CW01064124

HELM IDENTIFICATION GUIDES

BIRDS OF THE INDIAN SUBCONTINENT

HELM IDENTIFICATION GUIDES

BIRDS OF THE INDIAN SUBCONTINENT

Richard Grimmett, Carol Inskipp and Tim Inskipp
with the collaboration of Sarath Kotagama and Shahid Ali

Illustrated by Clive Byers, Daniel Cole, John Cox, Gerald Driessens, Carl D'Silva, Martin Elliott, Kim Franklin, Alan Harris, Peter Hayman, Craig Robson, Jan Wilczur and Tim Worfolk

CHRISTOPHER HELM
A & C Black • London

DEDICATIONS

To my parents Frank and Molly Grimmett for their wonderful support and understanding
Richard Grimmett

To all those who generously sent us information about birds of the subcontinent
Carol and Tim Inskipp

THE COLOUR PLATES
Clive Byers 119–127, 137–138, 141–153
Daniel Cole 1–6, 28–31, 38–39, 110–111
John Cox 32–35, 40
Gerald Driessens 26–27, 115–116
Carl D'Silva 14–25, 36–37, 78–82, 84–85, 88–95, 117–118, 139–140
Martin Elliott 52–58
Kim Franklin 61–62
Alan Harris 59, 64–67, 72–74, 96–109
Peter Hayman 41–51
Craig Robson 112–114, 128–136
Jan Wilczur 7–13, 75–77, 83, 86–87
Tim Worfolk 60, 63, 68–71

Christopher Helm (Publishers) Ltd, a subsidiary of A & C Black (Publishers) Ltd, 35 Bedford Row, London WC1R 4JH

0-7136-4004-9

A CIP catalogue record for this book is available from the British Library

Typeset and designed by D & N Publishing, Membury Business Park, Lambourn Woodlands, Hungerford, Berkshire, UK

Printed in the United Kingdom by Butler & Tanner Limited, Frome, Somerset

10 9 8 7 6 5 4 3 2 1

CONTENTS

THE INDIAN SUBCONTINENT

INTRODUCTION

This guide has been produced to fill a major gap in the ornithological literature, and represents the first work comprehensively to cover, in a field-guide form, all species occurring in the Indian subcontinent. Preparation of the text and plates has included extensive reference to museum specimens combined with considerable work in the field over almost all of the region. The guide should help observers identify all of the bird species recorded in the subcontinent, and it is hoped that, once basic identification skills have been acquired, birdwatchers will record their observations and use them to expand our knowledge of the distribution of the birds of the region, to further the conservation of threatened species, and to learn more about birds and the environment in which they live.

The guide covers the whole of the region that comprises the countries of India, Pakistan, Bangladesh, Sri Lanka, Nepal, Bhutan and the Maldives. The classic *Handbook of the Birds of India and Pakistan* by Sálim Ali and S. Dillon Ripley, which also covers the entire subcontinent and was first published in 1968–1975, lists about 1200 species. In recent years a number of additional species have been recorded in the region, and adopting the taxonomy used in *An Annotated Checklist of the Birds of the Oriental Region* (Inskipp *et al.* 1996) has produced a current total of 1295 species for the subcontinent.

Future fieldwork will certainly lead to major advances on this work, and existing published or unpublished material will undoubtedly have been missed or given insufficient attention. The authors (c/o the publishers, A & C Black) would be very grateful to receive, for use in future editions, any information which corrects or updates what is presented herein.

The book has drawn extensively from the literature, and published material up to mid 1997 has been reviewed.

Borders depicted in the maps in this book do not in any way impy an expression of opinion on the part of the authors as to the location of international or internal boundaries.

HISTORY OF ORNITHOLOGY IN THE INDIAN SUBCONTINENT

Apart from a few species described by 18th-century naturalists such as Carolus Linnaeus and John Latham, the investigation of the avifauna of the subcontinent began in earnest in the first half of the 19th century, with three main pioneers: Edward Blyth (based in Calcutta), Brian Hodgson (Nepal and Darjeeling) and Thomas Jerdon (mainly in peninsular India). The last-named's *Birds of India*, published in the 1860s, summarised what was known at that time about the avifauna of much of what is now the country of India. It was complemented by W. Legge's *History of the Birds of Ceylon* in 1880. Meanwhile, Allan Hume was amassing an enormous collection of bird skins, and nests and eggs, from all over the subcontinent, and he was aided by numerous other enthusiastic collectors. Much of the information he gathered from his many correspondents was published between 1873 and 1888 in his journal *Stray Feathers*. Another publication which began at that time was the *Journal of the Bombay Natural History Society*, and since 1886 this has been the premier source for papers on birds of the region. Just after this, the first work covering the entire subcontinent, the four-volume *Fauna of British India, Birds*, was produced by Eugene Oates and William Blanford. This contained descriptions of all the relevant species, but very abbreviated details of distribution and hardly any biological information.

In the early 20th century, a number of influential field ornithologists appeared on the scene, including E. C. Stuart Baker (based in Cachar, Assam, for a number of years), Charles Inglis (southwest India, Bihar and West Bengal), Claud Ticehurst (Pakistan), and Hugh Whistler (northwest India and Pakistan). Stuart Baker produced the second edition of the bird volumes of the *Fauna of British India* series during 1922 to 1930, including detailed accounts of habits and nests and eggs, but still very brief and unreferenced information on distribution. Ticehurst and Whistler began work on a comprehensive handbook of Indian birds, but this was never finished because of the untimely death of both men in the early 1940s. Whistler's manuscript (housed in the Natural History Museum, Tring, England) contains extensive accounts of the distribution of most relevant species and would have provided a sound basis for the future if the book had been published. In 1928, the first edition of his *Popular Handbook of Indian Birds* appeared, with an emphasis on field identification and habits, and many illustrations. Whistler's work highlighted the lack of knowledge of the birds of some areas of India and, at his instigation, the Bombay Natural History Society undertook a survey of the Eastern Ghats. This culminated in a lengthy report which pointed the way for further such work. Whistler made a survey of Jodhpur, Rajasthan, but 14 other surveys were carried out by one of the first Indian ornithologists, Sálim Ali, who went on to become renowned throughout India and beyond as a respected conservationist. The surveys led to the publication of several books by Sálim Ali, e.g. *The Birds Of Kutch, The Birds of Travancore and Cochin* and *The Birds of Sikkim*, but his *Book of Indian Birds*, first published in 1941 (and now in its 12th edition), probably did more to instill in the people of the region an interest in birds than did any other publication. Other significant ornithologists of this period were R. S. P. Bates (Kashmir), A. E. Jones (Himachal Pradesh), E. H. N. Lowther (Kashmir), Frank Ludlow (Bhutan and surrounding areas), and B. B. Osmaston and W. W. A. Phillips (Sri Lanka). Sálim Ali was accompanied on an expedition to the Mishmi Hills in Arunachal Pradesh by S. Dillon Ripley, which was the start of a collaboration that led to the publication of the *Handbook of the Birds of India and Pakistan* from 1968 to 1975. Ripley carried out surveys in Sri Lanka, Nepal and Nagaland, and in 1961 he published *A Synopsis of the Birds of India and Pakistan* which provided the taxonomic basis for the *Handbook*. The *Handbook* summarised the available data on all species and subspecies recorded in the subcontinent, with an emphasis on identification and, for the first time, provided illustrations of a large number of species and some distribution maps. It also revealed the gaps in knowledge for many species, especially relating to distribution, vocalisations, identification of birds of different subspecies and in various plumages, and breeding biology. Later editions of the *Handbook* incorporated coloured illustrations of nearly every species from *A Pictorial Guide to the Birds of the Indian Subcontinent*, but these were still inadequate for identification of difficult groups of birds and variation within species.

Other regional books with an emphasis on identification that have appeared in recent years include *A Guide to the Birds of Ceylon* by G. M. Henry (1955), which illustrates nearly every species; *Birds of Nepal* by Robert L. Fleming, Sr, Robert L. Fleming, Jr, and Lain Singh Bangdel (1976), which has led to a substantial number of Nepalis becoming interested in birds; *The Birds of Pakistan* by T. J. Roberts (1991–1992), a comprehensive two-volume work that is particularly useful for the author's original notes on habits and vocalisations; and *A Field Guide to the Birds of Sri Lanka* by Sarath Kotagama and Prithiviraj Fernando (1994), the Sinhalese version of which will, it is hoped, encourage many Sri Lankans to take up birdwatching. *A Guide to the Birds of Nepal* by Carol and Tim Inskipp (1985) contained identification sections on some of the more difficult groups of species and led ultimately to the production of the present book.

HOW TO USE THIS BOOK

Nomenclature

Taxonomy, sequence and nomenclature follow *An Annotated Checklist of the Birds of the Oriental Region* by Tim Inskipp, Nigel Lindsey and William Duckworth (1996). In cases where differences in taxonomic opinion exist in the literature, the species limits are fully discussed in that work, to which readers requiring further information should initially refer. The sequence of species is almost identical to that adopted in *Distribution and Taxonomy of Birds of the World* by C. G. Sibley and B. L. Monroe, Jr (1990), which was the first taxonomic sequence based on a relatively objective method of assessment. Although frequently criticised because it differs so radically from the so-called 'standard' sequence based on A. Wetmore (1930, A systematic classification for the birds of the world, *Proceedings of the United States National Museum* 76(24): 1–8), it is undoubtedly an improvement on the latter, which was never subjected to critical review. In addition, no single sequence has ever met with universal acceptance, as any user of bird books covering various regions will be aware, and even 'expert' users of such books are forced to turn to the indexes occasionally. The English names of birds are another contentious issue, with almost as many different names for some species as there are books describing them. The names adopted here are those which, in the opinion of the authors of the *Checklist*, are the most acceptable of the various alternatives. Alternative English and scientific names used in the main reference books for the region are given at the beginning of each species account. A capital letter in parentheses after each alternative name indicates the relevant book:

F Fleming, R. L., Sr, Fleming, R. L., Jr, and Bangdel, L. S. (1984) *Birds of Nepal*. Third edition. Avalok, Kathmandu.

I Ripley, S. D. (1961) *A Synopsis of the Birds of India and Pakistan*. Second edition. Bombay Natural History Society, Bombay.

K King, B. F., Dickinson, E. C., and Woodcock, M. W. (1975) *A Field Guide to the Birds of South-East Asia*. Collins, London.

N Inskipp, C., and Inskipp, T. (1991) *A Guide to the Birds of Nepal*. Second edition. Christopher Helm, London.

P Wijesinghe, D. P. (1991) *Checklist of the Birds of Sri Lanka*. Ceylon Bird Club, Colombo.

R Roberts, T. J. (1991–1992) *The Birds of Pakistan*. Two vols. Oxford University Press, Karachi.

Species Included

All species recorded in the subcontinent up to the end of 1996 have been described, with the exception of some reported very recently (see list below). Species with published records for the region which have since been discredited or require confirmation are included in boxed text. These include the following, which are illustrated and described: Plain-pouched Hornbill *Aceros subruficollis* (specimen now considered to be Wreathed Hornbill *A. undulatus*), Intermediate Parakeet *Psittacula intermedia* (now considered to be a hybrid), Rough-legged Buzzard *Buteo lagopus* (sight record requiring confirmation), Great-billed Heron *Ardea sumatrana* (sight records requiring confirmation), Soft-plumaged Petrel *Pterodroma mollis* (sight record requiring confirmation), Redwing *Turdus iliacus* (sight records now considered suspect), Willow Warbler *Phylloscopus trochilus* (one specimen was found to be a misidentified Greenish Warbler *P. trochiloides*, and two were collected by Col. Meinertzhagen), Giant Babax *Babax waddelli* (published record requires substantiation), Small Snowfinch *Montifringilla davidiana* (collected by Meinertzhagen), and Siberian Accentor *Prunella montanella* (collected by Meinertzhagen). The following have not been described or illustrated: Black-nest Swiftlet *Collocalia maxima* (specimens reidentified as Himalayan Swiftlets *C. brevirostris*), Great Black-backed Gull *Larus marinus* (specimen collected by Meinertzhagen but not preserved, and the published description is considered inadequate), Lesser Black-backed Gull *L. fuscus* (no specimens, and all sight records suspect), Mascarene Petrel *Pterodroma aterrima* (specimen lost and identification not confirmed), Eurasian Reed Warbler *Acrocephalus scirpaceus* (no definite records), and Olivaceous Warbler *Hippolais pallida* (sight records requiring confirmation). In addition, White-headed Petrel *Pterodroma lessoni* has been reported from Sri Lanka, but has not been fully accepted there.

Col. Richard Meinertzhagen collected a large number of birds in the subcontinent (and elsewhere) in the early 20th century, including several species which have not been recorded by other ornithologists. It has been demonstrated very recently that he falsified data relating to at least some of his specimens (Knox 1993; Rasmussen and Prys-Jones in prep.) and all of his records have, therefore, to be regarded as suspect.

Additional species have been recorded in recent years; at the time of writing no details have been published. These species are not described or illustrated in this book: Long-billed Dowitcher *Limnodromus scolopaceus* (Rajasthan, India), Pectoral Sandpiper *Calidris melanotos* (Punjab, India), Grey-faced Buzzard *Butastur indicus* (Andaman Islands), Trinidade Petrel *Pterodroma arminjoniana* (Tamil Nadu, India), Eared Pitta *Pitta phayrei* (Bangladesh), Swinhoe's Minivet *Pericrocotus cantonensis* (Bangladesh), Chinese Leaf Warbler *Phylloscopus sichuanensis* (Bhutan), Japanese Grosbeak *Eophona personata* (Arunachal Pradesh, India), and Pallas's Bunting *Emberiza pallasi* (Nepal).

Colour Plates and Plate Captions

All species are illustrated in colour except for Elliot's Laughingthrush *Garrulax elliotii* and Brown-cheeked Laughingthrush *G. henrici* (both very recently recorded in the subcontinent) and Moluccan Scops Owl *Otus magicus*. The last was collected in the Nicobar Islands in the 1960s, but only subsequently assigned to this species; the specimen was not available for illustration, and nothing has been published detailing how it differs from other populations of the species. Whenever possible, distinctive sexual and racial variation is shown, as well as immature plumages. While the guide has aimed to be as comprehensive as possible, some plumages recognisable in the field have not been covered owing to space limitations. The plates are largely in systematic order, although some species have been grouped out of sequence to enable useful comparisons to be made. Where possible, species depicted on any one plate have been drawn to the same scale.

The captions identify the figures illustrated, very briefly summarise the species' range, seasonality and habitats, and provide information on the most important identification characters. Figures are assigned to subspecies where these are distinct and racial variation has been mentioned in the text. Reference to the full text is essential for further information.

Species Accounts

The species accounts are divided into separate sections on identification, voice, habits, habitat, breeding, and distribution and status. In many cases, one or more references are appended.

'Family' Introductions

For each family or, in some instances, subfamily or even genus, a summary is given of plumage and physical characteristics, habits, habitat, breeding and movements.

Identification Section

Size This is given immediately after the subheading IDENTIFICATION and is the approximate body length of the species, including bill and tail, in centimetres. For most species, figures have been taken from what was felt to be the most reliable published source; with a few exceptions, no new measurements have been taken for this work, and the figures given are intended to provide a rough, comparative guide only. Length is expressed as a range when there is marked variation within the species (e.g. as a result of sexual dimorphism or racial differences).

Description The aim has been to cover comprehensively but concisely all important features that will assist observers in the field. Those species which are readily identifiable have been afforded the briefest of texts, while the more difficult species are described in much greater detail. The intention has been to compare with similar species, and to highlight the main identification features, rather than to provide full plumage descriptions. Male, female, breeding, non-breeding and immature plumages have been described where these are regarded as being distinct. The guide is aimed primarily at field observers, rather than those handling live birds or museum specimens (where greater attention to feather detail would be necessary).

The figures opposite illustrate the main plumage tracts and bare-part features, and are based on Grant and Mullarney (1988–1989). This terminology for bird topography has been used extensively in the species descriptions, and a full understanding of these terms is important if the reader is to make full use of this book; they are a starting point in putting together a description.

In the text of this book, 'crown' usually also includes the forehead, and 'throat' includes the chin; 'greater', 'median' and 'lesser coverts' refer to the greater, median and lesser secondary coverts; and the 'primary coverts' refer to the greater primary coverts. In instances where these general rules do not apply, the wording of the description makes this clear. Other terms have been used and are defined in the glossary. At times, and where considered to be self-explanatory, a looser terminology (e.g. upperparts, underparts, face) has also been employed. For species which are polytypic (i.e. contain two or more races, or subspecies), the description generally relates either to the nominate race or to the most widely distributed race occurring in the region. When appropriate, other races are mentioned in the section 'Racial variation'. This section covers the more distinctive subspecies occurring in the subcontinent which should be recognisable in the field, and particularly where variation has a significant bearing on the application of identification features. Coverage has necessarily been selective and subjective, and many widely accepted races have not been mentioned; readers are advised to consult Ali and Ripley (1987) for a more comprehensive listing. Hybrids are occasionally described when these are frequent in occurrence and are likely significantly to confuse or complicate field identification. They have not, however, been included for waterfowl, among which a remarkable variety of hybrids has been recorded (and almost anything is possible); see Gillham and Gillham (1996) for a good review of this issue.

We have attempted to be consistent in the use of terms for plumage colours, although we have aimed to keep these simple by confining ourselves largely to those which are currently in widespread use. An attempt to use a more discriminative and comprehensive nomenclature (Smithe 1975) was quickly abandoned, since colours in the natural world are infinitely more complex than are covered in Smithe's useful guide; moreover, such terms can be used only if readers are familiar with the swatches of colour and if artists have been able to follow them. Certain terms have been used frequently, and merit some explanation: cream is the colour of milk cream; buff is a deeper colour than cream, a dull brownish-yellow, with fulvous being deeper and stronger still;

DESCRIPTIVE PARTS OF A BIRD

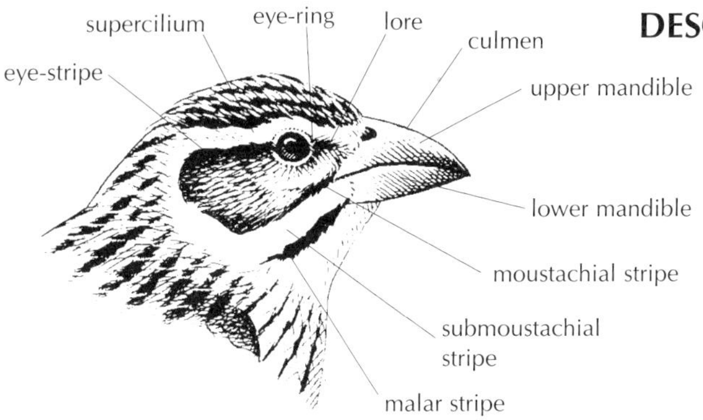

supercilium
eye-ring
lore
culmen
eye-stripe
upper mandible
lower mandible
moustachial stripe
submoustachial stripe
malar stripe

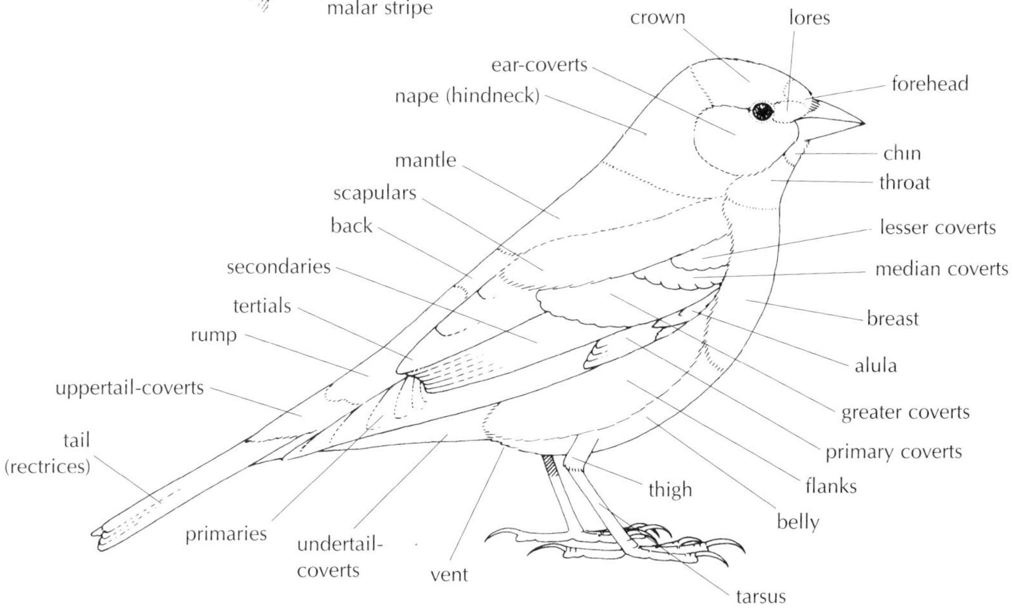

crown
lores
ear-coverts
forehead
nape (hindneck)
chin
throat
mantle
scapulars
back
lesser coverts
median coverts
secondaries
tertials
breast
rump
alula
uppertail-coverts
greater coverts
primary coverts
tail (rectrices)
flanks
thigh
belly
primaries
undertail-coverts
vent
tarsus

carpal joint
greater coverts
median coverts
lesser coverts
alula
primary coverts
primaries
back
rump
scapulars
secondaries
uppertail-coverts
tertials
tail

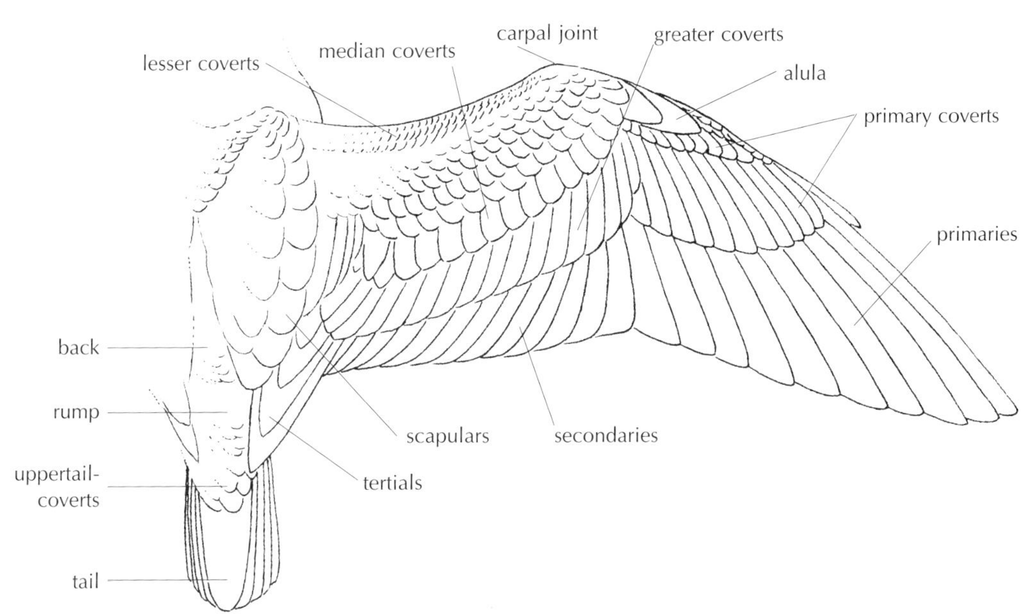

chestnut is reddish-brown (browner than rufous) and the colour of the fruit of a horse chestnut tree *Aesculus*; olive is the colour of a green olive; rufous is dull red, tinged with brown; and vinaceous is the colour of red wine. Trying to decide whether a colour was chestnut or rufous, cream or buff, and so on, to ensure differences between these colours are reflected in the colour plates, and to be wholly consistent over a six-year period is sure to have been too much for the first author! The use of 'pale' and 'dark' will, it is hoped, have added more precision. Apologies are offered for any shortcomings in this area. In compound colours, the dominant colour is placed last: thus, bluish-grey is greyer than greyish-blue.

Descriptions of varying plumages (age-related or seasonal) are provided where space has allowed. Juvenile plumage is the first plumage on fledging, and in many species it is looser, more fluffy, than subsequent plumages. In some families, juvenile plumage is retained only briefly after leaving the nest (e.g. pigeons), or hardly differs from adult plumage (e.g. many babblers), while in other groups it may be retained for the duration of long migrations or for many months (e.g. many waders). In some species (e.g. *Aquila* eagles), it may be several years before all juvenile feathers are finally moulted. The relevance of the juvenile plumage to field identification therefore varies considerably. Some species reach adult plumage after their first post-juvenile moult (e.g. larks), whereas others go though a series of immature plumages. The term 'immature' has been employed more generally to denote plumages other than adult, and is used either where a more exact terminology has not been possible or where more precision would give rise to unnecessary complexity. Terms such as 'first-winter' (resulting from a partial moult from juvenile plumage) or 'first-summer' (plumage acquired prior to the breeding season of the year after hatching) have, however, been used where it was felt that this would be useful.

Many species assume a more colourful breeding plumage, which is often more striking in the male compared with the female. This either can be realised through a partial (or in some species complete) body moult (e.g. waders) or results from the wearing-off of pale or dark feather fringes (e.g. redstarts and buntings). Wear can also influence feather coloration, as can bleaching caused by bright sunlight, with pale feathers fading more quickly than dark ones.

Voice

Voice has generally been mentioned only where it aids (or might aid) field identification, or is otherwise deemed noteworthy. It has not been included for species which are unlikely to be vocal in the subcontinent (e.g. skuas, boobies) or are generally vocal only at the nest (e.g. cormorants, egrets). Most species possess a considerably more varied vocabulary than can be covered in a guide of this size, with voice also differing between or within racial or biogeographical populations.

Song is the vocalisation used by males to claim or defend territories for breeding and/or feeding, to attract a mate, or to strengthen a pair-bond, and may be given by birds in their wintering quarters and on passage, as well as during the breeding season. Calls can serve the purpose of establishing or keeping contact, or giving alarm, or can be uttered for many other reasons.

While vocalisations are very difficult to describe, they can be essential in field identification. Pipits and *Phylloscopus* warblers, for example, include within their number many species which are extremely similar to one another in plumage, and which are often more easily separable by their calls. Locating some other species, especially in forest, can be a much easier task once the call has been learned. Time and effort spent in learning vocalisations is frequently rewarded, and once the observer has become familiar with a few calls he or she can quickly build on this.

Vocalisations are credited to source, unless they are drawn from the experience of the authors. Where possible, this guide has aimed to incorporate unpublished material obtained from recent field work in the region, although published material has frequently been incorporated when this is considered to be the best information available.

This section proved a very difficult one to write. Transcriptions are not easy to prepare and to follow, and are rarely satisfactory. Given that information has been drawn from many different sources, from observers of a wide range of nationalities, it has been impossible to be consistent in the presentation of vocalisations.

Habits

This summarises the species' main habits and behaviour, and focuses on those which help to locate and identify it.

Habitat

This section lists the main habitats where the species has been recorded, including those used at different seasons. If a species' habitat preferences within the subcontinent are not known or have not been recorded, as is not uncommonly the case with vagrants, this is stated.

Breeding

For species which breed in the subcontinent, the regional breeding season is given, along with a brief description of the nest and nest site. For a considerable number of species, information for the region is sparse or lacking, and data presented here are often from the 19th century or the early part of the 20th century.

Distribution and Status

A general description is given of the species' status as a resident, winter visitor, summer visitor, passage migrant or altitudinal migrant, and whether it is subject to local, long-distance or altitudinal movements. If a species is endemic to the region (i.e. it occurs nowhere else in the world) or is globally threatened, this is stated. One or two sentences describe its main distribution in the region, including breeding and non-breeding distributions if these are different; these do not usually include the listing of countries where the species is a vagrant, as this information is given under the country accounts, while lack of space has prevented the inclusion of the Andaman and Nicobar Islands under these introductory distribution descriptions for most relevant species.

This is followed by a summary statement of status, abundance and altitudinal range in both summer and winter for each country. As data on actual breeding records, with months and altitudes where appropriate, are few, it has not been possible to give comprehensive details on breeding and non-breeding ranges and abundance for most species. For example, many Himalayan species are recorded in summer over a wider altitudinal range than that within which they actually breed. The status, altitudinal ranges and distribution of birds in Bhutan are relatively poorly known in comparison with other countries in the region, and further work will undoubtedly expand the information given in this guide. The following symbols indicate the seven countries covered:

BD Bangladesh
BT Bhutan
IN India
LK Sri Lanka
MV Maldives
NP Nepal
PK Pakistan

Abundance is described using mainly the following terminology, which is based on a subjective assessment. Abundance decreases down the list:

Common
Fairly common
Frequent
Uncommon
Scarce
Rare
Vagrant

Key to the Maps

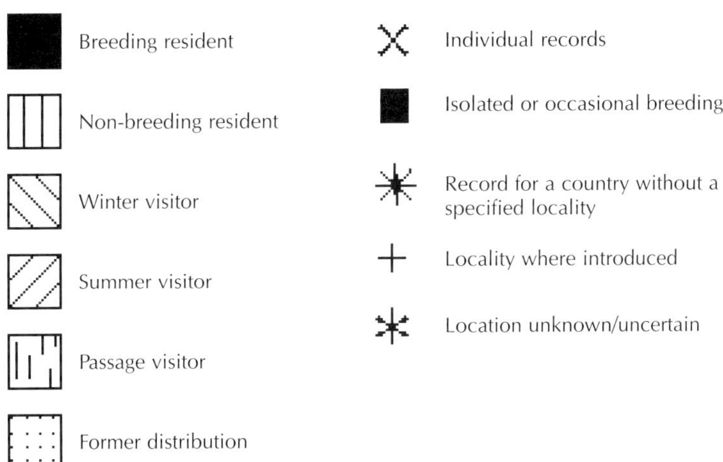

References

A huge number of references were used during the writing of this book, and not all are listed here. As part of the preliminary work, bibliographies were constructed for the constituent countries (these will be published elsewhere). The one for India currently includes over 10,500 entries, and it should not therefore be surprising if some relevant references have been overlooked or not reviewed. The main references relating to the region are marked with an asterisk (*) in the listed bibliography at the end of the book (p.859); these are not cited under individual species accounts. Those references which are cited provide additional information on identification, habits, habitat, breeding, distribution and status. The authors would be grateful to receive details of any important omissions from the cited references.

CLIMATE

There are great contrasts in climate within the subcontinent. The extremes range from the almost rainless Great Indian or Thar desert to the wet evergreen forests of the Khasi Hills, Meghalaya, where an annual rainfall of 1300 cm has been recorded at Cherrapunji (one of the wettest places on Earth), and to the arctic conditions of the Himalayan peaks, where only alpine flowers and cushion plants flourish at over 4900 m. There are similar contrasts in temperature ranges. In the Thar desert, summer temperatures soar as high as 50°C while winter temperatures drop to 0°C. On the Kerala coast, the annual and daily ranges of temperature and humidity are small; the average temperature is about 27°C and the average relative humidity is 60–80%.

Despite these variations, one feature dominates the subcontinent's climate, and that is the monsoons. Most of the rain in the region falls between June and September, during the southwest-monsoon season. During this period, cool, moisture-laden winds from the Indian Ocean bring heavy, intermittent rains. Typically, the monsoon begins in Kerala and the far northeast in late May or early June and moves north and west to extend over the rest of the area by the end of June, although it starts rather earlier in Sri Lanka and the Andaman Islands. On reaching the Western Ghats and the great barrier of the Himalayas, the air rises and cools and the moisture condenses, providing abundant rainfall along these ranges. In the Himalayas, the monsoon rains reach the east first and leave this area last, resulting in a higher rainfall over a longer period than in the western Himalayas. The air crossing the Himalayas is now dry, causing a rain shadow on the northern side of the mountains in regions such as Mustang and Dolpo in Nepal. The monsoon begins to retreat from the northwest at the beginning of September, and usually withdraws completely by mid October.

Rain continues, however, in the southern peninsula, and in the southeast around half the annual rain falls between October and mid December. This is brought by winds coming from the northeast during the northeast monsoon. In contrast, in much of the northern part of the subcontinent there is generally clear, dry weather in October, November and early December. Low-pressure systems from the west during this season do, however, bring some light to moderate precipitation to Pakistan and northern India. This falls as rain in the plains and as snow on the mountains. Some parts of northern and northwestern Pakistan, for example Chitral and Dir in the far north, receive their highest precipitation during these months.

The amount of rain varies from year to year, especially over areas of poor rainfall, such as Rajasthan, where it may even be as little as 30–40% of that of a normal year. Even when the total monsoon rain in an area is about average, it may fall over a very short period, bringing floods and drought in the same year.

MAIN HABITATS AND BIRD SPECIES

The bird habitats of the Indian subcontinent can be roughly divided into forest, scrub, wetlands (inland and littoral), marine, grassland, desert, and agricultural land. There is some overlap between habitats: for example, mangrove forest can also be considered as wetlands, as can seasonally flooded grassland. Many bird species require mixed habitat types.

Forests

There is a great variety of forest types in the region. Tropical forest ranges from coastal mangroves to wet, dense evergreen forest, dry deciduous forest and open-desert thorn forest. In the Himalayas, temperate forest includes habitats of mixed broadleaves, moist oak and rhododendron, and dry coniferous forest of pines and firs; higher up, subalpine forest of birch, rhododendron and juniper occurs.

The forest areas of the region are vitally important for many of its birds. Over half of the bird species in the subcontinent identified by BirdLife International as globally threatened and two-thirds of the region's endemic birds are dependent on forest.

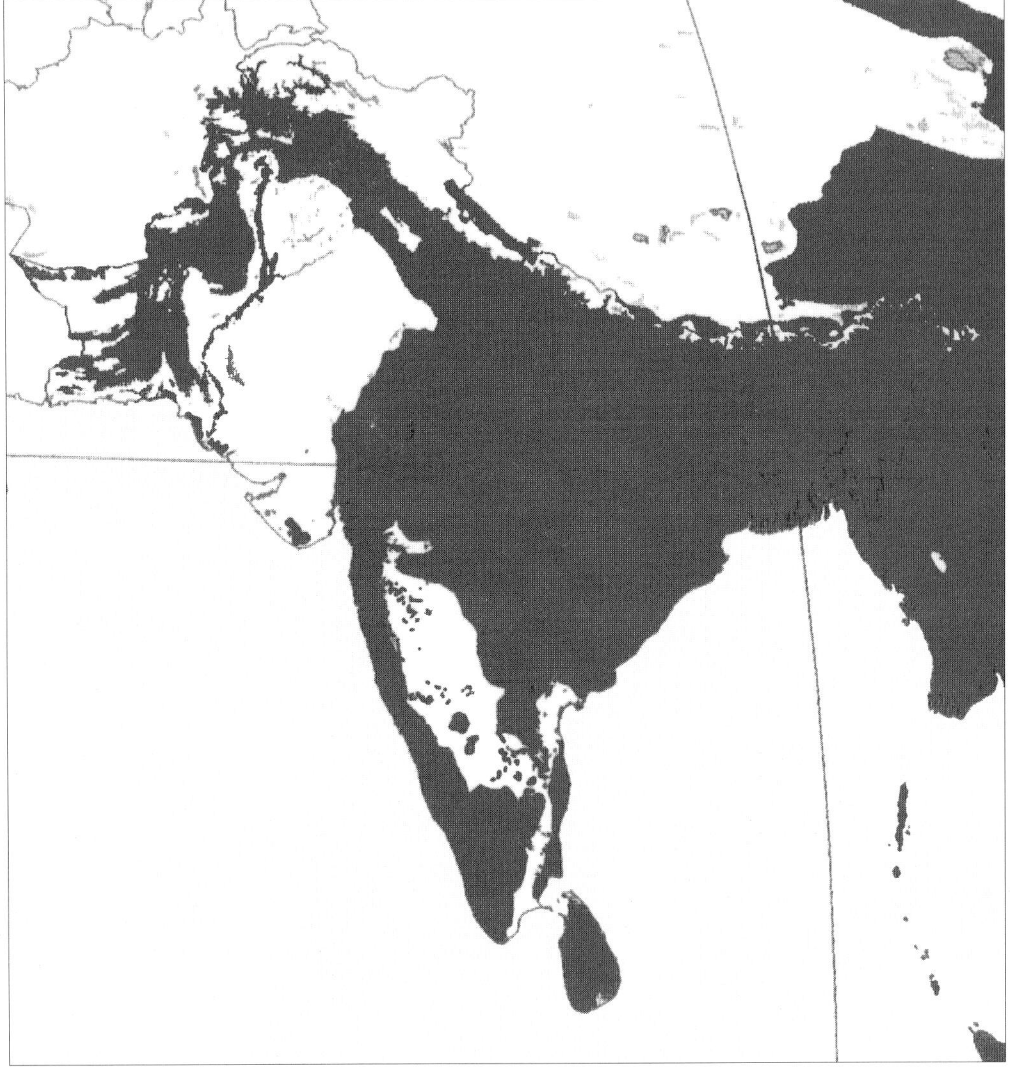

Original forest cover of the Indian subcontinent (source: World Conservation Monitoring Centre).

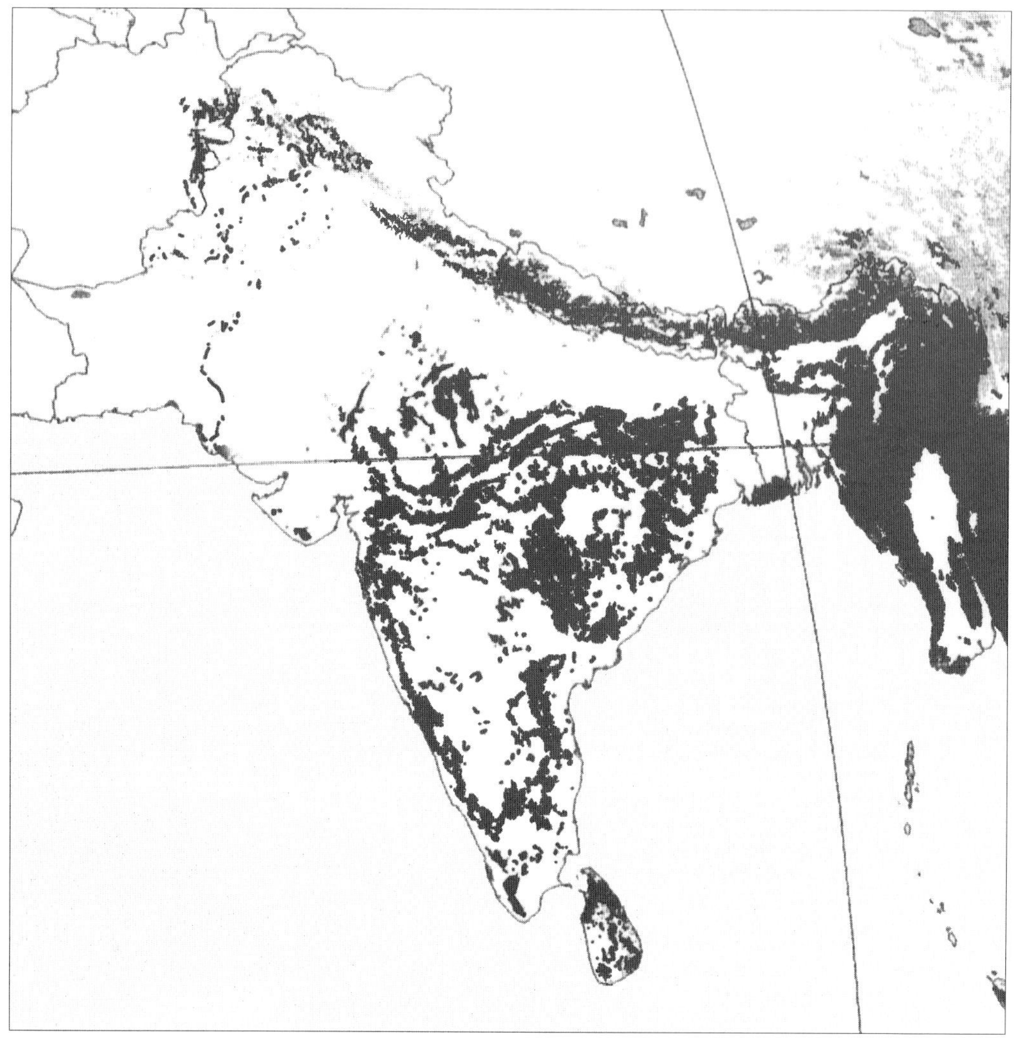

Current forest cover of the Indian subcontinent (source: World Conservation Monitoring Centre).

Primary tropical and subtropical broadleaved evergreen forest supports the greatest diversity of bird species. Significant areas of these forest habitats still remain in the eastern Himalayas and adjacent hills of northeast India, in the Western Ghats, in the Andaman and Nicobar Islands, and in Sri Lanka. They also contain a higher number of endemic and globally threatened species than any other habitat in the region. Species in this category include the Tawny-breasted Wren Babbler *Spelaeornis longicaudatus,* which is also restricted to the evergreen forest of the eastern Himalayas. Several species endemic to the Western Ghats are largely confined to evergreen broadleaved forest, among them the Black-and-orange Flycatcher *Ficedula nigrorufa* and Wynaad Laughingthrush *Garrulax delesserti.* Another endemic species inhabiting tropical evergreen forest is the Narcondam Hornbill *Aceros narcondami,* which is restricted to Narcondam Island in the Andamans.

Tropical deciduous forest, including moist and dry sal and teak forest, riverine forest and dry thorn forest, once covered much of the plains and lower hills of the subcontinent. Several widespread endemic species are chiefly confined to these habitats: they include the Plum-headed Parakeet *Psittacula cyanocephala,* which has a preference for moist deciduous forest, and the White-bellied Drongo *Dicrurus caerulescens,* which favours open dry deciduous forest. The only internationally threatened species restricted to deciduous forest is the White-naped Tit *Parus nuchalis,* which inhabits mainly tropical thorn forest in northwest India, with small numbers recorded very locally in moist deciduous forest in the south.

Temperate and subalpine forest grows in the Himalayas. These forest types support a relatively high proportion of species with restricted distributions, notably the White-throated Tit *Aegithalos niveogularis,* which frequents bushes in mixed forest and dwarf shrubberies near the treeline in the breeding season. Another endemic is the Pied Thrush *Zoothera wardii,* which breeds in open broadleaved forest in the Himalayas and hills of northeast India.

Scrub

Scrub has developed in the region where trees are unable to grow, either because soils are poor and thin, or because they are too wet, as at the edges of wetlands or in seasonally inundated floodplains. Scrub also grows naturally in extreme climatic conditions, as in semi-desert or at high altitudes in the Himalayas. In addition, there are now large areas of scrubland in the region where forest has been overexploited for fodder and fuel collection or grazing.

Relatively few birds in the subcontinent are characteristic of scrub habitats alone, but many are found in scrub mixed with grassland, in wetlands or at forest edges. Rather less than one-third of endemic birds in the region occupy habitats wholly or partly comprising scrub. One of the most interesting is the endangered Jerdon's Courser *Rhinoptilus bitorquatus*, which was known historically only from a few records in Andhra Pradesh, until it was rediscovered in 1986.

Wetlands

Wetlands are abundant in the region and support a rich array of waterfowl. As well as providing habitats for breeding resident species, they include major staging and wintering grounds for waterfowl breeding in central and northern Asia. The region possesses a wide range of wetland types, distributed almost throughout, including mountain glacial lakes, freshwater and brackish marshes, large water-storage reservoirs, village tanks, saline flats and coastal mangroves and mudflats. The results of the 1987–91 Asian Waterfowl Census, published in 1994 by the Asian Wetland Bureau (now Wetlands International-Asia Pacific) and the International Waterfowl and Wetlands Research Bureau, include detailed distribution maps for 200 Asian wetland species most commonly recorded during the period. A total of 33 of the subcontinent's wetland bird species is globally threatened, including the Spot-billed Pelican *Pelecanus philippensis*, Black-necked Crane *Grus nigricollis* and Indian Skimmer *Rynchops albicollis*.

A detailed directory of Indian wetlands compiled by WWF India and the Asian Wetland Bureau, describing their values, threats and conservation measures, was published in 1993. The subcontinent's most important wetland sites include Chilika Lake, a brackish lagoon in Orissa on the east Indian coast, which supports one of the largest concentrations of migrant waterfowl in the region. Wetlands in the Indus valley in Pakistan, notably the Chashma Barrage reservoir and Haleji Lake, form another major wintering refuge and staging area for a wide variety of waterfowl. The Sunderbans in the Ganges–Brahmaputra delta in Bangladesh and India include one of the largest contiguous areas of mangrove forest in the world; the mangroves support a rich and diverse avifauna. Although no comprehensive data are available, the coastal mudflats and estuaries are thought to be of great importance as staging and wintering areas. The extensive seasonally flooded man-made lagoons of Keoladeo Ghana National Park in Rajasthan are particularly diverse, and at least 332 bird species have been recorded there. Keoladeo is internationally renowned, especially for its wintering flock of the endangered Siberian Crane *Grus leucogeranus*; it is the only known site for this species in the region. The vast saline flats of the Ranns of Kutch in northwest India are important for migratory waterfowl and support breeding colonies of the Lesser Flamingo *Phoenicopterus minor*, herons and egrets. Wetlands in the moist tropical and subtropical forest of Assam and Arunachal Pradesh support two globally endangered species: the shy and little-known White-bellied Heron *Ardea insignis* and the White-winged Duck *Cairina scutulata*. Other wetlands in the region valuable for birds include the marshes, jheels and terai swamps of the Gangetic plain; Point Calimere and Pulicat Lake on India's east coast; the Haor basin of Sylhet and east Mymensingh in northeast Bangladesh; and the Brahmaputra floodplain in the Assam lowlands. Small water-storage reservoirs or tanks are a distinctive feature in India. Aggregations of these tanks provide important feeding and nesting areas for a wide range of waterbirds in some places; for example, a long-standing feature of the Deccan plateau has been its numerous tanks, which have been constructed near virtually every village.

Grasslands

The most important grasslands for birds in the subcontinent are the seasonally flooded grassland occurring across the Himalayan foothills and in the floodplains of the Indus and Brahmaputra rivers, the arid grassland of the Thar desert, and grasslands in peninsular India, especially those in Madhya Pradesh, Maharashtra and Karnataka. These lowland grasslands support distinctive bird communities, with a number of specialist endemic species.

Most of the region's endemic grassland birds are seriously at risk. These include three non-passerines, the Swamp Francolin *Francolinus gularis*, Lesser Florican *Sypheotides indica* and Indian Bustard *Ardeotis nigriceps*, which have gained much attention. A number of small passerines are in the same category, but have often been overlooked: Rufous-vented Prinia *Prinia burnesii*, Bristled Grassbird *Chaetornis striatus* and Finn's Weaver *Ploceus megarhynchus*. All of these threatened species face destruction and modification of their habitat.

Desert

The Thar desert is the largest desert in the region, covering an area of 200,000 km^2 in northwest India and Pakistan. Nearly 80% of the Thar lies in Rajasthan, and it also extends into parts of Punjab, Haryana, Gujarat and southeast Pakistan. There are other extensive arid areas in Pakistan: the hot deserts of the Chagai, a vast plain west of the main mountain ranges of Baluchistan, and the Thal, Cholistan and Sibi deserts in central and eastern Pakistan. The far northern mountain regions, which the monsoon winds do not penetrate, experience a cold-desert climate. The region's hot deserts are extensions of the Saharan and Arabian deserts and are also connected with semi-arid parts of peninsular India. As a result, there is only one bird species, Stoliczka's Bushchat *Saxicola macrorhyncha*, which is virtually endemic to the region. It is now found almost exclusively in the Thar desert (Rahmani and Sankaran 1995).

Seas

Seabirds occurring in the region comprise the skuas, petrels, storm-petrels, shearwaters, frigatebirds and boobies, most of which are passage migrants or vagrants, gulls (mainly winter visitors), terns and noddies (mainly residents, some winter or summer visitors and passage migrants), tropicbirds (residents and passage migrants), and phalaropes (one winter visitor and one vagrant). As a result of increased watching by dedicated observers, several seabirds have been added to the region's avifauna in recent years, notably the threatened Barau's Petrel *Pterodroma baraui*, which was first described for science only in 1963. Seabird breeding colonies in the subcontinent are concentrated chiefly in the Maldives and Lakshadweep. Terns and noddies are by far the most numerous breeding species, with the commonest being the Brown Noddy *Anous stolidus* and Sooty Tern *Sterna fuscata* in Lakshadweep and the Black-naped Tern *S. sumatrana* and Saunders's Tern *S. saundersi* in the Maldives.

IMPORTANCE FOR BIRDS

As many as 13% of the world's birds have been recorded in the Indian subcontinent. These include 141 endemic species, a total comprising over 10% of the region's avifauna.

New Species

New species are continually being added to the region's list. For example, recent surveys in the ornithologically poorly known state of Arunachal Pradesh revealed two laughingthrush species which were new to the subcontinent: Elliot's Laughingthrush and Brown-cheeked Laughingthrush. Both species had previously been recorded only in China. In 1991, the diminutive Nepal Wren Babbler *Pnoepyga immaculata* was first described from the Himalayan forest of Nepal (Martens and Eck 1991).

Extinct Species

Two species from the subcontinent may now be extinct. These are the Pink-headed Duck *Rhodonessa caryophyllacea* and the Himalayan Quail *Ophrysia superciliosa*, although some ornithologists consider that they could still survive.

Recent Rediscoveries

Two species endemic to India have been rediscovered recently. Jerdon's Courser was re-found in 1986, having last being recorded in 1900. The Forest Owlet *Athene blewitti* was located in 1997; the previous reliable record was as long ago as the 19th century.

Significant Families

Families (or other distinctive groupings of birds) with significant proportions of the world's species breeding in the subcontinent are: treecreepers Certhiinae (71%), accentors Prunellinae (62%), laughingthrushes Garrulacinae (55%), ioras Aegithininae (50%), long-tailed tits Aegithalidae (44%), babblers Timaliini (42%), flamingos Phoenicopteridae (40%), fairy bluebirds and leafbirds Irenidae (40%), dippers Cinclidae (40%), drongos Dicrurini (38%), and Asian barbets Megalaimidae (37%).

Reasons for Species-Richness

The Indian subcontinent is rich in species. This is partly because of its wide altitudinal range, extending from sea level up to the summit of the Himalayas, the world's highest mountains. Another reason is the region's highly varied climate and associated diversity of vegetation. The other major factor contributing to the subcontinent's species-richness is its geographical position in a region of overlap between three biogeographical provinces: the Indomalayan (South and Southeast Asia), Palearctic (Europe and Northern Asia), and Afrotropical (Africa) realms. As a result, species typical of all three realms occur. Most species are Indomalayan, typified by the ioras and minivets; some are Palearctic, including the accentors; and a small number, for instance the Spotted Creeper *Salpornis spilonotus*, originate in Africa.

Restricted-Range Species and Endemic Bird Areas

BirdLife International has analysed the distribution patterns of birds with restricted ranges, that is landbird species which have, throughout historical times (i.e. post-1800), had a total global breeding range of below 50,000 km^2 (about the size of Sri Lanka) (Stattersfield *et al.* 1998). A total of 99 restricted-range species breeds in the subcontinent, and a further four occur as non-breeding visitors from areas outside the region (BirdLife International 1998). BirdLife's analysis showed that restricted-range species tend to occur in places which are often islands or isolated patches of a particular habitat. These are known as centres of endemism, and are often called Endemic Bird Areas or 'conservation hotspots'. BirdLife has identified eight centres of endemism in the Indian subcontinent (see map overleaf).

The wet lowland and montane rainforest zones of the eastern Himalayas in India, Nepal and Bhutan (also extending into Myanmar and southwest China) form an important Endemic Bird Area. Further isolated endemic-rich areas of rainforest are on the coastal flanks of the Western Ghats and in southwestern Sri Lanka. The other Endemic Bird Areas are the western Himalayas in India, Nepal and Pakistan; the central Himalayas; the Assam plains, which lie in the floodplain of the Brahmaputra in Bangladesh and India; and the Andaman and Nicobar Islands in the Bay of Bengal. Seven of the subcontinent's eight Endemic Bird Areas are largely forest areas.

A total of 24 species occurs only in the eastern Himalayas. Nearly half of them are considered by BirdLife International to be at risk from loss or fragmentation of their habitat, and some pheasants and partridges are also thought to be threatened by hunting. Many of the birds are relatively poorly known, because much of the area has long been inaccessible for political and logistical reasons. More bird surveys have been carried out in recent years, and it is perhaps the most exciting area in the region for future work. Species which would certainly benefit from further study are Chestnut-breasted Partridge *Arborophila mandellii*, Dark-rumped Swift *Apus acuticauda* and Rusty-bellied Shortwing *Brachypteryx hyperythra*.

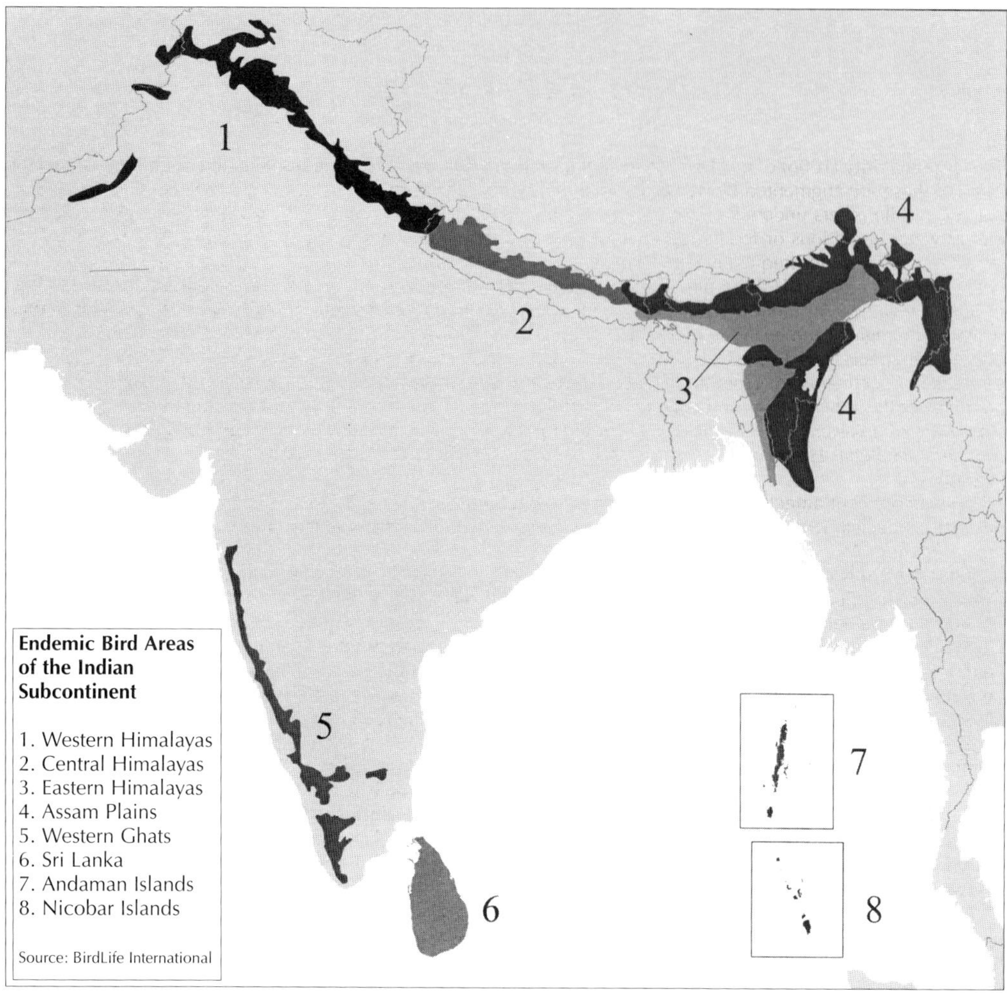

The 11 species endemic to the western Himalayas include the probably extinct Himalayan Quail, and three which are thought to be at risk of extinction: Western Tragopan *Tragopan melanocephalus,* Cheer Pheasant *Catreus wallichii* and Kashmir Flycatcher *Ficedula subrubra.* All three are threatened by habitat loss and deterioration, while the two pheasants also suffer from hunting.

The Central Himalayas Endemic Bird Area supports three endemic species: Hoary-throated Barwing *Actinodura nipalensis* (whose range extends into the eastern Himalayas) and Spiny Babbler *Turdoides nipalensis,* neither of which is considered threatened, and the recently discovered and very poorly known Nepal Wren Babbler.

Sri Lanka has almost as many endemic species (23) as the eastern Himalayas. Forest loss and disturbance have resulted in six of these species becoming seriously threatened, and a number of others are in significant decline. Two species are endangered: Green-billed Coucal *Centropus chlororhynchus* and Sri Lanka Whistling Thrush *Myophonus blighi.*

The Western Ghats support 16 endemic species, none of which is thought to be at risk of extinction. Most, however, are suffering to some extent from habitat damage and loss, mainly of forest.

The Andaman and Nicobar Islands form two Endemic Bird Areas and possess 15 endemic bird species, six found only on the Andamans, five only on the Nicobars and four on both groups of islands. While most of the endemic birds are not under immediate threat, their future prospects, if conservation measures are not implemented immediately, are bleak.

All three species endemic to the Assam Lowlands Endemic Bird Area are threatened: Manipur Bush Quail *Perdicula manipurensis,* Marsh Babbler *Pellorneum palustre* and Black-breasted Parrotbill *Paradoxornis flavirostris.* The Assam lowlands are also a refuge for two globally endangered species: the Greater Adjutant *Leptoptilos dubius,* a large stork, and the Bengal Florican *Houbaropsis bengalensis,* a bustard occupying wet grassland.

More Widespread Species

The subcontinent still supports very large populations of some large waterbirds and birds of prey, such as the Painted Stork *Mycteria leucocephala* and White-rumped Vulture *Gyps bengalensis,* which are now extirpated or rare in Southeast Asia.

MIGRATION

The large majority (1006) of the 1300 or so species recorded in the region are resident, although the numbers of some of these are augmented by winter visitors breeding farther north. Some residents are sedentary throughout the year, while others undertake irregular movements, either locally or more widely within the region, depending on water conditions or food supply. Many Himalayan residents are altitudinal migrants, the level to which they descend in winter frequently depending on weather conditions; for instance, the Grandala *Grandala coelicolor* summers at up to 5500 m and winters chiefly down to 3000 m, but it has been recorded as low as 1950 m in bad weather. A number of other residents in the subcontinent breed in the Himalayas and winter farther south in the region, one example being the endemic Pied Thrush, which spends the winter in Sri Lanka.

Eighteen species are exclusively summer visitors to the region. Most of these, such as the Lesser Cuckoo *Cuculus poliocephalus* and Common Swift *Apus apus*, winter in Africa. Several species breed chiefly to the north and west of the subcontinent and extend just into Pakistan and northwest India, for instance the European Bee-eater *Merops apiaster*. Some species move southeastwards, perhaps as far as Malaysia and Indonesia; the White-throated Needletail *Hirundapus caudacutus* and Asian Emerald Cuckoo *Chrysococcyx maculatus* are two such examples.

The subcontinent attracts 159 winter visitors, some of which are also passage migrants. There is also a small number of species (19) which are known only as passage migrants. The winter visitors originate mostly in northern and central Asia.

Organised study of bird migration was initiated in India in 1959, through bird-ringing projects by the Bombay Natural History Society. Two major field stations were established: Point Calimere Wildlife Sanctuary, Tamil Nadu, and the Keoladeo National Park, Rajasthan. Subsidiary field stations were periodically operated later. A total of 565 species was ringed during the first project period. The major habitats of the subcontinent were covered, resulting in the gathering of substantial data on species composition, distribution and dispersal, as well as on biometrics and migratory movements of the region's birds. The project's findings also included confirmation of the breeding origins of 20 waterfowl and 12 wader species, and helped to evaluate the role of certain key wetlands in the subcontinent as important wintering/passage sites for migratory waterfowl (Hussain 1996).

Information on migration routes in the region is still patchy, but it is believed that many of the subcontinent's winter visitors come through Pakistan, mainly en route to India and Sri Lanka. Ringing recoveries have shown that many winter visitors enter the subcontinent via the Indus plains. In 1967, the International Union for Conservation of Nature and Natural Resources, the International Waterfowl Research Bureau and the International Council for Bird Preservation (now BirdLife International) endorsed a resolution rating the Indus as the fourth major waterfowl migration flyway in order of world importance. There is less information about migration routes in the northeast of the region, but the Brahmaputra river and its tributaries are thought to form a flyway for birds from northeast Asia. Increasing evidence suggests that some birds breeding in the Palearctic, mainly non-passerines, migrate directly across the Himalayas to winter in the subcontinent. Birds have been seen flying over the highest regions of these ranges; for example, a flock of Bar-headed Geese *Anser indicus* was recorded flying as high as 9375 m over Sagarmatha in Nepal. Other birds follow the main valleys, such as those of the Kali Gandaki, Dudh Kosi and Arun in Nepal. Birds of prey, especially *Aquila* eagles, have also been found to use the Himalayas as an east–west pathway in autumn; the wintering area of these birds is unknown. The Spot-winged Starling *Saroglossa spiloptera* also undertakes east–west movements along the Himalayas, and it is possible that other species perform similar migrations.

A number of pelagic and coastal passage migrants and wintering species travel by oceanic or coastal routes. One identified coastal flyway lies on India's east coast, linking Point Calimere in Tamil Nadu with Chilika and Pulicat Lakes. Migration patterns of seabirds are particularly poorly understood, but there is now evidence that some species occur more regularly than previously thought, especially around the time of the southwest monsoon. In Sri Lanka, a mass migration of Bridled Terns *Sterna anaethetus* takes place in autumn; each year, an estimated half a million or more move southwards off the southwest coast within sight of land.

A few species which breed outside the region and winter in East Africa migrate through Pakistan and northwest India, examples being the Rufous-tailed Rock Thrush *Monticola saxatilis* and Red-backed Shrike *Lanius collurio*. As they occur mainly on autumn passage, they presumably use a different route in spring.

In addition to the subcontinent's residents, summer and winter visitors and passage migrants, nearly 100 species of vagrant have been recorded.

CONSERVATION

Religious Attitudes and Traditional Protection

The enlightened and benevolent attitudes towards wildlife of Hinduism and Buddhism have undoubtedly helped to conserve the rich natural heritage of the Indian subcontinent which still remains today. They are key factors in accounting for the abundance and tameness of birds in large parts of the region. The protection of wildlife has a long tradition in the history of much of the subcontinent. Indeed, one of the world's first wildlife sanctuaries was established in the 3rd century BC by King Devanampiyatissa in Sri Lanka.

India has a tradition of protection of all forms of animals dating from as early as 3000 years ago, when the Rig Veda mentioned the animals' right to live. Emperor Ashoka, influenced by the Buddhist way of life, ordered the protection of animals. Several communities, such as the Bishnois of Rajasthan, the Buddhists and the Jains, protect living creatures in daily life. Sacred groves, village tanks and temples where the hunting and killing of all forms of life are prohibited can be found throughout India. There are examples of villagers benefiting from their association with birds in unexpected ways. Bird droppings in Kokrebellur, for instance, help fertilise fields and act as amazingly effective natural fertiliser. Traditional farmers also recognise the role of raptors and owls in pest control. Indeed, in Kerala, there are farmers who put up perches in their fields to attract these birds, which save their crops from rodent damage. Unfortunately, however, many people nowadays are forgetting their traditional ways in the face of westernisation (Grewal 1994).

Current Threats

Birds in the region are currently confronted with many threats, the most important of which are habitat loss and deterioration. Root causes of loss of and damage to habitats are complex, interlinked and often controversial. Overpopulation is often blamed for the region's environmental ills; India is predicted to take over from China as the world's most populous nation by the year 2020. Other factors are, however, important: poverty, inequitable land distribution, insecurity of tenure, lack of political will, weak government, national debt (which encourages countries to overexploit their natural resources for export), damaging international policies, high demand from overseas for resources, and misguided national policies.

Threats extend to protected areas in parts of the region. For example, India's protected areas face livestock grazing and collection of fodder and fuelwood by local villagers whose vital basic needs have not been catered for, as well as occupation by political activists, exploitation for mining and lack of resources for park staff.

Threats to Forests

Both the extent and the quality of forest resources are declining throughout much of the region. India has suffered massive losses: forest covered more than 40% of its land mass barely a century ago; in 1997, the government estimated India's forest cover to be over 19% of the country's area, but only 11.2% of forest is dense forest (Forest Survey of India 1997). Nepal was once extensively forested, but by 1988 37% of the country was forest land and only 15% of the country carried dense forest. Bangladesh is one of Asia's poorest countries in terms of land under forest cover: its productive forest cover declined from 16% in the 1970s to only 6–7% in the 1990s, a reduction of 60% in 20 years, and much of what remains is heavily degraded (Collins *et al.* 1991; Rahman 1995). Natural forest cover in Sri Lanka has dwindled rapidly, from an estimated 89% in 1889 to 18.9% in 1983 (Collins *et al.* 1991). According to the United Nations Food and Agricultural Organization, only 2.8% of Pakistan's land is under forest. Bhutan, however, still retains much of its forest relatively intact, with 43% of its land area under high-density forest in 1991; the country possesses some of the best forest habitats left in the Himalayas.

The major threats to natural forest are overexploitation for fuelwood, timber and fodder, overgrazing which prevents forest regeneration, and the conversion of forest to other land uses: agriculture, notably shifting cultivation, tree plantations, urban land, and reservoirs through dam construction. The decline in Nepal's forest cover has been attributed partly to the breakdown of traditional management. All forest areas were nationalised in 1957 in an attempt to protect them, but in many areas forest depletion unfortunately accelerated instead, because people felt that the forest no longer belonged to them. The Forest Act of 1993 once again decentralised forest management, and many village communities have since started to manage their own forest resources.

In India, wood is the primary fuel for the rural population, and forest cover near cities is diminishing as a result of urban demand. India's forest can sustainably provide an estimated 41 million m^3 of fuelwood, yet annual demand is thought to be 240 million m^3. Fuelwood provides as much as 98% of Nepal's domestic energy supply and 37% of Pakistan's. With the rapid increase in the area of irrigated and cultivated land in India in recent years, many livestock-owners have been forced to rely on forest areas as grazing land for their herds. Of over 400 million cattle, about 90 million graze in forest, where the carrying capacity is estimated to be only 31 million (Forest Survey of India 1989).

Hydroelectric dams are an increasing threat, especially to Himalayan forest. In addition, they are very often built on rivers through the most fertile forest land in the subcontinent. By the late 1980s, it was estimated that several million hectares of reserve forest land had been lost through submergence and clearance for irrigated agriculture (Shyamsunder and Parameswarappa 1987).

Threats to Wetlands

Wetland destruction and degradation in the region are reducing the diversity of wetlands and the population numbers of many bird species. Major threats include overexploitation of wetland resources, as local demands often exceed wetlands' ability to regenerate. For example, 0.1 million people live around Chilika Lake in Orissa and most of them depend directly on the lake's resources for their sustenance and livelihood. Intensive prawn cultivation is another imminent threat to the lake, as well as to other coastal wetlands in India. Increasing hydro-electric developments are altering the characteristics and dynamics of entire river ecosystems in the region. Drainage and siltation of wetlands are other major threats. Many wetlands are becoming polluted by sewage, industrial effluents and agricultural fertilisers and pesticides, although these impacts have not been quantified on a national basis.

Almost half of Bangladesh is covered by wetlands, and these have suffered drastically. In the Ganges–Brahmaputra floodplain alone, approximately 2.1 million ha of wetlands have been lost to flood-control, drainage and irrigation developments. Indigenous protective management systems in the country have given way to short-term benefits for vested-interest groups (Khan *et al.* 1994).

Deforestation has resulted in habitat loss for some waterbirds. Swamp forest, which was once extensively distributed in Bangladesh, is now on the verge of disappearing. In the mangroves of the Bangladesh Sunderbans, the volume of sundari stands, the dominant tree species, has decreased by 40% since 1959 (Khan *et al.* 1994). Mangrove areas, too, have also been severely damaged in many parts of India and completely wiped out in some areas. For example, the dense mangrove forest which covered vast tracts of the state of Orissa a century-and-a-half ago now occupies only 226 km^2, and satellite imagery shows that about 2 km^2 are being lost every year (Anon. 1991).

While many of the region's natural wetlands have disappeared, new wetlands have been created. These include lakes and marshes upstream of dams and barrages on some rivers, certain of which now provide excellent habitat for waterbirds. Other wetlands have developed as a result of faulty drainage systems and overspill from irrigation canals. Rice production has also created large areas of seasonally useful habitat for some waterbirds in parts of the region, although in Bangladesh natural wetlands are being reclaimed for production of rice.

Threats to Grasslands

Grassland has been greatly reduced, fragmented and degraded by large-scale expansion of agriculture, conversion to other kinds of land use, drainage, and overgrazing. A recent study in the Kathiawad peninsula and the Malwa plateau, the stronghold of the Lesser Florican, revealed that between 1989 and 1994, in many areas, 40–70% of privately owned protected grasslands have been lost to agriculture, leased to graziers or ploughed up (Sankaran 1995).

Apart from grasslands located within protected areas, practically every grass-growing tract in the region is grazed by domestic livestock. Encroachment by graziers is also increasing in protected areas. Between 1951 and 1992 numbers of livestock grew by 52% in India, and in the period 1982–92 by as much as 30% in Pakistan and 31% in Bangladesh (Economic and Social Commission for Asia and the Pacific 1994). These large increases in livestock have led to widespread overgrazing, and this problem has been exacerbated as more and more grazing lands have been converted to other land uses.

Threats to Desert

The spread of irrigation has significantly reduced the habitat of desert birds. Between 1950 and 1990, the area under irrigation increased by 70% in Pakistan and by as much as 118% in India. The Indira Gandhi Nahar Project, the largest irrigation canal system in the world, which is under construction in the Thar desert, has undoubtedly had a profound effect on many desert birds. Recent work has shown that the canal and associated seepage wetlands, together with plantations alongside canals, have provided suitable habitats for generalist species such as some waterfowl, herons, babblers, munias and parakeets, but the specialist species of the desert such as the Indian Bustard and sandgrouse have been edged out (Rahmani and Sankaran 1995).

Similar trends have been observed in Pakistan, although the Sind Sparrow *Passer pyrrhonotus*, which is largely confined to that country, has benefited from the development of extensive irrigation systems and large canals with tree plantations (Roberts 1992).

Threats to Agricultural Habitats

Agricultural practices have become significantly intensified in recent years in most of the region, leading to increased production. In India, for example, rice production rose by 39% from 1982 levels to reach 73.7 million tonnes in 1992 (Economic and Social Commission for Asia and the Pacific 1994). Pesticide use has also increased, including use of the organochlorines DDT and aldrin, both of which have been proved to be particularly poisonous to birds. Between 1982 and 1988, the amount of DDT used or sold in India for agriculture increased six-fold and the amount of aldrin increased by a factor of ten (Economic and Social Commission for Asia and the Pacific 1994).

Pesticides build up in food chains, particularly affecting species at the apex, notably birds of prey. Pesticides leached from agricultural land contaminate rivers and streams and build up in aquatic food chains, thereby affecting fish and fish-eating birds. In Europe, such factors have been shown to cause widespread declines of numerous bird species, many of which were previously common, including birds of prey, shrikes and finches (Tucker and Heath 1994). Could the same be happening in the Indian subcontinent? This seems likely, although there is little direct evidence so far. Recent studies on the Lesser Fishing Eagle *Ichthyophaga humilis* in Corbett National Park found that none of the eggs in four nests hatched and eggshells from one nest revealed high levels of DDT (Naoroji 1995). No fewer than 18 Sarus Cranes *Grus antigone* were lost from Keoladeo Ghana National Park between 1988 and 1990, probably because of aldrin applied to fields around the park by local farmers (Muralidharan 1992).

Other Threats

Hunting is a major threat to some species in Pakistan (notably cranes and bustards) and in Bangladesh (particularly migratory waterfowl and waders). Local fishermen collect eggs of seabirds wherever they nest colonially in Pakistan and the Maldives. Persecution is so great in the Maldives that it seems doubtful whether many young of any seabird species now survive (Ash and Shafeeg 1995). Similar predation is also reported on the Black-bellied Tern *Sterna acuticauda*, River Tern *S. aurantia* and Small Pratincole *Glareola lactea* along rivers in Pakistan and may well account for the relative decline in these species (Roberts 1991). In parts of India and Nepal, hunting is on the increase as traditional values wane and is significant for several species, notably the threatened bustards – Indian Bustard, Macqueen's Bustard *Chlamydotis macqueeni*, Lesser Florican and Bengal Florican – and some pheasants, such as Blyth's Tragopan *Tragopan blythii* and Cheer Pheasant.

Until very recently there was a large domestic and international bird trade in India, but since 1991 all bird trade has been banned. Recent undercover operations have, however, revealed that thousands of birds are still regularly caught and traded, both within India and for export, although in much-reduced numbers compared with those previously traded. The species most commonly captured are the munias *Amandava* and *Lonchura*, the Hill Myna *Gracula religiosa* and parakeets *Psittacula*. A recent study found that the Edible-nest Swiftlet *Collocalia fuciphaga* is endangered on the Andaman and Nicobar Islands through collection of its nests for Chinese cuisine (Sankaran 1997).

Caged birds are popular in Pakistan, where Grey Francolins *Francolinus pondicerianus* are kept for their loud calling habits and Demoiselle Cranes *Grus virgo* as effective watchdogs (Roberts 1991). In recent years, in the Maldives, a very large trade seems to have developed in the marketing of wild birds as pets. Flightless flocks of waders and terns are a common sight in most villages (Ash and Shafeeg 1995).

Introduced species of fauna and flora are a common threat to native birds (and other wildlife) on a worldwide scale. In the subcontinent, large areas of natural habitat have been colonised by exotic plant species, such as the water hyacinth *Eichhornia*, which covers the surface of fresh waters, thus changing the habitat for many waterbirds. After being introduced to the Nicobar Islands, the Red-whiskered Bulbul *Pycnonotus jocosus* has competed so successfully with the Nicobar Bulbul *Hypsipetes nicobariensis* (which is endemic to the islands) that it may contribute towards its extinction.

Consequences

Losses and deterioration of habitats and other threats have resulted in widespread declines in bird populations, but we can only speculate on the changes which are occurring for most species. Apart from the annual waterfowl counts organised by Wetlands International and the International Waterfowl and Wetlands Research Bureau, and some studies on rare species, there is a lack of baseline data for monitoring most birds, especially common and widespread species.

A study of Nepal's forest birds (Inskipp 1989) found that only 16% of species had adapted to habitats heavily modified or created by people, such as groves, gardens, scrub, and trees and bushes at the edges of cultivation. Nearly all these species were common and widespread in Nepal; presumably, they once bred in forest edges and clearings. Considering the whole region, some bird species, such as Indian Grey Hornbill *Ocyceros griseus*, which naturally occurred in open deciduous forest have adapted well to human-modified habitats, such as secondary forest, gardens and roadside avenues. It seems likely that species which frequent scrub, such as the Grey-breasted Prinia *Prinia hodgsonii*, must have benefited as a result of forest clearance. Species which prefer open secondary habitats, as do some flycatchers, may well have increased as forest zones have become degraded. Most species in these categories, however, are fairly common and widespread, whereas many forest species have restricted ranges and specialised requirements. Hornbills need mature fruiting trees for feeding, and many babblers require forest with a well-developed understorey. Overall, it is likely that a far greater number of bird species have suffered from forest losses and degradation than have benefited from such changes.

In 1994, BirdLife International published a world list of 1111 bird species (11% of the world's avifauna) threatened with extinction, including 78 species which regularly occur in the Indian subcontinent (Collar *et al.* 1994). A book currently in preparation, the *Threatened Birds of Asia*, will describe all Asian species at risk of extinction, highlighting the threats they face and the conservation measures proposed to save them; data are being compiled by national co-ordinators in each country.

Conservation Measures

Traditional protection, religious beliefs, legal measures and the efforts of conservation organisations have all helped to counter, albeit only partially, the threats confronting birds in the subcontinent. Without them, the region's extinct and threatened bird species would be much greater in number.

In addition to the impact of religious beliefs and traditional protection (see p.24), legal conservation measures are in force in all countries in the subcontinent. The Convention on Biological Diversity has been ratified by all countries in the region. This commits member countries to conserve the variety of animals and plants within their jurisdiction and to aim to ensure that the use of biological resources is sustainable. All the subcontinent countries with major wetlands have ratified the Convention on Wetlands of International Importance, the Ramsar Convention. This requires the protection of wetlands of international importance, the promotion of wetlands and the fostering of their wise use.

There is widespread protected-area coverage. In 1990, India had 69 national parks and 410 sanctuaries covering more than 4% of the country's surface area. Particular emphasis is being given to protecting sites of high species diversity and endemism, such as the Western Ghats, as well as ecologically fragile areas. At least 35 protected areas in India are devoted primarily to bird conservation. The recently revised protected-areas system in Bhutan is especially impressive, covering 22% of the country and representing all of its major ecosystems. Large proportions of Nepal (10.6%) and Sri Lanka (12.1%) are also covered by protected areas. Protected-area coverage is 4.7% in Pakistan and 0.8% in Bangladesh.

Local, national and international non-governmental organisations have made a major impact on bird conservation. The main national and international organisations and their activities are listed below.

NATIONAL ORGANISATIONS

INDIA

Bombay Natural History Society (BNHS)
Address: Hornbill House, Dr Salim Ali Chowk, Shaheed Bhagat Singh Road, Bombay 400 023.
Publications: *Journal of the Bombay Natural History Society; Hornbill* magazine (quarterly).
The BNHS was founded in 1883, and is the largest non-governmental organisation in the subcontinent engaged in the conservation of nature and natural resources, education and research in natural history. The Society has an invaluable collection of over 26,000 bird specimens, held at its headquarters in Bombay. Its Nature Education Wing reaches over 10,000 students each year. The Salim Ali Nature Conservation Fund creates awareness, with training programmes for Indian Army officers, journalists and trekkers. Scientists have carried out vital ornithological research, including a national bird-ringing programme and studies on grassland birds.

Salim Ali Centre for Ornithology and Natural History (SACON)
Address: Kalampalayam, Coimbatore, Tamil Nadu 641 010.
Publication: SACON newsletter.
SACON came into being in 1990 and currently has 12 research staff. SACON's objectives are to:
(1) study India's biological diversity so as to promote its conservation and sustainable use;
(2) study the ecology of the Indian avifauna with special reference to its conservation;
(3) foster the development of professional wildlife research in India, by training postgraduates and forest-managers; and
(4) function as a regional nodal agency for the dissemination of information on biodiversity and its conservation.
Current work includes the conservation of birds on the Andaman and Nicobar Islands, and monitoring and conservation of the Lesser Florican.

Wildlife Institute of India (WII)
Address: Post Bag No. 18, Chandrabani, Dehradun 248 001.
The WII was set up in 1982. Its objectives are to:
(1) train biologists and managers for protected-area management and wildlife research;
(2) conduct and co-ordinate applied wildlife research, and evolve techniques relevant to the Indian situation;
(3) train educational and extension workers to acquire skills in eliciting public support for wildlife conservation;
(4) provide consultancy services in conservation matters to government and non-official agencies;
(5) create a database leading to a national wildlife information system; and
(6) provide conservation-orientation courses for those involved in land-use management.

Zoological Survey of India (ZSI)
Address: 27, Jawaharlal Nehru Road, Calcutta 700 016.
Publications: *Newsletter of the Zoological Survey of India; Annual Reports.*
The ZSI was established in 1916 and carries out surveys in the country. Its collections cover the whole of India. The National Zoological Collection of India at Calcutta houses more than a million specimens belonging to all the animal groups. Fourteen collecting stations are maintained in different ecological biotopes, such as the Desert Regional Station at Jodhpur and the high-altitude station at Solan.

NEPAL

Bird Conservation Nepal (BCN)
Address: Post Box 12465, Kathmandu.
Publication: *Danphe* newsletter (quarterly).
BCN (previously known as the Nepal Birdwatching Club) is the biggest and oldest society dedicated to the interest of ornithologists and birdwatching in Nepal. It was established in 1982 to promote an interest in birds among the general public, to encourage basic research on diverse aspects of bird biology and ecology, to identify the major threats to birds' continued survival, and to help conserve birds and their habitats. It provides the most up-to-date information on birds and their habitats all over Nepal. Conservation education activities are given high priority, to educate people on the importance of birds and their intimacy with people.

SRI LANKA

Ceylon Bird Club
Address: Ceylon Bird Club, 39 Chatham Street, Colombo 1.
Publication: *Ceylon Bird Notes* (monthly).
The Ceylon Bird Club, established in 1944, is the pioneer organisation devoted to the study and protection of birds in that country. In 1985, the Club created Sri Lanka's first formal Rarities Committee; its purpose is to scrutinise and evaluate all reports of rare and new birds and to establish the official record.

Field Ornithology Group of Sri Lanka (FOGSL)
Address: Department of Zoology, University of Colombo, Colombo 03.
Publication: *Malkoha* (quarterly).
FOGSL was founded in 1976. Since then, it has been closely associated with the University of Colombo. It is endeavouring to build up and consolidate knowledge of and concern for Sri Lankan birds, two types of activity representing the path to that goal. One is to study birds in the wild, so that it can confidently be stated which species need protection and in what manner they need it. The other is to engender among people a greater concern about birds, so that the threats to the Sri Lankan avifauna will be reduced.

BHUTAN

Royal Society for the Protection of Nature (RSPN)
Address: PO Box No. 325, Thimphu.
Publications: *Thrung Thrung* newsletter (half-yearly); *Rangzhin* magazine (quarterly).
The RSPN was established in 1985 and was the first non-governmental organisation dealing with the environment and allied concerns. During its initial phase, with no external funding, the RSPN devoted its attention to the monitoring and protecting of rare and endangered species, particularly the Black-necked Crane, and to lobbying on environmental matters. Since 1992, external sponsorship has enabled the RSPN to expand its conservation-awareness activities. The basic objective is to heighten public awareness of environmental issues through educational programmes, campaigns and publications.

PAKISTAN

Ornithological Society of Pakistan (OSP)
Address: Near Chowk Fara, Block 'D', PO Box 73, Dera Ghazi Khan 32200.
Publication: *Pakistan Journal of Ornithology*.
OSP is a national, non-profit-making, non-governmental organisation, established in 1993, and is the registered organisation focused on the conservation of bird habitats and their resources in Pakistan. It is deeply involved with the initiation and promotion of scientifically based action for bird conservation through the sustainable development of resources, with maximum community participation in conservation and development. OSP's mission is to help promote the protection, conservation and sustainable use of all kinds of habitat and their resources in and around Pakistan.

BANGLADESH

Nature Conservation Movement (NACON)
Address: Anisuzzaman Khan (Executive Director), 125–127 (2nd floor) Nohammadia Super Market, Sobhanbag, Dhaka 1207.
NACON is a non-governmental organisation working to improve information on wildlife, to raise awareness of the threats to wildlife, and to involve communities in wildlife conservation. NACON co-ordinates the Asian waterfowl census in Bangladesh and has undertaken other surveys, for example of birds and wildlife in the wetlands of the northeast, and in various protected areas controlled by the Forest Department.

Wildlife Society of Bangladesh
Address: Department of Zoology, University of Dhaka, Dhaka.
This society undertakes field studies of wildlife, promotes protection of wildlife, and has close connections with the Department of Zoology and with academic zoologists in Bangladesh.

Centre for Advanced Research in Natural Resources and Management (CARINAM)
Address: R. M. A. Rashid (President), 70 Kakrail, Dhaka 1000.
CARINAM undertakes surveys and studies mainly of wetland wildlife and resources, and has a wetland-resource study centre in Netrakona district.

INTERNATIONAL ORGANISATIONS

BirdLife International
Address: Wellbrook Court, Girton Road, Cambridge CB3 0NA, UK.
Publication: *World Birdwatch* magazine (quarterly).
BirdLife International (formerly the International Council for Bird Preservation) is now the world's leading authority on the status of the world's birds, their habitats and the urgent problems that face them. BirdLife aims to:
(1) prevent the extinction of any bird species;
(2) reduce the number of species that are globally threatened;
(3) enhance the conservation status of all bird species; and
(4) conserve crucial sites and habitats for birds.
Through its national co-ordinators, BirdLife is compiling detailed directories for Asia on threatened birds, important bird areas and endemic bird areas. Within the subcontinent, BirdLife International also has a programme to conserve the Western Tragopan in the Palas valley in Pakistan by working with local tribespeople.

Wetlands International – Asia Pacific
Address: Institute of Advanced Studies, University of Malaya, Lembah Pantai, 50603 Kuala Lumpur, Malaysia.
Publication: *Asian Wetland News.*
Wetlands International – Asia Pacific was created in October 1985 following the merger of the Asian Wetland Bureau with the International Waterfowl and Wetlands Research Bureau. The organisation is committed to promoting the protection and sustainable utilisation of wetlands and wetland resources in the Asia–Pacific region. It has been involved in surveys, monitoring and conservation of waterbirds and wetlands since 1954, and has co-ordinated the Asia Waterfowl Census since 1987. It also organises international and national conferences, workshops and meetings to encourage the exchange of information and experiences and training. An Asian–Pacific Migratory Waterbird Conservation Strategy 1996–2000 has recently been developed. This aims to enhance the long-term conservation of migratory waterbirds and their habitats in the region (Mundkur and Matsui 1996).

World Pheasant Association South Asia (WPA–SARO)
Address: c/o WWF India, 172-B Lodi Estate, New Delhi 110 023, India.
Publication: *WPA India News.*
WPA South Asia (WPA–SARO) was established by the World Pheasant Association in April 1992. The main purpose of this office was to further the aims of WPA in the South Asian region. Over the last five years, the office has initiated many short- and long-term field research projects leading to the production of useful data, not only on Galliformes, but also on other birds, mammals and their habitats. WPA–SARO has also been offering assistance by way of technical, material and financial help.

World Wide Fund for Nature (WWF)
WWF India
Address: 172-B Lodi Estate, New Delhi 110 023.
WWF India was established in 1969 and is the largest of the country's non-governmental conservation organisations. Today, the organisation's mission is 'to promote nature conservation and environmental protection as the basis for sustainable and equitable development'.
WWF Pakistan
Address: UPO Box 1439, University of Peshawar, Peshawar, N.W.F.P.
WWF's involvement in Pakistan dates from the mid 1960s. It is the largest non-governmental nature conservation organisation in Pakistan. Its conservation efforts include protecting wetlands, forest and wildlife on a sustainable basis, and working on air, water and land pollution issues.
WWF Nepal
Address: PO Box 7660, Lal Durbar, Kathmandu.
WWF started work in Nepal in 1967. In 1985, WWF initiated a countrywide programme with another non-governmental organisation, the King Mahendra Trust for Nature Conservation (see above), and in 1993 opened an office in Kathmandu. The WWF programme covers conservation education, protected-area and endangered-species management, and institutional strengthening, and today also encourages activities that integrate conservation with development.
WWF Bhutan
Address: PO Box 210, Thimphu.
WWF has been sponsoring conservation efforts in Bhutan since 1977, and a field office was established in 1992. Today, WWF is an important player in the country's conservation efforts, recognised by the Bhutanese Government. As part of its programme, WWF Bhutan is sponsoring baseline ornithological surveys in the country's protected areas, which must be among the least known in the region, as well as training Bhutanese in bird-survey and identification techniques.

Oriental Bird Club (OBC)
Address: The Lodge, Sandy, Bedfordshire SG19 2DL, UK.
Publications: *OBC Bulletin* (half-yearly); *Forktail* journal (annual).
The OBC was established in 1985. It aims to:
(1) encourage an interest in the birds of the Oriental region and their conservation;
(2) liaise with and promote the work of existing regional societies; and
(3) collate and publish material on Oriental birds.
The OBC offers grants to nationals in the region to encourage survey work useful for conservation and conservation awareness.

REFERENCES

Anon. (1991) Mangrove conservation. *Hornbill* 1991(4): 20.

Anon. (1996) *Asia–Pacific Migratory Waterbird Conservation Strategy: 1996–2000.* Wetlands International – Asia Pacific, Kuala Lumpur, Publication No. 117, and International Waterfowl and Wetlands Research Bureau – Japan Committee, Tokyo.

Ash, J. S., and Shafeeg, A. (1995) The birds of the Maldives. *Forktail* 10: 3–31.

Collar, N. J., Crosby, M. J., and Stattersfield, A. J. (1994) *Birds to Watch 2, the World List of Threatened Birds.* BirdLife International, Cambridge.

Collins, N. M., Sayer, J. A., and Whitmore, T. C. (1991) *The Conservation Atlas of Tropical Forests: Asia and the Pacific.* The World Conservation Union. Macmillan, London.

Economic and Social Commission for Asia and the Pacific. (1994) *Statistical Yearbook for Asia and the Pacific 1993.* Bangkok.

Forest Survey of India. (1989) *The State of Forest Report.* Government of India, Ministry of Environment and Forests.

Forest Survey of India. (1991) *The State of Forest Report.* Government of India, Ministry of Environment and Forests.

Gillham, E., and Gillham, B. (1996) *Hybrid ducks – Contribution towards an Inventory.* Privately published.

Grewal, B. (1994) *Threatened Birds of India.* Privately published.

Hussain, S. A. (1996) An overview of recent bird migration studies in India. Abstract. P.1 in Pan-Asian Ornithological Congress and XII BirdLife Asia Conference, Coimbatore, India, 9–16 November 1996.

Inskipp, C. (1989) *Nepal's Forest Birds: their Status and Conservation.* Monograph No. 4, International Council for Bird Preservation, Cambridge.

Inskipp, T., Lindsey, N., and Duckworth, W. (1996) *An Annotated Checklist of the Birds of the Oriental Region.* Oriental Bird Club, Sandy.

Khan, M. S., Haq, E., Huq, S., Rahman, A. A., Rashid, S. M. A., and Ahmed, H. (eds) (1994) *Wetlands of Bangladesh.* Bangladesh Centre for Advanced Studies, Dhaka.

Knox, A. G. (1993) Richard Meinertzhagen – a case of fraud examined. *Ibis* 135: 320–325.

Martens, J., and Eck, S. (1995) Towards an ornithology of the Himalayas: systematics, ecology and vocalizations of Nepal birds. *Bonner Zoologische Monographien* 38: 1–445.

Ministry of Environment and Forests. (1997) *State of Forest Report 1997.* Dehra Dun: Forest Survey of India.

Muralidharan, S. (1992) Poisoning the Sarus. *Hornbill* 1992(1): 2–7.

Naoroji, R. (1995) Conservation issues of some raptor species in the Himalayan foothills with emphasis on Mountain Hawk-Eagle and Lesser Greyheaded Fishing Eagle. Pp.32–34 in L. Vijayan (ed), *Avian Conservation in India.* SACON, Coimbatore.

Perennou, C., Mundkur, T., Scott, D. A., Folkestad, A., and Kvenild, L. (1994) *The Asian Waterfowl Census 1987–91: Distribution and Status of Asian Waterfowl.* AWB Publication 86. IWRB Publication 24. AWB, Kuala Lumpur, and IWRB, Slimbridge.

Rahman, S. (1995) Wildlife in Bangladesh: a diminishing resource. *TigerPaper* 22(3): 7–14.

Rahmani, A. R., and Sankaran, R. (1995) The Indian Thar desert. Pp.61–62 in L. Vijayan (ed), *Avian Conservation in India.* SACON, Coimbatore.

Rasmussen, P., and Prys-Jones, R. (in prep.) The Asian records of Richard Meinertzhagen.

Roberts, T. J. (1991–1992) *The Birds of Pakistan.* Two vols. Oxford University Press, Karachi.

Tucker, G., and Heath, M. (1994) *Birds in Europe: their Conservation and Status.* BirdLife International, Cambridge.

Sankaran, R. (1995) A fresh initiative to conserve the Lesser Florican. *Oriental Bird Club Bull.* 22: 42–44.

Sankaran, R. (1997) The impact of nest collection on the Edible-nest Swiftlet *Collacalia fuciphaga* in the Andaman and Nicobar Islands. SACON, Coimbatore.

Shyamsunder, S., and Parameswarappa, S. (1987) Forestry in India – the forester's view. *Ambio* 16: 332–337.

Stattersfield, A. J., Crosby, M. J., Long, A. J., and Wege, D. C. (1998) *Endemic Bird Areas of the World, Priorities for Biodiversity Conservation.* BirdLife International, Cambridge.

WWF India and AWB. (1993) *Directory of Indian Wetlands.* WWF INDIA, New Delhi; AWB, Kuala Lumpur.

ACKNOWLEDGEMENTS

The present work owes a very great debt to many ornithologists and birders both past and present. This guide would have been a lifetime's work were it not for the extensive and comprehensive foundations laid by E. C. S. Baker in the bird volumes of the *Fauna of British India including Ceylon and Burma* (1922–1930), and S. Ali and S. D. Ripley in their *Handbook of the Birds of India and Pakistan* (1968–1974). There have been tremendous advances over the past fifteen years, particularly in field identification, and the important work of Per Alström, Peter Clement, Urban Olsson, Pamela Rasmussen, Philip Round and Hadoram Shirihai has frequently been referenced.

A special word of appreciation should go to Nigel Redman and Christopher Helm, of Pica Press, who conceived the idea for this book, assembled a start-up team of authors and artists, and provided much encouragement in the early stages. We thank the publishers, A & C Black, who took over the project in 1992, and are especially grateful to Robert Kirk, who has managed the project, for his constant encouragement and understanding, and to David A. Christie for his editing.

The following people have been very willing to review identification texts, and their input has added much to this work: Raf Drijvers (finches, waders, warblers), Martin Elliot (gulls, terns), Clifford Frith (hornbills), David Gibbs (pigeons), Simon Harrap (babblers, nuthatches, treecreepers), Erik Hirschfeld (terns, waders), Paul Holt (warblers), Ted Hoogendoorn (gulls), Alan Kemp (hornbills), Paul Leader (terns), Steve Madge (crows, warblers), Klaus Malling Olsen (terns), John Marchant (waders), .Tony Marr (skuas), Pilai Poonswad (hornbills), Colin Richardson (terns), Jelle Scharringa (warblers), and David Wells (cuckoos). Martin Elliott drafted the accounts for the large gulls. Alan Harris provided useful information on the identification of female and juvenile flycatchers and redstarts, Philip Round on bush warblers, and Jan Wilczur on cormorants, and Nigel Collar obtained photographs of skins of Rusty-throated Wren Babbler. Andrew Robertson, Paul Willoughby, Phil Heath and Philip Round also provided valuable comments on the identification text and/or plates.

A number of people have kindly allowed access to important works in preparation or in press. Richard Porter provided RG with page proofs of *Field Guide to the Birds of the Middle East* (Porter *et al.* 1996); David Gibbs supplied RG with draft texts from his forthcoming book for Pica Press on pigeons of the world; and Nigel Redman sent RG pre-publication texts and copies of plates from *Shrikes* by Norbert Lefranc and Tim Worfolk (1997). David Wells provided information on cuckoos from his forthcoming book on the Malay peninsula, and draft texts and plates were also provided by A & C Black from I. J. Ferguson-Lees's book (in prep.) on raptors of the world. Such selfless assistance by so many people has been greatly appreciated.

Shahin Ansari, Chris Baker, Nigel Bean, Pete Davidson, Paul Holt, Graeme Green and Simon Mustoe provided considerable assistance to RG with the checking of plates and text against museum specimens and the literature. Their work revealed many an error or oversight, and frequently pinpointed new identification features. Of particular value was Pete Davidson's work on nightjars, herons, crakes and rosefinches, Nigel Bean's on pheasants, Chris Baker's on leafbirds and nightjars, and Graeme Green's work on thrushes, chats, flycatchers, petrels and tropicbirds. Nigel, and particularly Chris, took hundreds of photographs of museum specimens, which have greatly assisted the project. Per Alström provided valuable comments on the vulture plates.

The Natural History Museum at Tring, England, was an invaluable treasure house of information which has been a cornerstone for this work. Whatever standard this book might have reached has been possible only because of this magnificent resource, which is a monument to the many great fieldworkers who collected in the subcontinent during the late 19th and early 20th centuries. The frontiers will never again be pushed back, in the face of comparative hardship, to the extent that they were by those intrepid explorers. Too few people realise the priceless value of their efforts, the results of which should be preserved at all cost. Particular thanks from RG go to past and present staff at the NHM, Tring – Robert Prys-Jones, Michael Walters, Peter Colston, Cyril Walker, F. E. ('Effie') Warr, Don Smith and Mark Adams – for permission to use the collection and for their enthusiastic assistance.

Graeme, Carole, Louise and Julianna Green very kindly provided, on numerous occasions, both accommodation close to Tring and excellent hospitality for RG and others; without this, the project would have been even more of a financial liability! Staff at the Youth Hostel at Ivinghoe, near Tring, were also very hospitable.

Good company in the field has made birding in the subcontinent all the more enjoyable, informative and feasible. RG would like to thank the following for their great company in the region at various times over the past 18 years: Shahid Ali, Jonathan Eames, Dave Farrow, Dick Filby, M. S. Kulkarni, Rajiv Mathew, Chris Murphy, Les Norton, Mike Parr, Aasheesh Pittie, Nigel Redman, Craig Robson, S. Sridhar, Siraj Ahmed Taher, Colin Winyard and James Wolstencroft. Particular thanks are extended from RG to S. A. Hussain, David Melville, Mohammad Mumtaz Malik and T. J. Roberts for their considerable assistance with field work.

Many friends have encouraged us during the painful gestation of this book. Notably among these, RG would like to mention Mark Cocker, Adrian Long and Craig Robson. While this book has been written outside 'office hours', RG's past and present colleagues at BirdLife International – Colin Bibby, Nigel Collar, Mike Crosby, John Fanshawe, Christoph Imboden, Paul Jepson and Mike Rands – have always been supportive. Permission for the use of BirdLife office equipment has also been much appreciated. Irene Hughes has greatly assisted RG with word processing.

RG would like to thank Helen, as well as our two children George and Ella, for putting up with more self-centred obsession over the past six years than was ever reasonable, with too many holidays and weekends that never were. Helen has travelled with RG on long trips to the subcontinent; Helen also provided considerable editorial help, as well as assistance in so many other ways. The Grimmett family has always blessed RG with support and understanding which has made life and work possible. Many thanks also to the Taylor and Roseveare families for putting up with 'the book' and the absent son/brother-in-law.

CI and TI wish to warmly thank the many observers who sent us their bird records from the region during the writing of this book. Their contributions have greatly added to current knowledge of the distribution and status of the subcontinent's birds. We are especially grateful to Hem Sagar Baral, Raf Drijvers, Paul Holt, Krys Kazmierczak, Pratap Singh and Per Undeland. Thanks also go to Per Alström, Ramana Athreya, Ian Barber, M. Berlijn, Keith Betton, David Bishop, James Bland, Arun Bose, Axel Braunlich, Marc Brew, Neil Bostock, Seb Buckton, Hathan Choudhary, Anwaruddin Choudhury, Mark Cocker, D and J F Cooper, Rosemary Cooper, David Cottridge, Jack Cox Jr, Jon Curson, Jean-Marne Daulne, Edward Deumelmester, K. D. Dijkstra, Geoff Dobbs, Philippe Dubois, Alan Dunkley, Dave Farrow, Martin Flack, J. P. Fouarge, Usha Ganguli-Lachungpa, Brian Gee, Christian Goblet, Tika Ram Giri, Kaj Halberg, John Halliday, Simon Harrap, Andrew Harrop, Phil Heath, Morten Heegard, Joel Heinen, Pete Hines, Julian Hough, Ole Jakobsen, Paul Jepson, Björn Johansson, David Johnson, Madhusudan Katti, Chris Kightley, Ben King, Jean-Christopher Kovacs, Alan Lewis, Paul Mackenzie, Steve Madge, Jochen Martens, Rod Martins, Iwan Mauro, Frank Miallier, Taej Mundkur, Chris Murphy, Rishad Naoroji, Christian Perennou, Otto Pfister, Hans Christien Koie Poulsen, Rebecca Pradhan, Anders Priemé, Roger Prodon, Ian Puckrin, Asad Rahmani, Lars Bonne Rasmussen, Henning Vikkelso Rasmussen, Nigel Redman, Andy Robinson, Craig Robson, Jimmy Roberts, Mike Roberts, Andrew Robertson, Dave Showler, Don Taylor, Guy Thompson, Jugal Tiwari, sTim Toohig, Edward Vercrysse, Beat Wartmann, André Weiss, Walter Wettstein, Alan Wheeldon, David and Kay White, Paul Willoughby, John Woolner, Ron Youngman, and Michael Zerning.

Special thanks go to Bikram Grewal for the numerous Indian books, papers and reports he has sent us, which have been very useful for our work on the book. The two of us particularly appreciated Bikram's outstanding hospitality during our visits to Delhi and his enthusiasm and encouragement for the producing of this book.

The following provided CI with valuable comments on the texts on habits, habitat, and distribution and status: Prakash Gole (cranes), R. Kannan (hornbills), Rahul Kaul (gamebirds), Taej Mundkur (wetland birds and the book's introduction), Rishad Naoroji (birds of prey), Asad Rahmani (gamebirds, bustards, chats) and V. Santharam (woodpeckers).

TI would like to thank Aasheesh Pittie, V. Santharam, Siraj Taher and Per Undeland for providing comments on the maps.

CI is very grateful to Julie Reay for her enormous help with word processing and for always being prepared to take on extra work at short notice.

A number of people generously sent us their bird recordings and/or transcriptions of vocalisations. The authors thank Paul Holt and Craig Robson for their particularly large and valuable contributions. Thanks also go to Hem Sagar Baral, David Bishop, Seb Buckton, Scott Connop, Raf Drijvers, Jonathan Eames, Dave Farrow, Brian Gee, Paul Holt, Alan Lewis, Nigel Lindsey, Steve Madge, Pete Morris, Philip Round, Jelle Scharringa, Uthai Treesucon and Edward Vercrysse.

Useful information for the introduction was provided by Rahul Kaul (World Pheasant Association South Asia), Aleem Ahmed Khan (Pakistan NGOs) and Paul Thompson (Bangladesh NGOs).

The authors are especially grateful to David Butler, Mike Crosby and BirdLife International for the Endemic Bird Areas map of the subcontinent, and to Simon Blyth and the World Conservation Monitoring Centre for the forest-cover maps of the region.

Alan Harris is grateful to David Mead and Paul Leader for providing him with useful information, and also thanks the Natural History Museum at Tring. John Cox thanks David Gibbs, Craig Robson, Jenny Harris, Alan Pearson and Eustace Barnes. Daniel Cole acknowledges the help of Paul North, Michel Klat, Irene Charalambous, Steve Bishop and the World Pheasant Association. Martin Elliot is grateful to Mashuq Ahmad and Lars Jonsson.

GLOSSARY

See also figures on p.13, which cover bird topography.

Altitudinal migrant: a species which breeds at high altitudes (in mountains) and moves to lower levels and valleys in non-breeding season.
Arboreal: tree-dwelling.
Arm: the basal part of the wing, from where it joins the body outwards to the carpal joint.
Axillaries: the feathers in the armpit at the base of the underwing.
Biotope: a particular area which is substantially uniform in its environmental conditions and its flora and fauna.
Cap: a well-defined patch of colour or bare skin on the top of the head.
Carpal: the bend of the wing, or carpal joint.
Carpal patch: a well-defined patch of colour on the underwing in the vicinity of the carpal joint.
Casque: an enlargement on the upper surface of the bill, in front of the head, as on hornbills.
Cere: a fleshy (often brightly coloured) structure at the base of the bill and containing the nostrils.
Collar: a well-defined band of colour which encircles or partly encircles the neck.
Colonial: nesting or roosting in tight colonies; species which are loosely colonial have nests more widely spaced.
Commensalism: a rare situation in which species 'A' benefits from the presence of species 'B', but where 'B' is indifferent to the presence of 'A', neither gaining nor losing from that association.
Culmen: the ridge of the upper mandible.
Duar: the eastern section of the belt of alluvial soil stretching along the northern edge of the terai (see below) and up to about 600 m in the Himalayan foothills; found in northern West Bengal, Bhutan and adjacent upper Assam.
Eclipse plumage: a female-like plumage acquired by males of some species (e.g. ducks or some sunbirds) during or after breeding.
Edgings or edges: outer feather margins, which can frequently result in distinct paler or darker panels of colour on wings or tail.
Endemic: restricted or confined to a specific country or region.
Filoplume: a thin, hair-like feather.
Flight feathers: the primaries, secondaries and tail feathers (although not infrequently used to denote the primaries and secondaries alone).
Fringes: complete feather margins, which can frequently result in a scaly appearance to body feathers or wing-coverts.
Frugivorous: fruit-eating.
Gape: the mouth and fleshy corner of the bill, which can extend back below the eye.
Gonys: a bulge in the lower mandible, usually distinct on gulls and terns.
Graduated tail: a tail in which the longest feathers are the central pair and the shortest the outermost, with those in between intermediate in length.
Granivorous: feeding on grain or seeds.
Gregarious: living in flocks or communities.
Gular pouch: a loose and pronounced area of skin extending from the throat (e.g. on pelicans or hornbills).
Gular stripe: a usually very narrow (and often dark) stripe running down the centre of the throat.
Hackles: long and pointed neck feathers which can extend across mantle and wing-coverts (e.g. on junglefowls or Nicobar Pigeon).
Hand: the outer part of the wing, from the carpal joint to the tip of the wing.
Hepatic: used with reference to the rufous-brown morph of some (female) cuckoos.
Iris (plural irides): the coloured membrane which surrounds the pupil of the eye and which can be brightly coloured.
Jheel: a shallow lake in a low-lying natural depression, usually with floating and submerged vegetation, reedbeds and partially submerged trees.
Lappet: a wattle, particularly one at the gape.
Leading edge: the front edge of the forewing.
Local: occurring or common within a small or restricted area.
Mandible: the lower or upper half of the bill.
Mask: a dark area of plumage surrounding the eye and often covering the ear-coverts.
Melanistic: relating to a condition in which the plumage is dominated by black pigmentation.
Morph: a distinct plumage type which occurs alongside one or more other distinct plumage types exhibited by the same species.
Nomadic: of a wandering or erratically occurring species which has no fixed territory when not breeding.
Nominate: the first-named race of a species, that which has its scientific racial name the same as the specific name.
Nullah: a watercourse or ravine, usually dry.

Nuchal: relating to the hindneck, used with reference to a patch or collar.
Ocelli: eye-like spots of iridescent colour; a distinctive feature in the plumage of peafowls and Grey Peacock Pheasant.
Orbital ring: a narrow circular ring of feathering or bare skin surrounding the eye.
Pelagic: of the open sea.
pH: a measure of acidity: low pH indicates high acidity, high pH low acidity.
Plantation: a group of trees (usually exotic or non-native species) planted in close proximity to each other, used for timber or as a crop.
Primary projection: the extension of the primaries beyond the longest tertial on a closed wing; this can be of critical importance in identification (e.g. of larks or *Acrocephalus* warblers).
Race: subspecies, a geographical population whose members all show constant differences (e.g. in plumage or size) from those of other populations of the same species.
Rectrices (singular **rectrix**): the tail feathers.
Remiges (singular **remex**): the primaries and secondaries.
Rictal bristles: bristles, often prominent, at the base of the bill.
Shaft streak: a fine line of pale or dark colour in the plumage, produced by the feather shaft.
Shola: a patch of montane evergreen wet temperate forest, usually in a sheltered hill valley among rolling grassy hills from about 1500 m upwards, found in south India and Sri Lanka.
Speculum: the often glossy panel across the secondaries of, especially, dabbling ducks, often bordered by pale tips to these feathers and a greater-covert wing-bar.
Subspecies: see Race.
Subterminal band: a dark or pale band, usually broad, situated inside the outer part of a feather or feather tract (used particularly in reference to the tail).
Terai: the undulating alluvial, often marshy strip of land 25–45 km wide lying north of the Gangetic plain, extending from Uttar Pradesh through Nepal and northern West Bengal to Assam; naturally supports tall elephant grass interspersed with dense forest, but large areas have been drained and converted to cultivation.
Terminal band: a dark or pale band, usually broad, at the tip of a feather or feather tract (especially the tail); cf. Subterminal band.
Terrestrial: living or occurring mainly on the ground.
Trailing edge: the rear edge of the wing, often darker or paler than the rest of the wing; cf. Leading edge.
Vent: the area around the cloaca (anal opening), just behind the legs (should not be confused with the undertail-coverts).
Vermiculated: marked with narrow wavy lines, usually visible only at close range.
Wattle: a lobe of bare, often brightly coloured skin attached to the head (frequently at the bill-base), as on the mynas or the wattled lapwings.
Wing-linings: the entire underwing-coverts.
Wing panel: a pale or dark band across the upperwing (often formed by pale edges to the remiges or coverts), broader and generally more diffuse than a wing-bar.
Wing-bar: generally a narrow and well-defined dark or pale bar across the upperwing, and often referring to a band formed by pale tips to the greater or median coverts (or both, as in 'double wing-bar').

COLOUR PLATES
1–153

PLATE 1: NICOBAR SCRUBFOWL, SNOWCOCKS, PARTRIDGES AND FRANCOLINS

1 **NICOBAR SCRUBFOWL** *Megapodius nicobariensis* **Page 345**
Adult. Resident. Nicobars. Chestnut-brown upperparts, cinnamon-brown to brownish-grey underparts, and bare red facial skin. Forest undergrowth by sandy beaches.

2 **SNOW PARTRIDGE** *Lerwa lerwa* **Page 345**
Adult. Resident. Himalayas. Vermiculated dark brown and white upperparts, chestnut streaking on underparts, and red bill and legs. High-altitude rocky and grassy slopes with scrub.

3 **SEE-SEE PARTRIDGE** *Ammoperdix griseogularis* **Page 345**
Male (3a) and female (3b). Resident. Pakistan. Male has white eye-stripe and chestnut and black flank stripes. Female has cream supercilium and throat, grey flecking on neck, and pinkish-buff and grey vermiculations on mantle and breast. Dry rocky foothills, sand dunes and cultivation edges.

4 **TIBETAN SNOWCOCK** *Tetraogallus tibetanus* **Page 346**
Adult *T. t. aquilonifer*. Resident. Himalayas. White ear-covert patch, grey banding across breast, and white underparts with black flank stripes. High-altitude rocky slopes and alpine meadows.

5 **HIMALAYAN SNOWCOCK** *Tetraogallus himalayensis* **Page 346**
Adult. Resident. Himalayas. Chestnut neck stripes, whitish breast contrasting with dark grey underparts, and chestnut flank stripes. In flight, differs from Tibetan in wing pattern and rump/uppertail coloration (see text). High-altitude rocky slopes and alpine meadows.

6 **BUFF-THROATED PARTRIDGE** *Tetraophasis szechenyii* **Page 346**
Adult. Resident. Arunachal Pradesh. Large size, white-tipped tail, buff banding across scapulars and wings, orange-buff throat, and unstreaked mantle. Subalpine forest and shrubberies.

7 **CHUKAR** *Alectoris chukar* **Page 347**
Adult *A. c. chukar*. Resident. Pakistan hills and Himalayas. Black gorget encircling throat, barring on flanks, and red bill and legs. Open rocky or grassy hills; dry terraced cultivation.

8 **BLACK FRANCOLIN** *Francolinus francolinus* **Page 347**
Male (8a) and female (8b). Resident. N subcontinent. Male has black face with white ear-covert patch, rufous neck band, and black underparts with white spotting. Female has rufous hindneck, streaked appearance to upperparts, and heavily barred underparts. Cultivation, tall grass and scrub in plains and hills.

9 **PAINTED FRANCOLIN** *Francolinus pictus* **Page 348**
Male (9a) and female (9b). Resident. Peninsular India and Sri Lanka. Rufous-orange face (and often throat), and bold white spotting on upperparts and underparts. Tall grassland and cultivation with scattered trees; open thin forest.

10 **CHINESE FRANCOLIN** *Francolinus pintadeanus* **Page 348**
Male (10a) and female (10b). Resident. Manipur. Broad black moustachial stripe, and spotted mantle; underparts heavily spotted (male) or barred (female). Dry, open broadleaved forest and scrub in hills.

11 **GREY FRANCOLIN** *Francolinus pondicerianus* **Page 348**
Adult *F. p. interpositus*. Widespread resident in lowlands and low hills; unrecorded in northeast. Finely barred upperparts with shaft streaking, and finely barred underparts. Dry grass and thorn scrub.

12 **SWAMP FRANCOLIN** *Francolinus gularis* **Page 349**
Adult. Resident. From Nepal east to Assam. Rufous-orange throat, finely barred upperparts, and bold white streaking on underparts. Tall wet grassland, sugarcane fields.

13 **TIBETAN PARTRIDGE** *Perdix hodgsoniae* **Page 349**
Adult *P. h. hodgsoniae*. Resident. N Himalayas. Black patch on white face, rufous collar, and black and rufous barring on underparts. High-altitude semi-desert, rock and scrub slopes.

1
2
3b
3a
4
5
6
7
8b
8a
9b
9a
10b
10a
11
12
13
Dan Cole 95

PLATE 2: QUAILS AND BUTTONQUAILS

1 **COMMON QUAIL** *Coturnix coturnix* **Page 349**
Male (1a) and female (1b). Mainly winter visitor and passage migrant, also resident. Widespread in north. Male has black 'anchor' mark on throat; some males without 'anchor' and with rufous on throat. Female probably indistinguishable from female Japanese. Crops and grassland.

2 **JAPANESE QUAIL** *Coturnix japonica* **Page 350**
Male (2a) and female (2b). Winter visitor, probably breeds. Assam and Bhutan. Breeding male has rufous throat and foreneck; patterning of throat very variable on non-breeding male and, as female, probably indistinguishable from Common. Crops and grassland.

3 **RAIN QUAIL** *Coturnix coromandelica* **Page 350**
Male (3a) and female (3b). Widespread resident. Male has strongly patterned head and neck, black on breast, and streaking on flanks. Female smaller than female Japanese and Common, with unbarred primaries. Crops, grassland, grass and scrub jungle.

4 **BLUE-BREASTED QUAIL** *Coturnix chinensis* **Page 351**
Male (4a) and female (4b) Widespread resident; unrecorded in northwest. Male has black-and-white head pattern, slaty-blue flanks, and chestnut belly. Female has barred breast and flanks. Wet grassland, marshes and scrub.

5 **JUNGLE BUSH QUAIL** *Perdicula asiatica* **Page 351**
Male (5a) and female (5b) *P. a. asiatica.* Widespread resident; unrecorded in northwest and northeast. Male has barred underparts, rufous-orange throat, white moustachial stripe, and brown ear-coverts. Female has vinaceous-buff underparts, with head pattern similar to male. Dry grass and scrub, deciduous forest.

6 **ROCK BUSH QUAIL** *Perdicula argoondah* **Page 351**
Male (6a) and female (6b) *P. a. argoondah.* Resident. C and W India. Male has barred underparts, and vinaceous-buff ear-coverts and throat; lacks white moustachial stripe. Female has vinaceous-buff underparts, including throat and ear-coverts, and short whitish supercilium. Dry rocky and sandy areas with thorn scrub in plains and foothills.

7 **PAINTED BUSH QUAIL** *Perdicula erythrorhyncha* **Page 352**
Male (7a) and female (7b) Resident. Mainly Western and Eastern Ghats. Black spotting on upperparts and flanks, and red bill and legs. Male has white supercilium and throat. Female has rufous supercilium. Scrub in plains and foothills.

8 **MANIPUR BUSH QUAIL** *Perdicula manipurensis* **Page 352**
Male (8a) and female (8b) *P. m. manipurensis.* Resident. NE India. Dark olive-grey upperparts, and golden-buff underparts with black cross-shaped markings. Male has chestnut forehead and throat, which are brownish-grey on female. Tall moist grassland and scrub in foothills.

9 **SMALL BUTTONQUAIL** *Turnix sylvatica* **Page 378**
Male Mainly resident. Widespread, chiefly in lowlands in India. Very small size and comparatively long, pointed tail. Buff edges to scapulars form prominent lines, and rufous mantle and coverts are boldly fringed buff, creating scaly appearance. Scrub and grassland.

10 **YELLOW-LEGGED BUTTONQUAIL** *Turnix tanki* **Page 378**
Male (10a) and female (10b) Mainly resident; summer visitor to northwest. Widespread, chiefly in lowlands. Yellow legs and bill. Comparatively uniform upperparts (lacking scaly or striped appearance), buff coverts with bold black spotting. Pattern and coloration of underparts very different from Barred. Scrub and grassland, and crops.

11 **BARRED BUTTONQUAIL** *Turnix suscitator* **Page 379**
Male (11a) and female (11b) *T. s. taigoor.* Resident. Widespread, mainly in lowlands. Grey bill and legs, and bold black barring on sides of neck, breast and wing-coverts. Orange-rufous to orange-buff flanks and belly clearly demarcated from barred breast. Females (and some males) have black throat and centre of breast. Scrub and grassland, and open forest.

1b
2b
3b
3a
2a
1a
5b
4b
6b
4a
5a
6a
7b
7a
8a
8b
10a
11a
9
10b
11b
Daniel Cole 95

PLATE 3: PARTRIDGES AND SPURFOWL

1 HILL PARTRIDGE *Arborophila torqueola* **Page 352**
Male (1a) and female (1b). Resident. Himalayas and NE India. Male has rufous crown and white collar. Female has black barring on mantle, and lacks black border between rufous-orange foreneck and grey breast. Grey or brown legs and feet. Broadleaved forest.

2 RUFOUS-THROATED PARTRIDGE *Arborophila rufogularis* **Page 353**
Male (2a) and female (2b) *A. r. rufogularis*; male *A. r. intermedia* (2c). Resident. Himalayas, NE India and Bangladesh. Greyish-white supercilium, unbarred mantle, and black border between rufous-orange foreneck and grey breast (except *intermedia*). Broadleaved forest and secondary growth.

3 WHITE-CHEEKED PARTRIDGE *Arborophila atrogularis* **Page 353**
Adult. Resident. E Himalayas, NE India and Bangladesh. White cheeks, black mask and throat, barred upperparts, and orange-yellow on neck which is streaked with black. Bamboo thickets and forest undergrowth.

4 CHESTNUT-BREASTED PARTRIDGE *Arborophila mandellii* **Page 353**
Adult. Resident. E Himalayas and Assam. White half-collar, rufous-orange throat, and chestnut breast. Forest undergrowth.

5 MOUNTAIN BAMBOO PARTRIDGE *Bambusicola fytchii* **Page 354**
Adult. Resident. NE India and Bangladesh. Long tail, chestnut spotting on breast and upperparts, blackish spotting on flanks, and buffish supercilium. Dense grass and scrub in foothills.

6 RED SPURFOWL *Galloperdix spadicea* **Page 354**
Male (6a) and female (6b) *G. s. spadicea*; male *G. s. stewarti* (6c). Resident. India. Red facial skin and legs/feet. Male has brownish-grey head and neck, and rufous body. Female has black mottling on upperparts, and barred underparts. Male *stewarti* is deeper chestnut-red. Scrub, bamboo thickets and secondary growth.

7 PAINTED SPURFOWL *Galloperdix lunulata* **Page 354**
Male (7a) and female (7b). Resident. India. Dark bill and legs/feet. Male has chestnut-red upperparts and yellowish-buff underparts with spotting and barring. Female is dark brown, with chestnut supercilium and buff throat. Thorn scrub and bamboo thickets.

8 SRI LANKA SPURFOWL *Galloperdix bicalcarata* **Page 355**
Male (8a) and female (8b). Resident. Sri Lanka. Red facial skin and legs/feet. Male is boldly streaked and spotted with white. Female has chestnut upperparts with blackish vermiculations, rufous underparts, and dark brown crown. Dense forest.

1a
1b
2b
2a
2c
3
4
5
6a
6b
6c
7b
7a
8a
8b
Daniel Cole 95.

PLATE 4: HIMALAYAN QUAIL AND PHEASANTS

1 **HIMALAYAN QUAIL** *Ophrysia superciliosa* **Page 355**
Male (1a) and female (1b). Presumed extinct. W Himalayas in India. Red bill and legs/feet. Male has black-and-white head pattern. Female is boldly spotted and streaked with black. Long grass and brush on steep slopes.

2 **BLOOD PHEASANT** *Ithaginis cruentus* **Page 355**
Male (2a, 2c) and female (2b) *I. c. cruentus*; male *I. c. kuseri* (2d); male *I. c. tibetanus* (2e). Resident. Himalayas. Crested head, and red orbital skin and legs/feet. Male has grey upperparts streaked with white, and greenish underparts, and plumage is splashed with red. Female has grey crest and nape, rufous-orange face, dark brown upperparts, and rufous-brown underparts. High-altitude forest.

3 **WESTERN TRAGOPAN** *Tragopan melanocephalus* **Page 356**
Male (3a) and female (3b). Resident. W Himalayas. Male has orange foreneck, blackish underparts which are boldly spotted with white, and red hindneck. Female has dark grey-brown coloration to underparts. Temperate and subalpine forest.

4 **SATYR TRAGOPAN** *Tragopan satyra* **Page 356**
Male (4a) and female (4b). Resident. Himalayas. Male has red underparts with black-bordered white spots, and olive-brown coloration to upperparts. Female generally has rufous tone to underparts. Temperate and subalpine forest.

5 **BLYTH'S TRAGOPAN** *Tragopan blythii* **Page 357**
Male (5a) and female (5b) *T. b. blythii*; male *T. b. molesworthi* (5c). Resident. E Himalayas and NE India. Male has sandy-grey lower breast and belly, and yellow facial skin. Female has grey-brown underparts with indistinct spotting. Broadleaved forest, dense shrubberies and bamboo.

6 **TEMMINCK'S TRAGOPAN** *Tragopan temminckii* **Page 357**
Male (6a) and female (6b). Resident. E Himalayas in Arunachal Pradesh. Male has grey spotting on red underparts, and red coloration to upperparts. Female has prominent white spotting on underparts. Temperate and subalpine forest.

7 **KOKLASS PHEASANT** *Pucrasia macrolopha* **Page 357**
Male (7a) and female (7b) *P. m. macrolopha*; male (7c) *P. m. nipalensis*. Resident. W Himalayas. Male has bottle-green head and ear-tufts, chestnut on breast, and streaked appearance to body. Female has white throat and streaked body. Both sexes have wedge-shaped tail. Temperate and subalpine forest.

1b
1a
2b
2a
2c
2e
2d
3b
3a
4b
4a
5b
5a
5c
7b
6a
7a
7c
6b
Daniel Cole 95

PLATE 5: PHEASANTS

1 HIMALAYAN MONAL *Lophophorus impejanus* **Page 358**
Male (1a) and female (1b). Resident. Himalayas. Male is iridescent green, copper and purple, with white patch on back and cinnamon-brown tail. Female has white throat, boldly streaked underparts, and white crescent on uppertail-coverts. Summers on rocky and grass-covered slopes; winters in forest.

2 SCLATER'S MONAL *Lophophorus sclateri* **Page 358**
Male (2a) and female (2b). Resident. E Himalayas in Arunachal Pradesh. Male has tufted crest, white lower back and rump/uppertail-coverts, and broad white tip to the cinnamon-brown tail. Female has greyish-white rump/uppertail-coverts, and white tip to tail. Fir forest.

3 RED JUNGLEFOWL *Gallus gallus* **Page 359**
Male (3a) and female (3b). Resident. Himalayas, NE and E India, and Bangladesh. Male has orange and golden-yellow neck hackles, blackish-brown underparts, and rufous-orange panel on secondaries. Female has black-streaked golden 'shawl', and rufous-brown underparts streaked with buff. Forest undergrowth and scrub.

4 GREY JUNGLEFOWL *Gallus sonneratii* **Page 359**
Male (4a) and female (4b). Resident. Peninsular India. Male has 'shawl' of white and pale yellow spotting, and golden-yellow spotting on scapulars. Female has white streaking on underparts. Forest undergrowth, secondary growth, bamboo thickets.

5 SRI LANKA JUNGLEFOWL *Gallus lafayetii* **Page 359**
Male (5a) and female (5b). Resident. Sri Lanka. Male has orange-red underparts, yellow spot on comb, and purplish-black wings and tail. Female has white streaking on breast, and black-and-white patterning to belly. Forest.

6 KALIJ PHEASANT *Lophura leucomelanos* **Page 360**
Male (6a) and female (6b) *L. l. hamiltonii*; male *L. l. leucomelanos* (6c); male *L. l. melanota* (6d); male *L. l. lathami* (6e). Resident. Himalayas, NE India and Bangladesh. Both sexes have red facial skin and downcurved tail. Male has blue-black upperparts, and variable amounts of white on rump and underparts. Female varies from dull brown to reddish-brown, with greyish-buff fringes producing scaly appearance. Forest with dense undergrowth.

1b
1a
2a
2b
3a
3b
4a
4b
5a
5b
6c
6d
6b
6a
6e

PLATE 6: PHEASANTS

1 **TIBETAN EARED PHEASANT** *Crossoptilon harmani* **Page 360**
Adult. Resident. Himalayas in NE Arunachal Pradesh. Grey, with white throat and white nape band. Red facial skin. Long, broad and slightly downcurved tail. High-altitude forest.

2 **CHEER PHEASANT** *Catreus wallichii* **Page 361**
Male (2a, 2c) and female (2b). Resident. W Himalayas. Long, broadly barred tail, pronounced crest, and red facial skin. Male is more cleanly and strongly marked than female, with pronounced barring on mantle, unmarked neck, and broader barring across tail. Steep, craggy hillsides with scrub, secondary growth.

3 **MRS HUME'S PHEASANT** *Syrmaticus humiae* **Page 361**
Male (3a, 3c) and female (3b, 3d). Resident. NE India. Male is chestnut and blue-black, with white banding along scapulars and across wings, and has strongly barred tail. Female has narrow whitish wing-bars, and white tips to tail feathers. Both sexes have long graduated tail and red facial skin. Steep rocky slopes with forest and scrub.

4 **GREY PEACOCK PHEASANT** *Polyplectron bicalcaratum* **Page 361**
Male (4a) and female (4b). Resident. E Himalayas and Bangladesh. Male has prominent purple and green ocelli, particularly on wing-coverts and tail; tail is long and broad, and has short tufted crest. Female is smaller, with shorter tail and smaller and duller ocelli. Undergrowth in tropical and subtropical forest.

5 **INDIAN PEAFOWL** *Pavo cristatus* **Page 362**
Male (5a) and female (5b). Resident. India, SE Pakistan, Nepal and Bhutan. Male has blue neck and breast, and spectacular glossy green train of elongated uppertail-covert feathers with numerous ocelli. Female lacks elongated uppertail-coverts; has whitish face and throat and white belly. Primaries of female are brown (chestnut in male), although this is not depicted on plate. Forest undergrowth in wild; villages and cultivation where semi-feral.

6 **GREEN PEAFOWL** *Pavo muticus* **Page 362**
Male (6a) and female (6b). Former resident? NE India and Bangladesh. Male has erect tufted crest, and is mainly green, with long green train of elongated uppertail-covert feathers with numerous ocelli. Female lacks long train; otherwise is similar to male, but upperparts are browner. Dense forest.

1
2a
2b
2c
3a
3b
3c
3d
4a
4b
5a
5b
6a
6b

PLATE 7: GEESE AND SWANS

1 **MUTE SWAN** *Cygnus olor* **Page 364**
Adult (1a) and juvenile (1b). Vagrant. Pakistan and India. Adult has orange bill with black base and knob. Juvenile is mottled sooty-brown, and has grey bill with black base. Large rivers and lakes.

2 **WHOOPER SWAN** *Cygnus cygnus* **Page 364**
Adult (2a) and juvenile (2b). Vagrant. Pakistan, Nepal and India. Adult has yellow of bill extending as wedge towards tip. Juvenile is smoky-grey, with pinkish bill. Longer neck and more angular head shape than Tundra. Large rivers and lakes.

3 **TUNDRA SWAN** *Cygnus columbianus* **Page 365**
Adult (3a) and juvenile (3b). Vagrant. Pakistan, Nepal and India. Adult has yellow of bill typically as oval-shaped patch. Juvenile is smoky-grey, with pinkish bill. Smaller in size, and with shorter neck and more rounded head, compared with Whooper. Lakes.

4 **BEAN GOOSE** *Anser fabalis* **Page 365**
Adult (4a, 4b). Vagrant. Nepal, India and Bangladesh. Black bill with orange band, and orange legs. Has slimmer neck and smaller, more angular head than Greylag; head, neck and upperparts are darker and browner. In flight, lacks pale grey forewing of Greylag. Open country.

5 **GREATER WHITE-FRONTED GOOSE** *Anser albifrons* **Page 365**
Adult (5a, 5b) and juvenile (5c). Winter visitor. Pakistan, N India and Bangladesh. Adult has white band at front of head, black barring on belly, and orange legs and feet. Juvenile lacks frontal band and belly barring. Large rivers and lakes.

6 **LESSER WHITE-FRONTED GOOSE** *Anser erythropus* **Page 365**
Adult (6a, 6b) and juvenile (6c). Winter visitor. Pakistan and NE India. White frontal band of adult extends onto forehead. Both adult and juvenile have yellow eye-ring. See text for structural differences from Greater White-fronted. Wet grassland and lakes.

7 **GREYLAG GOOSE** *Anser anser* **Page 366**
Adult (7a, 7b) and juvenile (7c). Winter visitor. N subcontinent. Large grey goose with pink bill and legs. Shows pale grey forewing in flight. Grassland, crops, lakes and large rivers.

1b
2b
3b
1a
3a
2a
4b
5b
4a
5a
5c
6b
7b
6c
6a
7a
7c

PLATE 8: GEESE, WHISTLING-DUCKS, AND SHELDUCKS

1 **BAR-HEADED GOOSE** *Anser indicus* **Page 366**
Adult (1a, 1b) and juvenile (1c). Breeds in Ladakh; widespread winter visitor. Adult has white head with black banding, and white line down grey neck. Juvenile has white face and dark grey crown and hindneck. Plumage paler steel-grey, with paler grey forewing, compared with Greylag. Breeds by high-altitude lakes; winters near large rivers and lakes.

2 **SNOW GOOSE** *Anser caerulescens* **Page 366**
Adult white morph (2a, 2b). Vagrant. India. All white, with black wing-tips and pink bill and legs. See text for juvenile and blue morph. Grass by reservoirs.

3 **RED-BREASTED GOOSE** *Branta ruficollis* **Page 367**
Adult. Vagrant. India. Reddish-chestnut cheek patch and foreneck/breast, and black-and-white body pattern. Habitat in subcontinent unknown.

4 **FULVOUS WHISTLING-DUCK** *Dendrocygna bicolor* **Page 363**
Adult (4a, 4b) and juvenile (4c). Resident. Mainly NE India and Bangladesh. Larger than Lesser, with bigger, squarer head and larger bill. Shows white uppertail-coverts in flight. Adult and juvenile show rufous-brown crown and blackish line down hindneck. Freshwater wetlands.

5 **LESSER WHISTLING-DUCK** *Dendrocygna javanica* **Page 363**
Adult (5a, 5b) and juvenile (5c). Widespread resident. Chestnut uppertail-coverts and pronounced chestnut-maroon patch on forewing. Adult and juvenile show brown cap and lack pronounced blackish line down hindneck. Freshwater wetlands.

6 **RUDDY SHELDUCK** *Tadorna ferruginea* **Page 367**
Male (6a, 6b) and female (6c). Breeds in Himalayas; widespread winter visitor. Rusty-orange, with buff to orange head; white upperwing- and underwing-coverts contrast with black remiges in flight. Breeding male has black neck band. Freshwater wetlands.

7 **COMMON SHELDUCK** *Tadorna tadorna* **Page 367**
Male (7a, 7b), female (7c) and juvenile (7d, 7e). Has bred Baluchistan; widespread winter visitor. Adult has greenish-black head and neck, and largely white body with chestnut breast-band. Juvenile lacks breast-band and has sooty-brown upperparts. White upperwing- and underwing-coverts contrast with black remiges in flight. Freshwater and coastal wetlands.

1b
2b
1c
1a
2a
3
4b
5b
4c
5a
5c
4a
7b
7e
6b
7d
7c
6c
6a
7a
JPPW

PLATE 9: MISCELLANEOUS WATERFOWL

1 **WHITE-WINGED DUCK** *Cairina scutulata* **Page 368**
Male (1a, 1b); variant male (1c). Resident. NE India and Bangladesh. White upperwing- and underwing-coverts, and white head variably speckled with black. Small freshwater wetlands in tropical forest.

2 **COMB DUCK** *Sarkidiornis melanotos* **Page 368**
Male (2a, 2b), female (2c) and juvenile (2d). Resident. Widespread in India, also Nepal lowlands and Bangladesh. Whitish head, speckled with black, and whitish underparts. Upperwing and underwing blackish. Male has fleshy comb. Juvenile has pale supercilium, buff scaling on upperparts, and rufous-buff underparts with dark scaling on sides of breast. Freshwater wetlands in well-wooded country.

3 **COTTON PYGMY-GOOSE** *Nettapus coromandelianus* **Page 368**
Male (3a, 3b), eclipse male (3c), female (3d, 3e) and juvenile (3f). Widespread resident. Small size. Male has broad white band across wing, and female has white trailing edge to wing. Male has white head and neck and black cap. Eclipse male, female and juvenile have dark stripe through eye. Vegetation-covered freshwater wetlands.

4 **MANDARIN DUCK** *Aix galericulata* **Page 369**
Male (4a, 4b) and female (4c, 4d). Vagrant. Nepal, India and Bangladesh. Male has reddish bill, orange 'mane' and 'sails', and white stripe behind eye. Female and eclipse male have white 'spectacles' and white spotting on breast and flanks. In flight, shows dark upperwing and underwing, with white trailing edge, and white belly. Freshwater wetlands.

5 **WHITE-HEADED DUCK** *Oxyura leucocephala* **Page 364**
Male (5a) and female (5b). Winter visitor. Pakistan and N India. Swollen base to bill, and pointed tail which is often held erect. Male has white head with black cap. Female has dark bill and striped head. Large fresh waters, lakes and brackish lagoons.

6 **PINK-HEADED DUCK** *Rhodonessa caryophyllacea* **Page 374**
Male (6a) and female (6b). Probably extinct. Mainly NE India. Male has pink head and bill and dark brown body. Female has greyish-pink head and duller brown body. Pools and marshes in elephant-grass jungle.

7 **MARBLED DUCK** *Marmaronetta angustirostris* **Page 373**
Adult (7a, 7b). Breeds in Pakistan; winter visitor to N subcontinent. Shaggy hood, dark mask, and diffusely spotted body. Upperwing rather uniform and underwing very pale. Shallow freshwater lakes and ponds.

1b
2b
2c
1c
1a
2a
2d
3e
3b
3f
3c
3a
3d
4d
4b
5a
5b
4c
4a
7b
7a
6b
6a
JPPW

PLATE 10: DABBLING DUCKS

1 GADWALL *Anas strepera* **Page 369**

Male (1a, 1b) and female (1c, 1d). Widespread winter visitor. White patch on inner secondaries in all plumages. Male is mainly grey, with dark grey bill. Female has orange sides to bill and clear-cut white belly; otherwise similar to female Mallard. Freshwater wetlands.

2 FALCATED DUCK *Anas falcata* **Page 370**

Male (2a, 2b) and female (2c, 2d). Winter visitor. N subcontinent. Male has bottle-green head with maned hindneck, and elongated black-and-grey tertials; shows pale grey forewing in flight. Female has rather plain greyish head, a dark bill, and dark spotting and scalloping on brown underparts; shows greyish forewing and white greater-covert bar in flight. Lakes and large rivers.

3 EURASIAN WIGEON *Anas penelope* **Page 370**

Male (3a, 3b) and female (3c, 3d). Widespread winter visitor. Male has yellow forehead and forecrown, chestnut head, and pinkish breast; shows white forewing in flight. Female has rather uniform head, breast and flanks. In all plumages, shows white belly and rather pointed tail in flight. Male has distinctive whistled *wheeoo* call. Freshwater and coastal wetlands.

4 MALLARD *Anas platyrhynchos* **Page 370**

Male (4a, 4b) and female (4c, 4d). Breeds in Himalayas; widespread winter visitor. In all plumages, has white-bordered purplish speculum. Male has yellow bill, dark green head and purplish-chestnut breast. Female is pale brown and boldly patterned with dark brown. Bill variable, patterned mainly in dull orange and dark brown. Freshwater wetlands.

5 SPOT-BILLED DUCK *Anas poecilorhyncha* **Page 371**

Male (5a, 5b) and female (5c) *A. p. poecilorhyncha*; male *A. p. zonorhyncha* (5d, 5e). Widespread resident. Yellow tip to bill, dark crown and eye-stripe, and spotted breast. Nominate has red loral spot, and boldly scalloped flanks; white tertials and green speculum. *A. p. zonorhyncha* is more uniform sooty-black on upperparts and flanks; has mainly dark grey tertials, and blue speculum. Freshwater wetlands.

1d
1b
2d
2b
1a
2a
2c
2d
1c
3b
3d
4b
3c
4d
4a
3a
4c
5b
5e
5a
5d
JPPW
5c

PLATE 11: DABBLING DUCKS

1 **BAIKAL TEAL** *Anas formosa* **Page 373**
Male (1a, 1b) and female (1c, 1d, 1e). Winter visitor. N subcontinent. Grey forewing and broad white trailing edge to wing in flight. Male has striking head pattern. Female has dark-bordered white loral spot and buff supercilium; some females have white half-crescent on cheeks. Large rivers.

2 **COMMON TEAL** *Anas crecca* **Page 373**
Male (2a, 2b) and female (2c, 2d). Widespread winter visitor. Male has chestnut head with green band behind eye, and white stripe along scapulars. Female has rather uniform head, lacking stripy pattern of female Garganey. In flight, both sexes have broad white band along greater coverts, and green speculum with narrow white trailing edge; forewing of female is brown. Freshwater wetlands and brackish waters.

3 **SUNDA TEAL** *Anas gibberifrons* **Page 372**
Male (3a, 3b) and female (3c). Resident. Andamans. Brown, with variable white markings on head. In flight, shows white axillaries and broad white band across greater coverts. Freshwater wetlands and tidal creeks.

4 **GARGANEY** *Anas querquedula* **Page 372**
Male (4a, 4b) and female (4c, 4d). Widespread winter visitor. Male has white stripe behind eye, and brown breast contrasting with grey flanks; shows blue-grey forewing in flight. Female has more patterned head than female Common Teal, with pale supercilium, whitish loral spot, and dark cheek-bar; shows pale grey forewing and broad white trailing edge to wing in flight. Freshwater wetlands and coastal lagoons.

5 **NORTHERN PINTAIL** *Anas acuta* **Page 372**
Male (5a, 5b) and female (5c, 5d). Widespread winter visitor. Long neck and pointed tail. Male has chocolate-brown head, with white stripe down sides of neck. Female has comparatively uniform buffish head, and (as male) shows white trailing edge to secondaries and greyish underwing in flight. Freshwater wetlands and brackish lagoons.

6 **NORTHERN SHOVELER** *Anas clypeata* **Page 371**
Male (6a, 6b) and female (6c, 6d). Widespread winter visitor. Long spatulate bill and blue-grey forewing. Male has dark green head and chestnut flanks. Freshwater wetlands.

1b
1e
2b
2d
1d
1c
2c
2a
1a
3c
4d
4b
3b
4a
4c
3a
5d
6d
6b
5b
6a
5a
5c
6c

PLATE 12: DIVING DUCKS

1 **RED-CRESTED POCHARD** *Rhodonessa rufina* **Page 374**
Male (1a, 1b) and female (1c, 1d). Widespread winter visitor; unrecorded in Sri Lanka. Male has rusty-orange head, black neck and breast, and white flanks. Female has pale cheeks contrasting with brown cap. Both sexes have largely white flight feathers on upperwing, and whitish underwing. Large lakes and rivers.

2 **COMMON POCHARD** *Aythya ferina* **Page 374**
Male (2a, 2b), female (2c, 2d) and immature male (2e). Widespread winter visitor; unrecorded in Sri Lanka. Pale grey flight feathers result in different upperwing pattern from other *Aythya*. Male has chestnut head, black breast, and grey upperparts and flanks. Female has brownish head and breast contrasting with paler brownish-grey upperparts and flanks. Lakes and reservoirs.

3 **FERRUGINOUS POCHARD** *Aythya nyroca* **Page 375**
Male (3a, 3b) and female (3c). Breeds in Baluchistan, Kashmir and Ladakh; widespread winter visitor. Chestnut head, breast and flanks and white undertail-coverts. In flight, shows extensive white wing-bar and white belly. Freshwater pools, coastal lagoons.

4 **BAER'S POCHARD** *Aythya baeri* **Page 375**
Male (4a, 4b), immature male (4c) and female (4d). Winter visitor. Mainly NE India and Bangladesh. Greenish cast to dark head and neck, which contrast with chestnut-brown breast. White patch on foreflanks visible above water. Large rivers and lakes.

5 **TUFTED DUCK** *Aythya fuligula* **Page 376**
Male (5a, 5b), immature male (5c), female (5d, 5e) and female with scaup-like head (5f). Widespread winter visitor. Breeding male is glossy black, with prominent crest and white flanks. Eclipse/immature males are duller, with greyish flanks. Female is dusky brown, with paler flanks; some females may show scaup-like white face patch, but they usually also show tufted nape. Lakes and reservoirs.

6 **GREATER SCAUP** *Aythya marila* **Page 376**
Male (6a, 6b), immature male (6c), female (6d, 6e) and immature female (6f). Winter visitor. N subcontinent. Larger and stockier than Tufted, and lacking any sign of crest. Male has grey upperparts contrasting with black rear end. Female has broad white face patch, which is less extensive on juvenile/immature. Large lakes and rivers.

1d
1b
1a
1c
2d
2b
2a
2e
2c
3b
3a
3c
4b
4c
4a
4d
5b
5e
6b
6e
6f
5f
5d
6d
5c
6a
6c
5a

PLATE 13: MISCELLANEOUS DUCKS

1 **LONG-TAILED DUCK** *Clangula hyemalis* **Page 376**
Winter male (1a, 1b) and winter female (1c, 1d). Vagrant. Pakistan, Nepal and India. Both sexes show dark upperwing and underwing in flight. Winter male has dark cheek patch and breast, and long tail. Female and immature male variable, but usually with dark crown, cheek patch and breast. Lakes and large rivers.

2 **WHITE-WINGED SCOTER** *Melanitta fusca* **Page 377**
Male (2a, 2b) and female (2c). Vagrant. Pakistan. Both sexes show white secondaries in flight. Male black, with white crescent below eye. Female brown, with pale patch on lores and another on ear-coverts. Coastal waters.

3 **COMMON GOLDENEYE** *Bucephala clangula* **Page 377**
Male (3a, 3b) and female (3c, 3d). Winter visitor. N subcontinent. Stocky, with bulbous head. Male has dark green head, with large white patch on lores. Female and immature male have brown head, indistinct whitish collar, and grey body, with white wing patch usually visible at rest. Lakes and large rivers.

4 **SMEW** *Mergellus albellus* **Page 377**
Male (4a, 4b) and female (4c, 4d). Winter visitor. N subcontinent. Male is mainly white, with black markings. Immature male and female have chestnut cap, with white throat and lower ear-coverts. Lakes, rivers and streams.

5 **RED-BREASTED MERGANSER** *Mergus serrator* **Page 377**
Male (5a, 5b) and female (5c, 5d). Winter visitor. Mainly Pakistan, also India and Nepal. Male has spiky crest, white collar, ginger breast, and grey flanks. Female and immature male have chestnut head which merges with grey of neck. Slimmer than Common Merganser, and with finer bill; chestnut of head and upper neck contrasts less with grey lower neck than in Common Merganser. Coastal waters, large rivers and lakes.

6 **COMMON MERGANSER** *Mergus merganser* **Page 378**
Male (6a, 6b) and female (6c, 6d). Breeds in Ladakh; winters mainly in N subcontinent. Male has dark green head, and whitish breast and flanks (with variable pink). Female has chestnut head and greyish body. Lakes, rivers and streams.

1d
1b
2b
2c
1a
2a
1c
4b
4d
3b
3d
4c
3a
4a
6b
3c
5b
5d
6d
6a
5a
5c
6c

PLATE 14: YELLOW-RUMPED HONEYGUIDE AND WOODPECKERS

1 YELLOW-RUMPED HONEYGUIDE *Indicator xanthonotus* **Page 379**
Male (1a) and female (1b). Resident. Himalayas and NE India. Golden-yellow forehead, back and rump, streaked underparts, and square blackish tail. Male has pronounced yellow malar stripes. Near Giant Rock Bee nests on cliffs, and adjacent forest.

2 EURASIAN WRYNECK *Jynx torquilla* **Page 380**
Adult. Breeds in NW Himalayas; widespread in winter; unrecorded in Sri Lanka. Cryptically patterned with grey, buff and brown. Has dark stripe down nape and mantle, and long, barred tail. Summers in open forest; winters in open scrub, and cultivation edges.

3 SPECKLED PICULET *Picumnus innominatus* **Page 380**
Male (3a) and female (3b). Resident. Himalayas, hills of SW, E and NE India, and Bangladesh. Tiny size. Whitish underparts with black spotting, black ear-covert patch and malar stripe. Bushes and bamboo in forest and secondary growth.

4 WHITE-BROWED PICULET *Sasia ochracea* **Page 381**
Male (4a) and female (4b). Resident. Himalayas, NE India and Bangladesh. Tiny size. Rufous underparts, and white supercilium behind eye. Bushes and bamboo in forest and secondary growth.

5 RUFOUS WOODPECKER *Celeus brachyurus* **Page 386**
Male (5a) and female (5b). Resident. Himalayas, NE, E and W India, Bangladesh and Sri Lanka. Short black bill. Rufous-brown, with prominent black barring. Forest and secondary growth.

6 WHITE-BELLIED WOODPECKER *Dryocopus javensis* **Page 386**
Male (6a) and female (6b). Resident. Western and Eastern Ghats. Large black woodpecker with white belly. Male has red crown and moustachial stripe; red restricted to hindcrown on female. Forest and secondary growth with tall trees.

7 ANDAMAN WOODPECKER *Dryocopus hodgei* **Page 386**
Male (7a) and female (7b). Resident. Andaman Is. Large blackish woodpecker. Male has red crown and moustachial stripe; red restricted to hindcrown on female. Forest.

8 PALE-HEADED WOODPECKER *Gecinulus grantia* **Page 391**
Male (8a), female (8b) and juvenile male (8c). Resident. Himalayas, NE India and Bangladesh. Pale bill, golden-olive head, and dull maroon to maroon-brown underparts. Male has crimson on crown. Bamboo jungle.

9 BAY WOODPECKER *Blythipicus pyrrhotis* **Page 391**
Male (9a), female (9b) and juvenile male (9c). Resident. Himalayas, NE India and Bangladesh. Long pale bill, and rufous upperparts with dark brown barring. Male has red on sides of neck. Juvenile has streaked crown, and barring on underparts. Dense broadleaved forest and secondary growth.

10 HEART-SPOTTED WOODPECKER *Hemicircus canente* **Page 391**
Male (10a), female (10b) and juvenile (10c). Resident. Mainly hills of NE and E India. Prominent crest; very short tail. Black-and-white plumage, with heart-shaped black spots on tertials. Male has black crown, female has white crown, and juvenile has black spotting on white crown. Broadleaved forest and coffee plantations.

11 GREAT SLATY WOODPECKER *Mulleripicus pulverulentus* **Page 392**
Male (11a) and female (11b). Resident. Himalayas, NE India and Bangladesh. Huge, slate-grey woodpecker. Male has pinkish-red moustachial patch. Mature trees in tropical forest and forest clearings.

1b
1a
2
3b
3a
4b
4a
5b
5a
6b
6a
7a
7b
8b
8a
8c
10a
10b
10c
11a
9a
9b
9c
11b
C.D'S

PLATE 15: WOODPECKERS

1 **BROWN-CAPPED PYGMY WOODPECKER** *Dendrocopos nanus* **Page 381**
Male (1a) and female (1b) *D. n. nanus*; male *D. n. gymnopthalmus* (1c). Resident. Widespread; unrecorded in Pakistan. Very small. Has brown crown, brown coloration to upperparts, whitish underparts (streaked with brown, except in Sri Lanka), and white spotting on central tail feathers. Light forest and secondary growth.

2 **GREY-CAPPED PYGMY WOODPECKER** *Dendrocopos canicapillus* **Page 382**
Male (2a) and female (2b) *D. c. mitchellii*. Resident. Himalayas, NE India and Bangladesh. Very small. Has grey crown, blackish coloration to upperparts, diffuse blackish malar stripe, and dirty fulvous underparts streaked with black. Forest, and trees in cultivation.

3 **BROWN-FRONTED WOODPECKER** *Dendrocopos auriceps* **Page 382**
Male (3a) and female (3b). Resident. Hills of Baluchistan and Himalayas. Brownish forehead and forecrown, yellowish central crown, white-barred upperparts, prominent black moustachial stripe, pink undertail-coverts, and unbarred central tail feathers. Subtropical and temperate forest.

4 **FULVOUS-BREASTED WOODPECKER** *Dendrocopos macei* **Page 382**
Male (4a) and female (4b) *D. m. macei*; male *D. m. andamanensis* (4c). Resident. Himalayas, NE and E India, and Bangladesh. White barring on mantle and wing-coverts, diffusely streaked underparts, and buff wash to sides of head and neck. Upper mantle usually barred with white. Andaman race has black spotting on breast. Forest edges and open forest.

5 **STRIPE-BREASTED WOODPECKER** *Dendrocopos atratus* **Page 383**
Male (5a) and female (5b). Resident. NE Indian hills and Bangladesh. White barring on lower mantle and wing-coverts, prominently streaked underparts, white sides of head and neck, and olive-yellow wash to underparts. Upper mantle lacks white barring. Open forest.

6 **YELLOW-CROWNED WOODPECKER** *Dendrocopos mahrattensis* **Page 383**
Male (6a) and female (6b) *D. m. mahrattensis*. Resident. Widespread east of Indus R. Yellowish forehead and forecrown, white-spotted upperparts, poorly defined moustachial stripe, whitish undertail-coverts, and white barring on central tail feathers. Open woodland, open country with scattered trees.

7 **RUFOUS-BELLIED WOODPECKER** *Dendrocopos hyperythrus* **Page 384**
Male (7a) and female (7b). Resident. Himalayas, NE India and Bangladesh. Whitish face and rufous underparts. Lacks white 'shoulder' patch. Juvenile has barred underparts. Subtropical and temperate forest.

8 **CRIMSON-BREASTED WOODPECKER** *Dendrocopos cathpharius* **Page 384**
Male (8a) and female (8b) *D. c. cathpharius*; male *D. c. pyrrhothorax* (8c). Resident. Himalayas, NE India. Small white wing patch, streaked underparts, and variable crimson patch on breast. Male has extensive red on nape and hindneck. Broadleaved forest.

9 **DARJEELING WOODPECKER** *Dendrocopos darjellensis* **Page 384**
Male (9a) and female (9b). Resident. Himalayas, NE India. Small white wing patch, streaked underparts, and yellow patch on side of neck. Forest.

10 **GREAT SPOTTED WOODPECKER** *Dendrocopos major* **Page 385**
Male (10a) and female (10b). Resident. NE Indian hills. Extensive white 'shoulder' patch, unstreaked underparts, and black of moustachial stripe extending down side of breast. Male has black crown and crimson patch on nape. Oak and pine forest.

11 **SIND WOODPECKER** *Dendrocopos assimilis* **Page 385**
Male (11a) and female (11b). Resident. Widespread in Pakistan. Extensive white 'shoulder' patch, unstreaked underparts, and black moustachial stripe joining hindneck. Lacks black border to rear of ear-coverts of Himalayan. Dry forest and plantations.

12 **HIMALAYAN WOODPECKER** *Dendrocopos himalayensis* **Page 385**
Male (12a) and female (12b) *D. h. himalayensis*; *D. h. albescens* (12c). Resident. W Himalayas. White 'shoulder' patch, unstreaked underparts, and black rear border to ear-coverts. Forest.

1b
1a
1c
2b
2a
3a
3b
4b
4a
4c
5b
5a
6a
6b
7a
7b
8b
8a
8c
9a
9b
10a
10b
11a
11b
12a
12b
12c
C.D'S

PLATE 16: WOODPECKERS

1 **LESSER YELLOWNAPE** *Picus chlorolophus* **Page 387**
Male (1a) and female (1b) *P. c. chlorolophus*; male *P. c. chlorigaster* (1c). Resident. Himalayas, hills of India, Bangladesh and Sri Lanka. Tufted yellow nape, scarlet and white markings on head, and barring or spotting on underparts. Smaller, with less prominent crest and smaller bill, compared with Greater Yellownape. Forest, secondary growth, plantations.

2 **GREATER YELLOWNAPE** *Picus flavinucha* **Page 387**
Male (2a) and female (2b). Resident. Himalayas, NE and E India, and Bangladesh. Tufted yellow nape, yellow or rufous-brown throat, unbarred underparts, and rufous barring on secondaries. Forest and forest edges.

3 **LACED WOODPECKER** *Picus vittatus* **Page 387**
Male (3a) and female (3b). Recorded once in Bangladesh. Scaling on belly and flanks, unscaled olive-yellow foreneck and breast, broad black moustachial stripe, black tail, and reddish eye. Mangroves.

4 **STREAK-THROATED WOODPECKER** *Picus xanthopygaeus* **Page 388**
Male (4a) and female (4b). Widespread resident; unrecorded in Pakistan. Smaller than Scaly-bellied, with dark bill and pale eye. Streaked throat, scaling on breast, and indistinct barring on tail. Forest, secondary growth and plantations.

5 **SCALY-BELLIED WOODPECKER** *Picus squamatus* **Page 388**
Male (5a) and female (5b). Resident. Hills of Baluchistan and Himalayas. Larger than Streak-throated, with pale bill and reddish eye. Unstreaked throat and breast (except juvenile), and barred tail. Forest, scrub, and open country with large trees.

6 **GREY-HEADED WOODPECKER** *Picus canus* **Page 388**
Male (6a) and female (6b) *P. c. sanguiniceps*. Resident. Himalayas, NE and E India, and Bangladesh. Plain grey face, and uniform greyish-green underparts. Forest.

7 **HIMALAYAN FLAMEBACK** *Dinopium shorii* **Page 389**
Male (7a) and female (7b). Resident. Himalayas, NE India, and locally in hills of peninsula and Bangladesh. Smaller bill than Greater, with unspotted black hindneck, and brownish-buff centre of throat (and breast on some). Centre of divided moustachial stripe is brownish-buff (with touch of red on some males). Breast less heavily marked with black than on Common Flameback. Mature forest.

8 **COMMON FLAMEBACK** *Dinopium javanense* **Page 389**
Male (8a) and female (8b). Resident. Hills of SW and NE India and Bangladesh. Smaller bill than Greater, with unspotted black hindneck, and irregular line of black spotting down centre of throat. Moustachial stripe lacks clear white dividing line. Forest.

9 **BLACK-RUMPED FLAMEBACK** *Dinopium benghalense* **Page 389**
Male (9a) and female (9b) *D. b. benghalense*; male *D. b. psarodes* (9c). Widespread resident. Black eye-stripe and throat (lacking dark moustachial stripe), spotting on wing-coverts, and black rump. Sri Lankan *psarodes* has crimson upperparts. Light forest, plantations, groves and trees in open country.

10 **GREATER FLAMEBACK** *Chrysocolaptes lucidus* **Page 390**
Male (10a) and female (10b) *C. l. guttacristatus*; male *C. l. stricklandi* (10c). Resident. Himalayas, hills of India, Bangladesh and Sri Lanka. White or black-and-white spotted hindneck and upper mantle, large size, and long bill. Moustachial stripe is clearly divided. Sri Lankan race *stricklandi* has crimson upperparts. Forest and groves.

11 **WHITE-NAPED WOODPECKER** *Chrysocolaptes festivus* **Page 390**
Male (11a) and female (11b). Resident. Widespread in India, also W Nepal and Sri Lanka. White hindneck and mantle, and black scapulars and back forming V-shape. Moustachial stripe is clearly divided. Female has yellow crown. Light forest, scrub and scattered trees.

1a
1c
2b
2a
3b
3a
1b
5a
4b
4a
6b
5b
9b
9c
9a
6a
7b
7a
8b
10b
10a
11a
8a
10c
11b
C.D'S

PLATE 17: BARBETS

1 **GREAT BARBET** *Megalaima virens* **Page 392**
Adult *M. v. marshallorum.* Resident. Himalayas, NE India and Bangladesh. Large yellow bill, bluish head, brown breast and mantle, and streaked belly. Mainly subtropical and temperate forest.

2 **BROWN-HEADED BARBET** *Megalaima zeylanica* **Page 392**
Adult *M. z. caniceps* (2a) and adult *M. z. inornata* (2b). Widespread resident; unrecorded in Pakistan. Fine streaking on brown head and breast, brown throat, orange circumorbital skin and bill (when breeding), and white-spotted wing-coverts. Forest, wooded areas and trees near habitation.

3 **LINEATED BARBET** *Megalaima lineata* **Page 393**
Adult (3a) and paler variant (3b). Resident. Himalayan foothills, NE and E India, and Bangladesh. Bold white streaking on head and breast, and whitish throat. Less extensive circumorbital skin than Brown-headed. Open forest and well-wooded areas.

4 **WHITE-CHEEKED BARBET** *Megalaima viridis* **Page 393**
Adult (4a) and juvenile (4b). Resident. Western Ghats and hills of Tamil Nadu. White supercilium and cheeks contrasting with brown crown and nape. Whitish throat, and bold white streaking on breast. Wooded areas, gardens, groves.

5 **YELLOW-FRONTED BARBET** *Megalaima flavifrons* **Page 394**
Adult. Resident. Sri Lanka. Yellow forehead and malar stripe, and blue ear-coverts and throat. Forest and well-wooded gardens.

6 **GOLDEN-THROATED BARBET** *Megalaima franklinii* **Page 394**
Adult. Resident. Himalayas, NE India and Bangladesh. Yellow centre of crown and throat, greyish-white cheeks and lower throat, and broad black mask. Subtropical and temperate forest.

7 **BLUE-THROATED BARBET** *Megalaima asiatica* **Page 394**
Adult (7a) and juvenile (7b). Resident. Himalayas, NE India and Bangladesh. Blue 'face' and throat, red forehead and hindcrown, and black band across crown. Juvenile has duller head pattern. Open forest, groves and gardens.

8 **BLUE-EARED BARBET** *Megalaima australis* **Page 394**
Adult (8a) and juvenile (8b). Resident. E Himalayan foothills, NE India and Bangladesh. Small size, blue throat and ear-coverts, black malar stripe, and red patches on side of head. Juvenile lacks head patterning, but shows traces of blue on side of head and throat. Dense evergreen forest.

9 **CRIMSON-FRONTED BARBET** *Megalaima rubricapilla* **Page 395**
Adult *M. r. malabarica* (9a); adult (9b) and juvenile (9c) *M. r. rubricapilla.* Resident. Western Ghats and Sri Lanka. Small size. Both races have blue band down side of head and breast, and unstreaked green belly and flanks. In Western Ghats, *malabarica* has crimson cheeks, throat and breast. In Sri Lanka, *rubricapilla* has orange cheeks and throat. Juveniles are duller, but show traces of adult head pattern. Open wooded country.

10 **COPPERSMITH BARBET** *Megalaima haemacephala* **Page 395**
Adult (10a) and juvenile (10b). Resident. Widespread east of Indus R. Small size, crimson forehead and breast patch, yellow patches above and below eye, yellow throat, and streaked underparts. Juvenile lacks red on head and breast. Open wooded country and groves.

1
2a
2b
3a
3b
4a
4b
5
6
7a
7b
8a
8b
9a
9b
9c
10a
10b
C.D'S

PLATE 18: SMALL AND MEDIUM-SIZED HORNBILLS

1 **MALABAR GREY HORNBILL** *Ocyceros griseus* **Page 396**
Male (1a, 1b), female (1c) and immature (1d). Resident. Western Ghats. Orange or yellowish bill, lacking casque, and broad greyish-white supercilium. Darker grey upperparts than Indian Grey, with shorter, darker grey tail. Female has black patch at base of lower mandible. Immature has rufous fringes to upperparts. Open forest.

2 **SRI LANKA GREY HORNBILL** *Ocyceros gingalensis* **Page 396**
Male (2a, 2b), female (2c) and immature (2d). Resident. Sri Lanka. White underparts contrasting with grey upperparts. Lacks prominent supercilium. Male has cream-coloured bill with black patch at base. Female has mainly black bill with cream stripe along cutting edge. Older birds have white outer tail feathers. Forest and well-wooded areas.

3 **INDIAN GREY HORNBILL** *Ocyceros birostris* **Page 396**
Male (3a, 3b) and immature (3c). Widespread resident; unrecorded in Sri Lanka. Prominent black casque and extensive black at base of bill. Paler sandy brownish-grey upperparts than Malabar Grey, with longer tail that has dark subterminal band and elongated central feathers. Female similar to male, but with smaller bill and casque. Open forest and wooded areas with fruiting trees.

4 **MALABAR PIED HORNBILL** *Anthracoceros coronatus* **Page 399**
Male (4a, 4b), female (4c) and immature (4d). Resident. Western Ghats, E India and Sri Lanka. Axe-shaped casque with large black patch along upper ridge, white outer tail feathers, broad white trailing edge to wing, and pink throat patches. Orbital skin is blue-black on male, pinkish on female. Female's casque similar in shape and patterning to male's, although lacks black at posterior end; bill of female lacks black at tip. Open forest and large fruit trees near villages.

5 **ORIENTAL PIED HORNBILL** *Anthracoceros albirostris* **Page 398**
Male (5a, 5b), female (5c) and immature (5d). Resident. Himalayan foothills, NE India and E India, and Bangladesh. Cylindrical casque with black patch at tip, mainly black tail with white tips to outer feathers, and pale blue throat patch. Female has smaller casque, with black at posterior end, and black at tip of bill. Open forest, groves and large fruit trees near villages.

5a

PLATE 19: LARGE HORNBILLS

1 **GREAT HORNBILL** *Buceros bicornis* **Page 397**
Male (1a, 1b). Resident. Himalayas, NE India, Bangladesh and Western Ghats. Huge size, massive yellow casque and bill, and white tail with black subterminal band. Has white neck, wing-bars and trailing edge to wing which are variably stained with yellow. Sexes alike, although female has white iris and lacks black at ends of casque. Mature forest.

2 **BROWN HORNBILL** *Anorrhinus tickelli* **Page 397**
Male (2a, 2b) and female (2c, 2d). Resident. NE India. Medium-sized brown hornbill with stout yellowish bill. Male has white cheeks, throat and upper breast; rest of underparts rufous. Female is uniformly brown on underparts, and lacks white tips to flight feathers and tail. Broadleaved evergreen forest.

3 **RUFOUS-NECKED HORNBILL** *Aceros nipalensis* **Page 397**
Male (3a, 3b), female (3c) and immature (3d). Resident. Himalayas, NE India and Bangladesh. White terminal band to tail and white wing-tips. Red pouch. Male and immature have rufous head and neck. Female has black head and neck. Broadleaved evergreen forest.

4 **WREATHED HORNBILL** *Aceros undulatus* **Page 398**
Male (4a, 4b), female (4c) and immature (4d). Resident. E Himalayan foothills, NE India and Bangladesh. White tail and all-black wings. Has bill corrugations (except immature) and bar across pouch. Male has whitish head and neck and yellow pouch. Female has black head and neck with blue pouch. Broadleaved evergreen forest.

5 **NARCONDAM HORNBILL** *Aceros narcondami* **Page 398**
Male (5a, 5b), female (5c) and immature (5d). Resident. Narcondam I, Andamans. White tail and all-black wings. Bluish-white pouch. Male and immature have rufous head and neck. Female has black head and neck. High forest.

6 **PLAIN-POUCHED HORNBILL** *Aceros subruficollis* **Page 398**
Male (6a, 6b) and female (6c). [No definite records, but may possibly occur in the northeast. Very similar to Wreathed, but smaller. Lacks corrugations on bill, and has plain pouch. Mature forest.]

1a
1b
2a
2b
2c
2d
3a
3b
3c
3d
4a
4b
4c
4d
5a
5b
5c
5d
6a
6b
6c
C.D'S

PLATE 20: COMMON HOOPOE, TROGONS AND ROLLERS

1 **COMMON HOOPOE** *Upupa epops* **Page 399**
Adult (1a, 1b). Summer visitor to far north; resident and winter visitor to much of rest of subcontinent. Rufous-orange or orange-buff, with black-and-white wings and tail and black-tipped fan-like crest. Open country, cultivation and villages.

2 **MALABAR TROGON** *Harpactes fasciatus* **Page 400**
Male (2a), female (2b) and immature (2c) *H. f. malabaricus*; male *H. f. fasciatus* (2d). Resident. Western Ghats, hills of W Tamil Nadu, and Sri Lanka. Male has black or dark grey head and breast, pink underparts, and black-and-grey vermiculated wing-coverts. Female has dark cinnamon head and breast, pale cinnamon underparts, and brown-and-buff vermiculated coverts. Immature male has blackish or grey head and breast, and cinnamon underparts; coverts are vermiculated with grey on older birds. Dense broadleaved forest.

3 **RED-HEADED TROGON** *Harpactes erythrocephalus* **Page 400**
Male (3a), female (3b) and immature (3c). Resident. Himalayas, NE India and Bangladesh. Male has crimson head and breast, pink underparts, and black-and-grey vermiculated wing-coverts. Female has dark cinnamon head and breast, and brown-and-buff vermiculated coverts. Immature male has whitish underparts; older immatures resemble female, but have black-and-grey vermiculated coverts. Dense broadleaved forest.

4 **WARD'S TROGON** *Harpactes wardi* **Page 400**
Male (4a) and female (4b). Resident. E Himalayas in Bhutan and Arunachal Pradesh. Large trogon. Male is maroon, with deep pink forehead, supercilium and underparts; bill is also deep pink. Female is browner, with yellow forehead, supercilium and underparts. Broadleaved evergreen forest.

5 **EUROPEAN ROLLER** *Coracias garrulus* **Page 401**
Adult (5a, 5b) and juvenile (5c). Summer visitor to W Pakistan, Jammu and Kashmir; passage migrant in Pakistan and NW India. Turquoise head and underparts, and rufous-cinnamon mantle. Has black flight feathers and tail corners. Juvenile is much duller, and has whitish streaking on throat and breast; patterning of wings and tail helps separate from Indian Roller. Open woodland and cultivation.

6 **INDIAN ROLLER** *Coracias benghalensis* **Page 401**
Adult (6a, 6b) and immature (6c) *C. b. benghalensis*; adult *C. b. affinis* (6d). Widespread resident. Rufous-brown on nape and underparts, white streaking on ear-coverts and throat, and greenish mantle. Has turquoise band across primaries and dark blue terminal band to tail. Juvenile is duller than adult. *C. b. affinis* has purplish-brown underparts, blue streaking on throat, and dark corners to tail instead of dark terminal band. Cultivation, open woodland, gardens.

7 **DOLLARBIRD** *Eurystomus orientalis* **Page 402**
Adult (7a, 7b) and juvenile (7c) *E. o. cyanicollis*. Resident and partial migrant. Himalayas, NE and SW India, Bangladesh and Sri Lanka. Dark greenish, appearing black at distance, with red bill and eye-ring. In flight, shows turquoise patch on primaries. Tropical forest and forest clearings.

1a
1b
2a
2b
2d
2c
3c
3a
3b
4a
4b
5c
5b
5a
6b
6d
6c
6a
7b
7a
7c
C.D'S

PLATE 21: KINGFISHERS

1 **BLYTH'S KINGFISHER** *Alcedo hercules* **Page 402**
Adult. Resident. Mainly NE India. Dark greenish-blue ear-coverts. Has dark greenish-blue on head, scapulars and wings, with turquoise spotting. Shaded streams in dense tropical and subtropical forest.

2 **COMMON KINGFISHER** *Alcedo atthis* **Page 403**
Adult *A. a. benghalensis*. Widespread resident. Orange ear-coverts. Greenish-blue on head, scapulars and wings, and turquoise line down back. Fresh waters in open country, also mangroves and seashore in winter.

3 **BLUE-EARED KINGFISHER** *Alcedo meninting* **Page 403**
Adult (3a) and juvenile (3b). Resident. Himalayan foothills, NE, E and SW India, Bangladesh and Sri Lanka. Blue ear-coverts (except on juvenile). Lacks green tones to blue of head, scapulars and wings, and has deeper blue line down back compared with Common. Mainly streams in dense forest.

4 **ORIENTAL DWARF KINGFISHER** *Ceyx erithacus* **Page 403**
Adult (4a) and juvenile (4b) *C. e. erithacus*; adult *C. e. rufidorsa* (4c). Resident. Himalayan foothills, NE and SW India, and Bangladesh. Orange head with violet iridescence, and black upperparts with variable blue streaking. Juvenile duller, with whitish underparts and orange-yellow bill. Vagrant *C. e. rufidorsa* has rufous-orange upperparts with violet iridescence. Shady streams in moist broadleaved forest.

5 **BROWN-WINGED KINGFISHER** *Halcyon amauroptera* **Page 404**
Adult. Resident. E India and Bangladesh. Brownish-orange head and underparts. Brown mantle, wings and tail, and turquoise rump. Coastal wetlands.

6 **STORK-BILLED KINGFISHER** *Halcyon capensis* **Page 404**
Adult *H. c. capensis* (6a) and *H. c. intermedia* (6b). Widespread resident; unrecorded in Pakistan and NW India. Brown cap. Orange-buff collar and underparts, and blue upperparts. Cap lacking or poorly defined in Andaman and Nicobar Is. Shaded lakes and running waters.

7 **RUDDY KINGFISHER** *Halcyon coromanda* **Page 404**
Adult (7a) and juvenile (7b) *H. c. coromanda*. Resident. E Himalayan foothills, NE India and Bangladesh. Adult is rufous-orange with violet iridescence on upperparts. Juvenile has browner upperparts.

8 **WHITE-THROATED KINGFISHER** *Halcyon smyrnensis* **Page 405**
Adult. Widespread resident. White throat and centre of breast, brown head and most of underparts, and turquoise upperparts. White wing patch. Cultivation, forest edges, gardens, and freshwater and coastal wetlands.

9 **BLACK-CAPPED KINGFISHER** *Halcyon pileata* **Page 405**
Adult (9a) and juvenile (9b). Resident. Mainly coasts of India and Bangladesh. Black cap, white collar, purplish-blue upperparts, and pale orange underparts. Shows white wing patch in flight. Chiefly coastal wetlands.

10 **COLLARED KINGFISHER** *Todiramphus chloris* **Page 405**
Adult (10a) and juvenile (10b) *T. c. humii*; adult *T. c. davisoni* (10c); adult *T. c. occipitalis* (10d). Resident. Locally in E and W India, and Bangladesh. Dark bill, blue-green upperparts, and white or buff underparts with white or buff collar. Birds in Nicobar Is (*occipitalis*) have broad rufous-buff supercilium. Mainly coastal wetlands.

11 **CRESTED KINGFISHER** *Megaceryle lugubris* **Page 406**
Adult. Resident. Himalayas, NE India and Bangladesh. Much larger than Pied, with evenly barred wings and tail. Lacks supercilium, and has spotted breast. Mountain rivers, large rivers in foothills.

12 **PIED KINGFISHER** *Ceryle rudis* **Page 406**
Male (12a) and female (12b) *C. r. leucomelanura*; adult male *C. r. travancoreensis* (12c). Widespread resident. Smaller than Crested, with white supercilium, white patches on wings, and black band(s) across breast. Still fresh waters, slow-moving rivers and streams, also tidal creeks and pools.

1
2
3a
4a
4b
4c
3b
5
6b
6a
7b
8
9a
7a
10d
10a
10b
9b
11
12b
10c
12a
12c
C.D'S

PLATE 22: BEE-EATERS

1 **BLUE-BEARDED BEE-EATER** *Nyctyornis athertoni* **Page 406**
Adult. Resident. Himalayan foothills, NE and E India, Western Ghats, hills of W Tamil Nadu and Bangladesh. Large size, square-ended tail, and blue 'beard'. Has yellowish-buff belly and flanks with greenish streaking. Edges of broadleaved forest.

2 **GREEN BEE-EATER** *Merops orientalis* **Page 407**
Adult (2a, 2b) and juvenile (2c) *M. o. beludschicus*; *M. o. orientalis* (2d); *M. o. ferrugeiceps* (2e). Widespread resident and summer visitor. Small size. Blue cheeks, with black gorget, and golden to rufous coloration to crown. Green tail with elongated central feathers. Juvenile has square-ended tail. Open country.

3 **BLUE-CHEEKED BEE-EATER** *Merops persicus* **Page 407**
Adult (3a, 3b). Summer visitor and passage migrant. Pakistan and NW India. Chestnut throat, whitish forehead, turquoise-and-white supercilium, and turquoise-and-green ear-coverts. Green upperparts, underparts and tail, although may show touch of turquoise on rump, belly and undertail-coverts. Near water in arid areas.

4 **BLUE-TAILED BEE-EATER** *Merops philippinus* **Page 408**
Adult (4a, 4b) and juvenile (4c). Breeds in N and NE subcontinent; winters in peninsula and Sri Lanka. Chestnut throat. Forehead and supercilium are mainly green, and concolorous with crown, with touch of blue on supercilium. Green upperparts and underparts washed with brown and blue. Blue rump, tail and undertail-coverts. Juvenile differs from juvenile Blue-cheeked in having strong blue cast to tail. Near water in wooded country.

5 **EUROPEAN BEE-EATER** *Merops apiaster* **Page 408**
Adult (5a, 5b, 5c) and juvenile (5d). Summer visitor to Vale of Kashmir and N and W Pakistan mountains; passage migrant chiefly in Pakistan. Yellow throat, black gorget, blue underparts, chestnut crown and mantle, and golden-yellow scapulars. Juvenile is duller than adult, but still shows chestnut on crown and well-defined yellowish throat. Open country.

6 **CHESTNUT-HEADED BEE-EATER** *Merops leschenaulti* **Page 408**
Adult (6a, 6b) and juvenile (6c) *M. l. leschenaulti*; *M. l. andamanensis* (6d). Resident and partial migrant. Himalayas, NE, E, SW and SE India, Bangladesh and Sri Lanka. Chestnut crown, nape and mantle, and yellow throat with diffuse black gorget. Tail has slight fork. Juvenile washed-out version of adult, but crown and nape dark green on some; has rufous wash to lower throat, diffuse black gorget and turquoise rump. Near streams in deciduous forest.

1
2a
2b
2c
2d
2e
3a
3b
4a
4b
4c
5a
5b
5c
5d
6a
6b
6c
6d
C.D'S

PLATE 23: CUCKOOS

1 **PIED CUCKOO** *Clamator jacobinus* **Page 409**
Adult (1a) and juvenile (1b). Widespread resident and partial migrant. Adult is black and white with prominent crest. Crest smaller, upperparts browner and underparts more buffish on juvenile. Forest, well-wooded areas, also bushes in semi-desert.

2 **CHESTNUT-WINGED CUCKOO** *Clamator coromandus* **Page 409**
Adult (2a) and immature (2b). Breeds in Himalayas, NE India and Bangladesh; passage migrant in India; winter visitor to Sri Lanka. Prominent crest, whitish collar, and chestnut wings. Immature has rufous fringes to upperparts. Broadleaved forest.

3 **LARGE HAWK CUCKOO** *Hierococcyx sparverioides* **Page 410**
Adult (3a) and juvenile (3b). Breeds in Himalayas and NE India; scattered winter records in subcontinent. Larger than Common Hawk Cuckoo, with browner upperparts, strongly barred underparts, and broader tail banding. Juvenile has barred flanks and broad tail banding; head dark grey on older birds. Broadleaved forest.

4 **COMMON HAWK CUCKOO** *Hierococcyx varius* **Page 410**
Adult (4a) and juvenile (4b) *H. v. varius*. Widespread resident and partial migrant. Smaller than Large Hawk Cuckoo, with grey upperparts, more rufous on underparts, indistinct barring on belly and flanks, and narrow tail banding. Juvenile has spotted flanks and narrow tail banding. Well-wooded country.

5 **HODGSON'S HAWK CUCKOO** *Hierococcyx fugax* **Page 411**
Adult (5a) and juvenile (5b). Resident or summer visitor. Mainly E Himalayas and NE Indian hills. Stouter bill and shorter-looking tail than Common Hawk Cuckoo; typically darker slate-grey above, and underparts are more rufous and lack barring. Underparts of juvenile have broad spotting. Broadleaved evergreen and moist deciduous forest.

6 **INDIAN CUCKOO** *Cuculus micropterus* **Page 411**
Male (6a) and juvenile (6b). Breeds in Himalayas and E subcontinent. Brown coloration to upperparts and tail, broad barring on underparts, and pronounced white barring and spotting on tail. Juvenile has broad and irregular white tips to feathers of crown and nape and white tips to scapulars and wing-coverts. Forest and well-wooded country.

7 **EURASIAN CUCKOO** *Cuculus canorus* **Page 411**
Male (7a) and hepatic female (7b). Breeds in hills of Pakistan, Himalayas, and N, NE and C India; scattered winter records. Finer barring on whiter underparts than Oriental. Forest and well-wooded country.

8 **ORIENTAL CUCKOO** *Cuculus saturatus* **Page 412**
Male (8a) and hepatic female (8b). Breeds in Himalayas and NE India; winter visitor to Andamans and Nicobars. Broader barring on buffish-white underparts compared with Eurasian, and upperparts are a shade darker, with paler head. Hepatic female is slightly more heavily barred than Eurasian. Forest and well-wooded country.

9 **LESSER CUCKOO** *Cuculus poliocephalus* **Page 412**
Male (9a) and hepatic female (9b). Breeds in Himalayas and NE India; passage migrant in peninsula and Sri Lanka. Smaller than Oriental; hepatic female can be bright rufous and indistinctly barred on crown and nape. Forest and well-wooded country.

10 **BANDED BAY CUCKOO** *Cacomantis sonneratii* **Page 413**
Adult. Widespread resident; unrecorded in Pakistan. White supercilium, finely barred white underparts, and fine and regular dark barring on upperparts. Forest and wooded country.

11 **GREY-BELLIED CUCKOO** *Cacomantis passerinus* **Page 413**
Adult (11a), hepatic female (11b) and juvenile (11c). Summers in Himalayas; widespread resident or winter visitor farther south; unrecorded in northwest. Grey adult is grey with white vent and undertail-coverts. On hepatic female, base colour of underparts is mainly white, upperparts are bright rufous with crown and nape only sparsely barred, and tail is unbarred. Juvenile is either grey with pale barring on underparts, or similar to hepatic female, or intermediate.

12 **PLAINTIVE CUCKOO** *Cacomantis merulinus* **Page 413**
Adult (12a), hepatic female (12b) and juvenile (12c). Resident. NE India and Bangladesh. Adult has orange underparts. On hepatic female, base colour of underparts is pale rufous, and upperparts and tail are strongly barred. Juvenile has bold streaking on rufous-orange head and breast. Forest and wooded country.

1b
1a
2a
2b
4b
3b
3a
4a
6b
5b
6a
5a
8a
7b
7a
8b
9b
9a
10
11c
11a
11b
12a
12b
12c
C.D'S

PLATE 24: CUCKOOS AND COUCALS

1 **ASIAN EMERALD CUCKOO** *Chrysococcyx maculatus* **Page 414**
Male (1a), female (1b) and juvenile (1c). Summer visitor, mainly to E Himalayas, NE India and Bangladesh; winter visitor to Andamans and Nicobars. Male has emerald-green upperparts. Female has rufous-orange crown and nape and unbarred bronze-green mantle and wings. Juvenile has unbarred rufous-orange crown and nape, and rufous-orange wash to barred throat and breast. Evergreen forest.

2 **VIOLET CUCKOO** *Chrysococcyx xanthorhynchus* **Page 414**
Male (2a), female (2b) and juvenile (2c). Resident or summer visitor, mainly to NE Indian hills. Male has purple upperparts. Female has uniform bronze-brown upperparts, with only slight greenish tinge, and white underparts with brownish barring. Juvenile has extensive dark barring on crown and nape, and lacks rufous-orange wash to throat. Secondary evergreen forest and orchards.

3 **DRONGO CUCKOO** *Surniculus lugubris* **Page 415**
Adult (3a) and juvenile (3b). Summer visitor to Himalayas; resident farther south. Himalayas, NE, W, S and SE India, and Sri Lanka. Black, with white-barred undertail-coverts. Bill fine and downcurved, and tail has indentation. Juvenile is spotted with white. Forest and well-wooded areas.

4 **ASIAN KOEL** *Eudynamys scolopacea* **Page 415**
Male (4a) and female (4b). Mainly resident. Widespread. Male is greenish-black, with green bill. Female is spotted and barred with white. Open woodland, gardens and cultivation.

5 **GREEN-BILLED MALKOHA** *Phaenicophaeus tristis* **Page 415**
Adult. Resident. Himalayas, NE India and Bangladesh. Greyish-green coloration, green and red bill, red eye-patch, white-streaked supercilium, and white-tipped tail. Dense forest and thickets.

6 **BLUE-FACED MALKOHA** *Phaenicophaeus viridirostris* **Page 416**
Adult. Resident. Peninsular India and Sri Lanka. Greenish coloration, green bill, blue eye-patch, and bold white tips to tail. Scrub and secondary growth.

7 **SIRKEER MALKOHA** *Phaenicophaeus leschenaultii* **Page 416**
Adult. Widespread resident; unrecorded in northeast and parts of northwest. Sandy coloration, yellow-tipped red bill, dark mask with white border, and bold white tips to tail. Thorn scrub.

8 **RED-FACED MALKOHA** *Phaenicophaeus pyrrhocephalus* **Page 416**
Adult (8a) and juvenile (8b). Resident. Sri Lanka. Green bill, red face patch, black breast, and white malar stripe and underparts. Juvenile duller. Dense, tall, mainly evergreen forest.

9 **GREATER COUCAL** *Centropus sinensis* **Page 417**
Adult (9a) and juvenile (9b) *C. s. sinensis*. Widespread resident. Larger than Lesser, with brighter and more uniform chestnut wings. Juvenile is heavily barred. Tall grassland, scrub and groves.

10 **BROWN COUCAL** *Centropus andamanensis* **Page 417**
Adult (10a) and juvenile (10b). Resident. Andamans. Fawn-brown head and body, with chestnut wings. Juvenile is diffusely barred. Forest edges, gardens and cultivation.

11 **LESSER COUCAL** *Centropus bengalensis* **Page 417**
Adult breeding (11a), adult non-breeding (11b) and immature (11c). Resident. Himalayas, NE, E and SW India, and Bangladesh. Smaller than Greater, with duller chestnut wings; often with buff streaking on scapulars and wing-coverts. Non-breeding has pronounced buff shaft streaking on head and body, chestnut wings and black tail. Immature similar to non-breeding adult, but has barred wings and tail. Tall grassland, reedbeds and shrubberies.

12 **GREEN-BILLED COUCAL** *Centropus chlororhynchus* **Page 418**
Adult. Resident. Sri Lanka. Green bill. Wings are maroon-brown, and contrast less with head and body than on Greater. Tall forest with dense undergrowth.

1c
1b
1a
2c
2b
2a
3a
3b
4a
4b
5
6
7
8a
8b
9a
9b
10b
10a
11c
11b
11a
12
C.D'S

PLATE 25: HANGING PARROTS AND PARAKEETS

1 **VERNAL HANGING PARROT** *Loriculus vernalis* **Page 418**
Male (1a) and immature (1b). Resident. Mainly NE and E India, Western Ghats and Bangladesh. Small green parrot. Adult with red bill and red rump. Broadleaved forest.

2 **SRI LANKA HANGING PARROT** *Loriculus beryllinus* **Page 419**
Male (2a) and immature (2b). Resident. Sri Lanka. Adult has crimson crown, and orange cast to mantle. Broadleaved forest.

3 **ALEXANDRINE PARAKEET** *Psittacula eupatria* **Page 419**
Male (3a) and female (3b). Widespread resident; unrecorded in W Pakistan. Very large, with maroon shoulder patch. Male has black chin stripe and pink collar. Forest and well-wooded areas.

4 **ROSE-RINGED PARAKEET** *Psittacula krameri* **Page 419**
Male (4a) and female (4b). Widespread resident. Green head and blue-green tip to tail. Male has black chin stripe and pink collar. Forest, wooded areas and cultivation.

5 **SLATY-HEADED PARAKEET** *Psittacula himalayana* **Page 419**
Male (5a), female (5b) and immature (5c). Resident. Himalayas. Dark grey head, red-and-yellow bill, and yellow-tipped tail. Forest and well-wooded areas.

6 **GREY-HEADED PARAKEET** *Psittacula finschii* **Page 420**
Male (6a), female (6b) and immature (6c). Resident. NE India and Bangladesh. Grey head, red-and-yellow bill, yellowish-green upperparts, and yellow-cream tip to tail. Hill forest and cultivation.

7 **INTERMEDIATE PARAKEET** *Psittacula intermedia* **Page 420**
Male (7a) and female (7b). [Probably a hybrid. Trapped in Uttar Pradesh. Slaty-purple head with rufous-purple on forehead and around eye. Red upper mandible, and yellowish-white tip to tail. Habitat unknown.]

8 **PLUM-HEADED PARAKEET** *Psittacula cyanocephala* **Page 420**
Male (8a), female (8b) and immature (8c). Widespread resident; unrecorded in northwest and parts of northeast. Head is plum-red on male, pale grey on female. Yellow upper mandible, and white-tipped blue-green tail. Forest and well-wooded areas.

9 **BLOSSOM-HEADED PARAKEET** *Psittacula roseata* **Page 421**
Male (9a), female (9b) and immature (9c). Resident. Mainly NE Indian hills and Bangladesh. Head is pinkish on male, pale greyish-blue on female. Yellow upper mandible, and yellow-tipped tail. Well-wooded areas and open forest.

10 **MALABAR PARAKEET** *Psittacula columboides* **Page 421**
Male (10a), female (10b) and immature (10c). Resident. Western Ghats. Blue-grey head, breast and mantle. Blue primaries, and yellow tip to tail. Evergreen and moist deciduous forest.

11 **LAYARD'S PARAKEET** *Psittacula calthropae* **Page 421**
Male (11a), female (11b) and immature (11c). Resident. Sri Lanka. Blue-grey head and mantle, and green collar and underparts. Yellow tip to tail. Forest edges, plantations and gardens.

12 **DERBYAN PARAKEET** *Psittacula derbiana* **Page 422**
Male (12a) and female (12b). Resident. Arunachal Pradesh. Large size, and violet-grey head and underparts. Female has black bill. Conifer forest and cultivation.

13 **RED-BREASTED PARAKEET** *Psittacula alexandri* **Page 422**
Male (13a), female (13b) and immature (13c). Resident. Himalayan foothills, NE India and Bangladesh. Lilac-grey head and pink underparts. Open forest and secondary growth.

14 **NICOBAR PARAKEET** *Psittacula caniceps* **Page 422**
Male (14a) and female (14b). Resident. Nicobars. Large size and buffish-grey head. Tall forest.

15 **LONG-TAILED PARAKEET** *Psittacula longicauda* **Page 423**
Male (15a) and immature (15b) *P. l. tytleri*; male (15c) and female (15d) *P. l. nicobarica*. Resident. Andamans and Nicobars. Pinkish-red cheeks. Cultivation, gardens and forest.

1a
1b
2a
2b
3a
3b
4a
4b
5a
5b
5c
6a
6b
6c
7a
7b
8a
8b
8c
9a
9b
9c
10a
10b
10c
11a
11b
11c
12a
12b
13a
13b
13c
14a
14b
15a
15b
15c
15d
C.D'S

PLATE 26: SWIFTLETS AND NEEDLETAILS

1 **GLOSSY SWIFTLET** *Collocalia esculenta* **Page 423**
Adult (1a, 1b). Resident. Andamans and Nicobars. Small size, square-ended tail, glossy upperparts and breast, and white belly. Around habitation.

2 **INDIAN SWIFTLET** *Collocalia unicolor* **Page 423**
Adult (2a, 2b). Resident. Western Ghats, islets on Malabar coast, Sri Lanka. Uniform upperparts, with indistinct indentation to tail. Hills.

3 **HIMALAYAN SWIFTLET** *Collocalia brevirostris* **Page 424**
Adult (3a, 3b) Resident. Himalayas and NE India. Greyish rump band, and distinct indentation to tail. Open areas near forest.

4 **EDIBLE-NEST SWIFTLET** *Collocalia fuciphaga* **Page 424**
Adult (4a, 4b). Resident. Andamans and Nicobars. Narrow greyish rump band. Upperparts blacker and tail indentation narrower than on Himalayan. Coast and around habitation.

5 **WHITE-RUMPED NEEDLETAIL** *Zoonavena sylvatica* **Page 424**
Adult (5a, 5b). Resident. Himalayas, NE, E and SW India, and Bangladesh. Small size, white rump, and whitish belly and undertail-coverts. Broadleaved forest.

6 **WHITE-THROATED NEEDLETAIL** *Hirundapus caudacutus* **Page 425**
Adult (6a, 6b). Summer visitor. Himalayas and NE India. Well-defined white throat, prominent pale 'saddle', and white patch on tertials. Ridges, cliffs, upland grassland and river valleys.

7 **SILVER-BACKED NEEDLETAIL** *Hirundapus cochinchinensis* **Page 425**
Adult (7a, 7b). Resident. Hills of NE India and Bangladesh, Western Ghats and Sri Lanka. Poorly defined pale throat, prominent pale 'saddle', and dark lores. Broadleaved forest.

8 **BROWN-BACKED NEEDLETAIL** *Hirundapus giganteus* **Page 425**
Adult (8a, 8b). Resident. Hills of NE India and Bangladesh, Western Ghats and Sri Lanka. Large size, brown throat, indistinct 'saddle', and white lores. Pointed tail with prominent 'needles'. Broadleaved forest.

2a
2b
3a
3b
4a
4b
1a
1b
5a
5b
6a
7a
8a
6b
7b
8b
G. Driessens '95

PLATE 27: SWIFTS

1 COMMON SWIFT *Apus apus* **Page 426**
Adult (1a, 1b) and juvenile (1c, 1d). Mainly summer visitor. Baluchistan, Himalayas and Maldives. Uniform dark brown upperparts, lacking any contrast on upperwing. No white rump. Chiefly mountains.

2 PALLID SWIFT *Apus pallidus* **Page 427**
Adult (2a, 2b). Winter visitor. Pakistan. Pale grey-brown upperparts and underparts with dark eye-patch, and extensive pale throat. Shows contrast between dark outer primaries and inner wing-coverts and paler rest of wing. Coastal areas.

3 ASIAN PALM SWIFT *Cypsiurus balasiensis* **Page 426**
Adult (3a, 3b). Resident. Widespread; unrecorded in Pakistan. Small size and long, forked tail (usually held closed). Brown underbody with paler throat. Open country and cultivation with palms.

4 HOUSE SWIFT *Apus affinis* **Page 428**
Adult *A. a. affinis* (4a, 4b); adult *A. a. nipalensis* (4c, 4d). Widespread resident; unrecorded in parts of northwest. Stocky shape and comparatively short wings. Tail has square end or slight fork. White rump. Habitation, cliffs and ruins.

5 FORK-TAILED SWIFT *Apus pacificus* **Page 427**
Adult *A. p. leuconyx* (5a, 5b). Breeds in Himalayas and NE India; scattered winter records in peninsula. White rump, deeply forked tail, and white scaling on underparts. Open ridges and hilltops.

6 DARK-RUMPED SWIFT *Apus acuticauda* **Page 427**
Adult (6a, 6b). Resident. Meghalaya, Bhutan, and Mizoram? Blackish upperparts, including rump. Lacks distinct pale throat, and has whitish scaling on underparts. Rocky cliffs and gorges.

7 ALPINE SWIFT *Tachymarptis melba* **Page 426**
Adult (7a, 7b). Resident? Locally in subcontinent. Large size, white throat and brown breast-band, and white patch on belly. Mainly hills and mountains.

8 CRESTED TREESWIFT *Hemiprocne coronata* **Page 428**
Adult male (8a, 8b), female (8c, 8d), and juvenile (8e). Widespread resident; unrecorded in Pakistan. Large size and long, forked tail. Blue-grey upperparts and paler underparts, becoming whitish on belly and vent. Male has dull orange ear-coverts. Well-wooded areas and forest.

1a
1c
2a
3a
1b
1d
2b
3b
4a
5a
4c
6a
4b
5b
4d
6b
7a
8d
8c
7b
8a
8b
8e
G. Driessens '97

PLATE 28: SMALL AND MEDIUM-SIZED OWLS

1 **BARN OWL** *Tyto alba* **Page 429**
Adult *T. a. stertens* (1a); adult *T. a. deroepstorffi* (1b). Widespread resident. Unmarked white face, white to golden-buff underparts, and golden-buff and grey upperparts. In Andamans, *deroepstorffi* has rufous face and darker upperparts. Habitation and cultivation.

2 **GRASS OWL** *Tyto capensis* **Page 429**
Adult (2a, 2b). Resident. NE and SW India, and S Nepal. Whitish face and underparts, dark barring on flight feathers, golden-buff patch at base of primaries, and barred tail. Upperparts are heavily marked with dark brown. Tall grassland.

3 **ORIENTAL BAY OWL** *Phodilus badius* **Page 429**
Adult. Resident. NE and SW India, and Sri Lanka. Oblong-shaped, vinaceous-pinkish facial discs. Underparts vinaceous-pink, spotted with black; upperparts chestnut and buff, spotted and barred with black. Call is a series of eerie, upward-inflected whistles. Dense broadleaved forest.

4 **ANDAMAN SCOPS OWL** *Otus balli* **Page 430**
Adult. Resident. Andamans. Unstreaked dark rufous-brown upperparts with indistinct buff and dark brown markings; underparts finely vermiculated and spotted with dark brown and buff. Call is an abrupt *hoot...hoot-coorroo*. Cultivation and habitation.

5 **MOUNTAIN SCOPS OWL** *Otus spilocephalus* **Page 430**
Adult *O. s. spilocephalus* (5a); adult *O. s. huttoni* (5b). Resident. Himalayas, NE India and Bangladesh. Lacks prominent ear-tufts. Upperparts mottled with buff and brown; underparts indistinctly spotted with buff and barred with brown. Call is a double whistle, *toot-too*. Dense broadleaved forest.

6 **PALLID SCOPS OWL** *Otus brucei* **Page 430**
Adult (6a) and juvenile (6b). Resident. Pakistan and NW India. Pale, grey and rather uniform. Compared with Eurasian Scops, has less distinct scapular spots, and narrow dark streaking on underparts, which lack pale horizontal panels. Call is a resonant *whoop-whoop-whoop....* Stony foothills in semi-desert.

7 **EURASIAN SCOPS OWL** *Otus scops* **Page 431**
Adult brown (7a) and grey (7b) morphs. Summer visitor to N and W Pakistan mountains; winters in S Pakistan and NW India. Prominent white spots on scapulars, and streaked underparts with pale horizontal bands. Longer primary projection than Oriental Scops. Call is plaintive bell-like whistle. Scrub in dry rocky hills and valleys.

8 **ORIENTAL SCOPS OWL** *Otus sunia* **Page 431**
Adult *O. s. sunia* rufous (8a) and brown (8b) morphs; rufous specimen from Nicobars (8c). Resident. Himalayas, NE, W and S India, and Sri Lanka. Prominent ear-tufts. Prominent white scapular spots, streaked underparts and upperparts, and lacks prominent nuchal collar. Rufous morph distinct from Eurasian Scops; otherwise not distinguishable on plumage, although Oriental has shorter primary projection. Call is frog-like *wut-chu-chraaii*. Forest, wooded areas and habitation.

9 **COLLARED SCOPS OWL** *Otus bakkamoena* **Page 432**
Adult *O. b. gangeticus* grey morph (9a); adult *O. b. plumipes* rufous-brown morph (9b). Widespread resident; unrecorded in parts of northwest and northeast. Larger than other scops owls, with buff nuchal collar, finely streaked underparts, and indistinct buffish scapular spots. Iris dark orange or brown. Call is a subdued, frog-like *whuk*, repeated at irregular intervals. Forest and well-wooded areas.

1a
1b
2b
2a
3
4
5a
5b
6a
6b
7a
7b
8a
8c
8b
9a
9b
Dan Cole 95

PLATE 29: LARGE OWLS

1 EURASIAN EAGLE OWL *Bubo bubo* **Page 432**
Adult *B. b. hemachalana* (1a); adult *B. b. bengalensis* (1b). Widespread resident; unrecorded in parts of northwest, northeast and Sri Lanka. Very large, with upright ear-tufts. Upperparts mottled dark brown and tawny-buff; underparts heavily streaked. Call is a resonant *tu-whooh*. Cliffs, rocky hills, ravines and wooded areas.

2 SPOT-BELLIED EAGLE OWL *Bubo nipalensis* **Page 432**
Adult (2a) and immature (2b). Resident. Himalayas, NE India, Western Ghats and Bangladesh. Very large, with bold chevron-shaped spots on underparts. Upperparts dark brown, barred with buff.. Call is a deep hoot and a mournful scream. Dense forest.

3 DUSKY EAGLE OWL *Bubo coromandus* **Page 433**
Adult. Widespread resident; unrecorded in Sri Lanka. Large grey owl with prominent ear-tufts. Underparts greyish-white with brown streaking. Call is a deep, resonant *wo, wo,wo,wo-o-o-o-o*. Well-watered areas with extensive tree cover.

4 BROWN FISH OWL *Ketupa zeylonensis* **Page 433**
Adult. Widespread resident; unrecorded in Pakistan. Compared with other fish owls, has close dark barring on dull buff underparts, which also show finer streaking, and upperparts are duller brown with finer streaking. Calls include a soft, deep *hup-hup-hu* and a wild *hu-hu-hu-hu...hu ha*. Forest and well-wooded areas near water.

5 TAWNY FISH OWL *Ketupa flavipes* **Page 433**
Adult. Resident. Himalayas, NE India and Bangladesh. Pale orange upperparts with bold black streaking, bold orange-buff barring on wing-coverts and flight feathers, whitish patch on forehead, broad black streaking on pale rufous-orange underparts, and lack of black barring on underparts. Call is a deep *whoo-hoo* and a cat-like mewing. Banks of streams and rivers in dense broadleaved forest.

6 BUFFY FISH OWL *Ketupa ketupu* **Page 434**
Adult. Resident? Told from much larger Tawny Fish Owl by finer streaking on underparts, duller buffish-white to greyish-white barring on flight feathers and tail, and tendency towards heavier and more diffuse streaking on crown and nape. Rufous-orange coloration with heavier black streaking, and white forehead, help separate it from Brown Fish Owl. Call is monotonous *bup-bup-bup-bup-bup-bup-bup....* Forested streams in plains.

7 SNOWY OWL *Nyctea scandiaca* **Page 434**
Male (7a) and female (7b). Vagrant. Pakistan. Mainly white, with variable dark markings. Open country.

8 MOTTLED WOOD OWL *Strix ocellata* **Page 434**
Adult. Resident. Peninsular India. Concentric barring on facial discs, and white, rufous and dark brown mottling on upperparts; rufous on underparts. Call is a spooky, quavering *whaa-aa-aa-aa-ah*. Open wooded areas, groves around villages and cultivation.

9 BROWN WOOD OWL *Strix leptogrammica* **Page 434**
Adult *S. l. newarensis* (9a); adult *S. l. indranee* (9b). Resident. Himalayas, NE India, Eastern and Western Ghats, Bangladesh and Sri Lanka. Uniform facial discs, uniform brown upperparts with fine white barring on scapulars, and buffish-white underparts with fine brown barring. Calls include a *hoo-hoohoohoo(hoo)* and a loud eerie scream. Dense broadleaved forest.

10 TAWNY OWL *Strix aluco* **Page 435**
Adult *S. a. nivicola* (10a); adult *S. a. biddulphi* (10b). Resident. N Baluchistan, Himalayas and NE India. Grey to rufous-brown, with barred wings. Heavily streaked underparts, white markings on scapulars, dark centre to crown, and pale forecrown stripes. Call is a *too-tu-whoo*. Temperate forest.

11 HUME'S OWL *Strix butleri* **Page 435**
Adult. Resident. Makran coast, Pakistan. Buff underparts with dark barring, buff nuchal collar, and orange eyes. Call is a *whooo woohoo-woohoo*. Rocky gorges.

1a
1b
2a
2b
3
4
5
6
7a
7b
8
9a
9b
10a
10b
11
Dan Cole 95.

PLATE 30: SMALL AND MEDIUM-SIZED OWLS

1 COLLARED OWLET *Glaucidium brodiei* **Page 436**
Adult. Resident. Himalayas, NE India and Bangladesh. Very small and heavily barred. Spotted crown, streaking on flanks, and owl-face pattern on upper mantle. Call is a pleasant *toot..tootoot..toot*. Subtropical and temperate forest.

2 ASIAN BARRED OWLET *Glaucidium cuculoides* **Page 436**
Adult (2a) and immature (2b) *G. c. cuculoides*; adult *G. c. rufescens* (2c). Resident. Himalayas, NE India and Bangladesh. Small and heavily barred. Buff barring on wing-coverts and flight feathers, and streaked flanks. Call is a continuous bubbling whistle. Tropical, subtropical and temperate forest.

3 JUNGLE OWLET *Glaucidium radiatum* **Page 436**
Adult *G. r. radiatum* (3a); adult *G. r. malabaricum* (3b). Widespread resident; unrecorded in most of north-east. Small and heavily barred. Smaller than Asian Barred, with more closely barred upperparts and underparts. Rufous barring on wing-coverts and flight feathers, and barred flanks. Call is a loud *kao..kao..kao* followed by *kao..kuk*, and notes similar to Asian Barred's. Open tropical and subtropical forest.

4 CHESTNUT-BACKED OWLET *Glaucidium castanonotum* **Page 437**
Adult. Resident. Sri Lanka. Small and heavily barred. Back and wing-coverts are bright chestnut, diffusely barred with brown and some buff. Belly and flanks streaked. Call is a slow *kraw...kraw*.... Dense forest.

5 LITTLE OWL *Athene noctua* **Page 437**
Adult. Resident. Baluchistan and trans-Himalayas. Sandy-brown, with streaked breast and flanks, and streaked crown. Call is a plaintive *quew*, repeated every few seconds, and a soft barking. Cliffs and ruins in semi-desert.

6 SPOTTED OWLET *Athene brama* **Page 437**
Adult *A. b. indica* (6a); adult *A. b. brama* (6b). Widespread resident. White spotting on upperparts, including crown, and diffuse brown spotting on underparts. Pale facial discs and nuchal collar. Call is a harsh, screechy *chirurr-chirurr-chirurr...* followed by/alternated with *cheevak, cheevak, cheevak*. Habitation and cultivation.

7 FOREST OWLET *Athene blewitti* **Page 438**
Adult. Resident. C India. Rather dark grey-brown crown and nape, only faintly spotted with white. Wings (apart from inner coverts) and tail broadly banded blackish-brown and white, with white-tipped remiges and a broad white tail-tip (fresh plumage). Breast dark brown, and barring on upper flanks is broader and more prominent; rest of underparts white, much cleaner than on Spotted. Deciduous forest.

8 BOREAL OWL *Aegolius funereus* **Page 438**
Adult. Rare resident? NW Pakistan and NW India. Greyish facial discs bordered with black, and with angular upper edge. Call is a soft *po-po-po*.... Subalpine scrub.

9 BROWN HAWK OWL *Ninox scutulata* **Page 438**
Adult *N. s. lugubris* (9a); adult *N. s. obscura* (9b). Resident. Himalayas, NE, E and W India, Bangladesh and Sri Lanka. Hawk-like profile. Dark face, and rufous-brown streaking on underparts. Has dark brown underparts in Andamans. Call is a soft, pleasant *oo..ok, oo..ok,*.... Forest and well-wooded areas.

10 ANDAMAN HAWK OWL *Ninox affinis* **Page 439**
Adult. Resident. Andamans. Rufous spotting on white underparts. Call is a loud *craw*. Mangrove forest.

11 LONG-EARED OWL *Asio otus* **Page 439**
Adult (11a, 11b). Mainly winter visitor to Pakistan and NW India; has bred. Heavily streaked underparts and long ear-tufts. Orange-brown facial discs and orange eyes. Stunted trees and poplar plantations in winter.

12 SHORT-EARED OWL *Asio flammeus* **Page 439**
Adult (12a, 12b). Widespread winter visitor and passage migrant. Streaked underparts and short ear-tufts. Buffish facial discs and yellow eyes. Open country.

1
2a
2b
2c
3a
3b
4
5
6a
6b
7
8
9a
9b
10
11a
11b
12a
12b
Dan Cole 95

PLATE 31: FROGMOUTHS AND NIGHTJARS

1 **SRI LANKA FROGMOUTH** *Batrachostomus moniliger* **Page 440**
Male (1a) and female (1b). Resident. Western Ghats and Sri Lanka. Smaller and shorter-tailed than Hodgson's, with bigger-looking head and bill. Male brownish-grey; female more rufous and less heavily marked. Song is a series of loud liquid chuckles. Dense tropical and subtropical evergreen forest.

2 **HODGSON'S FROGMOUTH** *Batrachostomus hodgsoni* **Page 440**
Male (2a) and female (2b). Resident. E Himalayas, NE India and Bangladesh. Larger, longer-tailed and more evenly proportioned than Sri Lanka Frogmouth. Male more rufous than male Sri Lanka, with underparts more heavily and irregularly marked with black, white and rufous. Female more uniform rufous than male. Subtropical evergreen forest.

3 **GREAT EARED NIGHTJAR** *Eurostopodus macrotis* **Page 440**
Adult (3a, 3b). Resident. Mainly NE India, Bangladesh and Western Ghats. Very large and richly coloured, with prominent ear-tufts. Fine rufous barring on black ear-coverts and throat, dark brown barring on buff underparts, and tail broadly banded with golden-buff and dark brown. Lacks pale spots on wings or tail. Song is a clear, wailing *pee-wheeeu*. Broadleaved moist forest and secondary growth.

4 **GREY NIGHTJAR** *Caprimulgus indicus* **Page 441**
Male (4a, 4b) and female (4c) *C. i. indicus*. Widespread resident; unrecorded in parts of northwest. Grey to grey-brown, and heavily marked with black. Lacks pale rufous-brown nuchal collar and buff or rufous edges to scapulars. Song is a loud, resonant *chunk-chunk-chunk-chunk....* Forest clearings and scrub-covered slopes.

5 **EURASIAN NIGHTJAR** *Caprimulgus europaeus* **Page 441**
Male (5a, 5b) and female (5c). Mainly summer visitor and passage migrant. Pakistan and NW Gujarat. Medium-sized, grey nightjar with regular, bold lanceolate streaking on crown, nape and scapulars (latter with buffish outer edges). Song is a continuous churring; soft *quoit quoit* in flight. Rocky slopes with scattered bushes.

6 **EGYPTIAN NIGHTJAR** *Caprimulgus aegyptius* **Page 444**
Male (6a, 6b). Summer visitor. SW Pakistan. Medium-sized, sandy nightjar with finely streaked crown, black 'inverted anchor-shaped' marks on scapulars, unbroken narrow white throat crescent; never shows any white on wings or tail. Song is a *kowrr..kowrr..kowrr...*; guttural *tuk-l tuk-l* in flight. Semi-desert.

7 **SYKES'S NIGHTJAR** *Caprimulgus mahrattensis* **Page 444**
Male (7a, 7b) and female (7c). Resident. Breeds in Pakistan and parts of NW India; winters south to C India. Small, grey nightjar. Has finely streaked crown, black 'inverted anchor-shaped' marks on scapulars, large white patches on sides of throat, and irregular buff spotting on nape forming indistinct collar. Has continuous churring song; low, soft *chuck-chuck* in flight. Breeds in semi-desert; wide variety of habitats in winter.

8 **LARGE-TAILED NIGHTJAR** *Caprimulgus macrurus* **Page 444**
Male (8a, 8b) and female (8c). Resident. Himalayas south to Bangladesh and C India. More warmly coloured and strongly patterned than Grey, with longer and broader tail. Has diffuse pale rufous-brown nuchal collar, well-defined buff edges to scapulars, buff tips to black-centred wing-coverts. Song is a series of loud, resonant calls: *chaunk-chaunk-chaunk,* repeated at the rate of about 100 per minute. Edges of tropical and subtropical forest.

9 **JERDON'S NIGHTJAR** *Caprimulgus atripennis* **Page 445**
Male (9a, 9b). Resident. C and S peninsula and Sri Lanka. More warmly coloured and strongly patterned than Grey. Has rufous band across nape/upper mantle, well-defined buff edges to scapulars, and broad, buff tips to black-centred coverts forming wing-bars. Song is a series of liquid, tremulous calls: *ch-wo-wo,* repeated at the rate of 13–20 per minute. Edges of moist forest and secondary growth.

10 **INDIAN NIGHTJAR** *Caprimulgus asiaticus* **Page 445**
Adult (10a, 10b). Widespread resident; unrecorded in most of northeast. Small. Has boldly streaked crown, rufous-buff nuchal collar, bold black centres and broad buff edges to scapulars, and relatively unmarked central tail feathers. Song is a far-carrying *chuk-chuk-chuk-chuk-tukaroo*; short sharp *qwit-qwit* in flight. Open wooded country in plains and foothills.

11 **SAVANNA NIGHTJAR** *Caprimulgus affinis* **Page 445**
Male (11a, 11b) and female (11c). Widespread resident; unrecorded in Sri Lanka. Crown and mantle finely vermiculated, scapulars edged with rufous-buff; male has largely white outer tail feathers. Song is a strident *dheet.* Open forest, stony areas with scrub.

1b
1a
2b
2a
3b
3a
4c
4b
5b
5a
4a
5c
6b
7b
8b
6a
7c
8c
7a
8a
9b
9a
10b
10a
11b
11c
11a
Dan Cole 95

PLATE 32: PIGEONS

1 **ROCK PIGEON** *Columba livia* **Page 446**
Adult *C. l. neglecta* (1a, 1b); adult *C. l. intermedia* (1c, 1d). Widespread resident; unrecorded in parts of northwest and northeast. Grey tail with blackish terminal band, and broad black bars across greater coverts and tertials/secondaries. Northern race *neglecta* has whitish back. Feral birds live in villages and towns; wild birds around cliffs and ruins.

2 **HILL PIGEON** *Columba rupestris* **Page 446**
Adult (2a, 2b, 3c). Resident. Himalayas. Similar to Rock, but has white band across tail contrasting with blackish terminal band. High-altitude villages and cliffs, mainly in Tibetan plateau country.

3 **SNOW PIGEON** *Columba leuconota* **Page 447**
Adult (3a, 3b, 3c). Resident. Himalayas. Slate-grey head, creamy-white collar and underparts, fawn-brown mantle, and white band across black tail. Cliffs and gorges in mountains with plentiful rainfall.

4 **YELLOW-EYED PIGEON** *Columba eversmanni* **Page 447**
Adult (4a, 4b). Winter visitor and passage migrant. Pakistan and N India. Smaller than Rock, with narrower and shorter black wing-bars. Yellow orbital skin and iris, brownish cast to upperparts, and extensive greyish-white back and upper rump. Plains cultivation.

5 **COMMON WOOD PIGEON** *Columba palumbus* **Page 447**
Adult (5a, 5b). Resident. Baluchistan and Himalayas east to Nepal. White wing patch and dark tail-band, buff neck patch, and deep vinous underparts. Scrub-covered and wooded hillsides.

6 **SPECKLED WOOD PIGEON** *Columba hodgsonii* **Page 448**
Male (6a) and female (6b). Resident. Himalayas and NE Indian hills. Speckled underparts, white spotting on wing-coverts, and lacks buff patch on neck. Male has maroon mantle and maroon on underparts, replaced by grey on female. Mainly oak-rhododendron forest.

7 **ASHY WOOD PIGEON** *Columba pulchricollis* **Page 448**
Adult (7a, 7b). Resident. Himalayas and NE Indian hills. Buff collar, slate-grey breast, becoming buff on belly and undertail-coverts, and uniform slate-grey upperparts. Broadleaved forest.

1b
1a
1c
1d
3c
2b
2a
3b
3a
4b
4a
5b
5a
7b
6b
6a
7a

PLATE 33: PIGEONS

1 NILGIRI WOOD PIGEON *Columba elphinstonii* **Page 448**
Adult (1a, 1b). Resident. Western Ghats. Checkerboard pattern on neck, maroon-brown upperparts, uniform slate-grey tail. Moist evergreen forest.

2 SRI LANKA WOOD PIGEON *Columba torringtoni* **Page 449**
Adult (2a, 2b). Resident. Sri Lanka. Checkerboard pattern on neck, slate-grey upperparts, including tail, and lilac- to purplish-grey underparts. Mainly hill forest.

3 PALE-CAPPED PIGEON *Columba punicea* **Page 449**
Adult (3a, 3b) and juvenile (3c). Resident. Eastern Ghats, NE India and Bangladesh. Pale cap, vinous-chestnut underparts, and maroon-brown mantle and wing-coverts with green-and-purple gloss. Juvenile initially lacks cap; upperparts browner, with chestnut fringes, and underparts mixed grey and rufous-buff. Tropical and subtropical forest and secondary growth.

4 ANDAMAN WOOD PIGEON *Columba palumboides* **Page 449**
Adult (4a, 4b). Resident. Andamans and Nicobars. Dark slate-grey upperparts and grey underparts, with paler head and neck, latter with indistinct checkerboard patterning. Dense evergreen forest.

5 GREEN IMPERIAL PIGEON *Ducula aenea* **Page 455**
Adult *D. a. sylvatica* (5a, 5b). Resident. Mainly Western Ghats, E and NE India, Bangladesh and Sri Lanka. Large size, metallic green upperparts and tail, and maroon undertail-coverts (darker than belly). Moist tropical broadleaved forest.

6 MOUNTAIN IMPERIAL PIGEON *Ducula badia* **Page 456**
Adult (6a, 6b). Resident. Himalayas, NE Indian hills and Western Ghats. Large size, brownish upperparts, dark brown band across base of tail, and pale buff undertail-coverts. Tall evergreen forest.

7 PIED IMPERIAL PIGEON *Ducula bicolor* **Page 456**
Adult (7a, 7b). Resident. Mainly Nicobars. Creamy-white, with black flight feathers and black terminal band to tail. Evergreen broadleaved forest.

1b
1a
2a
2b
3b
3a
3c
4b
4a
5b
5a
6b
6a
7b
7a

PLATE 34: DOVES

1 EUROPEAN TURTLE DOVE *Streptopelia turtur* **Page 450**
Adult (1a, 1b) and juvenile (1c). Vagrant. Pakistan, India and Maldives. Has white sides and tip to tail. Told from *meena* race of Oriental Turtle by smaller size and slimmer build; broader, paler rufous-buff fringes to scapulars and wing-coverts; more buffish- or brownish-grey rump and uppertail-coverts; and greyish-pink breast, becoming whitish on belly and undertail-coverts. Juvenile lacks neck-barring. Cultivation in drier mountains and valleys.

2 ORIENTAL TURTLE DOVE *Streptopelia orientalis* **Page 450**
Adult *S. o. meena* (2a, 2b); adult (2c, 2d) and juvenile (2e) *S. o. agricola*; adult *S. o. erythrocephala* (2f). Resident and winter visitor. Himalayas, NE India and Bangladesh south to C peninsular India, except arid northwest. Rufous-scaled scapulars and wing-coverts, brownish-grey to dusky maroon-pink underparts, and black and bluish-grey barring on neck sides. In all but one Indian race, has grey sides and tip to tail. Juvenile lacks neck-barring. Open forest.

3 LAUGHING DOVE *Streptopelia senegalensis* **Page 450**
Adult (3a, 3b). Widespread resident; unrecorded in most of Himalayas, the northeast and Sri Lanka. Slim, small, with fairly long tail. Brownish-pink head and underparts, uniform upperparts, and black stippling on upper breast. Dry cultivation and scrub-covered hills.

4 SPOTTED DOVE *Streptopelia chinensis* **Page 451**
Adult *S. c. suratensis* (4a, 4b); adult *S. c. tigrina* (4c). Widespread resident; unrecorded in most of northwest and N Himalayas. Spotted upperparts, and black-and-white chequered patch on neck sides. *S. c. tigrina* of NE subcontinent has buff scaling on upperparts. Cultivation, habitation and open forest.

5 RED COLLARED DOVE *Streptopelia tranquebarica* **Page 451**
Male (5a) and female (5b). Widespread resident; unrecorded in most of northwest, N Himalayas, S India and Sri Lanka. Male has blue-grey head, pinkish-maroon upperparts, and pink underparts. Compared with Eurasian Collared, female has darker buffish-grey underparts, darker fawn-brown upperparts, and is much smaller and more compact. Light woodland and trees in open country.

6 EURASIAN COLLARED DOVE *Streptopelia decaocto* **Page 451**
Adult (6a, 6b). Widespread resident; unrecorded in W Pakistan, most of Himalayas and SW India. Sandy-brown with black half-collar. Larger and longer-tailed than Red Collared Dove, with paler upperparts and underparts. Open dry country with cultivation and groves.

7 BARRED CUCKOO DOVE *Macropygia unchall* **Page 452**
Male (7a) and female (7b). Resident. Himalayas and NE Indian hills. Long, graduated tail, slim body and small head. Upperparts and tail rufous, barred with dark brown. Female more heavily barred on underparts than male. Dense broadleaved forest.

8 ANDAMAN CUCKOO DOVE *Macropygia rufipennis* **Page 452**
Male (8a) and female (8b). Resident. Andamans and Nicobars. Long, graduated tail, slim body and small head. Feathers of brown upperparts are fringed with rufous. Male has brown barring across breast and belly, and unmarked rufous head. Female has black mottling on crown and nape, and unbarred underparts. Dense forest.

9 EMERALD DOVE *Chalcophaps indica* **Page 452**
Male (9a) and female (9b, 9c) *C. i. indica*. Widespread resident; unrecorded in most of northwest. Stout and broad-winged, with very rapid flight. Green upperparts and black-and-white banding on back. Male has grey crown and white shoulder patch. Moist tropical and subtropical broadleaved forest.

1a
1b
2b
2f
2a
1c
2d
2c
3a
3b
2e
4b
4a
5b
5a
4c
6a
6b
7b
7a
8a
9c
9b
8b
9a

PLATE 35: GREEN PIGEONS

1 **NICOBAR PIGEON** *Caloenas nicobarica* **Page 453**
Male (1a, 1b). Resident. Mainly Nicobars. Stocky, metallic green pigeon with short white tail. Dense evergreen forest.

2 **ORANGE-BREASTED GREEN PIGEON** *Treron bicincta* **Page 453**
Male (2a) and female (2b). Resident. Himalayas, hills of India, Bangladesh and Sri Lanka. Smallest green pigeon. Central tail feathers of both sexes are grey. Male has orange breast, bordered above by lilac band, and green mantle. Female has yellow cast to breast and belly, and grey hindcrown and nape. Subtropical moist broadleaved forest.

3 **POMPADOUR GREEN PIGEON** *Treron pompadora* **Page 453**
Male (3a) and female (3b) *T. p. phayrei*; male *T. p. affinis* (3c); male *T. p. pompadora* (3d); male *T. p. chloroptera* (3e). Resident. Himalayas, hills of NE and SW India, Bangladesh and Sri Lanka. Both sexes told from Thick-billed Green by thin blue-grey bill (without prominent red base) and lack of prominent greenish orbital skin. Male has maroon mantle; where range overlaps with Thick-billed's, has diffuse orange patch on breast. Female lacks maroon mantle; tail shape and pattern help separate it from female Orange-breasted and Wedge-tailed Green. Tropical and subtropical moist broadleaved forest and well-wooded areas.

4 **THICK-BILLED GREEN PIGEON** *Treron curvirostra* **Page 454**
Male (4a) and female (4b). Resident. E Himalayas, NE India and Bangladesh. Both sexes told from Pompadour Green by thick bill with red base and by prominent greenish orbital skin. Male has maroon mantle, and green breast without orange wash. Tropical and subtropical forest and well-wooded areas.

5 **YELLOW-FOOTED GREEN PIGEON** *Treron phoenicoptera* **Page 454**
Adult *T. p. phoenicoptera* (5a); adult *T. p. chlorigaster* (5b, 5c). Widespread resident; unrecorded in most of Himalayas and northwest. Large size, broad olive-yellow collar, pale greyish-green upperparts, mauve shoulder patch, and yellow legs and feet. Populations in peninsular India and Sri Lanka have greenish-yellow belly and flanks. Deciduous forest and fruiting trees around villages and cultivation.

6 **PIN-TAILED GREEN PIGEON** *Treron apicauda* **Page 454**
Male (6a) and female (6b). Resident. Himalayas, NE India and Bangladesh. Both sexes have pointed central tail feathers, grey tail, green mantle, and lime-green rump. Male has pale orange wash to breast. Tall tropical and subtropical forest.

7 **WEDGE-TAILED GREEN PIGEON** *Treron sphenura* **Page 455**
Male (7a) and female (7b). Resident. Himalayas, NE India and Bangladesh. Both sexes have long wedge-shaped tail, indistinct yellow edges to wing-coverts and tertials, and dark green rump and tail. Male has maroon patch on upperparts (less extensive than on Pompadour Green) and orange wash to crown. Female has uniform green head (lacking grey crown of female Pompadour where ranges overlap). Subtropical and temperate broadleaved forest.

1b
1a
2b
2a
3a
3d
3e
3c
3b
4b
5a
5b
4a
5c
6a
7b
6b
7a

PLATE 36: BUSTARDS

1 **LITTLE BUSTARD** *Tetrax tetrax* **Page 456**
Male breeding (1a, 1b), male non-breeding (1c) and female (1d, 1e). Winter visitor. Pakistan and N India. Small, stocky bustard with white panel across secondaries and inner primaries. Non-breeding male less heavily marked on upperparts and whiter on underparts compared with female, and shows more white on wing. Breeding male has grey face, and black-and-white pattern on neck and breast. Grassland and short crops.

2 **GREAT BUSTARD** *Otis tarda* **Page 457**
Male breeding (2a, 2b) and female (2c, 2d). Vagrant. Pakistan. Very large, stocky bustard. In all plumages, has greyish head and upper neck, cinnamon lower neck, cinnamon upperparts with bold black barring, and white underparts. Patterning of white on wing differs from that of other bustards. Male larger than female, with thicker neck, and with more extensive white on wing (tertials and wing-coverts show more white). Short-grass plains.

3 **INDIAN BUSTARD** *Ardeotis nigriceps* **Page 457**
Male (3a, 3b) and female (3c). Resident. India. Very large bustard. In all plumages, has greyish or white neck, black crown and crest, uniform brown upperparts, and white-spotted black wing-coverts. Upperwing lacks extensive area of white. Male huge, with black breast-band, and with almost white neck only very finely vermiculated with dark grey. Female smaller; neck appears greyer owing to profuse dark grey vermiculations, and typically lacks black breast-band. Dry grassland with bushes.

4 **MACQUEEN'S BUSTARD** *Chlamydotis macqueeni* **Page 458**
Male (4a, 4b) and juvenile (4c). Mainly winter visitor to Pakistan and NW India; also breeds in S Pakistan. Medium-sized bustard. In all plumages, shows dark vertical stripe down neck. In flight, extensive white patch on outer primaries. Sexes similar, but female is smaller and lacks whitish panel across greater coverts. Juvenile very similar to female, but lacks black-tipped crest, neck stripe is finer, and white on wing is washed with buff and less prominent. Semi-desert with scattered shrubs and sandy grassland.

5 **BENGAL FLORICAN** *Houbaropsis bengalensis* **Page 458**
Male (5a, 5b) and female (5c, 5d). Resident. Lowlands in N India and S Nepal. Larger and stockier than Lesser Florican, with broader head and thicker neck. Male has black head, neck and underparts, and in flight wings are entirely white except for black tips. Female and immature are buff-brown to sandy-rufous, and have buffish-white wing-coverts with fine dark barring. First-summer male resembles adult male, but reverts to female-like plumage in second winter; full adult male plumage acquired by second summer. Tall grassland with scattered bushes.

6 **LESSER FLORICAN** *Sypheotides indica* **Page 458**
Male breeding (6a, 6b), male non-breeding (6c) and female (6d, 6e). Resident. Breeds in NW India; winters south to SE India; also summers in Nepal. Small, slim, long-necked bustard. Male breeding has spatulate-tipped head plumes, black head/neck and underparts, and white collar across upper mantle; white wing-coverts show as patch on closed wing, but has less white on wing than Bengal Florican. Non-breeding male similar to female, but has white wing-coverts. Female and immature are sandy or cinnamon-buff; separated from female/immature Bengal Florican by smaller size and slimmer appearance, heavily marked wing-coverts, and rufous coloration to barred flight feathers. Dry grassland and crops.

1c
1d
2a
2c
1e
1a
2b
1b
2d
3b
4b
3a
3c
4c
4a
5d
5b
6e
6d
5c
6c
5a
6a
6b
C.D'S

PLATE 37: CRANES

1 **SIBERIAN CRANE** *Grus leucogeranus* **Page 459**
Adult (1a, 1b) and immature (1c). Winter visitor. Mainly Keoladeo Ghana Bird Sanctuary. Adult is white, with bare red face, pinkish-red legs, and noticeably downcurved reddish bill. Immature has brownish bill and fully feathered head at first and is strongly marked with cinnamon-brown on head, neck, mantle and wings; by third winter, red mask is apparent and body feathers are mainly white. In flight, both adult and immature show black primaries which contrast with rest of wing. Freshwater marshes.

2 **SARUS CRANE** *Grus antigone* **Page 460**
Adult (2a, 2b) and immature (2c) *G. a. antigone*; adult *G. a. sharpii* (2d). Resident. Mainly NW India and W Nepal. Adult is grey, with bare red head and upper neck and bare greenish crown. In flight, black primaries contrast with rest of wing. Immature has rusty-buff feathering to head and neck, and upperparts are marked with brown; older immatures have dull red head and upper neck and lack green crown of adult. *G. a. sharpii* is darker grey than nominate, with elongated tertials concolorous with rest of upperparts. Cultivation in well-watered country.

3 **DEMOISELLE CRANE** *Grus virgo* **Page 460**
Adult (3a, 3b) and immature (3c). Winter visitor. Mainly W India; passage migrant in Pakistan. Small crane. Adult has black head and neck with white tuft behind eye, and grey crown; black neck feathers extend as a point beyond breast, and elongated tertials project as shallow arc beyond body, giving rise to distinctive shape. Immature similar to adult, but head and neck are dark grey, tuft behind eye is grey and less prominent, and has grey-brown cast to upperparts. In flight, Demoiselle is best separated at a distance from Common by black breast. Cultivation, large rivers and reservoirs.

4 **COMMON CRANE** *Grus grus* **Page 460**
Adult (4a, 4b) and immature (4c). Winter visitor. Mainly NW India. Adult has mainly black head and foreneck, with white stripe behind eye extending down side of neck. Immature has brown markings on upperparts; adult head pattern apparent on some by first winter. Crops, lakes and reservoirs.

5 **HOODED CRANE** *Grus monacha* **Page 461**
Adult (5a, 5b) and immature (5c). Vagrant. India. Small crane. Adult is uniform dark grey, with white head and upper neck and black forehead and forecrown; red patch on forecrown visible at close range. Immature has strong cinnamon wash to greyish-white head and neck. In flight, has almost uniform slate-grey upperwing and underwing. Plains and marshes.

6 **BLACK-NECKED CRANE** *Grus nigricollis* **Page 461**
Adult (6a, 6b) and immature (6c). Breeds in Ladakh; winters mainly in Bhutan. Adult is pale grey with contrasting black head, upper neck and bunched tertials; shows more contrast between black flight feathers and pale grey coverts than Common, and has black tail-band. Immature has buff or brownish head, neck, mantle and mottling to wing-coverts. Summers by high-altitude lakes; winters in fallow cultivation and marshes.

1b
1c
1a
2a
2d
2c
2b
3b
3c
3a
4a
4c
4b
5b
5c
5a
6a
6c
6b
C.D'S

PLATE 38: MASKED FINFOOT, RAILS AND CRAKES

1 **MASKED FINFOOT** *Heliopais personata* **Page 461**
Male (1a) and female (1b). Resident? Assam and Bangladesh. Large size, with yellow bill and green legs and feet. Pools in dense forest and mangrove creeks.

2 **ANDAMAN CRAKE** *Rallina canningi* **Page 462**
Adult (2a) and juvenile (2b). Resident. Andamans. Lacks white throat and barring on wing-coverts. Adult has chestnut upperparts and black-and-white barred underparts. Juvenile duller, with less pronounced barring on underparts. Forest marshes.

3 **RED-LEGGED CRAKE** *Rallina fasciata* **Page 462**
Adult (3a) and juvenile (3b). Resident. Assam. Broad black-and-white barring on underparts. Adult told from Slaty-legged by red legs, white or buff barring on wings, rufous-brown upperparts, and indistinct whitish to rufous-buff throat. Juvenile from juvenile Slaty-legged by red legs and conspicuous barring on wings. Marshes and paddy-field edges.

4 **SLATY-LEGGED CRAKE** *Rallina eurizonoides* **Page 462**
Adult (4a) and juvenile (4b). Resident. Mainly India and Sri Lanka. Broad black-and-white barring on underparts. Adult told from Red-legged by greenish or grey legs, lack of barring on wings, olive-brown mantle contrasting with rufous neck and breast, and prominent white throat. Juvenile from juvenile Red-legged by leg colour and lack of barring on wings. Marshes in well-wooded country.

5 **SLATY-BREASTED RAIL** *Gallirallus striatus* **Page 463**
Adult male (5a) and juvenile (5b) *G. s. albiventer.* Widespread resident; unrecorded in Pakistan. Straight, longish bill with red at base. Legs olive-grey. Adult has chestnut crown and nape, slate-grey foreneck and breast, white barring and spotting on upperparts, and barred undertail-coverts. Juvenile has rufous-brown crown and nape, and white barring on wing-coverts. Marshes, mangroves and paddy-fields.

6 **WATER RAIL** *Rallus aquaticus* **Page 463**
Adult (6a) and juvenile (6b) *R. a. korejewi.* Breeds in Kashmir; winter visitor, mainly to N subcontinent. Slightly downcurved bill with red at base. Legs pinkish. Adult has dark-streaked olive-brown upperparts, grey underparts, black-and-white barring on flanks, and white undertail-coverts. Juvenile has buff underparts, with blackish flank barring and rufous-buff undertail-coverts. Marshes.

7 **CORN CRAKE** *Crex crex* **Page 463**
Adult. Vagrant. Pakistan, India and Sri Lanka. Stout pinkish bill and legs. Rufous-chestnut on wings, and rufous-brown and white barring on flanks. Grassland and crops.

8 **BROWN CRAKE** *Amaurornis akool* **Page 464**
Adult. Resident. N and C subcontinent. Olive-brown upperparts, grey underparts, and olive-brown flanks and undertail-coverts; underparts lack barring. Marshes and vegetation bordering watercourses.

9 **WHITE-BREASTED WATERHEN** *Amaurornis phoenicurus* **Page 464**
Adult (9a) and juvenile (9b). Widespread resident. Adult has grey upperparts, and white face, foreneck and breast; undertail-coverts rufous-cinnamon. Juvenile has greyish face, foreneck and breast, and olive-brown upperparts. Thick cover close to fresh waters.

1b
1a
2b
2a
3b
3a
4b
4a
5a
5b
6b
6a
9b
8
7
9a

PLATE 39: CRAKES AND OTHER RALLIDS

1 BLACK-TAILED CRAKE *Porzana bicolor* **Page 464**
Adult. Resident. Himalayas and NE India. Red legs. Sooty-grey head and underparts, rufescent olive-brown upperparts, and sooty-black tail and undertail-coverts. Forest pools and marshes, paddy-field edges.

2 LITTLE CRAKE *Porzana parva* **Page 465**
Male (2a), female (2b) and juvenile (2c). Winter visitor and passage migrant. Pakistan, India and Bangladesh. Longer wings than Baillon's, with less extensive barring on flanks, and pronounced pale edges to scapulars and tertials. Adult also with red at base of bill. Female has buff underparts. Juvenile has more extensive barring on flanks than adult (but less than on Baillon's). Marshes.

3 BAILLON'S CRAKE *Porzana pusilla* **Page 465**
Adult (3a) and juvenile (3b). Breeds in Indian Himalayas; widespread winter visitor and passage migrant. Adult has rufous-brown upperparts extensively marked with white; barring on flanks extends farther forward than on Little, and bill is all green. Juvenile has buff underparts; compared with Little, wings are shorter, barring on underparts more extensive, and lacks pronounced pale fringes to tertials and scapulars. Marshes, edges of lakes and pools, and paddy-fields.

4 RUDDY-BREASTED CRAKE *Porzana fusca* **Page 466**
Adult (4a) and juvenile (4b). Widespread resident. Red legs, chestnut underparts, and black-and-white barring restricted to rear flanks and undertail-coverts. Juvenile dark olive-brown, with white-barred undertail-coverts and fine greyish-white mottling/barring on rest of underparts. Marshes, paddy-fields and canals.

5 SPOTTED CRAKE *Porzana porzana* **Page 465**
Adult (5a) and juvenile (5b). Widespread winter visitor; unrecorded in E India. Profuse white spotting on head, neck and breast. Stout bill, barred flanks, and unmarked buff undertail-coverts. Adult has yellowish bill with red at base, and grey head and breast. Juvenile has buffish-brown head and breast, and bill is brown. Marshes and lakes.

6 WATERCOCK *Gallicrex cinerea* **Page 466**
Male breeding (6a), juvenile male (6b), 1st-summer male (6c) and female (6d). Widespread resident. Male is mainly greyish-black, with yellow-tipped red bill and red shield and horn. First-summer male has broad rufous-buff fringes to plumage. Non-breeding male and female have buff underparts with fine barring, and buff fringes to dark brown upperparts. Juvenile has uniform rufous-buff underparts, and rufous-buff fringes to upperparts. Male is much larger than female. Marshes and flooded fields.

7 PURPLE SWAMPHEN *Porphyrio porphyrio* **Page 466**
Adult (7a) and juvenile (7b). Widespread resident. Large size, purplish-blue coloration, and huge red bill and red frontal shield. Juvenile greyer, with duller bill. Large marshes.

8 COMMON MOORHEN *Gallinula chloropus* **Page 467**
Adult (8a) and juvenile (8b). Widespread resident and winter visitor. White undertail-coverts and usually white line along flanks. Adult has red bill with yellow tip and red shield. Juvenile has dull green bill, and is mainly brown. Freshwater wetlands.

9 COMMON COOT *Fulica atra* **Page 467**
Adult (9a) and juvenile (9b). Widespread resident and winter visitor. Blackish, with white bill and shield. Juvenile grey-brown, with whitish throat and breast. Standing fresh waters.

1
2a
2b
3a
4b
2c
3b
5b
5a
4a
6b
6c
7a
7b
6a
6d
9b
8b
8a
9a

PLATE 40: SANDGROUSE

1 **TIBETAN SANDGROUSE** *Syrrhaptes tibetanus* **Page 468**
Male (1a, 1b) and female (1c). Resident. NW Indian Himalayas. Large and pin-tailed. White underparts. In flight, black flight feathers contrast with sandy coverts on upperwing, and underwing is mainly black except for white lesser coverts and trailing edge to primaries. Semi-desert in Tibetan plateau country.

2 **PALLAS'S SANDGROUSE** *Syrrhaptes paradoxus* **Page 468**
Male (2a, 2b) and female (2c). Vagrant. India. Large and pin-tailed. Black patch on belly, largely white underwing, and pale upperside to primaries. Male has narrow black gorget across breast. Arid plains and uplands.

3 **PIN-TAILED SANDGROUSE** *Pterocles alchata* **Page 468**
Male breeding (3a, 3b) and female (3c, 3d). Probably breeds; winter visitor to Pakistan and NW India. Pin-tailed. White belly, with two (male) or three (female) narrow black bands across neck and breast. Largely white underwing and pale grey upperside to primaries. Desert and semi-desert.

4 **CHESTNUT-BELLIED SANDGROUSE** *Pterocles exustus* **Page 469**
Male (4a, 4b) and female (4c, 4d). Widespread resident; unrecorded in Himalayas, the northeast and Sri Lanka. Pin-tailed, with dark underwing and blackish-chestnut belly. Female has buff banding across upperwing-coverts and lacks black gorget across throat, which are useful distinctions at rest from Black-bellied. Desert and sparse thorn scrub.

5 **SPOTTED SANDGROUSE** *Pterocles senegallus* **Page 469**
Male (5a, 5b) and female (5c). Breeds in S Pakistan and Rajasthan; winters in Pakistan and NW India. Pin-tailed. Rather pale upperwing with dark trailing edge, and whitish belly with black line down centre. Flight call is bubbling *quitoo.* Sandy desert and arid foothills.

6 **BLACK-BELLIED SANDGROUSE** *Pterocles orientalis* **Page 470**
Male (6a, 6b) and female (6c). Breeds in Baluchistan; winters in Pakistan and NW India. Large, stocky and short-tailed. Has black belly, and white underwing-coverts contrast with black flight feathers. Semi-desert.

7 **CROWNED SANDGROUSE** *Pterocles coronatus* **Page 470**
Male (7a, 7b) and female (7c). Resident. Mainly Pakistan. Small, compact and short-tailed. Blackish flight feathers contrast with coverts on both surfaces of wing. Male has bold buff spotting on scapulars and upperwing-coverts, and black-and-white markings on head. Female uniformly barred and spotted, including on belly, and has orange-buff throat. Desert.

8 **PAINTED SANDGROUSE** *Pterocles indicus* **Page 470**
Male (8a, 8b) and female (8c). Resident. N Pakistan and India. Small, stocky, and heavily barred. Underwing dark grey. Male has chestnut, buff and black bands across breast, and unbarred orange-buff neck and inner wing-coverts. Female heavily barred all over, with yellowish face and throat. Arid low hills.

9 **LICHTENSTEIN'S SANDGROUSE** *Pterocles lichtensteinii* **Page 471**
Male (9a, 9b) and female (9c). Resident. SW Pakistan. Small, stocky, and heavily barred. Underwing dark grey. Male has buff and black bands across breast and barred neck. Female heavily barred all over, including on face and throat. Stony hills in desert.

1a
1c
1b
2c
2a
2b
3d
3c
3a
3b
4d
4b
4a
4c
5a
5b
5c
6b
6a
7b
7a
6c
7c
8b
9b
8a
8c
9c
9a

PLATE 41: EURASIAN WOODCOCK AND SNIPES

1 **EURASIAN WOODCOCK** *Scolopax rusticola* **Page 471**
Adult (1a, 1b). Breeds in Pakistan hills and Himalayas; winters in Himalayas, Indian hills and Sri Lanka. Bulky, rufous-brown wader with broad, rounded wings. Crown and nape banded black and buff; lacks sharply defined mantle and scapular stripes. Dense, moist forest, also plantations in S India.

2 **SOLITARY SNIPE** *Gallinago solitaria* **Page 472**
Adult (2a, 2b). Resident and winter visitor. Baluchistan, Himalayas and NE India. Large, dull-coloured snipe with long bill. Compared with Wood Snipe, has less striking head pattern, white spotting on ginger-brown breast, and rufous barring on mantle and scapulars (with finer white mantle and scapular stripes). Note, legs should be yellowish. High-altitude marshes and streams.

3 **WOOD SNIPE** *Gallinago nemoricola* **Page 472**
Adult (3a, 3b). Breeds in Himalayas and NE India; winters in Himalayas, S Indian hills and Sri Lanka. Large, with heavy and direct flight. Bill relatively short and broad-based. More boldly marked than Solitary, with buff and blackish head stripes, broad buff stripes on blackish mantle and scapulars, and warm buff neck and breast with brown streaking. Legs greenish. Breeds in alpine meadows and dwarf scrub; winters in forest marshes.

4 **PINTAIL SNIPE** *Gallinago stenura* **Page 473**
Adult (4a), juvenile (4b), flight (4c, 4d) and tail (4e). Widespread winter visitor; unrecorded in parts of the northwest and northeast and Himalayas. Compared with Common, has more rounded wings, and slightly slower and more direct flight. Lacks well-defined white trailing edge to secondaries, and has densely barred underwing-coverts and pale (buff-scaled) upperwing-covert panel (more pronounced than shown). Feet project noticeably beyond tail in flight. Marshes.

5 **SWINHOE'S SNIPE** *Gallinago megala* **Page 473**
Adult (5a), juvenile (5b), flight (5c, 5d) and tail (5e). Winter visitor. Mainly NE subcontinent and S India. Very similar to Pintail. In flight, is heavier, with longer bill and more pointed wings, and feet only just project beyond tail. Some birds quite dusky on neck, breast and flanks, unlike Pintail. Marshes.

6 **GREAT SNIPE** *Gallinago media* **Page 473**
Adult (6a), juvenile (6b), flight (6c, 6d) and tail (6e). Winter visitor. S India and Sri Lanka. Medium-sized, bulky snipe, with broader wings than Common, and slower and more direct flight. Heavily barred underwing, narrow but distinct white wing-bars, and prominent white at sides of tail. Marshes.

7 **COMMON SNIPE** *Gallinago gallinago* **Page 474**
Adult (7a), juvenile (7b), flight (7c, 7d) and tail (7e). Breeds in NW Himalayas; widespread winter visitor. Compared with Pintail, wings are more pointed, and has faster and more erratic flight; shows prominent white trailing edge to wing and white banding on underwing-coverts. Marshes and paddy stubbles.

8 **JACK SNIPE** *Lymnocryptes minimus* **Page 474**
Adult (8a, 8b, 8c). Widespread winter visitor. Small, with short bill. Flight weaker and slower than that of Common, with rounded wing-tips. Has divided supercilium but no crown-stripe. Mantle and scapular stripes very prominent. Marshes and paddy stubbles.

1a
1b
3b
2a
2b
3a
4a
4b
4c
4d
4e
5e
5a
5b
5c
5d
6a
6b
6c
6d
6e
7a
7b
7c
7d
7e
8a
8b
8c

PLATE 42: GODWITS AND CURLEWS

1 BLACK-TAILED GODWIT *Limosa limosa* **Page 475**
Male breeding (1a), female breeding (1b), non-breeding (1c), juvenile (1d) and flight (1e, 1f) *L. l. limosa;* non-breeding *L. l. melanuroides* (1g). Widespread winter visitor. White wing-bars and white tail-base with black tail band. In breeding plumage, has blackish barring on underparts and white belly. In non-breeding plumage, is more uniform on upperparts and breast than Bar-tailed. Juvenile has cinnamon underparts and cinnamon fringes to dark-centred upperparts. *L. l. melanuroides* has narrower wing-bar. Mainly fresh waters.

2 BAR-TAILED GODWIT *Limosa lapponica* **Page 475**
Male breeding (2a), female breeding (2b), non-breeding (2c), juvenile (2d) and flight (2e, 2f). Widespread winter visitor, mainly to coasts. Lacks wing-bar and has barred tail. Breeding male has chestnut-red underparts. Breeding female has pale chestnut or cinnamon underparts, although many as non-breeding. Non-breeding has dark streaking on breast and streaked appearance to upperparts. Juvenile similar to non-breeding, but with buff wash to underparts and buff edges to mantle/scapulars. Estuaries and lagoons.

3 WHIMBREL *Numenius phaeopus* **Page 475**
Adult *N. p. phaeopus* (3a, 3b, 3c); adult *N. p. variegatus* (3d, 3e). Widespread winter visitor, mainly to coasts. Smaller than both curlews, with shorter bill. Distinctive head pattern, with whitish supercilium and crown-stripe, dark eye-stripe, and dark sides of crown. *N. p. variegatus* has barred underwing-coverts and mainly brown rump and back. Flight call distinctive, *he-he-he-he-he-he-he*. Estuaries, tidal creeks and mangroves.

4 EURASIAN CURLEW *Numenius arquata* **Page 476**
Adult *N. a. orientalis* (4a, 4b, 4c). Widespread winter visitor, mainly to coasts. Large size and long, curved bill. Rather plain head. Underwing-coverts are white and rump/back mainly white; white ground colour to belly and vent. Has distinctive mournful *cur-lew* call. Estuaries, tidal creeks and mangroves.

5 EASTERN CURLEW *Numenius madagascariensis* **Page 476**
Adult (5a, 5b, 5c). Vagrant. Bangladesh. Mainly coastal. Dark back and rump and heavily barred underwing-coverts and axillaries. Underparts typically washed with pale brown, including belly and vent (although rather paler buff on some).

1a
1b
1c
1d
1e
1f
1g
2a
2b
2c
2d
2e
2f
3a
3b
3c
3d
3e
4a
4b
4c
5a
5b
5c

PLATE 43: *TRINGA* SANDPIPERS

1 **SPOTTED REDSHANK** *Tringa erythropus* **Page 476**
Adult breeding (1a), adult non-breeding (1b, 1c, 1d), and juvenile (1e). Widespread winter visitor. Red at base of bill, and red legs. Longer bill and legs than Common Redshank, and upperwing comparatively uniform. Non-breeding plumage is paler grey above and whiter below than Common. Underparts mainly black in breeding plumage. Juvenile has grey barring on underparts, and upperparts heavily spotted with white. Mainly fresh waters, also coastal waters.

2 **COMMON REDSHANK** *Tringa totanus* **Page 477**
Adult breeding (2a), adult non-breeding (2b, 2c, 2d) and juvenile (2e). Breeds in NW Himalayas; widespread winter visitor. Orange-red at base of bill, and orange-red legs. Shorter bill and legs than Spotted Redshank, and with broad white trailing edge to wing. Non-breeding plumage is grey-brown above, with grey breast. Neck and underparts heavily streaked in breeding plumage. Juvenile has brown upperparts with buff spotting and fringes. Fresh and coastal waters.

3 **MARSH SANDPIPER** *Tringa stagnatilis* **Page 477**
Adult breeding (3a), adult non-breeding (3b, 3c, 3d). Widespread winter visitor. Smaller and daintier than Common Greenshank, with proportionately longer legs and finer bill. Legs greenish or yellowish. Upperparts are grey and foreneck and underparts white in non-breeding plumage. In breeding plumage, foreneck and breast streaked and upperparts blotched and barred. Juvenile has dark-streaked upperparts with buff fringes. Mainly freshwater wetlands.

4 **COMMON GREENSHANK** *Tringa nebularia* **Page 478**
Adult breeding (4a) and non-breeding (4b, 4c, 4d). Widespread winter visitor. Stocky, with long, stout bill and long, stout greenish legs. Upperparts are grey and foreneck and underparts white in non-breeding plumage. In breeding plumage, foreneck and breast streaked and upperparts untidily streaked. Juvenile has dark-streaked upperparts with fine buff or whitish fringes. Wide range of freshwater and saltwater wetlands.

5 **NORDMANN'S GREENSHANK** *Tringa guttifer* **Page 478**
Adult breeding (5a), adult non-breeding (5b, 5c) and juvenile (5d). Winter visitor. India, Bangladesh and Sri Lanka. Stockier than Common Greenshank, with shorter, yellowish legs, and deeper bill with blunt tip. Breeding adult has black spotting on breast and prominent white notching on scapulars and tertials. Non-breeding has paler and more uniform upperparts than Common. Juvenile has rather uniform upperparts, with paler fringes to wing-coverts, and strongly bicoloured bill. Freshwater and coastal wetlands.

6 **GREEN SANDPIPER** *Tringa ochropus* **Page 479**
Adult breeding (6a) and non-breeding (6b, 6c, 6d). Widespread winter visitor. Greenish legs. Compared with Wood Sandpiper, has indistinct (or non-existent) supercilium behind eye and darker upperparts. In flight, underwing very dark. Mainly freshwater wetlands.

7 **WOOD SANDPIPER** *Tringa glareola* **Page 479**
Adult breeding (7a), adult non-breeding (7b, 7c, 7d) and juvenile (7e). Widespread winter visitor. Yellowish legs, prominent supercilium, and heavily spotted upperparts. Freshwater and coastal wetlands.

1a
1b
1e
2e
1c
1d
2a
2b
2c
2d
3a
3b
3d
3c
4a
4b
4c
4d
5a
5b
5d
5c
6a
6b
6c
6d
7a
7b
7e
7c
7d

PLATE 44: MISCELLANEOUS WADERS

1 **TEREK SANDPIPER** *Xenus cinereus* **Page 479**
Adult breeding (1a, 1b), adult non-breeding (1c, 1d) and juvenile (1e). Widespread winter visitor, mainly to coasts, also inland. Longish, upturned bill and short yellowish legs. In flight, shows prominent white trailing edge to secondaries and grey rump and tail. Adult breeding has blackish scapular lines. Mainly coastal wetlands.

2 **COMMON SANDPIPER** *Actitis hypoleucos* **Page 480**
Adult breeding (2a, 2b) and juvenile (2c, 2d). Breeds in Himalayas; widespread winter visitor. Horizontal stance and constant bobbing action distinctive. White wing-bar and brown rump and centre of tail in flight. In breeding plumage, has irregular dark streaking and barring on upperparts, lacking in non-breeding. Juvenile has buff fringes and dark subterminal crescents to upperparts. Breeds by mountain streams and rivers; winters at freshwater and coastal wetlands.

3 **GREY-TAILED TATTLER** *Heteroscelus brevipes* **Page 480**
Adult breeding (3a), adult non-breeding (3b, 3c, 3d) and juvenile (3e). Vagrant. Bangladesh. Uniform grey wings and rump/tail. Stocky, with short yellow legs. Prominent supercilium, usually extending beyond eye; primaries extend to tail-tip. Adult breeding has barring on breast and flanks. Adult non-breeding uniform grey on upperparts and breast. Juvenile has indistinct white spotting on upperparts. Coastal wetlands.

4 **RUDDY TURNSTONE** *Arenaria interpres* **Page 480**
Adult breeding (4a), adult non-breeding (4b, 4c, 4d) and juvenile (4e). Widespread winter visitor to coasts. Short bill and orange legs. In flight, shows white stripes on wings and back and black tail. In breeding plumage, has complex black-and-white neck and breast pattern and much chestnut-red on upperparts; duller and less strikingly patterned in non-breeding plumage. Juvenile has buff fringes to upperparts, and blackish breast. Rocky coasts and tidal mudflats.

5 **ASIAN DOWITCHER** *Limnodromus semipalmatus* **Page 481**
Adult breeding (5a), adult non-breeding (5b, 5c) and juvenile (5d). Comparatively larger than shown (slightly smaller than Bar-tailed Godwit). Winter visitor to coasts of India, Bangladesh and Sri Lanka. Broad-based black bill with swollen tip, and square-shaped head. Shows diffuse pale wing-bar and grey tail in flight. Underparts brick-red in breeding plumage. Upperparts and underparts heavily streaked in non-breeding plumage. Juvenile has buff fringes to upperparts and wash to breast. Intertidal mudflats and mudbanks.

6 **GREAT KNOT** *Calidris tenuirostris* **Page 481**
Adult breeding (6a), adult non-breeding (6b, 6c, 6d) and juvenile (6e). Winter visitor, chiefly to coasts. Larger than Red Knot, and often with slightly downcurved bill. Adult breeding heavily marked with black on breast and flanks, with chestnut patterning to scapulars. Adult non-breeding typically more heavily streaked on upperparts and breast than Red Knot, and juvenile is more strongly patterned than that species. Intertidal flats and tidal creeks.

7 **RED KNOT** *Calidris canutus* **Page 481**
Adult breeding (7a), adult non-breeding (7b, 7c, 7d) and juvenile (7e). Winter visitor, chiefly to coasts. Stocky, with short, straight bill. Much larger than stints. Adult breeding is brick-red on underparts. Adult non-breeding whitish on underparts and uniform grey on upperparts. Juvenile has buff fringes and dark subterminal crescents to upperparts. Mainly intertidal mudflats.

1a
1c
1e
1b
1d
2a
2c
2b
2d
3c
3d
3a
3b
3e
4a
4b
4e
4d
4c
5a
5b
5d
5c
6c
6d
6a
6b
6e
7d
7a
7b
7e
7c

PLATE 45: STINTS AND SANDERLING

1 SANDERLING *Calidris alba* **Page 482**
Adult breeding (1a, 1b), adult non-breeding (1c, 1d, 1e) and juvenile (1f). Winter visitor, mainly to coasts. Stocky, with short bill. Very broad white wing-bar. Adult breeding usually shows some rufous on sides of head, breast and upperparts. Non-breeding is pale grey above and very white below. Juvenile chequered black-and-white above. Sandy beaches.

2 LITTLE STINT *Calidris minuta* **Page 482**
Adult breeding fresh (2a) and worn (2b), adult non-breeding (2c, 2d) and juvenile (2e, 2g, dull variant 2f). Widespread winter visitor. More rotund and upright than Temminck's. In flight, shows grey sides to tail; has weak *pi-pi-pi* flight call. Adult breeding has pale mantle V, rufous wash to face, neck sides and breast, and rufous fringes to upperpart feathers. Non-breeding has untidy, mottled/streaked appearance, with grey breast sides. Juvenile has whitish mantle V, greyish nape, and rufous fringes to upperparts. Freshwater and coastal wetlands.

3 RED-NECKED STINT *Calidris ruficollis* **Page 483**
Adult breeding fresh (3a) and worn (3b), adult non-breeding (3c, 3d) and juvenile (3e, 3g, dull variant 3f). Winter visitor. India, Bangladesh and Sri Lanka. Very similar to Little. Adult breeding typically has unstreaked rufous-orange throat, foreneck and breast, white sides of lower breast with dark streaking, and rather plain greyish tertials and wing-coverts. Adult non-breeding subtly different in shape from non-breeding Little, and with paler and more uniform upperparts. Juvenile lacks prominent mantle V; has different coloration and patterning to lower scapulars and wing-coverts, and grey-centred, whitish- or buffish-edged tertials. Mainly coastal.

4 TEMMINCK'S STINT *Calidris temminckii* **Page 483**
Adult breeding (4a, 4b), adult non-breeding (4c, 4d) and juvenile (4e, 4f). Widespread winter visitor. More elongated than Little, and with more horizontal stance. In flight, shows white sides to tail; flight call a purring trill. Legs yellowish. In all plumages, lacks mantle V and is usually rather uniform, with complete breast-band and indistinct supercilium. Freshwater and coastal wetlands.

5 LONG-TOED STINT *Calidris subminuta* **Page 484**
Adult breeding (5a), adult non-breeding (5b, 5c, 5d) and juvenile (5e). Winter visitor. Mainly E subcontinent. Long and yellowish legs, longish neck, and upright stance. In all plumages, has prominent supercilium and heavily streaked foreneck and breast. In winter, upperparts more heavily marked than Little's. Freshwater and coastal wetlands.

6 SHARP-TAILED SANDPIPER *Calidris acuminata* **Page 484**
Adult breeding (6a), adult non-breeding (6b) and juvenile (6c, 6d, 6e). Vagrant. Pakistan and Sri Lanka. Rufous crown and prominent white supercilium. Adult non-breeding has breast-band of fine streaking. Adult breeding has dark markings over entire underparts. Juvenile has buff wash to lightly streaked breast. Freshwater and coastal wetlands.

1f
1d
1a
1c
1e
1b
2a
2c
2b
2d
2e
2f
2g
3a
3c
3d
3e
3f
3b
3g
4d
4a
4c
4e
4b
4f
5c
5d
5a
5b
5e
6e
6b
6a
6c
6d

PLATE 46: MISCELLANEOUS WADERS

1 **DUNLIN** *Calidris alpina* **Page 484**
Adult breeding (1a, 1b), adult non-breeding (1c, 1d) and juvenile (1e). Winter visitor, mainly to coasts, also inland. Shorter legs and bill compared with Curlew Sandpiper, and with dark centre to rump. Adult breeding has black belly. Adult non-breeding darker grey-brown than Curlew Sandpiper, with less distinct supercilium. Juvenile has streaked belly, rufous fringes to mantle, and buff mantle V. Mainly coastal wetlands, also flooded fields.

2 **CURLEW SANDPIPER** *Calidris ferruginea* **Page 485**
Adult breeding (2a, 2b), adult non-breeding (2c, 2d) and juvenile (2e, 2f). Winter visitor, mainly to coasts, also inland. More elegant than Dunlin, and with longer, more downcurved bill. Adult breeding has chestnut-red head and underparts. Adult non-breeding paler grey than Dunlin, with more distinct supercilium. Juvenile has strong supercilium, buff wash to breast, and buff fringes to upperparts. Mainly coastal wetlands, also inland waters.

3 **BUFF-BREASTED SANDPIPER** *Tryngites subruficollis* **Page 485**
Adult (3a) and juvenile (3b, 3c, 3d). Vagrant. India and Sri Lanka. Small size and short bill. Face and underparts buff. Upperparts neatly fringed with buff. Short grass, mud and seashore.

4 **SPOON-BILLED SANDPIPER** *Calidris pygmea* **Page 482**
Adult breeding (4a), adult non-breeding (4b, 4c) and juvenile (4d). Winter visitor. India, Bangladesh and Sri Lanka. Spatulate tip to bill. Adult winter has paler grey upperparts than Little Stint, with more pronounced white supercilium, forehead and cheeks. Adult breeding more uniform rufous-orange on face and breast compared with Little. Juvenile very similar to Little Stint, but shows more white on face and darker eye-stripe and ear-coverts (masked appearance). Intertidal mudflats.

5 **BROAD-BILLED SANDPIPER** *Limicola falcinellus* **Page 485**
Adult breeding (5a, 5b), adult non-breeding (5c, 5d) and juvenile (5e, 5f). Winter visitor to coasts. Distinctive shape: legs set well back and downward-kinked bill. Supercilium is divided. Adult breeding has bold streaking on neck and breast contrasting with white belly. Non-breeding has dark patch at bend of wing and streaked upperparts. Juvenile has buff mantle/scapular lines and streaked breast. Intertidal mudflats and tidal creeks.

6 **RUFF** *Philomachus pugnax* **Page 486**
Male breeding (6a, 6b, 6c), female breeding (6d), adult male non-breeding (6e, 6f), juvenile female (6g, 6h) and juvenile male (6i). Widespread winter visitor and passage migrant. Distinctive shape, with long neck, small head and short, slightly downcurved bill. Non-breeding and juvenile have neatly fringed upperparts, juvenile with buff underparts. Breeding birds have black and chestnut markings on upperparts, male with striking ruff. Freshwater wetlands and intertidal mudflats.

1a
1c
1e
1d
1b
2a
2c
2e
2d
2f
3a
3b
3c
3d
2b
4a
4b
4d
4c
5b
5a
5c
5e
5d
5f
6a
6f
6h
6d
6b
6e
6i
6g
6c

PLATE 47: PHALAROPES, COURSERS AND EURASIAN THICK-KNEE

1 **RED-NECKED PHALAROPE** *Phalaropus lobatus* **Page 486**
Adult breeding (1a), adult non-breeding (1b, 1c) and juvenile (1d). Winter visitor, mainly in offshore waters of Pakistan, NW and SE India and Sri Lanka. Typically seen swimming. More delicately built than Red Phalarope, with fine bill. Adult breeding has white throat and red stripe down side of grey neck. Adult non-breeding has grey upperparts. Juvenile has orange-buff mantle and scapular lines. Winters at sea.

2 **RED PHALAROPE** *Phalaropus fulicaria* **Page 487**
Adult breeding (2a), adult non-breeding (2b, 2c) and juvenile (2d). Vagrant. India. Typically seen swimming. Stockier than Red-necked Phalarope, with stouter bill. Adult breeding has red neck and underparts and white face patch. Adult non-breeding has uniform pale grey mantle, scapulars and rump. Juvenile has dark upperparts evenly fringed with buff. Habitat not recorded in subcontinent.

3 **GREATER PAINTED-SNIPE** *Rostratula benghalensis* **Page 487**
Adult male (3a), adult female (3b) and juvenile (3c). Widespread resident. Rail-like wader, with broad, rounded wings and longish, downcurved bill. White or buff 'spectacles' and 'braces'. Adult female has maroon head and neck and dark greenish wing-coverts. Adult male and juvenile duller, and have buff spotting on wing-coverts. Freshwater marshes, vegetated pools and mangroves.

4 **JERDON'S COURSER** *Rhinoptilus bitorquatus* **Page 498**
Adult (4a, 4b). Resident. Andhra Pradesh. Huge eye, and short yellow bill with black tip. Broad supercilium, and brown and white bands across breast. Thin scrub forest in rocky foothills.

5 **CREAM-COLOURED COURSER** *Cursorius cursor* **Page 499**
Adult (5a, 5b) and juvenile (5c). Resident and winter visitor. Pakistan and NW India. Pale sandy upperparts and underparts. Adult has sandy-rufous forehead, grey nape and pale lores. Juvenile has buffish crown and dark scaling on upperparts. Sand dunes and stony desert.

6 **INDIAN COURSER** *Cursorius coromandelicus* **Page 499**
Adult (6a, 6b). Widespread resident in plains. Grey-brown upperparts and orange underparts, with dark belly. In flight, shows white band across uppertail-coverts. Juvenile has brown barring on chestnut-brown underparts. Open dry country and dry river beds.

7 **EURASIAN THICK-KNEE** *Burhinus oedicnemus* **Page 488**
Adult (7a, 7b, 7c) and juvenile (7d). Widespread resident. Sandy-brown and streaked. Short yellow-and-black bill, striking yellow eye, and long yellow legs. Desert, stony hills, open dry forest and fields.

1a
1b
1d
1c
2a
2d
2c
2b
3a
3b
3c
4a
4b
6b
5b
5c
5a
6a

PLATE 48: MISCELLANEOUS WADERS, JACANAS

1 **EURASIAN OYSTERCATCHER** *Haematopus ostralegus* **Page 489**
Adult breeding (1a, 1b) and non-breeding (1c). Winter visitor to coasts. Black and white, with broad white wing-bar. Bill reddish. White collar in non-breeding plumage. Sandy and rocky coasts, and coral reefs.

2 **IBISBILL** *Ibidorhyncha struthersii* **Page 490**
Adult (2a, 2b) and juvenile (2c). Resident. Himalayas. Adult has black face, downcurved dark red bill, and black and white breast-bands. Juvenile has brownish upperparts with buff fringes, faint breast-band, and dull legs and bill. Mountain streams and rivers with shingle beds.

3 **BLACK-WINGED STILT** *Himantopus himantopus* **Page 490**
Adult (3a, 3b) and immature (3c). Widespread resident. Slender appearance, long pinkish legs, and fine straight bill. Juvenile has browner upperparts with buff fringes. Freshwater wetlands, brackish marshes and saltpans.

4 **PIED AVOCET** *Recurvirostra avosetta* **Page 490**
Adult (4a, 4b) and juvenile (4c). Breeds in Pakistan and Kutch; widespread winter visitor and passage migrant. Upward kink to black bill. Distinctive black-and-white patterning. Juvenile has brown and buff mottling on mantle and scapulars. Alkaline and brackish ponds, and coastal wetlands.

5 **CRAB-PLOVER** *Dromas ardeola* **Page 498**
Adult (5a, 5b) and juvenile (5c). Winter visitor to coasts; breeds in Sri Lanka. Black-and-white plumage, with stout black bill and very long blue-grey legs. Juvenile like washed-out version of adult. Intertidal mudflats, coral reefs and coastal rocks.

6 **PHEASANT-TAILED JACANA** *Hydrophasianus chirurgus* **Page 487**
Adult breeding (6a, 6b) and non-breeding (6c). Widespread resident. Extensive white on upperwing, and white underwing. Adult breeding has brown underparts and long tail. Adult non-breeding and juvenile have white underparts with dark line down side of neck and dark breast-band. Freshwater wetlands.

7 **BRONZE-WINGED JACANA** *Metopidius indicus* **Page 488**
Adult (7a, 7b) and immature (7c). Widespread resident; largely absent from Pakistan and Sri Lanka. Dark upperwing and underwing. Adult has white supercilium, bronze-green upperparts, and blackish underparts. Juvenile has orange-buff wash on breast, short white supercilium, and yellowish bill. Freshwater wetlands.

8 **GREAT THICK-KNEE** *Esacus recurvirostris* **Page 489**
Adult (8a, 8b). Widespread resident. Upturned black-and-yellow bill, and white forehead and 'spectacles'. In flight, shows grey mid-wing panel and black secondaries. Stony banks of larger rivers and lakes; coastal wetlands.

9 **BEACH THICK-KNEE** *Esacus neglectus* **Page 489**
Adult (9a, 9b). Resident. Andamans. Stouter and straighter bill than Great Thick-knee. Forehead and lores mainly black. In flight, shows grey secondaries and white inner primaries. Sandy and muddy shores and coral reefs.

1a
1c
2a
2c
1b
3a
3c
3b
2b
4b
4a
4c
6a
5b
5a
5c
6c
6b
7b
7c
7a
9a
8b
9b
8a

PLATE 49: PRATINCOLES AND PLOVERS

1 **COLLARED PRATINCOLE** *Glareola pratincola* **Page 499**
Adult breeding (1a, 1b, 1c), adult non-breeding (1d) and juvenile (1e). Breeds in Pakistan; winter visitor to India and Sri Lanka. White trailing edge to secondaries. Pronounced fork to tail, with tail-tip reaching tips of closed wings on adult at rest. Dry bare ground around wetlands.

2 **ORIENTAL PRATINCOLE** *Glareola maldivarum* **Page 500**
Adult breeding (2a, 2b, 2c), adult non-breeding (2d) and juvenile (2e). Widespread resident; no recent records for Pakistan. Lacks white trailing edge to secondaries. Only shallow tail-fork, tail-tip falling well short of wing-tip at rest. Often with strong peach-orange wash on underparts in breeding plumage. Dry bare ground around wetlands, and lowland fields.

3 **SMALL PRATINCOLE** *Glareola lactea* **Page 500**
Adult breeding (3a, 3b, 3c) and non-breeding (3d). Widespread resident. Small size, with sandy-grey coloration. White panel across secondaries and blackish underwing-coverts in flight. Large rivers and lakes with sand or shingle banks.

4 **EUROPEAN GOLDEN PLOVER** *Pluvialis apricaria* **Page 491**
Adult breeding (4a, 4b) and non-breeding (4c, 4d). Vagrant. Pakistan and India. Stockier than Pacific Golden, with shorter and stouter bill and shorter legs. Underwing-coverts and axillaries largely white. In non-breeding plumage, supercilium is usually less distinct and is rather plain-faced. Grassland and mud on lakeshores and in estuaries.

5 **PACIFIC GOLDEN PLOVER** *Pluvialis fulva* **Page 491**
Adult breeding (5a, 5b), adult non-breeding (5c, 5d). Widespread winter visitor. Golden-yellow markings on upperparts, and dusky grey underwing-coverts and axillaries. Slimmer-bodied, longer-necked and longer-legged than Grey Plover, and with narrower white wing-bar and dark rump. Mudbanks of wetlands, ploughed fields and grassland.

6 **GREY PLOVER** *Pluvialis squatarola* **Page 492**
Adult breeding (6a), adult non-breeding (6b, 6c, 6d) and juvenile (6e). Winter visitor, mainly to coasts. Greyish upperparts, white underwing, and black axillaries. Stockier, with stouter bill and shorter legs, than Pacific Golden. Whitish rump and prominent white wing-bar. Sandy shores, mudflats and tidal creeks.

1a
1d
1b
1c
1e
2a
2b
2d
2e
2c
3d
3a
3b
3c
4a
4b
4c
4d
5a
5c
5d
5b
6a
6b
6c
6d
6e

PLATE 50: PLOVERS

1 **COMMON RINGED PLOVER** *Charadrius hiaticula* **Page 492**
Adult breeding (1a) and non-breeding (1b, 1c). Widespread winter visitor. Prominent breast-band and white hindcollar. Prominent wing-bar in flight. Adult has orange legs and bill-base. Non-breeding and juvenile have prominent whitish supercilium and forehead compared with Little Ringed. Mudbanks of freshwater and coastal wetlands.

2 **LONG-BILLED PLOVER** *Charadrius placidus* **Page 492**
Adult breeding (2a) and non-breeding (2b, 2c). Winter visitor, mainly to N subcontinent; unrecorded in Pakistan. Like a large Little Ringed, but has longer tail with clearer dark subterminal bar, and more prominent white wing-bar; ear-coverts never black, and has less distinct eye-ring than Little Ringed. Shingle banks of large rivers.

3 **LITTLE RINGED PLOVER** *Charadrius dubius* **Page 493**
Adult breeding (3a) and non-breeding (3b, 3c). Widespread resident and winter visitor. Small size, elongated and small-headed appearance, and uniform upperwing. Legs yellowish or pinkish. Adult breeding has striking yellow eye-ring. Adult non-breeding and juvenile have less distinct head pattern. Freshwater and coastal wetlands.

4 **KENTISH PLOVER** *Charadrius alexandrinus* **Page 493**
Adult male breeding (4a) and non-breeding (4b, 4c) *C. a. alexandrinus*; breeding *C. a. seebohmi* (4d). Breeds locally in Pakistan, India and Sri Lanka; widespread winter visitor. Small size and stocky appearance. White hindcollar and usually small, well-defined patches on sides of breast. Male has rufous cap. Sandy seashores, sandy banks of freshwater wetlands and saltpans.

5 **LESSER SAND PLOVER** *Charadrius mongolus* **Page 494**
Male breeding (5a), female breeding (5b) and adult non-breeding (5c, 5d). Breeds in N Himalayas, India; winters on coasts of subcontinent. Larger and longer-legged than Kentish, lacking white hindcollar. Told from Greater Sand by smaller and stouter bill (with blunt tip), and shorter dark grey or dark greenish legs. In flight, feet do not usually extend beyond tail and white wing-bar is narrower across primaries. Breeding male typically shows full black mask and forehead and more extensive rufous on breast compared with Greater Sand (although variation exists in these characters). Breeds in Tibetan plateau country; winters on coastal wetlands.

6 **GREATER SAND PLOVER** *Charadrius leschenaultii* **Page 494**
Male breeding (6a), female breeding (6b) and adult non-breeding (6c, 6d). Winter visitor to coasts. Larger and lankier than Lesser Sand, with longer and larger bill, usually with pronounced gonys and more pointed tip. Longer legs are paler, with distinct yellowish or greenish tinge. In flight, feet project beyond tail and has broader white wing-bar across primaries. Coastal wetlands.

7 **CASPIAN PLOVER** *Charadrius asiaticus* **Page 495**
Male breeding (7a) and adult non-breeding (7b, 7c, 7d). Winter visitor. India, Sri Lanka and Maldives. Slim bill, slender appearance and complete breast-band. White underwing-coverts and greenish or brownish legs best distinctions from Oriental. Mudflats and coast.

8 **ORIENTAL PLOVER** *Charadrius veredus* **Page 495**
Male breeding (8a), adult non-breeding (8b, 8c, 8d). Vagrant. India and Sri Lanka. Larger than Caspian, with very long yellowish or pinkish legs. Has brown underwing-coverts Mudflats and coast.

9 **BLACK-FRONTED DOTTEREL** *Elseyornis melanops* **Page 495**
Adult breeding. Not to scale. Vagrant. India. Short, black-tipped red bill; black stripe through eye, black breast-band, and purplish scapular patch. Mainly stony beds of rivers and streams.

1a
1b
1c
2a
2b
2c
3a
3b
3c
4a
4b
4c
4d
5a
5b
5c
5d
6a
6b
6c
6d
7a
7b
7c
7d
8a
8b
8c
8d
9

PLATE 51: LAPWINGS

1 **NORTHERN LAPWING** *Vanellus vanellus* **Page 495**
Adult male breeding (1a) and adult non-breeding (1b, 1c). Winter visitor to N subcontinent. Black crest, white (or buff) and black face pattern, black breast-band, and dark green upperparts. Has very broad, rounded wing-tips. Wet grassland, marshes, fallow fields, and wetland edges.

2 **YELLOW-WATTLED LAPWING** *Vanellus malarbaricus* **Page 496**
Adult (2a, 2b) and juvenile (2c). Resident. Mainly in India. Yellow wattles and legs. White supercilium, dark cap, and brown breast-band. Open dry ground.

3 **RIVER LAPWING** *Vanellus duvaucelii* **Page 496**
Adult (3a, 3b). Resident. N subcontinent; unrecorded in Pakistan. Black cap and throat, grey sides to neck, and black bill and legs. Black patch on belly. Mainly sandbanks and shingle banks of rivers, also estuaries.

4 **GREY-HEADED LAPWING** *Vanellus cinereus* **Page 496**
Adult non-breeding (4a, 4b) and juvenile (4c). Winter visitor. Nepal, mainly NE India, and Bangladesh. Yellow bill with black tip, and yellow legs. Grey head, neck and breast, latter with diffuse black border, and black tail-band. River banks, marshes and wet fields.

5 **RED-WATTLED LAPWING** *Vanellus indicus* **Page 497**
Adult (5a) and juvenile (5b) *V. i. indicus*; adult *V. i. atronuchalis* (5c, 5d). Widespread resident. Black cap and breast, red bill with black tip, and yellow legs. *V. i. atronuchalis* has black head, neck and breast, with white patch on ear-coverts. Open flat ground near water.

6 **SOCIABLE LAPWING** *Vanellus gregarius* **Page 497**
Adult breeding (6a, 6b) and non-breeding (6c). Winter visitor, now mainly to Pakistan and N and NW India. Dark cap, with white supercilia which join at nape. Adult breeding has yellow wash to sides of head, and black-and-maroon patch on belly. Non-breeding and immature have streaked breast. Dry fallow fields and scrub desert.

7 **WHITE-TAILED LAPWING** *Vanellus leucurus* **Page 497**
Adult (7a, 7b) and juvenile (7c). Breeds in Baluchistan; winters in N subcontinent. Blackish bill, and very long yellow legs. Plain head. Tail all white, lacking black band of other *Vanellus* plovers. Freshwater marshes and marshy lake edges.

1a
1b
1c
2c
2a
3b
2b
4c
3a
4a
4b
5d
5a
5b
5c
6b
6a
6c
7a
7c
7b

PLATE 52: SKUAS

1 BROWN SKUA *Catharacta antarctica* **Page 501**
Adult (1a) and juvenile (1b). Visitor. India, Sri Lanka and Maldives. Larger and more powerful than South Polar, with broader-based wings and larger bill. Usually darker, lacking contrast between pale head and underbody and darker upperbody; can be very similar to South Polar in general colour and appearance, but upperparts of adult are more heavily and irregularly splashed with pale markings. Juvenile warmer, more rufous-brown, in colouration, and upperparts more uniform (lacking pronounced pale splashes of adult). Coastal waters.

2 SOUTH POLAR SKUA *Catharacta maccormicki* **Page 501**
Adult pale morph (2a), adult intermediate (2b), adult dark morph (2c) and juvenile (2d). Visitor. India, Sri Lanka and Maldives. Slightly smaller and slighter than Brown Skua, with finer bill. Pale morph distinctive: pale sandy-brown head and underbody contrasting with dark brown mantle and upperwing- and underwing-coverts. Dark morph lacks heavy pale streaking/mottling of Brown, and usually has pale forehead, dark cap/head and paler hindneck; uniform (unbarred) underwing-coverts, axillaries and uppertail- and undertail-coverts are best distinctions from dark juvenile Pomarine Jaeger. Intermediates also occur. Juvenile has pale to mid grey head and underparts, and dark grey upperparts. Coastal waters.

3 POMARINE JAEGER *Stercorarius pomarinus* **Page 502**
Adult dark morph breeding (3a), adult pale morph breeding (3b), adult pale morph non-breeding (3c), juvenile pale morph (3d) and juvenile dark morph (3e, 3f). Visitor. Pakistan, India and Sri Lanka. Larger and stockier than Parasitic Jaeger, with heavier bill and broader-based wings. Adult breeding has long, broad central tail feathers twisted at end to form swollen tip (although tips can be broken off). Adult non-breeding similar to immature (see text), but has uniform dark underwing-coverts; broader round-tipped central tail feathers best distinction from Parasitic. Juvenile variable, typically dark brown with broad pale barring on uppertail- and undertail-coverts and underwing-coverts; head, neck and underparts never appear rufous-coloured as on some juvenile Parasitic (although others appear virtually identical to Pomarine); note also the second pale crescent on outer underwing on most birds, diffuse vermiculations (never streaking) on nape and neck, and blunt-tipped or almost non-existent projection of central tail feathers. Coastal waters.

4 PARASITIC JAEGER *Stercorarius parasiticus* **Page 502**
Adult dark morph breeding (4a), adult pale morph breeding (4b), adult pale morph non-breeding (4c), juvenile pale morph (4d), juvenile intermediate morph (4e) and juvenile dark morph (4f). Visitor to coasts, mainly Pakistan. Smaller and more lightly built than Pomarine Jaeger, with slimmer bill and narrower-based wings. Adult breeding has pointed tip to elongated central tail feathers. Occurs in both pale and dark morphs. Adult non-breeding has more pointed tail-tip compared with non-breeding Pomarine. Juvenile more variable than juvenile Pomarine, ranging from grey and buff with heavy barring to completely blackish-brown, and many have rusty-orange to cinnamon-brown cast to head and nape (not found on Pomarine); except for all-dark juveniles, further distinctions from Pomarine are dark streaking on head and neck and pale tips to primaries. Coastal waters.

2c
1a
2a
2b
1b
2d
3f
3d
3a
3e
3b
3c
4a
4b
4f
4e
4d
4c

PLATE 53: LARGE GULLS

1 YELLOW-LEGGED GULL *Larus cachinnans* **Page 505**

Adult non-breeding (1a), 1st-winter (1b) and 2nd-winter (1c) *L. c. cachinnans*; adult non-breeding *L. c. barabensis* (1d). Widespread winter visitor. Much larger and broader-winged than Mew Gull. Adult has paler grey upperparts than Heuglin's; may show faint streaking on head in non-breeding plumage. Juvenile and first-year told from Heuglin's by paler inner primaries, and much paler underwing-coverts with dark barring; diffusely barred tail, dark greater-covert bar, and lack of distinct mask and patch of mottling on breast help separate it from juvenile Pallas's; brown mottling on mantle best distinction from first-winter Pallas's. Second-year has paler grey mantle than second-year Heuglin's; diffusely barred tail, dark greater-covert bar, and lack of distinct mask help separate it from first-year Pallas's. *L. c. barabensis* may occur in region; adult has darker upperparts than nominate, and usually more black and less white on primaries. Coasts and inland waters.

2 HEUGLIN'S GULL *Larus heuglini* **Page 506**

Adult non-breeding (2a), 1st-winter (2b) and 2nd-winter (2c) *L. h. taimyrensis*; adult non-breeding (2d), 1st-winter (2e) and 2nd-winter (2f) *L. h. heuglini*. Winter visitor, mainly to coasts. Darkest large gull of region. Adult has darker grey upperparts than Yellow-legged. Juvenile and first-year told from Yellow-legged by dark inner primaries and darker underwing-coverts, and usually broader dark tail-band; mainly dark tail, dark greater-covert bar, dark underwing, and lack of distinct mask help separate it from juvenile Pallas's; brown mottling on mantle further distinction from first-winter Pallas's. Second-year has darker grey mantle and darker upperwing and underwing than second-year Yellow-legged. *L. h. taimyrensis* bulkier and broader-winged than *L. h. heuglini*, and upperparts of adult are a shade paler. Coasts and inland waters.

3 PALLAS'S GULL *Larus ichthyaetus* **Page 506**

Adult breeding (3a), adult non-breeding (3b), 1st-winter (3c), 2nd-winter (3d) and 3rd-summer (3e). Widespread winter visitor. Angular head with gently sloping forehead, crown peaking behind eye. Bill large, 'dark-tipped', with bulging gonys. Adult breeding has black hood with bold white eye-crescents, and yellow bill with red tip and black subterminal band; white tips to primaries contrasting with black subterminal marks, and white wedge-shaped patch on outer wing contrasting with pale grey coverts. Adult non-breeding has largely white head with variable black mask (and white eye-crescents). First-winter has grey mantle and scapulars; told from second-winter Yellow-legged by head pattern (as adult non-breeding), absence of dark greater-covert bar, and more pronounced dark tail-band. Second-winter has largely grey upperwing, with dark lesser-covert bar and extensive black on primaries and primary coverts. Third-winter as adult non-breeding, but with more black on primaries. Coasts and inland lakes and large rivers.

1b
1c
1a
2f
2d
1d
2e
2a
2b
2c
3b
3d
3e
3a
3c

PLATE 54: SMALL GULLS

1 **MEW GULL** *Larus canus* **Page 504**
Adult non-breeding (1a), 1st-winter (1b), 1st-summer (1c) and 2nd-winter (1d). Visitor. N subcontinent. Smaller and daintier than Yellow-legged, with shorter and finer bill. Adult has darker grey mantle than Yellow-legged, with more black on wing-tips; bill yellowish-green, with dark subterminal band in non-breeding plumage, and dark iris. Head and hindneck heavily marked in non-breeding (unlike adult non-breeding Yellow-legged). First-winter/first-summer have uniform grey mantle; unbarred greyish greater coverts forming mid-wing panel, narrow black subterminal tail-band, and well-defined dark tip to greyish/pinkish bill best distinctions from second-year Yellow-legged (which also has grey mantle). Second-winter has black on primary coverts. Lakes and large rivers in region, also coasts elsewhere.

2 **WHITE-EYED GULL** *Larus leucophthalmus* **Page 503**
Adult breeding (2a) and 1st-winter (2b). Vagrant. Maldives. Dark mantle and upperwing, and blackish underwing. Slim, dark bill. Prominent crescents above and below eye. Smaller and slimmer than Sooty. Adult has black hood, and grey mantle and upperwing. First-year has grey-brown mantle and upperwing, and dark ear-coverts and nape. Fishing ports and harbours.

3 **SOOTY GULL** *Larus hemprichii* **Page 504**
Adult breeding (3a), 1st-winter (3b) and 2nd-winter (3c). Breeds in Pakistan; visitor to coasts elsewhere. Dark upperwing and underwing. Heavy, long, two-toned bill. Adult has brown hood, and greyish-brown mantle and upperwing; bill yellow with black-and-red tip. First-winter and second-winter have rather uniform brownish head and breast, and dark tail-band; bill initially greyish with black tip, becoming similar to adult during second winter. Coasts.

4 **BROWN-HEADED GULL** *Larus brunnicephalus* **Page 507**
Adult breeding (4a), adult non-breeding (4b), 1st-winter (4c) and juvenile (4d). Breeds in Ladakh; widespread winter visitor and passage migrant. Slightly larger than Black-headed, with more rounded wing-tips, and broader bill which is dark-tipped at all ages. Adult has broad black wing-tips and oval-shaped white patch on outer primaries; underside to primaries largely black and underwing-coverts greyer; iris pale yellow (rather than brown as in adult Black-headed). In breeding plumage, hood paler brown (especially on face) than Black-headed's. Juvenile and first-winter have broad black wing-tips contrasting with white patch on primary coverts. Coasts and large inland lakes and rivers.

5 **BLACK-HEADED GULL** *Larus ridibundus* **Page 507**
Adult breeding (5a), adult non-breeding (5b) and 1st-winter (5c). Widespread winter visitor and passage migrant. Smaller than Brown-headed Gull, with finer bill and narrower and more pointed wings. Distinctive white 'flash' on upperwing. Bill blackish-red and hood uniform dark brown in breeding plumage. In non-breeding and first-winter plumages, bill tipped black and head largely white with dark ear-covert patch. Coasts and large inland lakes and rivers.

6 **SLENDER-BILLED GULL** *Larus genei* **Page 507**
Adult breeding (6a), adult non-breeding (6b) and 1st-winter (6c). Resident in Pakistan; winter visitor to Nepal, India and Sri Lanka. Head white throughout year, although may show grey ear-covert spot in winter. Gently sloping forehead and longish neck. Iris pale, except in juvenile. Adult has variable pink flush on underparts. Coastal waters.

7 **LITTLE GULL** *Larus minutus* **Page 508**
Adult breeding (7a), adult non-breeding (7b), 1st-winter (7c) and 2nd-winter (7d). Vagrant. India. Small gull, with short legs, blackish bill, and buoyant flight. Adult has dark grey underwing, and lacks black on upperwing. Black M-mark across upperwing when immature. Coastal and inland waters.

1b
1c
1d
1a
2b
2a
3b
3c
3a
4c
4b
4a
4d
5c
5b
5a
6b
6c
6a
7c
7d
7b
7a

PLATE 55: LARGE TERNS

1 **GULL-BILLED TERN** *Gelochelidon nilotica* **Page 509**
Adult breeding (1a, 1b), adult non-breeding (1c), 1st-winter (1d) and juvenile (1e). Breeds locally in Pakistan and N India; widespread in winter. Stout, gull-like black bill and more gull-like appearance than Sandwich Tern. Grey rump and tail concolorous with back. Black half-mask in non-breeding and immature plumages. Juvenile less heavily marked on upperparts than juvenile Sandwich. Coastal and freshwater wetlands.

2 **CASPIAN TERN** *Sterna caspia* **Page 509**
Adult breeding (2a, 2b), adult non-breeding (2c) and juvenile (2d). Breeds in Pakistan, Gujarat and Sri Lanka; widespread in winter. Large size and broad-winged/short-tailed appearance. Red bill and black underside to primaries. Upperwing pattern poorly defined in immature plumages. Coastal and large inland waters.

3 **RIVER TERN** *Sterna aurantia* **Page 510**
Adult breeding (3a, 3b), adult non-breeding (3c), 1st-winter (3d) and juvenile (3e). Widespread resident; unrecorded in Sri Lanka. Adult breeding has orange-yellow bill, black cap, and whitish underparts. Large size, stocky appearance and stout yellow bill (with dark tip) help separate adult non-breeding and immature from Black-bellied. Large inland waters.

4 **LESSER CRESTED TERN** *Sterna bengalensis* **Page 510**
Adult breeding (4a, 4b), adult non-breeding (4c), 1st-winter (4d) and juvenile (4e). Occurs offshore almost all year; breeds in Pakistan. Orange to orange-yellow bill, smaller and slimmer than Great Crested's, with paler grey upperparts (adult) or paler and less boldly patterned upperwing (immatures). Mainly offshore waters; also tidal creeks and harbours.

5 **GREAT CRESTED TERN** *Sterna bergii* **Page 511**
Adult breeding (5a, 5b), adult non-breeding (5c), 1st-winter (5d) and juvenile (5e) *S. b. velox*; adult non-breeding *S. b. cristata* (5f). Resident. Coasts of subcontinent. Lime-green to cold yellow bill. Larger and stockier than Lesser Crested, with darker grey upperparts (adult) or darker and more strongly patterned upperwing (immatures). Mainly offshore waters; also tidal channels.

6 **SANDWICH TERN** *Sterna sandvicensis* **Page 511**
Adult breeding (6a, 6b), adult non-breeding (6c) and 1st-winter (6d). Visitor. Mainly W coasts. Slim black bill with yellow tip, and more rakish appearance than Gull-billed. White rump and tail contrast with greyer back. U-shaped black crest in non-breeding and first-winter/first-summer plumages. Juvenile more heavily marked than juvenile Gull-billed, and has black rear crown and nape. Coasts, tidal creeks and open sea.

1e
1d
1c
1b
1a
2d
2c
2b
2a
5e
5c
5d
5a
5b
5f
4e
4c
4d
4a
4b
3b
6d
6c
6b
3a
3c
6a
3e
3d

PLATE 56: SMALL TERNS

1 **ROSEATE TERN** *Sterna dougallii* **Page 512**
Adult breeding (1a, 1b), adult non-breeding (1c), 1st-summer (1d), 1st-winter (1e) and juvenile (1f). Resident and summer visitor. India, Sri Lanka and Maldives. Pale grey upperparts and rump concolorous with back, long tail with white outer feathers, broad white trailing edge to wing, and rather stiff and rapid flight action. In breeding plumage, has more black at bill-tip than Common Tern, and pink flush to underparts. Juvenile has black bill and legs, black subterminal marks to upperpart feathers, and largely black crown. Coastal waters and offshore islands.

2 **BLACK-NAPED TERN** *Sterna sumatrana* **Page 512**
Adult breeding (2a), adult non-breeding (2b), 2nd-winter (2c) and juvenile (2d). Resident. Mainly Maldives, Andamans and Nicobars. Adult very pale greyish-white, with black bill and black mask and nape band. Juvenile has black subterminal marks to upperpart feathers, and head pattern similar to adult but with black streaking on crown. Inshore waters around islands and lagoons.

3 **COMMON TERN** *Sterna hirundo* **Page 513**
Adult breeding (3a, 3b), adult non-breeding (3c), 1st-winter (3d) and juvenile (3e) *S. h. hirundo*; adult breeding *S. h. longipennis* (3f, 3g). Breeds in Ladakh; widespread winter visitor, mainly to coasts. Grey mantle contrasts with white rump and uppertail-coverts. In breeding plumage, has orange-red bill with black tip, and pale grey wash to underparts. Upperparts, underparts and bill darker in *longipennis*. Juvenile has orange legs and bill-base. Mainly coastal waters, also large inland waters.

4 **ARCTIC TERN** *Sterna paradisaea* **Page 513**
Adult breeding (4a, 4b), adult non-breeding (4c) and juvenile (4d). Vagrant. India. Uniform translucent primaries, and shorter legs than Common. In breeding plumage, has dark red bill normally lacking black tip. Juvenile has white secondaries which form white trailing edge to wing. Recorded inland in region, but usually found on coasts.

5 **WHITE-CHEEKED TERN** *Sterna repressa* **Page 515**
Adult breeding (5a, 5b), adult non-breeding (5c) and juvenile (5d). Breeds off Maharashtra coast; offshore waters of Pakistan, W India, Lakshadweep and Maldives in non-breeding season. Smaller than Common, with darker grey upperparts and uniform grey rump and tail concolorous with back. Underwing has dark trailing edge and pale central panel. In breeding plumage, darker grey on underparts than Common, and with white cheeks. Offshore waters.

1e
2d
2c
1f
1d
1b
2a
2b
1a
1c
3c
3b
3d
3e
3a
3f
3g
4c
4d
4a
4b
5d
5c
5b
5a

PLATE 57: SMALL TERNS

1 **LITTLE TERN** *Sterna albifrons* **Page 514**
Adult breeding (1a, 1b), adult non-breeding (1c) and juvenile (1d) *S. a. albifrons*; adult breeding *S. a. sinensis* (1e). Resident; breeds locally, widespread in non-breeding season. Fast flight with rapid wingbeats, long bill, and narrow-based wings. Adult breeding has white forehead and black-tipped yellow bill. Adult non-breeding and immature have blackish bill, black mask and nape band, and dark lesser-covert bar. Juvenile has dark subterminal marks to upperpart feathers. *S. a. sinensis* has longer tail and white primary shafts. Mainly freshwater lakes and rivers, also coastal waters.

2 **SAUNDERS'S TERN** *Sterna saundersi* **Page 514**
Adult breeding (2a, 2b) and 1st-winter (2c). Breeds in Pakistan, Gujarat, Sri Lanka and Maldives?; in non-breeding season on W and S Indian coasts. Adult breeding as Little Tern, but more rounded white forehead patch (lacking short white supercilium), broader black outer edge to primaries, and grey rump and centre of tail. Coastal waters.

3 **BLACK-BELLIED TERN** *Sterna acuticauda* **Page 515**
Adult breeding (3a, 3b), adult non-breeding (3c) and juvenile (3d). Widespread resident; unrecorded in Sri Lanka. Much smaller than River Tern, with orange bill (with variable black tip) in all plumages. Adult breeding has grey breast and black belly and vent. Adult non-breeding and immatures have white underparts, and black mask and streaking on crown. Breeds on large rivers; also other inland waters in winter.

4 **WHISKERED TERN** *Chlidonias hybridus* **Page 516**
Adult breeding (4a, 4b), adult non-breeding (4c, 4d), 1st-winter (4e) and juvenile (4f). Breeds in Kashmir and Assam; widespread in winter. In breeding plumage, white cheeks contrast with black cap and grey underparts. In non-breeding plumage, distinguished from White-winged by larger bill, grey rump concolorous with back and tail, and different patterning of black on head. Juvenile generally lacks pronounced dark lesser-covert bar and has black and buff markings on mantle/scapulars. Inland and coastal waters.

5 **WHITE-WINGED TERN** *Chlidonias leucopterus* **Page 517**
Adult breeding (5a), adult non-breeding (5b, 5c), 1st-summer (5d) and juvenile (5e). Widespread winter visitor. In breeding plumage, black head and body contrast with pale upperwing-coverts, and has black underwing-coverts. In non-breeding plumage, smaller bill, whitish rump contrasting with grey tail, and bold black ear-covert patch and nape line are distinctions from Whiskered. Worn birds in first-summer plumage show pale wing-covert panel. Juvenile has pronounced dark lesser-covert bar and more uniform dark mantle/scapulars than Whiskered. Mainly freshwater wetlands, also coasts.

6 **BLACK TERN** *Chlidonias niger* **Page 517**
Adult breeding (6a), adult non-breeding (6b, 6c), 1st-winter (6d) and juvenile (6e). Passage migrant/vagrant. India and Sri Lanka. In breeding plumage, black head and underbody and uniform grey upperwing and underwing. Non-breeding and juvenile have black patch on side of breast; distinguished from juvenile White-winged by less contrast between mantle and upperwing-coverts and by grey rump and tail. Marshes, pools and lakes.

1b
1d
1c
2b
2c
1e
1a
2a
3c
3d
3a
3b
4f
4e
4b
4c
4d
4a
6c
5e
6e
6d
5c
5d
6a
6b
5a
5b

PLATE 58: TERNS, NODDIES AND INDIAN SKIMMER

1 **WHITE TERN** *Gygis alba* **Page 519**
Adult (1a, 1b, 1c) and juvenile (1d). Breeds on Maldives. Adult all white, with beady black eye and upturned bill. Juvenile has buff and brown barring and spotting on upperparts. Pelagic, except when breeding.

2 **BRIDLED TERN** *Sterna anaethetus* **Page 516**
Adult breeding (2a, 2b), adult non-breeding (2c) and juvenile (2d, 2e). Breeds off Maharashtra coast, Lakshadweep and Maldives?; offshore waters of Pakistan, W India and Sri Lanka in non-breeding season. Smaller and more elegant than Sooty Tern. In breeding plumage, white forehead patch extends over eye as broad white supercilium, and has brownish-grey mantle and wings. Juvenile has greyish-white crown, dark mask and white forehead and supercilium (shadow-pattern of adult), buffish fringes to mantle and wing-coverts, and brownish patch on side of breast. Mainly offshore waters.

3 **SOOTY TERN** *Sterna fuscata* **Page 516**
Adult (3a, 3b), 1st-summer (3c) and juvenile (3d, 3e). Breeds off Maharashtra coast, Lakshadweep and Maldives?; seas adjacent to breeding islands in non-breeding season. Larger and more powerful than Bridled Tern, with blacker upperparts, more extensive blackish underside to primaries (contrasting with white under-wing-coverts), and white forehead patch not extending over eye. Juvenile has sooty-black head and breast contrasting with whitish lower belly, bold white spotting on mantle, scapulars and upperwing-coverts, and pale underwing-coverts. Pelagic, except when breeding.

4 **BROWN NODDY** *Anous stolidus* **Page 518**
Adult (4a, 4b, 4c) and juvenile (4d, 4e). Breeds in Lakshadweep and Maldives; also recorded off other coasts. Brown, with coverts paler than flight feathers, pale panel across upperwing-coverts. Bill stouter, proportionately shorter and noticeably downcurved compared with Black and Lesser. Pelagic, except when breeding.

5 **BLACK NODDY** *Anous minutus* **Page 518**
Adult (5a, 5b). Vagrant. India and Sri Lanka. Blacker than Brown Noddy, with all-dark upperwing and underwing. Paler and greyer centre of tail contrasts with darker upperparts. Slim, straight bill longer than head. Pelagic.

6 **LESSER NODDY** *Anous tenuirostris* **Page 518**
Adult (6a, 6b). Breeds on Maldives; vagrant to India and Sri Lanka. Long, slim bill as Black Noddy. Pale greyish lores contrasting with black patch in front of eye. Upperwing-coverts slightly paler than remiges, underwing-coverts concolorous with remiges, and paler and greyer tail centre contrasting with darker upperparts. Pelagic, except when breeding.

7 **INDIAN SKIMMER** *Rynchops albicollis* **Page 503**
Adult (7a) and juvenile (7b). Resident. N and C subcontinent. Adult has large, drooping orange-red bill, and black mantle and wings contrasting with white underparts. Juvenile has whitish fringes to mantle and upperwing-coverts, and dull orange bill with black tip. Mainly larger rivers.

1b
1d
1c
1a
3e
3d
3c
3b
3a
2e
2d
2b
2a
2c
4d
5b
5a
4a
4e
4b
6a
6b
4c
7b
7a

PLATE 59: KITES, BAZAS AND OSPREY

1 **OSPREY** *Pandion haliaetus* **Page 519**
Adult (1a, 1b). Breeds in Himalayas; widespread in winter. Long wings, typically angled at carpals, and short tail. Has whitish head with black stripe through eye, white underbody and underwing-coverts, and black carpal patches. Large inland waters and coastal waters.

2 **JERDON'S BAZA** *Aviceda jerdoni* **Page 520**
Adult (2a, 2b) and juvenile (2c, 2d). Resident. E Himalayas, hills of India, Bangladesh and Sri Lanka. Long and erect, white-tipped crest. Long, broad wings (pinched in at base) and fairly long tail. Pale rufous head, indistinct gular stripe, rufous-barred underparts and underwing-coverts, and bold barring across primary tips. At rest, closed wings extend well down tail. Juvenile has whitish head, and narrower dark barring on tail. Broadleaved evergreen forest.

3 **BLACK BAZA** *Aviceda leuphotes* **Page 520**
Adult (3a, 3b, 3c). Resident. Himalayan foothills, NE and S India, Bangladesh and Sri Lanka. Largely black, with long crest, white breast-band, and greyish underside to primaries contrasting with black underwing-coverts. Broadleaved evergreen forest.

4 **BLACK-SHOULDERED KITE** *Elanus caeruleus* **Page 521**
Adult (4a, 4b, 4c) and juvenile (4d). Widespread resident; unrecorded in parts of northwest and northeast. Small size. Grey and white with black 'shoulders'. Flight buoyant, with much hovering. Juvenile has brownish-grey upperparts with pale fringes, with less distinct shoulder patch. Grassland with cultivation and open scrub.

5 **RED KITE** *Milvus milvus* **Page 521**
Adult (5a, 5b, 5c). Vagrant. Nepal and India. Long and deeply forked rufous-orange tail. Wings long, and usually sharply angled. Rufous underparts and underwing-coverts, whitish head, pale band across upperwing-coverts, and striking whitish patches at base of primaries on underwing. Recorded in region in semi-desert.

6 **BLACK KITE** *Milvus migrans* **Page 522**
Adult (6a, 6b, 6c) and juvenile (6d, 6e) ***M. m. lineatus*****; adult (6f) and juvenile (6g)** ***M. m. govinda*****.** Widespread resident and winter visitor. Shallow tail-fork. Much manoeuvring of arched wings and twisting of tail in flight. Dark rufous-brown, with variable whitish crescent at primary bases on underwing, and pale band across median coverts on upperwing. Juvenile has broad whitish or buffish streaking on head and underparts. *M. m. lineatus* larger than *govinda*, with broader wings and generally more prominent whitish primary patch. Mainly around habitation, also mountains.

7 **BRAHMINY KITE** *Haliastur indus* **Page 522**
Adult (7a, 7b) and juvenile (7c, 7d). Widespread resident; unrecorded in parts of northwest and northeast. Small size and kite-like flight. Wings usually angled at carpals. Tail rounded. Adult mainly chestnut, with white head, neck and breast. Juvenile mainly brown, with pale streaking on head, mantle and breast, large whitish patches at bases of primaries, and cinnamon-brown tail. Inland and coastal waters.

1a
1b
2a
2b
2c
2d
4d
4a
4b
4c
3a
3b
3c
5a
5b
5c
6a
6b
6c
6d
6e
6f
6g
7a
7b
7c
7d
AH.

PLATE 60: SEA EAGLES AND FISH EAGLES

1 **WHITE-BELLIED SEA EAGLE** *Haliaeetus leucogaster* **Page 523**
Adult (1a, 1b), juvenile (1c, 1d) and immature (1e). Resident. Mainly coasts and offshore islands. Soars and glides with wings pressed forward and in pronounced V. Distinctive shape, with slim head, bulging secondaries, and short wedge-shaped tail. Adult has white head and underparts, grey upperparts, white underwing-coverts contrasting with black remiges, and mainly white tail. Juvenile has pale head, whitish tail with brownish subterminal band and pale wedge on inner primaries. Immatures show mixture of juvenile and adult features. Mainly coastal habitats.

2 **PALLAS'S FISH EAGLE** *Haliaeetus leucoryphus* **Page 523**
Adult (2a, 2b), juvenile (2c, 2d) and immature (2e). Resident. N subcontinent. Soars and glides with wings flat. Long, broad wings and protruding head and neck. Adult has pale head and neck, dark brown upperwing and underwing, and mainly white tail with broad black terminal band. Juvenile less bulky, looks slimmer-winged, longer-tailed and smaller-billed than juvenile White-tailed; has dark mask, pale band across underwing-coverts, pale patch on underside of inner primaries, all-dark tail, and pale crescent on uppertail-coverts. Older immatures have whitish tail with mottled band. Mainly larger rivers and lakes, also tidal creeks.

3 **WHITE-TAILED EAGLE** *Haliaeetus albicilla* **Page 524**
Adult (3a, 3b), juvenile (3c, 3d) and immature (3e). Widespread winter visitor. Huge, with broad parallel-edged wings, short wedge-shaped tail, and protruding head and neck. Soars and glides with wings level. Adult has large yellow bill, pale head, and white tail. Juvenile has whitish centres to tail feathers, pale patch on axillaries, and variable pale band across underwing-coverts. Bill becomes yellow with age. Coasts, large lakes and rivers.

4 **GREY-HEADED FISH EAGLE** *Ichthyophaga ichthyaetus* **Page 524**
Adult (4a, 4b) and juvenile (4c, 4d). Widespread resident; unrecorded in Pakistan. Adult told from Lesser Fish Eagle by largely white tail with broad black subterminal band, darker and browner upperparts, and rufous-brown breast. Juvenile has pale supercilium, boldly streaked head and underparts, diffuse brown tail barring, and whitish underwing with pronounced dark trailing edge. Slow-running waters, lakes and tidal lagoons in wooded country.

5 **LESSER FISH EAGLE** *Ichthyophaga humilis* **Page 524**
Adult (5a, 5b) and juvenile (5c, 5d). Resident. Himalayas. Adult differs from Grey-headed in smaller size, greyish tail, paler grey upperparts, white patch at base of outer primaries on underwing, and greyer underparts. Juvenile browner than adult, with paler underwing and paler base to tail; lacks prominent streaking of juvenile Grey-headed, and has clear-cut white belly and different tail pattern. Forested streams and lakes.

1a
1b
1c
1e
1d
2b
2d
2a
2e
2c
3e
3b
3d
3c
3a
4d
4b
4c
4a
5b
5d
5a
5c

PLATE 61: VULTURES

1 LAMMERGEIER *Gypaetus barbatus* **Page 525**
Adult (1a, 1b), juvenile (1c) and immature (1d). Resident. Pakistan and Himalayas. Huge size, long and narrow pointed wings, and large wedge-shaped tail. Adult has blackish upperparts, wings and tail, and cream or rufous-orange underparts contrasting with black underwing-coverts. Juvenile has blackish head and neck and grey-brown underparts. Mountains.

2 EGYPTIAN VULTURE *Neophron percnopterus* **Page 525**
Adult (2a, 2b, 2c), immature (2d, 2e) and juvenile (2f). Resident. Widespread in Pakistan, Nepal and India, except the northeast. Small vulture with long, pointed wings, small and pointed head, and wedge-shaped tail. Adult mainly dirty white, with bare yellowish face and black flight feathers. Juvenile blackish-brown with bare grey face. With maturity, tail, body and wing-coverts become whiter and face yellower. Around habitation.

3 WHITE-RUMPED VULTURE *Gyps bengalensis* **Page 526**
Adult (3a, 3b, 3c) and juvenile (3d, 3e, 3f). Widespread resident; unrecorded in Sri Lanka. Smallest of the *Gyps* vultures. Adult mainly blackish, with white rump and back, and white underwing-coverts. Key features of juvenile are dark brown coloration, streaking on underparts and upperwing-coverts, dark rump and back, whitish head and neck, and all-dark bill: in flight, underbody and lesser underwing-coverts distinctly darker than on Long-billed, while whitish panel on underwing narrower than on Eurasian Griffon; similar in coloration to juvenile Himalayan, but much smaller and less heavily built, with narrower-looking wings and shorter tail, underparts less heavily streaked, and lacks prominent streaking on mantle and scapulars. Around habitation.

4 LONG-BILLED VULTURE *Gyps indicus* **Page 526**
Adult (4a, 4b, 4c) and juvenile (4d, 4e) *G. i. indicus*; adult *G. i. tenuirostris* (4f). Widespread resident; unrecorded in Sri Lanka. Adult has pale sandy-brown body and upperwing-coverts, blackish head and neck, white downy ruff, comparatively slim bill, and pale cere, and lacks pale streaking on underparts; in flight, lacks broad whitish band across median underwing-coverts shown by Eurasian Griffon, and has whiter rump and back. Much smaller and less heavily built than Himalayan Griffon, with slimmer bill. Juvenile has blackish bill (yellowish/greenish on adult nominate), blackish cere, feathery buff neck ruff, and some whitish down on head and neck (except in *tenuirostris*): distinguished from juvenile Eurasian Griffon by darker brown upperparts with more pronounced pale streaking, paler and less rufescent underparts with less distinct pale streaking, and pale pinkish culmen (possibly not shown by very young birds, and juvenile *tenuirostris* has all-dark bill); best distinctions from juvenile White-rumped are paler and less clearly streaked underparts, paler underwing-coverts, paler lesser and median upperwing-coverts (owing to heavy streaking), and whitish rump and back. *G. i. tenuirostris* completely lacks white down on grey head and neck (both adult and immature); bill appears longer and slimmer than on nominate, and adult and sub-adult have blackish bill and cere with pinkish culmen (i.e. as juvenile of nominate). Around habitation.

1a
1b
1c
1d
2b
2c
2e
2a
2d
2f
3d
3b
3a
3e
4c
3f
3c
4f
4d
4b
4a
4e
KHEF

PLATE 62: VULTURES

1 **HIMALAYAN GRIFFON** *Gyps himalayensis* **Page 527**
Adult (1a, 1b, 1c) and juvenile (1d, 1e, 1f). Resident. Himalayas. Larger than Eurasian Griffon, with broader body and slightly longer tail. Wing-coverts and body pale buffish-white, contrasting strongly with dark flight feathers and tail; underparts lack pronounced streaking; legs and feet pinkish with dark claws, and has yellowish cere. Immature has brown feathered ruff, with bill and cere initially black (yellowish on adult), and has dark brown body and upperwing-coverts boldly and prominently streaked with buff (wing-coverts almost concolorous with flight feathers), and back and rump also dark brown; streaked upperparts and underparts and pronounced white banding across underwing-coverts are best distinctions from Cinereous Vulture; very similar in plumage to juvenile White-rumped Vulture, but much larger and more heavily built, with broader wings and longer tail, underparts more heavily streaked, and streaking on mantle and scapulars. Mountains.

2 **EURASIAN GRIFFON** *Gyps fulvus* **Page 527**
Adult (2a, 2b, 2c) and juvenile (2d, 2e, 2f). Resident. Breeds in hills of Pakistan and Himalayas; winters south to plains of Pakistan, N and NW India. Larger than Long-billed, with stouter bill. Key features of adult are blackish cere, whitish head and neck, rufescent-buff upperparts, rufous-brown underparts and thighs with prominent pale streaking, and dark grey legs and feet; rufous-brown underwing-coverts usually show prominent whitish banding (especially across medians). Immature richer rufous-brown on upperparts and upperwing-coverts (with prominent pale streaking) than adult; has rufous-brown feathered neck ruff, more whitish down covering grey head and neck, blackish bill (yellowish on adult), and dark iris (pale yellowish-brown in adult). Semi-desert, dry open plains and hills.

3 **CINEREOUS VULTURE** *Aegypius monachus* **Page 528**
Adult (3a, 3b) and juvenile (3c). Breeds in Pakistan; winters mainly in Pakistan and Himalayas. Very large vulture with broad, parallel-edged wings. Soars with wings flat. At a distance appears typically uniformly dark, except for pale areas on head and bill. Adult blackish-brown with paler brown ruff; may show paler band across greater underwing-coverts, but underwing darker and more uniform than on *Gyps* species. Juvenile blacker and more uniform than adult. Breeds in mountains; forages in wide range of habitats.

4 **RED-HEADED VULTURE** *Sarcogyps calvus* **Page 528**
Adult (4a, 4b, 4c) and immature (4d, 4e, 4f). Resident. Mainly Nepal and India. Comparatively slim and pointed wings. Adult has bare reddish head and cere, white patches at base of neck and upper thighs, and reddish legs and feet; in flight, greyish-white bases to secondaries show as broad panel. Juvenile has white down on head; pinkish coloration to head and feet, white patch on upper thighs, and whitish undertail-coverts are best features. Open country near habitation, and well-wooded hills.

1a
1d
1b
1e
2e
2b
1f
1c
2a
2d
2c
2f
3a
3c
3b
4b
4d
4a
4e
4c
4f
KHEF

PLATE 63: SHORT-TOED SNAKE EAGLE, SERPENT EAGLES AND BLACK EAGLE

1 **SHORT-TOED SNAKE EAGLE** *Circaetus gallicus* **Page 528**
Pale phase (1a, 1b, 1c), dark phase (1d), gliding (1e) and soaring (1f). Resident. Pakistan, S Nepal and India. Long and broad wings, pinched in at base, and rather long tail. Head broad and rounded. Soars with wings flat or slightly raised; frequently hovers. Pattern variable, often with dark head and breast, barred underbody, dark trailing edge to underwing, and broad subterminal tail-band; can be very pale on underbody and underwing. Open dry plains and hills.

2 **CRESTED SERPENT EAGLE** *Spilornis cheela* **Page 529**
Adult (2a, 2b) and juvenile (2c, 2d) *S. c. cheela*; adult (2e) *S. c. davisoni*; soaring (2f). Widespread resident; unrecorded in most of northwest and northeast. Broad, rounded wings. Soars with wings held forward and in pronounced V. Adult has broad white bands across wings and tail; hooded appearance at rest, with yellow cere and lores, and white spotting on brown underparts. Juvenile has blackish ear-coverts, whitish head and underparts, and narrower barring on tail. *S. c. davisoni* of Andamans and Nicobars is small, with buff underparts and underwing-coverts, and narrower white banding on wings and tail. Forest and well-wooded country.

3 **SMALL SERPENT EAGLE** *Spilornis minimus* **Page 529**
Adult (3a, 3b) and juvenile (3c, 3d) *S. m. minimus*; adult *S. m. klossi* (3e, 3f). Resident. Nicobars. Very small. *S. m. minimus* has white scaling on black crest, cinnamon-grey underparts with white barring, broad grey central band across uppertail, and broad white central band and some white at base on undertail. Juvenile *minimus* has buff tips to crown, crest and upperparts, and full second pale band across uppertail. *S. m. klossi* has cinnamon scaling on black crest, blackish gular stripe, plain cinnamon underparts, and narrow black banding on white undertail. Forest near rivers.

4 **ANDAMAN SERPENT EAGLE** *Spilornis elgini* **Page 530**
Adult (4a, 4b) and juvenile (4c, 4d). Resident. S Andaman Is. Adult has dark brown underparts and underwing-coverts with white spotting, brownish-grey banding on uppertail, narrow greyish-white barring on underside of remiges, and two narrow greyish-white bands across undertail. Juvenile paler brown, with white fringes to feathers of crown and nape, dark ear-covert patch, and more prominent banding on underside of wings and tail. Open forest and forest clearings.

5 **BLACK EAGLE** *Ictinaetus malayensis* **Page 539**
Adult (5a, 5b) and juvenile (5c, 5d). Resident. Himalayas, hills of India, Bangladesh and Sri Lanka. Distinctive wing shape, and long tail. Flies with wings raised in V, with primaries upturned. At rest, long wings extend beyond tip of tail. Adult dark brownish-black, with striking yellow cere and feet; in flight, shows whitish barring on uppertail-coverts, and faint greyish barring on tail and underside of remiges (cf. dark morph of Changeable Hawk Eagle, Plate 71). Juvenile has dark-streaked buffish head, underparts and underwing-coverts. Broadleaved forest in hills and mountains.

1e
1f
1a
1b
1c
1d
2c
2a
2b
2d
2f
2e
3c
3e
3a
3f
3b
3d
4a
4c
4b
4d
5c
5a
5d
5b
Tim Worfolk

PLATE 64: HARRIERS

1 **EURASIAN MARSH HARRIER** *Circus aeruginosus* **Page 530**
Adult male (1a, 1b, 1c), adult female (1d, 1e, 1f) and juvenile (1g) *C. a. aeruginosus*; adult male (1h, 1i, 1j, 1k), immature male (1l), adult female (1m, 1n, 1o) and juvenile (1p, 1q) *C. a. spilonotus*. Widespread winter visitor; unrecorded in parts of W Pakistan and NE India. Broad-winged and stocky. Glides and soars with wings in noticeable V. Male *aeruginosus* has pale head, brown mantle and upperwing-coverts contrasting with grey secondaries/inner primaries; female mainly dark brown, except for cream on head and on leading edge of wing. Juvenile *aeruginosus* may be entirely dark. Male *spilonotus* has blackish or streaked head, and black mantle and median coverts with feathers boldly edged with white; larger and stouter than Pied, and never as cleanly marked. Female *spilonotus* has white uppertail-coverts, dark-barred greyish flight feathers and tail, cream head and breast with dark streaking, and diffuse rufous streaking on underparts. Juvenile *spilonotus* is rather dark, with pale breast-band and pale patch at base of underside of primaries; head usually mainly cream, with variable dark streaking (paler than shown). Reedbeds, marshes, lakes and coastal lagoons.

2 **PIED HARRIER** *Circus melanoleucos* **Page 532**
Adult male (2a, 2b, 2c), adult female (2d, 2e, 2f), immature male (2g) and juvenile (2h, 2i, 2j). Breeds in Assam; winter visitor mainly to NE subcontinent, Western Ghats and Sri Lanka. Male has black head, upperparts and breast, white underbody and forewing, and black median-covert bar. Female has white uppertail-covert patch, dark-barred greyish remiges and rectrices, pale leading edge to wing, and pale underwing. Juvenile has pale markings on head, rufous-brown underbody, white uppertail-covert patch, and dark underwing with pale patch on primaries. Open grassland and cultivation.

1a
1b
1c
1d
1e
1f
1g
1h
1i
1j
1k
1l
1m
1n
1o
1p
1q
2a
2b
2c
2d
2e
2f
2g
2h
2i
2j

PLATE 65: HARRIERS

1 **HEN HARRIER** *Circus cyaneus* **Page 531**
Adult male (1a, 1b, 1c), female (1d, 1e, 1f) and immature male (1g). Winter visitor. Mainly Pakistan, Himalayas and NW India. Comparatively broad-winged and stocky. Male has dark grey upperparts, extensive black wing-tips, lacks black secondary bars, and has dark trailing edge to underwing. Female has broad white band across uppertail-coverts, narrow pale neck-collar, and rather plain head pattern (usually lacking dark ear-covert patch). Juvenile has streaked underparts as female, but with rufous-brown coloration. Open country in plains and foothills.

2 **PALLID HARRIER** *Circus macrourus* **Page 531**
Adult male (2a, 2b, 2c), female (2d, 2e, 2f), immature male in flight (2g) and juvenile (2h, 2i). Widespread winter visitor; unrecorded in parts of northeast and W Pakistan. Slim-winged and fine-bodied, with buoyant flight. Folded wings fall short of tail-tip, and legs longer than on Montagu's. Male has pale grey upperparts, dark wedge on primaries, very pale grey head and underbody, and lacks black secondary bars. Immature male may show rusty breast-band and juvenile facial markings. Female has distinctive underwing pattern: pale primaries, irregularly barred and lacking dark trailing edge, contrast with darker secondaries which have pale bands narrower than on female Montagu's and tapering towards body (although first-summer Montagu's more similar in this respect), and lacks prominent barring on axillaries. Typically, female has stronger head pattern than Montagu's, with more pronounced pale collar, dark ear-coverts and dark eye-stripe, and upperside of flight feathers darker and lacking banding; told from female Northern by narrower wings with more pointed hand, stronger head pattern, and patterning of underside of primaries. Juvenile has unstreaked orange-buff underparts and underwing-coverts; on underwing, primaries evenly barred (lacking pronounced dark fingers), without dark trailing edge, and usually with pale crescent at base; head pattern more pronounced than Montagu's, with narrower white supercilium, more extensive dark ear-covert patch, and broader pale collar contrasting strongly with dark neck sides. Open country in plains and foothills.

3 **MONTAGU'S HARRIER** *Circus pygargus* **Page 532**
Adult male (3a, 3b, 3c), female (3d, 3e, 3f), immature male (3g) and juvenile (3h, 3i). Widespread winter visitor. Folded wings reach tail-tip, and legs shorter than on Pallid. Male has black band across secondaries, extensive black on underside of primaries, and rufous streaking on belly and underwing-coverts. Female differs from female Pallid in distinctly and evenly barred underside to primaries with dark trailing edge, broader and more pronounced pale bands across secondaries, barring on axillaries, less pronounced head pattern, and distinct dark banding on upperside of remiges. Juvenile has unstreaked rufous underparts and underwing-coverts, and darker secondaries than female; differs from juvenile Pallid in having broad dark fingers and dark trailing edge to hand on underwing, and paler face with smaller dark ear-covert patch and less distinct collar. Open country in plains and foothills.

1b
1g
1e
1a
1c
1f
1d
2c
2g
2f
2a
2b
2e
2d
2h
2i
3b
3h
3g
3i
3c
3a
3f
3d
3e

PLATE 66: ACCIPITERS

1 **CRESTED GOSHAWK** *Accipiter trivirgatus* **Page 533**
Male (1a, 1b) and juvenile (1c, 1d) *A. t. indicus.* Resident. Mainly Himalayas, NE and SW India, and Sri Lanka. Larger size and crest are best distinctions from Besra. Short and broad wings, pinched in at base. Wing-tips barely extend beyond tail-base at rest. Male has dark grey crown and ear-coverts, black submoustachial and gular stripes, and rufous-brown streaking on breast and barring on belly and flanks. Female has browner crown and ear-coverts, and browner streaking and barring on underparts. Juvenile has rufous or buffish fringes to crown, crest and nape feathers, streaked ear-coverts, and buff/rufous wash to streaked underparts (barring restricted to lower flanks and thighs). Dense broadleaved tropical and subtropical forest.

2 **SHIKRA** *Accipiter badius* **Page 533**
Male (2a, 2b), female (2c, 2d) and juvenile (2e, 2f) *A. b. dussumieri.* Widespread resident, except in parts of northwest. Adults paler than Besra and Eurasian Sparrowhawk. Underwing pale, with fine barring on remiges, and slightly darker wing-tips. Male has pale blue-grey upperparts, indistinct grey gular stripe, fine brownish-orange barring on underparts, unbarred white thighs, and unbarred or only lightly barred central tail feathers. Female has upperparts more brownish-grey. Juvenile has pale brown upperparts, more prominent gular stripe, and streaked underparts; told from juvenile Besra by paler upperparts and narrower tail barring, and from Eurasian Sparrowhawk by streaked underparts. Open woods and groves.

3 **NICOBAR SPARROWHAWK** *Accipiter butleri* **Page 534**
Male (3a, 3b) and juvenile (3c, 3d) *A. b. butleri*; juvenile (3e, 3f) from Great Nicobar. Resident. Nicobars. Very short primary projection. Male has pale blue-grey upperparts, mainly whitish underparts and underwing-coverts, indistinct gular stripe, and unbarred tail with narrow diffuse terminal band. Female slightly browner on upperparts, with marginally stronger barring on breast. Juvenile of nominate race has rufous upperparts with dark brown feather centres, rufous-buff underparts with browner streaking, and dark banding on rufous-cinnamon secondaries and tail. The single juvenile specimen from Great Nicobar has much browner and darker upperparts and may represent an undescribed race. Tall trees.

4 **CHINESE SPARROWHAWK** *Accipiter soloensis* **Page 534**
Adult (4a, 4b) and juvenile (4c, 4d). Winter visitor. Nicobars. Narrow and pointed wings, with long primary projection at rest. Adult has blue-grey head and upperparts, indistinct grey gular stripe, and rufous-orange breast; distinctive underwing pattern, with unbarred remiges and coverts, blackish wing-tips and dark grey trailing edge. Sub-adults show some dark barring on underside of flight feathers. Juvenile has dark brown upperparts, pronounced dark gular stripe, and rufous-brown spotting and barring on underparts; compared with juvenile Japanese Sparrowhawk, crown is a darker slate-grey than mantle, lacks distinct supercilium, and has distinctive underwing pattern (dark grey wing-tips and trailing edge, largely unmarked greyish-brown to pale rufous coverts). Forest and wooded country.

1a
1b
1c
1d
2d
2e
2f
2a
2b
2c
4a
4b
4c
4d
3a
3b
3c
3d
3e
3f
AH.

PLATE 67: ACCIPITERS

1 **JAPANESE SPARROWHAWK** *Accipiter gularis* **Page 535**
Male (1a, 1b), female (1c, 1d) and juvenile (1e, 1f). Winter visitor. Locally in India. Very small. Long primary projection. In all plumages, pale bars on tail generally broader than dark bars (reverse on Besra). Underpart patterning of adults rather different from Besra; juveniles more similar. Male has dark bluish-grey upperparts, pale rufous to pale grey underparts (some with fine grey barring), and dark crimson iris. Female has browner upperparts, whitish underparts with grey-brown barring, indistinct gular stripe, and yellow iris. Juvenile has brown to rufous streaking and barring on underparts. Probably forest.

2 **BESRA** *Accipiter virgatus* **Page 535**
Adult male (2a, 2b), female (2c, 2d) and juvenile (2e, 2f) *A. v. virgatus.* Resident. Himalayas, NE and SW India, Bangladesh and Sri Lanka. Small, with short primary projection. Upperparts darker than Shikra (Plate 66), and prominent gular stripe and streaked breast should separate it from Eurasian Sparrowhawk; underwing strongly barred compared with Shikra. In all plumages, resembles Crested Goshawk (Plate 66), but considerably smaller, lacks crest, and has longer and finer legs. Male has dark slate-grey upperparts, broad blackish gular stripe, and bold rufous streaking on breast and barring on belly. Female browner on upperparts, with blackish crown and nape. Juvenile told from juvenile Shikra by darker, richer brown upperparts, broader gular stripe, and broader tail barring. Breeds in dense broadleaved forest; also open wooded country in winter.

3 **EURASIAN SPARROWHAWK** *Accipiter nisus* **Page 535**
Male (3a, 3b), female (3c, 3d) and juvenile (3e, 3f) *A. n. melaschistos.* Resident and winter visitor. Breeds in Baluchistan and Himalayas; winters in Himalayan foothills and south to S India. Upperparts of adult darker than Shikra (Plate 66), with prominent tail barring, and uniform barring on underparts and absence of prominent gular stripe should separate it from Besra; underwing strongly barred compared with Shikra. Male has dark slate-grey upperparts and reddish-orange barring on underparts. Female dark brown on upperparts, with dark brown barring on underparts. Juvenile has dark brown upperparts and barred underparts. Well-wooded country and open forest.

4 **NORTHERN GOSHAWK** *Accipiter gentilis* **Page 536**
Male (4a), female (4b, 4c) and juvenile (4d, 4e). Winter visitor and resident? Mainly Pakistan and Himalayas. Very large, with heavy, deep-chested appearance. Wings comparatively long, with bulging secondaries. Male has grey upperparts (greyer than female Eurasian Sparrowhawk), white supercilium, and finely barred underparts. Female considerably larger, with browner upperparts. Juvenile has heavy streaking on buff-coloured underparts. Forest.

1a
1b
1d
2a
2b
2d
1c
1e
1f
2c
2e
2f
3a
3b
3c
3d
3e
3f
4a
4b
4c
4d
4e
AH.

PLATE 68: BUZZARDS AND ORIENTAL HONEY-BUZZARD

1 **ORIENTAL HONEY-BUZZARD** *Pernis ptilorhyncus* **Page 520**
Male (1a, 1b, 1c), female (1d), juvenile (1e) and soaring (1f). Widespread resident; absent in parts of NW and NE subcontinent and SE India. Wings and tail long and broad, and has narrow neck and small head. Soars with wings flat. Has small crest. Very variable in plumage, with underparts and underwing-coverts ranging from dark brown through rufous to white, and unmarked, streaked or barred; often shows dark moustachial stripe and gular stripe, and gorget of streaking across lower throat. Lacks dark carpal patch. Male has grey face, greyish-brown upperparts, two black tail-bands, usually three black bands across underside of remiges, and dark brown iris. Female has browner face and upperparts, three black tail-bands, four narrower black bands across remiges, and yellow iris. Juvenile has finer and less distinct banding across underside of remiges, three or more tail-bands, and extensive dark tips to primaries; cere yellow (grey on adult) and iris dark. Well-wooded country.

2 **WHITE-EYED BUZZARD** *Butastur teesa* **Page 536**
Adult (2a, 2b, 2c), juvenile (2d, 2e) and soaring (2f). Widespread resident; absent in parts of the northwest, northeast and south. Longish, rather slim wings, long tail, and buzzard-like head. Pale median-covert panel. Flight *Accipiter*-like. Adult has black gular stripe, white nape patch, barred underparts, dark wing-tips, and rufous tail; iris yellow. Juvenile has buffish head and breast streaked with dark brown, with moustachial and throat stripes indistinct or absent; rufous uppertail more strongly barred; iris brown. Dry open country.

3 **COMMON BUZZARD** *Buteo buteo* **Page 537**
Adult *B. b. japonicus* (3a, 3b, 3c, 3d); adult *B. b. refectus* (3e, 3f); soaring (3g). Breeds in Himalayas; widespread in winter. Stocky, with broad rounded wings and moderate-length tail. Most compact *Buteo* in region. Plumage variable; some much as Long-legged and Upland. *B. b. japonicus* typically has rather pale head and underparts, with variable dark streaking on breast and brown patch on belly/thighs; tail dark-barred grey-brown. *B. b. refectus* dark brown to rufous-brown, with variable amounts of white on underparts; tail dull brown with some dark barring, or uniform sandy-brown. *B. b. vulpinus* (not illustrated) usually has rufous tail. Open-country habitats.

4 **LONG-LEGGED BUZZARD** *Buteo rufinus* **Page 537**
Adult (4a, 4b, 4c, 4d), juvenile (4e, 4f) and soaring (4g). Breeds in Himalayas; winters in Pakistan, Himalayas, Assam and Bangladesh. Larger and longer-necked than Common, with longer wings and tail (appears more eagle-like); soars with wings in deeper V. Variable in plumage. Most differ from Common in having paler head and upper breast, rufous-brown lower breast and belly, more uniform rufous underwing-coverts, more extensive black carpal patches, larger pale primary patch on upperwing, and unbarred pale orange uppertail. Rufous and black morphs much as those of Common. Juvenile generally less rufous, with narrower and more diffuse trailing edge to wing, and lightly barred tail which on many is pale greyish-brown; best distinguished from Common by larger size, different structure, and more prominent carpal patches and dark belly. Breeds in forested hills; winters in open-country habitats.

5 **UPLAND BUZZARD** *Buteo hemilasius* **Page 538**
Adult (5a, 5b, 5c, 5d), juvenile (5e, 5f) and gliding (5g). Breeds in Nepal?; winters in Himalayas and N India. Larger, longer-winged and longer-tailed than Common (appearing more eagle-like); soars with wings in deeper V. Tarsus always at least three-quarters feathered. Plumage variable. 'Classic' pale morph has combination of large white primary patch on upperwing, greyish-white tail (with fine bars towards tip), whitish head and underparts with dark brown streaking, brown thighs forming dark U-shape, and extensive black carpal patches (*japonicus* race of Common can be very similar); never has rufous tail or rufous thighs as Long-legged. 'Blackish morph' probably not distinguishable on plumage from those of Common/Long-legged. Juvenile has narrower and more diffuse trailing edge to wing, and more prominently barred tail. Open country in hills and mountains.

6 **ROUGH-LEGGED BUZZARD** *Buteo lagopus* **Page 538**
Adult (6a, 6b), juvenile (6c) and gliding (6d). [One published record; confirmation desirable. Long wings and tail. Adult has broad black subterminal band on white tail, dark belly, and whitish underwing-coverts with large black carpal patches. Juvenile lacks black tail-band.]

1a
1b
1c
1d
1e
1f
2a
2b
2c
2d
2e
2f
3a
3b
3c
3d
3e
3f
3g
4a
4b
4c
4d
4e
4f
4g
5a
5b
5c
5d
5e
5f
5g
6a
6b
6c
6d
Tim Worfolk

PLATE 69: AQUILA EAGLES

1 **LESSER SPOTTED EAGLE** *Aquila pomarina* **Page 539**
Adult (1a, 1b, 1c), juvenile (1d, 1e, 1f), immature (1g) and gliding (1h). Resident. N subcontinent; largely unrecorded in Pakistan. Stocky, medium-sized eagle with rather short and broad wings, buzzard-like head and smallish bill; rather short tail. Wings angled down at carpals when gliding and soaring. Told from Greater Spotted by slightly narrower wings and longer tail, pale buff-brown upperwing- and underwing-coverts contrasting with dark flight feathers (although some Greater Spotted can be similar), and double whitish carpal crescent on underwing. In some plumages can resemble Steppe (Plate 70), but shows prominent double whitish carpal crescents, lacks distinct barring on underside of primaries, and has dark chin; also smaller, with less protruding head and smaller bill, shorter wings with less deep-fingered tips, and smaller trousers exposing long, thin-looking feathered tarsus. Wooded areas in lowlands.

2 **GREATER SPOTTED EAGLE** *Aquila clanga* **Page 540**
Adult (2a, 2b, 2c), juvenile (2d, 2e, 2f), juvenile '*fulvescens*' (2g, 2h) and gliding (2i). Breeds in NW subcontinent; winters mainly in N subcontinent. Medium-sized eagle with rather short and broad wings, stocky head, and short tail. Wings distinctly angled down at carpals when gliding, almost flat when soaring. Heavier than Lesser Spotted, with broader wings and squarer hand, and shorter tail; dark brown upperwing- and underwing-coverts show little contrast with flight feathers (although some can be similar to Lesser Spotted), and usually lacks second whitish carpal crescent on underwing. Compared with Steppe Eagle (Plate 70), has less protruding head in flight, with shorter wings and less deep-fingered wing-tips; at rest, trousers less baggy, and bill smaller with rounded nostril and shorter gape; lacks adult Steppe's barring on underside of flight and tail feathers, dark trailing edge to wing, and dark chin. Pale variant '*fulvescens*' distinguished from juvenile Imperial Eagle (Plate 70) by structural differences, lack of pale wedge on inner primaries, and unstreaked underparts. Juvenile has bold whitish tips to dark brown coverts. Mainly inland waters.

3 **GOLDEN EAGLE** *Aquila chrysaetos* **Page 542**
Adult (3a, 3b, 3c), juvenile (3d, 3e), sub-adult (3f) and gliding (3g). Resident. Baluchistan and Himalayas. Large, with long and broad wings (with pronounced curve to trailing edge), long tail, and distinctly protruding head and neck. Wings clearly pressed forward and raised (with upturned fingers) in pronounced V when soaring. Adult has pale panel across upperwing-coverts, gold crown and nape, and two-toned tail. Juvenile has white base to tail and white patch at base of flight feathers. Rugged mountains above treeline.

1a
1b
1c
1d
1e
1f
1g
1h
2i
2a
2b
2c
2d
2e
2f
2g
2h
3a
3b
3c
3d
3e
3f
3g
Tim Worfolk

PLATE 70: AQUILA EAGLES

1 **TAWNY EAGLE** *Aquila rapax* **Page 540**
Adult (1a, 1b, 1c, 1d, 1e), juvenile (1f, 1g), sub-adult (1h) and gliding (1i). Widespread resident; unrecorded in the northeast and Sri Lanka. Compared with Steppe, hand of wing does not appear so long and broad, tail slightly shorter, and looks smaller and weaker at rest; gape-line ends level with centre of eye, and adult has yellowish iris. Differs from the spotted eagles (Plate 69) in more protruding head and neck in flight, baggy trousers, yellow iris, and oval nostril. Adult extremely variable, from dark brown through rufous to pale cream, and unstreaked or streaked with rufous or dark brown. Dark morph very similar to adult Steppe (which shows much less variation); distinctions include less pronounced barring and dark trailing edge on underwing, dark nape, and dark throat. Rufous to pale cream Tawny uniformly pale from uppertail-coverts to back, with undertail-coverts same colour as belly (contrast often apparent on similar species). Pale adults also lack prominent whitish trailing edge to wing, tip to tail and greater-covert bar (present on immatures of similar species). Characteristic, if present, is distinct pale inner-primary wedge on underwing. Juvenile also variable, with narrow white tips to unbarred secondaries; otherwise as similar-plumaged adult. Many (possibly all) non-dark Tawny have distinctive immature/sub-adult plumage: dark throat and breast contrasting with pale belly, and can show dark banding across underwing-coverts; whole head and breast may be dark. Desert, semi-desert and cultivation.

2 **STEPPE EAGLE** *Aquila nipalensis* **Page 541**
Adult (2a, 2b, 2c), juvenile (2d, 2e, 2f), immature (2g, 2h) and gliding (2i). Widespread winter visitor to N and C subcontinent. Broader and longer wings than Greater and Lesser Spotted (Plate 69), with more pronounced and spread fingers, and more protruding head and neck; wings flatter when soaring, and less distinctly angled down at carpals when gliding. When perched, clearly bigger and heavier, with heavier bill and baggy trousers. Adult separated from adult spotted eagles by underwing pattern (dark trailing edge, distinct barring on remiges, indistinct/non-existent pale crescents in carpal region), pale rufous nape patch and pale chin. Juvenile has broad white bar across underwing, double white bar on upperwing, and white crescent across uppertail-coverts; prominence of bars on upperwing and underwing much reduced on older immatures, and such birds are very similar to some Lesser Spotted (see that species). Wooded hills, open country and lakes.

3 **IMPERIAL EAGLE** *Aquila heliaca* **Page 541**
Adult (3a, 3b, 3c), juvenile (3d, 3e, 3f), sub-adult (3g, 3h) and gliding (3i). Winter visitor. Mainly Pakistan and NW India. Large, stout-bodied eagle with long and broad wings, longish tail, and distinctly protruding head and neck. Wings flat when soaring and gliding. Adult has almost uniform upperwing, small white scapular patches, golden-buff crown and nape, and two-toned tail. Juvenile has pronounced curve to trailing edge of wing, pale wedge on inner primaries, streaked buffish body and wing-coverts, uniform pale rump and back (lacking distinct pale crescent shown by other species), and white tips to median and greater upperwing-coverts. Open country in plains, deserts and around wetlands.

1c
1d
1d
1h
1e
1f
1a
1b
1i
1g
2f
2b
2c
2g
2a
2h
2d
2e
3h
2i
3c
3g
3b
3a
3e
3f
3d
3i
Tim Worfolk

PLATE 71: EAGLES AND HAWK EAGLES

1 **BONELLI'S EAGLE** *Hieraaetus fasciatus* **Page 542**
Adult (1a, 1b, 1c), juvenile (1d, 1e, 1f) and soaring (1g). Widespread resident; unrecorded in most of north-east, east and Sri Lanka. Medium-sized eagle with long and broad wings, distinctly protruding head, and long square-ended tail. Soars with wings flat. Adult has pale underbody and forewing, blackish band along underwing-coverts, whitish patch on mantle, and pale greyish tail with broad dark terminal band. Juvenile has ginger-buff to reddish-brown underbody and underwing-coverts (with variable dark band along greater underwing-coverts), uniform upperwing, and pale crescent on uppertail-coverts and patch on back. Well-wooded country in plains and hills.

2 **BOOTED EAGLE** *Hieraaetus pennatus* **Page 543**
Pale morph (2a, 2b, 2c), dark morph (2d, 2e) and soaring (2f). Breeds in Baluchistan and Himalayas; widespread in winter, but unrecorded in parts of northwest, northeast and east. Smallish eagle with long wings and long square-ended tail. Glides and soars with wings flat or slightly angled down at carpal. Always shows white shoulder patches, pale median-covert panel, pale wedge on inner primaries, white crescent on uppertail-coverts, and greyish undertail with darker centre and tip. Head, body and wing-coverts whitish, brown or rufous respectively in pale, dark and rufous morphs.

3 **RUFOUS-BELLIED EAGLE** *Hieraaetus kienerii* **Page 543**
Adult (3a, 3b), juvenile (3c, 3d) and soaring (3e). Resident. Himalayas, hills of NE and SW India, Bangladesh and Sri Lanka. Smallish, with buzzard-shaped wings and tail. At rest, wing-tips extend well down tail. Glides and soars with wings flat. Adult has blackish hood and upperparts, white throat and breast, and (black-streaked) rufous rest of underparts. Juvenile has white underparts and underwing-coverts, dark mask and white supercilium, and dark patches on breast and flanks. Moist broadleaved forest.

4 **CHANGEABLE HAWK EAGLE** *Spizaetus cirrhatus* **Page 544**
Adult pale morph (4a, 4b), dark morph (4c, 4d) and juvenile (4e, 4f) *S. c. limnaetus*; adult *S. c. cirrhatus* (4g, 4h); soaring (4i). Resident. Widespread in subcontinent; unrecorded in Pakistan. Narrower, more parallel-edged wings than Mountain Hawk Eagle. Soars with wings flat (except in display, when both wings and tail raised). Adult *limnaetus* lacks prominent crest, and has boldly streaked underparts and narrower tail barring compared with Mountain; dark morph told from Black Eagle (Plate 63) by structural differences, greyish undertail with diffuse dark terminal band, and extensive greyish bases to underside of remiges. Juvenile generally whiter on head than juvenile Mountain. Nominate *cirrhatus* best told from Mountain by wing shape, patterning of breast and underwing-coverts, and dark vent and undertail-coverts. Broadleaved forest and well-wooded country.

5 **MOUNTAIN HAWK EAGLE** *Spizaetus nipalensis* **Page 544**
Adult (5a, 5b) and juvenile (5c, 5d) *S. n. nipalensis*; adult *S. n. kelaarti* (5e); soaring (5f). Resident. Himalayas, hills of India and Sri Lanka. Prominent crest. Wings broader than on Changeable, with more pronounced curve to trailing edge. Soars with wings in shallow V. Distinguished from Changeable by extensive barring on underparts, whitish-barred rump, and stronger dark barring on tail. Juvenile told from juvenile Changeable by more extensive dark streaking on crown and sides of head, white-tipped black crest (useful in N subcontinent only), buff-barred rump, and fewer, more prominent tail-bars. *S. n. kelaarti* smaller, with rufous barring on underparts, and underwing-coverts buff and almost unmarked. Forested hills and mountains.

1g
1a
1d
1b
1e
1f
1c
2d
2b
2c
2a
2e
2f
3e
3a
3c
3b
3d
4h
4a
4c
4d
4f
4e
4g
4b
5e
4i
5f
5a
5c
5d
5b
Tim Worfolk

PLATE 72: FALCONETS AND FALCONS

1 **COLLARED FALCONET** *Microhierax caerulescens* **Page 545**
Adult (1a, 1b, 1c) and juvenile (1d). Resident. Himalayas and NE Orissa. Very small. Rather shrike-like when perched. Flies with rapid beats interspersed with long glides. Adult has white collar, black crown and eye-stripe, and rufous-orange underparts. Juvenile has rufous-orange on forehead and supercilium, and white throat. Edges of broadleaved tropical forest.

2 **PIED FALCONET** *Microhierax melanoleucos* **Page 546**
Adult (2a, 2b, 2c). Resident. E Himalayas and NE India. Larger than Collared Falconet. Adult has white underparts and lacks white hindcollar. Forest clearings and wooded foothills.

3 **LESSER KESTREL** *Falco naumanni* **Page 546**
Male (3a, 3b, 3c), immature male (3d, 3e) and female (3f, 3g, 3h). Widespread passage migrant. Slightly smaller and slimmer than Common Kestrel. Flapping shallower and stiffer. Claws whitish (black on Common). Male has uniform blue-grey head (without dark moustachial stripe), unmarked rufous upperparts, blue-grey greater coverts, and almost plain orange-buff underparts. In flight, underwing whiter with more clearly pronounced darker tips to primaries; tail often looks more wedge-shaped. First-year male more like Common; best distinguished by structural differences and unmarked rufous mantle and scapulars. Female and juvenile have less distinct moustachial stripe than Common, and lack any suggestion of dark eye-stripe; underwing tends to be cleaner and whiter, with primary bases unbarred (or only lightly barred) and coverts less heavily spotted, and dark primary tips more pronounced. Open grassland and cultivation.

4 **COMMON KESTREL** *Falco tinnunculus* **Page 546**
Male (4a, 4b, 4c) and female (4d, 4e, 4f). Resident in mountains of Pakistan, Himalayas and Western Ghats and Sri Lanka; widespread winter visitor. Long, rather broad tail; wing-tips more rounded than on most falcons. Frequently hovers. Male has greyish head with diffuse dark moustachial stripe, rufous upperparts heavily marked with black, and grey tail with black subterminal band. Female and juvenile have rufous crown and nape streaked with black, diffuse and narrow dark moustachial stripe, rufous upperparts heavily barred and spotted with black, and dark barring on rufous tail; underwing more heavily barred than male's. Open country.

5 **RED-NECKED FALCON** *Falco chicquera* **Page 547**
Adult (5a, 5b, 5c) and juvenile (5d). Widespread resident; unrecorded in most of the northeast, W Pakistan and Sri Lanka. Powerful falcon with pointed wings and longish tail. Flight usually fast and dashing. Adult has rufous crown and nape, pale blue-grey upperparts, white underparts finely barred with black, and grey tail with broad black subterminal band. Juvenile has lightly streaked crown, and rufous fringes and more extensive dark barring on upperparts. Open country with trees.

1a
1b
1c
1d
2a
2b
2c
3a
3b
3c
3d
3e
3f
3g
3h
4a
4b
4c
4d
4e
4f
5a
5b
5c
5d
AH.

PLATE 73: FALCONS

1 AMUR FALCON *Falco amurensis* **Page 547**

Male (1a, 1b), female (1c, 1d), immature male (1e, 1f) and juvenile (1g). Widespread passage migrant; unrecorded in Pakistan. In all plumages, has red to pale orange cere, eye-ring, legs and feet. Frequently hovers. Male dark grey, with rufous thighs and undertail-coverts and white underwing-coverts. First-year male shows mixture of adult male and juvenile characters. Female has dark grey upperparts, short moustachial stripe, whitish underparts with some dark barring and spotting, and orange-buff thighs and undertail-coverts; uppertail barred; underwing white with strong dark barring. Juvenile has rufous-buff fringes to upperparts, rufous-buff streaking on crown, and boldly streaked underparts. Open country.

2 SOOTY FALCON *Falco concolor* **Page 548**

Adult (2a, 2b) and juvenile (2c, 2d). Summer visitor. Makran coast, Pakistan. Slim, with very long wings and tail (latter wedge-shaped at tip). Adult entirely pale grey with blackish flight feathers; older males can be almost black. Juvenile has narrow buff fringes to upperparts, and yellowish-brown underparts and underwing-coverts which are diffusely streaked. Rocky areas and desert.

3 MERLIN *Falco columbarius* **Page 548**

Male (3a, 3b) and female (3c, 3d). Winter visitor. N subcontinent. Small and compact, with short, pointed wings. Flight typically swift, with rapid beats interspersed with short dashing glides, when wings often closed into body. Male has blue-grey upperparts, broad black subterminal tail-band, weak moustachial stripe, and diffuse patch of rufous-orange on nape. Female and juvenile have weak moustachial stripe, brown upperparts with variable rufous/buff markings, and strongly barred uppertail. Open country.

4 EURASIAN HOBBY *Falco subbuteo* **Page 549**

Adult (4a, 4b) and juvenile (4c, 4d). Breeds in Himalayas; widespread winter visitor; unrecorded in Sri Lanka. Slim, with long pointed wings and medium-length tail. Hunting flight swift and powerful, with stiff beats interspersed with short glides. Adult has broad black moustachial stripe, cream underparts with bold blackish streaking, and rufous thighs and undertail-coverts. Juvenile has dark brown upperparts with buffish fringes, pale buffish underparts which are more heavily streaked, and lacks rufous thighs and undertail-coverts. Well-wooded areas; also open country in winter.

5 ORIENTAL HOBBY *Falco severus* **Page 549**

Adult (5a, 5b) and immature (5c, 5d). Resident. Mainly Himalayas and NE India. Similar to Eurasian Hobby in structure, flight action and appearance, although slightly stockier, with shorter tail. Adult has complete blackish hood, bluish-black upperparts, and unmarked rufous underparts and underwing-coverts. Juvenile has browner upperparts, and heavily streaked rufous-buff underparts. Open wooded hills.

1a
1b
1f
1d
2b
1g
2d
1c
1e
2c
3b
2a
3d
5a
3a
3c
4a
5c
4b
5d
4d
4c
5b
AH.

PLATE 74: LARGE FALCONS

1 LAGGAR FALCON *Falco jugger* **Page 550**

Adult (1a, 1b, 1c) and juvenile (1d, 1e). Widespread resident; unrecorded in parts of northeast and east and Sri Lanka. Large falcon, although smaller, slimmer-winged and less powerful than Saker. Adult has rufous crown, fine but prominent dark moustachial stripe, dark brown upperparts, and rather uniform uppertail; underparts and underwing-coverts vary, can be largely white or heavily streaked, but lower flanks and thighs usually wholly dark brown; may show dark panel across underwing-coverts. Juvenile similar to adult, but crown duller and underparts very heavily streaked, and has greyish bare parts; differs from juvenile Peregrine in paler crown, finer moustachial stripe, and unbarred uppertail. Open arid country and cultivation in plains and low hills.

2 SAKER FALCON *Falco cherrug* **Page 550**

***F. c. cherrug* (2a, 2b, 2c, 2d); *F. c. milvipes* (2e).** Winter visitor. Mainly Pakistan, Gujarat and Nepal. Large falcon with long wings and long tail. Wingbeats slow in level flight, with lazier flight action than Peregrine. At rest, tail extends noticeably beyond closed wings (wings fall just short of tail-tip on Laggar and are equal to tail on Peregrine). Adult has paler crown, less clearly defined moustachial stripe and paler rufous-brown upperparts than Laggar; underparts generally not so heavily marked as on Laggar, with flanks and thighs usually clearly streaked and not appearing wholly brown (although some overlap exists); outer tail feathers more prominently barred. Juvenile has greyish cere, and greyish legs and feet; otherwise similar to adult, but crown more heavily marked, moustachial stripe stronger, underparts more heavily streaked, and upperparts darker brown. *F. c. milvipes* has broad orange-buff barring on upperparts. Desert and semi-desert, mainly in hills and mountains.

3 PEREGRINE FALCON *Falco peregrinus* **Page 551**

Adult (3a, 3b) and juvenile (3c, 3d) *F. p. peregrinator*; adult (3e, 3f) and juvenile (3g, 3h) *F. p. babylonicus*; adult *F. p. calidus* (3i, 3j). Widespread resident and winter visitor. Heavy-looking falcon with broad-based and pointed wings and short, broad-based tail. Flight strong, with stiff, shallow beats and occasional short glides. *F. p. calidus* has slate-grey upperparts, broad and clean-cut black moustachial stripe, and whitish underparts with narrow blackish barring; juvenile *calidus* (not illustrated) has browner upperparts, heavily streaked underparts, broad moustachial stripe, and barred uppertail. *F. p. peregrinator* has dark grey upperparts with more extensive black hood (and less pronounced moustachial stripe), and rufous underparts with dark barring on belly and thighs; juvenile *peregrinator* has darker brownish-black upperparts than adult, and paler underparts with heavy streaking. *F. p. babylonicus* ('Barbary Falcon') has pale blue-grey upperparts, buffish underparts with only sparse streaking and barring, rufous on crown and nape, and a narrower dark moustachial stripe; juvenile *babylonicus* has darker brown upperparts with narrow rufous-buff fringes, heavily streaked underparts and underwing-coverts, and only a trace of rufous on forehead and supercilium. Breeds in hills, mountains and stony semi-desert; winters around inland and coastal wetlands.

1a
1b
1c
1e
1d
2b
2d
2a
2c
2e
3b
3d
3i
3a
3c
3j
3e
3h
3g
3f

PLATE 75: GREBES AND LOONS

1 **LITTLE GREBE** *Tachybaptus ruficollis* **Page 552**
Adult breeding (1a) and non-breeding (1b, 1c). Widespread resident; unrecorded in parts of northwest and northeast. Small size. In breeding plumage, has rufous cheeks and neck sides and yellow patch at base of bill. In non-breeding plumage, has brownish-buff cheeks and flanks. Mainly freshwater wetlands.

2 **RED-NECKED GREBE** *Podiceps grisegena* **Page 552**
Adult breeding (2a) and non-breeding (2b, 2c). Winter visitor. N Pakistan, N and NW India. Large size. Black-tipped yellow bill. Black crown extends to eye, and has dusky cheeks and foreneck in non-breeding plumage. White cheeks and reddish foreneck in breeding plumage. Lakes.

3 **GREAT CRESTED GREBE** *Podiceps cristatus* **Page 552**
Adult breeding (3a) and non-breeding (3b, 3c). Breeds in NW subcontinent; winter visitor to N subcontinent. Large and slender-necked, with pinkish bill. Black crown does not extend to eye, and has white cheeks and foreneck in non-breeding plumage. Rufous-orange ear-tufts and white cheeks and foreneck in breeding plumage. Lakes, reservoirs and coastal waters.

4 **HORNED GREBE** *Podiceps auritus* **Page 553**
Adult breeding (4a) and non-breeding (4b, 4c). Winter visitor. Pakistan and India. Triangular-shaped head, with crown peaking at rear. White cheeks contrasting with black crown and white foreneck in non-breeding plumage. Yellow ear-tufts and rufous neck and breast in breeding plumage. Lakes and coastal waters.

5 **BLACK-NECKED GREBE** *Podiceps nigricollis* **Page 553**
Adult breeding (5a) and non-breeding (5b, 5c). Breeds in Baluchistan; winters mainly in Pakistan, NW India and Nepal. Steep forehead, with crown peaking in centre. Dusky ear-coverts contrast with white throat and sides of head in non-breeding plumage. Yellow ear-tufts, black neck and breast and rufous flanks in breeding plumage. Reed-edged lakes; also coastal waters in winter.

6 **RED-THROATED LOON** *Gavia stellata* **Page 576**
Adult breeding (6a) and non-breeding (6b, 6c). Vagrant. Pakistan. Upturned-looking bill and rounded head. In non-breeding plumage, paler grey and whiter than Black-throated. Red throat in breeding plumage. Coastal waters and lakes.

7 **BLACK-THROATED LOON** *Gavia arctica* **Page 576**
Adult breeding (7a) and non-breeding (7b, 7c). Vagrant. India. Straight bill and square-shaped head. Black-and-white appearance in non-breeding plumage. Black throat and black-and-white chequered upperparts in breeding plumage. Flooded land, lakes and coastal waters.

1b
2c
1c
2b
1a
2a
3b
3c
3a
5c
4c
5b
4a
4b
5a
7c
6c
6a
7a
6b
7b
JPPW

PLATE 76: TROPICBIRDS AND BOOBIES

1 **RED-BILLED TROPICBIRD** *Phaethon aethereus* **Page 553**
Adult (1a, 1b) and juvenile (1c). Visitor to coastal waters. Adult has red bill, white tail-streamers, black barring on mantle and scapulars, and much black on primaries. Juvenile has yellow bill with black tip, and black band across nape; shows more black on primaries than juvenile Red-tailed. Pelagic.

2 **RED-TAILED TROPICBIRD** *Phaethon rubricauda* **Page 554**
Adult (2a, 2b) and juvenile (2c). Breeds in Nicobars. Adult has red bill and red tail-streamers; lacks black barring on mantle, back and rump; wings largely white (with black primary shafts). Juvenile has grey or black bill, and lacks black nape band; shows less black on primaries than juvenile Red-billed and White-tailed. Pelagic.

3 **WHITE-TAILED TROPICBIRD** *Phaethon lepturus* **Page 554**
Adult (3a, 3b) and juvenile (3c). Resident on Maldives; visitor to coasts of India and Sri Lanka. Smaller and more graceful than other tropicbirds. Adult has yellow or orange bill, black diagonal bar across inner upperwing, and white tail-streamers. Juvenile has yellow bill, and lacks black band across nape; shows more black on primaries than juvenile Red-tailed. Pelagic.

4 **MASKED BOOBY** *Sula dactylatra* **Page 554**
Adult (4a), immature (4b) and juvenile (4c, 4d). Breeds on Maldives and Lakshadweep?; visitor to W coastal waters. Large and robust booby. Adult largely white, with black mask and black flight feathers and tail. Juvenile has brown head, neck and upperparts, with whitish collar and whitish scaling on upperparts; underbody white, and shows much white on underwing-coverts. Head, upperbody and upperwing-coverts of immature become increasingly white with age. Pelagic.

5 **RED-FOOTED BOOBY** *Sula sula* **Page 555**
Adult white morph (5a, 5b), intermediate morph (5c), immature (5d, 5e) and juvenile (5f). Breeds on Maldives and Lakshadweep?; visitor to coastal waters. Small and graceful booby. Adult has bluish bill, pinkish facial skin and red feet. White, brown and intermediate morphs occur. Juvenile has greyish legs and dark bill; underwing uniformly dark. Immature variable; immature white morph has diffuse breast-band. Pelagic.

6 **BROWN BOOBY** *Sula leucogaster* **Page 555**
Adult (6a) and immature (6b). Breeds on Lakshadweep?; visitor to coasts and coastal waters. Dark brown, with sharply demarcated white underbody and underwing-coverts. Juvenile has dusky brown underbody, with pale panel across underwing-coverts. Pelagic.

1b
2b
3b
2a
3a
1a
2c
1c
3c
5e
5c
5a
5f
5d
5b
4b
6a
4c
4d
6b
4a

PLATE 77: DARTER AND CORMORANTS

1 **DARTER** *Anhinga melanogaster* **Page 556**
Adult male breeding (1a, 1b, 1c) and immature (1d). Widespread resident; unrecorded in parts of the northwest, northeast and Himalayas. Long, slim head and neck, dagger-like bill, and long tail. Often swims with most of body submerged. Adult has white stripe down side of neck, lanceolate white scapular streaks, and white streaking on wing-coverts. Juvenile buffish-white below, with buff fringes to coverts forming pale panel on upperwing. Mainly inland waters, also coastal waters.

2 **PYGMY CORMORANT** *Phalacrocorax pygmeus* **Page 556**
Adult breeding (2a, 2b), non-breeding (2c) and immature (2d). Vagrant. Pakistan. Averages larger and bulkier than Little. Adult breeding has chestnut head and upper neck (becoming nearly black prior to breeding) with more profuse white plumes than breeding Little. Non-breeding and immature very similar to Little, although tend to be browner on body and with more extensive whitish mottling on breast and belly; chin and throat whitish, gradually merging into brown of foreneck (on Little, chin more clearly demarcated). Inland and coastal waters.

3 **LITTLE CORMORANT** *Phalacrocorax niger* **Page 557**
Adult breeding (3a, 3b), non-breeding (3c) and immature (3d). Widespread resident; unrecorded in parts of the northwest, northeast and Himalayas. Smaller than Indian, with shorter bill, rectangular-shaped head and shorter neck. Lacks yellow gular pouch. Adult breeding all black, with a few white plumes on forecrown and sides of head. Non-breeding browner (and lacks white head plumes), with whitish chin. Immature has whitish chin and throat, and foreneck and breast a shade paler than upperparts, with some pale fringes. Inland and coastal waters.

4 **INDIAN CORMORANT** *Phalacrocorax fuscicollis* **Page 557**
Adult breeding (4a, 4b), non-breeding (4c) and immature (4d). Widespread resident; unrecorded in parts of the northwest, northeast and Himalayas. Smaller and slimmer than Great, with thinner neck, slimmer oval-shaped head, finer-looking bill, and proportionately longer tail. In flight, looks lighter, with thinner neck and quicker wing action. Larger than Little, with longer neck, oval-shaped head and longer bill. Adult breeding glossy black, with tuft of white behind eye and scattering of white filoplumes on neck. Non-breeding lacks white plumes; has whitish throat, and browner-looking head, neck and underparts. Immature has brown upperparts and whitish underparts. Inland and coastal waters.

5 **GREAT CORMORANT** *Phalacrocorax carbo* **Page 558**
Adult breeding (5a, 5b), non-breeding (5c) and immature (5d). Widespread resident; unrecorded in parts of the northwest, northeast and Western Ghats. Larger and bulkier than Indian, with thicker neck, larger and more angular head, and stouter bill. Adult breeding glossy black, with orange facial skin, white cheeks and throat, white head plumes and white thigh patch. Non-breeding more blackish-brown, and lacks white head plumes and thigh patch. Immature has whitish or pale buff underparts. Inland and coastal waters.

1b
1d
1a
1c
2b
3b
3c
2d
2c
3d
3a
2a
4b
5b
4d
5c
4c
5d
5a
4a

PLATE 78: EGRETS AND POND HERONS

1 **LITTLE EGRET** *Egretta garzetta* **Page 558**
Adult breeding (1a) and non-breeding (1b, 1c). Widespread resident; unrecorded in parts of the northwest and northeast. Slim and graceful. Typically, has black bill, black legs with yellow feet, and greyish lores (lores reddish during courtship). Some can be very similar to Western Reef. Inland and coastal waters.

2 **WESTERN REEF EGRET** *Egretta gularis* **Page 559**
Adult white morph breeding (2a) and non-breeding (2b), adult dark morph non-breeding (2c) and intermediate morph (2d). Resident. Mainly W and SE coast. Bill longer and stouter than Little's and usually appearing very slightly downcurved. Legs also slightly shorter and thicker-looking. Bill and lores usually yellowish. Coastal waters.

3 **PACIFIC REEF EGRET** *Egretta sacra* **Page 559**
Adult white morph breeding (3a) and non-breeding (3b), adult dark morph non-breeding (3c) and juvenile dark morph (3d). Resident. Andamans and Nicobars. Legs shorter and stouter than Western Reef's, and is stockier, with shorter and thicker neck. White throat of dark morph is inconspicuous. Coastal waters.

4 **GREAT EGRET** *Casmerodius albus* **Page 562**
Adult breeding (4a, 4b) and non-breeding (4c). Widespread resident; unrecorded in parts of the northwest and northeast. Large size, very long neck and large bill. Black line of gape extends behind eye. Bill is black and lores blue in breeding plumage. In non-breeding plumage, bill yellow and lores pale green. Inland and coastal waters.

5 **INTERMEDIATE EGRET** *Mesophoyx intermedia* **Page 562**
Adult breeding (5a) and non-breeding (5b, 5c). Widespread resident; unrecorded in parts of the northwest and northeast. Smaller than Great, with shorter bill and neck. Black gape-line does not extend beyond eye. Bill is black and lores yellow-green during courtship. Has black-tipped yellow bill and yellow lores outside breeding season. Inland and coastal waters.

6 **CATTLE EGRET** *Bubulcus ibis* **Page 563**
Adult breeding (6a, 6b) and non-breeding (6c). Widespread resident; unrecorded in parts of the northwest and northeast. Small and stocky, with short yellow bill and short legs. Has orange-buff on head, neck and mantle in breeding plumage. Damp grassland, paddy-fields and inland waters.

7 **INDIAN POND HERON** *Ardeola grayii* **Page 563**
Adult breeding (7a, 7b) and non-breeding (7c). Widespread resident; unrecorded in parts of the northwest and northeast. Whitish wings contrast with dark saddle. Adult breeding has yellowish-buff head and neck and maroon-brown mantle/scapulars. Head, neck and breast streaked/spotted in non-breeding plumage. Inland and coastal wetlands.

8 **CHINESE POND HERON** *Ardeola bacchus* **Page 563**
Adult breeding (8a, 8b) and non-breeding (8c). Resident and winter visitor? Mainly NE India and Andamans. In breeding plumage, has maroon-chestnut head and neck and slaty-black mantle/scapulars. Non-breeding and immature plumages probably not separable from those of Indian Pond Heron. Inland and coastal waters.

1a
1b
1c
2a
2b
2c
2d
3a
3b
3c
3d
4a
4b
4c
5a
5b
5c
6a
6b
6c
7a
7b
7c
8a
8b
8c
C.D'S

PLATE 79: LARGE HERONS

1 **GREY HERON** *Ardea cinerea* **Page 560**
Adult (1a, 1b, 1c) and immature (1d). Resident, passage migrant and winter visitor. Widespread; unrecorded in parts of the northwest and northeast. In flight, black flight feathers contrast with grey upperwing- and underwing-coverts. Adult has whitish head and neck with black head plumes, and black patches on belly. Immature has dark cap with variable crest, and greyer neck; lacks or has reduced black on belly. Inland and coastal waters.

2 **GOLIATH HERON** *Ardea goliath* **Page 560**
Adult (2a, 2b). Visitor or resident? Mainly NE India. Huge size and large, dark bill. Black legs and feet. Rufous on head and neck. Adult has purplish-chestnut underparts and underwing-coverts. Rivers.

3 **WHITE-BELLIED HERON** *Ardea insignis* **Page 561**
Adult (3a, 3b). Resident. E Himalayan foothills. Large size and very long neck (much longer than shown on plate). Bill blackish, and legs and feet grey. Grey foreneck and breast contrast with white belly. In flight, has uniform dark grey upperwing, and white underwing-coverts contrasting with dark grey flight feathers. Wetlands in tropical and subtropical forest.

4 **GREAT-BILLED HERON** *Ardea sumatrana* **Page 561**
Adult (4a, 4b). [Vagrant? Possibly recorded in Nicobars. Large size and large bill. Grey head, neck and underparts, and grey upperwing and underwing. Breeding birds have white scapular plumes. Habitat unrecorded in region.]

5 **PURPLE HERON** *Ardea purpurea* **Page 561**
Adult (5a, 5b) and juvenile (5c, 5d). Resident and winter visitor? Widespread; unrecorded in parts of the northwest and northeast. Rakish, with long, thin neck. Adult has chestnut head and neck with black stripes, grey mantle and upperwing-coverts, and dark chestnut belly and underwing-coverts. Juvenile has buffish neck and underparts, and brownish mantle and upperwing-coverts with rufous-buff fringes. Mainly inland waters with tall cover.

1b
2b
1c
1d
1a
2a
3a
4b
3b
4a
5b
5d
5c
5a
C.D'S

PLATE 80: BITTERNS AND NIGHT HERONS

1 **LITTLE HERON** *Butorides striatus* **Page 564**
Adult (1a, 1b) and juvenile (1c). Widespread resident; unrecorded in parts of the northwest and northeast. Small, stocky and short-legged. Adult has dark greenish upperparts and greyish underparts. Juvenile has buff streaking on upperparts and dark-streaked underparts. Inland waters with dense shrub cover, and mangroves.

2 **BLACK-CROWNED NIGHT HERON** *Nycticorax nycticorax* **Page 564**
Adult (2a, 2b) and juvenile (2c). Widespread resident; unrecorded in parts of the northwest and northeast. Stocky, with thick neck. Adult has black crown and mantle contrasting with grey wings and whitish underparts. Juvenile boldly streaked and spotted. Immature has unstreaked brown mantle/scapulars. Inland and coastal waters.

3 **MALAYAN NIGHT HERON** *Gorsachius melanolophus* **Page 565**
Adult (3a, 3b) and immature (3c). Resident and partial migrant in Western Ghats, NE India and Nicobars; winter visitor to Sri Lanka. Stocky, with stout bill and short neck. Adult has black crown and crest and rufous-brown upperparts. Immature finely vermiculated with white, grey and rufous-buff, and with bold white spotting on crown and crest. Streams and marshes in evergreen forest.

4 **LITTLE BITTERN** *Ixobrychus minutus* **Page 565**
Adult male (4a, 4b), female (4c) and juvenile (4d). Resident in Kashmir and Assam; widely recorded elsewhere in India and Pakistan. Male has black crown and mantle/scapulars, and buff neck. Female has brown mantle/scapulars, with brownish-buff streaking on foreneck and breast. Juvenile has warm buff upperparts streaked with dark brown, and brown streaking on underparts. Reedbeds.

5 **YELLOW BITTERN** *Ixobrychus sinensis* **Page 565**
Adult male (5a, 5b) and juvenile (5c). Widespread resident. Yellowish-buff wing-coverts contrast with dark brown flight feathers. Male has pinkish-brown mantle/scapulars. Female has brown streaking on buff mantle/scapulars, and rufous-buff streaking on foreneck and breast. Juvenile has rufous-buff upperparts streaked with rufous-brown, and rufous streaking on underparts. Reedbeds and flooded paddy-fields.

6 **CINNAMON BITTERN** *Ixobrychus cinnamomeus* **Page 566**
Adult male (6a, 6b), female (6c) and juvenile (6d). Widespread resident. Uniform-looking cinnamon-rufous wings and tail. Male has cinnamon-rufous crown, hindneck and mantle/scapulars. Female has dark brown crown and mantle, and dark brown streaking on foreneck and breast. Juvenile has buff mottling on dark brown upperparts, and is heavily streaked with dark brown on underparts. Reedbeds and flooded paddy-fields.

7 **BLACK BITTERN** *Dupetor flavicollis* **Page 566**
Adult (7a, 7b) and juvenile (7c). Widespread resident. Blackish upperparts including wings, with orange-buff patch on side of neck. Juvenile has rufous fringes to upperparts. Reedbeds.

8 **GREAT BITTERN** *Botaurus stellaris* **Page 567**
Adult (8a, 8b). Widespread winter visitor. Stocky. Cryptically patterned with golden-brown, blackish and buff. Wet reedbeds.

1b
1a
1c
2b
2a
2c
3b
3c
3a
4b
4a
4c
4d
5b
5c
5a
6b
6a
6c
6d
7b
7a
7c
8a
8b
C.D'S

PLATE 81: FLAMINGOS, IBISES AND EURASIAN SPOONBILL

1 GREATER FLAMINGO *Phoenicopterus ruber* **Page 567**
Adult (1a, 1b), immature (1c) and juvenile (1d). Resident and winter visitor. Breeds in Gujarat; widespread visitor to plains. Larger than Lesser, with longer and thinner neck. Bill larger and less prominently kinked. Adult has pale pink bill with prominent dark tip, and variable amount of pinkish-white on head, neck and body; in flight, crimson-pink upperwing-coverts contrast with whitish body. Immature has greyish-white head and neck, and white body lacking any pink; pink on bill develops with increasing age. Juvenile brownish-grey, with white on coverts; bill grey, tipped with black, and legs grey. Shallow brackish lakes, mudflats and saltpans.

2 LESSER FLAMINGO *Phoenicopterus minor* **Page 567**
Adult (2a, 2b), immature (2c) and juvenile (2d). Breeds in Gujarat; widespread in Indian and Pakistan plains in non-breeding season. Smaller than Greater Flamingo; neck appears shorter, and bill is smaller and more prominently kinked. Adult has black-tipped dark red bill, dark red iris and facial skin, and deep rose-pink on head, neck and body; blood-red centres to lesser and median upperwing coverts contrast with paler pink of rest of coverts. Immature has greyish-brown head and neck, pale pink body, and mainly pink coverts; bill coloration develops with increasing age. Juvenile mainly grey-brown, with dark-tipped purplish-brown bill and grey legs. Salt and brackish lagoons and saltpans.

3 GLOSSY IBIS *Plegadis falcinellus* **Page 568**
Adult breeding (3a), non-breeding (3b) and juvenile (3c). Resident and winter visitor. Mainly W and S subcontinent. Small, dark ibis with rather fine downcurved bill. Adult breeding deep chestnut, glossed with purple and green, with metallic green-and-purple wings; has narrow white surround to bare lores. Adult non-breeding duller, with white streaking on dark brown head and neck. Juvenile similar to adult non-breeding, but is dark brown with white mottling on head, and only faint greenish gloss to upperparts. Inland wetlands.

4 BLACK-HEADED IBIS *Threskiornis melanocephalus* **Page 568**
Adult (4a) and immature (4b). Widespread resident; unrecorded in parts of E India and the northwest. Stocky, mainly white ibis with stout downcurved black bill. Adult breeding has naked black head, white lower-neck plumes, variable yellow wash to mantle and breast, and grey on scapulars and elongated tertials. Adult non-breeding has all-white body and lacks neck plumes. Immature has grey feathering on head and neck, and black-tipped wings. Inland and coastal wetlands.

5 BLACK IBIS *Pseudibis papillosa* **Page 569**
Adult. Widespread resident in lowlands of Pakistan, Nepal and India. Stocky, dark ibis with relatively stout downcurved bill. Has white shoulder patch and reddish legs. Adult has naked black head with red patch on rear crown and nape, and is dark brown with green-and-purple gloss. Immature dark brown, including feathered head. Marshes, lakes and fields.

6 EURASIAN SPOONBILL *Platalea leucorodia* **Page 569**
Adult breeding (6a) and juvenile (6b). Widespread resident; unrecorded in parts of India and the northwest. White, with spatulate-tipped bill. Adult has black bill with yellow tip; has crest and yellow breast patch when breeding. Juvenile has pink bill; in flight, shows black tips to primaries. Mainly inland wetlands.

1a
1b
1c
1d
2a
2b
2c
2d
3a
3b
3c
4a
4b
5
6a
6b
C.D'S

PLATE 82: PELICANS

1 **GREAT WHITE PELICAN** *Pelecanus onocrotalus* **Page 570**
Adult breeding (1a), adult non-breeding (1b, 1c), immature (1d) and juvenile (1e). Mainly a winter visitor to N subcontinent; breeds in Gujarat. Adult and immature have black underside to primaries and secondaries which contrast strongly with white (or largely white) underwing-coverts. Feathering of forehead narrower than on Dalmatian, and tapers to a point at bill-base (as orbital skin more extensive). Adult breeding has white body and wing-coverts tinged with pink, bright yellow pouch and pinkish skin around eye. Adult non-breeding has duller bare parts and lacks pink tinge and white crest. Immature has variable amounts of brown on wing-coverts and scapulars. Juvenile has largely brown head, neck and upperparts, including upperwing-coverts, and brown flight feathers; upperwing appears more uniform brown, and underwing shows pale central panel contrasting with dark inner coverts and flight feathers; greyish pouch becomes yellower with age. Large lakes and lagoons.

2 **DALMATIAN PELICAN** *Pelecanus crispus* **Page 570**
Adult breeding (2a), adult non-breeding (2b, 2c) and immature (2d). Winter visitor. Mainly S Pakistan and NW India. In all plumages, has greyish underside to secondaries and inner primaries (becoming darker on outer primaries) lacking strong contrast with pale underwing-coverts, and often with whiter central panel. Forehead feathering broader across upper mandible (orbital skin more restricted than on White). Legs and feet always dark grey (pinkish on White). Larger than Spot-billed Pelican, with cleaner and whiter appearance at all ages; lacks 'spotting' on upper mandible, and bill usually darker than pouch. Adult breeding has orange pouch and purple skin around eye, and curly or bushy crest. Adult non-breeding more dirty white; pouch and skin around eye paler. Immature dingier than adult non-breeding, with some pale grey-brown on upperwing-coverts and scapulars. Juvenile has pale grey-brown mottling on hindneck and upperparts, including upper-wing-coverts; pouch greyish-yellow. Large inland waters and coastal lagoons.

3 **SPOT-BILLED PELICAN** *Pelecanus philippensis* **Page 571**
Adult breeding (3a, 3b), adult non-breeding (3c), immature (3d) and juvenile (3e). Resident. Breeds in S and NE India and Sri Lanka; widespread in non-breeding season. Much smaller than Great White and Dalmatian, with dingier appearance, rather uniform pinkish bill and pouch (except in breeding condition), and black spotting on upper mandible (except juveniles). Tufted crest/hindneck usually apparent even on young birds. Underwing pattern similar to that of Dalmatian (and quite different from Great White), showing little contrast between wing-coverts and flight feathers and with paler greater coverts producing distinct central panel. Adult breeding has cinnamon-pink rump, underwing-coverts and undertail-coverts; head and neck appear greyish; has purplish skin in front of eye, and pouch is pink to dull purple and blotched with black. Adult non-breeding dirtier greyish-white, with pouch pinkish. Immature has variable grey-brown markings on upperparts. Juvenile has brownish head and neck, brown mantle and upperwing-coverts (fringed with pale buff), and brown flight feathers; spotting on bill initially lacking (and still indistinct at 12 months). Large inland and coastal waters.

1a
1b
1c
1d
1e
2c
2a
2d
3b
2b
3d
3e
3c
3a
C.D'S

PLATE 83: FRIGATEBIRDS

1 GREAT FRIGATEBIRD *Fregata minor* **Page 575**
Adult male (1a), adult female (1b), juvenile (1c) and immature (1d). Visitor. Coasts of India, Sri Lanka and Maldives. Adult male is only frigatebird with all-black underparts. Adult female has black cap and pink eye-ring; also has grey throat and black neck sides, and lacks spur of white on underwing. Juvenile and immature have rufous or white head, blackish breast-band and largely white underparts, which are gradually replaced by adult plumage; lack white spur on underwing (shown by all Lesser and some Christmas Island Frigatebirds); inseparable from some juvenile and immature Christmas Island, although any black on belly will indicate Great. Pelagic.

2 LESSER FRIGATEBIRD *Fregata ariel* **Page 575**
Adult male (2a), adult female (2b), immature male (2c) and juvenile (2d). Visitor to coasts of India, Sri Lanka and Maldives; has bred. Smaller and more finely built than other two frigatebirds. Adult male entirely black except for white spur extending from breast sides onto inner underwing. Adult female has black head and red eye-ring; also black throat, white neck sides, white spur extending from white breast onto inner underwing, and black belly and vent. Juvenile and immature have rufous or white head, blackish breast-band and much white on underparts, which are gradually replaced by adult plumage; always show white spur on underwing (lacking on Great); any black on belly indicates Lesser rather than Christmas Island. Pelagic.

3 CHRISTMAS ISLAND FRIGATEBIRD *Fregata andrewsi* **Page 576**
Adult male (3a), adult female (3b), immature male (3c) and juvenile (3d). Visitor. Coasts of India and Sri Lanka. Adult male has black underparts except for large white patch on belly. Adult female has black head and pink eye-ring; also black throat, white neck sides, white spur extending from white breast onto inner underwing, black wedge on side of breast, and white belly and vent. Juvenile has buffish to white head, blackish breast-band, and white underparts, with black head of female and black head and breast of male acquired gradually; some show white spur on underwing (always lacking on Great), and lower belly always remains white (gradually becoming black on both Lesser and Great). Pelagic.

1d
1b
1a
1c
2b
2d
2a
2c
3c
3b
3d
3a

PLATE 84: STORKS

1 PAINTED STORK *Mycteria leucocephala* **Page 571**
Adult (1a, 1b) and immature (1c, 1d). Widespread resident in plains; unrecorded in parts of the northwest and northeast. Adult has downcurved yellow bill, bare orange-yellow or red face, and red legs; white barring on mainly black upperwing-coverts, pinkish tertials, and black barring across breast. Juvenile dirty greyish-white, with grey-brown (feathered) head and neck and brown lesser coverts; bill and legs duller than adult's. Inland and coastal wetlands.

2 ASIAN OPENBILL *Anastomus oscitans* **Page 572**
Adult breeding (2a) and non-breeding (2b, 2c). Widespread resident in plains; unrecorded in parts of the northwest and northeast. Stout, dull-coloured 'open bill'. Largely white (breeding) or greyish-white (non-breeding), with black flight feathers and tail; legs usually dull pink, brighter in breeding condition. Juvenile has brownish-grey head, neck and breast, and brownish mantle and scapulars slightly paler than the blackish flight feathers. Mainly inland wetlands.

3 WOOLLY-NECKED STORK *Ciconia episcopus* **Page 572**
Adult (3a, 3b). Widespread resident; unrecorded in parts of the northwest, northeast and E India. Stocky, largely blackish stork with 'woolly' white neck, black 'skullcap', and white vent and undertail-coverts. In flight, upperwing and underwing entirely dark. Freshwater wetlands in open wooded country.

4 WHITE STORK *Ciconia ciconia* **Page 573**
Adult (4a, 4b). Widespread winter visitor and passage migrant. Mainly white stork, with black flight feathers, and striking red bill and legs. Generally has cleaner black-and-white appearance than Asian Openbill. Grassland and fields.

5 ORIENTAL STORK *Ciconia boyciana* **Page 573**
Adult (5a, 5b). Winter visitor. Mainly NE India. Larger than White Stork, with larger, slightly upturned, black bill. Usually shows prominent greyish-white outer webs to secondaries. Lores red (black on White). Wet meadows and marshes.

1b
1d
2c
1a
1c
2b
2a
3b
3a
4b
4a
5a
5b
C.D'S

PLATE 85: STORKS

1 **BLACK STORK** *Ciconia nigra* **Page 572**
Adult (1a, 1b) and immature (1c). Winter visitor and passage migrant. Mainly N subcontinent. Adult mainly glossy black, with white lower breast and belly, and red bill and legs; in flight, white underparts and axillaries contrast strongly with black neck and underwing. Juvenile has brown head, neck and upperparts; bill and legs greyish-green. Inland wetlands.

2 **BLACK-NECKED STORK** *Ephippiorhynchus asiaticus* **Page 573**
Adult (2a, 2b) and immature (2c, 2d). Widespread resident in lowlands. Large, black-and-white stork with long red legs and huge black bill. In flight, wings white except for broad black band across coverts, and tail black. Male has brown iris; yellow in female. Juvenile has fawn-brown head, neck and mantle, mainly brown wing-coverts, and mainly blackish-brown flight feathers; legs dark. Mainly inland wetlands.

3 **LESSER ADJUTANT** *Leptoptilos javanicus* **Page 574**
Adult breeding (3a) and non-breeding (3b, 3c). Widespread resident in lowlands; unrecorded in Pakistan. Flies with neck retracted, as Greater Adjutant. Smaller than Greater, with slimmer bill. Adult has glossy black mantle and wings, largely black underwing (with white axillaries), and largely black neck ruff (appearing as black patch on breast sides in flight); in breeding plumage, has narrow white fringes to scapulars and inner greater coverts. Juvenile similar to adult, but upperparts dull black and head and neck more densely feathered. Inland wetlands.

4 **GREATER ADJUTANT** *Leptoptilos dubius* **Page 574**
Adult breeding (4a, 4b, 4c) and immature (4d). Resident. Mainly Assam; rare elsewhere. Larger than Lesser Adjutant, with stouter, conical bill. Adult breeding has bluish-grey mantle, silvery-grey panel across greater coverts, greyish or brownish underwing-coverts, and more extensive white neck ruff. Adult non-breeding and immature have darker grey mantle and inner wing-coverts, and brown greater coverts (which barely contrast with rest of wing). Marshes and lakes.

1b
1a
1c
2d
2b
2a
2c
3c
3b
4c
3a
4a
4d
4b
C.D'S

PLATE 86: PETRELS AND STORM-PETRELS

1 **CAPE PETREL** *Daption capense* **Page 577**
Adult (1a, 1b). Vagrant. Sri Lanka. Black head, white underparts, white-and-black chequered upperparts, and black tail-band. Pelagic.

2 **BARAU'S PETREL** *Pterodroma baraui* **Page 577**
Adult (2a, 2b). Visitor. India and Sri Lanka. Blackish eye-stripe, blackish M-mark across upperwing, dark rump and tail. Largely white underwing with black band on leading and trailing edges. Pelagic.

3 **SOFT-PLUMAGED PETREL** *Pterodroma mollis* **Page 578**
Adult (3a, 3b). [Vagrant? Possibly recorded in Sri Lanka. Grey breast-band, grey crown, and fairly uniform dark upperwing which may show darker M-mark. Pelagic.]

4 **BULWER'S PETREL** *Bulweria bulwerii* **Page 578**
Adult (4a, 4b). Vagrant. India, Sri Lanka and Maldives. Small and dark, with long and pointed tail. Pale band across greater coverts. Smaller than Jouanin's, with finer bill and weaker flight, with rapid beats interspersed with twisting glides. Pelagic.

5 **JOUANIN'S PETREL** *Bulweria fallax* **Page 578**
Adult (5a, 5b). Visitor. India and Sri Lanka. All dark, with long, pointed tail. Larger and broader-winged than Bulwer's, with stouter bill. Flight more powerful, with 'shearing' or long glides interspersed with steady flapping. Smaller and with less languid flight than Wedge-tailed Shearwater. Pelagic.

6 **WILSON'S STORM-PETREL** *Oceanites oceanicus* **Page 581**
Adult (6a, 6b). Visitor. W and S coastal waters. Dark underparts and underwing. White rump band. Feet project noticeably beyond tail. Pelagic.

7 **WHITE-FACED STORM-PETREL** *Pelagodroma marina* **Page 581**
Adult (7a, 7b). Visitor. SW Indian coastal waters. White supercilium and dark mask, white underparts and underwing-coverts, grey rump, and peculiar bounding flight. Pelagic.

8 **SWINHOE'S STORM-PETREL** *Oceanodroma monorhis* **Page 582**
Adult (8a, 8b). Visitor. India and Sri Lanka. All-dark storm-petrel, lacking white rump band. Tail slightly forked, and feet do not project beyond tail. Pelagic and coastal waters.

9 **WHITE-BELLIED STORM-PETREL** *Fregetta grallaria* **Page 581**
Adult (9a, 9b). Vagrant. Maldives. Black head, and white underwing-coverts, underbody and undertail-coverts. Pelagic.

10 **BLACK-BELLIED STORM-PETREL** *Fregetta tropica* **Page 581**
Adult (10a, 10b). Vagrant. India and Sri Lanka. Black head, white underwing-coverts and white flanks, with black line down centre of belly and undertail coverts. Pelagic.

1a
1b
3a
3b
2b
4b
2a
5b
5a
4a
7a
8b
6a
6b
8a
7b
9a
9b
10a
10b

PLATE 87: SHEARWATERS

1 **STREAKED SHEARWATER** *Calonectris leucomelas* **Page 579**
Adult (1a, 1b). Visitor. India and Sri Lanka. White underparts and underwing-coverts and large size. Variable dark streaking on whitish head, and pale bill with dark tip. Pelagic, inshore waters.

2 **WEDGE-TAILED SHEARWATER** *Puffinus pacificus* **Page 579**
Pale morph (2a) and dark morph (2b, 2c). Visitor. India, Sri Lanka and Maldives. Large size, long pointed or wedge-shaped tail, fine greyish bill with dark tip, and pale legs and feet. Comparatively broad rounded wings and languid flight. Two colour morphs; dark morph has all-dark underwing. Pelagic.

3 **FLESH-FOOTED SHEARWATER** *Puffinus carneipes* **Page 579**
Adult (3a, 3b). Visitor. India, Sri Lanka and Maldives. Large, dark, broad-winged shearwater. Pink legs and feet. Greyish patch on underside of primaries. Stout pinkish bill with dark tip. Offshore.

4 **SOOTY SHEARWATER** *Puffinus griseus* **Page 579**
Adult (4a, 4b). Vagrant. Sri Lanka. Sooty-brown, with whitish flash on underwing-coverts. Slim, pointed wings, and strong, deliberate flight action with stiff flapping and long glides. Offshore and pelagic waters.

5 **SHORT-TAILED SHEARWATER** *Puffinus tenuirostris* **Page 580**
Adult (5a, 5b). Vagrant. Pakistan and Sri Lanka. Sooty-brown, with pale grey underwing-coverts. Much as Sooty, but shorter bill and steeper forehead. Inshore, offshore and pelagic waters.

6 **AUDUBON'S SHEARWATER** *Puffinus lherminieri* **Page 580**
Adult (6a, 6b). Resident or breeding visitor? India, Sri Lanka and Maldives. Dark brown upperparts, white underparts with dark on breast sides; white wing-linings, axillaries and flanks, with broad dark margins to underwing. Flies with fairly fast wingbeats interspersed with short glides. Offshore and pelagic waters.

7 **PERSIAN SHEARWATER** *Puffinus persicus* **Page 580**
Adult (7a, 7b). Visitor. Pakistan and India. Slightly larger than Audubon's, with less extensive white on underwing and brownish axillaries and flanks. Offshore and pelagic waters.

1a
1b
3a
3b
2a
2b
2c
4a
4b
5a
5b
6a
6b
7a
7b
JPPW

PLATE 88: PITTAS, BROADBILLS, ASIAN FAIRY BLUEBIRD AND LEAFBIRDS

1 BLUE-NAPED PITTA *Pitta nipalensis* **Page 582**
Male (1a), female (1b) and juvenile (1c). Resident. Himalayas, NE India and Bangladesh. Large and stocky, with fulvous underparts. Male has glistening blue hindrown and nape. Female has smaller greenish-blue patch on nape. Juvenile brown, spotted and streaked with buff. Broadleaved evergreen forest.

2 BLUE PITTA *Pitta cyanea* **Page 582**
Male (2a), female (2b) and juvenile (2c). Resident. NE India and Bangladesh. Pinkish-red hindcrown and black spotting on underparts. Male has blue upperparts. Female has dark olive upperparts. Juvenile dark brown, spotted and streaked with rufous-buff. Broadleaved evergreen forest.

3 HOODED PITTA *Pitta sordida* **Page 583**
Adult (3a) and juvenile (3b). Summer visitor or resident? Himalayas, NE India and Bangladesh. Black head with chestnut crown, and green breast and flanks. Juvenile has white patch on wing-coverts and black scaling on crown. Broadleaved evergreen and moist deciduous forest.

4 INDIAN PITTA *Pitta brachyura* **Page 583**
Adult (4a) and juvenile (4b). Resident. Breeds in Himalayan foothills and NE India; winters in S India and Sri Lanka. Bold black stripe through eye, white throat and supercilium, buff lateral crown-stripes, and buff breast and flanks. Juvenile duller, with black scaling on lateral crown. Mainly broadleaved forest.

5 MANGROVE PITTA *Pitta megarhyncha* **Page 583**
Adult (5a) and juvenile (5b). Resident? Sunderbans, Bangladesh. Similar to Indian Pitta, but larger and longer bill, uniform rufous-brown crown with narrow buffish supercilium, and deeper blue wing-coverts and rump. Juvenile duller, with black scaling on crown. Mangroves.

6 SILVER-BREASTED BROADBILL *Serilophus lunatus* **Page 584**
Male (6a) and female (6b). Resident. Himalayan foothills, NE India and Bangladesh. Stout bluish bill, dusky supercilium, pale chestnut tertials, and white-and-blue on wing. Broadleaved evergreen and semi-evergreen forest.

7 LONG-TAILED BROADBILL *Psarisomus dalhousiae* **Page 584**
Adult (7a) and juvenile (7b). Resident. Himalayan foothills, NE India and Bangladesh. Green, with black cap, and yellow 'ear' spot and throat. Juvenile has green cap. Broadleaved and semi-evergreen forest.

8 ASIAN FAIRY BLUEBIRD *Irena puella* **Page 585**
Male (8a) and female (8b). Resident. Himalayan foothills, hills of NE, E and S India, Bangladesh and Sri Lanka. Male has glistening violet-blue upperparts and black underparts. Female and first-year male entirely dull blue-green. Evergreen and moist deciduous forest.

9 BLUE-WINGED LEAFBIRD *Chloropsis cochinchinensis* **Page 585**
Male (9a), female (9b) and juvenile (9c) *C. c. jerdoni*; male (9d), female (9e) and juvenile (9f) *C. c. cochinchinensis*. Resident. Peninsular India, hills of NE India and Bangladesh. Nominate has blue wing panel and sides to tail in all plumages (lacking in *jerdoni*). Male has smaller black throat patch than Golden-fronted, with yellowish forehead. Female nominate has bluish-green throat and turquoise moustachial stripe; juvenile has greenish head with hint of turquoise moustachial. Female and juvenile *jerdoni* have yellowish border to turquoise throat. Open forest and well-wooded areas.

10 GOLDEN-FRONTED LEAFBIRD *Chloropsis aurifrons* **Page 585**
Adult *C. a. aurifrons* (10a); adult (10b) and juvenile (10c) *C. a. frontalis*. Resident. Himalayas, NE, E, S and SW India, Bangladesh and Sri Lanka. Lacks blue on wings and tail. Adult has golden-orange forehead. Juvenile head green, with hint of turquoise moustachial stripe. Broadleaved forest and secondary growth.

11 ORANGE-BELLIED LEAFBIRD *Chloropsis hardwickii* **Page 586**
Male (11a), female (11b) and juvenile (11c). Resident. Himalayas, NE India and Bangladesh. Male has orange belly, and black of throat extends to breast. Female has orange belly centre and large blue moustachial stripe. Juvenile has green head; some with touch of orange on belly. Broadleaved forest.

1a
1b
1c
2a
2b
2c
3a
3b
4a
4b
5a
5b
6a
6b
7a
7b
8a
8b
9a
9b
9c
9d
9e
9f
10a
10b
10c
11a
11b
11c
C.D'S

PLATE 89: SHRIKES

1 **RED-BACKED SHRIKE** *Lanius collurio* **Page 586**
Male (1a), female (1b) and first-winter (1c). Autumn passage migrant. Pakistan and NW India. Male lacks broad black forehead, has rufous mantle, and lacks white wing patch. Female has grey cast to head and nape, and dark brown tail. First-winter similar to female, but has barred upperparts. Bushes and cultivation in dry country.

2 **RUFOUS-TAILED SHRIKE** *Lanius isabellinus* **Page 587**
Male (2a), female (2b) and first-winter (2c) *L. i. phoenicuroides*; male (2d), female (2e) and first-winter (2f) *L. i. isabellinus*. Breeds in Baluchistan; winters mainly in NW subcontinent. Typically, has paler sandy-brown/grey-brown mantle and warmer rufous rump and tail than Brown. Male has small white patch at base of primaries. Female has grey-brown ear-coverts. Open dry scrub.

3 **BROWN SHRIKE** *Lanius cristatus* **Page 587**
Male (3a) and first-winter (3b) *L. c. cristatus*; male *L. c. lucionensis* (3c). Widespread winter visitor; unrecorded in Pakistan. Compared with Rufous-tailed, typically has darker rufous-brown upperparts (lacking clear contrast between crown and mantle and between mantle and tail); also thicker bill and more graduated tail. *L. c. lucionensis* has grey cast to crown. Forest edges and scrub.

4 **BURMESE SHRIKE** *Lanius collurioides* **Page 588**
Male (4a), female (4b) and immature (4c). Passage migrant. Mainly NE India. Male has dark grey crown and nape, dark chestnut mantle, white tail sides, and chestnut rump. Female has whitish forehead, and paler chestnut mantle than male. Immature has brownish-grey crown with indistinct dark and buff barring, rufous mantle with some diffuse dark barring, and rufous rump and uppertail-coverts. Secondary growth, and bushes in cultivation.

5 **BAY-BACKED SHRIKE** *Lanius vittatus* **Page 588**
Adult (5a), immature (5b) and juvenile (5c). Widespread resident; unrecorded in the northeast and Sri Lanka. Adult has black forehead and mask contrasting with pale grey crown and nape, deep maroon mantle, whitish rump, and white patch at base of primaries. Juvenile told from juvenile Long-tailed by smaller size and shorter tail, more uniform greyish/buffish base colour to upperparts, pale rump, and more intricately patterned wing-coverts and tertials (see text). First-year like washed-out version of adult; lacks black forehead. Open dry scrub, and bushes in cultivation.

6 **LONG-TAILED SHRIKE** *Lanius schach* **Page 588**
Adult (6a) and juvenile (6b) *L. s. erythronotus*; adult *L. s. caniceps* (6c); adult *L. s. tricolor* (6d). Widespread resident. Adult has grey mantle, rufous scapulars and upper back (except *caniceps*), narrow black forehead, rufous sides to black tail, and small white patch on primaries. Juvenile has (dark-barred) rufous-brown scapulars, back and rump; dark greater coverts and tertials fringed rufous. Himalayan *tricolor* has black hood. Bushes in cultivation, open forest, gardens.

7 **GREY-BACKED SHRIKE** *Lanius tephronotus* **Page 589**
Adult (7a) and juvenile (7b). Breeds in Himalayas; winters in Himalayas and adjacent plains in N and NE India and Bangladesh. Adult has dark grey upperparts (no rufous on scapulars and upper back); usually lacks white primary patch. Juvenile has cold grey base colour to upperparts. Bushes in cultivation, scrub and secondary growth.

8 **LESSER GREY SHRIKE** *Lanius minor* **Page 589**
Adult (8a) and juvenile (8b). Vagrant. India. Adult has black forehead (lacking on first-winter). Smaller than other 'grey shrikes', with mainly black secondaries, and long extension of primaries beyond tertials. Open dry country with bushes.

9 **SOUTHERN GREY SHRIKE** *Lanius meridionalis* **Page 590**
Adult (9a) and juvenile (9b) *L. e. lahtora*. Resident. Mainly N, NW and W subcontinent. Adult has pale grey mantle, white scapulars, bold white markings on black wings and tail, greyish rump, and all-white underparts. Juvenile has sandy cast to grey upperparts, buff tips to tertials and coverts, and grey mask. Scrub and open forest in dry country.

10 **GREAT GREY SHRIKE** *Lanius excubitor* **Page 589**
Adult *L. e. homeyeri*. Vagrant. Pakistan and India. Lacks black forehead; has pale grey mantle, white band at base of secondaries, and white rump.

1b
1a
2c
2f
1c
2a
2e
3b
2b
2d
3c
4b
3a
4a
4c
6d
5a
5c
6b
6a
5b
6c
7b
7a
10
8b
8a
9b
9a
C.D'S

PLATE 90: JAYS, MAGPIES, TREEPIES AND MANGROVE WHISTLER

1 **MANGROVE WHISTLER** *Pachycephala grisola* **Page 590**
Adult. Resident. Sunderbans in India and Bangladesh, and Andamans. Drab grey-brown upperparts and breast, and thick black bill. Mangroves.

2 **EURASIAN JAY** *Garrulus glandarius* **Page 591**
Adult *G. g. bispecularis*. Resident. Himalayas, NE India and Bangladesh. Pinkish- to reddish-brown head and body, black moustachial stripe, and blue barring on wings. White rump contrasts with black tail in flight. Temperate forest, mainly broadleaved.

3 **BLACK-HEADED JAY** *Garrulus lanceolatus* **Page 591**
Adult. Resident. NW mountains of Pakistan and Himalayas. Black face and crest, streaked throat, and pinkish-fawn body; blue barring on wings and tail. Mixed temperate forest.

4 **SRI LANKA BLUE MAGPIE** *Urocissa ornata* **Page 591**
Adult. Resident. Sri Lanka. Chestnut head and wings, blue body, and white-tipped blue tail. Evergreen broadleaved forest.

5 **YELLOW-BILLED BLUE MAGPIE** *Urocissa flavirostris* **Page 592**
Adult (5a) and juvenile (5b) *U. f. cucullata*; adult *U. f. flavirostris* (5c). Resident. Himalayas and NE India. Yellow bill, and white crescent on nape. Nominate eastern race has yellow wash to underparts. Juvenile has olive-yellow bill. Temperate mixed forest.

6 **RED-BILLED BLUE MAGPIE** *Urocissa erythrorhyncha* **Page 592**
Adult (6a) and juvenile (6b) *U. e. occipitalis*. Resident. Himalayas, NE India and Bangladesh. Red bill, and white hindcrown and nape. Juvenile has more extensive white crown. Broadleaved forest and trees in cultivation.

7 **COMMON GREEN MAGPIE** *Cissa chinensis* **Page 592**
Adult. Resident. Himalayas, NE India and Bangladesh. Green, with red bill and legs, black mask, chestnut wings, and white tips to tertials and tail feathers. Broadleaved evergreen and moist deciduous forest.

8 **RUFOUS TREEPIE** *Dendrocitta vagabunda* **Page 593**
Adult (8a) and immature (8b) *D. v. vagabunda*; adult *D. v. pallida* (8c). Widespread resident; unrecorded in Sri Lanka. Slate-grey hood, buffish underparts and rump, pale grey wing panel, and whitish subterminal tail-band. Juvenile has brown hood. Open wooded country, and gardens with trees and bushes.

9 **GREY TREEPIE** *Dendrocitta formosae* **Page 593**
Adult (9a) and immature (9b). Resident. Himalayas, NE India, Eastern Ghats and Bangladesh. Dark grey face, grey underparts and rump, and black wings with white patch at base of primaries. Juvenile duller version of adult. Broadleaved forest and secondary growth.

10 **WHITE-BELLIED TREEPIE** *Dendrocitta leucogastra* **Page 594**
Adult. Resident. Western Ghats and SE India. Black face, white nape and underparts, white rump, and black wings with white patch. Evergreen hill forest and secondary growth.

11 **COLLARED TREEPIE** *Dendrocitta frontalis* **Page 594**
Adult. Resident. Himalayas and NE India. Black face and throat, grey nape and underparts, rufous lower belly and vent, rufous rump, and black tail. Broadleaved evergreen forest.

12 **ANDAMAN TREEPIE** *Dendrocitta bayleyi* **Page 594**
Adult (12a) and immature (12b). Resident. Andamans, where the only treepie. Blue-grey hood, rufous-brown upperparts, bright rufous underparts, blackish tail, and white patch on wing. Juvenile has brownish hood. Dense evergreen forest.

4
1
2
3
5a
8a
5b
5c
8b
8c
6a
10
9b
6b
9a
7
11
12a
12b
C.D'S

PLATE 91: BLACK-BILLED MAGPIE, HUME'S GROUNDPECKER, SPOTTED NUTCRACKER, CHOUGHS AND CROWS

1 **BLACK-BILLED MAGPIE** *Pica pica* **Page 595**
Adult *P. p. bactriana*. Resident. Mountains of N and W Pakistan, and Himalayas in N India and N Bhutan. Black and white, with long metallic green/purple tail. Open cultivated upland valleys.

2 **HUME'S GROUNDPECKER** *Pseudopodoces humilis* **Page 595**
Adult. Resident. Himalayas in extreme N India and Nepal. Downcurved black bill. Sandy-brown upperparts, buffish underparts, and white tail sides. Tibetan steppe country.

3 **SPOTTED NUTCRACKER** *Nucifraga caryocatactes* **Page 595**
Adult *N. c. multipunctata* (3a); adult *N. c. hemispila* (3b). Resident. Mountains of NW Pakistan and Himalayas. Mainly brown, with white spotting on head and body (*multipunctata* more heavily spotted and with white tips to wing feathers). Coniferous forest.

4 **RED-BILLED CHOUGH** *Pyrrhocorax pyrrhocorax* **Page 596**
Adult (4a) and juvenile (4b). Resident. Mountains of W Pakistan and Himalayas. Curved red bill (shorter and orange-brown on juvenile). High mountains, alpine pastures and cultivation.

5 **YELLOW-BILLED CHOUGH** *Pyrrhocorax graculus* **Page 596**
Adult. Resident. Mountains of W Pakistan and Himalayas. Almost straight yellow bill (olive-yellow on juvenile). High mountains, alpine pastures and cultivation.

6 **EURASIAN JACKDAW** *Corvus monedula* **Page 596**
Adult. Resident. Mountains of W and N Pakistan, and NW Himalayas. Small size. Grey nape and hindneck. Adult has pale grey iris. Open cultivated valleys.

7 **HOUSE CROW** *Corvus splendens* **Page 597**
Adult *C. s. splendens* (7a); adult *C. s. zugmayeri* (7b). Widespread resident. Two-toned appearance (contrast varying with race), with paler nape, neck and breast. Around human habitation and cultivation.

8 **ROOK** *Corvus frugilegus* **Page 597**
Adult (8a, 8b) and juvenile (8c). Winter visitor. Pakistan. Long, pointed bill, steep forehead, and baggy 'trousers'. Adult has bare white skin at base of bill and on throat. Cultivation and pastures.

9 **CARRION CROW** *Corvus corone* **Page 598**
Adult *C. c. orientalis* (9a, 9b); adult *C. c. sharpii* (9c). Resident (*C. c. orientalis*) and winter visitor (*C. c. sharpii*). Mountains of Pakistan and NW India. Comparatively straight bill and flat crown. Race *sharpii* two-toned like House Crow, but has black head and breast and grey mantle. Open country with cultivation.

10 **LARGE-BILLED CROW** *Corvus macrorhynchos* **Page 598**
Adult *C. m. intermedius* (10a, 10b); adult *C. m. culminatus* (10c, 10d). Widespread resident. All black, lacking paler collar of House Crow. Domed head, and large bill with arched culmen. Wide range of habitats, except deserts and semi-deserts.

11 **BROWN-NECKED RAVEN** *Corvus ruficollis* **Page 598**
Adult (11a, 11b). Resident. Pakistan. Brown cast to head, neck and breast; lacks prominent throat hackles. Slimmer than Common Raven, with different call. Desert.

12 **COMMON RAVEN** *Corvus corax* **Page 599**
Adult *C. c. subcorax* (12a, 12b). Resident. Pakistan and NW India (*C. c. subcorax*), and high Himalayas (*C. c. tibetanus*). Very large; long and angular wings, prominent throat hackles, wedge-shaped tail, and deep resonant call. Race *subcorax* in lowland desert and semi-desert; *tibetanus* in dry rocky areas above treeline.

1
2
3a
3b
4a
4b
5
6
7b
7a
8a
8b
8c
10b
10a
9a
10c
9c
9b
10d
11b
11a
12a
12b
C.D'S

PLATE 92: WOODSWALLOWS, ORIOLES AND CUCKOOSHRIKES

1 **ASHY WOODSWALLOW** *Artamus fuscus* **Page 599**
Adult (1a, 1b). Resident. Mainly E, SE and S subcontinent. Slate-grey head, pinkish-grey underparts, and narrow whitish horseshoe-shaped band across uppertail-coverts. Open wooded country.

2 **WHITE-BREASTED WOODSWALLOW** *Artamus leucorynchus* **Page 600**
Adult (2a, 2b). Resident. Andamans. Slate-grey head, white underparts, and broad white band across lower rump and uppertail-coverts. Forest clearings.

3 **EURASIAN GOLDEN ORIOLE** *Oriolus oriolus* **Page 600**
Male (3a), female (3b) and immature (3c) *O. o. kundoo*; male *O. o. oriolus* (3d). Summer visitor to W Pakistan, Himalayas and N plains; resident in N and C India; winters farther south. Male golden-yellow, with black mask and mainly black wings. Female and immature variable, usually with streaking on underparts and yellowish-green upperparts. Open woodland, and trees in cultivation.

4 **BLACK-NAPED ORIOLE** *Oriolus chinensis* **Page 601**
Male (4a), female (4b) and immature (4c). Winter visitor to Kerala and Bangladesh; resident on Andamans and Nicobars; status elsewhere uncertain. Large, stout bill; nasal call. Male has yellow mantle and wing-coverts concolorous with underparts. Female and immature probably not safely separable from Slender-billed by plumage. Broadleaved forest and well-wooded areas.

5 **SLENDER-BILLED ORIOLE** *Oriolus tenuirostris* **Page 601**
Male (5a), female (5b) and immature (5c). Breeds in E Himalayas and NE India; winters west to C Nepal and Bihar. Long, slender, slightly downcurved bill, and woodpecker-like *kick* call are most reliable features from Black-naped. Adult has black stripe through eye and band across nape (diffuse or indistinct on immature). Well-wooded areas.

6 **BLACK-HOODED ORIOLE** *Oriolus xanthornus* **Page 601**
Male (6a), female (6b) and immature (6c). Widespread resident; unrecorded in Pakistan. Adult has black head and breast. Immature has yellow forehead, black-streaked white throat, and yellow breast. Open broadleaved forest and well-wooded areas.

7 **MAROON ORIOLE** *Oriolus traillii* **Page 602**
Male (7a), female (7b) and immature (7c). Resident. Himalayas, NE India and Bangladesh. Maroon rump and tail. Male has maroon underparts. Female has whitish belly and flanks, streaked with maroon-grey. Immature has brown-streaked white underparts. Dense broadleaved forest.

8 **LARGE CUCKOOSHRIKE** *Coracina macei* **Page 602**
Male *C. m. nipalensis* (8a); female (8b) and juvenile (8c) *C. m. macei*. Widespread resident; unrecorded in northwest. Large. Pale grey upperparts and greyish-white underparts with variable amounts of faint grey barring. See text for sexual and racial variation. Open woodland, and trees in cultivation.

9 **BAR-BELLIED CUCKOOSHRIKE** *Coracina striata* **Page 603**
Male (9a), female (9b) and immature (9c). Resident. Andamans. Smaller than Large Cuckooshrike, with darker grey upperparts and crimson iris. Female entirely barred below. First-year has rufous cast to throat and breast. Forest.

10 **BLACK-WINGED CUCKOOSHRIKE** *Coracina melaschistos* **Page 603**
Male (10a) and female (10b). Resident. Breeds in Himalayas and NE Indian hills; winters mainly in Himalayan foothills, E and NE India and Bangladesh. Male slate-grey, with black wings and bold white tips to tail feathers. Female paler grey, with faint barring on underparts. Open forest and groves.

11 **BLACK-HEADED CUCKOOSHRIKE** *Coracina melanoptera* **Page 604**
Male (11a) and female (11b). Widespread resident; unrecorded in Pakistan. Male has slate-grey head and breast, and pale grey mantle. Female has whitish supercilium, barred underparts, and pale grey back and rump contrasting with blackish tail; broad white fringes to coverts and tertials. Open broadleaved forest and secondary growth.

12 **PIED TRILLER** *Lalage nigra* **Page 604**
Male (12a) and female (12b). Resident. Nicobars. Male has white supercilium and black upperparts. Female has slate-grey upperparts and faintly barred underparts. Forest edges and secondary growth.

1a
1b
3a
3b
3c
3d
2b
2a
4a
4b
4c
8c
8b
8a
5a
5b
5c
9c
9b
9a
6a
6b
6c
7c
7a
7b
10b
10a
11b
11a
12a
12b
C.D'S

PLATE 93: MINIVETS, BAR-WINGED FLYCATCHER-SHRIKE AND FANTAILS

1 **ROSY MINIVET** *Pericrocotus roseus* **Page 604**
Male (1a) and female (1b). Resident. Breeds in Himalayas and NE India; winters mainly in NE and E India and Bangladesh. Male has grey-brown upperparts, white throat, and pinkish underparts and rump. Female has greyish forehead, white throat, pale yellow underparts, and dull olive-yellow rump. Forest.

2 **ASHY MINIVET** *Pericrocotus divaricatus* **Page 605**
Male (2a) and female (2b). Winter visitor. Mainly C and S India. Grey and white, lacking any yellow or red in plumage. Male has black 'hood'. Light forest.

3 **SMALL MINIVET** *Pericrocotus cinnamomeus* **Page 605**
Male (3a) and female (3b) *P. c. malabaricus*; male (3c) and female (3d) *P. c. pallidus*. Widespread resident. Much racial variation. Male has dark grey to pale grey upperparts, black to dark grey throat, and deep orange to mainly white underparts. Female's underparts vary from mainly orange-yellow to mainly white. Open wooded areas.

4 **WHITE-BELLIED MINIVET** *Pericrocotus erythropygius* **Page 606**
Male (4a) and female (4b). Resident. Mainly N and C India. Both sexes have white wing patch and orange rump. Male has black head and upperparts, and white underparts with orange breast. Female has brown upperparts and white underparts. Dry open scrub and forest.

5 **GREY-CHINNED MINIVET** *Pericrocotus solaris* **Page 606**
Male (5a) and female (5b). Resident. Himalayas and NE India. Male has grey chin and pale orange throat, grey ear-coverts, slate-grey upperparts, and orange-red underparts and rump. Female has grey forehead, supercilium and ear-coverts, whitish chin and whitish sides to yellow throat. Moist broadleaved forest.

6 **LONG-TAILED MINIVET** *Pericrocotus ethologus* **Page 606**
Male (6a) and female (6b) *P. e. favillaceus*. Resident. Breeds in N Baluchistan, Himalayas, NE India and Bangladesh; winters south to C India. Male has extension of red wing patch down secondaries. Female has narrow, indistinct yellow forehead and supercilium, grey ear-coverts, and paler yellow throat than breast. Distinctive *pi-ru* whistle. Forest; also well-wooded areas in winter.

7 **SHORT-BILLED MINIVET** *Pericrocotus brevirostris* **Page 607**
Male (7a) and female (7b). Resident. Himalayas and NE India. Male lacks extension of red wing patch down secondaries. Female has yellow forehead and cast to ear-coverts, and deep yellow throat concolorous with rest of underparts. Distinctive monotone whistle. Broadleaved forest and forest edges.

8 **SCARLET MINIVET** *Pericrocotus flammeus* **Page 607**
Male (8a) and female (8b). Resident. Himalayas, hills of India, Bangladesh and Sri Lanka. Large. Isolated red (male) or yellow (female) patch on secondaries. Forest.

9 **BAR-WINGED FLYCATCHER-SHRIKE** *Hemipus picatus* **Page 607**
Male (9a) and female (9b) *H. p. picatus*; male *H. p. capitalis* (9c). Resident. Himalayas, hills of India, Bangladesh and Sri Lanka. Dark cap contrasting with white throat; white wing patch and white rump. Broadleaved forest and forest edges.

10 **YELLOW-BELLIED FANTAIL** *Rhipidura hypoxantha* **Page 608**
Male. Resident. Himalayas, NE India and Bangladesh. Long fanned tail, yellow supercilium, dark mask, and yellow underparts. Forest.

11 **WHITE-THROATED FANTAIL** *Rhipidura albicollis* **Page 608**
Adult *R. a. canescens* (11a); adult *R. a. albogularis* (11b). Resident. Himalayas, NE India, Bangladesh and Indian peninsula. Narrow white supercilium and white throat; lacks spotting on wing-coverts. Forest, secondary growth and wooded areas.

12 **WHITE-BROWED FANTAIL** *Rhipidura aureola* **Page 609**
Adult (12a) and juvenile (12b) *R. a. aureola*. Widespread resident. Broad white supercilium, blackish throat, white breast and belly, and white spotting on wing-coverts. Forest and wooded areas.

2b
1a
1b
5a
2a
3b
4b
5b
4a
3c
3a
6a
6b
7b
7a
3d
8a
9b
9c
9a
8b
12b
11a
11b
10
12a
C.D'S

PLATE 94: DRONGOS

1 **BLACK DRONGO** *Dicrurus macrocercus* **Page 610**
Juvenile (1a), immature (1b) and adult (1c). Widespread resident. Adult has glossy blue-black underparts and white rictal spot. Tail-fork may be lost during moult. First-winter has black underparts with bold whitish fringes. Juvenile has uniform dark brown upperparts and underparts. Around habitation and cultivation.

2 **ASHY DRONGO** *Dicrurus leucophaeus* **Page 610**
Immature (2a) and adult (2b) *D. l. longicaudatus*; adult *D. l. hopwoodi* (2c); adult *D. l. salangensis* (2d). Breeds in Himalayas and NE Indian hills; winters in plains in peninsula and Sri Lanka. Adult has dark grey underparts and slate-grey upperparts with blue-grey gloss; iris bright red. First-winter has brownish-grey underparts with indistinct pale fringes. Juvenile as juvenile Black. E Himalayan *hopwoodi* paler grey. Vagrant *salangensis* has white lores and ear-coverts. Breeds in forest; winters in well-wooded areas.

3 **WHITE-BELLIED DRONGO** *Dicrurus caerulescens* **Page 611**
Immature (3a) and adult (3b) *D. c. caerulescens*; adult *D. c. leucopygialis* (3c). Widespread resident; unrecorded in Pakistan, the northeast or Sri Lanka. Whitish from belly downwards in all plumages, except in Sri Lanka, where one race (*leucopygialis*) has white restricted to vent and undertail-coverts. Open forest and well-wooded areas.

4 **CROW-BILLED DRONGO** *Dicrurus annectans* **Page 611**
Immature (4a) and adult (4b). Summer visitor/resident? in Himalayan foothills and NE India; winters in NE India and Bangladesh. Adult has stout bill, and widely splayed tail with shallow fork. First-winter has white spotting on breast and belly. Moist broadleaved forest.

5 **BRONZED DRONGO** *Dicrurus aeneus* **Page 611**
Juvenile (5a) and adult (5b). Resident. Himalayan foothills, NE India, Bangladesh and Eastern and Western Ghats. Adult small, with shallow tail-fork, and heavily spangled. Juvenile has brown underparts, and duller and less heavily spangled upperparts. Moist broadleaved forest.

6 **LESSER RACKET-TAILED DRONGO** *Dicrurus remifer* **Page 612**
Immature (6a) and adult (6b). Resident. Himalayan foothills, NE India and Bangladesh. Tufted forehead without crest, square-ended tail, and smaller size and bill than Greater Racket-tailed. Moist broadleaved forest.

7 **SPANGLED DRONGO** *Dicrurus hottentottus* **Page 612**
Juvenile (7a) and adult (7b). Resident. Himalayan foothills, NE India, Bangladesh and Eastern and Western Ghats. Broad tail with upward-twisted corners, and long downcurved bill. Adult has extensive spangling, and hair-like crest. Moist broadleaved forest.

8 **ANDAMAN DRONGO** *Dicrurus andamanensis* **Page 612**
Adult. Resident. Andamans. Large bill, and long broad tail with shallow fork twisted inwards at tip. Forest.

9 **GREATER RACKET-TAILED DRONGO** *Dicrurus paradiseus* **Page 614**
Immature (9a) and adult (9b) *D. p. ceylonicus*; adult *D. p. grandis* (9c). Widespread resident; unrecorded in Pakistan. Larger and with larger bill than Lesser Racket-tailed. Typically, has crest and forked tail; crest much reduced in some races and on immatures. *D. p. lophorhinus* of wet zone in Sri Lanka has long, deeply forked tail and lacks terminal rackets of other races (see fig. p.613). Broadleaved forest and bamboo jungle.

1c
2b
3b
3a
1b
2a
3c
2d
1a
2c
5a
4b
4a
5b
6a
6b
9c
9a
8
7b
9b
7a
C.D'S

PLATE 95: BLACK-NAPED MONARCH, ASIAN PARADISE-FLYCATCHER, IORAS, WOODSHRIKES, BOHEMIAN WAXWING AND DIPPERS

1 **BLACK-NAPED MONARCH** *Hypothymis azurea* **Page 614**
Male (1a) and female (1b) *H. a. styani*; male (1c) and female (1d) *H. a. ceylonensis*. Widespread resident; unrecorded in Pakistan. Male mainly blue, with black nape and gorget (except in Sri Lanka, where black often absent or indistinct). Female duller, with grey-brown mantle and wings. Broadleaved forest and well-wooded areas.

2 **ASIAN PARADISE-FLYCATCHER** *Terpsiphone paradisi* **Page 615**
White male (2a), rufous male (2b) and female (2c). Widespread resident. Male has black head and crest, with white or rufous upperparts and long tail-streamers. Female has reduced crest and lacks streamers. Forest and well-wooded areas.

3 **COMMON IORA** *Aegithina tiphia* **Page 615**
Male breeding (3a), male non-breeding (3b) and female (3c) *A. t. humei*; male breeding *A. t. multicolor* (3d); male breeding *A. t. tiphia* (3e). Widespread resident; unrecorded in the northwest. Lacks white on tail. Crown and mantle of breeding males vary from uniformly black, to black mixed with much yellow on mantle, to uniformly yellowish-green. Females very similar to non-breeding males. Open forest and well-wooded areas.

4 **MARSHALL'S IORA** *Aegithina nigrolutea* **Page 616**
Male breeding (4a) and female (4b). Resident. N and C peninsular India. Extensive white on black tail. Male has broad yellow hindcollar. Scrub and groves.

5 **LARGE WOODSHRIKE** *Tephrodornis gularis* **Page 616**
Male (5a) and female (5b) *T. g. pelvica*. Resident. Himalayan foothills, NE, E and SW India, and Bangladesh. Larger than Common Woodshrike; lacks white supercilium and white on tail. Broadleaved forest and well-wooded areas.

6 **COMMON WOODSHRIKE** *Tephrodornis pondicerianus* **Page 616**
Male (6a) and juvenile (6b). Widespread resident. Smaller than Large Woodshrike, with broad white supercilium and white tail sides. Open broadleaved forest, secondary growth and well-wooded areas.

7 **BOHEMIAN WAXWING** *Bombycilla garrulus* **Page 617**
Adult male. Vagrant. Pakistan, Nepal, India. Prominent crest, black throat, and waxy red and yellow markings on wings. Open country with fruiting trees and bushes.

8 **WHITE-THROATED DIPPER** *Cinclus cinclus* **Page 617**
Adult (8a) and juvenile (8b) *C. c. cashmeriensis*; adult *C. c. leucogaster* (8c). Resident. Himalayas. Adult has white throat and breast. Juvenile has dark scaling on grey upperparts and grey scaling on whitish underparts. Mountain streams.

9 **BROWN DIPPER** *Cinclus pallasii* **Page 618**
Adult (9a) and juvenile (9b) *C. p. tenuirostris*. Resident. Himalayas, NE India and Bangladesh. Adult entirely brown. Juvenile has white or rufous-buff spotting on brown upperparts and underparts. Mountain streams and small lakes.

2c
2a
2b
3a
3d
3e
1a
1b
3b
3c
1c
1d
4a
4b
5a
6a
6b
7
5b
8a
8c
9a
9b
8b
C.D'S

PLATE 96: ROCK THRUSHES AND WHISTLING THRUSHES

1 **RUFOUS-TAILED ROCK THRUSH** *Monticola saxatilis* **Page 618**
Male breeding (1a), female (1b) and 1st-winter male (1c). Breeds in Baluchistan; passage migrant in Pakistan and Ladakh. Orange-red uppertail-coverts and tail in all plumages. Male has bluish head/mantle, white back and orange underparts, which are obscured by pale fringes in non-breeding and first-winter plumages. Female has scaling on upperparts, and orange wash to scaled underparts. Open rocky hillsides.

2 **BLUE-CAPPED ROCK THRUSH** *Monticola cinclorhynchus* **Page 619**
Male breeding (2a), female (2b) and 1st-winter male (2c). Summer visitor to Himalayas and NE India; winters mainly in Western Ghats and Assam hills. Male has white wing patch and blue-black tail; blue crown and throat and orange underparts, obscured by pale fringes in non-breeding and first-winter plumages. Female has uniform olive-brown upperparts; lacks buff neck patch of Chestnut-bellied and orange-red tail of Rufous-tailed. Summers in open dry forest; winters in moist forest and well-wooded areas.

3 **CHESTNUT-BELLIED ROCK THRUSH** *Monticola rufiventris* **Page 619**
Male (3a), female (3b), juvenile male (3c) and juvenile female (3d). Resident. Himalayas and NE India. Male has chestnut-red underparts and blue rump and uppertail-coverts; lacks white on wing. Female has orange-buff neck patch, dark barring on slaty olive-brown upperparts, and heavy scaling on underparts. Juvenile has pale spotting on upperparts; male with blue on wing. Open forest on rocky slopes.

4 **BLUE ROCK THRUSH** *Monticola solitarius* **Page 620**
Male breeding (4a), female (4b) and 1st-winter male (4c) *M. s. pandoo*; male *M. s. philippensis* (4d). Resident and winter visitor. Breeds in Baluchistan and Himalayas; widespread in winter. Male indigo-blue, obscured by pale fringes in non-breeding and first-winter plumages. Female has bluish cast to slaty-brown upperparts, and buff scaling on underparts. Vagrant *philippensis* has rufous breast and belly. Breeds on open rocky slopes; winters in dry rocky areas.

5 **SRI LANKA WHISTLING THRUSH** *Myophonus blighi* **Page 620**
Male (5a) and female (5b). Resident. Sri Lanka. Male brownish-black, with glistening blue on forehead, supercilium and shoulders. Female brown, with blue shoulders. Mountain streams in moist, dense forest.

6 **MALABAR WHISTLING THRUSH** *Myophonus horsfieldii* **Page 620**
Adult (6a) and juvenile (6b). Resident. Hills of C and W India. Adult blackish, with blue forehead and shoulders. Juvenile more sooty-brown, and lacks blue forehead. Rocky hill streams in forest and well-wooded areas.

7 **BLUE WHISTLING THRUSH** *Myophonus caeruleus* **Page 621**
Adult (7a) and juvenile (7b). Resident. N Baluchistan, Himalayas and NE India. Adult blackish, spangled with glistening blue; yellow bill. Juvenile browner, and lacks blue spangling. Forest and wooded areas, usually close to streams.

1a
1c
2a
1b
2c
2b
3a
3b
3c
3d
4d
4a
4b
6a
4c
5b
5a
6b
7a
7b

PLATE 97: *ZOOTHERA* THRUSHES

1 **PIED THRUSH** *Zoothera wardii* **Page 621**
Male (1a), female (1b) and juvenile (1c). Resident. Breeds in Himalayas and NE India; winters in Sri Lanka and Tamil Nadu. Male black and white, with white supercilium and wing-bars. Female has buff supercilium and wing-bars, and scaled underparts. Juvenile has buff streaking on mantle and breast. Open broadleaved forest and secondary growth.

2 **ORANGE-HEADED THRUSH** *Zoothera citrina* **Page 621**
Male (2a), female (2b) and juvenile (2c) *Z. c. citrina*; male *Z. c. cyanotus* (2d). Widespread resident. Adult has orange head and underparts; male with blue-grey mantle, female with olive-brown wash to mantle. Juvenile has buffish-orange streaking on upperparts and mottled breast. *Z. c. cyanotus* has vertical black head stripes. Damp, shady places in forest and well-wooded areas.

3 **SIBERIAN THRUSH** *Zoothera sibirica* **Page 622**
Adult male (3a), female (3b) and 1st-winter male (3c). Winter visitor. Manipur hills and Andamans. Male slate-grey, with white supercilium; buff supercilium, throat and greater-covert bar in first-winter plumage. Female has buff supercilium and scaling on underparts, but lacks wing-bars of Pied. Forest.

4 **SPOT-WINGED THRUSH** *Zoothera spiloptera* **Page 622**
Adult (4a) and juvenile (4b). Resident. Sri Lanka. Adult has white wing-bars, black face markings, and black spotting on underparts. Juvenile has diffuse head pattern, buff streaking on mantle, and scaled breast. Moist forest and well-wooded areas.

5 **PLAIN-BACKED THRUSH** *Zoothera mollissima* **Page 623**
Adult (5a) and juvenile (5b). Resident. Himalayas and NE India. Adult lacks (or has indistinct) wing-bars, and has heavy black scaling on belly and flanks. Juvenile has buff streaking on upperparts and heavy black scaling and barring on underparts. Summers on rocky and grassy slopes with bushes; winters in forest and open country with bushes.

6 **LONG-TAILED THRUSH** *Zoothera dixoni* **Page 623**
Adult (6a) and juvenile (6b). Resident. Himalayas and NE India. Adult has prominent wing-bars; belly and flanks more sparsely marked than on Plain-backed, flanks more barred than scaled, and is longer-tailed. Juvenile has buff streaking on upperparts; underparts similar to adult's. Undergrowth in forest; in winter, also open country with bushes.

7 **SCALY THRUSH** *Zoothera dauma* **Page 623**
Adult (7a) and juvenile (7b) *Z. d. dauma*; adult *Z. d. imbricata* (7c). Breeds in Himalayas, hills of NE and W India and Sri Lanka; N birds winter south to Orissa. Boldly scaled upperparts and underparts. Juvenile has spotted breast. Sri Lankan *imbricata* smaller, with longer bill, and rufous-buff underparts. Forest; also well-wooded areas in winter.

8 **LONG-BILLED THRUSH** *Zoothera monticola* **Page 624**
Adult (8a) and juvenile (8b). Resident. Himalayas and NE India. Huge bill and short tail. Differs from Dark-sided in dark slate-olive upperparts and darker, more uniform sides of head and underparts. Juvenile has buff streaking on upperparts. Moist, dense forest.

9 **DARK-SIDED THRUSH** *Zoothera marginata* **Page 624**
Adult (9a) and juvenile (9b). Resident. Himalayas and NE India. Long bill and short tail. Differs from Long-billed in rufescent-brown upperparts, more strongly marked sides of head and underparts, and rufous panel on wing. Juvenile has buff streaking on upperparts. Moist, dense forest near streams.

1a
1b
1c
2a
2b
2c
2d
3a
3b
3c
4a
4b
5a
5b
6a
6b
7a
7b
7c
8a
8b
9a
9b

PLATE 98: *TURDUS* THRUSHES

1 **TICKELL'S THRUSH** *Turdus unicolor* **Page 625**
Male (1a), female (1b) and 1st-winter male (1c). Resident. Summers in Himalayas; winters mainly farther east and south in India. Small thrush. Male pale bluish-grey, with whitish belly and vent. Female and first-winter male have pale throat and submoustachial stripe and dark malar stripe. Open forest and well-wooded areas.

2 **BLACK-BREASTED THRUSH** *Turdus dissimilis* **Page 625**
Male (2a) and female (2b). Resident in NE India; winters south to Bangladesh. Male has black head and upper breast, and orange lower breast and flanks. Female has plain face, spotted breast, and orange lower breast and flanks. Broadleaved evergreen forest; also scrub and mangroves in winter.

3 **WHITE-COLLARED BLACKBIRD** *Turdus albocinctus* **Page 625**
Male (3a), female (3b) and juvenile (3c). Resident. Himalayas and NE India. Male black, with white collar. Female brown, with variable pale collar. Juvenile has bold spotting on orange-buff underparts. Forest and forest edges.

4 **GREY-WINGED BLACKBIRD** *Turdus boulboul* **Page 626**
Male (4a), female (4b) and juvenile male (4c). Resident. Himalayas and NE India. Male black, with greyish wing panel. Female olive-brown, with pale rufous-brown wing panel. Juvenile has orange-buff streaking on upperparts, and very variable orange-buff markings on underparts; wing panel similar to adult's. Forest and forest edges.

5 **EURASIAN BLACKBIRD** *Turdus merula* **Page 626**
Male *T. m. kinnisii* (5a); male (5b) and female (5c) *T. m. nigropileus*; male (5d) and female (5e) *T. m. maximus*. Resident. Himalayas, hills of peninsular India and Sri Lanka. Very variable. Males can be black, grey, or brownish-grey with darker cap. Females can be dark brown, brown with whitish belly, or grey. In Himalayas, summers on grassy and rocky slopes with scrub, winters in junipers; farther south, in moist forest and well-wooded areas.

6 **CHESTNUT THRUSH** *Turdus rubrocanus* **Page 627**
Male (6a) and female (6b) *T. r. rubrocanus*; male *T. r. gouldii* (6c). Resident. Himalayas and NE India. Chestnut upperparts and underparts. Male *rubrocanus* has pale collar; female has more uniform brownish-grey head/neck. *T. r. gouldii* has darker head/neck and lacks collar. Summers in coniferous and mixed forest; winters in open wooded areas.

7 **KESSLER'S THRUSH** *Turdus kessleri* **Page 627**
Male (7a) and female (7b). Winter visitor. E Himalayas. Male has black head, creamy-white mantle and breast-band, and chestnut back and belly. Female has brownish head, pale mantle and breast-band, and ginger-brown belly. Shrubberies, juniper stands and fields.

8 **GREY-SIDED THRUSH** *Turdus feae* **Page 628**
Male (8a) and female (8b). Winter visitor. NE India. White supercilium; rufescent-olive upperparts, crown and ear-coverts. Male has grey flanks. Habitat unrecorded in region.

9 **EYEBROWED THRUSH** *Turdus obscurus* **Page 628**
Male (9a) and 1st-winter female (9b). Winter visitor. E Himalayas. White supercilium, greyish crown and ear-coverts, and orange flanks. Open forest.

1c
1a
1b
6c
6a
6b
2a
2b
3c
3a
3b
4a
4b
4c
5a
5c
5b
5d
5e
9a
9b
7a
7b
8a
8b
AH.

PLATE 99: *TURDUS* THRUSHES AND SHORTWINGS

1 **DARK-THROATED THRUSH** *Turdus ruficollis* **Page 628**
Male (1a), female (1b) and 1st-winter female (1c) *T. r. ruficollis*; male (1d), female (1e) and 1st-winter female (1f) *T. r. atrogularis.* Winter visitor. N subcontinent. Uniform grey upperparts and wings. *T. r. ruficollis* has red throat and/or breast, and red on tail; first-winter with rufous wash to supercilium and breast. *T. r. atrogularis* has black throat and/or breast; first-winter with grey streaking on breast and flanks. Forest, forest edges, cultivation and pastures with scattered trees.

2 **DUSKY THRUSH** *Turdus naumanni* **Page 629**
Male (2a) and 1st-winter (2b) *T. n. eunomus.* Winter visitor. Himalayas and NE India. Prominent supercilium, spotting across breast and down flanks, and chestnut on wing. Cultivation and pastures with scattered trees.

3 **FIELDFARE** *Turdus pilaris* **Page 629**
Adult. Vagrant. India. Blue-grey head and rump/uppertail-coverts, chestnut-brown mantle, and orange-buff wash to spotted breast. Fields and orchards.

4 **SONG THRUSH** *Turdus philomelos* **Page 629**
Adult. Vagrant. Pakistan and India. Small size, olive-brown upperparts, and spotted breast. Head rather plain, lacking supercilium. Thorn scrub.

5 **MISTLE THRUSH** *Turdus viscivorus* **Page 630**
Adult (5a) and juvenile (5b). Resident. Baluchistan and W Himalayas. Large size, pale grey-brown upperparts, whitish edges to wing feathers, and spotted breast. Summers in open coniferous forest and shrubberies; winters on grassy slopes and at forest edges.

6 **GOULD'S SHORTWING** *Brachypteryx stellata* **Page 630**
Adult (6a) and juvenile (6b). Resident. Himalayas. Adult with chestnut upperparts, slate-grey underparts and white star-shaped spotting on belly and flanks. Juvenile streaked rufous on upperparts and breast. Breeds in shrubberies near treeline and among boulders in alpine zone; winters in forest.

7 **RUSTY-BELLIED SHORTWING** *Brachypteryx hyperythra* **Page 631**
Male (7a) and female (7b). Resident. Himalayas. Male has fine white supercilium, blue upperparts, and rufous-orange underparts. Female has olive-brown upperparts and pale rufous-orange underparts. Winters in forest undergrowth and thickets.

8 **WHITE-BELLIED SHORTWING** *Brachypteryx major* **Page 631**
Adult *B. m. major* (8a); adult *B. m. albiventris* (8b). Resident. Hills of SW India. Slaty-blue upperparts and breast, and white belly. Flanks rufous in nominate *major.* Dense undergrowth in ravines and evergreen forest.

9 **LESSER SHORTWING** *Brachypteryx leucophrys* **Page 631**
'Blue' male (9a) and female (9b). Resident. Himalayas, NE India and Bangladesh. Smaller and shorter-tailed than White-browed, with pinkish legs. Undergrowth in moist broadleaved forest and secondary growth.

10 **WHITE-BROWED SHORTWING** *Brachypteryx montana* **Page 632**
Male (10a), female (10b), immature male (10c) and juvenile (10d). Resident. Himalayas and NE India. Male dark slaty-blue, with fine white supercilium. Undergrowth in moist forest and thickets in ravines.

1a
1b
1c
1f
1d
1e
2a
2b
3
4
5b
5a
6a
6b
7a
7b
10a
10b
10c
10d
8a
8b
9a
9b

PLATE 100: FLYCATCHERS

1 **BROWN-CHESTED JUNGLE FLYCATCHER** *Rhinomyias brunneata* **Page 632**
Adult. Winter visitor/resident on Nicobars; vagrant to Andamans. Dark brown, with rufescent-brown tail, scaling on throat, brown breast, and long bill. Mainly forest.

2 **SPOTTED FLYCATCHER** *Muscicapa striata* **Page 632**
Adult. Summer visitor to Baluchistan and Himalayas in Pakistan; passage migrant in Pakistan and NW India. Large size, large and mainly dark bill, streaking on forehead and crown, indistinct eye-ring, and streaked throat and breast. Breeds in open conifer forest.

3 **DARK-SIDED FLYCATCHER** *Muscicapa sibirica* **Page 633**
Adult (3a) and juvenile (3b). Breeds in Himalayas and NE India; winter quarters poorly known. Small dark bill, and long primary projection. Breast and flanks heavily marked, with narrow white line down centre of belly. Juvenile has spotted upperparts and finely marked breast. Temperate and subalpine forest.

4 **ASIAN BROWN FLYCATCHER** *Muscicapa dauurica* **Page 633**
Fresh-plumaged adult (4a), worn adult (4b) and juvenile (4c). Breeds in Himalayan foothills and hills of C and W India; winters in S, C and E India and Sri Lanka. Large bill with prominent pale base to lower mandible; shorter primary projection than Dark-sided. Pale underparts, with light brownish wash to breast and flanks. Open forest and wooded areas.

5 **RUSTY-TAILED FLYCATCHER** *Muscicapa ruficauda* **Page 634**
Adult (5a) and juvenile (5b). Breeds in Himalayas; winters mainly in SW India. Rufous uppertail-coverts and tail, rather plain face, and pale orange lower mandible. Forest.

6 **BROWN-BREASTED FLYCATCHER** *Muscicapa muttui* **Page 634**
Adult. Breeds in NE India; winters in SW India and Sri Lanka. Large bill with entirely pale lower mandible, pale legs and feet, and rufous-buff edges to greater coverts and tertials. Dense thickets in evergreen forest.

7 **FERRUGINOUS FLYCATCHER** *Muscicapa ferruginea* **Page 635**
Adult (7a) and juvenile (7b). Probably summer visitor. Breeds in Himalayas and NE India. Rufous-orange uppertail-coverts and tail, rufous-orange flanks and undertail-coverts, and grey cast to head. Moist forest.

8 **YELLOW-RUMPED FLYCATCHER** *Ficedula zanthopygia* **Page 635**
Male (8a), female (8b) and 1st-winter male (8c). Vagrant. India. Yellow rump, and white on wing. Male has black upperparts and yellow underparts. Female and first-winter have greyish-olive upperparts. Undergrowth along rivers and streams.

9 **SLATY-BACKED FLYCATCHER** *Ficedula hodgsonii* **Page 635**
Male (9a) and female (9b). Resident. Himalayas and NE India. Male has orange underparts, deep blue upperparts, and black tail with white at base. Female has greyish-olive underparts, lacking well-defined white throat, and lacks rufous on tail. Forest.

10 **RUFOUS-GORGETED FLYCATCHER** *Ficedula strophiata* **Page 636**
Male (10a), female (10b) and juvenile (10c). Resident. Himalayas and NE India. Rufous gorget, and white sides to black tail. Female duller than male. Juvenile with orange-buff spotting on upperparts. Forest.

1
2
3a
3b
4a
4b
4c
5a
5b
6
7a
7b
8a
8b
8c
9a
9b
10a
10b
10c
AH.

PLATE 101: FLYCATCHERS

1 **RED-THROATED FLYCATCHER** *Ficedula parva* **Page 636**
Male (1a) and female (1b) *F. p. parva*; male *F. p. albicilla* (1c). Widespread winter visitor and passage migrant; has bred in W Himalayas. White sides to tail. Male has red throat. Female and many males have creamy-white to greyish-white underparts. *F. p. albicilla* has grey breast-band. Open forest, bushes and wooded areas.

2 **KASHMIR FLYCATCHER** *Ficedula subrubra* **Page 636**
Male (2a), female (2b) and juvenile (2c). Resident. Breeds in NW Himalayas; winters in Sri Lanka and Western Ghats. Male has more extensive red on underparts than Red-throated, with diffuse black border to throat and breast. Female and first-winter male differ from Red-throated in having rufous on throat and (often more pronounced) on breast, and often continuing as wash onto belly and/or flanks, and also slightly darker grey-brown upperparts. Breeds in deciduous forest; winters in wooded areas.

3 **WHITE-GORGETED FLYCATCHER** *Ficedula monileger* **Page 637**
Adult (3a) and juvenile (3b) *F. m. monileger*; adult *F. m. leucops* (3c). Resident. Himalayas and NE India. White throat and black gorget. Supercilium whitish or orange-buff. Moist broadleaved forest.

4 **SNOWY-BROWED FLYCATCHER** *Ficedula hyperythra* **Page 637**
Male (4a), female (4b) and juvenile (4c). Resident. Himalayas and NE India. Small size and short tail. Both sexes with rufous-brown wings. Male has short white supercilium, slaty-blue upperparts, and orange throat/breast. Female has orange-buff supercilium and eye-ring. Moist broadleaved forest.

5 **LITTLE PIED FLYCATCHER** *Ficedula westermanni* **Page 637**
Male (5a), female (5b), juvenile male (5c) and juvenile female (5d) *F. w. collini*; female *F. w. australorientis* (5e). Resident. Himalayas, NE India and Bangladesh. Male black and white, with broad white supercilium. Female has grey-brown upperparts, brownish-grey wash to breast, and rufous cast to rump/uppertail-coverts. Breeds in forest; winters in open wooded country.

6 **ULTRAMARINE FLYCATCHER** *Ficedula superciliaris* **Page 638**
Male (6a), female (6b), 1st-summer male (6c) and juvenile (6d) *F. s. superciliaris*; male *F. s. aestigma* (6e). Resident. Breeds in Himalayas and NE India; winters south to S India. Male has deep blue upperparts and sides of neck/breast, and white underparts; white supercilium in W Himalayas. Female has greyish-brown breast-side patches and lacks rufous on rump/uppertail-coverts. First-year males, and some females, show blue on upperparts. Breeds in forest; winters in open woodland and wooded areas.

7 **SLATY-BLUE FLYCATCHER** *Ficedula tricolor* **Page 638**
Male (7a), female (7b) and juvenile (7c) *F. t. tricolor*; male (7d) and female (7e) *F. t. cerviniventris*. Resident. Mainly Himalayas and NE India. Male has white throat and white on tail; belly and flanks greyish-white or orange-buff. Female has rufous tail; throat white or orange-buff. Breeds in subalpine shrubberies and forest undergrowth; winters in forest undergrowth, ravines and tall grass.

1a
1b
1c
2a
2b
2c
3a
3b
3c
4a
4b
4c
5a
5b
5c
5d
5e
6a
6b
6c
6d
6e
7a
7b
7c
7d
7e
AH.

PLATE 102: FLYCATCHERS, INCLUDING NILTAVAS

1 **SAPPHIRE FLYCATCHER** *Ficedula sapphira* **Page 639**
Male (1a), female (1b), immature male (1c) and juvenile male (1d). Resident. Himalayas and NE India. Small size, slim appearance and tiny bill. Orange throat and breast contrast with white belly. Male has blue breast sides and bright blue or brown-and-blue upperparts. Female has rufous uppertail-coverts and tail. Juvenile has buff breast and white belly and flanks. Evergreen broadleaved forest.

2 **BLACK-AND-ORANGE FLYCATCHER** *Ficedula nigrorufa* **Page 639**
Male (2a) and female (2b). Resident. Western Ghats. Male rufous-orange and black; female duller. Evergreen sholas and moist thickets in ravines.

3 **VERDITER FLYCATCHER** *Eumyias thalassina* **Page 640**
Male (3a), female (3b) and juvenile male (3c). Resident. Breeds in Himalayas and NE India; widespread in winter. Male greenish-blue, with black lores. Female duller and greyer, with dusky lores. Juvenile has orange-buff spotting, with turquoise cast to upperparts and underparts. Open forest and wooded areas.

4 **DULL-BLUE FLYCATCHER** *Eumyias sordida* **Page 640**
Adult (4a) and juvenile (4b). Resident. Sri Lanka. Both sexes ashy-blue, with greyish-white belly, black lores and cobalt-blue forehead and supercilium. Female slightly duller than male. Forest and well-wooded areas.

5 **NILGIRI FLYCATCHER** *Eumyias albicaudata* **Page 640**
Male (5a), female (5b) and juvenile male (5c). Resident. Western Ghats. White on tail-base. Male indigo-blue, with blue-grey belly, black lores and bright blue forehead and supercilium. Female blue-grey, paler on underparts. Juvenile has buff spotting on upperparts and blackish scaling on white underparts. Evergreen biotope in hills.

6 **LARGE NILTAVA** *Niltava grandis* **Page 641**
Male (6a), female (6b) and juvenile male (6c). Resident. Himalayas and NE India. Large size. Male dark blue, with brilliant blue crown, neck patch and shoulder patch. Female has rufous-buff forecrown and lores, rufescent wings and tail, and buff throat patch. Juvenile has rufous underparts with blackish barring. Moist broadleaved forest.

7 **SMALL NILTAVA** *Niltava macgrigoriae* **Page 641**
Male (7a), female (7b) and juvenile male (7c). Resident. Himalayas and NE India. Small size. Male dark blue, with brilliant blue forehead and neck patch. Female has indistinct blue neck patch and rufescent wings and tail; lacks oval throat patch of female Rufous-bellied. Juvenile has diffuse brown streaking on underparts. Bushes in broadleaved forest; also reed and grass jungle in plains in winter.

8 **RUFOUS-BELLIED NILTAVA** *Niltava sundara* **Page 642**
Male (8a), female (8b) and juvenile female (8c). Resident. Himalayas and NE India. Male has brilliant blue crown and neck patch, and orange on underparts extending to vent. Female and juvenile have oval-shaped throat patch. Undergrowth in forest and secondary growth.

9 **VIVID NILTAVA** *Niltava vivida* **Page 642**
Male (9a) and female (9b). Resident. NE Indian hills. Different head shape from Rufous-bellied. Male lacks glistening blue crown and nape of Rufous-bellied, and black of throat is indented by orange wedge. Female has buffish throat, but lacks oval-shaped throat patch. Undergrowth in broadleaved evergreen forest.

1a
1b
1c
1d
2a
2b
3a
3b
3c
4a
4b
5a
5b
5c
6a
6b
6c
7a
7b
7c
8a
8b
8c
9a
9b
AH

PLATE 103: BLUE FLYCATCHERS

1 **WHITE-TAILED FLYCATCHER** *Cyornis concretus* **Page 642**
Male (1a) and female (1b). Resident. Breeds in Arunachal Pradesh; winters in Assam and Mizoram. Large size, and white on tail. Male has white belly and undertail-coverts. Female has white patch on lower throat. Dense forest.

2 **WHITE-BELLIED BLUE FLYCATCHER** *Cyornis pallipes* **Page 643**
Male (2a), female (2b) and juvenile female (2c). Resident. Western Ghats and hills of W Tamil Nadu. Large bill, and lacks white at base of tail. Male indigo-blue, with white belly and unmarked undertail-coverts. Female has orange-red throat and breast and greyish head. Juvenile has unmarked buff throat and white belly. Undergrowth in dense evergreen forest.

3 **PALE-CHINNED FLYCATCHER** *Cyornis poliogenys* **Page 643**
Adult (3a) and juvenile (3b) *C. p. poliogenys*; adult *C. p. vernayi* (3c). Resident. Himalayan foothills, NE and E India, and Bangladesh. Nominate has greyish head, well-defined cream throat, and creamy-orange breast and flanks which merge with belly. More uniform creamy-orange underparts, thin eye-ring, and pale pinkish legs help separate *vernayi* from Tickell's Blue. Juvenile has diffusely marked upperparts, well-defined buff throat, and barring on flanks. Undergrowth in broadleaved forest.

4 **PALE BLUE FLYCATCHER** *Cyornis unicolor* **Page 644**
Male (4a), female (4b) and juvenile male (4c). Resident. Himalayas and NE India. Male pale blue, with whiter belly. Female has uniform greyish underparts. Juvenile has bold orange-buff spotting on scapulars and heavily scaled underparts. Moist broadleaved forest and secondary growth.

5 **BLUE-THROATED FLYCATCHER** *Cyornis rubeculoides* **Page 644**
Male (5a), female (5b) and juvenile male (5c). Resident. Breeds in Himalayas and NE India; winters in E Himalayan foothills and south to Bangladesh, SW India and Sri Lanka. Male has blue throat (some with orange wedge) and well-defined white belly and flanks. Female has narrow and poorly defined creamy-orange throat, orange breast well demarcated from white belly, and creamy lores. Juvenile has poorly defined pale throat, prominently spotted scapulars, and barred breast. Open forest and wooded areas.

6 **HILL BLUE FLYCATCHER** *Cyornis banyumas* **Page 644**
Male (6a) and female (6b). Resident. Himalayas and NE India. Long bill and long primary projection. On both sexes, orange of breast and flanks merges gradually with white of belly. Male has blackish ear-coverts. Female has dark lores and sharp demarcation between ear-coverts and creamy-orange throat. Dense, moist broadleaved forest.

7 **TICKELL'S BLUE FLYCATCHER** *Cyornis tickelliae* **Page 645**
Male (7a), female (7b) and juvenile (7c) *C. t. tickelliae*. Resident. Peninsular and NE India, and Sri Lanka. Male has orange throat and breast with clear horizontal division from white flanks and belly (except in Sri Lanka). Female has greyish-blue upperparts. Juvenile of both sexes has cerulean-blue on wings and weak scaling on breast. Open dry forest and wooded areas.

8 **PYGMY BLUE FLYCATCHER** *Muscicapella hodgsoni* **Page 645**
Male (8a) and female (8b). Resident. Himalayas and NE India. Small size, short tail, fine bill, and flowerpecker-like appearance and behaviour. Underparts entirely orange on male and orange-buff on female. Dense, moist broadleaved forest.

9 **GREY-HEADED CANARY FLYCATCHER** *Culicicapa ceylonensis* **Page 646**
Adult. Resident. Breeds in Himalayas, hills of India, Bangladesh and Sri Lanka; winters in Himalayan foothills, and plains in Pakistan and E and NE India. Grey head and breast, yellow rest of underparts, and greenish upperparts. Forest and wooded areas.

1a
1b
2a
2b
2c
3a
3c
3b
4c
4a
4b
5a
5b
5c
6a
6b
7a
7b
7c
8a
8b
9
AH.

PLATE 104: CHATS

1 **COMMON NIGHTINGALE** *Luscinia megarhynchos* **Page 646**
Adult. Vagrant. Pakistan and India. Rufous uppertail-coverts and long rufous tail, indistinct head markings, and pale fringes to wing-coverts and remiges. Bushes.

2 **SIBERIAN RUBYTHROAT** *Luscinia calliope* **Page 646**
Male (2a) and female (2b). Winter visitor. Himalayan foothills, peninsular and NE India and Bangladesh. Olive-brown upperparts and tail, and white supercilium and moustachial stripe. Male has ruby-red throat and grey breast. Female has olive-buff wash to breast. Legs pale brown. Bushes and thick undergrowth.

3 **WHITE-TAILED RUBYTHROAT** *Luscinia pectoralis* **Page 647**
Male (3a), female (3b) and juvenile female (3c) *L. p. pectoralis*; male *L. p. tschebaiewi* (3d). Resident. Breeds in Himalayas; winters mainly in Himalayan foothills and NE India. Male has ruby-red throat, black breast-band and white on tail. Female has grey upperparts, grey breast-band and white tip to tail. Legs black. Male *tschebaiewi* has white moustachial stripe, sometimes shown also by female. Breeds in subalpine scrub, and on alpine slopes; winters in scrub and tall grass in marshes.

4 **BLUETHROAT** *Luscinia svecica* **Page 647**
Male non-breeding (4a) and 1st-winter female (4b) *L. s. svecica*; male breeding *L. s. abbotti* (4c). Summer visitor to NW Himalayas; widespread in winter. White supercilium and rufous tail sides. Variable blue, black and rufous patterning to throat and breast. First-winter female may have just black submoustachial stripe and band of black spotting across breast. Summers in scrub along streams and lakes; winters in scrub and tall grass.

5 **FIRETHROAT** *Luscinia pectardens* **Page 648**
Male (5a), female (5b) and 1st-winter male (5c). Winter visitor? Mainly NE India. Male has white on tail, and flame-orange throat and breast bordered at sides with black. Female has mainly orange-buff underparts. First-winter male has blue on back and rump, with tail as male and underparts as female. Dense bushes and woodland.

6 **INDIAN BLUE ROBIN** *Luscinia brunnea* **Page 648**
Male (6a), female (6b) and juvenile (6c). Resident. Breeds in Himalayas and NE Indian hills; winters in Sri Lanka, hills of NE and SW India, and E Himalayan foothills. Male has blue upperparts and orange underparts, with white supercilium and black ear-coverts. Female has olive-brown upperparts, and buffish underparts with white throat and belly. Breeds in forest undergrowth; winters in forest, secondary scrub and plantations.

7 **SIBERIAN BLUE ROBIN** *Luscinia cyane* **Page 649**
Male (7a), female (7b) and 1st-winter male (7c). Vagrant. Nepal and India. Male has blue upperparts and white underparts. Female usually has blue on uppertail-coverts and tail. First-winter male similar to female, but with blue on mantle. Dense bushes.

8 **RUFOUS-TAILED SCRUB ROBIN** *Cercotrichas galactotes* **Page 651**
Adult. Southward passage migrant through Pakistan and NW India; also breeds in Pakistan. Long rufous tail, tipped white and with black subterminal markings. Sandy-grey upperparts and creamy-white underparts, with whitish supercilium and dark eye-stripe and moustachial stripe. Dry scrub jungle.

1
2a
2b
3d
3b
3a
3c
4b
4a
5a
5b
4c
7a
5c
6a
7b
7c
6b
8
6c

PLATE 105: CHATS

1 **ORANGE-FLANKED BUSH ROBIN** *Tarsiger cyanurus* **Page 649**
Male (1a), female (1b) and juvenile (1c). Resident. Breeds in Himalayas; winters in Himalayas and NE Indian hills. White throat, orange flanks, blue tail, and redstart-like stance. Male has blue upperparts and breast sides. Female has olive-brown upperparts and breast sides. Juvenile has bold spotting on scapulars. Forest understorey.

2 **GOLDEN BUSH ROBIN** *Tarsiger chrysaeus* **Page 649**
Male (2a), female (2b) and juvenile (2c). Resident. Himalayas and NE Indian hills. Orange to orange-buff underparts, with orange tail sides. Male has broad orange supercilium, dark mask, and orange scapulars. Female duller, with less distinct supercilium. Juvenile has adult tail pattern, and pale legs. Summers in subalpine shrubberies and forest undergrowth; winters in forest undergrowth and dense scrub.

3 **WHITE-BROWED BUSH ROBIN** *Tarsiger indicus* **Page 650**
Male (3a), female (3b) and juvenile (3c). Resident. Himalayas and NE Indian hills. Upright stance, long tail, and long and fine supercilium. Male has slaty-blue upperparts and rufous-orange underparts. Female has olive-brown upperparts and dirty orange-buff underparts. Forest undergrowth.

4 **RUFOUS-BREASTED BUSH ROBIN** *Tarsiger hyperythrus* **Page 650**
Male (4a), female (4b) and juvenile (4c). Resident. Breeds in Himalayas; winters south to NE Indian hills. Carriage and profile as Orange-flanked. Male has dark blue upperparts, glistening blue supercilium and shoulders, and rufous-orange underparts. Female has blue tail and orange-buff throat. Summers in bushes at forest edges; winters in moist forest undergrowth.

5 **ORIENTAL MAGPIE ROBIN** *Copsychus saularis* **Page 651**
Male (5a), female (5b) and juvenile (5c) *C. s. saularis.* Widespread resident; unrecorded in most of the northwest. Black/slate-grey and white, with white on wing and at sides of tail. Juvenile scaled with dark brown on throat and breast. Gardens, groves and open broadleaved forest.

6 **WHITE-RUMPED SHAMA** *Copsychus malabaricus* **Page 651**
Male (6a), female (6b) and juvenile (6c) *C. m. malabaricus*; male *C. m. albiventris* (6d). Resident. Himalayan foothills, NE, E and W India, Bangladesh and Sri Lanka. Long, graduated tail and white rump. Male has glossy blue-black upperparts and breast, and rufous-orange underparts. Female duller, with brownish-grey upperparts. Tail of juvenile as adult's. Male *albiventris* of Andamans has white belly. Undergrowth in broadleaved forest.

7 **INDIAN ROBIN** *Saxicoloides fulicata* **Page 652**
Male (7a) and female (7b) *S. f. cambaiensis*; male *S. f. fulicata* (7c). Widespread resident. Reddish vent and black tail in all plumages. Male has white shoulders and black underparts. Female has greyish underparts. In Sri Lanka and S India, upperparts of male glossy blue-black. Dry stony areas with scrub, and cultivation edges.

1a
1c
2a
2b
1b
3b
2c
3a
3c
4a
7c
4b
7b
7a
4c
6a
5c
6b
5a
6c
5b
6d

PLATE 106: REDSTARTS

1 **RUFOUS-BACKED REDSTART** *Phoenicurus erythronota* **Page 652**
Male breeding (1a), 1st-winter male (1b) and female (1c). Winter visitor. Hills of Pakistan and W Himalayas. Large size. Male has rufous mantle and throat, white on wing, and black mask; heavily obscured by pale fringes in non-breeding and first-winter plumages. Female has double buffish wing-bar. Dry hills and valleys with scrub.

2 **BLUE-CAPPED REDSTART** *Phoenicurus coeruleocephalus* **Page 653**
Male breeding (2a), female (2b), 1st-winter male (2c) and juvenile male (2d). Resident. Himalayas. Male has blue-grey cap, black tail, and white on wing; heavily obscured by pale fringes in non-breeding and first-winter plumages. Female has grey underparts, prominent double wing-bar, blackish tail, and chestnut rump. Juvenile heavily barred, with wings and tail as adult. Summers on rocky slopes with open forest; winters in open forest and secondary growth.

3 **BLACK REDSTART** *Phoenicurus ochruros* **Page 653**
Male (3a), female (3b) and juvenile (3c) *P. o. phoenicuroides*; male *P. o. rufiventris* (3d). Resident. Breeds in Pakistan mountains and Himalayas; widespread in winter. Male has black or dark grey upperparts, black breast, and rufous rest of underparts. Female has dusky brown underparts, with orange-buff wash to lower flanks and vent. Breeds in Tibetan steppe habitat; winters in cultivation and plantations.

4 **COMMON REDSTART** *Phoenicurus phoenicurus* **Page 654**
Male breeding (4a), 1st-winter male (4b) and female (4c). Spring passage migrant. Mainly Pakistan. Male has grey upperparts, white forehead, black throat, and rufous-orange underparts; heavily obscured by pale fringes in non-breeding and first-winter plumages. Female has buff-brown upperparts and buffish underparts. Arid areas.

5 **HODGSON'S REDSTART** *Phoenicurus hodgsoni* **Page 654**
Male breeding (5a) and female (5b). Winter visitor. Himalayas and NE Indian hills. Male (both breeding and non-breeding) has grey upperparts, white wing patch, and black throat and breast. Female has dusky brown upperparts and grey underparts. First-winter male as female. Stony river beds with trees, and bushes in cultivation.

6 **WHITE-THROATED REDSTART** *Phoenicurus schisticeps* **Page 654**
Male (6a), female (6b) and juvenile (6c). Resident and winter visitor. Himalayas; unrecorded in Pakistan. Both sexes with white throat, white wing patch, rufous rump and dark tail. Summers in shrubberies on rocky slopes and forest edges; winters in meadows and cultivation and on bush-covered slopes.

7 **DAURIAN REDSTART** *Phoenicurus auroreus* **Page 655**
Male non-breeding (7a) and female (7b). Resident. Himalayas and NE Indian hills. Both sexes have white patch on wing. Mantle of male black (worn) or brown with black mottling (fresh). Summers in open forest and trees in cultivation; winters in bushes and secondary growth.

8 **WHITE-WINGED REDSTART** *Phoenicurus erythrogaster* **Page 655**
Male (8a), female (8b) and juvenile male (8c). Resident and winter visitor. Himalayas. Large size and stocky appearance. Male has white cap and large white patch on wing. Female has buff-brown upperparts and buffish underparts. Breeds in rocky alpine meadows; winters in stony pastures and scrub patches.

1a
1b
2a
2c
1c
2b
2d
3d
3a
4b
4a
5a
3b
4c
5b
3c
6c
8a
8b
6a
6b
7a
7b
8c

PLATE 107: REDSTARTS, BLUE ROBINS, GRANDALA AND FORKTAILS

1 **BLUE-FRONTED REDSTART** *Phoenicurus frontalis* **Page 655**
Male (1a), female (1b) and juvenile (1c). Resident. Breeds in Himalayas; winters in Himalayan foothills, NE India and Bangladesh. Orange rump and tail sides, with black centre and tip to tail. Male has blue head and upperparts and chestnut-orange underparts. Female has dark brown upperparts and underparts, with orange wash to belly. Breeds in subalpine shrubberies; winters in bushes and open forest.

2 **WHITE-CAPPED WATER REDSTART** *Chaimarrornis leucocephalus* **Page 656**
Adult (2a) and juvenile (2b). Resident. Breeds in Himalayas and NE Indian hills; winters south to Baluchistan and Bangladesh. White cap, and rufous tail with broad black terminal band. Mainly mountain streams and rivers.

3 **PLUMBEOUS WATER REDSTART** *Rhyacornis fuliginosus* **Page 656**
Male (3a), female (3b) and juvenile (3c). Resident. Breeds in Himalayas and NE Indian hills; winters south to Bangladesh. Male slaty-blue, with rufous-chestnut tail. Female and first-year male have black-and-white tail and white spotting on grey underparts. Mountain streams and rivers.

4 **WHITE-BELLIED REDSTART** *Hodgsonius phaenicuroides* **Page 656**
Male (4a) and female (4b). Resident. Himalayas. Long, graduated tail. Male has white belly and rufous tail sides. Female has white throat and belly, and chestnut on tail. Breeds in subalpine shrubberies; winters in thick undergrowth and forest edges at lower levels.

5 **WHITE-TAILED ROBIN** *Myiomela leucura* **Page 657**
Male (5a), female (5b) and juvenile female (5c). Resident. Himalayas and NE Indian hills. White patches on tail. Male blue-black, with glistening blue forehead and shoulders. Female olive-brown, with whitish lower throat. Undergrowth in moist broadleaved forest.

6 **BLUE-FRONTED ROBIN** *Cinclidium frontale* **Page 657**
Male (6a) and female (6b). Resident. Himalayas. Long, graduated tail, lacking any white or rufous. Male deep blue, with glistening blue forehead. Female has dark brown tail and uniform pale brown underparts. Thickly vegetated gullies and dense vegetation at forest edges.

7 **GRANDALA** *Grandala coelicolor* **Page 658**
Male (7a) and female (7b). Resident. Himalayas. Slim and long-winged. Male purple-blue, with black wings and tail. Female and immature male have white patches on wing and streaked head and underparts. Rocky slopes and stony meadows; alpine zone in summer, lower altitudes in winter.

8 **LITTLE FORKTAIL** *Enicurus scouleri* **Page 658**
Adult. Resident. Himalayas and NE Indian hills. Small and plump, with short tail. White forehead. Mountain streams; also slower-moving streams in winter.

9 **BLACK-BACKED FORKTAIL** *Enicurus immaculatus* **Page 658**
Adult. Resident. Himalayan foothills, NE India and Bangladesh. Black crown and mantle, and more white on forehead than Slaty-backed. Fast-flowing streams in moist broadleaved forest.

10 **SLATY-BACKED FORKTAIL** *Enicurus schistaceus* **Page 659**
Adult. Resident. Himalayas and NE India. Slaty-grey crown and mantle; less white on forehead and larger bill than Black-backed. Fast-flowing streams in forest and wooded lake margins.

11 **WHITE-CROWNED FORKTAIL** *Enicurus leschenaulti* **Page 659**
Adult. Resident. E Himalayan foothills and NE Indian hills. Large size; white forehead and forecrown, black breast and black mantle. Fast-flowing waters in tropical evergreen forest.

12 **SPOTTED FORKTAIL** *Enicurus maculatus* **Page 659**
Adult (12a) and juvenile (12b) *E. m. maculatus*. Resident. Himalayas and NE Indian hills. Large size; white forehead, white spotting on mantle, and black breast. Rocky streams in forest.

1a
1b
1c
2a
2b
3a
3b
3c
4a
4b
5a
5b
5c
6a
6b
7a
7b
9
11
8
12a
12b
10

PLATE 108: COCHOAS AND BUSHCHATS

1 **PURPLE COCHOA** *Cochoa purpurea* **Page 660**
Male (1a), female (1b) and juvenile male (1c). Resident. Himalayas and NE Indian hills. Lilac crown, wing panelling and tail (latter with dark tip). Male purplish-brown. Female has rufous-brown upperparts and brownish-orange underparts. Juvenile with bold orange-buff spotting and scaling; wings and tail adult. Mainly dense moist broadleaved forest.

2 **GREEN COCHOA** *Cochoa viridis* **Page 660**
Male (2a), female (2b) and juvenile female (2c). Resident. Himalayas and NE India. Mainly green, with bluish head, and blue tail with black band. Male has blue wing panelling. Female has green in blue wing panels. Juvenile with bold orange-buff spotting and scaling; wings and tail as adult. Dense broadleaved evergreen forest.

3 **STOLICZKA'S BUSHCHAT** *Saxicola macrorhyncha* **Page 660**
Male breeding (3a), male non-breeding (3b) and female (3c). Resident. Mainly Rajasthan, India. Male has white supercilium, white primary coverts, and much white on tail; upperparts and ear-coverts appear blackish when worn (breeding) and streaked when fresh (non-breeding). Female differs from female Common Stonechat in longer bill and tail, more prominent supercilium, and broad buffish edges and tips to tail feathers. Sandy desert plains with scattered bushes.

4 **HODGSON'S BUSHCHAT** *Saxicola insignis* **Page 661**
Male non-breeding (4a) and female (4b). Winter visitor. N Indian plains and Nepal terai. Large size. Male has white throat extending to form almost complete white collar, and more white on wing than Common Stonechat. Female has broad buffish-white wing-bars and tips to primary coverts. Tall vegetation along river beds and cane fields.

5 **COMMON STONECHAT** *Saxicola torquata* **Page 661**
Male breeding (5a), male non-breeding (5b) and female (5c) *S. t. indica*. Resident and winter visitor. Male has black head, white patch on neck, orange breast, and whitish rump (features obscured in fresh plumage); lacks white in tail. Female has streaked upperparts and orange on breast and rump. Tail darker than in White-tailed. Summers in open country with bushes, including high-altitude semi-desert; winters in scrub, reedbeds and cultivation.

6 **WHITE-TAILED STONECHAT** *Saxicola leucura* **Page 662**
Male breeding (6a) and female (6b). Resident. N subcontinent, mainly in plains. Male has largely white inner webs to tail feathers. Female has greyer upperparts than Common, with diffuse streaking, and paler grey-brown tail. Reeds and tall grassland.

7 **PIED BUSHCHAT** *Saxicola caprata* **Page 662**
Male breeding (7a), female (7b) and 1st-winter male (7c) *S. c. bicolor*. Widespread resident. Male black, with white rump and wing patch; rufous fringes to body in non-breeding and first-winter plumages. Female has dark brown upperparts and rufous-brown underparts, with rufous-orange rump. Mainly cultivation and open country with scattered bushes or tall grass.

8 **JERDON'S BUSHCHAT** *Saxicola jerdoni* **Page 663**
Male (8a) and female (8b). Resident. Mainly NE Indian plains and Himalayan foothills. Male has black upperparts, including rump and tail, and white underparts. Female similar to female Grey, but lacks prominent supercilium, and has longer, more rounded tail lacking rufous at sides. Tall grassland.

9 **GREY BUSHCHAT** *Saxicola ferrea* **Page 663**
Male (9a), female (9b) and juvenile (9c). Resident. Breeds in Himalayas and NE Indian hills; winters south to N Indian plains. Male has white supercilium and dark mask; upperparts grey to almost black, depending on extent of wear. Female has buff supercilium and rufous rump and tail sides. Bushes and secondary growth.

10 **BROWN ROCK-CHAT** *Cercomela fusca* **Page 667**
Adult. Resident. Mainly Pakistan and N India. Both sexes brown, with more rufescent underparts. Rocky hills, cliffs and old buildings.

1a
2c
1c
1b
2a
2b
3c
3a
6a
3b
4b
4a
6b
7a
7b
7c
5a
5c
5b
9a
8a
9b
8b
9c
10

PLATE 109: WHEATEARS

1 **HOODED WHEATEAR** *Oenanthe monacha* **Page 663**
Adult (1a), 1st-winter male (1b) and female (1c). Resident. S Baluchistan. Long bill. Male has white crown and largely white outer tail feathers; in winter, buffish or greyish wash to crown and pale fringes to upperparts and wings (first-winter male has tail as female). Female has rufous-buff rump and tail, with brown central tail feathers. Barren desert.

2 **HUME'S WHEATEAR** *Oenanthe alboniger* **Page 664**
Adult. Resident. Mainly Pakistan; vagrant to India. All-black head and largely white underparts. Told from *picata* race of Variable by stockier appearance and domed head, larger bill, glossy sheen to black of plumage (except when worn), black of throat does not extend so far down on breast and white of rump extending farther up lower back. Barren stony slopes with boulders.

3 **NORTHERN WHEATEAR** *Oenanthe oenanthe* **Page 664**
Male breeding (3a), female breeding (3b), and 1st-winter (3c). Passage migrant. Mainly Pakistan; vagrant elsewhere. Breeding male has blue-grey upperparts, black mask, and pale orange breast. Breeding female greyish to olive-brown above; lacks rufous on ear-coverts of Finsch's and never shows dark grey/black on throat. Compared with Isabelline, adult winter and first-winter have blackish centres to wing-coverts and tertials and show more white at sides of tail. Open stony ground and cultivation.

4 **FINSCH'S WHEATEAR** *Oenanthe finschii* **Page 665**
Male (4a) and female (4b) and 1st-winter female (4c). Winter visitor. Baluchistan. Male has creamy-buff to white mantle. Adult female and first-winter have rufous cast to ear-coverts, rather pale grey-brown upperparts, and broad black terminal band to tail. Dry stony hills and valleys.

5 **VARIABLE WHEATEAR** *Oenanthe picata* **Page 665**
Male (5a) and female (5b) *O. p. picata*; male (5c) and female (5d) *O. p. capistrata*; male (5e) and female (5f) *O. p. opistholeuca*. Breeds in Baluchistan and N Pakistan; winter visitor mainly to Pakistan and NW India. Very variable. Males can be mainly black, have black head with white underparts, or have white crown and white underparts. Females can be mainly sooty-brown or have greyish upperparts with variable greyish-white underparts. Unlike Pied, lacks prominent pale fringes to mantle/scapulars and wing feathers in fresh plumage. Breeds in barren valleys and low hills; winters in plains, stony desert foothills and cultivation.

6 **PIED WHEATEAR** *Oenanthe pleschanka* **Page 665**
Male (6a), female (6b), 1st-winter male (6c) and 1st-winter female (6d). Breeds in N Pakistan and NW India; also passage migrant in Pakistan. Different tail pattern from Variable (see text). On breeding male, white of nape extends to mantle, black of throat does not extend to upper breast, and breast is washed with buff. Non-breeding and first-winter male and female have pale fringes to upperparts and wings (not apparent on fresh-plumaged Variable). Breeding female best told from breeding female Variable by tail pattern. Open stony country with lowlands.

7 **RUFOUS-TAILED WHEATEAR** *Oenanthe xanthoprymna* **Page 666**
Male breeding (7a) and male non-breeding (7b). Breeds in Baluchistan; winter visitor to Pakistan and NW India. Rufous-orange lower back and rump, and rufous tail sides. Male has black lores. Summers on dry rocky slopes; winters in semi-desert.

8 **DESERT WHEATEAR** *Oenanthe deserti* **Page 666**
Male breeding (8a), male non-breeding (8b), female breeding (8c) and female non-breeding (8d). Breeds in NW Himalayas; winter visitor mainly to Pakistan and NW India. Sandy-brown upperparts, with largely black tail and contrasting white rump. Male has black throat (partly obscured when fresh). Female has blackish centres to wing-coverts and tertials in fresh plumage and largely black wings when worn (useful distinction from Isabelline). Breeds on barren plateaux; winters in barren semi-desert.

9 **ISABELLINE WHEATEAR** *Oenanthe isabellina* **Page 667**
Adult breeding (9a) and non-breeding (9b). Breeds in Pakistan; winters in Pakistan and NW India. Rather plain sandy-brown and buff. Breeds on stony plateaux and in valleys; winters in sandy semi-desert.

1a
1c
2
3a
3b
1b
4a
3c
5f
4b
4c
5a
5b
5e
6a
6b
6c
5d
5c
6d
7a
7b
8a
9a
8c
8b
8d
9b
Af.

PLATE 110: STARLINGS

1 **ASIAN GLOSSY STARLING** *Aplonis panayensis* **Page 668**
Adult (1a) and juvenile (1b). Resident on Andamans and Nicobars; visitor to the northeast. Adult glossy greenish-black, with bright red iris. Juvenile has blackish-brown upperparts with variable greenish gloss, and streaked underparts. Groves and forest edges.

2 **SPOT-WINGED STARLING** *Saroglossa spiloptera* **Page 668**
Male (2a) and female (2b). Resident? Himalayan foothills and NE India. White wing patch and whitish iris. Male has blackish mask, reddish-chestnut throat, and greyish upperparts. Female has browner upperparts, and greyish-brown markings on throat and breast. Juvenile has buff wing-bars. Open forest and well-wooded areas.

3 **WHITE-FACED STARLING** *Sturnus senex* **Page 668**
Adult (3a) and juvenile (3b). Resident. Sri Lanka. Adult has whitish face, grey upperparts with slight green gloss, and white-streaked greyish underparts; head can be all white. Juvenile has whitish supercilium and throat, dull brown upperparts, and dark grey underparts. Tall forest.

4 **CHESTNUT-TAILED STARLING** *Sturnus malabaricus* **Page 669**
Adult (4a) and juvenile (4b) *S. m. malabaricus*; adult *S. m. blythii* (4c). Resident in NE subcontinent and SW Indian hills; winter visitor to C and W India. Adult has grey upperparts, rufous underparts, and chestnut tail; head whiter in southern race *blythii*. Juvenile has rufous sides and tips to outer tail feathers. Open wooded areas.

5 **WHITE-HEADED STARLING** *Sturnus erythropygius* **Page 669**
Adult *S. e. andamanensis*. Resident. Andamans and Nicobars. Creamy-white head and underparts, grey mantle and back, and glossy greenish-black wings and tail. Forest clearings and cultivation.

6 **BRAHMINY STARLING** *Sturnus pagodarum* **Page 669**
Adult (6a) and juvenile (6b). Widespread resident; unrecorded in parts of northwest and northeast. Adult has black crest, and rufous-orange sides of head and underparts. Juvenile lacks crest; has grey-brown cap and paler orange-buff underparts. Dry, well-wooded areas and thorn scrub.

7 **PURPLE-BACKED STARLING** *Sturnus sturninus* **Page 670**
Adult male (7a) and female (7b). Vagrant. Pakistan and India. Male has pale grey head and underparts, purplish-black hindcrown patch and mantle, and white tips to median coverts and rear scapulars. Female and juvenile duller. Open wooded areas.

8 **WHITE-SHOULDERED STARLING** *Sturnus sinensis* **Page 670**
Male (8a), female (8b) and juvenile (8c). Vagrant. India. Male has silky-grey head and body and white shoulder patch; head and body may have rusty-orange wash. Female and juvenile browner, with less or no white on wing. Coloration of uppertail-coverts and tail help separate from Chestnut-tailed. Habitat unknown in subcontinent.

9 **ROSY STARLING** *Sturnus roseus* **Page 670**
Adult (9a) and juvenile (9b). Passage migrant in Pakistan; winter visitor mainly to India and Sri Lanka. Adult has blackish head with shaggy crest, pinkish mantle and underparts, and blue-green gloss to wings. Juvenile mainly sandy-brown, with stout yellowish bill, and broad pale fringes to wing feathers. Cultivation and damp grassland.

10 **COMMON STARLING** *Sturnus vulgaris* **Page 671**
Adult breeding (10a) and non-breeding (10b) and juvenile (10c). Mainly winter visitor to N subcontinent; also partly resident in Pakistan, and summer visitor to Kashmir. Adult metallic green and purple; heavily marked with buff in winter. Juvenile dusky brown with whiter throat. Cultivation and damp grassland.

11 **ASIAN PIED STARLING** *Sturnus contra* **Page 671**
Adult (11a) and juvenile (11b) *S. c. contra*; adult *S. c. superciliaris* (11c). Resident. Widespread in N and C subcontinent. Adult black and white, with orange orbital skin and large, pointed yellowish bill. Juvenile has black of plumage replaced by brown. Cultivation, damp grassland and habitation.

2b
1b
1a
2a
4b
3a
3b
4a
4c
6b
5
6a
7a
7b
8a
9a
8b
9b
8c
10b
11c
10c
11b
11a
10a

PLATE 111: MYNAS

1 **COMMON MYNA** *Acridotheres tristis* **Page 672**
Adult *A. t. tristis* (1a, 1b). Widespread resident; unrecorded in parts of the northwest and northeast. Brownish myna with yellow orbital skin, white wing patch and white tail-tip. Juvenile duller. Habitation and cultivation.

2 **BANK MYNA** *Acridotheres ginginianus* **Page 672**
Adult (2a, 2b) and juvenile (2c). Resident. Widespread in N and C subcontinent. Orange-red orbital patch, orange-yellow bill, and tufted forehead. Wing patch, underwing-coverts and tail-tip orange-buff. Juvenile duller than adult. Cultivation, damp grassland and habitation.

3 **JUNGLE MYNA** *Acridotheres fuscus* **Page 672**
Adult (3a) and juvenile (3b) *A. f. fuscus*; adult *A. f. mahrattensis* (3c). Resident. Himalayas south to Bangladesh and N Orissa, and W India. Tufted forehead, and white wing patch and tail-tip; lacks bare orbital skin. Juvenile browner, with reduced forehead tuft. Cultivation near well-wooded areas, and edges of habitation.

4 **WHITE-VENTED MYNA** *Acridotheres cinereus* **Page 673**
Adult (4a) and juvenile (4b). Resident. NE India and Bangladesh. Similar to Jungle Myna, but has uniform blackish-grey upperparts, uniform dark grey underparts strongly contrasting with white undertail-coverts, yellow bill, and reddish to orange-brown iris. Juvenile browner. Cultivation and grassland.

5 **COLLARED MYNA** *Acridotheres albocinctus* **Page 673**
Adult (5a) and juvenile (5b). Resident. Manipur and Assam. Whitish patch on neck sides. Neck patch smaller and brownish-white on juvenile. Cultivation and grassland.

6 **GOLDEN-CRESTED MYNA** *Ampeliceps coronatus* **Page 674**
Male (6a), female (6b) and juvenile (6c). Resident. Manipur and Assam. Golden-yellow forehead and crown, yellow throat, naked orange-yellow orbital patch, and yellow patch at base of primaries. Juvenile browner, with less yellow. Open moist forest.

7 **SRI LANKA MYNA** *Gracula ptilogenys* **Page 674**
Adult. Resident. Sri Lanka. Compared with Hill Myna, has stouter orange-red bill with dark blue base, and different shape and positioning of wattles. Forest and well-wooded country.

8 **HILL MYNA** *Gracula religiosa* **Page 674**
Adult (8a) and juvenile (8b) *G. r. indica*; adult *G. r. intermedia* (8c). Resident. Himalayan foothills, hills of India, Bangladesh and Sri Lanka. Large myna with yellow wattles, large orange to yellow bill, and white wing patches. Juvenile has duller yellowish-orange bill, paler yellow wattles, and less gloss to plumage. Moist forest and plantations.

1a
1b
2a
2b
3a
2c
3b
4a
4b
5b
3c
6a
5a
6b
8b
6c
8a
7
8c

PLATE 112: NUTHATCHES AND TREECREEPERS

1 **CHESTNUT-VENTED NUTHATCH** *Sitta nagaensis* **Page 675**
Adult. Resident. NE Indian hills. Whitish underparts with chestnut rear flanks, and chestnut undertail-coverts with white spots. Open forest.

2 **KASHMIR NUTHATCH** *Sitta cashmirensis* **Page 675**
Male (2a) and female (2b). Resident. Himalayas and Indian hills. Compared with female Chestnut-bellied, has uniform undertail-coverts and lacks clearly defined white cheeks. Larger and longer-billed than White-tailed, with more pronounced white cheeks, no white at base of tail, and different calls. Forest and groves.

3 **CHESTNUT-BELLIED NUTHATCH** *Sitta castanea* **Page 676**
Male (3a) and female (3b) *S. c. castanea*; male *S. c. almorae* (3c). Resident. Himalayas and Indian hills. Male has deep chestnut underparts and white cheeks. Female paler cinnamon-brown on underparts, although white cheeks more pronounced than on similar species; has pale fringes to undertail-coverts. Forest and groves.

4 **WHITE-TAILED NUTHATCH** *Sitta himalayensis* **Page 676**
Adult. Resident. Himalayas and NE Indian hills. White at base of tail (difficult to see); less distinct white cheek patch than Kashmir; uniform undertail-coverts. Forest.

5 **WHITE-CHEEKED NUTHATCH** *Sitta leucopsis* **Page 676**
Adult. Resident. W Himalayas. Black crown and nape, white face, and whitish underparts with rufous flanks and undertail-coverts. Coniferous and mixed forest.

6 **EASTERN ROCK NUTHATCH** *Sitta tephronota* **Page 677**
Adult. Resident. Baluchistan. Large, with very large bill. Long black eye-stripe, pale blue-grey upperparts, and whitish underparts. Rocky gorges and ridges.

7 **VELVET-FRONTED NUTHATCH** *Sitta frontalis* **Page 677**
Male (7a) and female (7b). Resident. Himalayas, Indian hills, Bangladesh and Sri Lanka. Violet-blue upperparts, black forehead, black-tipped red bill, and lilac underparts. Male has black eye-stripe. Open broadleaved forest and well-wooded areas.

8 **BEAUTIFUL NUTHATCH** *Sitta formosa* **Page 677**
Adult. Resident. E Himalayas and NE Indian hills. Large; blue-streaked black upperparts, and rufous-orange underparts. Dense forest.

9 **WALLCREEPER** *Tichodroma muraria* **Page 678**
Adult male breeding (9a) and adult non-breeding (9b). Resident. Himalayas; winters down to foothills and plains. Long, downcurved bill. Largely crimson wing-coverts; shows white primary spots in flight. Breeding male has black throat. Rock cliffs and gorges; also ruins and stony river beds in winter.

10 **EURASIAN TREECREEPER** *Certhia familiaris* **Page 678**
Adult *C. f. mandellii* (10a); adult *C. f. hodgsoni* (10b). Resident. Himalayas, NE India? Dull brown, unbarred tail, and whitish throat and breast. W Himalayan *hodgsoni* comparatively pale and grey above, with pronounced whitish streaking. Forest.

11 **BAR-TAILED TREECREEPER** *Certhia himalayana* **Page 679**
Adult. Resident. Pakistan mountains, W Himalayas and Arunachal Pradesh. Dark barring on tail, white throat, and dull whitish or dirty greyish-buff underparts. Forest; also well-wooded areas in winter.

12 **RUSTY-FLANKED TREECREEPER** *Certhia nipalensis* **Page 679**
Adult. Resident. Himalayas. Buffish supercilium continuing around dark ear-coverts, unbarred tail, white throat, and rufous flanks. Forest.

13 **BROWN-THROATED TREECREEPER** *Certhia discolor* **Page 679**
Adult *C. d. discolor* (13a); adult *C. d. manipurensis* (13b). Resident. Himalayas and NE India. Brownish-buff to cinnamon-orange throat and breast; unbarred tail. Forest.

14 **SPOTTED CREEPER** *Salpornis spilonotus* **Page 680**
Adult. Resident. N and C India. Long, downcurved bill, and shortish tail. Plumage spotted with white. Open deciduous forest and groves.

1
2a
2b
3a
3b
3c
4
5
6
7a
7b
8
9a
9b
10a
10b
11
12
13a
13b
14
Craig Robson '97

PLATE 113: TITS

1 **WHITE-CROWNED PENDULINE TIT** *Remiz coronatus* **Page 681**
Fresh male (1a), worn male (1b), female (1c) and juvenile (1d). Winter visitor to Pakistan and Punjab, India; breeds in Ladakh? Male has blackish mask and nape, whitish crown and whitish collar. Female has pale grey crown and collar, and lacks black nape band. Juvenile lacks dark mask. Reedbeds and riverain forest.

2 **FIRE-CAPPED TIT** *Cephalopyrus flammiceps* **Page 681**
Male breeding (2a), male non-breeding (2b), female (2c) and immature (2d) ***C. f. flammiceps.*** Breeds in Himalayas; resident in NE India; winters in Nepal and C India. Flowerpecker-like, with greenish upperparts and yellowish to whitish underparts. Lacks crest. Breeding male has bright orange-scarlet forecrown, chin and throat. Forest.

3 **RUFOUS-NAPED TIT** *Parus rufonuchalis* **Page 682**
Adult (3a) and juvenile (3b). Resident. Baluchistan and W Himalayas. Large size, extensive black bib (to upper belly), and grey belly. Coniferous forest.

4 **RUFOUS-VENTED TIT** *Parus rubidiventris* **Page 682**
Adult (4a) and juvenile (4b) ***P. r. rubidiventris*****; adult (4c) and juvenile (4d)** ***P. r. beavani.*** Resident. Himalayas and Nagaland. Smaller than Rufous-naped, with smaller black bib, and (where ranges overlap) has rufous belly. E Himalayan *beavani* has greyish belly. Forest.

5 **SPOT-WINGED TIT** *Parus melanolophus* **Page 682**
Adult (5a) and juvenile (5b). Resident. W Himalayas. Small size, broad white tips to median and greater coverts, rufous breast sides, and dark grey belly. Coniferous and mixed forest.

6 **COAL TIT** *Parus ater* **Page 683**
Adult (6a) and juvenile (6b). Resident. C and E Himalayas. Small size, whitish tips to median and greater coverts, olive-grey mantle, and creamy-buff underparts. Coniferous and mixed forest.

7 **GREY-CRESTED TIT** *Parus dichrous* **Page 683**
Adult. Resident. Himalayas. Greyish crest and upperparts, whitish collar, and orange-buff underparts. Broadleaved and mixed forest.

8 **GREAT TIT** *Parus major* **Page 683**
Adult (8a) and juvenile (8b) ***P. m. stupae*****; adult** ***P. m. tibetanus*** **(8c).** Resident. Widespread in hills of subcontinent. Black breast centre and line down belly, greyish mantle, greyish-white breast sides and flanks, and white wing-bar. Juvenile has yellowish-white cheeks and underparts, and yellowish-olive wash to mantle. *P. m. tibetanus* has greenish-olive cast to mantle. Forest and well-wooded country.

9 **GREEN-BACKED TIT** *Parus monticolus* **Page 684**
Adult (9a) and juvenile (9b). Resident. Himalayas and NE Indian hills. Green mantle and back, and yellow on underparts. Forest.

1a
1b
1c
1d
2a
2c
2d
2b
3b
3a
4d
4c
4b
4a
6b
6a
5b
7
8b
5a
9b
8a
9a
8c
Craig Robson '97

PLATE 114: TITS AND WINTER WREN

1 **WINTER WREN** *Troglodytes troglodytes* **Page 680**
Adult *T. t. neglectus* (1a); adult *T. t. nipalensis* (1b). Resident. Baluchistan and Himalayas. Small and squat, with stubby tail. Brown, with dark-barred wings, tail and underparts. Breeds on high-altitude rocky and bushy slopes; winters around villages and in forest undergrowth.

2 **WHITE-NAPED TIT** *Parus nuchalis* **Page 684**
Adult. Resident. NW and S India. Black mantle and wing-coverts (grey on Great Tit); much white on tertials and at bases of secondaries and primaries. Thorn-scrub forest.

3 **BLACK-LORED TIT** *Parus xanthogenys* **Page 684**
Male (3a) and juvenile (3b) *P. x. xanthogenys*; female *P. x. aplonotus* (3c); female *P. x. travancoreensis* (3d). Resident. Himalayas and peninsular hills. Black forehead and lores, uniform greenish upperparts with black streaking confined to scapulars, and olive rump; where range overlaps with that of Yellow-cheeked, wing-bars are yellowish. Open forest, forest edges and plantations.

4 **YELLOW-CHEEKED TIT** *Parus spilonotus* **Page 685**
Adult (4a) and juvenile (4b) *P. s. spilonotus*. Resident. E Himalayas and NE Indian hills. Yellow forehead and lores, black streaking on greenish mantle, and grey rump; where range overlap with that of Black-lored, wing-bars are white. Open forest.

5 **AZURE TIT** *Parus cyanus* **Page 685**
Adult. Winter visitor? N Pakistan Himalayas. White underparts, lacking yellow on breast; crown and ear-coverts white. River-bed bushes.

6 **YELLOW-BREASTED TIT** *Parus flavipectus* **Page 686**
Adult. Resident? N Pakistan Himalayas. Yellow breast and greyish head; chin and centre of throat greyish (show as faint bib). Dense thickets.

7 **YELLOW-BROWED TIT** *Sylviparus modestus* **Page 686**
Adult *S. m. modestus*. Resident. Himalayas and NE India. Very small, with slight crest and rather stubby bill. Olive-green upperparts, yellowish eye-ring, fine yellow supercilium, and yellowish-buff underparts. Broadleaved forest.

8 **SULTAN TIT** *Melanochlora sultanea* **Page 686**
Male (8a) and female (8b). Resident. C and E Himalayas and NE Indian hills. Large, bulbul-like tit. Blue-black (male) or blackish-olive (female), with bright yellow crest and underparts. Mainly evergreen broadleaved forest.

9 **WHITE-CHEEKED TIT** *Aegithalos leucogenys* **Page 686**
Adult (9a) and juvenile (9b). Resident. Baluchistan and W Himalayas. Black throat, cinnamon crown, yellowish iris, and grey-brown mantle. Juvenile has buffish-white throat and streaking on breast. Scrub forest.

10 **BLACK-THROATED TIT** *Aegithalos concinnus* **Page 687**
Adult (10a) and juvenile (10b) *A. c. iredalei*; adult *A. c. manipurensis* (10c). Resident. Himalayas and NE Indian hills. Chestnut or rufous crown, white chin and black throat, white cheeks, and grey mantle. Juvenile has white throat and indistinct black-spotted breast-band. Broadleaved and mixed forest and secondary growth.

11 **WHITE-THROATED TIT** *Aegithalos niveogularis* **Page 687**
Adult (11a) and juvenile (11b). Resident. W Himalayas. White forehead and forecrown and whitish throat; iris brownish. Diffuse blackish mask and cinnamon underparts, with darker breast-band. Juvenile has dusky throat, more prominent breast-band, and paler lower breast and belly. Bushes in forest and high-altitude shrubberies.

12 **RUFOUS-FRONTED TIT** *Aegithalos iouschistos* **Page 688**
Adult (12a) and juvenile (12b). Resident. C and E Himalayas. Broad black mask (reaching nape), dusky throat, rufous-buff crown centre and cheeks, and rufous underparts. Juvenile has paler crown-stripe, cheeks and underparts. Forest.

1a
1b
2
3a
3b
3d
4a
3c
5
4b
8a
6
8b
7
9b
10a
10c
9a
10b
12a
11b
11a
12b
Craig Robson '97

PLATE 115: MARTINS AND SWALLOWS

1 SAND MARTIN *Riparia riparia* **Page 689**
Adult (1a, 1b, 1c). Breeds in NE India; recorded W to Gujarat. White throat and half-collar and brown breast-band. Very similar to Pale Martin, but upperparts darker brown, breast-band clearly defined and tail-fork deeper. Around large waterbodies; in summer, around rivers and streams.

2 PALE MARTIN *Riparia diluta* **Page 688**
Adult (2a, 2b, 2c). Resident. Pakistan (and probably farther east). Upperparts paler and greyer than on Sand and Plain Martins; throat greyish-white; breast-band not clearly defined; tail-fork very shallow. Around large waterbodies.

3 PLAIN MARTIN *Riparia paludicola* **Page 689**
Adult (3a, 3b, 3c). Resident. Mainly N and C subcontinent. Pale brownish-grey throat and breast, merging into dingy white rest of underparts; some with suggestion of breast-band. Underwing darker than on Sand and Pale, flight weaker and more fluttering, and has shallower indent to tail. Upperparts darker than on Pale. Around rivers and lakes.

4 EURASIAN CRAG MARTIN *Hirundo rupestris* **Page 689**
Adult (4a, 4b, 4c). Resident. Breeds in Pakistan hills and Himalayas; winters in Western Ghats. Larger and darker than Pale Crag Martin. Upperparts and underwing-coverts darker brown; dusky throat, dusky brown flanks and vent, and more distinct pale fringes to undertail-coverts. Rocky cliffs and gorges.

5 ROCK MARTIN *Hirundo fuligula* **Page 690**
Adult (5a, 5b, 5c). Resident. C and S Pakistan. Smaller than Eurasian Crag Martin, with paler sandy-grey upperparts (especially rump), buffish-white throat, paler vent and undertail-coverts, and paler underwing-coverts. Rocky gorges and cliffs.

6 DUSKY CRAG MARTIN *Hirundo concolor* **Page 690**
Adult (6a, 6b, 6c). Resident. Mainly N and peninsular India. Upperparts and underparts dark brown and rather uniform. Cliffs, gorges and old buildings.

7 BARN SWALLOW *Hirundo rustica* **Page 690**
Adult (7a, 7b, 7c) and juvenile (7d) *H. r. rustica*; adult *H. r. tytleri* (7e). Breeds in Pakistan hills, Himalayas and NE India; widespread farther south in winter. Reddish forehead and throat, long tail-streamers, and blue-black breast-band. Juvenile duller and lacks tail-streamers. *H. r. tytleri* has rufous underparts. Cultivation, habitation, lakes and rivers.

8 PACIFIC SWALLOW *Hirundo tahitica* **Page 691**
Adult (8a, 8b, 8c) and juvenile (8d) *H. t. javanica*; adult *H. t. domicola* (8e, 8f). Resident. SW Indian hills, Andamans and Sri Lanka. Told from Barn by more extensive rufous on throat, lack of breast-band, dingy underparts and underwing-coverts, and blackish undertail-coverts with whitish fringes; lacks tail-streamers. *H. t. domicola* has metallic green gloss to upperparts (more purplish-blue in *javanica*). Grassy hills, rivers and habitation.

9 WIRE-TAILED SWALLOW *Hirundo smithii* **Page 691**
Adult (9a, 9b, 9c) and juvenile (9d). Widespread resident; unrecorded in parts of the northwest, northeast and southeast. Chestnut crown, glistening white underparts and underwing-coverts, and fine filamentous projections to outer tail feathers (often broken or difficult to see). Juvenile has brownish cast to blue upperparts, and dull brownish crown. Open country and cultivation near fresh waters.

1a
1b
1c
2a
2b
2c
3a
3b
3c
4a
4b
4c
5a
5b
5c
6a
6b
6c
7a
7b
7c
7d
7e
8a
8b
8c
8d
8e
8f
9a
9b
9c
9d
G. Driessens
97

PLATE 116: SWALLOWS AND MARTINS

1 **RED-RUMPED SWALLOW** *Hirundo daurica* **Page 691**
Adult (1a, 1b, 1c) and juvenile (1d) ***H. d. nipalensis*****; adult** ***H. d. hyperythra*** **(1e, 1f).** Widespread resident; unrecorded in parts of the northwest and northeast. Rufous-orange neck sides, rufous-orange rump, finely streaked buffish-white underparts, and black undertail-coverts. Six races in the subcontinent, differing mainly in strength of streaking on underparts and rump, prominence of collar, and coloration of underparts and rump. Summers in upland cultivation and grassy hills; winters in open country and forest clearings.

2 **STRIATED SWALLOW** *Hirundo striolata* **Page 692**
Adult (2a, 2b, 2c) and juvenile (2d). Summer visitor; resident? NE Indian hills and Bangladesh. Told from Red-rumped by larger size, stronger streaking on underparts and rump, and lack of or poorly defined rufous collar (although collar can be incomplete in some races of Red-rumped). Steep cliffs in hills.

3 **STREAK-THROATED SWALLOW** *Hirundo fluvicola* **Page 692**
Adult (3a, 3b, 3c) and juvenile (3d). Resident. Indus plains; widespread in N and C India. Small and compact, with slight fork to long, broad tail. Chestnut crown, streaked throat and breast, white mantle streaks, and brownish rump. Juvenile duller, with browner crown. Cultivation and open country near water.

4 **NORTHERN HOUSE MARTIN** *Delichon urbica* **Page 693**
Adult (4a, 4b, 4c). Summer visitor to W Himalayas; mainly passage migrant elsewhere. Adult told from Asian House Martin by combination of whiter underparts, longer and more deeply forked tail, and paler underwing-coverts. Juvenile (not illustrated) has less glossy upperparts, is rather dingy underneath, and has shallower tail-fork; is more like Asian. Cliffs and gorges.

5 **ASIAN HOUSE MARTIN** *Delichon dasypus* **Page 693**
Adult (5a, 5b, 5c). Resident. Himalayas. Adult told from Northern by dusky underparts, shallower fork to shorter tail, darker underwing, and (not always) dusky centres to undertail-coverts; rump patch often looks smaller and dirty white. Juvenile (not illustrated) has browner upperparts and stronger dusky wash to underparts. Grassy slopes with cliffs, and forest around mountain villages.

6 **NEPAL HOUSE MARTIN** *Delichon nipalensis* **Page 693**
Adult (6a, 6b, 6c). Resident. Himalayas and NE Indian hills. Square-cut tail (lacking indentation even when closed), narrow white rump band, blackish underwing-coverts, black undertail-coverts contrasting sharply with white belly, and blackish throat (only chin black on some). Mountain ridges with cliffs, forest, and around villages.

1e
1f
2c
2d
2b
1b
1c
2a
1a
1d
3c
3b
3d
3a
5b
4b
6b
4c
5c
6c
4a
5a
6a
G. Driessens '97

PLATE 117: BULBULS

1 **CRESTED FINCHBILL** *Spizixos canifrons* **Page 694**
Adult (1a) and juvenile (1b). Resident. NE Indian hills. Stout, pale bill, and crested appearance. Dark tip to tail. Adult has blackish crest and throat, and grey ear-coverts. Juvenile has blackish-brown crown and pale brown ear-coverts. Broadleaved forest and secondary growth.

2 **STRIATED BULBUL** *Pycnonotus striatus* **Page 695**
Adult. Resident. Himalayas and NE Indian hills. Crested, green bulbul with boldly streaked upperparts and finely streaked underparts. Broadleaved forest.

3 **GREY-HEADED BULBUL** *Pycnonotus priocephalus* **Page 695**
Adult. Resident. SW India. Crestless,grey-and-green bulbul. Greenish-yellow forehead, and yellowish bill and iris. Evergreen forest and dense thickets.

4 **BLACK-HEADED BULBUL** *Pycnonotus atriceps* **Page 695**
Adult olive-yellow morph (4a), adult grey morph (4b) and juvenile (4c) *P. a. atriceps*; adult *P. a. fuscoflavescens* (4d). Resident. NE India, Andamans and Bangladesh. Crestless black head, and yellow wing panel; yellow terminal band and black subterminal band to tail. Grey morph rare. Andaman race *fuscoflavescens* has olive-green crown and ear-coverts and brighter yellow underparts. Open forest.

5 **BLACK-CRESTED BULBUL** *Pycnonotus melanicterus* **Page 696**
Adult (5a) and juvenile (5b) *P. m. flaviventris*; adult *P. m. gularis* (5c); adult *P. m. melanicterus* (5d). Resident. Himalayas, NE, E and SW India, Bangladesh and Sri Lanka. Uniform wings and tail. Nominate race in Himalayas and NE and E India has black crest; other races lack crest and have ruby-red (SW India) or yellow (Sri Lanka) throat. Moist broadleaved forest and thick secondary growth.

6 **RED-WHISKERED BULBUL** *Pycnonotus jocosus* **Page 696**
Adult (6a) and juvenile (6b) *P. j. emeria*. Widespread resident; unrecorded in Pakistan, parts of N and NW India and Sri Lanka. Black crest, red 'whiskers', and white underparts with complete or broken breast-band. Juvenile duller and lacks 'whiskers'. Open forest and secondary growth.

7 **WHITE-EARED BULBUL** *Pycnonotus leucotis* **Page 696**
Adult *P. l. leucotis* (7a); adult *P. l. humii* (7b). Resident. Pakistan and NW India. White-cheeked bulbul with black crown and nape, and short or non-existent crest. Thorn scrub and dry, open cultivation.

8 **HIMALAYAN BULBUL** *Pycnonotus leucogenys* **Page 697**
Adult. Resident. N Pakistan hills and Himalayas. Brown crest and nape, and white cheeks with black crescent at rear. Dry scrub and secondary growth.

9 **RED-VENTED BULBUL** *Pycnonotus cafer* **Page 697**
Adult *P. c. humayuni* (9a); adult *P. c. bengalensis* (9b). Widespread resident. Black head with slight crest, and white rump. Mantle and breast vary from pale brown to blackish. Open deciduous forest and secondary growth.

10 **YELLOW-THROATED BULBUL** *Pycnonotus xantholaemus* **Page 697**
Adult. Resident. S Indian hills. Plain yellow-green head, bright yellow throat, and grey breast-band. Thorn jungle and moist deciduous habitats in stony hills.

11 **YELLOW-EARED BULBUL** *Pycnonotus penicillatus* **Page 698**
Adult. Resident. Sri Lanka. Blackish crown, yellow ear-tufts and ear-covert patch, and white tufts from lores. Forest.

1b
1a
2
3
5d
4b
4a
5a
5c
4c
4d
7b
5b
6a
7a
8
9a
6b
9b
10
11
C.D'S

PLATE 118: BULBULS

1 **FLAVESCENT BULBUL** *Pycnonotus flavescens* **Page 698**
Adult. Resident. NE Indian hills. Longer tail and stout black bill compared with Olive Bulbul. White supercilium, brownish crest, yellowish undertail-coverts, and greenish uppertail. Forest and secondary growth.

2 **WHITE-BROWED BULBUL** *Pycnonotus luteolus* **Page 698**
Adult. Resident. Peninsular India and Sri Lanka. White supercilium and crescent below eye, and dark eye-stripe and moustachial stripe. Otherwise nondescript. Dry scrub and forest edges.

3 **WHITE-THROATED BULBUL** *Alophoixus flaveolus* **Page 699**
Adult (3a) and juvenile (3b). Resident. Himalayas, NE India and Bangladesh. Brownish crest, white throat, and yellow breast and belly. Juvenile duller, with browner underparts. Undergrowth in evergreen forest and secondary growth.

4 **OLIVE BULBUL** *Iole virescens* **Page 699**
Adult. Resident. NE India and Bangladesh. Longish bill with pale lower mandible, pale olive-yellow underparts, pale rufous undertail-coverts, and rufous-brown tail. Evergreen forest and secondary growth.

5 **YELLOW-BROWED BULBUL** *Iole indica* **Page 699**
Adult (5a) and juvenile (5b) *I. i. indica.* Resident. Western Ghats and Sri Lanka. Yellow supercilium, eye-ring and underparts. Striking black bill and dark eye. Moist forest and secondary growth.

6 **ASHY BULBUL** *Hemixos flavala* **Page 700**
Adult. Resident. Himalayan foothills, NE India and Bangladesh. Grey crest and upperparts, black mask and tawny ear-coverts, and olive-yellow wing patch. Broadleaved forest; also forest edges in winter.

7 **MOUNTAIN BULBUL** *Hypsipetes mcclellandii* **Page 700**
Adult. Resident. Himalayas and NE India. Brown crest, greyish throat with white streaking, cinnamon-brown breast with buff streaking, and greenish upperparts. Forest and secondary growth.

8 **BLACK BULBUL** *Hypsipetes leucocephalus* **Page 700**
Adult (8a) and juvenile (8b) *H. l. psaroides;* adult *H. l. ganeesa* (8c). Resident. Himalayas, NE and SW India, and Sri Lanka. Slate-grey to blackish bulbul with shallow fork to tail; red bill, legs and feet. Juvenile lacks crest; has whitish underparts with diffuse grey breast-band, and brownish cast to upperparts. Mainly broadleaved forest and plantations.

9 **NICOBAR BULBUL** *Hypsipetes nicobariensis* **Page 701**
Adult. Resident. Nicobars. Drab bulbul with dark brown crown and nape, and whitish throat and breast merging into yellowish belly and undertail-coverts. Forest and secondary growth.

10 **GREY HYPOCOLIUS** *Hypocolius ampelinus* **Page 701**
Male (10a) and female (10b). Winter visitor. S Pakistan and Gujarat. Crested, with long tail and white on primaries. Male has black mask and tail-band. Female rather uniform sandy-brown. Thorn scrub and date-palm groves in semi-desert.

1
2
3a
3b
4
5b
5a
6
7
8a
8b
10b
9
8c
10a
C.D'S

PLATE 119: PRINIAS

1 **HILL PRINIA** *Prinia atrogularis* **Page 704**
Adult breeding (1a) and non-breeding (1b) *P. a. atrogularis*; adult breeding (1c) and non-breeding (1d) *P. a. khasiana*. Resident. E Himalayas and NE Indian hills. Black throat and breast with white spotting in breeding plumage. White supercilium and buffish underparts in non-breeding plumage. Compared with Striated Prinia, has finer bill and unstreaked upperparts. Scrub and grass.

2 **RUFOUS-VENTED PRINIA** *Prinia burnesii* **Page 703**
Adult *P. b. burnesii* (2a); adult *P. b. cinerascens* (2b). Resident. Indus plains in Pakistan and NW India; Brahmaputra plains in NE India. Large size, streaked upperparts, whitish lores/eye-ring, and broad tail. Nominate race has rufous vent. Tall grassland and reedbeds.

3 **STRIATED PRINIA** *Prinia criniger* **Page 703**
Adult breeding (3a) and non-breeding (3b) *P. c. criniger*. Resident. Himalayas, hills of Pakistan and NE India. Large size, streaked upperparts, and stout bill. Dark bill and lores, and indistinct streaking, in breeding plumage. Prominently streaked, with buff lores, in non-breeding plumage. Scrubby hillsides, and long grass in open forest.

4 **GREY-CROWNED PRINIA** *Prinia cinereocapilla* **Page 704**
Adult. Resident. Himalayan foothills and Assam. Orange-buff supercilium, dark blue-grey crown and nape, and rufous-brown mantle and back. Bushes at forest edges and secondary growth.

5 **RUFOUS-FRONTED PRINIA** *Prinia buchanani* **Page 705**
Adult (5a) and grey variant (5b). Resident. Pakistan and N and C India. Rufous-brown crown and broad white tips to tail. Upperparts uniform pale rufous-brown on juvenile. Scrub in semi-desert.

6 **RUFESCENT PRINIA** *Prinia rufescens* **Page 705**
Adult breeding (6a), adult non-breeding (6b) and juvenile (6c). Resident. E Himalayas, hills of NE and E India and Bangladesh. Large bill with paler lower mandible. Grey cast to crown, nape and ear-coverts in summer. In non-breeding plumage has more rufescent mantle and edgings to tertials, and has stronger buffish wash to throat and breast, compared with Grey-breasted. Buzzing call. Tall grassland, grass under forest and secondary growth.

7 **GREY-BREASTED PRINIA** *Prinia hodgsonii* **Page 705**
Adult breeding (7a) and non-breeding (7b) *P. h. rufula*; non-breeding *P. h. hodgsonii* (7c); male (7d) and female (7e) *P. h. pectoralis*. Widespread resident. Small size. Grey breast-band in summer. Where ranges overlap with Rufescent, non-breeding is best distinguished by fine dark bill, grey-brown tail, and greyish wash to sides of neck and breast. Laughing, high-pitched call. Bushes at forest edges, scrub and secondary growth.

2a
1a
1b
3a
2b
3b
1d
1c
4
5b
6c
6a
7b
5a
6b
7a
7c
7e
7d
Clive Byers

PLATE 120: PRINIAS, CISTICOLAS, WHITE-EYES AND TESIAS

1 **JUNGLE PRINIA** *Prinia sylvatica* **Page 706**
Adult breeding (1a) and non-breeding (1b) *P. s. gangetica.* Widespread in lowlands and foothills; unrecorded in Pakistan. Larger than Plain, with stouter bill, uniform wings, and different calls and song. Dry scrub and tall grass.

2 **YELLOW-BELLIED PRINIA** *Prinia flaviventris* **Page 707**
Adult breeding (2a) and juvenile (2b) *P. f. flaviventris.* Resident. Widespread in N subcontinent. White throat and breast and yellow belly. Slate-grey cast to crown and olive-green cast to upperparts. Juvenile has uniform yellowish olive-brown upperparts and yellow underparts. Tall grassland by wetlands.

3 **GRACEFUL PRINIA** *Prinia gracilis* **Page 706**
Adult *P. g. lepida.* Resident. Lowlands in N subcontinent. Small, with fine bill and streaked upperparts. Tall grass and scrub, especially by wetlands.

4 **STREAKED SCRUB WARBLER** *Scotocerca inquieta* **Page 702**
Adult. Resident. Pakistan hills. Vinaceous-buff supercilium and ear-coverts, black throat streaking, greyish upperparts, and boldly streaked crown. Dry stony and scrubby slopes.

5 **PLAIN PRINIA** *Prinia inornata* **Page 708**
Adult breeding (5a) and non-breeding (5b) *P. i. inornata*; breeding *P. i. franklinii* (5c). Widespread resident. Smaller than Jungle, with finer bill. Pale or rufous fringes to tertials, and different call and song. Tall crops, reeds, grassland, scrub and tall grass, and mangroves.

6 **ASHY PRINIA** *Prinia socialis* **Page 707**
Adult breeding (6a) and non-breeding (6b) *P. s. stewarti.* Widespread resident. Slate-grey crown and ear-coverts, red eyes, slate-grey or rufous-brown upperparts, and orange-buff wash to underparts. Sri Lankan race *brevicauda* has very short tail. Tall grass and scrub, open secondary growth and reedbeds.

7 **ZITTING CISTICOLA** *Cisticola juncidis* **Page 701**
Adult breeding (7a) and non-breeding (7b). Widespread resident. Small, with short tail that has prominent white tips. Bold streaking on buff upperparts, including nape, and thin whitish supercilium. Distinctive call and song. Fields and grassland.

8 **BRIGHT-HEADED CISTICOLA** *Cisticola exilis* **Page 702**
Male breeding (8a) and non-breeding (8b) *C. e. tytleri*; male breeding (8c) and non-breeding (8d) *C. e. erythrocephala.* Resident. Terai, NE and S Indian hills, and Bangladesh. Breeding males have unstreaked crown. Otherwise, typically unstreaked rufous nape, rufous supercilium and neck sides, and uniformly dark tail except for narrow buff tips. Distinctive call and song. Tall grassland; scrubby hillsides in S India.

9 **SRI LANKA WHITE-EYE** *Zosterops ceylonensis* **Page 708**
Adult. Resident. Sri Lanka. Dull green upperparts, and olive-yellow throat and breast. Dusky lores and white eye-ring. Forest, gardens and plantations.

10 **ORIENTAL WHITE-EYE** *Zosterops palpebrosus* **Page 709**
Adult. Widespread resident; unrecorded in parts of the northwest. Black lores and white eye-ring, bright yellow throat and breast, and whitish belly. Open broadleaved forest and wooded areas.

11 **CHESTNUT-HEADED TESIA** *Tesia castaneocoronata* **Page 709**
Adult (11a) and juvenile (11b). Resident. Himalayas and NE Indian hills. Adult has chestnut head and yellow underparts. Juvenile has dark rufous underparts. Thick undergrowth in moist forest.

12 **SLATY-BELLIED TESIA** *Tesia olivea* **Page 709**
Adult. Resident. Himalayas and NE Indian hills. Darker grey underparts than Grey-bellied. Crown often brighter than mantle. Bright orange lower mandible without dark tip. Thick undergrowth in moist, mainly evergreen forest.

13 **GREY-BELLIED TESIA** *Tesia cyaniventer* **Page 710**
Adult (13a) and juvenile (13b). Resident. Himalayas, hills of NE India and Bangladesh. Paler grey underparts than Slaty-bellied, with almost whitish belly. Brighter supercilium than crown, and yellow lower mandible with dark tip. Thick undergrowth in moist forest.

1a
1b
2b
2a
3
5c
4
6a
5b
5a
8b
8a
6b
7b
7a
8c
9
11b
8d
10
11a
12
13b
13a
Clive Byers

PLATE 121: BUSH WARBLERS

1 ASIAN STUBTAIL *Urosphena squameiceps* **Page 710**
Adult. Vagrant. Nepal. Very short tail, long supercilium, rufous-brown upperparts, and white underparts. Pale pinkish legs and feet. Tropical broadleaved forest.

2 PALE-FOOTED BUSH WARBLER *Cettia pallidipes* **Page 711**
Adult *C. p. pallidipes* (2a); adult *C. p. osmastoni* (2b). Resident. Himalayas, NE India and S Andamans. Rufous-brown upperparts and whiter underparts compared with Brownish-flanked. Pale pinkish legs and feet. Tall grass and bushes at forest edges.

3 JAPANESE BUSH WARBLER *Cettia diphone* **Page 711**
Adult male (3a) and female (3b). Vagrant. India. Large size (especially male) and long tail. Rufous crown, stout bill, prominent supercilium, and buffy underparts. Scrub jungle, and bushes at forest edges.

4 BROWNISH-FLANKED BUSH WARBLER *Cettia fortipes* **Page 711**
Adult (4a) and 1st-winter? (4b) *C. f. fortipes*; adult *C. f. pallidus* (4c). Resident. Himalayas and NE India. Duskier underparts than Pale-footed, and more olive-tinged upperparts. Open forest and thickets.

5 CHESTNUT-CROWNED BUSH WARBLER *Cettia major* **Page 712**
Adult (5a) and juvenile (5b). Resident. Himalayas and NE Indian hills. Chestnut crown. Told from Grey-sided by larger size, rufous-buff on fore supercilium, and whiter underparts. Summers in rhododendron shrubberies and bushes in forest; winters in reedbeds.

6 ABERRANT BUSH WARBLER *Cettia flavolivacea* **Page 712**
Adult fresh (6a) and worn (6b). Resident. Himalayas and NE Indian hills. Greenish upperparts, and yellowish supercilium and underparts. Bushes at forest edges, long grass and bushes in pine forest.

7 YELLOWISH-BELLIED BUSH WARBLER *Cettia acanthizoides* **Page 712**
Adult. Resident. Himalayas. Small size, pale rufous-brown upperparts, whitish throat and breast, and yellowish belly and flanks. Bamboo stands.

8 GREY-SIDED BUSH WARBLER *Cettia brunnifrons* **Page 713**
Adult (8a) and juvenile (8b). Resident. Himalayas and NE India. Chestnut crown. Told from Chestnut-crowned by small size, shorter whitish supercilium, and greyer underparts. Summers in high-altitude shrubberies and bushes at forest edges; winters in scrub and forest undergrowth.

9 CETTI'S BUSH WARBLER *Cettia cetti* **Page 713**
Adult. Winter visitor and passage migrant. Pakistan and NW India. Large size with big tail; white breast and indistinct supercilium, greyish breast sides and flanks, and whitish tips to undertail-coverts. Reedbeds and tamarisks.

10 SPOTTED BUSH WARBLER *Bradypterus thoracicus* **Page 713**
Adult *B. t. thoracicus* (10a, 10b); adult *B. t. shanensis* (10c). Breeds in Himalayas; winters in foothills and NE Indian plains. Spotting on throat and breast (can be indistinct). Shortish bill, grey ear-coverts and breast, and olive-brown flanks; boldly patterned undertail-coverts. *B. t. shanensis* has brownish wash on breast, weaker spotting, whitish supercilium, and pale lower mandible. Summers in high-altitude shrubberies, grass and bushes; winters in reedbeds and tall grass.

11 LONG-BILLED BUSH WARBLER *Bradypterus major* **Page 714**
Adult worn (11a, 11b) and fresh (11c). Resident. W Himalayas. Spotting on throat and breast (can be indistinct). Long bill, white underparts and unmarked undertail-coverts. Bushy hillsides, and thickets at forest edges.

1
2b
4a
2a
3a
4c
4b
3b
5a
6a
6b
5b
8a
7
9
8b
10a
11a
10b
10c
11c
11b

PLATE 122: BUSH WARBLERS AND *LOCUSTELLA* AND *ACROCEPHALUS* WARBLERS

1 **CHINESE BUSH WARBLER** *Bradypterus tacsanowskius* **Page 714**
Adult (1a) and 1st-winter? (1b). Vagrant. Nepal and India. Grey-brown upperparts, and pale tips to undertail-coverts; underparts often with yellowish wash. Some have fine spotting on lower throat. Reedbeds, grass and bushes, and paddy-fields.

2 **BROWN BUSH WARBLER** *Bradypterus luteoventris* **Page 715**
Adult (2a, 2b). Resident. E Himalayas and NE Indian hills. Rufescent-brown upperparts, rufous-buff breast sides and flanks, rufous-buff supercilium, and lack of prominent pale tips to undertail-coverts. Lacks spotting on throat and breast. Grassy hills, and undergrowth in pine forest.

3 **RUSSET BUSH WARBLER** *Bradypterus seebohmi* **Page 715**
Adult. Resident. E Himalayas. Rich brown upperparts, brown breast sides and flanks, pale fringes to undertail-coverts, and blackish bill. Can have spotted breast. Forest edges and secondary growth.

4 **SRI LANKA BUSH WARBLER** *Bradypterus palliseri* **Page 715**
Adult (4a) and juvenile (4b). Resident. Sri Lanka. Large *Bradypterus* with dark olive-brown upperparts, orange-buff throat (lacking on juvenile), and olive-grey underparts with olive-yellow wash to belly. Dense forest undergrowth.

5 **LANCEOLATED WARBLER** *Locustella lanceolata* **Page 716**
Adult (5a, 5b). Winter visitor. Lowlands, mainly N subcontinent; unrecorded in Pakistan. Streaking on throat, breast and flanks (weak on some). See text for subtle differences from Grasshopper in undertail-coverts and tertials. Tall grassland, and bush/grassland.

6 **GRASSHOPPER WARBLER** *Locustella naevia* **Page 716**
Adult (6a, 6b). Widespread winter visitor. Olive-brown upperparts, indistinct supercilium, and (usually) unmarked or only lightly streaked throat and breast. Tall grassland, reedbeds and paddy-fields.

7 **RUSTY-RUMPED WARBLER** *Locustella certhiola* **Page 716**
Adult (7a) and juvenile (7b). Winters locally in subcontinent. Distinct supercilium, rufous rump and uppertail-coverts, and rather dark tail with white tips. Juvenile has yellowish wash to underparts and light spotting on breast. Reedbeds and paddy-fields.

8 **MOUSTACHED WARBLER** *Acrocephalus melanopogon* **Page 717**
Adult. Mainly winter visitor. Pakistan and N and NW Indian plains. Broad white supercilium, blackish eyestripe, and boldly streaked rufous-brown mantle. Tall reedbeds and tamarisks.

9 **SEDGE WARBLER** *Acrocephalus schoenobaenus* **Page 717**
Adult. Vagrant. India. Broad white supercilium and streaked mantle. Head pattern less striking than Moustached's; also has buffish olive-brown coloration to upperparts, well-defined buffy fringes to tertials and greater coverts, and longer primary projection. Tall vegetation at wetland edges.

10 **BLACK-BROWED REED WARBLER** *Acrocephalus bistrigiceps* **Page 718**
Adult. Winter visitor. Mainly NE India and Bangladesh. Broad supercilium and blackish lateral crown-stripes. Short tail, long primary projection, and dark grey legs. Tall grass and paddy-fields.

11 **PADDYFIELD WARBLER** *Acrocephalus agricola* **Page 718**
Adult fresh (11a) and worn (11b). Widespread winter visitor; unrecorded in Sri Lanka; has bred Baluchistan. Prominent white supercilium behind eye, and stout bill with dark tip. Strong rufous cast to upperparts in fresh plumage. Reedbeds, damp grassland and paddy-fields.

12 **BLUNT-WINGED WARBLER** *Acrocephalus concinens* **Page 718**
Adult fresh (12a) and worn (12b). Summer visitor to W Himalayas; resident in Assam. Longer and stouter bill than Paddyfield, with pale lower mandible. Supercilium indistinct behind eye. Reedbeds, and tall grass near water.

13 **BLYTH'S REED WARBLER** *Acrocephalus dumetorum* **Page 719**
Adult fresh (13a) and worn (13b). Widespread winter visitor and passage migrant. Long bill, olive-brown to olive-grey upperparts and uniform wings. Comparatively indistinct supercilium barely apparent behind eye. Bushes and trees at edges of forest, cultivation and in wooded areas.

1a
1b
2a
2b
3
4a
4b
5a
5b
6a
6b
7a
7b
8
9
10
11a
11b
12a
12b
13a
13b

PLATE 123: LARGE *ACROCEPHALUS* WARBLERS AND GRASSBIRDS

1 **GREAT REED WARBLER** *Acrocephalus arundinaceus* **Page 719**
Adult. Vagrant. Pakistan and India. Differs from Clamorous Reed in shorter, stouter bill, longer primary projection, and shorter-looking tail. Lacks whitish tip to tail and (usually) streaking on breast. Reedbeds.

2 **ORIENTAL REED WARBLER** *Acrocephalus orientalis* **Page 720**
Adult worn (2a) and fresh (2b). Winter visitor. Mainly NE India. Smaller than Clamorous Reed, with shorter, squarer tail. Often has streaking on sides of neck and breast, and well-defined whitish tips to outer rectrices. Reedbeds.

3 **CLAMOROUS REED WARBLER** *Acrocephalus stentoreus* **Page 720**
Adult worn (3a) and fresh (3b) *A. s. brunnescens*; adult *A. s. meridionalis* (3c). Breeds locally in Pakistan, India and Sri Lanka; widespread in winter. Large size, long bill, short primary projection, whitish supercilium, and lacks white at tip of tail. Sri Lankan *meridionalis* darker brown above, and often smaller. Reedbeds and bushes around wetlands.

4 **THICK-BILLED WARBLER** *Acrocephalus aedon* **Page 720**
Adult. Widespread winter visitor; unrecorded in Pakistan and Sri Lanka. Short, stout bill and rounded head. 'Plain-faced' appearance, lacking prominent supercilium or eye-stripe. Tall grass and scrub, reeds and bushes.

5 **STRIATED GRASSBIRD** *Megalurus palustris* **Page 738**
Adult worn (5a) and fresh (5b). Resident. Lowlands in N and C subcontinent. Streaked upperparts, finely streaked breast and long, graduated tail. Has longer and finer bill and more prominent supercilium than Bristled. Tall damp grassland, reedbeds and tamarisks.

6 **BRISTLED GRASSBIRD** *Chaetornis striatus* **Page 739**
Adult. Local resident. Mainly lowlands in India and Nepal. Streaked upperparts and fine streaking on lower throat. Has shorter, stouter bill and less prominent supercilium than Striated, also shorter and broader tail with buffish-white tips. Tall grassland with bushes, and paddy-fields.

7 **RUFOUS-RUMPED GRASSBIRD** *Graminicola bengalensis* **Page 739**
Adult. Resident. Terai and NE plains. Rufous and whitish streaking on black upperparts, white-tipped blackish tail, and white underparts with rufous-buff breast sides and flanks. Tall grass and reeds near water.

8 **BROAD-TAILED GRASSBIRD** *Schoenicola platyura* **Page 739**
Adult fresh (8a) and worn (8b). Resident. Western Ghats and Sri Lanka. Stout bill, long and broad tail, unstreaked rufous-brown to greyish-brown upperparts, and whitish underparts. Tail diffusely barred. Tall grass and reeds on open hillsides.

1
2a
2b
3a
3b
3c
4
5a
6
5b
7
8a
8b
Clive Byers

PLATE 124: *HIPPOLAIS* AND *SYLVIA* WARBLERS

1 **BOOTED WARBLER** *Hippolais caligata* **Page 721**
Adult *H. c. caligata* (1a); adult *H. c. rama* (1b). Breeds in Pakistan; widespread in winter; unrecorded in parts of the northeast. Small size and *Phylloscopus*-like behaviour. Tail looks long and square-ended, and undertail-coverts look short. Often shows faint whitish edges and tip to tail and fringe to tertials. Breeds in tamarisks and reed-grass; winters in scrub and groves in dry habitats.

2 **UPCHER'S WARBLER** *Hippolais languida* **Page 722**
Adult. Summer visitor to Baluchistan. Large size and heavy appearance. Long, full tail is often swayed or flicked downwards. Grey upperparts, often with dark wings and tail. Tail usually shows white sides and tip; usually whitish fringes to wing-coverts and tertials. Open stony and bushy hillsides.

3 **GARDEN WARBLER** *Sylvia borin* **Page 783**
Adult. Vagrant. India. Rather featureless. Stout-billed, stocky appearance and plain face, with just faint suggestion of greyish supercilium, aid separation from *Hippolais* and *Acrocephalus* warblers. Forest undergrowth and bushes.

4 **GREATER WHITETHROAT** *Sylvia communis* **Page 784**
Male (4a) and female (4b). Passage migrant in Pakistan and NW India; has bred in Baluchistan. Larger and longer-tailed than Lesser, with broad, well-defined, sandy-brown to pale rufous-brown fringes to greater coverts and tertials, and orange-brown to pale brown (not grey) legs and feet. Standing crops and bushes.

5 **LESSER WHITETHROAT** *Sylvia curruca* **Page 784**
Adult *S. c. blythi* (5a); adult *S. c. minula* (5b); adult *S. c. althaea* (5c). Breeds in Pakistan hills and W Himalayas; widespread in winter. Brownish-grey upperparts, grey crown with darker ear-coverts, blackish bill, and dark grey legs and feet. *S. c. althaea* is largest and darkest race; *minula* the most finely built, with pale, sandy grey-brown upperparts. Scrub.

6 **MÉNÉTRIES'S WARBLER** *Sylvia mystacea* **Page 785**
Male (6a) and female (6b). Summer visitor. Baluchistan. Small size, with long tail. Male has blackish hood, reddish-brown eye-ring, and pinkish wash to throat and breast, with white submoustachial line. Female/first-winter has rather uniform sandy grey-brown upperparts (lacking darker mask), dark tail, and pale legs and feet. Scrub in semi-desert.

7 **DESERT WARBLER** *Sylvia nana* **Page 785**
Adult. Winter visitor. Pakistan and NW India. Small size, sandy-brown upperparts, rufous rump and tail, yellow iris, and yellowish legs and feet. Scrub in desert and rocky hills.

8 **BARRED WARBLER** *Sylvia nisoria* **Page 785**
Male (8a) and 1st-winter (8b). Vagrant. Pakistan and India. Large size, stout bill, and pale edges and tips to tertials and wing-coverts. Adult has yellow iris and variable barring on underparts. First-winter barred on undertail-coverts and occasionally on flanks. Bushes.

9 **ORPHEAN WARBLER** *Sylvia hortensis* **Page 786**
Adult male (9a), adult female (9b) and 1st-winter (9c). Summer visitor to Pakistan; winters mainly in India. Larger and bigger-billed than Lesser Whitethroat. Adult has blackish crown, pale grey mantle, blackish tail, and pale iris. First-year has crown concolorous with mantle, with darker grey ear-coverts; see text for differences from Lesser Whitethroat. Breeds on bush-covered hillsides; winters in scrub and groves.

1a
1b
2
3
4a
5b
5a
4b
5c
6a
7
6b
9a
8a
9b
8b
9c
Clive Byers

PLATE 125: TAILORBIRDS, WHITE-BROWED TIT WARBLER AND *PHYLLOSCOPUS* WARBLERS

1 **MOUNTAIN TAILORBIRD** *Orthotomus cuculatus* **Page 722**
Adult (1a) and juvenile (1b). Resident. E Himalayas, NE India and Bangladesh. Long bill, yellowish supercilium, greyish throat and breast, and yellow belly. Juvenile has olive green crown and nape. Evergreen forest and secondary growth.

2 **COMMON TAILORBIRD** *Orthotomus sutorius* **Page 723**
Male (2a) and female (2b) *O. s. guzuratus*; male *O. s. sutorius* (2c). Widespread resident. Rufous forehead, greenish upperparts, and whitish underparts including undertail-coverts. Bushes in gardens, cultivation edges and forest edges.

3 **DARK-NECKED TAILORBIRD** *Orthotomus atrogularis* **Page 723**
Male (3a) and female (3b). Resident. E Himalayas, NE India and Bangladesh. Male has black on throat and breast. Female has yellow at bend of wing and on undertail-coverts. Dense scrub and edges of evergreen forest.

4 **WHITE-BROWED TIT WARBLER** *Leptopoecile sophiae* **Page 723**
Male (4a) and female (4b) *L. s. sophiae*; male (4c) and female (4d) *L. s. obscura*. Resident. N Himalayas from Pakistan to W Nepal. Whitish supercilium, rufous crown, and lilac and purple in plumage. Dwarf scrub in semi-desert.

5 **WILLOW WARBLER** *Phylloscopus trochilus* **Page 724**
Adult. [Two published records, now considered unreliable. Much as Common Chiffchaff, but paler legs, orange at base of bill, and longer primary projection. Often with yellow on supercilium and breast. Bushes and trees].

6 **COMMON CHIFFCHAFF** *Phylloscopus collybita* **Page 724**
Adult fresh (6a) and worn (6b) *P. c. tristis*; adult *P. c. collybita* (6c). Winter visitor. N subcontinent. Brownish to greyish upperparts; olive-green edges to wing-coverts, remiges and rectrices. Black bill and legs. No wingbar. *P. c. collybita* has olive crown and mantle and yellow supercilium and underparts. Forest, bushes, crops and reedbeds.

7 **MOUNTAIN CHIFFCHAFF** *Phylloscopus sindianus* **Page 725**
Adult. Pakistan and NW India; breeds in Himalayas, winters in plains and foothills. Much as Common Chiffchaff, but generally lacks olive-green tone to back and to edges of wing-coverts, remiges and rectrices. Different call. Breeds in bushes; winters in riverain trees and bushes.

8 **PLAIN LEAF WARBLER** *Phylloscopus neglectus* **Page 725**
Adult fresh (8a) and worn (8b). Breeds in hills of Baluchistan and Kashmir; winters mainly in Pakistan lowlands. Much as Common Chiffchaff, but smaller, with shorter tail, no olive-green or yellow in plumage, and different call. Breeds in juniper and pine forest; winters in open wooded areas.

9 **DUSKY WARBLER** *Phylloscopus fuscatus* **Page 726**
Adult. Winter visitor. Himalayan foothills, NE India and Bangladesh. Brown upperparts and whitish underparts, with buff flanks. Prominent supercilium, and hard *chack* call. Bushes and long grass.

10 **SMOKY WARBLER** *Phylloscopus fuligiventer* **Page 726**
Adult *P. f. fuligiventer* (10a); adult *P. f. tibetanus* (10b). Breeds in C and E Himalayas; winters in adjacent foothills and plains. Very dark, with short yellowish supercilium, and yellowish centre of throat and belly. *P. f. tibetanus* has greyish-white supercilium and belly centre. Breeds in high-altitude shrubberies; winters in dense undergrowth near water.

11 **RADDE'S WARBLER** *Phylloscopus schwarzi* **Page 728**
Fresh autumn (11a) and worn winter (11b). Vagrant. Nepal, India and Bangladesh. Stout bill, long buffish-white supercilium contrasting with dark eye-stripe, orangish legs and feet; call different from Dusky's. In fresh plumage, can show pronounced greenish-olive cast to upperparts and buffish-yellow cast to supercilium and underparts. Bushes and undergrowth.

1a
1b
2a
2b
2c
3a
3b
4a
4b
4c
4d
5
6a
6b
6c
7
8a
8b
9
10a
10b
11a
11b
Clive Byers

PLATE 126: *PHYLLOSCOPUS* WARBLERS

1 **TICKELL'S LEAF WARBLER** *Phylloscopus affinis* **Page 726**
Fresh. Breeds in Himalayas; widespread in winter; unrecorded in Sri Lanka. Dark greenish to greenish-brown upperparts, and bright yellow supercilium concolorous with throat and breast. Some worn birds paler on supercilium and underparts. Breeds in open country with bushes; winters in bushes at edges of forest and cultivation.

2 **BUFF-THROATED WARBLER** *Phylloscopus subaffinis* **Page 727**
Fresh. Vagrant? to India. Yellowish-buff underparts, buffish-yellow supercilium, and extensive dark tip to lower mandible. Habitat in region unknown.

3 **SULPHUR-BELLIED WARBLER** *Phylloscopus griseolus* **Page 727**
Fresh. Breeds in hills of W Pakistan and W Himalayas; winters mainly in N and C India. Dark greyish upperparts, bright yellow supercilium, and dusky yellow underparts strongly washed with buff. Soft *quip* call. Breeds on stony bushy slopes; winters in rocky areas and around old buildings.

4 **BUFF-BARRED WARBLER** *Phylloscopus pulcher* **Page 728**
Fresh *P. p. pulcher*. Resident. Himalayas and NE Indian hills. Buffish-orange wing-bars, yellowish supercilium and wash to underparts, white on tail, and small yellowish rump patch. Breeds in subalpine shrubberies and forest; winters in broadleaved forest.

5 **ASHY-THROATED WARBLER** *Phylloscopus maculipennis* **Page 728**
Fresh. Resident. Himalayas and NE Indian hills. Small size, greyish throat and breast, yellow belly and flanks, white supercilium and crown-stripe, yellow rump, and white on tail. Forest; also secondary growth in winter.

6 **LEMON-RUMPED WARBLER** *Phylloscopus chloronotus* **Page 729**
Fresh *P. c. chloronotus* (6a); fresh *P. c. simlaensis* (6b). Resident. Breeds in Himalayas; winters lower down and in NE Indian hills. Yellowish crown-stripe and rump band, dark lateral crown-stripes, and whitish underparts. Forest; also secondary growth in winter.

7 **BROOKS'S LEAF WARBLER** *Phylloscopus subviridis* **Page 729**
Fresh (7a) and worn (7b). Breeds in Pakistan Himalayas; winters in plains and hills in Pakistan and N India. Yellow supercilium and ear-coverts; variable yellow wash to throat and breast. Lacks dark lateral crown-stripes and obvious pale rump band. Summers in coniferous and mixed forest; winters in bushes and well-wooded areas.

8 **HUME'S WARBLER** *Phylloscopus humei* **Page 730**
Fresh (8a) and worn (8b) *P. h. humei*. Breeds in Himalayas; winters in plains. Lacks rump band and well-defined crown-stripe. Has buffish or whitish wing-bars and supercilium. Bill appears all-dark, and legs are normally blackish-brown. Breeds in coniferous forest and subalpine shrubberies; winters in forest and secondary growth.

9 **YELLOW-BROWED WARBLER** *Phylloscopus inornatus* **Page 730**
Fresh. Winter visitor. E Himalayas, NE and S India, and Bangladesh. Lacks rump band and well-defined crown-stripe. Has yellowish/whitish wing-bars and supercilium. Bill has orange at base. Groves and open forest.

10 **ARCTIC WARBLER** *Phylloscopus borealis* **Page 731**
Fresh. Vagrant. Andamans. Buzzing *dziit* call. Prominent supercilium falls short of forehead; broad eye-stripe reaches bill-base. Mangroves and groves.

11 **GREENISH WARBLER** *Phylloscopus trochiloides* **Page 731**
Fresh (11a) and worn (11b) *P. t. viridanus*; fresh *P. t. trochiloides* (11c); fresh (11d) and worn (11e) *P. t. nitidus*. Breeds in Himalayas and NE Indian hills; widespread in winter. Slurred, loud *chli-wee* call. No crown-stripe; fine wing-bar (sometimes two). Breeds in forest and subalpine shrubberies; winters in well-wooded areas.

12 **PALE-LEGGED LEAF WARBLER** *Phylloscopus tenellipes* **Page 732**
Fresh. Vagrant. India. Pale legs and feet, pale tip to bill, metallic *pink* call. Often buff wash to ear-coverts and olive-brown cast to upperparts, especially rump. Collected on a boat.

13 **LARGE-BILLED LEAF WARBLER** *Phylloscopus magnirostris* **Page 732**
Fresh. Breeds in Himalayas; winters in NE and S India, and Sri Lanka. Clear, loud *der-tee* call. Large, with large dark bill. Very bold yellow-white supercilium and broad dark eye-stripe. Breeds in forest along mountain rivers; winters in evergreen sholas.

14 **TYTLER'S LEAF WARBLER** *Phylloscopus tytleri* **Page 733**
Fresh (14a) and worn (14b). Breeds in W Himalayas; winters mainly in Western Ghats. Slender, mainly dark bill, long fine supercilium, no wing-bars, shortish tail. Breeds in coniferous forest and subalpine shrubberies; winters in broadleaved forest.

1
2
3
4
5
6a
7b
6b
8b
8a
7a
9
10
11d
11a
11c
11e
11b
13
14a
12
14b
Clive Byers

PLATE 127: *PHYLLOSCOPUS, SEICERCUS* AND *ABROSCOPUS* WARBLERS

1 **WESTERN CROWNED WARBLER** *Phylloscopus occipitalis* **Page 733**
Fresh. Breeds in N Pakistan hills and W Himalayas; winters in India, Nepal and Bangladesh. Crown-stripe, large size, greyish-green upperparts, and greyish-white underparts. Head pattern tends to be less striking than on Blyth's Leaf. Forest.

2 **EASTERN CROWNED WARBLER** *Phylloscopus coronatus* **Page 733**
Fresh. Winter visitor. E Himalayan foothills and NE Indian hills. Crown-stripe, yellowish undertail-coverts, large size. Darker, purer green upperparts than Western Crowned; more uniform wings with finer wing-bar than Blyth's Leaf. Broadleaved forest.

3 **BLYTH'S LEAF WARBLER** *Phylloscopus reguloides* **Page 734**
Fresh *P. r. reguloides* (3a); fresh *P. r. kashmiriensis* (3b). Breeds in Himalayas; winters in foothills and adjacent plains. Crown-stripe, yellowish on underparts, and broad wing-bars with dark panel across greater coverts. Forest.

4 **YELLOW-VENTED WARBLER** *Phylloscopus cantator* **Page 734**
Fresh. Resident. E Himalayas and NE Indian hills. Yellow crown-stripe with blackish at sides; yellow throat, white belly, and yellow undertail-coverts. Breeds in evergreen broadleaved forest; winters also in deciduous forest.

5 **GOLDEN-SPECTACLED WARBLER** *Seicercus burkii* **Page 735**
Adult. Breeds in Himalayas and NE Indian hills; winters lower down in same hills, also in Bangladesh and E India. Yellow eye-ring, and yellowish-green face. Forest understorey.

6 **GREY-HOODED WARBLER** *Seicercus xanthoschistos* **Page 735**
Adult *S. x. xanthoschistos* (6a); adult *S. x. albosuperciliaris* (6b). Resident. Himalayas and NE Indian hills. *Phylloscopus*-like appearance. Whitish supercilium, and grey crown with pale central stripe; yellow underparts and no wing-bars. Forest and secondary growth.

7 **WHITE-SPECTACLED WARBLER** *Seicercus affinis* **Page 736**
Adult. Resident. Mainly E Himalayas and NE Indian hills. White eye-ring, grey crown and supercilium, well-defined blackish lateral crown-stripes; greenish lower ear-coverts, and yellow lores and chin. Forest.

8 **GREY-CHEEKED WARBLER** *Seicercus poliogenys* **Page 736**
Adult. Resident. E Himalayas and NE Indian hills. White eye-ring, and dark grey head with poorly defined lateral crown-stripes; grey ear-coverts, grey lores and white chin. Evergreen broadleaved forest.

9 **CHESTNUT-CROWNED WARBLER** *Seicercus castaniceps* **Page 736**
Adult. Resident. Himalayas and NE Indian hills. Chestnut crown, white eye-ring, and grey ear-coverts; white belly, yellow rump and wing-bars, and white on tail. Mainly oak forest.

10 **BROAD-BILLED WARBLER** *Tickellia hodgsoni* **Page 737**
Adult. Resident. E Himalayas and NE Indian hills. Chestnut crown and greyish-white supercilium; grey throat and breast, yellow belly, white on tail, and no wing-bars. Understorey in evergreen broadleaved forest.

11 **RUFOUS-FACED WARBLER** *Abroscopus albogularis* **Page 737**
Adult. Resident. E Himalayas and NE Indian hills. Rufous face, and black on throat; yellow breast and white belly, whitish rump, no wing-bars, no white on tail. Bamboo.

12 **BLACK-FACED WARBLER** *Abroscopus schisticeps* **Page 737**
Adult *A. s. schisticeps* (12a); adult *A. s. flavimentalis* (12b). Resident. Himalayas and NE Indian hills. Black mask, yellow supercilium and throat, and grey crown. Moist broadleaved forest.

13 **YELLOW-BELLIED WARBLER** *Abroscopus superciliaris* **Page 738**
Adult. Resident. Himalayas, hills of NE India and Bangladesh. White supercilium and greyish crown; white throat and breast, yellow underparts, no wing-bars, no white on tail. Bamboo.

14 **GOLDCREST** *Regulus regulus* **Page 694**
Adult male (14a) and juvenile (14b). Resident. Himalayas. Small size; yellow centre to crown. Mainly coniferous forest.

1
3a
3b
2
4
5
6a
6b
7
8
9
10
11
12a
12b
13
14a
14b

PLATE 128: LAUGHINGTHRUSHES

1 ASHY-HEADED LAUGHINGTHRUSH *Garrulax cinereifrons* **Page 740**
Adult. Resident. Sri Lanka. Greyish head, rufous-brown upperparts, and deep buff underparts with whiter throat. Dense wet forest and bamboo thickets.

2 WHITE-THROATED LAUGHINGTHRUSH *Garrulax albogularis* **Page 740**
Adult. Resident. Himalayas, and Assam. White throat and upper breast, rufous-orange belly, and broad white tip to tail. Broadleaved and mixed forest and secondary growth.

3 WHITE-CRESTED LAUGHINGTHRUSH *Garrulax leucolophus* **Page 740**
Adult. Resident. Himalayas, NE India and Bangladesh. White crest and black mask, white throat and upper breast, and chestnut mantle. Broadleaved forest and secondary growth.

4 LESSER NECKLACED LAUGHINGTHRUSH *Garrulax monileger* **Page 741**
Adult. Resident. Himalayas, NE India and Bangladesh. Smaller than Greater Necklaced. Olive-brown primary coverts, narrow necklace thinning at centre, blackish lores, incomplete lower black border to ear-coverts (see also p.741). Moist broadleaved forest and secondary growth.

5 GREATER NECKLACED LAUGHINGTHRUSH *Garrulax pectoralis* **Page 742**
Adult. Resident. Himalayas, NE India and Bangladesh. Larger and bigger-billed than Lesser Necklaced. Blackish primary coverts, broad necklace, pale lores, and complete black moustachial stripe bordering white, black or black-and-white ear-coverts. (see also p.741). Moist broadleaved forest and secondary growth.

6 RUFOUS-NECKED LAUGHINGTHRUSH *Garrulax ruficollis* **Page 742**
Adult. Resident. Himalayas, NE India and Bangladesh. Black face and throat, rufous patch on neck side, rufous vent. Forest edges, secondary growth and bushes in cultivation.

7 STRIATED LAUGHINGTHRUSH *Garrulax striatus* **Page 742**
Adult *G. s. vibex* (7a); head of *G. s. cranbrooki* (7b). Resident. Himalayas and NE India. Crested appearance, white streaking on head and body, stout black bill. Broadleaved forest.

8 CHESTNUT-BACKED LAUGHINGTHRUSH *Garrulax nuchalis* **Page 743**
Adult. Resident. NE Indian hills. White ear-coverts and sides of throat, black chin and centre of throat, grey crown, and rufous mantle. Scrub-covered ravines.

9 YELLOW-THROATED LAUGHINGTHRUSH *Garrulax galbanus* **Page 743**
Adult. Resident. Hills of NE India and Bangladesh. Yellowish lower belly and vent, black chin, pale olive-brown upperparts, and mainly grey tail with white tips. Tall grass with trees and bushes, also forest edges.

10 WYNAAD LAUGHINGTHRUSH *Garrulax delesserti* **Page 743**
Adult. Resident. Western Ghats. Slate-grey crown with blackish ear-coverts, and white throat contrasting with grey breast. Mainly moist evergreen forest.

11 RUFOUS-VENTED LAUGHINGTHRUSH *Garrulax gularis* **Page 743**
Adult. Resident. Himalayan foothills, hills of NE India and Bangladesh. Rufous flanks and vent, yellow chin, rufous-brown upperparts, and rufous outer tail lacking white tips. Mainly dense evergreen undergrowth.

12 MOUSTACHED LAUGHINGTHRUSH *Garrulax cineraceus* **Page 744**
Adult. Resident. NE Indian hills. Black moustachial stripe breaking into black streaking on side of throat; grey-buff supercilium, and general greyish-olive coloration. Undergrowth in moist forest and secondary growth.

13 RUFOUS-CHINNED LAUGHINGTHRUSH *Garrulax rufogularis* **Page 744**
Adult *G. r. rufogularis* (13a); adult *G. r. occidentalis* (13b). Resident. Himalayas and NE India. Rufous chin and throat, black barring on upperparts, irregular black spotting on underparts, and rufous-orange tips to tail and vent. Undergrowth in broadleaved forest.

14 SPOTTED LAUGHINGTHRUSH *Garrulax ocellatus* **Page 744**
Adult. Resident. Himalayas. White spotting on chestnut upperparts, black throat and barring on breast, and white tips to chestnut, grey and black tail. Undergrowth in forest and rhododendron shrubberies.

1
2
3
5
4
7a
6
7b
8
13b
9
13a
10
12
11
14
Craig Robson '97

PLATE 129: LAUGHINGTHRUSHES

1 **GREY-SIDED LAUGHINGTHRUSH** *Garrulax caerulatus* **Page 745**
Adult *G. c. caerulatus.* Resident. Himalayas and NE India. Black face with blue orbital skin, black scaling on rufous-brown crown, and white underparts. Undergrowth in moist forest and bamboo thickets.

2 **SPOT-BREASTED LAUGHINGTHRUSH** *Garrulax merulinus* **Page 745**
Adult. Resident. NE Indian hills. Bold brown spotting on throat and breast; uniform rufescent olive-brown upperparts, wings and tail. Undergrowth in moist forest and bamboo thickets.

3 **WHITE-BROWED LAUGHINGTHRUSH** *Garrulax sannio* **Page 745**
Adult. Resident. NE Indian hills. Broad buffish-white supercilium and buffish-white patch on cheeks. Forest undergrowth, secondary growth and bamboo thickets.

4 **NILGIRI LAUGHINGTHRUSH** *Garrulax cachinnans* **Page 746**
Adult. Resident. SW Indian hills. Rufous throat and breast, rufous ear-coverts. Forest undergrowth and scrub.

5 **GREY-BREASTED LAUGHINGTHRUSH** *Garrulax jerdoni* **Page 746**
Adult *G. j. fairbanki* (5a); adult *G. j. jerdoni* (5b); adult *G. j. meridionale* (5c). Resident. Western Ghats. Grey or grey-streaked white throat and breast, greyish ear-coverts. Two races lack black chin. Thickets with wild raspberry.

6 **STREAKED LAUGHINGTHRUSH** *Garrulax lineatus* **Page 746**
Adult *G. l. lineatus* (6a); adult *G. l. imbricatus* (6b). Resident. Pakistan hills and Himalayas. Fine white streaking on mantle and underparts; otherwise, rather uniform brown or greyish and brown. Scrub-covered hills, secondary growth and bushes in cultivation.

7 **STRIPED LAUGHINGTHRUSH** *Garrulax virgatus* **Page 747**
Adult. Resident. NE hills. Chestnut wing-coverts, white shaft streaking on upperparts and underparts, whitish supercilium and ear-covert patch, chestnut throat. Undergrowth in evergreen forest and secondary growth.

8 **BROWN-CAPPED LAUGHINGTHRUSH** *Garrulax austeni* **Page 747**
Adult. Resident. NE Indian hills. Rufous-brown and white scaling on underparts, buff shaft streaking and spotting on rufous-brown head, rufous-brown wings. Bamboo thickets and bushes in cultivation.

9 **BLUE-WINGED LAUGHINGTHRUSH** *Garrulax squamatus* **Page 747**
Adult. Resident. Himalayas and NE India. White iris, black supercilium, rufous and bluish wing panels, black rear edge to wing, chestnut uppertail-coverts, and rufous-tipped tail. Undergrowth in moist forest and bamboo thickets.

10 **SCALY LAUGHINGTHRUSH** *Garrulax subunicolor* **Page 748**
Adult. Resident. Himalayas. Yellow iris, olive and blue-grey wing panels, olive uppertail-coverts, and white-tipped tail; lacks black supercilium. Undergrowth in moist forest and rhododendron shrubberies.

11 **VARIEGATED LAUGHINGTHRUSH** *Garrulax variegatus* **Page 749**
Adult *G. v. variegatus* (11a); adult *G. v. similis* (11b). Resident. W and C Himalayas. Grey or olive, with black patches on greyish wings, rufous-buff forehead and malar stripe, and black throat. Forest undergrowth and rhododendron shrubberies.

12 **BLACK-FACED LAUGHINGTHRUSH** *Garrulax affinis* **Page 749**
Adult *G. a. bethelae.* Resident. Himalayas. Black supercilium and ear-coverts, white malar stripe and neck-side patch, and grey-tipped tail. Forest and shrubberies above treeline.

13 **CHESTNUT-CROWNED LAUGHINGTHRUSH** *Garrulax erythrocephalus* **Page 749**
Adult *G. e. erythrocephalus* (13a); adult *G. e. chrysopterus* (13b); adult *G. e. nigrimentus* (13c). Resident. Himalayas and NE India. Chestnut on head, dark scaling/spotting on mantle and breast, olive-yellow wings, and olive-yellow tail sides. Undergrowth in forest and bushes in cultivation.

14 **RED-FACED LIOCICHLA** *Liocichla phoenicea* **Page 750**
Adult. Resident. Himalayas and NE India. Crimson ear-coverts and neck sides, crimson and orange on wing, and rufous-orange tip to black tail. Undergrowth in moist forest and thickets.

1
2
3
5a
5b
4
11a
5c
6b
11b
6a
7
12
8
13c
9
10
13a
14
13b
Craig Robson '97

PLATE 130: BABBLERS, INCLUDING SCIMITAR BABBLERS

1 **ABBOTT'S BABBLER** *Malacocincla abbotti* **Page 750**
Adult. Resident. Himalayan foothills, NE India and Bangladesh. Top heavy, with large bill. Unspotted white throat and breast, grey lores and supercilium, rufous uppertail-coverts and tail, and rufous-buff flanks and vent. Thickets in moist forest.

2 **BUFF-BREASTED BABBLER** *Pellorneum tickelli* **Page 751**
Adult. Resident. NE Indian hills. Buff lores, buff throat and breast (some with brown streaking); longish square-ended tail. Undergrowth in moist forest and bamboo thickets.

3 **SPOT-THROATED BABBLER** *Pellorneum albiventre* **Page 751**
Adult *P. a. albiventre.* Resident. E Himalayan foothills, hills of NE India and Bangladesh. White throat with diffuse grey spotting, olive-brown breast and flanks, and grey lores and supercilium; rounded tip to short tail. Scrub and secondary growth.

4 **MARSH BABBLER** *Pellorneum palustre* **Page 751**
Adult. Resident. NE India and Bangladesh. Bold streaking on breast and flanks, grey fore-supercilium, olive-brown crown concolorous with mantle, and rufous-buff wash to breast. Reedbeds and tall grassland.

5 **PUFF-THROATED BABBLER** *Pellorneum ruficeps* **Page 752**
Adult *P. r. ruficeps* (5a); adult *P. r. mandellii* (5b). Resident. Himalayan foothills, hills of NE India and Bangladesh. Rufous-brown to chestnut crown, and bold brown spotting on breast. Forest undergrowth and secondary growth.

6 **BROWN-CAPPED BABBLER** *Pellorneum fuscocapillum* **Page 752**
Adult *P. f. fuscocapillum.* Resident. Sri Lanka. Brown cap, and deep cinnamon to pale cinnamon-buff sides of head and underparts. Forest undergrowth and thick scrub.

7 **LARGE SCIMITAR BABBLER** *Pomatorhinus hypoleucos* **Page 752**
Adult. Resident. Hills of NE India and Bangladesh. Large; dull bill. Grey ear-coverts, breast sides and flanks, rufous on neck sides. Reeds, tall grass and forest undergrowth.

8 **SPOT-BREASTED SCIMITAR BABBLER** *Pomatorhinus erythrocnemis* **Page 753**
Adult. Resident. Hills of NE India and Bangladesh. White throat, well-defined brown spotting on breast, rufous lores and ear-coverts, and olive-brown breast sides and flanks. Forest undergrowth and secondary growth.

9 **RUSTY-CHEEKED SCIMITAR BABBLER** *Pomatorhinus erythrogenys* **Page 753**
Adult *P. e. erythrogenys.* Resident. Himalayas. Rufous down sides of neck, breast and flanks. E Himalayan birds can have noticeably grey or grey-streaked throat and breast. Forest undergrowth and thick scrub.

10 **INDIAN SCIMITAR BABBLER** *Pomatorhinus horsfieldii* **Page 754**
Adult *P. h. horsfieldii* (10a); adult *P. h. melanurus* (10b). Resident. Hills of peninsular India and Sri Lanka. Yellow bill and white supercilium. Breast sides and flanks grey to blackish in peninsular India, olive-brown to chestnut-brown in Sri Lanka. Forest and secondary growth.

11 **WHITE-BROWED SCIMITAR BABBLER** *Pomatorhinus schisticeps* **Page 753**
Adult *P. s. schisticeps.* Resident. Himalayan foothills, hills of NE India and Bangladesh. White centre to breast and belly, chestnut sides to neck and breast, and usually has slate-grey crown. Forest and secondary growth.

12 **STREAK-BREASTED SCIMITAR BABBLER** *Pomatorhinus ruficollis* **Page 754**
Adult. Resident. Himalayas and NE India. Olive-brown streaking on breast and belly, distinct rufous neck patch extending diffusely across nape. Smaller and smaller-billed than White-browed, with olive-brown crown. Forest undergrowth and dense scrub.

13 **RED-BILLED SCIMITAR BABBLER** *Pomatorhinus ochraceiceps* **Page 755**
Adult *P. o. austeni.* Resident. NE Indian hills. Fine orange-red bill, white throat and white/pale buff breast, uniform buffish olive-brown crown. Forest undergrowth and bamboo thickets.

14 **CORAL-BILLED SCIMITAR BABBLER** *Pomatorhinus ferruginosus* **Page 755**
Adult *P. f. ferruginosus* (14a); adult *P. f. formosus* (14b). Resident. E Himalayas and NE India. Stout red bill, rufous/rich buff underparts, white malar stripe and upper throat. Nominate race has blackish crown. Undergrowth in moist forest and bamboo thickets.

15 **SLENDER-BILLED SCIMITAR BABBLER** *Xiphirhynchus superciliaris* **Page 755**
Adult. Resident. Himalayas and NE India. Long, downcurved black bill, feathery white supercilium, deep rufous underparts. Undergrowth in moist forest and bamboo thickets.

1
2
3
5b
6
4
5a
7
8
10b
10a
9
11
12
15
14a
13
14b
Craig Robson '97

PLATE 131: WREN BABBLERS

1 **LONG-BILLED WREN BABBLER** *Rimator malacoptilus* **Page 756**
Adult. Resident. E Himalayas and NE Indian hills. Downcurved bill, dark moustachial stripe, fine buff shaft streaking on upperparts, broad buff streaking on underparts. Forest undergrowth and ravines.

2 **STREAKED WREN BABBLER** *Napothera brevicaudata* **Page 756**
Adult. Resident. NE Indian hills. Grey face, diffuse grey throat streaks, rufous-brown underparts, untidily streaked upperparts. Moist forest on rocky ground and ravines.

3 **EYEBROWED WREN BABBLER** *Napothera epilepidota* **Page 756**
Adult *N. e. roberti* (3a); adult *N. e. guttaticollis* (3b). Resident. E Himalayas and NE Indian hills. Prominent supercilium and dark eye-stripe, dark spotting on throat and breast, white spots on wing-coverts. Moss-covered boulders and logs in dense forest.

4 **SCALY-BREASTED WREN BABBLER** *Pnoepyga albiventer* **Page 757**
Adult white (4a) and fulvous morph (4b) *P. a. albiventer*; adult *P. a. pallidior* (4c). Resident. Himalayas and NE Indian hills. Larger than Winter Wren (Plate 114). Buff spotting on crown and sides of neck. Tall herbage in moist forest.

5 **NEPAL WREN BABBLER** *Pnoepyga immaculata* **Page 757**
Adult white (5a) and fulvous morph (5b). Resident. Nepal Himalayas. Narrow black centres to underpart feathers; lack of buff spotting on crown, neck sides and wings. Tall herbage in dense forest.

6 **PYGMY WREN BABBLER** *Pnoepyga pusilla* **Page 757**
Adult white (6a) and fulvous morph (6b). Resident. Himalayas and NE India. Same size as Winter Wren (Plate 114). Lacks buff spotting on crown and neck sides. Tall herbage in moist forest.

7 **RUFOUS-THROATED WREN BABBLER** *Spelaeornis caudatus* **Page 758**
Adult. Resident. E Himalayas. Rufous-orange throat and breast, and barring on flanks; grey ear-coverts. Mossy rocks and ferns in denser forest.

8 **RUSTY-THROATED WREN BABBLER** *Spelaeornis badeigularis* **Page 758**
Adult. Resident. Mishmi Hills, E Arunachal Pradesh. Rusty-chestnut throat, white and black bars/spots on breast and flanks, olive-brown ear-coverts. Moist subtropical forest.

9 **BAR-WINGED WREN BABBLER** *Spelaeornis troglodytoides* **Page 758**
Adult. Resident. E Himalayas. Finely barred wings and long barred tail, white spotting on crown and sides of neck, and white throat and breast with diffuse dark spotting. Undergrowth in moist forest.

10 **SPOTTED WREN BABBLER** *Spelaeornis formosus* **Page 759**
Adult. Resident. E Himalayas, hills of NE India and Bangladesh. Broad, dark brown barring on rufous-brown wings and tail, irregular white flecking on grey-brown upperparts. Denser undergrowth in moist forest.

11 **LONG-TAILED WREN BABBLER** *Spelaeornis chocolatinus* **Page 759**
Adult *S. c. chocolatinus* (11a); adult *S. c. oatesi* (11b). Resident. NE Indian hills. White or rufous-buff throat and breast. Buff and brown spotting in *chocolatinus*; blackish spotting in *oatesi*. Dense undergrowth in forest and hillsides with moss-covered rocks.

12 **TAWNY-BREASTED WREN BABBLER** *Spelaeornis longicaudatus* **Page 759**
Adult. Resident. NE Indian hills. Grey lores and ear-coverts, orange-buff underparts without prominent black or white spotting. Thick undergrowth in moist forest.

13 **WEDGE-BILLED WREN BABBLER** *Sphenocichla humei* **Page 760**
Adult *S. h. humei* (13a); adult *S. h. roberti* (13b). Resident. Indian E Himalayas and NE Indian hills. Conical yellow bill. Blackish underparts with white shaft streaking in *humei*; white scaling on underparts in *roberti*. Evergreen forest with bamboo.

1
2
3a
4b
4c
4a
3b
6b
5b
5a
10
6a
8
11b
7
11a
12
9
13a
13b
Craig Robson '97

PLATE 132: BABBLERS

1 **RUFOUS-FRONTED BABBLER** *Stachyris rufifrons* **Page 760**
Adult. Resident. E Himalayan foothills, NE and E Indian hills, and Bangladesh. Grey supercilium, olive-brown ear-coverts concolorous with nape, white throat and buff underparts. Thick undergrowth in open forest and ravines.

2 **RUFOUS-CAPPED BABBLER** *Stachyris ruficeps* **Page 760**
Adult. Resident. E Himalayas and NE and E Indian hills. Yellowish-buff supercilium and ear-coverts which contrast with nape, pale yellow throat, and yellowish-buff underparts. Dense undergrowth in moist forest.

3 **BLACK-CHINNED BABBLER** *Stachyris pyrrhops* **Page 761**
Adult. Resident. Himalayas. Black chin and lores, and orange-buff underparts. Undergrowth in open forest and secondary growth.

4 **GOLDEN BABBLER** *Stachyris chrysaea* **Page 761**
Adult *S. c. chrysaea* (4a); adult *S. c. binghami* (4b). Resident. Himalayas, hills of NE India and Bangladesh. Yellow crown with black streaking, black mask, and yellow underparts. Dense undergrowth in moist forest.

5 **GREY-THROATED BABBLER** *Stachyris nigriceps* **Page 761**
Adult *S. n. nigriceps* (5a); adult *S. n. coltarti* (5b). Resident. Himalayas, hills of NE India and Bangladesh. Blackish crown with white streaking, whitish supercilium, and grey or black-and-white throat. Forest undergrowth and secondary growth.

6 **SNOWY-THROATED BABBLER** *Stachyris oglei* **Page 762**
Adult. Resident. Arunachal Pradesh hills. Broad white supercilium and throat, black eye-stripe, and white spotting on neck sides. Dense scrub in rocky ravines; evergreen forest in winter.

7 **TAWNY-BELLIED BABBLER** *Dumetia hyperythra* **Page 762**
Adult *D. h. hyperythra* (7a); adult *D. h. albogularis* (7b). Resident. Peninsular India, S Nepal and Sri Lanka. Rufous-brown forehead and forecrown and orange-buff underparts, with white throat in most of range. Tall grass and scrub.

8 **DARK-FRONTED BABBLER** *Rhopocichla atriceps* **Page 762**
Adult *R. a. atriceps* (8a); adult *R. a. nigrifrons* (8b). Resident. Western Ghats and Sri Lanka. Stocky, with black on head, brown upperparts, and whitish underparts. Dense undergrowth in evergreen biotope.

9 **STRIPED TIT BABBLER** *Macronous gularis* **Page 763**
Adult. Resident. Himalayan foothills, hills of NE, E and S India, and Bangladesh. Rufous-brown cap, pale yellow supercilium, and finely streaked pale yellow throat and breast. Forest undergrowth.

10 **CHESTNUT-CAPPED BABBLER** *Timalia pileata* **Page 763**
Adult. Resident. Himalayan terai and foothills, and N and NE Indian plains. Chestnut cap and black mask contrasting with white forehead and supercilium. Tall grass, reedbeds and scrub.

11 **YELLOW-EYED BABBLER** *Chrysomma sinense* **Page 763**
Adult *C. s. sinense* (11a); adult *C. s. hypoleucum* (11b). Widespread resident; unrecorded in parts of the northwest and northeast. Yellow iris and orange eye-ring, white lores and supercilium, and white throat and breast. Tall grass, bushes and reeds.

12 **JERDON'S BABBLER** *Chrysomma altirostre* **Page 764**
Adult *C. a. altirostre* (12a); adult *C. a. griseigulare* (12b). Resident. Plains of Pakistan and the northeast, and C Nepal terai. Brown iris, grey lores and supercilium, and grey throat and breast. Reedbeds and tall grassland.

1
2
3
4a
4b
5a
5b
6
7a
7b
8a
8b
9
10
11a
11b
12a
12b
Craig Robson '97

PLATE 133: *TURDOIDES* BABBLERS, BABAXES AND MESIAS

1 **SPINY BABBLER** *Turdoides nipalensis* **Page 764**
Adult (1a, 1b). Resident. Nepal Himalayas. White patterning on face, and black shaft streaking on white or buff throat and breast. Dense scrub.

2 **COMMON BABBLER** *Turdoides caudatus* **Page 764**
Adult. Widespread resident; unrecorded in most of NE and E India, W Pakistan and Sri Lanka. Unstreaked whitish throat and breast centre. Dry scrub in plains and low hills.

3 **STRIATED BABBLER** *Turdoides earlei* **Page 765**
Adult. Resident. Plains of N subcontinent. Brown mottling on fulvous throat and breast. Reedbeds and tall grass in wet habitats.

4 **SLENDER-BILLED BABBLER** *Turdoides longirostris* **Page 765**
Adult. Resident. Lowlands of C Nepal and NE subcontinent. Unstreaked dark rufous-brown upperparts, white throat and buff underparts, and curved black bill. Tall grass and reeds.

5 **LARGE GREY BABBLER** *Turdoides malcolmi* **Page 765**
Adult. Resident. Pakistan, W Nepal and Indian peninsula. White sides to long, graduated tail; unmottled pinkish-grey throat and breast. Open dry scrub and cultivation.

6 **RUFOUS BABBLER** *Turdoides subrufus* **Page 766**
Adult. Resident. SW Indian hills. Grey forehead and forecrown, black-and-yellow bill, blackish lores, unstreaked rufous underparts. Tall grass and bamboo at forest edges.

7 **JUNGLE BABBLER** *Turdoides striatus* **Page 766**
Adult *T. s. striatus* (7a); adult *T. s. orientalis* (7b); adult *T. s. somervillei* (7c). Widespread resident; unrecorded in parts of the northwest and northeast. Uniform tail; variable dark mottling and streaking on throat and breast. Deciduous forest and cultivation.

8 **ORANGE-BILLED BABBLER** *Turdoides rufescens* **Page 766**
Adult. Resident. Sri Lanka. Orange bill, cinnamon-rufous underparts, and greyish crown and nape. Wet-zone forest.

9 **YELLOW-BILLED BABBLER** *Turdoides affinis* **Page 767**
Adult *T. a. affinis* (9a); adult *T. a. taprobanus* (9b, 9c). Resident. Peninsular India and Sri Lanka. Creamy-white crown, dark mottling on throat and breast, and pale rump and tail-base. Juvenile and *taprobanus* more similar to Jungle Babbler (see text). Scrub.

10 **CHINESE BABAX** *Babax lanceolatus* **Page 767**
Adult. Resident. Mizoram. Rufous-brown crown, dark chestnut submoustachial stripe, and broad chestnut streaking on breast sides and flanks, with buffish-white underparts. Open forest and thick vegetation on hill-sides.

11 **GIANT BABAX** *Babax waddelli* **Page 768**
Adult. [Doubtful resident in NE Sikkim. Submoustachial stripe diffuse or absent; greyish underparts, with diffuse dark brown streaking evenly across breast and belly. Dry high-altitude scrub.]

12 **SILVER-EARED MESIA** *Leiothrix argentauris* **Page 768**
Male (12a) and juvenile female (12b). Resident. Himalayas and NE Indian hills. Black crown, grey ear-coverts, orange-yellow throat and breast, and crimson wing panel. Bushes and forest undergrowth in ever-green biotope.

13 **RED-BILLED LEIOTHRIX** *Leiothrix lutea* **Page 768**
Male (13a) and juvenile female (13b) *L. l. calipyga*. Resident. Himalayas and NE Indian hills. Red bill, yellowish-olive crown, yellow throat and orange breast, and forked black tail. Forest undergrowth.

1a
1b
2
3
4
5
6
7a
7b
7c
9a
9b
9c
8
10
11
13b
12b
12a
13a
Craig Robson '97

PLATE 134: CUTIA, SHRIKE BABBLERS, BARWINGS AND MINLAS

1 **CUTIA** *Cutia nipalensis* **Page 769**
Male (1a) and female (1b). Resident. Himalayas and NE Indian hills. Grey crown and dark mask, and black barring on flanks. Female has spotted mantle. Mossy broadleaved forest.

2 **BLACK-HEADED SHRIKE BABBLER** *Pteruthius rufiventer* **Page 769**
Male (2a) and female (2b). Resident. Himalayas and NE Indian hills. Male has grey throat and breast, black head without white supercilium, and rufous-brown mantle. Female has black on nape and olive mantle. Dense, moist broadleaved forest.

3 **WHITE-BROWED SHRIKE BABBLER** *Pteruthius flaviscapis* **Page 769**
Male (3a) and female (3b). Resident. Himalayas and NE Indian hills. Male has rufous tertials, white supercilium, and grey mantle. Female has grey crown and olive mantle. Mainly broadleaved forest.

4 **GREEN SHRIKE BABBLER** *Pteruthius xanthochlorus* **Page 770**
Male *P. x. occidentalis* (4a); male *P. x. xanthochlorus* (4b); male *P. x. hybridus* (4c). Resident. Himalayas and NE Indian hills. Grey crown and nape, white wing-bar, and yellowish underparts. Forest.

5 **BLACK-EARED SHRIKE BABBLER** *Pteruthius melanotis* **Page 770**
Male (5a) and female (5b). Resident. Himalayas and NE Indian hills. Black patch on ear-coverts; no chestnut on forehead. Moist broadleaved forest.

6 **CHESTNUT-FRONTED SHRIKE BABBLER** *Pteruthius aenobarbus* **Page 770**
Male *P. a. aenobarbulus* (6a); adult female *P. a. intermedius* (6b). Resident. Meghalaya. Chestnut forehead; lacks black patch on ear-coverts. Edges of evergreen forest.

7 **WHITE-HOODED BABBLER** *Gampsorhynchus rufulus* **Page 771**
Adult (7a) and juvenile (7b). Resident. E Himalayas and NE Indian hills. Adult has white head and underparts. Juvenile has rufous-orange crown. Bamboo jungle and forest undergrowth.

8 **RUSTY-FRONTED BARWING** *Actinodura egertoni* **Page 771**
Adult *A. e. egertoni* (8a); adult *A. e. lewisi* (8b). Resident. Himalayas and NE Indian hills. Rufous front to head, unstreaked grey crown and nape. Undergrowth in moist forest and secondary growth.

9 **HOARY-THROATED BARWING** *Actinodura nipalensis* **Page 771**
Adult. Resident. Himalayas. Prominent buffish-white shaft streaking on crown and nape, black moustachial stripe, and greyish throat and breast. Mossy forest.

10 **STREAK-THROATED BARWING** *Actinodura waldeni* **Page 772**
Adult *A. w. waldeni* (10a); adult *A. w. daflaensis* (10b). Resident. NE Indian hills. Diffuse streaking on tawny-brown or greyish underparts, lack of bold shaft streaking on crown and nape, and unstreaked mantle. Mossy forest.

11 **BLUE-WINGED MINLA** *Minla cyanouroptera* **Page 772**
Adult. Resident. Himalayas and NE Indian hills. Blue on crown and on wings and tail; vinaceous-grey underparts. Bushes in forest and well-wooded country.

12 **CHESTNUT-TAILED MINLA** *Minla strigula* **Page 772**
Adult. Resident. Himalayas and NE Indian hills. Orange crown, black-and-white barring on throat, and yellow sides to tail. Forest.

13 **RED-TAILED MINLA** *Minla ignotincta* **Page 773**
Male (13a) and female (13b). Resident. Himalayas and NE Indian hills. White supercilium contrasting with dark crown and ear-coverts, and yellowish and red (or pink) on tail. Moist forest.

1a
1b
2a
2b
3a
3b
4c
4a
4b
5a
5b
6a
6b
7b
7a
8a
8b
9
10a
10b
11
12
13a
13b
Craig Robson '97

PLATE 135: FULVETTAS, YUHINAS AND FIRE-TAILED MYZORNIS

1 **GOLDEN-BREASTED FULVETTA** *Alcippe chrysotis* **Page 773**
Adult *A. c. chrysotis* (1a); adult *A. c. albilineata* (1b). Resident. Himalayas and NE Indian hills. Blue-grey and yellow fulvetta with silvery-grey ear-coverts. Bamboo.

2 **YELLOW-THROATED FULVETTA** *Alcippe cinerea* **Page 773**
Adult. Resident. Himalayas and NE Indian hills. Yellow supercilium, black lateral crown-stripes and greyish crown, and yellow throat and breast. Undergrowth in moist subtropical forest.

3 **RUFOUS-WINGED FULVETTA** *Alcippe castaneceps* **Page 773**
Adult. Resident. Himalayas and NE Indian hills. Chestnut crown streaked with buffish-white, black wing-bar, and white supercilium. Undergrowth in moist forest.

4 **WHITE-BROWED FULVETTA** *Alcippe vinipectus* **Page 774**
Adult *A. v. kangrae* (4a); adult *A. v. austeni* (4b); adult *A. v. chumbiensis* (4c). Resident. Himalayas and NE Indian hills. Broad white supercilium. Some races have streaked throat. Subalpine shrubberies and bushes in temperate and subalpine forest.

5 **BROWN-THROATED FULVETTA** *Alcippe ludlowi* **Page 775**
Adult. Resident. E Himalayas. No white supercilium or dark lateral crown-stripe; has prominent rufous-brown streaking on throat. Undergrowth in rhododendron forest.

6 **STREAK-THROATED FULVETTA** *Alcippe cinereiceps* **Page 774**
Adult. Resident. NE Indian hills. Lacks white supercilium; has brownish-buff crown and mantle, and greyish ear-coverts. Dense scrub and bamboo.

7 **RUFOUS-THROATED FULVETTA** *Alcippe rufogularis* **Page 775**
Adult. Resident. E Himalayas and NE Indian hills. Rufous collar, broad white supercilium, blackish lateral crown-stripes, uniform brown wings. Bamboo stands and undergrowth in moist tropical forest.

8 **RUSTY-CAPPED FULVETTA** *Alcippe dubia* **Page 775**
Adult. Resident. NE Indian hills. Rufous forehead, white supercilium, prominent buff streaking on neck sides, uniform brown wings. Dense undergrowth in forest.

9 **BROWN-CHEEKED FULVETTA** *Alcippe poioicephala* **Page 776**
Adult. Resident. Hills of India and Bangladesh. Nondescript, lacking any patterning to head or wings. Undergrowth in moist forest and secondary growth.

10 **NEPAL FULVETTA** *Alcippe nipalensis* **Page 776**
Adult. Resident. Himalayas, hills of NE India and Bangladesh. Grey head with black lateral crown-stripes. Undergrowth in moist forest.

11 **STRIATED YUHINA** *Yuhina castaniceps* **Page 778**
Adult *Y. c. rufigenis* (11a); adult *Y. c. castaniceps* (11b). Resident. Himalayas and NE Indian hills. White-tipped tail, grey or rufous crown with pale scaling, and rufous ear-coverts. Broadleaved forest.

12 **WHITE-NAPED YUHINA** *Yuhina bakeri* **Page 778**
Adult. Resident. Himalayas and NE Indian hills. Rufous crest, white nape, and white streaking on ear-coverts. Evergreen subtropical forest.

13 **WHISKERED YUHINA** *Yuhina flavicollis* **Page 778**
Adult *Y. f. flavicollis* (13a); adult *Y. f. albicollis* (13b). Resident. Himalayas and NE Indian hills. Rufous or yellowish hindcollar, black moustachial stripe. Broadleaved forest and secondary growth.

14 **STRIPE-THROATED YUHINA** *Yuhina gularis* **Page 779**
Adult. Resident. Himalayas and NE Indian hills. Streaked throat, and black and orange wing panels. Temperate forest.

15 **RUFOUS-VENTED YUHINA** *Yuhina occipitalis* **Page 779**
Adult. Resident. Himalayas. Grey crest, rufous lores and nape patch. Temperate and subalpine forest.

16 **BLACK-CHINNED YUHINA** *Yuhina nigrimenta* **Page 779**
Adult. Resident. Himalayas and NE Indian hills. Black lores and chin, black crest with grey streaking, and red lower mandible. Moist subtropical forest.

17 **WHITE-BELLIED YUHINA** *Yuhina zantholeuca* **Page 779**
Adult. Resident. Himalayas, NE India and Bangladesh. Olive-yellow upperparts and white underparts. Broadleaved forest.

18 **FIRE-TAILED MYZORNIS** *Myzornis pyrrhoura* **Page 780**
Male (18a) and female (18b). Resident. Himalayas. Emerald-green, with black mask. Subalpine shrubberies, mossy forest and bamboo.

1a
2
3
1b
4a
4c
4b
5
6
9
7
8
10
11b
11a
12
14
13b
13a
15
16
17
18a
18b
Craig Robson '97

PLATE 136: SIBIAS AND PARROTBILLS

1 **RUFOUS-BACKED SIBIA** *Heterophasia annectans* **Page 776**
Adult. Resident. E Himalayas and NE Indian hills. White and black streaking on nape, rufous back and rump, and black tail with white tips. Broadleaved evergreen forest.

2 **RUFOUS SIBIA** *Heterophasia capistrata* **Page 776**
Adult *H. c. capistrata* (2a); adult *H. c. nigriceps* (2b). Resident. Himalayas. Black cap, and rufous or cinnamon-buff nape and underparts; black and grey bands on rufous tail. Mainly broadleaved forest.

3 **GREY SIBIA** *Heterophasia gracilis* **Page 777**
Adult. Resident. NE Indian hills. Black cap, grey mantle, white underparts, and grey tail with black subterminal band. Mainly broadleaved forest.

4 **BEAUTIFUL SIBIA** *Heterophasia pulchella* **Page 777**
Adult *H. p. pulchella* (4a); adult *H. p. nigroaurita* (4b). Resident. NE Indian hills. Blue-grey crown, slate-grey upperparts and underparts, chestnut-brown tertials. Moist broadleaved forest.

5 **LONG-TAILED SIBIA** *Heterophasia picaoides* **Page 777**
Adult. Resident. E Himalayas and NE Indian hills. Long tail with white tips, and white patch on secondaries. Broadleaved forest.

6 **BEARDED PARROTBILL** *Panurus biarmicus* **Page 780**
Male (6a) and female (6b). Vagrant. Pakistan. Black and white on wings. Male has grey head with black moustache. Female and juvenile have plain buff head. Reedbeds.

7 **GREAT PARROTBILL** *Conostoma oemodium* **Page 780**
Adult. Resident. Himalayas. Huge conical yellow bill, greyish-white forehead, dark brown lores. Bamboo stands in forest.

8 **BROWN PARROTBILL** *Paradoxornis unicolor* **Page 781**
Adult. Resident. Himalayas. Stout yellowish bill, blackish lateral crown-stripes, dusky grey underparts. Bamboo stands and bushes.

9 **GREY-HEADED PARROTBILL** *Paradoxornis gularis* **Page 781**
Adult. Resident. Himalayas and NE Indian hills. Black lateral crown-stripes, black throat, grey crown and ear-coverts, whitish underparts. Forest, bushes and bamboo.

10 **BLACK-BREASTED PARROTBILL** *Paradoxornis flavirostris* **Page 781**
Adult. Resident. Assam. Black patch on breast, and rufous-buff underparts. Reedbeds and tall grass.

11 **SPOT-BREASTED PARROTBILL** *Paradoxornis guttaticollis* **Page 782**
Adult. Resident. NE Indian hills. Arrowhead-shaped spotting on breast, and pale buff underparts. Grass and scrub, also bushes and bamboo.

12 **FULVOUS PARROTBILL** *Paradoxornis fulvifrons* **Page 782**
Adult. Resident. Himalayas. Fulvous and olive-brown head markings, and fulvous throat and breast. Bamboo stands.

13 **BLACK-THROATED PARROTBILL** *Paradoxornis nipalensis* **Page 782**
Adult *P. n. nipalensis* (13a); *P. n. humii* (13b), *P. n. crocotius* (13c) and *P. n. poliotis* (13d). Resident. Himalayas and NE Indian hills. Grey or orange crown, blackish lateral crown-stripes and throat, white malar patch. Bamboo and dense forest undergrowth.

14 **LESSER RUFOUS-HEADED PARROTBILL** *Paradoxornis atrosuperciliaris* **Page 783**
Adult *P. a. atrosuperciliaris* (14a); adult *P. a. oatesi* (14b). Resident. E Himalayas and NE Indian hills. Small, with stouter bill than Greater Rufous-headed Parrotbill. Black eyebrow in *atrosuperciliaris* (indistinct in *oatesi*), whitish lores and buffish-orange ear-coverts. Bamboo stands, tall grass and scrub jungle.

15 **GREATER RUFOUS-HEADED PARROTBILL** *Paradoxornis ruficeps* **Page 783**
Adult *P. r. ruficeps* (15a); adult *P. r. bakeri* (15b). Resident. E Himalayas and NE Indian hills. Larger and longer-billed than Lesser. No black supercilium. Lores and ear-coverts deep rufous-orange. Bamboo stands and undergrowth in moist broadleaved forest.

1
2a
2b
3
5
4b
4a
6a
6b
7
10
8
9
11
12
15a
13a
14a
13b
13c
13d
14b
15b
Craig Robson '97

PLATE 137: LARKS

1 **SINGING BUSHLARK** *Mirafra cantillans* **Page 786**
Adult. Resident. Plains and foothills in Pakistan, India and Bangladesh. Stout bill, and rufous on wing; white outer tail feathers, weak and rather restricted spotting on upper breast, and whitish throat with brownish to rufous-buff breast-band. Slimmer, longer-tailed and smaller-billed than Rufous-winged. Open dry scrub, fallow cultivation and grassland.

2 **INDIAN BUSHLARK** *Mirafra erythroptera* **Page 787**
Adult *M. e. erythroptera*. Resident. Plains and plateaux in Pakistan and India; unrecorded in the northeast. Stout bill, and rufous on wing; rufous-buff on outer tail feathers, pronounced dark spotting on breast, dark spotting on ear-coverts and malar region, and more uniform whitish underparts. Hindclaw equal to hindtoe, and shows more rufous on wing than other bushlarks. Stony scrub and fallow cultivation.

3 **RUFOUS-WINGED BUSHLARK** *Mirafra assamica* **Page 787**
Adult *M. a. assamica* (3a); adult *M. a. affinis* (3b). Resident. Mainly plains and plateaux of N, E and S subcontinent. Stout bill, short tail, and rufous on wing; rufous-buff on outer tail feathers, pronounced dark spotting on breast, dark spotting on ear-coverts and malar region, and pale rufous-buff wash to underparts. Hindclaw longer than hindtoe. Upperparts grey and underparts more rufous in *assamica*. Stony scrub and fallow cultivation.

4 **BLACK-CROWNED SPARROW LARK** *Eremopterix nigriceps* **Page 790**
Male (4a) and female (4b, 4c). Resident. Pakistan and NW India. Male has brownish-black crown, nape and underparts. Female has stout bill, rather uniform head and upperparts, and dark grey underwing-coverts; probably inseparable from female Ashy-crowned. Sandy deserts.

5 **ASHY-CROWNED SPARROW LARK** *Eremopterix grisea* **Page 790**
Male. Widespread resident. Male has grey crown and nape, and brownish-black underparts. Female has stout greyish bill, rather uniform head and upperparts, and dark grey underwing-coverts; probably inseparable from female Black-crowned. Open dry scrub and dry cultivation.

6 **BAR-TAILED LARK** *Ammomanes cincturus* **Page 791**
Adult. Resident. Baluchistan. Blackish terminal bar to rufous tail; tertials orangey-buff and contrast with blackish primaries. Smaller and stockier than Desert, with shorter and finer bill. Low stony hills and gravelly plains.

7 **RUFOUS-TAILED LARK** *Ammomanes phoenicurus* **Page 792**
Adult. Resident. Plains in N Pakistan, S Nepal and India. Dusky grey-brown upperparts, rufous-orange underparts, prominent dark streaking on throat and breast, and rufous orange uppertail-coverts and tail, with dark terminal bar. Cultivation, open dry scrub.

8 **DESERT LARK** *Ammomanes deserti* **Page 792**
Adult. Resident. Pakistan and NW India. Tail largely grey-brown with rufous at sides; tertials grey-brown and contrast little with primaries. Larger and slimmer than Bar-tailed, with longer and broader bill. Low, dry rocky hills.

9 **GREATER HOOPOE LARK** *Alaemon alaudipes* **Page 792**
Adult (9a, 9b). Resident. Pakistan and Rann of Kutch. Longish downcurved bill and long legs. Black-and-white wing patterning prominent in flight. Desert.

10 **BIMACULATED LARK** *Melanocorypha bimaculata* **Page 793**
Adult (10a, 10b). Winter visitor. Pakistan and N and NW India. Large, with stout bill and short tail. Prominent white supercilium, black patch on side of breast, and white tip to tail. Semi-desert and fallow cultivation.

11 **TIBETAN LARK** *Melanocorypha maxima* **Page 793**
Adult (11a, 11b). Resident? Ladakh and Sikkim, India. Large, with long bill. Rather uniform head, blackish breast-side patch, white trailing edge to secondaries and tip to tail; crown, ear-coverts and rump can be rufous. Marshes around high-altitude bogs.

1
2
4a
3a
4b
3b
5
4c
6
10b
8
7
9b
10a
9a
11a
11b
Clive Byers

PLATE 138: LARKS

1 **GREATER SHORT-TOED LARK** *Calandrella brachydactyla* **Page 793**
Adult *C. b. dukhunensis* (1a); adult *C. b. longipennis* (1b, 1c). Widespread winter visitor; unrecorded in Sri Lanka and parts of India. Stouter bill than Hume's, with more prominent supercilium and eye-stripe; upperparts warmer, with more prominent streaking; dark breast-side patches often apparent. Breast of *dukhunensis* has warm rufous-buff wash, especially at sides. Open stony grassland, fallow cultivation and semi-desert.

2 **HUME'S SHORT-TOED LARK** *Calandrella acutirostris* **Page 794**
Adult. Summer visitor to Baluchistan and Himalayas; winters mainly in S Nepal and N India. Greyer and less heavily streaked upperparts than Greater, with pinkish uppertail-coverts; dark breast-side patch usually apparent, with greyish-buff breast-band. Head pattern less pronounced than Greater's, with rather uniform ear-coverts. Breeds in high-altitude semi-desert; winters in fallow cultivation.

3 **LESSER SHORT-TOED LARK** *Calandrella rufescens* **Page 794**
Adult *C. r. persica*. Winter visitor. Pakistan and India. Primaries extend beyond tertials. Bill large, short and stout. Broad gorget of fine streaking on breast, fine but clear streaking on upperparts, streaked ear-coverts; whitish supercilia appear to join across bill. Stony foothills.

4 **ASIAN SHORT-TOED LARK** *Calandrella cheleensis* **Page 794**
Adult *C. c. leucophaea*. Vagrant. Pakistan. Primaries extend beyond tertials. Bill small, short and stout. Broad gorget of diffuse streaking on breast, and diffuse streaking on upperparts. Open stony grassland, fallow cultivation and semi-desert.

5 **SAND LARK** *Calandrella raytal* **Page 795**
Adult *C. r. raytal* (5a); adult *C. r. adamsi* (5b). Resident. Widespread in N subcontinent. Small size, short tail, cold sandy-grey upperparts, and whitish underparts with fine sparse streaking on breast. Bill of *adamsi* comparatively fine. Banks of lakes, rivers, tidal creeks and coastal dunes.

6 **CRESTED LARK** *Galerida cristata* **Page 795**
Adult *G. c. chendoola*. Resident. Widespread in N subcontinent. Large size and very prominent crest. Sandy upperparts and well-streaked breast; broad, rounded wings, rufous-buff underwing-coverts and outer tail feathers. Desert, semi-desert, dry cultivation and coastal mudflats.

7 **MALABAR LARK** *Galerida malabarica* **Page 795**
Adult. Resident. Plains and hills in W peninsular India. Prominent crest, heavily streaked rufous upperparts, rufous-buff breast with heavy black spotting, and pale rufous outer tail feathers and underwing-coverts. Bill longer than Sykes's, and has buffish-white belly and flanks. Cultivation, grass-covered hills and open scrub.

8 **SYKES'S LARK** *Galerida deva* **Page 796**
Adult. Resident. Mainly C India. prominent crest and pale rufous outer tail feathers. Smaller than Malabar, with pale rufous underparts and finer and less extensive breast streaking. Stony, scrubby areas and dry cultivation.

9 **EURASIAN SKYLARK** *Alauda arvensis* **Page 796**
Adult. Winter visitor. Pakistan and N India. Large size with long tail; primaries extend beyond tertials. Pronounced whitish trailing edge to secondaries. Underparts whiter than on Oriental, has white outer tail feathers, and lacks rufous wing panel. Cultivation and grassland.

10 **ORIENTAL SKYLARK** *Alauda gulgula* **Page 797**
Adult *A. g. australis* (10a); adult *A. g. inconspicua* (10b). Widespread resident and winter visitor. Variable in coloration and prominence of streaking on upperparts and underparts. Fine bill, buffish-white outer tail feathers, and indistinct rufous wing panel. Grassland, cultivation and coastal mudflats.

11 **HORNED LARK** *Eremophila alpestris* **Page 797**
Male (11a) and female (11b) *E. a. longirostris*; male *E. a. albigula* (11c). Resident. High Himalayas. Male has black-and-white head pattern and black breast-band. Female streaked on crown and mantle. Breeds on stony ground and alpine pastures; winters in fallow cultivation, and on stony and sandy ground.

1a
4
2
1b
3
1c
8
5b
5a
7
6
11c
10a
11b
10b
11a
9

PLATE 139: FLOWERPECKERS AND SUNBIRDS

1 **THICK-BILLED FLOWERPECKER** *Dicaeum agile* **Page 798**
Adult. Widespread resident; unrecorded in parts of NE, NW and E subcontinent. Thick bill; diffuse malar stripe, streaking on breast, and indistinct white tip to tail. Forest and well-wooded country.

2 **YELLOW-VENTED FLOWERPECKER** *Dicaeum chrysorrheum* **Page 798**
Adult. Resident. Himalayas, hills of NE India and Bangladesh. Fine, downcurved bill; dark malar stripe and breast streaking breast, and orange-yellow vent. Open forest and forest edges.

3 **YELLOW-BELLIED FLOWERPECKER** *Dicaeum melanoxanthum* **Page 798**
Male (3a) and female (3b). Resident. Himalayas and NE Indian hills. Large size and stout bill; white centre of throat and breast, dark breast sides, and yellow belly and vent. Broadleaved forest.

4 **LEGGE'S FLOWERPECKER** *Dicaeum vincens* **Page 799**
Male (4a), female (4b) and juvenile (4c). Resident. Sri Lanka. Stout bill; white throat, yellow lower breast and belly. Male has bluish-black upperparts. Female has dark olive mantle and back. Forest and wooded gardens.

5 **ORANGE-BELLIED FLOWERPECKER** *Dicaeum trigonostigma* **Page 799**
Male (5a), female (5b) and juvenile male (5c). Resident. NE Indian hills and Bangladesh. Grey throat, orange rump contrasting with dark tail, orange on underparts. Juvenile has olive-yellow rump and belly centre. Edges of evergreen forest and mangroves.

6 **PALE-BILLED FLOWERPECKER** *Dicaeum erythrorynchos* **Page 799**
Adult *D. e. erythrorynchos.* Widespread resident; unrecorded in parts of NE and NW subcontinent. Pale bill, greyish-olive upperparts, pale grey underparts. Open broadleaved forest and well-wooded areas.

7 **PLAIN FLOWERPECKER** *Dicaeum concolor* **Page 800**
Adult *D. c. concolor* (7a); adult *D. c. virescens* (7b); adult *D. c. olivaceum* (7c). Resident. Mainly Himalayan foothills, hills of NE and SW India and Bangladesh. Dark bill. Nominate SW Indian race has darker olive-brown upperparts and paler greyish-white underparts than Pale-billed. Andaman *virescens* has yellowish lower belly. Himalayan *olivaceum* has olive-green upperparts. Edges of broadleaved forest and well-wooded areas.

8 **FIRE-BREASTED FLOWERPECKER** *Dicaeum ignipectus* **Page 800**
Male (8a), female (8b) and juvenile (8c). Resident. Himalayas and NE Indian hills. Male has metallic blue/green upperparts, and buff underparts with red breast. Female has olive-green upperparts and orange-buff throat and breast. Juvenile has duller upperparts and greyer underparts. Broadleaved forest and secondary growth.

9 **SCARLET-BACKED FLOWERPECKER** *Dicaeum cruentatum* **Page 800**
Male (9a), female (9b) and juvenile (9c). Resident. E Himalayan foothills, NE India and Bangladesh. Male has scarlet upperparts and black 'sides'. Female has scarlet rump contrasting with dark tail. Juvenile lacks scarlet rump, and has orange-red bill. Broadleaved forest and secondary growth.

10 **RUBY-CHEEKED SUNBIRD** *Anthreptes singalensis* **Page 801**
Male (10a), female (10b) and juvenile (10c). Resident. C and E Himalayan foothills, NE India and Bangladesh. Rufous-orange throat, yellow underparts. Male has metallic green upperparts and 'ruby' cheeks. Juvenile uniform yellow below. Open forest and forest edges.

11 **PURPLE-RUMPED SUNBIRD** *Nectarinia zeylonica* **Page 801**
Male (11a), female (11b) and juvenile (11c). Resident. Widespread in C and S India, Bangladesh and Sri Lanka. Male has narrow maroon breast-band, maroon head sides and mantle, and greyish-white flanks. Female has whitish throat, yellow breast, whitish flanks, and rufous-brown on wing. Juvenile uniform yellow below, with rufous-brown on wing. Cultivation and secondary growth.

12 **CRIMSON-BACKED SUNBIRD** *Nectarinia minima* **Page 802**
Male (12a), female (12b) and eclipse male (12c). Resident. Hills of W India. Smaller and finer-billed than Purple-rumped. Male has broad crimson breast-band and mantle. Female has crimson rump. Eclipse male has crimson back and purple rump. Evergreen forest and plantations.

1
2
3b
3a
4b
5b
6
4a
5a
5c
7c
4c
8c
7a
9c
8b
9b
7b
8a
9a
11c
10c
12c
11b
11a
10b
12b
12a
10a

PLATE 140: SUNBIRDS

1 **PURPLE-THROATED SUNBIRD** *Nectarinia sperata* **Page 802**
Male (1a) and female (1b). Resident. Plains of NE India and Bangladesh. Male has purple throat and maroon breast and belly. Female similar to female Purple, but smaller, with shorter bill. Open forest and gardens.

2 **OLIVE-BACKED SUNBIRD** *Nectarinia jugularis* **Page 803**
Male (2a), female (2b) and eclipse male (2c) ***N. j. andamanica*****; male** ***N. j. klossi*** **(2d).** Resident. Andamans and Nicobars. Male has olive-green upperparts and metallic purple-and-green throat. Female similar to female Purple, but brighter yellow below. Forest and scrub.

3 **PURPLE SUNBIRD** *Nectarinia asiatica* **Page 803**
Male (3a), female (3b, 3c) and eclipse male (3d). Widespread resident; unrecorded in parts of NE and NW subcontinent. Male metallic purple. Female has uniform yellowish underparts, with faint supercilium and darker mask (some greyer and whiter). Open deciduous forest and gardens.

4 **LOTEN'S SUNBIRD** *Nectarinia lotenia* **Page 803**
Male (4a), female (4b) and eclipse male (4c). Resident. C and S Indian peninsula and Sri Lanka. Sickle-shaped bill. Male has dusky-brown belly and vent. Female dark olive-green on upperparts; lacks supercilium and masked appearance of Purple. Well-wooded country.

5 **MRS GOULD'S SUNBIRD** *Aethopyga gouldiae* **Page 804**
Male (5a) and female (5b) ***A. g. gouldiae*****; male** ***A. g. dabryii*** **(5c).** Resident. Himalayas and NE Indian hills. Male has crimson mantle and back (reaching yellow rump), yellow belly, and blue tail. Female has pale yellow rump, yellow belly, short bill, and prominent white on tail. Forest.

6 **GREEN-TAILED SUNBIRD** *Aethopyga nipalensis* **Page 804**
Male (6a) and female (6b) ***A. n. nipalensis.*** Resident. Himalayas and NE India. Male has metallic blue-green crown, throat and tail, and maroon mantle. Female lacks prominent yellow rump; has long, graduated tail with white tips. Forest and secondary growth.

7 **BLACK-THROATED SUNBIRD** *Aethopyga saturata* **Page 805**
Male (7a) and female (7b). Resident. Himalayas and NE India. Male has black throat and breast, greyish-olive underparts, and crimson mantle. Female has dusky olive-green underparts and yellow rump. Bushes in forest and secondary growth.

8 **CRIMSON SUNBIRD** *Aethopyga siparaja* **Page 805**
Male (8a) and female (8f) ***A. s. seheriae*****; male (8b), eclipse male? (8c) and female (8d)** ***A. s. vigorsii*****; male (8e)** ***A. s. nicobarica.*** Resident. Himalayas, hills of India and Bangladesh; also N and NE plains in winter. Male has crimson mantle, scarlet throat and breast, and grey or yellowish-olive belly. Female has yellowish-olive to grey underparts; lacks yellow rump and prominent white on tail. Eclipse male/female can show red throat and breast. Bushes in forest, and groves.

9 **FIRE-TAILED SUNBIRD** *Aethopyga ignicauda* **Page 805**
Male (9a), eclipse male (9b) and female (9c). Resident. Himalayas and NE Indian hills. Male has red uppertail-coverts and red on tail. Female has yellowish belly, yellowish wash to rump, brownish-orange tail sides (which lack white at tip). Breeds in rhododendron shrubberies; winters in broadleaved and mixed forest.

10 **LITTLE SPIDERHUNTER** *Arachnothera longirostra* **Page 806**
Adult. Resident. E Himalayan foothills, hills of India and Bangladesh and adjacent plains. Very long downcurved bill, unstreaked upperparts, yellowish underparts. Wild bananas in moist broadleaved forest.

11 **STREAKED SPIDERHUNTER** *Arachnothera magna* **Page 806**
Adult. Resident. Mainly Himalayas and NE India. Very long downcurved bill, and boldly streaked upperparts and underparts. Moist broadleaved forest.

1b
1a
2b
2a
2d
2c
4b
4a
4c
3c
3b
3d
3a
5a
5b
5c
7a
7b
6b
6a
8f
8d
8e
8b
8c
8a
9c
9b
9a
10
11
C.D'G

PLATE 141: SPARROWS AND SNOWFINCHES

1 **HOUSE SPARROW** *Passer domesticus* **Page 807**
Male (1a) and female (1b). Widespread resident, except in parts of NE and NW subcontinent. Male has grey crown, black throat and upper breast, chestnut nape, and brownish mantle. Female has buffish supercilium and unstreaked greyish-white underparts. Breeds in habitation; also cultivation in winter.

2 **SPANISH SPARROW** *Passer hispaniolensis* **Page 807**
Male breeding (2a), male non-breeding (2b) and female (2c). Winter visitor. Pakistan, Nepal and N India. Male has chestnut crown, black breast and streaking on flanks, and blackish mantle with pale 'braces'; pattern obscured by pale fringes in non-breeding season. Female told from female House Sparrow by longer whitish supercilium, fine streaking on underparts, and pale 'braces'. Cultivation, semi-desert and reedbeds.

3 **SIND SPARROW** *Passer pyrrhonotus* **Page 808**
Male (3a) and female (3b). Resident. Pakistan and NW India. Smaller and slimmer than House, with finer bill. Male told from male House by chestnut on head restricted to crescent around ear-coverts; also grey ear-coverts, and small black throat patch. Female from female House by more prominent buffish-white supercilium, greyish ear-coverts, and warmer buffish-brown lower back and rump. Trees close to water.

4 **RUSSET SPARROW** *Passer rutilans* **Page 808**
Male (4a) and female (4b). Resident. Himalayas and NE Indian hills. Male lacks black cheek patch; has bright chestnut mantle, and yellowish wash to underparts. Female has prominent supercilium and dark eye-stripe, rufous-brown scapulars and rump, and yellowish wash to underparts. Open forest, forest edges and cultivation.

5 **DEAD SEA SPARROW** *Passer moabiticus* **Page 808**
Male (5a) and female (5b). Winter visitor. Baluchistan. Male has grey head with prominent buff supercilium and white submoustachial stripe; wing-coverts largely chestnut, and has yellow wash to underparts. Female has indistinct yellowish patch on neck, sandy-buff upperparts and yellow wash to underparts. Bushes near streams.

6 **EURASIAN TREE SPARROW** *Passer montanus* **Page 809**
Adult *P. m. malaccensis* (6a); adult *P. m. dilutus* (6b). Resident. Baluchistan, Himalayas, NE India, Eastern Ghats and Bangladesh. Chestnut crown, and black spot on ear-coverts. Habitation and cultivation.

7 **CHESTNUT-SHOULDERED PETRONIA** *Petronia xanthocollis* **Page 809**
Male (7a) and female (7b). Resident. Pakistan, Nepal and Indian peninsula. Unstreaked brownish-grey head and upperparts, and prominent wing-bars. Male and some females have yellow on throat. Open dry forest and scrub.

8 **ROCK SPARROW** *Petronia petronia* **Page 810**
Adult (8a) and juvenile (8b). Winter visitor. Pakistan. Striking head pattern, including pale crown-stripe, and whitish tip to tail. Dry stony ground in mountains.

9 **TIBETAN SNOWFINCH** *Montifringilla adamsi* **Page 810**
Adult (9a) and juvenile (9b). Resident. N Himalayas. Largely white or buffish-white wing-coverts. Adult has black throat, but head otherwise rather plain grey-brown. Rocky high-altitude semi-desert.

10 **WHITE-RUMPED SNOWFINCH** *Pyrgilauda taczanowskii* **Page 810**
Adult. Resident? and winter visitor. N Himalayas. White rump, black lores, white supercilium and throat, and streaked greyish upperparts. Rocky high-altitude semi-desert.

11 **SMALL SNOWFINCH** *Pyrgilauda davidiana* **Page 811**
Adult. [One published record, now considered doubtful. Small size, black forehead and throat, sandy-brown nape, white patch on primary coverts, and streaked mantle. High-altitude semi-desert.]

12 **RUFOUS-NECKED SNOWFINCH** *Pyrgilauda ruficollis* **Page 811**
Adult. Resident? N Himalayas. Cinnamon nape and neck sides, rufous patch at rear of ear-coverts, black malar stripe and white throat, and prominent wing-bars. High-altitude semi-desert and grassy plateaux.

13 **PLAIN-BACKED SNOWFINCH** *Pyrgilauda blanfordi* **Page 811**
Adult. Resident? and winter visitor. N Himalayas. Cinnamon nape and neck sides, black 'spur' dividing white supercilium, black throat; lacks wing-bars. High-altitude semi-desert.

1a
1b
3a
3b
2c
2a
4b
5a
2b
4a
6a
7a
5b
6b
8a
7b
9b
10
8b
9a
13
11
12
Clive Byers

PLATE 142: WAGTAILS

1 **FOREST WAGTAIL** *Dendronanthus indicus* **Page 812**
Adult. Mainly a winter visitor to NE and SW India, Bangladesh and Sri Lanka; breeds in Assam. Broad yellowish-white wing-bars, double black breast-band, olive upperparts, white supercilium, and whitish underparts. Paths and clearings in forest.

2 **WHITE WAGTAIL** *Motacilla alba* **Page 812**
Male breeding (2a), male non-breeding (2b) and juvenile (2c) *M. a. alboides*; male breeding (2d) and 1st-winter (2e) *M. a. personata*; male *M. a. leucopsis* (2f); male *M. a. ocularis* (2g); male *M. a. baicalensis* (2h); male *M. a. dukhunensis* (2i). Breeds in Himalayas; widespread in winter. Extremely variable. Head pattern and mantle colour (grey or black) indicate racial identification of breeding males. Non-breeding and first-winter birds often not racially distinguishable. Never has head pattern of White-browed. Breeds by running waters in open country; winters near water in open country.

3 **WHITE-BROWED WAGTAIL** *Motacilla maderaspatensis* **Page 813**
Adult (3a) and juvenile (3b). Widespread resident. Large black-and-white wagtail. Head black with white supercilium, and has black mantle. Juvenile has brownish-grey head, mantle and breast, with white supercilium. Freshwater wetlands.

4 **CITRINE WAGTAIL** *Motacilla citreola* **Page 813**
Male breeding (4a), adult female (4b), juvenile (4c) and 1st-winter (4d, 4e) *M. c. calcarata*; male breeding *M. c. citreola* (4f). Breeds in Baluchistan and Himalayas; widespread in winter. Broad white wing-bars in all plumages. Male breeding has yellow head and underparts, and black or grey mantle. Female breeding and adult non-breeding have broad yellow supercilium continuing around ear-coverts, grey upperparts, and mainly yellow underparts. Juvenile lacks yellow; has brownish upperparts, buffish supercilium (with dark upper edge) and ear-covert surround, and spotted black gorget. First-winter has grey upperparts, white surround to ear-coverts, dark border to supercilium, pale brown forehead, pale lores, all-dark bill, and white undertail-coverts; by early November, has yellowish supercilium, ear-covert surround and throat. Breeds in high-altitude wet grassland; winters at freshwater wetlands.

5 **YELLOW WAGTAIL** *Motacilla flava* **Page 814**
Male breeding (5a), adult female (5b), juvenile (5c) and 1st-winter (5d) *M. f. beema*; male *M. f. leucocephala* (5e); male (5f) and 1st-winter (5g) *M. f. lutea*; male *M. f. melanogrisea* (5h); male *M. f. superciliaris* (5i); male *M. f. zaissanensis* (5j); male *M. f. plexa* (5k); male *M. f. taivana* (5l); male (5m) and 1st-winter (5n) *M. f. thunbergi*. Breeds in W Himalayas; widespread in winter. Male breeding has olive-green upperparts and yellow underparts, with considerable variation in coloration of head depending on race. Female extremely variable, but often some features of breeding male. First-winter birds typically have brownish-olive upperparts, and whitish underparts with variable yellowish wash; some can closely resemble Citrine, but have narrower white supercilium which does not continue around ear-coverts. See text for other differences. Damp grasslands.

6 **GREY WAGTAIL** *Motacilla cinerea* **Page 814**
Male breeding (6a), adult female (6b) and juvenile (6c). Breeds in Baluchistan and Himalayas; widespread in winter. Longer-tailed than other wagtails. In all plumages, shows white supercilium, grey upperparts, and yellow vent and undertail-coverts. Male has black throat when breeding. Breeds by mountain streams; winters by slower streams in lowlands and foothills.

1
2b
2d
2e
3b
3a
2a
2f
2g
2i
2h
4f
2c
4e
4a
5d
4c
5c
4d
5a
5b
5e
4b
5g
6a
6b
5l
5f
6c
5n
5h
5i
5j
5k
5m
Clive Byers

PLATE 143: LARGE PIPITS

1 **RICHARD'S PIPIT** *Anthus richardi* **Page 815**
Adult (1a) and juvenile (1b). Widespread winter visitor. Large size and loud *schreep* call. Well-streaked upperparts and breast, pale lores, long and stout bill, and long hindclaw. Moist grassland and cultivation.

2 **PADDYFIELD PIPIT** *Anthus rufulus* **Page 815**
Adult *A. r. waitei* (2a); adult (2b) and juvenile (2c) *A. r. rufulus*. Widespread resident, except in parts of NE and NW subcontinent. Smaller than Richard's, with *chip-chip-chip* call. Well-streaked breast; lores usually look pale. Short grassland and cultivation.

3 **TAWNY PIPIT** *Anthus campestris* **Page 816**
Adult (3a), 1st-winter (3b) and juvenile (3c). Winter visitor. Mainly Pakistan and NW India. Loud *tchilip* or *chep* call. Adult and first-winter have plain or faintly streaked upperparts and breast. Juvenile more heavily streaked; useful features are dark lores, comparatively fine bill, rather horizontal stance, and wagtail-like behaviour. Stony semi-desert and fallow cultivation.

4 **BLYTH'S PIPIT** *Anthus godlewskii* **Page 816**
Adult (4a) and 1st-winter (4b). Widespread winter visitor. Call a wheezy *spzeeu*. Smaller than Richard's, with shorter tail and shorter and more pointed bill; shape of centres to adult median coverts distinctive if seen well, but this feature of no use in first-winter and juvenile plumage. Pale lores and well-streaked breast useful distinctions from Tawny. Grassland and cultivation.

5 **LONG-BILLED PIPIT** *Anthus similis* **Page 817**
Adult *A. s. jerdoni* (5a); adult *A. s. travancoriensis* (5b). Resident. Hills of Pakistan and India, and W Himalayan foothills; also N plains in winter. Considerably larger than Tawny, with very large bill and shorter-looking legs. Dark lores. Marked racial variation. Northern races (e.g. *jerdoni*) have greyish upperparts and warm buff colour to unstreaked or only lightly streaked underparts. Southern races (e.g. *travancoriensis*) darker grey-brown on upperparts and warm rufous-buff on underparts, with breast more heavily streaked/spotted. Breeds on rocky or scrubby slopes; winters in dry cultivation and scrub.

6 **UPLAND PIPIT** *Anthus sylvanus* **Page 820**
Adult (6a, 6b). Resident. Pakistan hills and Himalayas. Large, heavily streaked pipit with short and broad bill, and rather narrow, pointed tail feathers. Fine black streaking on underparts, whitish supercilium; ground colour of underparts varies from warm buff to rather cold and grey. Rocky and grassy slopes, and abandoned cultivation.

7 **NILGIRI PIPIT** *Anthus nilghiriensis* **Page 820**
Adult. Resident. SW Indian hills. Large, heavily streaked pipit. Compared with Paddyfield, has shorter tail, more heavily streaked upperparts, and streaked upper belly and flanks, and lacks malar stripe and patch. Call a weak *see-see*, quite unlike Paddyfield's. Grassy slopes.

1a
1b
2a
2b
2c
3a
3c
3b
4a
4b
5a
5b
6b
6a
7
Clive Byers

PLATE 144: PIPITS

1 **TREE PIPIT** *Anthus trivialis* **Page 817**
Adult *A. t. trivialis* (1a); adult *A. t haringtoni* (1b). Resident and winter visitor. Breeds in NW Himalayas; widespread in winter; unrecorded in Sri Lanka. Buffish-brown to greyish ground colour to upperparts (lacking greenish-olive cast), and buffish fringes to greater coverts, tertials and secondaries. *A. t. haringtoni* generally colder and greyer than nominate. Breeds on grassy slopes at treeline; winters in fallow cultivation and open country.

2 **OLIVE-BACKED PIPIT** *Anthus hodgsoni* **Page 818**
Adult fresh (2a) and worn (2b) *A. h. hodgsoni*; adult *A. h. yunnanensis* (2c). Resident and winter visitor. Breeds in Himalayas; widespread in winter, except NW and SE subcontinent. Greenish-olive cast to upperparts, and greenish-olive fringes to greater coverts, tertials and secondaries. Typically, has more striking head pattern than Tree Pipit. *A .h. yunnanensis* much less heavily streaked on upperparts than nominate race (and even less so than Tree). Open forest and shrubberies.

3 **MEADOW PIPIT** *Anthus pratensis* **Page 818**
Adult. Vagrant. Pakistan. Call a soft *sip-sip-sip*. Subtle differences from Tree are slimmer build, slimmer and weaker bill, and less boldly streaked breast but more boldly streaked flanks. Lacks prominent white supercilium, broad white wing-bars and distinct greenish edges to tertials and secondaries of Rosy Pipit. Open grassy areas.

4 **RED-THROATED PIPIT** *Anthus cervinus* **Page 819**
Adult male breeding (4a) and 1st-year (4b). Winter visitor. Mainly N subcontinent. Adult has reddish throat and upper breast, which tend to be paler on female and on autumn/winter birds. First-year has heavily streaked upperparts, pale 'braces', well-defined white wing-bars, strongly contrasting blackish centres and whitish fringes to tertials, pronounced dark malar patch, and more boldly streaked breast and (especially) flanks. Call a drawn-out *seeeeee*. Marshes, grassland and stubble.

5 **ROSY PIPIT** *Anthus roseatus* **Page 819**
Adult breeding (5a, 5b) and non-breeding (5c). Breeds in high Himalayas; winters in plains and foothills in N subcontinent. Always has boldly streaked upperparts, olive cast to mantle, and olive to olive-green edges to greater coverts, secondaries and tertials. Adult breeding has mauve-pink wash to underparts. Heavily streaked underparts and dark lores in non-breeding plumage. Call a weak *seep-seep*. Breeds on slopes above treeline; winters in marshes, damp grassland and cultivation.

6 **WATER PIPIT** *Anthus spinoletta* **Page 819**
Adult breeding (6a) and non-breeding (6b). Winter visitor. Pakistan, N India and Nepal. In all plumages, has lightly streaked upperparts, lacks olive-green on wing, has dark legs, and usually has pale lores; underparts less heavily marked than on Rosy and Buff-bellied Pipits. Orange-buff wash to supercilium and underparts in breeding plumage. Marshes, wet grassland and cultivation.

7 **BUFF-BELLIED PIPIT** *Anthus rubescens* **Page 820**
Adult breeding (7a) and non-breeding (7b). Winter visitor. Pakistan, N India and Nepal. In all plumages, has lightly streaked upperparts, lacks olive-green on wing, and has pale lores; underparts more heavily streaked, upperparts darker and legs paler compared with Water Pipit. Marshes, wet grassland and cultivation.

2b
1b
2a
3
1a
2c
4a
4b
5c
7b
5a
7a
5b
6b
6a

PLATE 145: ACCENTORS

1 **ALPINE ACCENTOR** *Prunella collaris* **Page 821**
Adult (1a) and juvenile (1b). Resident. Himalayas. Black barring on throat, grey breast and belly, and black band across greater coverts. Open stony slopes and rocky pastures.

2 **ALTAI ACCENTOR** *Prunella himalayana* **Page 821**
Adult. Winter visitor. Himalayas. White throat, with black gorget and spotting in malar region; white underparts, with rufous mottling on breast and flanks. Grassy and stony slopes and plateaux.

3 **ROBIN ACCENTOR** *Prunella rubeculoides* **Page 822**
Adult (3a) and juvenile (3b). Resident. Himalayas. Uniform grey head, rusty-orange band across breast, and whitish belly. Juvenile similar to juvenile Rufous-breasted, but lacks streaking on belly. Breeds in dwarf scrub and sedge clumps; winters around upland villages.

4 **RUFOUS-BREASTED ACCENTOR** *Prunella strophiata* **Page 822**
Adult (4a), 1st-winter? (4b) and juvenile (4c). Resident. Himalayas. Rufous band across breast, white-and-rufous supercilium, blackish ear-coverts, and streaking on neck sides and underparts. Juvenile similar to juvenile Robin Accentor, but has streaked belly. Breeds on high-altitude slopes; winters in bushes in cultivation and scrub.

5 **SIBERIAN ACCENTOR** *Prunella montanella* **Page 823**
Adult. [One published record, now considered doubtful. Orange-buff supercilium and throat, rufous streaking on mantle and often on flanks. Scrub].

6 **BROWN ACCENTOR** *Prunella fulvescens* **Page 823**
Adult (6a) and juvenile (6b) *P. f. fulvescens*. Resident. N Himalayas. White supercilium, faintly streaked upperparts, and pale orange-buff underparts which are usually unstreaked. Dry scrubby and rocky slopes; also around upland villages in winter.

7 **BLACK-THROATED ACCENTOR** *Prunella atrogularis* **Page 824**
Adult (7a) and 1st-winter female (7b). Winter visitor. W Himalayas. Orange-buff supercilium and submoustachial stripe, and black throat. Some have indistinct (or lack) black on throat, which instead is whitish; note heavily streaked mantle. Bushes near cultivation and dry scrub.

8 **RADDE'S ACCENTOR** *Prunella ocularis* **Page 823**
Adult. Vagrant. Pakistan. Whitish supercilium, dark brown crown, heavily streaked mantle, spotted malar stripe, and streaked flanks. Shrubs by mountain streams.

9 **MAROON-BACKED ACCENTOR** *Prunella immaculata* **Page 824**
Adult (9a) and juvenile (9b). Resident. C and E Himalayas. Grey head and breast, maroon-brown mantle, yellow iris, and grey panel across wing. Moist forest.

1a
2
1b
4a
3b
3a
4b
4c
5
8
7b
6a
7a
6b
9a
9b
Clive Byers

PLATE 146: WEAVERS AND AVADAVATS

1 **BLACK-BREASTED WEAVER** *Ploceus benghalensis* **Page 824**
Male breeding (1a, 1b) and non-breeding (1c, 1d). Resident. Mainly Indus and Gangetic plains. Breeding male has yellow crown and black breast-band; interesting variant has white ear-coverts and throat. In female and non-breeding plumages, breast-band can be broken by whitish fringes or restricted to small patches at sides, and may show indistinct, diffuse streaking on lower breast and flanks; head pattern as on female/non-breeding Streaked, except crown, nape and ear-coverts more uniform; rump also indistinctly streaked and, like nape, contrasts with heavily streaked mantle/back. Tall moist grassland and reedy marshes.

2 **STREAKED WEAVER** *Ploceus manyar* **Page 825**
Male breeding (2a), male non-breeding (2b) and female (2c). Widespread local resident. Breeding male has yellow crown, dark brown head sides and throat, and heavily streaked breast and flanks. Other plumages typically show boldly streaked underparts; can be only lightly streaked on underparts, when best told from Baya by combination of yellow supercilium and neck patch, heavily streaked crown, dark or heavily streaked ear-coverts, and pronounced dark malar and moustachial stripes. Reedbeds.

3 **BAYA WEAVER** *Ploceus philippinus* **Page 825**
Male breeding (3a), male non-breeding (3b) and female (3c) *P. p. philippinus*; male breeding (3d) and female (3e) *P. p. burmanicus*. Widespread resident; unrecorded in parts of NE and NW subcontinent. Breeding male *P. p. philippinus* has yellow crown, dark brown ear-coverts and throat, unstreaked yellow breast, and yellow on mantle and scapulars. Breeding male *burmanicus* has buff breast, and buff or pale grey throat. Female/non-breeding birds usually have unstreaked buff to pale yellowish underparts; can show streaking as prominent as on some poorly marked Streaked, but generally has less distinct and buffish supercilium, lacks yellow neck patch, and lacks pronounced dark moustachial and malar stripes. Head pattern of some (non-breeding males?) can, however, be rather similar to Streaked. Female *burmanicus* more rufous-buff on supercilium and underparts. Cultivation and grassland.

4 **FINN'S WEAVER** *Ploceus megarhynchus* **Page 826**
Male breeding (4a), female breeding (4b) and adult non-breeding (4c) *P. m. megarhynchus*. Resident. N India and SE Nepal. Large size and bill. Breeding male has yellow underparts and rump, and dark patches on breast (can show as complete breast-band). Breeding female has pale yellow to yellowish-brown head, and pale yellow to buffish-white underparts. Adult non-breeding and immature very similar to non-breeding Baya. Mainly grassland.

5 **RED AVADAVAT** *Amandava amandava* **Page 826**
Male breeding (5a), female (5b) and juvenile (5c). Widespread resident, except in parts of NE, NW and E subcontinent. Breeding male mainly red with white spotting. Non-breeding male and female have red bill, red rump and uppertail-coverts, and white tips to wing-coverts and tertials. Juvenile lacks red in plumage; has buff wing-bars, pink bill-base, and pink legs and feet. Tall wet grassland and reedbeds.

6 **GREEN AVADAVAT** *Amandava formosa* **Page 827**
Male (6a) and female (6b). Resident. Widespread in C India. Breeding male green and yellow, with red bill and barred flanks. Female much duller, with weak flank barring. Grass and low bushes, also tall grassland.

1a
1b
2a
2b
1c
1d
2c
3a
3c
3d
3e
3b
4a
4c
4b
6a
5c
5a
6b
5b
Clive Byers

PLATE 147: MUNIAS AND FINCHES

1 **INDIAN SILVERBILL** *Lonchura malabarica* **Page 827**
Adult (1a) and juvenile (1b). Widespread resident, except in NW and NE subcontinent and Himalayas. Adult has white rump and uppertail-coverts, black tail with elongated central feathers, and rufous-buff barring on flanks. Juvenile has buffish underparts, lacks flank barring, and has shorter tail. Dry cultivation, grassland and thorn scrub.

2 **WHITE-RUMPED MUNIA** *Lonchura striata* **Page 828**
Adult *L. s. striata* (2a); adult *L. s. acuticauda* (2b). Resident. Himalayan foothills, NE India and Bangladesh, and C and S India and Sri Lanka. Dark breast and white rump. Southern *L. s. striata* has clean black throat and breast, and unstreaked creamy-white or white belly. Northern *acuticauda* has pale streaking on ear-coverts, rufous-brown to whitish fringes to brown breast, and dingy underparts with faint streaking. Open wooded areas and scrub.

3 **BLACK-THROATED MUNIA** *Lonchura kelaarti* **Page 828**
Adult (3a) and immature (3b) *L. k. kelaarti*; adult *L. k. jerdoni* (3c). Resident. Hills of SW and E India, and Sri Lanka. Blackish face, throat and upper breast, and pinkish-cinnamon sides of neck and breast; underparts pinkish-cinnamon (*jerdoni*) or barred white and dark brown (*kelaarti*). Juvenile lacks black on head and breast and has uniform upperparts. Forest clearings, scrub and grassland.

4 **SCALY-BREASTED MUNIA** *Lonchura punctulata* **Page 829**
Adult (4a) and juvenile (4b) *L. p. punctulata*. Widespread resident; unrecorded in parts of the northwest. Adult has chestnut throat and upper breast, and whitish underparts with dark scaling. Juvenile has brown upperparts and buffish underparts; bill black. Open forest, bushes and cultivation.

5 **BLACK-HEADED MUNIA** *Lonchura malacca* **Page 829**
Adult (5a) and juvenile (5b) *L. m. malacca*; adult *L. m. atricapilla* (5c). Widespread resident in NE, E, C and S subcontinent. Black head, neck and upper breast, rufous-brown upperparts, white or chestnut lower breast and flanks, and black belly centre and undertail-coverts. Juvenile has uniform brown upperparts and buff to whitish underparts; bill blue-grey. Cultivation, marshes and tall grassland.

6 **JAVA SPARROW** *Lonchura oryzivora* **Page 829**
Adult (6a) and juvenile (6b). Introduced resident. Mainly around Colombo, Sri Lanka. Adult mainly grey, with pinkish-red bill, and black crown and throat contrasting with white cheeks. Juvenile much duller, with dusky white cheeks and pink base to grey bill. Cultivation and reedbeds.

7 **CHAFFINCH** *Fringilla coelebs* **Page 830**
Male non-breeding (7a) and female (7b). Winter visitor. Pakistan hills and N Himalayas. White wing-bars; lacks white rump. Male has blue-grey crown and nape, orange-pink face and underparts, and maroon-brown mantle. Female dull, with greyish-brown mantle and greyish-buff underparts. Upland fields with nearby bushes and forest.

8 **BRAMBLING** *Fringilla montifringilla* **Page 830**
Male breeding (8a), male non-breeding (8b) and female (8c). Winter visitor. Pakistan hills and N Himalayas. White rump and belly, and orange scapulars, breast and flanks. Upland fields and nearby bushes and forest.

1b
1a
2a
3a
2b
3c
3b
4a
4b
5b
5a
6a
6b
5c
7a
8a
8b
7b
8c

PLATE 148: FINCHES, INCLUDING MOUNTAIN FINCHES

1 **FIRE-FRONTED SERIN** *Serinus pusillus* **Page 831**
Male (1a), female (1b) and juvenile (1c). Baluchistan mountains and W and C Himalayas. Adult has blackish head with scarlet forehead. Juvenile has cinnamon-brown head. Breeds in Tibetan steppe habitat; winters on stony and bushy slopes.

2 **TIBETAN SISKIN** *Carduelis thibetana* **Page 832**
Male (2a) and female (2b). Breeds in E Himalayas?; winters in C and E Himalayas. Lacks large yellow patches on wing. Male mainly olive-green, with yellowish supercilium and underparts. Female heavily streaked, with indistinct yellowish wing-bars. Summers in mixed forest; winters in alders.

3 **YELLOW-BREASTED GREENFINCH** *Carduelis spinoides* **Page 831**
Male (3a), female (3b) and juvenile (3c) *C. s. spinoides*. Resident. Himalayas and NE India. Yellow supercilium and underparts, dark ear-coverts and malar stripe, and yellow patches on wing. Juvenile heavily streaked. Open forest, shrubberies and cultivation with nearby trees.

4 **BLACK-HEADED GREENFINCH** *Carduelis ambigua* **Page 831**
Male (4a) and female (4b). Resident? N Arunachal Pradesh. Yellow wing patches and tail sides, greenish mantle, greyish-white greater-covert bar, and greyish underparts. Male has dull black head. Open forest and shrubberies.

5 **EURASIAN SISKIN** *Carduelis spinus* **Page 832**
Male (5a) and female (5b). Vagrant. Nepal and India. Male has black crown and chin, and black-and-yellow wings. Female differs from female Tibetan Siskin in wing pattern and brighter yellow rump. Forest.

6 **EUROPEAN GOLDFINCH** *Carduelis carduelis* **Page 833**
Male (6a) and juvenile (6b) *C. c. caniceps*; male *C. c. major* (6c). Resident and winter visitor. Pakistan hills and W and C Himalayas. Red face (lacking on juvenile), and black-and-yellow wings with white tertial markings. Upland cultivation, shrubberies and open forest.

7 **TWITE** *Carduelis flavirostris* **Page 833**
Male (7a) and female (7b) *C. f. rufostrigata*; male *C. f. montanella* (7c). Resident. N Himalayas. Rather plain and heavily streaked, with small yellowish bill, buff wing-bars, and white edges to remiges and rectrices. Male has pinkish rump. *C. f. montanella* sandy-buff, and only lightly streaked below. High-altitude semi-desert.

8 **EURASIAN LINNET** *Carduelis cannabina* **Page 833**
Male breeding (8a), male non-breeding (8b) and female (8c). Winter visitor. Mainly Pakistan Himalayas. Told from Twite by greyish crown and nape contrasting with browner mantle, whitish lower rump and uppertail-coverts, and larger greyish bill. Forehead and breast crimson on breeding male. Open stony slopes and upland meadows.

9 **PLAIN MOUNTAIN FINCH** *Leucosticte nemoricola* **Page 834**
Adult breeding (9a) and juvenile (9b). Resident. Himalayas. Told from Brandt's by boldly streaked mantle with pale 'braces', and distinct patterning on wing-coverts (dark-centred, with well-defined wing-bars). Juvenile warmer rufous-buff than adult. Breeds on alpine slopes; winters in open forest and upland cultivation.

10 **BRANDT'S MOUNTAIN FINCH** *Leucosticte brandti* **Page 834**
Male breeding (10a) and 1st-summer (10b) *L. b. haematopygia*. Resident. Himalayas. Unstreaked to lightly streaked mantle, and rather uniform wing-coverts. More striking white panel on wing and more prominent white edges to tail compared with Plain. Adult breeding has sooty-black head and nape, and brownish-grey mantle with poorly defined streaking. Male has pink on rump. Alpine slopes.

1b
1a
2a
2b
1c
3b
4b
3a
3c
4a
6c
5a
5b
6a
9a
7c
6b
7a
8a
9b
7b
8b
10b
8c
10a

PLATE 149: FINCHES, INCLUDING ROSEFINCHES

1 **SPECTACLED FINCH** *Callacanthis burtoni* **Page 835**
Male (1a) and female (1b). Resident. Himalayas. Black wings with white tips to feathers. Blackish head with red (male) or orange-yellow (female) 'spectacles'. Juvenile has browner head with buff eye-patch, and buffish wing-bars. Open mixed forest.

2 **CRIMSON-WINGED FINCH** *Rhodopechys sanguinea* **Page 835**
Male (2a) and female (2b). Vagrant. Pakistan. Stout yellowish bill, pink on wing, dark cap, streaked brown mantle, and brown breast and white belly. Vagrants found in alpine grassland.

3 **TRUMPETER FINCH** *Bucanetes githagineus* **Page 835**
Male (3a) and juvenile (3b). Resident in Pakistan; winter visitor to NW India. Stocky, with very stout pinkish or yellow bill. Comparatively uniform wings and tail show traces of pink (except on juvenile). Dry rocky hills and semi-desert.

4 **MONGOLIAN FINCH** *Bucanetes mongolicus* **Page 836**
Male (4a) and female (4b). Resident in Pakistan and Ladakh; winter visitor to Baluchistan and Nepal. Whitish panels at bases of greater coverts and secondaries, whitish outer edges to tail, and bill is less stout than Trumpeter's. Dry stony slopes.

5 **DESERT FINCH** *Rhodospiza obsoleta* **Page 836**
Male breeding (5a) and female (5b). Resident. Baluchistan. Pink edges to wing-coverts and secondaries, white edges to remiges and outer edges to tail, and black centres to tertials. Adult breeding has black bill. Male has black lores. Dry steppe with scattered forest.

6 **RED CROSSBILL** *Loxia curvirostra* **Page 847**
Male (6a), female (6b) and juvenile (6c). Resident. Himalayas. Dark bill with crossed mandibles. Male rusty-red. Female olive-green, with brighter rump. Juvenile heavily streaked. Coniferous forest.

7 **BLANFORD'S ROSEFINCH** *Carpodacus rubescens* **Page 836**
Male (7a) and female (7b). Resident. C and E Himalayas. Slimmer bill than Common; male has more uniform head, duller crimson crown, and often distinct greyish cast to underparts. Female plain, lacks supercilium, has uniform wings and upperparts, and reddish or bright olive cast to rump and uppertail-coverts. Glades in coniferous and mixed forest.

8 **DARK-BREASTED ROSEFINCH** *Carpodacus nipalensis* **Page 837**
Male (8a) and female (8b). Resident. Himalayas. Slim, with slender bill. Male has maroon-brown breast-band, dark eye-stripe, and maroon-brown upperparts with indistinct dark streaking. Female has unstreaked underparts, lacks supercilium, and has streaked mantle, buffish wing-bars and tips to tertials, and olive-brown rump and uppertail-coverts. Breeds in high-altitude shrubberies; winters in forest clearings.

9 **COMMON ROSEFINCH** *Carpodacus erythrinus* **Page 837**
Male (9a) and female (9b) *C. e. roseatus*; male (9c) and female (9d) *C. e. erythrinus*. Breeds in Baluchistan and Himalayas; widespread in winter; unrecorded in Sri Lanka. Compact, with short, stout bill. Male has red head, breast and rump. Female has streaked upperparts and underparts, and double wing-bar. Breeds in high-altitude shrubberies and open forest; winters in cultivation with bushes.

10 **BEAUTIFUL ROSEFINCH** *Carpodacus pulcherrimus* **Page 842**
Male (10a) and female (10b) *C. p. pulcherrimus*. Resident. Himalayas. Male has pale lilac-pink supercilium, rump and underparts; upperparts grey-brown and heavily streaked. Female has poorly defined supercilium and heavily streaked underparts. Breeds in high-altitude shrubberies; winters on bush-covered slopes and cultivation with bushes.

11 **PINK-BROWED ROSEFINCH** *Carpodacus rodochrous* **Page 842**
Male (11a) and female (11b). Resident. Himalayas. Male has deep pink supercilium and underparts, and crimson crown. Female has buff supercilium and fulvous ground colour to rump, belly and flanks. Breeds in high-altitude shrubberies and open forest; winters in oak forest and on bushy slopes.

1a
2a
2b
1b
4a
4b
3a
3b
6b
5a
5b
6a
7a
7b
6c
9c
8b
8a
9d
11a
9a
10a
10b
9b
11b

PLATE 150: ROSEFINCHES

1 **VINACEOUS ROSEFINCH** *Carpodacus vinaceus* **Page 843**
Male (1a) and female (1b). Resident? Nepal and Indian Himalayas. Male dark crimson, with pink supercilium and pinkish-white tips to tertials. Female lacks supercilium; has whitish tips to tertials, and streaked underparts. Understorey in moist forest.

2 **DARK-RUMPED ROSEFINCH** *Carpodacus edwardsii* **Page 843**
Male (2a) and female (2b). Resident. C and E Himalayas. Male has pink supercilium and dark rump; maroon breast and flanks contrast with pink throat and belly. Female has narrow buff supercilium, pale tips to tertials, and brownish-buff underparts with lightly streaked throat and breast. High-altitude shrubberies and open forest; favours rhododendron.

3 **THREE-BANDED ROSEFINCH** *Carpodacus trifasciatus* **Page 843**
Male (3a) and female (3b). Vagrant. Bhutan. Both sexes have broad double wing-bars and white band down scapulars. Crimson of male's plumage replaced by orange-yellow on female. Upland village fields.

4 **SPOT-WINGED ROSEFINCH** *Carpodacus rodopeplus* **Page 844**
Male (4a) and female (4b). Resident. Nepal and Indian Himalayas. Male has pink supercilium and underparts, maroon upperparts, and pinkish tips to wing-coverts and tertials. Female has prominent buff supercilium, buff tips to tertials, and fulvous underparts with bold streaking on throat and breast. Breeds in rhododendron shrubberies; winters in forest understorey.

5 **WHITE-BROWED ROSEFINCH** *Carpodacus thura* **Page 844**
Male (5a) and female (5b) *C. t. thura*; female *C. t. feminus* (5c). Resident. Himalayas. Large size. Male has pink-and-white supercilium, pink rump and underparts, and heavily streaked brown upperparts. Female has prominent supercilium with dark eye-stripe, ginger-brown throat and breast (except northeastern *feminus*), and olive-yellow rump. Breeds in high-altitude shrubberies and open forest; winters on bushy hills.

6 **RED-MANTLED ROSEFINCH** *Carpodacus rhodochlamys* **Page 845**
Male (6a) and female (6b). Resident. Pakistan mountains and W Himalayas. Large size and large bill. Male has pink supercilium and underparts, and pale grey-brown upperparts with pinkish wash. Female pale grey and heavily streaked, with indistinct supercilium. Breeds in dry high-altitude shrubberies and forest; winters in well-wooded areas.

7 **STREAKED ROSEFINCH** *Carpodacus rubicilloides* **Page 845**
Male (7a) and female (7b). Resident. N Himalayas. Large size and long tail. Male has crimson-pink head and underparts and heavily streaked upperparts. Female lacks supercilium and has streaked upperparts. High-altitude semi-desert.

8 **GREAT ROSEFINCH** *Carpodacus rubicilla* **Page 845**
Male (8a) and female (8b). Resident. N Himalayas. Large size and long tail. Male has pale pink head and underparts, and pale sandy-grey and lightly streaked upperparts. Female lacks supercilium, and has lightly streaked pale sandy-brown upperparts; centres to wing-coverts and tertials pale grey-brown (much darker brownish-black on female Streaked). High-altitude semi-desert.

9 **RED-FRONTED ROSEFINCH** *Carpodacus puniceus* **Page 846**
Male (9a) and female (9b). Resident. N Himalayas. Large size, conical bill and short tail. On male, red of plumage contrasts with brown crown, eye-stripe and upperparts. Female lacks supercilium, is heavily streaked, and may show yellow/olive rump. High-altitude rocky slopes.

10 **CRIMSON-BROWED FINCH** *Propyrrhula subhimachala* **Page 846**
Male (10a) and female (10b). Resident. Himalayas and NE India. Short, stubby bill. Male has red forehead, throat and upper breast, greenish coloration to upperparts, and greyish underparts. Female has olive-yellow forehead and supercilium, greyish belly and greenish-olive upperparts. Breeds in high-altitude shrubberies; winters in forest undergrowth.

11 **SCARLET FINCH** *Haematospiza sipahi* **Page 847**
Male (11a), female (11b) and immature male (11c). Resident. Himalayas and NE India. Male scarlet. Female olive-green, with yellow rump. First-summer male has orange rump. Broadleaved forest.

1a
1b
2a
2b
3a
3b
4a
4b
5a
5b
5c
6a
6b
7a
7b
8a
8b
9a
9b
10a
10b
11a
11b
11c

PLATE 151: BULLFINCHES AND GROSBEAKS

1 **BROWN BULLFINCH** *Pyrrhula nipalensis* **Page 847**
Adult (1a) and juvenile (1b) *P. n. nipalensis.* Resident. Himalayas and NE India. Adult has grey-brown mantle, grey underparts, narrow white rump, and long tail. Juvenile has brownish-buff upperparts and warm buff underparts, and lacks adult head pattern. Dense moist forest.

2 **ORANGE BULLFINCH** *Pyrrhula aurantiaca* **Page 848**
Male (2a), female (2b) and juvenile (2c). Resident. W Himalayas. Male has orange head and body and orange-buff wing-bars. Female has grey crown and nape. Juvenile similar to female, but lacks grey on head. Open coniferous and mixed forest.

3 **RED-HEADED BULLFINCH** *Pyrrhula erythrocephala* **Page 848**
Male (3a), female (3b) and 1st-summer male (3c). Resident. Himalayas. Male has orange crown, nape and breast, and grey mantle. Female has yellow crown and nape. First-summer male has yellow breast. Mainly broadleaved forest.

4 **GREY-HEADED BULLFINCH** *Pyrrhula erythaca* **Page 848**
Male (4a) and female (4b). Resident. E Himalayas. Male has grey crown and nape (concolorous with mantle) and orange-red underparts. Female has grey crown and nape and brown mantle. Mixed forest and willow thickets.

5 **HAWFINCH** *Coccothraustes coccothraustes* **Page 849**
Adult male. Winter visitor. Mainly Pakistan, also Jammu. Stocky, short-tailed and huge-billed. Mainly orange-brown, with pale wing-covert band and black chin. Wild olive forest and orchards.

6 **BLACK-AND-YELLOW GROSBEAK** *Mycerobas icterioides* **Page 849**
Male (6a), female (6b) and juvenile male (6c). Resident. W Himalayas. Male usually lacks orange cast to mantle and rump; black of plumage duller than on Collared, and has black thighs. Female has pale grey head, mantle and breast, and peachy-orange rump and belly. Juvenile male has black wings and yellow rump. Coniferous forest.

7 **COLLARED GROSBEAK** *Mycerobas affinis* **Page 849**
Male (7a), female (7b) and juvenile male (7c). Resident. Himalayas. Male has orange cast to mantle; black of plumage strongly glossed, and thighs yellow. Female has olive-yellow underparts and rump and greyish-olive mantle. Juvenile male duller than adult, with black mottling on mantle. Mixed forest.

8 **SPOT-WINGED GROSBEAK** *Mycerobas melanozanthos* **Page 850**
Male (8a) and female (8b). Resident. Himalayas and NE India. Male has black rump and white markings on wings. Female yellow, boldly streaked with black; wing pattern similar to male's. Breeds in mixed forest; winters in broadleaved forest.

9 **WHITE-WINGED GROSBEAK** *Mycerobas carnipes* **Page 850**
Male (9a) and female (9b). Resident. Pakistan mountains and Himalayas. Male dull black and olive-yellow, with yellowish tips to greater coverts and tertials. Female similar, but black of plumage replaced by sooty-grey. Juniper shrubberies, and forest with junipers.

10 **GOLD-NAPED FINCH** *Pyrrhoplectes epauletta* **Page 850**
Male (10a) and female (10b). Resident. Himalayas. Small, with fine bill. White 'stripe' down tertials. Male black, with orange crown and nape. Female has olive-green on head, grey mantle, and rufous-brown wing-coverts and underparts. Undergrowth in oak–rhododendron forest and rhododendron shrubberies.

1a
1b
2a
2b
3b
2c
3a
4b
4a
3c
7c
5
6a
7a
7b
6b
9a
8a
6c
8b
9b
10a
10b

PLATE 152: BUNTINGS

1 **CRESTED BUNTING** *Melophus lathami* **Page 851**
Male (1a), female (1b) and 1st-winter male (1c). Resident. Himalayan foothills and hills of NE and C India. Always has crest and chestnut on wing and tail; tail lacks white. Male has bluish-black head and body. Female and first-winter male streaked on upperparts and breast; first-winter male darker and more heavily streaked than female, with olive-grey ground colour to underparts. Dry rocky and grassy hillsides, and terraced cultivation.

2 **YELLOWHAMMER** *Emberiza citrinella* **Page 851**
Male breeding (2a), male non-breeding (2b) and female (2c). Winter visitor. Nepal and Indian Himalayas. Chestnut rump and long tail. Most show yellow on head and underparts. (Note that hybrids with Pine Bunting can show variety of intermediate characters.) Upland cultivation.

3 **PINE BUNTING** *Emberiza leucocephalos* **Page 852**
Male breeding (3a), male non-breeding (3b) and female (3c). Winter visitor. Pakistan hills and Himalayas. Chestnut rump and long tail. Male has chestnut supercilium and throat, and whitish crown and ear-covert spot. Female has greyish supercilium and nape/neck sides, dark border to ear-coverts, usually some rufous on breast/flanks, and white belly. Fallow fields.

4 **ROCK BUNTING** *Emberiza cia* **Page 852**
Male (4a) and female (4b) *E. c. stracheyi*; male *E. c. par* (4c). Resident. Breeds in Pakistan mountains and W Himalayas; winters down to adjacent plains. Male has grey head, black lateral crown-stripes and border to ear-coverts, and rufous underparts. Female duller. *E. c. par* paler than *stracheyi*. Breeds on dry grassy and rocky slopes; winters in lowland fallow cultivation.

5 **GODLEWSKI'S BUNTING** *Emberiza godlewskii* **Page 853**
Male breeding (5a), male non-breeding (5b) and juvenile (5c). Resident. N Arunachal Pradesh. Greyish head with chestnut lateral crown-stripes and stripe behind eye. Wing-bars white. Dry rocky and bushy slopes.

6 **GREY-NECKED BUNTING** *Emberiza buchanani* **Page 853**
Male (6a), female (6b) and 1st-winter (6c). Breeds in Baluchistan; winters mainly in Pakistan and C and W India. Pinkish-orange bill, plain head and whitish eye-ring. Adult has blue-grey head, buffish submoustachial stripe and throat, and rusty-pink underparts. First-winter and juvenile often with only slight greyish cast to head and buffish underparts; light streaking on breast. Dry rocky and bushy hills.

7 **ORTOLAN BUNTING** *Emberiza hortulana* **Page 853**
Male (7a), female (7b) and 1st-winter (7c). Vagrant. Pakistan and India. Pinkish-orange bill, plain head and prominent eye-ring. Adult has olive-grey head and breast, and yellow submoustachial stripe and throat. Female streaked on crown and breast. First-winter and juvenile more heavily streaked on mantle, malar region and breast than Grey-necked. Orchards and open woodland.

8 **WHITE-CAPPED BUNTING** *Emberiza stewarti* **Page 853**
Male breeding (8a), male non-breeding (8b) and female (8c). Breeds in Pakistan mountains and W Himalayas; winters in foothills and valleys of Pakistan and NC India. Male has grey head, black supercilium and throat, and chestnut breast-band; pattern obscured in winter. Female has rather plain head with pale supercilium; crown and mantle uniformly and diffusely streaked, and underparts finely streaked and washed with buff. Dry grassy and rocky slopes; also fallow fields in winter.

9 **HOUSE BUNTING** *Emberiza striolata* **Page 854**
Male (9a) and female (9b). Resident. Pakistan and NW India. Lacks white on tail. Has black eye-stripe and moustachial stripe, and white supercilium and submoustachial stripe; throat and breast streaked, and underparts brownish-buff with variable rufous tinge. Female duller than male, with less striking head pattern. Dry rocky hills; also sandy plains in winter.

1c
1a
1b
2a
2c
2b
3a
3b
3c
4c
5b
4a
5a
5c
6a
7c
4b
7b
6c
6b
7a
8b
8a
9a
9b
8c

PLATE 153: BUNTINGS

1 **CHESTNUT-EARED BUNTING** *Emberiza fucata* **Page 854**
Male (1a), female (1b) and 1st-winter (1c). Resident and winter visitor. Breeds in W Himalayas; winters east to NE India and Bangladesh. Adult has chestnut ear-coverts, black breast streaking, and usually some chestnut on breast sides. Some first-winter birds rather nondescript, but plain head with warm brown ear-coverts and prominent eye-ring distinctive. Dry rocky and bushy hills.

2 **LITTLE BUNTING** *Emberiza pusilla* **Page 855**
Adult (2a) and 1st-winter (2b). Winter visitor. Himalayas, NE India and Bangladesh. Small size. Chestnut ear-coverts (and often supercilium and crown-stripe), and lacks dark moustachial stripe. Fallow cultivation and meadows.

3 **RUSTIC BUNTING** *Emberiza rustica* **Page 855**
Male breeding (3a) and 1st-winter (3b). Vagrant. Nepal. Striking head pattern, rufous streaking on breast, white belly, rufous on nape, and prominent white median-covert bar. Damp grassland.

4 **YELLOW-BREASTED BUNTING** *Emberiza aureola* **Page 855**
Male breeding (4a), male non-breeding (4b), female (4c) and juvenile (4d). Winter visitor. Mainly Nepal, NE India and Bangladesh. Male has black face and chestnut breast-band (obscured when fresh), and white inner wing-coverts. Female has striking head pattern, boldly streaked mantle, and prominent white median-covert bar. Juvenile streaked on breast and flanks. Cultivation and grassland.

5 **CHESTNUT BUNTING** *Emberiza rutila* **Page 856**
Male non-breeding (5a), female (5b) and 1st-winter male (5c). Winter visitor. Mainly NE India. Small size, chestnut rump, and little or no white on tail. Male has chestnut head and breast, which may be barely apparent in first-winter plumage. Female has buff throat and yellow underparts; head pattern less striking than on Yellow-breasted. Bushes near cultivation and forest clearings.

6 **BLACK-HEADED BUNTING** *Emberiza melanocephala* **Page 856**
Male breeding (6a), male non-breeding (6b), worn female (6c) and fresh female (6d). Winter visitor to N, W and WC India and SE Nepal; passage migrant in Pakistan. Male has black on head and chestnut on mantle. Female when worn may show ghost pattern of male; fresh female almost identical to Red-headed, but indicative features include rufous fringes to mantle and/or back, slight contrast between throat and greyish ear-coverts, and more yellowish underparts. Cereal crops.

7 **RED-HEADED BUNTING** *Emberiza bruniceps* **Page 856**
Male breeding (7a), male non-breeding (7b), fresh female (7c) and immature (7d). Winter visitor, mainly to NW and WC India; passage migrant in Pakistan. Male has rufous on head and yellowish-green mantle. Fresh female has throat paler than breast, often with suggestion of buffish breast-band; forehead and crown often virtually unstreaked. Smaller than Black-headed, with shorter and more conical bill. Cultivation.

8 **BLACK-FACED BUNTING** *Emberiza spodocephala* **Page 857**
Male breeding (8a), male non-breeding (8b) and female (8c). Winter visitor. Mainly Nepal and NE India. Male has greenish-grey head with blackish lores and chin, and yellow underparts. Non-breeding male with yellow submoustachial stripe and throat. Female has yellowish supercilium, yellow throat, olive rump, and white on tail. Long grass, paddy-fields and marsh edges.

9 **REED BUNTING** *Emberiza schoeniclus* **Page 857**
Adult male breeding (9a) and female (9b) *E. s. pallidior*; adult male non-breeding *E. s. pyrrhuloides* (9c). Winter visitor. Pakistan and NW India. Male has black head and white submoustachial stripe; head pattern obscured by fringes when fresh. Female has buff supercilium, brown ear-coverts, and black malar stripe. Reedbeds and irrigated crops.

10 **CORN BUNTING** *Miliaria calandra* **Page 858**
Adult. Vagrant. Pakistan and India. Stocky, with short tail and pale bill. Heavily streaked. Cultivation.

1a
1c
3a
3b
2b
2a
1b
5a
4d
4c
4b
5c
5b
4a
6d
6c
6b
8a
7d
6a
7a
7c
8b
7b
8c
10
9b
9a
9c

MEGAPODES Megapodiidae

Robust terrestrial birds which resemble pheasants, for example by scratching around in leaf litter when foraging. The family is characterised by its habit of laying its eggs in holes in the ground or in mounds of rotting vegetable matter and leaving them to be incubated by natural heat.

NICOBAR SCRUBFOWL *Megapodius nicobariensis* Plate 1

***M. freycinet*, Megapode (I)**

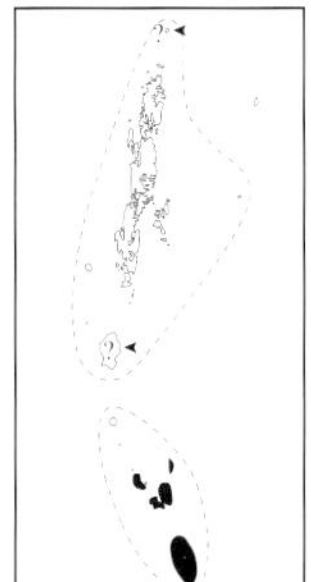

IDENTIFICATION 43 cm. Mainly brown, with bare red facial skin, slight crest, and large legs and feet. **Adult** shows extensive area of bare facial skin; chestnut-brown to greyish-brown crown, contrasting with paler, greyer supercilium and nape; chestnut-brown upperparts, and cinnamon-brown to brownish-grey underparts. **Immature** has less extensive bare facial skin (lores and area around eye), and generally has stronger cinnamon coloration to upperparts and underparts. **VOICE** Territorial call of male is a *kyououou-kyou-kou-koukoukoukoukou*, rising in pitch on the first note and gradually decreasing on the staccato series; contact call is a cackling *kuk-a-kuk-kuk* (Ali and Ripley 1987; Jones *et al.* 1995). **HABITS** Partly nocturnal. Keeps in pairs or in flocks of adults and young. Forages by scratching around in leaf litter. Birds often run about, calling noisily to one another. **HABITAT** Undergrowth in thick forest adjacent to sandy beaches on islands. **BREEDING** Throughout the year. Eggs are incubated in mounds of sand and rotting vegetation 0.1–2.1 m high. **DISTRIBUTION AND STATUS** Globally threatened. **IN:** endemic resident, apparently restricted to the Nicobar Is; locally common on the Great Nicobar group. **REFERENCES** Sankaran (1993, 1995a).

PARTRIDGES, FRANCOLINS, SNOWCOCKS, QUAILS AND PHEASANTS Phasianidae

Characteristically the Phasianidae are terrestrial, feeding and nesting on the ground, but many species roost in trees at night. They are good runners, often preferring to escape on foot rather than taking to the air. Their flight is powerful and fast, but, except in the case of the migratory quails, it cannot be sustained for long periods. Typically, they forage by scratching the ground with their strong feet to expose food hidden among dead leaves or in the soil, and some will dig with the bill. A wide range of vegetable food, including grain, seeds, fruit, buds, roots and leaves, is eaten, complemented by invertebrates such as insects, worms and snails. In the breeding season, males typically call at dawn and also often at dusk. Males of most pheasant species have spectacular courtship displays. Most Phasianidae lay their eggs on the ground in open scrapes with little or no lining. The young are able to run about and feed themselves a short time after hatching. The vast majority, except for a few of the quails, are residents; some Himalayan species move altitudinally with the seasons.

SNOW PARTRIDGE *Lerwa lerwa* Plate 1

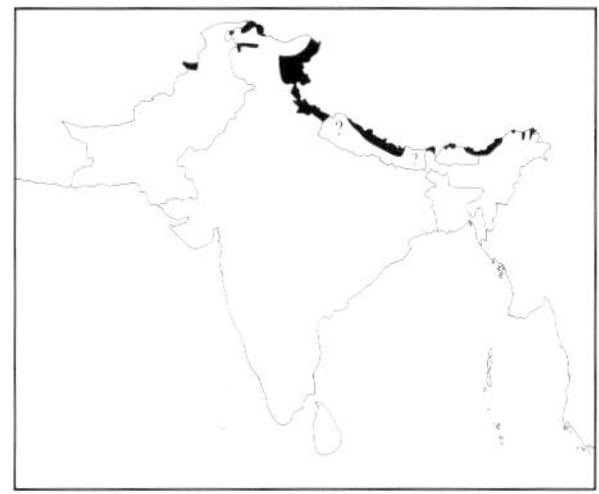

IDENTIFICATION 38 cm. Much smaller size, and uniformly barred upperparts, distinguish this species from the snowcocks. Shows a narrow white trailing edge to the wings in flight. Has head, neck, upper breast and upperparts finely vermiculated dark brown and white, and with a chestnut wash. Underparts are heavily streaked with chestnut. Bill, legs and feet are bright red. **VOICE** A loud, harsh and frequently repeated whistle. **HABITS** Usually in pairs in spring, and later in parties of up to 30 birds. Very tame where not hunted, standing on a rock to watch the observer, rather than flying away. When flushed, the flock disperses, plunging quickly downhill without calling, but with much clattering of wings. **HABITAT** Close to the snowline on steep rocky or grassy slopes interspersed with scattered dwarf juniper or rhododendron bushes. **BREEDING** May—July. Nest is well hidden under a rock or grass clump. **DISTRIBUTION AND STATUS** Resident. Himalayas from N Pakistan east to Arunachal Pradesh. Subject to altitudinal movements: summers mainly 4000–5000 m, winters down to 3050 m (–2000 m). **PK:** rare and local. **NP:** fairly common. **IN:** locally frequent in Sikkim. **BT:** locally common. **REFERENCES** Johnsgard (1988).

SEE-SEE PARTRIDGE *Ammoperdix griseogularis* Plate 1

IDENTIFICATION 26 cm. Both sexes are readily distinguishable from adult Chukar (p.347) by lack of black gorget around throat, and lack of bold black crescentic markings on flanks. In flight, shows rufous at sides of tail as on Chukar. **Male** has white eye-stripe bordered by black supercilium; pale grey throat and foreneck; patch of white flecking on sides of neck; pinkish breast; 'swept-back' black and chestnut flank stripes which cross the flanks horizontally rather than vertically; orange bill, and dull yellow legs. **Female** is rather uniform, and lacks distinctive head pattern and flank striping of male. Has cream throat and supercilium; greyish flecking on neck, which merges with

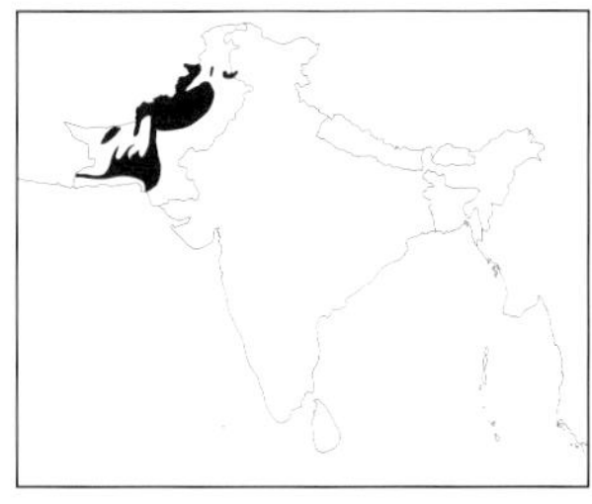

pinkish-buff and grey vermiculations of mantle and breast. **VOICE** A distinctive and far-carrying *wuii div, wuii div* and also *wuid-wuit*; flight call a fast *bwuit-bwuit-bwuit.* (Hollom *et al.* 1988). **HABITS** Normally in pairs when breeding and in small groups afterwards. Active in the early morning and at dusk, spending the hottest part of the day in shade. Very confiding where not hunted. Reluctant to fly when disturbed; escapes by rapid running and agile climbing. Wings produce a high-pitched squeaky noise which gives the bird its name. **HABITAT** Dry rocky foothills with light scrub, sand dunes, and edges of cultivation in narrow valleys. **BREEDING** March–June. Nests on the leeward side of a hill under a bush or rock or among stones. **DISTRIBUTION AND STATUS PK:** widespread, locally common and sedentary resident. **REFERENCES** Johnsgard (1988).

TIBETAN SNOWCOCK *Tetraogallus tibetanus* Plate 1

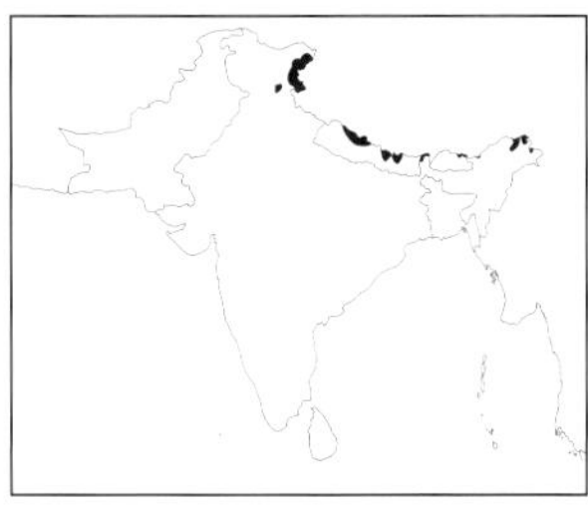

IDENTIFICATION 51 cm. From Himalayan Snowcock (below) by prominent white patch on ear-coverts offset against grey of head and neck, double band of grey across upper breast (absent, or just a single band, on some birds), white underparts with broad black flank stripes, and white striping on coverts and scapulars. In flight, wing pattern is very different, Tibetan showing only a small amount of white in primaries but extensive white in secondaries. Also has chestnut coloration on rump and uppertail-coverts. For differences from Buff-throated Partridge (below), which occurs in the easternmost Himalayas, see that species. Immature is similar to adult, but has grey breast mottled with dark brown and buff, and sides of throat are dark brown (rather than grey) and mottled with buff. **Juvenile** is much smaller, and lacks black flank stripes. **Racial variation** The nominate race of W Himalayas is much paler and sandier above than *T. t. aquilonifer* of C and E Himalayas. **VOICE** Not markedly different from Himalayan Snowcock. Three different calls: a subdued chuckling becoming louder and reaching a climax, a whistle, and a call reminiscent of Eurasian Curlew (p.476) (Ali and Ripley 1987). **HABITS** Similar to those of Himalayan Snowcock. **HABITAT** Bare rocky ridges and slopes sparsely covered with scrub or grass and alpine meadows. **BREEDING** May–August, varying locally. Nests among stones or under a rock on the leeward side of a hill. **DISTRIBUTION AND STATUS** Resident. Himalayas from Himachal Pradesh east to Arunachal Pradesh. Subject to altitudinal movements: in W Himalayas summers well above the tree-line, up to 5800 m; occasionally winters down to 3000 m. Farther east usually summers at 4500–5500 m; winters down to 3650 m. **NP:** locally fairly common. **IN:** status uncertain. **BT** fairly common. **REFERENCES** Johnsgard (1988).

HIMALAYAN SNOWCOCK *Tetraogallus himalayensis* Plate 1

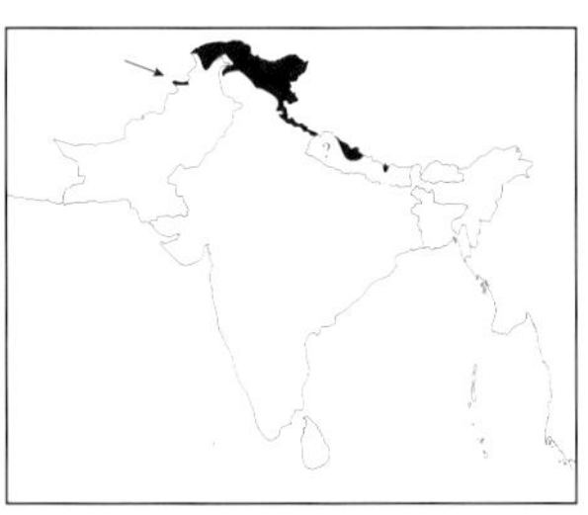

IDENTIFICATION 72 cm. Distinguished from Tibetan Snowcock (above) by broad dark chestnut stripes down sides of neck which join to form band across upper breast, greyish-white breast (variably barred with black) contrasting strongly with dark grey underparts (with chestnut and black flank streaking), and strong contrast between pale grey crown/mantle and dark grey back. Lacks white striping on scapulars and coverts which is a striking feature of Tibetan. In flight, wing pattern is very different, Himalayan showing extensive white in primaries but little or no white in secondaries. Also has greyish coloration on rump and uppertail-coverts. **Juvenile** is similar to but much smaller than adult, patterning is less well defined, and dark neck stripes join across nape. **VOICE** Far-carrying inflected whistle ending on two shorter, rising whistled notes, *cour-lee-whi-whi*, repeated at intervals, and reminiscent of Eurasian Curlew (p.476); also a *chok-chok-chok* which often accelerates into a rapid chatter (Roberts 1991). **HABITS** Keeps in pairs in the breeding season and later in flocks of up to 30 birds. Escapes by running uphill or, if pressed, by flying extremely swiftly downhill and covering a long distance before settling again. Flicks its heavy tail as it walks, showing the white undertail-coverts. Calls frequently. **HABITAT** Alpine pastures near the snowline, bare stony ridges and steep slopes. Sometimes found in the same areas as Tibetan Snowcock in Nepal, but usually at slightly higher altitudes. **BREEDING** April–June. Nest site is like that of Tibetan Snowcock. **DISTRIBUTION AND STATUS** Resident. Himalayas from N Pakistan east to Nepal. Subject to altitudinal movements: 4000–5500 m (–5900 m in Nepal, down to 2100 m in W Himalayas in severe winters). **PK:** common. **NP:** fairly common. **IN:** frequent in Kashmir. **REFERENCES** Johnsgard (1988).

BUFF-THROATED PARTRIDGE *Tetraophasis szechenyii* Plate 1

Pheasant-grouse (I)

IDENTIFICATION 64 cm. A very large, comparatively uniform phasianid with long and broad white-tipped tail. Given its range in subcontinent, likely to be confused only with female Sclater's Monal (p.358), but lacks white rump and prominent mantle streaking of that species. Distinctive features are bare red skin around eyes; orange-buff throat; greyish breast, spotted with black; prominent orange-buff and chestnut spotting on belly and flanks;

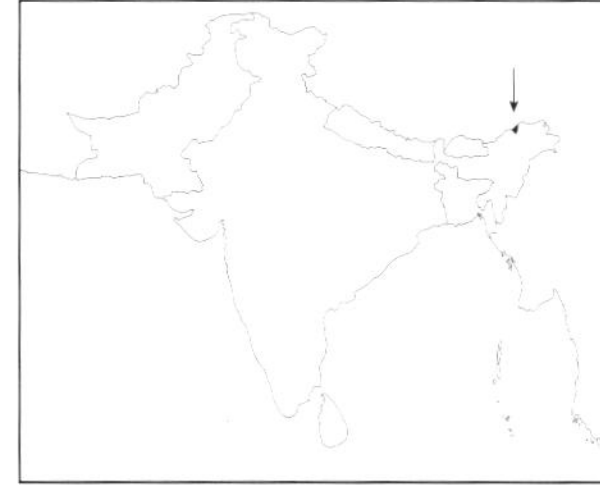

uniform grey crown/ear-coverts and uniform brown mantle; grey rump; and broad buffish and white tips to the wing-coverts, secondaries, tertials and scapulars (giving rise to distinctive banding on posterior upperparts). Sometimes occurs above the treeline and then possibly confusable with Tibetan Snowcock (p.346), but dark underparts, white tip to tail and lack of white in the wing on Buff-throated render identification straightforward even at long range. **Juvenile** is much smaller than (and unlikely to be seen away from) adult, is heavily barred with black and rufous-brown on the upperparts, which also have white shaft streaks, and the underparts are streaked with buff. **VOICE** Series of harsh, anxious cries. **HABITS** Usually in parties of four to six birds. When disturbed in forest, it escapes into trees and 'freezes', becoming difficult to detect because of its cryptic plumage. If flushed in open areas, it plummets downhill and into the nearest forest cover. Roosts in trees. **HABITAT** Well-vegetated rocky ravines or fir forest and rhododendron shrubberies in subalpine and alpine zones. **BREEDING** Details not recorded in the subcontinent and little known. Chicks found in Tibet late May–August. **DISTRIBUTION AND STATUS IN:** very rare and local resident in Arunachal Pradesh, 3350–4600 m. **REFERENCES** Johnsgard (1988).

CHUKAR *Alectoris chukar* — Plate 1

Chukor Partridge (F,I), Chukar Partridge (N)

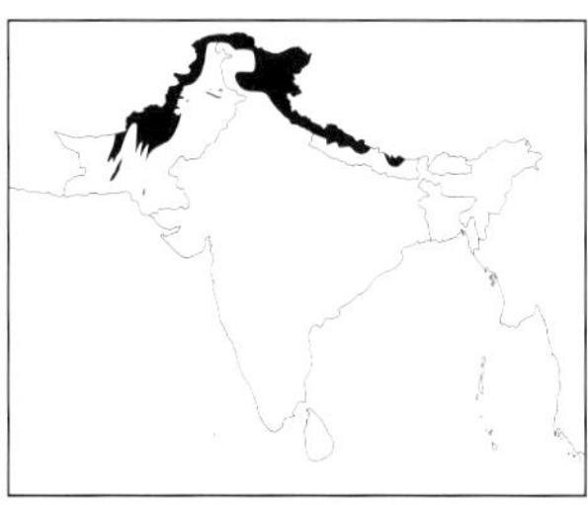

IDENTIFICATION 38 cm. A stocky, medium-sized partridge. Has black stripe through eye which extends to form black gorget, encircling creamy-white throat; broad chestnut and black rib-like bars on flanks, and bright red bill and legs. Displays rufous corners to tail in flight. **Juvenile** is much smaller, and initially lacks black gorget and flank barring. Underparts are whitish, with indistinct brown barring on breast and flanks; upperparts are brownish-grey with some white spotting and dark markings. **Racial variation** *A. c. pallescens* of NW part of range is paler and more extensively grey on upperparts, and has paler grey breast, compared with the nominate race. **VOICE** A rapidly repeated *chuck, chuck-aa*; when flushed, an anxious 'rolled-together' *chuck, chuck, chuck*. **HABITS** Keeps in flocks of up to 30 birds outside the breeding season. If flushed, the covey disperses, flying very fast and strongly, and in hilly regions flies downhill hugging the contours. Can move rapidly and with agility over rough ground. **HABITAT** Open, arid rocky hills, barren hillsides with scattered scrub, grassy slopes, dry terraced cultivation and stony ravines, often near a water source. **BREEDING** April–August, depending on altitude. Nests under a rock, bush or grass tussock on a rocky slope. **DISTRIBUTION AND STATUS** Sedentary resident. Widespread in hills of Pakistan and Himalayas from N Pakistan east to EC Nepal. Subject to some altitudinal movements: mainly 1200–3960 m (–5000 m in W Himalayas, down to 600 m in Pakistan). **PK:** now very rare on lower, more accessible foothills, locally fairly common higher up. **NP:** fairly common in the west. **IN:** well distributed; locally common. **REFERENCES** Johnsgard (1988), Malhotra and Pathania (1981), Pfister (1997).

BLACK FRANCOLIN *Francolinus francolinus* — Plate 1

Black Partridge (F,I)

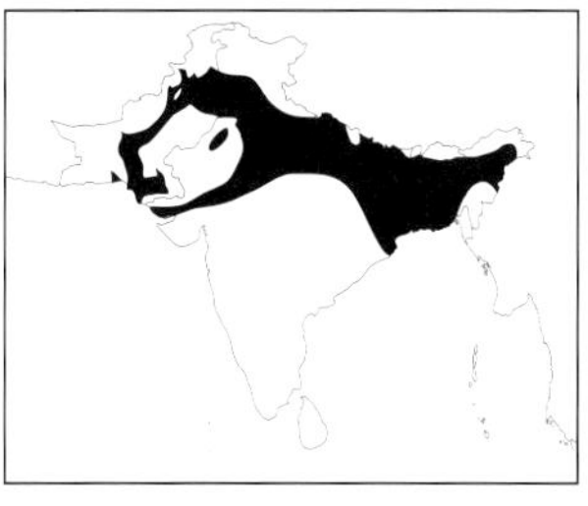

IDENTIFICATION 34 cm. **Male** unmistakable, with white ear-covert patch on otherwise black face, rufous collar, black upper mantle spotted with white, and black underparts with flanks boldly spotted with white. **Female** distinguished from female Painted Francolin (p.348) by rufous patch on hindneck, and pale buff to rufous-buff supercilium and ear-coverts divided by dark eye-stripe; furthermore, dark feathers of mantle and back are edged with buff, giving rise to mainly streaked (rather than spotted) appearance to upperparts (although may show small area of spotting on upper mantle), and general appearance of underparts is that they are heavily barred with black (rather than spotted with white), although breast can be spotted and underparts of some birds are much as on Painted. From Grey Francolin (p.348) by rufous hindneck, different head pattern, streaked rather than neatly barred appearance to upperparts, bold black barring on underparts, and black rather than chestnut on outer tail feathers in flight. See Chinese Francolin (p.348) for differences from that species. **VOICE** Loud, penetrating and harsh *kar-kar, kee, ke-kee*; frequently repeated. **HABITS** Found singly, in pairs or in groups of up to five birds. Roosts in thick ground cover. If much disturbed, escapes by running away swiftly, but otherwise flushes easily, flying off strongly and at great speed. Active in early morning and late afternoon, returning into cover during the heat of the day. Calls at any time of the day during the breeding season, often from a tree or stump. **HABITAT** Cultivation, tea estates and tall grass and scrub, especially near rivers and canals. Requires good ground cover and water close by. **BREEDING** March–October. Nests among grasses, dense scrub or in grain or sugarcane fields. **DISTRIBUTION AND STATUS** Resident. From Pakistan and NW India east to Arunachal Pradesh and Bangladesh. Hill birds make altitudinal movements: summers from the plains up to 2100 m (–2500 m in India). **PK:** now only locally common; up to 1220 m. **NP:** common and widespread. **IN:** widespread. **BT:** rare and local. **BD:** ?former resident; no recent records, but could still occur in very small numbers in the centre and northwest. **REFERENCES** Johnsgard (1988).

PAINTED FRANCOLIN *Francolinus pictus* Plate 1

Painted Partridge (I,P)

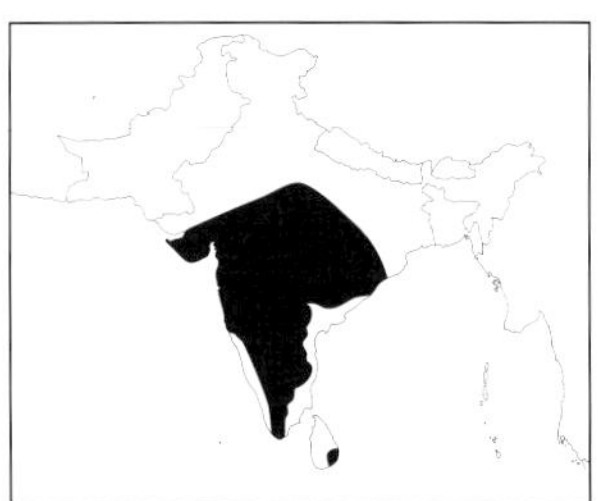

IDENTIFICATION 31 cm. Distinguished from female Black Francolin (p.347) and both sexes of Grey Francolin (below) by rather plain rufous-orange face and throat, bold white spotting on blackish mantle, and spotted (rather than barred) appearance to underparts. Sexes are often very similar in coloration; some females have whitish throat and/or less heavily spotted mantle (with buff edges to dark-centred feathers giving rise to streaked-looking lower mantle). Rufous-orange face and lack of rufous patch on hindneck are best features for separation from female Black Francolin, since patterning of mantle and underparts can be rather similar. Spotted and streaked appearance of upperparts and boldly marked underparts are always distinctive features from Grey Francolin. **Juvenile** like female, but more heavily marked on lower breast and flanks. **VOICE** A *click..cheek-cheek-keray*, almost indistinguishable from that of Black Francolin (p.347) (Ali and Ripley 1987). **HABITS** Usually keeps in pairs, sometimes in family parties. Leaves cover to forage in early morning and late afternoon. Very skulking, and if disturbed it will squat in cover. Male calls almost throughout the day during the breeding season, from a rock, stump or mound. **HABITAT** Generally occurs in wetter and thicker habitat than Grey Francolin and drier areas than Black. Tall thick grassland and cultivation with scattered trees and bushes, also glades in thin forest; partial to thick cover. **BREEDING** March–October, varying locally. Nests in mixed grass and scrub, sugarcane or other crops. **DISTRIBUTION AND STATUS** Endemic resident of India and Sri Lanka. From Gujarat north to S Uttar Pradesh, east to Orissa and south through the peninsula, and Sri Lanka. Subject to local movements, depending on food and water supplies. Hybridises with Black Francolin where the two species' ranges meet, e.g. in Rajasthan. **IN:** common and widespread, but declining. **LK:** rare, restricted to E foothills and lowlands of Uva province. **REFERENCES** Abdulali (1964), Johnsgard (1988), Kaul and Howman (1991).

CHINESE FRANCOLIN *Francolinus pintadeanus* Plate 1

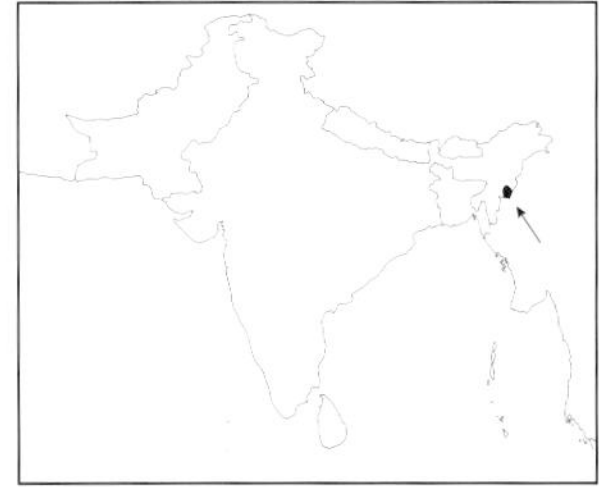

IDENTIFICATION 33 cm. Given its range, likely to be confused only with female Black Francolin (p.347). **Male** easily told from that species by orange-buff sides of crown, black moustachial stripe which divides white throat from white ear-coverts, lack of rufous on hindneck, extensive white spotting on upperparts, rufous in scapulars, and extensive white spotting on black breast and belly. **Female** is similar to male but duller, and white underparts are barred with black. Lack of rufous on hindneck, extensive white spotting on mantle, bold black moustachial stripe, and mottled/barred/spotted patterning to scapulars (with some rufous) are good distinctions from female Black. **Juvenile** has more buffish-orange ear-coverts, and lacks dark eye-stripe and moustachial stripe. More closely resembles female Black, but lack of rufous on hindneck and patterning of scapulars remain distinctive features. **VOICE** Loud, harsh, metallic *wi-ta-tak-takaa*, repeated after fairly long intervals (C. Robson). **HABITS** Little recorded in the subcontinent. Usually found singly or in pairs. Very skulking and remains under cover. **HABITAT** Dry open dipterocarp forest and oak scrub in hilly country. **BREEDING** Details not recorded in the subcontinent. March–September in Myanmar. Nests in scrub jungle or grass. **DISTRIBUTION AND STATUS IN:** very local resident in SE Manipur, common in drier areas. **REFERENCES** Johnsgard (1988).

GREY FRANCOLIN *Francolinus pondicerianus* Plate 1

Grey Partridge (F,I), Indian Grey Partridge (P)

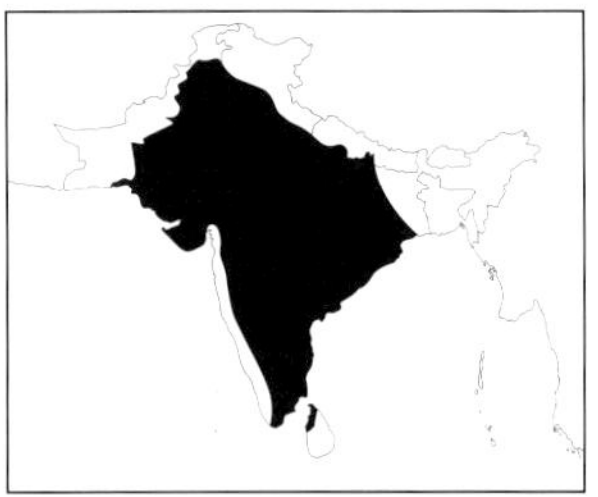

IDENTIFICATION 33 cm. **Adult** differs from female Black and Painted Francolins (p.347 and above) in having buffish-white or buffish-orange throat surrounded by necklace of black spotting, fine buff, chestnut, grey-brown and dark brown barring to upperparts (with distinct shaft streaking on coverts, scapulars and tertials), fine blackish-brown barring to entire underparts (without bold black or white markings), and chestnut (not black) on outer tail in flight. **Female** is unspurred. **Juvenile** is very similar, but head pattern is less pronounced and usually lacks the black necklace. **Racial variation** The nominate race of S peninsular India and Sri Lanka has a buffish-orange throat concolorous with supercilium and ear-coverts, and darker, more chestnut coloration to upperparts, and a stronger rufous wash to breast, compared with the other two races in the subcontinent *F. p. interpositus* and *F. p. mecranensis* (which are paler and greyer, and have a white throat). **VOICE** Rapidly repeated three-noted *khateeja-khateeja-khateeja*; also softer, more whistling *kila-kila-kila*, and when alarmed a high whirring *khirr-khirr* (Roberts 1991). **HABITS** Typically found in pairs or in groups of up to eight birds, which roost together in small thorny trees or shrubs. Well adapted to drought conditions. Usually escapes by running; seldom flies, but when pressed rises with a loud whirr of wings and alights again after only 50–100 m. Male calls from a vantage point. **HABITAT** Dry open grass plains and thorn scrub, often near dry cultivation, also stony semi-desert and sand dunes. **BREEDING** March–October, varying locally. Nests under a bush, rock or other shelter. **DISTRIBUTION AND STATUS** Resident. From Pakistan east to Bangladesh and south through the peninsula, and Sri Lanka. **PK:** common and widespread below 900 m. **NP:** uncommon, found below 200 m. **IN:** widespread and one of the commonest gamebirds; up to 500 m. **BD:** former resident. **LK:** common along N and W coast. **REFERENCES** Johnsgard (1988), Khan (1981), Lister (1951).

SWAMP FRANCOLIN *Francolinus gularis* — Plate 1

Swamp Partridge (F,I)

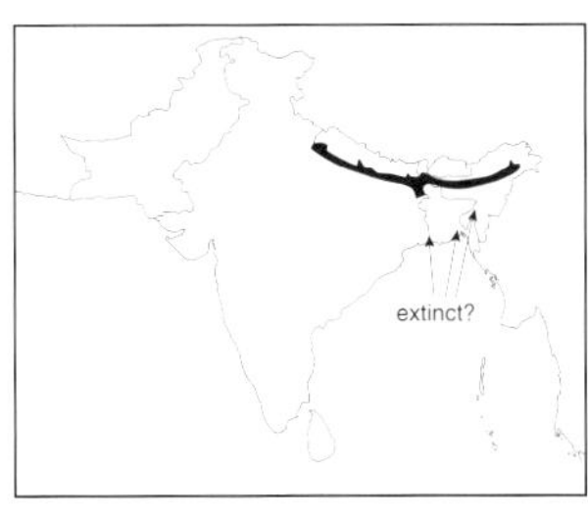

IDENTIFICATION 37 cm. Distinguished from other francolins by combination of rufous-orange throat and foreneck, brown upperparts finely barred with buff, broad white streaking to brown underparts, and buff supercilium and cheek-stripe (separated by dark brown eye-stripe). **Female** lacks spurs and has paler orange legs. Like Grey Francolin (p.348), shows chestnut on outer tail in flight. **VOICE** Gives a loud *kew-care* when alarmed (Fleming *et al.* 1984), occasional *qua, qua, qua* ascending in tone (Osmaston), and a harsh *chukeroo, chukeroo, chukeroo* preceded by several chuckles and croaks as if bird clearing throat in preparation (Tickell) (Ali and Ripley 1987). Advertising call is a long series of sharp notes, *chuill-chuill-chuill*, which is far-carrying and delivered at a rate of approximately ten calls in 8 seconds (P. Morris). **HABITS** Found in pairs or in groups of up to about six birds. In marshes often wades or climbs on to reeds in deep water. Forages in open grasslands and fields. When flushed, rises noisily with loud chuckling and whirring of wings. **HABITAT** Tall wet grasslands and swamps; also uses sugarcane fields adjacent to its natural habitats. **BREEDING** February–May. Nest is usually a thick pad of vegetation among reeds in shallow water. **DISTRIBUTION AND STATUS** Very local resident, endemic to the subcontinent. Formerly occurred from Nepal and N Uttar Pradesh, east across N India to Assam, at 50–200 m; current distribution is fragmented. **NP:** locally common in two protected areas. Globally threatened .**IN:** now virtually confined to protected areas in the terai and plains, where locally common. **BD:** ?former resident; no recent records, but could still occur in very small numbers. **REFERENCES** Javed (1993), Javed and Rahmani (1991), McGowan *et al.* (1995).

TIBETAN PARTRIDGE *Perdix hodgsoniae* — Plate 1

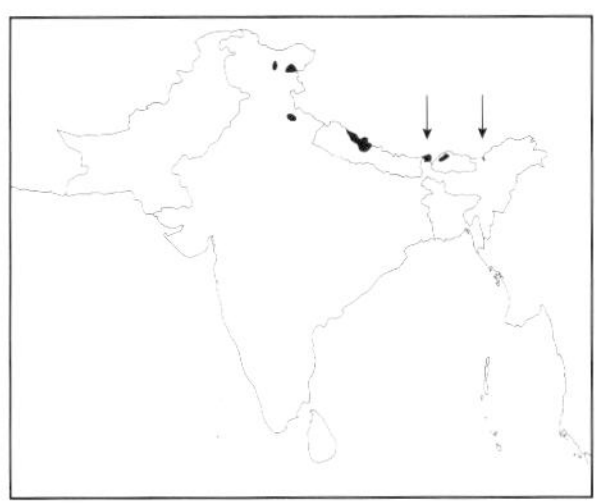

IDENTIFICATION 31 cm. **Adult** unmistakable, with bold, black ear-covert patch on whitish face, rufous collar not quite complete across breast, bold black barring on underparts forming variable black patch on belly, and rufous barring on flanks. **Juvenile** has crown and face dark brown, mottled with white, and lacks distinct black face patch. Further, lacks any rufous in plumage, and has underparts streaked and spotted with buff (without black barring). **Racial variation** *P. h. caraganae* of the NW Himalayas has paler rufous-orange collar and is paler overall compared with the nominate race, described above. **VOICE** A rattling and repeated *scherrrrreck-scherrrrreck*, uttered mostly in the morning and evening; when flushed, a shrill *chee, chee, chee, chee* (Ali and Ripley 1987). **HABITS** Keeps in coveys of up to about 15 birds outside the breeding season. When disturbed, birds run fast uphill, calling loudly. If pressed, they scatter in different directions and dive downhill, re-establishing contact later by uttering buzzing calls to each other. **HABITAT** Trans-Himalayan semi-desert and on rocky slopes with scattered *Caragana* and dwarf scrub. **BREEDING** May–July in Ladakh. Nests under a boulder or bush. **DISTRIBUTION AND STATUS** Resident. Extends marginally from Tibet into N Nepal, N India and N Bhutan. Winters at 3660–4100 m (down to 2800 m), summers up to 5200 m. **NP:** uncommon. **IN:** locally frequent. **BT:** fairly common in the northwest. **REFERENCES** Johnsgard (1988).

COMMON QUAIL *Coturnix coturnix* — Plate 2

IDENTIFICATION 20 cm. A very small and compact phasianid, usually seen only if flushed. Very like Japanese Quail (p.350) and female Rain Quail (p.350); see those species for comments on identification. In all plumages, has stripy head pattern (formed by distinct buff crown-stripe and supercilium), and prominent lanceolate buff streaks on mantle and scapulars. **Adult male** is very variable. Typically has blackish centre of throat, curving upwards towards ear-coverts to form 'anchor-shaped' pattern (although this may be poorly defined, or lacking, on some birds), below which is a whitish gorget across foreneck, which is usually separated from breast by band of rufous or blackish blotching. Breast varies from warm buff to rufous, with pale buff shaft streaking. Some males ('rufous morph') can have rufous (rather than white) throat sides and gorget, and rarely black 'anchor' can be absent and whole throat can be

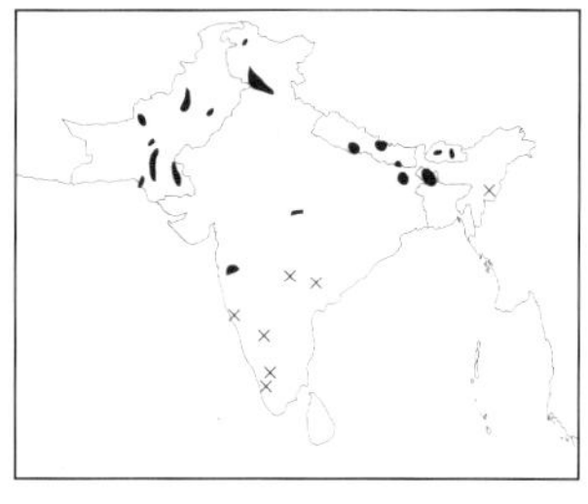

rufous. Many intermediates occur. **Female** lacks 'anchor' marking on throat, and has blackish spotting on buff breast. **VOICE** Song is a far-carrying *whit, whit-tit,* repeated in quick succession; frequently rendered as *wet-my-lips.* When flushed, a trilling, slightly rising *whreee* followed by short quiet *chak* notes (Cramp and Simmons 1980). **HABITS** Usually occurs singly or in pairs. Very secretive and keeps out of sight. If flushed, rises rapidly with whirring wingbeats and brief glides on downcurved wings, plunging into cover again after only 100–200 m or less. On arrival at breeding areas, males establish territories by singing persistently in early morning, evening and sometimes during the day or night. **HABITAT** Standing crops, paddy stubbles and grasslands, with vegetation dense and tall enough to conceal birds. **BREEDING** March–July. Nests in herbaceous vegetation. **DISTRIBUTION AND STATUS** Widespread but erratic visitor in winter and on passage. Mainly from Pakistan east to Assam and south to Maharashtra. Widely but very locally reported as resident in the north; probably under-recorded. Formerly very common locally in some years, especially on migration, but has declined. Its movements are very little known. **PK:** common passage migrant; a few breed and overwinter. **NP:** scarce winter visitor below 915 m, and passage migrant, possibly resident (–2900 m). **IN:** locally common. **BT:** probably resident, possibly also a passage migrant; locally common and breeds at 2135–3150 m. **BD:** local resident in the northwest, possibly migratory. **REFERENCES** Cramp and Simmons (1980), Johnsgard (1988), Martens and Eck (1995).

JAPANESE QUAIL *Coturnix japonica* — Plate 2

***C. coturnix japonica* (I)**

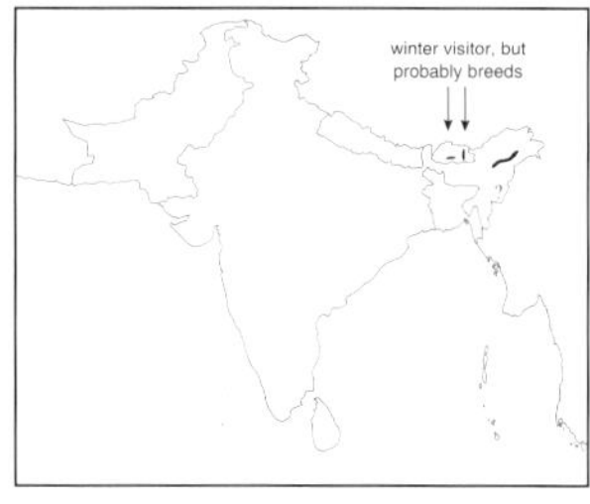

IDENTIFICATION 20 cm. Very similar to Common Quail (p.349). **Breeding male** has rufous face, throat and foreneck, with rufous often extending onto sides and upper part of breast. Some birds show faint dark 'anchor' marking on throat, as on Common. Tends to show more rufous on mantle, but upperparts of some Common appear identical in this respect. Coloration and patterning of breast and flanks is variable and much as Common. In non-breeding plumage, rufous colour on head is faint or absent, and head pattern is rather untidy and variable (for example, throat can be white with variable dark line down centre, or may be mottled with rufous, and/or have dark crescent at sides). Given considerable variation in head pattern of Common, there do not appear to be any features which are likely to be useful in the field. **Female** probably indistinguishable from female Common Quail, and, as that species, typically shows extensive black spotting across breast. **VOICE** A soft and muted *choo-pee-trrr,* the notes much harsher and blurred compared with Common Quail (Johnsgard 1988). Explosive, rasping, unmusical and often loud, barked *churck-churrr,* repeated at c. 10-second intervals (P. Holt). **HABITS** Like those of Common Quail. **HABITAT** Like that of Common Quail. **BREEDING** Details not recorded in the subcontinent. **DISTRIBUTION AND STATUS** Winter visitor to Assam and Bhutan; probably breeds. **IN:** rare. **BT:** locally fairly common in winter; probably breeds at 2800–3200 m; birds collected in Bhutan were apparently intermediate between this species and Common Quail. **REFERENCES** Johnsgard (1988), Ludlow and Kinnear (1937).

RAIN QUAIL *Coturnix coromandelica* — Plate 2

Black-breasted Quail (F,I)

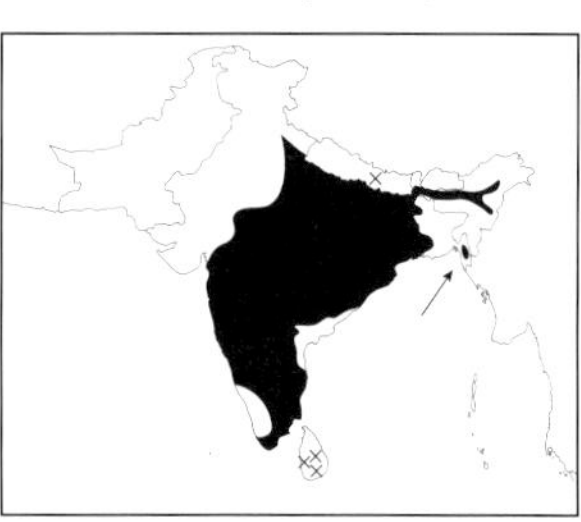

IDENTIFICATION 18 cm. Similar to Common and Japanese Quails (p.349 and above), although slightly smaller, with prominent crown-stripe and supercilium, and buff shaft streaking on mantle. Compared with those species, **male** Rain has more striking black-and-white pattern to head and neck, with black 'anchor' mark on throat, eye-stripe and moustachial, and black lower border to white band across foreneck being bold and clearly defined. Further, typically shows extensive black patch on breast and upper belly, contrasting with cinnamon-pink sides of neck and sides of breast, and bold black streaking on flanks. Some (immature?) males have black on underparts reduced to spotting on centre of breast and belly, when sides of breast are more extensively cinnamon-pink (with whitish shaft streaking). **Female** is very similar to female Common, but has unbarred primaries. **VOICE** A loud, metallic and high-pitched *whit-whit,* repeated in runs of three to five calls (Johnsgard 1988); also a short squeaky whistling note when flushed (Ali and Ripley 1987). **HABITS** Similar to those of Common Quail. Usually found singly or in pairs, sometimes in parties of up to six birds. Can be frequently heard throughout the day during the monsoon when breeding. **HABITAT** Standing crops, grasslands, paddy stubbles and grass and scrub jungle. **BREEDING** March–October, varying with locality and rainfall. Nests in standing crops or thin grass. **DISTRIBUTION AND STATUS** Resident, mainly confined to the subcontinent; some nomadic movements. From Pakistan east to Assam and Manipur, and south throughout the peninsula and Sri Lanka. **PK:** frequent monsoon visitor to the plains. **NP:** vagrant. **IN:** widespread and locally fairly common, mainly in the plains, also in the peninsular hills and to 2000 m in Himalayas. **BD:** vagrant. **LK:** rare winter visitor to lowlands and lower hills. **REFERENCES** Johnsgard (1988).

BLUE-BREASTED QUAIL *Coturnix chinensis* Plate 2

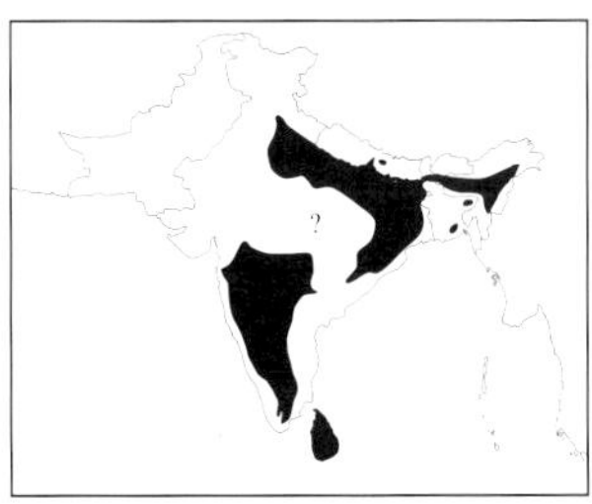

IDENTIFICATION 14 cm. **Male** unmistakable, with uniform slaty-blue forehead, sides of neck, breast and flanks, black-and-white patterning on head and foreneck, and reddish-chestnut belly and undertail-coverts. Extent of reddish-chestnut on underparts varies, on some extending to reach white band across foreneck. Patterning of upperparts also varies: some show blue-grey on crown, mantle and scapulars (and lack crown-stripe and shaft streaking); upperparts of others are more rufescent-brown with bold whitish shaft streaking, with darker brown crown and clearly defined crown-stripe. **Female** distinguished from female Common, Japanese and Rain Quails (p.349 and p.350) by much smaller size, rufous (or rufous-buff) forehead and broad supercilium, and barred breast and flanks; in addition, crown-stripe is finer, as is shaft streaking on hindneck, mantle and scapulars. Unbarred flight feathers are a further difference from Common and Japanese. Slaty-blue coloration of **immature male** is duller, and is said to be barred with black on sides of head and neck; chestnut on underparts is restricted to the centre of the belly or is absent. **VOICE** Typical call is a high-pitched series of two or three descending piping notes, *ti-yu* or *quee-kee-kew*; repeated weak *tir* notes may be uttered when flushed (Johnsgard 1988). **HABITS** Similar to those of Common Quail. Keeps in pairs or small family parties. **HABITAT** Wet grassland, marshes, paddy-field edges, dense grass at roadsides and scrub. **BREEDING** December–September, varying locally. Nests in a grass clump close to thick cover. **DISTRIBUTION AND STATUS** Resident; locally migratory depending on rainfall; a monsoon visitor in some places. From S Punjab, India, east to Assam and south to Tamil Nadu (distribution possibly disjunct), and Sri Lanka. **NP:** rare. **IN:** occurs widely but patchily and in small numbers, mainly in the plains, also up to 2000 m in peninsular hills; more frequent in the east. **BD:** vagrant. **LK:** resident throughout, most frequent in the dry lowlands. **REFERENCES** Johnsgard (1988).

JUNGLE BUSH QUAIL *Perdicula asiatica* Plate 2

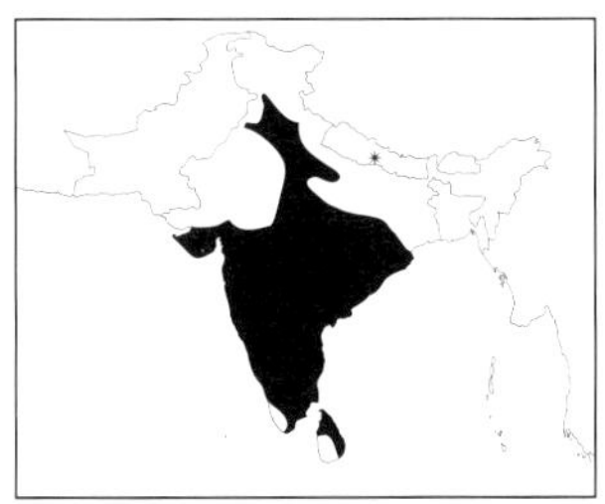

IDENTIFICATION 17 cm. **Male** has underparts heavily barred with black, and is very similar to male Rock Bush Quail (below). Best told by rufous-orange throat and supercilium (with supercilium edged above and below with creamy-white), whitish moustachial stripe, brownish ear-coverts, and orange-buff vent. **Female** is vinous-buff on the underparts, without black barring. From female Rock Bush Quail by striking head pattern, which is much as male Jungle, with rufous-orange throat distinct from rest of underparts. **Immature male** can be similar to female, but with some dark barring showing on underparts. **Racial variation** Five subspecies are recognised, with slight variation in coloration of upperparts of both sexes and underparts of female. **VOICE** A harsh grating *chee-chee-chuck, chee-chee-chuck*; also soft musical, whistling *whi-whi-whi-whi-whi* after a covey has been scattered (Ali and Ripley 1987). **HABITS** Found in coveys of up to 20 birds outside the breeding season. When roosting or when approached during the daytime, the birds bunch up and squat low before suddenly bursting into flight in all directions with a loud whirring of wings; they soon reassemble by making rallying calls to each other. Use a network of runs through the grass to move in single file between feeding grounds. **HABITAT** Dry grass and scrub jungle and both open and fairly dense deciduous forests, preferably on dry and stony ground. **BREEDING** Almost all months, varying locally. Nests at the base of a grass tussock in scrub. **DISTRIBUTION AND STATUS** Widespread resident, endemic to the subcontinent. From Gujarat east to Orissa, north to Himachal Pradesh and south throughout the peninsula and Sri Lanka. **NP:** extirpated, recorded only in 19th century. **IN:** fairly common in plains and hills below 1500 m. **LK:** rare resident in E hills and adjacent dry lowlands. **REFERENCES** Johnsgard (1988).

ROCK BUSH QUAIL *Perdicula argoondah* Plate 2

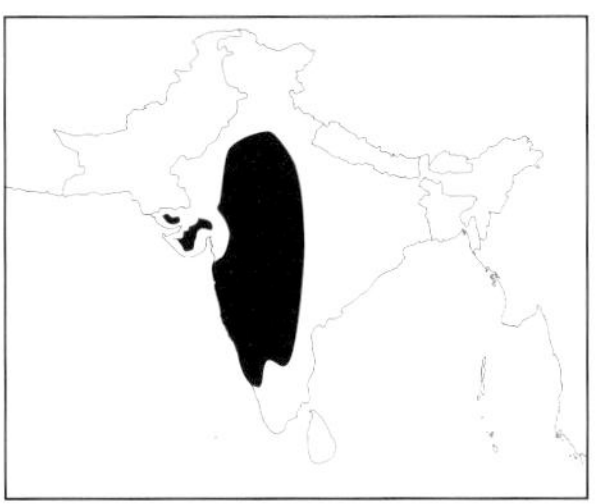

IDENTIFICATION 17 cm. **Male** is similar to Jungle Bush Quail (above), and like that species has white underparts heavily barred with black. Best told by subtle differences in head pattern. Has duller, more vinaceous-buff throat which is concolorous with ear-coverts, has creamy-white supercilium (variably washed with vinous-buff), and lacks white moustachial stripe. Also has buffish-white (not orange-buff) vent. **Female** is vinaceous to vinaceous-buff on the underparts, without black barring. Told from female Jungle by much plainer head pattern, with whitish supercilium behind eye, whitish chin, and with ear-coverts and throat concolorous with rest of underparts. Upperparts are more uniform, lacking bold blackish markings on scapulars and tertials (at least in adult birds). **Immature male** can be similar to female, but with more heavily marked upperparts (with buff barring and dark markings on scapulars) and with dark barring showing on underparts. **Racial variation** Three subspecies are recognised, with slight variation in coloration of upperparts of both sexes and underparts of female. **VOICE** As Jungle Bush Quail (Ali and Ripley 1987). **HABITS** Like those of

Jungle Bush Quail. **HABITAT** Dry rocky or sandy areas thinly vegetated with thorn scrub. Found in less well-vegetated and stonier country than Jungle Bush Quail. **BREEDING** Almost all year. Nests under a rock, bush or grass tussock. **DISTRIBUTION AND STATUS IN:** endemic resident, from Haryana south to N Kerala, and from Gujarat east to C Madhya Pradesh and C Andhra Pradesh; locally common. **REFERENCES** Johnsgard (1988).

PAINTED BUSH QUAIL *Perdicula erythrorhyncha* Plate 2

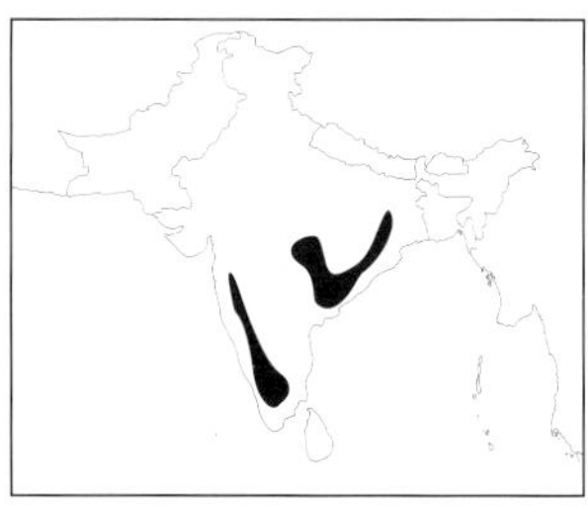

IDENTIFICATION 18 cm. A striking quail with bold black spotting on olive-brown upperparts, bold black spotting on breast and, especially, on rufous flanks, prominent white shaft streaks on scapulars and wing-coverts, and bright red bill and feet. **Male** is unmistakable, with white supercilia meeting across forecrown, black around eye, on forehead and on chin, and striking white throat. **Female** lacks black-and-white head pattern of male, and has fewer, or no, black spots on breast. Has rufous supercilium, lower ear-coverts and throat. **Juvenile male** has white shaft streaks on some mantle, throat and breast feathers, and supercilium and throat are white, washed with rufous. **VOICE** Male's breeding call is a pleasant triple *kirikee, kirikee*; when flushed, gives a short whistle like Common Quail; rally calls, given when scattered, are very soft whistles, *tu-tu-tu-tu-tutu-tutu-tuttu*, which rise gradually until they reach a certain pitch and the notes are then repeated a few times, before the calling dies down fairly rapidly (Ali and Ripley 1987). **HABITS** Similar to those of Jungle Bush Quail (p.351). Keeps in coveys of up to 15 birds for most of the year. Forages in more open areas in mornings and evenings. Often dustbathes at edges of tracks. **HABITAT** Thin scrub, and scrub at forest edges, often interspersed with cultivation. **BREEDING** Almost all year, varying locally. Nests under a rock, bush or grass tussock. **DISTRIBUTION AND STATUS IN:** endemic resident, mainly in Western and Eastern Ghats; locally distributed and common, 600–2000 m. **REFERENCES** Johnsgard (1988).

MANIPUR BUSH QUAIL *Perdicula manipurensis* Plate 2

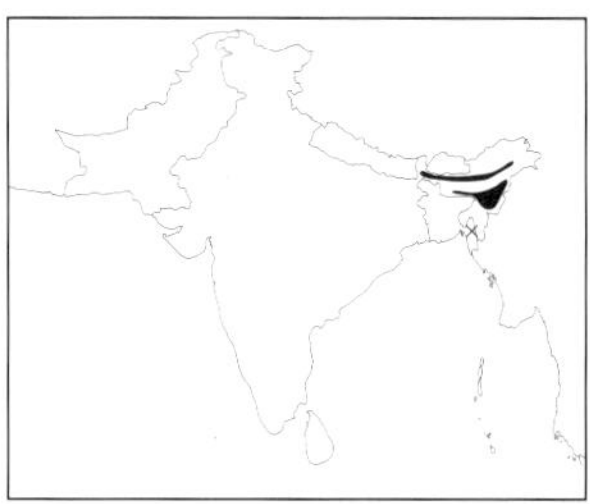

IDENTIFICATION 20 cm. Very distinctive, with dark olive-grey upperparts finely marked with black barring and spotting, and golden-buff underparts with black cross-shaped markings. **Male** has white lores, and chestnut forehead, supercilium, lower ear-coverts and throat. **Female** is less 'golden' underneath; has chestnut of head replaced by brownish-grey. **Racial variation** *P. m. inglisi* (north of the Brahmaputra R) differs from the nominate race (south of Brahmaputra), described above, in being less boldly marked with black on the upper- and underparts. **VOICE** Only described call (of a female) is a clear, softly whistled *whit-it-it-it-t-t*; each successive note is slightly higher in tone until the notes run together (Ali and Ripley 1987). **HABITS** Similar to those of Jungle Bush Quail (p.351). Associates in parties of six to eight birds. Very secretive and keeps in dense cover; most easily located by its distinctive call. Flight behaviour is similar to that of other bush quails. **HABITAT** Tall moist grassland and scrub in foothills, sometimes in swamps. **BREEDING** Poorly known. Fully fledged young found in mid January, nest taken among grass in mid May. **DISTRIBUTION AND STATUS** Very local resident endemic, now confined to NE India (Assam, Manipur, Meghalaya, Nagaland and West Bengal) and Bangladesh; in hills up to 1000 m. Globally threatened. **IN:** rare. **BD:** ?former resident in the southeast; no recent records, but could still occur in Chittagong Hill Tracts. **REFERENCES** Johnsgard (1988), McGowan *et al.* (1995).

HILL PARTRIDGE *Arborophila torqueola* Plate 3

Common Hill Partridge (F,I,K)

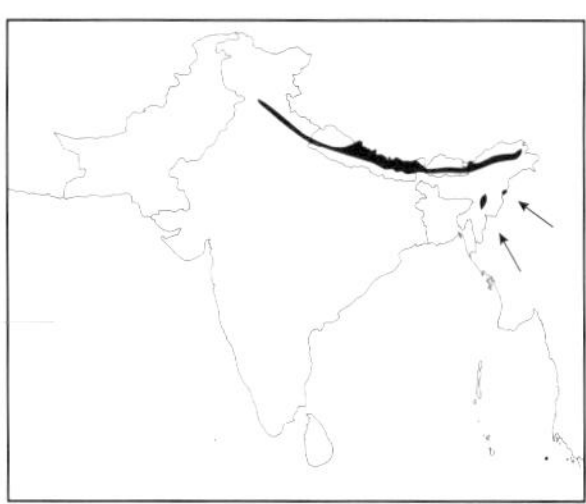

IDENTIFICATION 28 cm. **Male** told from Rufous-throated Partridge (p.353) by rufous (rather than olive-brown) crown and rufous-orange ear-covert patch, black eye-patch and eye-stripe, white neck sides streaked with black, and white half-collar separating throat from breast. **Female** is similar to male, but has olive-brown crown and ear-coverts and rufous foreneck (lacking white collar of male). More closely resembles Rufous-throated and best distinguished by buff supercilium, lack of black border between rufous foreneck and greyish breast, blackish barring to olive-brown mantle, diffuse rufous-buff fringes to breast, and greyish or brownish legs and feet. **Immature male** lacks the whitish supercilium and half-collar, and also chestnut on flanks, of adult male, and has white spotting on breast. **VOICE** A single, mournful, drawn-out whistle, repeated two or three times, followed by a series of three to six double whistles rendered as *bobwhite, bobwhite, bobwhite*; shrill continuous *kwikwikwikwikwik*, thought to be call of female, often precedes above call (Ali and Ripley 1987). **HABITS** Usually in pairs or, outside the breeding season, in coveys of five to ten birds. Digs for food among leaves and humus on the forest floor, birds keeping in contact by calling as they move through the forest. Roosts in coveys in trees. If disturbed, usually moves away on foot; if flushed, flies strongly, zigzagging around the trees, and usually settles after less than 100 m. **HABITAT** Ravines and slopes in undergrowth of moist, dense forest of oak and other evergreen broadleaves. **BREEDING** April–July. Nest is hidden in forest or scrub jungle. **DISTRIBUTION AND STATUS** Resident. Himalayas from Himachal Pradesh east to Arunachal Pradesh; NE India; mainly 1830–3050 m in Himalayas (400–4000 m in India, –3550 m in Bhutan), 2200–2600 m in hills of NE India. **NP:** fairly common and widespread. **IN, BT:** fairly common. **REFERENCES** Johnsgard (1988).

RUFOUS-THROATED PARTRIDGE *Arborophila rufogularis* Plate 3

Rufous-throated Hill Partridge (F,I)

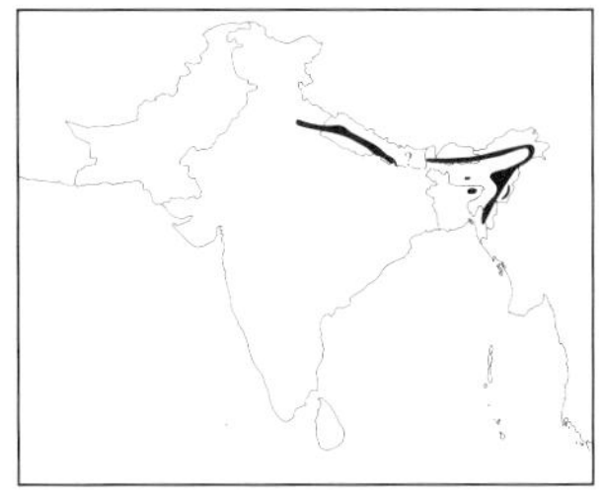

IDENTIFICATION 27 cm. Readily told from male Hill Partridge (p.352) by greyish forehead and olive-brown crown, rufous-orange throat and foreneck spotted with black, and lack of white half-collar. Both sexes more closely resemble female Hill, and are best told by greyish-white supercilium, white moustachial stripe which broadens beneath eye, narrow black band between rufous-orange foreneck and grey breast, uniform olive-brown mantle (although may show faint barring on lower back), darker grey breast, and pinkish-red to red legs and feet. Immature has more extensive white spotting on underparts, and unspotted rufous throat. **Racial variation** *A. r. intermedia* (hills east and south of the Brahmaputra R) is similar to the nominate race, described above, but throat is almost black, foreneck is brighter orange, and it lacks the black line dividing the orange of neck from the slate-grey breast. **VOICE** Mournful double whistle, *wheea-whu*, repeated constantly and on slightly ascending scale; the first note is prolonged and the second short and sharp. This call may be repeated two or three times and then followed by a series of ascending double notes. Members of a covey keep in contact by low whistled calls (Ali and Ripley 1987; Johnsgard 1988). **HABITS** Like those of Hill Partridge. **HABITAT** Thick understorey of broadleaved evergreen forest and secondary growth. **BREEDING** April–August. Nest varies, often a thick pad, sometimes has a dome and tunnel of growing grass; hidden in grass or dense undergrowth in forest. **DISTRIBUTION AND STATUS** Resident. Himalayas from N Uttar Pradesh east to Arunachal Pradesh; NE India and Bangladesh. Subject to vertical movements: mainly 1450–1830 m in Himalayas (460–2500 m), 600–1800 m in NE hills. Generally at lower altitudes than Hill Partridge, although ranges sometimes overlap. **NP:** scarce. **IN:** locally fairly common in Himalayas, locally frequent in NE hills. **BT:** common in the centre, very common in the east. **BD:** ?former resident in the northeast; no recent records, but could still occur in Chittagong Hill Tracts. **REFERENCES** Johnsgard (1988).

WHITE-CHEEKED PARTRIDGE *Arborophila atrogularis* Plate 3

White-cheeked Hill Partridge (I)

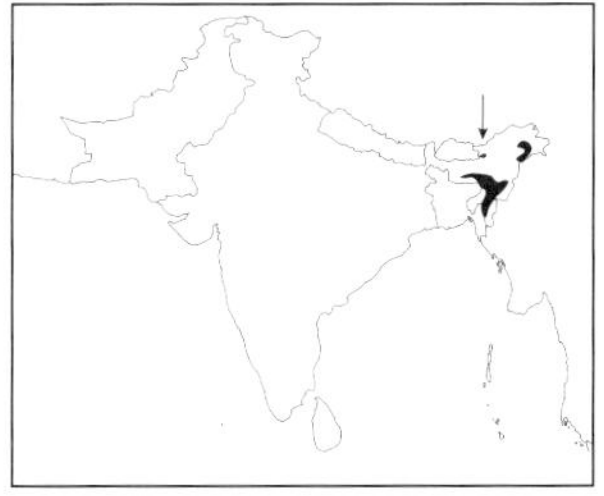

IDENTIFICATION 28 cm. Distinguished from other *Arborophila* partridges in the region by white patch on ear-coverts and whitish supercilium, black mask and throat (with black of throat extending to enclose white 'cheek' patch), black-streaked orange-yellow on hindneck and neck sides, and black streaking on white foreneck. Legs and feet are yellowish through to red. Mantle and back are olive-brown and heavily barred with black, and upperparts are very similar to female Hill Partridge (p.352), although hindneck is orange-yellow (rather than rufous-orange). Juvenile is much as adult. **VOICE** An accelerating and ascending series of 12–18 far-carrying, throaty *whew* notes that end abruptly (P. Holt from D. Allen recording). **HABITS** Like those of Hill Partridge (p.352). **HABITAT** Bamboo thickets and damp undergrowth in less dense broadleaved evergreen forest than those inhabited by Hill or Rufous-throated Partridges; also tea estates in Bangladesh. **BREEDING** March–July, varying with altitude. Nest varies, sometimes a hollow filled with leaves, or a thick pad of grass with a dome and tunnel of growing grass. **DISTRIBUTION AND STATUS** Resident. E Himalayas, NE India (Arunachal Pradesh, Assam, Manipur, Meghalaya, Mizoram, Tripura) and Bangladesh from the lower foothills up to 1500 m. **IN:** locally common, more frequent below 750 m. **BD:** very local in the northeast; could also still occur in Chittagong Hill Tracts. **REFERENCES** Johnsgard (1988).

CHESTNUT-BREASTED PARTRIDGE *Arborophila mandellii* Plate 3

Red-breasted Hill Partridge (I)

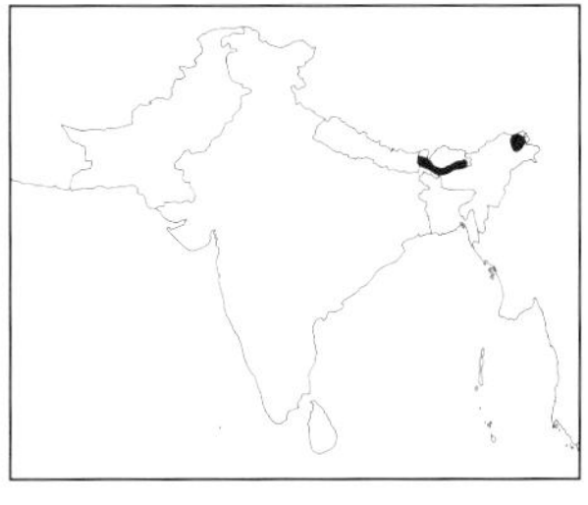

IDENTIFICATION 28 cm. Best told from other *Arborophila* partridges by white half-collar and broad chestnut breast-band. In addition, has rufous-orange ear-coverts, throat and foreneck, black division between orange foreneck and chestnut breast, black spotting on ear-coverts and sides of neck, and greyish supercilium. Sexes similar. **VOICE** Starts with repetition of *prrreet*, followed by a series of *prrr prrr-er-it*, ascending to a climax. **HABITS** Unknown in the wild. **HABITAT** Dense undergrowth in broadleaved evergreen forest. **BREEDING** Only one known nest: a pad of grass under a rock in forest, taken with eggs in early June; well-grown young in October. **DISTRIBUTION AND STATUS** Resident. E Himalayas from West Bengal east to Arunachal Pradesh; Assam; 350–2500 m and possibly higher. Globally threatened. **IN:** locally common in Arunachal Pradesh. **BT:** locally fairly common in Shemgang Zone. **REFERENCES** McGowan *et al.* (1995).

MOUNTAIN BAMBOO PARTRIDGE *Bambusicola fytchii* Plate 3

Bamboo Partridge (I)

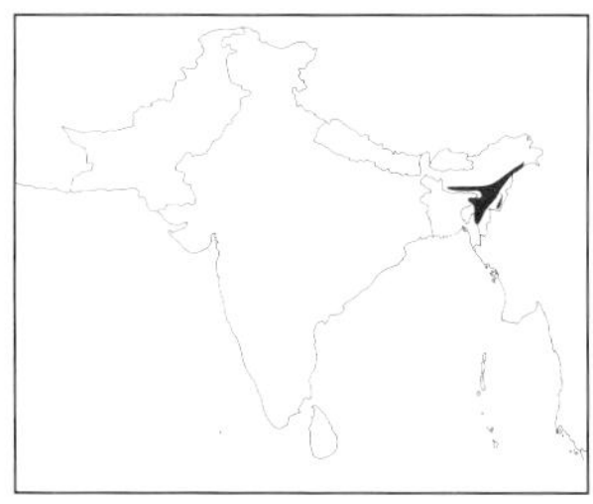

IDENTIFICATION 35 cm. A distinctive, comparatively long-tailed partridge with broad, buffish-white supercilium and dark eye-stripe, warm buff ear-coverts, throat and foreneck, rufous and chestnut spotting on breast, mantle and scapulars, diffusely barred tail, and bold blackish heart-shaped spotting on flanks. Shows rufous in primaries and sides of tail in flight. Sexes similar. **VOICE** Similar to call of Black Francolin (p.347) but less shrill and high-pitched, *che-chirree-che-chirree, chiree, chiree, chiree* (Ali and Ripley 1987). **HABITS** Associates in parties of up to five or six birds outside the breeding season. Shy, coming out in the open to feed only in early mornings and evenings. Males are very noisy in spring, crowing from a mound or tree stump. Difficult to flush, and then flies rapidly a short distance before landing in dense grass or in trees. **HABITAT** Dense grass in foothills and sometimes adjacent plains, scrub bordering paddy-fields, and scrub mixed with elephant grass along stream banks. Favours patches of *Alpinia*, a wild cardamom-like plant. Usually found near water. **BREEDING** March–May. Nests under a shrub or tree or in a grass clump. **DISTRIBUTION AND STATUS** Resident. NE India (Arunachal Pradesh, Assam, Manipur, Meghalaya, Mizoram, Nagaland) and Bangladesh, chiefly at low altitudes, but sometimes up to 2000 m. **IN:** now quite rare. **BD:** ?former resident in the northeast and southeast; no recent records, but could still occur in Chittagong Hill Tracts. **REFERENCES** Johnsgard (1988), McGowan *et al.* (1995).

RED SPURFOWL *Galloperdix spadicea* Plate 3

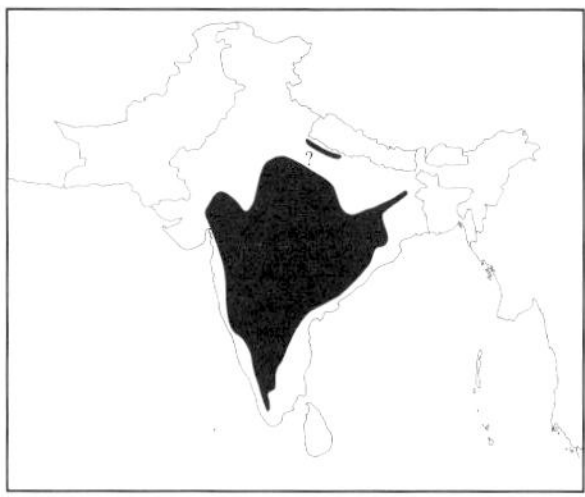

IDENTIFICATION 36 cm. Rufous-coloured partridge-like bird with comparatively long tail which is held partly fanned and with central ridge. Has red base to bill and eye-patch, and reddish legs and feet. **Male** is distinctive, with brownish-grey head and neck and darker brown crown, rufous upperparts and underparts scaled with grey and buff, and brownish-black unbarred tail. **Female** has browner head and neck, buffish-brown upperparts with bold blackish markings, rufous underparts with irregular blackish barring, and buff barring on tail. **Immature male** is like adult female, but more richly and deeply coloured, and more heavily marked with black. Rufous coloration of male, and dark mottling to upperparts and barred underparts of female, as well as red eye-patch and legs, are best distinctions from female and immature Painted Spurfowl (below). Also possibly confusable with female junglefowls (p.359–p.360), but those species have a laterally compressed tail (which is often held cocked), and prominent streaking on underparts. **Racial variation** *G. s. stewarti* of Kerala differs from the nominate race, described above, in being deeper chestnut-red on upperparts and underparts (and does not show obvious scaling to plumage); female of this race is generally darker and more heavily marked. Male *G. s. caurina* of Rajasthan and parts of Gujarat is paler than the nominate race, and rufous on upperparts is much reduced; female has paler, more rufous-brown upperparts, which are finely vermiculated with buff and dark brown (and lack bold black mottling shown by females of other two races). **VOICE** Male has a Grey Junglefowl-like crowing *ku-ruk-ku-rak* and a more hesitant, erratic, nervous cackling *kuk-kuk-ku-tuk*. Contact calls of both sexes include a slow, but accelerating sequence of up to eight low, gruff and pumped *wu-pu, wu-pu, wu-pu* notes (P. Holt). **HABITS** Found in pairs or in groups of three to five birds. Very wary, skulking and rarely flushed. When startled, runs off rapidly, dashing from one thicket to another. Roosts and often takes refuge in trees or dense thorny bushes. Scratches about among dead leaves under thickets, coming into the open on forest paths and field edges bordering forest only in early mornings or evenings. **HABITAT** Dense scrub near cultivation, dry and stony scrub-covered foothills, bamboo thickets and secondary growth; in S India also in coffee estates and lantana patches. **BREEDING** January–June, varying locally. Nests in dense scrub or bamboo. **DISTRIBUTION AND STATUS IN:** endemic resident, widespread and locally common from Uttar Pradesh south through the peninsula; foothills up to 1250 m. **REFERENCES** Johnsgard (1988).

PAINTED SPURFOWL *Galloperdix lunulata* Plate 3

IDENTIFICATION 32 cm. **Male** is unmistakable, with greenish-black head and neck spotted and barred with white, chestnut-red upperparts with black-bordered white spots, greenish-black wings and tail with white spotting on coverts, yellowish-buff breast and belly barred and spotted with black, and chestnut flanks. **Female** told from female Red Spurfowl (above) by dark olive-brown upperparts and breast (becoming paler brownish-buff on lower breast and belly), buff throat and malar stripe (variably mottled with chestnut), and chestnut forehead, supercilium and ear-coverts (with dark brown crown, and often with buffish mottling to rear of supercilium and across hindcrown). Lacks red orbital skin, and has dark bill and legs. **Juvenile** is similar to female, but more rufescent-brown in coloration,

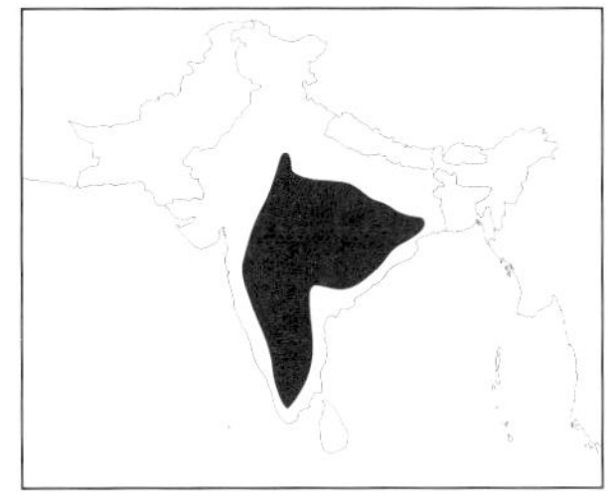

with irregular and indistinct rufous spotting, and rufous barring on rectrices and remiges. **VOICE** Call of male is poorly known and accounts are contradictory: described as 'cackling and very fowl-like' and also as a 'peculiar loud *chur, chur, chur,* rapidly repeated, and anything but fowl-like' (Ali and Ripley 1987). **HABITS** Keeps in pairs or in family parties of up to five birds. Even more skulking than Red Spurfowl. If disturbed, sprints away, clucking as it goes. If hard pressed, will fly a few metres, then land and run on again or hide in crevices and holes among rocks. **HABITAT** Generally in drier, rockier country than Red Spurfowl. Dry stony foothills covered with dense thorn scrub or bamboo thickets. **BREEDING** January–June. Nest is hidden under rocks or vegetation. **DISTRIBUTION AND STATUS IN:** locally frequent endemic resident, from E Rajasthan east to West Bengal and south through the peninsula; in foothills up to 1000 m. Range overlaps with that of Red Spurfowl. **REFERENCES** Johnsgard (1988), Prasad *et al.* (1992).

SRI LANKA SPURFOWL *Galloperdix bicalcarata* — Plate 3

Ceylon Spurfowl (I,P)

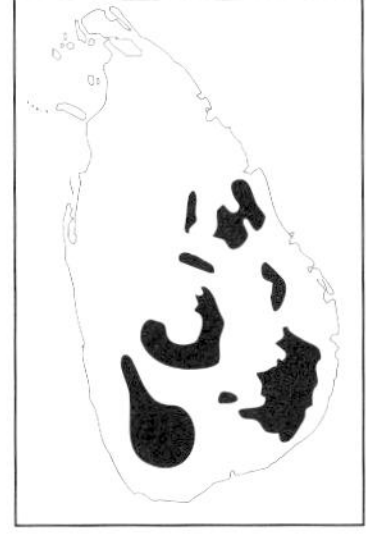

IDENTIFICATION 34 cm. **Male** is mainly blackish, with white throat, white streaking on upperparts, and bold white spotting on underparts (spots merging on belly to form white patch). Further, has chestnut rump and uppertail-coverts, and blackish tail. Both sexes have red bill, orbital skin and legs. **Female** has chestnut upperparts and brighter rufous underparts; body is finely vermiculated with black except on breast, which has irregular but more distinct black scaling. Has dark brown crown, and whitish chin and throat. **VOICE** A ringing series of trisyllabic whistles, each series on a higher note than the preceding one, and the last dropping suddenly to the starting note: *yuhuhu, yuhuhu, yuhuhu, yuhuhu, yuhuhu, yuhukeeyu,* replied to by other males in the neighbourhood (Henry 1971). **HABITS** Usually very shy and secretive, heard far more often than seen. Runs rather than flies to escape from danger, but if hard pressed it flies in a whirring partridge-like manner to the nearest cover. Has a high-strutting gait when moving about on the forest floor. **HABITAT** Tall, undisturbed, dense forest. **BREEDING** November–April, sometimes July and August. Nest is well concealed under a stone or bush. **DISTRIBUTION AND STATUS LK:** endemic resident, locally distributed in small numbers throughout the wet lowlands and hills, less frequent in the dry zone.

HIMALAYAN QUAIL *Ophrysia superciliosa* — Plate 4

Mountain Quail (I)

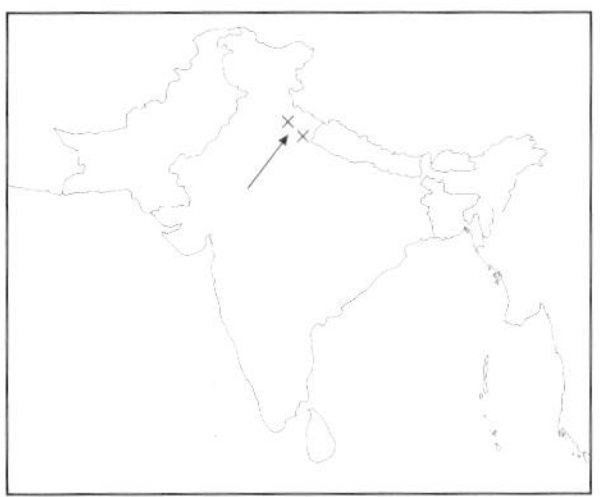

IDENTIFICATION 25 cm. A comparatively small, long-tailed phasianid with red bill and legs. **Male** has a complex black-and-white head pattern with black-bordered greyish-white supercilium, greyish-white eye-patch and patch on ear-coverts, and black throat with greyish-white border. Upperparts and underparts are dark slaty olive-brown with black streaks, except for undertail-coverts, which are black with greyish-white barring. **Female** has less striking head pattern, with narrow white eye-patch, pale vinaceous-grey supercilium and ear-coverts, and black sides of crown and stripe behind eye. Upperparts are cinnamon-brown and marked with black; underparts pale vinaceous-brown, streaked with black. **VOICE** A shrill whistle when disturbed. **HABITS** Poorly known. Old records indicate that it kept in coveys of six to 12 which rarely left thick cover and were very reluctant to take flight, preferring to run in and out between grass stalks. If flushed, birds flew slowly and heavily, soon dropped into vegetation, and reunited by using shrill whistles. **HABITAT** Long grass and brushwood on steep hillsides. **BREEDING** Unknown. **DISTRIBUTION AND STATUS** Globally threatened. **IN:** presumably once endemic to India; former status unknown, occurred in W Himalayas in N Uttar Pradesh, at 1650–2100 m; now presumed extinct, last confirmed sighting in 1890, but could possibly still survive. **REFERENCES** Rieger and Waltzhöny (1992), Kaul (1992), Sankaran (1990a).

BLOOD PHEASANT *Ithaginis cruentus* — Plate 4

IDENTIFICATION 38 cm. **Male** has lanceolate plumage, and is brightly coloured and unmistakable. Has bright red orbital patch; black forehead and 'spectacles'; crimson-red chin and throat; blue-grey upperparts streaked with white (and with apple-green in wing-coverts); apple-green underparts streaked with pale yellow-green; and crimson splashes on breast, tail-coverts and in tail. **Female** has dark brown upperparts and rufous-brown underparts. Has grey crest, nape and upper mantle, and rufous-orange forehead, face and throat. **Immature male** is less brightly coloured than adult male, with red bill and fleshy-grey orbital skin. **Immature female** is similar to adult female, but has brown crown, nape and upper mantle (concolorous with rest of upperparts). **Racial variation** Male *I. c. tibetanus* (E Bhutan and W Arunachal Pradesh) is quite distinctive compared with birds occurring to the west (described above): lacks black 'spectacles' (black around red orbital skin is largely replaced by red); has red forehead and forecrown, and extensive pinkish-red on breast. Male *I. c. kuseri* (E Arunachal Pradesh) differs further

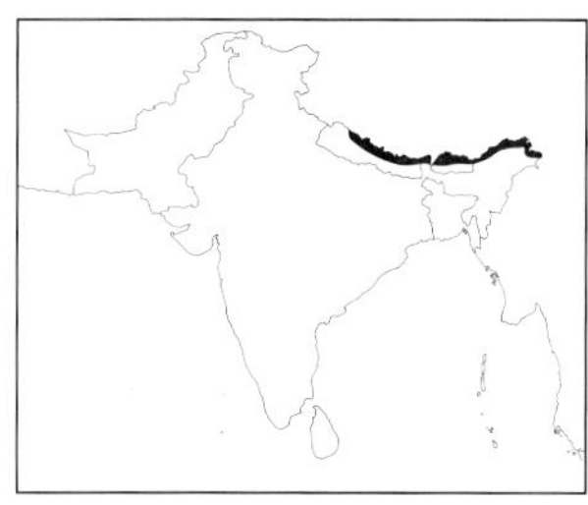

in having blackish crest and nape, black ear-coverts and sides of neck, black band across upper breast, and rest of breast entirely red. **VOICE** Call is a repeated *chuck*, and has a loud, grating *kzeeuuk-cheeu-cheeu-chee* (Fleming *et al.* 1984). **HABITS** Keeps in coveys of five to 30 or more. Tame and confiding. Rarely flies except to go to roost. Forages actively throughout the day, scratching the ground like a domestic fowl and turning over leaves and grasses with its feet; can dig down through snow, which often covers the vegetation. Roosts in trees or thickets, or on the ground. **HABITAT** Open fir and rhododendron forest and shrubberies of rhododendron, birch and juniper. Partial to dense bamboo clumps. Often near snow patches. **BREEDING** April–June. Builds a loose nest of grass and leaves under bushes or bamboo. **DISTRIBUTION AND STATUS** Resident. Himalayas from W Nepal east to Arunachal Pradesh. Subject to altitudinal movements: mainly 3200–4700 m (down to 1500 m in winter in India). **NP, IN:** locally fairly common. **BT:** common. **REFERENCES** Johnsgard (1986).

WESTERN TRAGOPAN *Tragopan melanocephalus* — Plate 4

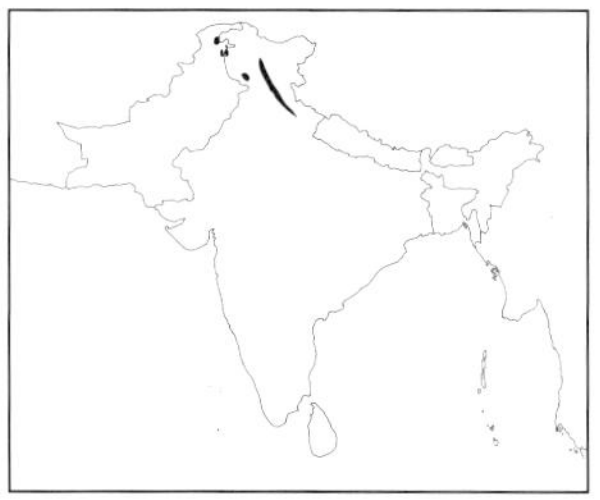

IDENTIFICATION Male 68–73 cm; female 60 cm. **Male** is strikingly different from male Satyr (below), having bright orange foreneck and upper breast, white-spotted black underparts (with red bases of feathers showing through on breast), and deep scarlet hindneck contrasting with intricately patterned black and grey-brown upperparts (which, as on Satyr, are spotted with white). In addition, has red facial skin, bluish throat, and bluish lappets and horns which are erected in display. **Female** is dull greyish-brown in coloration, intricately patterned with dark browns, greys and buffs; has slight rufescent tinge to crown and neck, and irregular white spotting on underparts. Very similar to female Satyr Tragopan, but has dark grey-brown (rather than rufous) coloration to underparts. In flight, possibly confusable with females of Koklass Pheasant (p.357) and Himalayan Monal (p.358). Best told from former by broad, rounded tail and stockier appearance, darker and more uniform coloration, and lack of white on throat. Female Himalayan Monal is heavily streaked on upperparts and underparts, has white throat and 'horseshoe' patch on rump, and has a loud shrieking flight call. **First-year male** is like a very dull version of adult male. Has dull brownish-red hindneck, and more uniformly grey upperparts and underparts with fewer, smaller white spots. White-spotted grey underparts would separate from first-year Satyr. **VOICE** Nasal, wailing *khuwaah*, repeated in bouts of 7–15 calls, uttered by male and female, usually at dawn and dusk (Roberts 1991). This call has been likened to the wailing of a child or goat. When alarmed, a more abrupt and anxious *waa, waa, waa.* **HABITS** Usually found singly or in pairs. Normally extremely wary and skulking, but sometimes forages in forest glades or on open slopes. Feeds on the ground, mainly in early morning and from late afternoon to dusk. Roosts in trees, where it is effectively concealed. Territorial in the breeding season. When displaying, males repeatedly expand and contract their horns and colourfully patterned lappets. **HABITAT** Dense undergrowth in undisturbed temperate and subalpine oak, coniferous and mixed forests. **BREEDING** May–early June. Builds a nest of sticks, lined with grass, in thick undergrowth. **DISTRIBUTION AND STATUS** Resident endemic of W Himalayas in Pakistan and India. Recently recorded from Pakistan, Kashmir and Himachal Pradesh; formerly occurred from N Pakistan east to N Uttar Pradesh. Subject to altitudinal movements: breeds at 2400–3600 m, winters down to 2000 m (–1735 m). Globally threatened. **PK, IN:** now rare and very local. **REFERENCES** Gaston *et al.* (1983), Johnsgard (1986), McGowan and Garson (1995).

SATYR TRAGOPAN *Tragopan satyra* — Plate 4

Crimson Tragopan (I), Crimson Horned Pheasant (F)

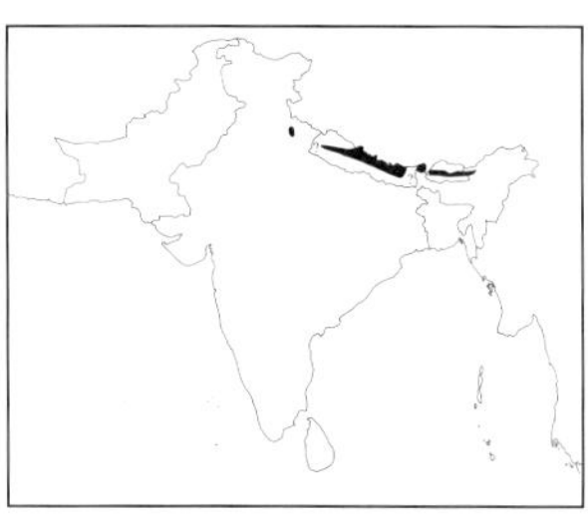

IDENTIFICATION Male 67–72 cm; female 57.5 cm. **Male** is unmistakable throughout much of its range. Has red neck, mantle and underparts (latter with black-bordered white spots), and intricately patterned olive-brown back, rump, uppertail-coverts and wing-coverts, spotted with white and mottled with red. In addition, has blue facial skin and throat, and bluish lappets and horns which are erected in display. **Female** varies from rufous-brown to ochraceous-brown in coloration, and is vermiculated, mottled and spotted with black and buff. Underparts are generally brighter and more rufescent than on other female tragopans. **First-year male** is more like female, but with black on head, and red on neck, upper mantle and breast; rest of upperparts and (paler) underparts are brownish-grey, finely vermiculated with dark brown and buff, with a few white spots. See other tragopan species for further identification features. **VOICE** A deep, wailing drawn-out call, given mainly at dawn, *wah, waah! oo-ah! oo-aaaaa!* uttered 12–14 times, the series rising in volume and becoming more protracted until it becomes almost a shriek. Also a *wah, wah* call uttered at any time of the day. When alarmed, or flushed, a more anxious *wak, wak* call (Johnsgard 1986). **HABITS** Similar to those of Western Tragopan (above). Usually wary, but tame where not hunted, such as in parts of Bhutan. **HABITAT** Moist oak and rhododendron forest with dense undergrowth and bamboo clumps; shrubberies on steep hillsides and narrow ravines, and mixed coniferous/broadleaved forest. **BREEDING** May–June. Builds a rough nest of sticks in branches of a forest tree. **DISTRIBUTION AND STATUS** Resident. Himalayas from N Uttar Pradesh and W Nepal east to W Arunachal Pradesh. Distribution now fragmented except in Bhutan. Subject to altitudinal movements: summers mainly at 2590–3800 m (2400–4500 m), winters down to 2000 m. **NP, IN:** uncommon. **BT:** fairly common. **REFERENCES** Johnsgard (1986), Khaling (1997), McGowan and Garson (1995).

BLYTH'S TRAGOPAN *Tragopan blythii* — Plate 4

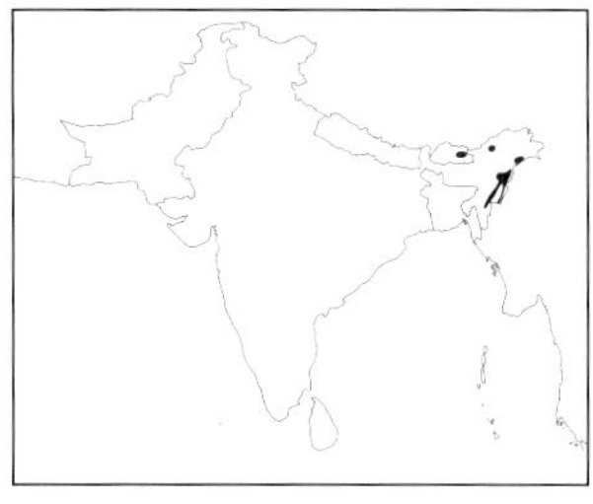

IDENTIFICATION Male 65–70 cm; female 58 cm. **Male** is similar to Satyr and Temminck's Tragopans (p.356 and below), but has sandy-grey breast and belly and orange-yellow facial skin. In addition, has broader red supercilium, and has clean division between red of hindneck and 'brown' upperparts, which have numerous brownish-maroon (as well as white) ocelli. **Female** distinguished from female Satyr by paler underparts lacking strong rufous tone, and from female Temminck's by paler underparts with much less distinct white spotting. **First-year male** is much as first-year male Satyr. Possible distinctions include less black on head (restricted to crown and nape, whereas head of Satyr is mainly black), more distinct whitish spotting on underparts (although less heavily and distinctly spotted than on first-winter Temminck's), and some brownish-maroon ocelli on upperparts. **Racial variation** *T. b. molesworthi* (NE Himalayas) differs from *T. b. blythii* (NE India, south of Brahmaputra R) in having a narrower band of red across breast and being paler and more uniform sandy-grey on rest of underparts (with lighter centres to feathers hardly apparent); underparts of *blythii* have a distinctly mottled/scaled appearance. Female *molesworthi* differs from *blythii* in being darker on the upperparts, with larger blackish markings, and with greyish (rather than reddish) tone to rump and uppertail-coverts. **VOICE** A deep *mao, mao* uttered in the early morning and again in the evening (Zeliang 1981) (for *T. b. blythii*; *T. b. molesworthi* undescribed). Male's courtship call a sonorous *wak*, sometimes lengthened to a *wa ak-ak* producing a kind of 'two-toned' effect (Johnsgard 1986). **HABITS** Similar to those of Western Tragopan (p.356); often in small parties of four or five. **HABITAT** Moist, evergreen broadleaved forest with a thick understorey; dense shrubberies and ringal bamboo on steep slopes. **BREEDING** Very poorly known in the wild. Nest with eggs found in April on cliff ledge. **DISTRIBUTION AND STATUS** Resident, subject to altitudinal movements. E Himalayas in E Bhutan and Arunachal Pradesh; NE India (Assam, Manipur, Mizoram and Nagaland). Globally threatened. **IN:** generally rare, but locally common in Nagaland; above 1800 m. **BT:** rare; 1800–3500 m. **REFERENCES** Ali *et al.* (1994), Baker (1928), Biswas (1968), Choudhury (1997), Johnsgard (1986), Katju (1996), Kaul *et al.* (1995), McGowan and Garson (1995).

TEMMINCK'S TRAGOPAN *Tragopan temminckii* — Plate 4

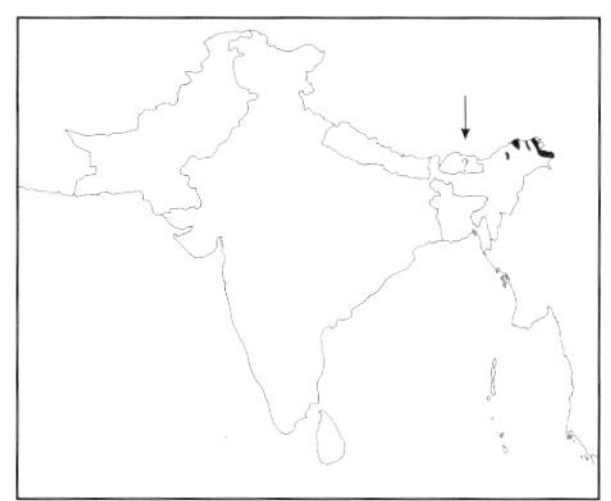

IDENTIFICATION Male 64 cm; female – no measurements. **Male** distinguished from male Satyr (p.356) by larger, greyish drop-shaped spotting (without black borders) on red underparts, brighter orange-red neck, mainly red upperparts (lacking Satyr's olive-brown tones to back and rump) with black-bordered greyish-white spotting, and more extensive (and brighter) blue facial skin. Easily told from male Blyth's (above) by coloration and patterning of upperparts and underparts. **Female** is much more conspicuously spotted with white on underparts than other female tragopans, and lacks the strong rufous tones of female Satyr. **First-year male** is very similar to first-year male Satyr, but has more prominent wedge-shaped white spotting on underparts. **VOICE** Series of six to nine eerie moaning notes, gradually increasing in length and volume, terminated by a curious nasal grumbling note: *woh...woah...woaah....waaah.... waaah....waaah....waaah....griiiik* (C. Robson). **HABITS** Similar to those of Western Tragopan (p.356), but very arboreal. Poorly known in the wild. **HABITAT** Dense undergrowth in damp, evergreen broadleaved forest and dense rhododendron and bamboo. **BREEDING** Details not recorded in the wild. **DISTRIBUTION AND STATUS IN:** rare resident in Arunachal Pradesh; 2100–3600 m. **REFERENCES** Johnsgard (1986).

KOKLASS PHEASANT *Pucrasia macrolopha* — Plate 4

Koklas Pheasant (I)

IDENTIFICATION Male 58–64 cm, female 52.5–56 cm. **Male** is unmistakable, with metallic green head and horn-like ear-tufts, yellowish-brown crest, white neck patch, streaked appearance to body, and variable amounts of chestnut on breast and belly. **Female** has white throat and short buff ear-tufts; upperparts are mottled black and brown, and finely streaked with buff, and buffish underparts are prominently streaked with black. Possibly confusable with female Kalij Pheasant (p.360), but that species has bare red facial skin, more uniform brownish upperparts, and a laterally compressed tail. In flight, told from female tragopans (p.356–p.357) by white throat, smaller size and 'streaked' appearance, and by longer, more sharply graduated tail. **Racial variation** Males of *P. m. castanea* and *biddulphi* (W Himalayas) have chestnut on hindneck and upper mantle, are mainly chestnut on breast and belly, and have

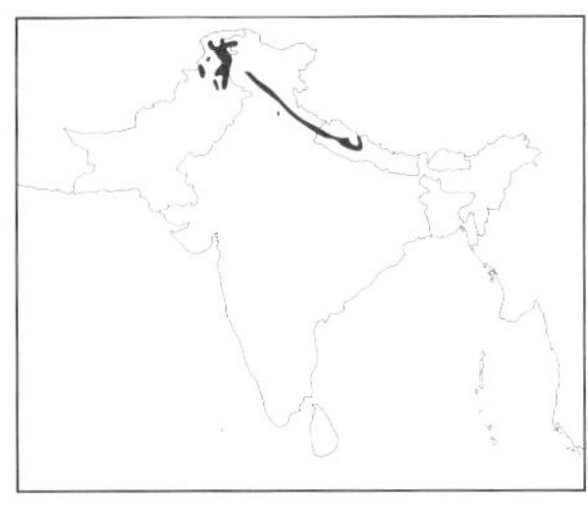

blackish flanks (streaked with white). Males of *P. m. macrolopha* and *nipalensis* (C Himalayas) have less chestnut in plumage (restricted to centre of breast and belly); mantle and sides of breast are pale grey (streaked with black) in *macrolopha* and black (streaked with buff) in *nipalensis*. **VOICE** A far-carrying and loud *kok, kark, kuk...kukuk*, uttered mainly at dawn and repeated at intervals with corvid-like raucousness. When flushed, a harsh *kwak-kwak-kwak*. Female's alarm call has been described as a higher-pitched, more melodic *qui-quik qui-quik qui-quik* (Roberts 1991). **HABITS** Usually occurs singly or in pairs, but in winter several birds may congregate in a loose party. Very secretive and wary. When disturbed, runs away quickly through undergrowth, or bursts upwards giving a noisy alarm before hurtling down the slope, twisting between the trees at great speed. Feeds mainly in early mornings and late afternoons in grassy glades. Roosts in trees, from where males crow at dawn almost throughout the year. Highly territorial during the breeding season. **HABITAT** Coniferous, oak and deodar forests with dense undergrowth of bushes and ringal bamboo. Favours steep slopes and ravines. **BREEDING** April–June. Nests under thick bushes. **DISTRIBUTION AND STATUS** Resident, subject to altitudinal movements. Himalayas from N Pakistan east to WC Nepal. **PK:** locally common; 2135–2745 m (1600–3350 m). **NP:** locally fairly common in the west; summers chiefly at 2680–3200 m (–3500 m), winters down to 2135 m. **IN:** fairly common; summers at 2100–3300 m, winters down to 1500 m. **REFERENCES** Johnsgard (1986).

HIMALAYAN MONAL *Lophophorus impejanus* — Plate 5

Impeyan Pheasant (F,I,K)

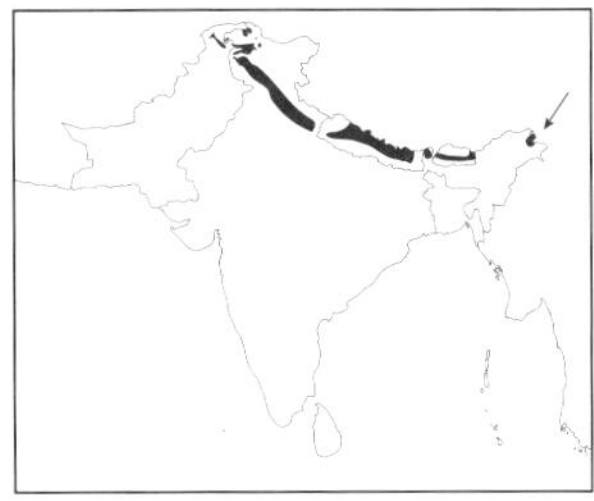

IDENTIFICATION Male 70 cm; female 63.5 cm. **Male** is unmistakable throughout much of its range, although see Sclater's Monal (below) for differences from that species. Has metallic green head and spatulate-tipped wire-like crest, brilliant metallic green and bronze on hindneck and mantle, iridescent blue and purple and green on wings and uppertail-coverts, cinnamon-brown tail, and velvety-black underparts. In flight, exhibits white on back. **Female** has dark brown upperparts with streaked appearance, and brown underparts with variable, broad pale streaking. Has prominent white throat, short crest, and bright blue orbital skin. In flight, shows whitish 'horseshoe' on uppertail-coverts, and broad rounded tail with rufous barring and narrow white tip. **First-year male** is similar to female, but with variable amounts of black spotting on white throat, and sometimes has a few metallic spots on the upperparts. **VOICE** A distinctive call, uttered by both sexes during the breeding season, is a series of upward-inflected whistles, *kur-leiu* or *kleeh-vick*, which are strung together, alternated with higher-pitched *kleeh* calls (Roberts 1991); reminiscent of the snowcocks (p.346) and Eurasian Curlew (p.476). Alarm call is a similar *kleeh-wick-kleeh-wick*, alternating with shorter, more urgent *kwick-kwick* cries (Roberts 1991). **HABITS** Loosely gregarious even in the breeding season, often three or four together. Feeds mainly by digging with its strong bill, and can dig deep in snow if necessary. Although cautious, it is less shy than most other Himalayan pheasants and can often be seen in summer foraging in alpine pastures. **HABITAT** Winters in oak, deodar, coniferous and rhododendron forests with grassy glades; sometimes remains above the snowline. In summer, moves up to the uppermost limit of trees and steep, rocky and grass-covered slopes above the treeline. **BREEDING** April–mid July. Nests on ground under a bush, rock or fallen trunk, usually in wooded habitats. **DISTRIBUTION AND STATUS** Resident. Himalayas from N Pakistan east to Arunachal Pradesh. Subject to altitudinal movements: in W Himalayas summers 2300–4875 m, winters mainly 2000–2500 m (down to 1500 m in India); from Nepal eastwards summers chiefly 2800–4575 m (from 2500 m), winters down to 2500 m (–2000 m). **PK:** widely distributed, but now generally rare, although locally fairly common. **NP:** widespread and locally common. **IN:** locally common, but has disappeared from parts of its former range. **BT:** common. **REFERENCES** Johnsgard (1986), Martens and Eck (1995).

SCLATER'S MONAL *Lophophorus sclateri* — Plate 5

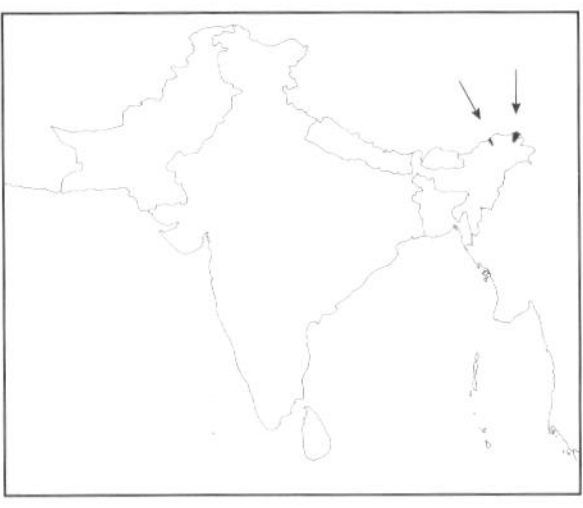

IDENTIFICATION Male 68 cm; female 63 cm. **Male** is similar to Himalayan Monal (above), with metallic green, blue and bronze coloration to head and upperparts, and velvety-black underparts. Distinguished from Himalayan by lack of spatulate-tipped crest (instead has short curly crown feathers), by white lower back, rump and uppertail-coverts, and by broad white tip to the cinnamon-brown tail. **Female** is similar to female Himalayan, but lacks crest and has contrastingly pale lower back, rump and uppertail-coverts (which are closely barred with brown and white; rufous-brown in coloration on Himalayan), and broad white terminal band to tail. Upperparts are darker overall, mantle is darker and more finely and cleanly streaked, and underparts are more uniform and lack bold splashes of greyish-white. Also bill is yellowish, and has more extensive area of blue skin around eye. **First-year male** similar to female, but is whiter on lower back, rump and uppertail-coverts; has cinnamon showing in tail, and black feathers on neck and breast. **VOICE** Alarm call is 'a shrill, harsh, plaintive cry' uttered repeatedly; also a wild ringing whistle like Himalayan Monal (above) but distinct in tone (Ali and Ripley 1987). **HABITS** Little known. Like those of Himalayan Monal (p.358). **HABITAT** Fir forest with dense rhododendron undergrowth. **BREEDING** Unknown. **DISTRIBUTION AND STATUS IN:** rare resident in E Himalayas in Arunachal Pradesh; 3000–4000 m. Globally threatened. **REFERENCES** Johnsgard (1986), Kaul *et al.* (1995), McGowan and Garson (1995).

RED JUNGLEFOWL *Gallus gallus* Plate 5

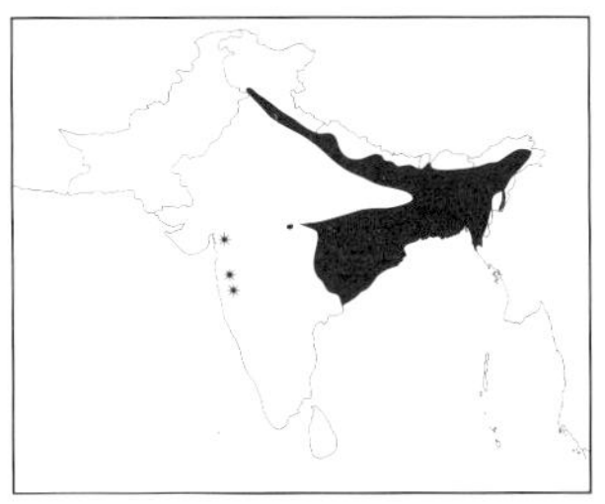

IDENTIFICATION Male 65–75 cm; female 42–46 cm. **Male** is unmistakable, with red comb and wattle, elongated rufous-orange and golden-yellow hackles across nape and mantle, blackish-brown underparts, crimson band across back, rufous secondaries, and long greenish-black, sickle-shaped tail. There is an eclipse plumage, after the summer moult, when the hackles are replaced by short, dark brown feathers, the central tail feathers are lacking, and the comb is duller and smaller: in this plumage, head and neck are dark brown, crimson band across back is more clearly apparent, and tail is much shorter. **Female** has 'shawl' of elongated (edged golden-buff, black-centred) feathers across nape and mantle, and naked reddish face. Rest of upperparts are rufous-brown, finely vermiculated with black, and has rufous-brown underparts streaked with buff. Possibly confusable with female Grey Junglefowl (below), but has more pronounced 'shawl' and lacks bold white streaking on underparts. Also possibly confusable with female Red Spurfowl (p.354), but is stockier, with laterally compressed tail which is often held cocked; fine streaking on breast, and black-streaked golden-buff 'shawl' are further distinctions. **First-year male** is superficially similar to adult male, but much duller; hackles are less developed (with prominent black centres), upperparts are an untidy mix of maroon and greenish-black, and lacks elongated central tail feathers. **VOICE** Calling of male at dawn and dusk, a loud *cock-a-doodle-doo*, very similar to the crowing of a domestic cockerel, but individual notes less pronounced. Both sexes utter a variety of cackling and clucking notes, when alarmed and when feeding. **HABITS** Keeps in small groups, usually one cock with several hens. Wary and very secretive, slinking into the undergrowth at the least disturbance. If flushed, rises, cackling, with a clatter of wings. In early mornings and late afternoons, comes into the open to forage on forest tracks, firebreaks and fields at forest edges. Roosts in trees and bamboo clumps. **HABITAT** Well-watered areas. Undergrowth in moist mixed forest and scrub jungle interspersed with patches of cultivation. **BREEDING** January–October. Nests under a bush or bamboo clump in forest. **DISTRIBUTION AND STATUS** Resident. Himalayas from Jammu and Kashmir east to Arunachal Pradesh; NE and E India and Bangladesh. Found chiefly up to 800 m (–2000 m locally). **NP:** locally common. **IN:** fairly common in protected areas. **BT:** common. **BD:** locally distributed throughout. **MV:** feral populations throughout. **REFERENCES** Johnsgard (1988).

GREY JUNGLEFOWL *Gallus sonneratii* Plate 5

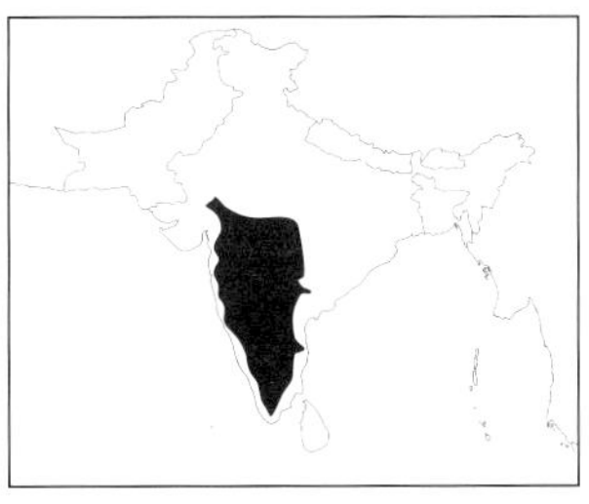

IDENTIFICATION Male 70–80 cm; female 38 cm. **Male** unmistakable, with red comb, face and wattles, 'shawl' of white and pale golden-yellow spotting across nape, neck and mantle, band of golden-yellow spotting on scapulars, grey underparts, back and rump streaked with white, and long sickle-shaped, purplish-black tail. There is an eclipse plumage in which neck hackles are short and brownish-black, the elongated central tail feathers are lacking and the comb is much reduced. **Female** is similar to Red Junglefowl (above), but has less extensive rufous-orange 'shawl' of elongated feathers across hindneck, and has bold white centres to feathers on underparts (giving rise to heavily streaked appearance). **First-year male** resembles adult male, but has much-reduced 'shawl' of yellowish-white spotting (barely extending onto mantle), spots on scapulars are smaller but brighter orange, comb and wattles are smaller, and lacks greatly elongated central tail feathers. **VOICE** Male's distinctive crowing call is a loud, staccato *kuk-ka-kurruk-ka*, repeated at regular intervals, and given perhaps four to five times per minute (P. Holt). **HABITS** Similar to those of Red Junglefowl, but not so gregarious; usually found singly, in pairs or in family parties. Normally very shy, never venturing far from cover, but tame where not hunted. **HABITAT** Undergrowth in broadleaved evergreen and deciduous forest, secondary growth, bamboo thickets and patches of cultivation in forest; in S India also in abandoned plantations; near a water source in summer. **BREEDING** February–May. Nest site is like that of Red Junglefowl. **DISTRIBUTION AND STATUS IN:** locally common endemic resident from S Rajasthan east to C Madhya Pradesh and south through the peninsula; locally common in the foothills, mainly up to 1500 m, but to 2400 m in Nilgiris. Frequently hybridises with Red Junglefowl. **REFERENCES** Johnsgard (1988).

SRI LANKA JUNGLEFOWL *Gallus lafayetii* Plate 5

Ceylon Junglefowl (I), *lafayetti* (P)

IDENTIFICATION Male 66–72.5 cm; female 35 cm. Similar to Red Junglefowl (above), but only junglefowl occurring naturally in Sri Lanka (although beware domestic hens). **Male** differs from that species in having orange-red breast and belly (streaked with chestnut), yellow centre to oblong-shaped comb, elongated deep orange feathering covering entire mantle and back, and purplish-black wings and tail (lacking rufous panel in

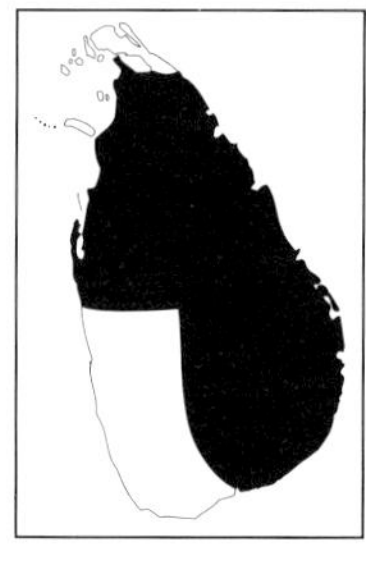

wing of Red). There is no distinct eclipse plumage as in Red Junglefowl. **Female** similar to female Red, but has less extensive rufous- and black-streaked 'shawl' across hindneck, white streaking on breast, with bold black-and-white patterning to feathers of lower breast and belly, and has prominent buff barring in wings. Possibly confusable with male Sri Lanka Spurfowl (p.355), but differs in shape and carriage, has rufous- and black-streaked 'shawl', and has comparatively uniform rufous-brown upperparts. **First-year male** has rufous-orange head and neck and deep rufous coloration to body; remiges and short rectrices are purplish-black, and has only poorly developed comb and wattles. **VOICE** The cock's crow is a staccato, musical ringing *chiok, chaw-choyik*, the terminal *ik* being higher on scale. The hen's cackle is a high-pitched metallic *kwikkuk kwikkukkuk....* (Henry 1971). **HABITS** Similar to those of Red Junglefowl. Non-breeding males often feed in large groups. **HABITAT** Confined to large forest patches. **BREEDING** January–March. Nests beside a log, at base of a tree or under a bush or rock. **DISTRIBUTION AND STATUS LK:** endemic resident, locally plentiful in protected areas and less inhabited areas throughout lowlands and in hills. Hybridisation with domestic hen has been recorded.

KALIJ PHEASANT *Lophura leucomelanos* — Plate 5

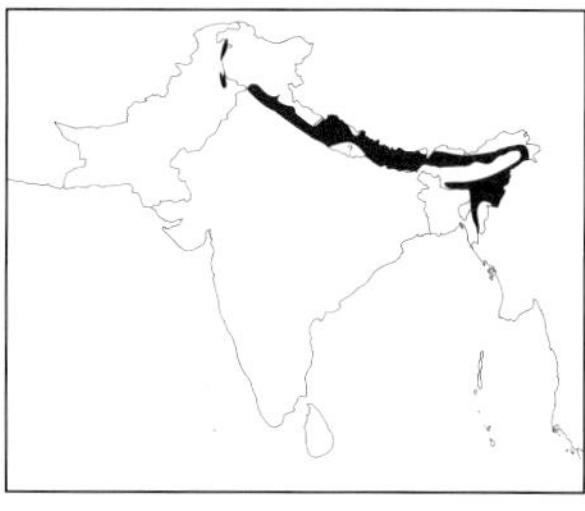

IDENTIFICATION Male 65–73 cm; female 50–60 cm. **Male** is essentially glossy blue-black on upperparts, with variable amounts of white on underparts and rump. Has bright red facial skin and wattles, and long, downcurved, laterally compressed tail. **Female** varies from dull brown to dark reddish-brown in coloration, with greyish-buff fringes giving scaly appearance. Has brown crest, red facial skin, and downcurved, laterally compressed brownish tail. Possibly confusable with female Koklass Pheasant (p.357), and best told by red facial skin, scaled (rather than streaked) upperparts and underparts, and different shape to tail. **Juvenile** is similar in coloration to female, but has blackish-brown and buff barring on upperparts. Assumes adult plumage in first year. **Racial variation** Male *L. l. hamiltonii* (W Himalayas) has a long white or pale grey-brown crest, broad white barring on rump, grey fringes to upperparts, and white to brownish-grey underparts. Male *L. l. leucomelanos* (C and E Nepal) has blue-black crest, white barring on rump, fairly uniform blue-black upperparts, and whitish breast. Male *L. l. melanota* (E Nepal to W Bhutan) has blue-black crest, blue-black rump (lacking white barring), and whitish breast. Male *L. l. moffitti* (C Bhutan) is entirely blue-black above and below, without white barring on rump. Male *L. l. lathami* (E Himalayas and NE India) has black crest, white barring on rump, and glossy blue-black underparts. There is some racial variation in female plumages, mainly in tone of upperparts, in prominence of pale scalloping on upperparts, and in mottling on, and coloration of, central tail feathers. **VOICE** Calls include a crowing which has been described as a loud, whistling chuckle or *chirrup*. When flushed, 'a series of guinea-pig-like squeaks and chuckles' or sharply repeated *koorchi, koorchi, koorchi* or a whistling *psee-psee-psee-psee* (Ali and Ripley 1987). **HABITS** Similar to those of Red Junglefowl (p.359). Found in pairs or family parties. Spends much time digging and scratching for food. Emerges into the open to forage at forest edges and on tracks in early mornings and late afternoons. Roosts in trees. **HABITAT** Frequents all types of forest with dense undergrowth and thickly overgrown steep gullies, usually not far from water. **BREEDING** March–October, varying locally. Nests in a scrape scantily lined with grass or dried vegetation among thick undergrowth, under a bush or rock or in a grass tussock. **DISTRIBUTION AND STATUS** Resident. Himalayas from N Pakistan east to Arunachal Pradesh; NE India and Bangladesh. Withdraws from higher levels in cold weather; mainly 245–3050 m (down to 35 m in Bangladesh, –3700 m in Nepal). **PK:** scarce and locally distributed, chiefly in foothills. **NP:** fairly common and widespread. **IN, BT:** common. **BD:** locally distributed in the northeast and southeast. **REFERENCES** Delacour (1977), Johnsgard (1988).

TIBETAN EARED PHEASANT *Crossoptilon harmani* — Plate 6

Eared Pheasant (I), *C. crossoptilon harmani* (E,I)

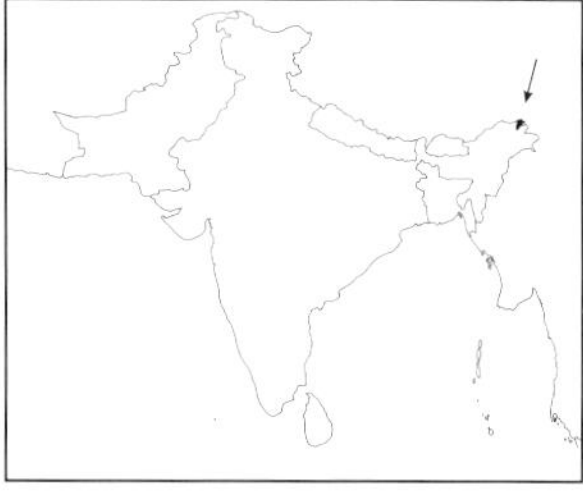

IDENTIFICATION 72 cm. Unmistakable, with bright red naked face, white throat connecting with band across nape, ashy-grey upperparts and underparts, blacker on neck and white on centre of belly, paler grey rump and uppertail-coverts, and broad blackish, downcurving tail (which is glossed with green, blue and purple). Sexes similar. **VOICE** Calls include an alarm note that is a sharp repeated *wrack*; a conversational cackling that terminates on a high *cucu cuco*; and a breeding call often uttered in unison by both sexes and sounding like a repeated *trip-crrra-ah*, becoming progressively louder and lasting up to 30 seconds (Johnsgard 1986). **HABITS** Gregarious, moving about in flocks of about five or ten birds in the non-breeding season. Very tame where not disturbed. When feeding, constantly gives a drawn-out cackle. Obtains much of its food by digging with its strong bill. Flies poorly and, if alarmed, either runs uphill and into the nearest bushes or flies into a nearby tree; otherwise flies heavily and very fast downhill for a long distance. **HABITAT** In Tibet, summers in patchy subalpine birch and rhododendron scrub and subalpine meadows; winters in spruce and pine forests. **BREEDING** Poorly known; May–July in Tibet. One nest was made of bark and pulp, lined with moss, and placed under a fallen tree. **DISTRIBUTION AND STATUS** Globally threatened. **IN:** only one confirmed record for the subcontinent: recently found at Towang, NE Arunachal Pradesh. Recorded at 2800–4600 m in China. **REFERENCES** Johnsgard (1986), McGowan and Garson (1995).

CHEER PHEASANT *Catreus wallichii* Plate 6

Chir Pheasant (I)

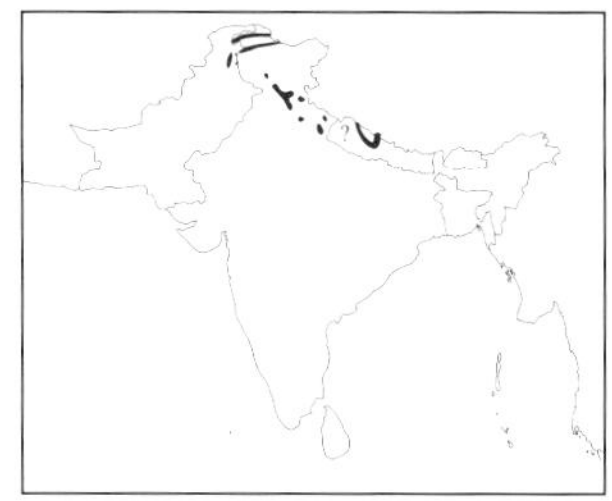

IDENTIFICATION Male 90–118 cm; female 61–76 cm. Typical views are of bird flying downhill, when buff, grey and brown coloration and long broadly banded tail are diagnostic. Both sexes have brown crest (longer on male) and red facial skin. **Male** has unmarked greyish throat and neck, heavily barred buff-and-black mantle and back, rufous rump barred with black, and greyish breast becoming more buffish on belly and flanks (with irregular black barring). Tail has broad buffish-white banding (with black-edged chestnut bands across outer feathers, and black-mottled grey-brown bands across central feathers). **Female** is similar to male, but has more rufescent upperparts, with prominent shaft streaking, is more heavily barred on breast, and has rufous-brown lower breast and belly scaled with buff, grey-brown rump mottled with black and buff, and narrower buff bands across tail. **Juvenile** is like female, but lacks crest and is less heavily marked. **VOICE** A far-carrying, loud *chir-a-pir, chir-a-pir, chir, chir chirwa, chirwa* (Ali and Ripley 1987). Also dusk and pre-dawn contact and chorus calls, which include high piercing whistles, *chewewoo,* interspersed with short *chut* calls and short staccato harsh notes (Young and Kaul 1987). **HABITS** Keeps in coveys of five or six outside the breeding season. Extremely wary and skulking. When disturbed, prefers to run off rapidly or crouch in thick undergrowth rather than fly. If flushed, rises noisily and dives downhill. Tends to feed in the same area day after day. Birds often roost together in trees. **HABITAT** Precipitous, often craggy hillsides with scrub and stunted trees and dissected by wooded ravines or with some scrub and grass cover; recently cleared areas with secondary growth. Strongly favours early successional habitats. **BREEDING** Late April–early June. Makes no nest; lays eggs in undergrowth on rough ground. **DISTRIBUTION AND STATUS** Resident, endemic to the subcontinent. Very local in Himalayas, from N Pakistan east to WC Nepal. Sedentary and with little altitudinal movement, mainly 1500–3050 m (down to 600 m in Pakistan). **PK:** very rare. **NP:** recent records from only a few localities. Globally threatened. **IN:** well distributed, but populations small and fragmented. **REFERENCES** Garson *et al.* (1992), Johnsgard (1986), McGowan and Garson (1995).

MRS HUME'S PHEASANT *Syrmaticus humiae* Plate 6

Mrs Hume's Barred-back Pheasant (I)

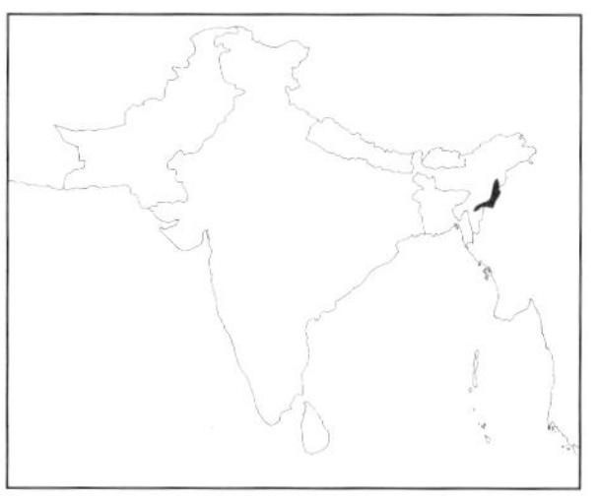

IDENTIFICATION Male 90 cm; female 60 cm. The only pheasant with long graduated tail in NE India. **Male** has bright red facial skin, glossy blue-black head, neck, upper breast and upper mantle, and mainly chestnut upperparts and underparts. Has broad white band along scapulars, white wing-bars (formed by broad white tips to greater coverts and secondaries), and white tips to tertials. Rump and uppertail-coverts are glossy blue-black, with fine white barring, and long greyish tail is narrowly banded with chestnut and black. **Female** is mainly grey-brown on upperparts, cryptically mottled and barred with black, and prominently spotted with white on mantle. Underparts are pale rufous-brown, barred with buff. Has suggestion of greyish band along scapulars, and narrow whitish wing-bars formed by tips to greater coverts and secondaries. Tail is shorter than male's; central tail feathers are sandy-brown, banded with black and rufous-brown and tipped with white, and outer feathers are chestnut with prominent white tips and black subterminal bands. **VOICE** Many vocalisations, including a very distinctive crowing *cher-a-per, cher-a-per, cher cher, cheria, cheria.* Also utters repeated cackling *waaak* notes and a sharp alarm note, *tuk tuk* (Johnsgard 1986). **HABITS** Very little known in the wild; probably similar to those of Cheer Pheasant (above). **HABITAT** Steep rocky slopes with open oak and pine forest and long grass, bracken and bushes. **BREEDING** April and May. Makes no nest; lays eggs under a bush, rock or grass clump. **DISTRIBUTION AND STATUS** Globally threatened. **IN:** very poorly known; an extremely local resident recorded from Manipur, Mizoram and Nagaland, at 1200–3000 m; only recent records are from Mizoram. **REFERENCES** Johnsgard (1986), Katju (1996), McGowan and Garson (1995).

GREY PEACOCK PHEASANT *Polyplectron bicalcaratum* Plate 6

Peacock-Pheasant (I)

IDENTIFICATION Male 64 cm; female 48 cm. **Male** is greyish-brown with short-tufted crest and long broad tail. Is finely spotted and barred with whitish, and strikingly marked with whitish-rimmed iridescent purple and green ocelli on mantle, wing-coverts, tertials, uppertail-coverts and tail. **Female** is similar, but is smaller, with shorter tail and shorter crest, and is more uniformly brown with smaller and duller ocelli on mantle, wing-coverts and tail. Older female very like male except for shorter tail. Immature male is very similar to female. **VOICE** A deep gut-

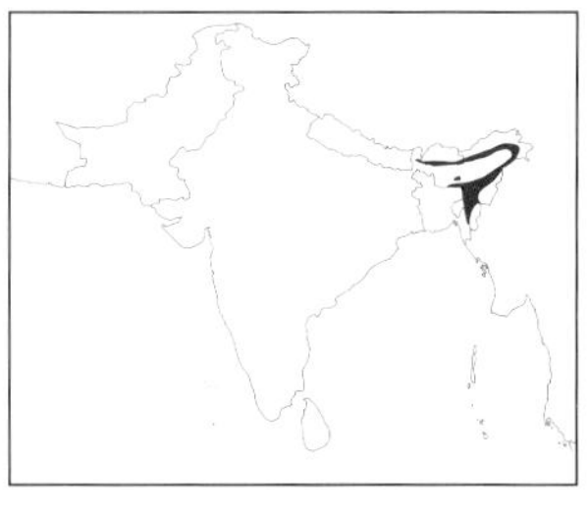

tural *hoo*, rapidly repeated about seven times, and soft chuckling notes. Also an *Ok-kok-kok-kok* (Ali and Ripley 1987). **HABITS** Keeps singly or in pairs, or in the breeding season in family groups. Extremely secretive, and skulks in dense vegetation at the least disturbance. Rarely seen and almost impossible to flush; most easily located by its call, and may be heard sporadically at any time of day in the breeding season. **HABITAT** Dense undergrowth in tropical moist, broadleaved evergreen and semi-evergreen forest. **BREEDING** March–June. Nests on ground among thick vegetation. **DISTRIBUTION AND STATUS** Resident. E Himalayas from Sikkim east to Arunachal Pradesh; Bangladesh; from base of the hills up to 1200 m. **IN:** common in undisturbed forest. **BT:** frequent. **BD:** rare and local in the northeast and southeast. **REFERENCES** Johnsgard (1986).

INDIAN PEAFOWL *Pavo cristatus* — Plate 6

Common Peafowl (F,I), Blue Peafowl (N)

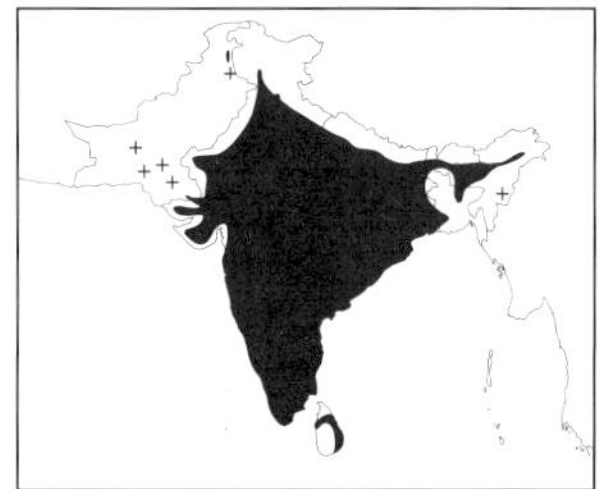

IDENTIFICATION Male 180–230 cm; female 90–100 cm. **Male** is unmistakable, with fan-like crest, glossy blue crown, neck, upper mantle and breast, metallic green lower mantle and back, and spectacular glossy green train. Train comprises numerous elongated uppertail-coverts with blue-centred, green and copper ocelli. **Female** lacks sweeping train. Has fan-like crest, whitish face and throat, chestnut-brown crown and hindneck, metallic green upper breast and mantle (barred with brown and buff), white belly, and brown back, rump and tail. Primaries are dark brown (chestnut on male). **First-year male** lacks train and is similar to female, but head and neck are usually blue, and primaries are chestnut with dark brown mottling. **Second-year male** more closely resembles adult male but has a short train, which lacks ocelli and is barred with green and brown. Length of train increases until fifth or sixth year. **VOICE** Trumpeting, far-carrying and mournful *kee-ow, kee-ow, kee-ow*. Also series of short, gasping screams, *ka-an...ka-an...ka-an*, repeated six to eight times, and *kok-kok* and *cain-kok* when alarmed. **HABITS** Gregarious, keeping in small flocks of usually one cock and three to five hens when breeding, and often in separate parties of adult males and of females with immatures in the non-breeding season. Roosts in tall trees. Emerges from dense thickets in early mornings and late afternoons to feed in forest clearings and fields at forest edges. Protected for religious or sentimental reasons in parts of India, where it has become very tame, but is quite shy and secretive where hunted. **HABITAT** In the wild state, in undergrowth in deciduous forest near streams; where semi-feral, lives in villages and cultivation. **BREEDING** January–September, varying locally. Wild birds nest among dense undergrowth, usually on the ground; semi-feral birds often nest on buildings. **DISTRIBUTION AND STATUS** Resident throughout much of India, also SE Pakistan, Nepal and Bhutan. Both wild and semi-feral populations occur; wild birds are endemic to the subcontinent. **PK:** wild birds are very local, common in the extreme south, rare elsewhere. **NP:** locally common; mainly up to 300 m. **IN:** locally very common, wherever protected; up to 1800 m (–2000 m). **BT:** uncommon and very local. **BD:** only one recent record, may now be extirpated. **LK:** common in protected areas in dry lowlands. **REFERENCES** Johnsgard (1986).

GREEN PEAFOWL *Pavo muticus* — Plate 6

Burmese Peafowl (I)

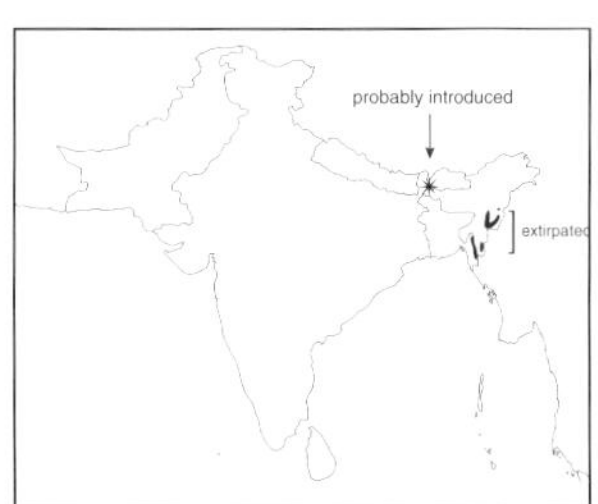

IDENTIFICATION Male 180–300 cm; female 100–110 cm. **Male** superficially resembles Indian Peafowl (above), but has erect tufted crest, blue and yellow facial skin, green neck and underparts, green coverts, and uniform brown tertials and secondaries. Has long train as on Indian Peafowl, but with stronger bronze, copper and purple hues. **Female** lacks long train and ocelli. Otherwise is similar to male except that lower back, rump, scapulars and tertials are blackish-brown, barred with buff and lightly glossed with green. Elongated golden-green uppertail-coverts, which fall short of tail tip, are barred with buff and brown. Tail is barred buff, brown and black. **First-year male** is similar to female, but has back and rump mostly golden-green, and stronger golden-green coloration to uppertail-coverts. **Second-year male** more closely resembles adult male, but long train lacks ocelli. **VOICE** Male has very loud, far-carrying *ki-wao* or *yee-ow*, often repeated. Female gives loud *aow-aa*, with emphasis on first syllable, often repeated with short intervals. (C. Robson) **HABITS** Similar to those of Indian Peafowl, but extremely shy everywhere and generally does not emerge into forest clearings and edges. **HABITAT** Dense forest near streams or clearings. **BREEDING** Mainly January–May, also July–September. Nests in dense forest. **DISTRIBUTION AND STATUS** Globally threatened. Resident. Recorded from NE India (Assam, Manipur, Mizoram and West Bengal) and Bangladesh, from plains up to 1000 m, but now believed extirpated in the subcontinent. **REFERENCES** Johnsgard (1986), McGowan and Garson (1995).

WHISTLING-DUCKS Dendrocygnidae AND SWANS, GEESE AND DUCKS Anatidae

All of the swans and most of the geese and ducks are winter visitors from farther north; only Bar-headed Goose and a few species of duck are breeding residents. Individuals (often injured adults) of most migratory species may be seen during the breeding season (June–August). All are associated with the aquatic environment, including fresh and marine waters. All ducks, swans and most geese undergo a simultaneous moult of their flight feathers after the breeding season and pass through a flightless period lasting a few weeks. Wildfowl are highly gregarious, typically migrating, feeding, roosting and resting together, often in mixed flocks, although they usually nest in pairs or loose groups. Many species have nocturnal feeding habits and make regular flights to and from their daytime roost at dawn and dusk. Most are chiefly vegetarian when adult, feeding on seed, algae, the greener parts of plants and roots, although they often supplement their diet with aquatic invertebrates; the last form the main diet of most young. The main foraging methods of wildfowl are diving, surface-feeding or dabbling, and grazing. They also upend, wade, filter and sieve water and debris for food, and probe with the bill. Wildfowl have a direct flight with sustained fast wingbeats, and characteristically they fly in V-formation. Most species, except for geese, Ruddy Shelduck and dabbling ducks, make a run along the surface of the water with wings beating before taking to the air. Wildfowl nest on the ground, or in holes in trees. The young can run, swim and feed themselves very soon after hatching. Extensive reference has been made to Cramp and Simmons (1977), del Hoyo *et al.* (1992), Harris *et al.* (1989), Madge and Burn (1988), and Perennou *et al.* (1994).

FULVOUS WHISTLING-DUCK *Dendrocygna bicolor* — Plate 8

Fulvous Treeduck (K), Large Whistling Teal (F,I,P)

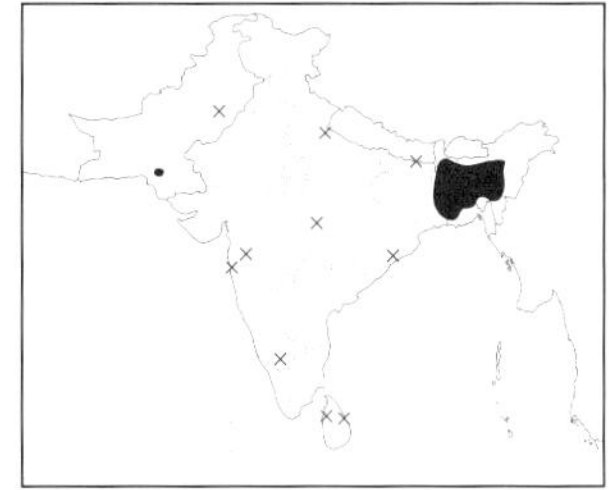

IDENTIFICATION 51 cm. Among a flock of the commoner Lesser Whistling-duck (below) is larger and lankier, with a proportionately larger and squarer head, and much larger bill. Like Lesser, has rather weak, deep-flapping flight, appears very dark on the upperwing and underwing, and is very noisy with repeated whistling. **Adult** told from Lesser by warmer rufous-orange coloration to head, with slightly darker rufous-brown crown, dark blackish line down hindneck, and pronounced fine, dark striations on neck. Streaking on the flanks is broad and usually prominent (often not apparent on Lesser). In flight, has a white (not maroon-chestnut) band across uppertail-coverts; upperwing-coverts have some chestnut-brown, but this is not so bright or prominent as the maroon-chestnut patch on forewing of Lesser. Sexes similar. **Juvenile** is usually accompanied by adults and is similar, but sides of head, foreneck and underparts are a paler, more uniform buff, and flank striping is less prominent. Best told from juvenile Lesser by differences in structure, brighter rufous-brown crown and dark line down hindneck, and dull chestnut-brown wing-coverts. For differences from Cotton Pygmy-goose (p.368) see that species, and from juvenile Comb Duck (p.368) see account for Lesser Whistling-duck. **VOICE** Very noisy in flight and at rest; a repeated whistle, *k-weeoo*. Also a harsh, repeated *kee* during disputes (Madge and Burn 1988). **HABITS** Keeps in small flocks and often associates with Lesser Whistling-duck. Shy and wary. Feeds chiefly at night, mainly by upending and dabbling, but can also dive well. Roosts during the day on undisturbed ground or waterbodies near its feeding grounds. **HABITAT** Marshes, flooded paddy-fields and shallow lakes and ponds with partly submerged trees and extensive emergent vegetation. **BREEDING** June–October. Nest of sticks is built in tree hole or in the fork of a large branch or old nest of other species; sometimes on the ground among tall bankside vegetation. **DISTRIBUTION AND STATUS** Resident and nomadic. Formerly widespread in the subcontinent, now mainly in NE India and Bangladesh; probably declining. **PK:** rare and irregular visitor, seldom remaining to breed. **NP:** vagrant. **IN:** locally common in Assam, scarce and sporadic elsewhere. **BD:** a local winter visitor. **LK:** winter vagrant to dry lowlands.

LESSER WHISTLING-DUCK *Dendrocygna javanica* — Plate 8

Lesser Treeduck (K), Lesser Whistling Teal (F,I,P)

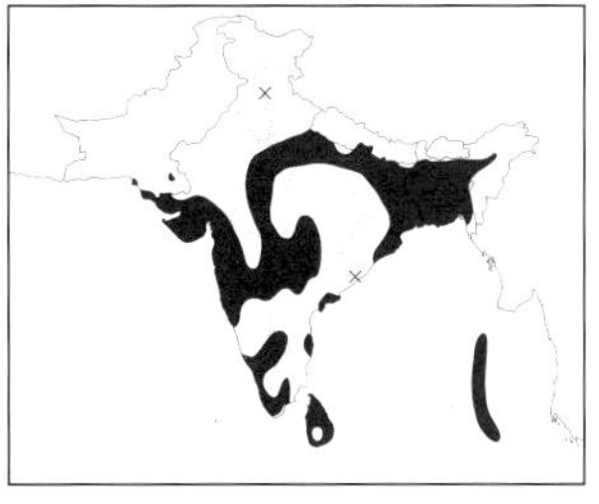

IDENTIFICATION 42 cm. Very noisy, and in flight appears very dark on the upper- and underwings. Smaller and more neatly proportioned than Fulvous Whistling-duck (above). Additional distinctions from that species are greyish-buff head and foreneck, lack of well-defined dark line down hindneck, and darker brown crown (contrasting more with sides of head). In flight, has maroon-chestnut (not white) band across uppertail-coverts and bright maroon-chestnut patch on forewing. Sexes similar. **Juvenile** is very similar to adult, but duller, greyish-buff on the underparts. Dark cap, absence of dark line down hindneck, and bright maroon-chestnut forewing are best plumage differences from juvenile Fulvous. Both Fulvous and Lesser are possibly confusable with juvenile Comb Duck (p.368), but that species is more heavily built, has stronger flight, and is comparatively silent (with no wittering and whistling); legs of Comb do not dangle well beyond tail in flight as they do on the whistling-ducks. Main plumage features of Comb are whitish supercilium, and brown crown and eye-stripe, dark scaling on sides of breast, and metallic blue-green gloss to wings. **VOICE** Incessant wittering call in flight; at rest, a clear whistled *whi-whee* as well as a subdued quacking. **HABITS** Similar to those of Fulvous Whistling-duck, but is more gregarious. Roosts in the daytime in trees or on partly submerged branches on undisturbed waters; near coasts, may loaf on the open sea or in lagoons. Dabbles in shallow waters, also dives in deeper water. **HABITAT** Flooded grassland and paddy-fields, freshwater marshes, and shallow pools and lakes, favouring those with plentiful fringe cover, emergent vegetation and partially submerged trees. Generally avoids open areas of water. **BREEDING** December–October, varying locally. Nest is built of twigs and grass or leaves, rushes and grass, in similar sites to those of Fulvous Whistling-duck. **DISTRIBUTION AND STATUS** Resident throughout much of the subcontinent. **PK:** mainly a monsoon visitor, partly resident; found chiefly in Sind, where common in summer. **NP:** locally common resident, winter visitor and passage migrant; mainly below 305 m (–1350 m). **IN:** locally common resident, subject to local movements depending on availability of water. **BD:** common winter visitor and local resident. **LK:** common resident in lowlands, rarely in hills.

WHITE-HEADED DUCK *Oxyura leucocephala* — Plate 9

White-headed Stiff-tailed Duck (I)

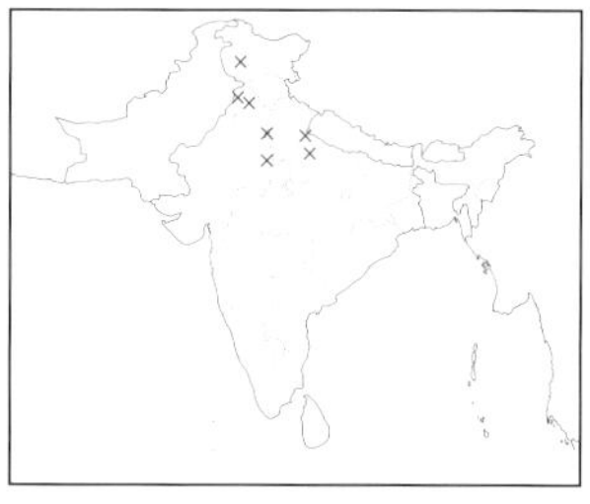

IDENTIFICATION 43–48 cm. A stocky duck with stiff tail, often held erect, and very broad-based bill which is swollen at base. Body is rufous-brown, barred finely with black. Upperwing is grey-brown, and underwing is grey with white axillaries, although this species is not often seen in flight. **Breeding male** has white head with black cap, and bright blue bill. **Eclipse male** has duller, less rufous body, grey bill, and black of cap more extensive and less clearly defined. **Female and juvenile** have grey bill, and striped head pattern (with dark cap, pale stripe below eye and dark stripe across cheeks). **Immature male** can have much black on head, which can even be all black, but by first spring has blue bill, and by second spring head is as adult. **VOICE** Silent except during display. **HABITS** Keeps singly, in pairs or in small parties. Very reluctant to fly, and when compelled to do so takes off laboriously. Prefers to escape by diving, or by swimming away while partially submerged. Feeds chiefly by diving, also by dabbling. **HABITAT** Large freshwater lakes and brackish lagoons. Requires waters of fairly high pH and with extensive submerged aquatic vegetation. **DISTRIBUTION AND STATUS** Very local and declining winter visitor to Pakistan and N India south to E Rajasthan and C Uttar Pradesh. Globally threatened. **PK:** mainly restricted to one or two lakes in the Punjab Salt Range; most birds depart by mid February. **IN:** rare.

MUTE SWAN *Cygnus olor* — Plate 7

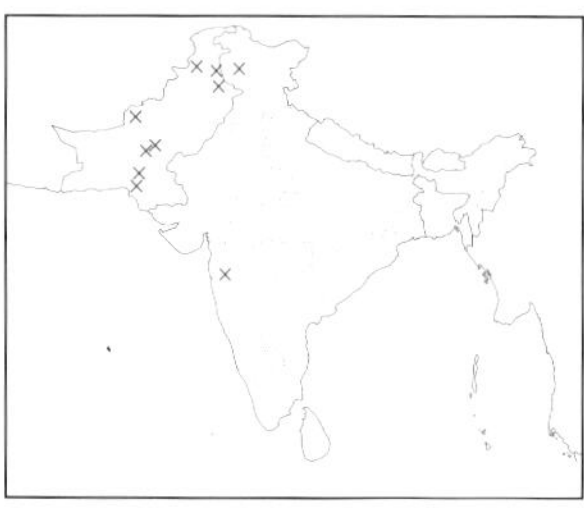

IDENTIFICATION 125–155 cm. Adult is large and white, although sometimes with rusty-orange staining on head and neck. Best told from other swans by orange bill with black base and black knob on forehead. Also, it shows a more curved S-shaped neck and longer, more pointed tail, and frequently holds wings strongly arched, giving rise to hunched appearance. In flight, it does not call but has noisy wingbeats, and pointed tail projects beyond prominent black feet. **Male** has brighter bill and larger knob than female. **Juvenile** is mottled sooty-brown and has grey bill with black base. During first winter plumage becomes mixed with white, resulting in two-toned or patchy appearance. By second winter is completely white, with adult bill. **VOICE** Generally silent except for quiet grunts and hisses. **HABITS** In the subcontinent it is shy and wary, and has mostly been found singly. Spends much time swimming and sits rather high in the water. Feeds mainly by submerging its head and neck, or by upending; also grazes on land. Rises heavily from the water, pattering some distance along the surface while flapping its wings powerfully before becoming airborne. Graceful in flight. **HABITAT** Lakes, large rivers and jheels. **DISTRIBUTION AND STATUS PK, IN:** winter vagrant.

WHOOPER SWAN *Cygnus cygnus* — Plate 7

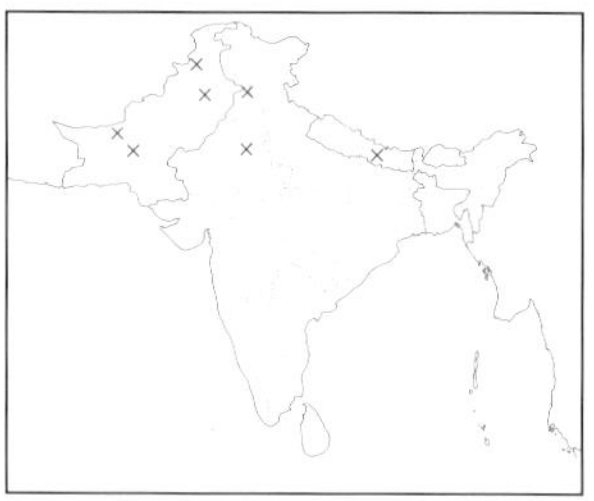

IDENTIFICATION 140–165 cm. **Adult** told from Mute Swan (above) by yellow base and black tip to bill, and lack of black frontal knob. Also, neck is usually held more erect, and never arches wings. Is very vocal at rest and in flight; has almost silent wingbeats, and feet reach end of tail in flight. From the very similar Tundra Swan (365) by more extensive yellow on bill, extending as a sharp wedge towards tip, by larger size and longer neck, and by more angular head shape owing to flatter forehead and larger wedge-shaped bill. **Juvenile** looks pale, uniform smoky-grey, with pinkish bill which has dark tip and cutting edges. Differs from juvenile Mute in bill coloration, body shape and carriage, and paler, more uniform coloration. During first winter plumage becomes whiter, and does not have two-toned appearance of Mute. Base of bill becomes whiter and black tip becomes more extensive with age. By second winter as adult. **VOICE** Much honking and trumpeting, deeper and stronger than Tundra's; typical flight call is a deep, resonant *hoop-hoop* (Madge and Burn 1988). **HABITS** Similar to those of Mute Swan. **HABITAT** Large rivers, lakes and jheels. **DISTRIBUTION AND STATUS PK, NP, IN:** winter vagrant.

TUNDRA SWAN *Cygnus columbianus* Plate 7

***C. cygnus bewickii* and *C. c. jankowskii* (I), Bewick's Swan *C. bewickii* (K)**

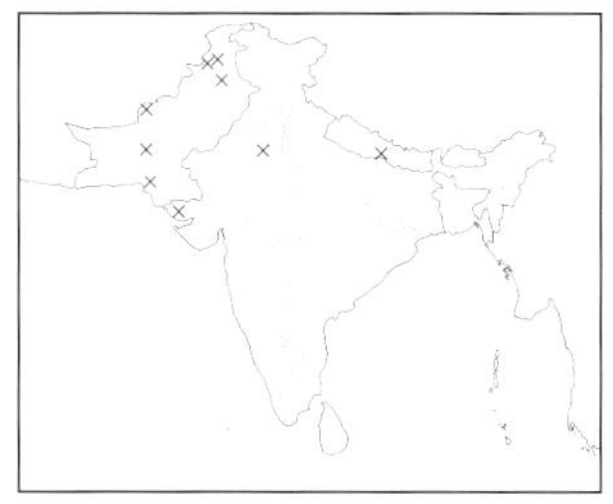

IDENTIFICATION 115–140 cm. **Adult** very similar to Whooper Swan (p.364), being all white with yellow and black bill. Distinguished from that species by more extensive black at tip of bill, with yellow typically reduced to oval-shaped patch. Other features include smaller size, with shorter and thicker neck, more rounded head, and smaller bill. **Immature** plumages are as Whooper, although juvenile is slightly paler and greyer, and second-winter birds usually show greyish-brown feathering on head and neck. Best told by smaller size and different shape. **VOICE** Similar to Whooper, with much honking and yelping, but calls typically higher-pitched; flight call is more yelping than trumpeting, a low *hoo-hoo-hoo* (Madge and Burn 1988). **HABITS** Similar to those of Mute Swan (p.364). **HABITAT** Lakes. **DISTRIBUTION AND STATUS PK, NP, IN:** winter vagrant.

BEAN GOOSE *Anser fabalis* Plate 7

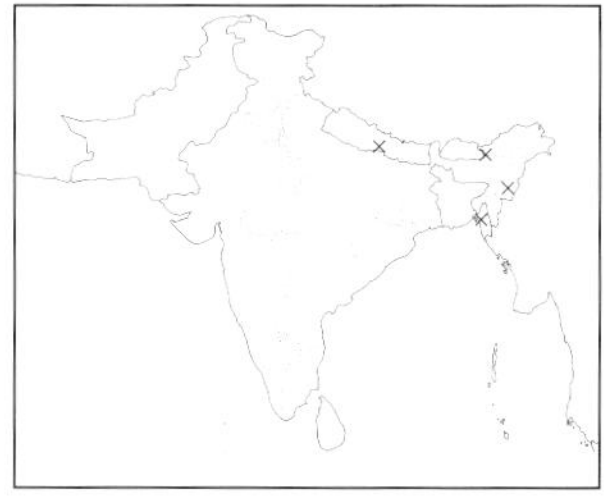

IDENTIFICATION 66–84 cm. Distinguished from adult and juvenile Greylag Goose (p.366) by slimmer appearance, with slimmer neck and smaller wedge-shaped head, black and orange bill, orange legs and feet, darker and browner head and neck contrasting with paler breast, and browner upperparts. **Juvenile** as adult, but with head and neck not so dark and contrasting, less distinct and browner fringes to feathers of upperparts, and more scaled appearance to breast and belly. Orange of bill and feet is duller and greyer. In flight, both adult and juvenile have darker and more uniform upperwing and underwing than Greylag (lacking latter's pale grey forewing and primary coverts), and have darker lower back. Some Bean have narrow whitish line around base of bill, although never as pronounced as on adult Greater and Lesser White-fronted Geese (below). Bill coloration is quite different, and lacks black barring on belly of adults of those two species. Bill coloration is also best distinction from juvenile Greater and Lesser White-fronted. **VOICE** Honking and cackling flight call, similar to other geese, but contains distinctive wittering *hank-hank* phrase. **HABITS** Details not recorded in the subcontinent. Similar to those of Greylag Goose. Shy and wary. **HABITAT** Occurs mainly on land in open country, and seldom found on water. **DISTRIBUTION AND STATUS NP, IN, BD:** winter vagrant.

GREATER WHITE-FRONTED GOOSE *Anser albifrons* Plate 7

White-fronted Goose (I)

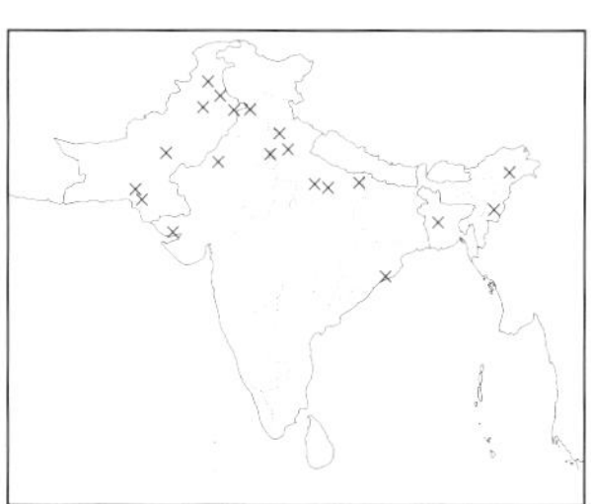

IDENTIFICATION 66–86 cm. **Adult** best told from Greylag Goose (p.366) by broad white band at front of head, browner coloration, black barring on belly, and orange legs and feet. Has more uniform upperwing in flight. White frontal band, black barring on belly, and orange-pink bill are best distinctions from Bean Goose (above). From adult Lesser White-fronted Goose (below) by shape of white frontal band, lack of yellow eye-ring, and less extensive black barring on belly; further, is larger and stockier, with longer neck, and has larger and longer bill with less steeply rising forehead. **Juvenile** lacks white frontal band and barring on belly, and is more difficult to tell from other 'grey' geese. From Greylag by smaller size and less stocky build, browner coloration, and orange legs and feet. Different structure and orange-pink bill are best distinctions from Bean. From juvenile Lesser White-fronted by lack of yellow eye-ring, and same structural differences as for adult. **VOICE** Cackling and honking flight call is higher-pitched than Bean's and contains distinctive musical *lyo-lyok* phrase (Madge and Burn 1988). **HABITS** Details not recorded in the subcontinent. Similar to those of Greylag Goose. **HABITAT** Large rivers and lakes. **DISTRIBUTION AND STATUS** Winter visitor to Pakistan, N India (south to Chilika Lake, Orissa) and Bangladesh. **PK:** vagrant. **IN:** rare. **BD:** vagrant. **REFERENCES** Harris *et al.* (1989).

LESSER WHITE-FRONTED GOOSE *Anser erythropus* Plate 7

IDENTIFICATION 53–66 cm. **Adult** really confusable only with Greater White-fronted Goose (above). Best distinguished by half-moon-shaped white frontal band on head (with white typically extending as point at front of

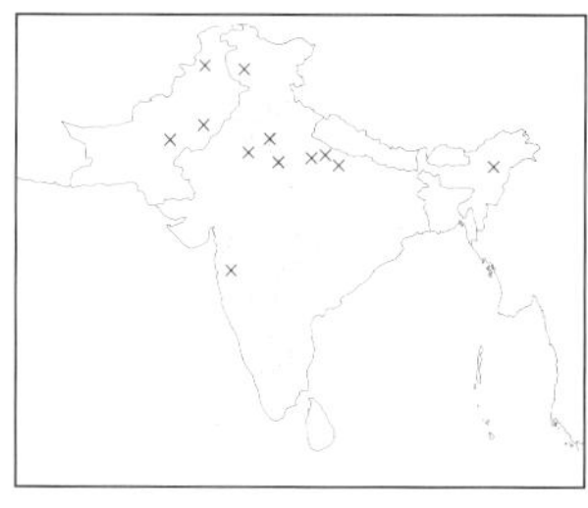

crown), and yellow eye-ring. Has slightly darker head and neck, and less extensive black barring on belly. Also has squarer-shaped head, with more steeply rising forehead, and is smaller and more compact, with stout triangular bill. **Juvenile** lacks white frontal band and black barring on belly, and is best distinguished from juvenile Greater White-fronted by yellow eye-ring, slightly darker head and neck, and the structural differences described above. **VOICE** Similar to that of Greater White-fronted, although squeakier and higher-pitched, and includes repeated *kyu-yu-yu* phrase (Madge and Burn 1988). **HABITS** Details not recorded in the subcontinent. Similar to those of Greylag Goose (below). Found in the region in ones or twos or in small groups of up to five, either separately or with Greylags. **HABITAT** Details not recorded in the subcontinent. Elsewhere, found on wet grassland and lakes. **DISTRIBUTION AND STATUS** Winter visitor to Pakistan and India (mainly to the north, east to Assam). Globally threatened. **PK:** vagrant. **IN:** rare. **REFERENCES** Harris *et al.* (1989).

GREYLAG GOOSE *Anser anser* — Plate 7

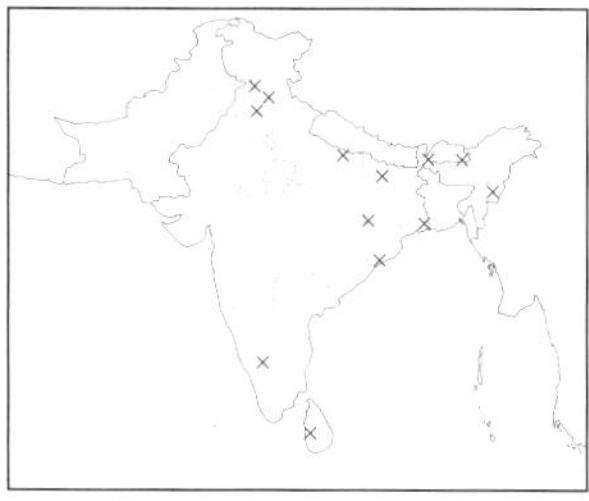

IDENTIFICATION 75–90 cm. Large, brownish-grey goose. **Adult** is easily told from Bar-headed Goose (below) by uniform greyish head and neck, stout pink bill, pink legs and feet, and darker, brownish-grey upperparts. **Juvenile** is similar to adult, but has less prominent pale fringes to upperparts, flanks and belly. In flight, upperwing-coverts are marked with brown and grey and contrast less with dark primaries than on Bar-headed. For differences from Bean Goose (p.365) and from Greater and Lesser White-fronted Geese (p.365), see those species. **VOICE** Loud cackling and honking, deeper than in other 'grey' geese, with repeated deep *aahng-ahng-ung* (Madge and Burn 1988). **HABITS** Assembles in considerable numbers wherever there is ample food and relative freedom from disturbance. Very shy and wary. Feeds chiefly by grazing; also by upending in shallow water. Almost entirely vegetarian; forages mainly at night on crops and wet grassland, and sometimes until well after sunrise. Spends the daytime swimming on large lakes or rivers or loafing on spits or in open fields. Continuously gabbles as it feeds and in flight. Flight is swift and strong, and often in V-formation. **HABITAT** Wet grassland and crops, lakes, large rivers and spits. A bird of open country. **DISTRIBUTION AND STATUS** Passage migrant and winter visitor. Winters mainly in the north, from Pakistan east to Manipur and south to Maharashtra. **PK:** locally frequent. **NP:** uncommon winter visitor and passage migrant; mainly below 275 m (–3050 m on passage). **IN:** locally common. **BT:** rare passage migrant. **BD:** local. **LK:** winter vagrant to wet lowlands.

BAR-HEADED GOOSE *Anser indicus* — Plate 8

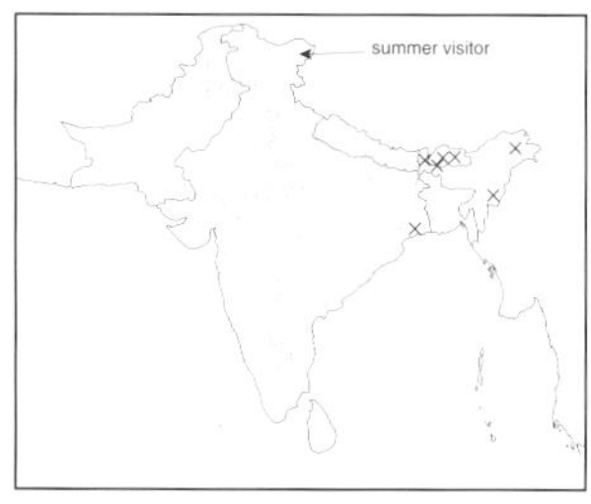

IDENTIFICATION 71–76 cm. **Adult** is very striking, and easily told from Greylag Goose (above) by black-banded white head, white line down dark grey neck, and paler steel-grey upperparts. Further, has black-tipped yellow bill, and orange-yellow legs and feet. **Juvenile** lacks distinctive head-and-neck pattern of adult. Has white forehead, cheeks and throat which contrast with dark grey crown and hindneck, and upperparts and underparts are more uniform. Attains adult plumage in first winter. In flight, both adult and juvenile show uniform pale grey forewing which contrasts with dark flight feathers. **VOICE** Honking flight call, but notes more nasal and more slowly uttered compared with Greylag. **HABITS** Rather similar to those of Greylag Goose. Gregarious throughout the year. Feeds mainly at night in cultivation or grassland on river banks, flying to and from its feeding grounds at dusk and dawn. Large flocks often spend the day resting on inaccessible sandbanks of large rivers. Tame and confiding on its breeding grounds, but very shy and wary in its winter quarters where it is hunted. **HABITAT** Breeds on swampy ground by lakes on high mountain plateaux. Winters near large rivers, lakes and reservoirs; also coastal islands in Sunderbans, Bangladesh. **BREEDING** End May and June. Nests on the ground, in a slight hollow thickly padded with down. **DISTRIBUTION AND STATUS** Breeds in Ladakh; widespread winter visitor to subcontinent. Arrives at wintering grounds about October/November; some remain until early May. **PK:** locally frequent winter visitor and passage migrant. **NP:** fairly common passage migrant, recorded up to 9375 m; sometimes winters below 275 m. **IN:** common on breeding grounds at 4300 m, widespread and locally common in winter. **BT:** rare passage migrant. **BD:** local winter visitor throughout. **REFERENCES** Pfister (1987), WWF India and AWB (1993).

SNOW GOOSE *Anser caerulescens* — Plate 8

IDENTIFICATION 65–84 cm. Occurs in two colour phases, with a white-phase bird recorded from the subcontinent. **Adult 'snow' phase** is all white, with pink bill and legs, and contrasting black wing-tips. **Juvenile**

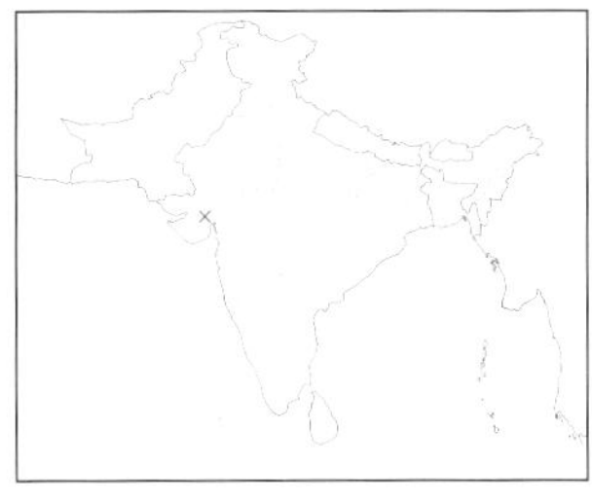

'snow' phase recalls juvenile Bar-headed Goose (p.366), but has pinkish-grey bill and legs, white neck and underparts, pale brownish-grey crown and hindneck, and all-white tail. **Adult 'blue' phase** has white head and upper neck contrasting with dark grey body; in flight, shows pale grey upperwing-coverts. **Juvenile 'blue' phase** has dark bill and dark grey head and neck. **VOICE** As other geese, but includes rather nasal and high-pitched *la-luk*, at distance not dissimilar to barking of a small dog (Madge and Burn 1988). **HABITS** Observed grazing with Bar-headed Geese. Not very shy. **HABITAT** Grass at reservoir edge. **DISTRIBUTION AND STATUS IN:** vagrant. **REFERENCES** Mundkur *et al.* (1992).

RED-BREASTED GOOSE *Branta ruficollis* — Plate 8

Siberian Red-breasted Goose (I)

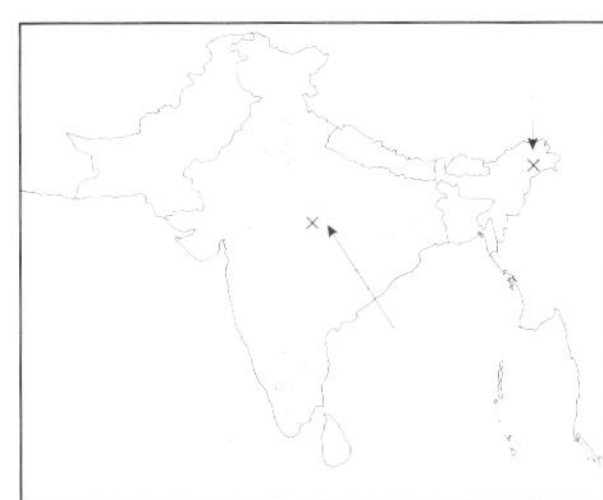

IDENTIFICATION 53–55 cm. Unmistakable, with reddish-chestnut cheek patch, foreneck and breast, and white surround to cheek patch and line down neck. Has black crown, hindneck and upperparts, and white band dividing chestnut breast from black belly. **Juvenile** is similar, but duller and not so clearly marked: chestnut is duller and upperparts browner. Wing-coverts are more extensively fringed with white (forming at least three complete white lines across closed wing). **VOICE** Flight call is a jerky *kik-yoik, kik-yik* (Madge and Burn 1988). **HABITS** Details not recorded in the subcontinent. Feeds almost entirely by grazing. Individuals may become mixed with other goose flocks. **HABITAT** Details not recorded in the subcontinent. **DISTRIBUTION AND STATUS IN:** vagrant, no recent records.

RUDDY SHELDUCK *Tadorna ferruginea* — Plate 8

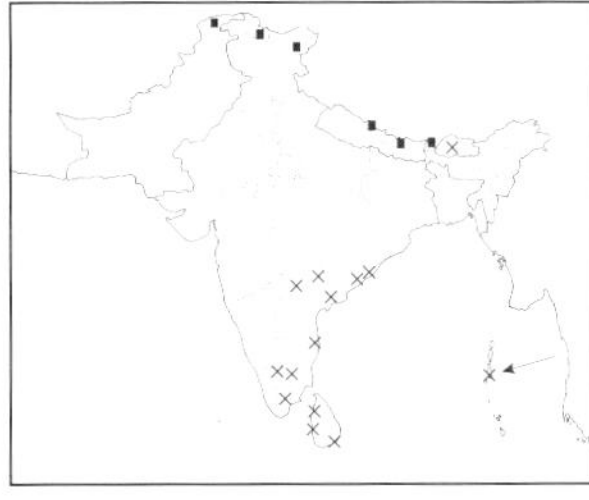

IDENTIFICATION 61–67 cm. Rusty-orange, goose-like duck, with buff to orange-buff head. In flight, white upperwing- and underwing-coverts contrast with blackish flight feathers, rump and tail. At close range, shows bottle-green gloss on secondaries. **Breeding male** has black neck-collar, which is less distinct or absent in non-breeding plumage. **Female** very similar to male, but lacks neck-collar and often has diffuse whitish face patch. **Juvenile** as female, but with browner and duller upperparts and underparts, and greyish tone to head. **VOICE** A honking *aakh* and trumpeted *pok-pok-pok-pok* when taking off (Madge and Burn 1988). **HABITS** Less gregarious than most other ducks, but flocks of thousands have occasionally been recorded at favoured winter quarters, e.g. Chilka Lake. Usually feeds by grazing on banks of rivers and lakes; also by wading in shallows, dabbling and upending. Extremely wary on its winter grounds, but can be very tame and confiding in its breeding areas. **HABITAT** Breeds around high-altitude lakes and swamps. Winters by large open lakes and rivers, especially where extensive sandbanks and sandy islets. Usually favours fresh waters. **BREEDING** May and June. Nests in a cliff hole thickly padded with down, often far from water. **DISTRIBUTION AND STATUS** Breeds in Ladakh, Sikkim and Nepal; widespread winter visitor to subcontinent, arriving in October/November, most departing by mid April. **PK:** winter visitor; probably also breeds in small numbers along N border. **NP:** common winter visitor below 305 m, regular on passage from the terai up to 4800 m; also a rare breeder at 4300 m. **IN:** common on breeding grounds in Ladakh, above 3650 m; elsewhere a locally common winter visitor and passage migrant. **BT:** winter visitor and passage migrant frequently recorded at 250–2745 m. **BD:** local winter visitor throughout. **LK:** winter vagrant to dry lowlands.

COMMON SHELDUCK *Tadorna tadorna* — Plate 8

Eurasian Shelduck (F)

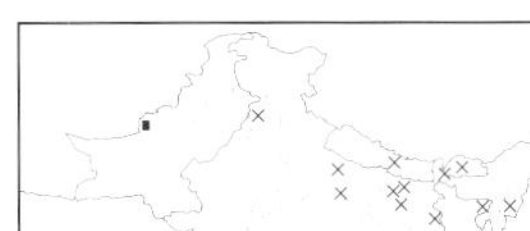

IDENTIFICATION 58–67 cm. **Male** has bright red bill and frontal knob, bottle-green head and neck, chestnut breast-band, and black scapular stripe. In flight, blackish flight feathers contrast with white upperwing- and underwing-coverts. **Eclipse male** is duller, with less distinct breast-band, fine grey barring on upperparts and underparts, and white mottling on face (as on female). **Female** is very similar to male, but is slightly smaller, with more rounded head; has duller greenish-black head (mixed with white adjacent to bill), duller bill lacking frontal knob, and narrow and duller chestnut breast-band. **Eclipse female** is duller and greyer, with indistinct breast-band and more extensive white on head: sometimes closely resembles juvenile. **Juvenile** is quite different from adult breeding plumage: lacks chestnut breast-band, and has sooty-brown crown, hindneck and upperparts, and white forehead, cheeks, foreneck and underparts. In flight, wing pattern similar to adult (although less contrasting), but shows well-defined white trailing edge to secondaries. **VOICE** Relatively silent; male utters low whistling call, and female a rapid *gag-ag-ag-ag-ag*. **HABITS** Often feeds by walking on mud and dabbling at the surface; also by wading in the shallows and upending. **HABITAT** Open lakes and large rivers; also coastal waters and salt lakes in Pakistan. **DISTRIBUTION AND STATUS** Has bred sporadically in Baluchistan, Pakistan. Winters in Pakistan, India south to Andhra Pradesh, Nepal and Bangladesh. **PK:** mainly a scarce winter visitor and passage migrant. **NP:** rare winter visitor and spring passage migrant below 275 m. **IN:** irregular and uncommon winter visitor. **BT:** very rare passage migrant. **BD:** local winter visitor.

WHITE-WINGED DUCK *Cairina scutulata* — Plate 9

White-winged Wood Duck (I)

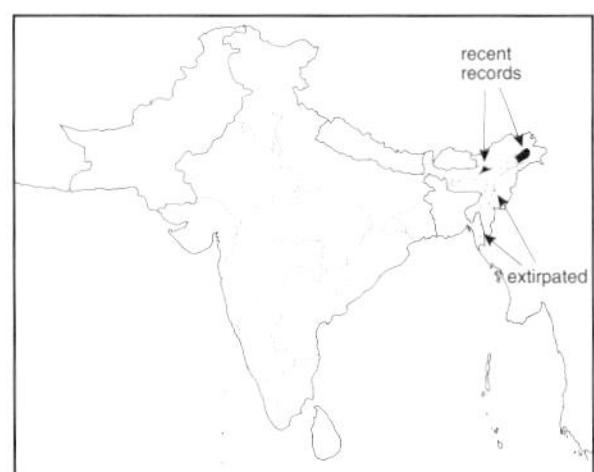

IDENTIFICATION 66–81 cm. A large, dark, forest-dwelling duck. Mainly blackish-brown (with greenish tone to upperparts), with whitish head profusely speckled with black. Has dull yellow or orange bill. White wing-coverts and inner edge to tertials, and blue-grey secondaries, are usually visible at rest. White upperwing- and underwing-coverts are very striking in flight. Head, neck and breast can be mainly white on some individuals. Sexes similar, although **female** is duller, with more heavily speckled head. **Juvenile** similar to female, although duller and browner, with brownish head. Possibly confusable with Comb Duck (below), but that species is entirely dark on the upperwing and underwing. **VOICE** A prolonged, vibrant, wailing honk in flight, often followed by nasal whistle (possibly from accompanying female); usually heard in evening en route to feeding areas (Madge and Burn 1988). **HABITS** Keeps singly, in pairs or in family parties. Flies to feeding grounds around dawn; at dusk returns to roost in trees in forest, either at the edge of the feeding site or deeper in forest. Feeds mainly by dabbling in very shallow water in the morning and evening, spending the middle of the day resting on a log or on the bank or floating in shade of a tree. **HABITAT** Small, stagnant and slow-flowing wetlands in forest; usually pools, streams and ditches in dense tropical moist forest, often with dead trees. **BREEDING** March–July. Nests in forest in tree holes lined with straw, leaves, grasses and roots, also on the ground. **DISTRIBUTION AND STATUS** Resident in NE India and Bangladesh, where formerly common and widespread. Has declined dramatically and range has contracted. Globally threatened. **IN:** now very rare in Assam and Arunachal Pradesh; also recorded in Manipur, Meghalaya and Nagaland, but current status there is unknown. **BD:** very rare resident in the southeast. **REFERENCES** Choudhury (1996a), Green (1993), Husain and Haque (1981), WWF India and AWB (1993), Yahya (1994).

COMB DUCK *Sarkidiornis melanotos* — Plate 9

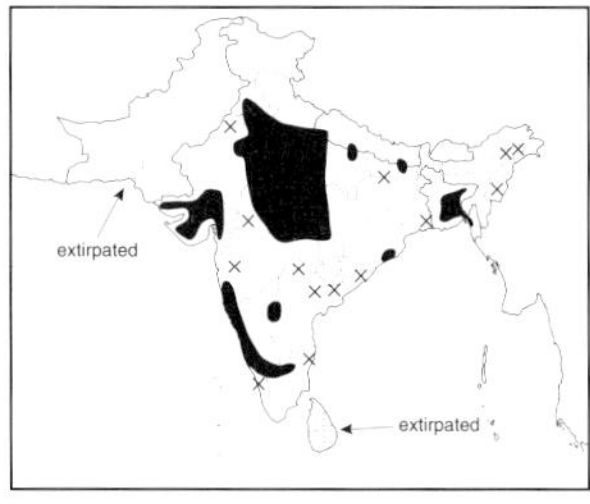

IDENTIFICATION 56–76 cm. **Male** is a large, stocky duck with white-speckled black head and neck, blackish upperparts glossed with bronze, blue and green, white breast with incomplete narrow black breast-band, white belly and undertail-coverts, and grey wash to flanks. Has gross, fleshy 'comb' at base of bill in summer, this much reduced in winter. In breeding plumage, has yellowish-buff wash to sides of head and neck. In flight, whitish underparts contrast strongly with very dark underwing, and 'comb' gives head an oblong-shaped appearance. **Female** lacks comb and is much smaller, duller on the upperparts, and often has brownish mottling on underparts. **Juvenile** has whitish supercilium, contrasting with (rufous-speckled) brown crown and eye-stripe, rufous-buff fringes to mantle and scapulars, and rufous-buff underparts with brown scaling on sides of breast. Wings have strong metallic blue-green sheen similar to adult. Head pattern and green in wing are best distinctions from juvenile Fulvous and Lesser Whistling-ducks (p.363). Like the whistling-ducks, also shows very dark upperwing and underwing in flight. **VOICE** Unlike the two whistling-ducks, generally silent, but sometimes utters low croak when flushed. **HABITS** Usually keeps in family parties or small flocks of 25–30. Feeds chiefly by grazing in marshes and wet grasslands; also by wading and dabbling in the shallows. Perches readily in trees. **HABITAT** Lowland pools, jheels and irrigation tanks with plentiful aquatic vegetation in well-wooded country. **BREEDING** July–September. Normally lays in a large unlined or sparsely lined hollow of a tree, standing in or close to water, sometimes some distance away, or occasionally in an old vulture's nest or hole in a wall or earth cliff. **DISTRIBUTION AND STATUS** Resident from Gujarat east to Bangladesh, north to Haryana and south to N Kerala and N Tamil Nadu; population concentrated mainly in India and declining; locally migratory, depending on water conditions. **PK:** formerly resident in Sind, probably now extirpated. **NP:** local and uncommon resident below 150 m. **IN:** widespread but generally uncommon resident. **BD:** rare breeder and passage migrant. **LK:** formerly a scarce resident in dry lowlands, now believed extirpated.

COTTON PYGMY-GOOSE *Nettapus coromandelianus* — Plate 9

Cotton Teal (F,I,P)

IDENTIFICATION 30–37 cm. A very small duck. **Male** has white head with black cap, white neck and underparts (flanks washed with grey), black breast-band, and greenish-black upperparts. Has white band across primaries and along secondaries. **Eclipse male** lacks breast-band; has greyish wash to face and neck, dark stripe

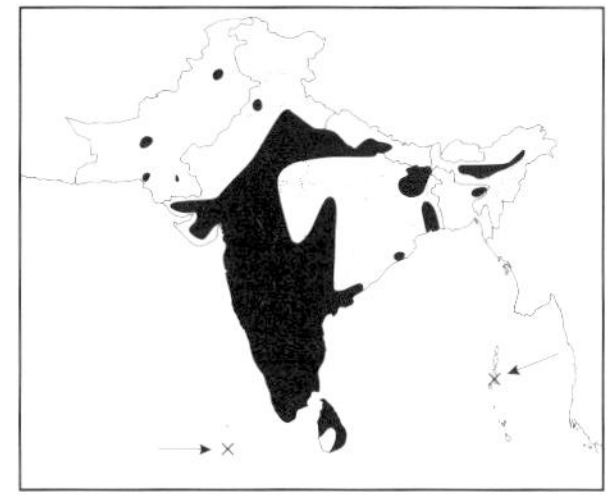

through eye, and grey mottling on breast and flanks. Retains wing pattern of breeding male. **Female** is duller than male, with dark eye-stripe, duller brownish-black upperparts with just a faint greenish gloss, and greyish-brown wash to neck and underparts, with dark mottling particularly on breast. Upperwing and underwing are dark, with fine white trailing edge to secondaries. **Juvenile** is similar to female, but lacks any greenish gloss to upperparts, is more heavily mottled on underparts, and has broader dark eye-stripe. Juvenile and female are conceivably confusable with Fulvous and Lesser Whistling-ducks (p.363). Smaller size, faster and stronger flight, paler and greyer face and underparts (with dark line through eye), and narrow white trailing edge to wing in flight are good features for separation from those species. Further, has cackling or quacking (not whistling call). **VOICE** Male utters sharp, staccato cackle, *car-car-carawak* or *quack, quack-quacky duck,* at rest and in flight; female utters weak *quack* (Madge and Burn 1988). **HABITS** Generally met with in pairs in the breeding season and in small flocks at other times; sometimes a few hundred together. Forages by dabbling and grazing among floating vegetation; picks food from the surface and dips head and neck under water. Usually escapes predators by flying off strongly and rapidly, but can dive if necessary. Awkward on land, but does perch on branches overhanging water. Confiding where not disturbed. **HABITAT** Vegetation-covered pools, irrigation tanks, channels and shallow lagoons. **BREEDING** May–September, varying locally. Nests in an unlined or sparsely lined hollow of a tree standing in or near water; sometimes in a hole in a building. **DISTRIBUTION AND STATUS** A locally distributed but widespread resident throughout much of the subcontinent up to 300 m (–1280 m in Nepal). Subject to local movements depending on water conditions. **PK:** irregular year-round visitor and very locally common resident. **NP:** frequent resident and summer visitor. **IN:** locally common, especially in deltaic West Bengal. **BD:** local resident; has recently declined. **LK:** resident in lowlands, regular in dry zone, very irregular and infrequent in wet zone. **MV:** vagrant?

MANDARIN DUCK *Aix galericulata* — Plate 9

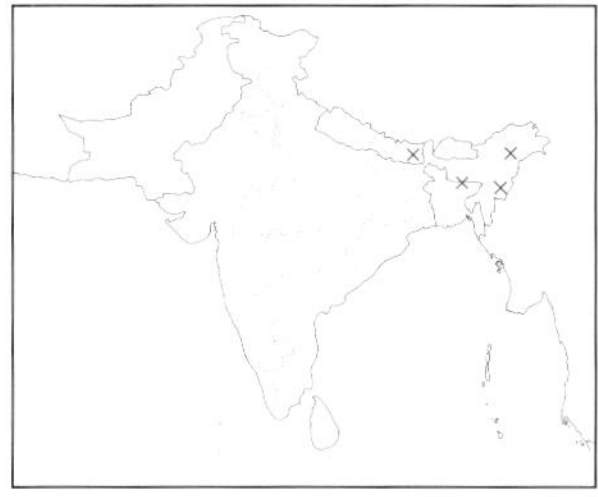

IDENTIFICATION 41–49 cm. **Male** is spectacular. Most striking features are pinkish-red bill, white band which sweeps back behind eye, elaborate orange 'mane' of elongated cheek and neck feathers, white-tipped orange 'sails', and black and white stripes on sides of breast. **Eclipse male** is like female, but with reddish (not greyish) bill, less distinct 'spectacles', shaggier crest, and glossier upperparts. **Female** has greyish head and shaggy hindneck, white 'spectacles', olive-brown upperparts, and white spotting on breast and flanks. In flight, both sexes appear bull-headed, show dark upperwing and underwing, with white trailing edge, and have contrasting white belly. In flight, and at a distance, recalls Eurasian Wigeon (p.370) because of white belly, but has darker and more uniform upperwing and underwing. **Juvenile** is similar to female, but with browner head, less distinct facial pattern ('spectacles' sometimes lacking), and more diffusely spotted breast and flanks. **VOICE** Silent except during display. **HABITS** In the region found singly, in pairs and in small parties of up to six birds. Habits otherwise not recorded in the subcontinent. Forages by dabbling and head-dipping in shallow water. Perches readily in trees. **HABITAT** In the region, recorded on rivers and once from a small stream. In its normal range, winters on flooded paddy-fields, marshes and open lowland rivers. **DISTRIBUTION AND STATUS NP, IN, BD:** winter vagrant.

GADWALL *Anas strepera* — Plate 10

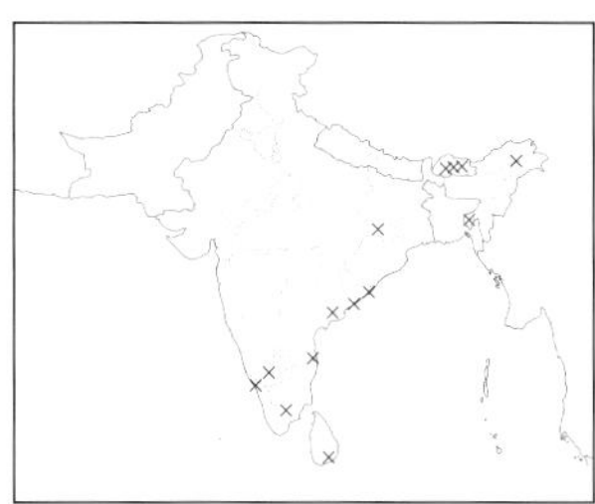

IDENTIFICATION 39–43 cm. **Male** is mainly grey, finely vermiculated with black and white. Has black rear end, dark grey bill, and white patch on secondaries which is often visible at rest. In flight, shows white patch on inner secondaries, contrasting with black outer secondaries and inner greater coverts, purplish-chestnut patch on median coverts, and grey flanks contrasting with white belly. **Eclipse male** is similar to female, but has more uniform grey upperparts and pale grey (rather than blackish-grey) tertials, and upperwing pattern of breeding male. **Female** is very similar to female Mallard (p.370), but is smaller, with squarer-shaped head, and duller and greyer general coloration, and has a finer bill which is dark grey with orange sides. Additional features in flight include white inner secondaries (lacking metallic speculum), and more contrasting whitish belly. **Juvenile** is very similar to female, but has orangey breast which is neatly and evenly streaked, and lacks female's clear-cut white belly. White in secondaries can be very indistinct in juvenile female. Distinguished from female and juvenile Falcated Duck (p.370) by dark crown and eye-stripe (Falcated has uniform greyish head), orange sides to bill, and white patch on inner secondaries in flight. **VOICE** Quiet except in aerial courtship chase, when male utters a short *wheck* and a low whistle, and female a repeated *gag-ag-ag-ag-ag.* **HABITS** Normally found in small parties. Behaviour is typical of dabbling ducks. Feeds mainly by dipping head into shallow water; sometimes also by upending. Usually shy and wary, and keeps close to emergent vegetation. **HABITAT** Freshwater marshes and lakes with extensive aquatic and emergent vegetation. **DIS-**

TRIBUTION AND STATUS Widespread winter visitor to the subcontinent, mainly south to C Karnataka. **PK:** common. **NP:** common; mainly below 915 m (–4750 m on passage). **IN:** locally common in the north. **BT:** uncommon. **BD:** locally common. **LK:** winter vagrant to dry lowlands. **REFERENCES** Harris *et al.* (1989).

FALCATED DUCK *Anas falcata* — Plate 10

Falcated Teal (F,I)

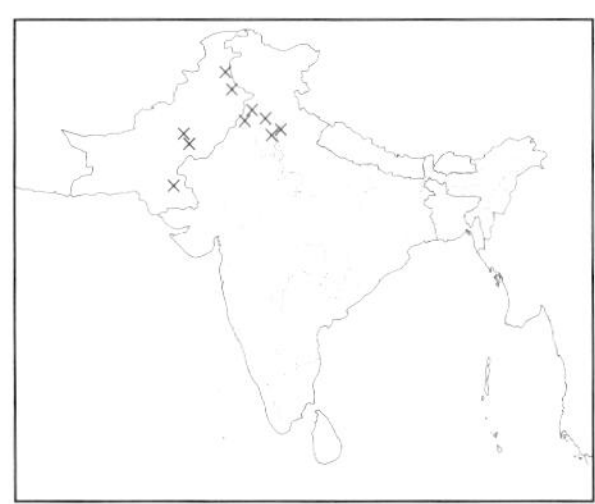

IDENTIFICATION 48–54 cm. **Male** is mainly grey, with bottle-green head and maned hindneck, long, downcurved, black-and-grey tertials, and black-bordered yellow patch at sides of vent. Shows pale grey forewing in flight. **Eclipse male** is similar to female, but has dark crown, hindneck and upperparts, and pale grey forewing. **Female and juvenile** have a rather plain, greyish head, greyish-white fringes to exposed tertials, and rufous-brown underparts. A white patch on sides of undertail-coverts is often striking. Confusion is possible with female and juvenile Eurasian Wigeon (below), and best distinguished from that species by rather long, dark grey bill, and dark scalloping and spotting on underparts. Further, normally shows quite full nape at rest. In flight, lacks striking white belly, has paler underwing, and has rounded (rather than pointed) tail compared with female Eurasian Wigeon. Also confusable with female Gadwall (p.369), and is best told from that by uniform greyish head and dark grey bill. In flight, it shows prominent whitish greater-covert wing-bar, and lacks the whitish patch on inner secondaries and white belly of female Gadwall. **VOICE** Has a distinctive, loud, piercing whistle in flight; utters a note very like the chuckling of a drake Mallard (below) while swimming (Smythies 1986). **HABITS** In the region usually found singly or in small flocks, but up to 80 seen together. Feeds mainly by dabbling and upending; usually keeps close to emergent vegetation. Often shy and wary. **HABITAT** Lakes and large rivers. **DISTRIBUTION AND STATUS** Winter visitor, mainly to Nepal, N India south to Gujarat, and Bangladesh. **PK:** vagrant. **NP:** locally distributed and uncommon, but regular below 915 m. **IN:** rare but regular visitor. **BD:** rare visitor, may be regular.

EURASIAN WIGEON *Anas penelope* — Plate 10

Wigeon (I,P)

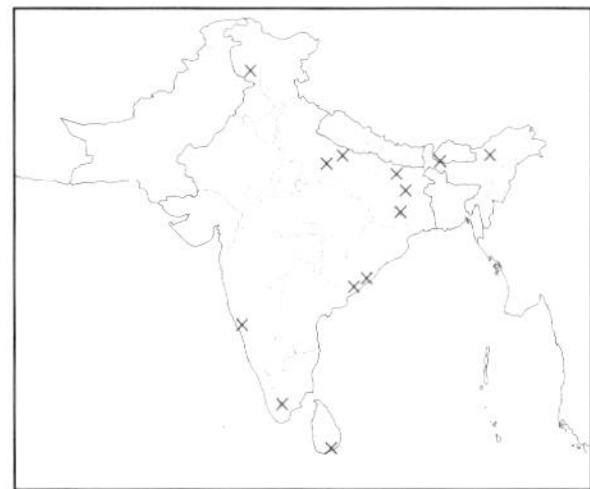

IDENTIFICATION 45–51 cm. **Male** has yellow forehead and forecrown on bright chestnut head, pinkish breast, grey mantle and flanks, and white band at rear end contrasting with black vent. In flight, shows white patch on forewing, although this is lacking on juvenile and first-winter males. **Eclipse male** is similar to female, but is more rufous on head and breast, and has white patch on forewing (sometimes visible at rest). **Female and juvenile** are typically uniform brown on head, becoming more chestnut-brown on breast and flanks. Lack prominent dark scalloping on underparts shown by most other female *Anas* species. In flight, all plumages feature prominent white belly contrasting with uniform breast and flanks, and pointed tail. Pointed tail may give rise to confusion in flight with female Northern Pintail (p.372), but Eurasian Wigeon is stockier and shorter-necked, with darker breast and flanks contrasting with clearly defined white belly. For differences from Falcated Duck (above), see that species. **VOICE** Male has a distinctive whistled *wheeooo* and female a low growled *krrr* (Madge and Burn 1988). **HABITS** Highly gregarious. Feeds chiefly by grazing, usually in compact parties on waterside grasslands and in wet paddy-fields; grazes more than other ducks. Also feeds by dabbling at the surface and by upending. **HABITAT** Frequents open lakes, reservoirs and rivers, also pools, marshes, tidal creeks and saltmarshes. Tends to avoid waters overgrown with vegetation and deep lakes. **DISTRIBUTION AND STATUS** Widespread winter visitor to the subcontinent. **PK:** common. **NP:** locally common; mainly below 250 m (–4570 m on passage). **IN:** widespread and locally common (–5000 m in Sikkim). **BT:** uncommon. **BD:** locally common winter visitor. **LK:** winter visitor to dry lowlands, more frequent in north.

MALLARD *Anas platyrhynchos* — Plate 10

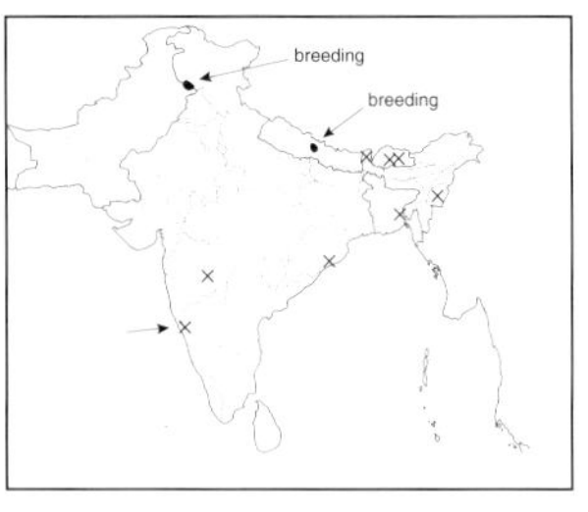

IDENTIFICATION 50–65 cm. A large, heavily built dabbling duck. **Breeding male** has bottle-green head, purplish-chestnut breast, mainly grey body, and black rear end. **Eclipse male** is similar to female, but with (less heavily marked) rusty-brown breast, blackish (glossed green) crown and eye-stripe, and uniform olive-yellow bill. **Female** is pale brown with darker crown and eye-stripe; has diffusely spotted or mottled breast, and dark brown subterminal and buff terminal fringes to feathers on upperparts and flanks. Bill is dull orange to olive-brown, marked with dark brown. **Juvenile** is similar to female, but with black crown and eye-stripe (similar to eclipse male), neatly streaked breast and streaked appearance to flanks, and (initially) dull reddish bill. Birds of feral stock can be very variable, with dark, pale and pied individuals occurring. Eclipse male, female and juvenile can be distinguished from corresponding plumages of Gadwall (p.369) by larger size, more rounded head, larger bill with different patterning and coloration, and in flight by white-bordered purplish-blue speculum (lacking white square on inner secondaries). **VOICE** Male has soft, rasping *kreep*, and female has distinctive, laughing *quack-quack-quack-quack*. **HABITS** A sociable duck, gathering in small flocks sometimes of up to 40–50 birds. Where hunted, rests by day on large open waterbodies and feeds at night. Often flights at dusk to flooded paddy-fields and marshes, where it feeds by dabbling, head-dipping, grazing or upending. **HABITAT** Freshwater marshes, reed-edged jheels and lakes. **BREEDING** Mid April–July. Nest is made of grass, rush leaves and down, and placed on the ground among thick vegetation cover. **DISTRIBUTION AND STATUS** Breeds in small numbers in Himalayas in Kashmir and Nepal; winters from Pakistan east to Manipur and south to Goa. **PK:** locally common, mainly in Punjab. **NP:** locally fairly common winter visitor and passage migrant from the terai up to 3050 m; also resident and breeds at 2620 m. **IN:** uncommon in the northwest and north, becoming less frequent east to Manipur and farther south (–5000 m in Sikkim). **BT:** uncommon. **BD:** rare winter visitor.

SPOT-BILLED DUCK *Anas poecilorhyncha* Plate 10

Spotbill Duck (I), Spotbill (F)

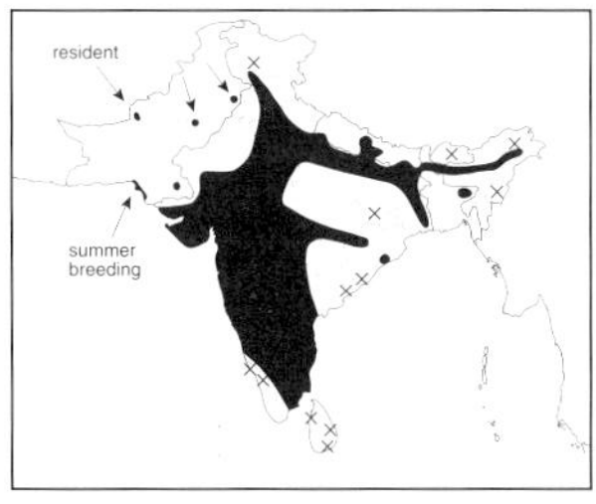

IDENTIFICATION 58–63 cm. A large, bulky dabbling duck. In all plumages (although see description of *A. p. zonorhyncha*), easily distinguished from other *Anas* species by yellow-tipped black bill, greyish-white head and neck with black crown and eye-stripe, blackish spotting on breast, white scalloping on flanks, and largely white tertials. In flight, wings appear dark except for white on tertials and white underwing-coverts. **Male** has prominent red loral spot and is more strongly marked than female and juvenile (the red loral spot is less conspicuous on female and lacking on juvenile). **Racial variation** *A. p. zonorhyncha*, which breeds in E Palearctic and occurs in NE India, is distinctively different from *A. p. poecilorhyncha* and *A. p. haringtoni*, which are covered by description above. Main differences are lack of red loral spot, diffusely marked breast, more uniform sooty-black upperparts and flanks, blue (rather than green) speculum, dark grey tertials (with whitish fringes), and dusky bar across cheeks. **VOICE** As Mallard (p.370). **HABITS** Very similar to those of Mallard, but is less quick taking off from water. Sociable; usually keeps in pairs or family parties, or in the non-breeding season in flocks of up to about 50. Feeds by dabbling, head-dipping, upending, and walking about among marsh vegetation. **HABITAT** Freshwater marshes, jheels, irrigation tanks, and pools with extensive emergent vegetation. **BREEDING** July–December, varying according to locality and water conditions. Builds a nest of grass and weeds on the ground among dense bankside vegetation or in a marsh. **DISTRIBUTION AND STATUS** Widespread resident in the subcontinent. **PK:** mainly a monsoon visitor, with a small overwintering population in S Sindh; common only in Tatta district. **NP:** resident and winter visitor, seen frequently; mainly below 915 m (–3290 m on passage). **IN:** locally common resident; nomadic and locally migratory; up to 1800 m in Kashmir and locally to 1200 m elsewhere. **BT:** rare passage migrant. **BD:** locally common winter visitor. **LK:** rare winter visitor to dry lowlands.

NORTHERN SHOVELER *Anas clypeata* Plate 11

Shoveller (F,I,P)

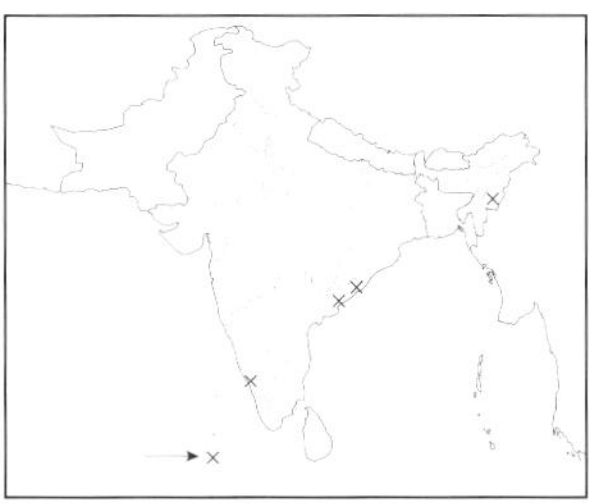

IDENTIFICATION 44–52 cm. Medium-sized dabbling duck with long spatulate bill. **Breeding male** has bottle-green head, white breast contrasting with chestnut flanks, black rear end, and long downcurving black-and-white scapulars. In flight, shows blue forewing, white bar across greater coverts, and green-glossed secondaries. **Eclipse male** recalls female, but is more rufous-brown, especially on flanks and belly, and has upperwing pattern of breeding male. Eye is yellow (usually dark in female). In sub-eclipse resembles breeding male, but has black scaling on breast and flanks and whitish facial crescent between bill and eye. **Female**'s brownish plumage recalls female Mallard (p.370), but has long spatulate bill. In flight, compared with Mallard, has faster wing action, and appears elongated at front and short-tailed at rear; has greyish-blue forewing and very dull speculum. **Juvenile** is similar to female: mantle is darker and more uniform, and underparts are more neatly spotted. Juvenile male has similar upperwing pattern to breeding male, whereas juvenile female lacks speculum or obvious white greater-covert bar. Juvenile male acquires adult-like plumage over gradual period, during which when can resemble sub-eclipse described above. **VOICE** Usually silent. Female has short descending series of quacks. **HABITS** Sociable; usually keeps in pairs or small parties. Often feeds by sweeping the bill from side to side while swimming, sifting the water for minute organisms and aquatic seeds; also upends or fully immerses its head and neck while swimming; sometimes feeds by wading, and occasionally dives. **HABITAT** Frequents all types of shallow fresh waters: lakes, jheels, irrigation tanks and reservoirs, small pools, flooded ditches, and rivers. **DISTRIBUTION AND STATUS** Widespread winter visitor to the subcontinent. Some arrive in August, small numbers sometimes remain until mid June. **PK:** common winter visitor and passage migrant. **NP:** locally common passage migrant, also a rare winter visitor;

mainly below 1350 m (–4570 m on passage). **IN:** common winter visitor. **BT:** uncommon winter visitor and passage migrant. **BD:** winter visitor, common in some years. **LK:** winter visitor to lowlands, rare in wet zone. **MV:** regular winter visitor.

SUNDA TEAL *Anas gibberifrons* — Plate 11

Grey Teal (I)

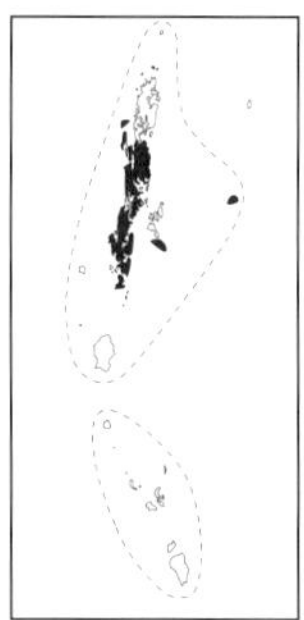

IDENTIFICATION 37–47 cm. A small, mainly brown duck. Many individuals are readily distinguished from other *Anas* species occurring in the Andaman Is by white markings on head. Typically has white throat and eye-patch, but occasionally head and neck are largely white. A significant proportion of birds have a rather uniform head, with just a narrow whitish eye-ring and only slightly paler throat, head therefore appearing not unlike that of Common Teal (p.373) although lacking dark stripe through eye. Compared with other teal species, has comparatively large head and slim neck. Bill is grey, sometimes mixed with pink. In flight, has white axillaries and stripe on underwing, and on upperwing has broad white band along greater-covert tips and green-glossed black speculum. Sexes similar. **VOICE** Calls mainly at night. Male has clear, low *preep*; female utters a loud, penetrating laughing series of quacks (Madge and Burn 1988). **HABITS** Usually associates in flocks of 20–30. Feeds mainly at night, by grazing in wet paddy-fields. Roosts in the daytime among mangrove trees or on rocks exposed at low tide. **HABITAT** Freshwater pools and marshes; tidal creeks and paddy-fields. **BREEDING** Only one definite record in the region: found nesting in a tree hole, with eggs in August. **DISTRIBUTION AND STATUS IN:** resident on Andaman Is; nomadic; once common, but has recently declined appreciably. **REFERENCES** Sankaran and Vijayan (1993), WWF India and AWB (1993).

NORTHERN PINTAIL *Anas acuta* — Plate 11

Common Pintail, Pintail (F,I,P)

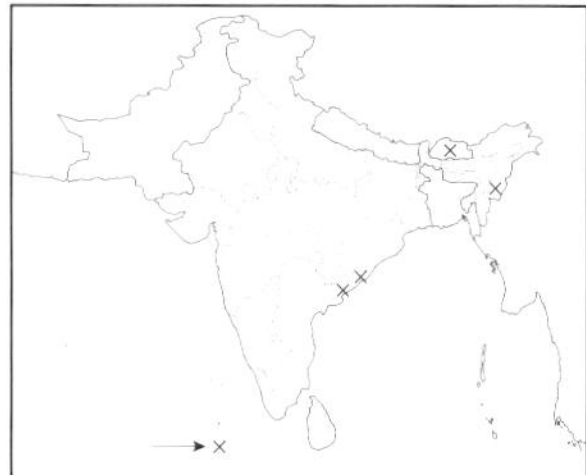

IDENTIFICATION 51–56 cm. A large, elegant dabbling duck with long, slender neck, long grey bill, and pointed tail which is held cocked when swimming. **Breeding male** has chocolate-brown head, with white stripe down sides of neck joining white foreneck and breast. Has greyish body, and yellowish-white and black ventral region. In flight, shows grey forewing, orange-buff band along greater coverts, and prominent white trailing edge to dull greenish speculum. **Eclipse male** resembles female, but is mottled grey above, has grey tertials, and has clear-cut grey sides to bill. Wing pattern is as breeding male. **Female** is easily distinguished from other female dabbling ducks by long neck, slender grey bill, pointed tail, and comparatively uniform buffish head lacking any eye-stripe or supercilium. In flight, shows combination of indistinct brownish speculum with broad white trailing edge, and greyish underwing. **Juvenile** as female, but with broader dark centres to flank feathers, and darker upperparts. **VOICE** Male a mellow *proop-proop* recalling male Common Teal (p.373); female has descending series of weak quacks, recalling Mallard (p.370), and a low croak when flushed (Madge and Burn 1988). **HABITS** Highly gregarious. Forages at night and in the early morning and evening in marshes and flooded paddy-fields, flying back to roost at a daytime refuge. Feeds mainly by upending, dabbling and head-dipping in shallow water; also grazes on land. Usually very shy and wary. **HABITAT** Open waters with aquatic vegetation, freshwater marshes, brackish lagoons, estuaries, wet paddy-fields. Avoids wooded areas. **DISTRIBUTION AND STATUS** Widespread winter visitor to the subcontinent. Arrives in Pakistan and NW India in September and October, most leaving by end March. **PK:** common. **NP:** common; mainly up to 915 m (–4650 m on passage). **IN:** common (–5000 m in Sikkim). **BT:** frequent. **BD:** common throughout. **LK:** common winter visitor to lowlands, more frequent in dry zone. **MV:** rare visitor.

GARGANEY *Anas querquedula* — Plate 11

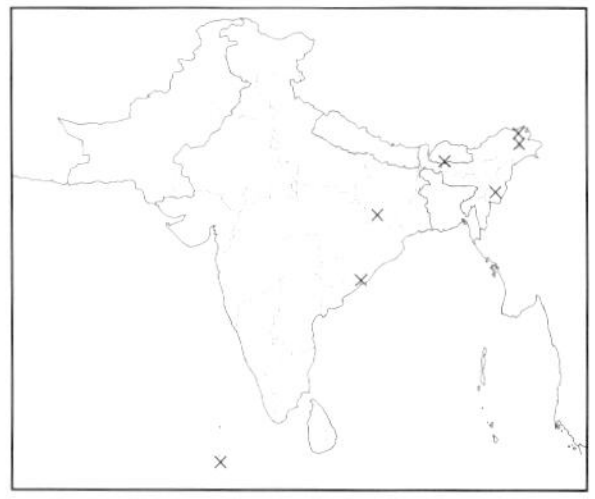

IDENTIFICATION 37–41 cm. **Breeding male** has downcurved white stripe behind eye, brownish breast contrasting with grey flanks, and long black-and-white striped scapulars. In flight, shows blue-grey forewing and broad white trailing edge to green speculum. **Eclipse male** is similar to female, but has upperwing pattern of breeding male. **Female** distinguished from female Common Teal (p.373) by more striking head pattern: typically, shows pale supercilium contrasting with dark eye-stripe, white loral spot and pale line beneath eye-stripe, dark cheek-bar, and whiter throat. Further, has more extensive white on belly, and more prominent whitish fringes to flank feathers. In flight, has greyish tone to forewing, and grey-brown speculum with broad white trailing edge (Common has more prominent white band along tips to greater coverts and narrower white trailing edge, with green speculum). For differences from Baikal Teal (p.373), see that species. **Juvenile** is similar to female, but has less distinct head pattern and lacks extensive white belly. **VOICE** Male has dry, crackling call in display or when alarmed; female has Common Teal-like quack.

HABITS Gregarious; gathers in aggregations of thousands in certain favoured daytime refuges. Where hunted, it is a nocturnal feeder. Feeds by dabbling, head-dipping in shallow water and picking from surface; sometimes upends. Usually shy and wary, preferring to keep among emergent vegetation. **HABITAT** Found on all types of water: marshes, jheels, village tanks and shallow lakes with plenty of vegetation; also coastal lagoons. **DISTRIBUTION AND STATUS** Widespread winter visitor to the subcontinent, one of the region's most common and widespread wintering ducks. Some arrive in August, small flocks occasionally remaining until May. **PK:** common on passage, with small numbers overwintering in S Sindh. **NP:** mainly a passage migrant, a few wintering; chiefly below 915 m (–4570 m). **IN:** common and widespread winter visitor (–4000 m). **BT:** uncommon. **BD:** common winter visitor. **LK:** common winter visitor to lowlands, more frequent in dry zone. **MV:** regular winter visitor.

BAIKAL TEAL *Anas formosa* — Plate 11

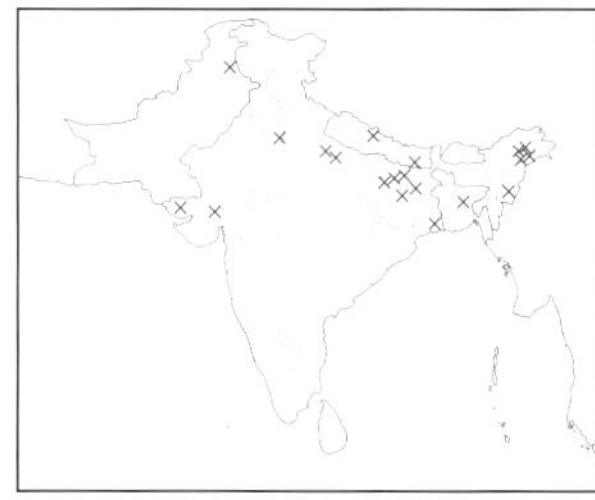

IDENTIFICATION 39–43 cm. **Breeding male** has complex head pattern of black, yellow, bottle-green and white. Other features include black-spotted pinkish breast, white line down sides of breast and grey flanks, black undertail-coverts, and long black, white and chestnut scapulars. Shows distinctive upperwing pattern in flight (see below), when black rear end and pointed tail are also very obvious and recall male Northern Pintail (p.372). **Eclipse male** is similar to female, but has darker and more rufous fringes to mantle, rufous breast and flanks, and less well-defined loral spot. **Female** closely resembles female Common Teal (below), and especially Garganey (p.372), but is larger than both and is best told by complex (although variable) head pattern: typical birds show buff supercilium broken above eye by dark crown, dark-bordered white loral spot, white throat which curves up to form half-moon-shaped cheek-stripe, and pale eye-ring with dark mark below forming vertical streak. Head pattern is variable, however, with some of the above-mentioned features often not apparent, most constant being dark-bordered loral spot (which is most prominent feature and visible at considerable range) and buff supercilium behind eye. By comparison, Garganey has more prominent whitish supercilium and pale horizontal cheek-stripe, and the loral spot is less prominent and not dark-bordered. In flight, upperwing pattern of both sexes is very distinctive and recalls that of Northern Pintail: forewing appears uniform greyish and the broad white trailing edge to secondaries is very striking. The chestnut greater-covert band of Baikal Teal, although diagnostic, is difficult to see, and belly also appears very white in flight. **Juvenile** similar to female, but has buffer and less distinct loral spot and mottled whitish belly. **VOICE** A chuckling *wot-wot-wot* by male, often uttered from flocks on water and in flight (Madge and Burn 1988). Female has a low quack. **HABITS** Found mainly singly or in pairs; once a party of eight to ten. Habits not otherwise recorded in the region. Feeds by dabbling, head-dipping and upending. **HABITAT** In the region, recorded on large rivers. **DISTRIBUTION AND STATUS** Mainly a winter visitor to the north, from Gujarat and Haryana east to Assam and south to S West Bengal. **PK, NP:** vagrant. **IN:** rare. **BD:** vagrant. **REFERENCES** Alström and Colston (1991), Crosby (1995), Eldridge and Harrop (1992).

COMMON TEAL *Anas crecca* — Plate 11

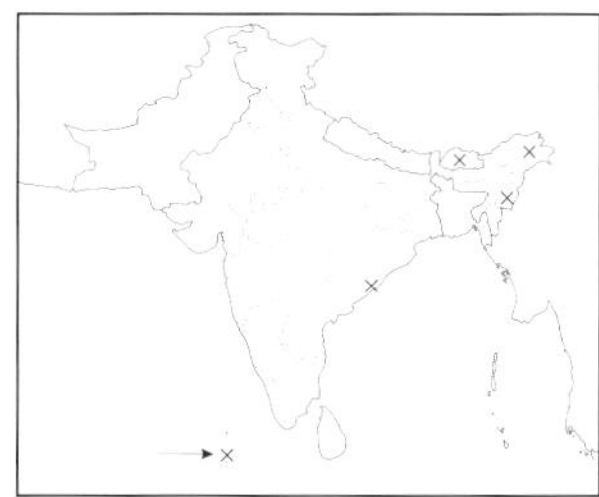

IDENTIFICATION 34–38 cm. A very small duck. **Male** has dark chestnut head, bottle-green band behind eye, white stripe along scapulars, and yellowish patch on undertail-coverts. **Eclipse male** and **juvenile** are much as female. **Female** differs from female Garganey (p.372) in more uniform head pattern, with less prominent supercilium; lacks prominent whitish loral spot and dark horizontal cheek-stripe which are usually apparent on Garganey. Bill is smaller and often shows touch of orange at base. Further, shows prominent white streak on outermost undertail-coverts. Additional features in flight include brownish (rather than greyish) forewing, broader white band across greater coverts, and green speculum. See Baikal Teal (above) for differences from that species. **VOICE** Male has distinctive, soft, throaty whistle, *preep preep*. Female usually silent, but utters a sharp *quack* when flushed. **HABITS** Found in both small and large flocks. Feeds by dabbling, head-dipping, upending, also by grazing on marshes and by night-time foraging in fields with other dabbling ducks. Rapid and agile in flight, often twisting and turning when disturbed. **HABITAT** Found on all kinds of shallow inland wetlands, including marshes, pools, lakes and rivers, and also on brackish waters. **DISTRIBUTION AND STATUS** Widespread winter visitor to the subcontinent, one of the most common wintering ducks. Some arrive in mid August and most leave by end March, a few remaining until May. **PK:** common. **NP:** common; mainly below 915 m (–4300 m on passage). **IN:** common (–5000 m in Sikkim). **BT:** frequent. **BD:** locally common. **LK:** scarce winter visitor to lowlands, more frequent in north. **MV:** occasional winter visitor.

MARBLED DUCK *Marmaronetta angustirostris* — Plate 9

Marbled Teal (I)

IDENTIFICATION 39–42 cm. **Adult** is pale brown with shaggy hood, dusky grey mask through eye, and diffuse white spotting on upperparts and underparts. In flight, has whitish underwing, uniform upperwing with pale brown coverts, and greyish flight feathers. **Juvenile** resembles adult, but has less prominent mask and less prominently

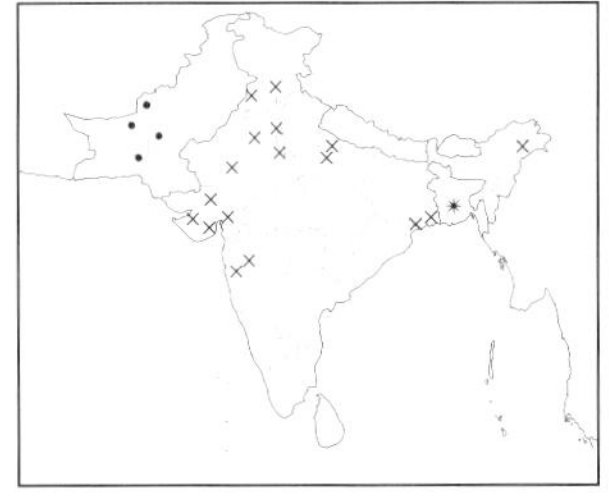

spotted flanks, and lacks shaggy hood. **VOICE** Silent except during display. **HABITS** Usually met with in pairs or small parties. Feeds mainly by dabbling in shallow water, occasionally by upending or diving. Rather shy and secretive, spending most of the day hiding in emergent vegetation or among partly submerged branches. When disturbed, flies low and drops into cover after a short distance. **HABITAT** Shallow freshwater lakes and ponds with extensive emergent and fringing vegetation; also inundated tamarisk bushes. **BREEDING** May–July. Nest is made of rushes and weeds and is hidden among marsh vegetation or on an island in a lake. **DISTRIBUTION AND STATUS** Breeds in Pakistan; winter visitor to N subcontinent south to C Maharashtra. Globally threatened. **PK:** now a locally distributed and rare breeding resident and winter visitor. **IN:** rare winter visitor. **BD:** winter vagrant, no recent records. **REFERENCES** WWF India and AWB (1993).

PINK-HEADED DUCK *Rhodonessa caryophyllacea* Plate 9

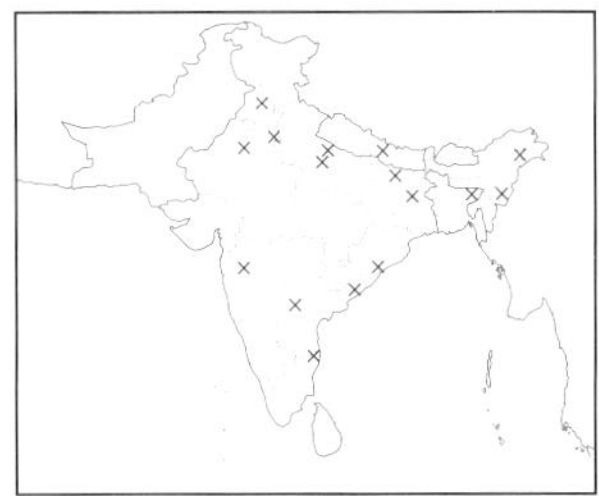

IDENTIFICATION 60 cm. Uniquely shaped duck, with long neck and body and triangular head. **Male** has combination of pink head and hindneck, and dark brown foreneck and body. In flight, pale fawn secondaries contrast with dark forewing, and pale pink underwing with dark body. **Female** is similar, but has paler, dull brown body, greyish-pink head, and brownish crown and hindneck. **Juvenile** similar to female, but with white fringes to body feathers. **VOICE** Male has a low, weak whistle and female a low quack (Madge and Burn 1988). **HABITS** Little known. Shy and secretive, and was rarely seen except when flushed. Outside the breeding season it was found in parties of six to eight, but flocks of 30–40 have been recorded. Fed by dabbling on the water surface, but could also dive; occasionally perched in trees. **HABITAT** Secluded pools and marshes in elephant-grass jungle. **BREEDING** Probably June and July. Only one nest recorded: built mainly of dry grass and concealed among tall grass on the ground. **DISTRIBUTION AND STATUS** Probably extinct; last confirmed wild sighting in 1935, in Bihar. Formerly found mainly in NE India, from Bihar east to Manipur and Orissa. Globally threatened. **NP:** one collected in 19th century. **IN:** once presumably resident. **BD:** former rare resident. After being discovered it was apparently always rare, the loss of its specialised habitat probably being the main cause of its disappearance. **REFERENCES** WWF India and AWB (1993).

RED-CRESTED POCHARD *Rhodonessa rufina* Plate 12

***Netta rufina* (F,I,N)**

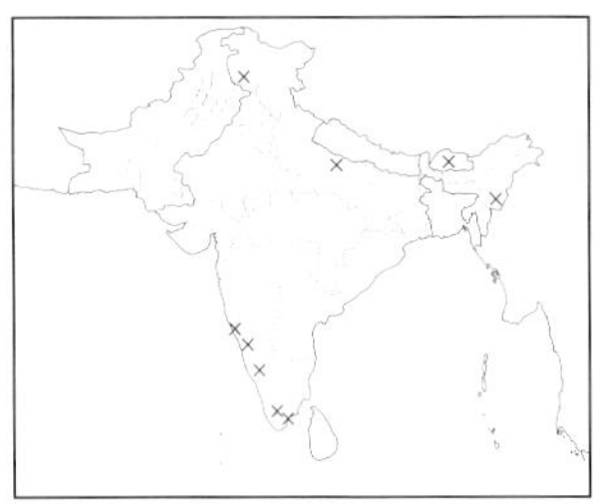

IDENTIFICATION 53–57 cm. A large, heavily built duck with large square-shaped head. Shape, carriage and flight action recall the dabbling ducks *Anas* rather than diving ducks *Aythya*. **Breeding male** has reddish bill, rusty-orange head, and white flanks contrasting with black breast and ventral region. In flight, shows white wing-bar (with flight feathers almost entirely white), and white underwing and flanks contrast with black breast and belly. **Eclipse male** very similar to female, but with reddish iris and bill. **Female** is mainly brown, with whitish cheeks contrasting with brown cap and nape, and brown bill with pink towards tip. In flight, shows broad white wing-bar and white underwing as male. **Juvenile** as female, but with all-dark bill. **VOICE** Silent away from breeding grounds. **HABITS** Usually feeds in small groups, but also forms large flocks. Feeds chiefly by diving; occasionally also by upending and head-dipping. **HABITAT** Large lakes with fairly deep open-water areas and plentiful submerged and fringing vegetation; sometimes on rivers. **DISTRIBUTION AND STATUS** Widespread winter visitor to the subcontinent, except Sri Lanka. Most arrive in the north in October and are gone by about mid March. **PK:** scarce, but has increased recently. **NP:** winter visitor and passage migrant, seen frequently; mainly below 915 m (–3050 m). **IN:** widespread and locally fairly common. **BT:** vagrant. **BD:** local winter visitor.

COMMON POCHARD *Aythya ferina* Plate 12

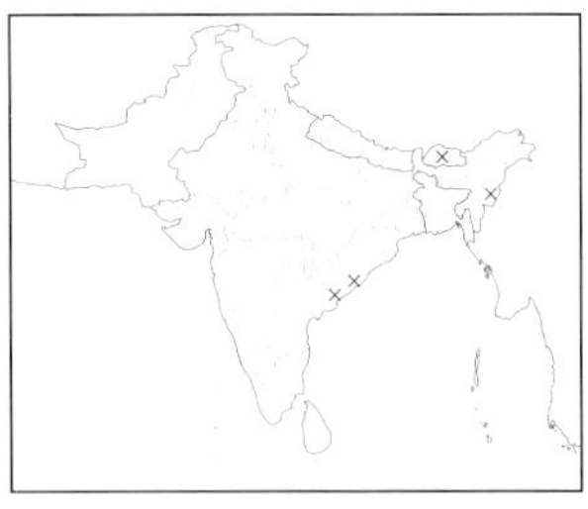

IDENTIFICATION 42–49 cm. Largest of the *Aythya* ducks, with large dome-shaped head. In all plumages, flight feathers are silvery-grey, and does not therefore show prominent white wing-bar of other *Aythya* species. **Breeding male** has chestnut head, and silvery-grey upperparts and flanks, which contrast with black breast and ventral region. **Eclipse male** and **immature male** recall breeding male, but have duller brown head, brownish-black breast and ventral region, and dull brownish-grey upperparts and flanks. **Female** has dull cinnamon- to chestnut-brown head, neck and breast contrasting with paler brownish-grey upperparts and flanks (in breeding season, upperparts and flanks become more uniformly brown); usually shows indistinct pale patch on lores, and pale throat and streak behind eye. Best distinctions from female Tufted Duck (p.376) are rounded head (lacking any sign of tuft), longer bill with grey central band, contrast between neck and breast and upperparts and flanks, dark eye, and different upperwing pattern in flight. Is larger and duller in coloration than Ferruginous Pochard (below), and lacks white undertail-coverts and white wing-bar of that species. **VOICE** Silent away from breeding grounds. **HABITS** Highly gregarious, often gathering in flocks of several hundred. Feeds chiefly by diving in open water, sometimes also by upending or dabbling. Where disturbed, it is mainly a nocturnal feeder. **HABITAT** Lakes, jheels and reservoirs with large areas of open water deep enough to allow diving; occasionally on rivers. **DISTRIBUTION AND STATUS** Widespread winter visitor to the subcontinent, except Sri Lanka. Most arrive in the north in mid October and leave by end March. **PK:** common. **NP:** a locally fairly common winter visitor and passage migrant; seen mainly below 915 m (–4570 m on passage). **IN:** widespread and locally common (–5000 m in Sikkim). **BT:** vagrant. **BD:** uncommon winter visitor.

FERRUGINOUS POCHARD *Aythya nyroca* — Plate 12

Ferruginous Duck (N,R), White-eyed Pochard (F,I)

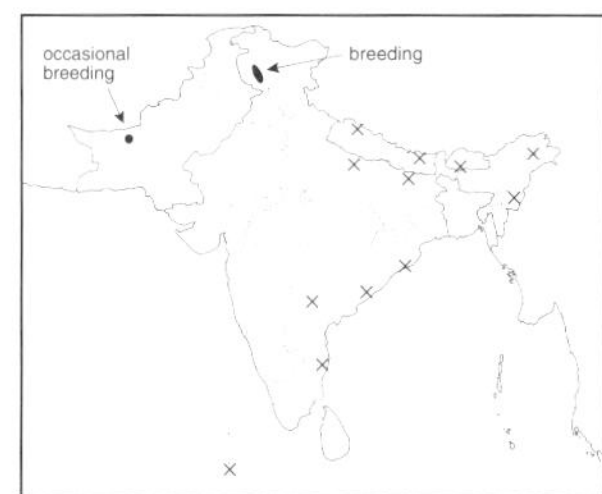

IDENTIFICATION 38–42 cm. Smallest of the *Aythya* species, with dome-shaped head recalling Common Pochard (p.374). In all plumages has chestnut-brown head, neck, breast and flanks, dark brown upperparts, and prominent white undertail-coverts. In flight, shows a more prominent white wing-bar, extending farther onto outer primaries than on other *Aythya* species; and males, in particular, show striking white belly, but this is not a useful feature on females. **Breeding male** is unmistakable, with rich chestnut head, neck and breast and white iris. **Eclipse male** resembles female, but is brighter on head and breast and has white iris. **Female** is chestnut-brown on head, neck, breast and flanks, and has dark iris. Distinguished from similar plumages of Common by smaller size, deeper chestnut-brown coloration to head etc, brownish back, white undertail-coverts, and extensive white wing-bar. Some female Tufted Ducks (p.376) show white undertail-coverts, but head, neck and breast of that species are browner, and has different head shape (usually with signs of crest). For differences from Baer's Pochard (below), see that species. **VOICE** Silent away from breeding areas. **HABITS** Usually met with in pairs or small groups. Feeds chiefly by diving and also by dabbling, head-dipping and upending. A shy duck, feeding mainly at night. Seeks refuge on the sea beyond the surf in coastal areas, flying inland at dusk to feed on village tanks. Secretive and not easily flushed, preferring to hide in reedbeds or dive to avoid danger. **HABITAT** Freshwater pools and irrigation tanks with extensive marginal and submerged aquatic vegetation; also coastal backwaters and lagoons. **BREEDING** May–July. Nest is a pad of rushes, lined with grasses and down feathers, and placed in reedbed close to the water's edge. **DISTRIBUTION AND STATUS** Breeds in Baluchistan, Pakistan, Kashmir and Ladakh; widespread winter visitor to the subcontinent south to NE Tamil Nadu. Globally threatened. **PK:** locally frequent; mainly a winter visitor and passage migrant. **NP:** chiefly a passage migrant, also a winter visitor; regularly seen below 915 m (–4575 m on passage). **IN:** breeds in Himalayas at 1500 m; widespread and locally common winter visitor. **BT:** uncommon winter visitor and passage migrant. **BD:** locally common winter visitor. **MV:** vagrant. **REFERENCES** WWF India and AWB (1993).

BAER'S POCHARD *Aythya baeri* — Plate 12

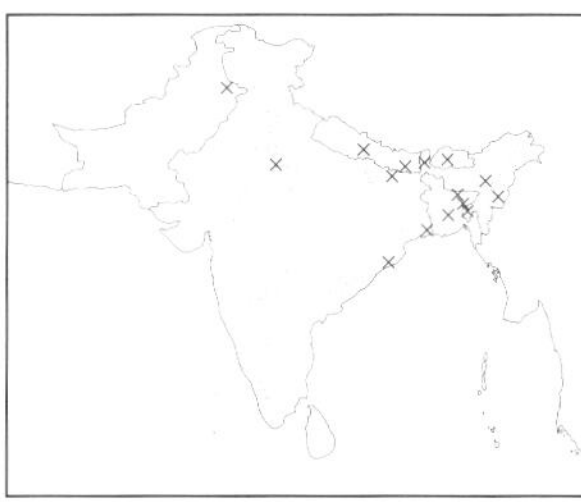

IDENTIFICATION 41–46 cm. In all plumages shows dark head and neck contrasting with warmer chestnut-brown breast, extensive white wing-bar, and white undertail-coverts. White patch on foreflanks usually visible above water when swimming. **Breeding male** has strong green gloss to dark head, and mahogany-brown breast with duller chestnut-brown flanks. **Eclipse male, immature male** and **female** have duller greenish-black head, variably mixed with dark chestnut-brown (greenish coloration barely apparent on some); breast is duller, more chestnut-brown in coloration, and not so clearly demarcated from foreneck. Iris is white in male and dark in female. Female has diffuse chestnut-brown loral patch, similar in colour to breast. Female and similar plumages most closely resemble female Tufted Duck (p.376) and are best told from that species by more domed head, lack of crest, darker head and neck contrasting with warmer brown breast, white foreflank patch, and more extensive white wing-bar in flight (with white extending farther onto primaries). Should not be confusable with Ferruginous Pochard (above), which is smaller, finer-billed, and uniform chestnut-brown on head, neck, breast and flanks. **Juvenile** as adult female, but is duller, lacks loral patch, and head is more chestnut-brown. **VOICE** Silent away from breeding areas. **HABITS** Little known in the wild. A shy duck, usually found in pairs or small parties. Feeds mainly by diving. Takes to the air more easily than other ducks in the genus, and is swift in flight. **HABITAT** Large rivers and lakes. **DISTRIBUTION AND STATUS** Winter visitor, mainly to NE India and Bangladesh. Globally threatened. **PK:** vagrant. **NP:** scarce but regular passage migrant, chiefly to Kosi Barrage. **IN:** locally fairly regular in the northeast, uncommon and erratic elsewhere. **BT:** vagrant. **BD:** regular winter visitor. **REFERENCES** WWF India and AWB (1993).

TUFTED DUCK *Aythya fuligula* Plate 12

Tufted Pochard (F)

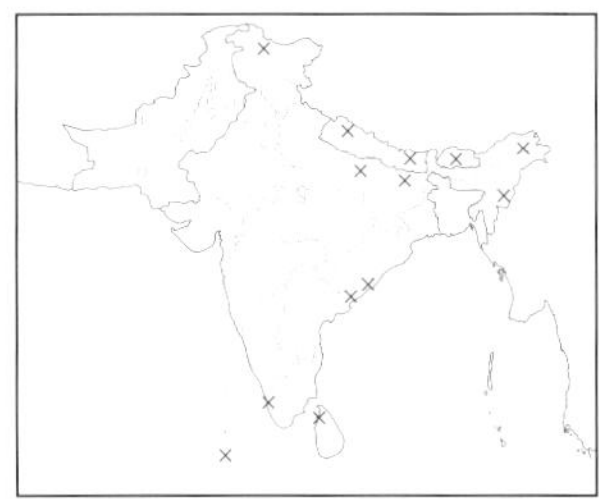

IDENTIFICATION 40–47 cm. **Breeding male** is mainly glossy black with contrasting white flanks and drooping crest. **Eclipse male** and **immature male** are duller brownish-black on head, breast and upperparts; have greyish flanks, duller grey bill, and crest which is shorter or apparently lacking. **Female** is dull brown, with darker upperparts, and usually shows signs of crest, although this can be indistinct or lacking. Can have white at the base of bill recalling Greater Scaup (below), or have white undertail-coverts recalling Ferruginous Pochard (p.375) or Baer's Pochard (p.375). Easily told from female Common Pochard (p.374) by square-shaped head (usually with signs of tuft), stouter bill, darker brown head and neck, dark blackish-brown upperparts, yellow iris, and in flight by broad white wing-bar. From female Ferruginous by head shape, darker brown (rather than warm chestnut) coloration to head, breast and flanks, yellow iris, and less extensive white wing-bar. For differences from Baer's and Greater Scaup, see those species. **VOICE** Silent away from breeding grounds. **HABITS** Gregarious; sometimes in flocks of several hundred. Feeds in the daytime, mainly by diving; also upends, dips head or picks items from surface. **HABITAT** Lakes and irrigation reservoirs with large open areas and deep enough to allow diving. **DISTRIBUTION AND STATUS** Widespread winter visitor to the subcontinent. **PK:** common but locally distributed; most arrive in late September and are gone by end March. **NP:** fairly common, some present all year; mainly below 915 m (–4900 m on passage). **IN:** widespread and locally common (–5000 m in Sikkim). **BT:** rare passage migrant. **BD:** locally common, sometimes oversummers; numbers increasing. **LK:** very rare. **MV:** fairly frequent winter visitor.

GREATER SCAUP *Aythya marila* Plate 12

Scaup Duck (I)

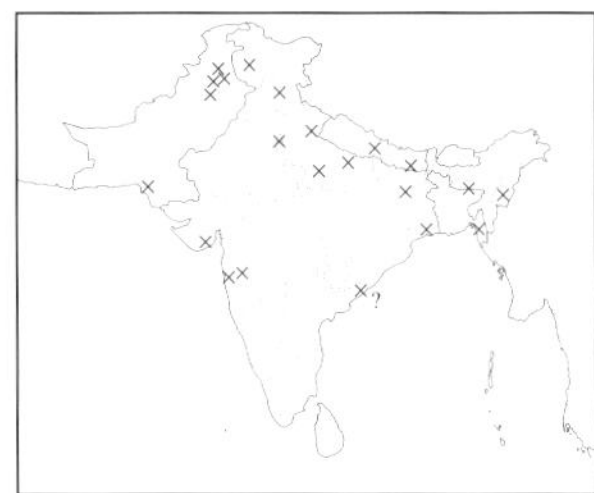

IDENTIFICATION 40–51 cm. Larger and stockier than Tufted Duck (above), with more rounded head and lacking any sign of crest. Bill is larger and wider, and has smaller black nail at tip than Tufted. **Breeding male** told from Tufted by greyish rather than black upperparts (at close range, lower mantle and back finely vermiculated with blackish), and green rather than purple gloss to blackish head. **Eclipse male** has brownish-black head, neck and breast, and upperparts are more strongly vermiculated with brownish-black. **Immature male** assumes adult-like although duller plumage during first winter, and is often similar in appearance to eclipse male. **Female** resembles female Tufted but, in addition to above-mentioned structural differences, has broad and contrasting white patch at base of bill (female Tufted sometimes shows white area at base of bill, but it is never so extensive and clear cut), and usually has greyish-white vermiculations ('frosting') on upperparts and flanks. Female shows pale patch on ear-coverts in summer, which is a further distinction from Tufted. **Juvenile** is warmer brown on head, breast and upperparts, has less white at base of bill (confined to lores), and often shows indistinct pale ear-covert patch. Structural differences and lack of crest are best means of separation from Tufted. **VOICE** Silent except during display. **HABITS** Details not recorded in the subcontinent. Gregarious in its regular winter quarters. Feeds mainly by diving, and when not feeding loafs in open water. A strong swimmer. **HABITAT** Found on large freshwater lakes and rivers in the region, but normally winters in coastal areas. **DISTRIBUTION AND STATUS** Winter visitor, mainly from Kashmir east to Manipur and south to Maharashtra. Possibly overlooked in coastal areas. **PK:** vagrant. **IN:** rare. **BD:** vagrant.

LONG-TAILED DUCK *Clangula hyemalis* Plate 13

Long-tail Duck (F,I)

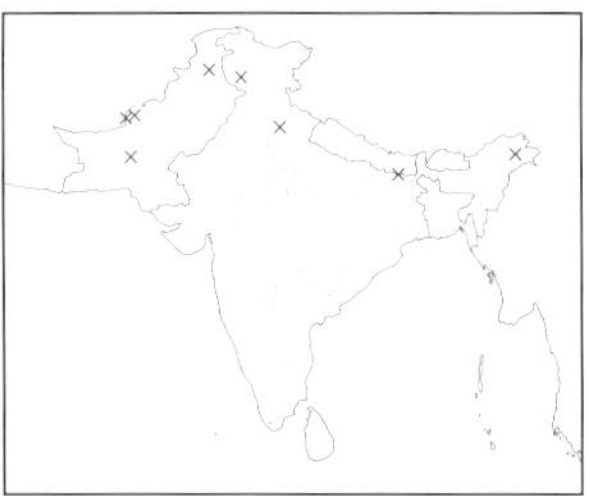

IDENTIFICATION 36–47 cm. A small, stocky duck with comparatively large head, stubby bill, and pointed tail which is elongated on male. Swims low in the water, and partially opens wings before diving. Shows uniform dark upperwing and underwing in flight. Winter **male** appears mainly white, with brownish-black cheek patch and breast, greyish face, long whitish scapulars, and long, pointed tail. In summer plumage has white eye-patch, but rest of head, neck and breast are dark chocolate-brown, and has broad chestnut fringes to blackish scapulars. **Immature male** resembles female, but usually shows male features such as pink band across bill and blackish breast. **Female** is very variable: in winter, usually has mainly white head with dark brown crown and cheek patch, and brown breast and upperparts contrasting with white flanks; in summer, has mainly brown head with whitish patches around eye and ring around neck. **VOICE** Silent except during display. **HABITS** Feeds almost exclusively by diving, often remaining underwater for many seconds. Flies low over the water and characteristically swings from side to side, showing the belly and back alternately. **HABITAT** Normally a sea duck, but found on freshwater lakes, jheels and large rivers in the subcontinent. **DISTRIBUTION AND STATUS PK, NP, IN:** vagrant.

WHITE-WINGED SCOTER *Melanitta fusca* — Plate 13

Velvet Scoter

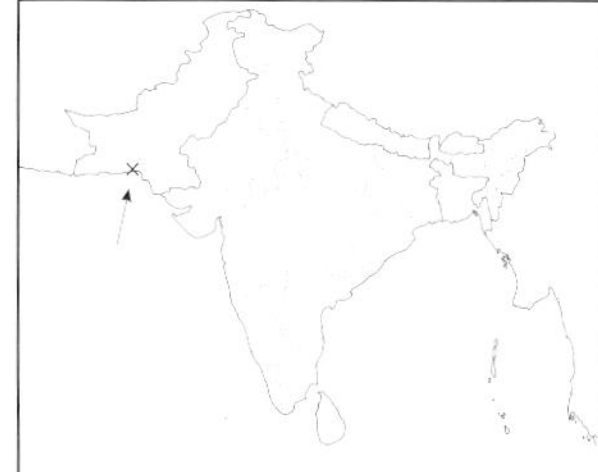

IDENTIFICATION 51–58 cm. A large, all-dark sea duck: both sexes have white secondaries which are prominent in flight. **Breeding male** is mainly black, with white iris and crescent below eye. Has orange-yellow sides to bill. **Immature male** is dull black, with duller bill, and lacks white crescent below eye. May show pale patch on lores. **Female** is brown, with diffuse whitish patch on lores and ear-coverts (sometimes lacking on fresh-plumaged birds). **VOICE** Silent except during display. **HABITS** Details not recorded in the region. Dives in shallow water for food, chiefly shellfish. **HABITAT** Coastal waters. **DISTRIBUTION AND STATUS PK:** vagrant. **REFERENCES** Hirschfeld *et al.* (1988).

COMMON GOLDENEYE *Bucephala clangula* — Plate 13

Goldeneye Duck (I), Goldeneye (F)

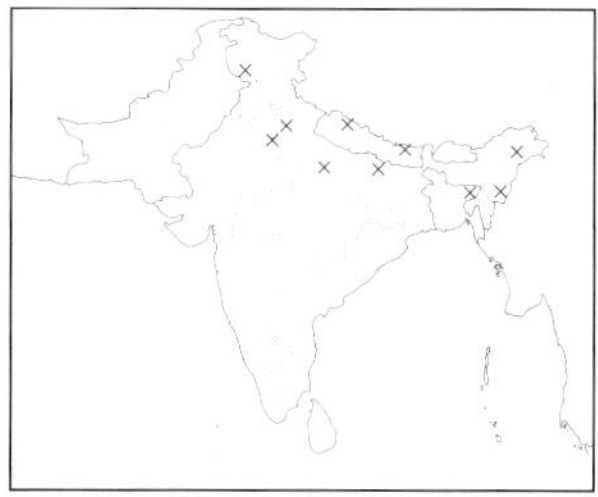

IDENTIFICATION 42–50 cm. A stocky duck with bulbous head. Swims with body flattened, and partially spreads wings when diving. Both sexes show extensive white on wing-coverts and white secondaries in flight. **Breeding male** has bottle-green head with striking white patch on lores, white breast and underparts, and black-and-white patterned upperparts. **Immature male** resembles female, but shows pale loral spot and has some white in scapulars. **Eclipse male** resembles female, but wing pattern is as breeding male. **Female** is distinctive, with chocolate-brown head, indistinct white collar, and greyish body with white wing patch usually visible at rest. **VOICE** Silent except during display. **HABITS** In the subcontinent found in parties of up to seven birds. Feeds mainly by diving in the daytime, group members often submerging simultaneously; occasionally dabbles and upends. Swift in flight, the wings producing a distinctive whistling sound. **HABITAT** Open-water areas in freshwater lakes and large rivers, particularly where they debouch from the hills. Avoids shallow waters with extensive aquatic vegetation. **DISTRIBUTION AND STATUS** Winter visitor, mainly to Pakistan, N India (from Kashmir east to Assam) and Nepal. **PK:** rare. **NP:** uncommon; chiefly below 915 m (–3050 m). **IN:** uncommon in the north. **BD:** vagrant.

SMEW *Mergellus albellus* — Plate 13

***Mergus albellus* (F,I,K,R)**

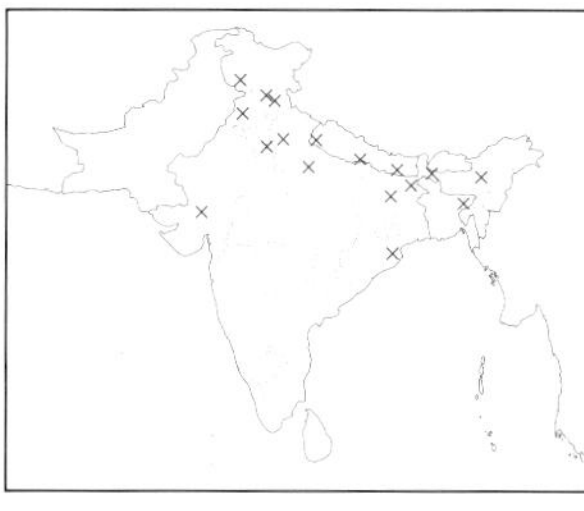

IDENTIFICATION 38–44 cm. A small, stocky 'sawbill' with comparatively large, square-shaped head. In flight, both sexes show dark upperwing with white wing-covert patch and trailing edge to secondaries. **Male** is mainly white, with black face, crest-stripe, breast stripes and back. Flanks are grey. **Female**, and **first-winter** and **eclipse male**, have chestnut cap with white throat and lower ear-coverts, and mainly dark grey body. **VOICE** Generally silent. **HABITS** Sociable, often in small groups; occasionally in large parties. Feeds diurnally, mainly by diving, members of a flock typically submerging in unison or in quick succession. Springs from the water easily, and is fast and agile in flight. **HABITAT** Freshwater lakes, rivers, jheels, and Himalayan streams where they debouch from the foothills onto the plains. **DISTRIBUTION AND STATUS** Winters from Pakistan east to Assam, south to Gujarat and Orissa. **PK:** scarce and irregular, usually seen only between late January and early February. **NP:** vagrant. **IN:** uncommon but regular winter visitor to the north. **BD:** vagrant. **REFERENCES** Crosby (1995).

RED-BREASTED MERGANSER *Mergus serrator* — Plate 13

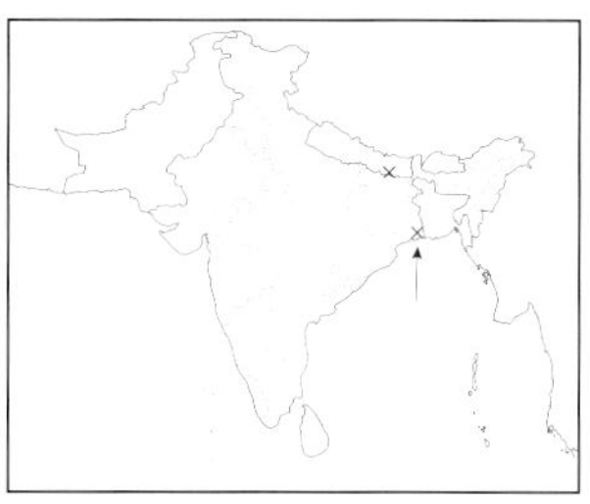

IDENTIFICATION 52–58 cm. A slim 'sawbill' with spiky crest. In flight, both sexes show white secondaries and wing-covert patch. **Male** told from male Common Merganser (p.378) by spiky crest on bottle-green head, white neck-collar, black-spotted ginger breast, and grey flanks. **Female**, and **eclipse** and **immature male**, more closely resemble respective plumages of Common and are best told by slimmer appearance, with slimmer bill, and narrower head with weaker and more ragged crest. Chestnut of head and upper neck is duller and contrasts less with grey lower neck and breast, and has browner body. In flight, white wing patch is broken by black bar, unlike on Common. **VOICE** Silent except during display. **HABITS** Similar to those of Common Merganser (p.378). **HABITAT** Coastal waters in Pakistan; large rivers and freshwater lakes. **DISTRIBUTION AND STATUS PK:** rare winter visitor to the Makran coast and passage migrant inland. **NP, IN:** vagrant.

COMMON MERGANSER *Mergus merganser* — Plate 13

Goosander (I,N,R), Merganser (F)

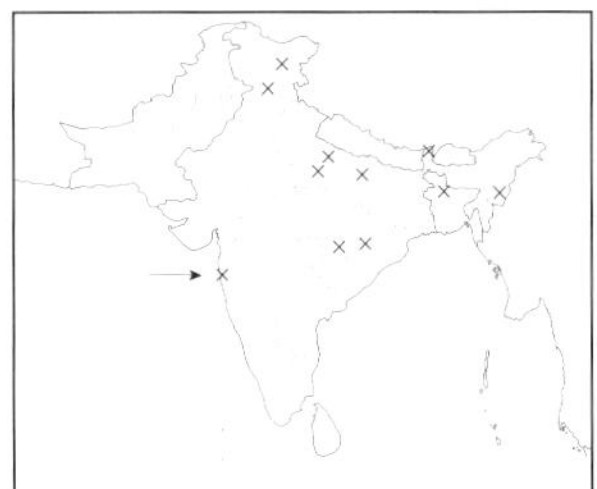

IDENTIFICATION 58–72 cm. A large, stocky 'sawbill' with bulbous head. **Breeding male** has bottle-green head, whitish breast and flanks, typically with salmon-pink wash, and black upperparts. Shows extensive white patch on wing-coverts and secondaries in flight. **Female**, and **eclipse** and **immature male**, have chestnut head and upper neck with shaggy crest, which contrasts with greyish body, and show white secondaries in flight. Eclipse male has upperwing pattern like breeding male. See Red-breasted Merganser (p.377) for differences from that species. **VOICE** Silent except during display. **HABITS** Sociable; usually found in small parties. Forages in the daytime, often fishing cooperatively. Feeds mainly by diving, usually after scanning with head submerged. An expert diver and swimmer; when feeding swims with the body low in the water, and when resting floats high and buoyantly. Flight usually follows the river course. **HABITAT** Lakes, fast-flowing and slow-moving rivers, and streams where these debouch into the plains; occasionally coastal waters in Pakistan. **BREEDING** June. No nest found in the region; in Tibet, nests in crevices in rock cliffs, lined with down. **DISTRIBUTION AND STATUS** Breeds in Ladakh; winters mainly in Pakistan, Nepal, Bhutan and N India, south to Bombay and S Madhya Pradesh and east to Assam. **PK:** scarce migrant and winter visitor. **NP:** fairly common winter visitor below 3000 m. **IN:** breeds at 3000–4000 m; mainly a winter visitor, fairly common in the E Himalayan foothills, rare in the northwest. **BT:** frequent winter visitor. **BD:** rare winter visitor.

BUTTONQUAILS Turnicidae

Small, plump terrestrial birds. They are found in a wide variety of habitats having a dry, often sandy substrate and low ground cover under which they can readily run or walk. Buttonquails are very secretive, and prefer to escape by walking away quickly. They fly with great reluctance, with weak whirring beats low over the ground, dropping quickly into cover. They are usually found singly, occasionally in pairs, and rarely in small parties, and typically can be located in the same place day after day. They feed on grass and weed seeds, grain, greenery and small insects, picking food from the ground surface, or scratching with the feet. Buttonquails are fond of dustbathing and sunbathing. The female is polyandrous. The main reference specific to buttonquails is Johnsgard (1991).

SMALL BUTTONQUAIL *Turnix sylvatica* — Plate 2

Little Bustard-Quail (F,I), Little Buttonquail (K)

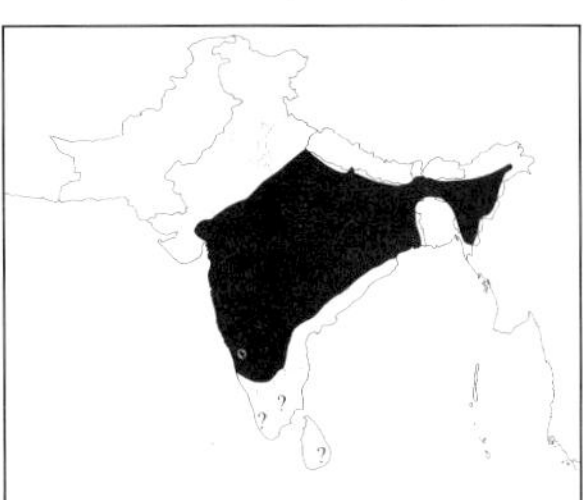

IDENTIFICATION 13 cm. **Adult** differs from Yellow-legged Buttonquail (below) in much smaller size, and comparatively long, pointed tail which is usually especially apparent in flight. Main plumage differences are broad, buff edges to scapulars, which show as prominent lines on upperparts, and rufous mantle and coverts which are broadly edged with buff (giving rise to scaly appearance). Rufous centres to buff-fringed coverts have black outer edge which may show as black spotting, but coverts are not so boldly spotted as on Yellow-legged. Underparts are similar to many Yellow-legged, with orange-buff lower throat and breast, and bold black spotting on sides of breast (becoming chestnut spotting on flanks). There is considerable variation in intricate patterning of crown, and centres to feathers of mantle and scapulars, such that sexing and distinguishing of breeding, non-breeding and first-year birds is unlikely to be possible in the field. Has blue-grey bill, and pale pink legs and feet. **VOICE** Female has booming call, which lasts one second and is repeated every 1–2 seconds for half a minute or more (Johnsgard 1991). **HABITS** Typical of the genus. **HABITAT** Scrub intermixed with grass at edges of cultivation and grassland. **BREEDING** Almost throughout the year. Nests in a sparsely lined scrape on the ground. **DISTRIBUTION AND STATUS** Mainly resident; summer visitor to the NW subcontinent. Pakistan, and from Gujarat and E Punjab, India, east to Assam and south to S Karnataka. **PK:** locally frequent and erratic during and immediately after the rains. **NP:** scarce and very local, presumably resident; 250 m. **IN:** locally fairly common; up to 2400 m in the outer Himalayas. **BD:** ?former resident; no recent records, but could still occur. **LK:** very rare in dry lowlands.

YELLOW-LEGGED BUTTONQUAIL *Turnix tanki* — Plate 2

Button Quail (F,I)

IDENTIFICATION 15–16 cm. Distinguished from Small Buttonquail (above) by larger size, rounded tail (lacking pin-tail of Small), and yellow legs and feet. Further, has more uniform upperparts, lacking scaly or stripy appearance, and has bold black spotting on otherwise fairly uniform buff coverts. Underparts (except on breeding female) are similar to Small, with orange-buff breast with bold black spotting on sides. Yellow legs and bill, more

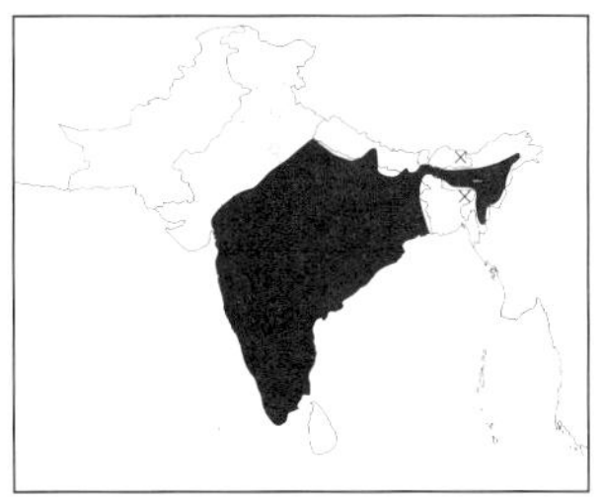

uniform upperparts, and unbarred underparts with whitish belly are best distinctions from Barred Buttonquail (below): see that species for further details. **Breeding female** is very distinctive, with unmarked rufous nape and upper mantle, and rufous-orange throat, sides of neck and breast. Mantle, scapulars and back are almost uniform brownish-grey with indistinct darker vermiculations. Crown is black, barred with buff, and usually lacks pale crown-stripe. **Non-breeding** and **immature female** have buff crown-stripe, and rufous collar across nape which is mixed with grey and less well defined than on breeding female (with overall pattern similar to mantle). Greyish mantle and scapulars are irregularly marked with black, and diffusely marked with rufous, with buff edges to some feathers (although these are nothing like as prominent as on Small). **Male** lacks rufous collar of female. Otherwise, upperparts show similar variation to female's (some greyish, and finely vermiculated, others marked with rufous and black). **VOICE** A low-pitched hoot, which is repeated with increasing strength and becomes a very human-like moan. **HABITS** Typical of the genus. Sometimes found with Small Buttonquail. **HABITAT** Grassland mixed with low scrub; also millet and other crops. **BREEDING** Almost throughout the year, varying with locality. Nest is a scrape on the ground, sometimes canopied by growing grass. **DISTRIBUTION AND STATUS** Mainly resident; summer visitor to the NW subcontinent. Pakistan, and from Gujarat and Punjab, India, east to Assam and south through the peninsula. **PK:** an irregular and locally distributed visitor, chiefly after spring rains or during the monsoon. **NP:** resident, fairly common at Chitwan, scarce elsewhere; up to 1500 m, mainly below 915 m. **IN:** uncommon resident; mainly up to 1200 m, locally to 2000 m. **BT:** rare. **BD:** rare? visitor, only one recent record.

BARRED BUTTONQUAIL *Turnix suscitator* — Plate 2

Common Bustard-Quail (F,I), Barred Bustard-Quail (P)

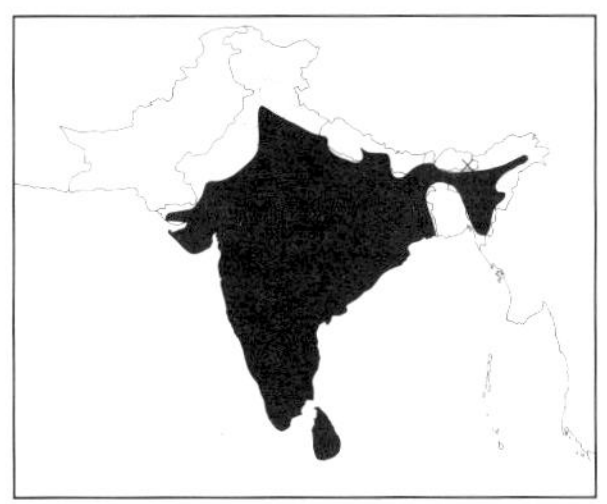

IDENTIFICATION 15 cm. In all plumages, distinguished from other buttonquails by bold black barring on buffish sides of neck, breast and wing-coverts, and warm orangey-rufous to orange-buff flanks and belly which are clearly demarcated from breast. Much larger than Small Buttonquail (p.378), and has blunt tail. Further differences from Yellow-legged Buttonquail (p.378) are more prominently marked upperparts (with buff streaking to mantle, scapulars and back, and bold black and rufous cross-barring), bluish-grey legs, and greyish bill (although bill can tend towards yellowish on some). Most show buff crown-stripe. **Female** generally, but not always, has black throat and centre of breast, with black and buff barring on breast sides and across lower breast. **Male** usually has greyish- or buffish-white throat, and has bold black and buff barring on neck sides and across whole of breast. Males of some races can have black throat. **Racial variation** Four races occur in the subcontinent, varying mainly in extent of black and rufous markings on upperparts and in depth of coloration of belly and flanks. **VOICE** Advertising call of female is a *drr-r-r-r-r-r*, similar to the sound of a distant motorcycle, lasting for 15 seconds or more, and usually prefaced by three or four long, deep *groo* notes, as well as a far-carrying booming call, *hoon-hoon-hoon-hoon* (Ali and Ripley 1987). **HABITS** Typical of the genus. **HABITAT** Grassland and scrub at edges of cultivation and near villages; also open deciduous forest, usually not far from water. **BREEDING** Almost throughout the year, varying with locality. Nest is a scrape on the ground, sometimes lined with grass and with a canopy of growing grass. **DISTRIBUTION AND STATUS** Resident. From Gujarat and E Punjab, India, east to Assam and south through the peninsula and Sri Lanka. Subject to local movements. **NP:** fairly common; up to 2050 m, chiefly below 300 m. **IN:** widespread and locally fairly common; from the plains up to 2500 m. **BT:** rare. **BD:** scarce. **LK:** common in the lowlands and lower hills.

HONEYGUIDES Indicatoridae

Small, dull-coloured and inconspicuous birds which inhabit forest or forest edge. All species eat insects, but a peculiarity shared by the family is that they also eat wax, usually as bee combs.

YELLOW-RUMPED HONEYGUIDE *Indicator xanthonotus* — Plate 14

Honeyguide (I), Orange-rumped Honeyguide (N,R), Himalayan Honeyguide (F)

IDENTIFICATION 15 cm. A finch-like, dark olive and grey bird with stout bill. Has a bright orange-yellow forehead, narrow olive-yellow edges to feathers of mantle and wings, golden-yellow lower back and rump, and dark, square-ended tail. Inner edges of tertials are white, forming parallel lines down back. Underparts are light grey, with diffuse dark grey streaking on belly and flanks. Male at honeycomb holds wings characteristically drooped, revealing bright back and rump. **Male** has broad golden-yellow malar stripes, which are ill-defined on the smaller **female**. **VOICE** A single *weet* uttered on the wing (Ali and Ripley 1987). **HABITS** Clings, often upside-down, to bee combs and pecks at wax. Also feeds on bees and other insects, which it catches in clumsy aerial sallies, returning to a favourite perch in the manner of a flycatcher. The male defends nests of the Giant

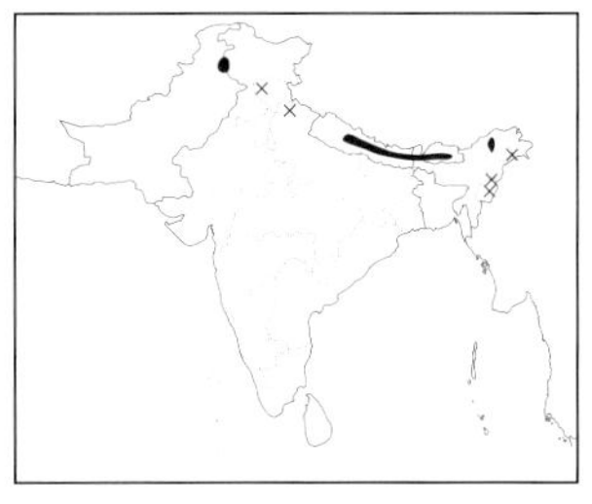

Rock Bee *Apis dorsata* and mates with females which visit the nests to feed. Typically slow-moving, or perches upright and motionless for long periods; easily overlooked. **HABITAT** Vicinity of Giant Rock Bee nests which are attached to vertical cliffs, and adjacent broadleaved and coniferous forest; often near water. **BREEDING** Probably May and June. Nest is unknown. **DISTRIBUTION AND STATUS** Resident, subject to altitudinal movements. Himalayas from Himachal Pradesh east to Arunachal Pradesh; NE India. Found at 1450–3500 m (–610 m in Nepal in winter); probably under-recorded. **PK:** presumed extirpated. **NP:** local and uncommon. **IN**: very rare and local. **BT:** local and uncommon. **REFERENCES** Cronin and Sherman (1976), Friedmann (1976).

WRYNECKS, PICULETS AND WOODPECKERS Picidae

Chiefly arboreal, and usually seen clinging to, and climbing up, vertical trunks and lateral branches. Typically, they work up trunks and along branches in jerky spurts, directly or in spirals, occasionally tapping the bark to disturb insects. Some species feed regularly on the ground, searching mainly for termites and ants. The bill of many species is powerful, for boring into wood to extract insects and for excavating nest holes. The long protrusile tongue is used for capturing prey. Woodpeckers feed chiefly on ants, termites, and grubs and pupae of wood-boring beetles; also on nectar and fruits, which are consumed seasonally. Most woodpeckers also hammer rapidly against tree trunks with their bill, producing a loud rattle, known as 'drumming', which carries considerable distances and is used to advertise and in defence of their territories. Their flight is strong and direct, with marked undulations. Many species excavate nest holes in live or rotten tree trunks or stumps, small woodpeckers invariably in branches. Many can be located by their characteristic loud calls. Most woodpecker species occur singly, in pairs or in family groups. Juvenile woodpeckers are generally similar to adults, although usually duller and less cleanly marked; they are therefore described in the text only where differences are noteworthy or could cause confusion. For the sake of simplicity, the facial stripe leading from the bill and bordering the ear-coverts has been referred to throughout as the moustachial stripe, although strictly speaking it may not always be so. The main references specific to woodpeckers are Short (1982) and Winkler *et al.* (1995).

EURASIAN WRYNECK *Jynx torquilla* — Plate 14

Wryneck (F,I)

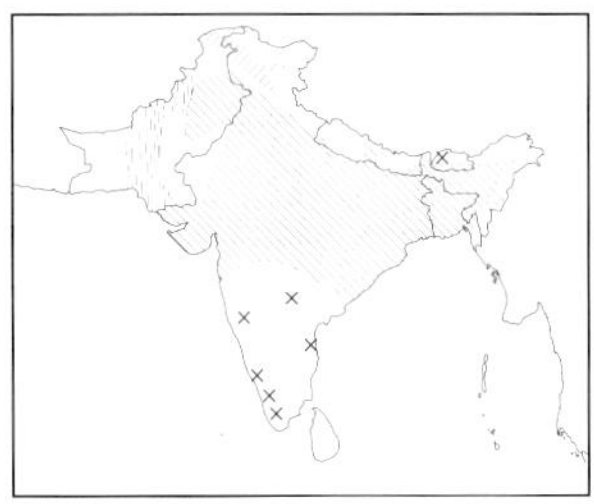

IDENTIFICATION 16–17 cm. A long-tailed aberrant woodpecker, with cryptic grey, buff and brown patterning reminiscent of nightjars and owls. Main features are dark stripe through eye, grey upperparts with irregular dark stripe down centre of nape and mantle, cross-barred tail, buff throat and breast which are finely barred with black, brown wings which are vermiculated, spotted and barred with buff, grey and black, and whitish belly and flanks which are finely marked with black. Some birds are strongly washed with rufous-buff on entire underparts. In flight, the long broad tail and shallowly undulating flight are distinctive. **VOICE** A piping *kek-kek-kek.* **HABITS** Rather sluggish and unobtrusive. Feeds mainly on the ground, hopping along with tail slightly raised and picking up ants and other insects. Can cling to tree trunks, although, unlike typical woodpeckers, it seldom uses its tail as a brace. If disturbed when feeding, it typically flies up on to a tree or bush. **HABITAT** Winters in open scrub country, edges of cultivation, and semi-desert; summers at edges of open forest and in orchards. **BREEDING** May–July, varying locally. Nests in a small tree hole. **DISTRIBUTION AND STATUS** Breeds in NW Himalayas, from Pakistan east to Himachal Pradesh, at 1500–3300 m; winters mainly from Pakistan east to Assam and south to Maharashtra and NE Andhra Pradesh. Breeders arrive in March/April and leave by about September. **PK:** frequent in winter and on passage, also a local breeding visitor. **NP:** frequent in winter and on passage; mainly below 915 m (–3445 m). **IN:** in winter and on passage fairly common in the north, very rare in the south; also a frequent breeding visitor to Kashmir. **BT:** rare passage migrant; 305–3750 m. **BD:** common winter visitor.

SPECKLED PICULET *Picumnus innominatus* — Plate 14

Spotted Piculet (F)

IDENTIFICATION 10 cm. A diminutive woodpecker with whitish 'face' broken by blackish ear-covert patch and malar stripe. Has yellowish-green upperparts, greyish crown, white to yellowish-white underparts heavily spotted with black (coalescing into bars on lower flanks), and short, square-ended blackish tail with white on central and outer feathers. **Male** has dull orange forehead and forecrown, barred with black, these colours lacking on **female**. **VOICE** A sharp *tsick*, a high-pitched *sik-sik-sik*, a *ti-ti-ti-ti*, and a remarkably loud drumming (Winkler *et al.* 1995). **HABITS** Usually found singly, and associates with mixed feeding parties of insectivorous

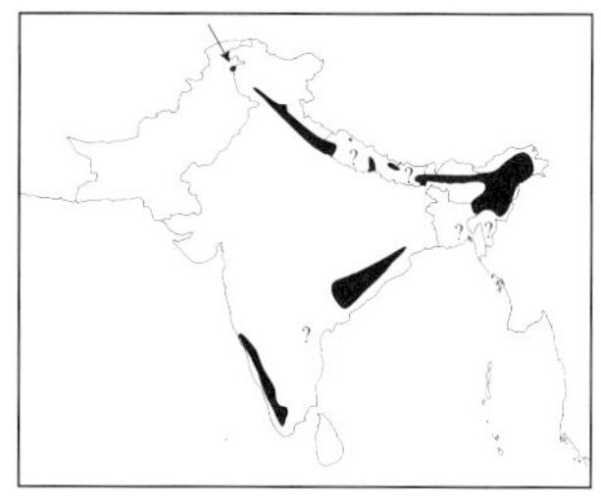

species. Eats mainly ants, and their eggs and pupae. Energetic and agile while feeding; small enough to forage on slender twigs of trees and shrubs, often feeding on small bushes close to the ground. Creeps along branches in typical woodpecker fashion, also clings upside-down to branches like a tit, and perches sideways across branches like a passerine. Can often be located by the sound of its vigorous pecking. **HABITAT** Bushes and bamboo undergrowth in broadleaved forest and secondary growth. **BREEDING** January–May, varying locally. Nests in a small hole bored into hollow bamboo or branch or stem of a small tree. **DISTRIBUTION AND STATUS** Resident. Himalayas from Pakistan and Jammu and Kashmir east to Arunachal Pradesh; hills of SW, E and NE India, and Bangladesh. Recorded mainly from base of the hills up to 2000 m (–2700 m). **PK:** rare and local; up to 1900 m. **NP:** locally fairly common; mainly 915–1830 m. **IN:** locally fairly common. **BT:** fairly common. **BD:** local. **REFERENCES** Short (1973).

WHITE-BROWED PICULET *Sasia ochracea* Plate 14

Rufous Piculet (F,I)

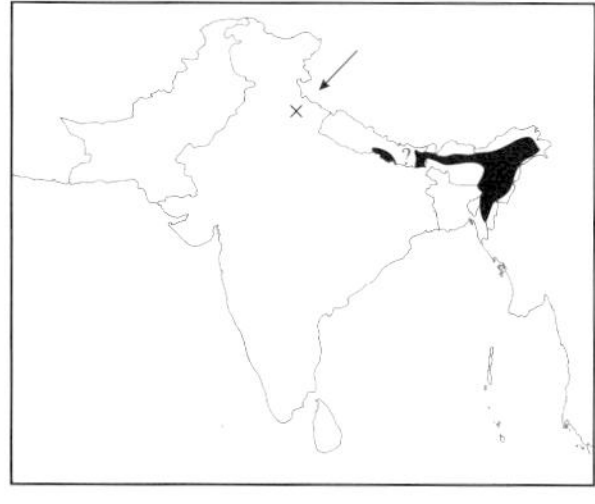

IDENTIFICATION 9–10 cm. A tiny woodpecker with 'tail-less' appearance. Has greenish-olive upperparts (variably washed with rufous) and rufous underparts, very short black tail, fine white supercilium behind eye, and red iris and orbital skin. **Male** has golden-yellow on forehead, which is lacking on **female**. **Juvenile** is similar to respective adult, but underparts are variably washed with grey or green. **VOICE** Rapid tinny drumming, often on bamboo, *tit..trrrrrrrrrrit*; call is a short, sharp *chi*; a rapid trill starting with the usual call, *chi.rrrrrrrra*; also loud tapping on bamboo (C. Robson). **HABITS** Similar to those of Speckled Piculet (p.380). Sometimes hops among leaf litter on the forest floor, cocking its tail like a wren. **HABITAT** Dense low vegetation in broadleaved forest and dense secondary growth. Has a preference for bamboo; often near water. **BREEDING** March–June. Nest is a tiny hole bored into a hollow bamboo. **DISTRIBUTION AND STATUS** Resident. Himalayas from N Uttar Pradesh and C Nepal east to Arunachal Pradesh; NE India and Bangladesh. Found locally at 250–2135 m (–2600 m). **NP:** uncommon. **IN:** generally uncommon; locally fairly common in E Himalayas. **BT:** frequent. **BD:** local in the northeast and south.

BROWN-CAPPED PYGMY WOODPECKER *Dendrocopos nanus* Plate 15

Pygmy Woodpecker (I), Brown-capped Woodpecker, Brown-crowned Pigmy Woodpecker (F), *Picoides nanus* (I), *Picoides moluccensis* (K), *Dendrocopos moluccensis* (R)

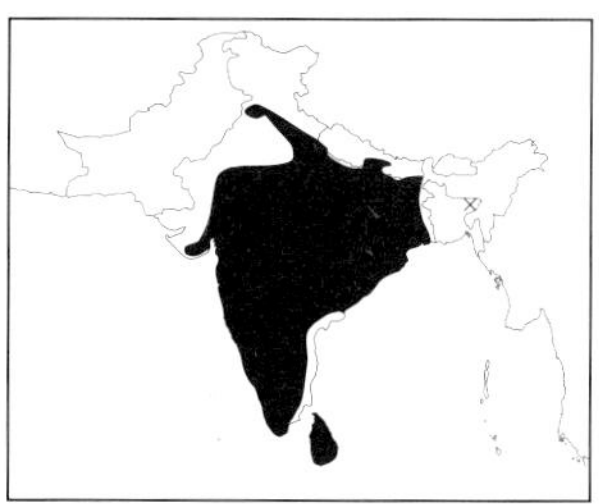

IDENTIFICATION 13 cm. A tiny woodpecker with white barring and spotting on upperparts, whitish supercilium, and broad brown band behind eye. Throughout most of range has streaked underparts. **Male** has small, often indistinct, crimson patch on sides of hindcrown, which is lacking on **female**. Distinguished from the very similar Grey-capped Pygmy Woodpecker (p.382) by brown (rather than grey) crown, which is distinctly warmer (fawn-coloured on some) than the brownish-black of mantle; background coloration to upperparts is browner; underparts are greyish-white to brownish-white, streaked (sometimes faintly) with brown, compared with the darker, fulvous and more heavily streaked underparts of Grey-capped. Further, throat is evenly mottled and streaked with brown (lacks diffuse greyish malar stripe, and whiter throat and submoustachial stripe typically shown by Grey-capped), and stripe behind eye is brown and concolorous with crown. White spotting on central tail feathers is a further feature (central tail feathers are all black on Grey-capped except in nominate race of that species). **Racial variation** Compared with *D. n. nanus*, described above, *D. n. gymnopthalmus* in Sri Lanka has darker brown crown concolorous with upperparts, and underparts are whiter (faintly washed with buff) and unstreaked (or only faintly so). Birds in SW peninsula (*P. n. cinereigula*) are intermediate. **VOICE** Vocabulary apparently limited to a rather feeble, unobtrusive drum and a surprisingly powerful rapid metallic rattle or chatter, *tik-ik-ik-ik-r-r-r*. Probably indistinguishable from the rattle of Grey-capped but, unlike that species, rarely (if ever?) gives isolated *pik* or *chik* calls (P. Holt). **HABITS** Very similar to those of Grey-capped. **HABITAT** Light deciduous forest and trees near cultivation, bamboo and secondary forest. **BREEDING** January–July, occasionally October and December, varying locally. Nest is a shaft with tiny entrance drilled into a small dead branch, at height of 7.8–13.7 m. **DISTRIBUTION AND STATUS** Resident, endemic to the subcontinent. N India from Punjab, Rajasthan and Gujarat, east to Bangladesh, south through the peninsula and Sri Lanka. **NP:** locally fairly common in far west, rare from central areas eastwards; below 250 m. **IN:** locally fairly common; plains up to 1200 m. **BD:** status uncertain, probably a rare resident. **LK:** resident in lowlands up to mid altitudes, more frequent in dry zone. **REFERENCES** Short (1973).

GREY-CAPPED PYGMY WOODPECKER *Dendrocopos canicapillus* Plate 15

Grey-crowned Pigmy Woodpecker (F,I), Grey-capped Woodpecker *Picoides canicapillus* (E,I,K)

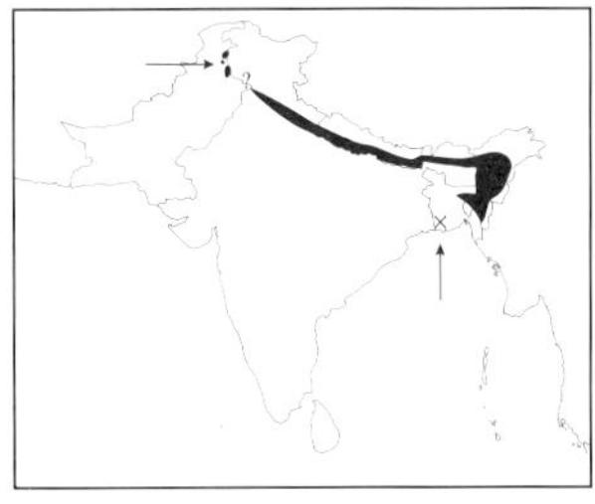

IDENTIFICATION 14 cm. A tiny woodpecker with white-barred black mantle and wings, broad whitish supercilium extending to sides of neck, and streaked underparts. **Male** has crimson on nape (see racial variation below), which is lacking on **female**. Distinguished from the very similar Brown-capped Pygmy Woodpecker (p.381) by grey (rather than brown) crown, which becomes blackish on sides and towards nape, by blackish (or brownish-black) stripe behind eye (warm brown and concolorous with crown on Brown-capped), and by deeper fulvous coloration to underparts, which are more heavily streaked with black. Further, tends to show diffuse blackish malar stripe, and indistinct whitish submoustachial stripe and throat, although throat and malar region can be untidily mottled and streaked and much as Brown-capped. Upperparts are blacker in background coloration, but difference is only very slight. Throughout most of range in subcontinent lacks white spotting on central tail feathers (see racial variation). **Racial variation** Male of *D. c. semicoronatus* has more extensive red on sides of crown, meeting in narrow band across nape, than *D. c. mitchellii* which occurs to the west, and this is a further distinction from Brown-capped. The nominate race, which occurs in NE India (S of Brahmaputra R) and Bangladesh, has paler, more buffish coloration to underparts (but still heavily streaked), is more brownish-black on upperparts, and has white spotting on central tail feathers; it is therefore less distinct from Brown-capped (although other, above-mentioned, features still hold). **VOICE** A high, quickly repeated *tit-tit-errrrrrr* (Fleming *et al.* 1984). Call is a weak single *kik* or *pit* (J. Scharringa). **HABITS** Often associates with foraging mixed parties of insectivorous birds. Feeds by probing, prying, tapping and hammering vigorously, often in the tree canopy, where it is easily overlooked; its small size enables it to forage on the outermost twigs. Creeps actively along branchlets and woody stems, often perching crosswise; also hangs upside-down from leaf clusters. **HABITAT** Both open and closed broadleaved forest and scattered trees in cultivation, secondary forest. **BREEDING** April–July, varying locally. Nests in a shaft with a tiny entrance hole drilled into underside of a thin branch. **DISTRIBUTION AND STATUS** Resident. Himalayas from N Pakistan east to Arunachal Pradesh; NE India and Bangladesh. **PK:** rare and very local; mainly a visitor, possibly resident, at 450–915 m. **NP:** fairly common from WC areas eastwards, rare farther west; most frequent below 365 m. **IN:** locally fairly common; plains up to 1700 m, occasionally to 2000 m. **BT:** fairly common; 250–1290 m. **BD:** status uncertain, local, not common. **REFERENCES** Short (1973).

BROWN-FRONTED WOODPECKER *Dendrocopos auriceps* Plate 15

Brown-fronted Pied Woodpecker (F,I), *Picoides auriceps* (I)

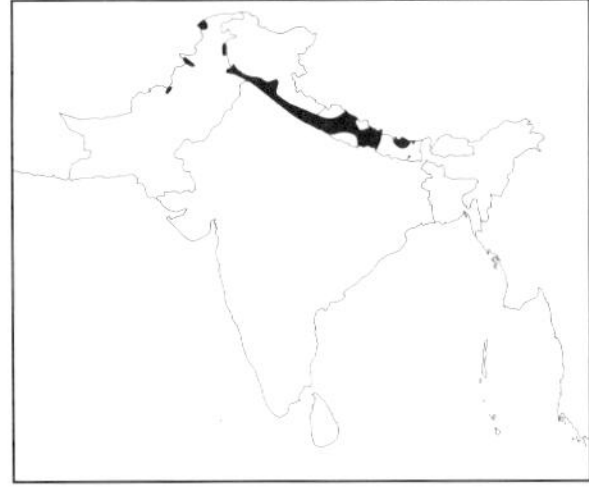

IDENTIFICATION 19–20 cm. A medium-sized 'pied' woodpecker, told from all others except Yellow-crowned Woodpecker (p.383) by yellowish coloration to crown. From Yellow-crowned by white-barred (rather than spotted) appearance to black mantle, by brownish forehead and forecrown, and by prominent black moustachial stripe and patch on sides of breast. Additional subtle differences include smaller bill, well-defined black streaking on underparts, pinkish undertail-coverts, all-black central tail feathers, and less heavily spotted inner wing-coverts. **Male** has red nape and yellow hindcrown. Band of red across nape is narrower than on male Yellow-crowned. **Female** has dull yellow hindcrown and nape (on Yellow-crowned, hindcrown and nape are browner than forecrown). **VOICE** Contact or advertising call is a series of rapidly repeated cries, *chitter-chitter-chitter-r-r-rh*; also short, sharp cries, *chik-chik* (Roberts 1991). **HABITS** Often associates with roving mixed feeding flocks. Forages mainly in the trees, sometimes on bushes in the forest understorey, very rarely on the ground. Feeds on insects, also pine seeds and fruit. **HABITAT** Subtropical and temperate forest of broadleaves, conifers and mixed stands; favours oaks and deodar. In Pakistan, typically associated with subtropical Chir Pine; in Nepal, found chiefly in dry broadleaved forest and conifers. **BREEDING** April and May. Nest hole is usually below 8 m. **DISTRIBUTION AND STATUS** Resident. Hills of N Baluchistan, Pakistan, and Himalayas from N Pakistan east to Nepal. Subject to altitudinal movements: breeds mainly at 1000–3000 m. **PK:** locally common; chiefly 900–1800 m. **NP:** fairly common at 1065–2440 m, uncommon up to 2950 m. **IN:** locally common.

FULVOUS-BREASTED WOODPECKER *Dendrocopos macei* Plate 15

Fulvous-breasted Pied Woodpecker (F,I), *Picoides macei* (E,I,K)

IDENTIFICATION 18–19 cm. A medium-sized woodpecker with white-barred black mantle and wings, black moustachial stripe, and lightly streaked dirty buff underparts. **Male** has red on crown, which is black on **female**. Throughout most of its range in subcontinent, really confusable only with Brown-fronted Woodpecker (above), which has brownish crown and yellow on nape, and with Crimson-breasted Woodpecker (p.384) and the larger Darjeeling Woodpecker (p.384). Easily told from the latter two species by white barring on black mantle, and lack of white 'shoulder' patches; in addition, male Fulvous-breasted has red (rather than black) crown.

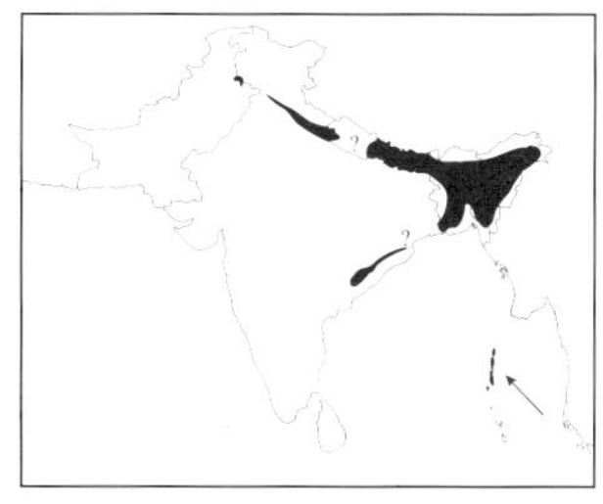

Very similar to Stripe-breasted Woodpecker (below) of NE subcontinent, and best told from that by less heavily streaked underparts (a few bold black streaks on sides of breast and fine diffuse streaking on belly and upper flanks). Further subtle differences include more pronounced white barring on black mantle (white bars at least as wide as black bars, and usually distinct on upper mantle), buffish wash to throat and sides of head and neck, buffish ground colour to underparts, and slightly smaller bill; in addition, red on head of male is less extensive (barely reaching onto nape, which it does on Stripe-breasted), and is duller and mixed with grey and black. **Racial variation** *P. m. andamanensis* of the Andaman Is is considerably smaller; has prominent black spotting (with distinct whitish fringes) on breast, streaking on ear-coverts, and a pale bill. Male has even duller red crown and nape (feathers are grey, tipped red), and female has brown tone to crown. **VOICE** An explosive *tchick*, quieter and less sharp than Stripe-breasted's, a rapid *pik-pipipipipipipipipi*, and a soft chattering *chik-a-chik-a-chit* (Ali and Ripley 1987; Winkler *et al.* 1995). *P. m. andamanensis* has a distinctive sonorous and staccato *chu-ik* call; sometimes a less disyllabic *kui*, usually given at intervals of 5–8 seconds. Also a loud ascending chattering, almost laughing *kut...ku...kut...kutt-rrr-it* (P. Holt). **HABITS** Often with mixed feeding flocks of other species. Forages chiefly on tree trunks and larger high branches. **HABITAT** Forest edges and open forest of broadleaves and broadleaves/conifers; on Andaman Is in open forest and trees in cultivation. **BREEDING** January–May, varying locally. Nest hole is usually 1–3 m up in a small tree. **DISTRIBUTION AND STATUS** Resident. Himalayas from Murree, Pakistan, and Himachal Pradesh east to Arunachal Pradesh; NE and E India and Bangladesh. Occurs from the plains up to 2000 m (–2745 m in Nepal). **PK:** local and rare; 600–900 m. **NP:** common from WC areas eastwards, frequent farther west. **IN:** common. **BT:** uncommon. **BD:** common throughout. **REFERENCES** Short (1973).

STRIPE-BREASTED WOODPECKER *Dendrocopos atratus* Plate 15

Stripe-breasted Pied Woodpecker (I), *Picoides atratus* (I,K)

IDENTIFICATION 21–22 cm. A medium-sized woodpecker with white-barred black mantle and wings, black moustachial stripe, and black-streaked underparts. **Male** has scarlet crown and nape, which are black on **female**. Easily confusable with Fulvous-breasted Woodpecker (p.382), and best told by boldly streaked underparts (especially on breast, and on some streaking extends onto lower throat). Further subtle differences include narrower white barring to black mantle (white bars narrower than black ones, and lacking on upper mantle, which is uniformly black), white throat, sides of head and neck (with greyish wash to ear-coverts), dull olive-yellow ground colour to underparts, and slightly longer bill; in addition, red on head of male is more extensive (extending onto nape) and is a brighter, purer scarlet. From Yellow-crowned Woodpecker (below) by crown colour and white-barred (rather than white-spotted) upperparts. From Crimson-breasted Woodpecker (p.384) and the larger Darjeeling Woodpecker (p.384) by white-barred black mantle, lack of white 'shoulder' patches, and male's scarlet (rather than black) crown. **VOICE** An explosive *tchick*, and a whinnying rattle (Boonsong and Round 1991; Winkler *et al.* 1995). **HABITS** Little known. Similar to those of Brown-fronted (p.382). **HABITAT** Open pine and oak forest. **BREEDING** End March–early May. Nest hole is usually less than 4 m from the ground in a small tree. **DISTRIBUTION AND STATUS IN:** resident at up to 1500 m in NE hills (Assam, Manipur, Meghalaya, Mizoram). **BD:** resident? **REFERENCES** Khan (1982).

YELLOW-CROWNED WOODPECKER *Dendrocopos mahrattensis* Plate 15

Yellow-fronted Pied Woodpecker (F,I,P), Yellow-fronted Woodpecker (R), *Picoides mahrattensis* (I,K)

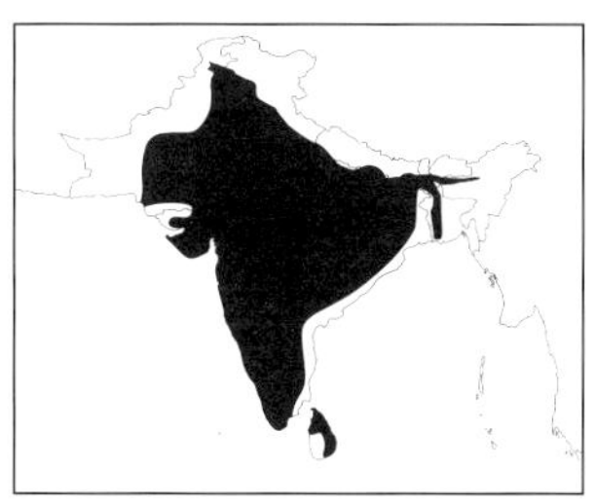

IDENTIFICATION 17–18 cm. Distinguished from Brown-fronted Woodpecker (p.382) by combination of yellowish forehead and forecrown, white-spotted mantle and wing-coverts, bold white barring on central tail feathers, and diffuse brown moustachial stripe and patch on sides of neck. Underparts are rather dirty grey, with fairly heavy brown streaking, and has small red patch on lower belly. Can show a slight crest. **Male** has scarlet hindcrown and nape, this colour being more extensive than on male Brown-fronted. **Female** has brownish hindcrown and nape (on Brown-fronted, hindcrown and nape are yellow and distinct from browner rest of crown). **Racial variation** *P. m. pallescens* of N and NW subcontinent has more heavily spotted and paler upperparts, and less noticeably streaked underparts, compared with the nominate race. **VOICE** Rather weak, shrill *peek-peek* calls, and a rapidly repeated *kik-kik-kik-r-r-r-r-h* (Roberts 1991). **HABITS** Often with mixed bands of insectivorous species. Found in the canopy and on trunks. Often feeds by excavating bark and dead wood. **HABITAT** Open wooded areas and open country with scattered trees, wooded gardens, groves and roadside avenues. Favours dry country. **BREEDING** February–July, also December; varies locally. Nest hole is usually 1–10 m above ground. **DISTRIBUTION AND STATUS** Resident throughout much of subcontinent east of Indus R, except Himalayas and most of NE India. Found mainly from the plains up to 1300 m; occasionally to 2000 m in S India. **PK:** frequent in plains; virtually absent from N foothill areas. **NP:** uncommon; mainly below 275 m (–1700 m). **IN:** locally common. **BD:** former resident only in the northwest?; no recent records. **LK:** resident in dry lowlands and adjacent low and medium hills; common in the southeast, infrequent elsewhere.

RUFOUS-BELLIED WOODPECKER *Dendrocopos hyperythrus* Plate 15

Rufous-bellied Sapsucker (F), *Picoides hyperythrus* (K), *Hypopicus hyperythrus* (E,F,I)

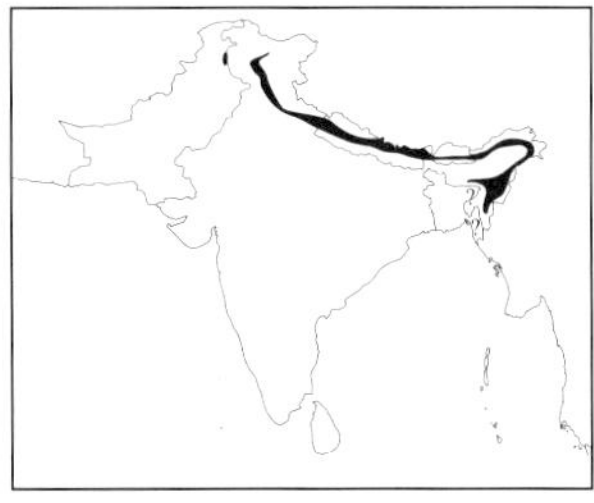

IDENTIFICATION 20 cm. A medium-sized woodpecker, easily told by combination of white-spotted and -barred mantle and wings, whitish face and absence of prominent black moustachial stripe (although does have faint dark markings in this area), and uniform and unstreaked rufous or chestnut underparts. **Male** has red crown and nape (extending down hindneck and across rear of neck sides in western populations). **Female** has black crown and nape which are spotted with white. **Juvenile** has blackish streaking on buff throat and blackish barring on rufous-buff underparts; upperparts are similar to adult, and both sexes show scarlet feather tips on blackish crown. Juvenile plumage can still be apparent in first winter. **VOICE** A rapid, high *tik-tik-tik-tik*, and a *titi-r-r-r-r-r* alarm call (Fleming *et al.* 1984). **HABITS** Often accompanies mixed feeding flocks of insectivorous birds. Usually forages in the upper forest storey on trunks and branches of large trees. Often feeds by probing and pecking at loose bark and in crevices; also bores holes into oak bark and drinks sap. **HABITAT** Moist subtropical and temperate forest. **BREEDING** April and May. Nest hole is 5–6 m up in a tree trunk. **DISTRIBUTION AND STATUS** Resident. Himalayas from Murree, Pakistan, and Jammu and Kashmir east to Arunachal Pradesh; NE India and Bangladesh. Recorded mainly at 1000–3300 m (800–4115 m). **PK:** scarce; usually 1520–1980 m. **NP:** locally fairly common; 2135–3400 m. **IN:** locally frequent. **BT:** common; 1000–3395 m. **BD:** ?former resident; no recent records, but may survive in Chittagong Hill Tracts.

CRIMSON-BREASTED WOODPECKER *Dendrocopos cathpharius* Plate 15

Crimson-breasted Pied Woodpecker (I), Small Crimson-breasted Pied Woodpecker (F), *Picoides cathpharius* (E,I,K)

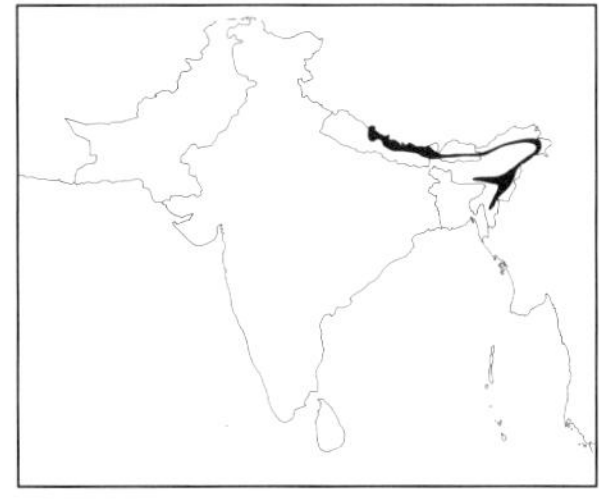

IDENTIFICATION 18 cm. Similar to Darjeeling Woodpecker (below), with white patches in wing and heavy black streaking on underparts, but is considerably smaller, with smaller bill. Best told by differing head pattern. **Male** has scarlet of nape extending to rear and sides of neck, while **female** has a diffuse, but fairly distinct, red patch at rear of ear-coverts. In addition, both sexes have a diffuse scarlet patch on breast (which is variable and may be lacking), lack heavy barring on flanks and thighs, and have indistinct scarlet streaking on undertail-coverts (wholly pale scarlet on Darjeeling). Easily told from the similar-sized Fulvous-breasted and Stripe-breasted Woodpeckers (p.382 and p.383) by unbarred black mantle and white wing patches, and additionally by black crown and scarlet nape of male. **Racial variation** Compared with the nominate race of C and E Himalayas, male *D. c. pyrrhothorax* of NE India south of Brahmaputra R has a larger scarlet patch on upper breast, and wholly scarlet undertail-coverts. Its underparts vary: some are similarly streaked to the nominate but have whiter background coloration; others have streaking on underparts coalescing to form black patch on breast. **VOICE** A loud monotonous *chip* or *tchick*, higher-pitched and less sharp than Darjeeling's, and a shrill *kee-kee-kee* (Boonsong and Round 1991; Winkler *et al.* 1995). **HABITS** Frequently feeds in the lower parts of trees and on bushes; favours dead trees. **HABITAT** Moist deciduous and broadleaved evergreen forest; favours oak/rhododendron forest. **BREEDING** April and May. Nest-site details are unknown. **DISTRIBUTION AND STATUS** Resident. Himalayas from WC Nepal east to Arunachal Pradesh; NE India. Recorded at 1500–2750 m (600–3900 m). **NP, IN, BT:** frequent. **REFERENCES** Short (1973).

DARJEELING WOODPECKER *Dendrocopos darjellensis* Plate 15

Darjeeling Pied Woodpecker (F,I), *Picoides darjellensis* (E,I,K)

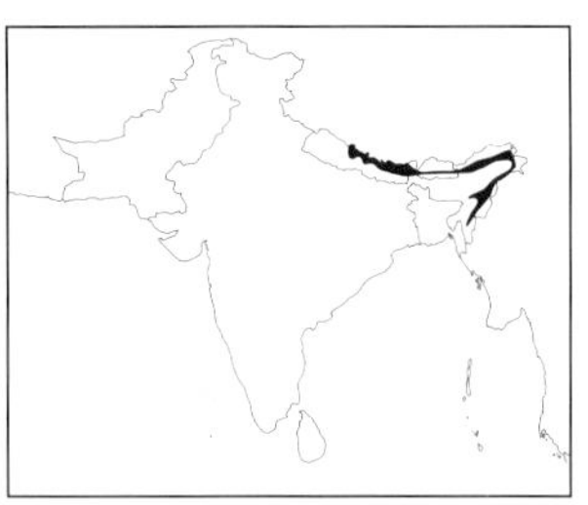

IDENTIFICATION 25 cm. A medium-sized black-and-white woodpecker which has black unbarred back and white wing patches. **Male** has black crown and scarlet nape; nape is black and concolorous with crown on **female**. Differs from Himalayan Woodpecker (p.385) in black streaking on yellowish-buff underparts (becoming more brownish on lower throat and upper breast), yellowish-buff to pale orange sides of neck, absence of black rear border to ear-coverts (black meets crown, or almost does, on Himalayan), and black crown and crimson nape patch of male. Told from the similar Crimson-breasted Woodpecker (above) by larger size and bill, less extensive scarlet patch on nape (of male), and yellowish-buff to pale orange neck sides; see Crimson-breasted for further differences. See Great Spotted Woodpecker (p.385) for differences from that species. **Juvenile** lacks yellowish-buff on sides of neck, and has browner coloration to upperparts. Juvenile male has dull red crown (black with some red tips on female). **VOICE** Includes single *tsik* calls, a rattling *di-di-di-d-dddddt*, and a *tchew-tchew-tchew-tchew* (Winkler *et al.* 1995). **HABITS** May accompany mixed-species flocks. Feeds in trees at varying heights, often high on moss-covered trunks and in canopy branches; also feeds on dead trees and mossy logs on forest floor. **HABITAT** Broadleaved, coniferous and mixed broadleaved/coniferous forest. **BREEDING** April and May. Nest hole is 1–2 m above ground. **DISTRIBUTION AND STATUS** Resident. Himalayas from Nepal east to Arunachal Pradesh; NE India. Recorded at 1700–3500 m throughout the year and to 4000 m in summer (down to 1300 m). Generally found at rather higher elevations than Crimson-breasted, although their altitudinal ranges overlap. **NP:** fairly common. **IN:** locally fairly common. **BT:** common. **REFERENCES** Short (1973).

GREAT SPOTTED WOODPECKER *Dendrocopos major* — Plate 15

***Picoides major* (I,K)**

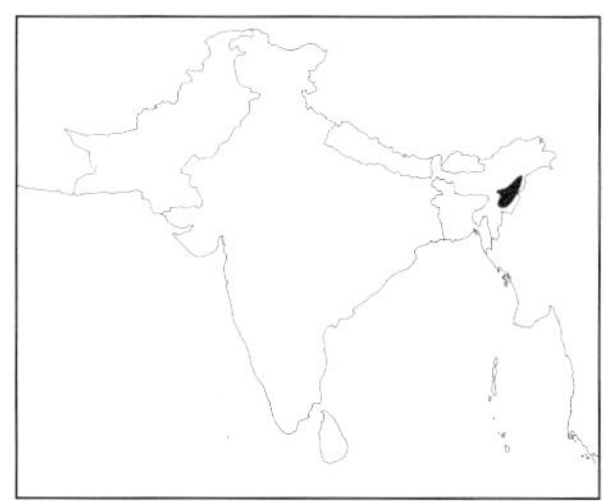

IDENTIFICATION 24 cm. A medium-sized black-and-white woodpecker with unbarred black back, white 'shoulder' patches, and unstreaked dirty buffish-brown underparts. May show some red on breast. **Male** has black crown with scarlet nape; **female** has all-black crown and nape. Most closely resembles Himalayan Woodpecker (below), but underparts are darker, dirty buffish-brown (paler, more buffish, on Himalayan, although some Himalayan are distinctly washed with brown on throat and breast); has black bar extending from rear of moustachial stripe down each side of breast (on some, bars almost joining to form band across breast); and crown of male is all black (scarlet on Himalayan, although see below); also, red of undertail-coverts is a deeper scarlet (rather than pinkish-red), and extends up centre of lower belly. In addition, whitish or brownish-buff patch on sides of neck is completely enclosed by black (with black of moustachial dividing to join both crown and black of upper mantle), a pattern which may be shown by Himalayan but much less clearly so. Unstreaked underparts and larger white 'shoulder' patch (extending noticeably onto median coverts) are best distinctions from Darjeeling Woodpecker (p.384). **Juvenile** has red crown, and therefore more closely resembles male Himalayan. **VOICE** A single *kix*, and a *krrarraarr* (Winkler *et al.* 1995). **HABITS** Not specifically recorded in the region. Mainly found singly. Will feed at all levels, but usually keeps in the upper storey on trunks and larger branches, especially in winter. **HABITAT** Oak and pine forest. **BREEDING** Unknown in region; presumably March and April, as in adjacent Myanmar. **DISTRIBUTION AND STATUS IN:** resident in NE hills (Assam, Manipur, Meghalaya, Nagaland), at 2000–3000 m; current status uncertain, no recent published records.

SIND WOODPECKER *Dendrocopos assimilis* — Plate 15

Sind Pied Woodpecker (I), *Picoides assimilis* (I)

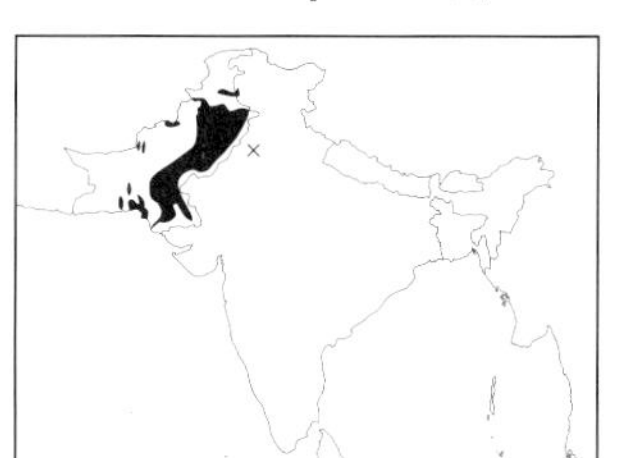

IDENTIFICATION 20–22 cm. A medium-sized black-and-white woodpecker with unbarred black back, white 'shoulder' patches, and unstreaked underparts. **Male** has scarlet crown; crown is entirely black on **female**. Very closely resembles Himalayan Woodpecker (below), although has different range and habitat. Subtle differences include slightly smaller size; absence of black border to rear of ear-coverts (black joins crown, or nearly does, on Himalayan); large white patch on forehead (on Himalayan, forehead is black or buffish or shows a narrow band of white); larger white 'shoulder' patch, with white extending onto scapulars; broader white barring on wings; and paler pinkish-red vent (red extends onto lower belly). Underparts vary from very white to faintly washed with buff, but are generally whiter than in *albescens* race of Himalayan. **VOICE** A rather weak, high-pitched *chir-rir-rirrh-rirrh*, and a *wicka toi-whit, toi-whit, toi-whit* (Roberts 1991; Winkler *et al.* 1995). **HABITS** Often occurs singly. Forages restlessly on slender branches of scrub and small trees. **HABITAT** Dry subtropical thorn forest, dry riverain forest, irrigated forest plantations in desert, and canal and roadside tree plantations. **BREEDING** March and April. Nest hole is 1–4 m above ground. **DISTRIBUTION AND STATUS PK:** widespread and locally frequent resident at up to 1500 m. **IN:** only one 19th-century record. **REFERENCES** Hargitt (1890).

HIMALAYAN WOODPECKER *Dendrocopos himalayensis* — Plate 15

Himalayan Pied Woodpecker (F,I), *Picoides himalayensis* (I)

IDENTIFICATION 23–25 cm. A medium-sized black-and-white woodpecker with unbarred black back, white 'shoulders', and unstreaked underparts. **Male** has scarlet crown, which is all black on **female**. Differs from Darjeeling Woodpecker (p.384) in unstreaked underparts, black rear edge to ear-coverts, and scarlet crown of male (although juvenile Darjeeling has reddish crown). For differences from Sind and Great Spotted Woodpeckers (above), see those species. **Racial variation** Western birds (*D. h. albescens*) are whitish or greyish-white on the underparts, rather than buff or yellowish (as in the eastern race *D. h. himalayensis*). **VOICE** A single *kit*, a rapid

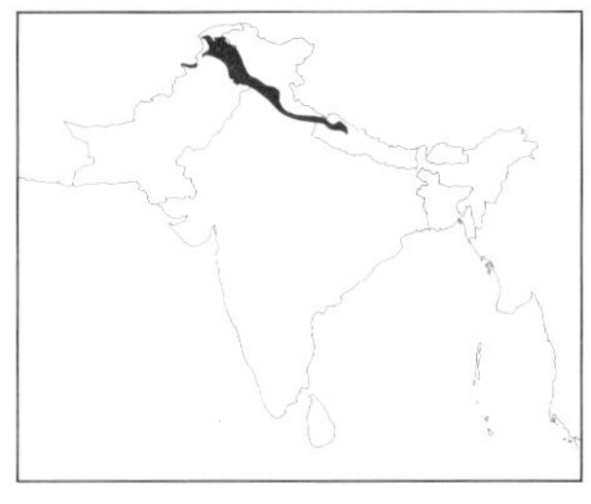

series of cries, *tri-tri-tri-tri*, and a rapid, high-pitched *chisik-chisik* (Roberts 1991; Winkler *et al.* 1995). **HABITS** Forages chiefly in the trees, hunting on trunks and on larger branches. Feeds on insects, beetle larvae and conifer seeds; wedges cone in cleft in bark or between trunk and branch, then hammers it to extract seeds. **HABITAT** Fir, pine, oak/rhododendron and mixed forest; favours coniferous forest. **BREEDING** April–June, varying locally. Nest hole is 2–15 m above ground. **DISTRIBUTION AND STATUS** Resident. W Himalayas from N Pakistan east to W Nepal, at 1980–3000 m (1500–3200 m in Pakistan). **PK:** common and sedentary; generally replaces Brown-fronted at higher altitudes. **NP, IN:** fairly common.

RUFOUS WOODPECKER *Celeus brachyurus* Plate 14

Brown Woodpecker (F), *Micropternus brachyurus* (E,F,I,K)

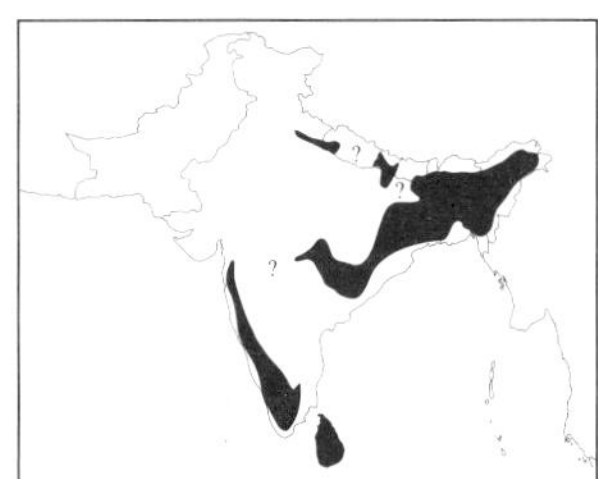

IDENTIFICATION 25 cm. A medium-sized, rufous-brown woodpecker with shaggy crest. Has short black bill, and is heavily barred with black on mantle, wings, flanks and tail. **Male** has small scarlet flash on ear-coverts. **Female** has pale buff ear-coverts. Smaller size, and black bill with distinct curve to culmen, are best distinctions from Bay Woodpecker (p.391); see that species for further differences. **VOICE** A high-pitched nasal *keenk, keenk, kenk*, and a diagnostic drumming like stalling engine *bdddd-d-d–d–dt* (Ali and Ripley 1987; Boonsong and Round 1991). **HABITS** Shy. Forages in trees at all heights; often seen digging into tree-ant nests, which it favours; also feeds on ground on fallen rotten logs, termite nests and cow dung. **HABITAT** Broadleaved forest and secondary growth, often mixed with bamboo. **BREEDING** February–June, also December, varying locally. Carves its nest in the papier-mâché nests of tree ants. The viciously stinging ants do not disturb incubating bird or nestlings. **DISTRIBUTION AND STATUS** Resident. Himalayas from Uttar Pradesh east to Arunachal Pradesh; NE and E India, and Bangladesh; W India from S Gujarat south through the peninsula and Sri Lanka. **NP:** uncommon; to 305 m (–1525 m). **IN:** locally fairly common; to 1000 m (–1500 m). **BT:** frequent below 700 m. **BD:** locally common. **LK:** scarce resident in lowlands and lower hills. **REFERENCES** Short (1973).

WHITE-BELLIED WOODPECKER *Dryocopus javensis* Plate 14

Indian Great Black Woodpecker (I)

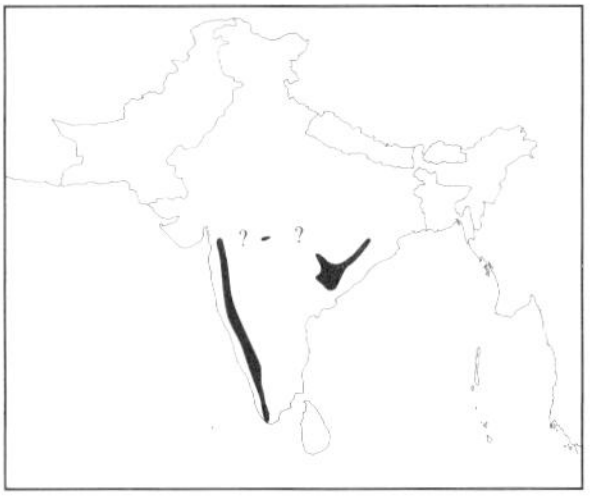

IDENTIFICATION 48 cm. A very large, mainly black woodpecker with broad white band across upper flanks and belly. Occasionally has white barring on lower flanks and lower belly. In flight, shows white rump, white underwing-coverts and small white patch at base of primaries. **Male** has scarlet moustachial stripe, forehead, crown and crest; **female** has scarlet restricted to hindcrown and crest. **VOICE** A resounding metallic *chiank* uttered every 2–3 seconds, three to four times in succession, and short ringing laugh or chuckle in flight (Ali and Ripley 1987). **HABITS** A noisy woodpecker, excavating and frequently hammering more loudly than other woodpeckers where it occurs. Forages on both live and dead trees, large fallen logs or dead stumps. Has slow, deliberate wingbeats rather like a crow's. **HABITAT** Prefers primary forest and forest edges, also secondary forest with large trees. Found mainly in moist deciduous, also in evergreen and semi-evergreen broadleaved forest and plantations; in SW India, favours bamboo and teak plantations and tall shade trees in coffee and cardamom plantations. **BREEDING** January–March. Nest hole is 6–16 m above ground, often with a shaft 50–60 cm deep. **DISTRIBUTION AND STATUS IN:** resident in the Surat Dangs and south through the Western Ghats, also Eastern Ghats; may be extirpated in Maharashtra; found at up to 1200 m; frequent, but very local in the heavy-rainfall zone north to Goa; thinly distributed, rare or sporadic elsewhere in most of its range. **REFERENCES** Short (1973).

ANDAMAN WOODPECKER *Dryocopus hodgei* Plate 14

***D. javensis hodgei* (I)**

IDENTIFICATION 38 cm. A large, brownish-black woodpecker. **Male** has scarlet moustachial stripe, forehead, crown and crest; **female** has scarlet restricted to hindcrown and crest. **VOICE** Has a loud, chattering *kuk-kuk-kuk* ending in a whistling *kui* (Ali and Ripley 1987). **HABITS** Very similar to those of White-bellied Woodpecker. **HABITAT** Large trees in evergreen forest. **BREEDING** February to March. **DISTRIBUTION AND STATUS** Common resident, endemic to Andaman Is. **REFERENCES** Davidar *et al.* (1997), Sankaran and Vijayan (1993).

LESSER YELLOWNAPE *Picus chlorolophus* Plate 16

Small Yellow-naped Woodpecker (F,I), Lesser Yellow-naped Woodpecker (N,P,R)

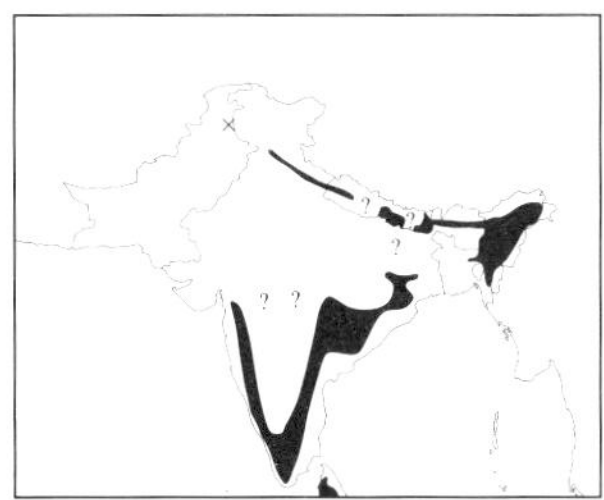

IDENTIFICATION 27 cm. Medium-sized, mainly green woodpecker with tufted yellow nape. Differs from Greater Yellownape (below) in smaller size and bill, less prominent yellow 'tuft' (resulting in more rounded shape to head), scarlet and white markings on head, maroon edges to secondaries which form indistinct panel on wing, white barring on primaries, and white barring on underparts. **Male** differs from female in having scarlet moustachial stripe and line above eye. **Racial variation** Birds in peninsular India and Sri Lanka (*P. c. chlorigaster* and *P. c. wellsi*) are smaller and darker green above than the nominate race (described above) and *P. c. simlae* of N and NE subcontinent; they have white spotting (rather than barring) on underparts, and lack distinct white stripes on sides of head (head is more uniform dark greyish-olive). Males of these two races have a mainly crimson crown and less extensive yellow on nape (females also show much crimson on rear crown but, as in other races, lack the crimson moustachial stripe). **VOICE** A buzzard-like, drawn-out *pee-oow* (R. Grimmett), and a descending series of shrill notes *kee kee kee kee kee* (Boonsong and Round 1991). **HABITS** Often accompanies roving mixed parties of insectivorous birds, such as minivets, babblers and drongos or other woodpecker species. Feeds chiefly in smaller trees, occasionally descending to understorey shrubs or fallen logs. Noisy and conspicuous. **HABITAT** Deciduous and broadleaved evergreen forest, secondary growth, bamboo, open woodlands; also rubber and coffee plantations in S India. **BREEDING** January–July, varying locally. Nest hole is 2–10.7 m, sometimes 20 m, above ground. **DISTRIBUTION AND STATUS** Resident. Mainly Himalayas from Himachal Pradesh east to Arunachal Pradesh; hills of NE, E, W and S India, Bangladesh and Sri Lanka. From lowlands up to 1800 m (–2135 m in Himalayas and Sri Lanka). **PK:** vagrant. **NP:** fairly common. **IN:** fairly common, more frequent in the foothills. **BT:** fairly common. **BD:** locally common. **LK:** resident in wet zone and adjacent areas of dry zone; frequent in wet zone. **REFERENCES** Short (1973).

GREATER YELLOWNAPE *Picus flavinucha* Plate 16

Large Yellow-naped Woodpecker (F,I), Greater Yellow-naped Woodpecker (N)

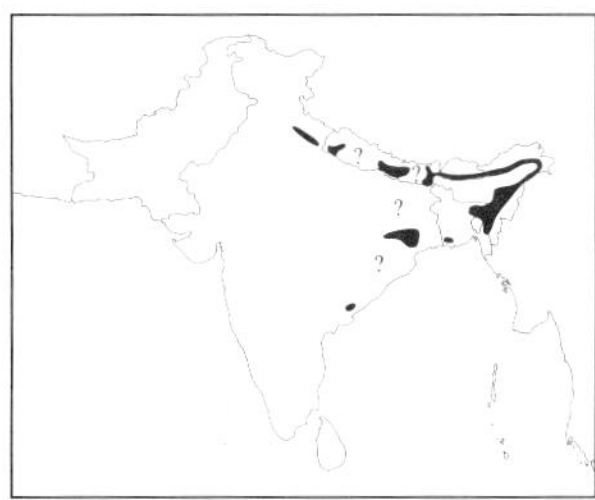

IDENTIFICATION 33 cm. A large, mainly green woodpecker with tufted yellow nape. Told from Lesser Yellownape (above) by larger size and bill, more prominent yellow crest (resulting in triangular-shaped head), brown on crown, and lack of red and white markings on head. Further differences include dark olive sides of neck adjoining dark-spotted white foreneck, uniform underparts, broad rufous barring on primaries, and colour of throat. **Male** has a pale yellow throat. **Female** has rufous-brown chin and throat, and is smaller, with smaller bill. **Juvenile** is much as adult: male has white or buff throat spotted with black. **VOICE** A plaintive, descending *pee-u ... pee-u* and a single metallic *chenk* (Ali and Ripley 1987); a hesitant *chup-chup* with a long interval between the notes, followed by a quick, high-pitched staccato roll (Smythies 1986). **HABITS** Often with mixed-species feeding flocks. Feeds at all levels, from tree bases to the highest branches. Shy and restless. **HABITAT** Deciduous and broadleaved evergreen forest and forest edges. **BREEDING** March–May. Nest hole is 3–6 m above ground. **DISTRIBUTION AND STATUS** Resident. Himalayas from N Uttar Pradesh east to Arunachal Pradesh; NE and E India and Bangladesh. Found mainly at 250–1500 m (–2500 m). **NP, IN, BT:** fairly common. **BD:** locally common. **REFERENCES** Short (1973).

LACED WOODPECKER *Picus vittatus* Plate 16

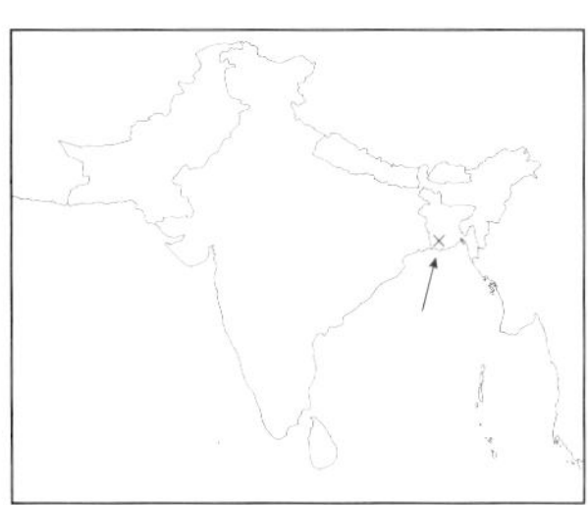

IDENTIFICATION 30–33 cm. A medium-sized, mainly greenish woodpecker. Has diffuse white supercilium and broad, dark moustachial stripe, dark olive scaling on belly and flanks, and olive-yellow rump. Adult distinguished from the similar and more widely distributed Streak-throated Woodpecker (p.388) by unstreaked olive-yellow throat, foreneck and breast, red or reddish-brown (rather than whitish) eye, broader and more clearly defined black moustachial stripe, more uniform grey ear-coverts, finer, less distinct white supercilium, and longer, blackish tail (Streak-throated has shorter, browner tail, with more distinct brownish-white barring). **Male** has scarlet forehead and crown, which are black on **female**. **Juvenile** is similar to respective adult, but with duller olive-brown underparts and less distinct scaling on belly. **VOICE** An explosive, shrill, falling *kweep* (Boonsong and Round 1991). **HABITS** Details not recorded in the region. Feeds low down in mangroves or on the ground. **HABITAT** Mangroves. **BREEDING** Details not recorded in the region. Probably April. **DISTRIBUTION AND STATUS BD:** only certain record is of one collected south of Khulna in the southwest in April 1958. **REFERENCES** Paynter (1970), Short (1973).

STREAK-THROATED WOODPECKER *Picus xanthopygaeus* Plate 16

Little Scaly-bellied Green Woodpecker (I), Small Scaly-bellied Woodpecker (F,P), *P. myrmecophoneus* (I).

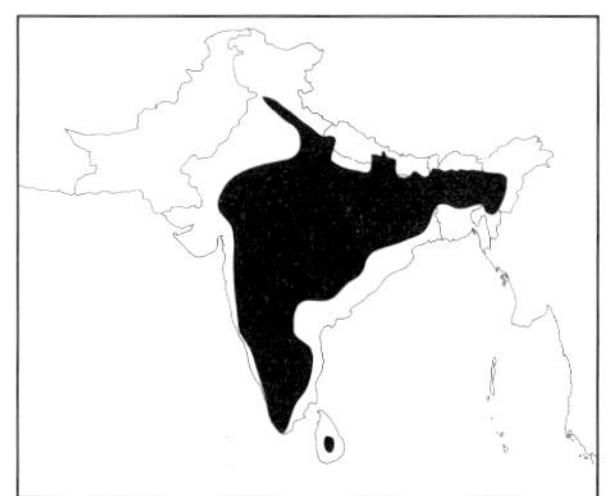

IDENTIFICATION 30 cm. A medium-sized, mainly greenish woodpecker with prominent white supercilium and cheek-stripe, olive scaling on breast, belly and flanks, and olive-yellow rump. Distinguished from similar Scaly-bellied Woodpecker (below) by smaller size, smaller and darker bill, pale eye, less prominent (often obscured) dark moustachial stripe, absence of black stripe below white supercilium, olive streaking on throat and upper breast, and comparatively uniform tail (lacking bold white barring of Scaly-bellied). For differences from Laced Woodpecker (p.387), which has a very restricted range (only one definite record) in the subcontinent, see that species. **Male** has scarlet forehead and crown, which are black (streaked with grey) on female. **Juvenile** is similar to adult, but has grey bases to feathers of mantle and scapulars, creating mottled appearance to upperparts. **VOICE** Rather silent, although known to give a sharp, single *queemp* (Winkler *et al.* 1995). **HABITS** Often joins mixed parties of insectivorous birds. Sometimes feeds on the ground. **HABITAT** Open broadleaved forest, secondary growth, bamboo and forest plantations; also rubber plantations in S India. In Sri Lanka, sometimes seen climbing about boulders on hillsides. **BREEDING** January–September, varying locally. Nest hole is usually 2.7–9.8 m above ground. **DISTRIBUTION AND STATUS** Resident. From Himachal Pradesh and Punjab, India, east to Bangladesh, south throughout the peninsula and Sri Lanka. **NP:** frequent below 465 m (–915 m). **IN:** locally fairly common in plains and foothills; in the peninsula and rarely in Himalayas, occurs at up to 1700 m. **BT:** rare. **BD:** scarce and local. **LK:** rare in dry-zone hills, confined to mid elevations.

SCALY-BELLIED WOODPECKER *Picus squamatus* Plate 16

Scaly-bellied Green Woodpecker (I), Large Scaly-bellied Woodpecker (F)

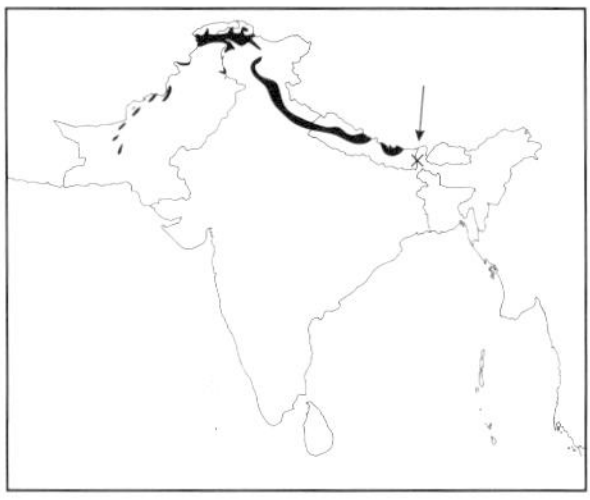

IDENTIFICATION 35 cm. A large, mainly greenish woodpecker with white supercilium and dark moustachial stripe, dark scaling on belly and flanks, and olive-yellow rump. Adult told from similar Streak-throated Woodpecker (above) by larger size, larger, pale (yellowish) bill, reddish eye, more prominent dark moustachial stripe, presence of black stripe below white supercilium, unstreaked throat and upper breast, more boldly scaled underparts (scaling thicker, darker and more clearly defined), and prominent whitish barring on tail. Further, is much more vocal than that species. White supercilium, scaled underparts, and male's red crown are best distinctions from Grey-headed Woodpecker (below). **Male** has scarlet forehead and crown, which are black (streaked with grey) on **female**. **Juvenile** is similar to adult, but has grey bases and pale tips to feathers of mantle and scapulars, creating mottled appearance to upperparts; significantly, also has dark spotting and scaling on throat and breast, which could cause confusion with Streak-throated (although is larger and has barred tail). **VOICE** The usual flight or contact call is *kuik-kuik-kuik*, usually repeated rapidly three or four times; advertising call is a melodious, inflected or two-noted quavering *klee-guh-kleeguh*, rapidly repeated seven or eight times; birds in visual contact utter subdued *chissuh-chissuh* (Roberts 1991). **HABITS** Hunts on tree trunks and often also on the ground. Feeds mainly on ants and termites. Noisy. **HABITAT** Coniferous, mixed oak/coniferous and mixed deciduous/coniferous forest; in Pakistan, also juniper scrub and bush-studded stream beds in desert; in Kashmir, fairly open country with large trees and orchards. **BREEDING** March–June. Nest hole is 2–6 m, sometimes 15 m, above ground. **DISTRIBUTION AND STATUS** Resident, subject to small seasonal altitudinal movements. Hills of Baluchistan, Pakistan, and Himalayas from N Pakistan east to Darjeeling. **PK:** common; 1500–3050 m (down to 600 m). **NP:** locally fairly common; 1850–3700 m, mainly below 3300 m. **IN:** fairly common; 1000–3300 m. **REFERENCES** Short (1973).

GREY-HEADED WOODPECKER *Picus canus* Plate 16

Black-naped Green Woodpecker (I), Grey-faced Woodpecker, Black-naped Woodpecker (F)

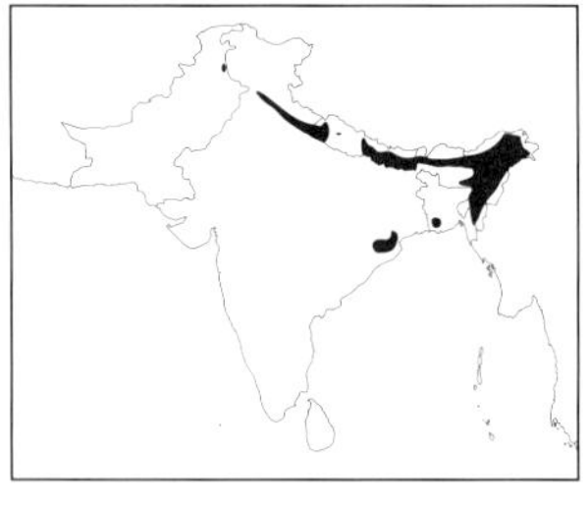

IDENTIFICATION 32 cm. A medium-sized greenish woodpecker with olive-yellow rump. Easily told from similar Scaly-bellied and Streak-throated Woodpeckers (above) by plain grey face and lack of white supercilium and cheek-stripe, and by uniform greyish-green underparts (lacking prominent scaling). Further, has red iris (pale in Streak-throated), and lacks prominent tail barring of Scaly-bellied. **Male** has scarlet forehead and forecrown and black hindcrown and nape (males of Streak-throated and Scaly-bellied have entire crown scarlet). **Female** has black forehead, crown and nape (streaked with grey). **Juvenile** similar to respective adult but duller, with greyer upperparts, and has whitish barring on underparts. **Racial variation** Birds in W Himalayas (*P. c. sanguiniceps*) are darker and greener on upperparts and underparts than those in E

Himalayas (*P. c. hessei*), which have golden or bronze sheen to upperparts and yellower underparts. **VOICE** A high-pitched *peeek, peeek, peeek, peeek*, usually in runs of four or five notes and fading at end; also chattering alarm cry (Ali and Ripley 1987). **HABITS** Often feeds by probing on the ground, moving about with heavy hops. Also forages in trees. **HABITAT** Moist subtropical and temperate forest; in Pakistan, mixed coniferous/deciduous forest; in Nepal, broadleaved forest, especially oaks; also well-wooded country. **BREEDING** May and June. Nest hole is 1–8 m above ground. **DISTRIBUTION AND STATUS** Resident. Himalayas in Murree, Pakistan, and from Himachal Pradesh east to Arunachal Pradesh; NE and E India, and Bangladesh. Mainly below 2200 m (–2600 m). **PK:** local and rare. **NP:** common. **IN:** locally common. **BT:** common. **BD:** locally common. **REFERENCES** Short (1973).

HIMALAYAN FLAMEBACK *Dinopium shorii* — Plate 16

Himalayan Golden-backed Three-toed Woodpecker (I), Himalayan Goldenback (K), Three-toed Golden-backed Woodpecker (F)

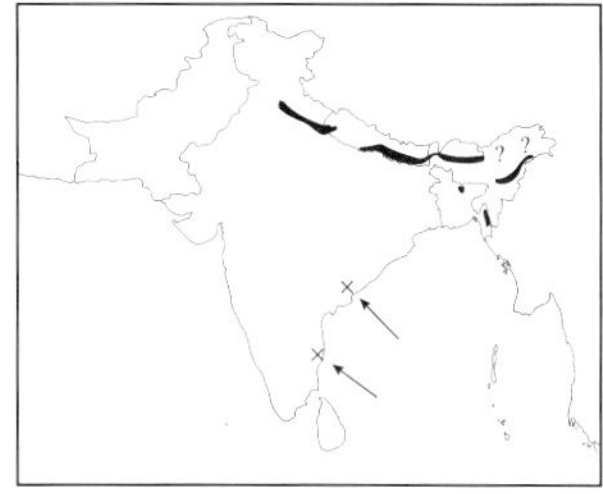

IDENTIFICATION 30–32 cm. A medium-sized woodpecker with golden-yellow upperparts (with variable orange or red suffusion), black-and-white face pattern, and scarlet rump. **Male** has scarlet crown and crest, and **female** has white-streaked black crest. Told from Greater Flameback (p.390) by smaller, weaker-looking bill, unspotted black hindneck and upper mantle, and brownish-buff centre of throat (with black spotting forming irregular border), with brownish-buff extending over upper breast (particularly striking on some birds). Further, has reddish or brown eyes, and has three (rather than four) toes. Breast is irregularly (and rather untidily) streaked and scaled with black, rather than black with bold white spotting as on Greater, and on some is almost unmarked (and buff-coloured). Female has white streaking to black crest (rather than spotting as on female Greater). Both sexes appear to show divided moustachial stripe, but much less clearly so than on Greater, and centre is brownish-buff (with touch of red on male). Is larger and larger-billed than Common Flameback (below), plumage differences from which are likely to be difficult to see in the field. Common tends to have a single broad dark moustachial, although some appear identical to Himalayan in this respect, and black crown of female Himalayan has more extensive and prominent white streaking. There are further subtle differences in patterning of throat and breast: Common has an irregular line of black spotting down centre of throat, lacking brownish-buff line of Himalayan; and breast of Common is more heavily marked with black. **VOICE** A rapid, repeated tinny *klak-klak-klak-klak-klak*, which is slower and softer than call of Greater Flameback (Fleming *et al.* 1984). **HABITS** Poorly recorded. Often with itinerant mixed-species flocks. **HABITAT** Tall mature broadleaved forest; sensitive to deforestation. **BREEDING** March–May. Nest-site details are unknown. **DISTRIBUTION AND STATUS** Resident. Himalayas from Himachal Pradesh and N Haryana east to Arunachal Pradesh; NE India and Bangladesh; also locally in the hills of the peninsula. From the lowlands up to 700 m. **NP:** locally common below 275 m. **IN, BT:** locally fairly common. **BD:** rare.

COMMON FLAMEBACK *Dinopium javanense* — Plate 16

Indian Golden-backed Three-toed Woodpecker (I), Common Goldenback (K)

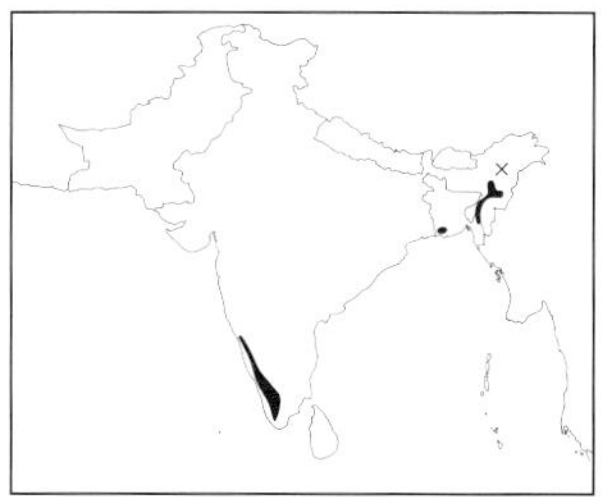

IDENTIFICATION 28–30 cm. A medium-sized woodpecker with golden-yellow upperparts, black-and-white face pattern, scarlet rump, and black spotting on underparts. **Male** has scarlet crest, and **female** has white-spotted black crest. Told from Greater Flameback (p.390) by smaller size and much smaller, weaker-looking bill, unspotted black hindneck and upper mantle, and reddish or brown eyes, and has three (rather than four) toes. Generally has solid black moustachial stripe, although this can appear divided on some birds, but moustachial is never as cleanly divided as on Greater and never shows that species' clear white oval centre. Further, female Common is more finely spotted with white on black crest. For differences from the very similar Himalayan Flameback (above), see that species. **VOICE** Rattle call faster, higher-pitched and less faltering than Greater Flameback's; nasal *wicka-wick-wicka* during display; drums less powerfully than Greater Flameback (P. Holt). **HABITS** Usually with mixed foraging parties of insectivorous birds, such as drongos. Hunts at all levels in the trees, but usually low down. **HABITAT** Mainly broadleaved evergreen and semi-evergreen forest in the peninsula; moist deciduous forest and wooded areas near habitation in NE India; mangroves in Bangladesh; in more humid habitats than Black-rumped. **BREEDING** January–June, varying locally. Nest hole is 2–10 m above ground. **DISTRIBUTION AND STATUS** Resident. Hills of SW and NE India, and Bangladesh; at up to 1700 m, favouring the foothills. **IN:** locally fairly common. **BD:** local in the south. **REFERENCES** Short (1973).

BLACK-RUMPED FLAMEBACK *Dinopium benghalense* — Plate 16

Lesser Golden-backed Woodpecker (F,I,R), Black-rumped Goldenback (K), Golden-backed Woodpecker (P)

IDENTIFICATION 26–29 cm. A medium-sized woodpecker with golden-yellow upperparts, black-and-white face pattern, and black streaking or scaling on underparts. **Male** has scarlet crown and crest; **female** has white-

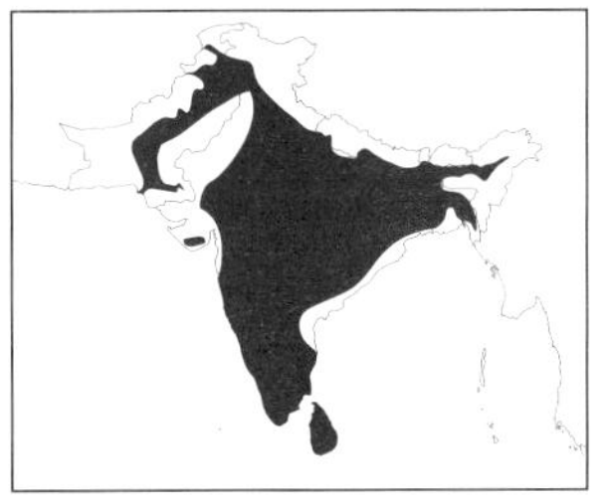

spotted black forehead and forecrown and scarlet hindcrown and crest. Best distinguished from other flamebacks by combination of black lower back and rump (though these areas are washed olive in population of SW India, and the feathers are often red-tipped in *D. b. psarodes*), less complex black-and-white head pattern (has white-spotted black throat and black stripe through eye, but lacks moustachial stripe), and (usually) white or buff spotting on black lesser and median coverts. Easily distinguished from the much larger White-naped Woodpecker (p.390) by black hindneck, golden-yellow mantle, and different head pattern. **Racial variation** Coloration of upperparts varies throughout subcontinent (can be olive-yellow or golden-yellow), as does prominence of white spots on wing-coverts. *D. b. psarodes* of Sri Lanka is strikingly different, having crimson mantle, coverts and tertials; distinguished from the crimson-backed race of Greater Flameback *C. l. stricklandi* (below) by smaller size, smaller dark bill, unspotted black hindneck, and different head pattern, in addition to which female *psarodes* has red crest. **VOICE** Contact call is a single, strident *kierk*; also a whinnying *kyi-kyi-kyi* (Roberts 1991). **HABITS** Usually with mixed foraging parties of insectivorous birds. Forages at all levels in the trees and also often on the ground. Feeds chiefly on ants. **HABITAT** Light forest, forest plantations, groves, trees around villages and cultivation, open wooded country, roadside avenues, canal-side plantations, wooded gardens; in S India, also rubber and coconut plantations. **BREEDING** Recorded in almost all months, varying locally. Nest hole is from less than 2 m up to 15.2 m above ground. **DISTRIBUTION AND STATUS** Resident throughout much of the subcontinent in plains and foothills. **PK:** locally common in the plains. **NP:** frequent below 365 m. **IN:** common in low country and foothills; in the north up to 1000 m (–1700 m); locally to 1000 m in the southwest; to 1200 m in rest of the peninsula. **BT:** one 19th-century record. **BD, LK:** common throughout.

GREATER FLAMEBACK *Chrysocolaptes lucidus* — Plate 16

Large Golden-backed Woodpecker (I), Greater Goldenback (K), Crimson-backed Woodpecker (P), Large Golden-backed Woodpecker (F)

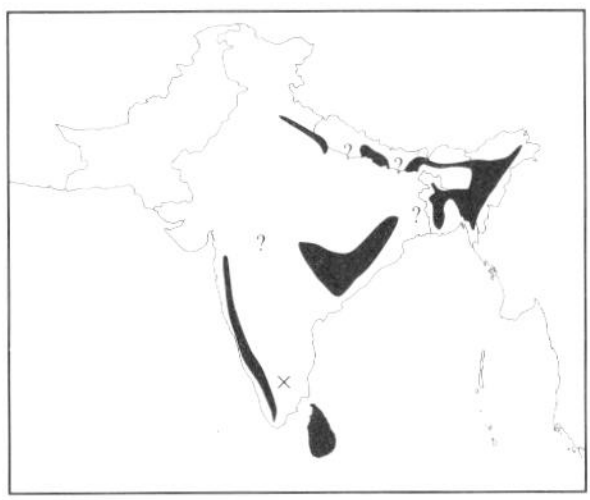

IDENTIFICATION 33 cm. A large woodpecker with golden-yellow upperparts, striking black-and-white face pattern, scarlet rump, and white spotting on black breast. **Male** has scarlet crown and crest, and **female** has white-spotted black crest. Told from very similar Himalayan and Common Flamebacks (p.389) by larger size and longer S-shaped neck, longer, stronger-looking bill, white or black-and-white spotted hindneck and upper mantle, pale eyes, and four (not three) toes. In addition, has clearly divided moustachial stripe (with obvious white oval centre), clean single black line down centre of throat, and white spotting on black breast; and female has white spotting on crown (rather than streaking as on Himalayan). **Racial variation** *C. l. stricklandi* of Sri Lanka is strikingly different, having crimson upperparts, pale bill, and broader black stripe through eye (and narrower white supercilium); differs from the crimson-backed race of Black-rumped Flameback (p.389), which occurs in Sri Lanka, in its larger size, larger, pale bill, white-spotted hindneck and upper mantle, and divided moustachial stripe. **VOICE** A sharp, metallic, monotone *di-di-di-di-di-di-di...* sounding like a giant cicada, and a lower-pitched, more rapid *di-i-i-i-i-t* in flight (Boonsong and Round 1991). **HABITS** Frequently associates with other woodpeckers, drongos and small insectivorous species. Visits chiefly large trees. Forages at all levels, especially on dead wood, sometimes also on the ground. **HABITAT** Broadleaved forest, groves, also mangroves in Bangladesh. **BREEDING** Recorded in all months, varying locally. Nest hole a distinctive elongated oval, usually 7.3–15.2 m above ground. **DISTRIBUTION AND STATUS** Resident. Himalayas from N Uttar Pradesh east to Arunachal Pradesh; hills of SW, E and NE India, Bangladesh and Sri Lanka. **NP:** frequent below 915 m (–1700 m). **IN:** fairly common; chiefly in foothills below 700 m (–1600 m) in the north; up to 1800 m in the southwest. **BT:** locally common in foothills. **BD:** locally common throughout. **LK:** rare resident in all zones, more frequent in wet zone. **REFERENCES** Short (1973).

WHITE-NAPED WOODPECKER *Chrysocolaptes festivus* — Plate 16

Black-backed Woodpecker (F,I), Black-backed Yellow Woodpecker (P)

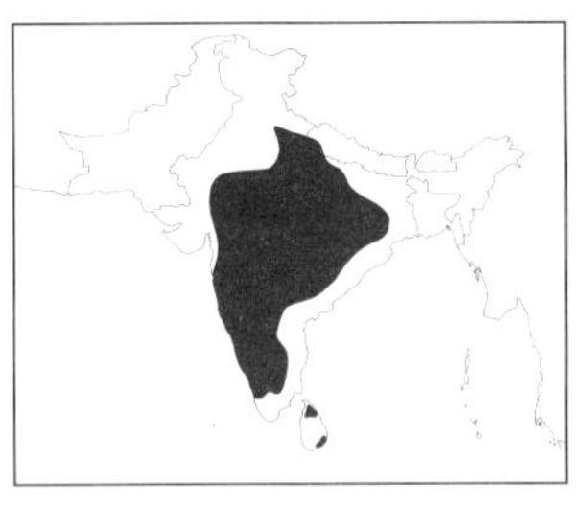

IDENTIFICATION 29 cm. A largish woodpecker bearing a resemblance to the flamebacks (p.389–390), with complex black-and-white head pattern, black-streaked white underparts, and golden-yellow coverts and tertials. Easily distinguished from the flamebacks by white hindneck and mantle contrasting with black scapulars and back (which form black V). Further, **female** has yellow crown and crest. Rump is black, as on Black-rumped (p.389). Has divided moustachial stripe and black line down centre of throat, as on Greater. **Male** has crimson crest. **Juvenile** male has buffish forehead and pinkish crest; female has yellow crest, tipped pink towards rear crown. **VOICE** Tinnier, higher-pitched and more hesitant rattle than other flamebacks; all phrases drop noticeably in pitch and are reminiscent of call of Crested

Kingfisher (p.406) (P. Holt). **HABITS** Forages on lower tree trunks, and occasionally on the ground on burnt grass and bare patches. **HABITAT** Light deciduous forest, scrub and scattered trees. **BREEDING** September–March, varying locally. Nest hole is 2–7 m above ground. **DISTRIBUTION AND STATUS** Resident, endemic to the subcontinent. From Uttar Pradesh, Rajasthan and E Gujarat east to W West Bengal, and south to Kerala and Sri Lanka. **NP:** uncommon in the far west; below 245 m. **IN:** locally fairly common; widely distributed throughout most of peninsula. **LK:** rare and local in dry lowlands.

PALE-HEADED WOODPECKER *Gecinulus grantia* Plate 14

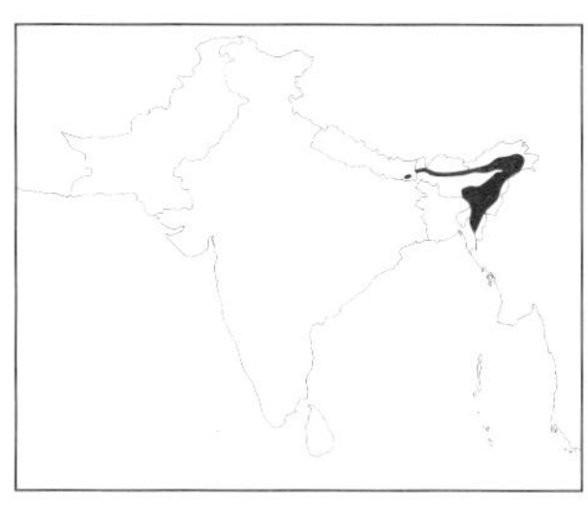

IDENTIFICATION 25 cm. A smallish, mainly unbarred woodpecker with pale bill. Easily distinguished by golden-olive head and neck, dull crimson to crimson-brown upperparts, brown primaries barred with buffish-pink, and dark olive underparts. **Male** differs from **female** in having crimson-pink on crown. **Juvenile** resembles female, but head is duller and upperparts are browner (although still with crimson cast); juvenile male has some crimson on crown. **VOICE** Drumming is loud, full, fairly short in duration and evenly pitched; territorial call is reminiscent of Bay Woodpecker's (below), a loud, strident comical phrase with shorter, stressed first note, *yi..wee-wee-wee;* calls are harsh, rather high-pitched and quickly repeated, *grritj-grrit-grrit, grridit..grrit-grrit* etc (C. Robson). **HABITS** Forages noisily and often low down on large bamboos and tree trunks, sometimes on fallen logs, and rarely also on the ground. **HABITAT** Chiefly in bamboo jungle; also moist broadleaved secondary forest. **BREEDING** March–May. Nest hole is excavated 1–6 m above ground in a rotten stump or dead tree. **DISTRIBUTION AND STATUS** Local resident in Himalayas from E Nepal east to Arunachal Pradesh; NE India and Bangladesh; mainly up to 1000 m (–1375 m in Bhutan). **NP:** very rare in the SE terai. **IN, BT:** uncommon. **BD:** rare, only one recent record.

BAY WOODPECKER *Blythipicus pyrrhotis* Plate 14

Red-eared Bay Woodpecker (I), Red-eared Rufous Woodpecker (F)

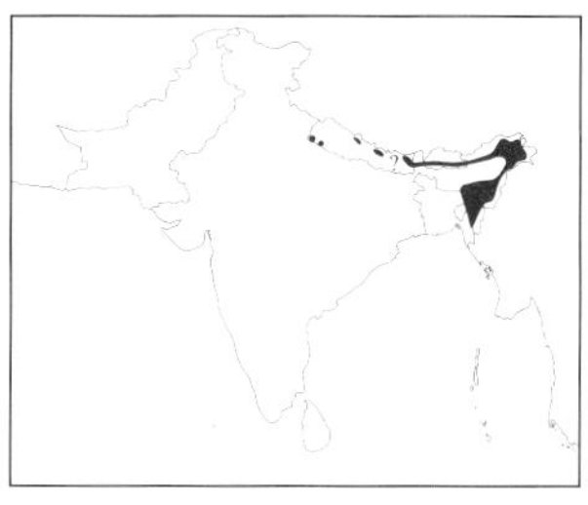

IDENTIFICATION 27 cm. A medium-sized, rufous woodpecker with broad dark brown barring on mantle and wings. Really confusable only with Rufous Woodpecker (p.386), but has long yellowish-white bill; is also larger, with more angular head shape, and has more broadly barred and brighter rufous upperparts, diffuse streaking on forehead and crown, and dark brown underparts. **Male** has prominent scarlet patch on sides of neck, extending onto nape. **Female** lacks scarlet patch. **Juvenile** has more prominent barring on mantle, diffuse rufous and dark brown barring on underparts, and more prominent pale streaking on head; juvenile male has diffuse scarlet patch on neck sides. **VOICE** Loud descending laughter, *keek, keek-keek-keek-keek-keek;* when flushed, or flying from tree to tree, a loud chattering *kerere-kerere-kerere* (Boonsong and Round 1991; Ali and Ripley 1987). **HABITS** Sometimes associates with mixed-species flocks. Most foraging takes place within a few metres of the ground on moss-covered trunks, dead stumps, fallen logs, also on the ground among roots; sometimes feeds higher up, keeping close to or on the trunk. Shy and elusive, heard much more often than seen. **HABITAT** Mature, evergreen broadleaved forest with thick undergrowth and adjoining dense secondary forest. **BREEDING** May and June. Nest hole is 1–4 m above ground. **DISTRIBUTION AND STATUS** Resident. Himalayas from W Nepal east to Arunachal Pradesh; NE India and Bangladesh. **NP:** local and uncommon; mainly 1525–2500 m (down to 75 m). **IN:** locally fairly common; plains up to 2000 m. **BT:** frequent; 380–2395 m. **BD:** very local in the southeast and northeast. **REFERENCES** Short (1973).

HEART-SPOTTED WOODPECKER *Hemicircus canente* Plate 14

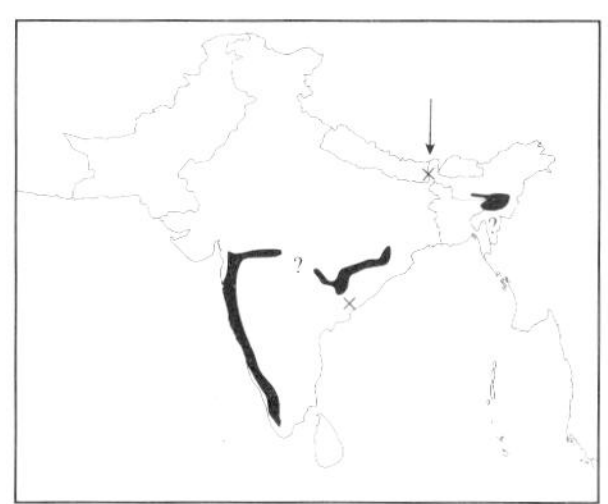

IDENTIFICATION 16 cm. A small, black-and-buff woodpecker. Looks top-heavy both at rest and in flight, with large crested head and very short tail (the latter obscured by wings at rest). Easily identified by prominent black crest, black heart-shaped spotting on white tertials and some coverts and scapulars, and white throat, becoming dusky olive or grey on rest of underparts. Shows white rump in flight. **Female** is similar to male, but has white forehead and forecrown. **Juvenile** is similar to female, but forehead and forecrown are spotted with black, and feathers of upperparts have narrow whitish fringes. **VOICE** Highly vocal. Calls include a weak, nasal inflected *ki-yew;* a high-pitched penetrating *kee...kee,* sometimes strung into a rapid Eurasian Wryneck-like trill; and a harsh quarrelsome *kirrrick,* often doubled or tripled; also short weak drumming (P. Holt). **HABITS** Frequently with mixed foraging parties of small insectivorous birds. Forages by creeping actively along outermost twigs and branches high in the trees, and most often among foliage; feeds mainly on live substrates. Often perches across branches like a passerine. Flight is weak and undulating. **HABITAT** Moist deciduous and broadleaved evergreen forest; favours teak and bamboo forest, and shade trees in S India coffee plantations. **BREEDING** November–April. Nest is a tiny hole drilled into a dead branch, usually 3–12 m above ground. **DISTRIBUTION AND STATUS IN**: a thinly distributed resident, mainly in hills of the southwest, northeast and east, also in Madhya Pradesh; locally frequent up to 1300 m. **BD:** ?resident; only one recent record. **REFERENCES** Short (1973).

GREAT SLATY WOODPECKER *Mulleripicus pulverulentus* Plate 14

Himalayan Great Slaty Woodpecker (I)

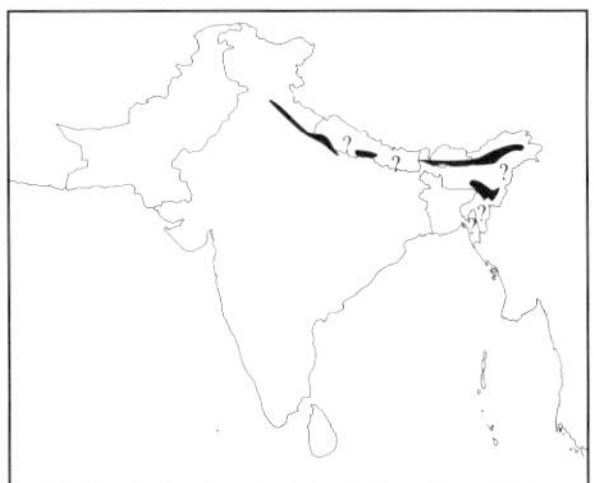

IDENTIFICATION 51 cm. A giant, serpentine slate-grey woodpecker with huge pale bill, long neck and long tail. Has yellowish-buff chin, throat and foreneck and fine white spotting on head, neck and underparts. **Male** differs from female in having pinkish-red moustachial patch and pinkish tips to feathers of lower throat. **Juvenile** has brown cast to upperparts. **VOICE** A loud, bleating call, not unlike that of a goat; a very loud cackle in flight; and a soft *whu-ick* given at rest and in flight (Ali and Ripley 1987; Boonsong and Round 1991). **HABITS** Forages chiefly on trunks and major branches in large trees. Hops slowly and jerkily in spirals up trunks and large branches with apparent difficulty; also perches across smaller branches. Birds follow each other in flight, which is less undulating than that of other woodpeckers, with slow deliberate wingbeats. Apparently has a large home range. **HABITAT** Climax sal and tropical broadleaved evergreen forest, also forest clearings with scattered tall, mature trees. **BREEDING** March–May. Nest is often 25 m or higher above ground. **DISTRIBUTION AND STATUS** Resident. Himalayas from Himachal Pradesh east to C Nepal and Sikkim east to Arunachal Pradesh; NE India and Bangladesh. **NP:** local, below 245 m; frequent in the west, rare in C areas. **IN:** uncommon; mainly up to 1000 m, and to 1200 m in the northeast. **BT:** uncommon. **BD:** ?former resident; no recent records, but may survive in Chittagong Hill Tracts. **REFERENCES** Short (1973).

ASIAN BARBETS Megalaimidae

Barbets are arboreal and usually found in the treetops. Despite their bright coloration, they can be very difficult to see, especially when silent, their plumage blending remarkably well with tree foliage. Barbets call persistently and monotonously in the breeding season, sometimes throughout the day; in the non-breeding season they are usually silent. They often sit motionless for long periods. They are chiefly frugivorous, many species favouring figs *Ficus*. Insects are also eaten, being caught by clumsy aerial sallies from treetops, and flower petals and nectar are taken when available. Barbets excavate their own nesting holes in trunks or branches of trees. Their flight is strong and direct, with deep woodpecker-like undulations.

GREAT BARBET *Megalaima virens* Plate 17

Great Hill Barbet (I), Great Himalayan Barbet (F)

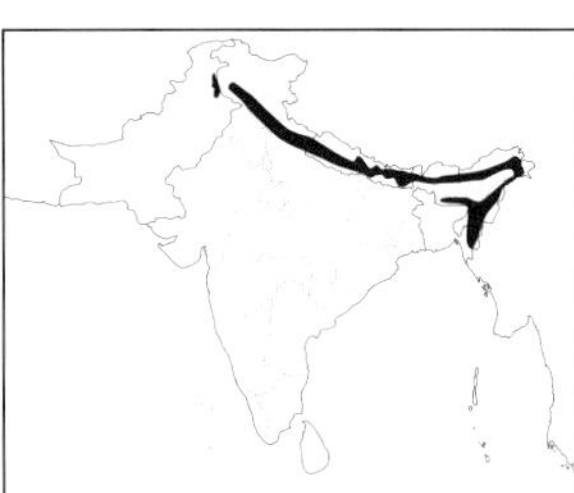

IDENTIFICATION 33 cm. Largest of the barbets and unmistakable, with large pale yellow bill, violet-blue head, brown breast and mantle, olive-streaked yellowish underparts, and red undertail-coverts. The only barbet with bluish head and red undertail-coverts. Some **racial variation**, birds in W Himalayas being duller and paler, with more extensive yellowish-green streaking on hindneck. **VOICE** A monotonous, incessant and far-reaching *piho, piho*, uttered throughout the day. A second call, a repetitious *tuk, tuk, tuk*, is often uttered in a duet (presumably by female); this call, sometimes given in isolation, is similar to but faster than that of Coppersmith Barbet (p.395) (Ali and Ripley 1987). **HABITS** Usually met with singly or in small groups of five or six, but congregates in feeding parties of up to 30 or more in fruit-laden trees. **HABITAT** Mainly moist subtropical and temperate forest; also well-wooded country. **BREEDING** April–July, varying with altitude. Nest hole is 3–5 m above ground. **DISTRIBUTION AND STATUS** Resident, subject to altitudinal movements. Himalayas in Murree, Pakistan, and from Jammu and Kashmir east to Arunachal Pradesh; NE India and Bangladesh. **PK:** common, but very local; 600–2600 m. **NP:** common; mainly 900–2200 m, summers chiefly above 1000 m. **IN:** common; summers at 1000–3000 m, winters down to 150 m; above 1200 m in Mishmi Hills. **BT:** common; 250–2900 m. **BD:** ?former resident; no recent records, but may survive in Chittagong Hill Tracts.

BROWN-HEADED BARBET *Megalaima zeylanica* Plate 17

Green Barbet (F,I,)

IDENTIFICATION 27 cm. A large, mainly green barbet with stout orange bill and bare patch around eye, and brown head and breast which are finely streaked with white. Best told from the similar Lineated Barbet (p.393)

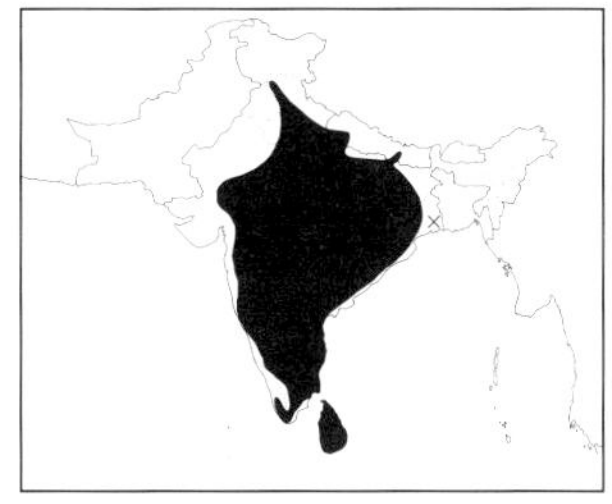

by much finer whitish streaking on head and breast (which look more uniformly brown), brown chin and throat concolorous with breast, and virtual absence of streaking on belly and flanks. In addition, has whitish-tipped wing-coverts (although rather indistinct in *inornata*), more extensive bare orange patch around eye which invariably extends to the bill (eye-patch becoming yellow in non-breeding season), and deeper reddish-orange bill (becoming orange-brown in non-breeding season). Orange bill and circum-orbital skin, and otherwise rather uniform brown head and breast, separate Brown-headed from the smaller White-cheeked Barbet (below) where the two species overlap in peninsular India. Some **racial variation** in extent of brown on breast and mantle and in prominence of streaking. Above-mentioned features apply to *M. z. caniceps* of N subcontinent. By comparison, *M. z. inornata* of W India has more uniform brown head and breast with less prominent streaking, while *M. z. zeylanica* of SW India and Sri Lanka has darker brown head and breast and more prominent streaking on nape and breast than *inornata*. **VOICE** Monotonous *kutroo, kutroo, kutroo* or *kutruk, kutruk, kutruk* uttered throughout the day. Lineated has similar call, but softer and mellower (Ali and Ripley 1987). **HABITS** Found singly or in small feeding groups, but parties of 20 or more sometimes gather with other frugivorous birds, such as green pigeons, bulbuls and mynas, in favoured fruiting trees. Particularly fond of figs. Very noisy in hot weather, often calling in chorus. **HABITAT** Broadleaved forest and wooded areas near habitation; fig and other fruiting trees along roadsides in towns and cities and in wooded gardens. **BREEDING** February–October, varying locally. Nest hole is 3–15 m above ground. **DISTRIBUTION AND STATUS** Resident, endemic to the subcontinent. From Himachal Pradesh east to C Nepal and West Bengal and south through the peninsula and Sri Lanka. **NP:** locally fairly common in the far west, status elsewhere uncertain; below 300 m. **IN:** locally common up to 800 m in Himalayas and to 1200 m in the south. **LK:** common resident in lowlands and lower hills.

LINEATED BARBET *Megalaima lineata* — Plate 17

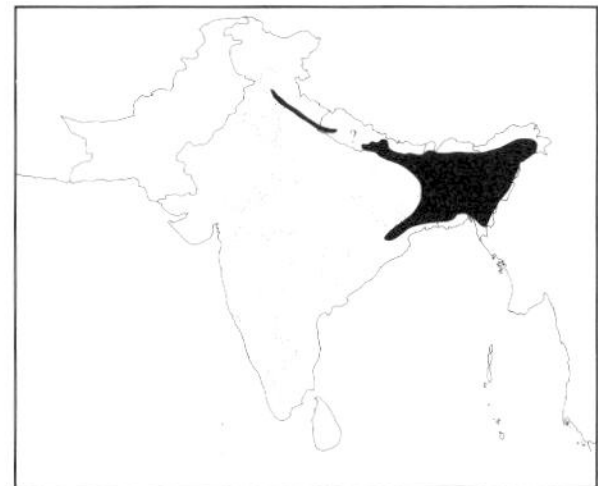

IDENTIFICATION 28 m. A large barbet with stout yellowish bill and bare patch around eye, and bold buffish-white streaking on pale brown head, mantle and breast. Told from the similar Brown-headed Barbet (p.392) by bold white streaking on head, upper mantle and breast (and extending onto centre of belly), with usually whitish chin and throat (although can be dusky brown on some); underparts can look white, streaked with brown. In addition, has less extensive naked yellowish patch around eye which (unlike on Brown-headed) is usually separated from the yellowish-coloured (not orange) bill, and uniform unspotted wing-coverts. Note also differences in range. **VOICE** A monotonous *kotur, kotur, kotur*, slightly mellower and softer than Brown-headed's (Ali and Ripley 1987). **HABITS** Very similar to those of Brown-headed. **HABITAT** Open deciduous forest; well-wooded gardens and roadside avenues with fig or other fruiting trees. **BREEDING** End March–mid June. Nest hole is 3–12 m above ground. **DISTRIBUTION AND STATUS** Resident. Himalayan foothills from Himachal Pradesh east to Arunachal Pradesh; NE and E India and Bangladesh. Up to 1000 m in W Himalayas and to 800 m in NE India. **NP:** common; up to 915 m. **IN:** locally fairly common. **BT:** frequent; 250–1000 m. **BD:** locally common.

WHITE-CHEEKED BARBET *Megalaima viridis* — Plate 17

Small Green Barbet (I)

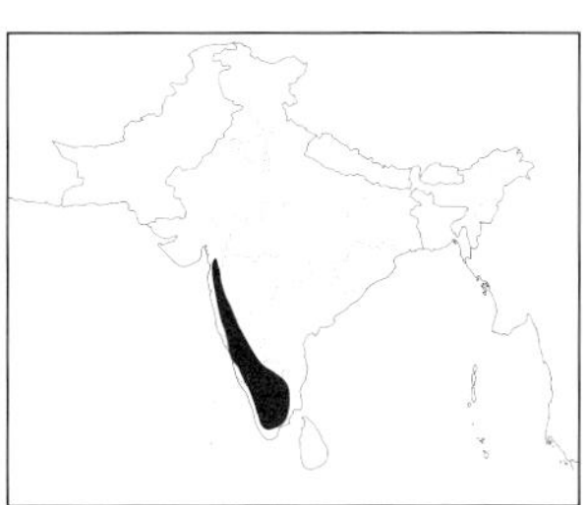

IDENTIFICATION 23 cm. A brown and green barbet with prominent white cheek patch and white spotting on underparts. Confusable only with Brown-headed Barbet (p.392), which also occurs in the Western Ghats and S peninsular India. Best distinguished by smaller size, shorter brownish bill, bold white cheek patch and white supercilium (contrasting with black around eye and dark brown crown and nape), whitish chin and throat, and bold white spotting on breast. **Juvenile** is similar, but brown of head is paler, and throat and breast are whiter (with indistinct brown streaking). **VOICE** Very similar to Brown-headed's, a *pucock, pucock, pucock*, uttered incessantly throughout the day (Ali and Ripley 1987). **HABITS** Similar to those of Brown-headed. Very pugnacious when feeding. Often climbs along branches and up trunks like a woodpecker. **HABITAT** Broadleaved evergreen and moist deciduous wooded areas, gardens and groves in towns, villages and cultivation. **BREEDING** December–June, varying locally. Nest hole is usually 2–10 m above ground. **DISTRIBUTION AND STATUS IN:** endemic resident, from the Surat Dangs south through the Western Ghats and east to C Tamil Nadu; common up to 1500 m; to 1800 m and occasionally to 2300 m in the Nilgiris.

YELLOW-FRONTED BARBET *Megalaima flavifrons* Plate 17

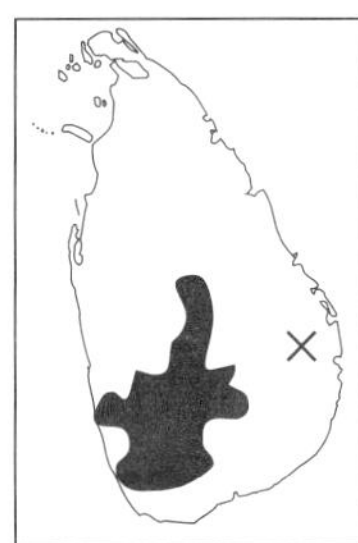

IDENTIFICATION 21 cm. A medium-sized, mainly green barbet. Easily distinguishable from Brown-headed and Crimson-fronted Barbets (p.392 and p.395), which also occur in Sri Lanka, by combination of yellow forehead, forecrown and malar stripe, and pale blue ear-coverts, throat and upper breast. In addition, has paler centres to green breast feathers, resulting in scaled appearance, and dark legs and feet. **VOICE** A rolling ascending *kowowowowowo*, which changes into a repetitive *kuiar, kuiar, kuiar* (Henry 1971). **HABITS** Similar to those of Brown-headed. **HABITAT** Broadleaved forest and well-wooded gardens. **BREEDING** Throughout the year, whenever conditions are favourable. Nest hole is 3–15 m above ground. **DISTRIBUTION AND STATUS LK:** endemic resident, common in wet lowlands and lower hills, most frequent at mid elevations; local in dry zone.

GOLDEN-THROATED BARBET *Megalaima franklinii* Plate 17

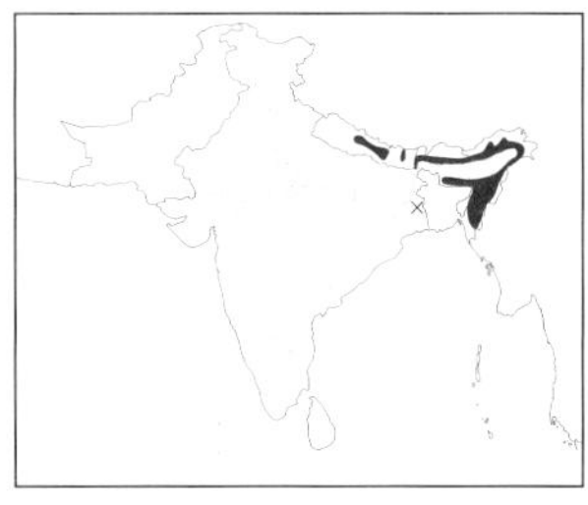

IDENTIFICATION 23 cm. A medium-sized barbet, easily told from Blue-throated Barbet (below) by yellow crown centre, chin and upper throat, greyish-white (not blue) cheeks and lower throat, and broad black stripe through eye. From below, possibly confusable with the much smaller Coppersmith Barbet (p.395), which also has a yellow throat, but Golden-throated has uniform green breast and belly (lacking red breast-band and streaked underparts) and has dark legs and feet. **VOICE** A wailing, repetitive *peeyu, peeyu*, recalling Great Barbet (p.392), but higher-pitched; also a monotonous *pukwowk, pukwowk, pukwowk* (Ali and Ripley 1987). **HABITS** Very similar to those of Brown-headed (p.392). **HABITAT** Moist broadleaved subtropical and temperate forest. **BREEDING** April–June. Nest hole is 2–5 m above ground. **DISTRIBUTION AND STATUS** Resident. Himalayas from WC Nepal east to Arunachal Pradesh; NE India and Bangladesh. Found at 400–2400 m east of Nepal. **NP:** frequent, but local; 1500–2400 m. **IN:** locally frequent. **BT:** common; 570–2300 m. **BD:** ?former resident; no recent records, but may survive in Chittagong Hill Tracts.

BLUE-THROATED BARBET *Megalaima asiatica* Plate 17

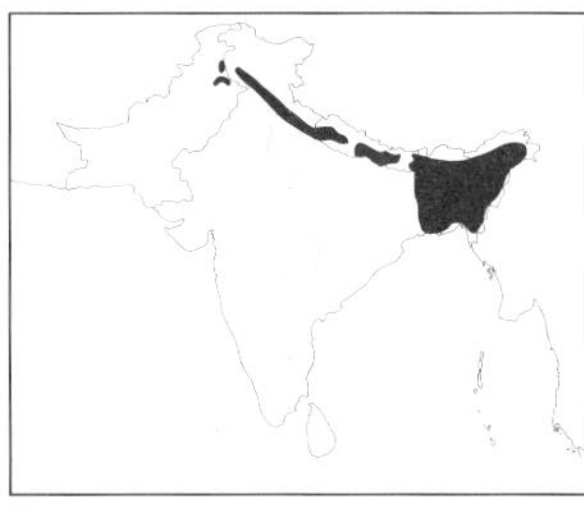

IDENTIFICATION 23 cm. A medium-sized barbet, easily told by combination of red forehead, black band across centre of crown, red hindcrown, and blue 'face', throat and upper breast. In NE subcontinent, possibly confusable with Blue-eared Barbet (below), but is larger, has red on crown, and has uniform blue sides of head. **Juvenile** is similar to adult, but head pattern is duller and poorly defined (with red of crown intermixed with green and black). **VOICE** A harsh and loud *took-a-rook, took-a-rook*, uttered very rapidly (King *et al.* 1975). **HABITS** Similar to those of Brown-headed (p.392). **HABITAT** Evergreen and deciduous trees, especially fig; open forest, groves near habitation and gardens. **BREEDING** March–July, depending on altitude. Nest hole is 2–8 m above ground. **DISTRIBUTION AND STATUS** Resident. Himalayas from N Pakistan east to Arunachal Pradesh; NE India and Bangladesh. Common. Generally at lower altitudes in summer than Golden-throated. **PK:** common, but very local; mainly 450–1675 m. **NP:** common below 1500 m; frequent up to 2100 m. **IN:** common; plains up to 2000 m. **BT:** common up to 1445 m. **BD:** locally common.

BLUE-EARED BARBET *Megalaima australis* Plate 17

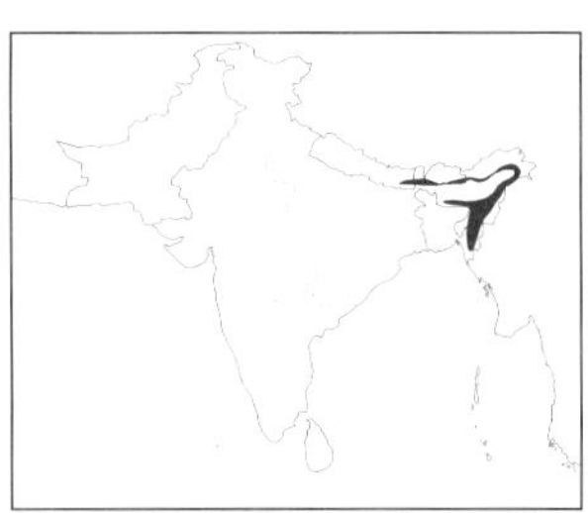

IDENTIFICATION 17 cm. A small barbet with blue throat and ear-coverts, and complex black and red patterning on head. Easily told from the larger Blue-throated Barbet (above) by blackish forehead and blue crown, more complex patterning on sides of head (with black malar stripe, red stripe behind eye, and red patches below eye and on sides of neck), and diffuse black gorget across upper breast. **Juvenile** is mainly green, with blue wash to 'face' and throat, and lacks black and red head markings. **VOICE** A disyllabic *tk-trrt*, repeated about 120 times per minute, and a throaty whistle (King *et al.* 1975). **HABITS** Similar to those of Coppersmith Barbet (p.395). Usually met with singly and perched at the top of a tall tree in thick forest. **HABITAT** Dense, broadleaved evergreen forest. **BREEDING** April–early June. Nest-hole details are unknown. **DISTRIBUTION AND STATUS** Resident. Himalayan foothills from E Nepal east to Arunachal Pradesh; NE India and Bangladesh. Occurs at up to 1200 m, more frequent below 760 m. **NP:** scarce and very local in the far east; 120–305 m. **IN:** uncommon. **BT:** locally fairly common; 380–450 m. **BD:** local.

CRIMSON-FRONTED BARBET *Megalaima rubricapilla* Plate 17

Crimson-throated Barbet (I), Ceylon Small Barbet (P)

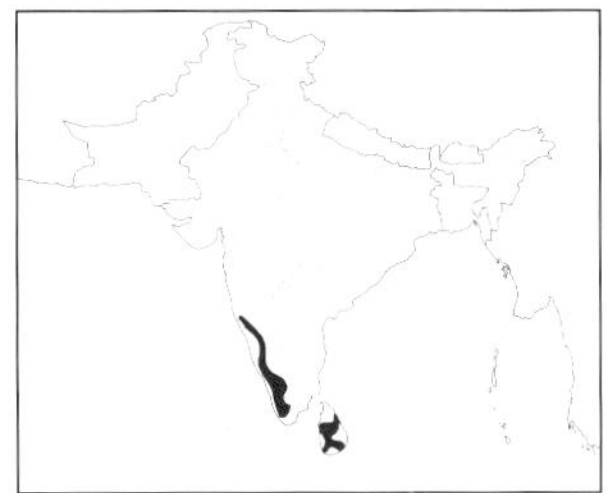

IDENTIFICATION 17 cm. A small colourful barbet, occurring as two distinctive races in the Western Ghats and Sri Lanka. *M. r. malabarica* (Western Ghats) is easily told from the similar-sized Coppersmith Barbet (below) by crimson cheeks, throat and breast, black streaking on breast, unstreaked green belly and flanks, and diffuse blue band down sides of head and breast. *M. r. rubricapilla* (Sri Lanka) more closely resembles Coppersmith and is best told by orange (rather than yellow) supercilium, cheeks, throat and upper breast, smaller and less distinct red patch on breast, unstreaked green belly and flanks, and diffuse blue patch on sides of head and neck. **Juveniles** of both subspecies are considerably duller than respective adult; they are predominantly green and show traces of adult head pattern. Juvenile *malabarica* has traces of red on forehead and throat; *rubricapilla* has trace of yellow on throat, blue wash on neck sides and moustachial stripe, and orange-yellow on cheeks and supercilium. Juvenile lacks striking 'face' pattern and streaked underparts of juvenile Coppersmith. **VOICE** Similar to that of Coppersmith (although possibly softer and quicker); a fast-delivered, repetitive, monotonous *poop, poop, poop...* etc (Ali and Ripley 1987). **HABITS** Similar to those of Coppersmith. Gathers in feeding parties outside breeding season. Often feeds in the canopy. **HABITAT** Restricted to moist evergreen biotope in Western Ghats, where it replaces Coppersmith, which occurs in deciduous biotope. Open wooded country with scattered fig trees in Sri Lanka. **BREEDING** December–September, varying locally. Nest hole is like that of Coppersmith. **DISTRIBUTION AND STATUS** Resident, endemic to the Western Ghats, India, and Sri Lanka. **IN:** common, but local; foothills up to 1200 m. **LK:** common resident in wet lowlands and lower hills up to 1300 m, local in dry zone.

COPPERSMITH BARBET *Megalaima haemacephala* Plate 17

Crimson-breasted Barbet (F,I,P)

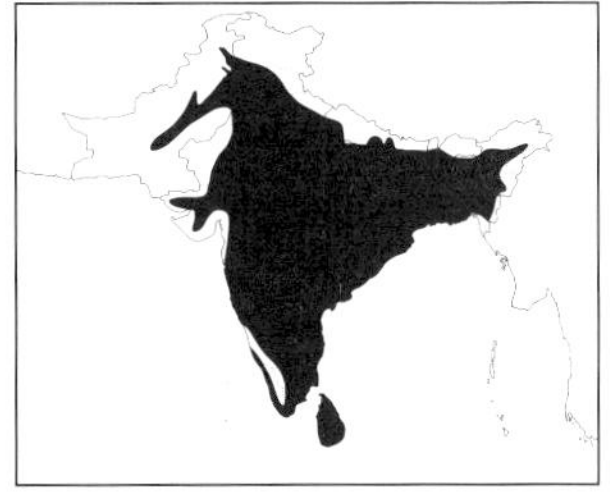

IDENTIFICATION 17 cm. A small, brightly coloured barbet, easily identified by combination of crimson forehead and patch on breast, yellow patches above and below eye contrasting with blackish hindcrown and sides of head, yellow throat, dark streaking on belly and flanks, and bright red legs and feet. **Juvenile** superficially resembles adult, but lacks red on forehead and breast; has prominent pale yellow patches above and below eye (surrounded by dark olive sides of head and moustachial stripe), whitish throat, olive-green breast-band, and broad olive-green streaking on belly and flanks. Both adult and juvenile might be confused with Crimson-fronted Barbet (above), which replaces Coppersmith in the evergreen forests of the Western Ghats and Sri Lanka; for differences, see that species. **VOICE** A loud metallic, repetitive and monotonous *tuk, tuk, tuk* (Ali and Ripley 1987). **HABITS** Usually found singly or in small parties, but flocks of up to 100 or more sometimes congregate on fruit-laden fig trees with other frugivorous birds such as green pigeons, bulbuls and mynas. Can cling to and climb up tree trunks like a woodpecker, using its short tail for support. In the early morning often suns itself from a bare treetop. Particularly vocal during the heat of day in summer. **HABITAT** Deciduous biotope, especially of fig trees. Open wooded country and groves near villages and cultivation; also wooded urban gardens. **BREEDING** November–September, varying locally. Nest is a shaft excavated in a dead branch or stump, 25–80 cm deep. **DISTRIBUTION AND STATUS** Resident throughout much of subcontinent east of the Indus R in plains and lower hills. **PK:** common. **NP:** common throughout below 915 m, frequent up to 1830 m. **IN:** common and widespread below 1500 m. **BT:** uncommon. **BD:** common. **LK:** common resident in dry lowlands and adjacent lower hills.

HORNBILLS Bucerotidae

Medium-sized to large birds with massive bills with variable-sized casque. They feed chiefly on wild figs *Ficus*, berries and drupes, supplemented by small animals, such as mice, lizards, snakes and insects. Mainly arboreal, but some species occasionally descend to the ground to feed. Flight is powerful and slow, and for most species consists of a few wingbeats followed by a sailing glide with the wing-tips upturned. In all but the smaller species, the wingbeats make a distinctive loud puffing sound audible for some distance. Hornbills often fly one after another in follow-my-leader fashion. Usually found in pairs or small parties, sometimes in flocks of up to 30 or more where food is abundant. Natural tree holes are used as nest sites. The incubating female plasters herself inside the hole using her own excreta, presumably for defence, and is fed by the male through a vertical slit. After she leaves the nest, the young replaster the hole. Many species are declining because of habitat loss and hunting. The main reference specific to hornbills is Kemp (1995), and measurements are taken from that work.

INDIAN GREY HORNBILL *Ocyceros birostris* Plate 18

Common Grey Hornbill (I), Gray Hornbill (F), *Tockus birostris* (F,I,R)

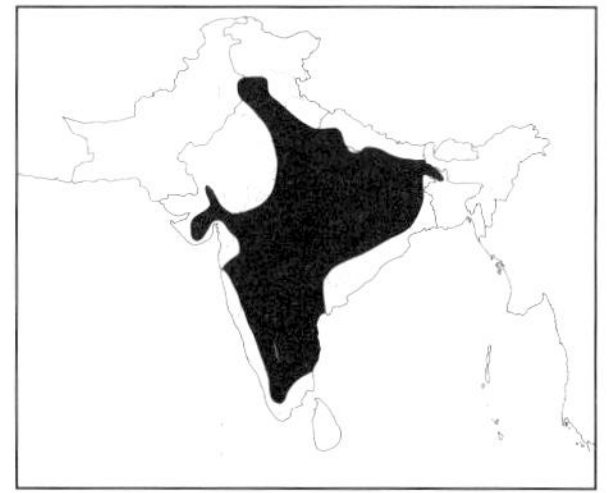

IDENTIFICATION 50 cm. The most widely distributed of the small 'grey' hornbills. Has broad greyish-white supercilium with dark grey ear-coverts, white tips to primaries and secondaries, and white-tipped tail. Has prominent blackish casque, and more extensive black at base of bill compared with Malabar Grey Hornbill (below). Further, lacks pale streaking on crown, sides of head, neck and breast, has paler sandy brownish-grey coloration to upperparts, and has white trailing edge to secondaries. Tail is also longer than on Malabar Grey, and paler brown with dark grey subterminal band and elongated central feathers. Calls are also different. **Female** is similar to male, but has smaller casque with less pronounced tip. **Immature** has bill as female's, but smaller and with smaller casque. Is similar in plumage to adult, although lacks white wing-tips, and has broader white stripe in centre of leading edge of primaries (indistinct on adults) which forms a pale panel on wing. **VOICE** Territorial call is a loud cackling and squealing *k-k-k-ka-e* or short, rapid piping *pi-pi-pi-pi-pipipieu-pipipieu-pipipieu*; normal contact call is kite-like *chee-ooww*. **HABITS** Usually found at medium levels in forest, where it is surprisingly inconspicuous when perched. Feeds on fruiting trees, often with other frugivorous species such as green pigeons, bulbuls and mynas. Occasionally descends to the ground to pick up fallen fruit or large insects, or to dust-bathe. Generally moves short distances from tree to tree. **HABITAT** Open deciduous forest, groves, gardens, cultivation, roadside avenues and orchards, wherever fruiting trees occur; favours large, old trees such as mango, tamarind, banyan and peepul. Prefers drier, more open habitats than Malabar Grey Hornbill. **BREEDING** March–June, varying locally. Nest hole is 3–8 m above ground. **DISTRIBUTION AND STATUS** Resident, endemic to the subcontinent. Subject to local movements, depending on fruiting seasons. From NE Pakistan east to Bangladesh and south through the peninsula. **PK:** scarce. **NP:** local and frequent; below 305 m (–760 m). **IN:** widespread and locally common; up to 1000 m (–1400 m). **BD:** ?former resident; no recent records. **REFERENCES** Hussain (1993), Shrestha (1993).

MALABAR GREY HORNBILL *Ocyceros griseus* Plate 18

***Tockus griseus* (I)**

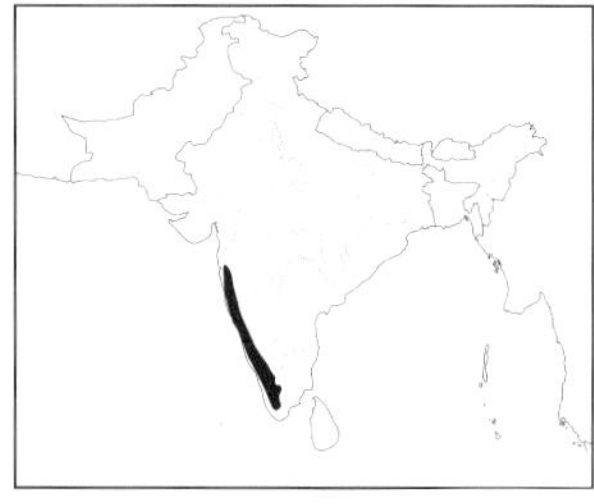

IDENTIFICATION 45 cm. A small, dark grey hornbill showing white wing-tips in flight. Has greyish-white supercilium which broadens behind eye and contrasts with darker ear-coverts. Similar to the more widely distributed Indian Grey Hornbill (above), but lacks prominent casque and has mainly orange or yellow bill. Further, has greyish-white streaking on sides of head, throat and neck, darker grey upperparts, rufous undertail-coverts, and shorter dark grey tail (with broken white terminal band as on Indian Grey). In flight, does not show white trailing edge to secondaries as on Indian Grey. Calls are also different. Sexes alike, although **female** has paler yellow bill lacking orange tinge and with black patch at base of lower mandible. **Immature** has smaller bill, lacking dark marks at base; also has rufous fringes to mantle and coverts, and less pronounced supercilium. **VOICE** A raucous *waa waa* recalling Alexandrine Parakeet (p.419), and a maniacal laughing *waa..waa..wa-wa-wa-wa-wa*. **HABITS** Very similar to those of Indian Grey Hornbill. **HABITAT** Open, broadleaved evergreen and moist deciduous forest, especially where figs are common. **BREEDING** January–April. Nest hole is mainly 9–18 m above ground. **DISTRIBUTION AND STATUS IN:** resident, endemic to Western Ghats; plains up to 1600 m; locally common, population now fragmented owing to habitat loss. **REFERENCES** Hussain (1993), Mudappa (1994), Mudappa and Kannan (1997).

SRI LANKA GREY HORNBILL *Ocyceros gingalensis* Plate 18

Ceylon Grey-Hornbill *Tockus gingalensis* (P), *T. griseus gingalensis* (I)

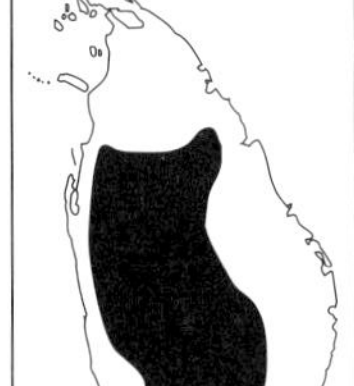

IDENTIFICATION 45 cm. The only grey hornbill occurring in Sri Lanka. Superficially resembles Malabar Grey Hornbill (above), which is confined to W peninsular India, but lacks broad greyish-white supercilium and has white underparts. In addition, has steel-grey wing-coverts (greyer than grey-brown mantle) with distinct black fringes, and browner crown than Malabar (both with buff shaft streaking) contrasting with dark grey ear-coverts. Outer tail feathers are almost entirely white on older birds (but otherwise are dark grey with white tips, as on Malabar). **Male** has mainly cream-coloured bill with black patches at base. **Female** has mainly black bill with cream stripe along cutting edge of upper mandible. **Immature** has smaller pale yellowish bill and less pronounced head pattern. **VOICE** A loud *kaa...kaa... kakakaka...* or *kuk...kuk-kuk-kuk ko ko kokoko* (Henry 1971). **HABITS** Very similar to those of Indian Grey Hornbill (above). **HABITAT** Forests and well-wooded areas. **BREEDING** April–August. Nest hole is 2–21 m above ground. **DISTRIBUTION AND STATUS LK:** endemic resident; lowlands and lower hills, more frequent in lowlands and in dry zone. **REFERENCES** Ginige and Kotagama (1993).

GREAT HORNBILL *Buceros bicornis* Plate 19

Great Pied Hornbill (I), Giant Hornbill (F)

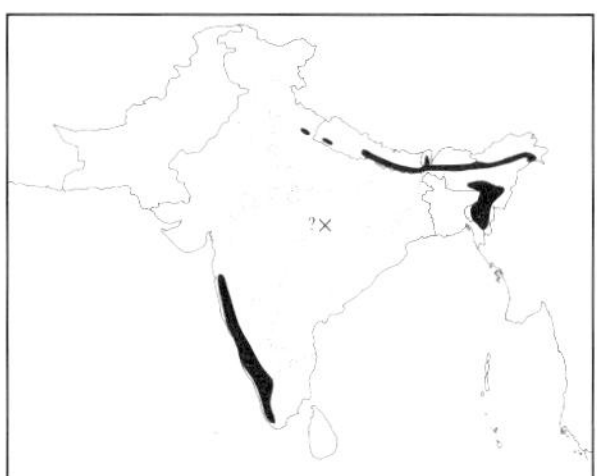

IDENTIFICATION 95–105 cm. A very large, pied hornbill. Easily distinguished from the other large hornbills by combination of large golden-yellow casque on huge downcurved bill, black face band contrasting with yellowish-white nape, neck and upper breast, and broad black band across white tail. In flight, shows broad whitish wing-bar and trailing edge to wing. As with neck and breast, white wing-bars and base of tail are typically stained yellow with preen-gland oils. Sexes very similar. **Male** has red iris, black circumorbital skin, and black at each end of casque. **Female** is smaller than male, with a smaller bill, has white iris and red circumorbital skin, and lacks black at ends of casque. **Immature** lacks casque until at least six months old. **VOICE** Typical calls are loud, deep and retching, often in a short series of notes and frequently given as a duet, *grongk-gonk grongk-gongk*; calls often become louder, more persistent and more raucous prior to flight; flight call is a loud *ger-onk*. Calls carry for a long distance (P. Morris). **HABITS** Often wary. Keeps to a very regular schedule of feeding circuits and roosting flights. Often flies high over the forest for long distances. Chiefly arboreal, but sometimes descends to ground to feed. In the non-breeding season, roosts communally in top branches of tall forest trees, where individuals are spaced over several neighbouring trees. **HABITAT** Mature broadleaved evergreen and moist deciduous forest. **BREEDING** February–April, varying locally. Nest hole is 18–25 m above ground. **DISTRIBUTION AND STATUS** Resident; may move seasonally, depending on fruit supplies. Mainly from N Uttar Pradesh east through the Himalayas to Arunachal Pradesh; NE India and Bangladesh; Western Ghats. **NP:** local and uncommon below 250 m; now mainly in protected areas. **IN:** locally fairly common, but declining; up to 1500 m in peninsular hills, mainly below 800 m (–2200 m) in Himalayas. **BT:** fairly common; 250–1400 m, locally to 1830 m. **BD:** vagrant. **REFERENCES** Hussain (1993), Kannan (1994).

BROWN HORNBILL *Anorrhinus tickelli* Plate 19

White-throated Brown Hornbill (I), *Ptilolaemus tickelli* (I,K)

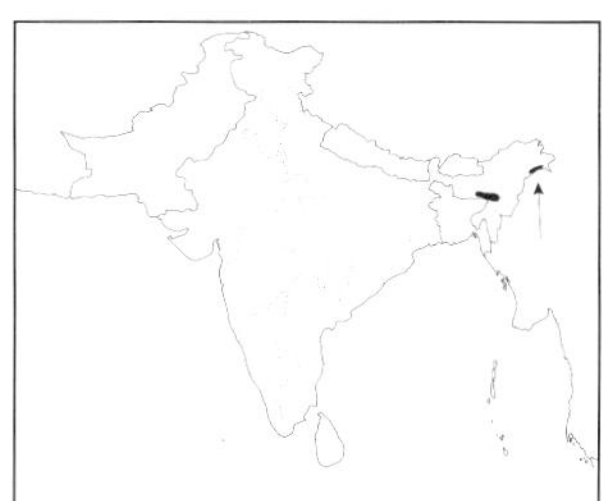

IDENTIFICATION 60–75 cm. A medium-sized brown hornbill. **Male** easily distinguished from Indian Grey Hornbill (p.396) by large and stout pale bill and casque, larger size, brown upperparts, whitish cheeks, throat and upper breast, and rufous-brown lower breast and belly. In flight, has white tips to all but central tail feathers and to primaries. Has blue circumorbital skin. **Female** is similar, although has entire underparts dusky brown, with pale streaking on crown and sides of head and rufous edging to feathers of throat and breast; lacks white tips to primaries and tail, but, like male, has small buffish-white panel across primaries. **Immature** is similar to adult male, but underparts are paler, has pale brown tips to wing-coverts, and orbital skin is pinkish. **VOICE** A high-pitched yelp; airy piercing screams, *kléé-ah*, very raptor-like (J. Scharringa). **HABITS** Often found with Oriental Pied Hornbill and other fruit-eating birds. Shy and restless; calls frequently. Usually keeps to the canopy of the highest forest trees. Flight is similar to that of other hornbills, but is relatively quiet. Normally flies only short distances through the canopy. **HABITAT** Evergreen broadleaved forest. **BREEDING** April–June. Nest hole is 4–9 m above ground. **DISTRIBUTION AND STATUS IN:** small population resident in the upper Brahmaputra valley (Arunachal Pradesh, Assam, Meghalaya); up to 1000 m. **REFERENCES** Hussain (1993).

RUFOUS-NECKED HORNBILL *Aceros nipalensis* Plate 19

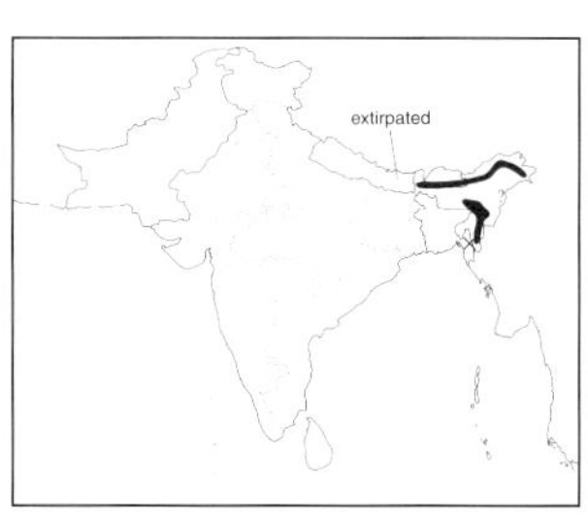

IDENTIFICATION 90–100 cm. The second-largest hornbill of the subcontinent, and really confusable only with Wreathed Hornbill (p.398). **Male** is easily distinguished from male Wreathed by bright rufous head, neck and underparts, black and white (rather than all-white) tail, scarlet gular pouch, and blue orbital skin. **Female**, being mainly black, more closely resembles female Wreathed and is best told by red throat and white terminal band to tail. In flight, both sexes show white wing-tips, unlike Wreathed, which has all-black wings. **Immature** is similar to adult male, but bill is smaller, unridged and unmarked; eyes are greenish-white, but other soft-part colours are undescribed. **VOICE** Short monosyllabic bark, repeated at regular one-second intervals, *kwuk-kwuk-kwuk...*, higher-pitched but otherwise similar to call of Great Hornbill (above) (P. Holt). **HABITS** Conspicuous, often perching in treetops in the open. Flies with deep undulations, resembling a woodpecker. Mainly arboreal, rarely feeding on the ground. **HABITAT** Tall, evergreen broadleaved forest. **BREEDING** April and May. Nest hole is 10–30 m above ground. **DISTRIBUTION AND STATUS** Resident. Himalayas from E Nepal east to Arunachal Pradesh; NE India and Bangladesh. Globally threatened. **NP:** probably extirpated; no records since 19th century. **IN:** small population in foothills below 1800 m; virtually all recent records are from Arunachal Pradesh. **BT:** fairly common; 150–2090 m. **BD:** ?former resident; no recent records, but may survive in Chittagong Hill Tracts. **REFERENCES** Hussain (1993).

WREATHED HORNBILL *Aceros undulatus* **Plate 19**

***Rhyticeros undulatus* (E,I,K)**

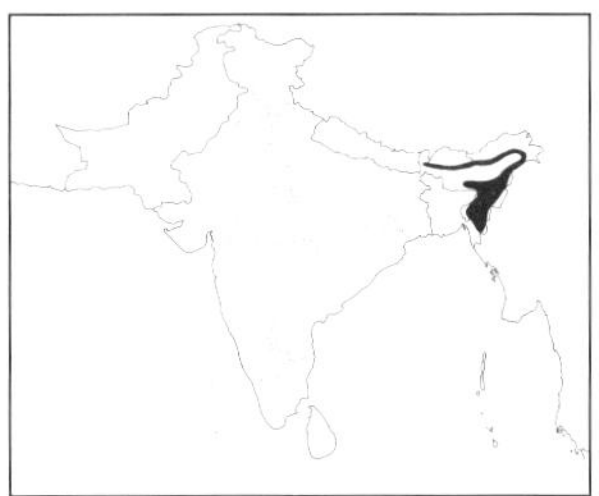

IDENTIFICATION 75–85 cm. **Male** is easily told from the slightly larger Rufous-necked Hornbill (p.397) by whitish sides of head, foreneck and upper breast (with rufous-brown crown and nape), and entirely white tail. Has yellow gular pouch and reddish circumorbital skin. **Female** has black head and neck, and more closely resembles female Rufous-necked, from which is best told by blue pouch, reddish circumorbital skin, and all-white tail. In flight, both sexes have all-black wings, unlike Rufous-necked. **Immature** is similar to adult male, but initially lacks casque and corrugations on bill; eyes are pale blue rather than red (adult male) or brown (adult female). Corrugations on sides of bill, and casque, begin to develop in first year, with new 'wreaths' added approximately once each year. For differences from the very similar Plain-pouched Hornbill (below), see that species. **VOICE** Very loud, gasping *uk-hweerk*, with emphasised second note; less harsh and grating than similar calls of Great Hornbill (p.397) (C. Robson). **HABITS** Often shy. Maintains highly regular feeding circuits and roosting flights. Frequently flies high above the canopy; glides less often than other large hornbills. In the non-breeding season, large flocks gather and follow each other in flight to roost together in tall trees or patches of giant bamboo. **HABITAT** Evergreen broadleaved forest and edges of forest clearings. **BREEDING** April and May. Nest hole recorded at 25 m above ground. **DISTRIBUTION AND STATUS** Resident. From West Bengal east to Arunachal Pradesh; NE India and Bangladesh. **IN:** locally fairly common in plains and foothills. **BT:** frequent; 250–655 m. **BD:** ?former resident; no recent records, but may survive in Chittagong Hill Tracts. **REFERENCES** Boonsong and Round (1991), Hussain (1993).

NARCONDAM HORNBILL *Aceros narcondami* **Plate 19**

***Rhyticeros (plicatus) narcondami*, Blyth's Hornbill (I)**

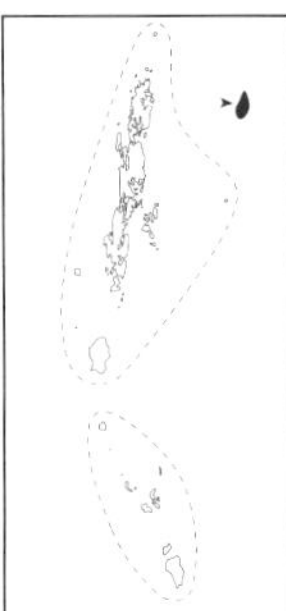

IDENTIFICATION 45–50 cm. A small hornbill with green-glossed black body and white tail. The only hornbill occurring on Narcondam I. Like small version of Rufous-necked Hornbill (p.397), but lacks black at base of tail and has bluish-white pouch. **Male** has rufous head and neck, yellowish-white bill with crimson at base, and blue circumorbital skin. **Female** has all-black head and neck, and iris is dark olive-brown (rather than reddish as in male). **Immature** is similar to adult male, but initially lacks casque; has less red at base of bill, and pale grey iris. Casque is grown, but not wreathed, by end of first year. **VOICE** A cackling *ka-ka-ka-ka-ka*. **HABITS** Noisy and confiding. Often undertakes leisurely flights in small parties from one part of the island to the other. Flight is heavy and slow. Feeds on wild fruits. **HABITAT** Mature forest. **BREEDING** Unknown. **DISTRIBUTION AND STATUS IN:** resident, endemic to Narcondam I, Andamans. Common, but considered globally threatened because of the island's small size and threats to the vegetation from feral goats. **REFERENCES** Hussain (1984), Prakash (1995), Sankaran and Vijayan (1993).

PLAIN-POUCHED HORNBILL *Aceros subruficollis* **Plate 19**

Rhyticeros plicatus* (K), *A. undulatus

IDENTIFICATION 65–70 cm. A medium-sized hornbill with black body and white tail. In all plumages very similar to Wreathed Hornbill (p.above), and best distinguished by smaller size with proportionately longer and narrower wings, cleaner ivory bill lacking corrugations on sides of mandible (although these also lacking on immature Wreathed until approximately one year old), and unmarked pouch. In flight, has all-black wings like Wreathed. **Male** has whitish head, neck and upper breast, with rufous-brown crown and nape, reddish-purple circumorbital skin, and bare yellow pouch. **Female** has black head and neck, dull pink circumorbital skin and blue pouch. **Immature** like adult male, but lacks casque and red at base of bill. **VOICE** A *keh-kek-kehk*, higher-pitched, more quacking and less booming than the normal two-noted call of Wreathed. **DISTRIBUTION AND STATUS** Globally threatened. A specimen collected from Margherita, Assam, is detailed in Kemp (1988, 1995), but has since been reidentified as a Wreathed Hornbill. **REFERENCES** Boonsong and Round (1991).

ORIENTAL PIED HORNBILL *Anthracoceros albirostris* **Plate 18**

Indian Pied Hornbill (I,K), Pied Hornbill (F), *A. malabaricus* (E,F,I)

IDENTIFICATION 55–60 cm. A medium-sized pied hornbill with large and strikingly patterned casque and bill. In flight, shows white trailing edge to wings. Very similar to the larger Malabar Pied Hornbill (p.399), and best distinguished by casque patterning and shape (cylindrical rather than axe-shaped, with black patch at tip, lacking

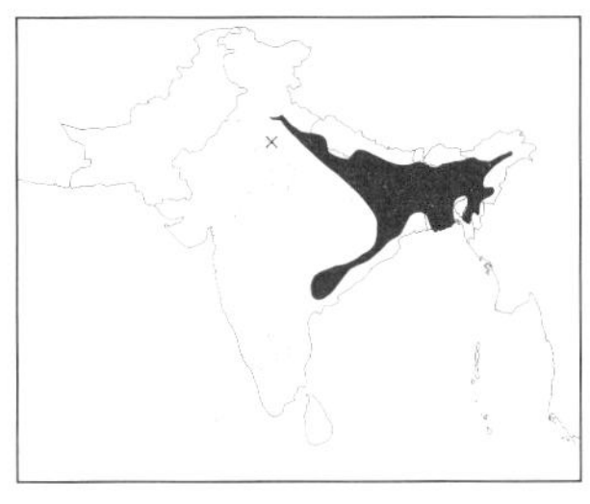

Malabar Pied's black patch along upper ridge). Also has mainly black tail with white tips to all but central feathers, narrower white trailing edge to secondaries, and pale blue (rather than pink) throat patches. Sexes are similar, but **female** is smaller, with marked sexual dimorphism in casque size, shape and amount of black pigmentation (unlike Malabar Pied). Female has less convex casque lacking projecting tip, and shows much black at tip of bill and some on posterior tip of casque (unlike Malabar Pied). Both sexes have pale blue circumorbital skin (blue-black on male and pinkish-white on female Malabar Pied). **Immature** has smaller bill and poorly developed casque with less black; orbital skin is whitish, with a tinge of pink posteriorly and blue anteriorly, and the throat patch is whitish-pink. **VOICE** A variety of loud, shrill, nasal squeals and raucous chucks, including loud cackling *kleng-kleng, kek-kek-kek-kek-kek* (Kemp 1995). **HABITS** Often feeds in parties together with Indian Grey Hornbill (p.396) and other frugivorous species. Quite shy. Mainly arboreal, but regularly feeds on the ground on fallen fruit, termites and other insects; also takes fish and nestling birds; sometimes hawks flying termites. **HABITAT** Open, moist broadleaved deciduous and evergreen forest; groves of large mangos, figs and other fruit trees near villages. **BREEDING** April and May. **DISTRIBUTION AND STATUS** Resident, subject to local movements depending on fruiting season. From Haryana east through the Himalayan foothills to Arunachal Pradesh; NE and E India, and Bangladesh. **NP:** local and fairly common below 250 m, probably declining. **IN:** locally common, but declining; plains up to 350 m. **BT:** frequent; 250–450 m. **BD:** local, the commonest hornbill. **REFERENCES** Frith and Frith (1983), Hussain (1993), Shrestha (1993).

MALABAR PIED HORNBILL *Anthracoceros coronatus* Plate 18

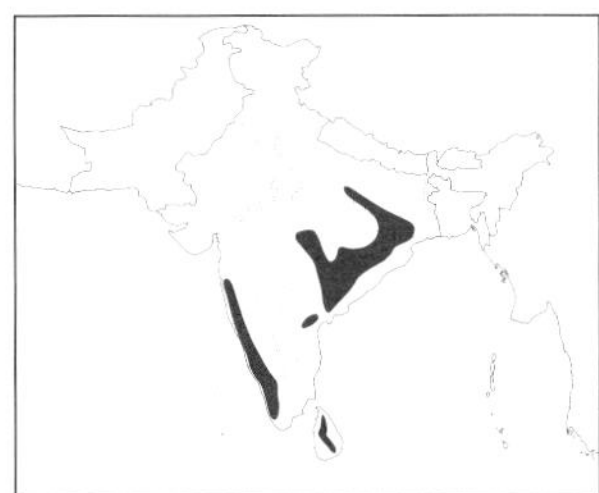

IDENTIFICATION 65 cm. A medium-sized pied hornbill with large and strikingly patterned casque and bill. In flight, shows broad white trailing edge to wings and white sides to tail. Very similar to the smaller Oriental Pied Hornbill (p.398), but has different casque shape and patterning (axe-shaped in both sexes, with pronounced tip, and large black patch along upper ridge). Also has white outer tail feathers (can show black at base of these, especially on immatures, but this is not so extensive as on Oriental Pied), broader white trailing edge to wings (with broad white tips to all but innermost secondaries), and pinkish throat patches. Sexes are similar; **female** has a slightly smaller casque than male (and lacks black at posterior end), although it is similar in shape (whereas Oriental Pied exhibits pronounced sexual dimorphism in casque shape), and has pinkish (blue-black on male) circumorbital skin. Bill lacks black at tip (unlike on female Oriental Pied). **Immature** has smaller bill than adult, with a poorly developed casque which has smaller black markings; bare facial skin is as on respective adults. **VOICE** A variety of loud, shrill squeals and raucous cackles, including a loud cackling *kleng-keng, kek-kek-kek-kek-kek-kek* which rises in pitch and volume (Kemp 1995). **HABITS** Very similar to those of Oriental Pied Hornbill. **HABITAT** Open, moist, broadleaved deciduous and evergreen forest; also large mangos, figs and other fruit trees near villages. **BREEDING** March–September, varying locally. Nest hole is 3.5–15 m above ground. **DISTRIBUTION AND STATUS** Resident, endemic to the subcontinent. Subject to seasonal local movements, depending on availability of fruit. Western Ghats, E India and Sri Lanka. **IN:** common in a few areas, but declining; up to 300 m. **LK:** local and moderately plentiful; now confined to more secluded forest of the dry lowlands. **REFERENCES** Frith and Frith (1983), Ginige and Kotagama (1993), Hussain (1993).

HOOPOES Upupidae

Hoopoes have a distinctive appearance, with a long decurved bill, short legs, rounded wings, and a mainly cinnamon-pink plumage with the wings boldly patterned black and white. They are insectivorous and forage on the ground.

COMMON HOOPOE *Upupa epops* Plate 20

Hoopoe (F,I,N,R)

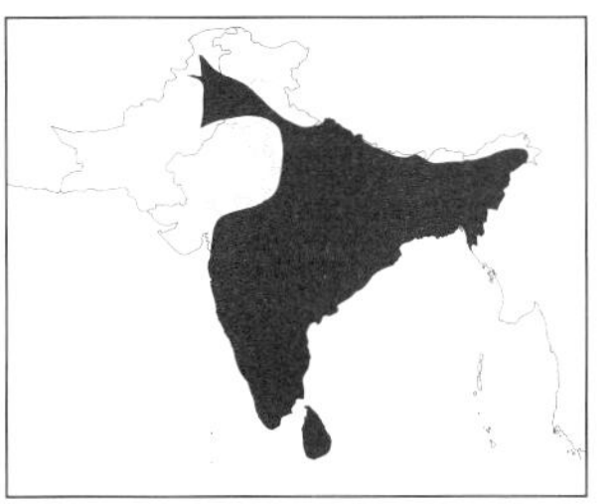

IDENTIFICATION 31 cm. Mainly rufous-orange or orange-buff, with striking black-and-white wings and tail, black-tipped fan-like crest which is usually held flat, and long, thin downcurved bill. Broad, rounded wings in flight. **VOICE** A pleasant, repetitive and mellow *poop, poop, poop*; similar to call of Oriental Cuckoo (p.412), which usually has four notes rather than two or three. **HABITS** Usually seen singly or in pairs; also in loose flocks when migrating. Perches and roosts in trees. Searches for food on the ground, running and walking about actively, probing and pecking. Feeds entirely on insects, particularly soft larvae. Flight is undulating, slow and butterfly-like, with irregular wingbeats. **HABITAT** Open country, lightly wooded areas, cultivation and villages.

Prefers areas where there is some grass or herb cover. **BREEDING** Late March–August, varying locally. Nests in a tree hollow or in hole in wall of a building. **DISTRIBUTION AND STATUS** Summer visitor to N and W Pakistan and the higher Himalayas east to Arunachal Pradesh; winters in SE Pakistan and NW India; resident and winter visitor throughout much of the rest of subcontinent. **PK:** common; breeds at up to 3050 m. **NP:** fairly common; resident up to 1500 m, summers to 4400 m (–5900 m on passage). **IN:** common summer visitor to Himalayas, common in the peninsula, especially in winter. **BT:** fairly common; 150–2870 m. **BD:** local resident. **LK:** resident in dry lowlands and E hills, occasionally recorded in the wet zone, possibly also a winter visitor. **MV:** rare visitor.

TROGONS Trogonidae

Brightly coloured, short-necked, medium-sized birds with a long tail, short rounded wings and a rather short, broad bill. All trogons are arboreal, in the subcontinent confined to dense forests, where they are inconspicuous in the gloomy forest light. They usually keep singly or in widely separated pairs. Characteristically, they perch almost motionless in upright posture for long periods in the middle or lower forest storey. Trogons eat mainly caterpillars, beetles, grasshoppers, cicadas and other insects; also leaves and berries. They capture flying insects on the wing when moving from one vantage point to another, twisting and turning with the agility of a flycatcher. Insects are also snatched while they hover in front of foliage, and occasionally by swooping to the ground. Indian trogons nest in unlined natural tree hollows or on top of broken tree stumps in dense forest.

MALABAR TROGON *Harpactes fasciatus* — Plate 20

Ceylon Trogon (P)

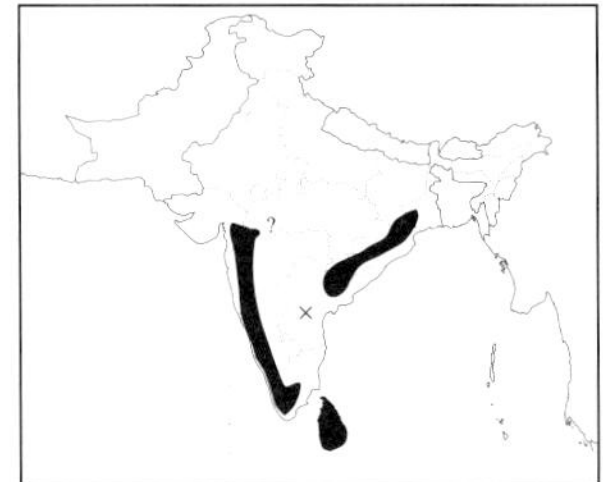

IDENTIFICATION 31 cm. The only trogon occurring in peninsular India and Sri Lanka. **Male** has dark head, neck and upper breast, cinnamon upperparts, and pink underparts with a narrow white breast-band. **Female** has cinnamon underparts, narrow buff breast-band, and dark cinnamon head, upper breast and upperparts; brown coverts and secondaries are finely vermiculated with buff (black, vermiculated with pale grey, on male). **Immature male** resembles female, but has brownish-black head and breast (grey in Sri Lankan race) contrasting with mantle, and dark of breast is separated from cinnamon underparts by broad white band. Often has traces of pink on underparts. Coverts are initially vermiculated with buff (later with grey). **Racial variation** Head, neck and upper breast are black in *H. f. malabaricus* of the peninsula and grey in *H. f. fasciatus* of Sri Lanka. **VOICE** A throaty, musical *cue-cue-cue*, and a low rolling *krr-r-r-r* when alarmed (Ali and Ripley 1987). **HABITS** Typical of those of the family in the region. **HABITAT** Middle storey of dense broadleaved evergreen, semi-evergreen and moist deciduous forest, preferably with an abundance of bamboo, in tropical and subtropical zones. **BREEDING** February–May, varying locally. Nests below 6 m from ground. **DISTRIBUTION AND STATUS** Resident, endemic to India and Sri Lanka. From the Surat Dangs south through the Western Ghats and east to C Tamil Nadu; patchily in E India; Sri Lanka. **IN:** locally frequent; plains up to 1500 m. **LK:** frequent in remaining humid forest of the wet zone, infrequent in dry and hill country.

RED-HEADED TROGON *Harpactes erythrocephalus* — Plate 20

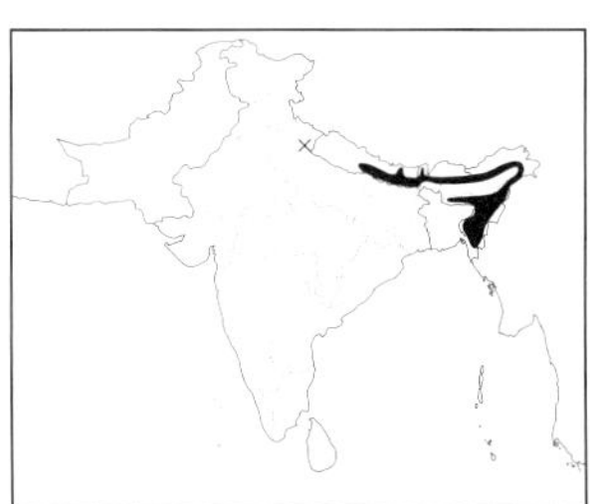

IDENTIFICATION 35 cm. **Male** has crimson head, neck and breast, prominent white breast-band, and pink on rest of underparts. **Female** is similar, with white breast-band and pink underparts, but has cinnamon head, neck and breast; brown coverts and secondaries are finely vermiculated with buff (black, vermiculated with pale grey, on male). **Immature** resembles female, but is buffish-white (rather than pink) on lower breast, belly and flanks. Older immature male resembles female (with pink underparts), but has pale grey (rather than buff) vermiculations on coverts. **VOICE** Song is five or more well-spaced notes in a descending sequence *tyaup, tyaup, tyaup, tyaup, tyaup...* (J. Scharringa). **HABITS** Typical of those of the family in the region. **HABITAT** Middle storey of dense broadleaved evergreen forest and mixed bamboo in tropical and subtropical zones. **BREEDING** April–July. Nests 1.5–5 m above ground. **DISTRIBUTION AND STATUS** Resident. Himalayas in N Uttar Pradesh and from C Nepal east to Arunachal Pradesh; NE India and Bangladesh. **NP:** now local and uncommon; mainly 250–1000 m. **IN:** locally fairly common in the northeast, uncommon elsewhere; terai up to 1800 m (–2400 m). **BT:** frequent; 245–2090 m. **BD:** local.

WARD'S TROGON *Harpactes wardi* — Plate 20

IDENTIFICATION 38 cm. Largest trogon in the subcontinent. **Male** is very distinctive, with maroon head, breast and mantle, pink forehead and supercilium, and pink underparts and outer tail feathers. Bill is also deep pink. Has large white patch at base of secondaries. **Female** is equally distinctive, with dark olive-brown head, breast and

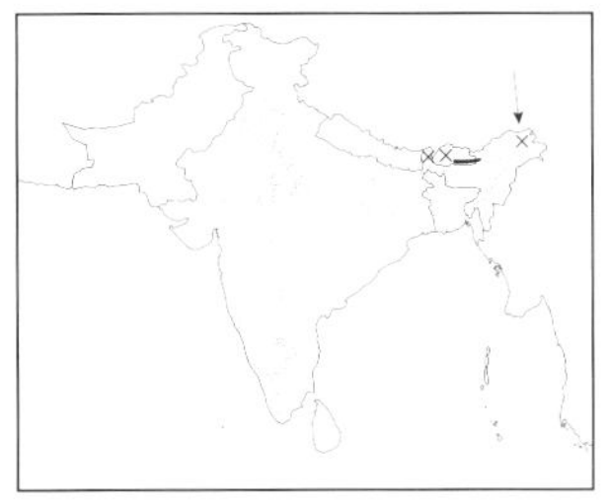

mantle (with maroon cast), yellow supercilium, and yellow underparts and outer tail feathers; coverts and secondaries are finely vermiculated with buff (pale grey on male). **VOICE** Rapid series of mellow *klew* notes, often slightly accelerating and dropping in pitch towards the end; very different from the slower, more evenly paced corvid-like *tyaup* notes of Red-headed Trogon (p.400) (P. Holt from K. D. Bishop recording). **HABITS** Typical of those of the family in the region. **HABITAT** Lower storey, undergrowth and bamboo in subtropical and temperate broadleaved evergreen forest. **BREEDING** Collected in breeding condition in early April. Nest not yet recorded. **DISTRIBUTION AND STATUS** Resident. Himalayas from Sikkim east to Arunachal Pradesh, at 1500–3200 m (down to 300 m). Globally threatened. **IN:** rare and local. **BT:** local and rare. **REFERENCES** Ganguli-Lachungpa (1996), Singh (1995), Tymstra *et al.* (1997).

ROLLERS Coraciidae

Stoutly built, medium-sized birds with large head and short neck. They are named for their habit of rolling or somersaulting in breeding display flights whilst uttering raucous cries. Large insects, crickets, beetles, flying termites, locusts and moths form their main food; they also eat frogs, lizards and small mammals. Typically, they keep singly or in widely spaced pairs. Flight is buoyant, with rather rapid deliberate wingbeats. Natural hollows in tree trunks or branches are their usual nest sites, although they sometimes use holes in walls or cliffs. The main reference specific to rollers is Fry *et al.* (1992).

EUROPEAN ROLLER *Coracias garrulus* — Plate 20

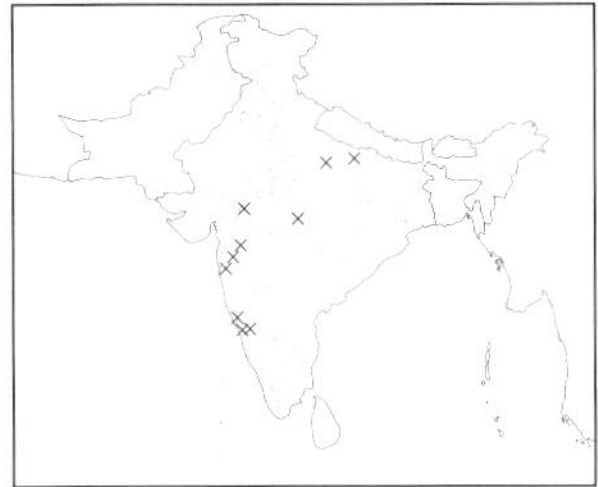

IDENTIFICATION 31 cm. **Adult breeding** differs from Indian Roller (below) in turquoise-blue head, neck and underparts (with brighter blue streaking on throat and breast), and rufous-cinnamon mantle and tertials. Primaries and secondaries are black, and has black corners to tail (lacks turquoise band across primaries and dark blue terminal band to tail, which are features of Indian). **Adult non-breeding** has paler blue head, neck and underparts, with brownish cast to nape and breast, and duller rufous-brown mantle. **Juvenile** is similar to adult non-breeding, but has brownish coloration to head, neck and breast; tail is more rounded, and more uniform pale greyish-blue, and lacks black tips to outer feathers, while ear-coverts, throat and breast are finely streaked with white. More easily confused with Indian, but has turquoise-blue cast to ear-coverts, crown and nape, which contrast with browner mantle, and different pattern to wings and tail (lacking dark terminal tail-band and turquoise patch in primaries). **VOICE** Calls include a *ack-er-ack, rack-kack* or *kacker*, a slower *krak*, and a sharper, mournful *kraa* (Cramp 1985). **HABITS** Similar to those of Indian Roller. Territorial in the breeding season. **HABITAT** Open woodland and cultivation; breeds in drier valleys. **BREEDING** May–July. Has an unlined nest in a typical roller site. **DISTRIBUTION AND STATUS** Breeding summer visitor to W Pakistan and Jammu and Kashmir; widely distributed on passage, mainly in Pakistan and NW India. Arrives end March–May; most birds pass through, some remaining to breed; return passage in July–October. **PK:** frequent; breeds mainly at 900–1300 m. **IN:** locally frequent; breeds from foothills up to 2000 m. **REFERENCES** Sangha (1995).

INDIAN ROLLER *Coracias benghalensis* — Plate 20

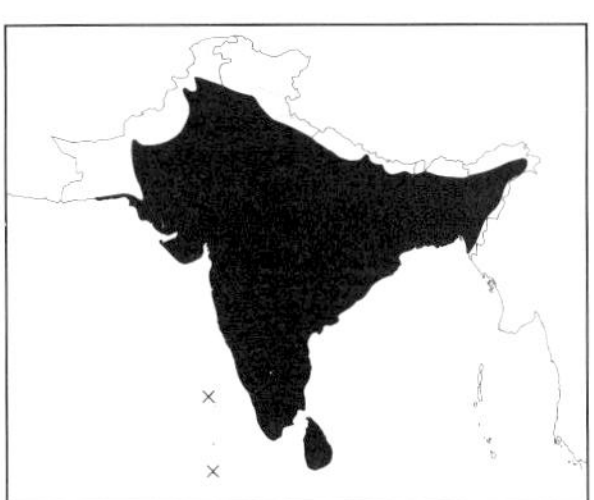

IDENTIFICATION 33 cm. Throughout most of range, readily distinguished by turquoise crown, rufous-brown nape, ear-coverts, throat and breast (contrasting with turquoise lower belly and vent), brownish olive-green mantle and tertials, and turquoise and deep blue in wings and tail. Has white streaking and lilac flush to ear-coverts, throat and breast. In flight, shows turquoise sides and dark blue terminal band to tail, turquoise panel across primaries, and turquoise underwing-coverts. Flight is direct but buoyant, with broad round-tipped wings. In NW subcontinent confusable with European Roller (above); see that species for differences. **Juvenile** resembles adult, but is duller; has more heavily streaked throat and breast, and mantle and tertials are drab brown. **Racial variation** *C. b. affinis* of NE subcontinent has strong purplish-blue flush to rufous-brownish underparts, blue (rather than whitish) streaking on throat, darker, deeper brownish-green upperparts, and deep purple-blue underwing-coverts; also lacks broad dark blue terminal band to tail, and outer tail is mainly turquoise with black tips to outer feathers. Juvenile of this race lacks purplish-blue flush to underparts and has whitish shaft streaking on throat; it is darker on upperparts and underparts than juvenile of nominate race, and tail pattern is as adult *affinis*. **VOICE** Call is a raucous *chack-chack-chack*, with various discordant screeches and shrieks. **HABITS** Spends most of the day on a prominent perch such as a telegraph wire, post or dead tree in open country, scanning for prey. Swoops leisurely down to capture prey on the ground. Often hunts until dusk is well advanced. Aggressively territorial throughout much of the year. Often attracted to fires, where it recklessly pursues insects. **HABITAT** Cultivation, gardens, groves near villages and open deciduous forest. **BREEDING** January–July, varying locally. Has an untidy nest of grass, bits of paper and rags in a typical roller site. **DISTRIBUTION AND STATUS** Resident throughout much of the subcontinent; subject to poorly understood local seasonal movements. **PK:** common and very widespread. **NP::** common below 1050 m (–3655 m). **IN:** common and very widespread; plains up to 1000 m, locally to 1500 m. **BT:** frequent; 275–620 m (–2440 m). **BD:** common throughout. **LK:** common resident in lowlands, most frequent in dry zone; visitor to mid altitudes. **MV:** rare winter visitor.

DOLLARBIRD *Eurystomus orientalis* — Plate 20

Broad-billed Roller (I), Dark Roller (F), Asian Broad-billed Roller (P)

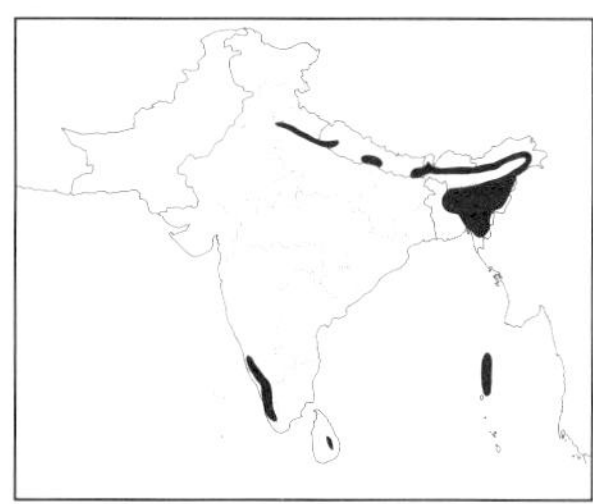

IDENTIFICATION 28 cm. At a distance, appears black with bright red bill. Flashes turquoise patch across primaries in flight. Shape is similar to that of Indian Roller (p.401), but has shorter and stouter bill, proportionately larger head and thicker neck, and shorter tail. Flight is also similar: buoyant, with broad round-tipped wings. At close range, has greenish-brown coloration to mantle, wing-coverts and underparts, and browner head. Has red eye-ring. **Juvenile** is similar, but has dull pinkish bill. **Racial variation** *E. o. laetior* and *E. o. irisi* of Western Ghats and Sri Lanka respectively have brighter, blue underparts and blacker head than *E. o. cyanicollis* of the Himalayan foothills and terai, and NE subcontinent. **VOICE** A raucous *check check*. **HABITS** Spends long periods in the daytime perched inactively on tops of dead trees, only occasionally making short flights after insects. Feeds chiefly in late afternoons and evenings, continuing until dark. Hawks insects on the wing; small parties gather and hawk in circles where insects are swarming. Capable of agile aerial manoeuvring when chasing prey. Territorial in the breeding season. **HABITAT** Tropical forest, forest clearings with scattered trees, and overgrown rubber plantations. **BREEDING** March–May. Has an unlined nest in a natural tree hollow or disused woodpecker or barbet hole. **DISTRIBUTION AND STATUS** Resident and partial migrant. Himalayas from N Haryana east to Arunachal Pradesh; NE India and Bangladesh; SW India and Sri Lanka. **NP:** local summer visitor; mainly below 365 m (–1300 m). **IN:** resident, locally fairly common; plains up to 1000 m (–2500 m). **BT:** locally fairly common resident; 250–825 m. **BD:** local winter visitor. **LK:** very rare resident in lowlands and lower hills, mainly in wet zone.

SMALL KINGFISHERS Alcedinidae, LARGE KINGFISHERS Halcyonidae AND PIED KINGFISHERS Cerylidae

Small to medium-sized birds with large head, long strong beak and short legs. Most kingfishers spend long periods perched singly or in well-separated pairs, watching intently for prey. Occasionally they jerk the tail, and on spotting quarry they typically bob head and body to help judge distance before plunging swiftly downwards to seize prey with bill; they usually return to the perch, where the prey item is beaten until immobile and then swallowed whole. They eat mainly fish, tadpoles and invertebrates; larger species also eat frogs, snakes, crabs, lizards and rodents. Their flight is direct and strong, with rapid wingbeats. When moving between perches by watercourses, they fly close to the surface. Kingfishers actively defend a territory throughout the year. Most dig nesting tunnels with their beak into steep earthen banks of watercourses, roadside cuttings, sides of dry ditches or dry forest ravines, sometimes far from water. The tunnels are up to 1.5 m long, terminating in a widened, unlined egg chamber. The main reference specific to kingfishers is Fry *et al.* (1992).

BLYTH'S KINGFISHER *Alcedo hercules* — Plate 21

Great Blue Kingfisher (F)

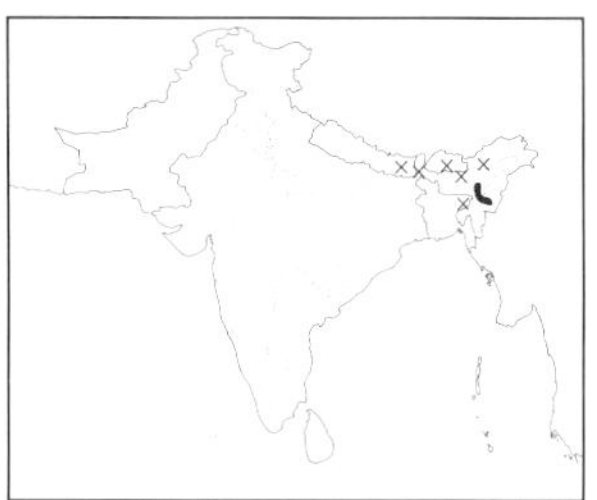

IDENTIFICATION 22 cm. A medium-sized, dark blue and orange, forest-dwelling kingfisher with large bill. Superficially like a giant Common Kingfisher (p.403) without orange ear-coverts. Best told from that species and from Blue-eared Kingfisher (p.403) by considerably larger size and larger and longer bill, darker greenish-blue (almost brownish-black) coloration to scapulars and wings (with prominent turquoise spotting on lesser and median coverts), which more strongly contrast in flight with brilliant blue back and rump, almost blackish crown with sharply contrasting turquoise spotting, and less distinct orange loral spot. **Female** same as male, but with red at base of lower mandible. **VOICE** Similar to Common, but louder and hoarser. The call, which is given in flight, consists of a shrill single note, more powerful and with a deeper tone than that of other members of the genus (J. Eames). **HABITS** Generally similar to those of Common, but is shy and poorly known. Perches inconspicuously in low bushes overhanging water to watch for prey. When disturbed, will first hop up into bush to conceal itself, then flies away if approached closer. **HABITAT** Shaded streams in dense, broadleaved evergreen tropical and subtropical forest. **BREEDING** March–June. **DISTRIBUTION AND STATUS** Resident, mainly in NE India (Arunachal Pradesh, Assam, Manipur, Sikkim). Globally threatened. **NP:** vagrant. **IN:** rare, in duars and foothills up to 1200 m. **BT:** rare; 400–1000 m. **BD:** vagrant. **REFERENCES** Athreya *et al.* (1997), Long *et al.* (1992).

COMMON KINGFISHER *Alcedo atthis* — Plate 21

Eurasian Kingfisher (F,N)

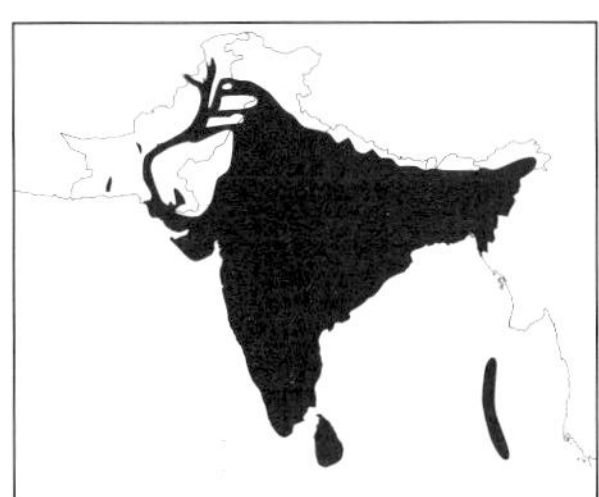

IDENTIFICATION 16 cm. A small, brilliant turquoise-blue and orange kingfisher, typically found in open country. Distinguished from the similar forest-dwelling Blue-eared Kingfisher (below) by orange ear-coverts, paler greenish-blue upperparts (crown, scapulars and wings) with paler turquoise-blue line down back, and paler orange underparts. For differences from juvenile Blue-eared, which also has rufous ear-coverts, and from Blyth's Kingfisher (p.402), see those species. **Juvenile** is similar to adult, but duller and greener above, with dusky scaling on breast. **Racial variation** *A. a. taprobana* of peninsular India and Sri Lanka is darker blue, less green, than the other two races occurring in the subcontinent, although not so blue as Blue-eared. **VOICE** A high-pitched shrill *chee*, usually repeated, and *chit-it-it* alarm call. **HABITS** Tame and confiding. Uses a post, reed, or bank at the water's edge as a vantage point, perching 1–2 m above the surface. Plunges headlong into the water to catch prey; may submerge completely, and sometimes hovers before diving. Flies swiftly and directly low over the water or trees, often calling. **HABITAT** Streams, rivers, canals, ditches, ponds and lakes in open country; avoids shady forest; also mangrove swamps and the seashore in winter. **BREEDING** November–June, varying locally. **DISTRIBUTION AND STATUS** Resident throughout much of subcontinent, except parts of the northwest. **PK:** partly resident, partly local migrant; common in lower Sindh, frequent elsewhere. **NP:** fairly common resident below 1000 m; frequent up to 1800 m (–3050 m). **IN:** common, partly resident and partly migratory; plains up to 2000 m (–3100 m). **BT:** uncommon; 250–2745 m. **BD:** common resident. **LK:** common resident throughout, less so in hills.

BLUE-EARED KINGFISHER *Alcedo meninting* — Plate 21

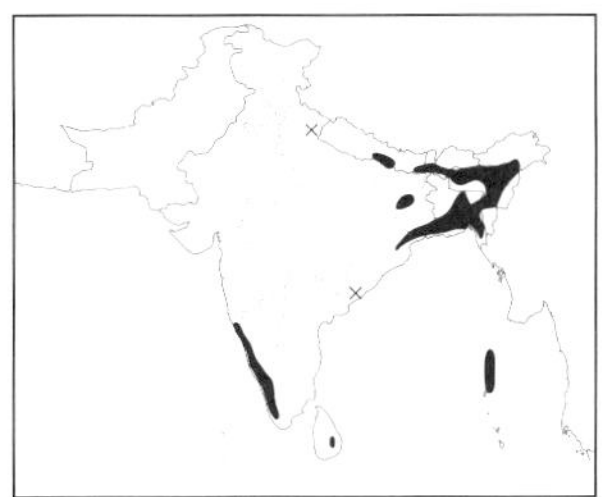

IDENTIFICATION 16 cm. A small, blue and orange, forest-dwelling kingfisher. Resembles the cosmopolitan Common Kingfisher (above), but distinguished by blue rather than orange ear-coverts (except in juvenile plumage), darker blue upperparts (lacking greenish tones to crown, scapulars and wings, and almost purplish-blue around cheeks, nape and upper mantle), darker brilliant blue line down centre of back and rump, and deeper orange underparts. Sexes alike. **Juvenile**, confusingly, has rufous-orange ear-coverts as on Common, but has darker blue upperparts (similar in coloration to adult) and lacks the broad blue moustachial stripe of that species (although can show short black moustachial which does not extend beyond ear-coverts). **VOICE** Call is typically a shrill, single *seet* or *tsit*, higher-pitched though quieter and less strident than Common Kingfisher's; contact calls are thin, shrill *striiiit, trrrrrt, tit.trrrreu* etc, in various combinations. Juvenile has a short, harsh *chit* similar to the call of Pygmy Wren Babbler (p.757) (C. Robson). **HABITS** Very similar to those of Common, but shy. **HABITAT** By streams in dense, shady, broadleaved evergreen tropical and subtropical forest or thick bamboo; also streams through patches of rice cultivation in Kerala, and tidal creeks fringed with mangroves in Andamans. **BREEDING** April–August. **DISTRIBUTION AND STATUS** Resident. Himalayan foothills from C Nepal east to SE Arunachal Pradesh; NE India and Bangladesh and south to Orissa; SW India and Sri Lanka. Recorded at up to 1000 m, occasionally 1500 m. **NP:** scarce and local in lowlands. **IN:** generally rare. **BT:** once collected in 19th century. **BD:** rare? resident. **LK:** very rare resident in lowlands and E foothills.

ORIENTAL DWARF KINGFISHER *Ceyx erithacus* — Plate 21

Black-backed Kingfisher, Three-toed Kingfisher (F,I), Oriental Kingfisher (N), Indian Three-toed Kingfisher (P)

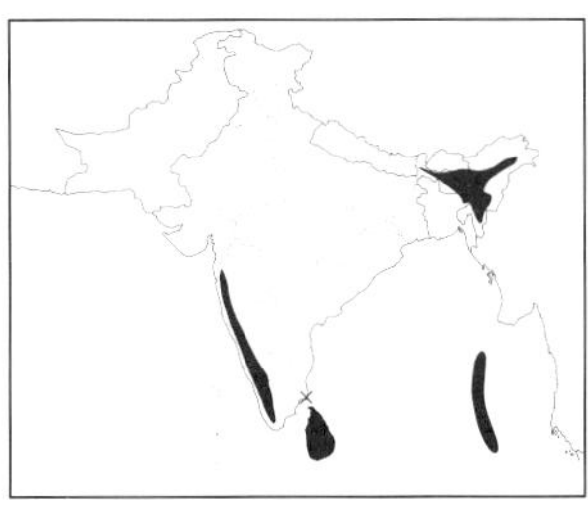

IDENTIFICATION 13 cm. A tiny forest kingfisher with coral-red bill. Has orange head, with variable violet iridescence on crown and nape, black mantle, back, scapulars and wings, with the coverts and scapulars boldly marked with blue, pale orange underparts, and orange rump and tail also with violet iridescence. Sexes similar. **Juvenile** is similar to adult, but duller. Bill is initially black, becoming pale yellow-orange. Underparts are whitish with orange breast-band, crown is more orange (less violet), and has less blue in upperparts. **Racial variation** *C. e. rufidorsa* has rufous-orange upperparts, with violet wash especially to crown and rump, and lacks blue flash (bordering white spot) at rear of ear-coverts of nominate race. Juvenile is similar to juvenile nominate, but head, mantle and coverts are rufous-orange. **VOICE** Call is a weak, thin *seet* or *tseet*, thinner and higher-pitched than Blue-eared's. Contact calls include a weak, shrill *tit-sreet* and *tit-tit* (C. Robson). **HABITS** Perches in a shaded position on a rock or low in vegetation. Takes aquatic prey just below the water surface; also frequently takes insects from the ground and from foliage. Wary; when disturbed, darts off, calling. **HABITAT** Shady, small streams in broadleaved evergreen and moist deciduous tropical forest. **BREEDING** February–September, varying locally. **DISTRIBUTION AND STATUS** Resident. Himalayan foothills from Sikkim east to Arunachal Pradesh; NE India and Bangladesh; SW India and Sri Lanka. **NP:** possibly collected in 19th century, but the specimen may have originated in India. **IN:** scarce resident up to 1000 m; subject to local movements, depending on water conditions; a specimen identified as *rufidorsa* was collected from Sikkim in July 1909, but may have been an aberrant individual. **BT:** rare and local. **BD:** scarce summer visitor. **LK:** scarce resident in lowlands and lower hills, most frequent in foothills of wet zone. **REFERENCES** Ripley and Beehler (1987).

BROWN-WINGED KINGFISHER *Halcyon amauroptera* — Plate 21

***Pelargopsis amauroptera* (I)**

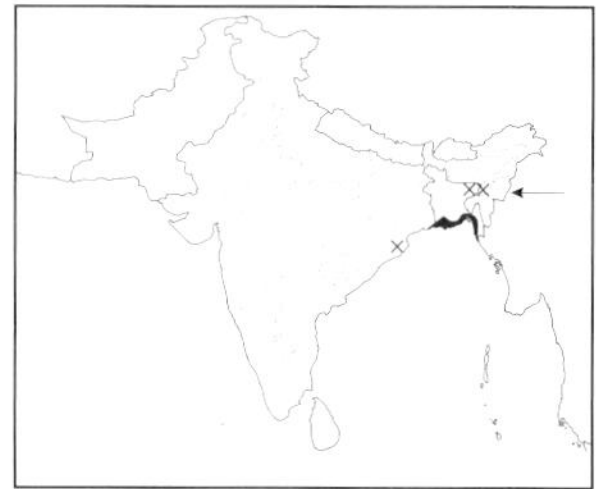

IDENTIFICATION 36 cm. A very large coastal kingfisher with huge red bill. Superficially resembles Stork-billed Kingfisher (below) and best distinguished by brown mantle, wings and tail which contrast strongly with turquoise rump and lower back (especially in flight). Lacks the brown cap of Stork-billed, and the entire head and underparts are rich brownish-orange. Sexes alike. **Juvenile** has pale fringes to mantle and wing-coverts, and fine dusky barring on nape and underparts. **VOICE** A deep laughing *cha-cha-cha-cha*, descending in pitch, and a pleasant mournful *chow-chow-chow* whistle. **HABITS** Usually watches from perch fairly high in mangroves. Captures prey by diving into the water or by landing on mud and seizing quarry from the surface; sometimes plunges into rough surf. Movements are slow and deliberate when perched. Flies like Stork-billed. **HABITAT** Restricted to coasts: mangrove swamps, tidal rivers and creeks. **BREEDING** Very poorly known. March and April. **DISTRIBUTION AND STATUS** Resident, possibly also a winter visitor. West Bengal, Orissa, Assam and Bangladesh. **IN:** locally common. **BD:** locally common resident or winter visitor. **REFERENCES** Daniel and Hussain (1975), Pandav (1997).

STORK-BILLED KINGFISHER *Halcyon capensis* — Plate 21

***Pelargopsis capensis* (F,I,N,P)**

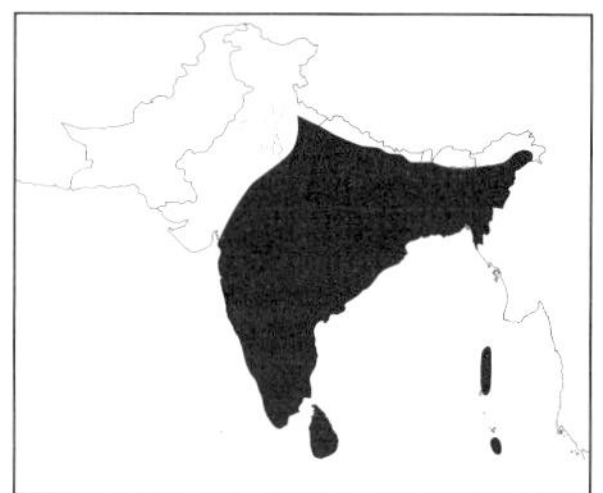

IDENTIFICATION 38 cm. A very large, predominantly freshwater kingfisher. Easily distinguished by huge coral-red bill, brownish cap, pale orange-buff collar and underparts, and blue-green upperparts. In flight, shows turquoise rump and lower back. Sexes alike. For differences from Brown-winged Kingfisher (above), see that species. **Juvenile** has dusky barring on underparts, especially on breast (forming a broad band). **Racial variation** *H. c. intermedia* of the Nicobar Is differs from the nominate race (described above) in that it lacks the brown cap, has an entirely orange-buff head with brown flecks on crown, and has much deeper blue upperparts. *H. c. osmastoni* of the Andaman Is has a paler grey-brown crown which contrasts less with the collar than in nominate race. **VOICE** An explosive, shrieking laugh, *ke-ke-ke-ke-ke*, and pleasant *peer, peer, pur* (Ali and Ripley 1987). Song is a long series of usually paired melancholy whistles, *iuu-iuu..iuu-iuu..iuu-iuu..iuu-iuu..iuu-iuu...* etc (the *i* being higher-pitched than the *uu*); frequently in duet with rasping calls (J. Scharringa). **HABITS** Rather sluggish, and heard more often than seen. Sits, often half-hidden, on a branch overhanging water, occasionally diving down to catch prey. Flight is strong, direct and steady. **HABITAT** Deeply shaded lakes, slow-moving rivers, streams and irrigation channels in well-wooded country; Screw Pine-lined coastal backwaters in Kerala; tidal creeks in mangrove forest and seashore in Andamans and Nicobars. **BREEDING** January–September, varying locally. **DISTRIBUTION AND STATUS** Resident. From Uttar Pradesh and Gujarat east through much of the subcontinent. **NP:** frequent below 760 m. **IN:** locally common in plains and foothills, occasionally up to 1200 m. **BD:** locally common. **LK:** mainly in dry lowlands, where common; also at mid altitudes.

RUDDY KINGFISHER *Halcyon coromanda* — Plate 21

IDENTIFICATION 26 cm. A medium-sized forest kingfisher. Unmistakable, with large coral-red bill, rufous-orange upperparts with brilliant violet gloss, and paler rufous underparts. In flight, shows striking bluish-white rump. Sexes alike. **Juvenile** lacks the violet gloss; is darker and browner on upperparts, and has bluer rump, faint blackish barring on rufous underparts, and blackish bill with orange-red tip. **Racial variation** *H. c. mizorhina* of the Andaman Is has a larger bill than the widespread nominate race, and much darker underparts often with violet wash on breast. **VOICE** Call not unlike that of White-throated Kingfisher (p.405), but more musical: a descending and high-pitched trill *tititititititi*. Song, uttered when perched, is a relatively soft and trilling *tyuur-rrrr*, incessantly repeated with one-second intervals (J. Scharringa). **HABITS** Secretive, shy and little known; heard more often than seen. **HABITAT** Pools and streams in dense broadleaved evergreen tropical and subtropical

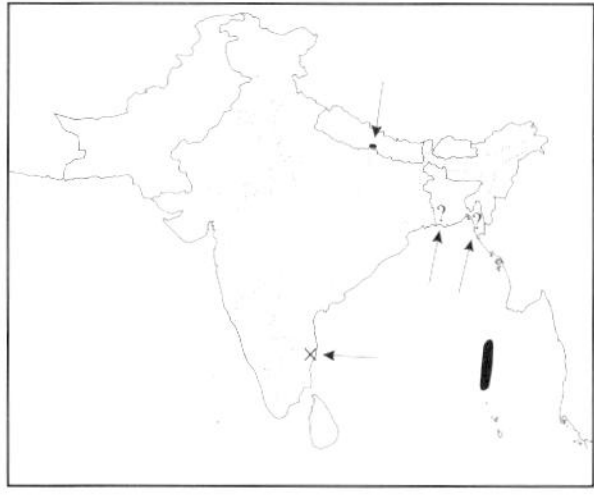

forest; also mangrove swamps. **BREEDING** March and April. **DISTRIBUTION AND STATUS** Resident, subject to poorly known movements. E Himalayan foothills from C Nepal and Sikkim east to Arunachal Pradesh; NE India and Bangladesh. **NP:** scarce and local. **IN:** generally rare; plains up to 1800 m. **BT:** rare; 275–610 m. **BD:** status uncertain, rare resident or winter visitor.

WHITE-THROATED KINGFISHER *Halcyon smyrnensis* Plate 21

White-breasted Kingfisher (F,I,P), Smyrna Kingfisher (I)

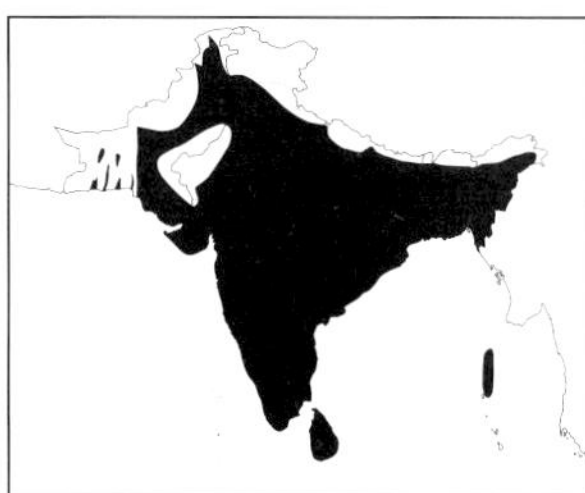

IDENTIFICATION 28 cm. A large, cosmopolitan kingfisher with large red bill, chocolate-brown head and most of underparts, white throat and centre of breast, and brilliant turquoise-blue upperparts including rump and tail. In flight, shows prominent white patches at base of black primaries. Sexes alike. **Juvenile** is duller, with brown bill and dark scalloping on breast. **VOICE** A loud rattling laugh. The song is a drawn-out musical whistle, *kililili* (Ali and Ripley 1987). **HABITS** Bold and noisy. Typically perches on fence posts, telegraph wires or branches. **HABITAT** Wide-ranging, often far from water. Cultivation, forest edges, gardens, dry deciduous forest, as well as streams, rivers, pools, canals, village tanks, ditches, coasts, and fish-curing yards; also mangroves on Andamans. **BREEDING** January–August, varying locally. **DISTRIBUTION AND STATUS** Resident throughout much of the subcontinent, except parts of the northwest. **PK:** common and sedentary in plains and lower valleys. **NP:** common below 1000 m, rarely above 1800 m (–3050 m). **IN:** common and subject to local movements; from plains up to 2250 m. **BT:** frequent; 250–1280 m. **BD:** common. **LK:** common throughout, less so at higher elevations.

BLACK-CAPPED KINGFISHER *Halcyon pileata* Plate 21

Black-capped Purple Kingfisher

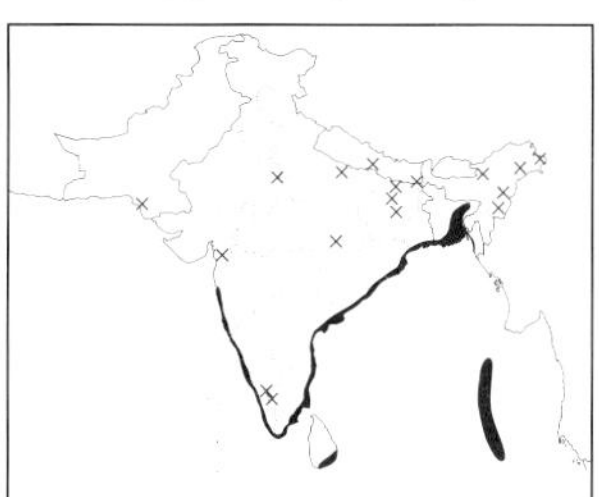

IDENTIFICATION 30 cm. A large, mainly coastal kingfisher with large coral-red bill, black cap contrasting with white throat and collar, deep purplish-blue upperparts and tail, black coverts contrasting with blue secondaries, and slightly brighter blue rump, white breast, and pale orange-buff belly and flanks. In flight, shows prominent white patches at base of primaries. Sexes alike. **Juvenile** has dusky scalloping on collar and breast. **VOICE** A distinctive, ringing cackle, *kikikikikiki*, similar to but higher-pitched than that of White-throated Kingfisher (above). **HABITS** Perches in open at edges of mangroves, forest or on telegraph wires. Uses the same lookout posts day after day. Dives down obliquely to catch prey; rarely plunges into water. Usually silent when flying off. **HABITAT** Rarely found far from the coast, although not restricted to salt water like Brown-winged. Mangrove swamps, seashore, estuaries, tidal creeks and rivers, often moving up rivers above tidal limits and sometimes farther inland along larger rivers. **BREEDING** Little known in the subcontinent. May. **DISTRIBUTION AND STATUS** Resident, subject to local movements. Mainly coasts of Bangladesh and India west to Maharashtra, and Sri Lanka; locally inland in India. **PK:** vagrant. **NP:** rare visitor. **IN:** locally frequent. **BD:** locally common winter visitor. **LK:**: regular winter visitor. **REFERENCES** Kylänpää (1998).

COLLARED KINGFISHER *Todiramphus chloris* Plate 21

White-collared Kingfisher (I), *Halcyon chloris* (I,K)

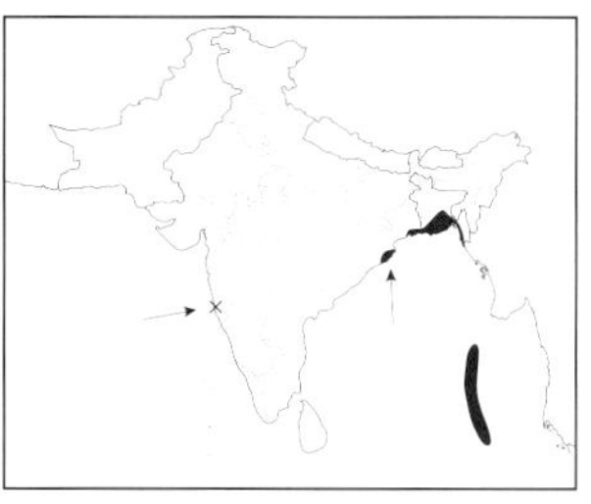

IDENTIFICATION 24 cm. A medium-sized coastal kingfisher with stout mainly blackish bill, blue-green crown and ear-coverts with short white supercilium, white collar, blue-green mantle and blue wings and tail, and white underparts. Sexes alike. **Juvenile** is generally duller, with dusky barring on buffish-white underparts, and has buff supercilium. **Racial variation** Birds in the Andaman Is (*T. c. davisoni*) and Nicobar Is (*T. c. occipitalis*) differ from *T. c. humii*, described above, in having blackish-green ear-coverts and lower border to nape, and buff wash on underparts. *T. c. davisoni* has a short buffish supercilium, while *occipitalis* is particularly distinctive in having broad rufous-buff supercilia which join at nape to form a second 'collar'. **VOICE** A raucous *krerk-krerk-krerk-krerk*. **HABITS** Similar to those of Black-capped (above). **HABITAT** Coastal areas, mangrove swamps and tidal creeks; also gardens and forest edges on Andamans. **BREEDING** March–August, varying locally. Unlike other kingfishers in the region, usually excavates its nest hole in a tree trunk; sometimes in a mud nest of tree ants or in a termite mound. **DISTRIBUTION AND STATUS** Resident. West Bengal, Orissa, Ratnigiri district on W coast; Bangladesh. **IN:** locally common. **BD:** local. **REFERENCES** Pandav (1997).

CRESTED KINGFISHER *Megaceryle lugubris* Plate 21

Greater Pied Kingfisher (I), Large Pied Kingfisher (F), *Ceryle lugubris* (F,I,K,R)

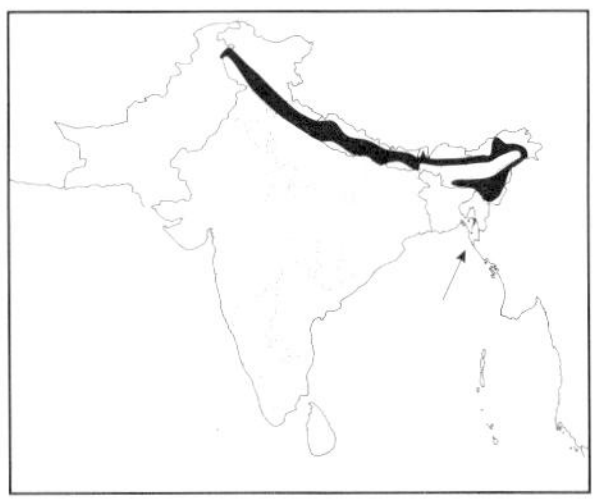

IDENTIFICATION 41 cm. A very large, crested, grey-and-white kingfisher. Distinguished from the much smaller Pied Kingfisher (below) by lack of white supercilium, presence of complete white neck-collar, finely spotted breast-band (sometimes mixed with rufous), dark grey back and rump finely spotted with paler grey, and dark grey wings and tail finely barred with white (lacking Pied's prominent white patches in wing). **Female** and **juvenile** are similar to male, but have pale rufous underwing-coverts. **VOICE** Usually silent, although has squeaky *aick* flight call and a loud, hoarse, grating trill (Ali and Ripley 1987; Boonsong and Round 1991). **HABITS** Keeps to favourite stretches of river; spends most of the day perched on branches close to and overhanging water or on rocks at the river's edge or in the middle, where the current is swift. Unlike Pied, does not hover, but dives from perch to catch fish, on which it feeds exclusively. **HABITAT** Rocky fast-flowing mountain streams and larger rivers in foothills; rarely by lakes. **BREEDING** March and April. **DISTRIBUTION AND STATUS** Resident. Himalayas from N Pakistan east to Arunachal Pradesh; NE India and Bangladesh. **PK:** rare. **NP:** frequent; 250-1800 m (–3000 m). **IN:** locally frequent; from base of hills up to 2000 m. **BT:** fairly common; 250–1980 m. **BD:** ?rare resident; no recent records, but may still occur in Chittagong Hill Tracts.

PIED KINGFISHER *Ceryle rudis* Plate 21

Lesser Pied Kingfisher (I), Small Pied Kingfisher (F)

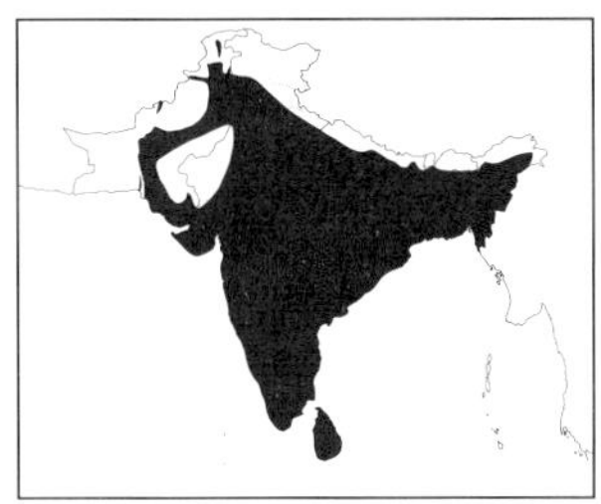

IDENTIFICATION 31 cm. A large, crested, black-and-white kingfisher. Distinguished by white-streaked black crown and crest, white supercilium contrasting with broad black eye-stripe and finely white-streaked black ear-coverts, white underparts with black breast-band, and black-and-white patterning of wings and tail. **Female** same as male, but has single (rather than double), usually broken, breast-band. For differences from the larger Crested Kingfisher (above), see that species. **Racial variation** *C. r. travancoreensis* of SW corner of peninsula differs from *C. r. leucomelanura*, described above, in having less prominent white markings on upperparts (appearing black above, spotted with white, rather than white, spotted with black). **VOICE** A sharp *chirruk chirruk*. **HABITS** Characteristically hunts by hovering over water with bill pointing down and fast-beating wings, then plunging vertically downwards when it sees a fish; sometimes checks its dive and hovers again closer to the water. Forages to a lesser extent by using a post or rock in water as a vantage point. **HABITAT** Slow-moving streams and rivers. All types of still waters in open country: ponds, lakes, canals, irrigation tanks, flooded ditches, jheels. Sometimes also tidal creeks and intertidal pools. **BREEDING** Almost throughout the year, varying locally. **DISTRIBUTION AND STATUS** Resident throughout much of the subcontinent, except parts of the northwest. **PK:** common in Punjab and lower Sind. **NP:** common below 915 m. **IN:** common below 1800 m. **BT:** uncommon and local. **BD:** locally common. **LK:** common throughout lowlands.

BEE-EATERS Meropidae

Brightly coloured birds with long decurved beak, pointed wings and very short legs. They feed almost entirely on flying insects, with Hymenoptera (bees, wasps and hornets) forming the major diet of most species. Their prey is caught on the wing, by making short, swift sallies like a flycatcher from an exposed perch such as a treetop, branch, post or telegraph wire; insects are pursued in a lively chase with a swift and agile flight. Apart from Blue-bearded and Green Bee-eaters, other species in the region also hawk insects in flight like swallows. Most species are sociable. Their flight is graceful and undulating, a few rapid wingbeats followed by a glide. Typically, bee-eaters nest in a tunnel up to 2 m long ending in an oval, unlined egg chamber, which is dug into sandy or earthen banks. The main reference specific to bee-eaters is Fry *et al.* (1992).

BLUE-BEARDED BEE-EATER *Nyctyornis athertoni* Plate 22

IDENTIFICATION 31–34 cm. A large green bee-eater with a broad square-ended tail (lacking elongated central tail feathers). **Adult** is easily distinguished by combination of blue forehead and 'beard', uniform green upperparts, broad greenish streaking on yellowish-buff belly and flanks, and yellowish-buff undertail-coverts and underside to tail. Shows yellowish-buff underwing-coverts in flight. **Juvenile** is similar to adult and has blue 'beard' even when very young. **VOICE** A gruff *gga gga ggr gr* or *kor-r-r kor-r-r* (Fry *et al.* 1992). **HABITS** Keeps singly or in pairs.

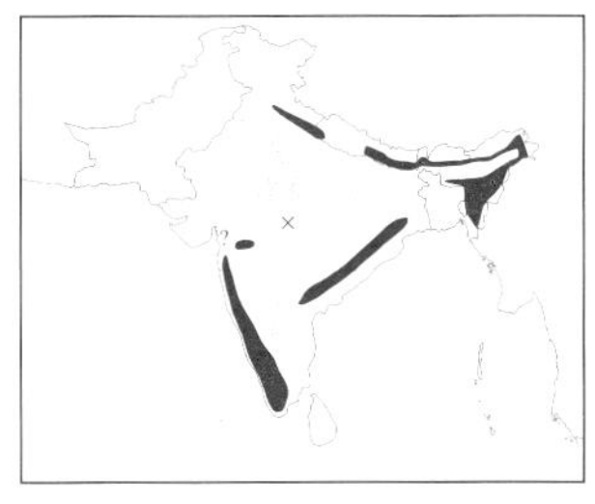

Shy, and spends much time perched inactively and inconspicuously among foliage in the middle or upper forest storey; sometimes in the open on tree-tops. Typically, sits in hunched posture with its tail hanging vertically. Rather sluggish. Makes aerial sallies after insects from a vantage point like other bee-eaters. Flight is laboured and deeply undulating. **HABITAT** Forest clearings and edges in dense broadleaved, evergreen and moist deciduous forest. **BREEDING** February–August, varying locally. Nests singly in the bank of a forest ravine or stream or roadside cutting. **DISTRIBUTION AND STATUS** Resident. Himalayan foothills from Himachal Pradesh east to Arunachal Pradesh; NE and E India, N Maharashtra and Bangladesh; Western Ghats and east to C Tamil Nadu. **NP:** uncommon; chiefly below 365 m (–2440 m). **IN:** local and frequent in low hills and adjacent plains (–1700 m). **BT:** frequent; 245–1980 m. **BD:** local. **REFERENCES** Lama (1995a).

GREEN BEE-EATER *Merops orientalis* — Plate 22

Little Green Bee-eater (P)

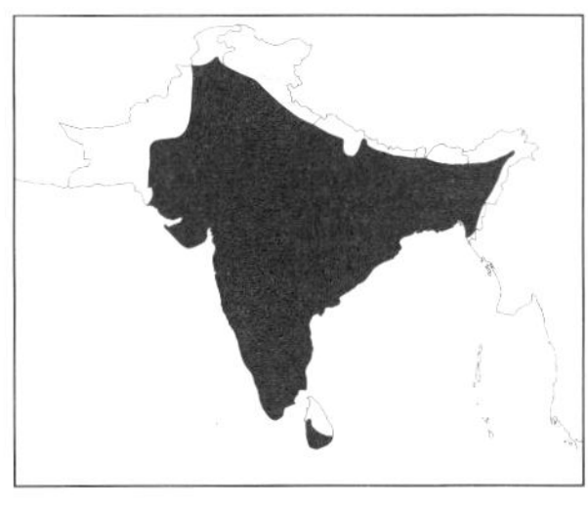

IDENTIFICATION 16–18 cm. A small green bee-eater with elongated central tail feathers. Distinguished from Blue-cheeked and Blue-tailed Bee-eaters (below and p.408) by much smaller size, different call, blue or green throat with black gorget, and variable golden-brown to rufous coloration to crown and nape. Green tail further separates from Blue-tailed. Proportionately longer central tail feathers and absence of bluish-white supercilium are additional distinctions from Blue-cheeked. In NE subcontinent (see racial variation), confusable with Chestnut-headed Bee-eater (p.408), but has blue cheeks and green throat, and elongated central tail feathers. **Juvenile** is similar to adult, but has paler fringes to upperparts and pale buff belly and flanks, and lacks black gorget and elongated central tail feathers; crown and mantle are uniform green, and throat varies from pale yellow to pale bluish-green. Confusable with juvenile Chestnut-headed, but is smaller, and lacks diffuse chestnut and black gorget on lower throat and turquoise rump of that species. **Racial variation** *M. o. beludschicus* of the NW subcontinent differs from the widely distributed nominate race in having blue throat (becoming green adjoining black gorget), and has green crown and nape with only a faint golden sheen. *M. o. ferrugeiceps* of the NE subcontinent has strong rufous cast to crown, nape and upper mantle, green (rather than blue) throat with blue cheeks, rufous wash to sides of breast, and is darker green in coloration compared with the nominate race. **VOICE** A pleasant, throaty trill, *tree-tree-tree*. **HABITS** Often associates in small, loose parties of about 15–20 birds or more. Perches on small trees, dead branches, posts, telegraph wires, and sometimes on the backs of cattle; then launches sallies to snap up a passing insect, and circles gracefully back to base. Large numbers gather noisily at sunset, before roosting communally in favoured trees. **HABITAT** Open country with scattered trees, cultivation; on coasts, favours sandy areas above high-water mark; also semi-desert and grazing land. **BREEDING** March–July, varying locally. Breeds singly or in loose colonies in tunnels dug into an embankment or in relatively flat sandy ground. **DISTRIBUTION AND STATUS** Resident or summer visitor throughout much of the subcontinent, except parts of the northwest. **PK:** partly resident, partly summer visitor; common in plains, sparse in foothills up to 1200 m. **NP:** common resident and summer visitor throughout the terai, fairly common in lower hills below 620 m (–2800 m). **IN:** common resident from plains up to 1500 m in Himalayas and to 1000 m in peninsular hills; subject to marked seasonal local movements, moves away from N areas in winter and wet areas during the monsoon. **BT:** resident or summer visitor?, frequent in foothills. **BD:** common resident. **LK:** common resident in dry lowlands, occasional visitor to wet zone.

BLUE-CHEEKED BEE-EATER *Merops persicus* — Plate 22

***M. superciliosus* (I,R)**

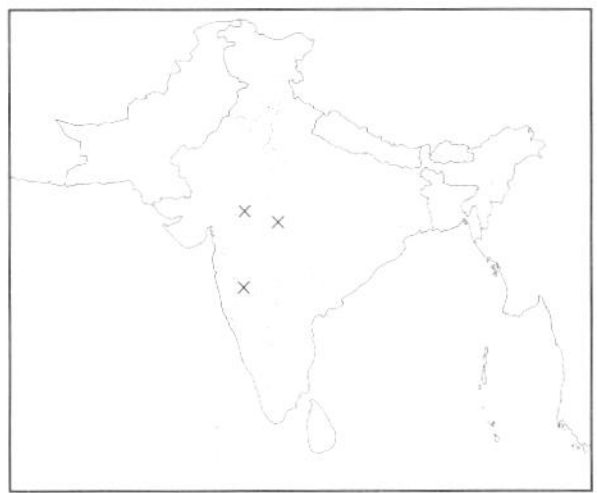

IDENTIFICATION 24–26 cm. A bright green bee-eater with green tail, chestnut throat and yellow chin. Distinguished from Blue-tailed Bee-eater (p.408) by bronze-green tail, whitish forehead and turquoise-and-white supercilium, turquoise and green on ear-coverts, and a more restricted area of chestnut on throat. Upperparts and underparts are a purer green (although may show turquoise wash to belly, rump, undertail-coverts and uppertail-coverts). Distinguished from Green Bee-eater (above) by much larger size, yellow chin and chestnut throat, lack of black gorget, presence of whitish forehead and turquoise supercilium above black mask, and different call. **Juvenile** has diffuse pale fringes to upperparts and underparts, lacks blue on supercilium and cheeks, has duller rufous throat, and lacks elongated central tail feathers. Very similar to juvenile Blue-tailed, but rump, uppertail-coverts and tail are generally green (some with a touch of turquoise), and has less extensive but more clearly defined rufous throat. **VOICE** A rolling *diririp*, more polysyllabic than European Bee-eater (p.408) (Fry *et al.* 1992). **HABITS** Keeps in loose flocks when foraging. Darts out from exposed perches such as telegraph wires to seize prey; also hawks insects in continuous flight. Eats mainly dragonflies and damselflies; also other flying insects. Roosts communally in trees outside breeding season. **HABITAT** Near water: jheels, irrigation tanks and reservoirs, canals and sandy seashores in arid areas. **BREEDING** April–August. Nests colonially in tunnels dug into gently sloping sandbanks or sandy seashore. **DISTRIBUTION AND STATUS** Widespread summer visitor and passage migrant to Pakistan and NW India. **PK:** common summer visitor; arrives early April–early May, some remain to breed, others pass through; return passage late August–November. **IN:** locally fairly common.

BLUE-TAILED BEE-EATER *Merops philippinus* Plate 22

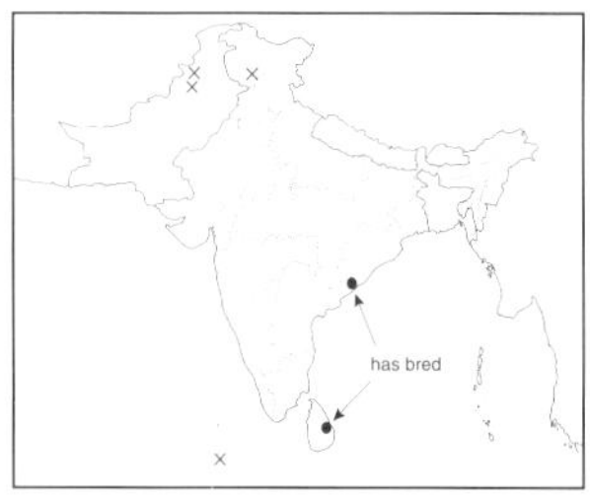

IDENTIFICATION 23–26 cm. A bright green bee-eater with blue tail, chestnut throat and yellow chin. Distinguished from Blue-cheeked Bee-eater (p.407) by blue rump and tail, and green forehead and supercilium which are concolorous with crown (with just a touch of blue on supercilium in front of eye). Chestnut of throat extends onto ear-coverts, and has streak of blue below black mask (but this is less extensive than on Blue-cheeked and, unlike on that species, is not adjoined by green on lower ear-coverts). Upperparts and underparts are washed with rufous and turquoise, and has turquoise undertail-coverts. Told from Green Bee-eater (p.407) by much larger size, blue rump and tail, yellow chin and chestnut throat, and lack of black gorget. **Juvenile** as Blue-cheeked, but with strong blue cast to rump, uppertail-coverts and tail, and more extensive but less well-defined rufous throat. **VOICE** As Blue-cheeked. **HABITS** Very similar to those of Blue-cheeked. Sometimes also hunts from treetops at forest edges and clearings. **HABITAT** Like Blue-cheeked Bee-eater keeps close to water, but inhabits more wooded, less dry country. **BREEDING** March–June. Nests colonially in a vertical river bank or sandy cliff. **DISTRIBUTION AND STATUS** Breeds mainly from N Pakistan east through N and NE India, S Nepal and Bangladesh; winters throughout the peninsula and Sri Lanka. **PK:** summer visitor to the northeast, common only in N Punjab. **NP:** locally fairly common summer visitor below 300 m (–1525 m); very rarely overwinters. **IN:** locally fairly common. **BD:** locally common resident, subject to local movements. **LK:** common winter visitor throughout, scarce breeding resident in dry E lowlands. **MV:** vagrant.

EUROPEAN BEE-EATER *Merops apiaster* Plate 22

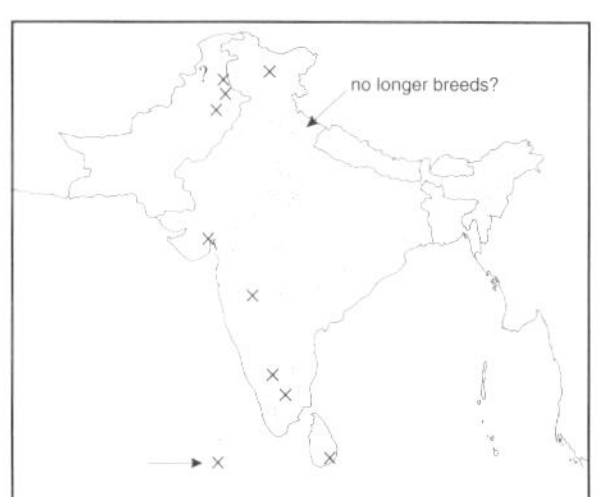

IDENTIFICATION 23–25 cm. A very distinctive, multicoloured bee-eater. **Adult** is identified by combination of yellow throat and black gorget, turquoise underparts, chestnut crown, nape, mantle and patch in wing-coverts, golden-yellow scapulars, and green tail. Sexes similar, although **female** is slightly paler, with green in scapulars and less chestnut in wing. **Juvenile** like washed-out version of adult, with pale fringes to feathers of upperparts and underparts. Lacks elongated central tail feathers and bright chestnut in wing-coverts; has yellowish-white throat (with diffuse and often very indistinct dark gorget), pale blue underparts, greenish tones to crown, nape and mantle, and greenish or dull buff scapulars. Chestnut in crown, and well-defined yellowish-white throat, are best distinctions from Blue-cheeked Bee-eater (p.407). **VOICE** A cheerful, throaty *threep*. **HABITS** Similar to those of Blue-cheeked Bee-eater, although not so gregarious. Feeds mainly on Hymenoptera. **HABITAT** Open country, cultivation, low foothills and vicinity of lakes and watercourses. **BREEDING** June and July. Nests singly or in groups of a few pairs in a steep bank. **DISTRIBUTION AND STATUS** Summer visitor mainly to Vale of Kashmir and drier W and N mountains of Pakistan; passage migrant chiefly to Pakistan. On passage end March–mid May and late July–September. **PK:** common. **IN:** widespread summer visitor to Vale of Kashmir. **LK, MV:** vagrant. **REFERENCES** Robson (1993a).

CHESTNUT-HEADED BEE-EATER *Merops leschenaulti* Plate 22

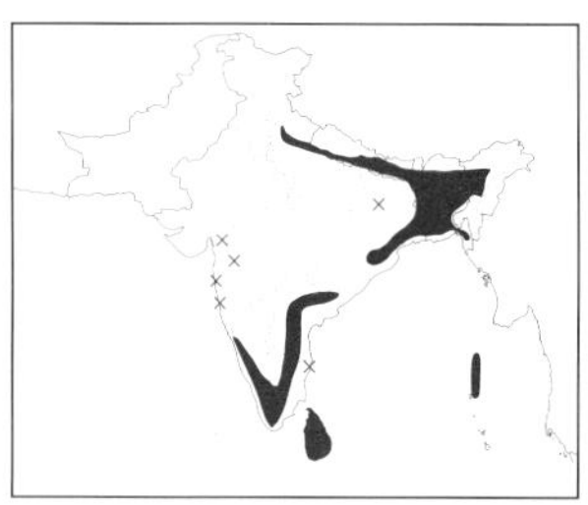

IDENTIFICATION 18–20 cm. A small chestnut and green bee-eater. Adult is distinguished from Green Bee-eater (p.407) (although caution needed with respect to *M. o. ferrugeiceps*) by combination of bright chestnut crown, nape and mantle, yellow throat with rufous on lower throat and diffuse black gorget, and turquoise rump. Tail broadens noticeably towards tip, and has a shallow fork. **Juvenile** is much duller, with chestnut of upperparts absent or reduced to a wash on crown (crown and nape are a uniform dark green on some). More easily confusable with Green; best told by larger size, rufous wash to lower throat, diffuse blackish gorget, and turquoise rump. **Racial variation** *M. l. andamanensis* of Andaman Is differs from the nominate race, described above, in having an indistinct black mask, and rufous on breast which adjoins rufous on throat. **VOICE** A *pruik* or *churit*, briefer and less melodious than calls of the larger bee-eaters (Fry *et al.* 1992). A mixture of *brip* notes and finch-like chips (S. Connop). **HABITS** Similar to those of

Blue-cheeked Bee-eater (p.407), but a forest bird; often launches sallies from treetops or feeds high above canopy. Gathers noisily at sunset in favoured communal roosting trees. **HABITAT** Vicinity of water in deciduous forest. **BREEDING** February–June. Nests in scattered small colonies in a sloping sandy bank of a stream or in sandy level ground. **DISTRIBUTION AND STATUS** Resident and partial migrant. Himalayas from Uttar Pradesh east to Arunachal Pradesh; from NE India south to Orissa and Bangladesh; SW and SE India, and Sri Lanka. **NP:** chiefly a summer visitor, some birds resident at lower altitudes; fairly common below 680 m, locally up to 1525 m (–2135 m). **IN:** resident, subject to migratory movements; moves out from heavy-rainfall areas during the monsoon; widespread, but local below 1000 m. **BT:** resident or summer visitor?; uncommon. **BD:** locally common resident. **LK:** irregular and infrequent resident from lowlands to mid altitudes. **REFERENCES** Lama (1994b).

OLD WORLD CUCKOOS Cuculidae

Have an elongated body with fairly long neck, tail varying from medium length to long and graduated, and quite long, decurved bill. Almost all Cuculidae are arboreal, inhabiting forests or well-wooded areas, and feed chiefly on hairy caterpillars. Apart from the malkohas *Phaenicophaeus*, male cuckoos are very noisy in the breeding season, calling frequently during the day, especially if cloudy, and often into the night. When not breeding they are silent and unobtrusive, and as a result their status and distribution at this season are very poorly known. Cuckoos are notorious for their nest parasitism: eggs are laid in the nests of other species, which then care for the young cuckoos. The breeding season of parasitic cuckoos is synchronised locally with that of their hosts. The malkohas, however, are non-parasitic and build their own nests.

PIED CUCKOO *Clamator jacobinus* — Plate 23

Pied Crested Cuckoo (F,I,P), Jacobin Cuckoo, *Oxylophus jacobinus*

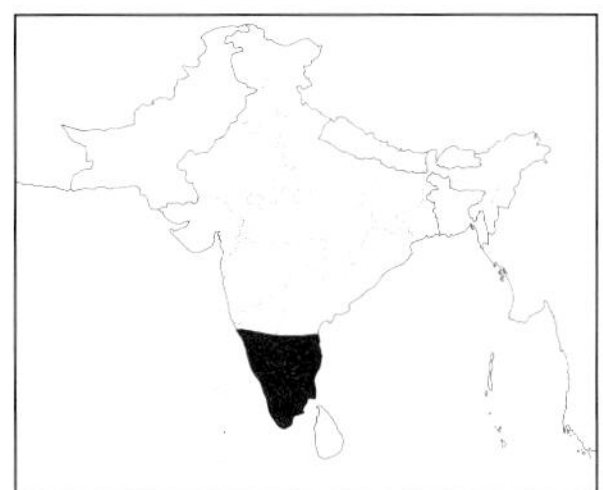

IDENTIFICATION 33 cm. A medium-sized pied cuckoo with prominent crest. **Adult** distinguished from Chestnut-winged Cuckoo (below) by smaller size, lack of white nuchal collar, black wings with white patch at base of primaries, all-white underparts (with faint buffish wash), and prominent white tips to tail feathers. **Juvenile** similar to adult, but has grey-brown upperparts, grey wash to throat and upper breast, with buffish wash to rest of underparts, smaller crest, smaller white wing patch, and paler bill. **VOICE** A loud, metallic, pleasant *piu...piu...pee-pee piu, pee-pee piu* or *piu...piu...piu*, uttered frequently day and night (Ali and Ripley 1987). **HABITS** Conspicuous and not at all shy, often perching in the open. Chiefly arboreal, but often also searches for food in low bushes and sometimes by hopping on ground. **HABITAT** Forests, groves and well-wooded country, including gardens and cultivation; bushes in semi-desert areas and reedbeds; also irrigated forest plantations in Pakistan, and scrub in Sri Lanka. **BREEDING** All year, varying locally. Brood-parasitic, mainly on *Turdoides* babblers. **DISTRIBUTION AND STATUS** Resident and partial migrant. Throughout much of the subcontinent, except parts of the northwest and Himalayas: summer visitor to the north, arriving in late May/June and leaving in September/October; resident in NE India and south of 15°S, dispersing widely in the monsoon and intermingling with summer visitors in C and E India and possibly elsewhere. **PK:** common summer visitor. **NP:** uncommon summer visitor; mainly below 365 m (–3660 m). **IN:** locally common in summer; plains up to 2600 m (–3800 m). **BD:** local summer visitor. **LK:** resident in lowlands and lower hills, more common in dry zone. **REFERENCES** Becking (1981), Serrao (1989).

CHESTNUT-WINGED CUCKOO *Clamator coromandus* — Plate 23

Red-winged Crested Cuckoo (F,I,P)

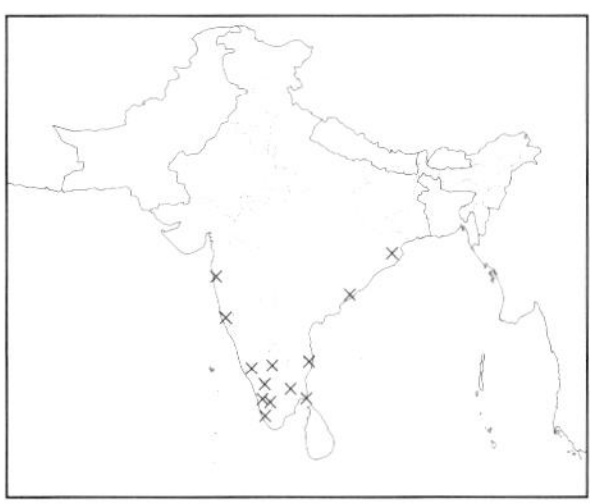

IDENTIFICATION 47 cm. A large, crested cuckoo with chestnut wings and very long black tail (latter with narrow greyish-white feather tips). **Adult** told from the smaller Pied Cuckoo (above) by white nuchal collar, mainly chestnut wings without white wing patch, and orange wash to throat and breast. **Juvenile** superficially resembles adult, but has shorter, rounded crest, broad rufous fringes to crown, mantle, scapulars and coverts, buff nuchal collar, whitish throat and breast, broad buff tips to rectrices, and paler bill. **Immature** is similar to adult (including adult-like crest), but retains some buff tips to scapulars and coverts, and broad buff tips to tail. **VOICE** Call is a series of double metallic whistles, *breep breep*. Also a harsh grating scream. **HABITS** Arboreal and rather retiring, favouring the canopy and usually inconspicuous when perched among foliage. Often descends to lower storey of bushes to feed. **HABITAT** Broadleaved evergreen and moist deciduous forest and cut-over scrub jungle. **BREEDING** March–August, varying locally. Brood-parasitic, mainly on Himalayan laughingthrushes, often Greater and Lesser Necklaced. **DISTRIBUTION AND STATUS** Breeds patchily in Himalayas from N Uttar Pradesh east to Arunachal Pradesh; NE India and Bangladesh; passage migrant to C and S India, and winter visitor to SW India and Sri Lanka. **NP:**

very local summer visitor; 250–365 m (down to 75 m). **IN:** rare; breeds in Himalayan foothills below 1500 m; regular passage migrant in the centre and south. **BT:** frequent summer visitor; 380–895 m. **BD:** local summer visitor below 1800 m. **LK:** rare but widespread winter visitor. **REFERENCES** Becking (1981), Choudhary (1996b).

LARGE HAWK CUCKOO *Hierococcyx sparverioides* Plate 23

***Cuculus sparverioides* (F,I,K,N)**

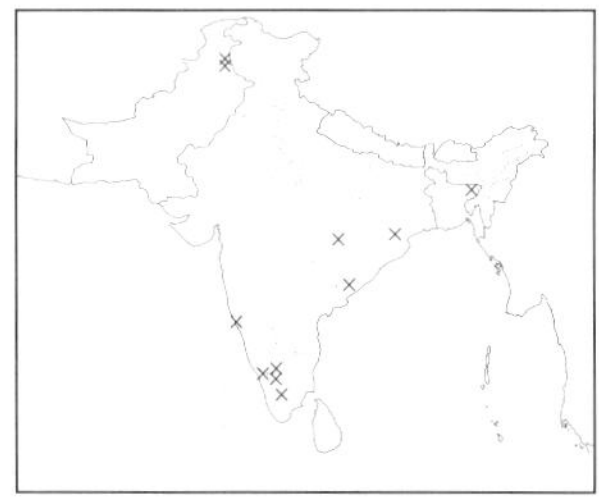

IDENTIFICATION 38 cm. A large cuckoo with comparatively broad, rounded wings. **Adult** distinguished from the very similar Common Hawk Cuckoo (below) by combination of larger size, brownish (rather than grey) mantle and wings contrasting with slate-grey head, blackish chin, grey streaking on throat and breast, irregular band of rufous across breast, broad dark brown barring on breast, belly and flanks, and much broader and stronger dark banding across tail (apparent on both upperside and underside). Underwing-coverts are white, barred with dark brown. **Juvenile** has brown upperparts, barred with rufous, with paler rufous nape (streaked dark brown); underparts are white, with variable rufous wash, with bold drop-shaped brown streaking on breast and barring on belly and flanks. Very similar to juvenile Common, but flanks tend to be more strongly barred rather than spotted, and dark tail-banding is broader (as adult). Rufous-fringed feathers to forehead and crown are quickly lost, and head is then a darker slate-grey than in similar plumage of Common, and shows blackish chin and grey streaking on throat (as adult). **VOICE** A shrill *pee-pee-ah...pee-pee-ah*, which is repeated, rising in pitch and momentum, climaxing in hysterical crescendo. Often calls throughout the night. **HABITS** Usually keeps well hidden among foliage of the forest canopy, even when calling. *Accipiter*-like in flight: flies low, with a few fast wingbeats followed by a glide, then rises up abruptly to land in a tree. **HABITAT** Usually broadleaved forest, especially oaks; sometimes mixed broadleaved/coniferous forest and groves. **BREEDING** April–July, varying locally. Brood-parasitic, on Streaked Spiderhunter (p.806), Lesser Shortwing (p.631) and presumably other species. **DISTRIBUTION AND STATUS** Breeds in Himalayas from Himachal Pradesh east to Arunachal Pradesh; NE India; scattered winter records from Nepal, Bangladesh and India south to Tamil Nadu. **PK:** ?vagrant; no recent confirmed records. **NP:** fairly common, March–October, 1830–3000 m; a few winter records 1800–2460 m. **IN:** locally fairly common in spring and summer in Himalayas, 900–2900 m; rare in winter in the south. **BT:** common in spring and summer; 1000–3025 m. **BD:** rare winter visitor and possibly passage migrant. **REFERENCES** Becking (1981).

COMMON HAWK CUCKOO *Hierococcyx varius* Plate 23

***Cuculus varius* (F,I,K,N)**

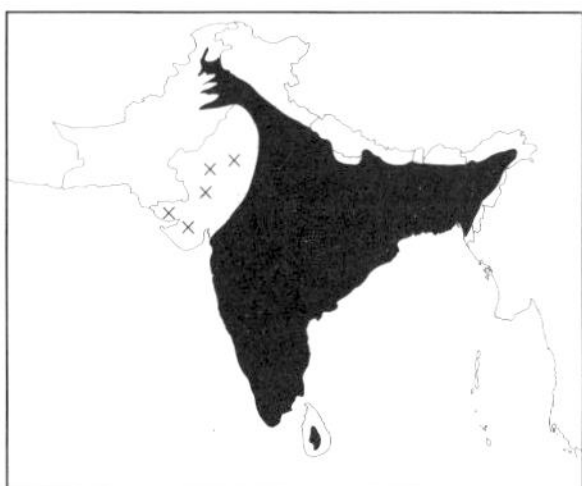

IDENTIFICATION 34 cm. A medium-sized cuckoo, similar in size to Eurasian Cuckoo (p.411). **Adult** very similar to Large Hawk Cuckoo (above), but is smaller and has greyer, more uniform upperparts (with crown and nape concolorous with mantle and wing-coverts). Throat is whitish, variably mottled or washed with grey, and lacks blackish chin and strong grey throat streaking of Large. Rufous on underparts is paler and more extensive than on Large (extending onto belly and flanks), and breast, belly and flanks have only faint dark barring. Underwing-coverts are washed with rufous, and only faintly barred. Banding on both surfaces of tail is narrower than on Large. **Juvenile** is similar to juvenile Large; flanks tend to be less heavily marked, with spots or chevron marks rather than strong dark barring (although underparts of some are very similar), while rufous banding across tail (below narrow dark banding) is typically brighter and more clearly defined than on Large, and usually shows more pronounced rufous tip to tail. **Racial variation** *H. v. ciceliae* of Sri Lanka differs from the widespread nominate race, described above, in being darker grey on upperparts (almost brownish-grey on mantle), with stronger streaking on throat and dark barring on underparts (and is virtually identical to Large in plumage, although tail-banding is narrower as on nominate Common). **VOICE** A shrill *pee-pee-ah...pee-pee-ah* etc (hence the alternative name 'Brainfever Bird'), like that of Large Hawk Cuckoo, but even more shrill and manic. **HABITS** Similar to those of Large Hawk Cuckoo, but more often seen because it frequents less thickly wooded country. Becomes more vocal during hot weather. **HABITAT** Well-wooded deciduous and semi-evergreen country, favouring groves, mangroves, orchards, gardens and cultivation; also irrigated forest plantations in Pakistan, and tea estates in Sri Lanka. **BREEDING** January–June, also later months, and varying locally. No certain evidence of which species it brood-parasitises. **DISTRIBUTION AND STATUS** Resident and partial migrant. Throughout much of the subcontinent, except parts of the northwest. **PK:** summer visitor, common only in Punjab. **NP:** common resident; below 1000 m (–1500 m). **IN:** widespread and locally common resident; plains up to 1200 m; subject to local movements, especially during the monsoon. **BT:** frequent resident; below 710 m (–1980 m). **BD:** common and widespread resident. **LK:** resident in hills, also a winter visitor. **REFERENCES** Becking (1981).

HODGSON'S HAWK CUCKOO *Hierococcyx fugax* Plate 23

***Cuculus fugax* (F,I,K)**

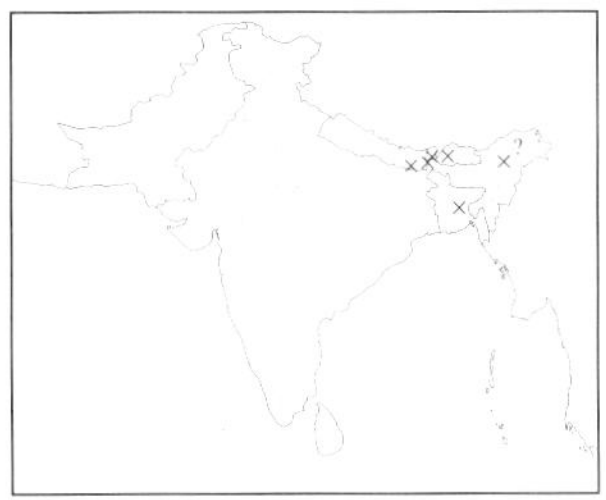

IDENTIFICATION 29 cm. A medium-sized cuckoo with dark grey upperparts, much rufous on underparts, and prominently banded tail. **Adult** distinguished from the similar Common Hawk Cuckoo (p.410) by smaller size, with shorter-looking tail, shorter, deeper-based bill, darker slate-grey upperparts, more pronounced slate-grey chin, and usually more extensive rufous on underparts, lacking barring on flanks. Throat and breast may show dark grey streaking. Has rufous tip to tail which is typically more pronounced than on Common. Frequently shows a single pale inner tertial (on both wings on some), which does not seem to be present on Common. Voice is also different. **Juvenile** has dark brown upperparts, with narrow buff feather fringes, and boldly spotted underparts. Told from juvenile Common by smaller size and stouter bill, darker brown and more uniform upperparts, and broader (squarer) and less drop-shaped spots on underparts. **Immature** birds have dark grey chin, ear-coverts and crown, rufous barring to upperparts, and strongly streaked underparts. Underparts, particularly flanks, are more strongly and clearly streaked than on Common, and dark grey chin, crown and nape contrast with rufous-barred mantle, recalling Large. **VOICE** A shrill, thin *gee-whiz...gee-whiz* etc, repeated up to 20 times and becoming more frantic and high-pitched. **HABITS** Little known in the subcontinent. Usually keeps to low trees or bushes, but moves higher in trees when calling. **HABITAT** Broadleaved evergreen and moist deciduous forest. **BREEDING** Very poorly known in the subcontinent. Probably April–June. **DISTRIBUTION AND STATUS** Resident, subject to altitudinal and migratory movements, or summer visitor, mainly to NE Indian hills and Himalayas in Sikkim, Arunachal Pradesh and Bhutan; probably overlooked. **NP:** vagrant. **IN:** status uncertain, no recent published records; 600–1800 m. **BT:** fairly common; 1400–2320 m. **BD:** vagrant. **REFERENCES** Becking (1981), Tymstra *et al.* (1997).

INDIAN CUCKOO *Cuculus micropterus* Plate 23

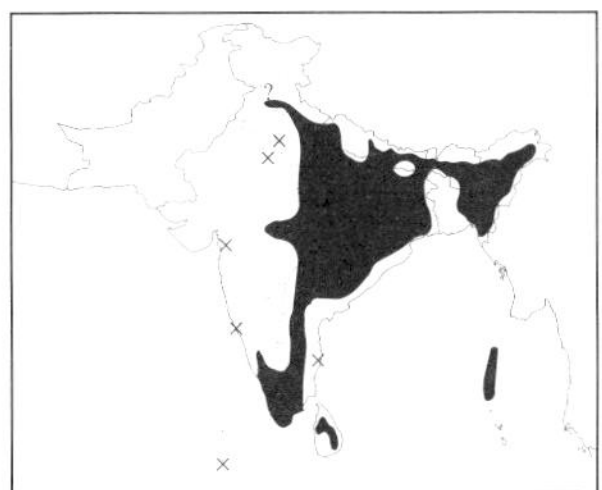

IDENTIFICATION 33 cm. A medium-sized, mainly grey-brown cuckoo with blackish barring on white underparts. Song is distinctive. **Adult male** distinguished from adult Eurasian Cuckoo (below) and Oriental Cuckoo (p.412) by browner coloration to mantle and wing-coverts, slightly contrasting with greyer head and breast, and broader, more widely spaced black barring on underparts. Typically, tail looks paler and browner than on Eurasian and Oriental, with broad (diffuse) dark subterminal band; also has broader white barring on outer tail feathers and larger white spots on shafts of central feathers (tail of adult Eurasian and Oriental is darker and more uniform, with small white notches on outer feathers and rather small white spots on central shafts). Indian has a brown or reddish-brown iris (yellow in Eurasian; yellow or brown in Oriental). **Female** is similar to male, but has rufous-buff wash to base of grey breast, and rufous suffusion to whitish barring of lower breast. There is said to be no hepatic morph. **Juvenile** told from juvenile Eurasian and Oriental by broad and irregular white tips to feathers of crown and nape and bold white tips to scapulars and wing-coverts; throat and breast are creamy-white with irregular brown markings, and barring on rest of underparts is broader and more irregular than on Eurasian and Oriental. **VOICE** A descending, four-noted whistle, *kwer-kwah..kwah-kurh*, often rendered as 'one more bottle'. **HABITS** Frequents the tops of forest trees and foliage of the canopy; sometimes flies hawk-like above the forest. Often calls at night during breeding season. **HABITAT** Forest, well-wooded country and groves. **BREEDING** Season poorly known; April and June and probably other months. Brood-parasitic on drongos, mainly Black Drongo (p.610) and Ashy Drongo (p.610). **DISTRIBUTION AND STATUS** Breeds in Himalayas from Punjab, India, east to Arunachal Pradesh and south through much of the E half of the subcontinent. Possibly only a summer visitor to Himalayas. **PK:** vagrant to NE foothills. **NP:** recorded February–September; common in spring and summer below 2100 m (–3800 m). **IN:** resident, subject to migratory movements; plains up to 2300 m; common in Himalayas in spring and summer, but further south uncommon and status uncertain. **BT:** common in spring and summer; 250–2895 m. **BD:** locally common resident. **LK:** common resident in dry lowlands, winter visitor to all zones. **MV:** rare. **REFERENCES** Becking (1981).

EURASIAN CUCKOO *Cuculus canorus* Plate 23

The Cuckoo (I), Common Cuckoo (K,P)

IDENTIFICATION 32–34 cm. A medium-sized, mainly grey cuckoo with white underparts barred with black. Song is distinctive. **Adult male** told from adult Indian Cuckoo (above) by uniform grey head, mantle and wing-coverts, finer and more narrowly spaced blackish barring on the underparts, and more uniform dark grey tail. Iris is yellow (rather than brown or brownish-red). Almost identical in appearance to Oriental Cuckoo (p.412) and best distinguished by song; for subtle differences, see that species. **Female** occurs in two colour morphs. Typically is very similar to male (sometimes indistinguishable), although usually has rufous wash to lower border of grey breast. There is also a hepatic morph which is rufous-brown above and whitish below, and strongly barred all over with dark brown. See Oriental

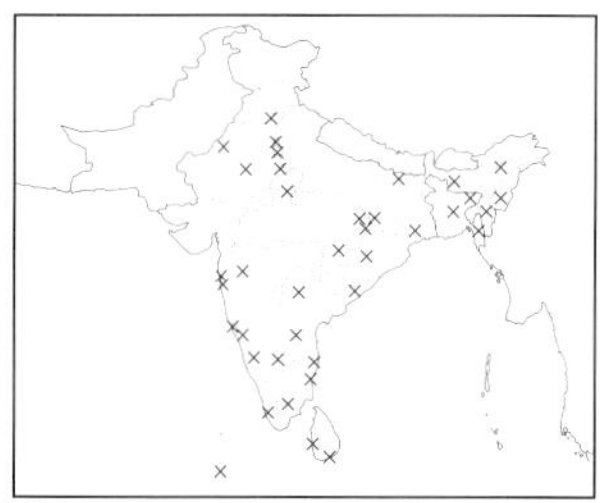

for differences from the hepatic morph of that species. **Juvenile** is very variable, some superficially resembling grey adult, others hepatic female. Always show whitish fringes to feathers of mantle, scapulars and wing-coverts, and in fresh plumage have white patch on nape. **VOICE** Male has a loud, pleasant, although repetitive *cuck-oo.....cuck-oo*; both sexes have a bubbling call, often described as a water-bubbling chuckle. **HABITS** Similar to those of Indian Cuckoo, but less vocal at night. Sometimes also feeds close to or on the ground, as well as in tree-tops. Often perches conspicuously in the open when calling in the breeding season. **HABITAT** Forest, well-wooded country and secondary growth; also montane dwarf scrub and alpine meadows. **BREEDING** March–September, varying locally. Brood-parasitic, mainly on small passerines: chiefly chats, warblers (*Acrocephalus*), wagtails and pipits, and buntings. **DISTRIBUTION AND STATUS** Breeds in hills of W Pakistan, Himalayas from N Pakistan east to Arunachal Pradesh, NE India, and patchily in N and C India. Arrives in March; isolated records in autumn and winter south through the peninsula and Sri Lanka. **PK:** common and widespread summer visitor; 1800–3650 m. **NP:** common 915–3800 m (–4250 m), uncommon lower down. **IN:** common summer visitor to Himalayas; 600–4100 m (–5250 m). **BT:** common summer visitor; 900–4060 m. **BD:** scarce passage migrant. **LK:** winter vagrant. **MV:** regular winter visitor. **REFERENCES** Becking (1981).

ORIENTAL CUCKOO *Cuculus saturatus* — Plate 23

Himalayan Cuckoo (F,I)

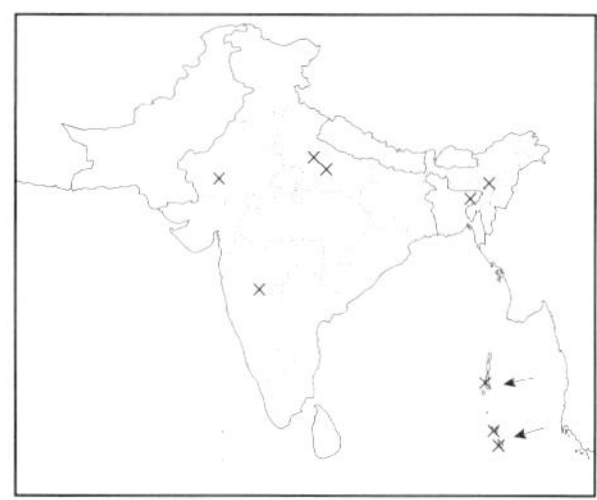

IDENTIFICATION 30–32 cm. A medium-sized, mainly grey cuckoo with whitish underparts strongly barred with blackish. See Indian Cuckoo (p.411) for differences from that species. **Adult male** is almost identical in appearance to Eurasian Cuckoo (p.411) (some indistinguishable) and safely distinguished only by song. Generally has more prominent, broader black barring on buffish-white (rather than pure white) underparts, and darker grey upperparts, sometimes showing contrast with paler head. Typically, lacks barring on leading edge of wing, resulting in mainly white patch below carpal joint. Often appears distinctly smaller than Eurasian, which can be further aid to identification. **Adult female**, like Eurasian, occurs as grey and rufous morphs. Compared with grey female Eurasian, is typically more extensively buff on breast, with broader black barring on breast and belly. Hepatic morph differs from hepatic female Eurasian in broader and more prominent black barring, especially on breast, back, rump and tail. **Juvenile** occurs in rufous and grey morphs; underparts are warmer buff and more prominently barred, and the barring is stronger on the upperparts and tail in rufous morph compared with Eurasian. **VOICE** A resonant *ho..ho..ho..ho,* easily confused with the call of Common Hoopoe (p.399), although has at least four notes (rather than the two or three of Common Hoopoe) and often preceded by a guttural *kkukh* and followed by a quiet series of six to eight disyllabic *bu-bu* notes (Cramp 1985). **HABITS** Similar to those of Indian Cuckoo (p.411), but usually keeps hidden among foliage and is less noisy at night. **HABITAT** Forest, well-wooded country and orchards. **BREEDING** May and June. Brood-parasitic, on *Phylloscopus* and *Seicercus* warblers. **DISTRIBUTION AND STATUS** Breeds in Himalayas from N Pakistan east to Arunachal Pradesh, and NE India; common winter visitor to Andamans and Nicobars; a few records of passage migrants south to Maharashtra. **PK:** frequent but local summer visitor; above 1800 m. **NP:** fairly common summer visitor, mid March–September; 1525–3355 m (down to 250 m). **IN:**locally common summer visitor; 1500–3300 m. **BT:** common summer visitor; 1525–3080 m. **BD:** vagrant. **REFERENCES** Becking (1981), Cramp (1985).

LESSER CUCKOO *Cuculus poliocephalus* — Plate 23

Small Cuckoo (F,I,P)

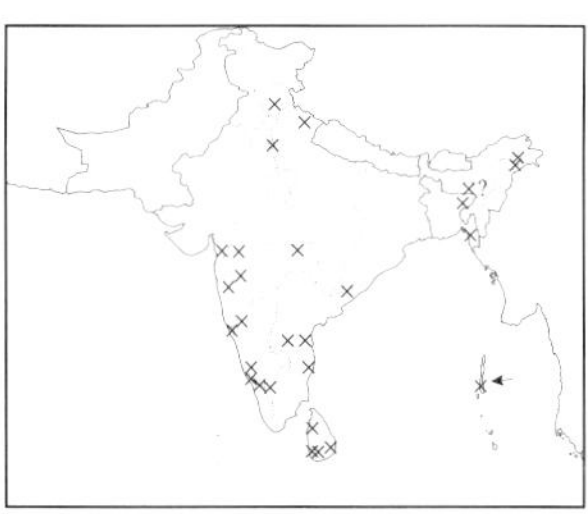

IDENTIFICATION 25 cm. **Adult male** best told from Oriental Cuckoo (above) by song; is also much smaller, and has finer bill. Otherwise, plumage is very similar. **Adult female** sometimes similar to male, but hepatic morph prevails, and is typically more rufous in coloration than hepatic Oriental (some with almost unmarked rufous crown, nape, rump and uppertail-coverts). **Juvenile** has dark grey-brown upperparts with variable, narrow whitish to rufous barring (and a few white spots on nape), and broadly barred underparts. **VOICE** A strong, cheerful song, rendered as *pretty-peel-lay-ka-beet* (Fleming *et al.* 1984); often one of the first birds to start singing at dawn. **HABITS** Similar to those of Indian Cuckoo (p.411). Frequently calls noisily in flight, often above the canopy as well as when perched. **HABITAT** Forest and well-wooded country. **BREEDING** May–July. Brood-parasitic, on *Cettia* warblers. **DISTRIBUTION AND STATUS** Breeds in Himalayas from N Pakistan east to Arunachal Pradesh; NE India. Migrates through the peninsula and Sri Lanka in autumn. **PK:** frequent but local summer visitor to Himalayas. **NP:** fairly common summer visitor, recorded mainly April–August; 1500–3660 m. **IN:** locally common summer visitor; 1200 m to the treeline. **BT:** fairly common summer visitor; 1400–3390 m. **BD:** vagrant. **LK:** rare, irregular winter visitor to lowlands and lower hills. **REFERENCES** Becking (1981).

BANDED BAY CUCKOO *Cacomantis sonneratii* — Plate 23

Indian Banded Bay Cuckoo (I), Bay-banded Cuckoo (P)

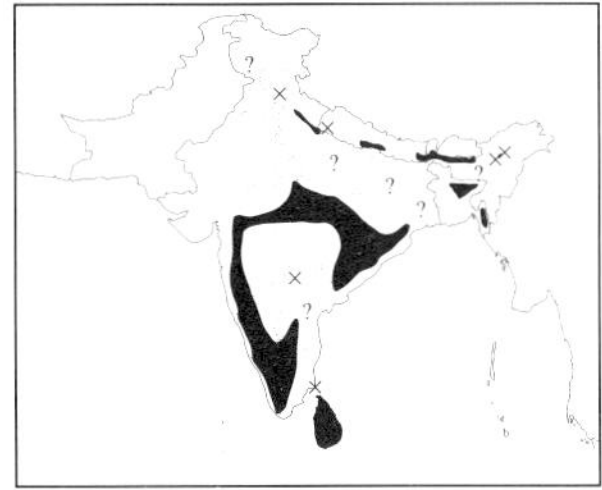

IDENTIFICATION 24 cm. A small rufous-brown and white cuckoo, strongly barred all over with dark brown. **Adult** distinguished from females and immatures of other small cuckoos by broad white supercilium (cross-barred with black), which encircles brown ear-coverts. Also, underparts are more uniformly whitish, with faint buff wash to belly and flanks, and are more finely and uniformly barred. Upperparts are also more finely and regularly barred, and barred central tail feathers are more extensively dark on each side of shaft. **Juvenile** is very similar to adult, but barring on underparts is broader and more diffuse, and crown and nape have some buff barring. **VOICE** A shrill, whistled *pi-pi-pew-pew*, the first two notes at the same pitch, the last two descending. **HABITS** Favours the bare branches of treetops, from which it calls, usually holding the tail depressed, wings drooping and rump feathers fluffed out. **HABITAT** Dense broadleaved forest in Nepal; lightly wooded country in India; forest edges, patches of shifting cultivation and open forest in Sri Lanka, where it prefers the intermediate belt of country between the wet and dry zones. **BREEDING** Variable and prolonged, mainly February–August. Brood-parasitic, primarily on Common Iora (p.615), also on minivets. **DISTRIBUTION AND STATUS** Resident. From N Uttar Pradesh east to Assam and Bangladesh; W, NC and E India, and Sri Lanka. **NP:** uncommon; mainly below 250 m (–2440 m). **IN:** resident, subject to local movements; widely scattered throughout in the monsoon, up to 1500 m, occasionally higher; uncommon in the north, locally fairly common in the Deccan and S India. **BT:** rare. **BD:** local resident. **LK:** common resident in lowlands and foothills, ascending E hills in winter. **REFERENCES** Becking (1981).

GREY-BELLIED CUCKOO *Cacomantis passerinus* — Plate 23

Indian Plaintive Cuckoo (I,P), Grey-bellied Plaintive Cuckoo (N,R), *C. merulinus passerinus* (E,F)

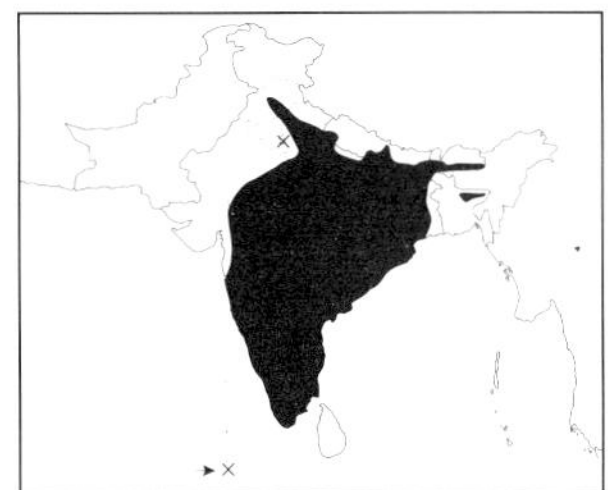

IDENTIFICATION 23 cm. **Adult** is a small, mainly grey cuckoo with grey belly and flanks, and white vent and undertail-coverts. Sexes alike, although hepatic morph of female is frequent. Lack of supercilium, largely unbarred tail, and less regularly (but more broadly) barred upperparts and underparts are best distinctions from Banded Bay Cuckoo (above). See Plaintive Cuckoo (below) for differences from that species. **Juvenile** appears to occur in two morphs and with intermediates. Some are similar to 'grey' adult, with uniform brownish-black upperparts (without distinct barring), dusky grey underparts with indistinct and diffuse buffish-grey barring mainly on belly and flanks (some are more heavily barred on underparts), and tail dark grey-brown with each feather finely notched with greyish-white. Other juveniles are more noticeably barred with rufous on upperparts, and underparts are similar to hepatic female; tail is dark brown, barred with rufous (and is similarly patterned to tail of Plaintive). Intermediates would seem to occur, e.g. with uniform grey upperparts and strong rufous barring on tail. **VOICE** A clear, interrogative *Pee-pipee-pee...pipee-pee*, ascending in scale and higher-pitched with every repetition; also a plaintive single whistle, *piteer*, frequently repeated at short intervals (Ali and Ripley 1987). **HABITS** Keeps mainly to the leafy tops of trees and bushes; sometimes descends briefly to the ground to pick up caterpillars, or sallies after insects. Very active and restless, repeatedly flying rapidly to different vantage points and calling; often flies quite long distances between resting places. When calling, holds the wings loosely, tail depressed and rump feathers fluffed out. **HABITAT** All types of lightly wooded country: open forest, groves, wooded gardens and shade trees in plantations. **BREEDING** May–September. Brood-parasitic, on *Prinia*, *Cisticola* and *Orthotomus* warblers. **DISTRIBUTION AND STATUS** Summers in Himalayas in N Pakistan and from Himachal Pradesh east to Bhutan; resident, subject to local movements, or winter visitor further south and throughout much of the peninsula. **PK:** local but frequent summer visitor; 600–1800 m. **NP:** summer visitor, frequent below 1400 m (–2135 m). **IN:** fairly common summer visitor to Himalayas, locally fairly common further south. **BT:** uncommon summer visitor; 250–1395 m (–2285 m). **BD:** local resident. **LK:** common winter visitor to lowlands and lower hills, more frequent in dry zone, also occasionally oversummers. **MV:** rare winter visitor. **REFERENCES** Becking (1981).

PLAINTIVE CUCKOO *Cacomantis merulinus* — Plate 23

Rufous-bellied Plaintive Cuckoo (I,N)

IDENTIFICATION 23 cm. A small, mainly grey cuckoo with orange on underparts. This species and Grey-bellied Cuckoo (above) are very variable, and further work is needed to confirm the features mentioned below. **Adult** differs from adult Grey-bellied in orange belly, flanks and vent. Sexes alike, although female frequently (perhaps mainly) occurs as a hepatic morph and therefore resembles Banded Bay Cuckoo (above) as well as the hepatic morph of Grey-bellied. Main differences from Banded Bay are smaller size, lack of pale supercilium, and rufous wash to throat and breast. From hepatic female Grey-bellied by duller rufous-brown upperparts, with more regular dark brown barring on crown and nape, and regular dark barring on rump and uppertail-coverts (on Grey-bellied, crown and nape are brighter rufous and only sparsely barred, and rump and uppertail-coverts are almost

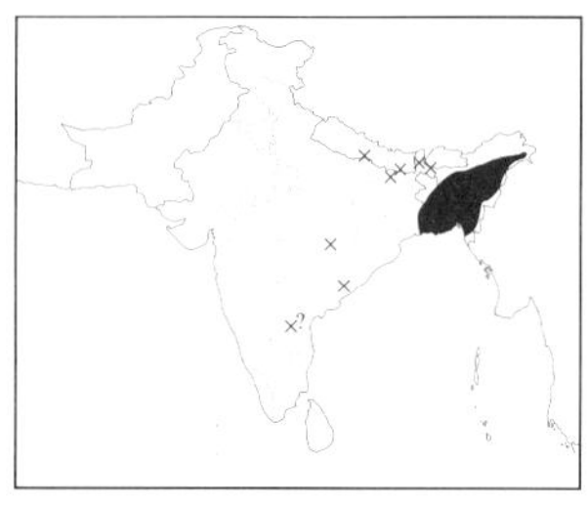

unmarked on some, boldly but sparsely streaked on others). Further, has dull rufous wash across most of underparts, becoming paler on lower belly and rear flanks (Grey-bellied has rufous wash on sides of throat and onto breast, but base colour of underparts is otherwise white). Also, patterning of central tail feathers differs in adult birds: on Plaintive, central feathers are strongly and evenly barred or notched with rufous (unbarred on adult Grey-bellied; central rectrices are almost unmarked except for black spot at tip, while others also have black line down each side of shaft with some black notching at outer edge). On underside of tail, feathers are heavily barred on Plaintive (unbarred or with regular barring and spotting on Grey-bellied). Note, however, that juvenile Grey-bellied can have tail pattern similar to Plaintive. **Juvenile** is distinct from hepatic and juvenile Grey-bellied. Has bold blackish streaking to rufous-orange crown and nape, and throat and breast are rufous-orange and streaked with dark brown; rest of underparts are more sparsely barred than on adult, and upperparts are paler rufous-orange and more sparsely barred. **VOICE** A mournful whistle, *tay..ta..tee*, the second note lower and the third note higher than the first (King *et al.* 1975); also a *tay..ta..ta..tay*, repeated with increasing speed and ascending in pitch (Smythies 1986). **HABITS** Very similar to those of Grey-bellied. **HABITAT** Very similar to that of Grey-bellied. **BREEDING** March–August. **DISTRIBUTION AND STATUS** Resident, subject to local movements. Mainly NE India and Bangladesh. **NP:** vagrant. **IN:** status uncertain; plains and hills up to 2000 m. **BT:** rare. **BD:** common and widespread. **REFERENCES** Tymstra *et al.* (1997).

ASIAN EMERALD CUCKOO *Chrysococcyx maculatus* — Plate 24

Emerald Cuckoo (F,I,P), *Chalcites maculatus* (E,F,I)

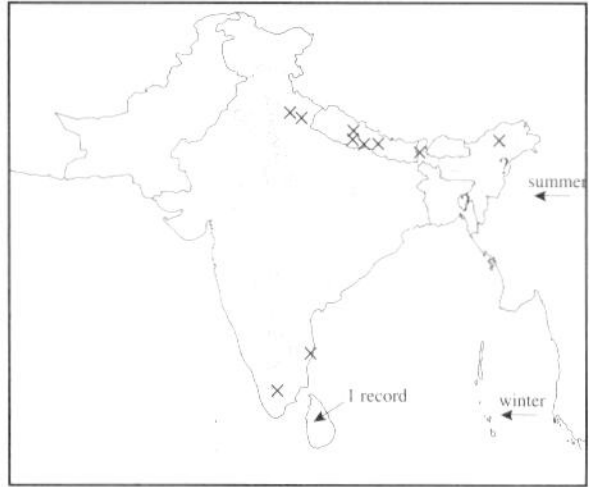

IDENTIFICATION 18 cm. **Male** is unmistakable. Upperparts and breast are iridescent emerald-green, and lower breast, belly and flanks are white and strongly barred with metallic brownish-green. **Subadult male** has whitish sides of head, throat and breast which are strongly barred, as rest of underparts. **Female** differs from female Violet Cuckoo (below) in rufous-orange crown and nape (with some dark barring), contrasting with (unbarred) bronze-green mantle and wings. Has yellow bill with dark tip. **Juvenile** differs from juvenile Violet in having unbarred rufous-orange crown and nape, and rufous-orange wash to barred throat and breast. Upperparts are green with rufous-orange barring (especially on mantle and scapulars), although upperparts of juvenile Violet are rather similar. In flight, shows whitish band (at base of primaries) on underside of wing (more rufous on Violet). **VOICE** A clear, loud three-noted whistle, and a sharp *chweek* call uttered in flight. Loud descending *kee-kee-kee-kee* (A. Lewis). **HABITS** Usually keeps to the leafy canopy of tall trees, but on arrival in spring often flies about conspicuously. Very active, moving rapidly from branch to branch and making sallies to capture flying insects. Has a habit of perching along a branch, rather than across it. Flight is fast and direct. **HABITAT** Evergreen broadleaved forest. **BREEDING** Poorly known. April–July. Brood-parasitic, on sunbirds and Little Spiderhunter (p.806). **DISTRIBUTION AND STATUS** Summer visitor to Bhutan Himalayas, NE India and Bangladesh; rare further west in Himalayas to N Uttar Pradesh and in Arunachal Pradesh; winter visitor to Andamans and Nicobars. **NP:** rare, April–September; 250 m and 1280–1800 m. **IN:** rare; recorded up to 2200 m. **BT:** frequent; 300–2200 m (–2745 m). **BD:** local summer visitor. **LK:** winter vagrant to lowlands. **REFERENCES** Becking (1981).

VIOLET CUCKOO *Chrysococcyx xanthorhynchus* — Plate 24

***Chalcites xanthorhynchus* (I)**

IDENTIFICATION 17 cm. A very small cuckoo; male is unmistakable, female and juvenile are more similar to corresponding plumages of Asian Emerald Cuckoo (above). **Adult male** is iridescent purple on upperparts, throat and breast, and white on the rest of the underparts, which are strongly barred with purplish-brown. **Female** differs from Asian Emerald in having uniform bronze-brown upperparts, with only a slight greenish tinge, and white underparts with brownish barring. **Juvenile** has rufous crown and nape with broad dark green barring, dark green upperparts with rufous barring, and white underparts with broad dark brown barring. Extensive dark barring to crown and nape and lack of rufous-orange wash on throat are best distinctions from juvenile Asian Emerald. **VOICE** A disyllabic and repeated *che-wick*, particularly in flight; also an accelerating trill (J. Scharringa). **HABITS** Very poorly known; presumably similar to those of Asian Emerald. **HABITAT** Tree clumps in secondary evergreen broadleaved forest, orchards. **BREEDING** Poorly known. Mainly brood-parasitic, on same species as Asian Emerald. **DISTRIBUTION AND STATUS** Resident or summer visitor mainly to hills of NE India (Arunachal Pradesh, Assam, Manipur, Meghalaya, Mizoram, Nagaland, Tripura) and NE Bangladesh. **IN:** rare; breeds in hills up to 1500 m (–2300 m). **BT:** rare. **BD:** rare. **REFERENCES** Becking (1981), Singh (1995).

DRONGO CUCKOO *Surniculus lugubris* Plate 24

Drongo-Cuckoo (I,N,P)

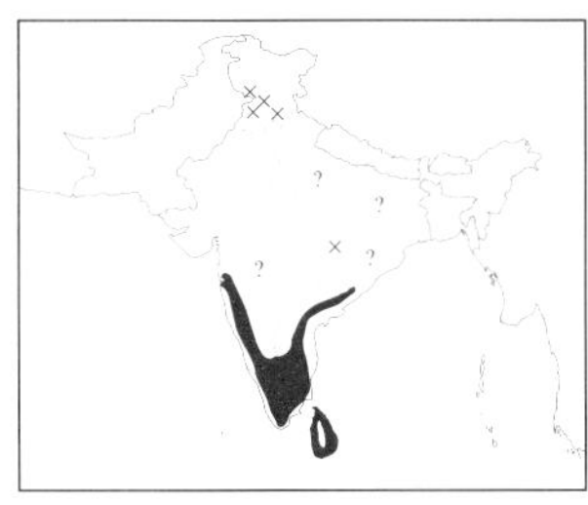

IDENTIFICATION 25 cm. A small, all-dark cuckoo, most likely to be confused with a drongo *Dicrurus* (p.609–p.614). **Adult** is almost entirely glossy black, except for fine white barring on very long undertail-coverts, white thighs, and tiny white patch on nape (last two features are difficult to see in the field). Best told from a drongo by fine, downcurved black bill, square-ended tail (with slight indentation), and combination of clean black belly and vent and white-barred undertail-coverts. **Juvenile** is dull black, spotted with white, and could more easily be confused with an immature drongo, especially Greater Racket-tailed (p.614) and Crow-billed (p.611). Best told by bill shape, and by long, white-barred undertail-coverts. **VOICE** A distinctive, ascending series of whistles, *pee-pee-pee-pee-pee-pee*, broken off and quickly repeated. **HABITS** Resembles a drongo, especially when perched upright, but is less active and flies like a cuckoo. Perches on a bare branch when calling, but otherwise usually keeps in the canopy foliage of trees and bushes. **HABITAT** Forest edges and clearings, open secondary forest, groves, orchards, and shade trees in tea plantations. **BREEDING** Poorly known. Probably December–October, varying locally. Found to be brood-parasitic, on Nepal Fulvetta (p.776) and Dark-fronted Babbler (p.762). **DISTRIBUTION AND STATUS** Summer visitor to Himalayas; elsewhere resident, subject to local movements. Mainly in Himalayas from N Uttar Pradesh east to Arunachal Pradesh; NE India and Bangladesh; Western Ghats, S and SE India, and Sri Lanka. **PK:** no confirmed records. **NP:** local summer visitor, March–early November; mainly below 1500 m (–2000 m). **IN:** locally common in Himalayas, not common elsewhere. **BT:** common summer visitor; 250–2250 m. **BD:** locally common resident. **LK:** rare resident in lowlands, visitor to hills. **REFERENCES** Becking (1981).

ASIAN KOEL *Eudynamys scolopacea* Plate 24

Koel (I), Common Koel (N,R), Koel Cuckoo (F), Indian Koel (P)

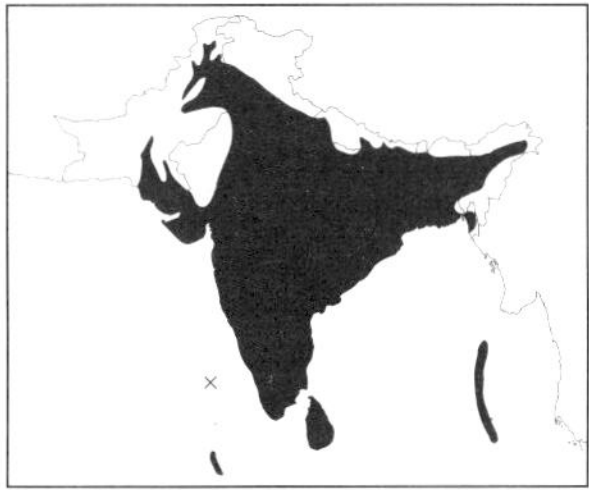

IDENTIFICATION 43 cm. A very large, long-tailed cuckoo. **Male** is glossy black all over (with green iridescence), with a dull lime-green bill and brilliant red eye. **Female** is brown above (with faint green gloss), spotted and barred with white and buff, and white below, strongly barred with dark brown. Also has striking red eye. **Juvenile** is blackish, with white or buff tips to wing-coverts and tertials, and variable white barring on underparts; tail is black, although shows pronounced rufous barring on some. **VOICE** A loud, rising and increasingly anxious *ko-el...ko-el...ko-el...ko-el...ko-el...ko-el*, and a bubbling, more rapid *koel..koel..koel..koel.* **HABITS** Typically keeps concealed in dense foliage when not feeding, although may sun itself from a treetop in early mornings. Usually seen when it flies hurriedly from one tree to another. Flight is fast, strong and direct. Feeds mainly on fruit and berries, especially *Ficus*; also invertebrates and birds' eggs. **HABITAT** Open woodland, gardens, orchards, groves around cultivation and villages, parks and other areas with scattered trees in towns and cities; irrigated plantations in Pakistan. **BREEDING** March–October, varying locally. Parasitises House Crow (p.597) and Large-billed Crow (p.598). **DISTRIBUTION AND STATUS** Throughout much of the subcontinent; summer visitor to parts of the northwest, resident elsewhere. **PK:** common in plains. **NP:** common throughout; below 1370 m, locally to 1800 m. **IN:** locally common; up to 1800 m in Himalayas and to 1000 m in peninsular hills. **BT:** uncommon resident or summer visitor. **BD:** common and widespread. **LK:** common in lowlands and lower hills. **MV:** widespread.

GREEN-BILLED MALKOHA *Phaenicophaeus tristis* Plate 24

Large Green-billed Malkoha (F,I), *Rhopodytes tristis* (E,F,I)

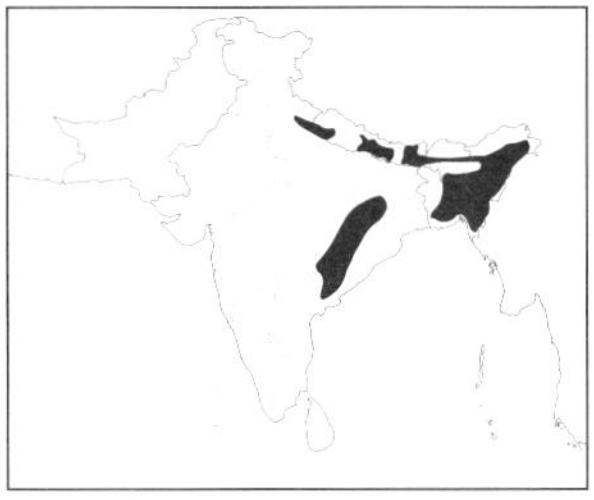

IDENTIFICATION 38 cm. A large, long-tailed cuckoo, greyish-green in coloration, with stout, lime-green bill, scarlet-red eye-patch, and broad white tips to the tail feathers. Replaces Blue-faced Malkoha (p.416) in northern parts of the subcontinent. Main differences from Blue-faced are larger size, red rather than blue eye-patch, black lores and white-streaked supercilium, paler greyish-green coloration to crown and nape, paler and more uniform buffish-grey underparts with fine black shaft streaking, and narrower white tips to tail feathers. **VOICE** A low croaking *ko...ko...ko*, and a peculiar chuckle when flushed (Ali and Ripley 1987). **HABITS** Rather shy; usually keeps out of sight in dense tangles of vegetation and thickly foliaged trees. Creeps and clambers unobtrusively through branches low down in dense vegetation. A weak flier, usually making only short laboured flights from one thicket to another. **HABITAT** Dense broadleaved evergreen and moist deciduous thickets. **BREEDING** April–August, varying locally. Builds a small untidy nest of twigs and rootlets, lined with green leaves, and placed 3–7 m up in a tangle of creepers. **DISTRIBUTION AND STATUS** Resident. Himalayas from N Uttar Pradesh east to Arunachal Pradesh; NE and E India, and Bangladesh.

NP: fairly common below 700 m, uncommon up to 2000 m. **IN:** locally fairly common; foothills up to 1800 m. **BT:** fairly common; 250–1700 m. **BD:** locally common.

BLUE-FACED MALKOHA *Phaenicophaeus viridirostris* Plate 24

Small Green-billed Malkoha (I), ***Rhopodytes viridirostris*** **(I,P)**

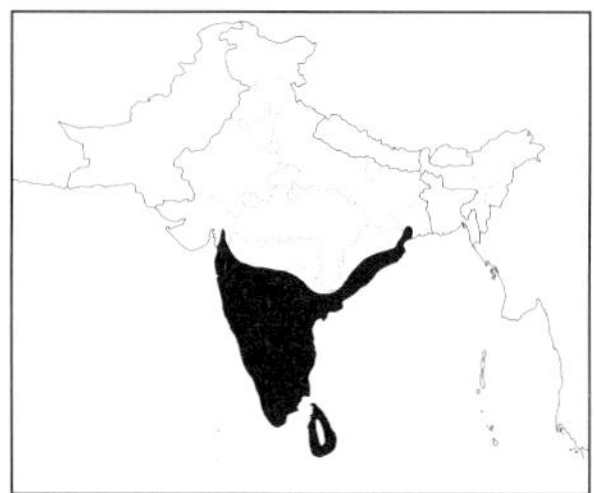

IDENTIFICATION 39 cm. A large, greenish-coloured, long-tailed cuckoo with lime-green bill, blue eye-patch, and broad white tips to rectrices. Differs from the larger Green-billed Malkoha (p.415) (which it replaces in S India and Sri Lanka) in having blue rather than red eye-patch, darker green coloration to head and nape (lacking pale-streaked supercilium), darker grey throat and breast with buffish streaking, distinctly buffish lower breast and belly, and broader white tips to tail feathers. **VOICE** A low croaking *kra* (Ali and Ripley 1987). **HABITS** Similar to those of Green-billed Malkoha. **HABITAT** Bushes and thorn scrub, such as *Euphorbia* and lantana, and open secondary forest. **BREEDING** Almost all year. Nest similar to that of Green-billed Malkoha, placed 1–2 m up in a thorn bush or bamboo clump. **DISTRIBUTION AND STATUS** Resident, endemic to the subcontinent. From S Gujarat and S Orissa south through the peninsula and Sri Lanka. **IN:** locally fairly common; plains and hills up to 1000 m. **LK:** common resident in dry lowlands and foothills, infrequent in wet zone.

SIRKEER MALKOHA *Phaenicophaeus leschenaultii* Plate 24

Sirkeer Cuckoo (F,I), Sirkeer, ***Taccocua leschenaultii*** **(E,F,I,P,R)**

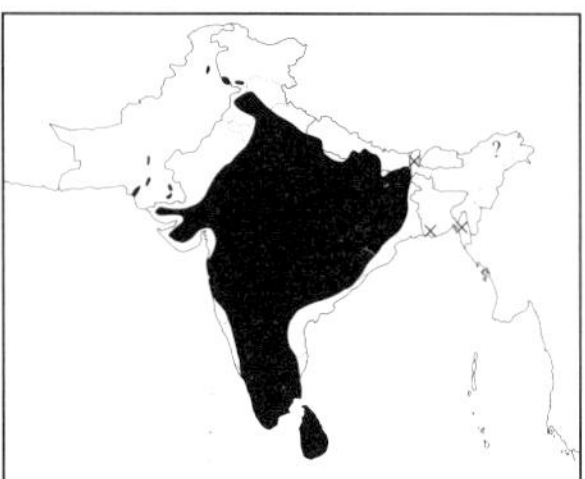

IDENTIFICATION 42 cm. **Adult** is distinctive. Has fine white line above and below dark facial skin, resulting in masked appearance, and yellow-tipped red bill. Mainly sandy grey-brown in coloration, with black shaft streaking on crown, mantle and breast; throat is buff, and belly is rufous-buff. Has long, graduated, white-tipped tail. **Immature** is very similar, but has indistinct buff fringes to wing-coverts, scapulars and tertials. **Juvenile** plumage appears to be retained for only a brief period after fledging: has broad dark brown streaking on head, mantle, throat and breast, and buff fringes to mantle, wing-coverts and tertials. **VOICE** Normally silent, but can utter a parakeet-like *kek-kek-kek-kerek-kerek-kerek,* or *kik-kik-kik* (Ali and Ripley 1987). **HABITS** Largely terrestrial. Stalks about the ground in search of food; sometimes clambers among shrubs and small trees or hops from branch to branch. Quite shy, taking refuge in patches of dense cover when observed. A poor flier; often just flaps laboriously from one bush to another. When alarmed, prefers to escape by running away quickly, darting in and out of thickets, keeping head down and body horizontal, looking more like a mammal than a bird. **HABITAT** Thorn scrub and acacia bushes in stony places; also semi-desert. **BREEDING** March–September, varying locally. Nest similar to that of Green-billed Malkoha (p.415), placed up to 6 m above ground in a *Euphorbia* or shrub. **DISTRIBUTION AND STATUS** Sedentary resident, endemic to the subcontinent. Throughout much of the subcontinent, except parts of the northeast, most of the northwest and extreme E India. **PK:** rare and local. **NP:** frequent in the far west, uncommon farther east; below 915 m (–1370 m). **IN:** generally uncommon; up to 1000 m in the peninsula, locally to 2100 m in Himalayas. **BD:** ?rare resident. **LK:** rare in dry lowlands and adjacent hills of the east.

RED-FACED MALKOHA *Phaenicophaeus pyrrhocephalus* Plate 24

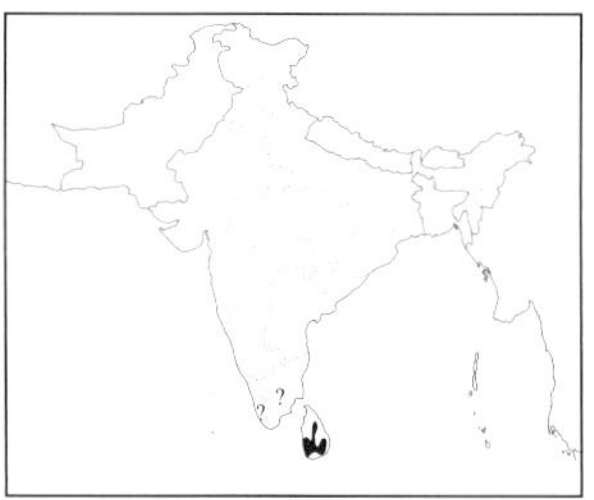

IDENTIFICATION 46 cm. A very large, dark green cuckoo with long graduated tail. **Adult** unmistakable. Most distinctive features are stout apple-green bill, large red face patch, whitish chin and malar stripe contrasting with black throat and breast, white flecking on crown and nape, striking white belly, and very broad white tips to tail feathers. **Juvenile** has smaller red face patch, brown streaking on crown and nape, and extensive greyish-white streaking on throat, neck sides and breast. **VOICE** Usually silent, but sometimes utters short yelping whistles, a low *kra* and a hollow *kok*. **HABITS** Similar to those of Green-billed Malkoha (p.415), but frequents the tree canopy. Typically, threads its way through foliage, creepers and branches. Often three or four birds together, and frequently associates with mixed feeding flocks of other species. Eats fruit and insects. **HABITAT** Tall, dense, broadleaved primary forest, mainly evergreen. **BREEDING** January, April and May. Nest is a shallow cup of twigs, grass and roots, placed in a shrub in dense forest. **DISTRIBUTION AND STATUS** Resident, probably endemic to Sri Lanka; two doubtful claims from Tamil Nadu and Kerala. Globally threatened. **LK:** rare and locally distributed in forest of wet zone and riverain forest of dry zone; restricted to protected areas.

COUCALS Centropodidae

Large, skulking birds with long graduated tail and weak flight. Coucals are terrestrial, frequenting dense undergrowth, bamboo, tall grassland or scrub jungle. They eat small mammals, lizards, snakes, frogs, nestlings, eggs, insects, spiders, crustaceans and molluscs.

GREATER COUCAL *Centropus sinensis* Plate 24

Crow-pheasant (I), Common Coucal (P), Large Coucal (F)

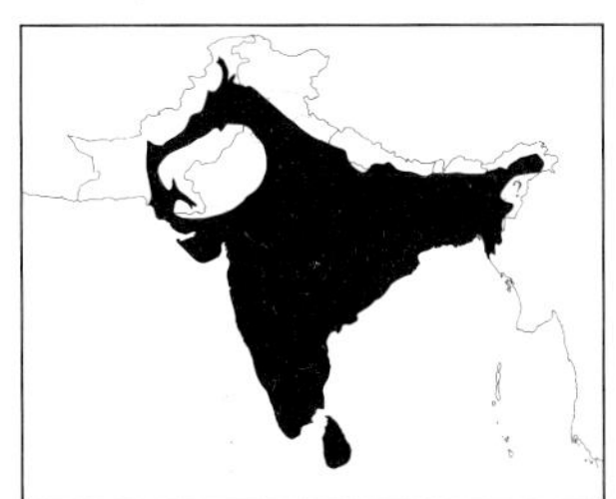

IDENTIFICATION 48 cm. Large, with glossy black head, body and tail, contrasting chestnut wings, and red eye. **Adult** differs from adult breeding Lesser Coucal (below) in much larger size, black underwing-coverts (difficult to see in the field), and brighter and more uniform chestnut wings. Non-breeding and immature Lesser are very distinctive (see that species). For differences from Green-billed Coucal (p.418), see that species. **Juvenile** (except for *C. s. parroti* of peninsular India, which resembles adult) has brownish-black head and body, with chestnut spotting on crown and nape (becoming barred on mantle), and diffuse whitish barring on entire underparts; chestnut-brown covert and flight feathers are barred with dark brown, and tail is narrowly barred with buff or greyish-white. **Immature** resembles adult, although head and body are duller black and has barred (juvenile) flight feathers and tail. **VOICE** A deep, resonant and primate-like *hoop-hoop-hoop-hoop-hoop-hoop-hoop*, descending and then rising towards the end of the series. Also has a popping *tok-tok-tok* call, and a harsh, rasping *skaah* (Boonsong and Round 1991). **HABITS** Walks sedately like a pheasant, with tail held horizontal, or skulks furtively through dense undergrowth. Hunts mainly on the ground; hops and runs strongly and actively when pursuing prey. Readily perches in trees, where it can clamber and hop about with ease. Flight is weak, slow and clumsy. When flying any distance, it usually hops from branch to branch to a tree-top, where it takes off and flutters and glides downwards. Feeds on a wide variety of small animal prey, also eggs and nestlings. **HABITAT** Tall grassland, bamboo or scrub jungle, shrubberies in cultivation and gardens, orchards, groves, and thick cover adjacent to wetlands. **BREEDING** Almost all year, varying locally. Nest is usually an untidy ball of twigs and leaves with a side entrance, placed in a thick bush or bamboo clump; sometimes a deep cup with a dome. **DISTRIBUTION AND STATUS** Resident throughout much of subcontinent, except parts of the north-west. **PK:** common and very widespread. **NP:** common throughout below 365 m, also very locally at 900 m in summer. **IN:** common from plains locally up to 2200 m. **BT:** uncommon; 400–1600 m. **BD:** locally common. **LK:** common resident in all zones; has recently extended into highest areas of hill country.

BROWN COUCAL *Centropus andamanensis* Plate 24

***C. sinensis andamanensis* (I)**

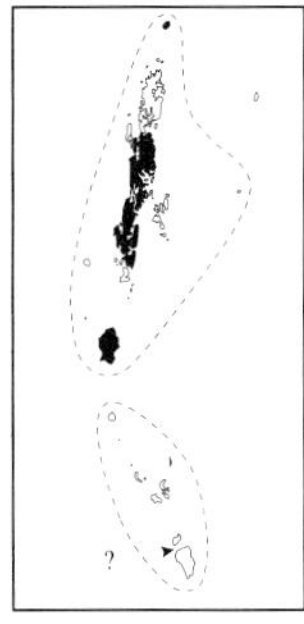

IDENTIFICATION 48 cm. The only coucal occurring in the Andamans. **Adult** resembles Greater Coucal (above), with striking chestnut wings, but head and body are fawn-brown (rather than glossy black), with darker brown rump and tail. Some have paler, dirty buff head and underbody, and greyish-buff tail which is distinctly darker towards tip. **Juvenile** is indistinctly and diffusely barred with brown on head, mantle and entire underparts. **VOICE** A rapid series of *hoop* notes, probably normally between 25 and 35, which start slowly and weakly and increase in intensity before ending abruptly (B. Gee). **HABITS** Like those of Greater Coucal. **HABITAT** Forest edges, gardens, cultivation, especially sugarcane, and mangroves. **BREEDING** May–July. Nest is like that of Greater. **DISTRIBUTION AND STATUS IN:** occurs only in the Andamans and Coco Is (Myanmar), possibly in the Nicobars; locally common on Andaman Is. **REFERENCES** Davidar *et al.* (1997), Gee (1995), Sankaran and Vijayan (1993).

LESSER COUCAL *Centropus bengalensis* Plate 24

Small Coucal (F), *C. toulou bengalensis* (E,F,I)

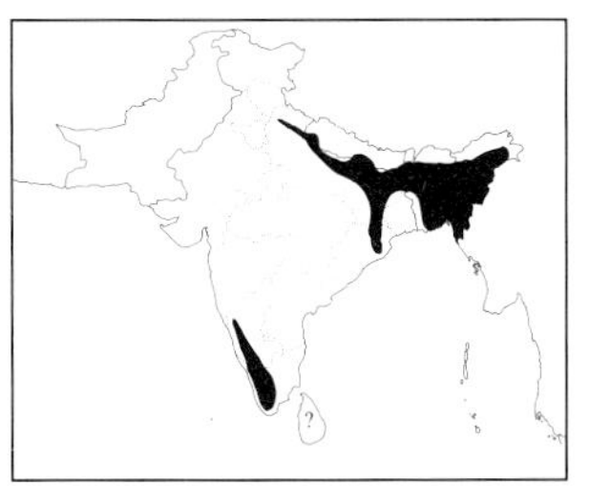

IDENTIFICATION 33 cm. **Adult breeding** like Greater Coucal (above), with chestnut mantle and wings contrasting with glossy black head, underparts and tail. Really distinguishable only by much smaller size, chestnut (rather than black) underwing-coverts, duller chestnut mantle and wings, and browner tertials and primary tips. Often shows buff streaking on some scapulars and wing-coverts (unlike Greater). **Adult non-breeding** is quite different from Greater. Has dark brown head and mantle with prominent buff shaft steaks, dark brown and rufous barring on rump and very long uppertail-coverts contrasting with blackish tail, buff underparts with pale streaking on throat and breast, and dark barring on sides of breast and flanks. Wings and tail are as adult breeding. **Juvenile** is similar to adult non-breeding, but has less distinct pale shaft streaking on upperparts, dark barring on crown, mantle and back, dark brown barring on wings, and narrow rufous barring on tail. **Immature** has head and body as adult non-breeding, but wings and tail are barred as on juvenile. **VOICE** Series of (usually six) deep, resonant *pwoop-pwoop-pwoop-pwoop* notes very similar to Greater, but rarely as hesitant, usually slightly faster and more interrogative, initially ascending and then descending and decelerating. Common call is a series of five to six *whoot* notes, the first two uttered at somewhat slow tempo, slightly faster from the third. The calls lack the deep resonance and volume of the regular call-notes of Greater. Heard less often is *kurook*, given in Ali and Ripley (1987) as *kulook* or *kirook* (Santharam and Nameer 1992). **HABITS** Similar to those of Greater, but feeds almost entirely on grasshoppers. Spends considerable periods perched and inactive. **HABITAT** Tall grassland, reedbeds, dense shrubberies at forest edges; in Nepal, also in Salima grass with bamboo clumps and scattered trees and bushes. **BREEDING** March–October, varying locally. Nest is similar to that of Greater, but smaller. **DISTRIBUTION AND STATUS** Resident; possibly a summer visitor to Himalayas. Himalayas from N Uttar Pradesh east to Arunachal Pradesh; NE India and Bangladesh; E and SW India. **NP:** local, mainly below 365 m; very locally summers up to 1400 m. **IN:** locally fairly common; lower hills of Himalayas, locally to 1800 m; also to 900 m in the southwest. **BT:** frequent; 400–1830 m. **BD:** locally common. **LK:** status uncertain, perhaps a vagrant to lowlands. **REFERENCES** Santharam and Nameer (1992).

GREEN-BILLED COUCAL *Centropus chlororhynchus* — Plate 24

Ceylon Coucal (I)

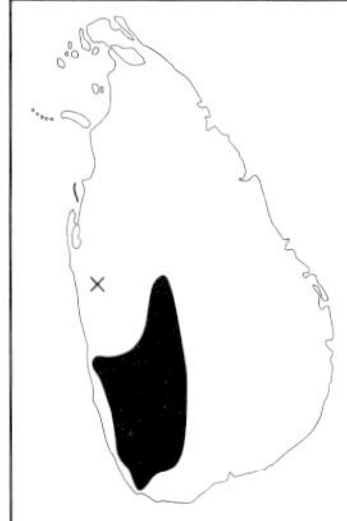

IDENTIFICATION 43 cm. Large, with blackish head, body and tail and maroon-brown wings. Differs from Greater Coucal (p.417), which also occurs in Sri Lanka, in green rather than black bill and in distinctive call. Head and underbody are duller and browner in coloration compared with Greater and, unlike that species, lacks striking contrast between (maroon-brown) wings and blackish body. There are no distinct juvenile or immature plumages. **VOICE** Similar to that of Greater, but is usually of only two or three syllables and is deeper, with a sonorous mournful quality: *hooo-poop* or *hooo-poo-poop*, the *poop* being lower-pitched than the *hooo* (Henry 1971). **HABITS** Similar to those of Greater, but very secretive and far better known by its call than by sight. May emerge from cover in early morning and after heavy rain. **HABITAT** Tall, damp forest with dense undergrowth of bamboo and cane brakes. **BREEDING** January–July. Only one nest known, a ball of twigs, roots and grass, lined with green leaves and placed among thorn cane brakes. **DISTRIBUTION AND STATUS** Globally threatened. **LK:** rare endemic resident, restricted to wet lowlands and adjoining foothills.

PARROTS Psittacidae

Have a short neck and short, stout hooked bill with the upper mandible strongly curved and overlapping the lower mandible. Most parrots are noisy and highly gregarious. They associate in family parties and small flocks and gather in large numbers at concentrations of food, such as paddy-fields and orchards, where some species cause much damage. Their diet is almost entirely vegetarian: fruit, seeds, buds, nectar and pollen. Typically, parrots use the foot to hold their food and the bill to crack and dehusk seeds or nuts before swallowing. When climbing about in trees, they often use the bill to grasp a branch and then step across it in a 'hand-over-hand' fashion. Most species nest in natural tree holes, often unlined, which they enlarge to suit their needs; some species use barbet or woodpecker holes. The flight of *Psittacula* parrots is swift, powerful and direct. The main references specific to parrots is Forshaw (1989).

VERNAL HANGING PARROT *Loriculus vernalis* — Plate 25

Indian Lorikeet (F,I)

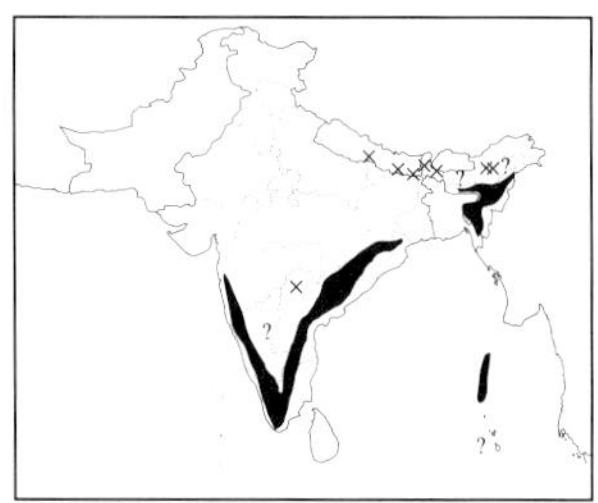

IDENTIFICATION 14 cm. A small (sparrow-sized), stocky green parrot with red rump and uppertail-coverts and red bill. **Adult** has yellowish-white iris. **Male** has turquoise throat patch. **Female** is similar, but lacks (or has much-reduced) turquoise throat patch. **Immature** is similar to female, but red rump and uppertail-coverts are mixed with green, and has brown iris. **VOICE** Distinctive di- or trisyllabic rasping flight call, *de-zeez-zeet*; occasionally given also by birds at rest (P. Holt). **HABITS** Wholly arboreal, spending most of the day feeding in the tops of tall trees, and may be overlooked. More easily seen in flight, when has short, rapid wingbeats followed by a brief pause, resulting in undulations. Very agile, clambering about trees using beak and feet, scampering along branches and hanging upside-down to reach flowers. **HABITAT** Broadleaved evergreen and moist deciduous forest. **BREEDING** January–May, varying locally. Nest hole is 2–10 m above ground, usually lined with strips of green leaves. **DISTRIBUTION AND STATUS** Resident, subject to poorly understood local movements; a winter visitor in some areas and a monsoon visitor in others. Mainly NE India and Bangladesh, Western Ghats, and E India from Orissa south to Tamil Nadu. **NP:** very rare; below 275 m. **IN:** locally common; plains up to 1000 m, to 1800 m in Nilgiris. **BD:** local resident.

SRI LANKA HANGING PARROT *Loriculus beryllinus* — Plate 25

Ceylon Lorikeet (I,P), Ceylon Hanging Parrot

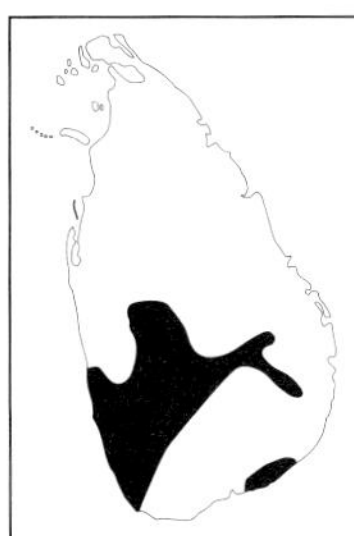

IDENTIFICATION 14 cm. Much the same as Vernal Hanging Parrot (p.418) in shape, behaviour and coloration. **Adult** has crimson forehead and crown, golden-orange cast to nape and mantle, and turquoise wash on throat. **Immature** has greyish-green forehead, orange cast to green crown (with a few patches of red), and only faint turquoise wash to throat. **VOICE** As Vernal Hanging Parrot. **HABITS** Very similar to those of Vernal Hanging Parrot. **HABITAT** Like that of Vernal. **BREEDING** January–August. Nest is like that of Vernal Hanging Parrot. **DISTRIBUTION AND STATUS LK:** endemic resident; common in hills and adjacent lowlands, mainly in foothills of wet zone.

ALEXANDRINE PARAKEET *Psittacula eupatria* — Plate 25

Large Indian Parakeet (I), Large Parakeet (F)

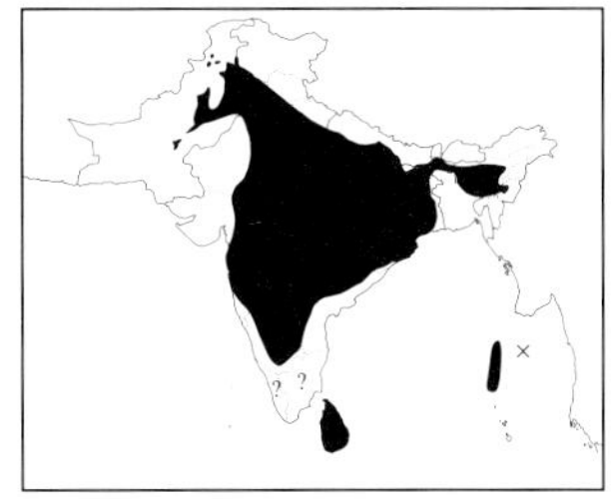

IDENTIFICATION 53 cm. A very large, all-green parakeet with huge red bill. Considerably larger than Rose-ringed Parakeet (below), and best told from that species by combination of larger size, maroon shoulder patch, and massive bill. Distinctive call and slower and more laboured flight are additional pointers. **Male** has black chin stripe joining pink and turquoise hindcollar, both of which are lacking on **female** and **immature**. **VOICE** A loud, guttural *keeak* or *kee-ah*, deeper and more raucous than that of Rose-ringed. **HABITS** Quite wary. Flocks in large numbers to raid orchards or crops; has wasteful feeding habits. Flies with deliberate wingbeats accompanied by a harsh loud scream. Hundreds or sometimes thousands gather noisily from all directions at sunset to roost communally (usually not with other species) in large, thickly foliaged trees in groves or forest. **HABITAT** Moist and dry deciduous forest and well-wooded areas; parks, gardens and trees around habitation, irrigated desert settlements with mature trees and plantations. **BREEDING** December–May, varying locally. Has a typical parrot nest hole, sometimes with a bed of wood chippings. **DISTRIBUTION AND STATUS** Resident, subject to local wanderings depending on food supply. From E Pakistan east through N India and S Nepal to NE India and Bangladesh, and south through the peninsula to S Karnataka; Sri Lanka. **PK:** common and local. **NP:** common; below 365 m (–1380 m). **IN:** common and widespread in the north, sporadic south of 18°N; plains up to 1600 m in Himalayas and to 900 m in peninsular hills. **BT:** uncommon; 250–400 m. **BD:** ?local resident; no recent records. **LK:** irregular resident in lowlands and lower hills, more frequent in dry zone. **REFERENCES** Lama (1995b).

ROSE-RINGED PARAKEET *Psittacula krameri* — Plate 25

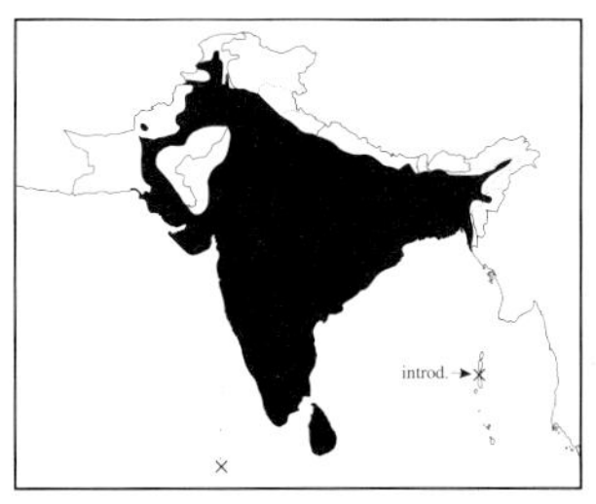

IDENTIFICATION 42 cm. An all-green parakeet with bright red bill. Differs from the similar Alexandrine Parakeet (above) in smaller size, lack of maroon shoulder patch, and smaller bill. Dark blue-green (rather than pale yellowish) dorsal aspect of tail is a further feature. **Male** has black chin stripe joining pink hindcollar. **Female** lacks the chin stripe and collar, and is all green (although it does have an indistinct pale green collar). **VOICE** A loud, shrill and variable *kee-ah*, higher-pitched and less guttural than Alexandrine's. **HABITS** A very adaptable species, often associated with habitation and cultivation. Feeding habits are like those of Alexandrine. Has enormous communal roosts, often with crows and mynas, in trees in gardens and groves near habitation. Constantly screeches and squabbles. **HABITAT** Deciduous forest, open woodland, secondary growth, cultivation, gardens and vicinity of habitation. **BREEDING** December–July, varying locally. Uses a typical parrot nest hole; also often uses holes in walls or cliffs. Frequently in loose colonies. **DISTRIBUTION AND STATUS** Resident throughout much of the subcontinent, except parts of the northwest, northeast and Himalayas. **PK:** common and widespread resident throughout Indus basin; moves up to Baluchistan valleys and to 915 m in Murree foothills. **NP:** common; below 365 m (–1370 m). **IN:** common. **BT:** uncommon; 250–305 m. **BD:** common. **LK:** common resident throughout lowlands, less common in hills. **MV:** introduced.

SLATY-HEADED PARAKEET *Psittacula himalayana* — Plate 25

IDENTIFICATION 41 cm. **Adult** is usually readily distinguished by grey head, stout red bill, and yellow-tipped tail. From below, underside of tail is strikingly yellow. Possibly confusable with female Plum-headed Parakeet (p.420), but is larger, head is a darker slate-grey with black chin stripe and half-collar, has a stouter red bill with pale yellow lower mandible, lacks yellowish collar, and has yellow (rather than white) tip to the tail. **Male** differs from **female** in having a maroon shoulder patch. **Immature** lacks slate-grey head, and is best told from female and immature Rose-ringed Parakeet (above) by dark, dull green head, yellow tip to tail (although this may

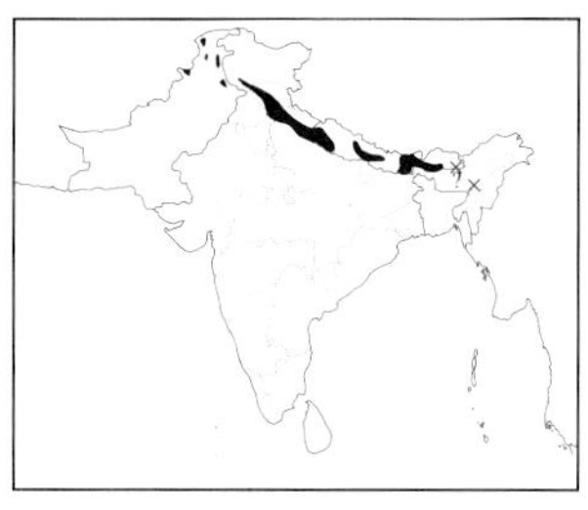

not be apparent on younger birds), and distinctive call. Very similar in all plumages to Grey-headed Parakeet (below); see that species for differences. **VOICE** A shrill *tooi..tooi*, deeper and harsher than the call of Plum-headed. **HABITS** Feeding behaviour is like that of Alexandrine (p.419). Very agile in flight, keeping in compact flocks, the birds twisting and turning through the trees in unison, then suddenly gliding upwards to alight. **HABITAT** Forest and well-wooded areas, especially near hill orchards and cultivation. **BREEDING** March–July, varying locally. Uses a typical parrot nest hole; sometimes loosely colonial. **DISTRIBUTION AND STATUS** Resident, subject to seasonal altitudinal movements and nomadic wanderings depending on food supply. Himalayas from N Pakistan east to Bhutan. **PK:** common, but very local; breeds 2135– 2400 m, winters down to 460 m. **NP:** fairly common; usually summers up to 2135 m and winters down to 1000 m (75–3260 m). **IN:** locally fairly common; breeds 1200–2500 m, winters down to 250 m. **BT:** frequent; 1220–1980 m, winters down to 610 m. **REFERENCES** Choudhary (1996a).

GREY-HEADED PARAKEET *Psittacula finschii* — Plate 25

Eastern Slaty-headed Parakeet (I)

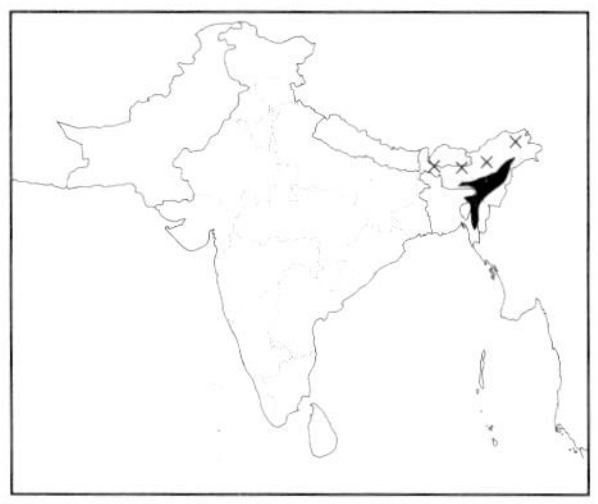

IDENTIFICATION 36 cm. Has more easterly distribution than Slaty-headed Parakeet (p.419). **Male** told from both sexes of that species by paler ashy-grey head, yellowish-green wash to upperparts (especially pronounced on nape), paler green underparts, and lilac-blue (more green on Slaty-headed) tail with paler yellowish-cream (rather than bright yellow) tip. **Female** is similar, but has darker green mantle (more closely resembling Slaty-headed in this respect), and lacks maroon shoulder patch. Within range in subcontinent both sexes are confusable with female and immature Blossom-headed Parakeet (p.421), but Grey-headed is larger, and has longer tail with more extensive yellowish-white tip, darker grey head with black chin stripe, marked blue-green collar, and larger red and pale yellow bill. **Immature** has brownish-green (darker than mantle) head (later becoming dull slate-grey), and lacks black chin stripe and half-collar of adult. Probably not separable in the field from immature Slaty-headed. **VOICE** Loud, short, shrill, high-pitched whistles with an upward inflection: *dreet..dreet..., sweet..sweet..., swit*, etc (C. Robson). **HABITS** Like those of Slaty-headed. **HABITAT** Hill forest and cultivation. **BREEDING** January–May. Uses a typical parrot nest hole; often loosely colonial. **DISTRIBUTION AND STATUS** Resident, subject to local movements. NE India (Arunachal Pradesh, Assam, Manipur, Meghalaya, Mizoram, Nagaland) and Bangladesh. **IN:** uncommon; from foothills up to 2100 m. **BD:** ?local resident.

INTERMEDIATE PARAKEET *Psittacula intermedia* — Plate 25

Rothschild's Parakeet (I)

IDENTIFICATION 36 cm. Best told from Plum-headed and Slaty-headed Parakeets (below and p.419) by coloration of head, which is slaty-purple with rufous-purple on forehead and around eye. Back and underparts are yellowish-green as on Plum-headed (darker and purer green on Slaty-headed). Rump and uppertail-coverts have slight bluish tinge (more blue on Plum-headed; green on Slaty-headed); tip of tail is yellowish-white (paler than on Slaty-headed); and outer webs of outer tail feathers are bluish-green with bright yellow tips (much as Plum-headed, but with brighter yellow tips). Upper mandible is red, as on Slaty-headed; lower mandible is described as yellow, but may be black. **VOICE** A monosyllabic, loud, throaty call, not unlike Rose-ringed's, has been reported (Sane *et al.* 1987). **DISTRIBUTION AND STATUS IN**: several specimens of unknown origin have been obtained; small numbers of live birds have recently appeared in Indian bird markets, reportedly trapped in the Uttar Pradesh plains. Some authorities suggested that this parakeet was a hybrid; others believed that there was a case for its being a distinct species. Recent evidence from captive-bred birds strongly suggests that this form is of hybrid origin. Found only in India. **REFERENCES** Biswas (1959), Husain (1959), Inskipp and Inskipp (1995a), Sane *et al.* (1987), Walters (1985).

PLUM-HEADED PARAKEET *Psittacula cyanocephala* — Plate 25

Blossom-headed Parakeet (F,I,P)

IDENTIFICATION 36 cm. A small-bodied, long-tailed parakeet with very rapid flight and distinctive high-pitched call. **Adult male** is easily distinguished throughout much of range by plum-red and purplish-blue head, yellow upper mandible, and white-tipped blue-green tail. Care is needed in NE parts of range, where it is replaced by Blossom-headed Parakeet (p.421); see that species for main differences. **Adult female** has greyish head and is possibly confusable with Slaty-headed Parakeet (p.419), although that species is typically a bird of the uplands rather than the plains. Is smaller-bodied and has daintier head and bill than Slaty-headed, main plumage distinctions from which are lilac cast to paler grey head (lacking black chin stripe and half-collar),

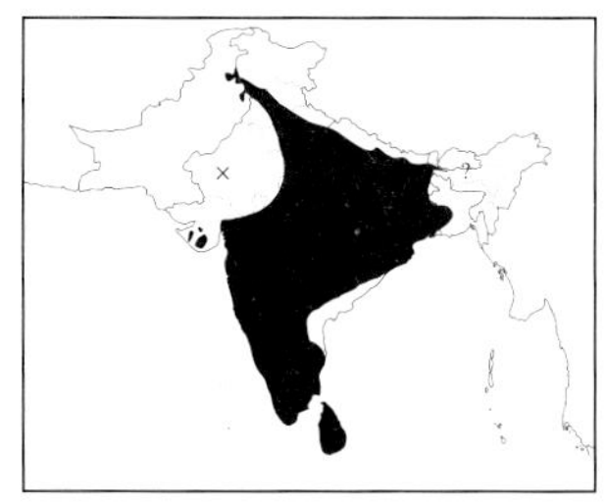

yellow (rather than red) upper mandible, yellowish collar and upper breast, and white (rather than yellow) tip to tail. **Juvenile** has green head, slightly darker than breast and mantle, and has buffish forehead, lores and cheeks. **VOICE** A shrill *tooi-tooi*, higher-pitched and less harsh than Slaty-headed's. **HABITS** Less associated with people than Rose-ringed (p.419). Roosts communally in large numbers in bamboo clumps or forest, birds continuing to screech even after dark. In flight, it can weave between forest trees with great agility. **HABITAT** Moist deciduous forest, well-wooded areas, and cultivation in forest clearings and at forest edges; open forest in Sri Lanka. **BREEDING** December–June, varying locally. Uses a typical parrot nest hole. **DISTRIBUTION AND STATUS** Resident, endemic to the subcontinent. Subject to local movements. Himalayas from NE Pakistan east to Bangladesh, south through much of the peninsula except parts of the northwest and northeast; Sri Lanka. **PK:** common and local resident. **NP:** fairly common below 500 m; frequent up to 1525 m. **IN::** locally common; plains up to 600 m, locally to 1500 m in Himalayas and to 1300 m in peninsular hills. **BD:** former resident. **LK:** resident in lowlands and lower hills, frequent in mid country, infrequent in dry zone. **REFERENCES** Husain and Sarker (1971).

BLOSSOM-HEADED PARAKEET *Psittacula roseata* Plate 25

Eastern Blossom-headed Parakeet (I)

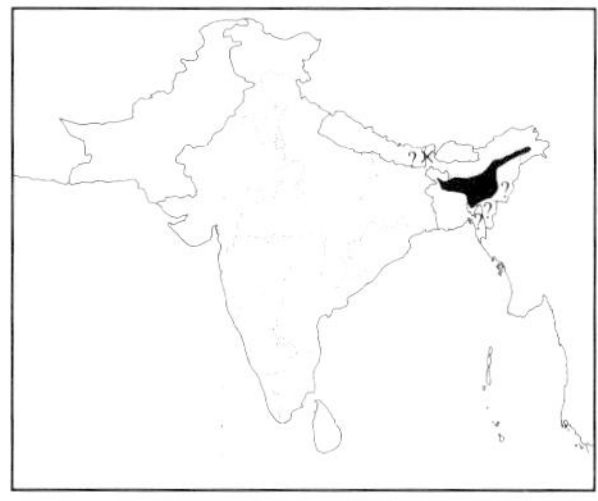

IDENTIFICATION 36 cm. Replaces Plum-headed Parakeet (p.420) in NE India. **Adult male** told by paler pink coloration to head (forecrown and cheeks are pink rather than red, and rear crown and nape are pale lilac-blue rather than purple). Also lacks turquoise collar, and has pale yellow (rather than white) tip to tail. **Adult female** is very similar to female Plum-headed, but has paler greyish-blue head, less distinct (barely apparent) yellowish-green hindcollar, maroon shoulder patch, green (rather than bluish-green) rump, uppertail-coverts and underwing-coverts, and pale yellow tip to tail. From Grey-headed Parakeet (p.420) by smaller size, shorter tail with only a small pale yellow tip, paler greyish-blue head (darker grey on Grey-headed), narrow yellowish-green collar, lack of black chin stripe, and smaller bill (yellow, with grey lower mandible). **VOICE** As that of Plum-headed. **HABITS** Like those of Plum-headed. **HABITAT** Well-wooded areas, open forest and cultivation in forest clearings. **BREEDING** January–May, varying locally. Uses a typical parrot nest hole. **DISTRIBUTION AND STATUS** Resident, subject to local movements. Mainly NE Indian hills (Arunachal Pradesh, Assam, Manipur, Meghalaya, Sikkim, Tripura, West Bengal) and Bangladesh. **NP:** several specimens recently located in the British Museum (Natural History), collected in 19th century. **IN:** current status uncertain, very few recent records; duars and foothills. **BD::** local resident. **REFERENCES** Athreya *et al.* (1997), Inskipp and Inskipp (1997).

MALABAR PARAKEET *Psittacula columboides* Plate 25

Blue-winged Parakeet (I)

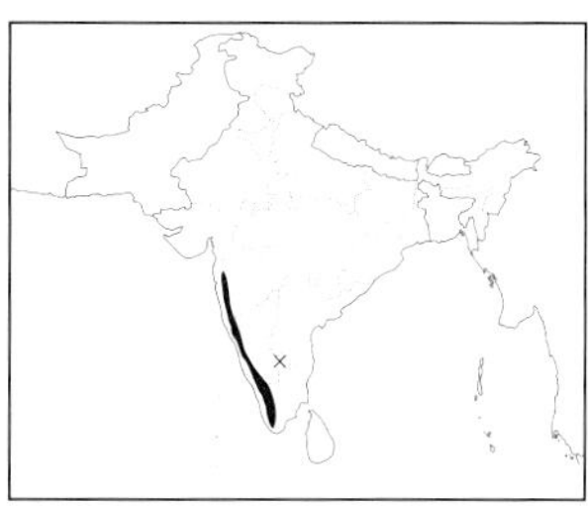

IDENTIFICATION 38 cm. **Adult male** has blue-grey head with green lores and cheeks, blue-green collar, pale blue-grey breast and mantle with variable pinkish tinge, blue-green lower back and rump, and blue primaries and yellow-tipped blue tail. **Adult female** is similar, but has blackish bill, lacks the blue-green collar of male (but has broader black collar across hindneck), and has greener lower mantle and back and greener lower breast and belly. **Immature** is greener than female, with indistinct dark collar; head is variably washed with dull turquoise and blue-grey. Blue in wings, yellow-tipped blue tail and different call help to separate from female and immature Rose-ringed Parakeet (p.420). **VOICE** Distinctive loud, discordant, jarring or scolding notes, coarser than those of other parakeets (given both in flight and at rest). **HABITS** Similar to those of Plum-headed (p.420), its counterpart in moist deciduous forest. Frequently associates with that species in intermediate habitats in low foothills, but at higher altitudes Malabar replaces Plum-headed. Mainly arboreal, feeding in the treetops. Will come to ground to feed on ripening crops in cultivation at forest edges or clearings. **HABITAT** Mainly tropical and subtropical broadleaved evergreen forest, sometimes also moist deciduous forest. **BREEDING** January–March. Uses a typical parrot nest hole 6–30 m above ground. **DISTRIBUTION AND STATUS IN:** endemic resident, subject to local movements; Western Ghats from N Maharashtra south to S Kerala; locally common, chiefly 500–1000 m, but occasionally in the plains and up to 1600 m.

LAYARD'S PARAKEET *Psittacula calthropae* Plate 25

IDENTIFICATION 31 cm. **Adult male** distinguished from other parakeets occurring in Sri Lanka by combination of bluish-grey coloration to head and mantle, with green lores and cheeks, broad green collar, green wings (with brighter lime-green lesser coverts), green underparts, violet-grey lower back and rump, and violet-blue tail with

yellowish tip. **Adult female** is very similar to male, but upper mandible is blackish (rather than red). Bill is initially orange-red, becoming blackish later. **Immature** is mainly green, with slightly darker head. Differs from female and immature Rose-ringed Parakeet (p.419) in violet-blue cast to lower back and rump, and yellow-tipped blue-green tail. **VOICE** A loud, harsh chattering scream, *ak..ak..ak..ak* (Henry 1971). **HABITS** Similar to those of Plum-headed (p.420), but more arboreal; usually keeps to the treetops and forages almost entirely in tall trees. Feeds and roosts in small flocks. **HABITAT** Edges of woods, forest clearings and wooded river banks; sometimes forest plantations and gardens with large trees. **BREEDING** Throughout the year. Uses a typical parrot hole, usually high up. **DISTRIBUTION AND STATUS LK:** endemic resident; frequent up to 1700 m in the wet zone and forested humid areas of the lowlands.

DERBYAN PARAKEET *Psittacula derbiana* Plate 25

Lord Derby's Parakeet (I)

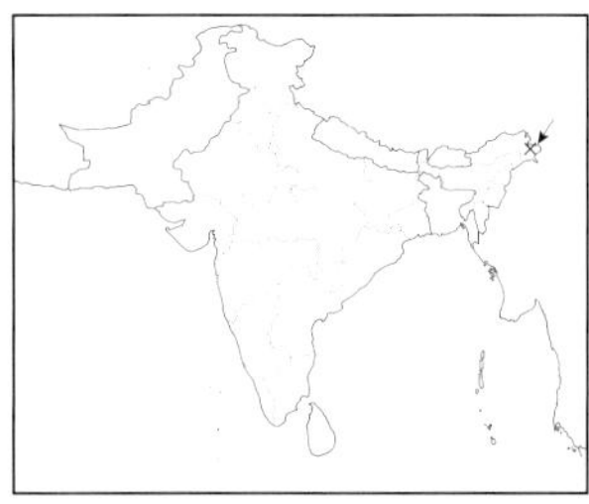

IDENTIFICATION 46 cm. **Adult male** has violet-grey crown and ear-coverts (brighter on forecrown, and blue-green around eyes), black forehead and chin stripe, striking greenish-yellow patch in wing-coverts, violet-grey breast and belly, and blue central tail feathers. **Adult female** is very similar, but has pinkish wash to violet-grey underparts and all-black bill (upper mandible is red on male). Larger size and coloration of underparts are best distinctions from female Red-breasted Parakeet (below), which occurs at much lower altitude. **Immature** has greener head, and is generally duller than adult; very young birds have orange-red bill. **VOICE** A prolonged raucous, metallic cry (Forshaw 1989). **HABITS** Poorly known in the subcontinent. Often in flocks of 40–50 birds. A serious pest in ripening crops; also feeds on pine cones and orchard fruits. **HABITAT** Conifer forest, and cultivation during harvest. **BREEDING** Very poorly known in the subcontinent. Visited nest hole in a tall, dead tree in late September. **DISTRIBUTION AND STATUS IN:** common, local resident in Arunachal Pradesh; breeds 2700–3500 m; presumably an altitudinal migrant. **REFERENCES** Singh (1995), Stonor (1952).

RED-BREASTED PARAKEET *Psittacula alexandri* Plate 25

Moustached Parakeet (N), Rose-breasted Parakeet (F)

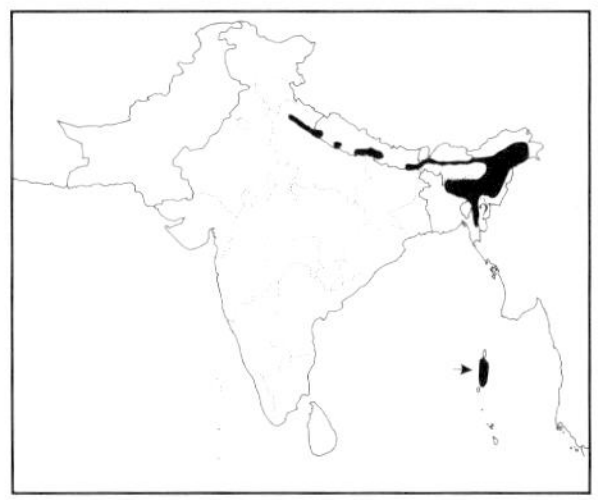

IDENTIFICATION 38 cm. **Adult male** is unmistakable throughout its range, with lilac-grey crown and ear-coverts (with variable pinkish wash), broad black chin stripe, deep lilac-pink breast and belly, greenish-yellow lesser wing-coverts contrasting with green mantle, and yellowish-tipped blue-green tail. **Adult female** is similar to male, but has blue-green tinge to head, purer peach-pink breast, and black (rather than red) upper mandible. **Immature** is duller than adult, with green underparts; has variable lilac-pink to lilac-grey coloration to crown and ear-coverts (crown is initially green). Bill is orange-red on young birds, becoming blackish later. **VOICE** A short, sharp nasal *kaink* (Ali and Ripley 1987). **HABITS** Generally keeps in small parties; in larger flocks when attacking crops. Usually quiet while feeding in treetops, the only signs of their presence being falling leaves and the fluttering of wings. Flight is slower than that of other *Psittacula*. Has large communal roosts in bamboo clumps or groves of trees. **HABITAT** Open deciduous forest, secondary growth, and shifting cultivation in hills. **BREEDING** February–April, varying locally. Uses a typical parrot nest hole, 3–10 m above ground. **DISTRIBUTION AND STATUS** Resident, subject to local movements depending on food supply. Himalayan foothills from N Uttar Pradesh east to Arunachal Pradesh; NE India and Bangladesh. **NP:** locally fairly common; below 365 m (–1370 m). **IN:** locally common; foothills up to 1500 m. **BT:** frequent; 250–610 m. **BD:** locally common resident.

NICOBAR PARAKEET *Psittacula caniceps* Plate 25

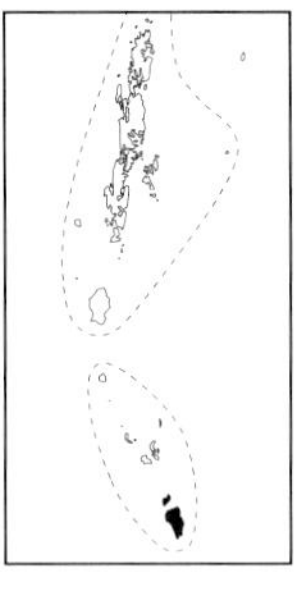

IDENTIFICATION 61 cm. **Adult male** is mainly yellowish-green, with buffish-grey head, black forehead and broad black chin stripe, and blackish flight feathers with bluish edges. **Adult female** has bluish-grey tinge to crown and nape, and black (rather than red) upper mandible. **Immature** is undescribed. **VOICE** A loud, raucous, corvid-like *kraan...kraan* (Ali and Ripley 1987); similar to that of Plum-headed Parakeet (p.420) (Forshaw 1989). **HABITS** Little known. Found singly or in small groups. Arboreal and usually keeps out of sight in upper branches of tall trees. Heard more often than seen, its calls carrying a long distance. Feeds on ripe fruit of *Pandanus*. **HABITAT** Tall forest. **BREEDING** Unknown. **DISTRIBUTION AND STATUS IN:** resident, endemic to Nicobar Is (Great Nicobar, Little Nicobar, Menschal and Kondul). **REFERENCES** Sankaran (1998).

LONG-TAILED PARAKEET *Psittacula longicauda* Plate 25

Red-cheeked Parakeet (I)

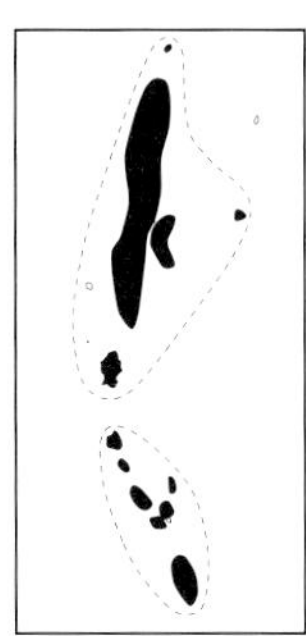

IDENTIFICATION 46–48 cm. **Adult male** has pinkish-red cheeks contrasting with dark green crown, broad black chin stripe, variable pale turquoise and lilac wash to green of mantle, and blue central tail and edges of primaries. **Adult female** is similar, but has black (rather than red) upper mandible; also is uniformly green above, and has paler, peach-coloured cheeks. **Immature** is uniform green, with less distinct cheek stripe; has touch of pinkish to ear-coverts, and yellowish edges to primaries. **Racial variation** *P. l. nicobarica* of the Nicobar Is differs from *P. l. tytleri* of the Andaman Is (described above) in being larger and more yellow-green on the upperparts (with variable, indistinct lilac or pinkish wash to nape, and turquoise wash to back). **VOICE** Similar to that of Rose-ringed Parakeet (p.419) (Ali and Ripley 1987). **HABITS** Little described from the region. Restless; dashes from one tree to another and twists and turns between forest trees at high speed with ease. Roosts communally. Huge flocks are a serious pest in ripening paddy. **HABITAT** Cultivation, gardens and nearby forest, mangroves. **BREEDING** February and March. Uses a typical parrot nest hole, 4–8 m above ground. **DISTRIBUTION AND STATUS IN:** common resident on Andaman and Nicobar Is. **REFERENCES** Sankaran and Vijayan (1993).

SWIFTS Apodidae AND TREESWIFTS Hemiprocnidae

Swifts in the region comprise the true swifts (Apodidae) and Crested Treeswift *Hemiprocne coronata.* They have long pointed wings, compact body, short bill with a wide gape and very short legs. Swifts spend most of the day swooping and wheeling through the sky with great agility and grace. Typical swift flight is a series of rapid shallow wingbeats interspersed with short glides. They feed entirely in the air, drink and bathe while swooping low over water, and regularly pass the night in the air. Normally, the Apodidae do not land on the ground or on vegetation, but their strong feet enable them to cling to vertical surfaces, such as tree trunks and cliff walls, when nesting or roosting. They eat mainly tiny insects, caught by flying back and forth among aerial concentrations of these with their large mouth open; they also pursue individual insects. They usually feed high in the air, except in bad weather; sometimes also from the surface of water, tree foliage and under the eaves of buildings. Where food is abundant, they often gather in mixed flocks of several species and with swallows and martins. On fine evenings, many swift species have a habit of flocking in tight concentrations near their roost or nest sites, the birds chasing each other and flying higher and higher while screaming or twittering in chorus. Swifts in the region roost communally, and many breed colonially. Most build a half-cup nest of plant material glued together and attached to a substrate with the birds' saliva. The main reference specific to swifts and treeswifts is Chantler and Driessens (1995).

GLOSSY SWIFTLET *Collocalia esculenta* Plate 26

White-bellied Swiftlet (I,K)

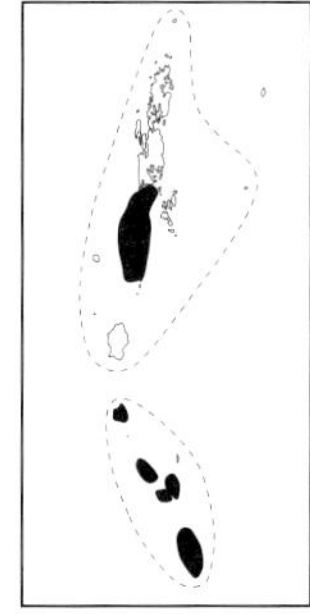

IDENTIFICATION 10 cm. Distinguished from Edible-nest and Himalayan Swiftlets (p.424), the two other swiftlets occurring in the Andaman and Nicobar Is, by smaller size, glossy blue-black upperparts, square-ended tail (without obvious indentation), white belly contrasting with dark grey throat and breast, and blackish undertail-coverts and underside to tail. Shows pale fringing and dark blotching on lower breast, and extent of white on underbody varies. **VOICE** A sharp twitter (Chantler and Driessens 1995). **HABITS** Gregarious and tame. **HABITAT** Hawks insects around homes and office buildings, often flying freely in and out. **BREEDING** December–April. Builds a typical swift nest in small or large colonies in buildings, such as factories and tool sheds. **DISTRIBUTION AND STATUS IN:** common resident on Andaman and Nicobar Is. **REFERENCES** Sankaran (1998), Sankaran and Vijayan (1993).

INDIAN SWIFTLET *Collocalia unicolor* Plate 26

Indian Edible-nest Swiftlet (I,P), *Aerodramus unicolor*

IDENTIFICATION 12 cm. A small brownish swiftlet with slight gloss to upperparts, and paler greyish-brown underparts. Has indistinct indentation to tail. Like other swiftlets, has bat-like flight with rapid flapping broken by banking and gliding; flight is rather slower than that of other swifts. No other swiftlets are known to occur within the range of this species. However, it differs from Himalayan Swiftlet (p.424), which could occur as a migrant, in smaller size, with less evident indentation to tail, and uniform (or occasionally very indistinctly paler) rump (comparatively well-defined greyish band on Himalayan). **VOICE** A harsh call-note, and feeble, but shrill, clicking or twittering *chit-chit* when roosting (Chantler and Driessens 1995). **HABITS** Birds roost clustered together in caves, clinging like small bats to vertical rock faces or to old nests, sometimes in huge numbers. In darkness, they make

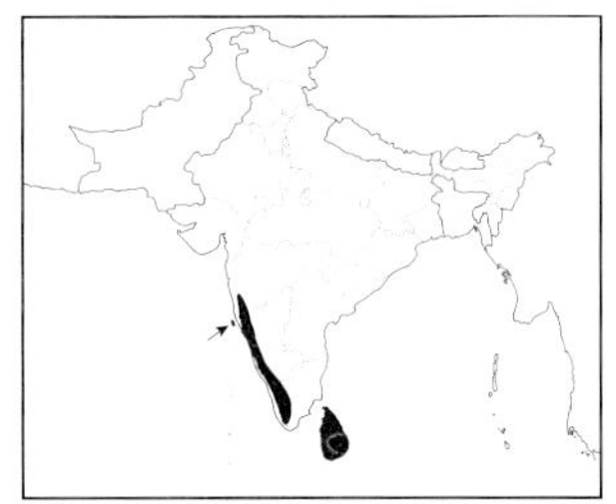

shrill clicking calls which enable them to navigate by echo-location. Leave the roost with a noisy rush of wings before dawn, returning at dusk. **HABITAT** Wanders erratically over large distances in the hills to feed. **BREEDING** March–September. Builds a typical swift nest in large colonies in caves in rocky islands and cliffs in the hills. **DISTRIBUTION AND STATUS** Resident. Western Ghats and islets on Malabar coast and Sri Lanka. **IN:** common; from sea level up to 2200 m. **LK:** small numbers breed throughout.

HIMALAYAN SWIFTLET *Collocalia brevirostris* — Plate 26

Edible Nest Swiftlet (F), *Aerodramus brevirostris*

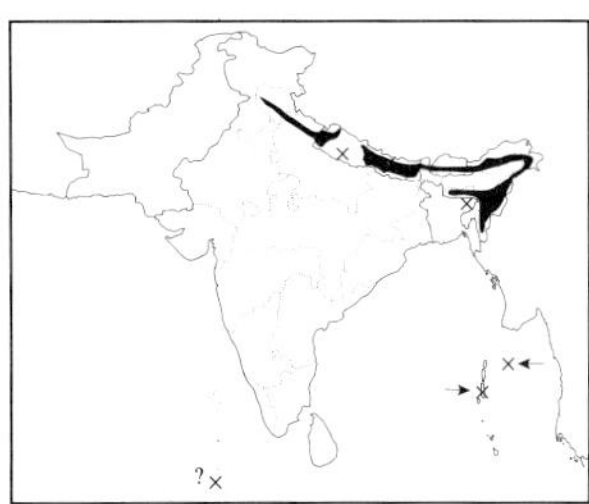

IDENTIFICATION 14 cm. A stocky brownish swiftlet with slight gloss to upperparts, and with pronounced indentation to tail. Has paler grey-brown underparts, and a comparatively distinct pale grey rump band (both with dark shaft streaking). Banking and gliding flight, interspersed with brief bat-like fluttering, is rather slower and more laboured than that of other swiftlets. The only swiftlet occurring throughout much of its range in the subcontinent, although could occur alongside Edible-nest Swiftlet (below) in Andaman Is. Distinguished from that species by larger size and more pronounced tail-fork, browner upperparts with less ostensible gloss (and showing slightly less contrast between upperparts and underparts), and tendency towards a broader but less clearly defined rump band. See Indian Swiftlet (p.423) for differences from that species. **VOICE** A low rattle-like call, and twittering *chit-chit* uttered at roost (Ali and Ripley 1987). **HABITS** Very similar to those of Indian. **HABITAT** Often forages over forest; roosts in caves. **BREEDING** April–June. Builds a typical swift nest in colonies, with nests close together, either at random or in rows, but not in clusters like those of House Swift. **DISTRIBUTION AND STATUS** Resident, subject to altitudinal movements. Mainly in Himalayas from W Himachal Pradesh east to Arunachal Pradesh; NE India. **NP:** fairly common; summers up to 4575 m, usually winters 915–2745 m and sometimes in the terai. **IN:** fairly common; foothills up to 3600 m. **BT:** common; up to at least 2800 m. **BD:** vagrant. **MV:** occasional winter visitor.

BLACK-NEST SWIFTLET *Collocalia maxima* — Not illustrated

Some specimens of Himalayan Swiftlet collected by Ludlow from Arunachal Pradesh and Bhutan and housed in the Natural History Museum, Tring, were reidentified as Black-nest Swiftlets (Medway 1961). The specimens were re-examined by T. and C. Inskipp in 1993 and confirmed as Himalayan Swiftlets. There are no records of Black-nest Swiftlet for the Indian subcontinent.

EDIBLE-NEST SWIFTLET *Collocalia fuciphaga* — Plate 26

Andaman Grey-rumped Swiftlet (I), *Aerodramus fuciphagus*

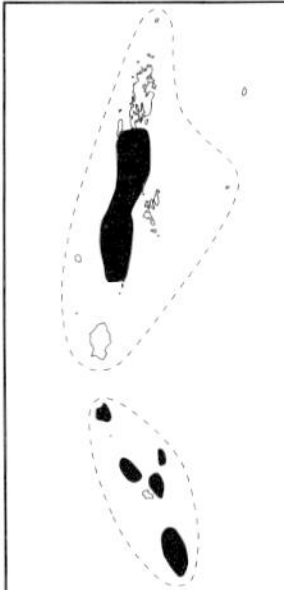

IDENTIFICATION 12 cm. One of three swiftlets known from the Andaman and Nicobar Is. Told from Glossy Swiftlet (p.423) by larger size, noticeable indentation to tail, blackish-brown coloration to upperparts (with much less noticeable gloss), and uniform, greyish-brown underparts. Further, has a narrow greyish (although sometimes very indistinct) rump band. For differences from Himalayan Swiftlet (above), see that species. **VOICE** A loud metallic *zwing* (Chantler and Driessens 1995). **HABITS** Very similar to those of Indian. **HABITAT** Prefers the coast and areas around human habitation. Hawks over mangrove swamps in the day, and roosts in caves and cliff fissures at night. **BREEDING** March–April. Nests are made entirely of saliva, and are collected commercially to make birds'-nest soup. Breeds communally in caves. **DISTRIBUTION AND STATUS IN:** common resident on Andaman Is; less common on Nicobar Is. **REFERENCES** Sankaran and Vijayan (1993).

WHITE-RUMPED NEEDLETAIL *Zoonavena sylvatica* — Plate 26

White-rumped Spinetail, *Chaetura sylvatica* (F,I)

IDENTIFICATION 11 cm. A small, stocky, broad-winged needletail. Has bulging secondaries, with wings pinched in at base and pointed at tip. Typically, flight action is fast with rapid wingbeats, and banking from side to side, interspersed with short glides on slightly bowed wings. Upperparts are mainly blue-black with contrasting white rump; throat and breast are grey-brown, merging into whitish lower belly and undertail-coverts. From

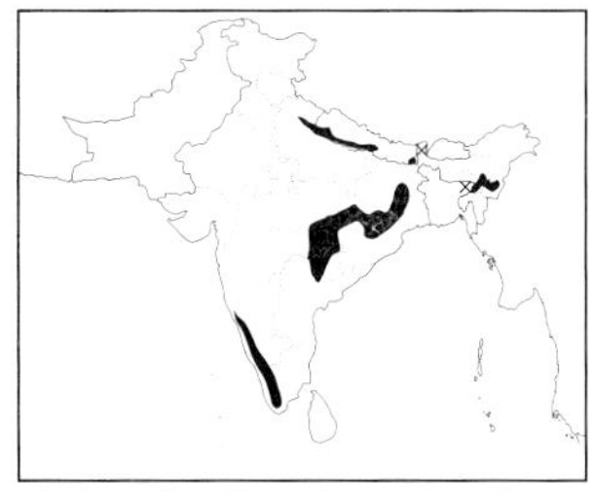

below, long white undertail-coverts contrast with black of sides and tip of undertail. 'Spines' at tip of tail are visible at close range. **VOICE** A twittering *chick..chick,* uttered on the wing (Ali and Ripley 1987). **HABITS** Keeps in flocks of up to 50 birds. Hawks over forest, sometimes descending to dash between trees with astonishing manoeuvrability. **HABITAT** Broadleaved evergreen and moist deciduous forest. **BREEDING** February–May. Nests solitarily in a hollow tree trunk or bole of a dead palm. **DISTRIBUTION AND STATUS** Resident, endemic to the subcontinent. Himalayas from N Uttar Pradesh east to Sikkim; NE, E and SW India, and Bangladesh. **NP:** local and uncommon, possibly resident; 150–250 m. **IN:** patchily distributed resident; foothills and hills up to 1700 m. **BD:** rare resident. **REFERENCES** Anon. (1994).

WHITE-THROATED NEEDLETAIL *Hirundapus caudacutus* Plate 26

White-throated Spinetail Swift (I), *Chaetura caudacuta* (E,F,I)

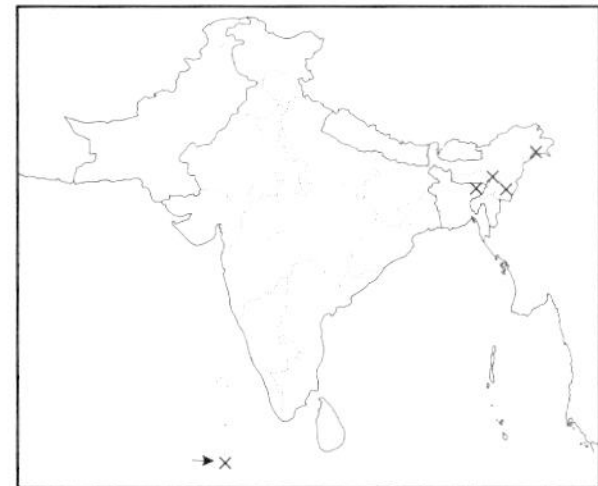

IDENTIFICATION 20 cm. A large, very powerful swift, with white hindflanks and undertail-coverts forming striking white 'horseshoe' crescent at rear end. As other large needletails, has pale 'saddle' on upperparts. A magnificent flier, combining very strong flapping with swooping, gliding and soaring, often at very high speeds. Best told from Silver-backed and Brown-backed Needletails (below) by clearly demarcated white throat, and white inner webs to tertials (showing as white patch, although this may be obscured). Additional differences from Brown-backed include smaller size, dark lores, and more contrasting pale 'saddle'. Compared with Brown-backed, tends to show shorter, square-ended tail projection beyond white undertail-coverts, and tail 'spines' are less distinct. **Juvenile** has black streaking and spotting on white of hindflanks, and black fringes to white undertail-coverts. **VOICE** Feeble, rapid metallic chittering, audible only at close range (P. Holt). **HABITS** Usually occurs singly or in loose parties. Roosts colonially in cliff fissures, also in trees. Skims low over mountain ridges and forest, and dashes around crags with amazing adroitness. Wings produce a vibrant swish as the birds fly past. Covers huge distances in a day's foraging. **HABITAT** Often seen over ridges, cliffs, forest, upland grasslands and river valleys. **BREEDING** Almost unknown in the subcontinent. Probably April. Elsewhere, nests at base of a tree hollow. **DISTRIBUTION AND STATUS** Summer visitor. Himalayas from N Pakistan east to Arunachal Pradesh; NE India. Suddenly appears and then disappears, making local status difficult to determine. **PK:** scarce summer visitor. **NP:** fairly common, recorded mainly March–June; up to 3200 m. **IN:** rather uncommon and local; 1200–4000 m. **BT:** fairly common; 450–3510 m. **BD, MV:** vagrant. **REFERENCES** Anon. (1994).

SILVER-BACKED NEEDLETAIL *Hirundapus cochinchinensis* Plate 26

Cochinchina Spinetail Swift (I), White-vented Needletail (F,K,N), *Chaetura cochinchinensis* (I)

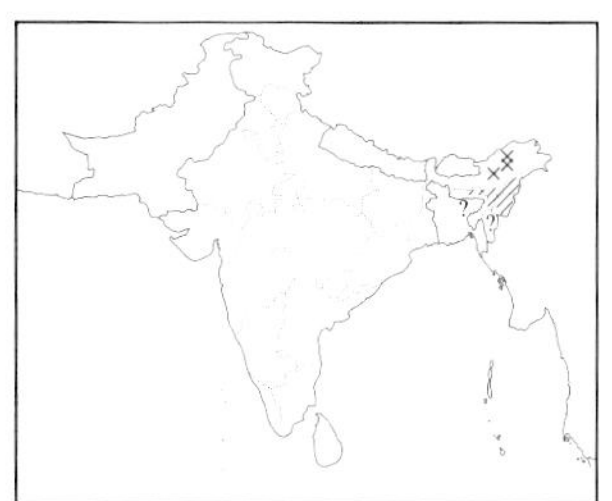

IDENTIFICATION 20 cm. Very similar to White-throated Needletail (above) and best told by lack of clearly demarcated white throat. Throat of Silver-backed is pale brown or grey and can appear distinctly pale greyish-white, but is never pure white and sharply divided from breast, and can be only minimally paler than rest of underparts. In addition, lacks white on inner web of tertials (which is often apparent as distinct white patch on White-throated), although tertials have a pale grey inner web which is sometimes visible in the field. More closely resembles Brown-backed Needletail (below), but is noticeably smaller and less powerful, usually shows distinctly paler throat and dark lores, and has more contrasting pale 'saddle' (pale brown at edges, with whitish centre). Compared with Brown-backed, tends to show shorter, square-ended tail projection beyond white undertail-coverts, and tail 'spines' are less distinct, although these features are rarely of much use in the field. **Juvenile** has brown fringes to white undertail-coverts. **VOICE** A soft rippling *trp-trp-trp-trp-trp* (Chantler and Driessens 1995). **HABITS** Very like those of White-throated Needletail. **HABITAT** Little known in the subcontinent. Mainly recorded hawking over forest in Nepal and over forested hills with clearings in Assam. **BREEDING** Virtually unknown. Probably May. **DISTRIBUTION AND STATUS** Resident. Nepal and NE India (Arunachal Pradesh, Assam, Manipur, Meghalaya, ?Mizoram); probably under-recorded because of confusion with White-throated Needletail. **NP:** status and movements are poorly understood; several records 250–2400 m, March–July. **IN:** locally common resident; 150–2400 m. **BD:** vagrant. **REFERENCES** Anon. (1994).

BROWN-BACKED NEEDLETAIL *Hirundapus giganteus* Plate 26

Large Brown-throated Spinetail Swift (I), Brown Needletail (K), Brown-throated Spinetail Swift (P), *Chaetura gigantea* (I)

IDENTIFICATION 23 cm. Largest and most powerful of the needletails; 'needles' of tail larger and longer than on other species and often easy to observe in the field. Best told from White-throated Needletail (above) by

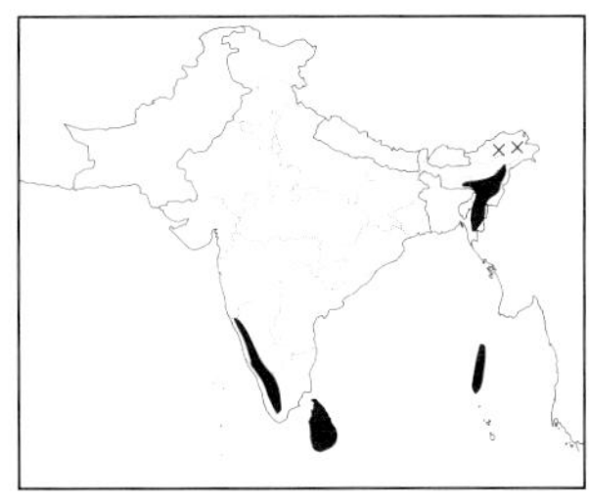

brownish throat (only slightly paler than rest of underparts, although may still show some contrast, and chin can be almost white). Also has white lores, although these can be difficult to see in the field. More likely to be confused with Silver-backed Needletail (p.425), but is noticeably larger and more powerful, and has less contrasting pale 'saddle' (uniformly pale brown, lacking silvery-white centre), longer and rounded or point-ended tail projection beyond white undertail-coverts, and white lores. **VOICE** As other two needletails; also a brittle, squeaked *cirrwiet* and a thin squeak, *chiek* (Chantler and Driessens 1995). **HABITS** Keeps in pairs, small parties or large scattered flocks. Flight and foraging behaviour are like those of White-throated Needletail. Roosts communally in the hollows of old trees. **HABITAT** Broadleaved evergreen and moist deciduous forest and forest clearings. **BREEDING** February–April. Nests solitarily in a depression in debris at the base of a hollow bole of an old tree. **DISTRIBUTION AND STATUS** Resident. Hills of NE India and Bangladesh; Western Ghats and Sri Lanka. **IN:** locally fairly common. **BD:** ?rare resident in the southeast; no recent records, but may still occur in Chittagong Hill Tracts. **LK:** very infrequent in lower hills, occasionally recorded in lowlands.

ASIAN PALM SWIFT *Cypsiurus balasiensis* — Plate 27

Palm Swift (F,I,P), *Cypsiurus parvus* (F,I,P), *C. batasiensis* (K)

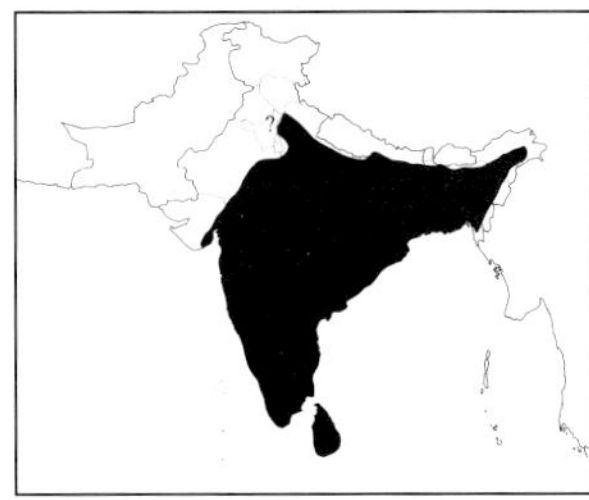

IDENTIFICATION 13 cm. A very slim-bodied, sooty-brown swift with fine scythe-shaped wings and deeply forked tail. Flight is rather slow and fluttering compared with most swifts; rapid fluttering wingbeats are interspersed with short glides. Throat is slightly paler than rest of underparts, and may also show a slightly paler rump. Differs from swiftlets in slender appearance and forked tail, which appears pointed when closed. Possibly confusable with Crested Treeswift (p.428), but is much smaller, with weaker, more fluttering flight, is browner in coloration (and does not show whiter belly and undertail-coverts), and has proportionately shorter tail. **VOICE** A trilling *te-he-he-he-he*. **HABITS** Usually hawks insects around palms. Roosts clinging to a palmyra leaf; also in thatched roofs of village houses in NE India. Twists and turns in the air with great agility. **HABITAT** Usually open country and cultivation, and closely associated with palms, especially palmyra and sometimes the betelnut palm; also forest clearings in NE India. **BREEDING** Almost all year, varying locally. Builds a typical swift nest attached to the underside of a palm; also in the eaves of thatched roofs of village houses in NE India. Breeds solitarily. **DISTRIBUTION AND STATUS** Resident. From Punjab, India, and E Gujarat east through most of the subcontinent south of the Himalayas. **NP:** uncommon in C and E terai. **IN:** local and widespread; mainly in plains, locally in hills to 1000 m. **BT:** locally common. **BD:** common and widespread. **LK:** locally common resident in lowlands and lower hills.

ALPINE SWIFT *Tachymarptis melba* — Plate 27

***Apus melba* (E,F,I,P)**

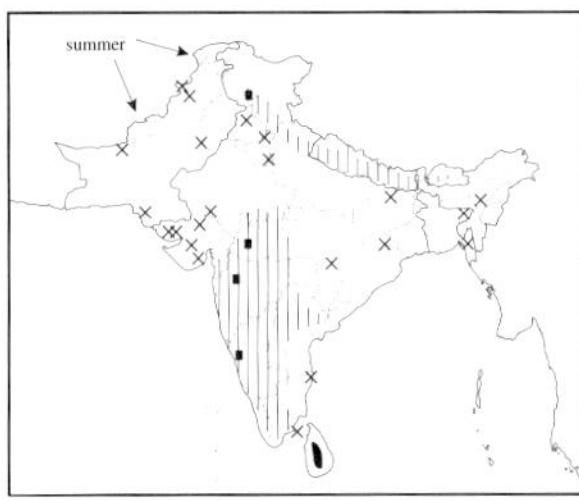

IDENTIFICATION 22 cm. Larger and more powerful than other swifts, with comparatively deep and slow wingbeats. Has mid-brown upperparts and wings, paler brown than Common Swift (below). Best told from other swifts by white throat with brown breast-band, and white breast and belly contrasting with brown underwing, flanks and vent. **VOICE** A high-pitched trilling *tri-hihihihi*. **HABITS** Gregarious, usually keeping in scattered flocks. May undertake long flights to avoid bad weather conditions. Roosts in clefts in rock faces. **HABITAT** Mainly hills and mountains with cliffs or old forts. May occur briefly over any habitat. **BREEDING** December–June, varying locally. Builds a typical swift nest in a cleft in a rocky cliff. **DISTRIBUTION AND STATUS** Resident. Locally in N and W Pakistan, Himalayas from N Pakistan east to Bhutan; from S Rajasthan east to N Andhra Pradesh, and south to Kerala and Sri Lanka. Subject to seasonal and altitudinal movements, and wanders erratically over long distances. **PK:** common but very local summer visitor. **NP:** fairly common and widespread, probably resident; summers mainly up to 2200 m (–3700 m), winters chiefly below 915 m. **IN:** mainly a summer visitor to Himalayas, but some winter in the foothills; resident in Western Ghats, also recorded breeding in N Maharashtra and W Madhya Pradesh; winter visitor to the peninsula; passage migrant to the north. **BT:** rare. **BD:** vagrant. **LK:** rare resident in hills, visitor to lowlands.

COMMON SWIFT *Apus apus* — Plate 27

The Swift (I), Black Swift (F)

IDENTIFICATION 17 cm. A large, uniformly dark brown swift with long scythe-shaped wings and deeply forked tail. Most likely to be confused with Fork-tailed Swift (p.427), but has uniform brown upperparts (lacking white rump) and lacks (or has much less distinct) pale scaling on the underparts. For differences from the very similar Pallid

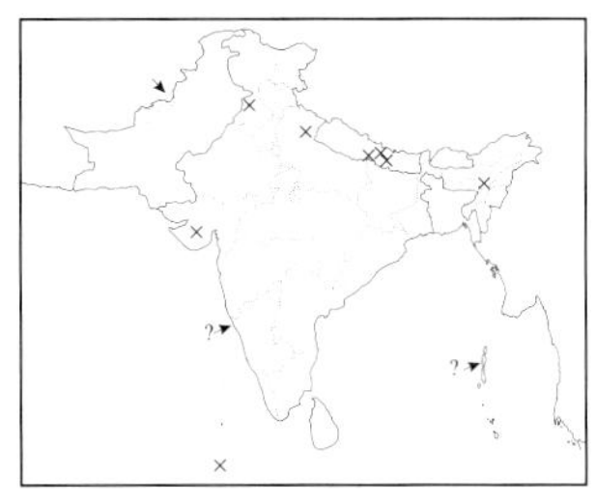

and Dark-rumped Swifts (below), see those species. **Juvenile** has whiter forehead and more extensive white throat, and extensive pale scaling on underparts (although not so prominent as on Fork-tailed). **VOICE** A high-pitched screaming *screee..screee..screee.* **HABITS** Similar to those of Alpine (p.426). **HABITAT** Chiefly in mountains, but can occur fleetingly over any habitat. **BREEDING** Poorly known in the region. Probably May and June. Nest is undescribed from the subcontinent; builds a typical swift nest in Europe. Breeds colonially in cracks in cliff faces in Pakistan. **DISTRIBUTION AND STATUS** Mainly a summer visitor. Baluchistan, Pakistan, and Himalayas from N Pakistan east to Nepal; Maldives. **PK:** common in mountains; 2400–4575 m. **NP:** local, recorded mainly mid March–July; 2000–3795 m. **IN:** locally common; mainly 1500–3300 m (–5700 m). **MV:**: regular visitor. **REFERENCES** Anon. (1979), Pfister (1997).

PALLID SWIFT *Apus pallidus* — Plate 27

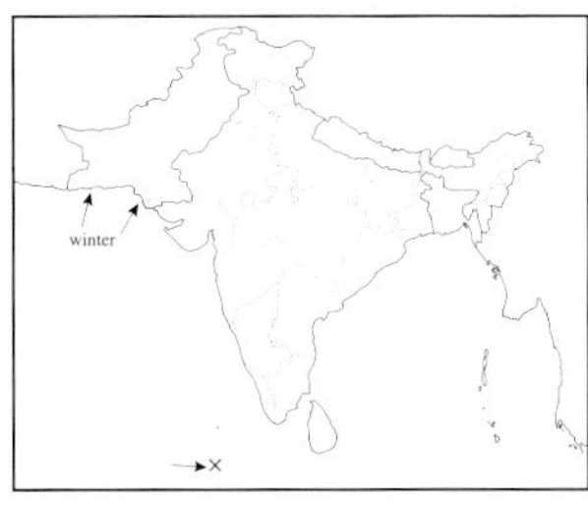

IDENTIFICATION 17 cm. A large, uniformly grey-brown swift, similar in shape and appearance to Common Swift (p.426), and with similar flight, but has slower wingbeats than latter. Is paler grey-brown in coloration than Common (appearing very pale in bright light), with more extensive pale throat and forehead, which contrasts with dark eye-patch. Has dark outer primaries and leading edge to wing, contrasting on both upperside and underside with pale rest of wing (especially with pale greater primary coverts on upperwing). Further, has pale fringes to feathers of underparts, resulting in scaly appearance, and shows greater contrasts between head and mantle and between mantle and wings (often giving rise to dark-saddled, pale-headed appearance). Caution is needed, however, since some adult (but especially juvenile) Common can show paler lores and more extensive white throat than is typical of that species, and juvenile Common has pale fringes to underparts. There are subtle structural differences: Pallid is bulkier and broader-winged, and has blunter tips to wings and slightly shallower fork to tail. **VOICE** A disyllabic *cheeu-eet* or *churr-ic* (Harris *et al.* 1989). **HABITS** Similar to those of Alpine (p.426) and Common. **HABITAT** Coastal areas. **DISTRIBUTION AND STATUS PK:** winter visitor to coastal regions; status unknown, but probably frequent in extreme west. **MV:** rare winter visitor. **REFERENCES** Harris *et al.* (1989).

FORK-TAILED SWIFT *Apus pacificus* — Plate 27

Large White-rumped Swift (F,I), Pacific Swift (R)

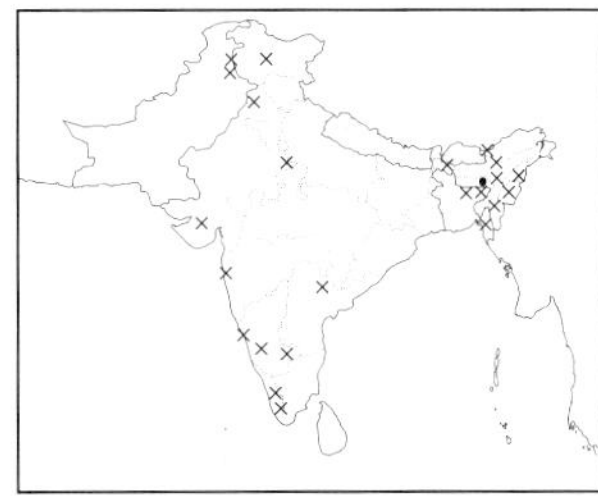

IDENTIFICATION 15–18 cm. A blackish swift with deeply forked tail and long scythe-shaped wings. The race breeding in the Himalayas (*A. p. leuconyx*) is smaller than the migrant nominate race and is most likely to be confused with House Swift (p.428). Best told by longer, deeply forked tail, distinct whitish fringes to feathers of underparts (giving rise to greyish cast to breast and belly at a distance), and slimmer-bodied and longer-winged appearance. The larger *A. p. pacificus* (18 cm) is more likely to be confused with Common Swift (p.426). Main differences from that species are prominent white rump, more extensive white throat, and distinct pale scaling on underparts; also appears slightly larger, longer-winged and more powerful than Common, with longer tail with deeper fork. **VOICE** Call is less wheezy and softer than Common's, a *sreee* (Chantler and Driessens 1995). **HABITS** A typical swift. **HABITAT** Favours hawking over open ridges or hilltops. **BREEDING** April–July. Builds a typical swift nest in small colonies inside fissures in cliff faces. **DISTRIBUTION AND STATUS** Breeds in Himalayas in Pakistan and from Himachal Pradesh east to Arunachal Pradesh; NE India; winter range is poorly known; isolated records throughout much of the peninsula south to Kerala. **PK:** rare and local summer visitor. **NP:** fairly common, possibly resident; movements are poorly understood; recorded mainly below 365 m in winter, up to 3800 m in summer. **IN:** locally fairly common in summer in Himalayas and NE hills from foothills up to 3600 m; status elsewhere is uncertain. **BT:** common summer visitor; 450–3670 m. **BD:** irregular winter visitor or passage migrant.

DARK-RUMPED SWIFT *Apus acuticauda* — Plate 27

Dark-backed Swift (I), Khasi Hills Swift (F)

IDENTIFICATION 17 cm. An all-dark swift recalling Fork-tailed Swift (above). Best told from that species by all-dark rump, and lack of clearly defined white throat. Throat is greyish-white, with dark streaking, and patterning merges with rest of underparts (which are more broadly fringed with white than on Fork-tailed). Does not appear quite so slim and long-winged as Fork-tailed, and tail-fork is sharper, with narrower and more pointed outer tail feathers. Very similar in shape to Common Swift (p.426), and best told from that species by heavily marked throat and bold scaling on the underparts (belly often appearing pale grey in strong light). Also has blacker upperparts (with greenish or bluish hue in good light), and tends to show pale silvery trailing edge to secondaries. **VOICE**

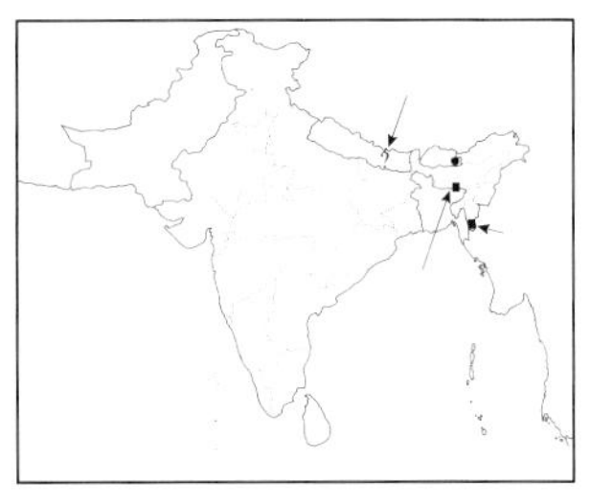

A very high-pitched call uttered by flocking birds in the vicinity of the breeding cliffs. **HABITS** Typical swift, but keeps close to its nesting cliffs while breeding, not wandering long distances to feed like other swifts. **HABITAT** Rocky cliffs and gorges. **BREEDING** End March–April. Builds a typical swift nest in a cleft in a rock cliff. **DISTRIBUTION AND STATUS** Resident, endemic to the subcontinent. The species was described from Nepal in 19th century, but no later records from there; the specimen may have originated in India. Globally threatened. **IN:** breeds in Meghalaya and probably Mizoram; vagrant to Andaman Is. **BT:** rare, breeds in the east.

HOUSE SWIFT *Apus affinis* — Plate 27

Little Swift, *A. nipalensis*

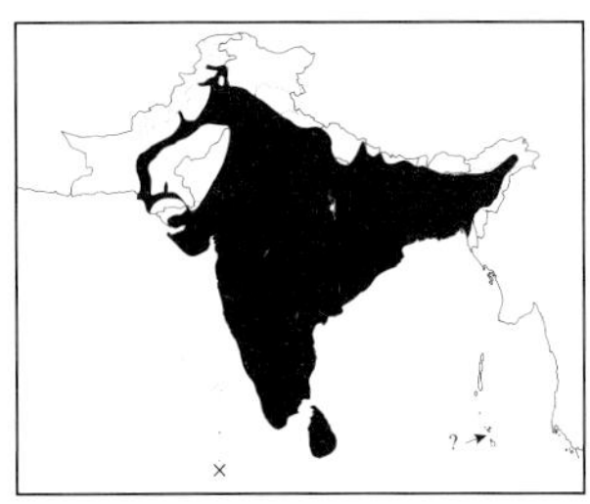

IDENTIFICATION 15 cm. A small, stocky, blackish swift with a broad white rump. Tail is either square-ended or has shallow fork. Readily told from Fork-tailed Swift (p.427), the only other white-rumped swift occurring in the subcontinent, by smaller size, shorter and broader wings, stout body and rather big head, and different tail shape. Flight is rather weak compared with that of Fork-tailed, consisting of a few rapid strokes of the wings followed by a long swooping glide and with many twists and turns. Blackish underparts are best feature for separation from White-rumped Needletail (p.424). **Racial variation** Four races are recognised from the subcontinent, sometimes grouped as two separate species: 'House Swift' (*A. a. nipalensis*) of the Himalayas and NE India, and 'Little Swift' (*A. a. affinis*, *A. a. galilejensis* and *A. a. singalensis*) of the subcontinent south and west of this range. Compared with 'House', where ranges adjoin, 'Little' has a square-ended tail and broader white rump band. Tail of 'Little' is more rounded when open, but can show slight notch; 'House' shows a slight fork to tail. **VOICE** A rapid and shrill *siksiksiksik-sik-sik-siksiksiksik* (Ali and Ripley 1987). **HABITS** Usually associates in large scattered flocks and keeps within a wide vicinity of its nesting area when breeding. **HABITAT** Villages, towns, cities, cliffs, old forts and ruins. **BREEDING** Almost all year, varying locally. Builds a typical swift nest in colonies; nests placed haphazardly one upon another, usually under the eaves or verandas of buildings, under bridges or arches, on cliffs or in caves. **DISTRIBUTION AND STATUS** Resident. Throughout much of the subcontinent except parts of the northwest. **PK:** common, partly resident, a summer visitor to the north. **NP:** common up to 2100 m; occurs up to 915 m all year, descends from higher levels in cold weather. **IN:** locally common; occurs February–November in Himalayas; elsewhere resident, subject to local movements, and presumably also winter visitor. **BT:** common; 250–1930 m. **BD:** common and widespread resident. **LK:** common resident in lowlands and lower hills. **MV:** irregular winter visitor. **REFERENCES** Abdulali (1966).

CRESTED TREESWIFT *Hemiprocne coronata* — Plate 27

Crested Swift (F,I), *H. longipennis coronata* (F,I)

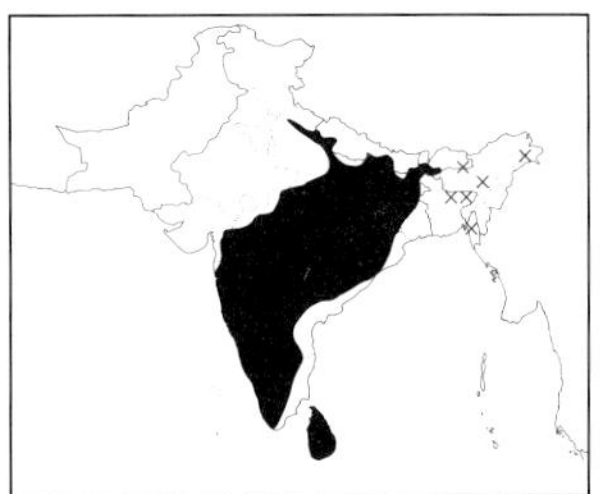

IDENTIFICATION 23 cm. A large swift with long, narrow, sickle-shaped wings and long, deeply forked tail which is usually held closed in flight, giving rise to point-tailed appearance. Typically, flies above tree canopy with mixture of rapid and rather heavy fluttering and periods of banking and gliding. In flight, appears mainly blue-grey with darker upperwing and tail, and whitish abdomen and undertail-coverts. At rest, both sexes show prominent dark green-blue crest, and wing-coverts are glossed with blue. **Male** has dull orange ear-coverts. **Female** has dark grey ear-coverts, forming dark mask, bordered below by whitish moustachial stripe. **Juvenile** has extensive white fringes to upperparts (especially noticeable on lower back and rump), and feathers of underparts are fringed with white and have grey-brown subterminal bands. **VOICE** A harsh *whit-tuck..whit-tuck* uttered in flight. **HABITS** Graceful swift, able to glide for long distances. Keeps in scattered parties and hawks insects. Does not wander far when foraging. Unlike the Apodidae swifts, perches readily in trees, often on exposed branches. **HABITAT** Well-wooded areas and forest, usually deciduous and in hilly country. **BREEDING** December–September, varying locally. Nest is a tiny shallow basin made of bark scales and small feathers, and glued to a slender bare branch. **DISTRIBUTION AND STATUS** Local resident, subject to local movements. From N Uttar Pradesh and SE Gujarat east throughout much of the subcontinent, except parts of the northeast, extreme east and Himalayas. **NP:** locally common; below 365 m (–1280 m). **IN:** widespread, but very local; generally not common. **BT:** rare. **BD:** vagrant. **LK:** resident in lowlands and lower hills, more common in dry zone.

BARN OWLS AND GRASS OWLS (Tytonidae), AND TYPICAL OWLS (Strigidae)

Characteristically, owls have a large and rounded head, big forward-facing eyes surrounded by a broad facial disc, and a short tail. Most are nocturnal and cryptically coloured and patterned, making them inconspicuous when resting during the day. They are well adapted for hunting in poor light; their hearing and sight are exceptionally acute, and their plumage, which is dense and soft, makes them almost noiseless in flight. When hunting, owls either quarter the ground or scan and listen for prey from a perch. Their diet consists of small animals, mainly birds, rodents, shrews and insects; many species also feed on frogs, lizards, snakes, fish and other invertebrates. Many owls, because of their nocturnal habits, are seldom seen and are poorly known. They are usually located by their distinctive and often weird calls, which are diagnostic of the species and advertise their presence and territories. Nocturnal owls usually spend the day roosting, and are invariably mobbed by other small birds when they are seen in the daytime. Most owls are sedentary and territorial. All nest in unlined natural holes in tree trunks, rocks or human habitations, in tree forks or in disused nest holes of other birds. The main references specific to owls are Burton (1984) and Voous (1988).

BARN OWL *Tyto alba* — Plate 28

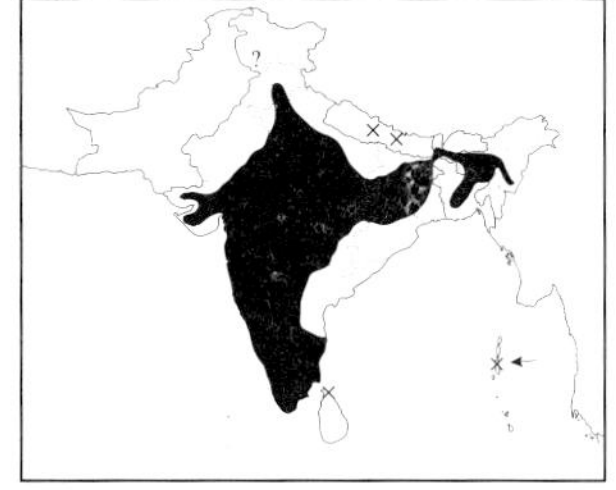

IDENTIFICATION 36 cm. A medium-sized, very pale owl, readily identified throughout much of region by combination of unmarked white face and contrasting black eyes, white to golden-buff underparts finely spotted with black, and golden-buff and grey upperparts which are finely spotted with black and white. Wings and tail appear very uniform in flight, lacking any prominent tail barring or wing patches. For differences from Grass Owl (below), see that species. **Racial variation** *T. a. deroepstorffi* of the Andaman Is differs from *T. a. stertens*, described above, in having rufous face and buffish underparts, and much darker upperparts which are heavily marked with rufous and dark brown. **VOICE** A variety of eerie screeching and hissing noises. **HABITS** Mainly crepuscular and nocturnal; usually roosts by day in a tree hollow, building, or groves. Hunts by quartering open country a few metres above the vegetation, often banking and hovering erratically before pouncing on prey. Sometimes perches on posts or low branches. **HABITAT** Closely associated with people: roosts and nests in buildings, especially under roofs, in cities, towns and villages, also in ruins, caves and wells; feeds in cultivation. **BREEDING** Almost all year, varying locally. Nests in hole in tree or building. **DISTRIBUTION AND STATUS** Resident. Widespread but very local in the subcontinent. **PK:** scarce and local, confined to Indus plains. **NP:** uncommon and very local; 1320 m. **IN:** widespread, local and uncommon; up to 1000 m in peninsular hills. **BD:** local. **LK:** uncommon in dry N lowlands, scarce elsewhere.

GRASS OWL *Tyto capensis* — Plate 28

Eastern Grass Owl, *Tyto longimembris* (F,I,K,N)

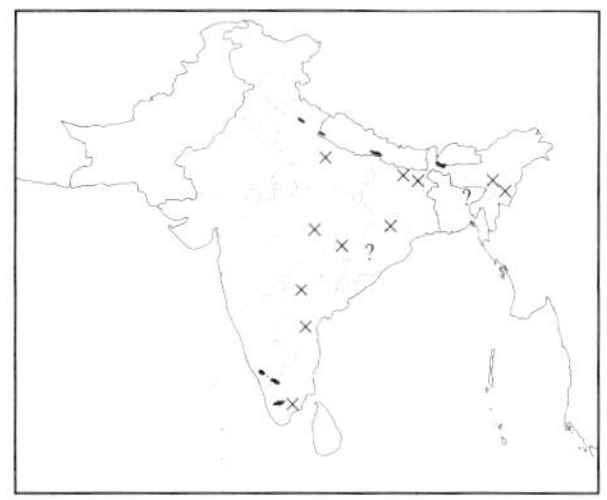

IDENTIFICATION 36 cm. A grassland owl resembling Barn Owl (above) in size and structure, with dark eyes, and whitish face and underparts. Upperparts are darker and contrast more with underparts than on Barn, being more heavily marked with dark brown (especially on crown and scapulars) and with golden-buff (particularly on nape). Further, has dark barring on flight feathers, with prominent golden-buff patch at base of primaries contrasting with dark primary tips, and has dark-barred white or buff tail which usually contrasts with dark uppertail-coverts. Most likely to be seen when flushed from grassland habitat, when confusable with Short-eared Owl (p.439). Best told from that species by mottled rather than streaked upperparts, lack of bold streaking on breast (although may show diffuse brown breast-band), and paler face with black eyes and pale bill. **VOICE** Like that of Barn. **HABITS** Terrestrial. Spends the day roosting in a small clearing in tall grass. Hunting behaviour is similar to that of Barn. If flushed, it flies a short distance and soon drops into cover again. **HABITAT** Tall grassland. **BREEDING** October–March. Nest is a pad of flattened grass, hidden among rank vegetation. **DISTRIBUTION AND STATUS** Local resident. From Uttar Pradesh east to Manipur; E and SW India. **NP:** rare and very local; 250 m. **IN:** rare and local; up to 1800 m in peninsular hills. **BD:** ?former resident; no recent records.

ORIENTAL BAY OWL *Phodilus badius* — Plate 28

Bay Owl (F,I,K,P)

IDENTIFICATION 29 cm. A stocky, medium-sized, strictly nocturnal owl with short, rounded wings and rapid flight action. Easily identified by distinctive head shape (with wide forehead, and oblong-shaped facial discs which protrude as broad 'ear-tufts'), very large all-dark eyes, white necklace, rich chestnut and buff upperparts spotted and barred with black, and vinaceous-pink facial discs and underparts, the latter also spotted with black. **VOICE** A series of eerie, musical, upward-inflected whistles (Boonsong and Round 1991). **HABITS** Strictly

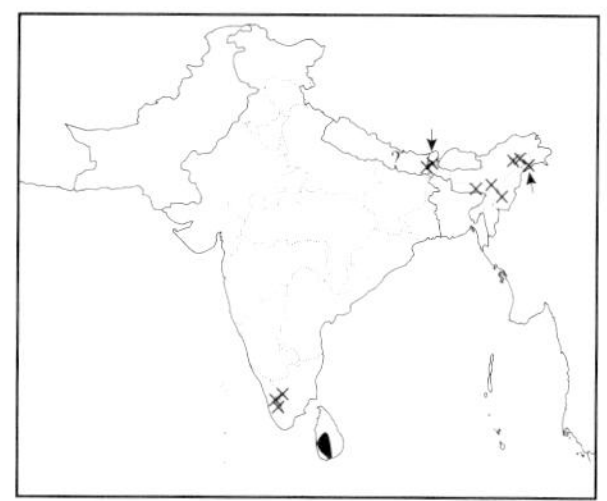

nocturnal and little known. Roosts in a hollow tree by day. Its short rounded wings aid rapid flight between trees in its forest habitat. **HABITAT** Dense evergreen broadleaved forest. **BREEDING** March–May. Nests in a hole in tree trunk or stump. **DISTRIBUTION AND STATUS** Resident. Nepal?, Sikkim, NE and SW India, and Sri Lanka. **NP:** one possible 19th-century record. **IN:** rare; foothills up to 1500 m in NE India. **LK:** rare in wet lowlands and lower hills. **REFERENCES** Hussain and Khan (1977), Kannan (1993a).

ANDAMAN SCOPS OWL *Otus balli* — Plate 28

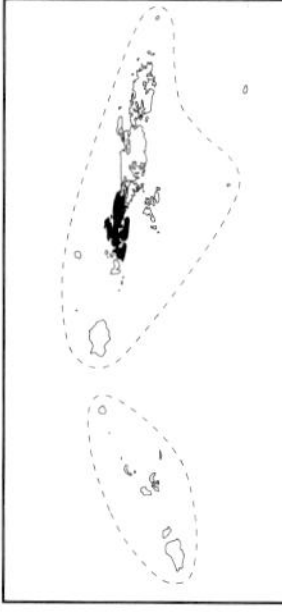

IDENTIFICATION 19 cm. Distinguished from Oriental Scops Owl (p.431), the only other scops owl known to occur in the Andaman Is, by unstreaked upperparts and underparts. Crown, nape and mantle are dark rufous-brown with sparse and indistinct buff and dark brown markings. Facial discs are buff. Underparts are finely vermiculated and spotted with dark brown, and diffusely marked with buff. **VOICE** An abrupt *hoot...hoot-coorroo* and a low clucking note (Ali and Ripley 1987). **HABITS** Totally nocturnal and poorly known. Eats caterpillars and other large insects. **HABITAT** Cultivation and around human habitation. **BREEDING** February–April. Nests in a tree hollow. **DISTRIBUTION AND STATUS IN:** Resident, endemic to Andaman Is; common in early 20th century; current status uncertain.

MOUNTAIN SCOPS OWL *Otus spilocephalus* — Plate 28

Spotted Scops Owl (F,I,R)

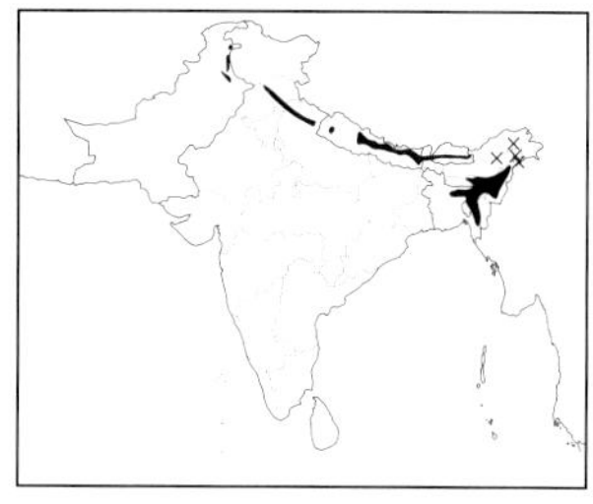

IDENTIFICATION 20 cm. A small montane scops owl. Told from similar species by unstreaked underparts, which are indistinctly spotted with buff and barred with brown, and by unstreaked upperparts, which are mottled with buff and brown (with crown and nape usually the most heavily marked parts of the bird). Lacks prominent ear-tufts, and has distinctive call. Often shows a paler band on upper mantle (forming diffuse 'collar'), and head can appear slightly paler than rest of upperparts. **Racial variation** Birds in the W Himalayas (*O. s. huttoni*) are grey or fulvous-brown, while those in the E Himalayas (*O. s. spilocephalus*) are rufous in coloration. **VOICE** A resonant and far-carrying flute-like double whistle, *toot-too*, repeated every 5–7 seconds. **HABITS** Entirely nocturnal and difficult to see, in common with all scops owls. Roosts during the day in a tree hollow. Begins calling about one hour before dark, and continues intermittently during night. Chiefly insectivorous. **HABITAT** Dense evergreen broadleaved temperate forest. **BREEDING** March–June. Nests in a natural tree hole or an abandoned nest hole of a barbet or woodpecker. **DISTRIBUTION AND STATUS** Resident. Himalayas from N Pakistan east to Arunachal Pradesh; NE India and Bangladesh. **PK:** mainly in Murree hills, where frequent above 1800 m in summer. **NP:** locally fairly common; 1830–2590 m (1525–2745 m). **IN:** locally frequent; breeds 1500–2600 m, and down to wet foothills in northeast. **BT:** frequent; 245–2285 m. **BD:** scarce and local.

PALLID SCOPS OWL *Otus brucei* — Plate 28

Striated Scops-Owl (I,R)

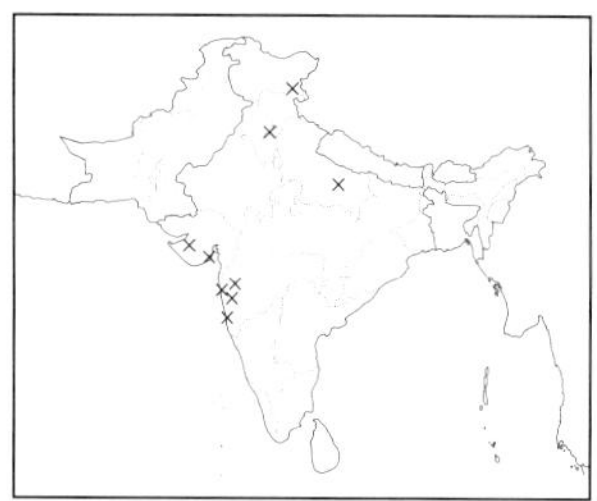

IDENTIFICATION 22 cm. A pale scops owl which is very similar to grey-morph Eurasian Scops Owl (p.431). Pallid is paler, greyer and more uniform above, lacking rufous-brown tones that Eurasian usually shows to its lower mantle, scapulars and coverts; pale spots on the lower scapulars are also more buff and less conspicuous (white and usually prominent on Eurasian, although may be lacking). The dark streaking on underparts tends to be narrower, as are the dark horizontal bars, and, importantly, Pallid lacks the prominent pale horizontal panels across underparts shown by Eurasian. The primary coverts of Pallid are more strongly patterned, with broad and distinct sandy-white bars. Also shows fewer, broader pale bars on tail (two to four rather than five to seven on central rectrices, with dark barring absent at tip). Pallid's facial disc is typically paler and plainer, lacking the darkening around eye shown by most Eurasian, and the ruff of black feathering bordering the disc is typically narrower and more sharply demarcated. It has a shorter primary projection, with tips of folded primaries never projecting beyond tail (usually projecting slightly on Eurasian). **Juvenile** is completely barred below and is very different in appearance from juvenile Eurasian, which closely resembles adult. **VOICE** A hollow, resonant, low-pitched *whoop-whoop-whoop...*, repeated at precise intervals, sometimes for as long as four minutes without a pause, and a longer and irregular *whoo*, possibly uttered by female (Roberts 1991). **HABITS** Spends the day in a rock crevice, under an overhang, in a tree hole or among thick foliage. Mainly insectivorous. **HABITAT** Semi-desert stony foothills, and rocky country; avoids the plains. **BREEDING** April and May. Nests in hole in a tree, wall or cliff. **DISTRIBUTION AND STATUS PK:** scarce resident and local migrant; summers in the hills, a few winter records from the plains. **IN:** rare visitor. **REFERENCES** Harris *et al.* (1996).

EURASIAN SCOPS OWL *Otus scops* — Plate 28

European Scops Owl (R)

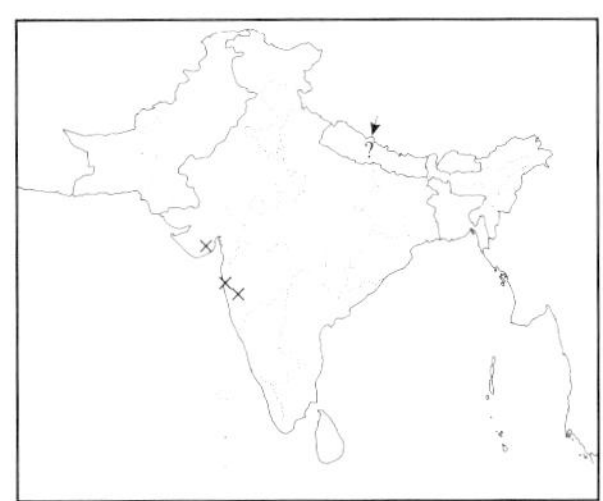

IDENTIFICATION 19 cm. Occurs as grey and brown morphs. Not safely distinguishable in the field from Oriental Scops Owl (below), although has different call and longer primary projection (see Oriental). Within range, most likely to be confused with Pallid Scops Owl (p.430) and best told from that species by prominent white spots on lower scapulars (if present), pale horizontal bars on underparts, and different call. See Pallid for further details. **VOICE** A clear, plaintive, bell-like whistle, *tyuu.....tyuu...*, repeated without interruption for many minutes; uttered by both sexes, the female's call slightly higher-pitched (Cramp 1985). **HABITS** Similar to those of Oriental Scops Owl. **HABITAT** Juniper scrub and Holly Oak in dry rocky hills and valleys. **BREEDING** Unknown in the region. Elsewhere, nests in a hole in tree trunk or wall. **DISTRIBUTION AND STATUS** Summer visitor to the mountains of N and W Pakistan; winters in Sind, Pakistan, and Gujarat and W Maharashtra. **PK:** common summer visitor to the north and west, 1500–3000 m; winter straggler to S plains. **NP:** possibly recorded. **IN:** rare; no recent published records.

MOLUCCAN SCOPS OWL *Otus magicus* — Not illustrated

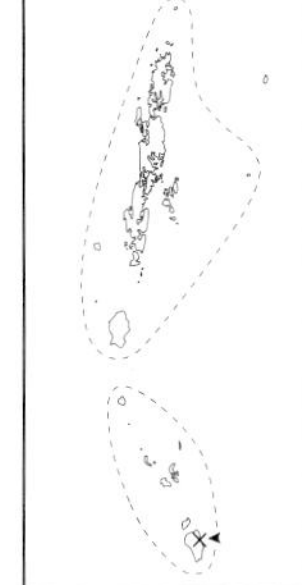

A specimen in the BNHS collection from the Nicobar Is, initially identified as *O. s. nicobaricus*, has been reidentified as this species (Abdulali 1980).

ORIENTAL SCOPS OWL *Otus sunia* — Plate 28

Scops Owl (F,I), Little Scops Owl (P), *O. scops* (E,I,K,P)

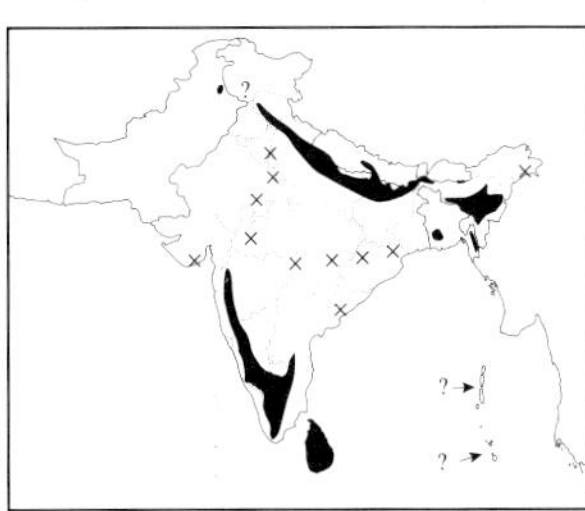

IDENTIFICATION 19 cm. Highly variable, with grey, brown and rufous morphs. The rufous morph is very different from any plumage of Eurasian Scops Owl (above); the other two morphs are not safely distinguishable from Eurasian in the field, except by vocalisations, although Oriental has more rounded wings and usually shows four or five primaries beyond the longest tertial (compared with six or seven on Eurasian). On range, rufous morph is most likely to be confused with Mountain Scops Owl (p.430), particularly with the nominate subspecies in the E Himalayas, but Oriental has prominently streaked underparts, streaking on crown and mantle, prominent ear-tufts (although not always held erect), and distinctive call. Also confusable with Collared Scops Owl (p.431), but is smaller, lacks prominent buff nuchal collar, has more heavily streaked underparts and more prominent white scapular spots, and call is also different. See Andaman Scops Owl (p.430) for differences from that species. **Racial variation** The Nicobar race, *O. s. nicobaricus*, is rufous, and differs from the rufous morph of the peninsula in having blackish-brown freckles and vermiculations on crown, nape and rest of upperparts. A specimen in the Natural History Museum, Tring, collected from the Nicobar Is, is quite different and warrants further investigation (upperparts and underparts are uniform bright rufous, and lack dark or pale markings (except for prominent white scapular spots); facial discs are also bright rufous, and lack pale or dark borders; primaries are only faintly barred). **VOICE** A rhythmic, resonant, frog-like *wut-chu-chraaii*, the first note musical, the last two more rasping; usually uttered regularly about once every 3–4 seconds, sometimes in continuous sequences of over one hundred calls (Roberts 1991). **HABITS** Hides by day in a densely foliaged tree, often close against the trunk or in dark tree hollow. Has a characteristic habit of compressing its plumage and stretching itself up while erecting the ear-tufts, almost closing the eyes; in this position it freezes, becoming almost indistinguishable from its bark- and lichen-covered perch. Hunts both in flight and by scanning from a perch. Mainly insectivorous. **HABITAT** Deciduous and evergreen broadleaved tropical and subtropical forest, orchards, groves around habitation and cultivation; also near street lights in cities in Sri Lanka. **BREEDING** February–May, varying locally. Nests in a hole in tree trunk or wall. **DISTRIBUTION AND STATUS** Resident, subject to some migratory movements. Mainly Himalayas in N Pakistan (Murree hills) and from W Himachal Pradesh east to Arunachal Pradesh; NE India, Bangladesh, W and S India, and Sri Lanka. **PK:** scarce and very local; 600–2000 m. **NP:** fairly common below 365 m (–1525 m). **IN:** locally fairly common; plains up to 1800 m, locally to 2300 m. **BT:** very local and rare?; 250 m. **BD:** locally common resident. **LK:** scarce resident throughout.

COLLARED SCOPS OWL *Otus bakkamoena* — Plate 28

O. lempiji

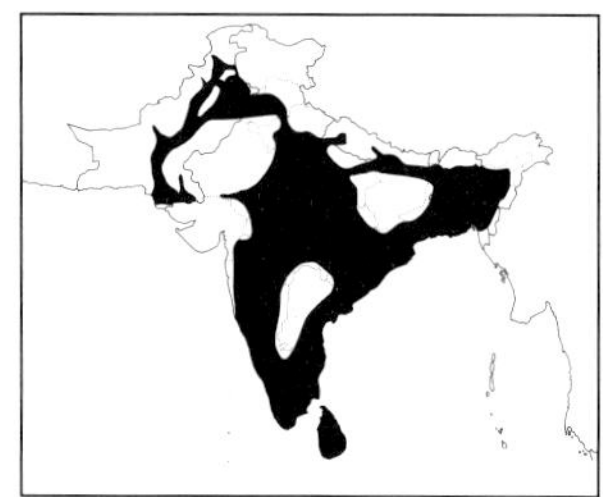

IDENTIFICATION 23–25 cm. Largest of the scops owls occurring in the subcontinent. Most likely to be confused with Oriental Scops Owl (p.431), but is larger, has prominent buff nuchal collar edged with dark brown, has more finely streaked underparts, lacks prominent white scapular spots (spots are buff and usually poorly defined), and call is also very different. Iris is typically dark orange or brown, rather than yellow as in Oriental. Very variable in coloration: can be pale grey-brown (e.g. in *O. b. deserticolor* from the drier parts of Pakistan) or warm rufous-brown (e.g. in the nominate race of Sri Lanka). **VOICE** Call lacks the resonance of those of the other scops owls, and does not carry very far: a subdued, frog-like, interrogative *whut* or *whuk*, usually repeated at irregular intervals but most often 4–6 seconds apart; female often responds with lower-pitched call, resulting in rapid two-noted duet (Roberts 1991). In C and E Himalayas, call is softer, less staccato, and with falling inflection (P. Holt). **HABITS** Very similar to those of Oriental Scops Owl. **HABITAT** Forest and well-wooded country, shady trees in orchards, groves, gardens and around cultivation; also irrigated plantations and riverain forest in Pakistan. **BREEDING** January–May, varying locally. Nests in a tree hole. **DISTRIBUTION AND STATUS** Resident. Throughout much of the subcontinent, except parts of the northwest and northeast and parts of C and E India. **PK:** common in plains and locally up to 2135 m in summer. **NP:** local; 185–1525 m. **IN:** locally common; plains and hills up to 1200 m in the peninsula, locally to 2400 m in E Himalayas. **BT:** frequent; 250–1830 m. **BD:** locally common. **LK:** common in lowlands and lower hills. **REFERENCES** Roberts and King (1986).

EURASIAN EAGLE OWL *Bubo bubo* — Plate 29

Eagle Owl (I), Northern Eagle Owl (K,R), Great Horned Owl (F), Rock Eagle Owl, *B. bengalensis*

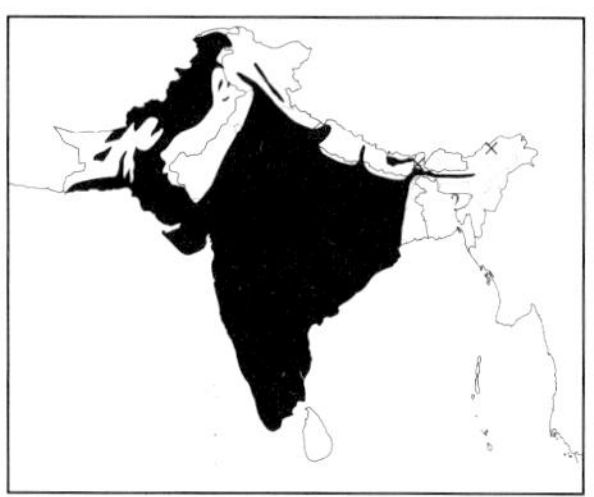

IDENTIFICATION 56–66 cm. A very large owl with bold dark brown streaking on breast, finer streaking and barring on belly, and dark brown and tawny-buff mottled upperparts. Has more upright ear-tufts, and broader streaking on breast, compared with Brown Fish Owl (p.433), which can occur in similar habitat. Legs are completely feathered. Eyes are orange, and bill is horn-brown. **Racial variation** *B. b. hemachalana* of NW subcontinent is larger and paler than *B. b. bengalensis*, described above, which is widely distributed throughout the subcontinent. **VOICE** A resonant *tu-whooh*, the second note rising in tone (Roberts 1991). **HABITS** Mainly nocturnal, roosting by day in a cleft or ledge of a rocky cliff, or among ruins, but usually perches on a prominent rock well before sunset and again after sunrise. Detects prey chiefly by scanning from a perch; also by making short flights over open country. **HABITAT** Rocky cliffs, steep earth banks, ruined forts, scrub-covered rocky hills, wooded areas with ravines, orchards and groves with old trees; in Pakistan, also disused irrigation channels overgrown with bushes. **BREEDING** October–May. Nests on ledge of an earth or rocky cliff; sometimes on ground under a bush or tree. **DISTRIBUTION AND STATUS** Resident. Throughout much of the subcontinent, except parts of the northwest and northeast and Sri Lanka. **PK:** widely and thinly distributed in hills; locally to 3200 m. **NP:** local; frequent up to 1800 m (–3415 m). **IN:** uncommon; plains up to 4300 m. **BD:** vagrant?

SPOT-BELLIED EAGLE OWL *Bubo nipalensis* — Plate 29

Forest Eagle Owl (F,I,P)

IDENTIFICATION 63 cm. A very large owl, easily distinguished by large, chevron-shaped spots on whitish underparts, buff-barred dark brown upperparts, and all-brown eyes. **Juvenile** is very distinctive: crown, mantle, coverts, rump and underparts are white and buff, with brown spotting and barring, and face is off-white. **VOICE** A low, deep, moaning hoot, and a far-carrying mournful scream, first rising and then falling in tone (Ali and Ripley 1987; Boonsong and Round 1991). **HABITS** Largely nocturnal, usually hiding by day among dense foliage in deep forest or thickly wooded valleys. A very bold and powerful owl, able to overcome large prey

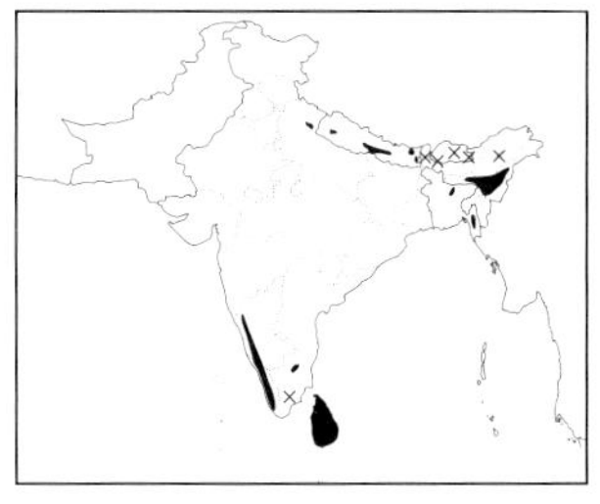

such as Kalij Pheasant (p.360); also takes hares, jackals, fawns, lizards and snakes. Hunts chiefly in forest, but may be seen at dusk at edge of clearings or by streams. **HABITAT** Heavy evergreen and moist deciduous tropical and subtropical broadleaved forest. **BREEDING** December–May, varying locally. Nests in a tree hollow, deserted raptor nest or cave or fissure in a rocky cliff. **DISTRIBUTION AND STATUS** Resident. Locally in Himalayas, mainly from N Uttar Pradesh east to Arunachal Pradesh; NE India and Bangladesh; Western Ghats, N Tamil Nadu and Sri Lanka. **NP:** rare and local; 305–2135 m. **IN:** rare; foothills up to 2100 m. **BT:** rare. **BD:** local. **LK:** rare resident throughout.

DUSKY EAGLE OWL *Bubo coromandus* — Plate 29

Dusky Horned Owl (F,I)

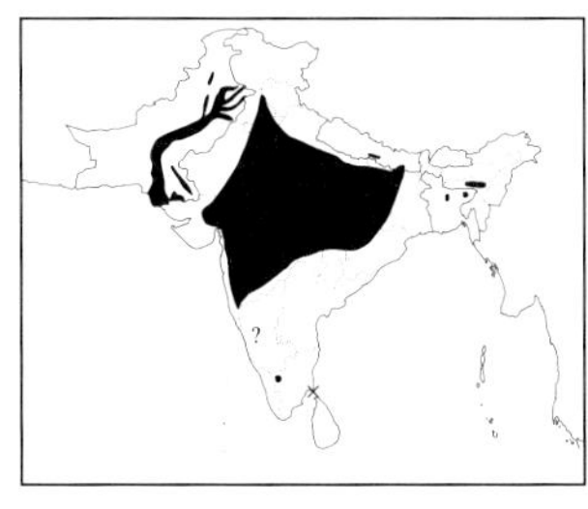

IDENTIFICATION 58 cm. A greyish-coloured eagle owl with large erect ear-tufts. Upperparts are greyish-brown, finely vermiculated with whitish, and with diffuse darker brown streaking; underparts are greyish-white, finely vermiculated and more strongly streaked with brown. Most likely to be confused with Brown Fish Owl (below), and best distinguished from that by more uniform grey-brown upperparts, less heavily streaked on mantle, and lacking any rufous tones. **VOICE** A deep, resonant *Wo, wo,wo,wo-o-o-o-o,* uttered day and night, the *wo* becoming progressively more silent; the call has been likened to a ping-pong ball bouncing to a halt (Ali and Ripley 1987). **HABITS** Generally roosts by day in a shady tree or sometimes in a thicket, emerging about an hour before sunset; sometimes hunts in daylight, especially in cloudy weather. Frequently begins calling in early afternoon and then continues intermittently, but can be heard at any time of day. **HABITAT** Well-watered areas with extensive tree cover in the plains: groves and roadside avenues of thickly foliaged trees near water; also irrigated forest plantations and scrub and tall grass near water in Pakistan. **BREEDING** November–April, varying locally. Usually nests in a deserted raptor nest high in a tree, often growing in or near water. **DISTRIBUTION AND STATUS** Sedentary resident. Pakistan; from C Punjab, India, east to SE Nepal and south to S Maharashtra; also locally in Assam, Meghalaya, Tamil Nadu and Bangladesh. **PK:** confined to well-watered plains, where frequent. **NP:** rare and very local; below 250 m. **IN:** widespread, generally uncommon. **BD:** rare and local.

BROWN FISH OWL *Ketupa zeylonensis* — Plate 29

***Bubo zeylonensis* (F,I)**

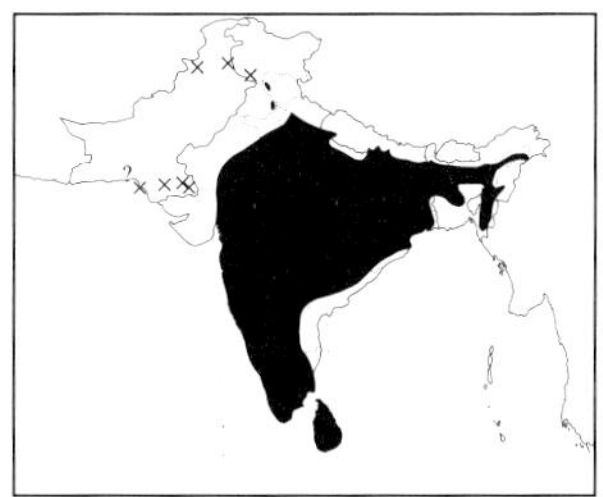

IDENTIFICATION 56 cm. A large brownish fish owl with stubby ear-tufts. Told from Tawny and Buffy Fish Owls (below and p.434) by combination of duller brown upperparts (with only dull rufous cast), finer dark brown streaking on crown, mantle and scapulars, finer streaking on dull buff underparts (with close cross-barring, lacking on other species), and lack of white above the bill. **VOICE** A soft, rapid, deep *hup-hup-hu*, a maniacal laugh, *hu-hu-hu-hu...hu ha,* and a mournful scream similar to that of Spot-bellied Eagle Owl (p.432) (Boonsong and Round 1991). **HABITS** Lives in pairs, generally roosting by day in a thickly foliaged tree, bamboo clump, ravine or hollow in an earth bank. Partly diurnal, emerging from its roosting place long before sunset, when the pair members begin to call to each other. Sometimes hunts in the day, especially in dull weather. Eats mainly fish, frogs and crabs. **HABITAT** Forest and well-wooded areas near water in tropical and subtropical zone. Favours mature trees, steep river banks, thickly vegetated ravines and village groves. **BREEDING** November–May, varying locally. Nests in a tree, on the ledge of a steep river bank or ruin, or in a deserted raptor's nest. **DISTRIBUTION AND STATUS** Sedentary resident. Mainly from E Gujarat and NW Uttar Pradesh east to Arunachal Pradesh and Bangladesh and south through the subcontinent, except the extreme east; also locally in Pakistan, Jammu and Kashmir, Himachal Pradesh and Punjab, India. **PK:** very rare. **NP:** uncommon; 75–1525 m. **IN:** widespread and uncommon in plains and hills, locally up to 1500 m. **BD:** local. **LK:** occurs throughout, more frequent in lowlands.

TAWNY FISH OWL *Ketupa flavipes* — Plate 29

***Bubo flavipes* (E,F,I)**

IDENTIFICATION 61 cm. A very large rufous-orange and brown fish owl. Told from the smaller Brown Fish Owl (above) by pale orange upperparts (much more richly coloured than on Brown) with bolder and more distinct black streaking, bold orange-buff barring on wing-coverts and flight feathers, and broader and more prominent black streaking on pale rufous-orange underparts, which lack black cross-barring on feathers, while often shows prominent whitish patch on forehead. See Buffy Fish Owl (p.434) for differences from that species. **VOICE** A deep *whoo-hoo* and a cat-like mewing (Baker 1927). **HABITS** Similar to those of Brown; sometimes fishes in bright

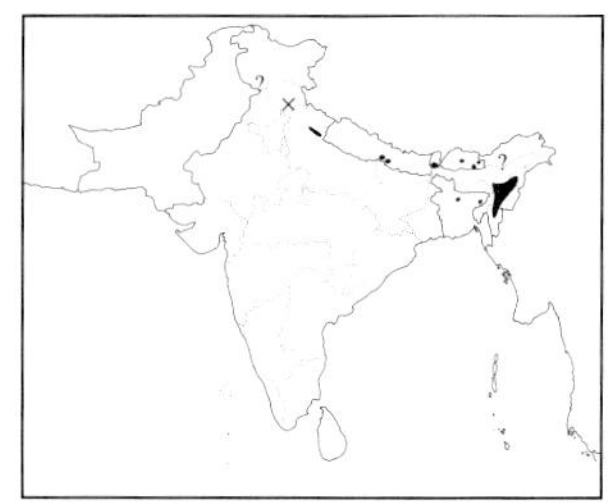

daylight. **HABITAT** Ravines, stream banks, rivers and pools in heavy broadleaved tropical and subtropical forest. **BREEDING** Poorly known. December–February in Assam. Nests in a disused raptor's nest or in hollow in a ravine or river bank. **DISTRIBUTION AND STATUS** Resident. Very locally in Himalayas from Himachal Pradesh east to Bhutan; NE India and Bangladesh. **NP:** very rare and local; 250–365 m. **IN:** rare; mainly foothills (–2450 m). **BT:** uncommon; 610–1330 m. **BD:** rare resident?

BUFFY FISH OWL *Ketupa ketupu* — Plate 29

Malay Fish Owl (I), *Bubo ketupu* (I)

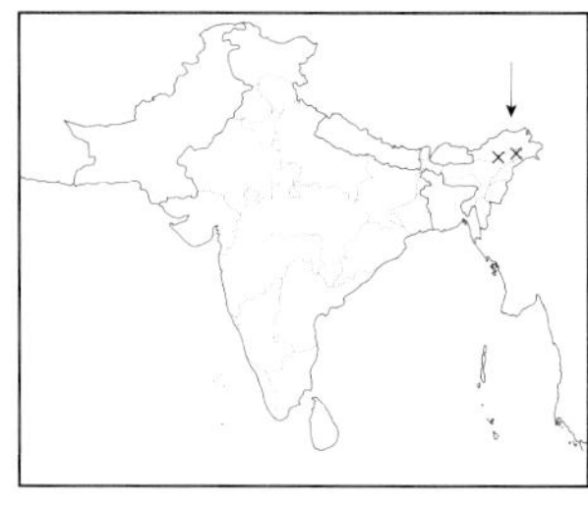

IDENTIFICATION 50 cm. Smallest of the fish owls. Distinguished from the much larger Tawny Fish Owl (p.433) by finer streaking on underparts, with only very fine shaft streaking on belly and flanks, duller buffish-white to greyish-white barring on flight feathers and tail (more orange-buff on Tawny), and tendency for crown and nape to be more heavily and diffusely streaked. From Brown Fish Owl (p.433) by white forehead (although not always apparent), more rufous-orange upperparts with thicker and more prominent black streaking, orange-buff underparts with more clearly defined black streaking on breast, and lack of black cross-barring on feathers of underparts. **VOICE** A long and monotonous *bup-bup-bup-bup-bup-bup-bup...* or *hup-hup-hup-hup-hup-hup...*, like a generator (Malaysia) (J. Scharringa). **HABITS** Details not recorded in the region. Very shy and fully alert by day as well as by night. **HABITAT** Forested streams in the plains. **BREEDING** Details not recorded in the region. In Malaysia, December–May; nests in a cave in a cliff or tree hollow. **DISTRIBUTION AND STATUS IN:** recorded in E Assam in early 20th century; presumably once resident, current status unknown, no recent published records. **REFERENCES** Baker (1922-30), Stevens (1915).

SNOWY OWL *Nyctea scandiaca* — Plate 29

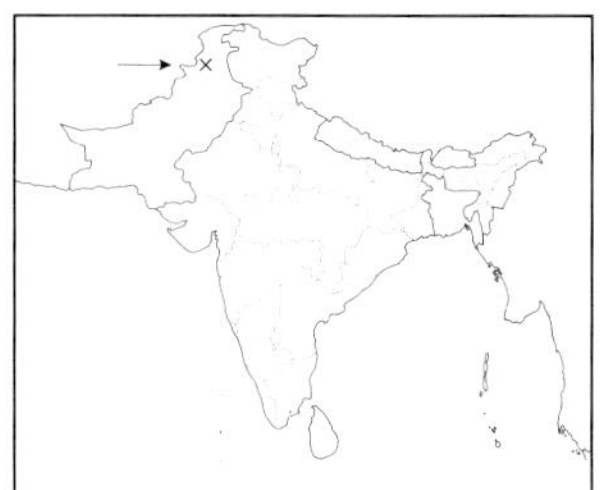

IDENTIFICATION 53–66 cm. A huge white owl with striking yellow eyes. **Male** is entirely pure white but for some brown spotting on wing-coverts and scapulars. **Female** and **immature** are white, heavily spotted and barred with brown on crown, mantle, wings and underparts. **VOICE** Usually silent outside breeding range. **HABITS** Details not recorded in the region. A powerful terrestrial owl, frequently active in daylight. Usually scans from an exposed perch, and also seeks prey by flying low and sometimes hovering. **HABITAT** Open country. **DISTRIBUTION AND STATUS PK:** vagrant.

MOTTLED WOOD OWL *Strix ocellata* — Plate 29

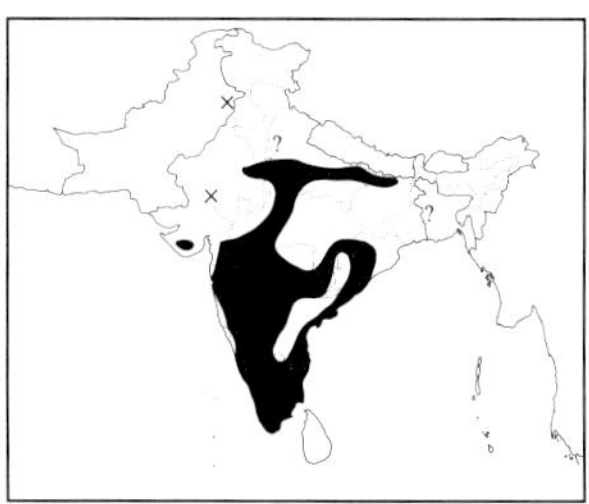

IDENTIFICATION 48 cm. Distinguished from Brown Wood Owl (below) by black concentric barring on pale facial discs, white, dark brown and rufous mottling on crown, nape and mantle, and whitish underparts barred with dark brown and mixed with rufous. Shows prominent white 'half-collar' on upper breast. Back and wings are barred and mottled dark brown and greyish-white, with some rufous (mainly on coverts and inner edges of remiges). **VOICE** A spooky, quavering *whaa-aa-aa-aa-ah*. Also a single, mellow, metallic hoot, and a harsh screech (Ali and Ripley 1987). **HABITS** Chiefly nocturnal. Keeps in pairs, which hide during the day in the shady refuge of a large tree. **HABITAT** Open wooded areas and groves of old, densely foliaged trees around villages and cultivation in the plains. **BREEDING** November–April, varying locally. Nests in a natural tree hole. **DISTRIBUTION AND STATUS** Resident, endemic to the subcontinent. Mainly from E Rajasthan east to Bihar and south through the peninsula, except in E India; also locally in N India and S Gujarat. **PK:** no recent records. **IN:** generally rather uncommon.

BROWN WOOD OWL *Strix leptogrammica* — Plate 29

IDENTIFICATION 47–53 cm. Told from Mottled Wood Owl (above) by uniform facial discs without black concentric barring, uniform brown crown and mantle, with fine white barring on scapulars, and buffish-white underparts finely barred with brown. Wings are much plainer brown (although coverts and tertials may be finely barred); flight feathers are dark brown, faintly barred paler brown and tipped whitish. **Racial variation** *S. l.*

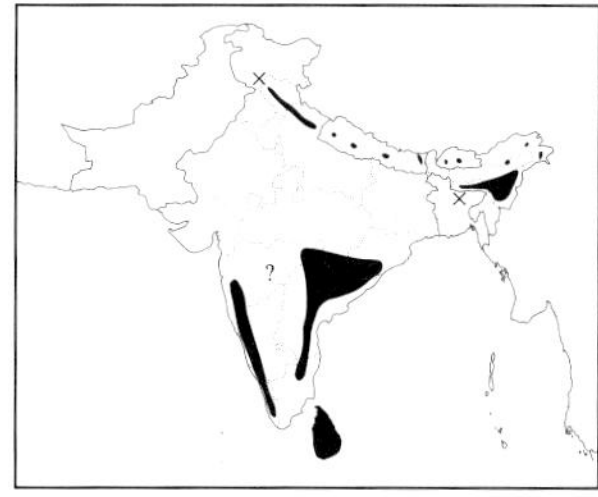

newarensis of the Himalayas has dark brown face, with prominent white eyebrows and pale lower rim to facial discs, and striking white band across foreneck, contrasting with dark brown sides to upper breast, and is much larger in size. *S. l. indranee* of the peninsula has more rufous facial discs and less prominent white eyebrows, while band on foreneck is smaller. **Juvenile** of *S. l. indranee* has prominent white-and-buff mottling on crown and mantle, buff, white and brown barring on wing-coverts, and whitish underparts without barring. Shows much down and quickly moults into adult plumage. **VOICE** Various calls described: a low double hoot, *tu-whoo,* and a sonorous squawk for *S. l. newarensis,* and a musical, hollow-sounding *tok...tu-hoo* and a variety of eerie shrieks and chuckles (Ali and Ripley 1987). Also: (1) *hoohoohoohoo(hoo),* one note followed after a slight pause by a vibrating sequence of three to four notes; (2) extremely loud and eerie scream, *eeeeooow,* similar to the screams of Brown Fish Owl (p.433) (Malaysia) (J. Scharringa). **HABITS** Virtually nocturnal. Roosts by day in pairs in large trees in heavy forest. Very shy; if disturbed, will compress itself to resemble a stump or fly off a long distance through the forest. **HABITAT** Dense broadleaved subtropical or temperate oak–rhododendron forest; also densely wooded gardens in Sri Lanka. **BREEDING** January–April, varying locally. Nests in a large tree, on a cliff ledge, or on the ground between tree roots or under rocks. **DISTRIBUTION AND STATUS** Resident. Locally in Himalayas from Jammu and Kashmir east to Arunachal Pradesh; NE India and Bangladesh; Eastern and Western Ghats, and Sri Lanka. **NP:** uncommon; 250–2700 m. **IN:** uncommon; 750 m up to at least 2500 m (–3900 m) in Himalayas, plains up to 1800 m in peninsula. **BT:** rare?; 2040–2745 m. **BD:** rare and local. **LK:** occurs throughout. **REFERENCES** Lama (1995b).

TAWNY OWL *Strix aluco* — Plate 29

Tawny Wood Owl (I)

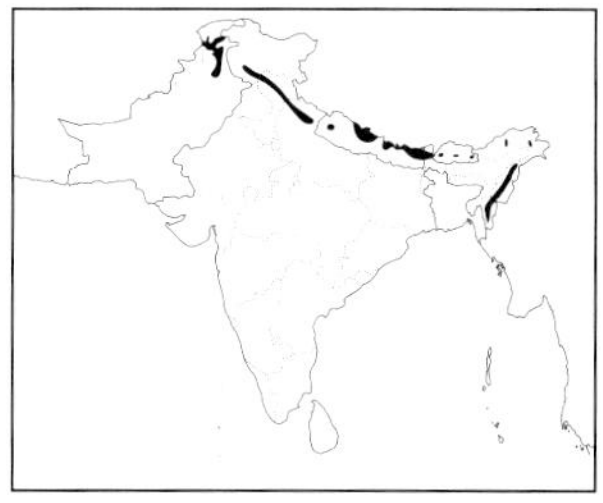

IDENTIFICATION 45–47 cm. A medium-sized Himalayan owl with large rounded head and broad rounded wings. Plumage varies from grey to rufous-brown in coloration, but always has dark streaking on sides of head, neck and entire underparts, pale forecrown stripes contrasting with dark forehead and centre of crown, dark eyes, prominent white markings on scapulars, and broad barring on wings and tail. **Racial variation** *S. a. biddulphi* of the W Himalayas is grey-brown and white in coloration, with broad streaking on upperparts, and is larger than *S. a. nivicola* of C and E Himalayas, which varies from rufous to dark brown and has barred rather than streaked upperparts. **VOICE** A trisyllabic *too-tu-whoo,* which is sometimes shortened to a two-noted *turr-whooh*; also a low-pitched *ku-wack-ku-wack* (Roberts 1991). **HABITS** Strictly nocturnal; seldom emerges before dusk. Typically, roosts in a tree, perched close to the trunk with half-closed eyes, partly concealed by leaves and resembling a dead stump. Hunts mainly by looking out and listening from a perch; also seizes birds from their roosting places or nests. **HABITAT** Temperate oak, rhododendron, pine and fir forest. **BREEDING** January–May, varying locally. Usually nests in a natural tree hollow. **DISTRIBUTION AND STATUS** Resident, subject to altitudinal movements. N Baluchistan, Pakistan, and Himalayas from N Pakistan east to Arunachal Pradesh; NE India. **PK:** frequent in the north. **NP:** frequent; 2000–4000 m. **IN:** widespread in Kashmir; 1800 m up to the treeline in Himalayas, 1200 m up to the treeline in NE hills. **BT:** uncommon; 2440-3120 m.

HUME'S OWL *Strix butleri* — Plate 29

Hume's Wood Owl (I)

IDENTIFICATION 37–38 cm. An arid-country owl. Bears a superficial resemblance to Tawny Owl (above), but, given range and habitat, is more likely to be confused in poor views with Barn Owl (p.429). Best distinguished by combination of pale coloration, whitish face with orange (rather than dark) iris, dark forehead dividing pale facial discs, buff collar around hindneck, buff-coloured underparts lightly barred with brown on breast, white scapular spots, and buff and brown barring on flight feathers and tail (underwing shows prominent dark carpal patch and barring on flight feathers, unlike Barn). **VOICE** A distinctive *whooo woohoo-woohoo,* the *woo* being higher-pitched than the *hoo*; also a rapid and agitated *hu-hu-hu-hu-hu...* etc (Cramp 1985). **HABITS** Unknown in the region. In the Middle East, roosts by day in rock crevices of gorges or sometimes in ruins. **HABITAT** Unknown in the region. Rocky gorges in Middle East. **BREEDING** Unknown in the region. In Middle East, nests in cavities and caves in steep walls of gorges. **DISTRIBUTION AND STATUS PK:** possibly a rare resident on SW Makran coast; only one record, in 1920, but the area is little visited by ornithologists. **REFERENCES** Cramp (1985).

COLLARED OWLET *Glaucidium brodiei* Plate 30

Collared Pygmy Owlet (F,I)

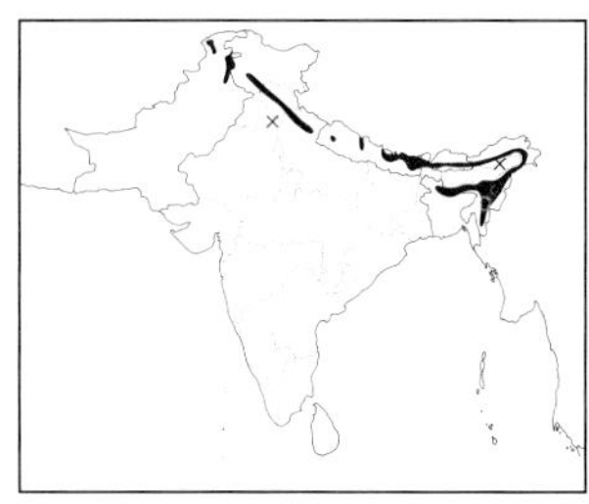

IDENTIFICATION 17 cm. A very small owl, occurring in rufous and grey-brown morphs. Is heavily barred with buff and grey-brown (or rufous and brown) on the upperparts. The underparts are similarly patterned, although is white on throat, centre of breast and centre of belly. Most similar to Jungle Owlet (below), but is much smaller, and has distinct buff (or rufous) 'spectacles' on upper mantle which frame blackish patches (creating pattern resembling an owl's face). Further, crown appears spotted rather than neatly and finely barred, and Collared has broad, diffuse streaking (rather than barring) on flanks. **VOICE** A pleasant, four-noted bell-like whistle, *toot..tootoot..toot*, uttered in runs of three or four and repeated at intervals (Ali and Ripley 1987). **HABITS** Keeps singly. Diurnal and crepuscular, often hunting in broad daylight. Usually seeks prey by watching and listening from a prominent perch. Calls persistently during the day in the breeding season, as well as at night. Can also often be located by the scolding cries of small birds mobbing the owl. **HABITAT** Subtropical broadleaved forest and temperate oak, rhododendron and fir forest. **BREEDING** March–July. Nests in a natural tree hole or one dug by barbets or woodpeckers. **DISTRIBUTION AND STATUS** Resident. Himalayas from N Pakistan east to Arunachal Pradesh; NE India and Bangladesh. **PK:** common, but very local, 1800–2750 m; down to foothills in winter. **NP:** fairly common and local; 1350–2900 m (610–3050 m). **IN:** fairly common; 900–3050 m. **BT:** fairly common; 300–3200 m. **BD:** very local.

ASIAN BARRED OWLET *Glaucidium cuculoides* Plate 30

Barred Owlet (F,I)

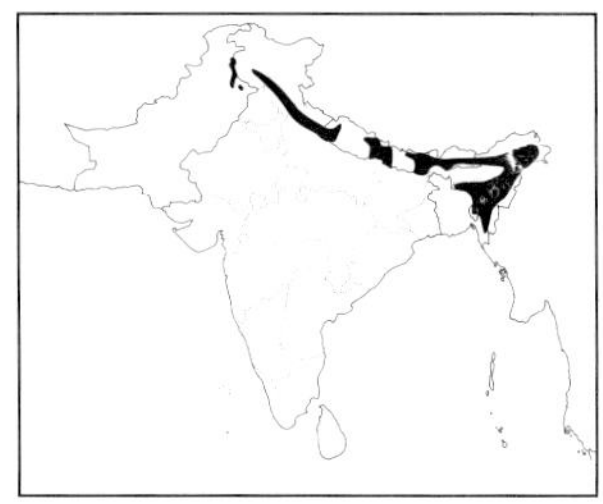

IDENTIFICATION 23 cm. A small owl, heavily barred on the upperparts and underparts. Best told from Jungle Owlet (below), where ranges overlap, by larger size and longer and fuller-looking tail, buff barring on wing-coverts and flight feathers (wings of Jungle are barred with rufous and contrast markedly with buff-barred mantle), and less finely barred upperparts and underparts, with lower flanks usually noticeably streaked (barring continues onto lower flanks on Jungle). Patterning of lower flanks varies, however, and on some appears barred (but more broadly and diffusely than on Jungle). **Juvenile** has buff spotting on crown, nape and mantle, and barring on breast and streaking on flanks is more diffuse. Possibly confusable with Spotted Owlet (p.437), but lacks white hindcollar of that species, and patterning of underparts is quite different. **Racial variation** Birds occurring in the E Himalayas and the NE subcontinent (*G. c. austerum* and *G. c. rufescens*) are more rufous than the nominate form, described above, having rufous-buff barring on more rufescent-brown upperparts and rufous-brown streaking on flanks. **VOICE** A crescendo of harsh squawks, and in the breeding season a continuous bubbling whistle, *wowowowowowowowo*, which lasts up to seven seconds; also has an occasional *woioioioioioi* followed by a higher-pitched *kek* (Ali and Ripley 1987). **HABITS** Mainly diurnal, often perching conspicuously on bare branches, from where it scans and listens for prey in the daytime. When alarmed, has a curious habit of wagging its tail. Like other small owls, has an undulating flight, a series of rapid wingbeats followed by a dipping glide. Puffs itself up into a ball before starting its bubbling call, and then gradually subsides to its normal size. **HABITAT** Broadleaved tropical and subtropical forest; also open temperate forest of oak, pine and rhododendron. **BREEDING** April and May. Nests in a natural tree hole or one dug by barbets or woodpeckers. **DISTRIBUTION AND STATUS** Resident. Himalayas from N Pakistan east to Arunachal Pradesh; NE India and Bangladesh. **PK:** frequent but local; 460–1800 m. **NP:** common; 245–2440 m (–2745 m). **IN:** locally common; foothills up to 2100 m, locally to 2700 m. **BT:** fairly common; 250–2700 m. **BD:** locally common.

JUNGLE OWLET *Glaucidium radiatum* Plate 30

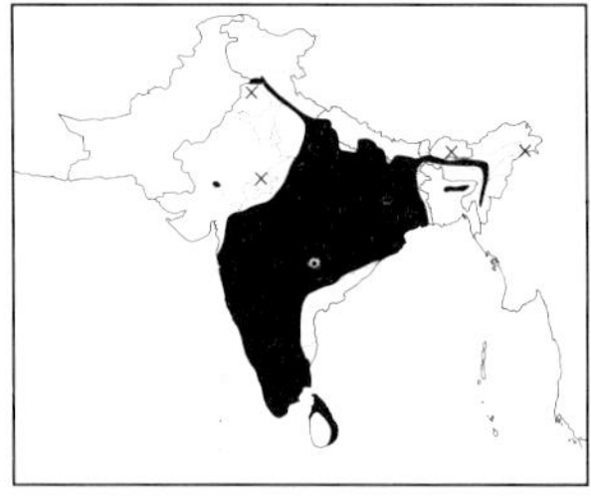

IDENTIFICATION 20 cm. A small owl, heavily barred on the upperparts and underparts. Note that this is the only *Glaucidium* species occurring in the Indian peninsula. Very similar in appearance to Asian Barred Owlet (above) and best told by smaller size, bright rufous barring on wing-coverts and flight feathers contrasting with buff barring on mantle (wings of Asian Barred are barred with buff and are therefore concolorous with mantle), more closely barred upperparts, and more closely barred underparts with bars continuing onto lower flanks (lower flanks are typically diffusely streaked on Asian Barred). Possibly confusable also with Collared Owlet (above), but is larger, has uniformly barred nape and mantle (lacking owl-face patterning of Collared), and has barred forehead and crown, and more uniformly barred underparts. Occurs in Sri Lanka, where it is confusable with Chestnut-backed Owlet (p.437); see that species for main differences. **Racial variation** Birds occurring in the Malabar coastal strip (*G. r. malabaricum*) differ from the nominate form, described above, in being more rufous, particularly across the breast and on the crown, mantle and scapulars. **VOICE** A loud, slow *kao..kao..kao* followed by a *kao..kuk*, which is repeated at an increasingly fast rate for several seconds. Also has an occasional *woioioioioioi* followed by a higher-pitched *kek*, as does Asian Barred Owlet (Ali and Ripley 1987). **HABITS** Mainly crepuscular, but sometimes active in the daytime, especially in dull weather. Spends the day in foliage or in a tree hollow. Easier to see than many owls, as it readily flies from its roost when disturbed. **HABITAT** Open broadleaved forest and secondary growth, mainly in tropical and subtropical zones. **BREEDING** March–May. Nests in a natural tree hole or one dug by barbets or woodpeckers. **DISTRIBUTION AND STATUS** Resident. Himalayas from Himachal Pradesh east to Bhutan; from NE Uttar Pradesh and E Gujarat south and east through the subcontinent, except much of the northeast and extreme E India. **NP:** common below 915 m (–1600 m). **IN:** common in plains and hills below 2000 m. **BT:** rare and local. **BD:** common and local. **LK:** common in dry lowlands and adjacent E hills.

CHESTNUT-BACKED OWLET *Glaucidium castanonotum* — Plate 30

G. radiatum castanonotum* (I), *G. cuculoides castanonotum

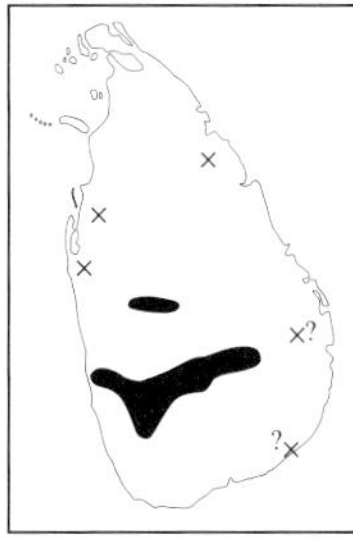

IDENTIFICATION 19 cm. A small owl, similar to Jungle Owlet (p.436), which also occurs in Sri Lanka. Back and wing-coverts are bright chestnut, narrowly and diffusely barred with brown and some buff (with rest of upperparts dark brown and narrowly barred with buff, much as on Jungle). Lower throat and band across breast are barred brown and buff as on Jungle, but belly and flanks are noticeably streaked (rather than barred). **VOICE** Distinctive series of (usually three to five) rather slow, resonant *kraw..kraw..kraw..kraw..kraw* notes that usually slow slightly towards the end. Somewhat reminiscent of one of the notes of Common Hawk Cuckoo (p.410) or Sri Lanka Frogmouth (p.440) (P. Holt). **HABITS** Shy and wary. Diurnal; often hunts and calls in daylight. Keeps in tops of tall trees. **HABITAT** Dense forest. **BREEDING** March–May. Nests in a tree hole. **DISTRIBUTION AND STATUS LK:** rare endemic resident in wet lowlands and hills.

LITTLE OWL *Athene noctua* — Plate 30

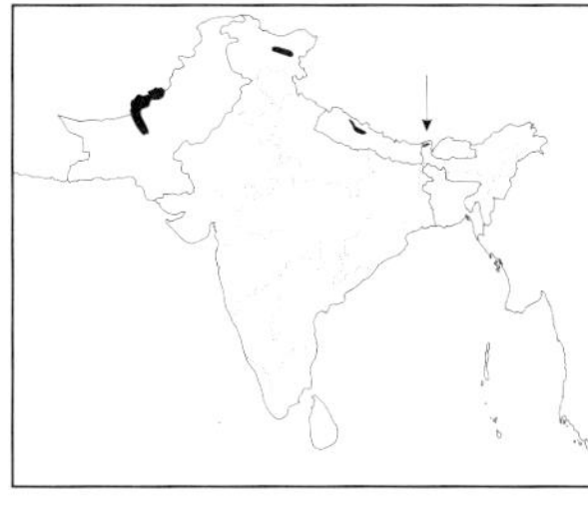

IDENTIFICATION 23 cm. A white-spotted, typically sandy-brown owl with bold streaking on underparts. In Baluchistan, its range overlaps with that of the widely distributed Spotted Owlet (below). Told from that species by streaked rather than spotted breast and flanks, neatly streaked crown with white streaks arranged in lines (rather than irregularly scattered spots across crown), and different call. **VOICE** A plaintive *quew* or *piu*, repeated every 2–3 seconds, and a soft barking *werro-werro*. **HABITS** Crepuscular and partly diurnal; when feeding young, may hunt at any time. Most prey is captured by pouncing from a vantage point, but also sometimes by running on the ground. When alarmed, stretches upwards and bobs its head in curious fashion. **HABITAT** Rocky and earth cliffs, gullies, bluffs of rivers and ruins in open semi-desert. **BREEDING** March–June. Nests in a hole in tree, rock, ruined wall or earth cliff. **DISTRIBUTION AND STATUS** Local resident. Baluchistan, Pakistan, Jammu and Kashmir, NW and WC Nepal and N Sikkim. **PK:** locally frequent; 600–2400 m. **NP:** scarce, in Tibetan plateau country; 2715–4155 m. **IN:** rare, in Ladakh; 3000–5000 m. **REFERENCES** Pfister (1997).

SPOTTED OWLET *Athene brama* — Plate 30

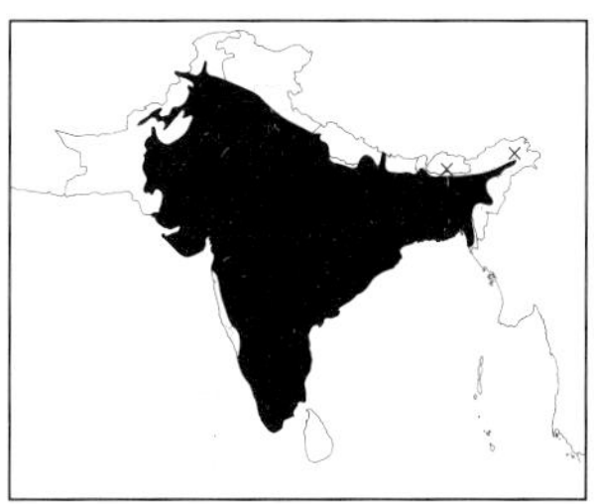

IDENTIFICATION 21 cm. Most likely to be confused with Jungle and Asian Barred Owlets (p.436), but easily distinguished by spotted rather than barred appearance (with prominent white spotting on crown, mantle and wing-coverts, and brown spotting rather than close dark barring on underparts). In addition, has pale facial discs and pale hindcollar. In arid regions of W Pakistan, its range overlaps with that of the very similar Little Owl (above); told from that species by spotted or barred rather than streaked breast and flanks, irregular white spotting on crown, and different call. Great care is needed to avoid overlooking the very poorly known Forest Owlet (p.438); see that species for main differences. **Racial variation** Birds in N India (*A. b. indica*) are paler, grey-brown in coloration compared with the nominate race of S India. **VOICE** A harsh, screechy *chirurr-chirurr-chirurr...* etc followed by or alternated with *cheevak, cheevak, cheevak,* and a variety of other discordant screeches and chuckles (Ali and Ripley 1987). **HABITS** Mainly crepuscular and nocturnal, although sometimes seen in broad daylight if disturbed. Hides by day in a tree hollow, shady branch of a mature tree, or chimney, or under roof. Frequently congregates around street lights at night while hunting insects. Usually in pairs or family groups. **HABITAT** Villages, towns, cities, ruins, cultivation, groves of old trees; in treeless semi-desert, frequents earth cliffs and ravines. **BREEDING** November–April, varying locally. Nests in a hole in a tree or wall, in building or in a chimney. **DISTRIBUTION AND STATUS** Sedentary resident. Throughout much of the subcontinent, except parts of the northeast and northwest and Himalayas. **PK:** common and widespread in plains, valleys and foothills; locally to 1600 m. **NP:** common below 1525 m (–2745 m). **IN:** generally common from plains locally up to 1400 m. **BT:** rare and local. **BD:** common throughout.

FOREST OWLET *Athene blewitti* Plate 30

Forest Spotted Owlet (I)

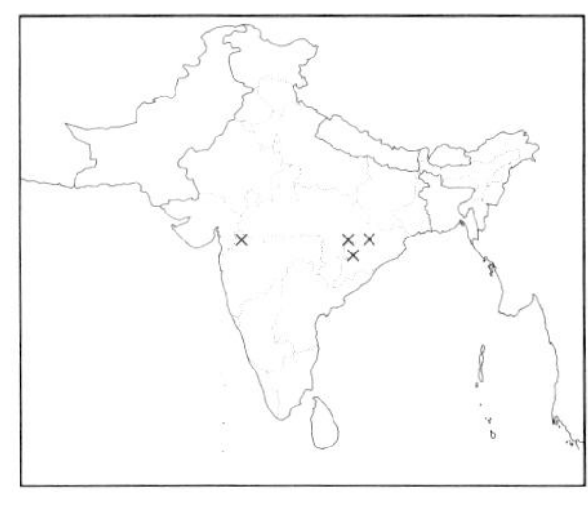

IDENTIFICATION 23 cm. A very poorly known forest-dwelling owl, similar to the smaller Spotted Owlet (p.437) in appearance, but structurally more like a *Glaucidium* owlet, with massive, heavily feathered legs and large claws. The crown, nape and mantle appear uniform cold grey-brown, with white speckles visible only at close range, and lacking the white collar of Spotted. Scapulars have some white tips and bars, but are more uniform and not so profusely and irregularly spotted as on Spotted. Wings (apart from the inner coverts) and tail are broadly banded blackish-brown and white, with white-tipped remiges and a broad white tail-tip in fresh plumage. Face is pale, without dark cheek patches. Breast almost uniformly dark brown, and barring on upper flanks is broader, stronger and more prominent; rest of underparts are white, much cleaner than Spotted's. **VOICE** A whinny like that of Spotted was probably made by this species (King *et al.* in press). **HABITS** Very poorly known. Diurnal and confiding. **HABITAT** Fairly open, secondary dry deciduous forest. Previously recorded in dense moist deciduous forest. **BREEDING** Unknown. **DISTRIBUTION AND STATUS** Globally threatened. **IN:** endemic resident; several specimens collected in 19th century in Satpura hills in SE Gujarat, N Maharashtra, SE Madhya Pradesh and W Orissa; sight records in S Bihar in 1950s unconfirmed; rediscovered in 1997 in NW Maharashtra. **REFERENCES** Ara (1953), King *et al.* (in press), Rasmussen and Collar (in press), Ripley (1976).

BOREAL OWL *Aegolius funereus* Plate 30

Tengmalm's Owl (I,R)

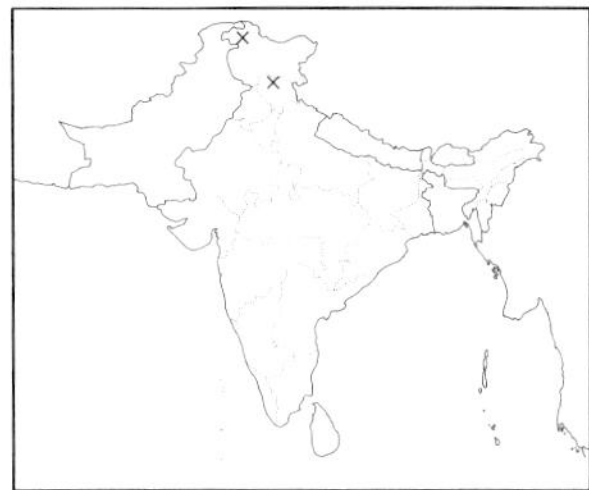

IDENTIFICATION 24–26 cm. Considerably smaller than Tawny Owl (p.435), but with similar although more rapid flight action. Has relatively large, square-shaped head, greyish-white facial discs encircled with black (with angular upper edge giving rise to alert expression), and white spotting on forehead and crown. Has grey-brown upperparts, with white spotting on scapulars and wing-coverts and barring on wings and tail, and whitish underparts with grey-brown streaking. **Juvenile** has uniform brown crown, mantle and underparts, and dark brown facial discs edged with white, retaining this plumage for several months. **VOICE** Commonest calls are a soft although far-carrying, regularly repeated *po-po-po...* etc, with number of units per phrase varying, as do tempo and pitch, and a squirrel-like smacking *yiop* or *chiak* (Cramp 1985). **HABITS** Unknown in the subcontinent. Elsewhere, it is strictly nocturnal, retiring to a shady tree during the day. Scans from a lookout on a tree or boulder and flies down to seize prey. **HABITAT** Subalpine juniper scrub and dwarf trees. **BREEDING** Unknown in the subcontinent. Elsewhere, usually nests in disused woodpecker hole. **DISTRIBUTION AND STATUS** Probably under-recorded and a rare resident in drier inner Himalayan ranges. **PK:** one record in the northwest. **IN:** once collected in Himachal Pradesh.

BROWN HAWK OWL *Ninox scutulata* Plate 30

Brown Boobook (R)

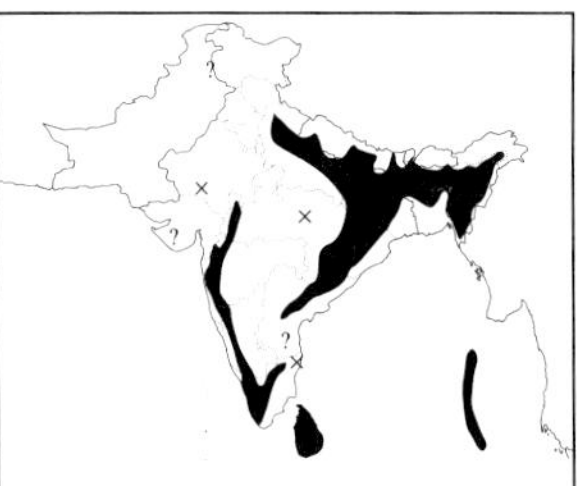

IDENTIFICATION 32 cm. A distinctive owl, best identified by hawk-like profile (with slim body, long tail and narrow head). Has uniform dark brown upperparts showing variable amounts of white spotting on scapulars, all-dark face except for white patch above bill (therefore lacking pale facial discs shown by many owl species), and bold rufous-brown streaking on underparts. **Racial variation** *N. s. obscura*, occurring in the Andaman and Nicobar Is, is almost entirely dark chocolate-brown, without broad streaking on the underparts; has indistinct white spotting on flanks and belly, and a whitish forehead. See Andaman Hawk Owl (p.439) for main differences from that species. **VOICE** A soft and pleasant *oo..ok, oo..ok, oo..ok,* in runs of 6–20 calls (Ali and Ripley 1987). **HABITS** Keeps singly or in pairs. Crepuscular and nocturnal, typically spending the day concealed in the top of a forest tree. Sometimes hunts in daylight in cloudy weather. Flies out from a tree stump to chase insects and returns to the same perch again; also eats frogs, lizards, and small birds and mammals. Flight is hawk-like, a series of rapid wingbeats followed by a glide. **HABITAT** Forest and well-wooded areas, often near water, in tropical and subtropical zones. **BREEDING** January–July, varying locally. Nests in a natural tree hollow. **DISTRIBUTION AND STATUS** Resident. Himalayas from N Uttar Pradesh east to Arunachal Pradesh; NE India and Bangladesh, and south through E India to C Andhra Pradesh;

W India from W Madhya Pradesh south to Kerala and east to C Tamil Nadu; Sri Lanka. **NP:** locally fairly common; below 1500 m. **IN:** locally frequent; foothills up to 1000 m. **BT:** rare and local?; 250–400 m. **BD:** common. **LK:** lowlands and lower hills, mainly in dry lowlands.

ANDAMAN HAWK OWL *Ninox affinis* — Plate 30

Andaman Brown Hawk Owl (I)

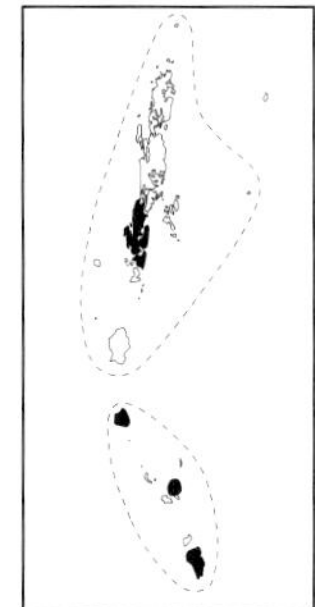

IDENTIFICATION 28 cm. Occurs alongside the all-dark endemic race of Brown Hawk Owl (p.438) in the Andaman and Nicobar Is. Readily told by smaller size, rufous spotting on white underparts, paler brown coloration to upperparts, more distinctly barred tail, and different call. **VOICE** A loud *craw*, quite different from the pleasant *oo..ok..* of Brown Hawk Owl (Ali and Ripley 1987). **HABITS** Little known; presumably similar to those of Brown Hawk Owl. Keeps singly or in pairs; perches on tall trees in fields and forest clearings; hawks insects at dusk. **HABITAT** Mangrove forest. **BREEDING** Unknown. **DISTRIBUTION AND STATUS IN:** Resident, endemic to Andaman and Nicobar Is (Great Nicobar, Car Nicobar, Trinkat and Camorta).

LONG-EARED OWL *Asio otus* — Plate 30

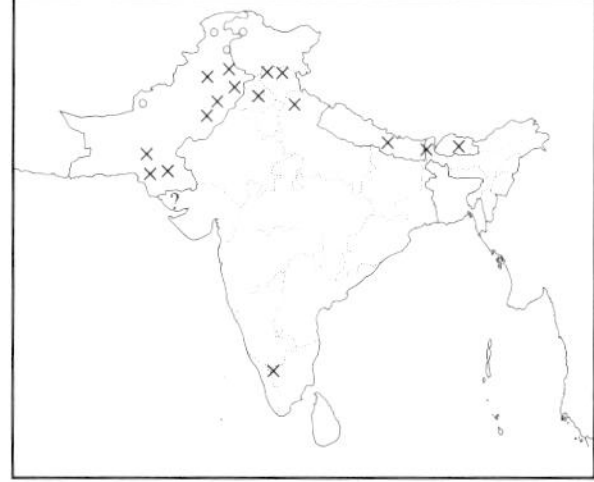

IDENTIFICATION 35–37 cm. A slim, medium-sized, heavily streaked owl with long ear-tufts which are typically held erect when at rest. Most likely to be confused with Short-eared Owl (below) when flushed during the day. Told from that species at rest by erect ear-tufts, orange-brown coloration to facial discs, orange (rather than yellow) iris, greyish (rather than buff) background coloration to upperparts, and more heavily streaked belly and flanks. Further differences in flight are orange-buff base coloration to primaries and tail feathers, with more pronounced dark barring, lack of prominent dark carpal patch, and more rounded wings and shorter tail. **VOICE** Territorial call of male is a long-drawn, subdued *oo* or *hu*. **HABITS** Strictly nocturnal. Hides in the daytime in trees; also in dense thickets in winter, when it sometimes roosts communally. When roosting, makes itself very slim: raises its ear-tufts and closes its eyes to slits, looking like a stump of decayed wood or a broken branch. Hunts by quartering open ground. **HABITAT** On passage and in winter, frequents stunted trees and poplar plantations. Recorded breeding in well-wooded coniferous areas and groves. **BREEDING** Very poorly known in the region. One breeding record in June. In Europe, uses a disused stick nest of another bird in trees and bushes. **DISTRIBUTION AND STATUS** Mainly a winter visitor to Pakistan and NW India (Jammu and Kashmir, Himachal Pradesh and Punjab); has bred in N and W Pakistan and Kashmir. **PK:** mainly a scarce winter visitor. **NP:** vagrant. **IN:** rare. **BT:** vagrant.

SHORT-EARED OWL *Asio flammeus* — Plate 30

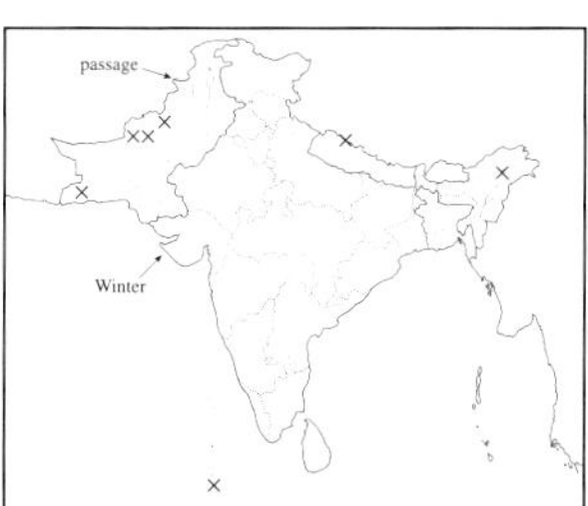

IDENTIFICATION 37–39 cm. A medium-sized, well-streaked owl, often seen hunting during the day. Confusion possible with both Long-eared Owl (above) and Grass Owl (p.429). Told from Long-eared at rest by short or apparently absent ear-tufts, buffish-white coloration to facial discs, yellow (rather than orange) iris, buff background coloration to upperparts, and non-existent or indistinct streaking on belly and flanks. Further differences in flight are buffish-white background coloration to primaries and tail, with less prominent dark barring, pronounced dark carpal patch, noticeable white trailing edge to wing, and narrower wings and longer tail. From Grass by heavily streaked upperparts and breast, and dark surround to yellow-and-black eyes (Grass Owl has very pale face with all-dark eyes). **VOICE** Usually silent outside breeding season. **HABITS** Keeps singly or in small flocks. Diurnal and crepuscular. A terrestrial owl, hunting by quartering low over open country in a deceptively leisurely manner. Has an irregular and rolling flight, frequently hovering and gliding on slightly raised wings and occasionally flying in wide circles. **HABITAT** Open country with scattered bushes, grassland and semi-desert. **DISTRIBUTION AND STATUS** Winter visitor and passage migrant. Throughout much of the subcontinent, except parts of the northwest, northeast, Himalayas and extreme E India. **PK:** scarce. **NP:** uncommon; up to 3350 m on passage. **IN:** generally uncommon; widespread in plains and peninsular hills up to 1400 m. **BD:** rare winter visitor. **LK:** irregular, but widespread. **MV:** irregular winter visitor.

ASIAN FROGMOUTHS Batrachostomidae

Frogmouths have the same cryptic colouring, soft plumage, wide gape and nocturnal habits as nightjars, but differ in some of their habits. They are more arboreal than nightjars, nesting and roosting in trees and hunting from them at night by pouncing on prey.

SRI LANKA FROGMOUTH *Batrachostomus moniliger* Plate 31

Ceylon Frogmouth (I,P)

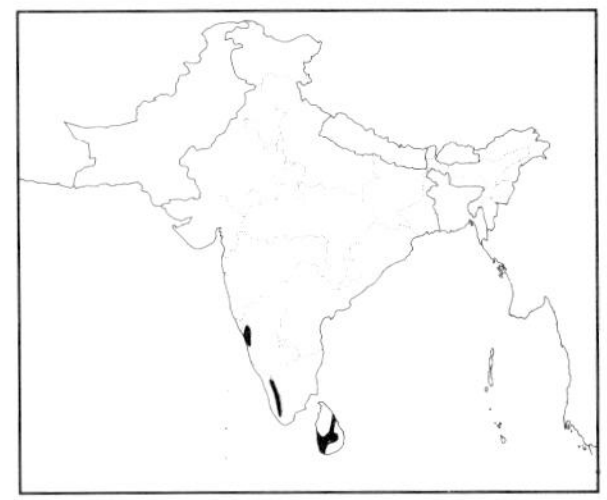

IDENTIFICATION 23 cm. Smaller and shorter-tailed than Hodgson's (below), with bigger-looking head and bill; the only frogmouth occurring in the Western Ghats and Sri Lanka. **Male** is brownish-grey in coloration, with irregular black-and-white markings and vermiculations. White markings typically form narrow 'collar' across upper mantle and irregular line of spotting across breast, and are usually prominent on scapulars, wing-coverts and belly/flanks. Is generally greyer than male Hodgson's, with more uniform underparts. **Female** is more uniform than male, and rufous to rufous-brown in coloration. Upperparts are irregularly spotted with black, with odd whitish spots on scapulars and coverts, and also belly/flanks. Often has white spotting on upper mantle forming irregular 'collar'. **VOICE** Fairly loud series of (usually seven to nine) rollicking liquid chuckles with a slightly quarrelsome quality: starts explosively, decelerates, and fades after 2–3 seconds; highly repetitive and often ventriloquial. Also gives a range of softer whistles, wheezes and croaks (P. Holt). **HABITS** Poorly known. Roosts by day in undergrowth in dense forest, where it is extremely difficult to see. Feeding habits are presumably the same as those of other frogmouths: they perch in a tree and descend with fast flight to pounce on moths, beetles and grasshoppers. **HABITAT** Bamboo and cane forest; dense tropical and subtropical broadleaved evergreen forest. **BREEDING** Mainly January–April. Nest is a well-flattened camouflaged cup on a horizontal branch or in a tree fork. **DISTRIBUTION AND STATUS** Local resident, endemic to Western Ghats in NW Karnataka and Kerala and Sri Lanka. **IN:** uncommon; below 1200 m. **LK:** rare resident, more records from the wet than dry zone. **REFERENCES** Kannan (1993b), Gaston and Zacharias (1996), Sugathan (1981).

HODGSON'S FROGMOUTH *Batrachostomus hodgsoni* Plate 31

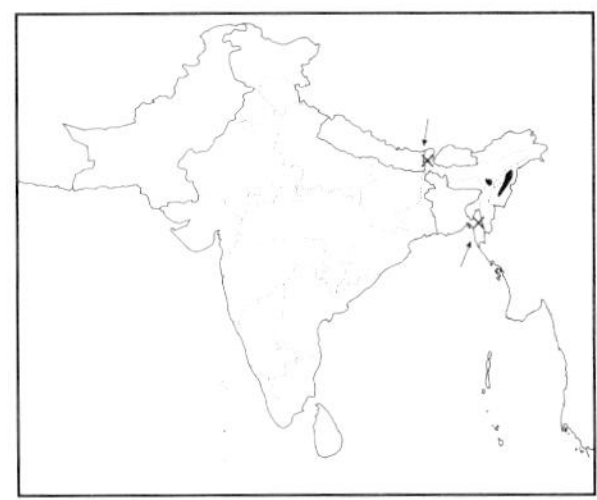

IDENTIFICATION 27 cm. Larger, longer-tailed and more evenly proportioned than Sri Lanka Frogmouth (above), although is the only frogmouth occurring in the NE subcontinent. **Male** is rufous-brown in overall coloration. Upperparts are heavily marked with black, especially on head, with irregular bold whitish markings particularly on scapulars and upper mantle (forming 'collar' on some birds). Underparts are heavily and irregularly marked with black, white and rufous. Is more rufous in coloration than male Sri Lanka Frogmouth, and underparts are more heavily marked. **Female** is more uniform rufous, with irregular black-tipped white spots on upper mantle, scapulars and underparts. **VOICE** Usual call is a series of soft burring *gwaa* notes with rising inflection. Also has quiet, descending whistles (Boonsong and Round 1991). **HABITS** Little known. Similar to those of Sri Lanka Frogmouth. **HABITAT** Subtropical broadleaved evergreen forest. **BREEDING** April–July. Nest and nest site are like those of Sri Lanka Frogmouth. **DISTRIBUTION AND STATUS** Resident. Sikkim, NE India (Arunachal Pradesh, Assam, Manipur, Tripura) and Bangladesh. **IN:** rare; 300–1800 m. **BD:** rare resident.

EARED NIGHTJARS Eurostopodidae AND NIGHTJARS Caprimulgidae

Small to medium-sized birds with long, pointed wings, and gaping mouth with long bristles which help to catch insects in flight. Nightjars are crepuscular and nocturnal in habit, with soft, owl-like, cryptically patterned plumage. By day they perch on the ground or lengthwise on a branch, and are difficult to detect. All their food, which consists of flying insects, especially moths, beetles and crickets, is caught on the wing. Typically, they fly erratically to and fro over and among vegetation, occasionally wheeling, gliding and hovering to pick insects from foliage. They often feed in loose parties. Nightjars are most easily located by their calls or songs, and are heard mainly between sunset and dark and again, briefly, in the earliest dawn. When disturbed, they are not easily flushed, and soon drop into cover again. Their eggs are usually laid on bare ground.

GREAT EARED NIGHTJAR *Eurostopodus macrotis* Plate 31

IDENTIFICATION 40–41 cm. A very large, richly coloured nightjar. In flight, told from other nightjars by combination of larger size, slower-flapping and more buoyant flight action (typically feeding higher in the air

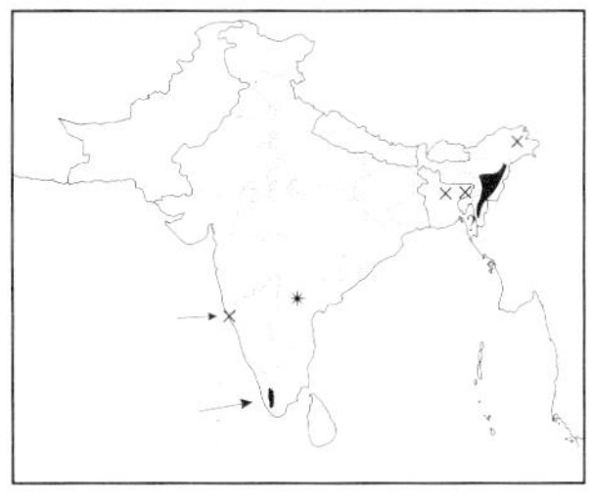

compared with others), and lack of white or buff spots on wings or tail. At rest, shows prominent ear-tufts, and is generally more richly marked with golden-buff and rufous than other nightjars. Has fine rufous barring on black ear-coverts and throat, buff underparts boldly barred with dark brown, and tail broadly banded with golden-buff and dark brown. **VOICE** Loud, eerie, haunting and hypnotic musical whistle, *pit...pee-wheeeu*, the first note often inaudible. Much more attractive and less metronomic than voice of most other night birds (P. Holt). **HABITS** Similar to those of other nightjars, but feeds much higher up. Emerges at dusk to circle high over the forest and forest clearings, descending lower as darkness gathers. **HABITAT** Evergreen and moist deciduous tropical and subtropical broadleaved forest and secondary jungle. **BREEDING** January–May, varying locally. Lays eggs on a bush-covered slope. **DISTRIBUTION AND STATUS** Resident, subject to local movements. Mainly in NE India, Bangladesh, Western Ghats in Goa, S Kerala. **IN:** from plains up to 1650 m in the northeast; local in foothills and up to 1000 m in Western Ghats. **BD:** rare or local resident. **REFERENCES** Singh (1995).

GREY NIGHTJAR *Caprimulgus indicus* — Plate 31

Indian Jungle Nightjar (I), Jungle Nightjar (F,N,R), Highland Nightjar (P)

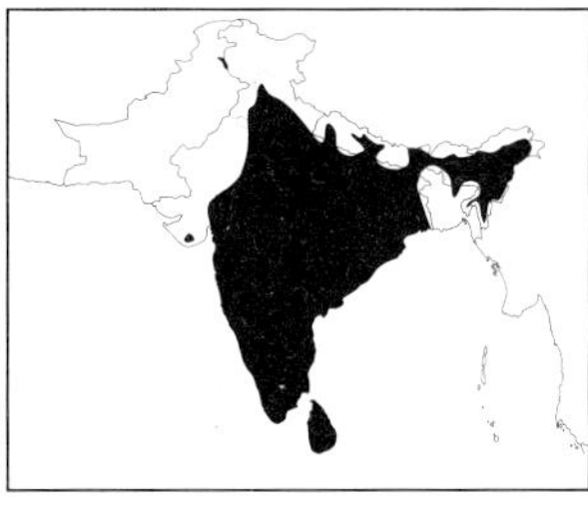

IDENTIFICATION (See also summary table.) 27–32 cm. Grey to grey-brown in coloration, and heavily marked with black; more cold-coloured and less strongly patterned than Large-tailed and Jerdon's Nightjars (p.444 and p.445). Has more uniform grey upperparts than those two species, lacking diffuse warm rufous-brown nuchal collar. Breast is dark grey-brown, lacking warm buff or brown tones. Further, has bold, irregular black markings on scapulars, usually lacking prominent pale edges (although some may show bold whitish or cold buff edges), variable but rather poorly defined greyish-white to rufous-buff spotting on coverts, and different tail pattern. Bold black markings on crown, mantle and scapulars, absence of rufous edges to scapulars, and different tail pattern are best distinctions from Savanna (p.445). See Eurasian (below) for differences from that species. **Male** has white spots on first four primaries, and white at tips of all but central tail feathers. **Female** has no white in primaries and no white in outer tail. **Racial variation** *C. i. hazarae* of Himalayas and NE subcontinent is larger and darker grey-brown in coloration compared with *C. i. indicus* and *C. i. kelaarti* of peninsular India/Sri Lanka; is more heavily marked with black, and has rufous-buff (rather than greyish-white or buffish) spotting on wing-coverts. **VOICE** Song of male is a loud, resonant *chunk-chunk-chunk-chunk...* etc, repeated rapidly at a rate of three or four notes per second, usually in a series of seven or eight before a brief pause; similar to call of Large-tailed, but the *chaunk* notes of that species are more widely spaced and resonant. Also has a more rapid, deeper and hoarser *quor-quor-quor*, possibly uttered by the female (Roberts 1991). **HABITS** A typical nightjar. **HABITAT** Forest clearings, open forest and scrub-covered hillsides. **BREEDING** February–June. Often lays eggs on a stony slope. **DISTRIBUTION AND STATUS** Resident, subject to local and altitudinal movements. Himalayas in N Pakistan and from W Himachal Pradesh east to Arunachal Pradesh; NE India and Bangladesh; south through C Punjab, E Rajasthan, E and S Gujarat, India, through the subcontinent. **PK:** common and very local summer visitor, mainly in Murree hills; 1800–2400 m. **NP:** fairly common; summers up to 2895 m, winters 180–915 m. **IN:** widespread and locally common; foothills up to 3000 m. **BT:** fairly common; 245–3390 m. **BD:** local. **LK:** rare in hills. **REFERENCES** Inskipp and Inskipp (1996).

EURASIAN NIGHTJAR *Caprimulgus europaeus* — Plate 31

European Nightjar (I,R)

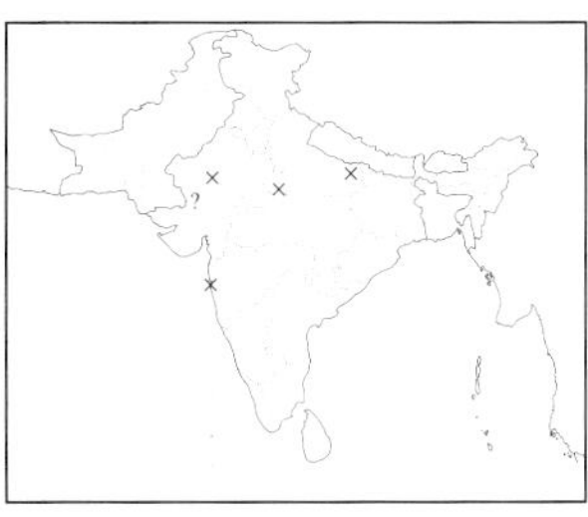

IDENTIFICATION (See also summary table.) 25 cm. A medium-sized, grey, well-streaked nightjar. Has regular, bold lanceolate streaking on crown, nape and scapulars, lacking on Savanna Nightjar (p.445), compared with which has longer wings and tail, and white throat patch is indistinct but generally complete; tail pattern of male is also different. More cleanly and regularly streaked than Grey (above), and generally paler grey in coloration. Has buffish outer edges to scapulars which form prominent line, and spotting on wing-coverts is usually more clearly defined. Rarely, can be pale sandy-grey or pale grey in coloration, when similar in appearance to Sykes's and Egyptian (p.444). Longer wings and tail, boldly streaked crown and scapulars, buff scapular line, and prominent buffish-white spots on coverts are main differences from Sykes's; see Egyptian for differences from that species. **Male** has white spots on first three primaries and on two pairs of outer tail feathers, whereas **female** lacks spots. **VOICE** Song of male comprises bouts of continuous purring and churring, very similar to that of Sykes's Nightjar but louder and varying in pitch; on the wing, male also has a low, soft *quoit quoit*, different from the *chuck-chuck* flight call of Sykes's (Roberts 1991). **HABITS** A typical nightjar. **HABITAT** Hills with rocky slopes and ridges and sparse bush cover. **BREEDING** May–August. Lays eggs on a stony slope or ravine. **DISTRIBUTION AND STATUS** Mainly a summer visitor and passage

IDENTIFICATION OF NIGHTJARS

Species	Size and structure	General coloration	Crown/nape
Grey Nightjar I = *C. i. indicus* H = *C. i. hazarae*	Medium. Well-proportioned, longish wings and tail, and large head	I - Uniform cold grey to grey-brown, heavily marked with black. H - Dark grey-brown, heavily marked with black	Variable. Heavily to very heavily marked with black drop-shaped streaks; some with irregular patches of rufous on nape. Streaking less regular and more extensive than on Large-tailed
Eurasian Nightjar	Medium. Long wings and tail, and small head	Grey, neat lanceolate streaking	Regular, bold, black lanceolate streaking
Egyptian Nightjar	Medium. Long wings and tail, and large head	Sandy with fine dark vermiculations and buff mottling	Relatively unmarked with fine dark streaking and irregular mottling
Sykes's Nightjar	Small. Shortish wings and tail, and large head	Grey, with buff mottling and restricted dark vermiculations. Some are as sandy as Egyptian	Variable, small dark arrowhead markings,more extensive than on Egyptian. Irregular buff spotting on nape gives suggestion of collar
Indian Nightjar	Small. Short wings and tail, and small head	Grey, with bold buff, black and some rufous markings	Bold, broad, black streaking on crown. Nape marked with rufous-buff, forming distinct collar
Large-tailed Nightjar	Large. Long-winged with long broad tail, and large head	More warmly coloured than Grey, with buff-brown tones, heavily marked with black and buff	Brownish-grey, with bold black streaks down centre. Diffuse pale rufous-brown band across nape
Jerdon's Nightjar	Medium. Relatively short-winged and short-tailed, and large head	Warmly coloured, as Large-tailed, though generally darker	As Large-tailed. More extensive rufous-brown coloration to nape and upper mantle
Savanna Nightjar	Medium. Shortish wings and tail, and large head	Dark brownish-grey, intricately patterned (without bold, dark streaking), but with variable rufous-buff markings	Variable. Some only finely vermiculated, others with black, arrowhead markings and others with irregular-shaped black markings

Scapulars/wing-coverts	Primaries	Tail	White throat patch
Scapulars heavily but irregularly marked with black, usually lacking well-defined buff or white edges (although pronounced pale edges may be prominent on some). Coverts with variable greyish-white to buffish spotting, usually poorly defined (I) or more rufous (H)	Male has small white spots on three or four primaries. On female, spots either lacking or small and rufous	I – Male variable, usually with white at tips of all but central tail feathers and with diffuse greyish margin at end. H – Male has more distinct blackish margin to white tips. Females of both races lack white on tail	Large central white spot on male, or buff in female
Bold lanceolate streaking on scapulars, with buff outer edge. Well-defined, regular pale buff spots on coverts	Male has large white spots on three primaries, and female has no spots	Outermost two tail feathers have broad white tips on male. No white tips on female	Indistinct, but generally complete white throat crescent
Scapulars relatively poorly patterned with buff and black inverted 'anchor-shaped' marks. Coverts with prominent irregular buff mottling	Male and female have no white spots	Tips on male are buff, but with no white spots	Generally has unbroken narrow white crescent
Scapulars relatively unmarked (with a few black inverted 'anchor-shaped' marks). Coverts with irregular and small buff markings	Male has large white spots on three or four primaries. Female's primary spots are buffish	On male, two outermost pairs have broad white tips. On female, tail is unmarked or has buffish tip to outer tail	Broken, large white patches at sides; some have complete crescent
Bold triangular black centres and broad rufous-buff fringes to scapulars. Coverts with bold buff- or rufous buff spotting	Both sexes have small white or buffish spots on four primaries	Both sexes have broad white tips to outer two tail feathers	Generally broken. Large white patches at sides, lacking on some
Scapulars have well-defined buff edges with bold wedge-shaped black centres. Coverts boldly tipped buff	Male has white spots on four primaries. Female lacks these or has smaller buff spots	Male has extensive white tips to two outermost feathers. Female has less extensive buff tips to outer two feathers	Large central white throat patch on both sexes
Much as Large-tailed	As Large-tailed	As Large-tailed	As Large-tailed
Scapulars variably marked, but most show rufous-buff outer web. Coverts variably marked with rufous-buff, showing as distinct spotting on some	Male has large white spots on four primaries, with buff to rufous-buff wash on female	Outer two tail feathers are mainly white on male, but not on female	Large white patches at sides

migrant. Pakistan and NW Gujarat. **PK:** common and widespread; summers in the dry inner mountain ranges of Chitral and Gilgit and throughout the Baluchistan hills; passage migrant in the Indus plains. **IN:** uncommon autumn passage migrant.

EGYPTIAN NIGHTJAR *Caprimulgus aegyptius* Plate 31

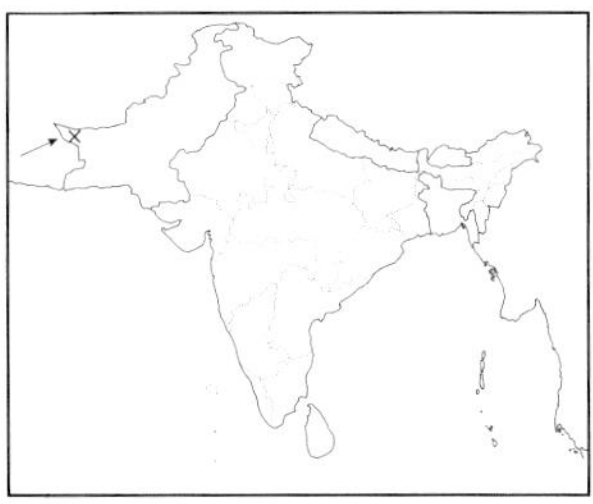

IDENTIFICATION (See also summary table.) 25 cm. A medium-sized sandy nightjar. Larger than Sykes's (below), with longer wings and tail. Very similar in plumage to some Sykes's, although crown and nape are relatively unmarked, with only fine dark streaking (Sykes's generally shows more pronounced small dark arrowhead-shaped markings on crown, and irregular buff spotting on nape forms indistinct collar); in addition, never shows any white in wings or tail. Some Eurasian (p.441) can be similarly coloured, but Egyptian has finely streaked crown, relatively unmarked scapulars with buff mottling and black 'inverted anchor-shaped' marks (lacking Eurasian's bold dark lanceolate streaking and white outer edges to scapulars), and coverts have prominent irregular buff mottling. **VOICE** Male's song comprises a regular and rapidly repeated *kowrr..kowrr..kowrr* etc, slowing down and becoming more regular towards the end, with chugging quality of distant motorboat; also a disyllabic and guttural *tuk-l tuk-l*, uttered in flight (Cramp 1985). **HABITS** Details not recorded in the region. Presumably the same as for other nightjars. **HABITAT** Semi-desert. **BREEDING** May–July. Eggs are laid on bare ground in the shelter of a boulder. **DISTRIBUTION AND STATUS PK:** rare summer visitor, confined to extreme W borders of the Chagai in the southwest.

SYKES'S NIGHTJAR *Caprimulgus mahrattensis* Plate 31

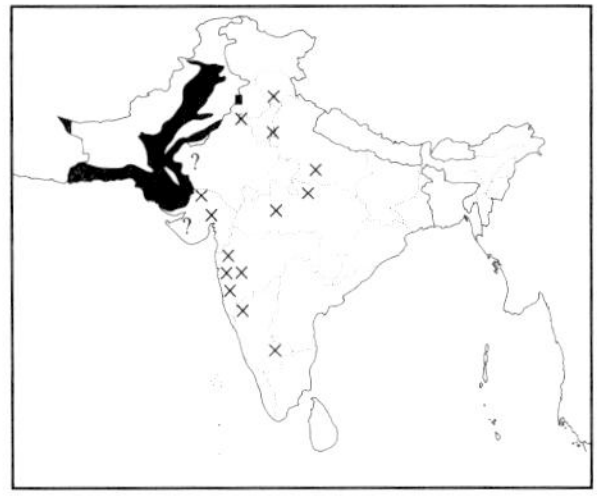

IDENTIFICATION (See also summary table.) 23 cm. A small, grey nightjar, generally lacking in warm brown or rufous markings. For differences from Eurasian and Egyptian (p.441 and above), which are similarly coloured, see those species. Compared with Indian, which is similarly proportioned, crown is much less heavily marked, lacks well-defined rufous-buff nuchal collar, scapulars are relatively unmarked (with a few black 'inverted anchor-shaped' marks), and central tail feathers are more strongly barred. **Male** has large white spots on first three primaries and white tips to outermost tail feathers. **Female** has buffish primary spots and buffish tips to outer tail feathers (latter may be lacking on some). **VOICE** Song of male comprises bouts of continuous purring and churring, very similar to Eurasian Nightjar's (p.441) but quieter and not varying in pitch; on the wing, male also has a low, soft *chuck-chuck*, which is different from the *quoit* call of Eurasian. **HABITS** A typical nightjar. Often calls while on the ground. Roosts on the ground, preferring the shade of a bush. **HABITAT** Breeds in semi-desert and sand dunes with scattered thorn bushes. Favours canalside roads or embankments when hunting, but avoids well-irrigated country. In winter, occurs in a wide variety of habitats. **BREEDING** February–August. Eggs are laid on bare ground in arid country in the shelter of a bush. **DISTRIBUTION AND STATUS** Resident, with some migratory movements. Breeds in Pakistan and Kutch; possibly breeds in Punjab, Saurashtra and Rajasthan, India; winters south to S Karnataka and east to C Uttar Pradesh. **PK:** common resident, subject to local movements. **IN:** rare resident and winter visitor. **REFERENCES** Abdulali and Hussain (1971).

LARGE-TAILED NIGHTJAR *Caprimulgus macrurus* Plate 31

Long-tailed Nightjar (F,I)

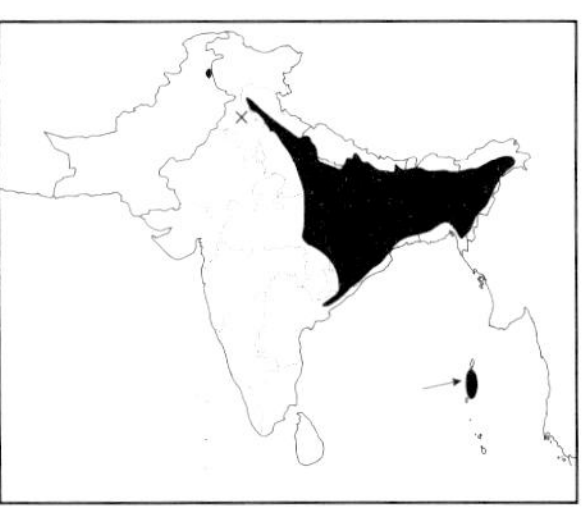

IDENTIFICATION (See also summary table.) 33 cm. A large, richly coloured nightjar, with longer and broader tail than Grey (p.441). More warmly coloured and strongly patterned than Grey, with grey and buff-browns contrasting strongly with black and warm buff markings. Further differences include diffuse pale rufous-brown nuchal collar, well-defined buff edges and bold wedge-shaped black centres to scapulars, broad buff tips to coverts forming wing-bar(s), and more extensive white or buff in outer tail feathers (lacking darker terminal bar shown by male Grey). **Male** has white spots on first four primaries and extensive white tips to outer two tail feathers. **Female** has buff rather than white primary spots and tips to outer tail feathers. **VOICE** Male's song is a series of loud, resonant calls: *chaunk-chaunk-chaunk-chaunk...* etc, repeated slowly and deliberately 4–20 times at the rate of about 100 per minute; call is usually likened to the sound of an axe striking a log; caution is needed, however, since shorter and softer calls have been noted which are similar to those of Grey Nightjar (Roberts 1991). **HABITS** A typical nightjar. Often squats on forest paths and roads at night. **HABITAT** Clearings and edges of tropical and subtropical forest; well-wooded ravines, also bamboo and semi-cultivation in NE India and mangrove swamps on Andaman Is. **BREEDING** February–May, varying locally. Lays eggs on bare ground or on a few dry leaves among scrub. **DISTRIBUTION AND STATUS** Resident and partial migrant. Himalayas in Murree, Pakistan, and from W Himachal Pradesh east to Arunachal Pradesh, south to Bangladesh, E Madhya Pradesh and NE Andhra Pradesh. **PK:** scarce and very local summer visitor; 460–900 m. **NP:** possibly resident; fairly common below 915 m, uncommon up to 1525 m. **IN:** locally fairly common; foothills up to 1800 m in Himalayas in summer, to 2400 m in the northeast. **BT:** uncommon. **BD:** common and widespread.

JERDON'S NIGHTJAR *Caprimulgus atripennis* — Plate 31

Horsfield's Jungle Nightjar, Long-tailed Nightjar (P), *C. macrurus atripennis* (I)

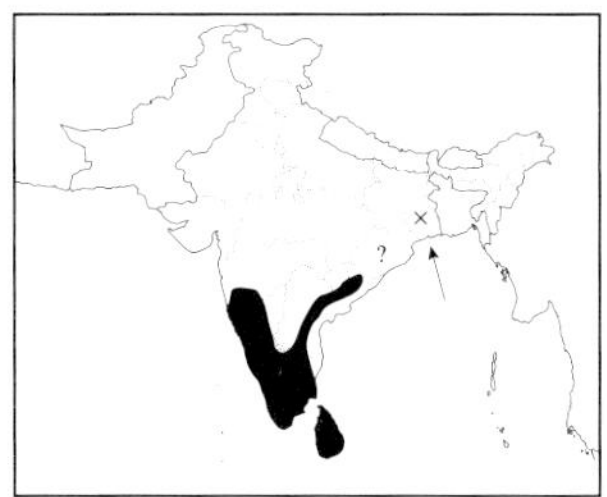

IDENTIFICATION (See also summary table.) 28 cm. A medium-sized, dark and richly coloured nightjar. More warmly coloured and strongly patterned than Grey (p.441), with browns and buffs contrasting more with black markings. Further differences include broad, diffuse rufous-brown band across nape/upper mantle, well-defined buff edges to scapulars, which have bold wedge-shaped black centres, and broad buff tips to coverts forming wing-bar, as well as more extensive white or buff in outer tail feathers (lacking darker terminal bar shown by male Grey). Smaller and shorter-tailed than Large-tailed (p.444), and is darker in coloration (with darker brown mantle and deeper rufous-brown band across nape), although otherwise very similar in plumage. **Male** has white spots on first four primaries and extensive white tips to outer two tail feathers. **Female** has buff rather than white primary spots (which may be lacking), and less extensive buff tips to outer tail feathers. **VOICE** A series of loud, liquid tremulous calls: *ch-wo-wo*, repeated at the rate of about 13–20 per minute. **HABITS** As those of Large-tailed. **HABITAT** Favours clearings and edges of bamboo and secondary jungle in evergreen and moist deciduous broadleaved forest; also well-wooded ravines in India. **BREEDING** February–July, varying locally. Lays eggs on bare ground among scrub. **DISTRIBUTION AND STATUS** Resident, endemic to the subcontinent. From S Maharashtra east to S Orissa and south through the peninsula and Sri Lanka. **IN:** locally fairly common; chiefly in foothills and up to 2000 m. **LK:** common in lowlands and lower hills of dry zone.

INDIAN NIGHTJAR *Caprimulgus asiaticus* — Plate 31

Common Indian Nightjar (I), Common Nightjar (P), Little Nightjar (F)

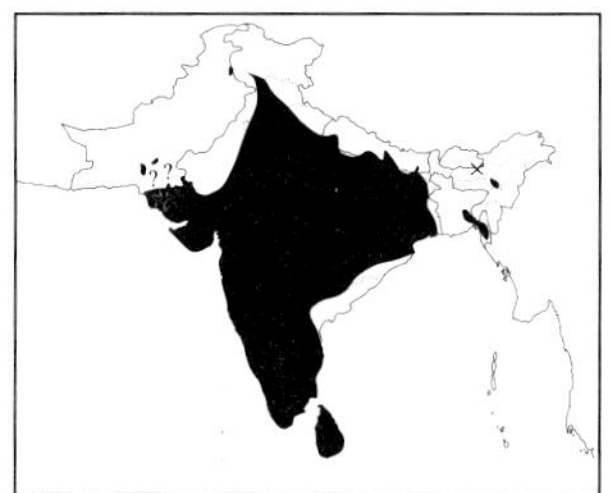

IDENTIFICATION (See also summary table.) 24 cm. A small, generally grey nightjar, although some are paler sandy-grey and others more brownish-grey in coloration. Best told by combination of small size and relatively short wings and tail, boldly streaked crown, rufous-buff markings on nape forming distinct collar, bold black centres and broad buff edges to scapulars, prominent buff or rufous-buff spotting on wing-coverts, and pale, relatively unmarked central tail feathers. In general appearance can be rather similar to Large-tailed Nightjar (p.444), although is much smaller and has pronounced rufous collar. Patterning of wings and tail is similar on both sexes. **VOICE** A far-carrying *chuk-chuk-chuk-chuk-tukaroo*, likened to ping-pong ball bouncing to rest on a hard surface; male in flight also has a short, sharp *qwit-qwit* (Roberts 1991). **HABITS** A typical nightjar. Often on cart tracks and roads after sunset. **HABITAT** Thinly wooded and scrub country, fallow cultivation with thickets, young plantations, and overgrown gardens in rural areas in dry plains and foothills. **BREEDING** January–October, varying locally. Lays eggs on ground in thin scrub. **DISTRIBUTION AND STATUS** Resident, subject to local movements. Mainly from S Pakistan and S Jammu and Kashmir south and east through the subcontinent, except N and C Nepal and much of the NE subcontinent and extreme E India. **PK:** locally common in the south. **NP:** movements uncertain, possibly resident; rare. **IN:** locally fairly common, and widespread; foothills up to 1500 m. **BD:** rare resident? **LK:** common in dry lowlands and lower hills, infrequent in wet zone.

SAVANNA NIGHTJAR *Caprimulgus affinis* — Plate 31

Franklin's Nightjar (F,I)

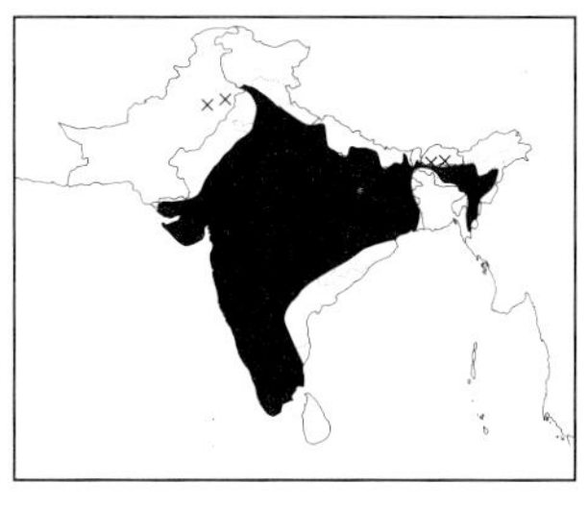

IDENTIFICATION (See also summary table.) 23 cm. A medium-sized, dark brownish-grey nightjar. Compared with Grey and Eurasian (p.441), crown and mantle are finely vermiculated, and lack bold dark streaking; has more uniform coverts with fine dark vermiculations and irregular rufous-buff markings, and scapulars are usually edged with rufous-buff. Male has distinctive tail pattern. **Male** has white spots on first four primaries, and outer tail feathers are all white except for greyish tips. **Female** has rufous-buff primary spots and lacks white in tail. **VOICE** A strident and shrill *dheet*, vehemently uttered at rest and in flight (Roberts 1991). **HABITS** A typical nightjar. **HABITAT** Open forest, stony hillsides and ravines with scattered scrub, dry stream beds with grass tussocks and bushes, and grassland with rocky outcrops. **BREEDING** March–August. Lays eggs on ground in a dry watercourse or in thin deciduous forest.

DISTRIBUTION AND STATUS Resident, subject to local movements. From N Pakistan east through S Nepal to NE India and Bangladesh; south through E Punjab, C Rajasthan and Gujarat, India, and throughout the peninsula except the extreme east. **PK:** common spring migrant to NW foothills, some remaining to breed. **NP:** movements unclear, possibly resident; common and widespread, but rather local; up to 250 m (–915 m). **IN:** locally common; plains and foothills up to 1800 m (–2400 m). **BT:** rare; 245–305 m. **BD:** local.

PIGEONS AND DOVES Columbidae

Pigeons and doves (small pigeons) are easily recognised by their stout compact body, rather short neck, and small head and bill. Their flight is swift and direct, with fast wingbeats, and on take-off and alighting the tail is widely fanned. Most species are gregarious outside the breeding season. Seeds, fruits, buds and leaves form their main diet, but many species also eat small invertebrates; terrestrial pigeons run about actively when feeding. Their voices are a soft plaintive cooing or booming, which is often monotonously repeated. Many pigeons have display flights in the breeding season, and males court females with a bowing display, bobbing the head with neck and breast puffed out while crooning. Pigeons build a shallow scanty nest of twigs, stems or roots in a tree, or on a ledge of a cliff or building. Many species in the subcontinent are migratory or nomadic, depending on food supplies. The main reference specific to pigeons is Goodwin (1967).

ROCK PIGEON *Columba livia* — Plate 32

Blue Rock Pigeon (F,I,P)

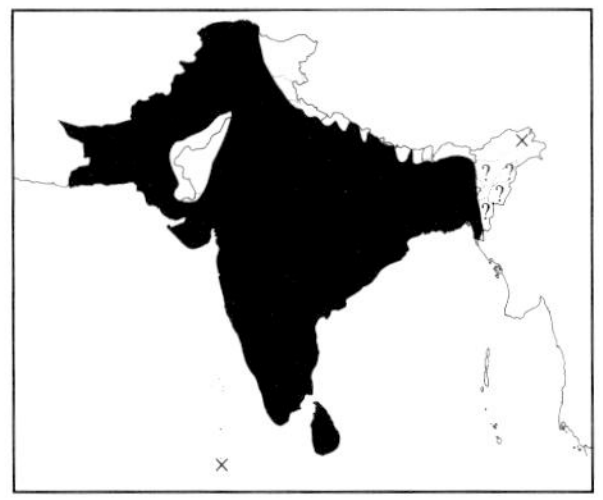

IDENTIFICATION 33 cm. **Adult** is greyish, with metallic green-and-purple sheen on neck, blackish terminal band on grey tail, and short, broad black bars across inner wing. Occurs throughout the subcontinent as feral and semi-feral populations, which vary considerably in coloration and patterning. In the high Himalayas, most similar to Hill Pigeon (below), but is darker grey and lacks whitish tail-band of that species. See also Yellow-eyed Pigeon (p.447). **Juvenile** is browner, with less pronounced iridescence, and black bar on greater coverts is less well developed; many feathers have pale fringes, resulting in scaly appearance. **Racial variation** *C. l. neglecta* of NW and N subcontinent typically has pale grey to whitish back, and is slightly paler grey on underparts, compared with *C. l. intermedia* of peninsular India and Sri Lanka, which has a grey back, almost concolorous with mantle and rump. **VOICE** A deep *gootr-goo, gootr-goo,...* etc uttered by courting male, and a deep, nasal *goo, goo, goo.* **HABITS** Lives in colonies all year. Wild birds roost on cliff ledges and in fissures in cliffs and ruins. Feeds chiefly in cultivation, mainly on seeds; also eats green shoots. **HABITAT** Large numbers of feral birds inhabit villages, towns and cities; wild birds frequent cliffs, gorges and ruins. **BREEDING** Almost all year, varying locally. Nests in holes and crevices of cliffs and ruined walls in the wild; feral birds nest in buildings, well shafts or holes in large tree trunks. **DISTRIBUTION AND STATUS** Resident. Throughout much of the subcontinent, except parts of the northwest and northeast. Both feral and wild populations occur. **PK:** common and widespread; from sea level up to 3355 m. **NP:** common and widespread; summers up to 4270 m, winters to at least 2810 m. **IN:** widespread and locally common; plains up to at least 3300 m. **BT:** common. **BD:** common throughout, mainly feral birds. **LK:** rare in coastal dry lowlands; breeds on offshore islands; feral birds common. **MV:** feral birds. **REFERENCES** Gibbs *et al.* (in press).

HILL PIGEON *Columba rupestris* — Plate 32

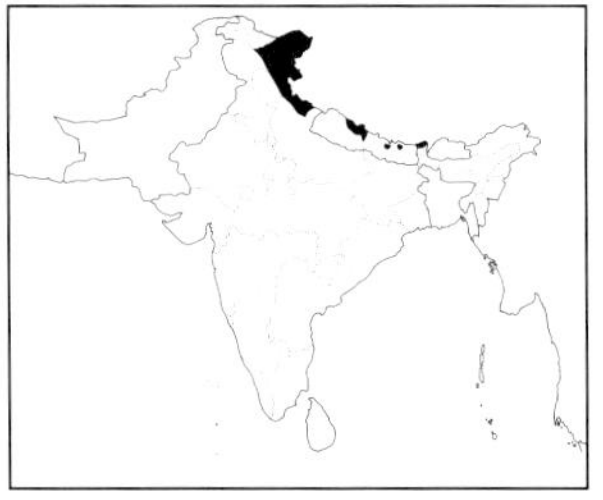

IDENTIFICATION 33 cm. A pale grey pigeon of the high Himalayas. **Adult** has metallic green-and-purple sheen on neck and breast, white band across tail, white back contrasting with grey rump, and blackish bars across inner wing. Paler grey coloration, and white band across centre of tail contrasting with blackish terminal band, are best distinctions from Rock Pigeon (above); further, white patch on back tends to be more extensive and more clearly defined than on Rock. **Juvenile** is generally browner than adult, and lacks iridescence; feathers of neck and breast are fringed with rusty-buff, and coverts are fringed with creamy-buff. **VOICE** A high-pitched, quickly repeated *gut-gut-gut-gut* (Ali and Ripley 1987). **HABITS** Similar to those of wild Rock. Often very tame. Feeds on grain in cultivation and along mule tracks. **HABITAT** Rocky cliffs, gorges, villages and *Caragana* scrub at high altitude, mainly in open trans-Himalayan country. **BREEDING** April–July. Nests in a hole or crevice in a cliff face or wall. **DISTRIBUTION AND STATUS** Resident, subject to altitudinal movements. Himalayas from N Pakistan east to Sikkim. **PK:** scarce in northernmost valleys. **NP:** common in trans-Himalayan areas; usually summers 2900–5490 m, sometimes winters down to 1650 m. **IN:** locally common; breeds 3000–5500 m, and forages above 6000 m in summer; winters above 1500 m. **REFERENCES** Gibbs *et al.* (in press).

SNOW PIGEON *Columba leuconota* Plate 32

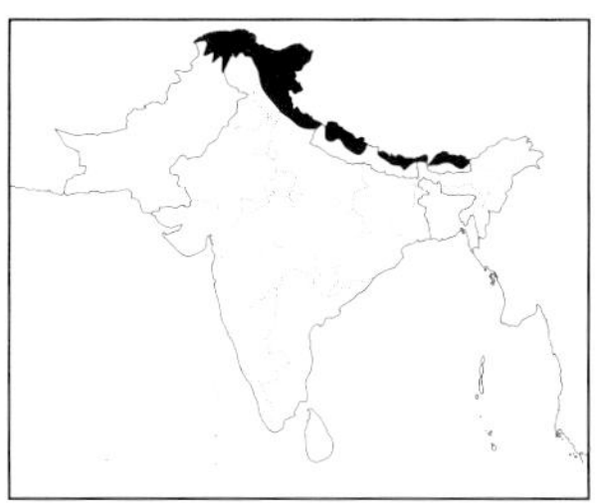

IDENTIFICATION 34 cm. A distinctive pigeon of the high Himalayas. **Adult** has slate-grey head, creamy-white collar and underparts, fawn-brown mantle contrasting with pale grey wing-coverts, white back contrasting with blackish rump and uppertail-coverts, and white band across blackish tail. At rest, tail pattern is similar to that of Hill Pigeon (p.446), but in flight white band is in shape of inverted V. **Juvenile** is similar to adult, but has greyish-buff wash to neck, breast and rest of underparts, and fine whitish fringes to coverts and scapulars. **VOICE** A prolonged, high-pitched *coo-ooo-ooo*, and during courtship utters a short croaking call not unlike a hiccup (Roberts 1991). **HABITS** Keeps in pairs and small parties in summer and in large flocks in winter. Forages on grass and rocky slopes and cultivation; in summer also at the edge of melting snow-fields. Eats mainly seeds and small bulbs. **HABITAT** Cliffs and gorges in mountains with plentiful rainfall; absent in dry steppe regions. **BREEDING** May–July. Nests colonially on ledges, in fissures of rock cliffs and in caves. **DISTRIBUTION AND STATUS** Resident, subject to altitudinal movements. Himalayas from N Pakistan east to Arunachal Pradesh. **PK:** frequent in restricted habitat in the north; 3050 m to at least 4060 m in summer, occasionally down to 1000 m in winter. **NP:** common and widespread; summers 3000–5200 m (–5700 m), winters above 1500 m. **IN:** locally common; breeds 3000–5100 m, winters down to 1500 m, occasionally to 750 m. **BT:** common.

YELLOW-EYED PIGEON *Columba eversmanni* Plate 32

Eastern Stock Pigeon (I), Pale-backed Pigeon, Pale-backed Eastern Stock Dove (R)

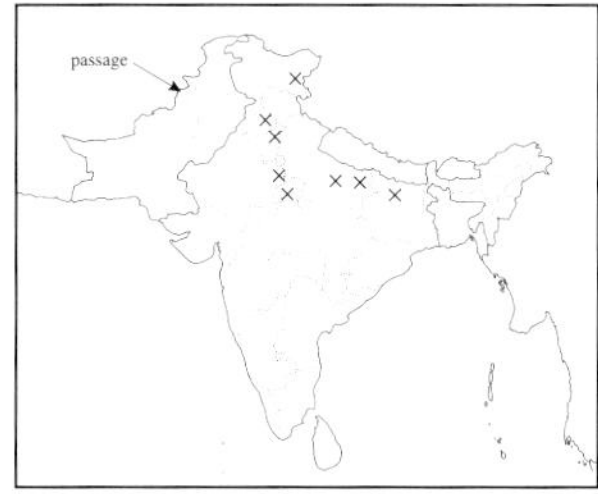

IDENTIFICATION 30 cm. **Adult** smaller and daintier than Rock Pigeon (p.446), and generally appearing paler. Iris and orbital skin are yellowish, and tip of bill can be distinctly yellowish (on Rock, iris is pale grey, dull brown or yellow, and orbital skin and bill are grey). Has diffuse greyish-brown fringes to grey mantle, scapulars, wing-coverts and tertials, usually resulting in pronounced brownish cast to upperparts; upperparts can, however, appear more uniformly grey (and much as Rock, although paler), or more uniformly brown and lacking distinct fringes. Black wing-bars are narrower and shorter than on Rock, with black confined to bases of a few inner greater coverts and (not always) tertials; and often has black bases to a few median coverts which may show as a third 'wing-bar'. Has purplish cast to grey crown and nape (lacking on Rock), and purplish-grey on the breast can be particularly extensive on some birds. Further, shows more extensive area of greyish-white on back and upper rump than in *neglecta* race of Rock; dark fringes to pale grey lower rump and uppertail-coverts are typically more pronounced; and green-and-purple iridescence on neck, mantle and breast is less extensive and less apparent. There is a slight difference in tail pattern: dark terminal band is less clear-cut than on Rock, and shows a diffuse paler, grey subterminal band. **Juvenile** is similar to adult (e.g. with yellow orbital skin), but iris is tinged brown, and lacks green-and-purple gloss. **VOICE** Usually silent, but gives quiet *oo-oo-oo* in breeding season (Gibbs *et al.* in press). **HABITS** Similar to those of Rock, but roosts in groves. Forages in small parties or flocks in nearby fields, often with Rock. Mainly granivorous; also eats mulberries plucked from trees. **HABITAT** Plains cultivation. **DISTRIBUTION AND STATUS** Winter visitor and passage migrant. Pakistan and N India (from Punjab and Jammu and Kashmir, east to N Bihar and south to N Madhya Pradesh). Globally threatened. **PK:** scarce; mainly in plains west of the Indus R or in immediate riverain areas. **IN:** generally rare, but large numbers have been seen in Harike, Punjab. **REFERENCES** Aspinall (1996), Cramp (1985), Crosby (1995), Robson (1996a).

COMMON WOOD PIGEON *Columba palumbus* Plate 32

Wood Pigeon (F,I)

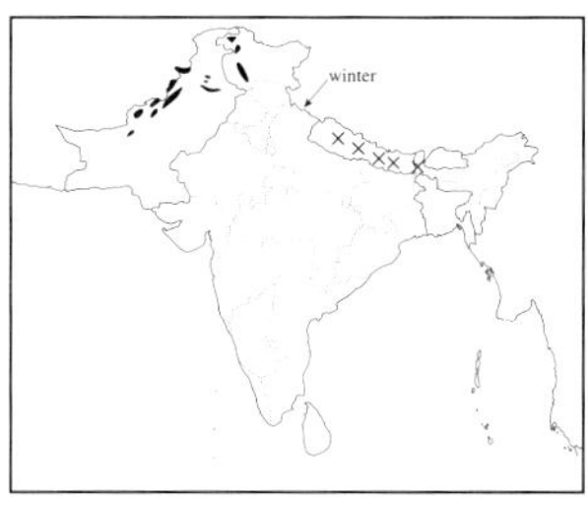

IDENTIFICATION 43 cm. Larger than Ashy Wood Pigeon (p.448). **Adult** has paler, grey-brown mantle, scapulars and inner wing-coverts (contrasting with grey of outer coverts), deep vinaceous underparts, white patch visible at bend of wing at rest, and more restricted patch of buff feather tips on sides of neck. In flight, white in coverts shows as prominent crescent, brownish mantle contrasts with grey back and rump, grey undertail-coverts are concolorous with base of tail, and shows distinct banding on tail: from above, grey band across centre of tail, which is only a shade paler than blackish terminal band; from below, however, central band is greyish-white and much more pronounced. **Juvenile** is duller and browner, and lacks green gloss and buff patch on neck. **VOICE** A deep, 'laid-back' and throaty *kookooo-koo... kookoo*, repeated three or four times. **HABITS** Usually found in small parties; sometimes in large flocks in the non-breeding season. Feeds on grain picked from crop stubbles, and acorns, berries and buds plucked from bushes and trees. Clambers among foliage while feeding; may hang upside-down to reach food items. **HABITAT** Scrub-covered and wooded hillsides, valleys and nullahs with oaks, junipers and firs; also cultivation. **BREEDING** April–August.

Nests on a horizontal branch or fork of a tree. **DISTRIBUTION AND STATUS** Resident, subject to erratic seasonal and altitudinal movements over considerable distances, depending on food supplies. Baluchistan, Pakistan, and from N Pakistan east to Kashmir; winters east to West Bengal. **PK:** scarce and very local resident; 700–2500 m. **NP:** erratic winter visitor, occurs in large flocks in some years but absent in others; 950–2275 m. **IN:** breeds 1500–3500 m, winters down to 800 m.

SPECKLED WOOD PIGEON *Columba hodgsonii* Plate 32

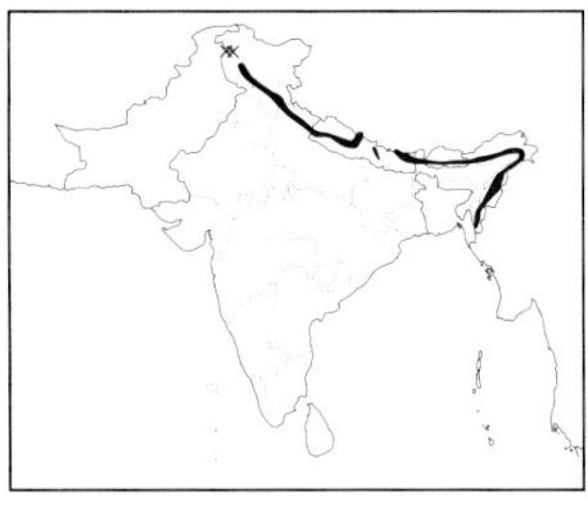

IDENTIFICATION 38 cm. Both sexes differ from Ashy Wood Pigeon (below) in lack of buff patch on neck, and in having white spotting on wing-coverts, 'speckled' underparts, and dark grey vent and undertail-coverts which are concolorous with underside of tail. Has dark grey bases to neck feathers, resulting in stippled effect. Like Ashy, shows very dark underwing and blackish uppertail and undertail in flight. **Male** has maroon mantle and wing-coverts, and maroon streaking on breast, becoming more solidly maroon on belly and flanks (with grey and buff feather edges resulting in pronounced 'speckling'). **Female** has brownish slate-grey upperparts and more uniform pale grey underparts, latter with dark grey feather centres giving rise to speckled effect. **Juvenile** is similar to female, but neck patterning is less distinct; has finer white tips to coverts, and underparts are more diffusely patterned. **VOICE** A deep *whock-whr-ooooo whroo* (Ali and Ripley 1987). **HABITS** Usually in pairs or small flocks. Mainly frugivorous and arboreal; sometimes feeds on grain in crop stubbles. Clambers about trees when feeding, like Common Wood Pigeon (p.447). **HABITAT** Mainly broadleaved oak/rhododendron forest, sometimes open country. **BREEDING** May and June. Nests in forest trees. **DISTRIBUTION AND STATUS** Resident, subject to irregular movements depending on food supplies. Himalayas from N Pakistan east to Arunachal Pradesh; NE Indian hills. **PK:** rare visitor. **NP:** resident, frequently recorded 1500–3050 m. **IN:** locally frequent resident; 1100–4000 m. **BT:** fairly common; from 1720 m up to at least 3355 m. **REFERENCES** Kaul *et al.* (1995), Singh (1995).

ASHY WOOD PIGEON *Columba pulchricollis* Plate 32

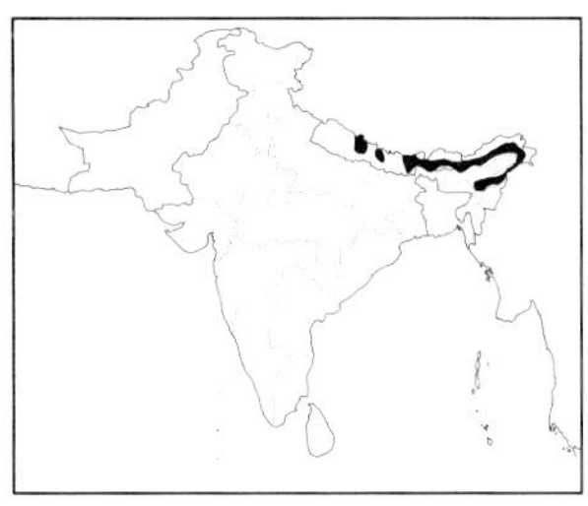

IDENTIFICATION 36 cm. **Adult** distinguished from Speckled Wood Pigeon (above) by combination of dark slate-grey upperparts, no white spotting on wing-coverts, uniform dark slate-grey breast without 'speckling', and creamy-buff belly and undertail-coverts which contrast with dark underside of tail. Has buff collar (at close range, rufous-buff tips to neck feathers contrast with dark bases, forming checkerboard pattern), and metallic green-and-purple sheen to lower neck and back. From Common Wood Pigeon (p.447) by dark grey appearance and smaller size, uniform slate-grey wings with no white wing patch, uniform blackish tail, and buff undertail-coverts. **Juvenile** has browner upperparts, with less distinct patterning on neck, and has rufous fringes to feathers of breast and belly. **VOICE** Deep, slightly booming *whuoo...whuoo...whuoo*, usually in well-spaced series of two to five (C. Robson). **HABITS** Keeps singly, in pairs or in small flocks. Chiefly arboreal and frugivorous; wanders in search of fruiting trees. Typically, sits very quietly, concealed among foliage in the canopy. **HABITAT** Dense broadleaved oak/rhododendron/chestnut subtropical and temperate forest. **BREEDING** Poorly known. May–August. Nests in trees. **DISTRIBUTION AND STATUS** Resident, subject to irregular movements. Himalayas from W Nepal east to Arunachal Pradesh; NE India. **NP:** frequent; 1100–2440 m. **IN:** status uncertain; 1200–3200 m, locally down to base of foothills. **BT:** uncommon; 1800–2100 m.

NILGIRI WOOD PIGEON *Columba elphinstonii* Plate 33

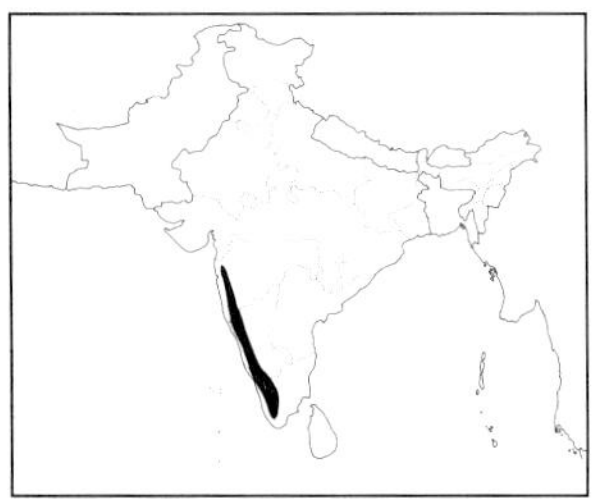

IDENTIFICATION 42 cm. A large, dark pigeon. Given its distribution, most likely to be confused with Mountain Imperial Pigeon (p.456). Is smaller than that species, with rapid flight action and more compact, streamlined appearance on the wing. Has darker maroon-brown upperparts, with uniform slate-grey tail (tail is distinctly banded on Mountain Imperial). **Adult** has black-and-white chequered pattern on hindneck, and purple-and-green gloss on mantle, foreneck and breast. **Juvenile** is similar to adult, but has less distinct chequered patterning on hindneck, almost lacks purple-and-green iridescence, and has chestnut fringes to mantle and coverts. **VOICE** A langur-like *who*, followed by three or four deep, quickly repeated *who-who-who* owl-like notes (Ali and Ripley 1987). **HABITS** Similar to those of Ashy (above). Occasionally also feeds on the forest floor. **HABITAT** Moist broadleaved evergreen forest; also cardamom sholas with tall shade trees in Kerala. **BREEDING** March–July. Nests in a moderate-sized tree, usually at elevations above 1000 m. **DISTRIBUTION AND STATUS IN:** resident, endemic to Western Ghats from N Maharashtra south to S Kerala and S Tamil Nadu; subject to nomadic movements; uncommon to common from foothills up to 2000 m. **REFERENCES** Gaston and Zacharias (1996).

SRI LANKA WOOD PIGEON *Columba torringtoni* Plate 33

Ceylon Wood Pigeon (I,P)

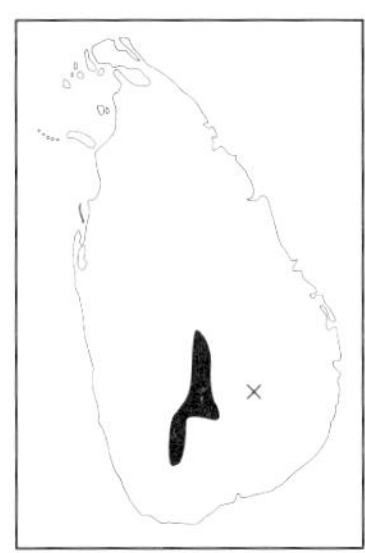

IDENTIFICATION 36 cm. A medium-sized, dark pigeon. **Adult** has dark slate-grey upperparts, including wings and tail, and lilac-grey head, neck and underparts (with darker, more purplish-grey breast); has black hindneck with white stippling, and strong purplish (and weaker green) gloss on mantle, sides of neck and breast. Given its distribution, really confusable only with Green Imperial Pigeon (p.455), but smaller size, checkerboard pattern on neck, grey upperparts including tail, and darker underparts with grey rather than maroon undertail-coverts are good distinctions. **Juvenile** has slaty-black upperparts, and diffuse chestnut fringes to grey underparts, and lacks adult's lilac and purplish coloration to head, neck, mantle and breast; feathers of hindneck are broadly tipped with grey. **VOICE** Mainly silent, but has a deep, owl-like *hoo* in courtship display (Henry 1971). **HABITS** Very shy. Usually in pairs except when roosting and feeding. Feeds in the forest canopy on fruits and berries, especially wild cinnamon. **HABITAT** Forest; sometimes fruiting trees in gardens and around villages. **BREEDING** Very little known. Nests above 7 m in trees. **DISTRIBUTION AND STATUS** Globally threatened. **LK:** endemic resident; breeds above 1650 m, regularly moves down to 300 m. **REFERENCES** Hoffmann (1984).

PALE-CAPPED PIGEON *Columba punicea* Plate 33

Purple Wood Pigeon (I,P)

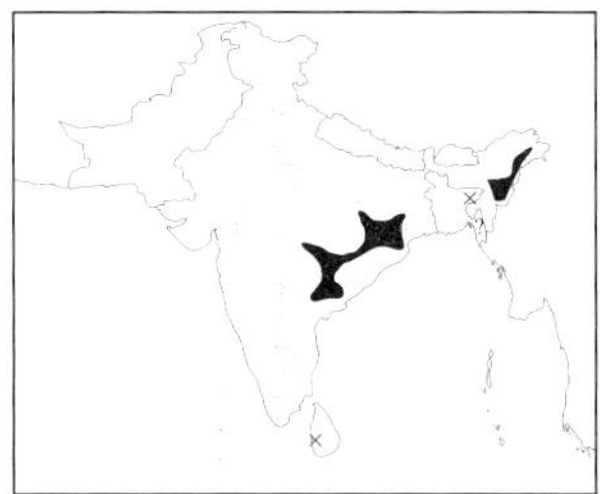

IDENTIFICATION 36 cm. **Adult** has greyish-white to grey crown and nape, giving rise to pale cap (which on some can be very striking and 'silvery-white' but on others much less distinct). Throat, foreneck and rest of underparts are vinaceous-chestnut, and mantle and wing-coverts are maroon-brown with metallic green-and-purple sheen. Uppertail-coverts and tail are dark slate-grey. Sexes are similar, but cap of female averages darker grey (although some are as pale as males). **Juvenile** initially has chestnut-brown cap, with pale grey feathers appearing progressively on forehead and over eye. Upperparts are browner with chestnut fringes, with less green-and-purple iridescence, and underparts are mixed grey and rufous-buff. **VOICE** A soft mew. **HABITS** Usually keeps singly or in small parties; also congregates where food is abundant. Feeds in trees on fruits and wild figs, on seeding bamboo, and on grain in fields. Perches quietly and inconspicuously among foliage. Has rather slow flight compared with others of the genus. **HABITAT** Forest, secondary growth and cultivation in tropical and subtropical zones. **BREEDING** May–August. Nests in a bush or bamboo clump in forest. **DISTRIBUTION AND STATUS** Resident. Mainly Eastern Ghats and NE India and Bangladesh. Globally threatened. **IN:** very rare and local; recorded recently only from Assam, but much of the species' range has been little visited by modern ornithologists. **BD:** rare resident? **LK:** vagrant. **REFERENCES** Choudhury (1994), Gibbs *et al.* (in press).

ANDAMAN WOOD PIGEON *Columba palumboides* Plate 33

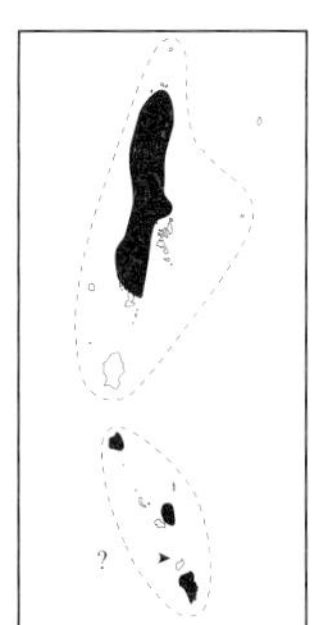

IDENTIFICATION 41 cm. **Male** has whitish head (with bluish-grey wash) merging into silvery-grey neck (on which dark grey feather bases form indistinct checkerboard patterning). Has dark slate-grey upperparts, and paler blue-grey underparts; upper mantle and breast have metallic green sheen, and feathers of rest of upperparts are variably fringed with metallic purple. Underwing and underside of tail appear almost blackish in flight. Has reddish cere, reddish bill with yellowish-white tip, and purplish-red orbital skin. **Female** has slightly darker, but still pale blue-grey, head and neck. **Juvenile** lacks metallic green and purple sheens and is darker and browner. Within its range, and especially when not seen well, adult is confusable with Green Imperial Pigeon (p.455), but that species has metallic green upperparts, including wings and tail, and paler grey underparts with contrasting maroon or chestnut undertail-coverts. Caution is required especially with respect to the Nicobar race of Green Imperial, which has darker (bluer, less metallic green) upperparts. From below, Andaman shows contrast between greyish-white throat and foreneck and darker grey breast, which is not apparent on Green Imperial. **VOICE** Series of lengthy, mellow, purring notes, usually a double *crroo-crroo* delivered every 6–9 seconds or so; readily confused with call of Green Imperial Pigeon, but less 'owl-like' and lacks the *currr* introductory notes often given by that species (P. Holt). **HABITS** Keeps in pairs or small parties. Wanders from one island to another in search of fruiting trees. Feeds on wild figs and other fruits. **HABITAT** Dense broadleaved evergreen forest. **BREEDING** Unknown. **DISTRIBUTION AND STATUS IN:** resident, endemic to Andaman and Nicobar Is (all three subgroups: Great Nicobar, Nancowry, and Car Nicobar and Batti Malv); uncommon on Andamans. **REFERENCES** Davidar *et al.* (1997), Sankaran (1998).

EUROPEAN TURTLE DOVE *Streptopelia turtur* — Plate 34

Turtle Dove (I), Western Turtle Dove (R)

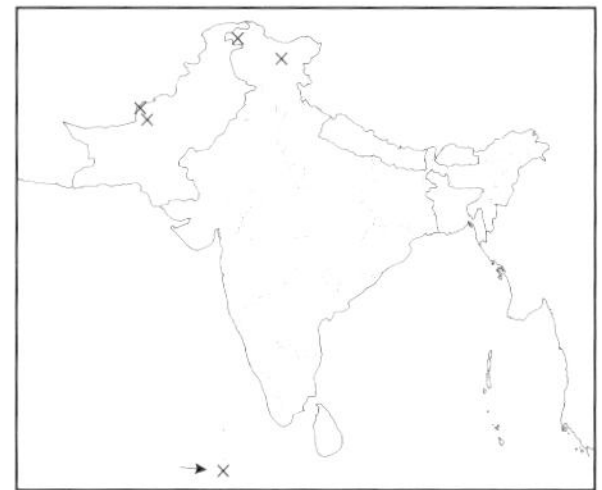

IDENTIFICATION 33 cm. **Adult** very closely resembles the resident W Himalayan race of Oriental Turtle Dove (below) *S. o. meena*, and like that race, has white sides and tip to tail (which are greyish in other races of Oriental). Distinguished from *meena* race of Oriental by a combination of features. Is smaller in size, slimmer in build, with proportionately longer, finer tail, and has more rapid, less heavy flight action. Shows little or no contrast between pale grey crown and nape, whereas *meena* has more contrasting grey crown and warm brown nape; has broader, paler rufous-buff fringes to scapulars and wing-coverts, compared with more contrasting rounded blackish centres and bright rufous fringes to these feathers on *meena*; and rump and uppertail-coverts tend to be more buffish- or brownish-grey (darker, bluish-grey, on Oriental). The black neck feathers are typically tipped white or greyish-white, forming three or four distinct rows, whereas these feathers are typically tipped bluish-grey on Oriental, forming four to six discrete rows. Breast is greyish-pink on European (lacking brown or rufous tones of Oriental), becoming whitish on belly and undertail-coverts (more extensive and strikingly so than on *meena*). **Juvenile** lacks neck-barring of adult; has head and underparts sandy-grey, with buff fringes to greyish-centred feathers of scapulars and wing-coverts. More closely resembles Eurasian Collared Dove (p.451) in this plumage, but note scaled appearance to upperparts and lack of broken neck-ring. Distinguished from juvenile Oriental by paler head, mantle and underparts, less prominent pale fringes (with paler centres) to wing-coverts and scapulars, and less sharply defined, more buff-tinged fringes to primaries compared with well-defined rufous margins on Oriental. **VOICE** A throaty purr, *rroorrrr, rroorrrr, rroorrr*, uttered mainly on the breeding grounds. **HABITS** Similar to those of Oriental Turtle Dove. **HABITAT** Open cultivation, mainly in drier mountain valleys. **DISTRIBUTION AND STATUS PK, IN, MV:** vagrant. **REFERENCES** Hirschfeld (1992), Gibbs *et al.* (in press).

ORIENTAL TURTLE DOVE *Streptopelia orientalis* — Plate 34

Rufous Turtle Dove (F,I,P), Eastern Rufous Turtle Dove (R)

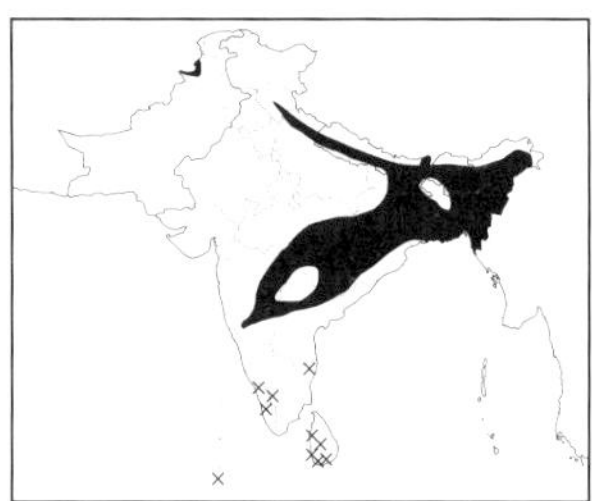

IDENTIFICATION 33 cm. A stocky, dusky-plumaged dove, recalling Rock Pigeon (p.446) in shape and flight action. Usually readily distinguished throughout its range by combination of rufous-scaled scapulars and wing-coverts, brownish-grey to dusky maroon-pink underparts, and black and (usually) bluish-grey barring on sides of neck. See European Turtle Dove (above), however, for main differences from that species. In flight, has dusky grey underwing and, in all but one Indian race, grey sides and tip to tail (white on other *Streptopelia* species occurring in the subcontinent). **Immature** is quite different in coloration, with buffish-grey head and underparts, and pale buff fringes to dark-centred feathers of scapulars and wing-coverts. In this plumage more closely resembles Eurasian Collared Dove (p.451), but is stockier in appearance, lacks black neck-ring and has scaled upperparts. **Racial variation** Compared with other races in the subcontinent, the W Himalayan race *S. o. meena* has white rather than grey sides and tip to tail, white rather than grey undertail-coverts, and paler underparts. *S. o. agricola* (E Himalayas and NE India) has deeper vinaceous-pink tinge to head, neck and underparts. *S. o. erythrocephala* of peninsular India has reddish-brown head, neck and mantle. **VOICE** A hoarse, mournful, repeated *goor... gur-grugroo.* **HABITS** Found singly or in pairs when breeding, and in small parties in winter; may form flocks when migrating. A ground-feeder, gleaning grain from cultivation; also eats grass, bamboo and weed seeds, and often forages on dusty tracks. **HABITAT** Open forest, mainly broadleaved, sometimes coniferous, often near cultivation and orchards. **BREEDING** May–July. Nests in a bush, young tree or bamboo clump. **DISTRIBUTION AND STATUS** Resident and winter visitor to Himalayas, NE India, Bangladesh and C and E peninsular India south to N Karnataka. Winter visitor to much of N and W India south to S Maharashtra, except the arid northwest. Subject to local migratory movements, depending on food supply. **PK:** widespread and common summer visitor to N Himalayas, breeding 2135–3350 m; winters in foothills. **NP:** common resident and winter visitor; summers 365–4570 m, winters mainly below 1370 m, occasionally up to 2000 m. **IN:** locally common resident and winter visitor; breeds in Himalayas from foothills up to 4000 m, winters in foothills. **BT:** common resident; foothills up to at least 4060 m. **BD:** locally common resident and winter visitor. **LK:** rare winter visitor, mainly to the north. **MV:** irregular winter visitor.

LAUGHING DOVE *Streptopelia senegalensis* — Plate 34

Little Brown Dove (F,I)

IDENTIFICATION 27 cm. A slim, small dove with fairly long tail, most likely to be confused with Spotted Dove (p.451). Distinguished by smaller size and slighter appearance, brownish-pink coloration to head, neck and breast, uniform unspotted upperparts, and black stippling on upper breast. **Juvenile** has duller pinkish-brown head, neck and breast (lacking black stippling), and whitish fringes to fawn-brown scapulars and grey coverts. Lack of black neck-ring, and slimmer appearance with longer tail, help separate from adult Eurasian Collared Dove (p.451).

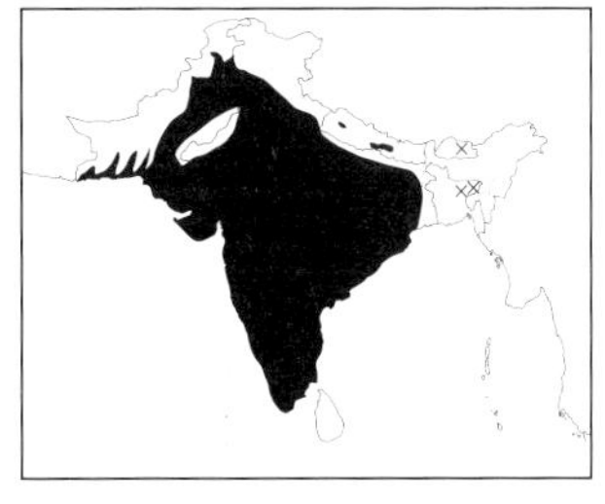

VOICE A soft, pleasant *coo-rooroo-rooroo* or *cru-do-do-do-do*. **HABITS** Similar to those of Oriental Turtle Dove (p.450), but often congregates in flocks where food is abundant, sometimes with Eurasian Collared and Red Collared Doves (below). **HABITAT** Cultivation around villages, and stony and scrub-covered hills in dry country. **BREEDING** Almost all year. Nests in a low bush, *Euphorbia* clump or date palm. **DISTRIBUTION AND STATUS** Resident, subject to local and some altitudinal movements. Throughout much of the subcontinent, except most of the Himalayas, the northeast and Sri Lanka. **PK:** common and widespread resident; summers locally up to 2400 m. **NP:** scarce, status and movements uncertain; recorded 610–2440 m. **IN:** common resident; plains up to 1500 m in peninsular hills. **BT:** uncommon. **BD:** vagrant.

SPOTTED DOVE *Streptopelia chinensis* — Plate 34

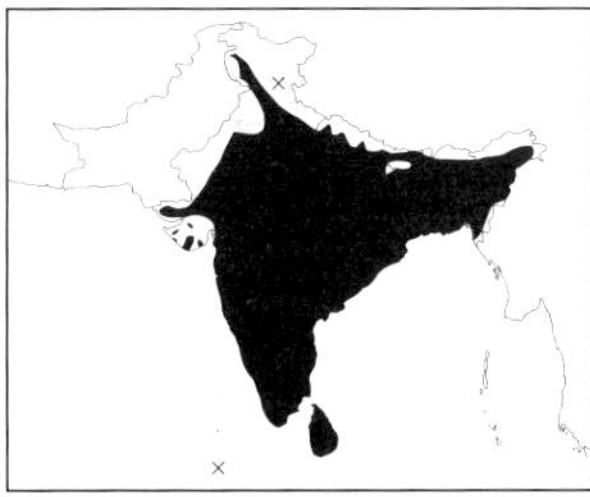

IDENTIFICATION 30 cm. Superficially resembles Eurasian Collared Dove (below), but upperparts are scaled or spotted with pinkish-buff (rather than uniform sandy-brown). Further, has extensive black-and-white chequered patches on sides of neck which meet on nape, grey cast to crown and ear-coverts contrasting with strongly vinaceous-pink tinged upper nape and neck sides, throat and breast, and darker grey-brown rump and tail with blackish base to outer tail feathers. **Juvenile** is paler and browner, lacks chequered patch on sides of neck, and has faintly barred mantle and scapulars, and narrow rufous fringes to wing-coverts. **Racial variation** Compared with other races in the subcontinent, *S. c. tigrina* of NE India (south of Brahmaputra R) and Bangladesh lacks the heavily spotted appearance on the upperparts, having narrow buff fringes at tips of the feathers. **VOICE** A soft, mournful *krookruk-krukroo..., kroo-kroo-kroo* (Ali and Ripley 1987). **HABITS** Similar to those of Oriental Turtle Dove (p.450). When disturbed, bursts upwards with a noisy clatter of wings, then glides down to settle nearby. **HABITAT** Gardens, cultivation, around villages and towns, open moist deciduous forest; also subtropical pine forest in Pakistan; prefers more wooded and wetter habitats than Laughing or Eurasian Collared Doves. **BREEDING** Almost all year, varying locally. Nests fairly low down in a tree, thorn bush, bamboo clump or palm. **DISTRIBUTION AND STATUS** Resident, subject to local movements. Throughout much of the subcontinent, except most of the northwest and N Himalayas. **PK:** common summer visitor to subtropical pines in Himalayan foothills; a few winter in adjacent plains. **NP:** common resident below 1500 m, frequent up to 2000 m (–4000 m). **IN:** common and widespread resident; plains up to 2400 m in Himalayas, to 1500 m in peninsular hills. **BT:** common resident; 250–1830 m. **BD, LK:** common resident throughout. **MV:** vagrant. **REFERENCES** Gibbs *et al.* (in press).

RED COLLARED DOVE *Streptopelia tranquebarica* — Plate 34

Red Turtle Dove (F,I,K,N)

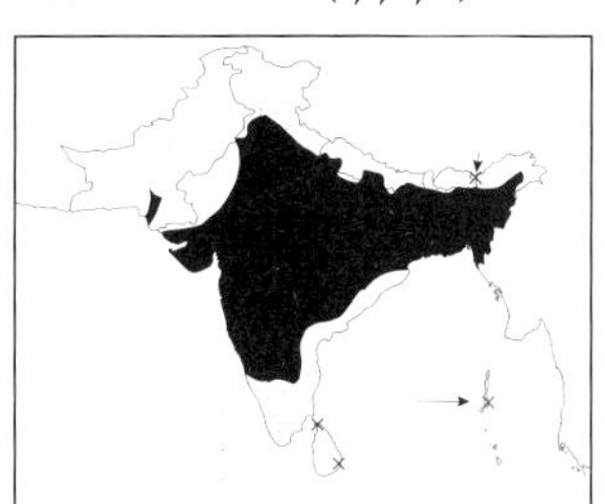

IDENTIFICATION 23 cm. A small, stocky dove with black half-collar and striking greyish-white sides to tail. **Male** easily distinguished from the similar Eurasian Collared Dove (below) by blue-grey head, pinkish-maroon mantle and wing-coverts, and deep pink underparts. **Female** is very similar in coloration to Eurasian, but has darker buffish-grey underparts and slightly darker fawn-brown upperparts, and is much smaller and more compact. In flight, shows greyer underwing-coverts, distinctly shorter tail with less white at tip of outer feathers, and white undertail-coverts. **Juvenile** lacks neck-collar, and feathers of upperparts and breast are fringed with buff; primary coverts have rufous tips. **VOICE** A harsh, rolling, repeated *groo-gurr-goo*. **HABITS** Similar to those of Laughing Dove (p.450), but less associated with human habitation and cultivation than other doves. **HABITAT** Open country and cultivation with some trees, scrub jungle, and light woodland; in Pakistan, prefers more wooded areas such as canal or roadside plantations. **BREEDING** All year, varying locally. Nests in trees 3–8 m above ground. **DISTRIBUTION AND STATUS** Resident, subject to local movements. Throughout much of the subcontinent, except most of the northwest, N Himalayas, S and extreme E India. **PK:** mainly a summer visitor, a few overwintering in lower Sind; common in Punjab plains. **NP:** fairly common resident throughout below 300 m; uncommon in summer up to 1370 m. **IN:** locally fairly common resident; plains up to 1300 m. **BT:** rare. **BD:** common resident throughout. **LK:** vagrant to dry coastal lowlands; has bred once. **REFERENCES** Gibbs *et al.* (in press).

EURASIAN COLLARED DOVE *Streptopelia decaocto* — Plate 34

Indian Ring Dove (F,I), Collared Dove (K,P)

IDENTIFICATION 32 cm. A sandy-brown dove with black half-collar, white sides to tail, and white underwing-coverts. Confusable really only with female Red Collared Dove (above), but is larger, with longer tail, and has paler fawn upperparts, paler pinkish-grey underparts with grey undertail-coverts, more white at tip of tail, and

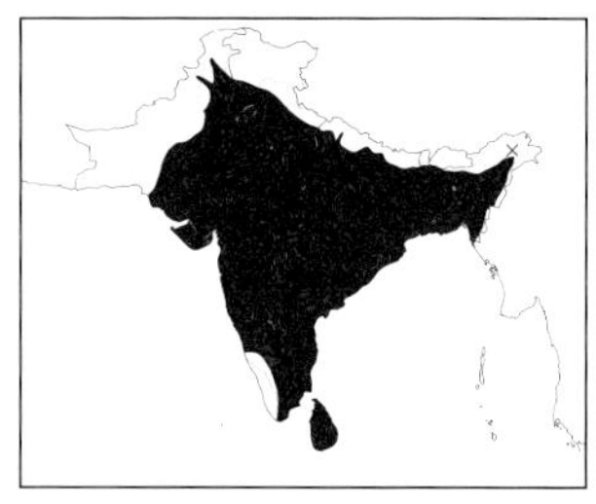

whiter underwing. **Juvenile** lacks neck-collar, and feathers of upperparts are fringed with buff. **VOICE** A pleasant, repeated cooing, *kukkoo ... kook.* **HABITS** Similar to those of Laughing Dove (p.450). **HABITAT** Open dry country with cultivation and groves of deciduous trees; also desert areas in Pakistan. **BREEDING** All year, varying locally. Nests low down in a bush or small tree, occasionally in outbuildings. **DISTRIBUTION AND STATUS** Resident, subject to marked seasonal and altitudinal movements. Throughout much of the subcontinent, except W Pakistan, most of Himalayas and SW India. **PK:** common resident in the plains; summer visitor to the cultivated valleys of Baluchistan and NW Pakistan. **NP:** fairly common resident; below 400 m (–2440 m). **IN:** widespread and locally common; plains up to 2400 m in summer in W Himalayas. **BT:** fairly common and local; 240–350 m. **BD:** common throughout. **LK:** common in dry N coastal belt.

BARRED CUCKOO DOVE *Macropygia unchall* — Plate 34

Bar-tailed Cuckoo Dove (I), Long-tailed Cuckoo Dove (F)

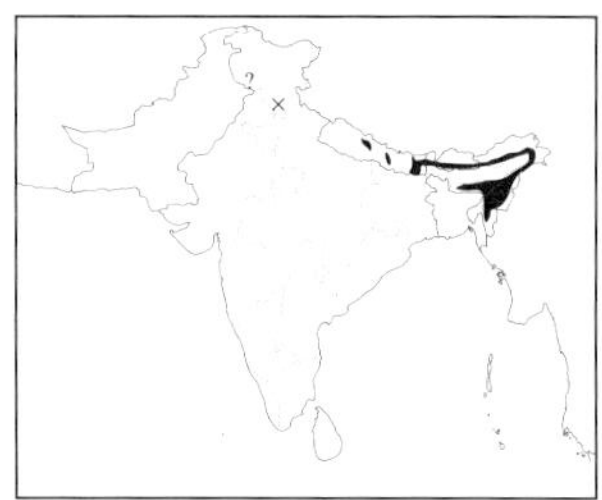

IDENTIFICATION 41 cm. A distinctive, forest-dwelling dove with long, graduated tail and slim body. Long tail and upright stance give species a cuckoo-like appearance. Upperparts and tail are rufous and profusely barred with dark brown. **Male** has buffish head and underparts, metallic purple-and-green gloss to crown and nape, extending onto upper breast, and limited dark brown barring on neck sides and upper breast. Lower breast and rest of underparts lack barring. **Female** and **juvenile** have yellowish-brown head, neck and breast which are barred with dark brown, with green-and-purple gloss restricted to nape and sides of neck. **VOICE** A very deep *croo-umm*, the second syllable a booming note, audible a long way off. Heard in the distance as a low, muffled single *umm* repeated at short intervals (Ali and Ripley 1987). **HABITS** Found in pairs and small flocks. Feeds on berries, acorns and shoots in forest trees, clambering about and sometimes swinging upside-down to reach food items. Also gleans grain and seeds from cultivation in forest clearings. **HABITAT** Dense broadleaved evergreen and secondary forest in tropical, subtropical and temperate zones. **BREEDING** May–July. Nests 2–8 m up in small forest tree. **DISTRIBUTION AND STATUS** Resident. Himalayas from WC Nepal east to Arunachal Pradesh; NE Indian hills. **NP:** scarce in centre and east; 250–2800 m. **IN:** locally frequent; 150–2700 m. **BT:** fairly common; 250–2590 m.

ANDAMAN CUCKOO DOVE *Macropygia rufipennis* — Plate 34

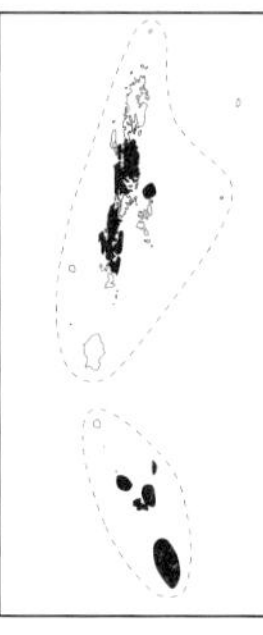

IDENTIFICATION 41 cm. A slim rufous and brown dove with a long graduated tail. Feathers of brown upperparts are fringed with rufous. In flight, shows rufous flash across (inner webs of) primaries and rufous underwing-coverts. Note that Barred Cuckoo Dove (above) does not occur in the Andaman and Nicobar Is. **Male** has brown barring across breast and belly, and unmarked rufous head. **Female** and **juvenile** have black mottling on crown and nape, and unbarred underparts. **VOICE** A hoarse, deep, subdued croaking *o-o-o-o-ah*, repeated several times (Ali and Ripley 1987). **HABITS** Similar to those of Barred Cuckoo Dove. **HABITAT** Dense broadleaved evergreen and secondary forest. **BREEDING** Unknown. Possibly February. **DISTRIBUTION AND STATUS IN:** resident, endemic to Andaman Is, Nancowry subgroup and Great Nicobar Is; locally frequent on Andamans, scarce on Nicobars. **REFERENCES** Davidar *et al.* (1997), Sankaran (1998).

EMERALD DOVE *Chalcophaps indica* — Plate 34

Green-winged Pigeon (K), Bronze-winged Dove (P)

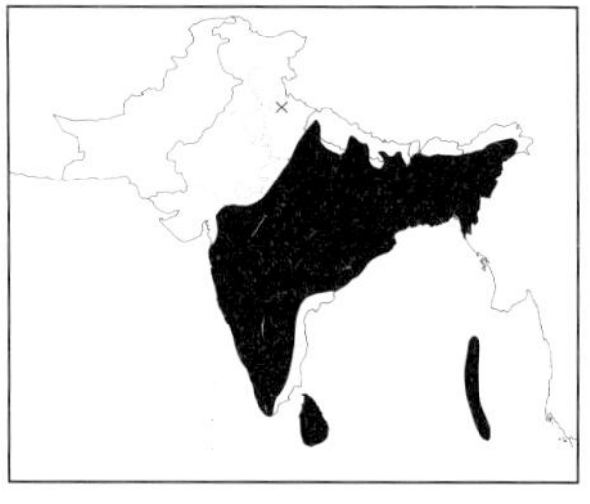

IDENTIFICATION 27 cm. A stout, broad-winged, short-tailed pigeon with emerald-green upperparts. Typically very rapid in flight, and allows only brief views on being flushed from forest floor, when shows black-and-white banding on back. **Male** has grey crown, white forehead and supercilium, and deep vinaceous-pink head sides and underparts; has white shoulder patch. **Female** is warm brown on crown, neck and underparts, has forehead and supercilium suffused with grey, and shoulder patch is generally warm brown. Some females (presumably older birds) are more similar to males. **Juvenile** resembles female, but has dark grey barring on buffy-white forehead, narrow buff fringes (and some dark subterminal bars) to neck and underparts, dark brown tertials with chestnut tips, brown primaries with chestnut edges and tips, rufous-brown rump, and brownish bill. **Racial variation** Male of Sri Lankan race *C. i. robinsoni* has grey of crown extending as broad line down sides of neck to upper mantle. **VOICE** A mournful, booming *tk-hoon...tk-hoon* (Henry 1971). **HABITS** Keeps singly or in pairs. Feeds on the ground, often on forest tracks, on seeds, grain and fallen berries. Frequently seen flying away rapidly and directly through the forest, only a few metres from the ground. **HABITAT** Broadleaved evergreen and moist deciduous forest and dense secondary growth, mainly in the tropical and subtropical zones. **BREEDING** Almost all year, varying locally. Nests in trees, shrubs and bamboo clumps in forest. **DISTRIBUTION AND STATUS** Sedentary resident. Mainly Himalayas from W Nepal east to Arunachal Pradesh, and south to Bangladesh, SE Gujarat and south through the rest of the subcontinent. **NP:** locally common; mainly below 365 m (–1200 m). **IN:** locally common; occurs patchily throughout up to 1800 m. **BT:** frequent; 245–930 m. **BD:** locally common throughout. **LK:** common resident throughout. **REFERENCES** Gibbs *et al.* (in press).

NICOBAR PIGEON *Caloenas nicobarica* — Plate 35

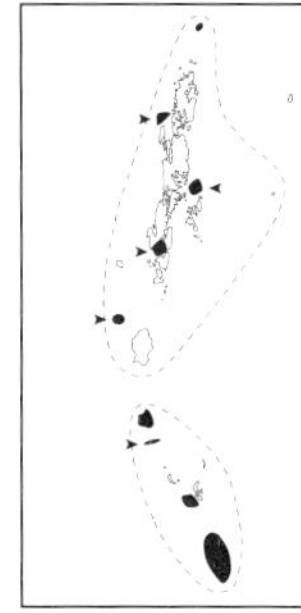

IDENTIFICATION 41 cm. A stocky, short-tailed pigeon. At rest, **adult** has long blue-black, metallic green and copper neck hackles which extend across mantle, metallic green-and-bronze back and wing-coverts, and white tail. **Juvenile** is duller, lacks neck hackles, and has a blackish tail. **Immature** has hackles, but tail remains black. **VOICE** Typically silent, although has harsh guttural croak. A short deep but soft cooing (Heinroth in Goodwin 1967). A pig-like grunting given when threatening others (Goodwin 1967). **HABITS** Occurs singly or in small parties. Forages actively on the forest floor for fruits and seeds. When disturbed, it flies up swiftly with a noisy flutter into thick foliage in the treetops. Readily flies long distances from island to island in search of food. **HABITAT** Dense broadleaved evergreen forest where human interference is least. **BREEDING** January–April. Nests in forest trees, often several nests in one tree. **DISTRIBUTION AND STATUS IN:** resident on Nicobar Is (Nancowry, Camorta and Car Nicobar), where locally common; straggler to Andaman Is. **REFERENCES** Sankaran and Vijayan (1993).

ORANGE-BREASTED GREEN PIGEON *Treron bicincta* — Plate 35

Orange-breasted Pigeon (K)

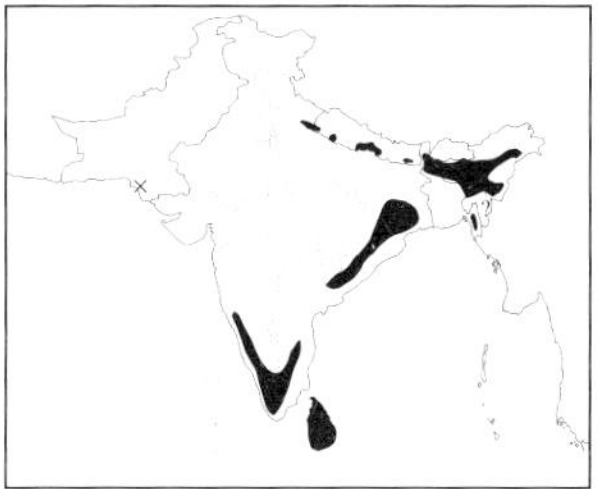

IDENTIFICATION 29 cm. **Male** distinguished from other green pigeons by combination of small size, orange breast bordered above by lilac band, and yellowish-green forehead merging into pale blue-grey hindcrown and nape. Mantle is uniformly green, unlike on male Pompadour Green Pigeon (below) and Thick-billed Green Pigeon (p.454). Central tail feathers are grey with slightly paler tip (green on Pompadour and Thick-billed). At rest, tail therefore appears grey rather than green, while, in flight, shows pronounced pale grey tips to rest of tail feathers, which are dark slate-grey (as on other species). **Female** lacks lilac and orange on breast, and is best told from other green pigeons by combination of strong yellow cast to breast and belly, green forehead and forecrown merging into grey hindcrown and nape, and grey central tail feathers. In Sri Lanka, lacks pronounced yellow throat of female Pompadour there. **VOICE** Mellow, wandering whistle, as other green pigeons; also a subdued gurgling (Ali and Ripley 1987). **HABITS** Normally found in small flocks, which unite into large ones where food is plentiful. Often in mixed feeding parties with other fruit-eating birds, such as other green pigeons, barbets and hornbills. Usually keeps to the tops of tall trees, coming to the ground to drink or to pick up earth at salt-licks. Eats ripe wild figs and other fruits and berries. Clambers about twigs with great agility to reach fruit, sometimes hanging upside-down. Keeps well concealed in the foliage; when approached, 'freezes' and becomes very hard to detect. When flushed, the wings make a loud clatter as the bird bursts out of tree. Often suns itself in treetops in early mornings and evenings. **HABITAT** Broadleaved evergreen and moist deciduous forest and well-wooded country in the subtropical zone. **BREEDING** December–September, varying locally. Nests in a moderate-sized tree or cane brake. **DISTRIBUTION AND STATUS** Resident, subject to local movements. Himalayas from N Uttar Pradesh east to S Arunachal Pradesh; NE India, Bangladesh, hills of E, S and SW India, and Sri Lanka. **PK:** vagrant. **NP:** locally distributed below 305 m; common at Chitwan, uncommon or rare elsewhere. **IN:** uncommon; from plains up to 1000 m in peninsular hills, to 1500 m in Himalayas. **BT:** local and uncommon. **BD:** local resident. **LK:** common in lowlands, more frequent in dry zone; occasional visitor to foothills.

POMPADOUR GREEN PIGEON *Treron pompadora* — Plate 35

Pompadour Pigeon (K), Gray-fronted Green Pigeon (F)

IDENTIFICATION 28 cm. **Male**, with maroon mantle, resembles Thick-billed Green Pigeon (p.454). Main differences are thinner blue-grey bill (without prominent red base), and lack of extensive greenish orbital skin. Where ranges overlap, male Pompadour has diffuse orange patch on breast, greenish-yellow throat, and uniform chestnut undertail-coverts, which are further differences from Thick-billed. **Female** lacks maroon mantle, as does female Thick-billed, and is best told by differences in bill and orbital skin (as for male). Also, where ranges overlap, undertail-coverts appear streaked rather than barred. Told from female Orange-breasted Green Pigeon (above) by green breast and belly, and tail pattern. Tail shape and coloration are best distinctions, for both sexes, from Wedge-tailed Green Pigeon (p.455); see that species. **Racial variation** *T. p. phayrei* of Himalayas and NE

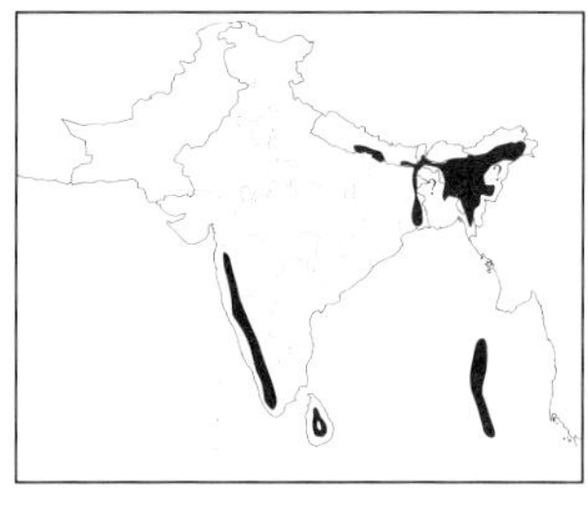

subcontinent has orange wash to breast and chestnut undertail-coverts (male), and both sexes have grey cap. *T. p. affinis* of S India lacks orange wash to breast and has cinnamon undertail-coverts (male), and cap of both sexes is paler blue-grey. *T. p. pompadora* of Sri Lanka has yellowish forehead and pronounced yellow throat in both male and female, and male has buffish-white undertail-coverts. *T. p. chloroptera* of Andaman and Nicobar Is is much larger, with heavier bill; maroon mantle of male is less extensive (not extending onto wing-coverts, which are green); has bright lime-green rump, and undertail-coverts are grey-green and tipped with pale yellow. **VOICE** A wandering series of pleasant whistles. A series of soft, high-pitched oscillating whistles, similar to that of some other green pigeons, e.g. Wedge-tailed (S. Buckton). **HABITS** Like those of Orange-breasted. **HABITAT** Broadleaved evergreen and moist deciduous forest and well-wooded areas in tropical and subtropical zones. **BREEDING** December–July, varying locally. Nests in a moderate-sized tree, cane brake or bamboo clump. **DISTRIBUTION AND STATUS** Resident, subject to local movements. Himalayas from WC Nepal east to Arunachal Pradesh; NE India, Bangladesh, hills of SW India, and Sri Lanka. **NP:** local below 250 m; fairly common at Chitwan, uncommon or rare elsewhere. **IN:** locally common; plains up to 1200 m in Western Ghats, to 1500 m in the northeast. **BT:** local and rare. **BD:** local. **LK:** common in lowlands and lower hills, more common in dry zone. **REFERENCES** Gibbs *et al.* (in press).

THICK-BILLED GREEN PIGEON *Treron curvirostra* Plate 35

Thick-billed Pigeon (K)

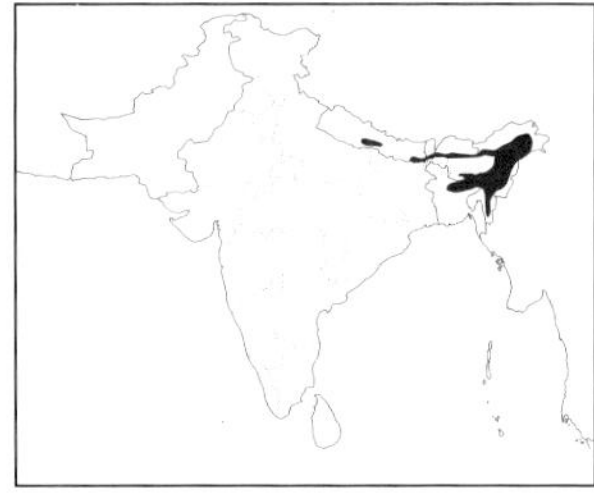

IDENTIFICATION 27 cm. **Male** closely resembles Pompadour Green Pigeon (p.453), having maroon mantle. Main differences are thicker bill with striking red base and cere, extensive area of bare greenish orbital skin, green breast without orange wash, and different undertail-covert pattern. Shorter (inner) undertail-coverts are green, tipped with white (giving rise to barred effect), and longer undertail-coverts are pale cinnamon. **Female** lacks maroon mantle, and can be told from other female green pigeons by bill size and coloration, and greenish orbital skin (as male). Compared with female Pompadour, undertail-coverts appear barred rather than streaked. **Juvenile** is like female, but has more olive (rather than grey) crown, and bill is more slender, with a less distinctly curved culmen. **VOICE** A pleasant wandering whistle, as other green pigeons. Song typical for the genus, quiet and warbling, consisting of a series of whistling and cooing notes which rise and fall in pitch (P. Morris). **HABITS** Like those of Orange-breasted (p.453). **HABITAT** Forest and well-wooded country in tropical and subtropical zones. **BREEDING** April–June. Nests in a small tree or bamboo clump. **DISTRIBUTION AND STATUS** Resident, subject to local movements. Himalayas from C Nepal east to Arunachal Pradesh; NE India and Bangladesh. **NP:** scarce and local; below 455 m. **IN:** uncommon; from plains up to at least 1500 m. **BT:** local and rare. **BD:** local.

YELLOW-FOOTED GREEN PIGEON *Treron phoenicoptera* Plate 35

Green Pigeon (I), Yellow-footed Pigeon (K), Yellow-legged Green Pigeon (P), Bengal Green Pigeon (F)

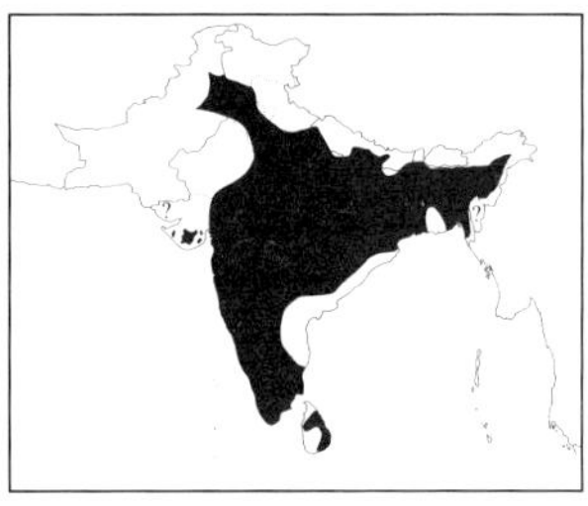

IDENTIFICATION 33 cm. A large green pigeon, best distinguished by combination of grey cap and pale greenish-yellow forehead and throat, broad olive-yellow band around neck, narrow grey band across upper mantle, pale greyish-green upperparts, olive-yellow band across base of grey tail, mauve shoulder patch, and yellow legs and feet. Sexes are similar, although female is duller. **Racial variation** Birds occurring in peninsular India and Sri Lanka (*T. p. chlorigaster* and *T. p. phillipsi*) have greenish-yellow belly and flanks almost concolorous with yellow of breast. Belly and flanks are grey in the northern race (*T. p. phoenicoptera*) and clearly demarcated from breast. Intermediates occur. **VOICE** Pleasant wandering whistling, as other green pigeons. **HABITS** Like those of Orange-breasted (p.453). **HABITAT** Fig and other fruiting trees in deciduous forest, groves around villages and cultivation, overgrown gardens and roadside avenues in tropical and subtropical zones. **BREEDING** March–June. Nests in a moderate-sized tree. **DISTRIBUTION AND STATUS** Resident, subject to local movements. Throughout most of the subcontinent, except much of the northwest, Himalayas and extreme E India. **PK:** common and irregular year-round visitor to the Punjab plains; uncommon in Sind. **NP:** widespread and locally fairly common below 250 m, uncommon up to 1400 m. **IN:** widespread and locally common; plains up to 1000 m. **BD:** common. **LK:** rare, confined to E foothills and adjacent lowlands.

PIN-TAILED GREEN PIGEON *Treron apicauda* Plate 35

Pin-tailed Pigeon (K)

IDENTIFICATION Male 42 cm; female 39 cm. A large green pigeon, best distinguished by extended and pointed central tail feathers on both sexes. Also has mainly grey tail (with greenish tip to central feathers)

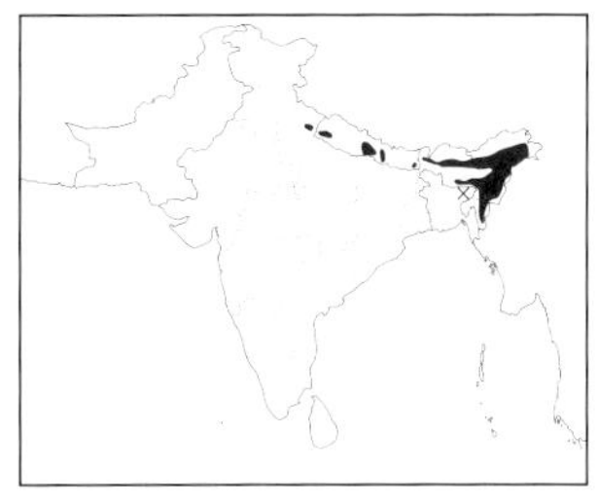

contrasting with bright, lime-green rump and uppertail-coverts, which is best distinction from female Wedge-tailed Green Pigeon (below) if central tail feathers are broken or missing. Green crown, wing-coverts and back are additional differences from male Wedge-tailed. Has blue cere and bill-base and naked blue lores (lores are feathered on Wedge-tailed). **Male** has longer central tail feathers, pale orange wash to breast, and more pronounced grey cast to upper mantle compared with **female**. **VOICE** A distinctive, deep, tuneful short melody. After the initial note all notes are paired, *oou...ou-ruu...oo-ru...ou-rooou*. Much richer, less meandering and more tuneful than the flatter song of Wedge-tailed (P. Holt from U. Treesucon recording). **HABITS** Like those of Orange-breasted (p.453). **HABITAT** Tall broadleaved forest, especially evergreen, in tropical and subtropical zones. **BREEDING** April–June. Nests in a bush or bamboo clump. **DISTRIBUTION AND STATUS** Resident, subject to local movements. Himalayas from N Uttar Pradesh east to Arunachal Pradesh; NE India and Bangladesh. **NP:** scarce; mainly below 305 m (–915 m). **IN:** locally fairly common; base of hills up to 1800 m (–2745 m). **BT:** frequent; 250–730 m. **BD:** rare, possibly a nomad from neighbouring hills.

WEDGE-TAILED GREEN PIGEON *Treron sphenura* Plate 35

Wedge-tailed Pigeon (K)

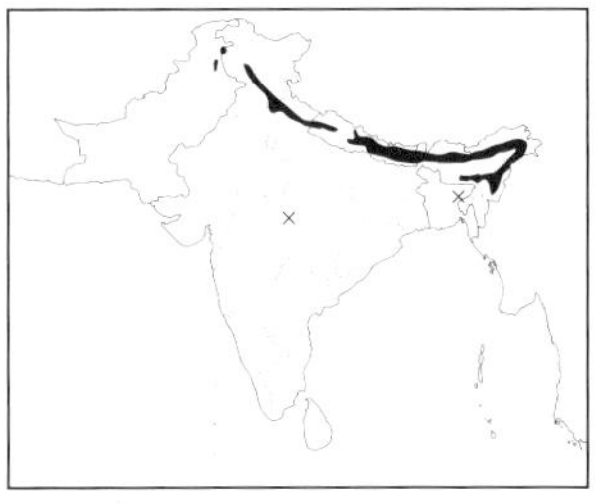

IDENTIFICATION 33 cm. **Male** told from male Pompadour Green Pigeon (p.453) by larger size, longer, wedge-shaped tail, less extensive maroon patch on upperparts (confined to inner wing-coverts, scapulars and lower mantle), darker olive-green back and rump, and only indistinct, fine yellow edges to greater coverts and tertials. In flight, shows more uniform tail, lacking pale grey terminal band of Pompadour. Orange wash to crown, less distinct orange wash on breast, and very long pale cinnamon undertail-coverts are further differences where ranges overlap. **Female** is mainly green, lacking orange coloration to crown and breast and maroon wing-coverts and mantle of male. Longer undertail-coverts are yellowish-white with grey-green centres. Told from female Pompadour by differences in tail shape and coloration, and lack of prominent yellow in wing (features as male); also has uniform green head (lacking grey crown of female Pompadour where ranges overlap). Tail shape, maroon patch on upperparts (male), and dull olive-green rump, uppertail-coverts and central tail feathers are best distinctions from Pin-tailed Green Pigeon (p.454); see that species for further differences. **VOICE** A series of wandering mellow whistles, like that of other green pigeons, although notes deeper with more hooting compared with Thick-billed Green Pigeon (p.454). **HABITS** Like those of Orange-breasted (p.453), but less gregarious than other green pigeons, usually keeping in small flocks. **HABITAT** Broadleaved forest in subtropical and temperate zones. **BREEDING** April–August. Nests in trees. **DISTRIBUTION AND STATUS** Resident, subject to seasonal and altitudinal movements. Himalayas in N Pakistan and from Kashmir east to Arunachal Pradesh; NE India and Bangladesh. **PK:** rare and very local, possibly resident. **NP:** locally fairly common; mainly 1525–2000 m (–2800 m). **IN:** locally fairly common; plains up to 2500 m. **BT:** fairly common; 610–2100 m. **BD:** rare, possibly a nomad from neighbouring hills.

GREEN IMPERIAL PIGEON *Ducula aenea* Plate 33

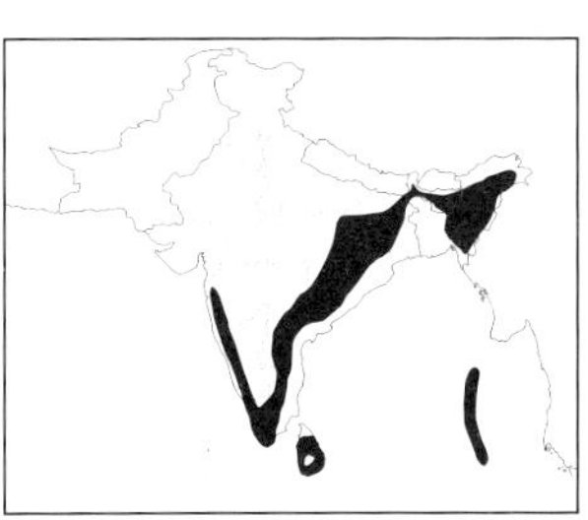

IDENTIFICATION 43–47 cm. A very large pigeon, best told from Mountain Imperial Pigeon (p.456) by dark metallic bronze-and-green upperparts. Has uniform dark green tail (distinctly banded on Mountain Imperial), and maroon undertail-coverts, contrasting with, and appearing darker than, grey breast and belly. **Racial variation** *D. a. nicobarica* from the Nicobar Is has darker (less metallic) and more bluish or purplish upperparts than races occurring elsewhere in the subcontinent; further, underparts are purer grey, lacking lilac wash, and undertail-coverts are brown or grey (darker than or concolorous with rest of underparts). **VOICE** Lengthy deep, hollow and resonant *currr-whoo*, with emphasis on the Eurasian Eagle Owl-like second syllable; often only this second syllable is audible at any range. Ventriloquistic and hard to locate. Also rhythmic purring notes (P. Holt). **HABITS** Keeps singly or in pairs, and gathers in small flocks when feeding on fruiting trees, often associating with other frugivorous birds. Flies at a considerable height well above the treetops when moving between feeding grounds. Although flight appears leisurely, with slow flaps, it is swift and powerful. Other habits are similar to those of green pigeons (see Orange-breasted, p.453). **HABITAT** Tropical broadleaved evergreen, moist deciduous and secondary forest with fruiting trees. **BREEDING** February–December, varying locally. Nests below 10 m in a forest sapling. **DISTRIBUTION AND STATUS** Resident, subject to local movements. Mainly Western Ghats, E and NE India, Bangladesh and Sri Lanka. **IN:** locally fairly common resident; usually below 300 m, occasionally up to 600 m. **BD:** scarce winter visitor. **LK:** regular resident in lowlands and lower hills.

MOUNTAIN IMPERIAL PIGEON *Ducula badia* Plate 33

Imperial Pigeon (F,I)

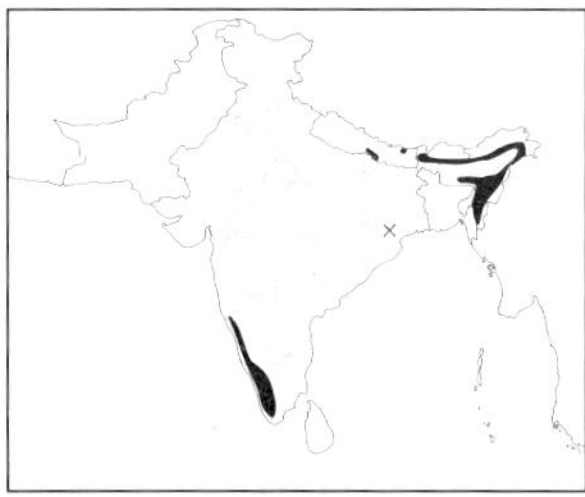

IDENTIFICATION 43–51 cm. A very large pigeon, best told from Green Imperial Pigeon (p.455) by brownish upperparts, creamy-white chin and throat, dark brown base to paler grey-brown tail, resulting in two-toned (rather than uniform) tail pattern, and pale buff undertail-coverts which are paler (not darker) than belly and vent. For differences from Nilgiri and Andaman Wood Pigeons (p.448 and p.449), see those species. **Juvenile** has rufous fringes to mantle and wing-coverts, with chestnut leading edge to wing, and tail pattern is less well defined. **VOICE** A deep, resonant, booming double note preceded by a click (heard at close range), *klip-whroom, whroom*; the second *whroom* is deeper and louder (Gibbs *et al.* in press). **HABITS** Very similar to those of Green Imperial. Seen mostly when flying high above the forest from one feeding ground to another, or in the breeding season when birds regularly make late-afternoon flights in wide circles high over the trees. **HABITAT** Tall broadleaved evergreen forest in tropical, subtropical and temperate zones. **BREEDING** January–August, varying locally. Nests 5–8 m up in a forest sapling. **DISTRIBUTION AND STATUS** Resident, subject to local movements. Himalayas from Nepal east to Arunachal Pradesh; NE India and Western Ghats. **NP:** rare and local, probably resident; 250–1250 m. **IN:** locally common; up to 2000 m in Western Ghats, to 2300 m in Himalayas and NE Indian hills. **BT:** fairly common; 250–2440 m. **REFERENCES** Gibbs *et al.* (in press), Lama (1995a).

PIED IMPERIAL PIGEON *Ducula bicolor* Plate 33

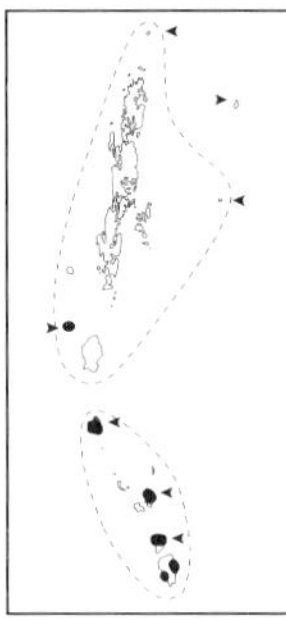

IDENTIFICATION 41 cm. Creamy-white, except for black flight feathers and black in tail. Has blue-grey bill, and dark eye contrasting with white head. **Juvenile** has diffuse ginger-buff tips to feathers of head, upperparts and underparts. **VOICE** Described as a chuckling *hu-hu-hu*, and a domestic pigeon-like and often repeated *cru-croo* (Ali and Ripley 1987). Deep and resonant purring, *wrrooom*, repeated at 1–3-second intervals, and similar to notes of other imperial pigeons (P. Holt from U. Treesucon recording). **HABITS** Frugivorous and arboreal. Usually occurs in small parties in the tops of tall trees; gathers in large flocks and wanders from island to island, wherever food is plentiful. The wings make a loud clatter as the bird takes flight. **HABITAT** Broadleaved evergreen forest; favours mangroves. **BREEDING** January–March. Nests 7–8 m up in tree. **DISTRIBUTION AND STATUS IN:** common resident on Nicobar Is; possibly only a seasonal visitor to Andaman Is, where rare. **REFERENCES** Sankaran and Vijayan (1993).

BUSTARDS Otididae

Medium-sized to large terrestrial birds of desert, semi-desert, grasslands and arid scrub. Typically, they have fairly long legs, stout body, long neck and short bill. Most species have ornamental feathers, such as crests and neck plumes, which are exhibited in display. The wings are broad and long, and in flight the neck is outstretched. Their flight is powerful and can be very fast, although bustards prefer to escape by running or by crouching on the ground, relying on their cryptic coloration to avoid detection. When feeding, bustards have a steady, deliberate gait. They are more or less omnivorous, and feed opportunistically on large insects, such as grasshoppers and locusts, young birds, shoots, leaves, seeds and fruits. Most bustards in the region are, as a consequence of hunting, very wary and difficult to approach. Many species are gregarious, especially in winter. Males perform elaborate and spectacular displays in the breeding season. The nest is a shallow depression on the ground, and the female alone incubates and takes care of the young. The main reference specific to bustards is Johnsgard (1991).

LITTLE BUSTARD *Tetrax tetrax* Plate 36

Otis tetrax

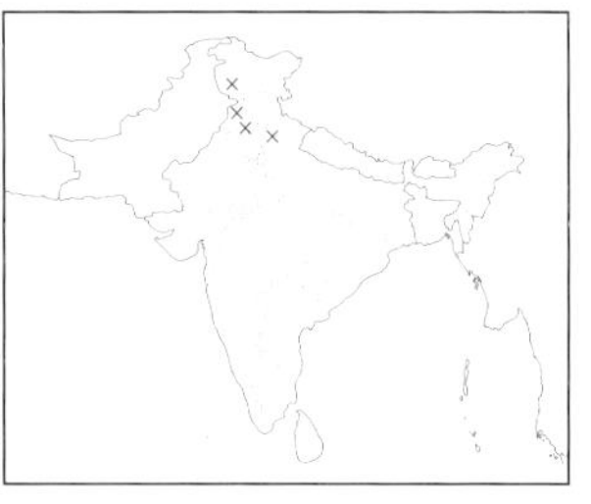

IDENTIFICATION 40–45 cm. Distinguished from other bustards by small size and stocky appearance, rapid 'winnowing' flight action on stiff, noticeably bowed wings (instead of the steady wingbeats of other bustards), and large amount of white in wing. Lesser Florican (p.458) is much slimmer, and in female and non-breeding plumages is generally paler in coloration, with more prominent dark arrowhead markings on upperparts, warmer buff-coloured wing-coverts, and less distinct streaking and mottling on breast (cf. profuse narrow barring on breast of female Little). **Breeding male** has black foreneck and upper breast, with white neck V and band across upper breast, pale slate-grey face, sandy-brown upperparts vermiculated with grey and black, white lower breast and belly, and broad white panel in wing (with white greater coverts, white secondaries with narrow black subterminal bar, and mainly white inner primaries). **Non-breeding male** lacks grey face and black-and-white neck pattern; resembles adult female, but is less heavily marked on head, neck and upperparts, and has cleaner white underparts, occasionally with a few black chevrons on flanks. Wing pattern is as breeding male, and therefore shows more white in wing than female. **Female** is warm buff-brown, with extensive black streaking on head and neck; has coarse blackish blotching and vermiculations on upperparts (giving darker overall impression than male), black barring and chevrons on breast and flanks (more conspicuous than on non-breeding male), broader black bar across secondaries, and often black bar across white greater coverts. **Juvenile** has blackish crown, streaked with buff; upperparts are duller and more heavily streaked and vermiculated, and underparts are less strongly barred. White area in wing is less extensive owing to dark-barred buffish primaries and outer greater coverts, and with barring on inner primaries and secondaries. **Immature** birds retain juvenile primaries, and therefore show less white in wing than adults until second winter. **VOICE** Gives hoarse grunt when flushed. **HABITS** Usually found in small parties. Flight is swift and direct, with occasional erratic turns. Male produces an extraordinary whistling sound in flight, a result of emarginated seventh primary (Cramp and Simmons 1980). **HABITAT** Open grassland, short crops. **DISTRIBUTION AND STATUS** Winter visitor. Pakistan and N India (Jammu and Kashmir, Punjab and NW Uttar Pradesh). **PK:** rare and erratic. **IN:** vagrant. **REFERENCES** Cramp and Simmons (1980).

GREAT BUSTARD *Otis tarda* — Plate 36

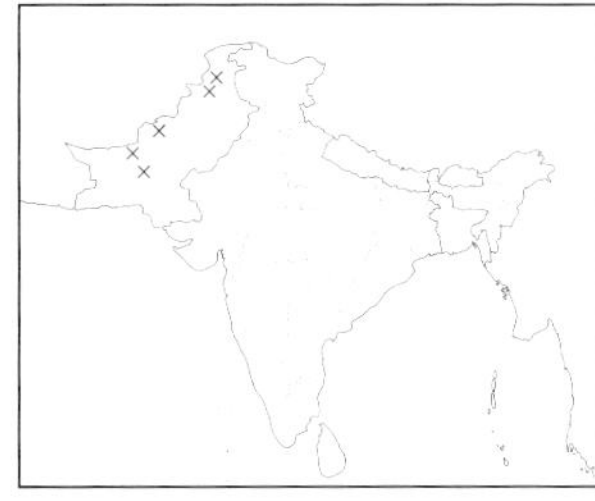

IDENTIFICATION 75–105 cm. A very large, stocky, broad-winged bustard. In all plumages, distinguished from other bustards by combination of greyish head and upper neck, cinnamon coloration to lower neck, cinnamon upperparts with bold black barring, and white underparts. Take-off is ponderous and flight action is stiff, with wingbeats slow and heavy. Upperwing pattern differs from that of other bustards, and always shows white at base of primaries and secondaries. **Breeding male** is huge, with thick neck. Has swept-back white whiskers, deep cinnamon-chestnut breast-band and lower neck, and shows large white panel on closed wing, with mainly white outer tertials. In flight, has more extensive area of white in wing than female (tertials and wing-coverts show more white). **Non-breeding male** is similarly very large, with much white in wing; crown is mixed with black, neck and breast are mainly grey (with cinnamon restricted to lower hindneck and sides of upper breast), and it lacks white whiskers. **Female** is similar to non-breeding male, but is much smaller, and has thinner neck and smaller-looking head; cinnamon of upperparts is not so warm-toned as on male, and female shows less white on closed wing and in flight (with median and greater coverts grey and cinnamon, barred with black). **Juvenile** is similar to female, but has black crown with buff tips, rest of head and neck grey, mixed with cinnamon and buff, paler cinnamon upperparts with finer barring, and less white in wing (tertials, as well as wing-coverts, mainly barred with buff and blackish). **Immature** birds take up to six years to acquire adult plumage. **VOICE** Largely silent outside breeding season. **HABITS** Similar to those of Indian Bustard (below). **HABITAT** Plains with short grass. **DISTRIBUTION AND STATUS PK:** vagrant. **REFERENCES** Cramp and Simmons (1980).

INDIAN BUSTARD *Ardeotis nigriceps* — Plate 36

Great Indian Bustard (F,I,N,R), *Choriotis nigriceps* (I)

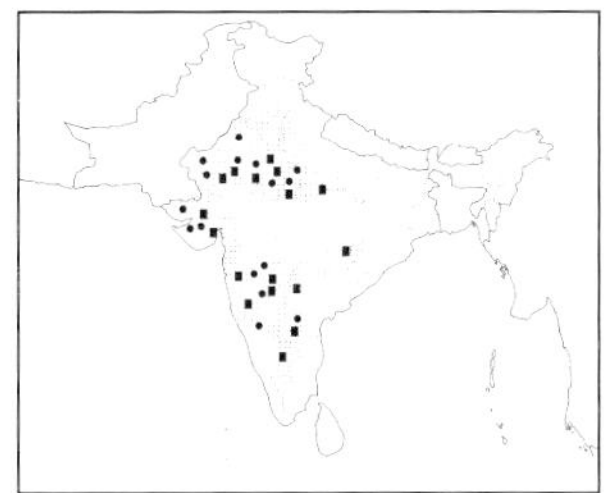

IDENTIFICATION 92–122 cm. A very large, thin-necked bustard, with angular head and long, pointed bill typically held upwards. In all plumages, told from other bustards by combination of greyish-white head and neck, with black forehead, crown and crest, grey-brown upperparts (with rufous tinge) finely vermiculated with black, white-spotted black wing-coverts, and white underparts. Flight action is stiff, with wingbeats slow and heavy, recalling a large bird of prey. Upperwing pattern differs from that of other bustards in being mainly dark and lacking extensive area of white; wing-coverts are tipped with white, with narrow greater-covert bar. Has white tips to outer tail feathers. **Male** is huge, with almost white head and neck (neck is only very finely vermiculated with dark grey); has black breast-band and can show black thigh patches. **Female** is similar to male, but is appreciably smaller (75% of male's size); head and neck appear greyer owing to profuse dark grey vermiculations; can show white supercilium, and typically lacks black breast-band. **Immature** is similar to female, but has buff spotting on crown, hindneck and mantle. **VOICE** Alarm call is a bark or bellow; in display, has a deep booming moan (Ali and Ripley 1987). **HABITS** Normally keeps in small parties, but gathers in flocks during the early monsoon. Feeds chiefly in early mornings and late afternoons. Flight is steady, quite close to the ground, and can be sustained for long distances. Males gather on traditional sites to perform their displays: the throat sac is greatly distended, and the bird emits a deep boom and struts with cocked tail and drooping wings. **HABITAT** Arid and semi-arid grasslands with a good cover of bushes; also adjacent open dry deciduous forest. **BREEDING** Mainly March–September, locally also in other months. Nests in open areas with low vegetation, usually fallow fields or scrub. **DISTRIBUTION AND STATUS** Resident, now endemic to India. Moves seasonally in search of food and breeding sites. Most birds are now in Rajasthan; smaller numbers in Gujarat, Madhya Pradesh, Maharashtra, Karnataka and Andhra Pradesh. Formerly ranged from the

Indus R east to W Orissa and south to Tamil Nadu; numbers and range have declined since 1830. Globally threatened. **PK:** vagrant. **NP:** possibly recorded in 19th century. **IN:** uncommon, declining. **REFERENCES** Rahmani (1989a), Rahmani and Manakadan (1990a).

MACQUEEN'S BUSTARD *Chlamydotis macqueeni* Plate 36

Houbara (I), Houbara Bustard *C. undulata*

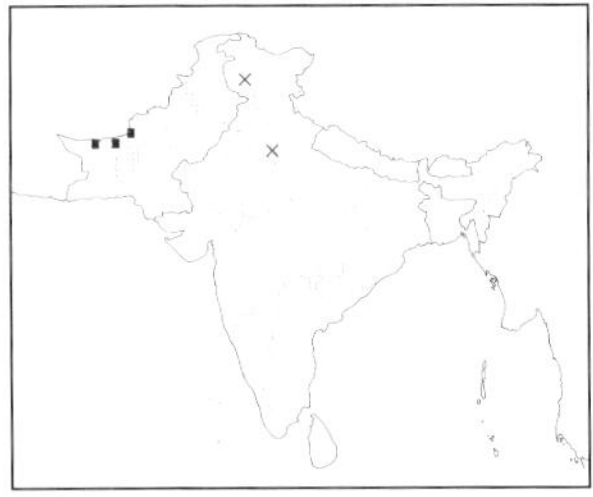

IDENTIFICATION 55–65 cm. Medium-sized, comparatively slim bustard with rather long tail, and slim neck which in all plumages shows a dark vertical stripe. In flight, extensive white patch on outer primaries (contrasting with black primary coverts and inner primaries) helps to separate it from other bustards. **Male** has crested appearance, with elongated white crown feathers broadly tipped with black. Further, has black feathering down neck which is more extensive on lower neck, and overhangs breast sides when not displaying. Upperparts are sandy, finely vermiculated with grey and black, with vermiculations joining to form distinct dark bars. **Female** is similar to male, but smaller; black-tipped crest and line of black feathering down neck are reduced. In flight, has buff subterminal tips to primaries and lacks whitish greater-covert panel of male. **Juvenile** is very similar to female, but lacks black crest, and crown is uniform; neck stripe is finer, and white patterning in wing is washed with buff and less prominent. **VOICE** Virtually silent. **HABITS** Chiefly nocturnal in Pakistan, where disturbance is high. Extremely shy and wary. Strongly attracted to mustard crops. In courtship display, the male runs and walks while spreading the crown plumes, raising the neck plumes and retracting the neck. **HABITAT** Gently undulating country, semi-desert with sand dunes and sparsely scattered hardy shrubs, sandy grasslands; also mustard fields in winter. **BREEDING** March and April. Lays eggs in a scrape under a bush. **DISTRIBUTION AND STATUS** Chiefly a winter visitor to Pakistan and NW India. **PK:** widespread, but scarce; mainly winter visitor and passage migrant; a few breed in the Makran and Chaggai. **IN:** scarce winter visitor, mainly to Rajasthan and N Gujarat. **REFERENCES** Cramp and Simmons (1980), Osborne *et al.* (1984), Rahmani (1995).

BENGAL FLORICAN *Houbaropsis bengalensis* Plate 36

Eupodotis bengalensis

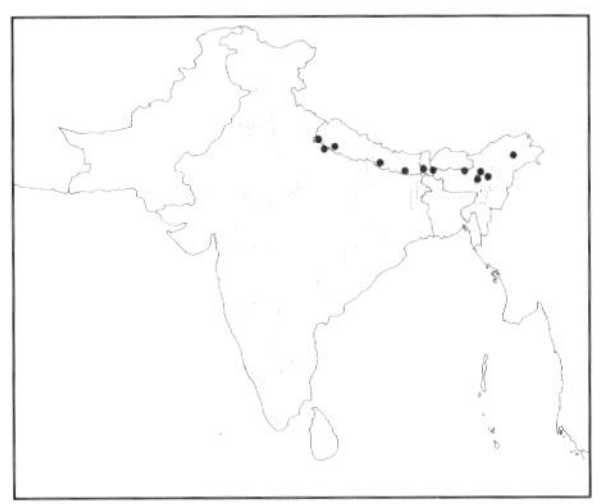

IDENTIFICATION 66 cm. A medium-sized, well-proportioned bustard, considerably larger and stouter than Lesser Florican (p.456) and with broader head and thicker neck. **Male** has black head, neck, breast and underparts, sandy to cinnamon-buff upperparts with fine black vermiculations and bold black arrowhead markings, and white wing-coverts showing as a conspicuous patch on closed wing. In addition to structural differences, black throat, shaggy hindneck and breast and lack of white hindcollar are further differences from male Lesser. In flight, wings are entirely white except for black outermost primaries and primary tips. **Female**, which is slightly larger than male, and **immature** are buff-brown to sandy-rufous in coloration. They have a dark brown crown and buff crown-stripe, narrow dark brown streak down side of neck, arrowhead-shaped black markings and vermiculations on upperparts, and buffish-white wing-coverts (with fine dark barring) which show as a pale area on closed wing. In flight, pale wing-coverts contrast with blackish barring on primaries and secondaries. Size, structure, pale and less prominently marked wing-coverts, and buff rather than rufous background coloration to barred flight feathers separate it from Lesser. **First-summer male** resembles adult male, but reverts to female-like plumage in second winter; full adult male plumage acquired by second summer. **VOICE** Normally silent, but when disturbed utters a shrill, metallic *chik-chik-chik* (Ali and Ripley 1987). **HABITS** Usually solitary, although small groups of males gather briefly in the breeding season. Forages in short-grass areas in the early mornings and late afternoons, retiring into adjacent tall grass cover at other times. Most easily seen in the breeding season, when males perform striking displays, leaping above the grassland, in early mornings and evenings. **HABITAT** Tall grassland with scattered bushes and interspersed with areas of short grass, such as regrowth after burning. **BREEDING** March–August, varying locally. Nests in grassland. **DISTRIBUTION AND STATUS** Resident. Currently in small and highly fragmented populations almost entirely in protected areas, mainly in Uttar Pradesh, Assam and S Nepal; small numbers in Arunachal Pradesh and N West Bengal. Formerly common in the terai and duars from NW Uttar Pradesh east to NE India and Bangladesh. Globally threatened. **NP, IN:** rare and local. **BD:** ?former resident; no recent records, but could occur in very small numbers in the extreme northwest. **REFERENCES** Inskipp and Inskipp (1983), Narayan (1990), Rahmani (1996), Rahmani *et al.* (1992).

LESSER FLORICAN *Sypheotides indica* Plate 36

Likh (I), *Eupodotis indica*

IDENTIFICATION 46–51 cm. A small, slim, long-necked bustard. Considerably smaller and slimmer than Bengal Florican (above), with smaller head and finer neck. Flight action is also different, with more rapid

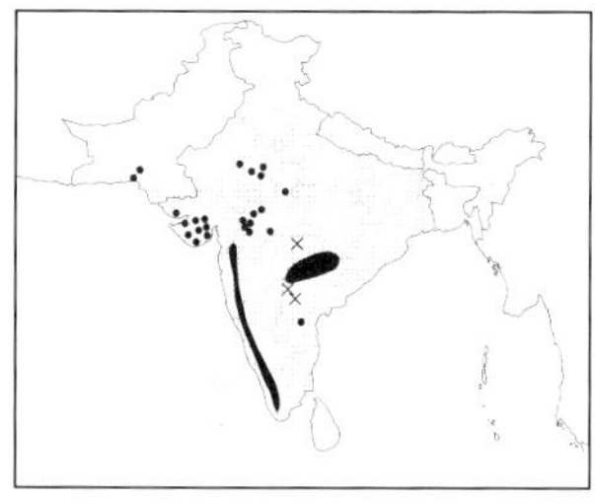

wingbeats. **Breeding male** has black head with four to six amazing spatulate-tipped head plumes (sometimes lacking); black neck, breast and underparts, and sandy-grey, cinnamon-tinged upperparts with fine black vermiculations and bold black arrowhead markings. Has white wing-coverts, which show as a patch on closed wing. White throat, black head plumes and white 'collar' (across upper mantle) are further differences from male Bengal. In flight, white of wing is restricted to coverts, which contrast with a black carpal bar and barred flight feathers. **Non-breeding male** is similar to female, but has white wing-coverts. **Female**, which is slightly larger than male, and **immature** are sandy or cinnamon-buff, with black-streaked crown and narrow buff crown-stripe, and black streaking on foreneck, and have black arrowhead markings and vermiculations on upperparts (giving dark overall appearance to upperparts). Small size, slim structure, heavily marked wing-coverts, and rufous rather than buff background coloration to barred flight feathers separate from female and immature Bengal. **VOICE** A frog-like croak is uttered during display, and when disturbed gives a short whistle (Ali and Ripley 1987). **HABITS** Less shy than other bustards. When flushed, flies off with fast wingbeats, covering some distance before landing and running into cover. Males are conspicuous during the breeding season, when they repeatedly jump into the air and perform a spectacular display flight. **HABITAT** Dry grasslands with scattered bushes, cotton and millet crops. **BREEDING** July–October. Nests in a bare patch in short grass or crops. **DISTRIBUTION AND STATUS** Resident, endemic to the subcontinent. Subject to migratory movements over much of its range, depending on rainfall. Now very rare: breeding is restricted to W and E Gujarat, SE Rajasthan and W Madhya Pradesh; disperses south to SE India in non-breeding season. Numbers and range have declined sharply since at least 1870; formerly recorded from S Pakistan east to West Bengal and from N Uttar Pradesh south throughout the peninsula; its main breeding range included much of W India. Globally threatened. **PK:** vagrant. **NP:** very rare summer visitor; mainly below 250 m (–1310 m). **IN:** rare and declining. **BD:** former visitor. **REFERENCES** Sankaran (1990b, 1995b), Sankaran *et al.* (1992).

CRANES Gruidae

Stately long-necked, long-legged birds with tapering body, and long inner secondaries which hang over the tail. The flight is powerful, with the head and neck extended forwards and legs and feet stretched out behind. Flocks of cranes often fly in V-formation; they sometimes soar at considerable heights. Most cranes are gregarious outside the breeding season, and flocks are often very noisy. Cranes have a characteristic resonant and far-reaching musical trumpet-like call. A wide variety of plant and animal food is taken, including seeds, tubers, shoots, leaves, buds, crustaceans, frogs, lizards, small fish and large insects. The bill is used to probe and dig for plant roots and to graze and glean vegetable material above the ground. Both sexes have a spectacular and beautiful dance in which the cranes bow, leap in the air and toss vegetation about while uttering loud calls and bugle sounds. Dancing takes place throughout the year, although most frequently prior to breeding; single individuals, pairs or a whole flock may dance. Cranes are monogamous, and some species pair for life. Both parents undertake nest-building, incubation and care of the young. The main references specific to cranes are Johnsgard (1983) and Perennou *et al.* (1994).

SIBERIAN CRANE *Grus leucogeranus* Plate 37

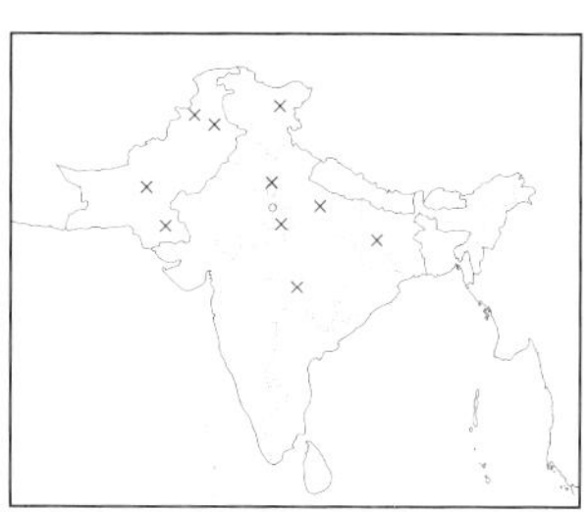

IDENTIFICATION 120–140 cm. **Adult** at rest appears all white with bare red face, pinkish-red legs, and noticeably downcurved reddish bill; long, downcurved white tertials conceal black primaries at rest. **Immature** initially has brownish bill and fully feathered head, and is strongly marked with cinnamon-brown on head, neck, mantle and wings, with some white body feathers acquired during first winter. By third winter red mask is apparent and body feathers are mainly white, and full adult plumage is attained by fourth winter. In flight, both adult and immature show black primaries which contrast with rest of wings; at a distance possibly confusable with White Stork (p.573), but that species has black secondaries, lacks red mask and has a straight red bill. **VOICE** Much less vocal than other cranes in the region, and generally heard only in period just before going to roost. Utters a pleasing musical *ahooya* in flight, and alarm call is a subdued *krroum* or *turr* (Cramp and Simmons 1980). **HABITS** When feeding, usually keeps in family parties of parents and one or two young; formerly also seen in small flocks. Family parties have winter feeding territories, unlike most cranes. Almost entirely vegetarian; feeds by probing for aquatic plants while wading in marshes or flooded areas. **HABITAT** Freshwater marshes with aquatic vegetable food in waters of wading depth. **DISTRIBUTION AND STATUS** Winter visitor and passage migrant to Pakistan and N India. Globally threatened. **PK:** very rare passage migrant; no confirmed records since 19th century, although presumably overflies the country annually en route to India. **IN:** very rare and local winter visitor, recorded regularly only at Keoladeo Ghana National Park, Rajasthan. **REFERENCES** Cramp and Simmons (1980), WWF India and AWB (1993).

SARUS CRANE *Grus antigone* **Plate 37**

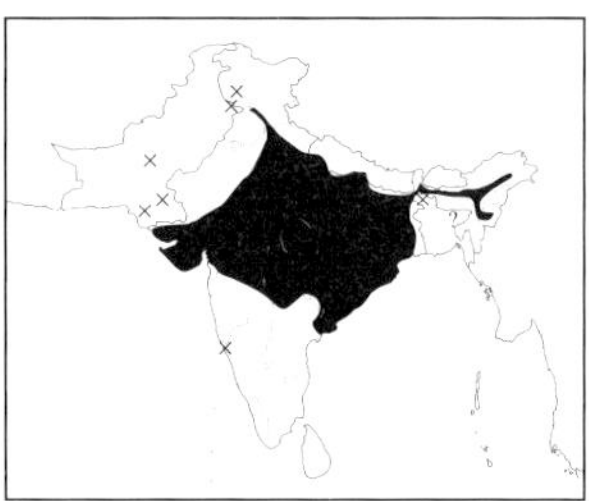

IDENTIFICATION 156 cm. A huge, mainly pale grey crane with reddish legs. **Adult** has naked scarlet head and upper neck (except for ashy-green crown), and very large bill. **Immature** is heavily marked with brown on upperparts, and head and neck are covered with buff or rusty-buff feathers. Older immatures have bare head and upper neck duller than adult, and lack greenish crown. In flight, both adult and immature show black primaries which contrast with grey of rest of wing. **Racial variation** Eastern race *G. a. sharpii,* which occurs in NE subcontinent, is darker grey in coloration compared with the widespread nominate race, with tertials concolorous with body. **VOICE** A very loud trumpeting, usually as a duet by paired birds at rest or on the wing (Ali and Ripley 1987). **HABITS** Normally keeps in pairs or family parties of three or four birds, although sometimes in flocks of 70 or more. Very tame in C and W India and Nepal where it is undisturbed. Usually makes regular daily flights to and from roosting sites. **HABITAT** Open cultivation in well-watered country, marshes, jheels, lakes and large rivers. **BREEDING** July–December, varying locally. Nest is a huge pile of vegetation built on a mound in marsh or pool, or on a bund in flooded paddy-fields. **DISTRIBUTION AND STATUS** Resident, subject to local movements. Recently recorded mainly from Gujarat and Rajasthan east to E Uttar Pradesh and S Madhya Pradesh. Formerly ranged from Pakistan and N India (from Kashmir) east to Assam and south to N Andhra Pradesh. **PK:** vagrant. **NP:** uncommon and local in W terai; declining. **IN:** locally common in the west and centre; has declined. **BD:** ?former resident; few recent records. **REFERENCES** Meine and Archibald (1996), Sonobe and Usui (1993).

DEMOISELLE CRANE *Grus virgo* **Plate 37**

***Anthropoides virgo* (F,I,K,R)**

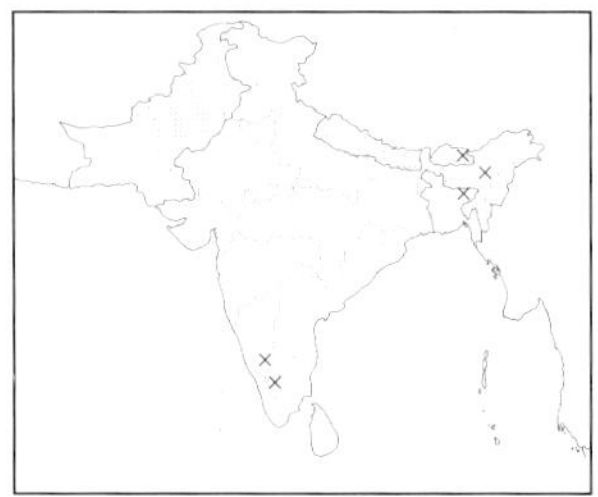

IDENTIFICATION 90–100 cm. Smallest of the cranes occurring regularly in the subcontinent, and mainly grey in coloration, with short, fine bill. **Adult** has mainly black head and neck with downcurved white tuft behind eye, and grey crown; black feathers of neck often extend as a point beyond breast; and elongated grey and black tertials project as a shallow arc beyond body, giving rise to distinctive shape. **Immature** is initially almost entirely grey, with slate-grey on foreneck, and with shorter all-grey tertials. By first winter is similar to adult, but head and neck are dark grey and less contrasting, tuft behind eye is grey and less prominent, and elongated feathers of foreneck and tertials are shorter and protrude less than in adult plumage; has grey-brown cast to mantle, coverts and tertials. In flight, both adult and immature show black flight feathers which contrast with pale grey of rest of wing. Easily confused at a distance with Common Crane (below). Elongated breast feathers, sleek appearance of elongated tertials, relatively short bill (shorter than head), and black of throat extending onto breast are best features for separating distant Demoiselle from Common at rest. In flight, Demoiselle is best separated at a distance by black breast; in addition, the legs and neck appear relatively shorter, and the wings shorter and broader-based. **VOICE** Flight call is a *garrooo,* higher-pitched than that of Common; courtship call is more guttural than Common's, a rasping *krruorrr* (Cramp and Simmons 1980). **HABITS** Highly gregarious and sometimes found with Common Cranes. Mainly vegetarian; feeds in morning and late afternoon in winter crops and stubble fields, and retires for rest of day to sandbanks in rivers and edges of jheels. **HABITAT** Cultivation, large rivers with sandbanks and reservoirs. In Pakistan, rests in remote desert areas on migration. **DISTRIBUTION AND STATUS** Winter visitor and passage migrant. Recently recorded mainly from Pakistan and from Gujarat and Rajasthan south to N Karnataka and east to C Uttar Pradesh. Formerly widespread and common in winter from Pakistan east through N India to Bihar and Orissa and south to S Andhra. **PK:** now a frequent passage migrant from mid to late March and late September–early October; no winter flocks nowadays. **NP:** now an uncommon passage migrant; once common, flying along river valleys in large flocks. **IN:** locally common in NW, W, NC and C areas. **BT, BD:** vagrant. **REFERENCES** Ullman (1991).

COMMON CRANE *Grus grus* **Plate 37**

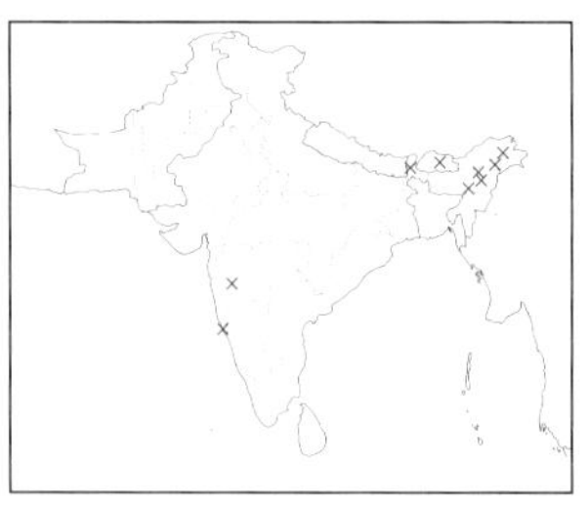

IDENTIFICATION 110–120 cm. **Adult** is mainly greyish, and best told from other cranes by largely black head and foreneck, with white stripe behind eye extending down neck sides; red patch on crown is visible at close range. **Immature** lacks head pattern of adult: head and neck are buff or grey, tinged with brown, and mantle and wing-coverts have variable amounts of brown. Immature acquires head pattern of adult by second winter, with whitish stripe behind eye apparent on some by first winter. In flight, both adult and immature show black primaries and secondaries which contrast with grey wing-coverts. For separating distant Common from Demoiselle Crane (above), see latter species. **VOICE** Flight call is a loud, trumpeting *krrooah;* birds on the ground utter other similar bugling calls, often involving bonded pairs, including typical *kroo-krii-kroo-krii* duet. **HABITS** Similar to those of Demoiselle Crane, with which it often associates. **HABITAT** Winter crops, rivers with sandbanks, jheels and reservoirs. **DISTRIBUTION AND STATUS** Winter visitor. Recently recorded mainly from Gujarat and N Madhya Pradesh. Formerly common in winter from Pakistan and N India east to West Bengal and south to N Andhra Pradesh. **PK:** regular but scarce passage migrant; overwinters only in the extreme southeast. **NP:** now a scarce winter visitor and passage migrant, recorded up to 3050 m. **IN:** locally fairly common winter visitor, especially in the northwest. **BT:** rare passage migrant. **BD:** former winter visitor; no confirmed records in 20th century. **REFERENCES** Choudhury (1996b).

HOODED CRANE *Grus monacha* — Plate 37

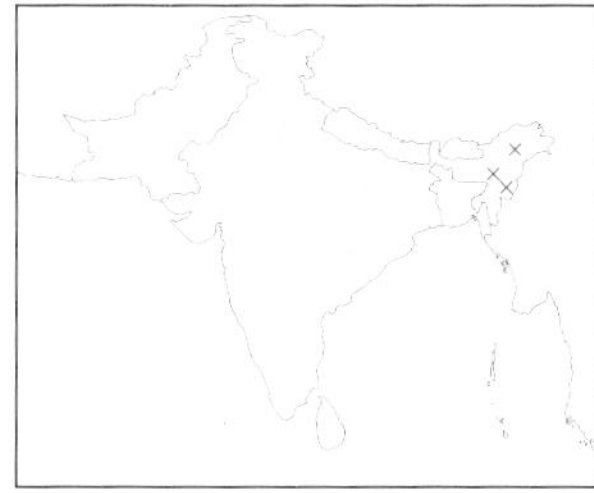

IDENTIFICATION 97 cm. A small, well-proportioned crane. **Adult** is uniform dark grey with contrasting white head and upper neck, and has black forehead and forecrown, with red patch visible on forecrown at close range. **Immature** has strong cinnamon wash to greyish-white head and neck, which contrast less with dark grey of lower neck, and lores and forehead are usually dark grey; has indistinct rufous-brown fringes to wing-coverts. In flight, both adult and immature show almost uniform slate-grey upperwing and underwing, with only slightly darker flight feathers. **VOICE** Adults give a loud *kurrk* or *kurr*, and immatures a throaty *piii* (Sonobe and Usui 1993). **HABITS** Unknown in the region. Similar to those of other cranes. **HABITAT** Plains and marshes. **DISTRIBUTION AND STATUS IN:** vagrant in 19th century.

BLACK-NECKED CRANE *Grus nigricollis* — Plate 37

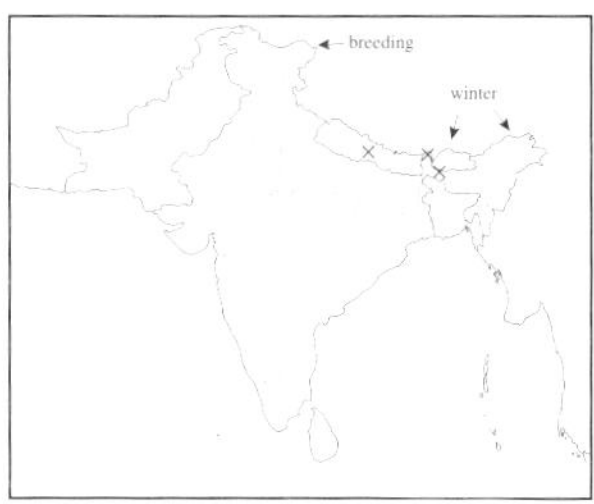

IDENTIFICATION 139 cm. **Adult** is mainly pale grey, with contrasting black head and upper neck, and black rear end created by extended and bunched tertials; red crown and white patch behind eye are visible at close range. **Immature** has buff or brownish head, neck, mantle and mottling to wing-coverts. By second winter, plumage is as adult. In flight, both adult and immature show black primaries and secondaries which contrast with pale grey wing-coverts (showing more contrast than Common Crane, p.460), as well as black tail-band (which is lacking on Common). **VOICE** Variety of calls, most slightly higher-pitched than those of Common, but difficult to distinguish (P. Holt). **HABITS** A typical crane. Gregarious in winter. Undisturbed by local Buddhist people, and is very tame. **HABITAT** Summers by high-altitude lakes in trans-Himalayan country; winters in wet fallow and stubble fields and marshes, in Bhutan also in marshes with a thick growth of dwarf bamboo. **BREEDING** May–July. Nest is a huge pile of vegetation on marshy ground. **DISTRIBUTION AND STATUS** Breeding summer visitor to Ladakh, 4000–4800 m; now winters in Bhutan, and a few in Arunachal Pradesh; recently attempted to breed in Sikkim. Globally threatened. **NP:** vagrant. **IN:** rare summer visitor. **BT:** locally common and regular winter visitor to traditional sites in valleys, 1950–3050 m. **REFERENCES** Chacko (1992), Gole (1992, 1996), Hussain (1986), Pfister (1997), WWF India and AWB (1993).

FINFOOTS Heliornithidae

Finfoots have an elongated neck, a graduated, long, stiff tail, broadly lobed toes and a strong bill. They inhabit waters overhung by forest or thick vegetation.

MASKED FINFOOT *Heliopais personata* — Plate 38

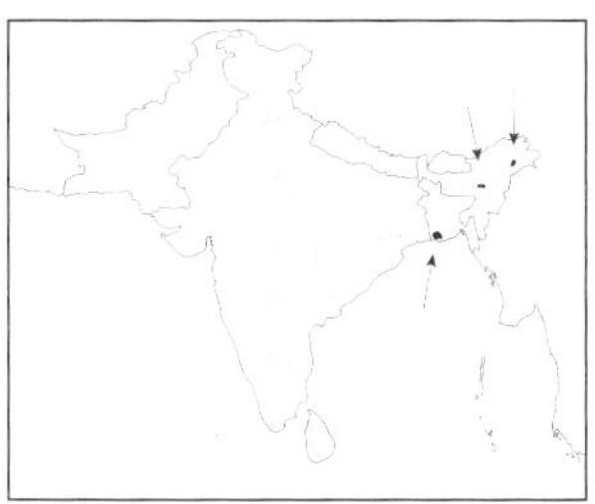

IDENTIFICATION 56 cm. A large, grebe-like bird with huge yellow or orange bill and day-glo green legs and feet. **Male** has black forehead, throat and foreneck, white stripe extending from behind eye down side of neck separating black of foreneck from grey hindneck, and olive-brown upperparts. **Female** is similar to male, but has white centre to throat and foreneck. **Immature** is similar to female, but has grey rather than black forehead. **VOICE** A high-pitched bubbling sound, and a loud grunting quack (Ali and Ripley 1987). **HABITS** Usually solitary, in pairs or in family parties. Territorial. Shy and retiring, typically keeping close to the cover of marginal vegetation. Swims well, normally with much of the body above water; but, if alarmed, will sink until only head and part of neck are visible, or skitters away along water surface. On land, escapes by running away rapidly like a rail and bolting into thick cover. Can climb with agility among fallen trunks and branches, and often perches on boughs overhanging water. Avoids taking wing, but can fly fast and quite strongly. Eats aquatic invertebrates and small fish. **HABITAT** Perennial pools in dense forest, mangrove creeks. **BREEDING** Poorly known in the region, but July in Assam. Nest is a platform of twigs placed 1 m above water on a horizontal branch or fallen tree in dense swamp forest. **DISTRIBUTION AND STATUS IN:** no recent published records; formerly rare resident or visitor to Assam. **BD:** rare resident or visitor. **REFERENCES** WWF India and AWB (1993).

RAILS, GALLINULES AND COOTS Rallidae

Small to medium-sized birds with moderate to long legs for wading and short rounded wings. Their body is laterally compressed, enabling them to run through reeds and undergrowth. Long toes facilitate walking over soft mud. With the exception of the Common Moorhen and Common Coot, which spend much time swimming in the open, rails are mainly terrestrial. Many occur in marshes and are very skulking, so their habits are poorly known and they are under-recorded, especially in winter, when they are generally silent. Typically, they emerge from thick cover in the early morning and at dusk. At the least sign of danger they bolt into cover with head and tail lowered. They fly reluctantly and feebly, with legs dangling, for a short distance and then drop into cover again. The majority are heard more often than seen, and are most voluble at dusk and at night. Their calls consist of strident or raucous repeated notes. Rails walk with constantly bobbing head and jerking tail and a high-stepping gait, and can clamber with agility among reeds. They swim with rhythmic movements of the head and neck and jerk the tail. They eat insects, crustaceans, amphibians, fish and vegetable matter. The nest is usually a pad of vegetation, well concealed, and built on the ground, on broken reeds or on floating mats of vegetation. The main reference specific to rails is Perennou *et al.* (1994).

ANDAMAN CRAKE *Rallina canningi* Plate 38

Andaman Banded Rail (I)

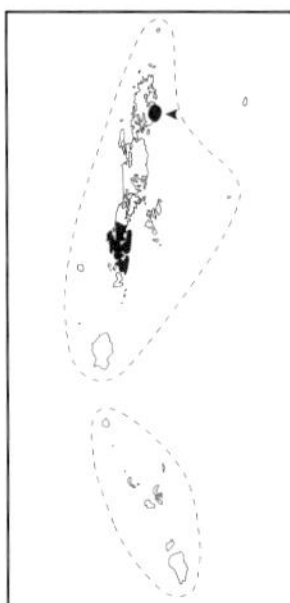

IDENTIFICATION 34 cm. A deep chestnut-coloured crake with bold black-and-white barring on underparts. Confusion possible only with Red-legged and Slaty-legged Crakes (below), although neither has been recorded from the Andaman Is. Differs from those species in much larger size, deep ruddy-chestnut head, neck, breast and upperparts, large and striking apple-green bill, and lack of white on throat. Additional distinctions from Red-legged are green legs and lack of prominent white barring on wing-coverts and flight feathers (although Andaman can show indistinct warm buff barring on outer coverts and outer primaries). **Juvenile** has duller chestnut head, breast and upperparts, and greyish belly (tinged with chestnut) which is narrowly banded with whitish. **VOICE** A deep throaty croak, *kroop.. kroop*, and a sharp *chick, chick* when alarmed (Ali and Ripley 1980). **HABITS** Similar to those of other rails, but poorly known. **HABITAT** Marshes in or at the edge of forest. **BREEDING** June–August. Nests on ground in marshes, or sometimes in forest not close to water. **DISTRIBUTION AND STATUS** Globally threatened. **IN:** resident, endemic to Andaman Is (N and S Andaman and possibly other islands); formerly common, but very few recent records.

RED-LEGGED CRAKE *Rallina fasciata* Plate 38

Red-legged Banded Crake (I)

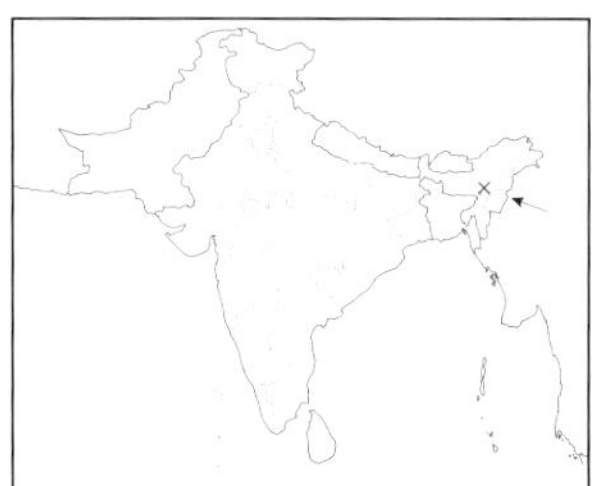

IDENTIFICATION 23 cm. A rufous-brown crake with striking black-and-white barring on underparts. Told from the commoner Slaty-legged Crake (below) by red legs, prominent white or buffish spotting and barring on scapulars, wing-coverts and exposed flight feathers, warm rufous-brown upperparts (with chestnut-orange head, neck and breast), slightly broader and less numerous black bars on underparts, indistinct whitish to rufous-buff throat, and broad red orbital ring. Extensive black-and-white barring on underparts, and pale barring on wing-coverts, are best distinctions from Ruddy-breasted and Black-tailed Crakes (p.466 and p.464), which also have red legs. See Andaman Crake (above) for differences from that species. **Juvenile** has warm brown head, neck and breast, and less distinct buff or white barring on scapulars and wing-coverts. From juvenile Slaty-legged by leg colour, upperpart coloration, and conspicuous barring on wings. **VOICE** A long descending trill, and a loud series of nasal *pek* calls given at roughly half-second intervals (Boonsong and Round 1991). **HABITS** A typical rail. **HABITAT** Dense forest. **BREEDING** Unknown in region. August and September in Burma. Nest is like that of Slaty-legged. **DISTRIBUTION AND STATUS IN:** presumably resident; recorded only in Assam, at 800 m; no recent records.

SLATY-LEGGED CRAKE *Rallina eurizonoides* Plate 38

Banded Crake (F,I,P), Slaty-legged Banded Crake

IDENTIFICATION 25 cm. A rufous and olive-brown crake with black-and-white barring on underparts. **Adult** told from the very similar but much rarer Red-legged Crake (above) by larger size, greenish to dark grey legs, lack of white-and-black barring on wing-coverts, dark olive-brown upperparts contrasting with rufous head,

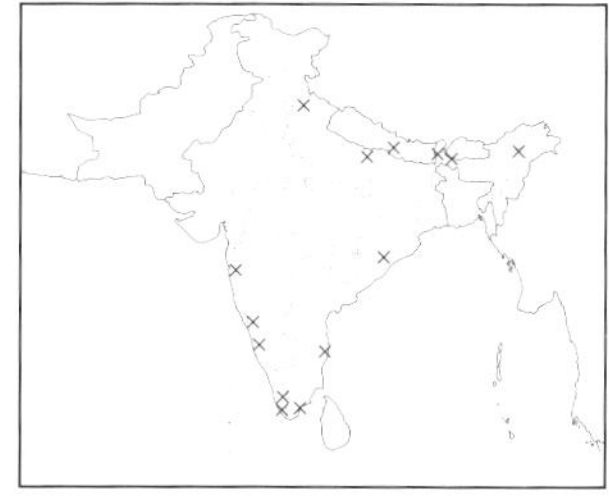

neck and breast, narrower and more numerous white bars on underparts, more prominent white chin and throat, and dull greyish-pink orbital ring. See Andaman Crake (p.462) for differences from that species. **Juvenile** has dark olive-brown head, neck and breast concolorous with mantle, and dull brown rather than crimson iris. Differs from juvenile Red-legged in leg colour, dark olive-brown rather than warm brown upperparts, and lack of conspicuous barring on wings. **VOICE** A *kek-kek, kek-kek,...* etc, a loud drumming croak, *krrrrrrrrr-ar-kraa-kraa-kraa*, a subdued *kok*, and a *krrrr* alarm call (Ali and Ripley 1987). **HABITS** A typical rail. Partly nocturnal. **HABITAT** Marshes in well-wooded country. **BREEDING** June–September. Nests up to 1 m above ground among dense vegetation, sometimes away from water. **DISTRIBUTION AND STATUS** Resident and local migrant. Mainly India (breeding) and Sri Lanka. **NP:** vagrant. **IN:** uncommon but widespread; plains and hills, up to 1600 m in Himalayas. **LK:** winter visitor throughout, favouring hills.

SLATY-BREASTED RAIL *Gallirallus striatus* Plate 38

Blue-breasted Banded Rail (F,I,P), ***Rallus striatus*** **(F,I,K)**

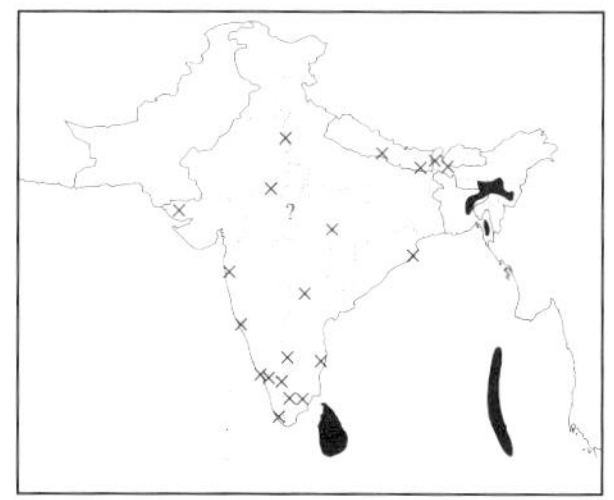

IDENTIFICATION 27 cm. Bill is relatively long and stout, with orange or red at base. **Adult** has chestnut crown and nape, whitish chin and throat, grey head sides, foreneck and breast, fine white barring and spotting on upperparts, and white barring on dark grey belly, flanks and undertail-coverts. Straighter bill, chestnut crown and nape, barred upperparts and olive-grey legs are the best features to separate it from Water Rail (below). **Female** is very similar to male, but with whitish central belly. **Juvenile** has rufous-brown crown and nape streaked with dark brown, olive-brown upperparts streaked with dark brown, browner underparts, and brown (rather than red) iris. Bill shape, rufous-brown crown and nape, and white barring on wing-coverts are best distinctions from juvenile Water Rail. **Racial variation** *G. s. obscurior* of the Andaman Is is darker overall than the widely distributed *G. s. albiventer*, with more blackish coloration to upperparts and darker slate on sides of head, foreneck and breast. **VOICE** A sharp *cerrk* (Boonsong and Round 1991). **HABITS** A typical rail. **HABITAT** Reedy marshes, mangroves, edges of village tanks or flooded paddy-fields. **BREEDING** Almost all year, varying locally. Nests in marshes, on ground or on reed debris. **DISTRIBUTION AND STATUS** Widespread resident, subject to local movements. From Gujarat and Haryana east to Manipur and south through much of the subcontinent. **NP:** vagrant, possibly resident. **IN:** uncommon; plains up to 1300 m. **BD:** local. **LK:** rare resident in all zones, possibly also a winter visitor.

WATER RAIL *Rallus aquaticus* Plate 38

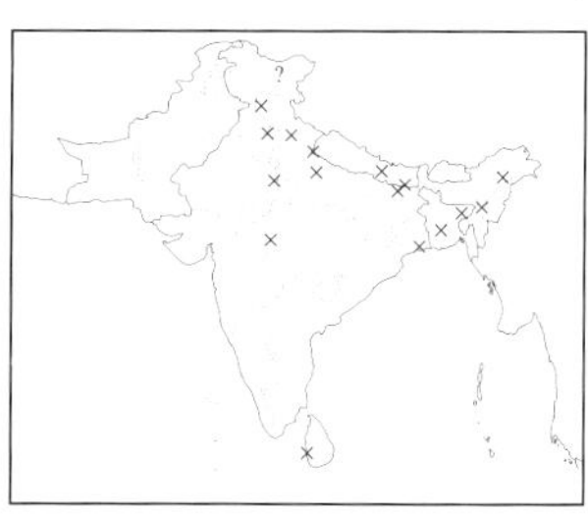

IDENTIFICATION 23–28 cm. **Adult** is a distinctive rail, with relatively long and slightly downcurved reddish bill, grey face and underparts, with black-and-white barring on flanks, black-streaked olive-brown upperparts, and white undertail-coverts. Told from adult Slaty-breasted Rail (above) by bill shape, coloration and patterning of upperparts (lacking fine white barring), broader black-and-white barring on flanks, and white undertail-coverts (although see racial variation). Legs are pinkish to pinkish-brown. **Juvenile** has upperparts like adult; bill is duller, underparts are buff with extensive dark brown mottling and stronger blackish barring on flanks, and undertail-coverts are warm rufous-buff. From juvenile Slaty-breasted by lack of rufous on crown and nape, conspicuous dark mottling on breast and flanks, and lack of narrow white barring on wing-coverts. **Racial variation** *R. a. indicus*, which winters in the NE subcontinent, has dark brown line through eye, creating grey supercilium above it, and neck and breast are browner than in *R. a. korejewi*, which breeds in Kashmir; *indicus* also has whitish chin and throat, and has blackish barring on white or buff undertail-coverts. **VOICE** Most frequently heard call, often likened to a squealing pig, is a grunting *grui..grui..grui...* etc that rises in pitch and then dies away; also a *tic tic tiç wheee-ooo*; courtship song is a *tyick-tyick-tyick*, often followed by a trilling *tyyurr* (Cramp and Simmons 1980). **HABITS** A typical rail. **HABITAT** Reedy marshes. **BREEDING** May–August. Nests among thick vegetation in marshes. **DISTRIBUTION AND STATUS** Breeds in Kashmir (and Ladakh?). Scattered winter records in N and NE India, Nepal, Bangladesh and Sri Lanka. **PK:** locally frequent winter visitor and passage migrant, mainly in Punjab. **NP:** rare and local winter visitor and passage migrant in the lowlands. **IN:** common in summer in Kashmir at 1500 m; widespread in winter, but few records. **BD:** rare passage migrant. **LK:** vagrant.

CORN CRAKE *Crex crex* Plate 38

Corncrake (P)

IDENTIFICATION 27–30 cm. Main features are stout pinkish bill and legs, rufous-chestnut wings (brightest on wing-coverts, and especially conspicuous in flight), buff-brown upperparts boldly streaked with dark brown, and

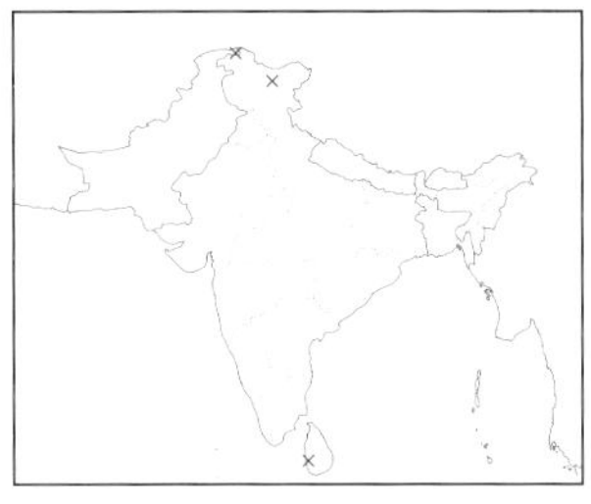

rufous-brown and white barring on flanks and undertail-coverts. Has variable amounts of grey on head sides, neck and breast, which is most prominent on breeding male and absent (replaced by buff) in juvenile plumage. **VOICE** Song of male, occasionally heard on migration, is a loud rasping *crex-crex, crex-crex,...* etc. **HABITS** Unknown in the region. Similar to those of other rails; crepuscular. **HABITAT** Confined to grasslands and standing crops. **DISTRIBUTION AND STATUS PK, IN, LK:** vagrant.

BROWN CRAKE *Amaurornis akool* — Plate 38

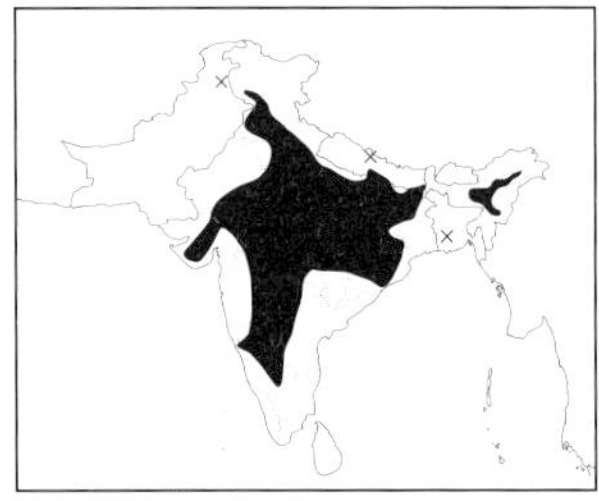

IDENTIFICATION 28 cm. A large, dusky crake, without barring on flanks or other prominent markings. **Adult** distinguished from other crakes by combination of dark olive-brown upperparts, ash-grey sides of head and underparts, with dusky olive-brown flanks and undertail-coverts, whitish throat, and greenish bill. Legs are pinkish-brown to purple. Most likely to be confused with immature Common Moorhen (p.467), but note that that species has white lateral undertail-coverts and whitish border to flanks. For differences from Black-tailed Crake (below), see that species. **Juvenile** as adult, but has brown rather than red iris. **VOICE** Poorly known, but variously described as 'a short plaintive note', 'a shrill rattle-like call' and a long-drawn-out vibrating whistle (Ali and Ripley 1987). **HABITS** A typical rail. **HABITAT** Reedy marshes, grass margins of streams, and emergent vegetation bordering watercourses. **BREEDING** May–August, varying locally. Nests in or near marshes. **DISTRIBUTION AND STATUS** Resident, subject to local movements. Mainly from Kashmir east to NE India and Bangladesh and south to S Karnataka. **PK:** rare and very local. **NP:** common at Chitwan, uncommon elsewhere; below 365 m. **IN:** uncommon; plains up to 800 m. **BD:** ?former resident; no recent records.

WHITE-BREASTED WATERHEN *Amaurornis phoenicurus* — Plate 38

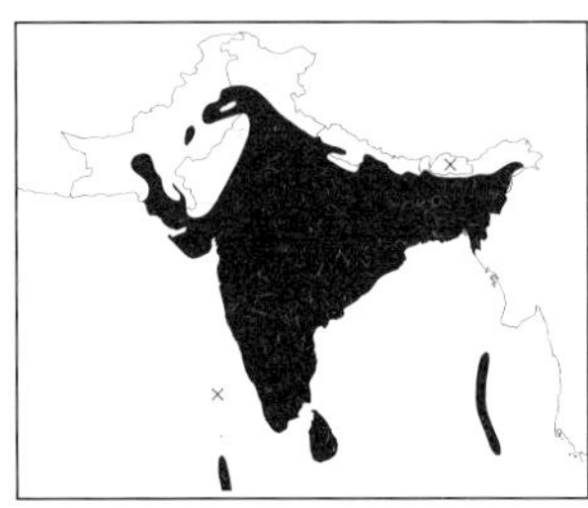

IDENTIFICATION 32 cm. **Adult** is very striking, with white face, foreneck and breast, dark slate-grey hindneck, upperparts and flanks, and rufous-cinnamon lower belly, vent and undertail-coverts. Has lime-green bill with red base, and long greenish legs. **Immature** is similar to adult, but has greyish cast to white face, foreneck and breast, and dark olive-brown upperparts. **VOICE** Usually silent except during the monsoon breeding season, when calls include a metallic *krr-kwaak-kwaak, krr-kwaak-kwaak* etc and a *kook..kook..kook,* usually preceded by loud roars, croaks and chuckles (Ali and Ripley 1987). **HABITS** Similar to those of other rails, but is less shy than most of the family; often feeds in the open and on quite dry land. Clambers among bushes and bamboo clumps with ease. Very noisy in the breeding season, sometimes calling throughout the night. **HABITAT** Occurs wherever water is surrounded by some thick cover: reedy marshes, edges of flooded paddy-fields, ponds, ditches. Often seen in villages and in public parks in towns and cities. **BREEDING** June–October. Nests on the ground, in dense undergrowth or thick bushes at the water's edge. **DISTRIBUTION AND STATUS** Resident throughout much of the subcontinent, except most of the northwest and Himalayas. **PK:** patchily distributed; frequent in Punjab, common in Sind. **NP:** fairly common below 915 m, rare up to 1370 m. **IN:** widespread and common; up to 1500 m. **BT:** rare. **BD:** occurs locally throughout. **LK:** common throughout, except the highest hills. **MV:** widespread.

BLACK-TAILED CRAKE *Porzana bicolor* — Plate 39

Elwes's Crake (F,I), *Amaurornis bicolor*

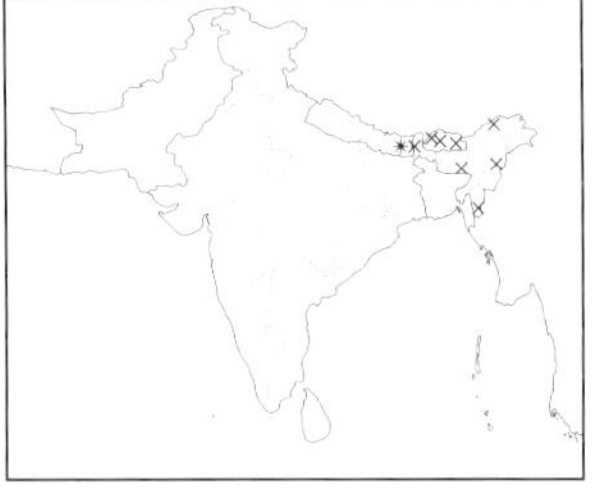

IDENTIFICATION 25 cm. **Adult** is grey and rufous-brown, and really confusable only with Brown Crake (above). Distinguished from that species by smaller size, indistinct whitish chin (whitish seldom extending onto throat), more uniform sooty-grey head, neck and underparts, bright rufescent olive-brown upperparts, sooty-black tail and undertail-coverts, and red patch at base of bill (brighter in breeding season). **Immature** has brown rather than red iris. **VOICE** Quite harsh rasping notes, often followed by a prolonged trill which is more obviously descending than that of Ruddy-breasted Crake (p.466) (Boonsong and Round 1991). **HABITS** Very skulking and poorly known. Probably like those of other rails. **HABITAT** Pools or marshy areas, sometimes in forest, and dense undergrowth bordering paddy-fields. **BREEDING** May–August in Khasi hills. Nests on wet ground in undergrowth; sometimes low down in bushes and trees. **DISTRIBUTION AND STATUS** Resident in Himalayas from E Nepal? east to Arunachal Pradesh; NE India. **NP:** possibly collected in the far east. **IN:** rare in Himalayas, common in Khasi hills; foothills up to 3600 m. **BT:** uncommon; 2285–2800 m (–700 m).

LITTLE CRAKE *Porzana parva* Plate 39

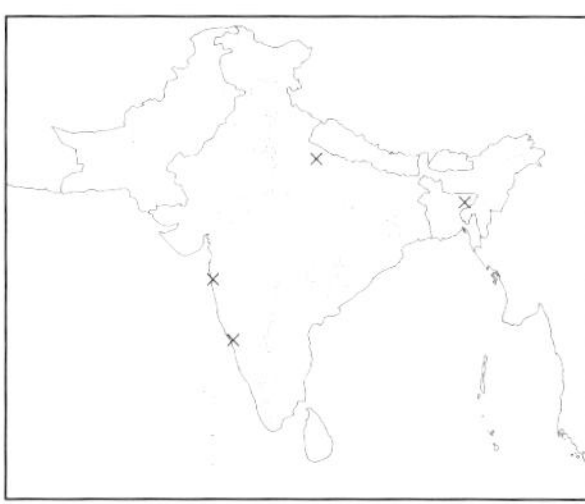

IDENTIFICATION 20–23 cm. A small, slim crake. Long wings (primaries extending well beyond tertials at rest) and long tail help to separate it from the similar Baillon's Crake (below) in all plumages. **Male** has grey face and underparts, with white barring on rear flanks, white barring on blackish undertail-coverts, warm brown upperparts prominently striped with buff and black (with some sparse white markings), and red base to green bill. In winter, the breast and belly are finely barred with buff. Features distinguishing it from adult Baillon's are duller brown upperparts, less extensive barring on underparts, more pronounced pale fringes to tertials and scapulars, and red base to bill; less heavily flecked with white above than Baillon's, and lacks the small, wavy, ring-shaped white spots of that species. **Female** is quite different from male: has some grey on supercilium and cheeks, but otherwise underparts are buff, with brown-and-buff barring to rear flanks and undertail-coverts. Not confusable with female Baillon's, which has greyish underparts. Red at base of bill, deep red iris, longer wings, restricted barring on rear flanks, and pronounced pale edge to tertials (see below) are best distinctions from immature Baillon's. **Juvenile** and **first-winter** are more heavily barred with brown on flanks than adult female, and lack red iris. From immature Baillon's by longer wings and tail, paler and broader sandy-buff scapular and tertial fringes (latter form buff stripe along outer edge of closed tertials), and paler olive-brown coloration to upperparts; upperparts have less extensive white flecking, which is usually restricted to inner mantle, back and greater coverts (on Baillon's usually extending over most of upperparts, with coverts heavily flecked); barring on flanks is largely restricted to rear flanks (on Baillon's, covers upper flanks and extends onto belly); and supercilium is more pronounced and contrasts noticeably with dark crown. Has yellow, and sometimes some reddish-orange, at base of lower mandible, whereas Baillon's has fairly uniform olive-green bill. In all plumages, noticeably smaller than Spotted Crake (below), and lacks that species' profuse white spotting on head, neck and breast and its unmarked buff undertail-coverts. **VOICE** Usually silent away from the breeding areas. Nevertheless, the song, which may be heard on migration, is a repeated, loud, nasal *quek...quek...quek...* etc, sometimes accelerating and then falling in pitch to end with *ak-uk-u-u-u-u*, before the series is resumed; also a *quek* contact call and a *tyiick* alarm call (Cramp and Simmons 1980). **HABITS** A typical rail. Mainly crepuscular. **HABITAT** Marshes with dense reed cover. **DISTRIBUTION AND STATUS** Winter visitor and passage migrant. Mainly Pakistan and India. **PK:** scarce to rare. **IN:** rare. **BD:** vagrant. **REFERENCES** Harris *et al.* (1996).

BAILLON'S CRAKE *Porzana pusilla* Plate 39

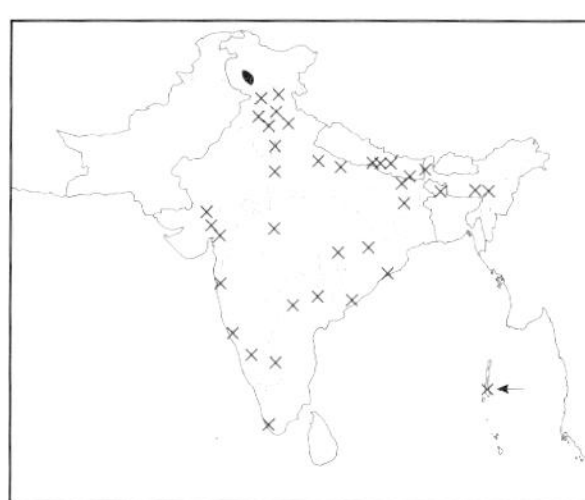

IDENTIFICATION 17–19 cm. A small crake with short wings and tail. **Male** has blue-grey face and underparts, white barring on blackish flanks, vent and undertail-coverts, rufous-brown upperparts prominently striped with black and liberally marked with white streaks and ring-shaped spots, and an all-green bill. **Female** is similar to male, but usually has paler throat, and paler greyish underparts often flecked with buff. **Juvenile** and **first-winter** have upperparts similar to adult, but face and underparts are buff, with whitish chin and throat. Easily confused with the much rarer Little Crake (above); see that species for main differences. Noticeably smaller than Spotted Crake (below), and lacks that species' profuse white spotting on head, neck and breast and its unmarked buff undertail-coverts. **VOICE** Usually silent away from the breeding areas. The song, which may be heard on migration, is a rattling rasp, *trrrrr-trrrr...*, sounding like a fingernail being drawn across a comb; also a *tyiuk* alarm call (Cramp and Simmons 1980). **HABITS** A typical rail. Mainly crepuscular. **HABITAT** Reedy marshes, edges of lakes and pools with emergent vegetation, and flooded paddy-fields. **BREEDING** May–August in Kashmir. Nest usually has a partial canopy of plant stems, and is built in a marsh, in a paddy-field or at a lake edge. **DISTRIBUTION AND STATUS** Breeds in Kashmir and Uttar Pradesh; winter visitor or passage migrant throughout much of the subcontinent. **PK:** scarce winter visitor and passage migrant. **NP:** scarce winter visitor and passage migrant, possibly breeds; mainly in the lowlands (–1370 m). **IN:** common in Kashmir in summer up to 1800 m; status elsewhere uncertain. **BD:** vagrant. **LK:** rare winter visitor to lowlands and middle hills. **REFERENCES** Harris *et al.* (1996).

SPOTTED CRAKE *Porzana porzana* Plate 39

IDENTIFICATION 22–24 cm. In all plumages, separable from other crakes by profuse white spotting on head, neck and breast, and unmarked buff undertail-coverts. **Male** has blue-grey supercilium, throat and foreneck, and grey-wash to breast, red base to rather stout yellowish bill, blackish-streaked olive-brown upperparts profusely marked with white, and brown and white barring on flanks. **Female** is similar to male, but has less grey on head, neck and breast, which can be more profusely spotted with white. Legs of both sexes are olive-green. **Juvenile** is

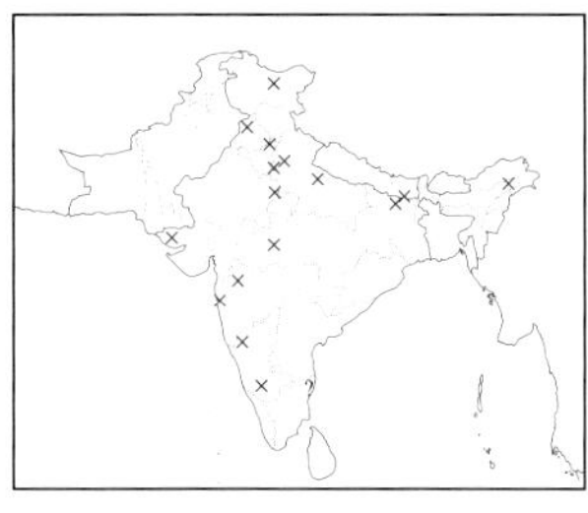

similar to female, but grey of head, neck and breast is replaced with buffish-brown, breast is not so heavily spotted with white, and bill is brown with paler base. **VOICE** Usually silent away from the breeding areas. The song, sometimes heard on migration, is a swishing *h-wet..h-wet...*, often likened to sound of a whiplash. **HABITS** A typical rail; mainly crepuscular. **HABITAT** Reedy swamps; reed-edged jheels, reservoirs and canals. **DISTRIBUTION AND STATUS** Winter visitor. From Pakistan east to Assam and south to Karnataka, except E India and Bangladesh. **PK:** scarce winter visitor and passage migrant. **NP:** vagrant. **IN:** widespread but rare winter visitor, recorded mainly in the west.

RUDDY-BREASTED CRAKE *Porzana fusca* — Plate 39

Ruddy Crake (F,I,P), *Amaurornis fuscus* (F,P)

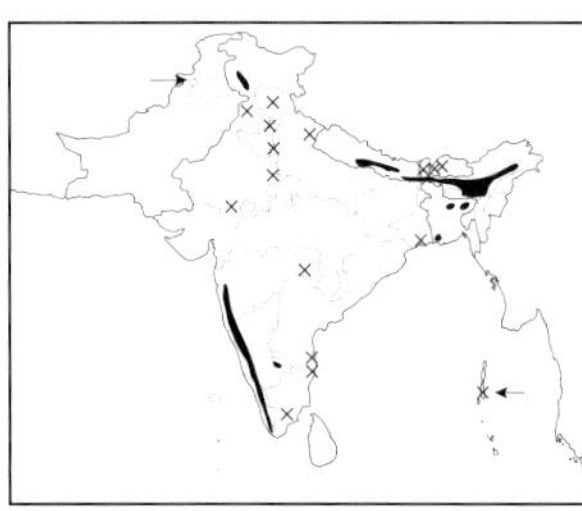

IDENTIFICATION 22 cm. **Adult** best separated from other crakes by combination of dull chestnut underparts, unmarked dark olive-brown upperparts, indistinct dark brown and white barring on rear flanks and undertail-coverts, and red legs. Red legs, smaller size, chestnut underparts, and barring on flanks separate it from Brown Crake (p.464). Red-legged Crake (p.462) is more strikingly banded on the underparts, is brighter rufous on head, neck and breast, and has white markings on wing-coverts and flight feathers. **Juvenile** is dark olive-brown, with variable greyish-white mottling, streaking or fine barring on underparts; undertail-coverts are prominently barred with white; has pale chin and throat, and some chestnut mottling on forehead and around face. Iris is brown (rather than red as in adult). **VOICE** A single soft *crake*, uttered at considerable intervals; a loud metallic *tewk*, repeated at intervals of 2–3 seconds, often followed by a squeaky trilling recalling Little Grebe (p.552), and a short *chuck* when feeding (Ali and Ripley 1987; Boonsong and Round 1991). **HABITS** A typical rail. **HABITAT** Reedy marshes, edges of flooded paddy-fields and canals with emergent vegetation. **BREEDING** June–September, varying locally. Nests on marshy ground among grass, reeds or rice plants; stalks sometimes bent over to form a canopy. **DISTRIBUTION AND STATUS** Resident, subject to local and altitudinal movements. Mainly NW Pakistan, Kashmir, Nepal, NE India, Western Ghats, Bangladesh and Sri Lanka; scattered records elsewhere in India. **PK:** rare to scarce in foothills. **NP:** local resident below 370 m, uncommon visitor up to 1280 m. **IN:** common in Kashmir, uncommon elsewhere; up to 1830 m in Himalayas and to 2000 m in Western Ghats. **BT**: rare resident or summer visitor; 2135–2400 m. **BD:** local resident and winter visitor. **LK:** scarce resident throughout, except highest hills.

WATERCOCK *Gallicrex cinerea* — Plate 39

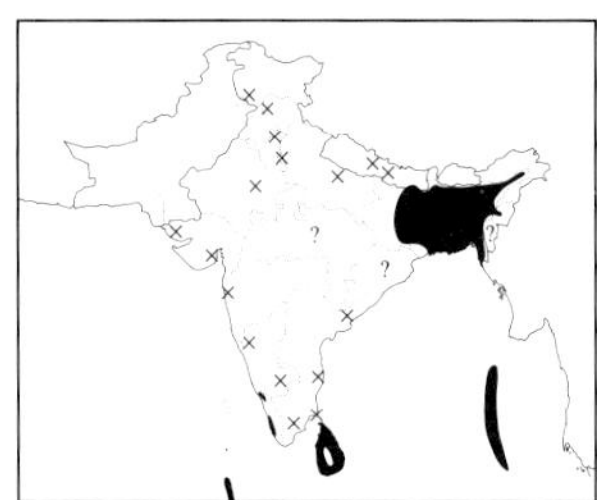

IDENTIFICATION Male 43 cm; female 36 cm. Large and lanky, with long, slim neck and huge legs and feet. **Breeding male** is mainly greyish-black in coloration, with yellow-tipped red bill and red frontal shield and horn. Legs and feet are red. Has warm buff fringes to scapulars, wing-coverts and tertials, and buff undertail-coverts are generally barred with blackish. **First-year male** is heavily marked with rufous-buff fringes to feathers of head, neck and body. **Non-breeding male** and **female** are mainly buff in coloration, with yellowish bill, olive-green legs and feet, and small yellowish triangular shield on forehead. Face, neck and underparts are buff, with underparts narrowly barred with brown; have blackish-brown crown, and blackish-brown upperparts with broad buff fringes to mantle and wings. Female is considerably smaller than non-breeding male. **Juvenile** is similar to non-breeding adult, but is uniform rufous-buff on underparts, and feathers of upperparts are fringed with rufous-buff. **VOICE** A series of 10–12 *kok-kok-kok...* notes, followed by a deep, hollow *utumb-utumb-utumb...* repeated 10–12 times, and then by five or six *kluck-kluck-kluck* notes (Ali and Ripley 1987). **HABITS** Very similar to those of other rails. Mainly crepuscular, also emerging from cover to feed in cloudy weather. In the breeding season during the monsoon, males call persistently. **HABITAT** Reedy marshes, flooded paddies or sugarcane fields, canals, ponds and ditches with emergent vegetation. **BREEDING** May–September, varying locally. Nest is a deep cup or dome of vegetation in reedbeds or paddy-fields. **DISTRIBUTION AND STATUS** Resident in well-watered areas; disperses widely in the monsoon. Widespread, but mainly in the northeast and Sri Lanka. **PK:** very local, summer visitor; common in lower Sindh, a few in Punjab. **NP:** rare monsoon visitor; below 1280 m. **IN:** frequent and local in the plains. **BD:** local resident throughout. **LK:** resident in the lowlands; rare in the dry zone, more frequent in wet zone. **MV:** uncommon resident or breeding visitor.

PURPLE SWAMPHEN *Porphyrio porphyrio* — Plate 39

Purple Coot (P), Purple Gallinule (F)

IDENTIFICATION 45–50 cm. A very large rail, mainly purplish-blue in coloration, with huge red bill, and red frontal shield. Has long, stout red legs and huge feet, and white undertail-coverts. **Juvenile** is duller than adult,

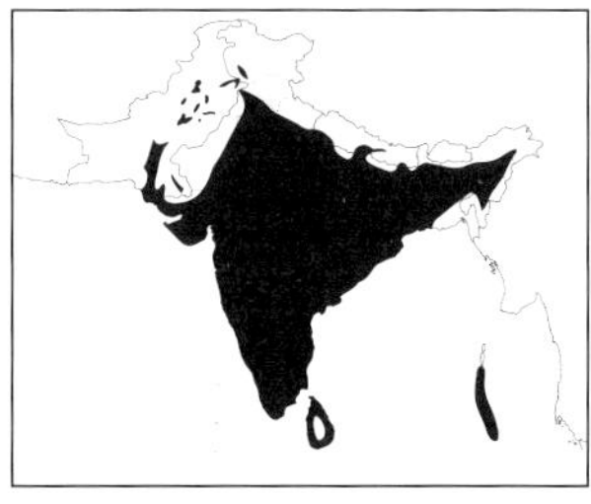

with pale throat, grey wash to face, foreneck and breast, duller red bill (which is blackish at first), and duller legs and feet. **VOICE** Very variable: alarm call is an explosive, nasal, rising *cooah*; song is a long series of powerful, nasal rattles, rendered as *quinquinkrrkrr...* etc, and contact calls include a soft *chuck-chuck* (Cramp and Simmons 1980). **HABITS** Typically found in small parties, and in bigger numbers in extensive marshes. Diurnal, and where undisturbed is not shy. Forages mainly within reedbeds and readily clambers about reeds. **HABITAT** Large marshes and extensive reedbeds bordering jheels and lakes. **BREEDING** April–September, varying locally. Nest is a bulky mass of vegetation placed on a floating islet or just above water in reeds or rushes. **DISTRIBUTION AND STATUS** Resident, subject to local movements. Throughout much of the subcontinent, except parts of the northwest, northeast and Himalayas. **PK:** common resident. **NP:** chiefly a winter visitor and passage migrant below 915 m (–1370 m); also breeds. **IN:** locally common and widespread; plains, up to 1500 m in Kashmir. **BD:** locally common resident. **LK:** common resident in lowlands.

COMMON MOORHEN *Gallinula chloropus* — Plate 39

Moorhen (I,P), Waterhen, Indian Gallinule (F)

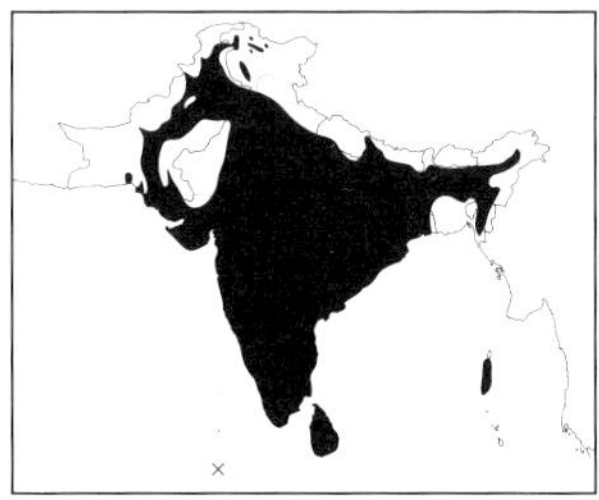

IDENTIFICATION 32–35 cm. **Adult breeding** has yellow-tipped red bill and red frontal shield, red irides, blackish head and neck, slate-grey underparts, and dark olive-brown upperparts; very striking white lateral undertail-coverts and white border to flanks, and yellow-green legs with red above knee. **Adult non-breeding** has duller brownish-red bill and duller legs. **Juvenile** has white undertail-coverts and flank line (although latter sometimes missing), which help distinguish it from Brown Crake (p.464); is mainly brown, with whitish throat, grey wash to breast and flanks, and variable whitish patch on belly, and has dull green bill and legs. **Immature** resembles non-breeding adult, but has duller body plumage, with grey of underparts washed with brown and buff, whitish throat, and less prominent pale border to flanks. **VOICE** Advertising call is a loud, explosive *kurr-ik* and *kark*; also a *cuk cuk cuk* and *kekuk* alarm calls, and a soft, muttering territorial call, *kook..kook..* (Cramp and Simmons 1980). **HABITS** Found singly, in pairs or in small parties; may gather in flocks of 50 or more in winter. Usually forages in the open; spends most of day swimming among aquatic plants; also feeds on land. Generally escapes danger by swimming into vegetation, but can dive well if necessary. Slow and heavy in flight, and patters along the water before becoming airborne. **HABITAT** Marshes, lakes, jheels, ponds, village tanks and ditches with emergent aquatic vegetation. **BREEDING** March–September, varying locally. Nest is a large mass of vegetation in reedbeds, placed a little above the water level. **DISTRIBUTION AND STATUS** Resident and winter visitor. Throughout most of the subcontinent, except parts of the northwest, northeast and Himalayas. **PK:** common and very widespread resident. **NP:** locally common resident and winter visitor, mainly in the lowlands (–4575 m on passage). **IN:** widespread and common resident and winter visitor; breeds up to 2400 m in Kashmir and to 2000 m in the Nilgiris. **BD:** local resident. **LK:** resident in the lowlands, more common in the dry zone. **MV:** has bred.

COMMON COOT *Fulica atra* — Plate 39

Coot (F,I), Eurasian Coot (N), Black Coot (R)

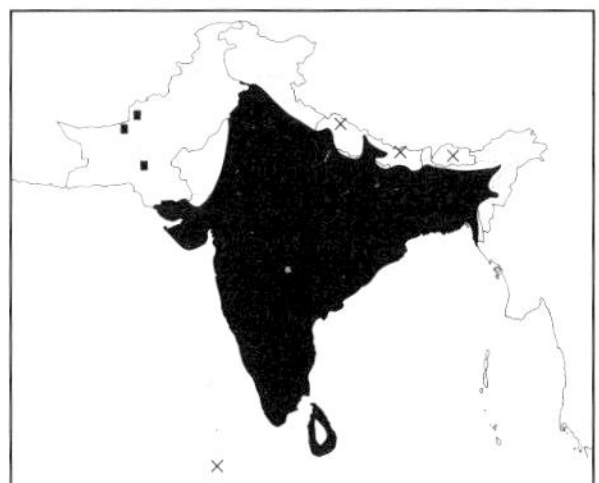

IDENTIFICATION 36–38 cm. **Adult** is entirely greyish-black, with white bill and frontal shield, red irides, and large dull green legs and feet. Shows paler trailing edge to secondaries in flight. **Juvenile** is paler grey-brown, with whitish chin, throat and breast; has brown irides, greyish-white bill, and indistinct shield. **Immature** is similar to adult, but duller, with whitish throat and paler greyish underparts. **VOICE** A great variety of calls, including a high-pitched *pyee* and a series of long, often soft *dp..dp..* calls. **HABITS** Gregarious, especially in winter, when it gathers in enormous flocks in some places. Diurnal and not shy. Forages chiefly for aquatic vegetation in open water, mainly by diving; also by sieving plant material from the surface. When disturbed, prefers to skitter away along the water surface rather than fly. Takes to the air with difficulty, after prolonged pattering across the water. **HABITAT** Lakes, jheels and irrigation tanks with large areas of open water and marginal emergent vegetation. **BREEDING** May–December, varying locally. Nest is a large mass of vegetation among reeds, a little above the water level. **DISTRIBUTION AND STATUS** Resident and winter visitor. Throughout much of the subcontinent, except parts of the northwest, northeast and Himalayas. **PK:** common and widespread winter visitor; occasionally breeds. **NP:** uncommon winter visitor and passage migrant; from the terai up to 3500 m (–5000 m). **IN:** widespread and common resident and winter visitor; breeds locally up to 2500 m in Himalayas, also widely and erratically in plains. **BT:** rare. **BD:** scarce resident. **LK:** rare resident in N dry lowlands, a few records in south. **MV:** vagrant. **REFERENCES** Tymstra *et al.* (1997).

SANDGROUSE Pteroclidae

Cryptically patterned terrestrial birds resembling pigeons in size and shape. The body is plump, with a small head, short bill, and short legs feathered down to, and sometimes including, the toes, and the wings are long and pointed. Most sandgrouse are wary and, when disturbed, rise with a clatter of wings, flying off rapidly and directly with fast regular wingbeats. They walk and run well, foraging mainly for small hard seeds picked up from the ground and sometimes also eating green leaves, shoots, berries, small bulbs and insects. They need to drink every day, and will frequently travel long distances to waterholes. Most sandgrouse have regular drinking times which are characteristic of each species, and they often visit traditional watering places; sometimes thousands of birds may gather in a drinking flock. Most species are gregarious except when breeding. The nest is a shallow unlined scrape, normally in the open or occasionally among stones, shrubs or grass tufts. The young leave the nest as soon as they hatch, and follow their parents to forage for food. The references specific to sandgrouse are Cramp (1985) and Johnsgard (1991).

TIBETAN SANDGROUSE *Syrrhaptes tibetanus* — Plate 40

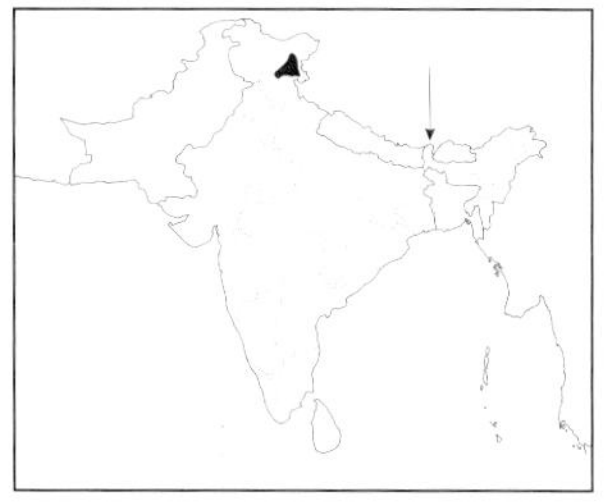

IDENTIFICATION 48 cm. A large, pin-tailed sandgrouse, the only one occurring on the Tibetan Plateau. Both sexes are distinctive, with pale orange face and throat, fine black barring on crown and breast, sandy upperparts with bold black spotting on scapulars, and white lower breast and belly. In flight, shows blackish upperside to flight feathers (with white trailing edge to primaries), which contrast with sandy wing-coverts; underwing is mainly dark, except for white lesser coverts and narrow white trailing edge to underside of primaries. For differences from Pallas's (below), see that species. **Male** has unbarred sandy mantle and wing-coverts, and fawn wash across lower breast. **Female** is similar to male, but has fine black barring on mantle, coverts and tertials, and more extensive black barring on breast. **Immature** is similar to female, but has only faint traces of pale orange on throat. **VOICE** Calls include deep, disyllabic *guk-guk* or *caga-caga* notes, said to be more musical than calls of most other sandgrouse (Johnsgard 1991). **HABITS** Drinks irregularly, unlike most sandgrouse. Usually tame, flying only when approached quite closely, and even then landing again a short distance away. **HABITAT** High-altitude, barren, stony semi-desert. **BREEDING** Details not recorded in the region. From late June in Tibet. Lays eggs in a depression on bare stony ground. **DISTRIBUTION AND STATUS IN:** resident, breeds in Ladakh (where locally common), N Himachal Pradesh and Sikkim, 4200–5400 m; sometimes moves to lower elevations in winter. **REFERENCES** Pfister (1997), Robson (1993b).

PALLAS'S SANDGROUSE *Syrrhaptes paradoxus* — Plate 40

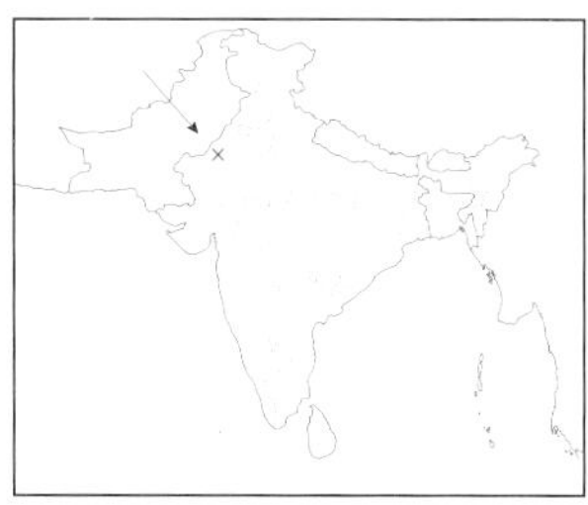

IDENTIFICATION 30–41 cm. A large, pin-tailed sandgrouse with elongated outer primaries. Both sexes are distinctive, with pale orange throat and patch on sides of head, pale grey breast, sandy upperparts with bold black spotting and barring, prominent black patch on belly, and largely white underwing in flight. Superficially resembles Tibetan Sandgrouse (above), but major differences are black patch on belly, mainly white underwing (with narrow black band along underside of secondaries and inner primaries), and pale upperside to primaries with black leading edge. **Male** has narrow gorget of black barring across breast, unbarred sandy wing-coverts, and unspotted hindneck and crown. **Female** lacks black gorget, and has extensive black barring on mantle and wing-coverts, blackish spotting on crown and hindneck, and narrow black bar across lower throat. **VOICE** A low-pitched, chattering *cu-ruu cu-ruu cu-ou-ruu* (Cramp 1985). **HABITS** A typical sandgrouse. **HABITAT** Unknown in the region. Elsewhere, inhabits open, arid plains and uplands. **DISTRIBUTION AND STATUS IN:** vagrant to Rajasthan. Breeds in C Asia; erratic irruptions formerly occurred when birds dispersed widely, but the species has decreased.

PIN-TAILED SANDGROUSE *Pterocles alchata* — Plate 40

Large Pintail Sandgrouse

IDENTIFICATION 31–39 cm. The only pin-tailed sandgrouse with brilliant white belly and two or (on female) three black breast lines. Underwing is mainly white, with fine black leading and trailing edges, underside of primaries becoming blacker towards tip; upperside of primaries appears pale grey, with darker trailing edge to inner primaries. **Male breeding** has black chin and eye-stripe, black-framed chestnut-buff breast-band, olive-green upperparts with yellowish spotting, and vinaceous-chestnut outer wing-coverts which are outlined with white and black. **Male non-breeding** has similar-plumaged underparts and coverts, but has buff upperparts (including crown), strongly barred with black, and whitish chin. **Female breeding** has upperparts, including crown and hindneck, barred with golden-buff, grey and black, this patterning spreading onto wing-coverts, and barring widening on outer coverts. Has black bar across lower throat, in addition to the two across breast. **Female**

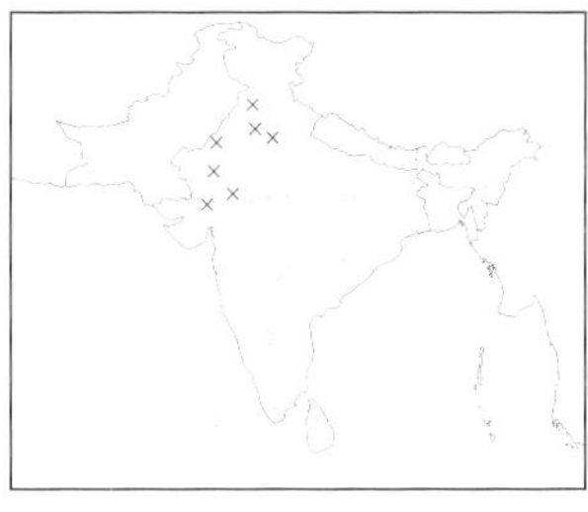

non-breeding lacks grey barring on upperparts; throat is spotted with black, but lacks clear black band across lower throat. **Juvenile** is similar to respective non-breeding adult, but with patterning less well defined, and lacks pintail. **VOICE** Flight calls are variously described as a loud, ringing *catar-catar*, a nasal *ga-ga-ga* and an abrupt, guttural *gang gang* (Cramp 1985). **HABITS** A typical sandgrouse. Highly gregarious in winter and on migration. Flights to water in huge flocks in early mornings and late afternoons, and also at midday in very hot weather. Rests during the heat of the day and at night. Very difficult to approach. **HABITAT** Arid, sandy desert, scrub desert, and fallow land in partly cultivated semi-desert. **BREEDING** Details not recorded in the region. May–July in Iraq. Loosely colonial. Lays eggs in a depression on high open ground. **DISTRIBUTION AND STATUS** Probably breeds; winter visitor to Pakistan and NW India (Punjab, Haryana, Delhi, Rajasthan and Gujarat). **PK:** scarce and rather local winter visitor; small numbers probably remain to breed in extreme SW Baluchistan and on the Afghan border around Chaman. **IN:** straggler. **REFERENCES** Cramp (1985).

CHESTNUT-BELLIED SANDGROUSE *Pterocles exustus* — Plate 40

Indian Sandgrouse (F,I)

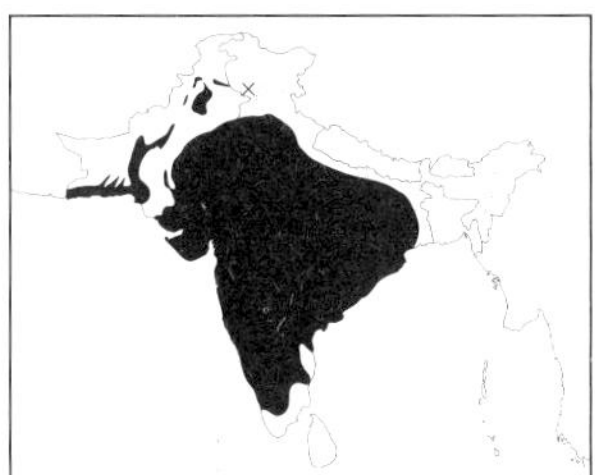

IDENTIFICATION 31–33 cm. The only pin-tailed sandgrouse with dark underwing, dark belly and black breast line, these features being shown by both sexes. Most likely to be confused with Black-bellied Sandgrouse (p.470), but is smaller and slimmer; male has elongated central tail feathers, and shows all-dark underwing in flight (with white trailing edge to primaries). **Male** is dusky buff, with yellowish wash to face; has black-fringed yellowish spots on wing-coverts, and diffuse blackish-chestnut belly. **Female** is heavily spotted with black on breast and barred with black on upperparts, and belly patch is dark brown and indistinctly barred with rufous. Has buff banding across wing-coverts and lacks black collar, which are also distinctions (in addition to underwing pattern) from female Black-bellied. **Juvenile** is similar to female, but is duller, has less heavily barred upperparts, and has shorter tail. **VOICE** A chuckling, guttural *whit kt-arr* (Cramp 1985). **HABITS** A typical sandgrouse. Usually keeps in flocks of up to 30 birds outside the breeding season or when flying to drink. Flies to drinking places in early to mid morning, also sometimes in early afternoon in very hot weather; birds usually land some distance from water and gather in numbers, before flying or walking to the water's edge. **HABITAT** Sandy deserts, barren plains, sparse thorn scrub, and fallow fields and stubbles at the desert edge. **BREEDING** January–May, varying locally; sometimes also other months. Lays eggs in a scrape on open ground, usually sheltered by a bush or lump of earth. **DISTRIBUTION AND STATUS** Resident, subject to erratic local movements depending on food supply and rainfall. Pakistan and from Gujarat, Rajasthan and C Punjab east to C West Bengal and south through the peninsula to S Kerala and S Tamil Nadu. **PK:** widespread and common. **IN:** common and widespread, less frequent in the far east and south.

SPOTTED SANDGROUSE *Pterocles senegallus* — Plate 40

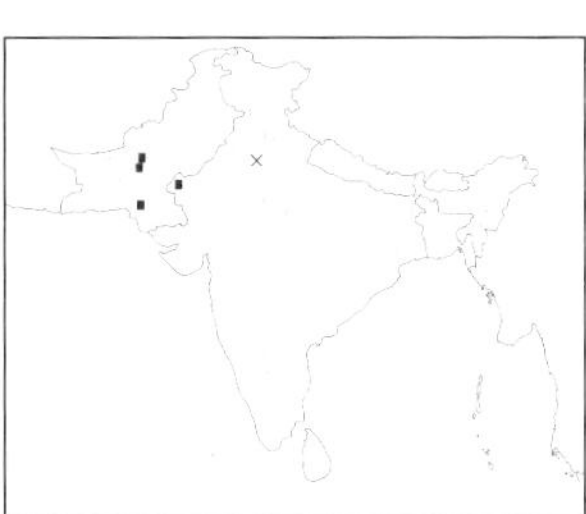

IDENTIFICATION 30–35 cm. Most likely to be confused with Crowned Sandgrouse (p.470), but has long pointed tail, is slimmer-bodied with narrower-based and more pointed wings, and has distinctive flight call. Upperwing appears rather pale, with indistinct dark trailing edge, and underwing lacks Crowned's strong contrast between black remiges and whitish coverts. Lacks black banding across breast shown by Chestnut-bellied and Black-bellied Sandgrouse (above and p.470). **Male** is sandy olive-brown above, with buff spotting on wing-coverts, and has greyish supercilium and unmarked breast. Main plumage differences from male Crowned are lack of black-and-white patterning to head, and presence of black centre to belly. For further differences, see that species. **Female** is boldly spotted with black on upperparts and breast. Told from female Crowned by warmer orange-buff coloration, sparser but more prominent spotting on upperparts and breast, unbarred lower breast and belly, and black centre to belly and vent. **Juvenile** is similar to female, but lacks orange throat and is more finely barred. Unbarred belly, with black line down centre, help separate it from juvenile Crowned. **VOICE** A distinctive and far-carrying *quitoo quitoo* (Cramp 1985). **HABITS** A typical sandgrouse. More gregarious than Chestnut-bellied; usually in flocks of 100 or more birds outside the breeding season or in flights to drinking places. Gathers in huge concentrations at water in areas of water scarcity. Regularly flies to water about two hours after sunrise, and also in the evening in hot weather; birds fly in directly to the water's edge, or may even land on the water. **HABITAT** Barren sandy desert and arid stony foothills. **BREEDING** June and July. Lays eggs in a hollow on bare clay flats or sand and clay areas. **DISTRIBUTION AND STATUS** Breeds in N Sindh and S Baluchistan, Pakistan and Rajasthan; winters in Pakistan and NW India (W Gujarat and W Rajasthan). **PK, IN:** common but erratic winter visitor and passage migrant; small numbers breed. **REFERENCES** Harris *et al.* (1996), Sangha (1995).

BLACK-BELLIED SANDGROUSE *Pterocles orientalis* — Plate 40

Imperial Sandgrouse (F,I)

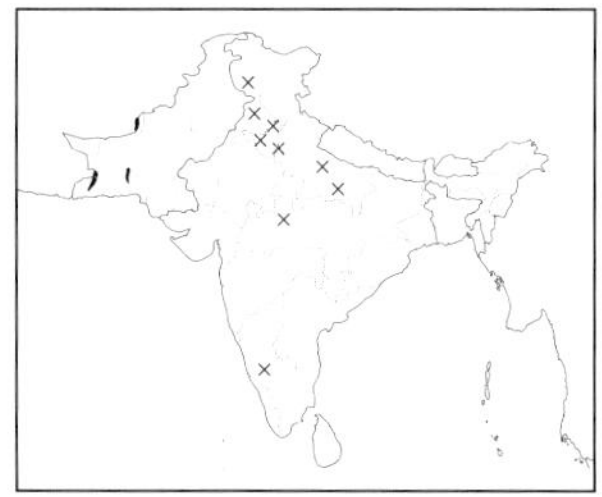

IDENTIFICATION 33–35 cm. A large, stocky sandgrouse, lacking pin-tail; both sexes show black belly, and narrow black gorget across breast. Most likely to be confused with Chestnut-bellied Sandgrouse (p.469), but is stockier, with broader-based wings, lacks elongated central tail feathers, and has white underwing-coverts which contrast strongly with black flight feathers. **Male** has greyish head, neck and upper breast, black-and-chestnut throat, and yellow-ochre upperparts with dark feather centres. **Female** is heavily spotted with black on upper breast and upperparts. Boldly patterned underparts separate it from other female sandgrouse except Chestnut-bellied (but has black throat-collar and white underwing-coverts, and lacks buff banding across wing of that species). **Juvenile** is similar to female, but very soon resembles dull version of respective adult. **VOICE** A soft, gurgling *tchowrrr rerr-rerr* (Cramp 1985). **HABITS** A typical sandgrouse. Makes daily flights to water two hours or so after sunrise, and less regularly in the late afternoon. Very wary; flocks may circle over drinking places before landing. **HABITAT** Thorn scrub in semi-desert and fallow cultivation at the desert edge. **BREEDING** Little known in the region. May. Lays eggs in a hollow on bare open ground. **DISTRIBUTION AND STATUS** Breeds in Baluchistan, Pakistan; winters in Pakistan and NW India (W Rajasthan and W Gujarat). **PK:** mainly a winter visitor, common in Punjab, uncommon in Sindh; also a regular passage migrant; a few pairs breed. **IN:** erratic; occurs locally in huge numbers.

CROWNED SANDGROUSE *Pterocles coronatus* — Plate 40

Coronetted Sandgrouse (I)

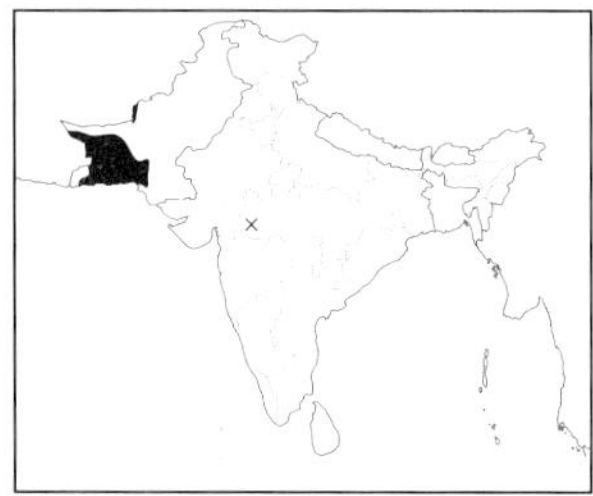

IDENTIFICATION 27–29 cm. A small and compact, short-tailed sandgrouse. Most likely to be confused with Spotted Sandgrouse (p.469), but has short, white-tipped tail, shows blackish flight feathers which contrast with wing-coverts on upperwing and underwing, lacks black line down centre of belly, and has distinctive flight call. **Male** is sandy-brown, with prominent buff spotting on scapulars and coverts. Main differences from male Spotted are black-and-white pattern to head, darker rufous crown, and more prominent buff spotting on upperparts. **Female** is sandy-buff all over, heavily spotted and barred with black. Told from female Spotted by colder coloration, less prominent spotting, barred lower breast and belly, and lack of black centre to belly and vent. Possibly confusable also with female Lichtenstein's Sandgrouse (p.471), but has orange-buff throat. **Juvenile** is similar to female, but has whiter throat and is more finely barred. **Immature** resembles respective adult, but head pattern of young male is indistinct (and more closely resembles male Spotted). **VOICE** A loud, guttural chatter, *ch-ga ch-ga-ra* (Harris *et al.* 1996). **HABITS** Very similar to those of other sandgrouse, but has a more upright posture. Usually allows close approach. Typically, flies to drink in the early morning in flocks of up to 30 birds; settles a few hundred metres from the water until a large party gathers, and then cautiously walks to drinking place. **HABITAT** Very barren and arid desert regions. **BREEDING** April–June. Lays eggs in a hollow on open ground. **DISTRIBUTION AND STATUS PK:** common and quite local resident, mainly west of the Indus R; subject to some local movements, depending on food availability. **IN:** no records since 19th century. **REFERENCES** Briggs (1931), Harris *et al.* (1996).

PAINTED SANDGROUSE *Pterocles indicus* — Plate 40

Close-barred Sandgrouse (F,I)

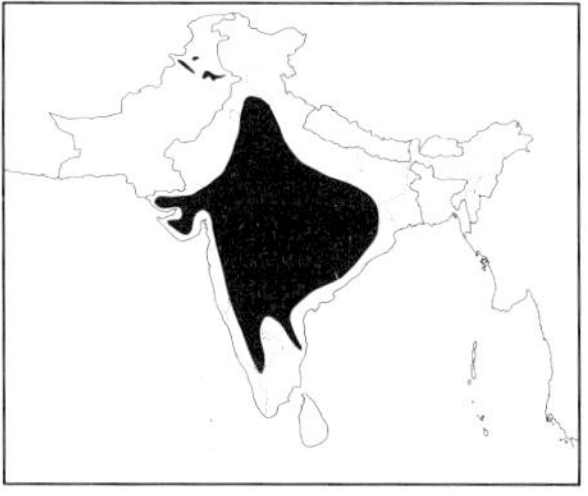

IDENTIFICATION 28 cm. A strongly barred sandgrouse without pin-tail. Both sexes show brownish-grey underwing in flight. Most closely resembles Lichtenstein's Sandgrouse (p.471), although there is no overlap in ranges. **Male** has white forehead divided by black cross-band, heavily barred upperparts, and strongly banded breast. Is more richly coloured and strongly marked than Lichtenstein's, and has unbarred buffish-orange face and inner wing-coverts, and a chestnut (rather than blackish) band encircling base of neck. **Female** is heavily barred all over, and lacks male's patterning on head and underparts. Is similar to female Lichtenstein's, but has unspotted creamy face and throat, more broadly and coarsely barred upperparts with warmer buff and rufous tones, and darker, more densely barred belly; and outer greater coverts are unbarred and show as distinct buff area in wing. Possibly confusable with female Chestnut-bellied Sandgrouse (p.469), but that species is distinctly pin-tailed, has a darker underwing, and has a boldly spotted breast which is bordered below by a broad unmarked buff band. Grey underwing helps separate it from female Crowned Sandgrouse (above), although there is no overlap in ranges; that species is much paler fawn above and is paler below, becoming whiter towards belly. **Immature** is similar to female, but is more closely barred. **VOICE** A clucking *yek-yek-yek* when flushed, and a *chirik-chirik* flight call (Ali and

Ripley 1987). **HABITS** A typical sandgrouse, but less gregarious than other species, usually keeping in twos, threes, or small groups of up to ten. Normally sits tight and allows close approach, and if flushed lands again after a short flight. Drinks only after dusk, usually settling some distance from water before moving in to drink. **HABITAT** Low hills with scattered thorn scrub or open rocky and grassy areas; firebreaks in deciduous forest and shallow rocky ravines. **BREEDING** Almost all months, varying locally. Lays eggs in a scrape on stony ground, under a small bush or grass clump. **DISTRIBUTION AND STATUS** Resident, subject to local movements. N Pakistan and India from W Gujarat, E Rajasthan and S Punjab east to S Bihar and E Orissa and throughout much of the peninsula south to N Tamil Nadu. **PK:** rather rare and local. **IN:** widespread, but generally uncommon.

LICHTENSTEIN'S SANDGROUSE *Pterocles lichtensteinii* — Plate 40

Close-barred Sandgrouse *P. indicus* (I)

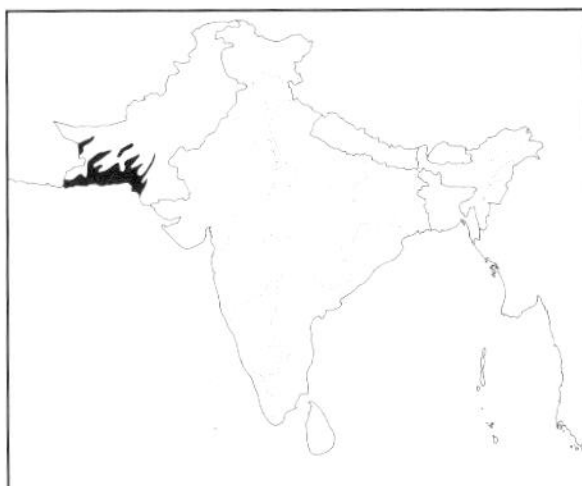

IDENTIFICATION 24–26 cm. A closely barred sandgrouse without pin-tail. Both sexes look rather pale grey and buff in coloration, and show strong contrast between blackish remiges and paler barred coverts on upperwing; underwing is uniform grey. **Male** is almost entirely barred with black, except for white forehead and forecrown crossed by two black bands, golden-buff banding across closed wing, and yellowish-buff and black banding across breast. Similar to male Painted Sandgrouse (p.470), although there is no overlap in ranges, but is greyer in coloration and more uniformly barred (e.g. on neck and inner wing-coverts). **Female** is heavily barred all over, and lacks patterning of head and bands across breast of male. For differences from female Painted, see that species. Possibly confusable with female Crowned Sandgrouse (p.470), but has barred face and throat, lacks pale buff spotting on upperwing-coverts and scapulars, and has uniform grey underwing. **Juvenile** is similar to female, but more finely barred. **First-winter** as respective adult, but male may lack black-and-white patterning to head, and breast-banding may be poorly defined. **VOICE** Flight call is a *wheet-wheet-wheet* and a *qwee-oo*, and also a guttural *krerwerwerwer* (Harris *et al.* 1996). **HABITS** Very similar to those of Painted. **HABITAT** Low stony hills with scattered scrub in desert and dry rocky nullahs. **BREEDING** Mainly May and June. Lays eggs in a hollow in soil, shaded in the lee of a bush. **DISTRIBUTION AND STATUS PK:** locally frequent resident in the south, west of the Indus R. **REFERENCES** Harris *et al.* (1996).

WADERS

Accounts for the following six families (Scolopacidae, Rostratulidae, Jacanidae, Burhinidae, Charadriidae and Glareolidae) have drawn extensively on Hayman *et al.* (1986), and to a lesser extent on Cramp *et al.* (1983), Colston and Burton (1988) and Rosair and Cottridge (1995).

WOODCOCKS AND SNIPES Scolopacidae: subfamily Scolopacinae

Woodcocks and snipes are small to medium-sized waders with a very long bill, fairly long legs and cryptically patterned plumage. They feed mainly by probing in soft ground and also by picking from the surface. Their diet consists mostly of worms, tiny molluscs, larvae and aquatic invertebrates. If approached, they usually first crouch on the ground and 'freeze', preferring to rely on their protective plumage pattern to escape detection, and are often not flushed until almost trodden on. They inhabit marshy ground.

EURASIAN WOODCOCK *Scolopax rusticola* — Plate 41

Woodcock (F,I,P)

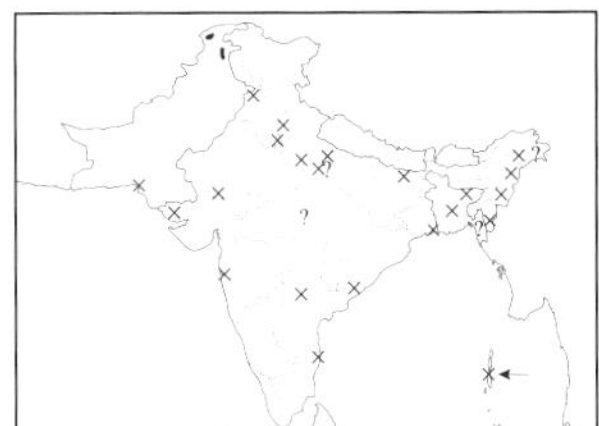

IDENTIFICATION 33–35 cm. A bulky, rufous-coloured wader, usually seen when flushed from forest floor or when roding (displaying in flight) at dusk. Has black-and-buff-banded crown and nape, black loral stripe, and large rearward-set black eye. Upperparts are intricately barred and mottled with rufous, black and buff, and lack sharply defined mantle or scapular stripes. In flight, appears heavy and broad-winged compared with Wood and Solitary Snipes (p.472), and rather uniform and rufous-coloured (being especially rufous on back, rump and wing-coverts). Further, has rufous spotting on flight feathers and dark subterminal band to tail. **VOICE** Usually silent when flushed, although sometimes gives harsh *schaap* call. In roding display, male gives a sharp *chiwich*, which is regularly repeated. **HABITS** Solitary, crepuscular and nocturnal, passing the day in thick cover. When flushed, flies off without calling, only the wings making a swishing sound; zigzags away with wavering wing movements and quickly drops into cover again. Most easily located by the male's characteristic roding display flight in the breeding season: at dawn and dusk, he makes a regular circuit low over the treetops with slow, deliberate wingbeats while calling. **HABITAT** Damp forest with thick undergrowth and marshy glades; temperate rhododendron and fir forest in Himalayas, ravines in sholas and evergreen forest, cardamom and coffee plantations with marshy streams in S India. **BREEDING** April–July in Himalayas. Nest is a depression on the ground, lined with leaves and hidden among undergrowth, usually near a stream. **DISTRIBUTION AND STATUS** Breeds in hills of Pakistan and Himalayas from NW Pakistan east to Arunachal Pradesh; winters at lower elevations in Himalayas, and hills of NE, W and S India and Sri Lanka; isolated records of passage migrants elsewhere. Breeds 1830–3900 m; winters 900–2100 m (down to 100 m in Nepal). **PK:** rare and local in moister temperate Himalayan forest; winters in adjacent foothills and valleys. **NP, IN:** locally fairly common. **BT:** common. **BD:** vagrant. **LK:** rare winter visitor to higher hills; passage migrant to wet lowlands.

SOLITARY SNIPE *Gallinago solitaria* — Plate 41

***Capella solitaria* (E,F)**

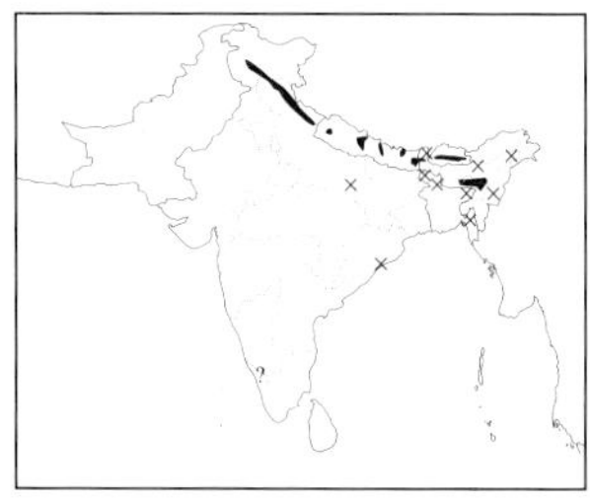

IDENTIFICATION 29–31 cm. A large, dull-coloured snipe. Colder-coloured and less boldly marked than Wood Snipe (below), with less striking head pattern. Crown-stripe and supercilium are less clearly defined, being dark-speckled and greyish-white in colour. Further, has gingery-brown breast finely spotted and barred with white, and rufous barring on mantle and scapulars, with finer white mantle and scapular stripes. Bill is longer and can appear slightly upturned, and legs are yellowish. In flight, has longer, narrower and more pointed wings than Wood, and has fine white wing-bar (formed by white tips to primary and greater coverts) and inconspicuous white trailing edge; as on Wood, underwing and flanks are heavily barred. Larger and colder-coloured than Pintail, Swinhoe's and Common Snipes (p.473 and p.474). **Juvenile** is similar to adult. **VOICE** When flushed, a harsh *kensh*, deeper than Common's. In aerial display, utters a deep *chok-achock-a* call, combined with a mechanical bleating produced by outer tail feathers (Hayman *et al.* 1986). **HABITS** Usually seen singly. If flushed, zigzags away, flying more heavily and slowly than Common Snipe, giving a louder, harsher call, and soon settles again. In common with other snipes, male has an aerial 'drumming' display in the breeding season. **HABITAT** High-altitude bogs and marshy edges and beds of mountain streams; in Assam, wet paddy-field stubbles bordered by scrub. **BREEDING** Not described from the region. In Mongolia, nest is a well-concealed, unlined hollow in a damp willow thicket. **DISTRIBUTION AND STATUS** Resident, subject to altitudinal movements, and winter visitor. Mainly Baluchistan, Pakistan, and Himalayas from NW Pakistan east to Arunachal Pradesh; NE India. **PK:** rare and local resident; 1525–2750 m. **NP:** uncommon and local winter visitor and passage migrant, recorded in most months, probably also resident and breeding, seen displaying at 4260 m in May; mainly 2135–4000 m, regularly winters at 3795 m (down to 915 m). **IN:** uncommon; summers 2400–4600 m, winters from 1200 m to at least 3000 m, locally down to the foothills, rarely to plains. **BT:** uncommon, probably resident. **BD:** vagrant.

WOOD SNIPE *Gallinago nemoricola* — Plate 41

***Capella nemoricola* (F,P)**

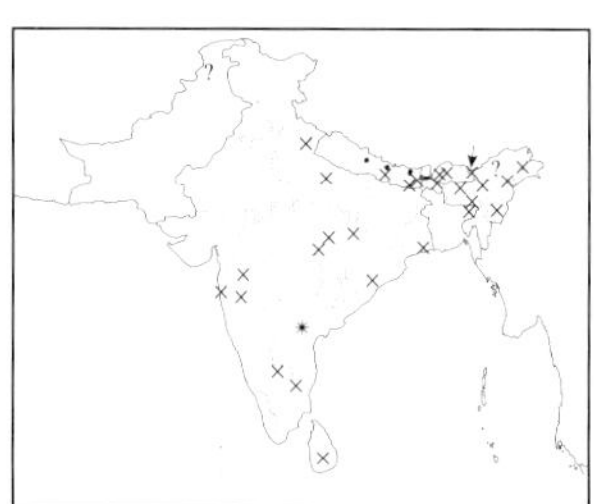

IDENTIFICATION 28–32 cm. A large, bulky and boldly marked snipe with broad wings and heavy and direct flight. Underwing and most of belly and flanks are heavily barred. Bill is relatively short and deep-based. **Adult** is more boldly marked than Solitary Snipe (above), with more striking head pattern and boldly marked upperparts. Has well-defined buff crown-stripe and supercilium, contrasting with blackish crown sides and eye-stripe, and mantle and scapulars are dark brown with broad golden-buff fringes forming two sets of parallel stripes. Patterning of neck and breast is also different, being warm buff and streaked with dark brown. Legs are dull greyish-green (yellow on Solitary). Upperwings appear rather uniform in flight, lacking any white trailing edge, although grey-buff fringes to coverts result in paler mid-wing panel. Head pattern and boldly striped upperparts readily separate it from Eurasian Woodcock (p.471). **Juvenile** has finer, less prominent, whitish mantle and scapular stripes (centres to these feathers are dark brown, lacking fine rufous barring of Solitary). **VOICE** In breeding area, utters a long series of nasal notes from the ground, *check-check-check...*, with approximately four notes per second in a sequence lasting 20 seconds or more; in display flight a nasal *che-dep, che-dep, che-dep, ip-ip-ip, ock, ock*; and a *che-dep, che-dep* is given when flushed (Buckton and Morris 1993). **HABITS** Normally found singly. Has a slow, heavy, wavering flight and soon settles after being flushed. Male performs an aerial display in the breeding season, flying in a wide circle c. 10 m above ground while calling. **HABITAT** Breeds in alpine meadows with scattered bushes and few streams; also dwarf scrub in barren boulder-strewn areas. Winters in swampy ground in and at edge of forest, in cover too thick for Common Snipe.**BREEDING** Very poorly known. Probably May and June. No first-hand authentic records of the nest. **DISTRIBUTION AND STATUS** Resident. Breeds in Himalayas from NW Himachal Pradesh east to Arunachal Pradesh; NE India, 3000–5000 m; winters mainly at lower elevations in Himalayas (–3050 m in

Nepal) and in hills of S India. Probably overlooked. Globally threatened. **NP:** rare altitudinal migrant, possibly resident. **IN:** scarce altitudinal migrant and winter visitor. **BT:** rare. **BD:** vagrant. **LK:** probably a rare winter visitor to higher hills. **REFERENCES** Buckton and Morris (1993).

PINTAIL SNIPE *Gallinago stenura* Plate 41

***Capella stenura* (F,P)**

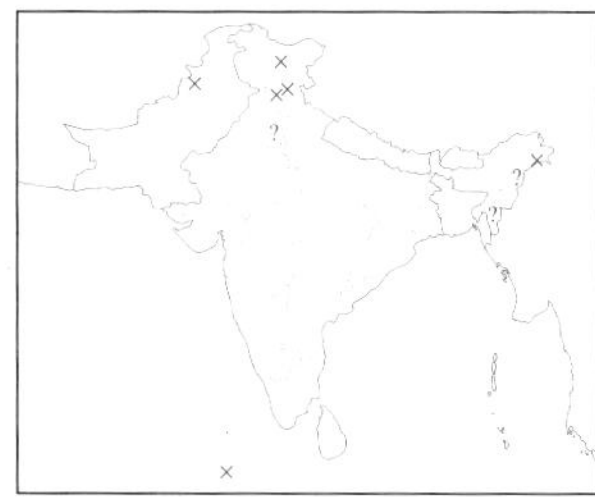

IDENTIFICATION 25–27 cm. A medium-sized, strongly marked snipe. Very similar to Common Snipe (p.474), showing dark brown and buff stripes on head, warm buff coloration to breast, and prominent mantle and scapular stripes, but generally more grey and not so warm-toned in plumage. Most easily told from Common in flight, when slightly broader, more rounded wings, stockier appearance, and its slightly slower, more direct and deliberate flight, with more laboured take-off, can be seen. Bill appears comparatively short and blunt-tipped. Further, lacks well-defined white trailing edge to secondaries (although secondaries show diffuse pale tips in fresh plumage, especially from below), has densely barred underwing-coverts (with underwing appearing uniformly dark), and has more prominent, buff-scaled, upperwing-covert panel; also has smaller area of white in centre of belly, shorter tail with toes protruding farther in flight, and deeper flight call. At rest, shows little or no tail projection beyond closed wings, with more bulk in front of legs, compared with Common, while head is more rounded, with comparatively larger eye; median-covert panel is strongly contrasting. There tends to be a subtle difference from Common in head pattern: Pintail usually shows bulging supercilium in front of eye, with little or no contrast between supercilium and cheeks, and the eye-stripe is often narrow in front of eye and poorly defined behind. Width and coloration of edges to lower large scapulars are similar on inner and outer webs, creating a scalloped appearance (see Common for comparison). In the hand, narrow pin-like outer tail feathers immediately distinguish Pintail from Common. **Juvenile** similar to adult, but has finer mantle and scapular stripes and narrower buff fringes to wing-coverts. For differences from the rarer Swinhoe's Snipe (below), see that species. **VOICE** A short rasping *tetch* when flushed, deeper and less anxious than Common's. **HABITS** Usually solitary; sometimes in small groups or flocks in favourable feeding areas. If flushed, flies off with little or no zigzagging, usually dropping into cover more quickly than Common Snipe. Feeds mainly in mornings and evenings and at night. **HABITAT** Damp paddy-fields and marshy pool edges; sometimes on quite dry ground, unlike Common; also coasts in Bangladesh. **DISTRIBUTION AND STATUS** Winter visitor to much of the subcontinent, except parts of the northwest and northeast and Himalayas. First arrives in late August, leaves by mid May. **PK:** status uncertain, mainly a passage migrant. **NP:** winter visitor and passage migrant; frequent below 1370 m. **IN:** widespread and locally common winter visitor. **BD:** common winter visitor throughout. **LK:** common winter visitor, most frequent in lowlands. **MV:** regular winter visitor. **REFERENCES** Carey (1993), Carey and Olsson (1995).

SWINHOE'S SNIPE *Gallinago megala* Plate 41

***Capella megala* (P)**

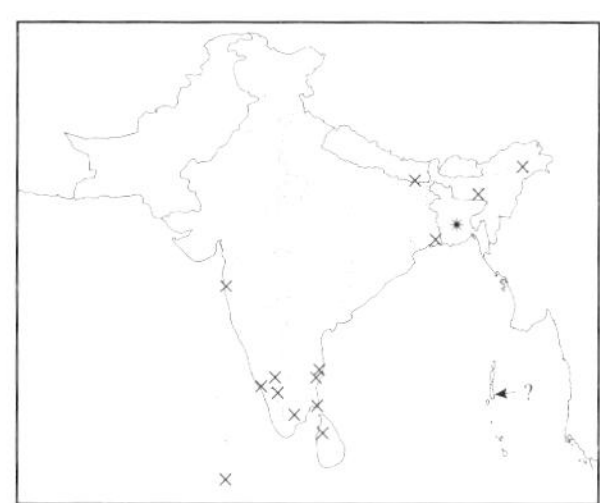

IDENTIFICATION 25–27 cm. In many respects similar to the commoner Pintail Snipe (above): has profusely barred underwing-coverts, lacks distinct white trailing edge to wing, and shows pale median-covert panel on upperwing. These features help to distinguish it from Common Snipe (p.474). Reluctant to be flushed, and flight is rather slow and direct, even compared with Pintail. In flight, appears larger and heavier than Pintail, wings appear longer and more pointed, and bill is longer; the toes only just project beyond the tail, much less so than on Pintail. At rest, tail extends noticeably beyond folded wings. Some birds in spring can appear quite dusky on sides of head, neck, breast and flanks (and are distinct from Pintail), but plumage often as Pintail. Shape of outer tail feathers is intermediate between Pintail and Common. **VOICE** Calls less often than Pintail and Common, and can be silent on flushing, unlike those two. Call is similar in pitch to Pintail's, but thinner, with a slight slur, sounding rather flat or low at times. **HABITS** Very similar to those of Pintail. **HABITAT** Very similar to that of Pintail. **DISTRIBUTION AND STATUS** Winter visitor to NE subcontinent and S India. **NP:** vagrant. **IN:** widespread, but scarce. **BD:** scarce. **LK, MV:** vagrant. **REFERENCES** Carey (1993).

GREAT SNIPE *Gallinago media* Plate 41

***Capella media* (P)**

IDENTIFICATION 27–29 cm. A bulky, medium-sized snipe. In flight, appears larger than Pintail and Common Snipes (above and p.474), with broader, more rounded wings, and slower, more direct and level flight. Shows broad white tips to median, greater and primary coverts, forming narrow but distinct wing-bars, has much white at sides of tail, especially prominent when tail is spread before landing, and has strongly barred flanks and belly. The pale lines on mantle and scapulars are relatively indistinct, and the head pattern is not so well defined. Further differs from Common in that underwing-coverts are entirely barred, pale trailing edge to wing is poorly defined, and bill appears relatively broader and shorter. At rest, best distinctions from those two species are broad

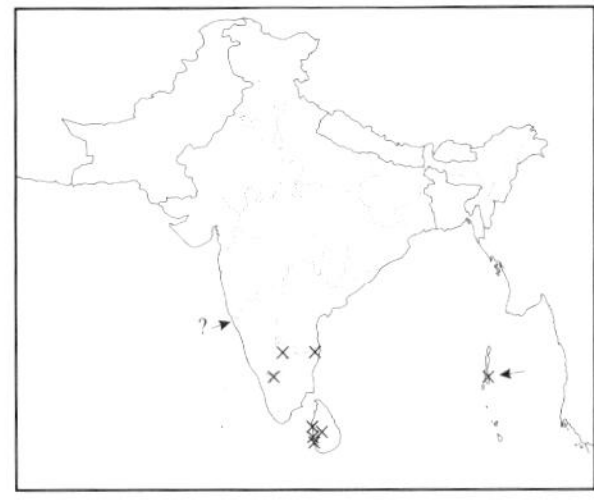

white tips to greater and median coverts, and extensive barring on flanks and belly (with only a small unbarred area on central belly). Best told from Wood Snipe (p.472) by white wing-bars, more prominent white at sides of tail, and less distinct scapular lines (with rufous barring to buff-edged feathers); head pattern is also less well defined. **Juvenile** is very similar to adult, but has narrower white tips to greater and median coverts and has black barring on white outer tail feathers (although white tail corners are still apparent). **VOICE** Almost always gives a long single or double croak, *etch-etch*, when flushed (Hayman *et al.* 1986). **HABITS** Found singly. When flushed, usually rises silently, or occasionally utters a hoarse croak, and soon settles again; flight is slower, straighter and without the zigzagging or towering of Common Snipe, and with the bill held more horizontal. **HABITAT** Marshy habitats; also on drier ground. **DISTRIBUTION AND STATUS IN:** very rare winter visitor to the south. **LK:** vagrant.

COMMON SNIPE *Gallinago gallinago* — Plate 41

Fantail Snipe (F,I), *Capella gallinago* (F,P)

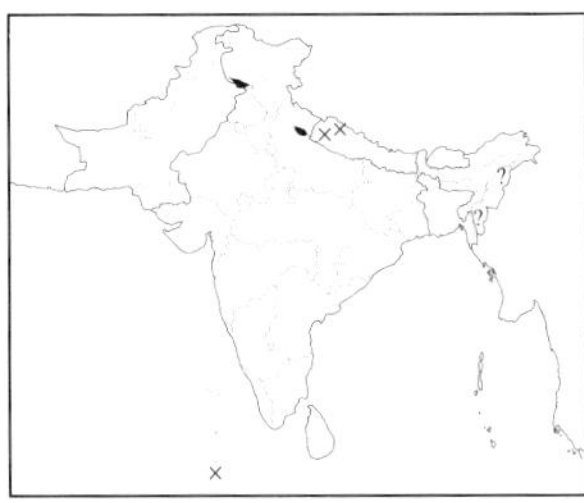

IDENTIFICATION 25–27 cm. Like Pintail Snipe (p.473), shows dark brown and buff stripes on head, warm buff coloration to breast, and prominent mantle and scapular stripes. In flight, wings appear slightly narrower and more pointed than Pintail's, body looks slimmer and bill longer, and has more abrupt take-off and erratic, faster getaway. Further, shows prominent white trailing edge to secondaries, white patterning on underwing-coverts (with median and greater coverts broadly tipped with white), more extensive white belly patch, and rather indistinct upperwing-covert panel. At rest, very difficult to tell from Pintail, although shows noticeable projection of tail beyond wings and only a poorly defined median-covert panel; typically, buff supercilium contrasts with white cheek-stripe, and bulges less in front of eye. Usually broad and buff edges to outer webs of lower scapulars contrast with narrower and browner inner webs. **Juvenile** is very similar to adult, but has finer mantle and scapular stripes and narrower buff fringes to wing-coverts. **VOICE** When flushed, gives an anxious rising, grating *scaaap*, which usually sounds higher-pitched and more urgent than Pintail Snipe's call. **HABITS** Usually found singly, occasionally in flocks. Mainly crepuscular and nocturnal, but will feed in the daytime where undisturbed. If flushed, rises steeply with rapid zigzagging while uttering a hoarse cry, circles high up, and then lands some distance away. Male has a 'drumming' display in the breeding season: circles high over his territory with fast wingbeats, then dives steeply, the air vibrating in his outer tail feathers producing a distinctive humming sound. **HABITAT** Marshes, flooded paddy stubbles, muddy edges of rivers and pools. **BREEDING** Late April–mid June. Nest is a shallow depression lined with grasses, well hidden in marshy ground. **DISTRIBUTION AND STATUS** Breeds in Himalayas in Kashmir and N Uttar Pradesh; winter visitor throughout much of the subcontinent, except parts of the northwest and northeast and Himalayas, arrives from end August and leaves by end May. **PK:** common and widespread winter visitor, also a passage migrant. **NP:** locally fairly common; winter visitor and passage migrant below 1500 m (–4700 m on passage). **IN:** breeds 1600–4500 m in Himalayas; common and widespread winter visitor, less frequent than Pintail Snipe in the south. **BT:** uncommon passage migrant. **BD:** common winter visitor throughout. **LK:** rare winter visitor to lowlands. **MV:** regular winter visitor. **REFERENCES** Carey (1993), Carey and Olsson (1995).

JACK SNIPE *Lymnocryptes minimus* — Plate 41

***Gallinago minima* (I), *Capella minima* (F,P)**

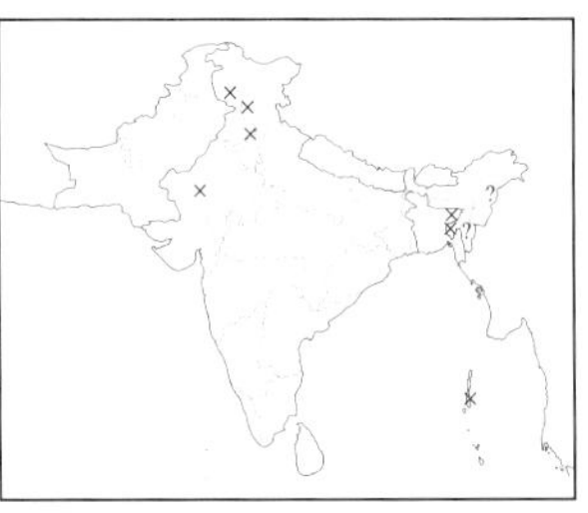

IDENTIFICATION 17–19 cm. A small snipe with boldly striped upperparts. Has habit of rising silently and only when almost trodden on. When feeding, seems to bob body constantly. In flight, told from Common Snipe (above) by smaller size and shorter bill, weaker, slower and more level flight, narrower but blunt-ended paddle-like wings, and proportionately longer tail. Further, has all-dark, wedge-shaped tail, with toes not extending beyond, and more uniform upperwing, lacking prominent white trailing edge. At rest, shows dark upperparts with strongly contrasting broad buff mantle and scapular lines, buff supercilium which divides in front of eye, and no central crown-stripe. **VOICE** Almost always silent when flushed, but very occasionally gives a subdued *gah* (Hayman *et al.* 1986). **HABITS** Almost always solitary. Usually crepuscular and nocturnal; rarely flies in the daytime unless disturbed. If flushed, flies off silently, more slowly than Common Snipe and without zigzagging, and soon drops into cover. **HABITAT** Marshes and wet paddy stubbles. **DISTRIBUTION AND STATUS** Winter visitor throughout much of the subcontinent, except parts of the northwest and northeast and Himalayas; first arrives in early September, leaving by mid April. **PK:** scarce passage migrant and winter visitor. **NP:** rare passage migrant and winter visitor; below 1500 m. **IN:** widespread winter visitor, fairly common in the northwest, generally uncommon elsewhere. **BD:** scarce and local winter visitor to the northeast. **LK:** rare winter visitor, mainly in lowlands.

GODWITS, SANDPIPERS, CURLEWS, PHALAROPES etc
Scolopacidae: subfamily Tringinae

The Tringinae are wading birds with quite long to very long legs and a long bill. They feed on small molluscs, crustaceans, insects and worms and inhabit freshwater and coastal wetlands.

BLACK-TAILED GODWIT *Limosa limosa* — Plate 42

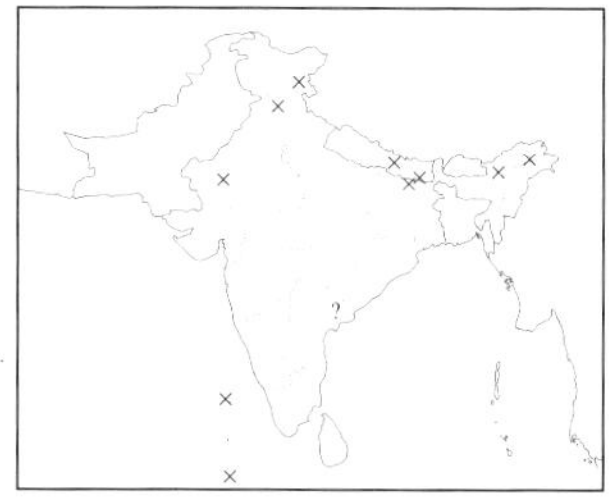

IDENTIFICATION 36–44 cm. Best distinguished from Bar-tailed Godwit (below) in flight, when it shows prominent white wing-bar and white rump band contrasting with black tail. At rest, is larger and lankier, with longer legs, and has longer and straighter bill (although see *L. l. melanuroides* below). **Adult breeding** differs from breeding male Bar-tailed in being more orange-red on head, neck and breast, with blackish barring on lower breast and belly, and belly is otherwise mainly white rather than chestnut-red. Mantle and scapulars tend to be more unevenly patterned, with old grey feathers mixed with chestnut- and black-banded new feathers. **Female** is distinctly larger than male, and is duller, retaining a greater proportion of grey non-breeding plumage. **Adult non-breeding** is similar to non-breeding Bar-tailed, but has less prominent supercilium, and is more uniform grey on neck, breast and upperparts (lacking dark-streaked appearance to mantle, scapulars and coverts of Bar-tailed). **Juvenile** told from juvenile Bar-tailed by less prominent supercilium, cinnamon coloration to head, neck and underparts, and evenly marked upperparts with dark rounded centres and neat cinnamon fringes to mantle, scapulars and wing-coverts. **Racial variation** The eastern race *L. l. melanuroides*, wintering in NE subcontinent, is noticeably different from the more widespread *L. l. limosa*, described above. It is smaller (and more similar in size and structure to Bar-tailed), and shows a markedly narrower wing-bar in flight. Male in breeding plumage has deeper and more extensive red on underparts. Non-breeding plumage is darker grey on head, neck and breast. **VOICE** A quiet *kek-kek* occasionally uttered in flight. **HABITS** Feeds mainly by walking slowly and probing in open soft mud or in shallows; also by picking prey from the surface. Feeds in deeper water than most other waders; sometimes wades up to the belly and probes with head and neck almost completely submerged. **HABITAT** Chiefly fresh waters: shallows and mudbanks of rivers, lakes, reservoirs and marshes, occasionally tidal waters, brackish lagoons and coastal saltpans. **DISTRIBUTION AND STATUS** Widespread winter visitor. Mainly S Pakistan, India except for parts of the northwest and east and Himalayas; Bangladesh and Sri Lanka; arrives from late August, leaves by mid May. **PK:** common winter visitor, mainly to lower Sindh; a few flocks oversummer. **NP:** scarce and local passage migrant; below 1525 m. **IN:** widespread winter visitor, locally common. **BD, LK:** locally common winter visitor. **MV:** vagrant.

BAR-TAILED GODWIT *Limosa lapponica* — Plate 42

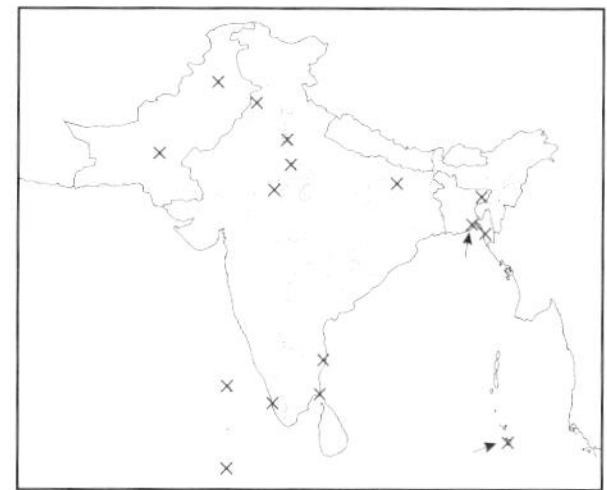

IDENTIFICATION 37–41 cm. Best separated from Black-tailed Godwit (above) in flight, by finely barred tail and lack of prominent wing-bar. At rest, it is stockier and shorter-necked, has shorter legs, and has a shorter, more upturned bill. Care is needed to avoid overlooking the much rarer Asian Dowitcher (p.481); for differences, see that species. **Adult male breeding** differs from breeding male Black-tailed in being a deeper chestnut-red on head, neck and entire underparts, lacking prominent blackish barring on breast and belly; mantle and scapulars are more uniformly patterned, with narrow chestnut fringes to dark-centred feathers. **Female breeding** has pale chestnut or cinnamon neck and underparts, with upperparts similar to male's, although many appear as non-breeding. **Adult non-breeding** has more prominent supercilium than Black-tailed, shows dark streaking on brownish-grey neck and breast, and has dark centres and brownish-grey fringes to feathers of upperparts, giving streaked appearance. **Juvenile** similar to non-breeding adult, but has buffish wash to neck and breast and bright buff edges to mantle and scapular feathers. **VOICE** A barking *kak-kak* and deep *kirruc* (Hayman *et al.* 1986). **HABITS** Similar to those of Black-tailed, but often feeds in shallower water than that species. **HABITAT** Intertidal zone of estuaries and lagoons, and saltpans. Very rarely on inland waters. **DISTRIBUTION AND STATUS** Winter visitor. Pakistan, India, Bangladesh, Sri Lanka and Maldives, chiefly on the coasts; first arrives in late July, leaving by mid May. **PK:** common on coast; a small number oversummer. **IN:** widespread; most frequent in the northwest. **BD:** scarce but regular on coast. **LK:** rare on dry-zone coast. **MV:** annual visitor in small numbers.

WHIMBREL *Numenius phaeopus* — Plate 42

IDENTIFICATION 40–46 cm. Is smaller than Eurasian Curlew (p.476), with shorter bill, often with more marked downward kink, and has distinctive flight call. Further, has prominent whitish supercilium and crown-stripe, contrasting with blackish eye-stripe and sides to crown, resulting in more striking head pattern. **Juvenile** is very similar in plumage to adult. Characteristic head pattern is best distinction from juvenile Eurasian Curlew. **Racial variation** The eastern race *N. p. variegatus*, which winters in NE subcontinent, differs from *N. p. phaeopus* in

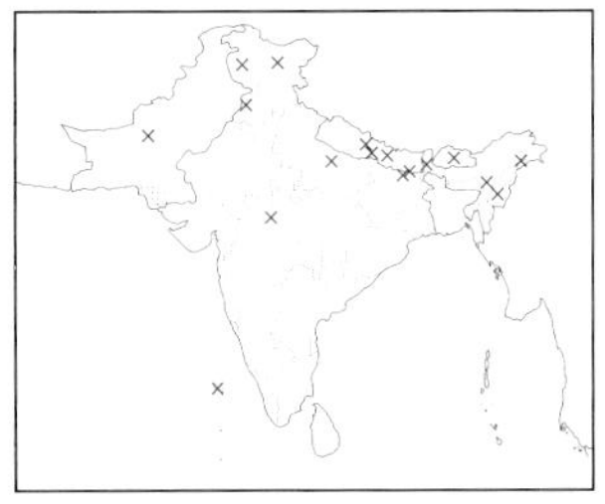

having entire back and rump marked heavily with brown (lacking prominent white back V of *phaeopus*), and underwing-coverts are heavily barred with brown (rather than being mainly white as in *phaeopus*). **VOICE** A distinctive, whistled *he-he-he-he-he-he-he*, flat-toned and at times laughter-like. **HABITS** Walks about on mud and feeds chiefly by picking from the surface, also by probing. Often eats crabs, also other molluscs and crustaceans. Almost invariably calls in flight. **HABITAT** Mainly intertidal coastal mudflats and mudbanks of tidal creeks and mangroves, but on all coasts in Sri Lanka; occasionally on inland waters when on passage. **DISTRIBUTION AND STATUS** Winter visitor mainly to coasts of the subcontinent, a few oversummering; first arrives mid July, and leaves by mid May. **PK:** common winter visitor to Makran and Sindh coast. **NP:** scarce passage migrant; below 1350 m. **IN:** locally fairly common in winter on coast, uncommon inland. **BT:** vagrant, once at 3250 m. **BD:** local winter visitor. **LK:** common winter visitor to lowlands, more frequent in dry zone. **MV:** regular winter visitor.

EURASIAN CURLEW *Numenius arquata* — Plate 42

Curlew (F,I,P)

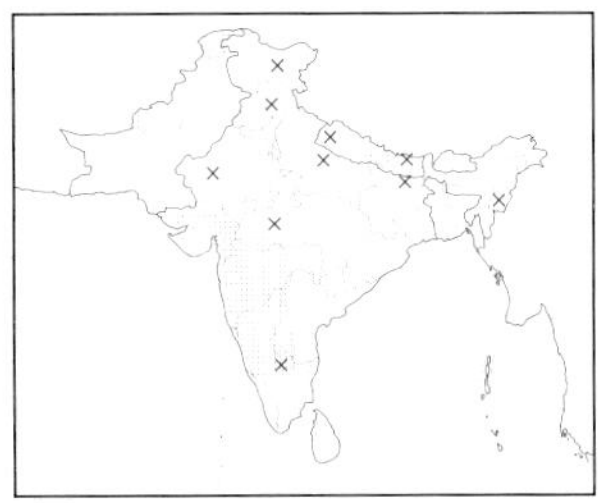

IDENTIFICATION 50–60 cm. Confusion most likely with Whimbrel (p.475), and best told by combination of larger size, much longer bill, more uniform head pattern, paler plumage (race *orientalis*), and mournful flight call. Head typically looks rather uniform, but can show dark eye-stripe and surprisingly distinct pale supercilium. Very similar to the much rarer Eastern Curlew (below); see that species for main differences. **Juvenile** is similar in plumage to adult, but with shorter bill. More closely resembles Whimbrel, but lacks blackish sides to crown and pale crown-stripe. **VOICE** Typically a mournful, rising *cur-lew*, and an anxious *were-up* when alarmed. Its song, a beautiful sequence of bubbling phrases, accelerating and rising in pitch, is often heard in winter and on passage (Hayman *et al.* 1986). **HABITS** Usually keeps singly or in small groups. Generally wary and difficult to approach. Feeds by walking on mud and probing deeply, also by picking from the surface. Flocks often fly in V-formation. Vocal throughout the year; frequently calls in flight. **HABITAT** Intertidal mudflats, tidal estuaries and creeks, mudbanks of mangroves; also uncommonly on large rivers and inland lakes. **DISTRIBUTION AND STATUS** Widespread winter visitor, mainly on coasts; first arrives in early August, departing by May. **PK:** common winter visitor to coast; scarce winter visitor and passage migrant inland; a few oversummer. **NP:** common winter visitor to the terai at Kosi Barrage, scarce passage migrant elsewhere up to 3050 m. **IN:** widespread winter visitor, locally common on coast. **BD:** locally common winter visitor. **LK:** regular winter visitor to coast, most frequent in the north. **MV:** regular winter visitor; some oversummer.

EASTERN CURLEW *Numenius madagascariensis* — Plate 42

Far Eastern Curlew

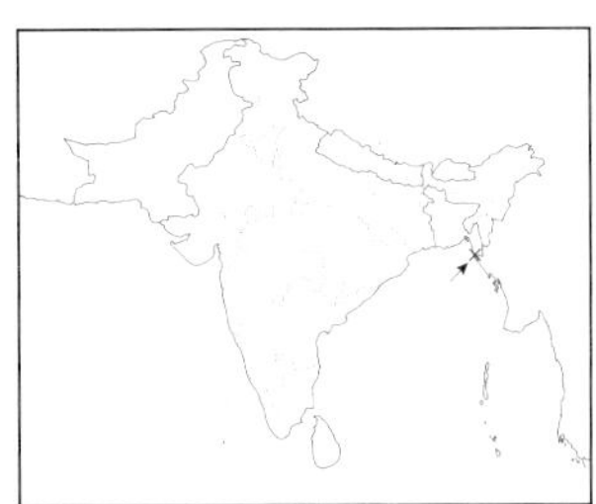

IDENTIFICATION 60–66 cm. Largest of the curlews, with an extremely long downcurved bill. Best told from Eurasian Curlew (above) in flight by dark back and rump (lacking prominent white back V of Eurasian) and by heavily barred axillaries and underwing-coverts (white and usually unbarred on Eurasian). More difficult to separate at rest. In breeding plumage, ground colour of underparts is brownish-buff, becoming paler, more creamy-buff, on lower belly and vent (ground colour of Eurasian's breast and belly is much whiter), although underbody of non-breeding birds is paler creamy-buff and more like that of Eurasian. In breeding plumage, upperpart feathers often have rufous notches and edges, giving the bird a warmer appearance than Eurasian. **Juvenile** closely resembles adult, and has warm buff wash to belly and vent, but bill is distinctly shorter. **VOICE** Typically, a flatter call than Eurasian's, *coor-ee*, and when agitated gives a strident *ker ker-ee-ker-ee* (Hayman *et al.* 1986). **HABITS** Similar to those of Eurasian. **HABITAT** Mainly coastal: mudflats, sand spits and tidal creeks. **DISTRIBUTION AND STATUS BD:** vagrant. **REFERENCES** Higgins and Davis (1996).

SPOTTED REDSHANK *Tringa erythropus* — Plate 43

IDENTIFICATION 29–32 cm. A medium-sized, slender wader with long, fine straight bill and long red legs. Really confusable only with Common Redshank (p.477). Has longer, thinner bill, with red confined to base of lower mandible, longer, usually brighter red legs, and more slender appearance. More easily told in flight, by lack of broad white trailing edge to wing and distinctive flight call. Has fast, direct flight action with rapid wingbeats, quite distinct from other *Tringa*. **Adult non-breeding** distinguished from Common by more prominent white supercilium in front of eye (contrasting with dark lores), paler grey upperparts, and whiter underparts with only faint grey wash to breast. **Adult breeding** is unmistakable, with entire head, neck and underparts sooty-black, and upperparts black, spotted with white. Moulting birds have patches of black on underparts. Birds in

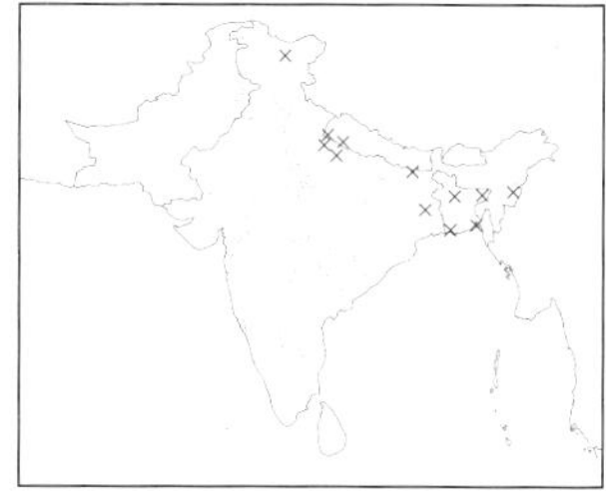

first-summer plumage have dark barring on underparts and dark-mottled upperparts. **Juvenile** similar to non-breeding adult, but has darker grey upperparts more heavily spotted with white, and underparts are finely barred with grey. **VOICE** A distinctive *tu-ick* flight call, and shorter *chip* alarm call. **HABITS** Solitary or in small flocks, often with other waders. Feeds by picking from the surface, often after a short dash. Frequently also forages in water, often in compact flocks; either sweeps the bill from side to side or probes rapidly, often submerging the head and neck completely. Swims readily, and upends like a surface-feeding duck to reach the bottom mud. **HABITAT** Mainly fresh waters: muddy banks and shallow waters of rivers and lakes; also tidal estuaries and creeks. **DISTRIBUTION AND STATUS** Winter visitor to much of the subcontinent, except most of the Himalayas and the east; first arrives in early September, leaving by May. **PK:** frequent winter visitor and passage migrant. **NP:** local and frequent winter visitor and passage migrant; below 1350 m. **IN:** widespread and locally common winter visitor. **BD:** frequent winter visitor, mainly to the northeast. **LK:** rare winter visitor to dry lowlands.

COMMON REDSHANK *Tringa totanus* — Plate 43

Redshank (P)

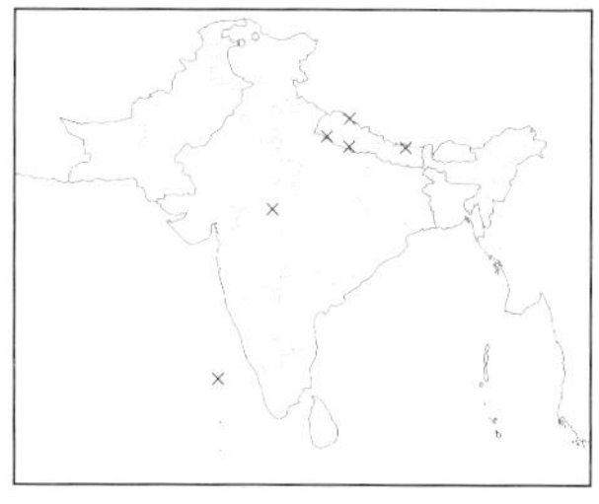

IDENTIFICATION 27–29 cm. A medium-sized wader with straight bill and moderately long orange-red legs. Really confusable only with Spotted Redshank (p.476). Has shorter, stouter bill and shorter, more orange-red legs, and is stockier in appearance. More easily told in flight, by striking white secondaries and inner primaries forming broad white trailing edge to wing, and distinctive flight call. Note that Ruff (p.486) may also have red legs. **Adult non-breeding** distinguished from Spotted Redshank by darker grey-brown coloration to upperparts, strong grey wash to breast (usually with fine streaking), and lack of prominent supercilium in front of eye. **Adult breeding** has brighter orange-red legs and base to bill, heavily streaked neck and underparts, and browner upperparts variably marked with dark brown and cinnamon. **Juvenile** quite different from juvenile Spotted, with brown upperparts entirely fringed and spotted with buff, underparts heavily streaked with dark brown, and dull orange legs and base to bill. **VOICE** Very noisy. Typically, an anxious *teu-hu-hu*, and a mournful *tyuuu* on the ground. **HABITS** Found singly or in small groups, often with other waders. Generally wary and noisy, often giving its alarm call. Feeds by walking briskly and picking from the surface; also probes, and wades in shallow water. **HABITAT** Marshes, muddy edges of rivers and lakes, mudbanks of mangroves, tidal creeks and estuaries, saltpans and brackish pools. **BREEDING** May–July. Nest is a deep grass-lined depression hidden in a grass tussock in a marsh. **DISTRIBUTION AND STATUS** Breeds in Himalayas in Kashmir, Ladakh and Sikkim; winter visitor to much of the subcontinent, except most of the Himalayas and NC and NE India, arriving from late July and leaving by end May. **PK:** common and widespread winter visitor to coast; small numbers inland. **NP:** local winter visitor below 915 m (–4270 m on passage); frequent at Kosi Barrage, uncommon elsewhere. **IN:** fairly common on breeding grounds in Ladakh and Sikkim, breeds 3300–5000 m; common and widespread in winter. **BD:** common winter visitor throughout; non-breeders oversummer. **LK:** very common winter visitor to coasts. **MV:** regular winter visitor. **REFERENCES** Pfister (1997).

MARSH SANDPIPER *Tringa stagnatilis* — Plate 43

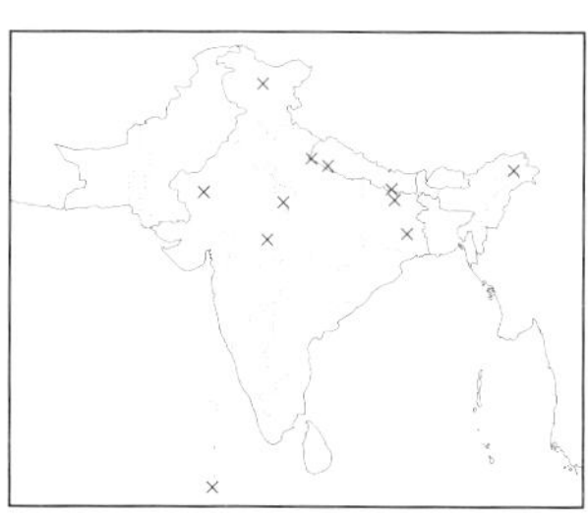

IDENTIFICATION 22–25 cm. A slender, graceful wader with fine, straight black bill and long, slender greenish legs. Really confusable only with Common Greenshank (p.478). Is smaller in size and daintier in appearance (head looks small and rounded, neck thinner and body rather bulbous); bill is finer and straight, and legs are proportionately longer and thinner. **Adult non-breeding** has pale grey upperparts and very white underparts. The pale lores, forehead and chin create a pale-faced appearance. Bend of wing often looks strikingly dark compared with rest of upperparts. **Adult breeding** is boldly spotted and streaked on neck, breast and flanks, and pinkish-buff to greyish-olive upperparts are variably blotched and barred with black. Corresponding plumage of Common Greenshank is greyer above and appears irregularly streaked rather than spotted and barred. Legs of Marsh can be more yellowish when breeding. **Juvenile** upperparts appear streaked blackish, with feathers notched and fringed with buff, and head sides, hindneck and upper mantle are streaked dark grey and white. Appears more buffish in coloration than juvenile Common Greenshank. Moults early, so usually similar to non-breeding adult on arrival in subcontinent. **VOICE** An abrupt, dull *yup*; also rapid, excitable series of *kiu-kiu-kiu...* notes. **HABITS** A particularly graceful wader. Usually solitary or in small groups or flocks, often with other waders, dabbling ducks or egrets. Forages actively, often in water or at the water's edge, also on mud; picks delicately from the surface, making frequent rapid darts to seize prey; probes occasionally. **HABITAT** Pools, lakes, flooded paddy-fields and marshes; much less often on intertidal mudflats, brackish lagoons and saltpans. **DISTRIBUTION AND STATUS** Widespread winter visitor, mainly to W and NE subcontinent; first arrives in late July, leaves by mid May. **PK:** common passage migrant; small numbers overwinter in Punjab. **NP:** uncommon passage migrant and winter visitor; below 1300 m. **IN:** widespread and locally common winter visitor. **BD:** scarce winter visitor. **LK:** common winter visitor to lowlands, more frequent in dry zone. **MV:** irregular winter visitor.

COMMON GREENSHANK *Tringa nebularia* — Plate 43

Greenshank (F,I,P)

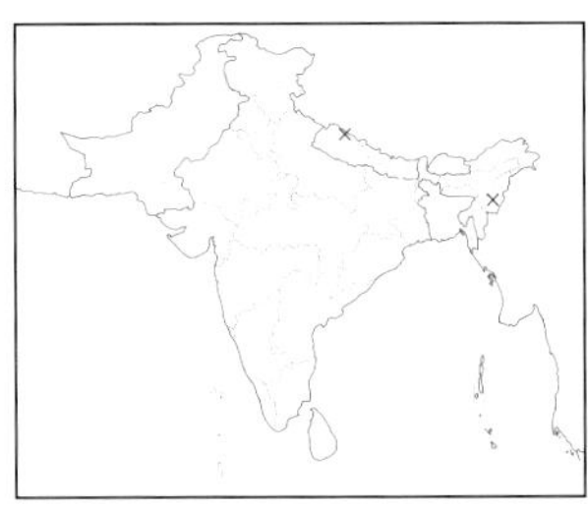

IDENTIFICATION 30–34 cm. A stocky, medium-sized wader with stout, slightly upturned bill and long, stout greenish legs. Told from Marsh Sandpiper (p.477) by larger size and stockier appearance, stouter, slightly upturned bill, thicker, proportionately shorter legs, and distinctive alarm and flight calls. Great care is needed to avoid overlooking the much rarer Nordmann's Greenshank (below); for differences, see that species. **Adult non-breeding** has grey upperparts, finely streaked hindneck and crown, and white underparts. **Adult breeding** is spotted and streaked on head, neck and breast, and greyish feathers of upperparts have variable black centres and white fringes, usually giving rise to (untidy) streaked appearance. **Juvenile** has more heavily streaked head and neck than non-breeding birds, and upperparts are darker, with mantle and scapular feathers fringed or notched with buff or white. **VOICE** A loud, ringing *tu-tu-tu*, and sometimes a more throaty *kyoup-kyoup-kyoup*. **HABITS** Usually forages singly, although may gather in small parties to roost. Generally wary and, when alarmed, bobs head and body nervously up and down. Feeds actively, chiefly in shallow water or at the water's edge; detects prey mainly by sight, and makes frequent rapid runs to seize fast-moving prey. Flies strongly and sometimes erratically. Gives its distinctive call when flushed, and frequently in flight. **HABITAT** Wide range of fresh- and saltwater wetlands: freshwater marshes, banks of rivers, irrigation tanks, jheels and lakes, brackish pools, mangroves, coastal lagoons and mudflats, tidal creeks and saltpans. **DISTRIBUTION AND STATUS** Winter visitor throughout much of the subcontinent, a few oversummering; first arrives in late July, with most gone by early May. **PK:** common and widespread winter visitor, recorded in all months. **NP:** widespread and common winter visitor and passage migrant, a few summer records; winters chiefly below 370 m, up to 4800 m on passage. **IN:** widespread and locally common winter visitor. **BT:** winter visitor and passage migrant; frequent from 245 m up to at least 2745 m. **BD:** common winter visitor throughout. **LK:** common winter visitor to lowlands, more frequent in dry zone. **MV:** frequent winter visitor; some oversummer.

NORDMANN'S GREENSHANK *Tringa guttifer* — Plate 43

Spotted Greenshank (I)

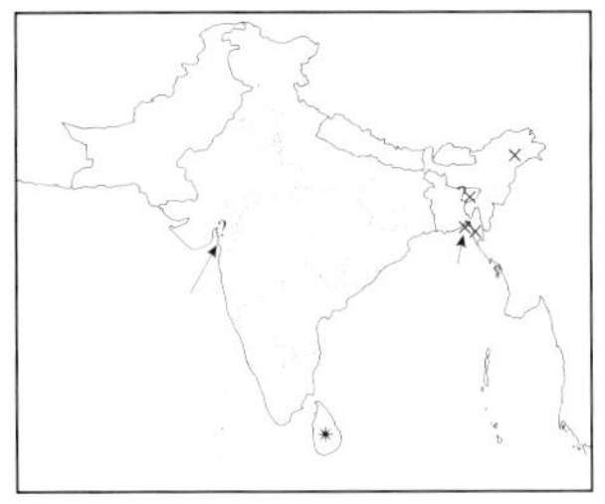

IDENTIFICATION 29–32 cm. Similar to Common Greenshank (above), although overall impression is at times not unlike that of Terek Sandpiper (p.479). Compared with Common, Nordmann's appears deeper-breasted, with flat belly and pronounced ventral angle behind the legs; has shorter and thicker neck, and larger and more bulbous head. Legs are proportionately shorter and thicker than on Common, with the tibia shorter and sometimes hidden by belly. The bill is proportionately longer, heavier, deeper-based and more blunt-tipped and, when seen head-on, is clearly much broader and lacks a well-defined culmen ridge. In flight, the toes of Nordmann's project only slightly beyond the tail (all of feet project on Common), and appears stockier, with broader-based wings; underwing-coverts are pure white (faintly barred with brown on Common). Legs are yellow (on Common usually greenish, but sometimes yellowish). **Adult non-breeding** has very pale head, and pale grey upperparts are generally paler and more uniform than on Common. Lacks dark subterminal crescents to scapulars and coverts, and also lacks fine dark notching to outer edge of tertials of non-breeding Common. Underparts are white and unmarked, lacking fine dark streaking across breast (although breast streaking can also be absent on Common). **Adult breeding** is streaked with black on head and neck, and breast is variably spotted with black (breast of Common typically has fine dark streaking); dark grey to blackish scapulars and tertials are deeply notched with white. Upperparts in full breeding plumage appear heavily spangled (blackish scapulars of Common have a narrow white fringe, with fine black notching, giving rise to a streaked appearance, and tertials are grey-centred with white fringe and fine blackish notching). **Juvenile** has foreneck and breast typically white, with brown wash across breast (may be lightly streaked, although less heavily so than is typical for juvenile Common). Crown is grey-brown, and white supercilium is pronounced. Wing-coverts appear rather uniform, with pale fringes, and mantle and scapulars have narrow fringe of white notching; tertials are more similar to those of Common. Bill of juvenile is strongly bicoloured. **VOICE** Call is a *kwork* or *gwaak*, quite different from the call of Common (Kennerley and Bakewell 1991). **HABITS** Wary and usually silent. Has rather a horizontal stance, unlike Common Greenshank. Feeding behaviour is similar to that of Terek Sandpiper: makes rapid runs after prey with beak held low; often feeds up to belly in water. Flies strongly. **HABITAT** Coastal mudflats, banks of larger rivers and wet grassland. **DISTRIBUTION AND STATUS** Winter visitor. Globally threatened. **IN:** vagrant. **BD:** scarce. **LK:** vagrant. **REFERENCES** Kennerley and Bakewell (1991), Robson (1991).

GREEN SANDPIPER *Tringa ochropus* Plate 43

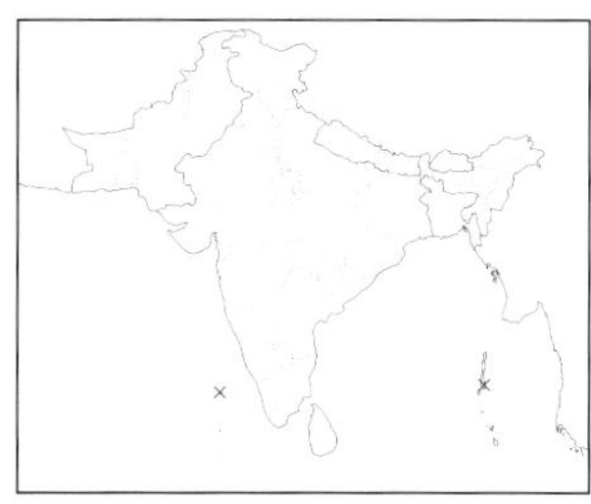

IDENTIFICATION 21–24 cm. A stocky sandpiper with dark greenish-brown upperparts and white belly and vent. Really confusable only with Wood Sandpiper (below), but note the shorter greenish legs and stockier appearance, darker, less heavily spotted upperparts, and supercilium indistinct or absent behind eye. In flight, the loud ringing call, very dark underwing, strongly contrasting with white belly and vent, and striking white rump are distinctive. **Adult breeding** has white streaking on crown and neck, heavily streaked breast, and prominent whitish spotting on upperparts (most noticeable on the scapulars and tertials). **Adult non-breeding** is more uniform on head and breast, and is less distinctly spotted on upperparts. **Juvenile** has browner upperparts with buff spotting. **VOICE** A ringing *tluee-tueet* and *tuee-weet-weet.* **HABITS** Usually solitary when feeding; may gather in small flocks when on migration. Shy, and bobs rear body when nervous. Difficult to approach and flies off readily, giving its characteristic call. Forages in marginal vegetation and shallows, picking prey from the water or mud. **HABITAT** Favours small waters often not used by other waders, such as edges of narrow ditches, small streams, village tanks and pools; also marshes, wet rice fields, banks of jheels, rivers and lakes. Rare in coastal habitats. **DISTRIBUTION AND STATUS** Winter visitor throughout much of the subcontinent, a few oversummering; first arrives at end July, with most gone by end April. **PK:** common and widespread winter visitor and passage migrant; noted at 2700–4200 m in Chitral in July, but no evidence of breeding. **NP:** common passage migrant up to 4250 m; fairly common winter visitor below 370 m. **IN:** widespread and locally common winter visitor; up to 2000 m in peninsular hills. **BT:** frequent winter visitor and passage migrant; 240–3000 m. **BD:** common winter visitor throughout. **LK:** uncommon winter visitor throughout.

WOOD SANDPIPER *Tringa glareola* Plate 43

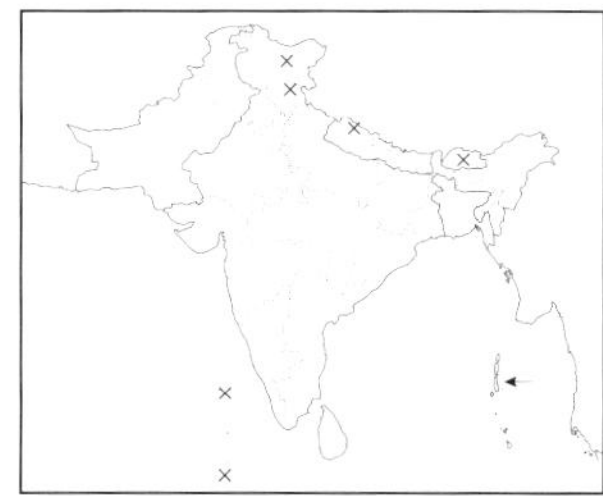

IDENTIFICATION 18–21 cm. A slim, well-proportioned sandpiper with heavily spotted upperparts, distinct whitish supercilium, and streaked breast ending in breast-band. In flight, white rump contrasts with brown back and wings. Easily distinguished from Green Sandpiper (above) by longer, yellowish legs and slimmer appearance, heavily speckled upperparts, and prominent supercilium behind eye. In flight, by the call, slimmer body and narrower wings, toes projecting clearly beyond tail, paler underwing contrasting less with white underparts, and paler brown upperparts contrasting less with smaller white rump. **Adult breeding** has heavily streaked breast and barred flanks, and upperparts are barred and spotted with pale grey-brown and white. **Adult non-breeding** has more uniform grey-brown upperparts, spotted whitish, and breast is brownish and lightly streaked. **Juvenile** has warm brown upperparts heavily speckled with warm buff, and lightly streaked buff breast. **VOICE** A soft *chiff-if* or *chiff-if-if.* **HABITS** Often forages in scattered parties, and frequently occurs in flocks on migration. Feeds in shallow water and on mud by probing, picking from the surface and sweeping its bill from side to side in water. Usually towers away when flushed, giving distinctive call. **HABITAT** Fond of shallow waters with emergent vegetation; marshes, village tanks, lakes, wet paddy-fields, mudflats and tidal creeks. **DISTRIBUTION AND STATUS** Winter visitor throughout much of the subcontinent; arrives mainly in August, leaves by mid May. **PK:** common and widespread passage migrant, with considerable numbers overwintering. **NP:** uncommon winter visitor, frequent on passage; below 3780 m. **IN:** widespread and locally common winter visitor. **BT:** rare passage migrant. **BD:** common winter visitor and passage migrant throughout. **LK:** common winter visitor to lowlands, less frequent in hills; vagrant in summer. **MV:** annual winter visitor.

TEREK SANDPIPER *Xenus cinereus* Plate 44

Tringa terek* (I,P), *Tringa cinerea

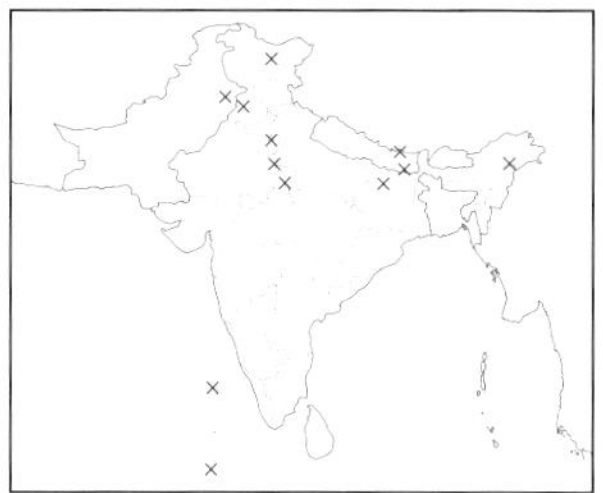

IDENTIFICATION 22–25 cm. A stocky wader with long upturned bill and short yellow-orange legs. In flight, combination of prominent white trailing edge to secondaries and grey rump and tail is unique. Fast, erratic feeding action and rapid, shallow wingbeats recall Common Sandpiper (p.480). **Adult breeding** is grey-brown above, with bold black scapular lines, and has prominent grey-brown patches on sides of breast. **Adult non-breeding** is uniform brownish-grey above, lacking distinct scapular lines. **Juvenile** is similar to adult breeding, but has buff fringes and dark subterminal marks to feathers of upperparts. **VOICE** A soft, pleasant whistle, *hu-hu-hu,* and a sharper *twit-wit-wit-wit* recalling Common. **HABITS** Solitary or in scattered groups when feeding; often gathers in small flocks to roost. A very active feeder, running here and there erratically to chase prey; also probes deeply, and sometimes feeds in shallow water. **HABITAT** Mudbanks of mangrove creeks, intertidal sand- and mudflats and coastal lagoons. **DISTRIBUTION AND STATUS** Winter visitor mainly to coasts of the subcontinent, uncommon inland on passage, possibly also winters in small numbers at freshwater sites in India and Pakistan; first arrives in early August, and most leave by mid May. **PK:** common winter visitor to Indus delta and

Makran coast, a few recent inland records. **NP:** vagrant. **IN:** widespread, locally common winter visitor to the coast; generally uncommon on passage inland, but regular in Punjab. **BD:** common winter visitor; some non-breeders oversummer. **LK:** rare winter visitor to dry-zone coast. **MV:** irregular winter visitor.

COMMON SANDPIPER *Actitis hypoleucos* Plate 44

Tringa hypoleucos

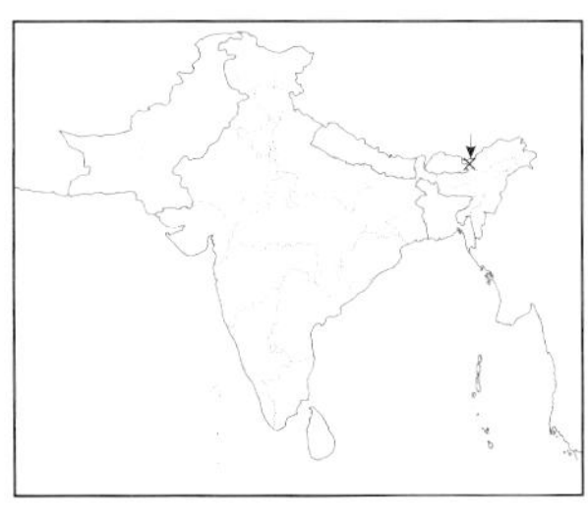

IDENTIFICATION 19–21 cm. Smallest of the *Tringa*-type sandpipers, and with olive-brown upperparts strongly contrasting with white underparts. Horizontal stance, long tail projecting well beyond closed wings, and constant bobbing action when feeding are distinctive features. In flight, prominent white wing-bar, olive-brown rump and centre of tail, and highly distinctive action (rapid shallow beats and bowed-wing glides) are diagnostic. **Adult breeding** has irregular dark streaking and barring on upperparts, and prominent (streaked) olive-brown patches on sides of breast, separated from wing by wedge of white which is lacking on Green Sandpiper (p.479). **Adult non-breeding** is duller and more uniform above, with less distinct breast patches. **Juvenile** has distinctive buff fringes and dark subterminal bands to feathers of mantle, scapulars and wing-coverts, and buff and dark brown notches on tertials. **VOICE** An anxious *wee-wee-wee* when flushed or alarmed. Song, a repeated *kittie-needie,* is often heard in the winter quarters. **HABITS** Invariably solitary in non-breeding season. Characteristically, rocks rear body and bobs head constantly when feeding. Runs along the water's edge and picks prey from ground or vegetation. Flies low over the water, with rapid, shallow wingbeats alternating with brief glides on stiff downcurved wings. **HABITAT** Winters in freshwater and coastal wetlands, and when inland often on small waterbodies: village tanks, banks of streams, rivers, canals, lakes, tidal creeks, coastal lagoons and rocky coasts. Breeds on mountain streams and rivers. **BREEDING** May and June. Nest is a shallow depression lined with dead leaves and grass, sheltered by a bush or boulder, on a shingle islet in a Himalayan stream. **DISTRIBUTION AND STATUS** Breeds in Himalayas from Pakistan east to N Uttar Pradesh, possibly east to W Nepal, and winters throughout much of the subcontinent; first arrives in early August, leaving by end May. **PK:** common and widespread winter visitor; considerable numbers breed in the north, 2285–3630 m. **NP:** common winter visitor and passage migrant, possibly breeds; winters below 1370 m (–5400 m on passage). **IN:** locally common breeder in Himalayas, 1800–3200 m and probably higher; common and widespread winter visitor; plains and hills, up to 2100 m in Nilgiris. **BT:** fairly common winter visitor and passage migrant. **BD, LK:** common winter visitor throughout. **MV:** regular winter visitor. **REFERENCES** Martens and Eck (1995).

GREY-TAILED TATTLER *Heteroscelus brevipes* Plate 44

Tringa brevipes

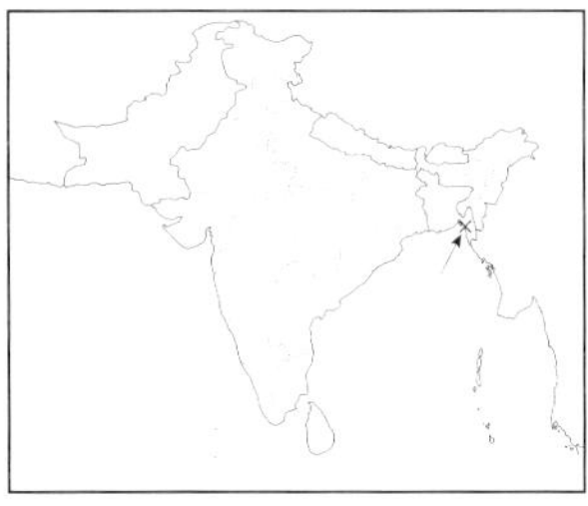

IDENTIFICATION 24–27 cm. A stocky, cold grey and white wader with stout, straight bill and bright yellowish legs. In all plumages, shows prominent white supercilium contrasting with dark eye-stripe, uniform grey wings lacking prominent wing-bar, grey rump and tail, and grey underwing contrasting with white belly. Combination of these features help separate it from Red Knot (p.481) in non-breeding plumage. Very similar to Wandering Tattler *Heteroscelus incanus* (which has not been recorded in the subcontinent, but could occur as a vagrant). Supercilium is broader and longer than on that species, usually extending beyond eye, and with rather indistinct orbital ring; also, folded primaries extend to level with or just past tail (more noticeably beyond tail on Wandering), and nasal groove extends to just over half length of bill (three-quarters on Wandering), although this last feature is very difficult to see in the field. Typical flight call is also different (see below). **Adult breeding** White underparts are barred and streaked with dark grey, except for plain white belly, vent and undertail-coverts. (Breeding Wandering has darker and broader grey barring covering almost all of underparts.) **Adult non-breeding** has uniform pale grey neck, breast and flanks. **Juvenile** is finely spotted with white on scapulars, wing-coverts and tertials. **VOICE** Typical call is a *tu-weet, tu-weet,* recalling Common Ringed Plover (p.492), and alarm call is a *tuu-tuu-tuu.* **HABITS** Often quite tame. Frequently bobs head and rear body up and down. Flies fast and low, and raises wings vertically on alighting. **HABITAT** Mudflats, mangrove creeks and rocky shores on coast. **DISTRIBUTION AND STATUS BD:** vagrant. **REFERENCES** Hirst and Procter (1995).

RUDDY TURNSTONE *Arenaria interpres* Plate 44

Turnstone (F,I,P)

IDENTIFICATION 23 cm. A stout wader with black bill and short orange legs. Unmistakable, especially in flight, when in all plumages reveals unique pattern of white stripes on wings and back, and prominent black tail-band. **Adult breeding** has complex black-and-white patterning on head, neck and breast, and chestnut-red and black upperparts. **Adult non-breeding** is duller, with brownish head, but retains black neck-and-breast pattern and some chestnut on scapulars. **Juvenile** upperparts are brown, with neat buffish fringes, and black breast contrasts with white underparts and throat. **VOICE** A rolled *trik-tuk-tuk-tuk* or a shorter *tuk-er-tuk,* and when flushed may

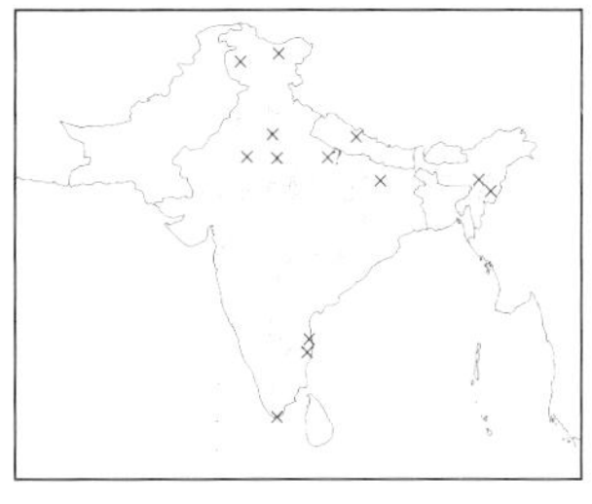

give sharp *chick-ik* or *kuu* (Hayman *et al.* 1986). **HABITS** Often feeds in small parties. Runs actively on the shore, turns over pebbles and shells and flicks seaweed to catch prey sheltering beneath; also probes into soft sand and pokes into rock crevices and among detritus at the high-water mark in search of food. Sometimes scavenges on carrion washed up by the tide. Flight is strong and direct, usually low over the shore. **HABITAT** Rocky coasts; also tidal mudflats and sandy shores in Pakistan and Gulf of Kutch; rarely inland waters. **DISTRIBUTION AND STATUS** Winter visitor, mainly to coasts of the subcontinent; first arrives in mid August, and most leave by mid May. **PK:** frequent winter visitor to the coast. **NP:** vagrant, once at 2590 m. **IN:** uncommon winter visitor, mainly to the NW coast. **BD:** winter visitor; non-breeders oversummer. **LK:** common winter visitor. **MV:** regular winter visitor; some oversummer.

ASIAN DOWITCHER *Limnodromus semipalmatus* — Plate 44

Snipe-billed Godwit (I)

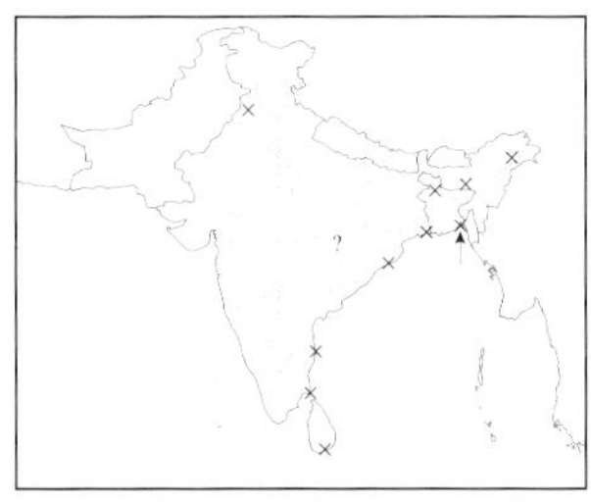

IDENTIFICATION 34–36 cm. In all plumages, closely resembles the commoner and more widely distributed Bar-tailed Godwit (p.475). Best told by straight, broad-based all-black bill, which has pronounced swollen tip; also by smaller size and stouter appearance, with deep-chested look and short neck, and square-shaped head with steeply rising forehead. Has distinctive 'sewing-machine' feeding action (stationary, usually in deep water, with rapid probing of substrate). In flight, shows diffuse pale wing-bar, greyish tail, and dark barring or spotting on whitish lower back and rump; prominent white V of nominate race of Bar-tailed is lacking (although beware eastern race *L. l. baueri*, which could occur in the subcontinent and has heavily barred lower back and rump). **Adult breeding** has reddish-chestnut face, neck and underparts, prominently barred flanks, and chestnut fringes to dark feathers of mantle and scapulars. Female is duller chestnut below than male. **Adult non-breeding** is greyish above, with prominent dark centres to feathers of mantle and scapulars creating strongly streaked appearance; underparts are whitish, densely streaked with dark grey except on throat and belly. Has more prominent white supercilium and more heavily marked flanks compared with adult non-breeding Bar-tailed. **Juvenile** recalls non-breeding adult, but with strong buffish wash to throat and breast, and prominent buff fringes to blackish feathers of mantle, scapulars and tertials. **VOICE** A yelping *chep-chep* or *chowp* and a soft, moaning *kiaow* with a human-like quality (Hayman *et al.* 1986). **HABITS** Often feeds and flies in tight flocks. Mixes with godwits and other waders at roost. Flight is powerful and often aerobatic. **HABITAT** Mainly intertidal mudflats and mudbanks of large tidal rivers. **DISTRIBUTION AND STATUS** Winter visitor to coasts of India, Bangladesh and Sri Lanka. **IN:** probably regular in very small numbers on the E coast south to Tamil Nadu. **BD:** rare. **LK:** winter vagrant to dry-zone coasts.

GREAT KNOT *Calidris tenuirostris* — Plate 44

Eastern Knot (I)

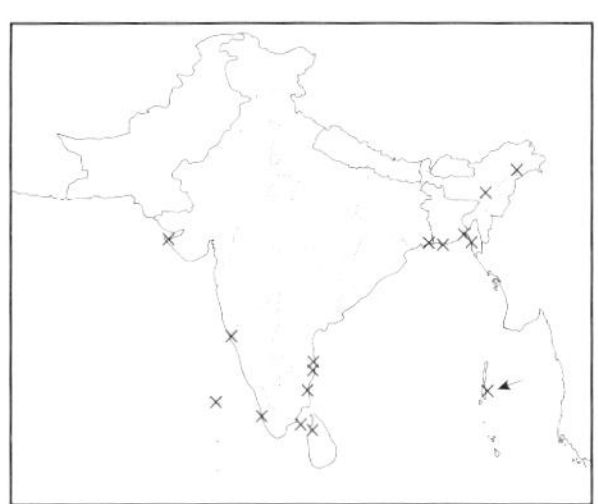

IDENTIFICATION 26–28 cm. Larger than Red Knot (below), with longer and often slightly downcurved bill. Also is less neatly proportioned, with head looking proportionately smaller and neck and body longer, at times recalling Ruff (p.486). At rest, closed wings extend beyond tail, while in flight shows more clearly defined white rump contrasting with grey tail. **Adult breeding** is heavily streaked with black on head, neck and mantle, and boldly spotted with black on breast and flanks, and has chestnut patterning to scapulars. Spotting on breast often merges to form solid black patch. Most likely to be confused with moulting male Ruff (which can look very similar in plumage, but has orangey legs). **Adult non-breeding** is more heavily streaked on the upperparts than Red Knot, usually showing prominent streaking on mantle and scapulars, and with a more densely marked breast. **Juvenile** has darker centres and contrasting white fringes to feathers of mantle, scapulars and wing-coverts, and more heavily marked breast, compared with juvenile Red Knot. **VOICE** A low disyllabic *nyut nyut*. **HABITS** Usually found in small parties, often with godwits and other waders. Feeds slowly, chiefly by probing deeply into mud or sand. Flight is strong and direct. **HABITAT** Intertidal mud- or sandflats and tidal creeks. **DISTRIBUTION AND STATUS** Winter visitor to coasts of the subcontinent. **PK:** rare winter visitor to coast, October–early June. **IN:** local and uncommon winter visitor. **BD:** scarce or irregular passage migrant and winter visitor. **LK:** rare on dry-zone coasts.

RED KNOT *Calidris canutus* — Plate 44

Knot (I,P)

IDENTIFICATION 23–25 cm. A neatly proportioned, rather plump, short-legged wader with short, straight bill. All plumages are similar to those of Curlew Sandpiper (p.485), but has quite different bill shape and proportions and

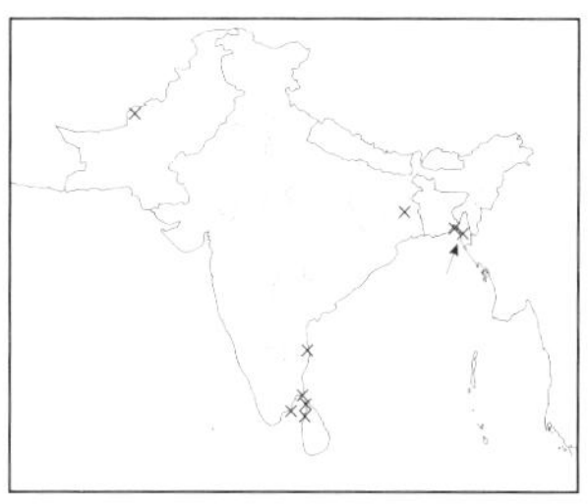

white rump is barred with grey. Unlike Curlew Sandpiper, it rarely feeds by wading in water. **Adult breeding** is brick-red on the entire underparts, with upperparts patterned rufous and black. **Adult non-breeding** is pale grey on the upperparts and whitish on the underparts, finely marked with grey on breast and flanks. Told from other non-breeding-plumaged calidrids except Great Knot (p.481) by combination of larger size and proportions and straight bill. See Great Knot for main differences from that species. **Juvenile** has prominent buff-ish-white fringes and dark subterminal crescents to feathers of brownish-grey mantle, scapulars and wing-coverts, and buff wash on breast and flanks. **VOICE** A low, short *knutt ... knutt,* although often silent. **HABITS** Details not recorded in the region. Highly gregarious in the non-breeding season. Feeds chiefly by probing in soft mud, also by picking from surface. **HABITAT** Mainly extensive intertidal mudflats. **DISTRIBUTION AND STATUS** Winter visitor, chiefly to coasts. **PK, IN, BD:** vagrant. **LK:** uncommon winter visitor to dry-zone coast.

SANDERLING *Calidris alba* Plate 45

***Crocethia alba* (K)**

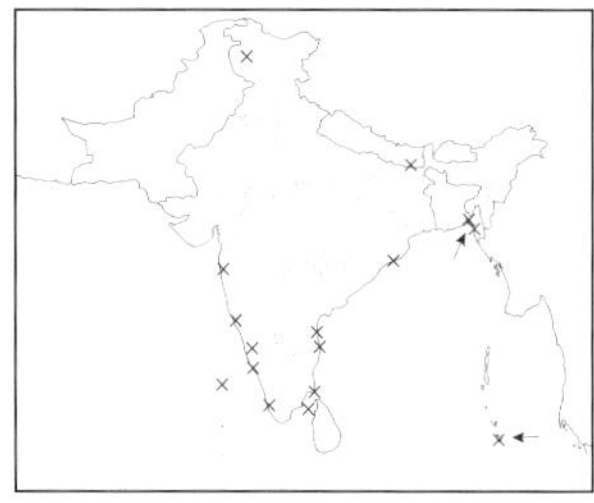

IDENTIFICATION 20 cm. Stocky, with thick, straight black bill, and the broadest white wing-bar of any calidrid. **Adult non-breeding** is pale grey above and very white below, with indistinct white supercilium, grey smudge through eye, and grey patch on sides of breast. Has blackish lesser wing-coverts, which are especially noticeable in flight but also show at rest as black patch at bend of wing (unless concealed by breast feathers). **Adult breeding** varies in appearance: brightest individuals have much rufous on sides of head, breast and mantle; in fresh plumage, rufous colouring is concealed by grey feather tips, with upperparts appearing mottled black and grey (or buff-brown), and breast white with dark streaking. Rufous birds possibly confusable with Little and Red-necked Stints (below and p.483), but Sanderling is considerably larger, with broader wing-bar, has rufous centres to scapulars and coverts, and also patterned tertials, and lacks hindtoe. Sides of head are distinctly streaked compared with Red-necked. **Juvenile** is similar to adult non-breeding, but has black streaking on crown and hindneck, chequered black-and-white mantle and scapulars, and buff wash to streaked sides of breast. **VOICE** Call is a liquid *plit.* **HABITS** Forages in small parties along the shoreline. Extremely active; runs swiftly after retreating waves, stopping suddenly to snatch minute animals cast ashore or to probe in the sands. **HABITAT** Sandy beaches. **DISTRIBUTION AND STATUS** Winter visitor chiefly to coasts, very rare inland; arrives mainly in September, with most gone by mid May. **PK:** common. **NP:** vagrant. **IN:** locally fairly common. **BD:** local; some oversummer. **LK:** irregular. **MV:** local and rather uncommon.

SPOON-BILLED SANDPIPER *Calidris pygmea* Plate 46

Spoonbill Sandpiper, *Eurynorhynchus pygmea*

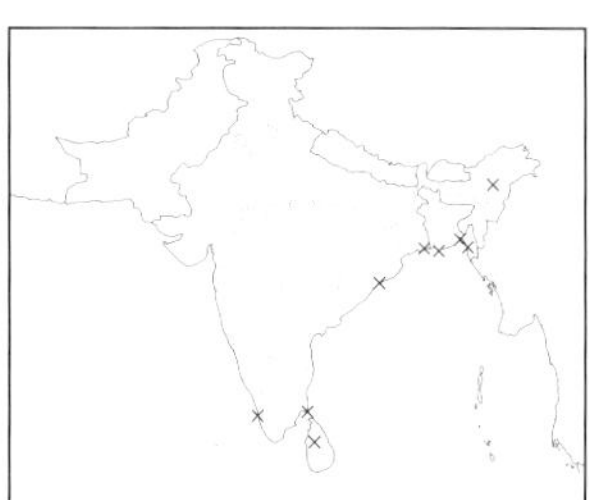

IDENTIFICATION 14–16 cm. Similar in all plumages to Little Stint (below) and best told by broad, spatulate tip to bill (although bill shape can be difficult to see side-on). Also appears larger and stockier, and approaches size and general appearance of Broad-billed Sandpiper (p.485). Has different feeding action, running quickly across mud, stopping for periods to feed by sweeping submerged bill-tip from side to side (sometimes pivoting on the spot or even moving backwards). Does not probe in slow, deliberate fashion like Little. **Adult non-breeding** is similar in plumage to Little, but upperparts are paler grey in coloration. Has more pronounced white supercilium, forehead and cheeks, and underparts appear cleaner and whiter. **Adult breeding** has more uniform rufous-orange face and breast compared with Little (recalling Red-necked Stint, p.483). Upperparts are more uniformly fringed with buff, and lacks buff V on mantle. **Juvenile** is very similar in plumage to Little Stint, but shows more white on face and darker eye-stripe and ear-coverts (resulting in masked appearance), and has upperparts more uniformly fringed with buff. **VOICE** A quiet rolled *preep* or a shrill *wheet* (Hayman *et al.* 1986). **HABITS** Found singly, or in small groups scattered among flocks of other small waders, and rarely in large flocks. Feeds mostly by sweeping bill from side to side in shallow water while walking along; also observed moving feet up and down and then stepping back to jab bill into the trampled area. **HABITAT** Intertidal mudflats. In Bangladesh, suitable sites are dynamic and can change within a year. **DISTRIBUTION AND STATUS** Winter visitor. India, Bangladesh and Sri Lanka. Globally threatened. **IN:** very rare, mainly on E coast. **BD:** local and regular on the coast in winter; the most important known wintering ground for this species worldwide. **LK:** vagrant.

LITTLE STINT *Calidris minuta* Plate 45

IDENTIFICATION 13–15 cm. In all plumages, differs from Temminck's Stint (p.483) in more rounded, upright appearance, stouter and straighter all-black bill, and dark legs. Tail does not extend beyond closed wings. Has

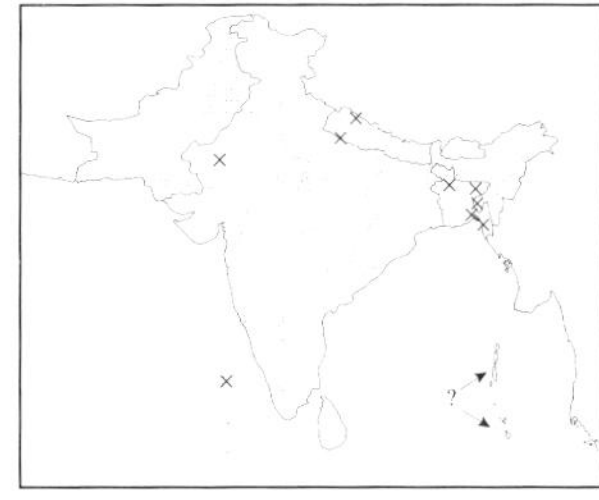

grey (not white) sides to tail visible in flight, and distinctive flight call. Is generally more active, with much running and furtive pecking. Often occurs in flocks on tidal mudflats, unlike Temminck's, although also frequently seen inland and in similar habitats to Temminck's. **Adult non-breeding** is brownish-grey above and white below, with grey patches on sides of breast. Differs from adult non-breeding Temminck's in appearing paler above, with more prominent dark centres to feathers of upperparts giving rise to streaked or mottled (and less uniform) appearance. Usually has pale centre to breast, without prominent pectoral band shown by Temminck's, and has more obvious white supercilium. **Adult breeding** is warmer, more rufous, in coloration than adult breeding Temminck's, especially on head and breast. Further, has a more extensive white throat, shows cream V on mantle, and feathers of scapulars, tertials and greater coverts are more extensively and evenly fringed with rufous. **Juvenile** is similar to adult breeding (quite different from juvenile Temminck's), but usually has more prominent pale mantle V, and more prominent white supercilium which typically splits above the eye; nape and hindneck are distinctly greyer than crown and mantle. For differences from Long-toed Stint (p.484) and the much rarer but very similar Red-necked Stint (below), see those species. **VOICE** In flight, a weak *pi, pi, pi.* **HABITS** Gregarious; often gathers in flocks mixed with Dunlins (p.484) and Curlew Sandpipers (p.485). An active wader, rapidly picks at the surface and frequently darts about to catch tiny prey items; probes occasionally. Flies in tight flocks when disturbed, twisting and turning in unison. **HABITAT** Mudflats, coastal lagoons, tidal creeks, marshes, paddy-fields and lakes. **DISTRIBUTION AND STATUS** Winter visitor. Much of the subcontinent, except parts of the northwest and northeast and most of Himalayas; first arrives in late July, with most gone by mid May. **PK:** common winter visitor to coast, passage migrant inland. **NP:** uncommon winter visitor, mainly to the lowlands (–3050 m on passage). **IN:** widespread and locally common winter visitor, most frequent on coasts. **BD:** local winter visitor; some non-breeders oversummer. **LK:** common winter visitor to lowlands. **MV:** regular winter visitor. **REFERENCES** Harris *et al.* (1996).

RED-NECKED STINT *Calidris ruficollis* — Plate 45

Eastern Little Stint (I), Rufous-necked Stint (K)

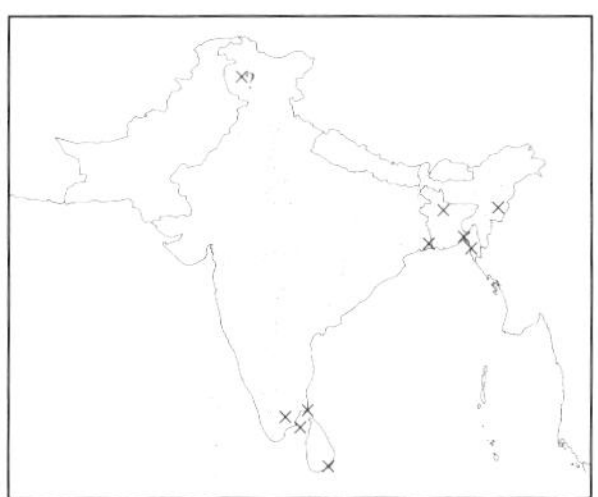

IDENTIFICATION 13–16 cm. Very subtle structural differences from Little Stint (p.482) include stouter, deeper-tipped bill, shorter legs, and longer wings which give rise to more elongated appearance. In flight, some birds show more extensive white at base of inner primaries compared with Little. **Adult non-breeding** is almost identical to Little, but is cleaner and paler grey above, with clearer and less extensive dark centres to mantle and scapulars, and markings on sides of breast are more clearly defined. **Adult breeding** typically shows unstreaked rufous-orange face and upper breast, contrasting with white underparts, with only a small whitish patch on chin; sides of lower breast are white, overlaid with dark streaking. By comparison, adult breeding Little Stint is uniformly streaked on ear-coverts, sides of neck and breast, overlaid with rufous-brown wash, and has extensive white throat. Lack of prominent buff V on mantle, and greyish-white rather than rufous fringes to tertials and wing-coverts, are further differences from Little. Initially, grey fringes to feathers of mantle and scapulars give overall grey appearance to upperparts; later, these feathers wear to reveal rufous edges (when contrast with rather uniform greyish wing-coverts is distinctive). In this later plumage, confusion is possible with breeding-plumaged Sanderling (p.482), but that species has deeper chestnut coloration to head and breast with more prominent dark streaking and spotting, and chestnut patterning to wing-coverts and tertials; Sanderling is also larger and dumpier, has a broader white wing-bar, and has a distinctive flight call. **Juvenile** is similar to Little, but more variable. Compared with Little, lacks or has only indistinct V on mantle; also has less distinct supercilium behind eye, and, unike on Little, the supercilium does not usually split in front of eye; tertials are grey with whitish or buffish edges (rather than blackish with rufous edges), and bases to lower scapulars are grey with dark subterminal marks and whitish fringes (rather than wholly blackish centres with rufous fringes). Often shows pinkish-grey wash on sides of breast, with extensive diffuse streaking (Little has orangey wash with a few sharp streaks). **VOICE** Much as that of Little, a *chit* or *prip,* slightly coarser and perhaps lower-pitched (Hayman *et al.* 1986). **HABITS** Very similar to those of Little. **HABITAT** Mainly coastal. **DISTRIBUTION AND STATUS** Winter visitor. Mainly E coasts of India and Bangladesh. **IN:** status uncertain; presumably overlooked because of similarity to Little Stint. **BD:** winter visitor inland and on coast; some non-breeders oversummer. **LK:** very rare. **REFERENCES** Harris *et al.* (1996), Robson (1996b).

TEMMINCK'S STINT *Calidris temminckii* — Plate 45

IDENTIFICATION 13–15 cm. In all plumages, told from Little Stint (p.482) by elongated appearance and rather crouching, horizontal stance, with tail extending noticeably beyond closed wings at rest. Further, has finer, slightly downcurved bill with paler base, yellowish or greenish legs, prominent white sides to tail in flight, and distinctive flight call. Is typically less active, and rather 'skulking' in behaviour. In some respects resembles a small Common Sandpiper (p.480), and jerky wing action in flight recalls Little Ringed Plover (p.493). **Adult non-breeding** is brownish-grey above and white below. Differs from adult non-breeding Little in darker and more uniform upperparts,

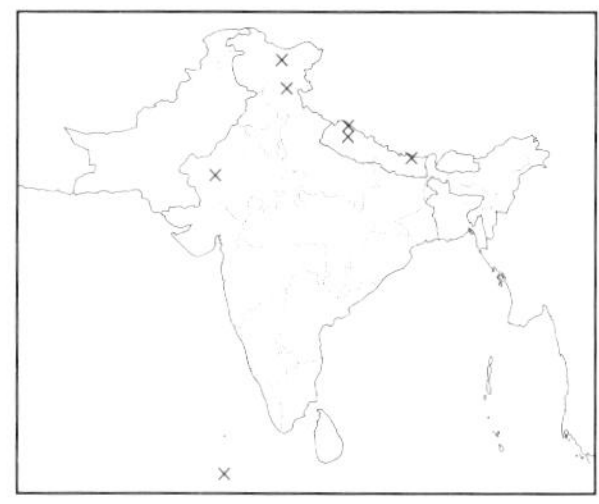

brownish-grey breast-band, and less distinct supercilium. **Adult breeding** is similar in pattern to non-breeding, but has browner head and breast, and browner upperparts with irregular dark centres and rufous edges to feathers of mantle and scapulars. It is quite different from adult breeding Little, lacking buff V on mantle; also lacks regular and extensive rufous fringes to scapulars, tertials and greater coverts, and has only an indistinct pale throat. **Juvenile** is similar to adult non-breeding, but is browner, and feathers of upperparts are evenly fringed with buff, with black subterminal crescents; quite unlike juvenile Little. **VOICE** A trilling, cicada-like *trrrrrit.* **HABITS** Usually found singly, in small groups or in flocks of up to 20 birds. Unobtrusive and easily overlooked. Forages more among vegetation at wetland margins than other stints. Feeds more slowly than Little Stint, runs about less, covers a smaller area of ground, and methodically searches for food; picks prey from vegetation, mud or sand. When disturbed it often crouches, and if flushed typically towers jerkily upwards and flies off swiftly in a tight, wheeling flock. **HABITAT** Favours vegetated freshwater habitats: marshes, pools, lakes, wet fields and river banks; also less often on brackish marshes, mudflats and tidal lagoons. **DISTRIBUTION AND STATUS** Winter visitor. Throughout much of the subcontinent, except parts of the northwest, northeast and Himalayas; first arrives in late August, leaves by end May. **PK:** common winter visitor, mainly to Punjab. **NP:** common and widespread winter visitor and passage migrant; below 1370 m (–4710 m on passage). **IN:** widespread and locally common winter visitor. **BT:** common but very local winter visitor and passage migrant. **BD:** uncommon winter visitor. **LK:** rare winter visitor to dry-zone coasts. **MV:** rare on passage.

LONG-TOED STINT *Calidris subminuta* — Plate 45

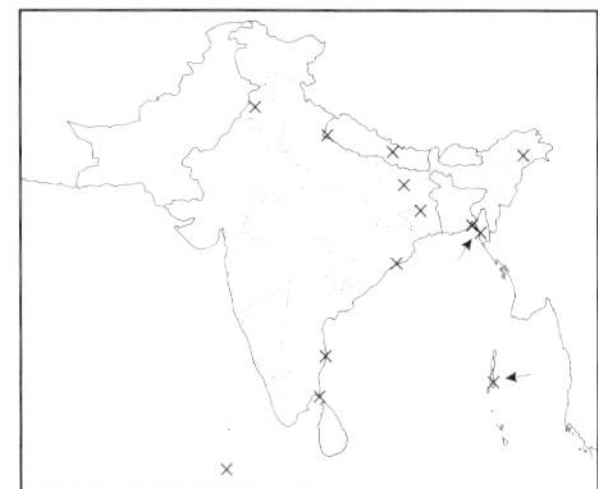

IDENTIFICATION 13–15 cm. Fairly distinctive in all plumages, recalling a miniature Wood Sandpiper (p.479). Compared with Little Stint (p.482), has longer, yellowish legs, upright stance and longish neck, and finer, slightly downcurved bill with paler base. Shape and plumage features are quite different from those of Temminck's Stint (p.483). In **adult non-breeding plumage**, further differences from Little are more heavily marked upperparts with prominent, dark centres to feathers, more prominent supercilium and darker eye-stripe and ear-coverts (giving rise to masked appearance), and more heavily marked foreneck and breast showing as a distinct breast-band. **Adult breeding** and **juvenile** are similar in plumage to respective plumages of Little, with prominent rufous fringes to feathers of mantle, scapulars and tertials, but have rufous crown, prominent white supercilium, and strong brown streaking on foreneck and breast. Juvenile has particularly striking dark-bordered buff Vs on mantle and scapulars. **VOICE** A soft *prit* or *chirrup,* similar to but less purring than that of Curlew Sandpiper (p.485). **HABITS** Often feeds with other stints; runs about energetically to pick up tiny invertebrates. Towers like a Temminck's Stint if flushed. **HABITAT** Freshwater and brackish marshes, lakes, river banks and intertidal mudflats. **DISTRIBUTION AND STATUS** Winter visitor. Mainly E subcontinent. **NP:** vagrant. **IN:** widespread and uncommon. **BD:** scarce. **LK:** irregular, mainly on coast. **MV:** rare.

SHARP-TAILED SANDPIPER *Calidris acuminata* — Plate 45

Asian Pectoral Sandpiper (I,P)

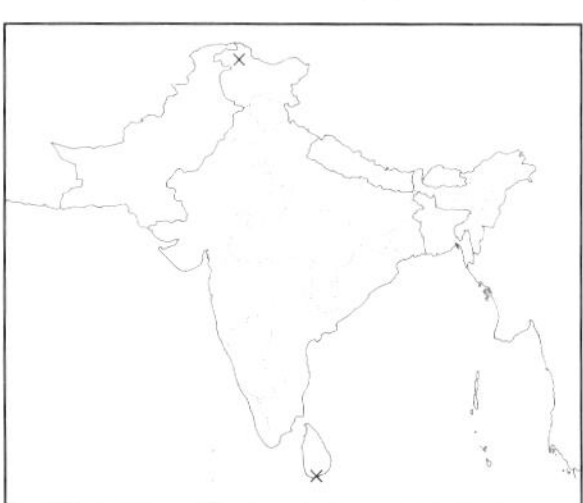

IDENTIFICATION 17–21 cm. Recalls Wood Sandpiper (p.479) in shape, or a very large Long-toed Stint (above) in both shape and plumage. Legs are pale, usually yellowish or greenish. **Adult non-breeding** has rufous tinge to crown, prominent white supercilium which broadens behind eye, breast-band of fine dark streaking, and dark-streaked brownish upperparts. **Adult breeding** has rufous crown and prominent white supercilium, bold dark spotting and arrowhead markings on entire underparts, and bright rufous fringes to feathers of mantle and scapulars. **Juvenile** is similar to breeding adult, but lacks bold markings on underparts; breast is lightly streaked, and washed with warm buff. **VOICE** A soft *trrt* or *wheep,* often in a short twittering sequence recalling Barn Swallow (p.690) (Hayman *et al.* 1986). **HABITS** Feeds by picking and probing, and is frequently hidden among vegetation. Typically, crouches when disturbed. **HABITAT** Freshwater lakes and marshes, tidal lagoons and intertidal mudflats; often on grassland and drier edges of wetlands. **DISTRIBUTION AND STATUS PK, LK:** vagrant. The Kashmir record noted in Ali and Ripley (1987) was from Gilgit, Pakistan.

DUNLIN *Calidris alpina* — Plate 46

IDENTIFICATION 16–22 cm. Told from Curlew Sandpiper (p.485), in all plumages, by shorter legs and less elegant gait, shorter, less downcurved bill, dark centre to rump, and distinctive call. Bill is much longer, and noticeably downcurved, compared with Sanderling (p.482) and the smaller Little Stint (p.482). For differences from Broad-billed Sandpiper (p.485), see that species. **Adult non-breeding** differs from adult non-breeding Curlew

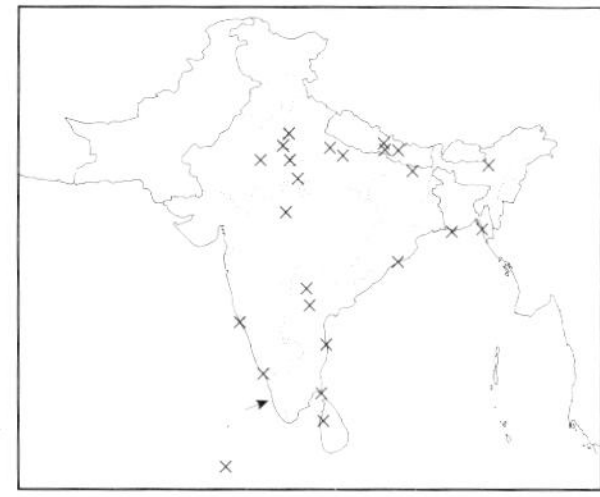

Sandpiper in being a slightly darker grey-brown above, with less distinct whitish supercilium. Confusion is possible with adult non-breeding Sanderling, but that species is paler grey above and whiter below, with broader white wing-bar. **Adult breeding** is distinctive, with black patch on belly, dark-streaked foreneck and breast, and dark-streaked rufous-brown crown, mantle and scapulars. **Juvenile** has rufous-buff wash to face and breast, with dark brown streaking on lower breast and belly, neat rufous fringes to dark feathers of mantle (often with faint buff V formed by fringes to scapulars), and neat buff fringes to wing-coverts. **VOICE** A slurred *screet*, quite different from calls of similar species. **HABITS** Usually in flocks, often with other waders. Typically, has a hunched posture when foraging; makes short runs over wet mud and wades near the water's edge. Pecks or probes, often making a series of vigorous, rapid jabs into mud. Flies swiftly in close packs, with erratic changes of direction performed in unison. **HABITAT** Intertidal mudflats, seashore, tidal creeks, river banks, sand bars and flooded fields. **DISTRIBUTION AND STATUS** Winter visitor mainly to coasts of the subcontinent, with small numbers inland; first arrives in early August, with most gone by late May. **PK:** common winter visitor to the coast; small numbers along major rivers all winter; a few possibly oversummer. **NP:** scarce passage migrant and winter visitor; below 1370 m. **IN:** widespread winter visitor mainly to NW and W coasts, where locally common, uncommon inland. **BD:** rare winter visitor, mainly to coasts. **LK:** rare winter visitor to coast, occasionally inland. **MV:** probably a rare and local winter visitor.

CURLEW SANDPIPER *Calidris ferruginea* — Plate 46

***C. testacea* (I)**

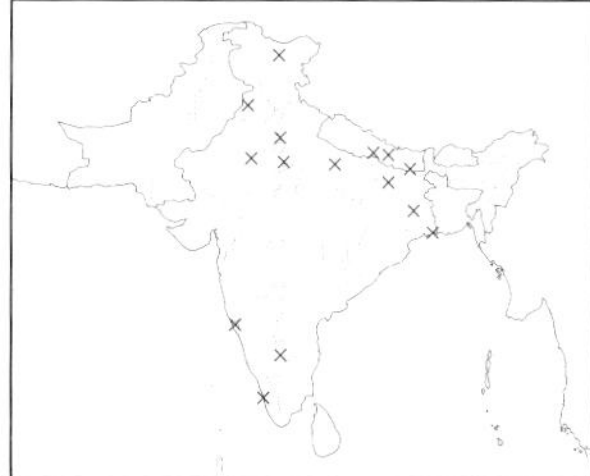

IDENTIFICATION 18–23 cm. Distinguished from Dunlin (p.484) and Broad-billed Sandpiper (below), in all plumages, by longer legs and more elegant gait, longer, more downcurved bill, broad white rump band, and distinctive call. **Adult non-breeding** differs from adult non-breeding Dunlin in being slightly paler grey above, with more distinct white supercilium. **Adult breeding** is distinctive, with most of head and underparts chestnut-red, with white chin; has black-centred, white-fringed scapulars, and more uniformly grey coverts. **Juvenile** is also distinctive, with prominent white supercilium, pale peach wash across faintly streaked breast, and neat buff fringes to grey-brown feathers of upperparts (with black subterminal crescents visible at close range). **VOICE** A low, purring *prrriit*. **HABITS** Keeps in flocks, often with other waders. Feeds on wet mud in a similar manner to Dunlin; also by wading in deeper water than that used by other *Calidris*, immersing head and bill below the surface. **HABITAT** Mainly on coast, intertidal mudflats, seashore, saltpans; rare inland on lakes and rivers. **DISTRIBUTION AND STATUS** Winter visitor mainly to coasts of the subcontinent, with small numbers inland; first arrives in last week of July, with most gone by end April. **PK:** common winter visitor to coasts, passage migrant inland; a few probably oversummer. **NP:** rare passage migrant. **IN:** widespread winter visitor, common on extreme S and SE coasts, very common on migration on W coast, uncommon inland. **BD:** common winter visitor, some non-breeders oversummer; on coast and inland. **LK:** common winter visitor to dry lowlands, infrequent in wet zone. **MV:** common winter visitor.

BUFF-BREASTED SANDPIPER *Tryngites subruficollis* — Plate 46

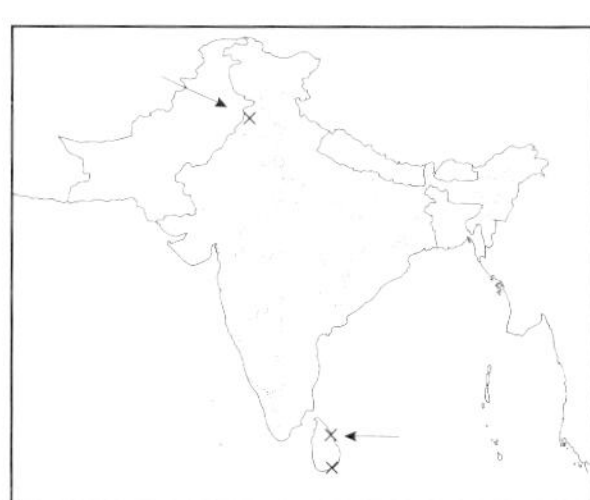

IDENTIFICATION 18–20 cm. Recalls a diminutive Ruff (p.486), with shorter and straighter bill, large eyes, and bright yellow legs. In flight, lacks obvious wing-bar and has more uniform uppertail-coverts. Underwing pattern is characteristic, with black markings on primary coverts, primaries and secondaries. **Adult** has unmarked buff face and underparts, with beady black eyes, black streaking on crown and hindneck, and neat buff fringes to dark feathers of upperparts. **Juvenile** is very similar, but has buff centres and dark subterminal crescents to pale-fringed feathers of mantle and scapulars. **VOICE** Generally silent. **HABITS** Usually very tame. Feeds actively by picking prey from the ground and from vegetation; walks quickly and often changes direction. Does not wade. Flight is rapid and erratic. **HABITAT** Dry short-grass areas, dry mud and seashore. **DISTRIBUTION AND STATUS IN, LK:** vagrant. **REFERENCES** Robson (1996a).

BROAD-BILLED SANDPIPER *Limicola falcinellus* — Plate 46

IDENTIFICATION 16–18 cm. In all plumages, told from Dunlin (p.484) by longer bill with noticeable downward kink at tip. Also appears shorter-bodied and stockier, with rearward-set legs. **Adult non-breeding** differs from Dunlin in having prominent white supercilium, with noticeable 'split' before eye, contrasting with dark eye-stripe. Further, has dark inner wing-coverts forming patch at bend of wing (sometimes obscured by breast feathers), more heavily streaked upperparts, and stronger breast-band of dark streaking. Dark inner wing-coverts show as dark leading edge to wing in flight (recalling Sanderling (p.482)). **Adult breeding** has prominent split

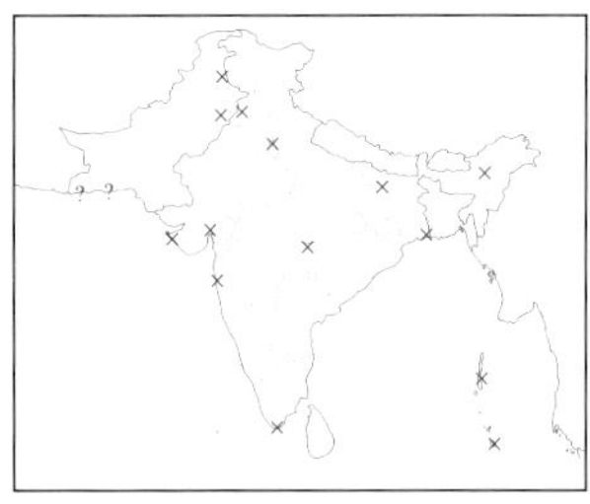

supercilium contrasting with dark sides and centre of crown, bold brown streaking on sides of head, neck and breast sharply demarcated from white underparts, and rufous-fringed mantle and scapular feathers with whitish mantle and scapular lines. Birds in worn breeding plumage can appear uniformly very dark on upperparts. **Juvenile** is similar to adult breeding, but wing-coverts are neatly fringed with buff, and breast is washed with buff and only lightly streaked. Confusion possible with juvenile Dunlin, but Broad-billed has more prominent supercilium and unstreaked white belly. **VOICE** A distinctive buzzing *chrrreet*, and a shorter *tzit* or *trr* (Hayman *et al.* 1986). **HABITS** Usually found singly in winter and in small flocks when on passage. Feeds in a similar manner to Dunlin, by pecking and probing. **HABITAT** Mudbanks of creeks, intertidal mudflats and brackish lagoons. **DISTRIBUTION AND STATUS** Winter visitor to coasts of the subcontinent, uncommon inland on passage; first arrives in late July, leaves by end May. **PK:** frequent to scarce on the coast; a few probably oversummer. **IN:** local on the coast, common in the extreme southeast, uncommon inland. **BD:** local and common on the coast. **LK:** very rare on dry-zone coast.

RUFF *Philomachus pugnax* Plate 46

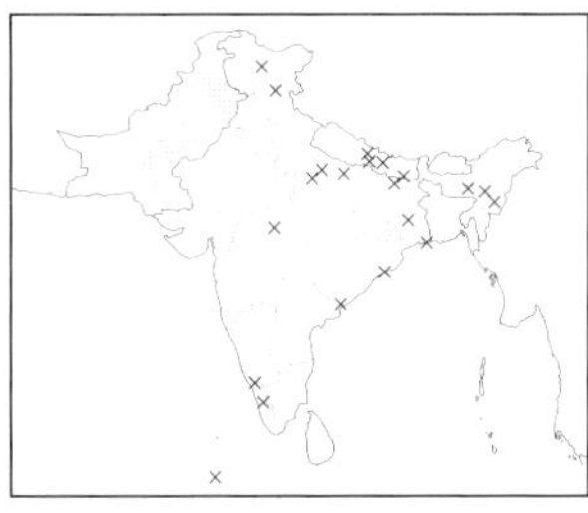

IDENTIFICATION Male 26–32 cm; female 20–25 cm. A deep-bellied, slim-necked wader with rather small head. Has medium-length, slightly downcurved bill and rather long yellowish or orangey legs. In all plumages, lacks prominent supercilium and, in flight, shows narrow white wing-bar and prominent white sides to uppertail-coverts. Male is considerably larger than female. **Adult non-breeding** is grey-brown above, with feathers fringed buffish-white, and mainly white below. Some non-breeding males can have whitish head, neck and breast. **Adult male breeding** in full plumage has elaborate ruff which can be variably white, black, brown or barred. Mantle and scapulars are also very variable, typically irregularly patterned with black and chestnut. **Adult female breeding** lacks ruff. Head, neck and breast are rufous-brown marked with darker brown, and feathers of mantle and scapulars show irregular chestnut and black markings. **Juvenile** has warm buff head and underparts, and neat buffish fringes to dark feathers of upperparts, resulting in scaly appearance. **VOICE** Generally silent. **HABITS** Gregarious, often in small parties or flocks with other waders; often congregates in flocks of many thousands on first arrival in NW India and when on passage. Walks purposefully, picking prey from surface and vegetation and probing into mud. When stationary, has an upright posture with head raised. **HABITAT** Freshwater lakes, pools and marshes, flooded fields, grassland and intertidal mudflats; also feeds on fallen grain on roads and in ports. **DISTRIBUTION AND STATUS** Widespread winter visitor or passage migrant. Mainly Pakistan; India except parts of the northwest, east and Himalayas; Bangladesh and Sri Lanka. First arrives in early August, with most gone by mid April. **PK:** common passage migrant, mainly in spring; a few overwinter in Sind. **NP:** scarce passage migrant; below 1310 m. **IN:** widespread winter visitor, common in the northwest, north and extreme southeast. **BD:** passage migrant and local winter visitor. **LK:** winter visitor to dry lowlands. **MV:** rare winter visitor.

RED-NECKED PHALAROPE *Phalaropus lobatus* Plate 47

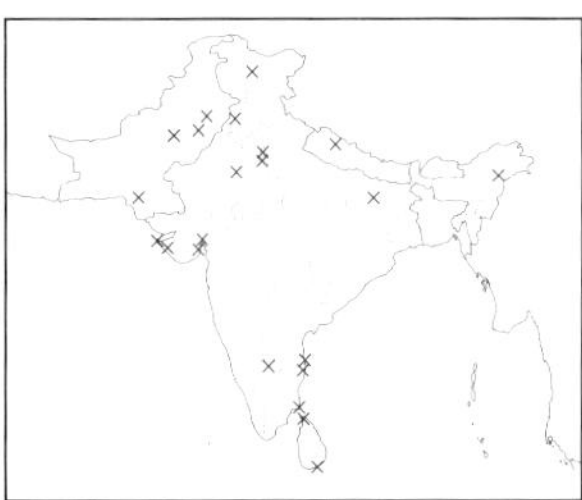

IDENTIFICATION 18–19 cm. Smaller and daintier than Red Phalarope (p.487), with smaller head and needle-fine bill. Has faster, more jerky flight action (usually rather stint-like). **Adult non-breeding** differs from other winter-plumaged waders, except Red Phalarope, in showing prominent black mask and cap (latter sometimes much reduced), with dark line running down hindneck. In flight, has prominent white wing-bar, and dark grey upperwing-coverts contrast with mantle. Compared with Red in winter plumage, has darker grey upperparts, with broader white edges to feathers forming mantle and scapular lines. Bill is wholly black. Underwing shows contrasting dark trailing edge and markings on coverts (these features lacking on Red). Some birds in their first summer are similar to non-breeding adult. **Adult female breeding** is unmistakable, having slate-grey head with white crescent above eye and white throat, red band down sides of neck, slate-grey hindneck and breast, and prominent buff scapular stripes. **Adult male breeding** is duller, with less striking head pattern. **Juvenile** is similar in plumage to juvenile Red, but shows prominent orange-buff mantle and scapular lines. **First-winter** is like adult non-breeding, but blackish-centred (juvenile) feathers of mantle and scapulars are retained late into year. **VOICE** A single *twick*, lower-pitched than call of Red (Hayman *et al.* 1986). **HABITS** Wintering birds are mainly pelagic and gregarious, often in flocks of up to 100 or more. Very tame when on migration at inland pools. Swims buoyantly, and characteristically spins around; at fresh waters, darts erratically here and there to pick insects from the surface or emergent vegetation. Also wades when foraging. Flight over long distances is swift and in close-packed flocks, like that of a stint. **HABITAT** Winters at sea; on migration, also occurs on saltpans, shallow pools and jheels inland. **DISTRIBUTION AND STATUS** Winter visitor. Chiefly offshore from the coasts of Pakistan, NW and SE India and Sri Lanka; arrives mainly in September, leaves by late May. **PK:** common winter visitor, normally 32–48 km offshore. **NP:** vagrant, one at

3050 m. **IN:** common winter visitor off coasts of Gujarat and Tamil Nadu; rare on passage inland and at coast. **LK:** scarce but regular winter visitor, mainly to SE coast. **REFERENCES** Higgins and Davis (1996).

RED PHALAROPE *Phalaropus fulicaria* Plate 47

Grey Phalarope

IDENTIFICATION 20–22 cm. Larger and bulkier than Red-necked Phalarope (p.486), with larger head and stouter bill. Has slower wingbeats and often less erratic flight, with longer and slightly broader wings and fuller tail. **Adult non-breeding** differs from other winter-plumaged waders, except Red-necked Phalarope, in showing dark mask and cap (latter sometimes much reduced). In flight, darker grey wing-coverts contrast with pale grey mantle and scapulars, and has broad white wing-bar. Distinguished from non-breeding Red-necked by more uniform, and paler grey, mantle and scapulars. Bill usually has yellow or yellowish-brown tinge at base (although this may be lacking on some). **Adult female breeding** is unmistakable, with entire neck and underparts brick-red, white face patch, black crown and front of face, yellow bill with black tip, and rufous fringes to feathers of mantle and scapulars. **Adult male breeding** is similar but duller, with less striking head pattern, and usually has white belly. **Juvenile** is similar in plumage to juvenile Red-necked, with buffish foreneck and breast, but has dark feathers of upperparts more evenly fringed with paler buff (lacking prominent mantle and scapular lines of Red-necked). Broader bill usually shows yellowish at base. **First-winter** is like adult non-breeding, but blackish-centred (juvenile) feathers of mantle and scapulars are retained late into year. **VOICE** A shrill *wit*, recalling Sanderling (p.482) (Hayman *et al.* 1986). **HABITS** Similar to those of Red-necked. **HABITAT** Unknown in subcontinent. Elsewhere, similar to that of Red-necked. **DISTRIBUTION AND STATUS IN:** vagrant, one 19th-century record. **REFERENCES** Higgins and Davis (1996).

PAINTED-SNIPES Rostratulidae

Frequent marshes and superficially resemble snipes, but have spectacular plumages.

GREATER PAINTED-SNIPE *Rostratula benghalensis* Plate 47

Painted Snipe (F,I,P)

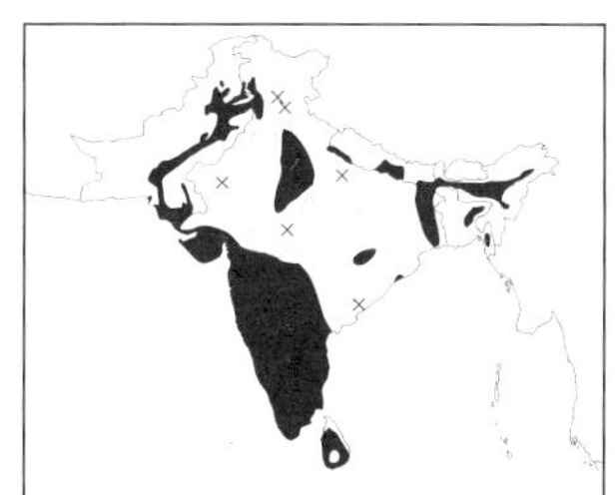

IDENTIFICATION 25 cm. A rail-like wader with long, slightly downcurved bill. Flight is weak and rail-like, with dangling legs and rather broad and rounded wings. **Adult female** has striking white 'spectacles' and white 'braces', which join with buff scapular lines. Also has maroon head and neck, becoming blacker on breast, buff crown-stripe, and dark greenish mantle and wing-coverts. **Adult male** is smaller and duller; 'spectacles' are buff, head and neck lack maroon coloration, and wing-coverts are boldly spotted with golden-buff. In flight, both sexes show golden-buff barring on flight feathers; wing-coverts of male appear mainly golden-buff. **Juvenile** resembles adult male, but wing-coverts are greyer, with smaller buff spots. **VOICE** Occasionally an explosive *kek* when flushed; female has soft *koh koh* in display (Hayman *et al.* 1986). **HABITS** Found singly or in small flocks. Chiefly crepuscular or nocturnal. Skulking, and reluctant to fly if approached; rises heavily and with legs trailing, and lands in cover again a short distance away. Feeds by probing in mud, or by sweeping bill from side to side in shallow water while bobbing rear body. Movements are slow and deliberate. Has a roding display flight like Eurasian Woodcock (p.471). **HABITAT** Freshwater marshes, pools and ditches thickly vegetated with reeds and with mud patches; also mangroves in Bangladesh. **BREEDING** Almost all year, varying locally. Nest is a pad of grass or reeds well hidden among thick vegetation. **DISTRIBUTION AND STATUS** Resident, subject to local movements depending on water conditions. Widespread, but few records from parts of NW, C and E India. **PK:** frequent and widespread, but local in Indus Basin. **NP:** widespread but uncommon; mainly below 350 m (–1370 m). **IN:** widespread and locally fairly common; in the plains, up to 1800 m in Himalayas. **BD:** local. **LK:** regular but rare in lowlands and lower hills.

JACANAS Jacanidae

Jacanas characteristically have very long toes, which enable them to walk over floating vegetation. They inhabit freshwater lakes, ponds and marshes.

PHEASANT-TAILED JACANA *Hydrophasianus chirurgus* Plate 48

IDENTIFICATION 31 cm (39–58 cm in breeding season). Extensive white in upperwing, and white underwing, distinguish this from Bronze-winged Jacana (p.488) in all plumages. Like that species, has very long legs and toes which dangle behind in flight. **Adult breeding** is elaborate and unmistakable. Has white head and foreneck, orange-yellow hindneck, dark brown body contrasting with white of wings, and long downcurved tail. **Adult**

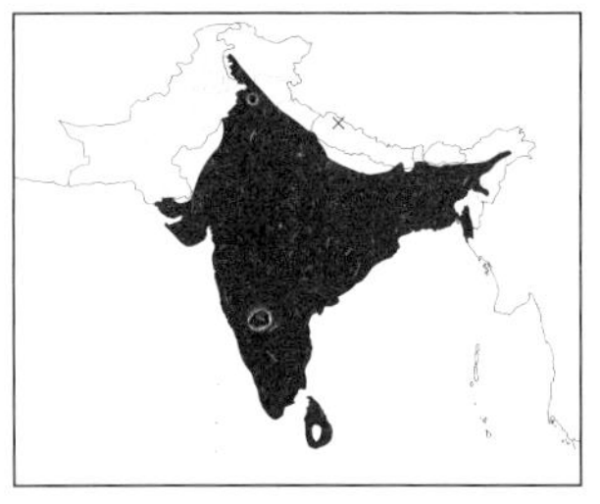

non-breeding lacks long tail and has white underparts, and is confusable with juvenile Bronze-winged. Best told by daintier appearance, finer dark bill, dark brown neck line contrasting with yellow sides of neck, and brown breast-band. **Juvenile** is duller than non-breeding adult. Breast-band can be less prominent, has pale buff on sides of neck stripe, and has rufous fringes to wing-coverts and rufous cap. **VOICE** A distinctive *me-e-ou* or *me-oup* in the breeding season, and a nasal *tewu* (Hayman *et al.* 1986). **HABITS** Gregarious outside the breeding season. Walks or rests on floating vegetation; usually found in the open and is quite tame. Forages actively throughout the day; eats mainly seeds and roots and also aquatic invertebrates. Swims well and floats buoyantly. Flight is slow and flapping, with the large feet dangling behind. **HABITAT** Lakes, jheels, pools and village tanks well vegetated with floating aquatic plants. **BREEDING** May–September, varying locally. Builds a flimsy nest of grasses and water weeds on floating or emergent aquatic vegetation. **DISTRIBUTION AND STATUS** Resident, subject to local movements. Throughout much of the subcontinent, except most of Himalayas. **PK:** widespread and common in major rice-growing areas of Sind; summer visitor to Punjab. **NP:** mainly a summer visitor, although recorded in all months; breeds up to 1525 m (–3050 m on passage); fairly common in the terai at Kosi, rare elsewhere. **IN:** widespread and generally common resident; summers up to 1500 m in Himalayas (–3800 m, presumably on passage). **BD:** local resident throughout. **LK:** common resident in lowlands.

BRONZE-WINGED JACANA *Metopidius indicus* Plate 48

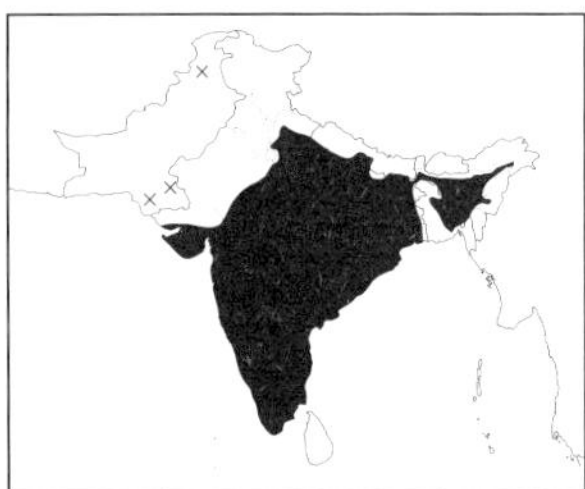

IDENTIFICATION 28–31 cm. Very dark upperwing and underwing distinguish this species from Pheasant-tailed Jacana (p.487) at all times. **Adult** has white supercilium contrasting with glossy black head, black neck and underparts, and bronze-green upperparts. Further, has rufous-chestnut rump, uppertail-coverts and tail. Bill is yellow, with bright red shield. **Juvenile** could be confused with juvenile and non-breeding adult Pheasant-tailed Jacana, but lacks brown band down sides of neck and brown breast-band, and has strong orange-buff wash to foreneck and breast; has short, white supercilium, but this does not extend beyond eye. Bill is broader and yellowish. **VOICE** A short, harsh grunt and a wheezy, piping *seek-seek-seek* (Hayman *et al.* 1986). **HABITS** Similar to those of Pheasant-tailed, and often found with that species. If alarmed, will partially submerge its body among aquatic vegetation. **HABITAT** Similar to that of Pheasant-tailed Jacana. **BREEDING** June–September, soon after the start of the SW monsoon. Nest is a pad of rushes or weed stems, although eggs are sometimes laid directly on to floating leaves. **DISTRIBUTION AND STATUS** Resident. Mainly from Gujarat and NW Uttar Pradesh east through the Nepal lowlands to NE India and Bangladesh and south throughout the peninsula. **PK:** vagrant. **NP:** fairly common throughout the lowlands, uncommon up to 915 m. **IN:** widespread and generally common resident. **BD:** local.

THICK-KNEES Burhinidae

Medium-sized to large waders, mainly crepuscular or nocturnal, and with cryptically patterned plumages. Their flight is swift and low over the ground, with legs stretched out behind.

EURASIAN THICK-KNEE *Burhinus oedicnemus* Plate 47

Stone Curlew (I,K,R), Stone-curlew, Stone-Plover (P)

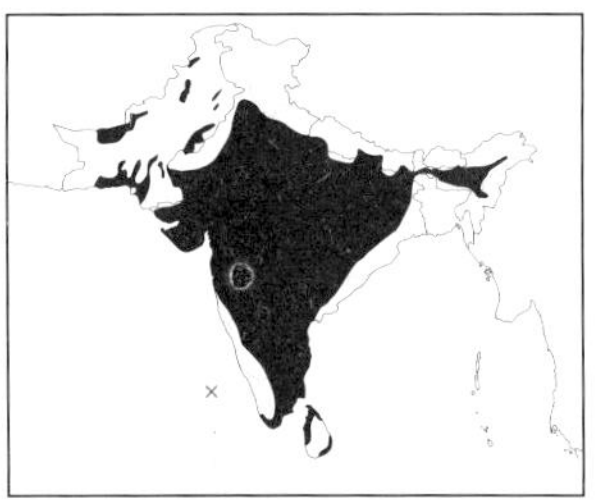

IDENTIFICATION 40–44 cm. Unmistakable wader. Mainly sandy-brown in coloration, strongly streaked with dark brown. Has very large yellow eye, short black-and-yellow bill, and long, stout, yellowish legs. At rest, most striking plumage features are white supercilium and cheek-stripe, dark submoustachial stripe, and black and white bands across wing-coverts. In flight, shows white patches on primaries. **VOICE** Typical territorial call starts with slurred whistles which build up in pitch and volume to a series of clear, loud *cur-lee* calls and then die away; other calls are variants of *cur-lee* (Hayman *et al.* 1986). **HABITS** Usually in pairs, also in small groups. Typically, spends the day sitting in the shade. Very wary; if suspicious, runs off furtively with its head low, then squats and flattens itself on the ground, relying on camouflage for concealment. When foraging, makes short runs, stopping to capture prey with swift snatch; eats mainly insects, worms, small reptiles and mice. If undisturbed, will remain in the same place day after day. **HABITAT** Thorn-scrub desert, sand-dune desert, stony hills, open dry forest, dry river beds, fields, orchards and village groves; favours dry country with scrub patches. **BREEDING** February–August. Nest is an unlined scrape at the base of a bush, stone or grass tussock in stony area. **DISTRIBUTION AND STATUS** Resident, subject to local movements depending on rainfall. Throughout much of the subcontinent. **PK:** scarce resident. **NP:** frequent resident; below 915 m (–1310 m). **IN:** widespread and locally fairly common resident; up to 1000 m in Himalayas and peninsular hills. **BT:** very local and rare, probably resident. **BD:** winter visitor. **LK:** regular but infrequent and local resident in dry lowlands, mainly on coasts, rare in wet zone.

GREAT THICK-KNEE *Esacus recurvirostris* — Plate 48

Great Stone Plover (I,N,P), *E. magnirostris recurvirostris* (F,I,K), *Burhinus recurvirostris* (R)

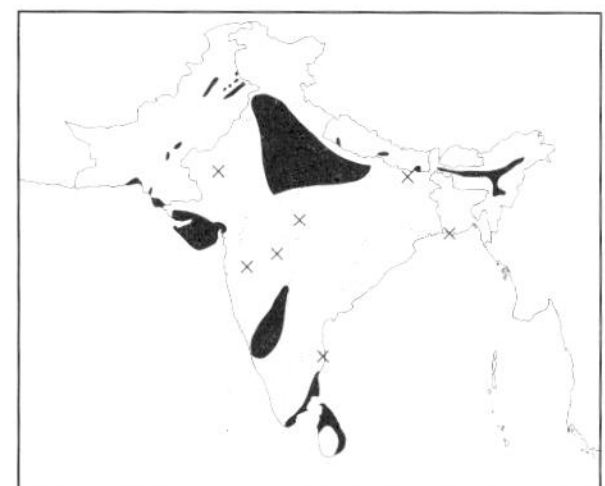

IDENTIFICATION 49–54 cm. A huge sandy grey-brown thick-knee, unmistakable throughout most of its range. Has large, slightly upturned black-and-yellow bill, and yellow eye. At rest, most striking features are white forehead and 'spectacles' contrasting with black ear-coverts, and blackish and whitish bands across wing-coverts. In flight, has grey panel on wings and white patches on primaries. For differences from Beach Thick-knee (below), see that species. **VOICE** Territorial call is a wailing whistle of two or more syllables, given with rising inflection; alarm call is a loud, harsh *see-eek* (Hayman *et al.* 1986). **HABITS** Similar to those of Eurasian Thick-knee (p.488), but usually rests during the day in full sun close to the water's edge. If disturbed, relies on camouflage, and then either runs off or flies away in a rather jerky fashion. Feeds chiefly on crabs, also molluscs, insects and small reptiles, amphibians, fish, small mammals and birds' eggs. **BREEDING** February–June. Nest is a shallow scrape in an exposed situation, such as a sandbank, rocky island or reservoir bank, lined with pebbles and well camouflaged. **HABITAT** Mainly stony beds of larger rivers; also lakes with stony shores, saltmarshes, estuaries and saltpans. **DISTRIBUTION AND STATUS** Resident, subject to local movements depending on water conditions. Widespread, but local. **PK:** scarce and local resident. **NP:** frequent, local resident and winter visitor; below 245 m (–1310 m). **IN:** generally uncommon in the plains. **BD:** local winter visitor. **LK:** common resident in dry lowlands, mainly in coastal areas. **REFERENCES** Mundkur (1991a).

BEACH THICK-KNEE *Esacus neglectus* — Plate 48

***E. magnirostris magnirostris* (I)**

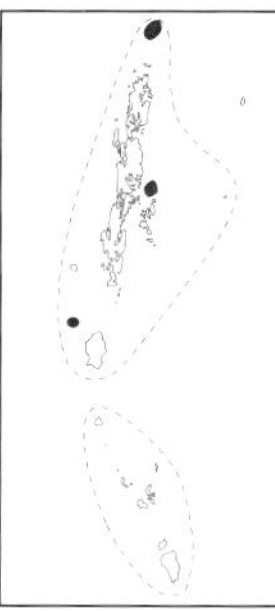

IDENTIFICATION 53–57 cm. A very large, sandy grey-brown thick-knee, closely resembling Great Thick-knee (above). Has different head pattern, with mainly black forehead and lores, and more black on sides of crown and ear-coverts (enclosing white supercilium). Also is larger, with thicker and straighter bill. Shows stronger black-and-white patterning on closed wings. In flight, has different wing pattern from Great, with grey (rather than mainly black) secondaries and white inner primaries. **VOICE** Territorial call is a harsh wailing *wee-loo*, and has a *quip* or *peep* alarm call. **HABITS** Similar to those of Great Thick-knee. Sometimes associates with Crab-plovers (p.498). Feeds on crabs and shellfish. **HABITAT** Sandy and muddy shores and reefs on coast. **BREEDING** March and April. Nest is a scrape in sand or shingle on the shore, above the high-water mark. **DISTRIBUTION AND STATUS IN:** widespread resident on Andaman Is, ?Nicobar Is.

OYSTERCATCHERS, AVOCETS AND STILTS Charadriidae: subfamily Recurvirostrinae

Oystercatchers are seashore waders with all-black or black and white plumage. The bill is long, stout, orange-red and adapted for opening shells of bivalve molluscs. Stilts and avocets have a long bill, and longer legs in proportion to the body than any other birds except flamingos. They inhabit marshes, lakes and pools. The unusual Ibisbill is placed in the same subfamily.

EURASIAN OYSTERCATCHER *Haematopus ostralegus* — Plate 48

Oystercatcher (F,I,P), Common Oystercatcher (K)

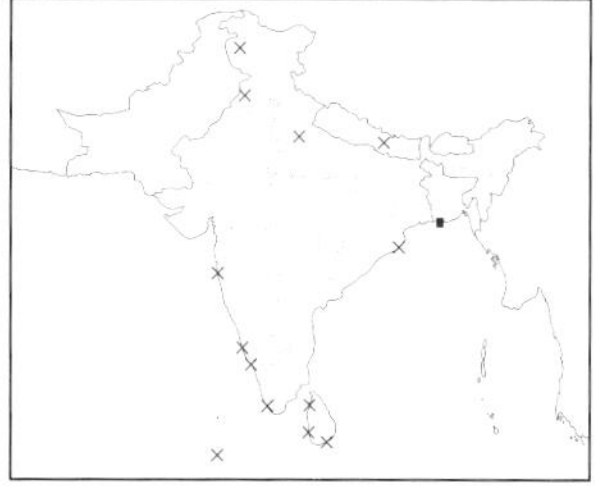

IDENTIFICATION 40–46 cm. Unmistakable black-and-white wader with long, stout, orange-red bill. Shows broad white wing-bar in flight. Has stout pinkish legs, and red eye and eye-ring. **Adult breeding** has entirely black neck and breast contrasting with white underparts. **Adult non-breeding** and **first-winter** have white collar on foreneck and duller bill. **Juvenile** has brownish-black upperparts with buffish-white fringes, but no white collar. Lacks red eye-ring, and has dull yellowish-brown bill. **VOICE** A piping *pi ..peep..peep..peep* and *pi-peep.* **HABITS** Scattered flocks feed and roost on the seashore with other waders. Flight is strong and direct, with shallow wingbeats. Feeds mainly on bivalve molluscs, also marine worms and small crustaceans. Runs about on intertidal wet sand, probing for food; also dislodges molluscs from rocks. **HABITAT** Sandy and rocky coasts. **BREEDING** Nest is a hollow scrape on a shingle beach. **DISTRIBUTION AND STATUS** Winter visitor to coasts of the subcontinent and small offshore islands; rare inland. **PK:** common winter visitor to coasts throughout Makran and Sindh; small numbers oversummer. **NP:** vagrant. **IN:** winter visitor, locally fairly common on NW coast, uncommon on other coasts, rare inland. **BD:** ?vagrant; has bred. **LK:** scarce winter visitor to dry-zone coast. **MV:** vagrant. **REFERENCES** Stanford (1937, 1954).

IBISBILL *Ibidorhyncha struthersii* Plate 48

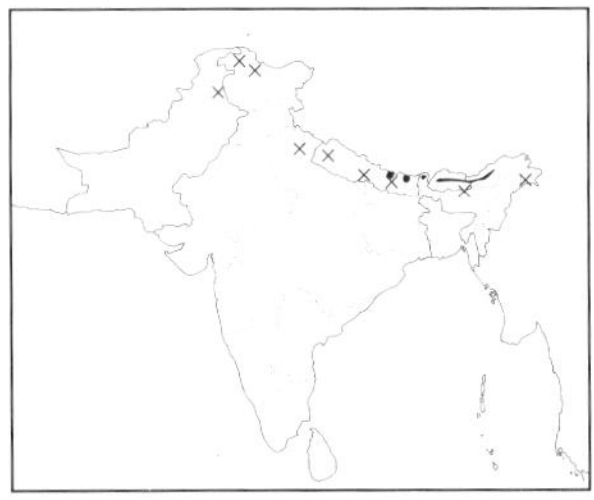

IDENTIFICATION 38–41 cm. A distinctive wader with lead-grey upperparts, white underparts, and strongly downcurved dark red bill. In flight, shows white patch at base of inner primaries and blackish tail-band. **Adult breeding** has black face, bordered with white, white and black breast-bands, and bright red bill and legs. **Adult non-breeding** is similar, but black on face is mottled with white, and has white lores and chin. Bill is duller, and legs are greyish-pink. **Juvenile** has whitish or brown face, dark cap, diffuse brown breast-band, buff fringes to brown upperparts, and dull-coloured bill and legs. **VOICE** A ringing *klew-klew* and a rapid *tee-tee-tee-tee* (Hayman *et al.* 1986). **HABITS** Single birds, pairs or small groups forage inconspicuously and quietly in mountain rivers and streams. Usually quite wary; if alarmed, nervously bobs its head and wags its tail. Seeks aquatic invertebrates by walking slowly through the water, using its long decurved bill to probe around and under stones; frequently wades belly-deep and picks up floating invertebrates while remaining at a favoured spot for long periods. Sometimes rakes small stones on river bed to dislodge prey. **HABITAT** Fast-flowing mountain streams and rivers with shingle beds. **BREEDING** End March–mid May. Nest is a hollowed-out bowl lined with small pebbles, sited on a shingle bank or island. **DISTRIBUTION AND STATUS** Resident, subject to altitudinal movements. Himalayas, mainly from Jammu and Kashmir east to Arunachal Pradesh. **PK:** vagrant. **NP:** frequent resident; breeds 3800–4200 m, winters mainly below 915 m. **IN:** breeds 1700–4500 m; descends to base of the hills in winter in the east. **BT:** fairly common resident; summers 2250–4480 m, winters 240–2250 m. **REFERENCES** Pierce (1986).

BLACK-WINGED STILT *Himantopus himantopus* Plate 48

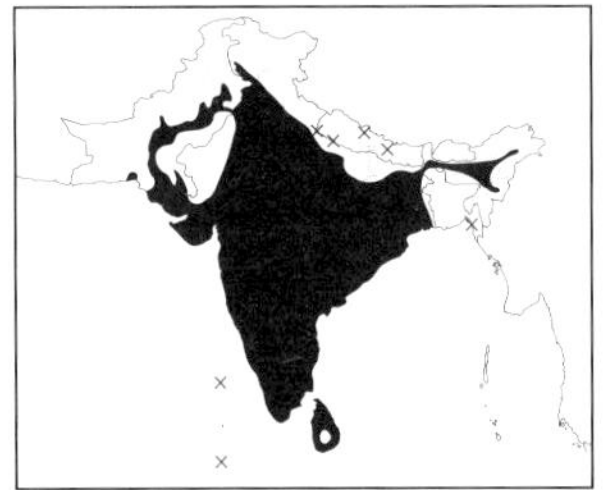

IDENTIFICATION 35–40 cm. An elegant, very long-legged, black-and-white wader with fine, straight black bill. Black upperwing strongly contrasts with white back V in flight. **Adult** at rest shows mainly white head, neck and underbody, contrasting with upperparts, and reddish-pink legs. Both sexes can have dusky grey on crown, nape and hindneck. **Female** has browner mantle and scapulars than male. **Juvenile** has brown upperparts with buffish fringes, and strong grey wash to crown and hindneck. **VOICE** A noisy wader, readily agitated; calls include a *kek .. kek* and an anxious *kikikikiki.* **HABITS** Gregarious throughout the year; sometimes breeds in colonies. A graceful wader which walks slowly and deliberately. Forages on dry mud and by wading, sometimes in water up to the belly and in deeper water than other waders; also by free-floating in deep saltpans. Picks prey from the surface, probes in soft mud and sweeps bill from side to side; sometimes immerses head and neck in water. Eats insects and also other aquatic invertebrates and small fish. **HABITAT** Freshwater and brackish marshes, pools, village tanks, reservoirs, saltpans and shallow margins of lakes. **BREEDING** March–August, depending on SW monsoon. Nest is a scrape, lined with whatever is conveniently available, on a mound or islet surrounded by shallow water or on a dry bank in saltmarshes and reservoirs. Often in mixed colonies with terns, plovers and Small Pratincoles. **DISTRIBUTION AND STATUS** Resident, subject to local movements, especially in winter. Throughout much of the subcontinent. **PK:** common resident. **NP:** uncommon passage migrant; mainly below 1380 m (–3355 m). **IN:** widespread and common resident; breeds at 1500 m in Kashmir (–3505 m on passage). **BD:** local winter visitor. **LK:** common resident in dry lowlands, possibly also a winter visitor. **MV:** uncommon visitor.

PIED AVOCET *Recurvirostra avosetta* Plate 48

Avocet (F,I,P)

IDENTIFICATION 42–45 cm. A striking, white-and-black wader with pronounced upward curve to black bill. Has blue-grey legs. **Adult** has prominent black cap and hindneck, black bands across wing-coverts and scapulars and black wing-tips, which combine to form striking pattern at rest and in flight. **Juvenile** has black of plumage obscured by dark brown, and white of mantle and scapulars is mottled with brown and buff. **VOICE** A throaty *quib..quib.* **HABITS** Gregarious for most of the year; usually nests in colonies. Characteristically, feeds by sweeping bill and head from side to side in shallow water; also often swims and upends like a dabbling duck, and picks prey from the surface of water or mud. Diet consists of small crustaceans, molluscs and insects. **HABITAT** Favours shallow alkaline or brackish pools; also tidal creeks, saltpans, estuarine mudflats and marshes. **BREEDING** Little known in the region. Probably April–June. Nest is a shallow scrape on open ground near water. **DISTRIBUTION AND STATUS** Breeds in W and S Pakistan and Kutch; widespread winter visitor and passage migrant, but mainly

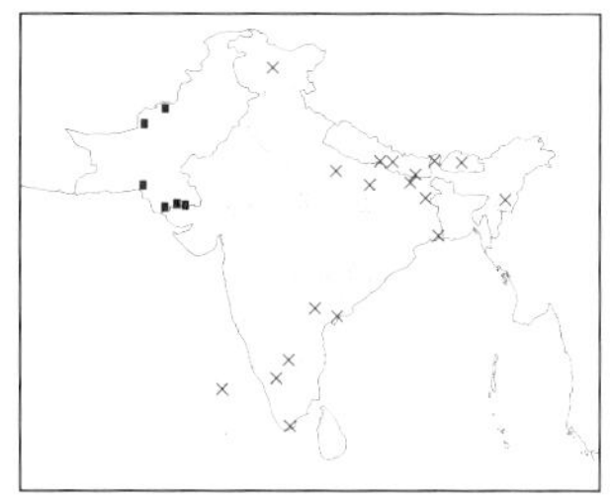

in the northwest. **PK:** erratic but frequent year-round visitor; breeds sporadically. **NP:** rare passage migrant; below 275 m. **IN:** widespread, mainly a locally common winter visitor, present all year in Gujarat (–4200 m on passage in Sikkim). **BT:** vagrant. **BD:** local winter visitor, mainly to coasts. **LK:** regular and local migrant in small numbers to dry lowlands.

PLOVERS AND LAPWINGS Charadriidae: subfamily Charadriinae

Plovers and lapwings are small to medium-sized waders with rounded head, short neck and short bill. Typically, they forage by running in short spurts, pausing and standing erect, then stooping to pick up prey. Their flight is swift and direct.

EUROPEAN GOLDEN PLOVER *Pluvialis apricaria* Plate 49

Golden Plover (I), Eurasian Golden Plover, Greater Golden Plover (K,R)

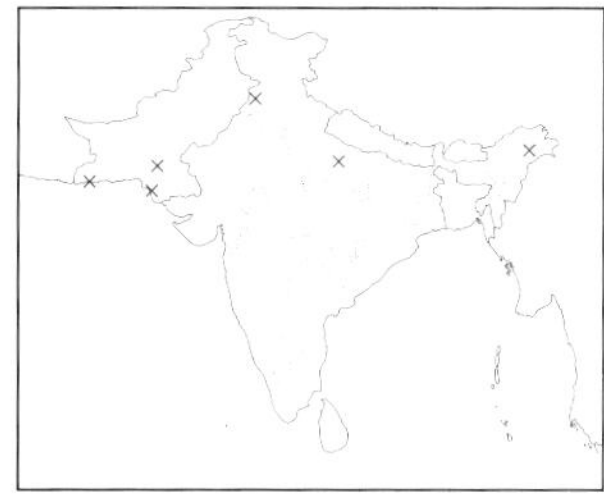

IDENTIFICATION 26–29 cm. A larger, stockier version of Pacific Golden Plover (p.491). Has white underwing-coverts and axillaries (grey on Pacific Golden), and subtly different flight call. Main differences are structural: has shorter neck and larger-looking head, bill appears shorter and stouter, and legs look shorter (owing to shorter tibia); at rest, primary tips fall roughly level with tail-tip (clearly longer on Pacific Golden), and tertials are rather short (fall far short of tail and a greater length of primaries is exposed). In flight, toes do not project beyond tail (noticeable projection on Pacific). **Adult breeding** as Pacific Golden. Subtle differences in plumage include narrower black centre to foreneck, narrower white band on forehead, supercilium and neck sides, more white on flanks, and more finely spangled upperparts, and the undertail-coverts show no or very little black. **Adult non-breeding** generally shows less distinct supercilium, with rather plain face compared with Pacific Golden. Underparts tend to be more golden-buff in coloration and more distinctly spotted. **Juvenile** much as Pacific Golden; the centre of breast and belly are more distinctly spotted, upperparts more finely spangled, and wing-coverts are concolorous with mantle and scapulars (usually distinctly paler on Pacific Golden). **VOICE** A plaintive *too-lee* or *tloo.* **HABITS** Similar to those of Pacific Golden Plover. Single birds or flocks recorded with Pacific Golden or other waders. **HABITAT** Grassland, estuaries, and muddy margins of lakes. **DISTRIBUTION AND STATUS PK, IN:** vagrant. **REFERENCES** Harris *et al.* (1989), Alström and Colston (1991).

PACIFIC GOLDEN PLOVER *Pluvialis fulva* Plate 49

Eastern Golden Plover (F,I,P), Asiatic Golden Plover *P. dominica* (F,I,K,R)

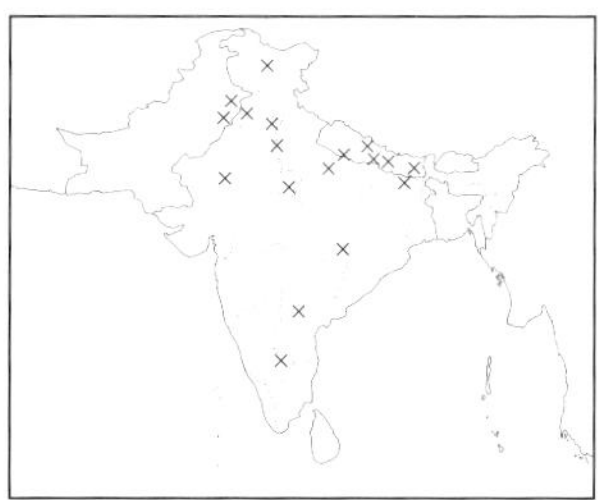

IDENTIFICATION 23–26 cm. In all plumages, told from Grey Plover (p.492) by golden-yellow markings on upperparts, dusky grey underwing-coverts and axillaries, lack of whitish rump, and finer white wing-bar. Is also slimmer-bodied, with longer neck and small bulbous head, and bill is finer. Legs appear longer (owing to proportionately longer tibia). **Adult breeding** has black on face, foreneck, breast and belly which is strikingly bordered by white. **Adult non-breeding** and **juvenile** have yellowish-buff wash to supercilium, cheeks and neck (unlike Grey Plover, on which the background coloration is greyish or white), and foreneck, breast and belly are mottled with dusky brown and generally lack 'golden' coloration; usually show more pronounced supercilium which often curves down as diffuse crescent behind ear-coverts, and also a dark patch on rear ear-coverts. See European Golden Plover (above) for differences from that species. **VOICE** An abrupt disyllabic *chi-vit* recalling Spotted Redshank (p.476), and a more plaintive *tu-weep* or *chew you.* **HABITS** Associates in flocks, which scatter when feeding; sometimes several hundred birds together on spring and autumn passage. Very wary and, if disturbed, rise almost simultaneously in a compact flock, twisting and turning rapidly in unison. Has typical plover feeding behaviour. Eats beetles, earthworms, grasshoppers and other insects. **HABITAT** Muddy banks of rivers, lakes and pools, ploughed fields, wet grassland, coasts and coastal lagoons. **DISTRIBUTION AND STATUS** Widespread winter visitor; first arrives in early August, leaves by end May. **PK:** scarce and local. **NP:** common in the terai at Kosi, rare elsewhere (–2950 m on passage). **IN:** widespread, common in the northeast and southeast, less frequent elsewhere. **BD:** common throughout. **LK:** common in lowlands. **MV:** common winter visitor.

GREY PLOVER *Pluvialis squatarola* — Plate 49

Black-bellied Plover (F)

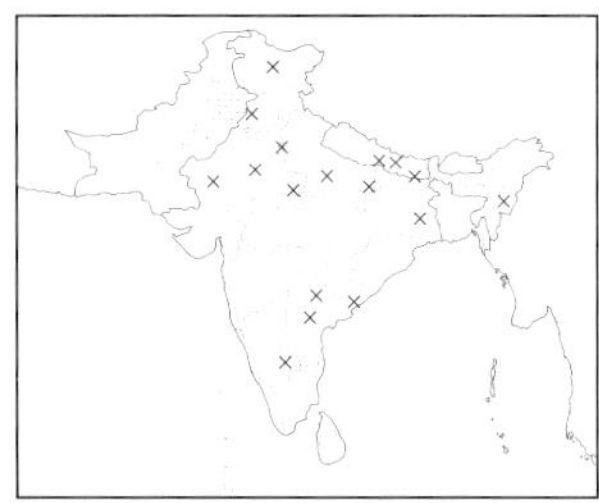

IDENTIFICATION 27–30 cm. Larger and stockier than Pacific Golden Plover (p.491), with larger-looking head, stouter bill, and shorter-looking legs. Plumage differences always include greyer coloration to upperparts, whitish rump, broader white wing-bar, and white underwing with contrasting black axillaries. **Adult breeding** has black face, foreneck, breast and belly, with a striking white border to sides of face and neck. Black feathers of upperparts are boldly spangled with silvery-white. **Adult non-breeding** and **juvenile** have indistinct whitish supercilium, and diffuse grey streaking on whitish underparts. In juvenile plumage, feathers of mantle and scapulars are spotted with buff, but not so brightly as on Pacific Golden. **VOICE** A mournful *chee-woo-ee*. **HABITS** Similar to those of Pacific Golden Plover, but usually less gregarious; often in pairs or small groups and with other wader species. **HABITAT** Mainly coastal, in intertidal zones of sandy shores and mudflats, tidal and mangrove creeks; also inland on lakes and pools. **DISTRIBUTION AND STATUS** Winter visitor mainly to coasts of the subcontinent; erratically inland, mainly on passage; first arrives in early August, most leaving in late April. **PK:** common in tidal creeks and mangroves on Sind and Makran coasts; occasionally recorded inland and passage. **NP:** vagrant. **IN:** widespread, mainly on coasts; common in the south-east, uncommon on passage inland. **BD:** locally common; some oversummer. **LK:** common on coasts. **MV:** common winter visitor.

COMMON RINGED PLOVER *Charadrius hiaticula* — Plate 50

Ringed Plover (I,P)

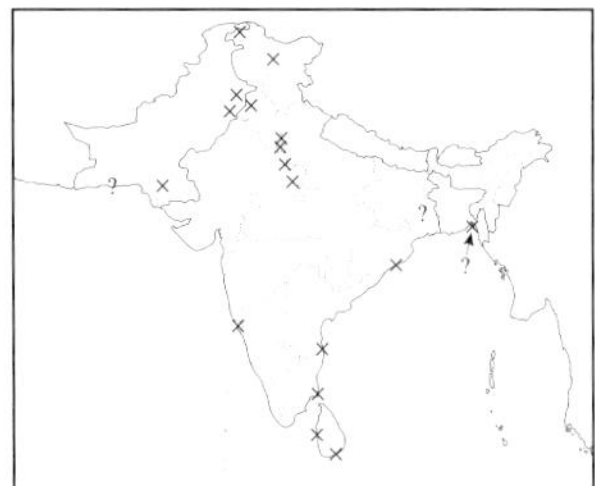

IDENTIFICATION 18–20 cm. A stocky plover, with prominent breast-band and white hindneck-collar. Told from Little Ringed Plover (p.493) by larger size and stockier appearance, prominent white wing-bar in flight, and distinctive call. **Adult non-breeding** has brownish-black breast-band and ear-coverts. More prominent whitish forehead and supercilium, and orangey legs and base to bill, are further differences from Little Ringed. **Adult breeding** has black breast-band extending as dark collar around lower hindneck, black ear-coverts and band across forecrown, and prominent white forehead disjunct from white supercilium behind eye. Orange base to bill and orange legs are especially distinctive, and lacks prominent yellow eye-ring of Little Ringed. **Juvenile** has extensive brown patches on sides of breast, sometimes joining to form breast-band, uniform brown crown and ear-coverts, and buff fringes to upperparts. Compared with juvenile Little Ringed, has larger breast-side patches and more prominent whitish forehead and supercilium; legs are olive-yellow and similar in coloration to Little Ringed's. Best features to separate Common Ringed from juvenile and non-breeding adult Kentish Plover (p.493) are larger size and heavier build, yellowish base to bill, more extensive patches on sides of breast, and different call. Also confusable with juvenile and non-breeding adult Lesser Sand Plover (p.494), but is smaller and stockier, with shorter legs and neck, and has white hindcollar. See also Long-billed Plover (below). **VOICE** Contact call, invariably given in flight, is a soft *too-li* or *tooee*; becomes a long *tooweep* when alarmed (Hayman *et al.* 1986). **HABITS** Similar to those of Little Ringed. **HABITAT** Mudbanks of tidal creeks, mangroves and freshwater lakes, and intertidal mudflats. **DISTRIBUTION AND STATUS** Winter visitor to the subcontinent. Status uncertain, probably overlooked because of confusion with Little Ringed Plover; possibly occurs regularly in very small numbers inland and along the E Indian coast south to Sri Lanka. **PK:** scarce but regular on the Karachi coast. **IN:** rare and widespread. **BD:** vagrant. **LK:** uncommon in the lowlands. **MV:** annual in small numbers.

LONG-BILLED PLOVER *Charadrius placidus* — Plate 50

Long-billed Ringed Plover (I), Long-billed Ring Plover (F)

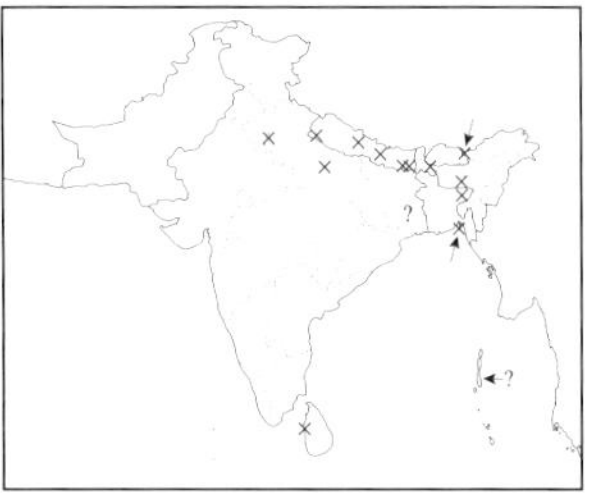

IDENTIFICATION 19–21 cm. Resembles a very large Little Ringed Plover (p.493), with long and slim-bodied appearance, small-looking head and yellowish legs, and rather jerky flight is also similar. Distinguishable from that species by much larger size and longer bill, and, in flight, wings appear broader and tail longer. Has more prominent white greater-covert wing-bar and fine white trailing edge to secondaries, and greyish outer webs to secondaries and inner primaries form indistinct wing panel. Has clearer dark subterminal tail-band than Little Ringed. Flight call is also different. **Adult non-breeding** shows narrow brownish-black breast-band, dark band across forecrown, white forehead, and buffish-white supercilium behind eye. Head pattern is more contrasting than that of adult non-breeding Little Ringed. **Adult breeding** has fine black breast-band, black band across forecrown, and white forehead and supercilium. Lacks black ear-coverts, and has less distinct eye-ring than Little Ringed. **Juvenile** is like a large juvenile Little Ringed. Lacks dark band across forecrown, has indistinct buffish supercilium, brown breast-band, and buff fringes to upperparts. Juvenile plumage is lost quickly, and this species may not occur in this plumage in the subcontinent. **VOICE** A clear, penetrating *piwee* (Hayman *et al.* 1986). **HABITS** Similar to those of Little Ringed, but usually solitary. **HABITAT** Shingle banks of large rivers. **DISTRIBUTION AND STATUS** Winter visitor to Nepal, N and NE India and Bhutan. **NP:** rare winter visitor and passage migrant; below 1380 m. **IN:** rare but regular winter visitor. **BT:** rare passage migrant; 1280–2745 m. **BD, LK:** vagrant. **REFERENCES** De Silva and Perara (1993), Robson (1993a).

LITTLE RINGED PLOVER *Charadrius dubius* — Plate 50

Little Plover, Little Ring Plover (F)

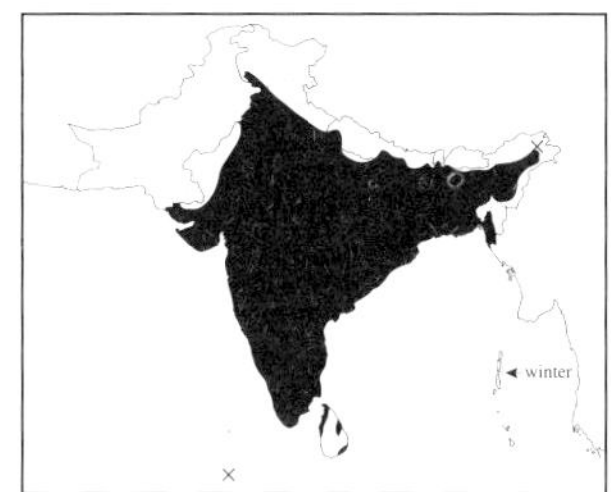

IDENTIFICATION 14–17 cm. A small, slim and long-bodied plover with prominent breast-band and white hindneck-collar. Distinguished from Common Ringed (p.492) by smaller size, more rounded head and slim-bodied appearance (with long wings and tail, and small-looking head), as well as by uniform upperwing with only a very narrow wing-bar, and distinctive call. Legs are yellowish or pinkish. Flight action is characteristic, with jerky 'oarsman-like' wingbeats. For differences from the much larger Long-billed Plover (p.492), see that species. **Adult non-breeding** has brownish cap with whitish forehead, indistinct supercilium, and blackish-brown breast-band (narrower, and sometimes broken, at centre). Head pattern is more uniform than that of Common Ringed (far less well-defined white forehead and supercilium). **Adult breeding** has broad black mask and frontal band, white forehead, bold yellow eye-ring, and black breast-band. Yellow eye-ring, narrow white division between black frontal band and brown crown, and mainly dark bill (with a touch of yellowish at base) help to separate it from adult breeding Common Ringed. **Juvenile** is similar to adult non-breeding, but has prominent buff fringes to pale brown upperparts. Head pattern is more uniform compared with juvenile Common Ringed, with buffish forehead merging with crown and indistinct supercilium, giving hooded appearance. **VOICE** A clear, descending *pee-oo* and a shorter *peeu*. **HABITS** Keeps in pairs or small flocks, which scatter over a wide area when feeding and are often mixed with other waders. If disturbed, will rise almost simultaneously in a compact flock and fly off rapidly, low over the ground, veering and swerving in unison. Feeding behaviour is typical of the plovers: makes short runs, then pauses and stoops stiffly without bending the legs to pick up small invertebrates. During pauses, has a habit of rapidly vibrating a foot on the mud, probably to attract prey to the surface. Typically, carries the head low and drawn into the shoulders. **HABITAT** Sand, shingle and mud margins of lakes, pools and rivers, wet grassland and paddy-fields, intertidal areas on seashore, mudflats and tidal creeks. **BREEDING** March–August, varying locally. Nest is a small unlined hollow on shingle or among sparse vegetation. **DISTRIBUTION AND STATUS** Widespread resident and winter visitor. **PK:** common and widespread, especially along rivers and lakes. **NP:** common and widespread below 1500 m (–2745 m). **IN:** common and widespread. **BT:** rare. **BD:** common winter visitor and local resident. **LK:** common on the coast, rare inland. **MV:** probably an annual visitor in small numbers. **REFERENCES** Giri and Choudhary (1997).

KENTISH PLOVER *Charadrius alexandrinus* — Plate 50

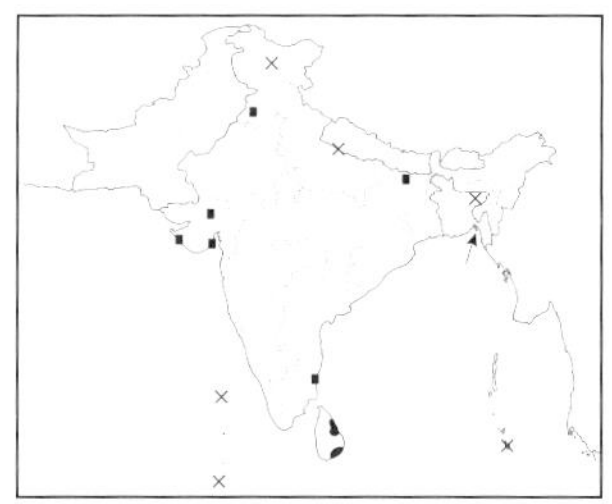

IDENTIFICATION 15–17 cm. Smaller size and stockier appearance, white hindneck-collar, and more white at sides of tail are best features to separate this species from Lesser Sand Plover (p.494). Except for male in breeding plumage, confusion is also possible with Common Ringed Plover (p.492), but appears shorter in body, with big-looking head, and has rearward-set legs. Legs usually appear blackish, but may be tinged with brown or be olive-yellow. Upperparts are paler, more sandy-grey, has smaller and better-defined patches on sides of breast, and has more prominent white forehead and supercilia (V-shaped when seen front-on). Call is also distinctive. **Adult non-breeding** has sandy grey-brown crown and ear-coverts, whitish forehead and supercilium, and neat sandy-brown patches on sides of breast. **Adult male breeding** has black eye-stripe and forecrown, rufous wash to centre and rear of crown, and narrow black patches on sides of breast. **Adult female breeding** lacks rufous on crown, and often lacks black markings of male, and is then similar to adult non-breeding. **Juvenile** is also similar to non-breeding adult, but has buff fringes to feathers of upperparts, breast patches are paler and more diffuse, and forehead is buff, with buffish supercilium. **Racial variation** Breeding male *C. a. seebohmi* of Sri Lanka and S India differs from breeding male of the nominate race in lacking rufous on crown; dark bar across forecrown and dark ear-coverts may be obscure, and often has white lores. Female *seebohmi* can have darker brown upperparts than female of nominate. **VOICE** A soft *pi..pi..pi*, recalling Little Stint (p.4820); a rattling trill, *prrr* or *prrrtut* (harsher than similar call of Lesser Sand); and a plaintive *whoheet*. **HABITS** Gait and feeding behaviour typical of other plovers (see Little Ringed, p.above), but runs about more rapidly. **HABITAT** Sandy seashores, sandy margins of lakes and ponds, sandy and shingle banks and islands of rivers, and saltpans. **BREEDING** March–August, varying locally. Nest is a slight depression in a dry river bed, bund, gypsum heap or saltpan, or on seashore. **DISTRIBUTION AND STATUS** Breeds locally in Pakistan, N and S India and Sri Lanka; winters throughout much of the subcontinent. **PK:** mainly resident and common in lower Sind, fairly widespread in Punjab in winter, locally and erratically distributed elsewhere. **NP:** locally common winter visitor and passage migrant below 1380 m; possibly breeds. **IN:** widespread and locally common. **BT:** rare. **BD:** common winter visitor, ?and resident. **LK:** common resident in dry lowlands, and uncommon winter visitor to coastal areas of lowlands. **MV:** occasionally recorded in winter.

LESSER SAND PLOVER *Charadrius mongolus* Plate 50

Mongolian Plover

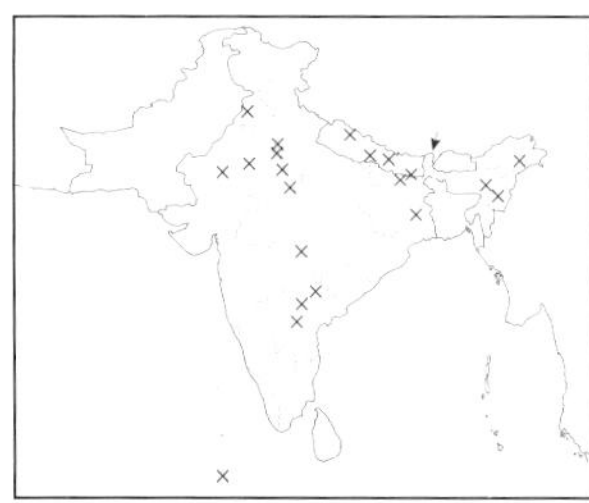

IDENTIFICATION 19–21 cm. A medium-sized, long-legged *Charadrius* plover. Very similar in all plumages to Greater Sand Plover (below), from which best told by a combination of the following features: smaller size and more neatly proportioned appearance, with rounder head; smaller and stouter bill, without bulging gonys and with blunter tip; and shorter dark grey or grey-green legs, with tibia noticeably shorter than tarsus. There is much variation in these features, however, and some birds can be very difficult to identify. In flight, feet do not usually extend beyond tail, wing-bar is narrower across primaries, shows less white at sides and tip of tail (lacking dark subterminal bar), and has different flight call. Except in breeding plumage, possibly confusable also with Kentish and Common Ringed Plovers (p.492 and p.493), but is larger and lankier, has longer legs, and lacks white hindcollar. **Adult non-breeding** has grey-brown upperparts and ear-coverts, prominent pale supercilium and forehead, and grey-brown patches at side of breast. Upperparts often appear a darker shade of brown than on Greater (colour of wet rather than dry sand). **Adult male breeding** has black mask, sometimes marked with white, and rufous-orange breast and hindneck. There is variation in male breeding plumage of both Greater and Lesser, although full black forehead and mask typically present on Lesser apparently does not occur on Greater, and rufous-orange breast-band is typically more extensive on Lesser. **Adult female breeding** is similar to adult non-breeding, but with pale orange breast-band, and often shows dark mask. **Juvenile** is similar to adult non-breeding, but has buffish patches on breast sides and buff fringes to upperparts. **VOICE** A hard *chitik, chi-chi-chi* and *kruit-kruit,* which are rather short and sharp (Harris *et al.* 1996). **HABITS** Gait and feeding behaviour typical of other plovers (see Little Ringed, p.493). **HABITAT** Breeds in high-altitude semi-desert on drying-out edges of lakes and marshes. Winters on coasts, mainly on intertidal mudflats and tidal creeks, also on rocky and sandy shores; rarely on lakes and rivers inland on passage. **BREEDING** June–mid July. Nest is an unlined hollow on dry margins of marshes or lakes. **DISTRIBUTION AND STATUS** Breeds in Ladakh, Lahul and Sikkim, India, above 3400 m and possibly also in Baltistan, Pakistan; winters on coasts of the subcontinent. Begins to arrive in early August, most leaving by late May; some birds oversummer. Rare on passage inland. **PK:** common on the coast. **NP:** rare winter visitor and spring passage migrant; mainly below 275 m (–3050 m). **IN:** locally common on breeding grounds in Ladakh, 3900–5500 m; locally common winter visitor on coasts. **BD:** common winter visitor. **LK:** common winter visitor in lowlands. **MV:** common and regular winter visitor. **REFERENCES** Harris *et al.* (1996), Alström and Colston (1991), Pfister (1997).

GREATER SAND PLOVER *Charadrius leschenaultii* Plate 50

Large Sand Plover (I,P)

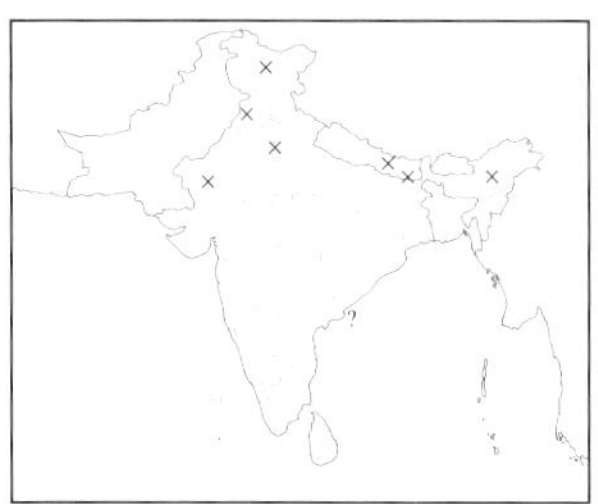

IDENTIFICATION 22–25 cm. A medium-sized, lanky plover, very similar to Lesser Sand Plover (above) in all plumages. Best told from that species by combination of larger size and lankier appearance; squarer-shaped head; longer and larger bill, usually with pronounced gonys and more pointed tip; longer legs, with tibia appearing almost as long as tarsus; and paler legs (usually with distinct yellowish or greenish tinge), often with darker knee and toe joints. Beware of variation in these features. In flight, feet typically extend noticeably beyond tail, wing-bar is broader across primaries, shows more white at sides and tip of tail, and has different flight call; dark subterminal band to tail is a further good distinction from Lesser. For differences from Caspian Plover (p.495), see that species. **Adult non-breeding** has grey-brown upperparts, crown and ear-coverts, prominent pale supercilium and forehead, and grey-brown patches at sides of breast. **Adult male breeding** has black mask with white patch on sides of forehead, and rufous-orange breast-band and sides of neck. Does not show solid black mask and forehead which is often shown by Lesser Sand, and rufous breast-band tends to be narrower. **Adult breeding female** is similar to non-breeding adult, but with orange breast-band. **Juvenile** is similar to non-breeding adult, but has buffish patches on sides of breast and buff fringes to upperparts. **VOICE** A trilling *prrrirt* or *kyrrrr...trrr,* softer and longer than Lesser Sand's, recalling Ruddy Turnstone (p.480) (Harris *et al.* 1996). **HABITS** Gait and feeding behaviour typical of other plovers (see Little Ringed, p.493). **HABITAT** Mainly on sandy shores, intertidal mudflats and saltpans; also on muddy areas of mangroves and rocky coasts; vagrant to inland rivers. **DISTRIBUTION AND STATUS** Winter visitor to the coasts of the subcontinent; arrives mainly in late August, most leave by mid May, a small number oversummer. Rare inland. **PK:** common. **NP:** vagrant. **IN:** locally common on coasts. **BD:** local. **LK:** common in dry lowlands, occasionally recorded in wet zone. **MV:** regular in small numbers. **REFERENCES** Harris *et al.* (1996), Alström and Colston (1991).

CASPIAN PLOVER *Charadrius asiaticus* Plate 50

Sand Plover (I)

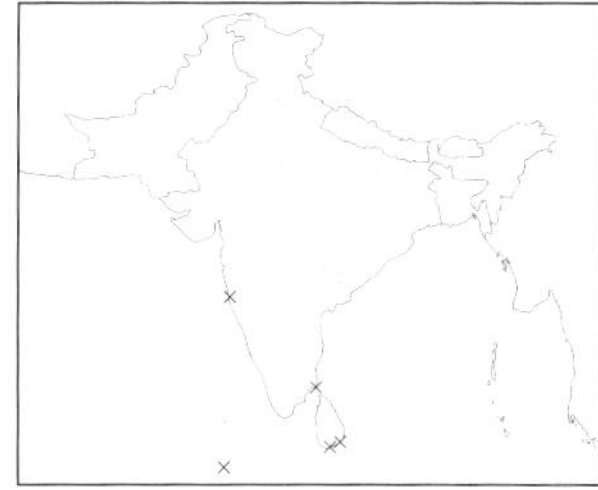

IDENTIFICATION 18–20 cm. A medium-sized, long-legged and long-winged plover. Distinguished from Oriental Plover (below) by mostly white underwing-coverts and axillaries, and narrow white wing-bar (formed by tips to greater coverts and white bases to primaries); also smaller, and not quite so long-legged. **Adult non-breeding** has prominent white supercilium, uniform brownish upperparts, and mottled grey-brown breast. Best features to separate it from non-breeding Greater Sand Plover (p.494) are slender appearance with tapering rear end, slimmer bill, narrower wing-bar, complete breast-band, and more pronounced supercilium with dark-capped appearance. **Adult male breeding** has chestnut breast-band with a black lower border. Whitish supercilium and face contrast strongly with brown crown and stripe behind eye. **Adult female breeding** is similar to adult non-breeding, but some show chestnut on breast. **Juvenile** as adult non-breeding, but with rufous and buff fringes to feathers of upperparts. **VOICE** A loud, sharp *tyup*, a long rattling *tptptptptp*, a soft piping *tik*, and a shrill whistled *kwhitt* (Hayman *et al.* 1986). **HABITS** Unknown in the subcontinent. Elsewhere, gait and feeding behaviour typical of other plovers (see Little Ringed, p.493). **HABITAT** Usually on dry grassland, dry mud near fresh water or, rarely, on intertidal mud. **DISTRIBUTION AND STATUS** Winter visitor. **IN:** vagrant. **LK:** rare winter visitor to dry lowlands, occasionally recorded in wet zone. **MV:** vagrant. **REFERENCES** Kazmierczak *et al.* (1993), Robson (1996a).

ORIENTAL PLOVER *Charadrius veredus* Plate 50

C. asiaticus veredus

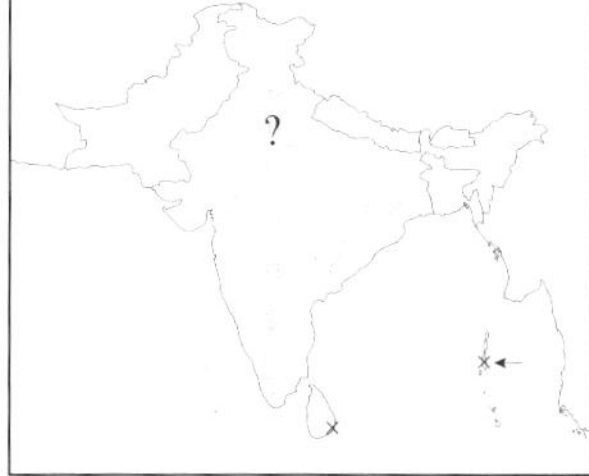

IDENTIFICATION 22–25 cm. A medium-sized, long-legged and long-winged *Charadrius* plover. Told from Caspian Plover (above) by larger size and longer neck and legs, brown underwing-coverts and axillaries (giving uniformly dark underwing), and uniformly dark upperwing typically lacking any sign of white wing-bar. Legs are yellowish or pinkish (usually greenish or brownish on Caspian). **Adult non-breeding** has prominent buffish supercilium, brownish upperparts, with fine rufous fringes in fresh plumage, and brownish-buff breast. **Adult male breeding** has mainly whitish head and neck (with dark rear crown), and pale chestnut band across breast with black lower border. **Adult female breeding** and **first-summer male** are similar to adult non-breeding, but may show some chestnut on breast. **Juvenile** as adult non-breeding, but has broad buff fringes to feathers of upperparts. Buff supercilium is less prominent than on Caspian, and underparts are warmer buff than in adult non-breeding. **VOICE** Flight call is a sharp whistled *chip-chip-chip* (Hayman *et al.* 1986). **HABITS** Details not recorded in the subcontinent. Similar to those Caspian. **HABITAT** Usually winters on dry grassland; on passage, may also be on dry mud near fresh water or, rarely, intertidal mud. **DISTRIBUTION AND STATUS IN:** vagrant to Andaman Is. **LK:** vagrant. **REFERENCES** Hoffman (1996).

BLACK-FRONTED DOTTEREL *Elseyornis melanops* Plate 50

Australian Black-fronted Plover (I), *Charadrius melanops* (I)

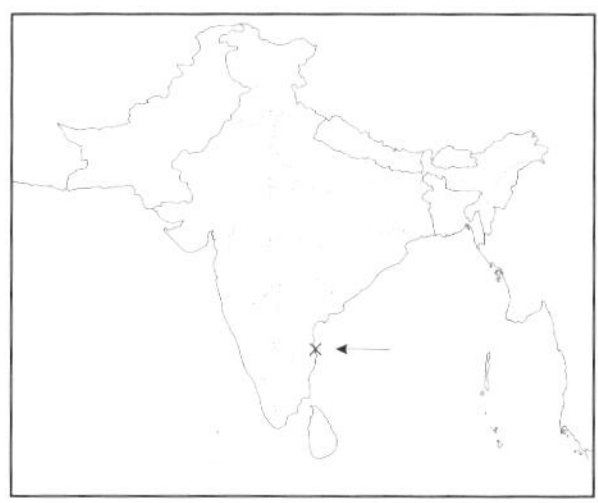

IDENTIFICATION 16–18 cm. **Adult** has red eye-ring and black-tipped red bill, broad black stripe through eye and white supercilium, black breast-band, and purplish-chestnut scapular patch. In flight, shows black wing-tips and greyish panel across wing-coverts on upperwing, and mainly white underwing-coverts contrasting with black flight feathers. **Juvenile** similar to adult, although duller, and breast-band is incomplete; lacks purplish-chestnut scapular patch, and has coverts streaked brown and chestnut. **VOICE** An explosive, high-pitched *dip* and a soft *tink-tink* (Hayman *et al.* 1986). **HABITS** Feeds chiefly by picking from the surface, also by probing. Typically, bobs its head when standing erect. Flight is swift, with flitting wing movements, and while in the air it often calls repeatedly. **HABITAT** Occurs mainly on stony or shingle beds of rivers and streams; also on estuaries in Australia. **DISTRIBUTION AND STATUS IN:** vagrant.

NORTHERN LAPWING *Vanellus vanellus* Plate 51

Lapwing (I), Eurasian Lapwing (F)

IDENTIFICATION 28–31 cm. A stocky, short-legged plover with broad, rounded wings, and distinctive slow-flapping flight with rather erratic wingbeats. Unmistakable in all plumages, with black crest, black and white (or buff) face pattern, black breast-band contrasting with white underparts, and dark glossy green upperparts. In flight, upperwing is entirely dark except for buffish-white at tips of outer primaries, and white at base of tail contrasts with broad black subterminal band; white underwing-coverts contrast strongly with black underside to

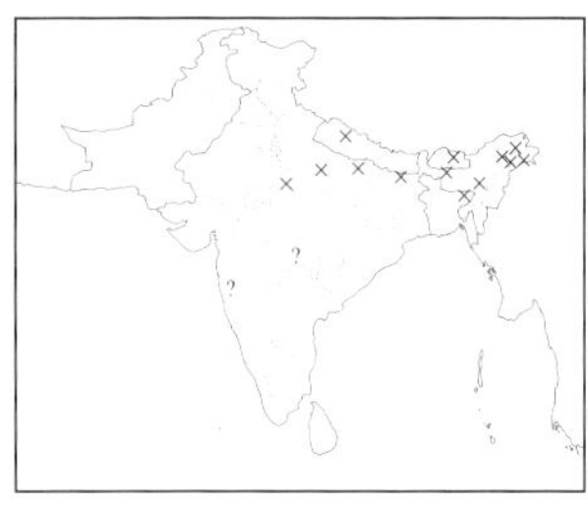

flight feathers. **Adult breeding** has very long black crest and strongly contrasting black and white face pattern. Chin and throat are all black on male and usually marked with white on female. **Adult non-breeding** has buff wash to lores, supercilium and cheeks. **Juvenile** like non-breeding adult, but with prominent buff fringes to mantle, scapulars and wing-coverts. **VOICE** A mournful *eu-whit* (Hayman *et al.* 1986). **HABITS** Found in pairs or small flocks. Feeding behaviour is similar to that of Red-wattled Lapwing (p.497). **HABITAT** Wet grassland, marshes, lake margins, shingle river banks; sometimes on dry stubbles and fallow fields. **DISTRIBUTION AND STATUS** Winters from Pakistan east to NE India. **PK:** locally common winter visitor to N Punjab and NW Pakistan; arrives in the plains by late October, often leaves by early February. **NP:** uncommon winter visitor; below 1380 m (–2700 m). **IN:** fairly common in the northwest, occurs in small numbers east to Uttar Pradesh, and erratically in the northeast. **BT:** very rare passage migrant; 2600 m. **BD:** vagrant. **REFERENCES** Anon. (1994).

YELLOW-WATTLED LAPWING *Vanellus malarbaricus* — Plate 51

***Hoplopterus malabaricus* (R)**

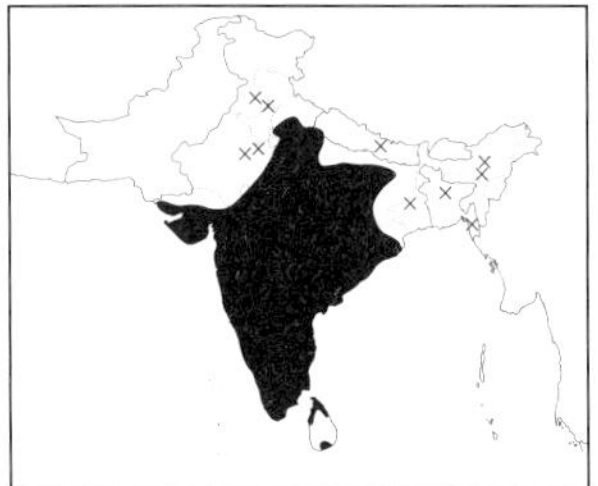

IDENTIFICATION 26–28 cm. **Adult** is easily identified by lobe-shaped yellow wattles, long yellow legs, and black cap contrasting with white supercilium. Has sandy-brown upperparts and breast contrasting with white belly, with a narrow dark breast-band. In flight, shows white greater-covert wing-bar contrasting with black flight feathers, and white tail with black subterminal band. **Juvenile** has small and dull yellow wattles. Has brown cap, and prominent buff fringes and dark subterminal bars to feathers of upperparts. Chin is white (black or brown on adult). **VOICE** A strident *chee-eet* and a hard *tit-tit-tit.* **HABITS** Keeps in pairs, and sometimes in small flocks in non-breeding season. Foraging behaviour similar to that of Red-wattled Lapwing (p.497). Flight is buoyant and with rather slow wingbeats. **HABITAT** Dry stubbles and fallow fields, stony ground, abandoned cultivation, bare gravel plains, and open dry country with very short grass; on drier ground than Red-wattled. **BREEDING** March–August, varying locally. Nest is a scrape on dry bare ground, unlined or lined with pebbles or goat/sheep droppings. **DISTRIBUTION AND STATUS** Resident, endemic to the subcontinent, occurring mainly in India; subject to local movements, moving away from wetter areas in monsoon. **PK:** chiefly a summer visitor to the south, frequent only in lower Sindh. **NP:** mainly a rare winter visitor to the terai, but recorded in all months. **IN:** widespread and locally common resident. **BD:** very local, ?resident. **LK:** common resident in dry lowlands.

RIVER LAPWING *Vanellus duvaucelii* — Plate 51

Spur-winged Lapwing (F,I), *V. spinosus* (E,I), *Hoplopterus duvaucelii*

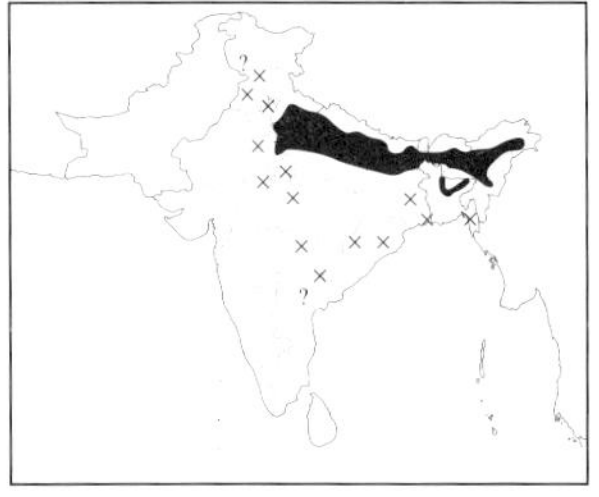

IDENTIFICATION 29–32 cm. A distinctive, riverain lapwing. In all plumages, has black cap and throat with diffuse white border, grey sides to neck, and cold sandy-brown upperparts and breast-band contrasting with white belly. Has small black patch in centre of belly, and black legs and bill. In flight, shows broad white greater-covert wing-bar contrasting with black flight feathers, and broad black terminal band to tail; from below, white underwing-coverts contrast with black flight feathers. **Juvenile** is similar to adult, but black of head is partly obscured by white tips, and has buff fringes and dark subterminal marks to feathers of upperparts. **VOICE** A sharp, insistent, high-pitched *did, did, did,* sometimes ending with *did-did-do-weet* (Ali and Ripley 1987). **HABITS** Usually occurs singly, in pairs or in small groups. Feeding behaviour similar to that of Red-wattled Lapwing (p.497). Often has a rather hunched posture, with head drawn in. **HABITAT** Sandy and shingle banks and islands of rivers; also estuarine coasts in Bangladesh. **BREEDING** March–June. Nest is a shallow scrape on an open sand or shingle bar in a river. **DISTRIBUTION AND STATUS** Resident, subject to some local movements. From Himachal Pradesh east through N India, and the Himalayan foothills to NE India and Bangladesh. **NP:** common and widespread below 915 m; occasionally summers locally up to 1380 m. **IN:** locally common in the north. **BT:** frequent; 250–2280 m. **BD:** scarce resident.

GREY-HEADED LAPWING *Vanellus cinereus* — Plate 51

Hoplopterus cinereus

IDENTIFICATION 34–37 cm. A stocky, yellow-legged lapwing. Has striking upperwing pattern, with white greater coverts and secondaries contrasting with sandy-brown inner wing-coverts and black primaries. Tail has broad black terminal band. At close range, shows red iris and patch of bare yellow skin in front of eye. Possibly confusable with White-tailed Lapwing (p.497), but black-tipped yellow bill, shorter-looking legs,

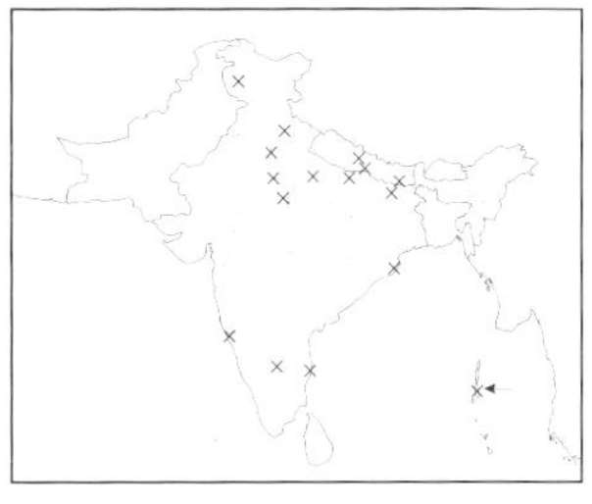

stockier appearance and black tail-band are differences in all plumages. **Adult breeding** has grey head and neck, with broad blackish breast-band. In **non-breeding** plumage, head and neck are browner and breast-band less prominent. **Juvenile** has brownish head and neck, lacks the dark breast-band, and has prominent buff fringes to feathers of upperparts. **VOICE** A plaintive *chee-it, chee-it* (Ali and Ripley 1987). **HABITS** Found in small parties or flocks of up to 50 birds. Behaviour to that of Red-wattled Lapwing (below), with which it often feeds. **HABITAT** River banks, marshes, wet stubbles or grazing pastures. **DISTRIBUTION AND STATUS** Winter visitor to Nepal, India (mainly the northeast) and Bangladesh. **NP:** regular winter visitor to the Kathmandu valley at 1310 m; rare passage migrant elsewhere below 275 m. **IN:** regularly winters in the northeast, rare elsewhere. **BD:** occurs locally throughout.

RED-WATTLED LAPWING *Vanellus indicus* — Plate 51

***Hoplopterus indicus* (R)**

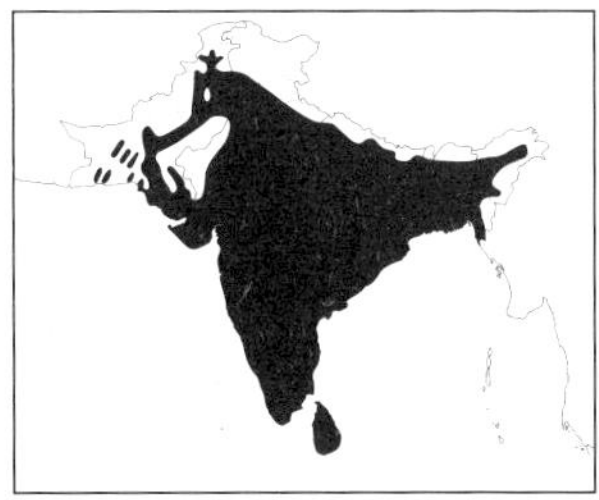

IDENTIFICATION 32–35 cm. **Adult** is unmistakable, with black crown, throat and centre to breast which contrast with white cheeks, sides of breast and belly. Has black-tipped red bill, red wattle, iris and eye-ring, and yellow legs. In flight, shows white greater-covert wing-bar and black band across tail. **Juvenile** is considerably duller, with whitish throat. Distinguishable from other juvenile lapwings by red base to bill, red iris, and black on breast. **Racial variation** *V. i. atronuchalis* of E India is very different from the nominate race, described above. Head and breast are entirely black except for white ear-coverts, and black of hindneck is separated from brown mantle by narrow white band. **VOICE** Very vocal: an agitated, penetrating *did he do it, did he do it,* and a less intrusive *did did did.* **HABITS** Keeps in pairs or small flocks of up to about 12 birds. A vigilant and noisy bird; when alarmed, calls loudly and frantically while circling overhead. Feeding behaviour is similar to that of other plovers: walks or runs in short spurts, then stops and probes with body tilted forward; also vibrates its foot rapidly on surface to flush out invertebrates. Forages mainly during the night and in early morning and evening. Usually flies slowly and with deep flaps. **HABITAT** Any open flat ground near water. **BREEDING** March–September, varying locally. Nest is a scrape on open bare ground near water, with the rim built up with pebbles or small mammal droppings; nests on flat pebbled roofs in some parts of India. **DISTRIBUTION AND STATUS** Resident throughout much of the subcontinent; subject to local movements. **PK:** common throughout the irrigated country of Sind and Punjab; mainly resident. **NP:** common and widespread below 1050 m (–1340 m). **IN:** common and widespread; plains up to 1800 m. **BT:** uncommon; 250–450 m. **BD:** locally common throughout. **LK:** common in lowlands and lower hills. **REFERENCES** Mundkur (1985).

SOCIABLE LAPWING *Vanellus gregarius* — Plate 51

Sociable Plover (P), *Chettusia gregaria* (R)

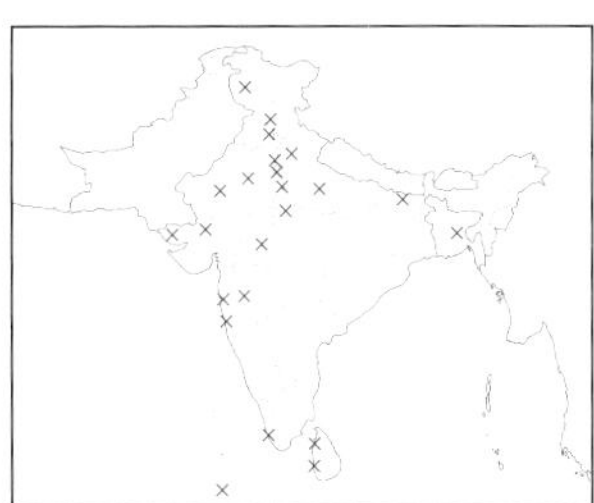

IDENTIFICATION 27–30 cm. Distinguished in all plumages by dark crown contrasting with prominent white or buff supercilia (which join to form a V at the nape), and black bill and legs. In flight, white secondaries contrast with black primaries and sandy-brown upperwing-coverts; underwing is white, with black primaries. Has black subterminal tail-band, unlike White-tailed Lapwing (below). **Adult breeding** has black crown and eye-stripe contrasting strongly with white supercilium; yellowish-buff wash to face, and black-and-maroon patch on belly. **Adult non-breeding** and **juvenile** have duller head pattern and white belly, and both show variable dark streaking on neck and breast. Juvenile additionally has prominent buff fringes and dark subterminal crescents to scapulars and coverts. **VOICE** Rather quiet away from breeding areas. **HABITS** In Pakistan in recent years, recorded as singles or in small parties of up to 12 birds. Feeding behaviour is similar to that of Red-wattled Lapwing (above). **HABITAT** Dry fallow fields, stubbles, scrub desert and wilderness; occasionally grassy margins of lakes and rivers. **DISTRIBUTION AND STATUS** Winter visitor. Now rare, but formerly regular and fairly common in Pakistan, NW India and Uttar Pradesh, occurring erratically east to West Bengal and south to Kerala and Sri Lanka. Globally threatened. **PK:** rare passage migrant and winter visitor. **IN:** rare winter visitor, mainly to the north and northwest. **BD:** vagrant. **LK:** scarce and irregular winter visitor to lowlands. **MV:** vagrant.

WHITE-TAILED LAPWING *Vanellus leucurus* — Plate 51

***Chettusia leucura* (R)**

IDENTIFICATION 26–29 cm. A plain-headed lapwing with large black eye, all-black bill, and very long yellow legs. Wing pattern is similar to that of Sociable and Grey-headed Lapwings (above and p.496), with white

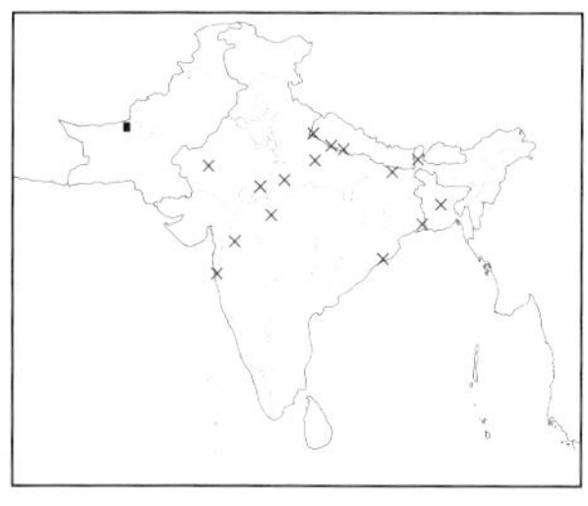

secondaries contrasting with black primaries, but White-tailed is the only lapwing with an all-white tail. **Adult** has uniform sandy-brown head, upperparts and breast, becoming grey on lower breast and with pinkish wash on belly. Has indistinctly paler lores, supercilium and throat. **Juvenile** has dark subterminal marks and pale fringes to feathers of upperparts, and paler neck and breast than adult; crown is mottled with dark brown. **VOICE** Calls include a *pet-oo-wit* and *pee-wick*, recalling Northern Lapwing (p.495). **HABITS** Usually in small parties in winter and in larger flocks when migrating. Habits similar to those of other lapwings. Usually feeds in shallow water, by pecking at the surface and by foot-dabbling; also probes on land. **HABITAT** Freshwater marshes and marshy edges of lakes and jheels. **BREEDING** Probably May–July. Nest is a scrape on the ground with little or no lining, sited on small islet in a lake. **DISTRIBUTION AND STATUS** Breeds in Baluchistan, Pakistan; winters in Pakistan, N India south to N Maharashtra and C Orissa, S Nepal and Bangladesh. **PK:** breeds very locally in small numbers; a common winter visitor and passage migrant; seen mainly early September–mid March. **NP:** very rare winter visitor to the W terai. **IN:** locally fairly common winter visitor to the north and northwest. **BD:** vagrant.

CRAB-PLOVER Glareolidae: subfamily Dromadinae

The Crab-plover is the only species in the subfamily Dromadinae.

CRAB-PLOVER *Dromas ardeola* — Plate 48

Crab Plover

IDENTIFICATION 38–41 cm. A large, mainly white wader with big head and short, stout black bill. Legs are very long, and blue-grey. **Adult** has black mantle, inner scapulars and flight feathers, giving a striking pattern at rest and in flight. In flight, shows whitish panels across primary coverts and base of primaries. May show dark speckling on crown and nape. **Juvenile** looks like washed-out version of adult. Has black streaking on nape, grey rather than black mantle and inner scapulars, and paler grey flight feathers; outer scapulars, wing-coverts and tertials have brownish cast. **VOICE** Nasal, yappy *kirruc* flight call recalls a tern or Bar-tailed Godwit. When in series, *kwerk-kwerk-kwerk-kwerk*, more like goose or flamingo (P. Holt from N. Lindsey recording). **HABITS** Found singly, in pairs and in small parties, but hundreds recorded at traditional roost sites. Mainly crepuscular, and usually very wary, taking flight at a distance. Feeds chiefly on crabs, also mudskippers and crustaceans, which it hunts in a typical plover-like manner, either on mudflats or in shallow water. Flies with neck and legs extended. **HABITAT** Feeds on intertidal mudflats and coral reefs; roosts on reefs, sand spits and coastal rocks. **BREEDING** Details not recorded in the region. Adults feeding young on Gulf of Kutch coast in mid September and December. Elsewhere, nests in burrows excavated in sandbanks or under rocks. **DISTRIBUTION AND STATUS** Chiefly a winter visitor to the coasts of the subcontinent; breeds in Sri Lanka. **PK:** rare winter visitor and passage migrant. **IN:** a regular and locally distributed winter visitor with an important concentration in the Gulf of Kutch, Gujarat. **BD:** vagrant. **LK:** scarce resident on N and NW coasts, occasionally recorded in south. **MV:** common and widespread, possibly resident. **REFERENCES** Mundkur (1991b), Palmes and Briggs (1986).

PRATINCOLES AND COURSERS Glareolidae: subfamily Glareolinae

Coursers and pratincoles have an arched and pointed bill, wide gape and long, pointed wings. Coursers are long-legged and resemble plovers; they feed on the ground. Most pratincoles are short-legged; they catch most of their prey in the air, although they also feed on the ground. All pratincoles live near water, whereas coursers frequent dry grassland and desert.

JERDON'S COURSER *Rhinoptilus bitorquatus* — Plate 47

***Cursorius bitorquatus* (I)**

IDENTIFICATION 27 cm. **Adult** has broad buffish supercilium and narrow crown-stripe, orange throat patch, and white and brown banding across breast. Has huge eye, with prominent pale eye-ring, short yellow bill with black tip, and long yellow legs. In flight, shows broad black tail-band, and white patch at tip of black primaries. **Juvenile** is undescribed. **VOICE** Poorly described; a plaintive cry (Ali and Ripley 1987). **HABITS** Very poorly known, as the species is largely nocturnal. Usually found singly or in pairs or small parties. **HABITAT** Bare patches of open ground among thin scrub forest in rocky foothills. **BREEDING** Unknown. **DISTRIBUTION AND**

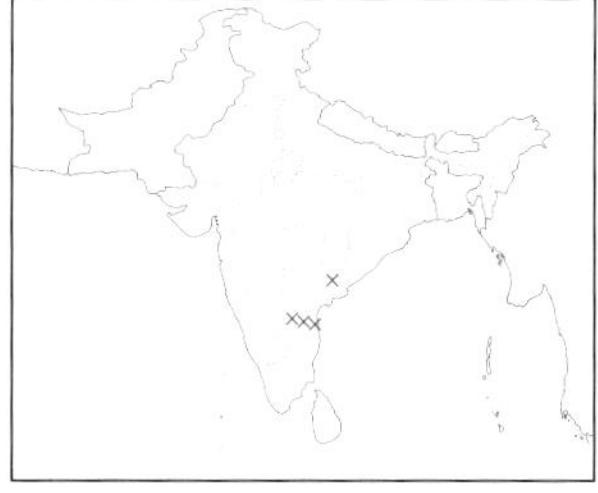

STATUS Globally threatened. **IN:** very rare, local and sedentary endemic resident; in 19th century recorded from the Penner and Godavari valleys in Eastern Ghats in E Andhra Pradesh; no records since 1900 until its rediscovery in 1986, when found nearby in the Lankamalai foothills in S Andhra Pradesh. **REFERENCES** Bhushan (1986, 1990a, 1990b).

CREAM-COLOURED COURSER *Cursorius cursor* — Plate 47

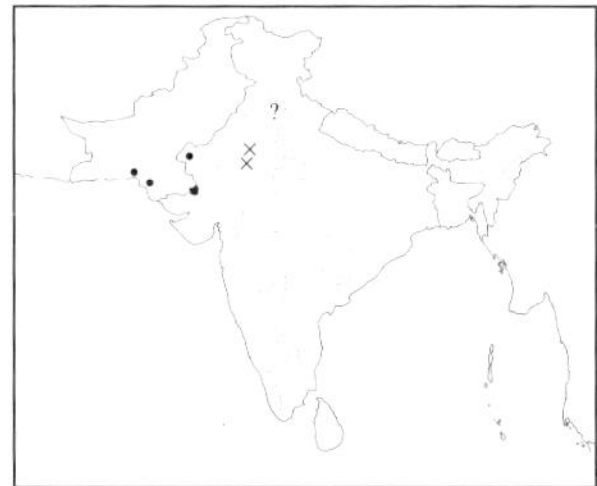

IDENTIFICATION 21–24 cm. **Adult** distinguished from Indian Courser (below) by uniform pale, sandy underparts concolorous with upperparts, sandy-rufous forehead and grey nape, and pale lores. In flight, both species are very dark on the underwing. Cream-coloured shows stronger upperwing contrast between sandy coverts and secondaries and black primaries and primary coverts; also, uppertail-coverts are concolorous with the rump and tail, and belly is whitish and without a dark centre. **Juvenile** has less distinct head pattern than adult; crown is buffish with indistinct dark markings, and feathers of upperparts have dark subterminal bars and pale tips. **VOICE** Commonest call is a sharp piping whistle, and utters penetrating *praak-praak* in flight (Cramp *et al.* 1983). **HABITS** Keeps in pairs or scattered parties; sometimes found with Indian Courser. Diurnal. Usually tame, and prefers to run off rather than fly; when alert, has a very erect posture. When foraging, runs rapidly in short bursts and pauses to bend down and pick up prey in the manner of a plover; also often digs in dry ground for insects and insect larvae. Often feeds on beetles and other insects attracted to the dung of livestock. Flight is direct and rapid, with powerful regular wingbeats and legs extending slightly beyond the tail. **HABITAT** Open arid desert country, sand dunes and stony desert. Often near villages where livestock are penned at night. **BREEDING** Poorly known in the region. Eggs found in Pakistan in May. Nest is an unlined scrape in sand in an exposed situation. **DISTRIBUTION AND STATUS** Breeds in S Sindh and Baluchistan, Pakistan, and Rajasthan; winter visitor to Pakistan and NW India (Rajasthan and Gujarat). **PK:** scarce. **IN:** regular in most arid parts. **REFERENCES** Rahmani and Manakadan (1990b).

INDIAN COURSER *Cursorius coromandelicus* — Plate 47

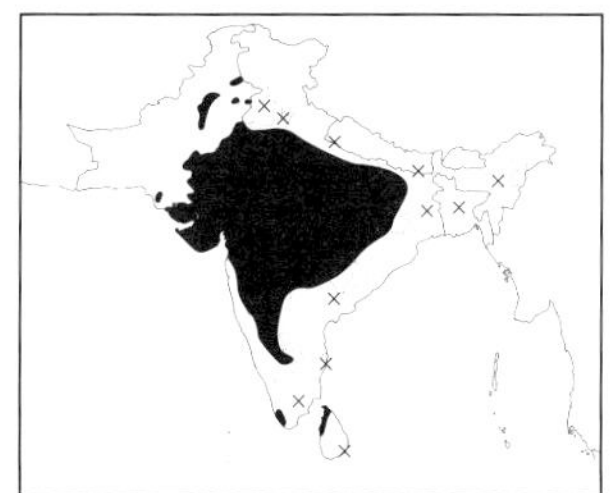

IDENTIFICATION 23 cm. **Adult** distinguished from Cream-coloured Courser (above) by rich orange underparts contrasting with grey-brown upperparts, and by blackish centre of belly, chestnut crown, and black lores. In flight, shows white band across uppertail-coverts and, as Cream-coloured, very dark underwing. **Juvenile** has dark brown crown, pale lores, strong brown-and-cream barring and blotching on upperparts, and brown markings on pale chestnut-brown underparts. Initially lacks dark patch on belly. **VOICE** Usually silent. A low *gwut* or *wut* (Hayman *et al.* 1986). **HABITS** Similar to those of Cream-coloured, but usually shy and readily takes to the wing. May occur with that species where their habitats overlap. **HABITAT** Dry fallow fields, wilderness, stony plains, dry river beds. Favours less arid habitats than those preferred by Cream-coloured. **BREEDING** March–August, varying locally. Nest is an unlined scrape on bare soil on fallow or uncultivated land. **DISTRIBUTION AND STATUS** Resident, subject to local movements depending on rainfall. Locally throughout most of the plains of the subcontinent. **PK:** scarce and erratic throughout Punjab and Sindh. **NP:** rare and local in the terai. **IN:** locally common and widespread, but patchily distributed. **BD:** ?former resident; no recent records. **LK:** resident in dry N, NW and SE coastal belt.

COLLARED PRATINCOLE *Glareola pratincola* — Plate 49

Common Pratincole, European Pratincole (P)

IDENTIFICATION 16–19 cm. A graceful, at times tern-like wader, with long, pointed wings and forked tail. In all plumages has red underwing-coverts, although this can be surprisingly difficult to see in the field. **Adult breeding** has cream throat bordered by black gorget, and red base to black bill. Told from Oriental Pratincole (p.500) by deeper fork to tail (with elongated outer feathers reaching at least to end of closed primaries at rest), paler brown mantle and wing-coverts contrasting more with dark primaries and secondaries, white trailing edge to secondaries on both upperwing and underwing (although at times visible only at close range), and more extensive red base to bill (reaching to nostril of upper mandible). **Adult non-breeding** is duller than adult breeding, with mottled breast, buffish-white throat and gorget of faint streaking; red at base of bill is less extensive. Tail length and tail-fork and white trailing edge to wing remain the best features to distinguish it from non-breeding Oriental. **Juvenile** has shorter outer tail feathers which fall short of closed wings at rest; feathers of

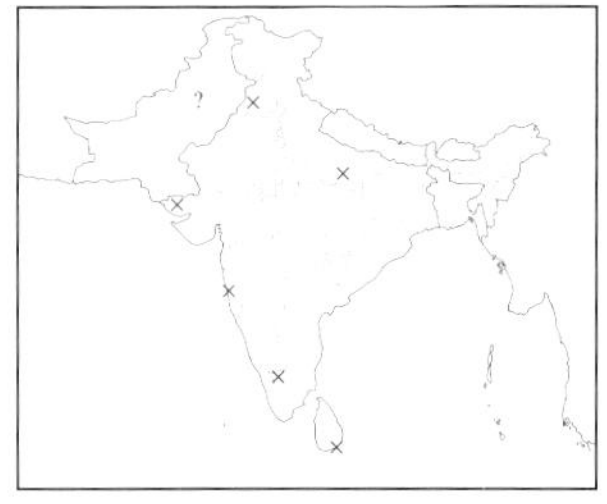

mantle, scapulars and wing-coverts are prominently fringed with buff, with black subterminal marks. Told with great difficulty from juvenile Oriental by white trailing edge to wing, and slightly longer tail with more pronounced fork. **VOICE** A *kirik..kirik..kirik* and a rolled-together *pirrit.. pirrit.. pirrit,* along with a variety of other calls, all of which have tern-like qualities. **HABITS** Gregarious throughout the year. Usually crepuscular, and also active in overcast conditions; rests during the hot part of the day, squatting on the ground. Hawks insects with its mouth wide open in powerful swallow-like flight. Also feeds on the ground in the manner of a plover, making short dashes to capture prey. Eats larger insects, mainly moths, beetles and flying ants; favours swarming species. **HABITAT** Open, dried-out bare ground around seasonal lakes, swamps and tidal creeks. **BREEDING** Late March–May. Breeds colonially. Lays eggs on the ground or in a shallow scrape on sun-baked grassland or stubble fields, often on burnt patches. **DISTRIBUTION AND STATUS** Breeds in Pakistan; winter visitor to India and Sri Lanka. **PK:** summer visitor, mainly to lower Sindh, where common; rare straggler to Punjab. **IN:** widespread, but rare. **LK:** rare in SE coastal areas.

ORIENTAL PRATINCOLE *Glareola maldivarum* — Plate 49

Indian Large Pratincole, Large Indian Pratincole, *G. pratincola* (F,I)

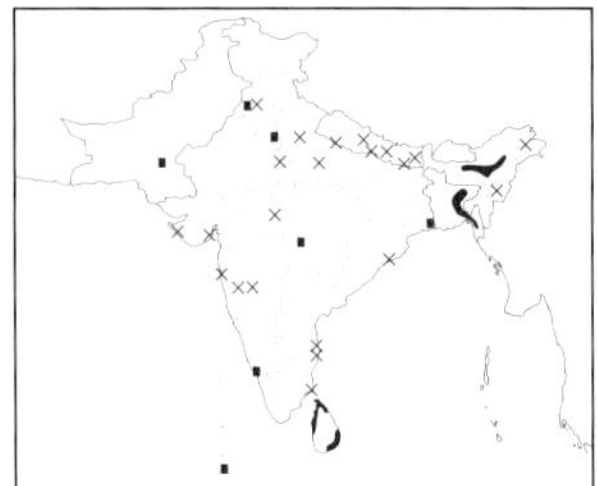

IDENTIFICATION 23–24 cm. Closely resembles Collared Pratincole (p.499) in all plumages, and, like that species, has red underwing-coverts. **Adult breeding** distinguished from Collared by shorter tail with much shallower fork (outer feathers falling roughly halfway between tips of primaries and tertials at rest), darker brown upperparts contrasting less with dark primaries, lack of white trailing edge to secondaries (although white trailing edge can be very difficult to see on Collared, even in fresh plumage, and is at times missing owing to feather wear), and less extensive red at base to bill (not reaching nostril as on Collared). Many Oriental in breeding plumage have strong peachy-orange coloration to breast and belly, unlike Collared. **Adult non-breeding** lacks the black-bordered creamy-yellow throat and peach-coloured breast of breeding-plumaged adult: best told from Collared by shorter tail and lack of white tailing edge. Usually warmer-coloured below than Collared (with orange wash often still apparent). **Juvenile** told with great difficulty from juvenile Collared by lack of white trailing edge to wing (although has very narrow buffish-white tips to secondaries, but this is rarely apparent in the field), and shorter tail (although tail of juvenile Collared falls short of closed wing). **VOICE** Sharp *kyik* or *chik-chik* or *chet* calls, as well as a loud *cherr* and a rising *tooeet* (Hayman *et al.* 1986). **HABITS** Like those of Collared Pratincole. **HABITAT** Dried-out bare flats by larger rivers and marshes, also low-lying pastures and fields, often near water. **BREEDING** March–July, varying locally. Breeds colonially. Nest site like that of Collared Pratincole. **DISTRIBUTION AND STATUS** Widespread in the subcontinent. **PK:** only one record, of a few breeding pairs in Sindh in the 19th century. **NP:** rare passage migrant; below 1310 m. **IN:** resident, subject to local migratory movements; very locally distributed when breeding, more widespread in winter. **BD:** local resident. **LK:** resident in dry lowlands, favours coastal areas. **MV:** common visitor, occasionally breeds.

SMALL PRATINCOLE *Glareola lactea* — Plate 49

Small Indian Pratincole (I,P), Little Pratincole (N)

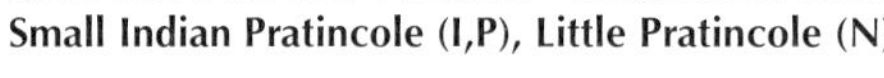

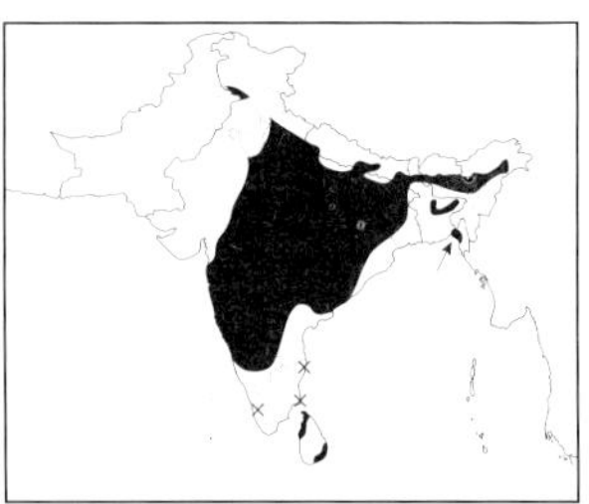

IDENTIFICATION 16–19 cm. A small, stocky pratincole. Easily distinguished from other pratincoles by smaller size, pale sandy-grey coloration, square-ended tail (or with very shallow fork), and striking wing pattern in flight. Upperwing has white panel across secondaries contrasting with grey wing-coverts and black primaries and tips to secondaries; on underwing, blackish coverts contrast with white panel across secondaries and pale underparts. **Adult breeding** has black lores and buff wash to throat and breast. **Non-breeding adult** (briefly) lacks black lores and has faint streaking on throat. **Juvenile** has indistinct buff fringes and pale brown subterminal bars to feathers of upperparts; throat and upper breast are ringed by small brownish spots, and tail is tipped buffish-brown. **VOICE** A high-pitched, rattling *tiririt.* **HABITS** Very similar to those of Collared (p.499), but often hawks insects later in the evening. **HABITAT** Chiefly large rivers with banks of sand or shingle; also lakes. **BREEDING** February–June, varying locally. Breeds colonially, sometimes with terns. Lays eggs in shallow scrape or none at all on a river sandbank; also on rocky and sandy ground on reservoir island. **DISTRIBUTION AND STATUS** Resident and partial migrant throughout much of the subcontinent; moves downstream outside the breeding season, when more frequent in estuaries and coastal areas. **PK:** common; mainly a summer breeding visitor to the Indus, occasionally winters in S Indus. **NP:** locally common resident and local migrant; below 305 m. **IN:** widespread and locally common resident. **BT:** local and common resident. **BD:** local common resident. **LK:** local resident in dry lowlands, favouring coastal areas.

SKUAS, JAEGERS, SKIMMERS, GULLS AND TERNS Laridae

This family comprises the subfamilies Larinae and Alcinae. The latter includes the auks, largely coastal and oceanic birds of the northern hemisphere, none of which has been recorded in the subcontinent. The Larinae is subdivided into tribes.

SKUAS AND JAEGERS Tribe Stercorariini

Aerial seabirds resembling brownish-plumaged gulls, with a strong, hooked bill, long, pointed wings, short legs and webbed feet. They can often be distinguished from gulls by their faster, stiffer wingbeats. Skuas and jaegers are predatory, and well known for their habit of persistently harrying gulls, terns and other seabirds on the wing until they drop or disgorge food, which the skua then skilfully catches in mid-air. Skuas and jaegers are fast and agile in pursuit, following every twist and turn of their victim. They breed in the high latitudes of both hemispheres and migrate to lower latitudes of the same or the opposite hemisphere. In the Indian subcontinent, skuas and jaegers are non-breeding visitors or passage migrants to coastal waters; they are sometimes storm-driven, occurring after monsoon gales. Present knowledge indicates that they are uncommon, rare or vagrants to the region, but they are under-recorded; more sea-watching from coasts or observations from boats offshore would undoubtedly produce more records. The main references specific to skuas and jaegers are Harrison (1983) and Malling Olsen and Larsson (1997).

BROWN SKUA *Catharacta antarctica* — Plate 52

Catharacta skua*, Antarctic Skua (I), *C. lonnbergi

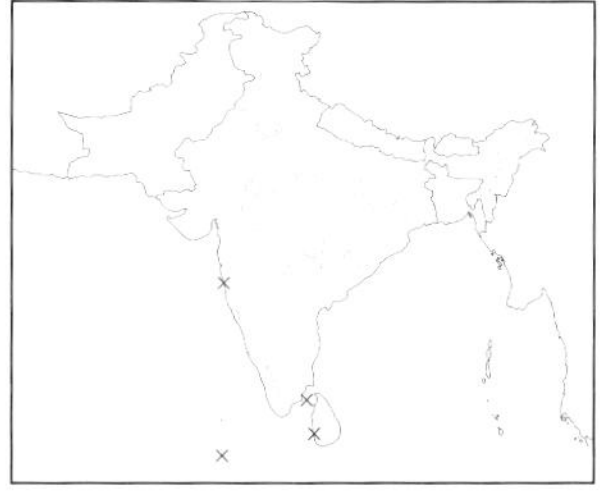

IDENTIFICATION 63 cm. A large, broad-winged skua showing broad white patches at base of upper- and underside of primaries. Larger and more powerful than South Polar Skua (below), with broader-based wings and larger bill. At rest, primaries do not usually extend beyond tail. **Adult** told from dark-morph South Polar by warmer brown coloration to upperparts and underparts, and pale streaking and rufous-brown mottling on mantle and scapulars, which often show fairly large white blotches (upperparts are uniformly dark on dark-morph South Polar Skua). Some birds can be paler brown on upperparts and underparts, but lack contrast between head, underbody and mantle shown by intermediate-morph South Polar. **Juvenile** is warmer brown on upperparts and underparts, some with rufous-brown coloration to underparts. **HABITS** A typical skua, but relatively powerful. Normal flight is purposeful, direct and almost laboured, with steady shallow wingbeats, but is swift, dashing and hawk-like when in pursuit of gulls and terns. **HABITAT** Coastal waters. **DISTRIBUTION AND STATUS** Rare visitor. **IN:** vagrant. **LK:** regular visitor in small numbers to W coastal waters during SW monsoon. **MV:** rare visitor. **REFERENCES** Balachandran (1991), Devillers (1977), Harrison (1987), Warakagoda (1994).

SOUTH POLAR SKUA *Catharacta maccormicki* — Plate 52

McCormick's Skua, *Catharacta skua* (I), *Stercorarius maccormicki*

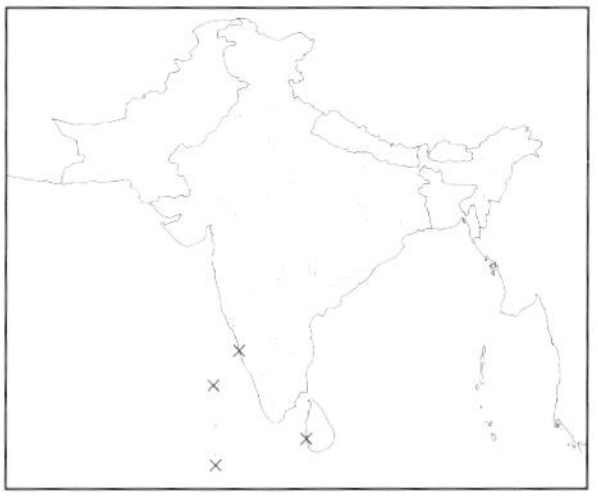

IDENTIFICATION 53 cm. A large, broad-winged skua with white 'flashes' at base of upper- and underside of primaries. A little smaller and slighter than Brown Skua (above), with bill shorter and not so deep. At rest, primaries usually extend beyond tail. **Adult** of pale morph is distinctive, with pale sandy-brown head and underbody contrasting with dark brown upperwing- and underwing-coverts and mantle. Dark bill and eye stand out against pale head, and usually shows paler collar. Dark morph is uniformly dark brown or blackish, lacking warm brown coloration and streaked and mottled appearance of Brown; can show pale nape and pale band across forehead, which, if present, are good distinctions from that species. Possibly confusable with dark juvenile Pomarine Jaeger (p.502), but is larger and broader-winged, has uniform underwing-coverts, axillaries, and uppertail- and undertail-coverts (only exceptionally unbarred on dark juvenile Pomarine), and has more prominent white 'flashes' at base of upperside of primaries. Intermediates occur which typically show uniform pale brown hindneck, with darker cap or head, and buff or pale brown underparts which contrast with blackish underwing-coverts; they, too, often show a pale nape and band across forehead, and also lack the warm coloration and streaked appearance of adult Brown Skua. **Juvenile** is greyer than adult, with pale to mid grey head and underparts, and dark grey upperparts. Subsequent immatures are much as respective adults. **HABITS** Similar to those of Brown Skua. Follows ships. **HABITAT** Coastal waters. **DISTRIBUTION AND STATUS IN:** vagrant to Lakshadweep. **LK:** vagrant. **MV:** rare visitor. **REFERENCES** Alström and Colston (1991), Harrison (1988).

POMARINE JAEGER *Stercorarius pomarinus* Plate 52

Pomatorhine Skua (I,P), Pomarine Skua (R)

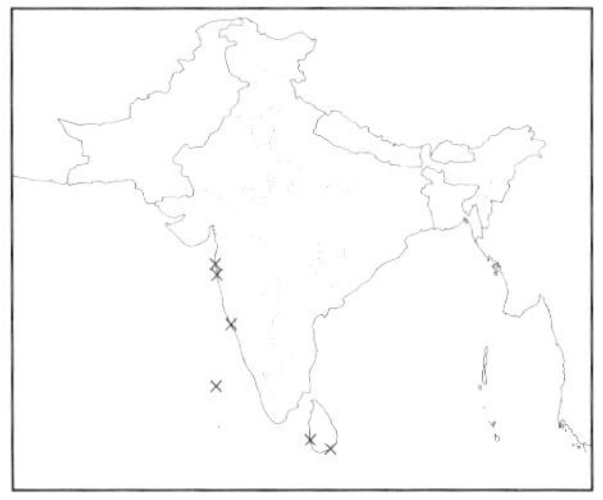

IDENTIFICATION 56 cm. Larger and stockier than Parasitic Jaeger (below), with heavier bill. In flight, appears slower and heavier, with deeper chest and broader-based wings. **Adult breeding** told from Parasitic by longer and broader central tail feathers which are twisted at end to form swollen tip (although tips can be broken off). Both pale and dark morphs occur (latter is much rarer). Pale morph has blacker mantle and wing-coverts than pale-morph Parasitic. Prominent pink base to bill, brighter yellow neck, more prominent breast-band, dark flank barring, and darker and more raggedly patterned vent are additional features which help to separate it from pale-morph Parasitic. **Adult non-breeding** has shorter tail, lacking swollen tip. In pale morph, cap becomes indistinct, neck and breast are diffusely barred with brown, and mantle and scapulars are barred with buff; also has prominent pale barring to uppertail- and undertail-coverts. Uniform dark underwing-coverts separate adult non-breeding from immature plumages. Safely distinguished from non-breeding Parasitic only by size and shape and by broader round-tipped central tail feathers, which on some can be quite long. **Juvenile** is variable, although is typically dark brown with broad, pale barring on uppertail- and undertail-coverts and on underwing-coverts; never appears rufous-coloured on head, neck and underparts as some juvenile Parasitic do (although other Parasitic are virtually identical in appearance to Pomarine). In addition to structural differences mentioned above, best distinctions from juvenile Parasitic are whitish bases to underside of primary coverts which on most birds form a prominent second pale crescent on underwing (never as clear-cut on Parasitic), diffuse vermiculated patterning (never streaking) on nape and neck, and blunt-tipped or almost non-existent projection of central tail feathers. Further indicative features are more strikingly dark-tipped bill; lack of (or very indistinct) pale tips to primaries; more strongly barred uppertail- and undertail-coverts (combination of strongly barred uppertail-coverts and dark uniform head is diagnostic of Pomarine); and more contrastingly barred underwing-coverts and axillaries. Dark-morph juveniles occur, some being uniform sooty-black with white only at base of primaries; they differ little in subsequent immature plumages, and are not distinguishable by plumage from juvenile dark-morph Parasitic. **First-winter** similar to juvenile, but scapulars and upperwing-coverts lack pale fringes. **Second-winter** is similar to adult non-breeding, but underparts and underwing-coverts are heavily barred. **Third-winter** has whiter belly and may show unbarred greater underwing-coverts. **HABITS** Often associates with feeding flocks of terns. Like the skuas, parasitises gulls and terns. Flight is direct and powerful, with steadily flapping wingbeats. **HABITAT** Coastal waters, often near mouths of creeks or promontories with feeding terns; also often well offshore. **DISTRIBUTION AND STATUS** Regular visitor. **PK:** a scarce visitor, occurring mainly in winter, also seen in April, June and September. **IN:** rare visitor, recorded in March, October and November. **LK:** regular summer visitor to W and S coastal waters; moves with Bridled Terns along W coast. **REFERENCES** Cramp and Simmons (1983), Harris *et al.* (1989), Jonsson (1992), Sinclair (1977).

PARASITIC JAEGER *Stercorarius parasiticus* Plate 52

Parasitic Skua (I), Arctic Skua (P,R)

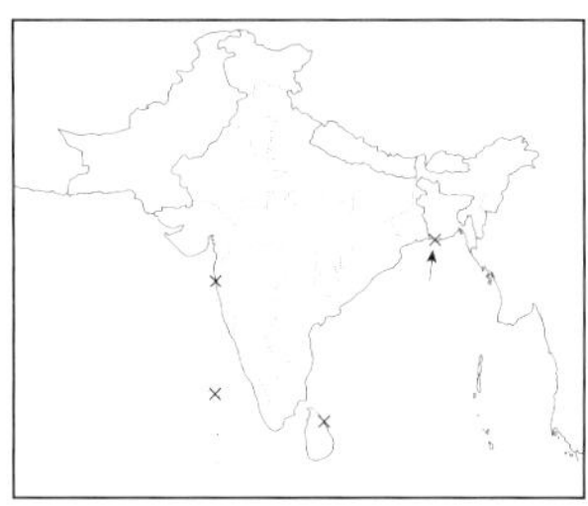

IDENTIFICATION 45 cm. Smaller and more lightly built than Pomarine Jaeger (above), with slimmer bill and narrower-based wings. **Adult breeding** has pointed ends to elongated central tail feathers, which are narrower and lack swollen tip of Pomarine. Occurs in both pale and dark morphs. Pale morph has paler grey-brown mantle and wing-coverts than pale-morph Pomarine; can also show a breast-band and dark vent, although these are rarely as striking as on some Pomarine. **Adult non-breeding** loses clean-cut appearance, having pale feather fringes to mantle, white barring on rump and vent, and diffuse barring on head and neck, with cap partly obscured. Has less contrasting pale base to bill and more pointed tip to tail compared with non-breeding Pomarine. **Juvenile** is more variable than juvenile Pomarine, ranging from grey and buff in colour, and heavily barred, to completely blackish-brown. Many juveniles have rusty-orange to cinnamon-brown cast to head and nape, which is not found on Pomarine. Except for all-dark juveniles, has dark streaking on head and neck and pale tips to primaries, which further help to separate it from Pomarine. See Pomarine for further differences. **First-/second-/third-winter** (except for dark morphs) progressively resembles adult non-breeding; belly becomes whiter, and underwing-coverts less noticeably barred (being uniformly dark when adult). Differences from respective immature plumages of Pomarine are size and structure, slimmer bill with less distinct pale base, dark streaking on head and nape, less obvious barring on underwing, flanks and vent, more uniform rump and uppertail-coverts, and pointed central tail feathers. **HABITS** Commonly associates with terns and gulls. Feeding behaviour is typical of jaegers. Normal flight is buoyant, with jerky wingbeats alternating with glides; swift, dashing and falcon-like when in pursuit. **HABITAT** Coastal waters, often near mouths of major creeks, rivers and lagoons with roosting and feeding terns and gulls. **DISTRIBUTION AND STATUS** Regular visitor. **PK:** frequent visitor in small numbers, mainly from the post-monsoon months until the following spring; also a regular spring migrant. **IN, BD, LK:** vagrant. **REFERENCES** Cramp and Simmons (1983), Harris *et al.* (1989), Jonsson (1992), Malling Olsen (1989), Sinclair (1977).

SKIMMERS Tribe Rynchopini

Have very long wings, a short forked tail, a long bill and short red legs and toes, and are black above and white below. They frequent rivers, lakes and coastal waters.

INDIAN SKIMMER *Rynchops albicollis* Plate 58

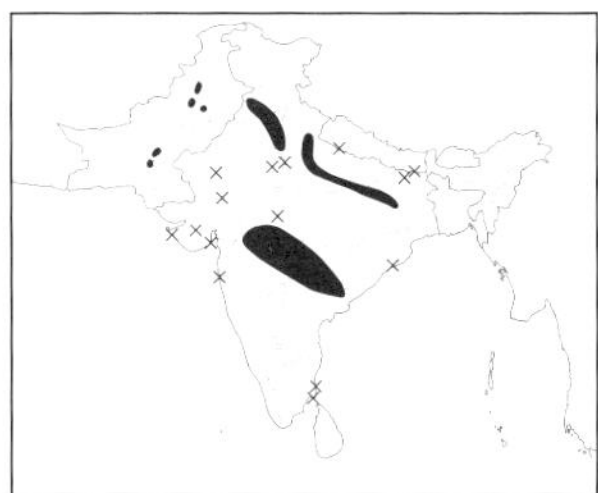

IDENTIFICATION 40 cm. **Adult** is very distinctive, with large, drooping orange-red bill (with lower mandible projecting noticeably beyond upper), black crown and nape contrasting with white forehead and collar, and black mantle and wings contrasting with white underparts. In flight, shows broad white trailing edge to upperwing, white underwing with blackish primaries, and white rump and tail with black central tail feathers. In non-breeding plumage, upperparts are duller and browner. **Juvenile** has dark brown upperparts with whitish to buffish fringes to mantle and wing-coverts, diffuse cap and pale collar, dull orange bill with black tip, and dull orange (rather than bright red) legs and feet. **VOICE** A nasal *kap, kap* (Ali and Ripley 1987). **HABITS** Forages singly or in flocks; roosts communally on sandbanks. Feeds chiefly in the early morning or near dusk, but also active on bright moonlit nights. Flight is fast, powerful and graceful, resembling that of a *Sterna* tern. Systematically quarters the water surface, and has a characteristic skimming feeding method: flies close to the surface with the tip of its much longer lower mandible in the water and bill held open; when prey is detected, snaps its shorter upper mandible down while simultaneously pulling its head down and back. Eats mainly fish. **HABITAT** Mainly larger rivers with sandbanks, also reservoirs; rare on inland lakes and inshore coastal waters on passage and in winter. **BREEDING** Mid February–May. Colonial, in association with terns and Small Pratincoles. Nest is an unlined hollow on open bare sand on islands in rivers. **DISTRIBUTION AND STATUS** Resident, subject to migratory movements depending on water conditions. Large rivers of Pakistan, mainly N and C India, Nepal and Bangladesh. Globally threatened. **PK:** now a rare breeding summer visitor to the Indus R and tributaries. **NP:** an irregular and now rare visitor, chiefly to Kosi Barrage. **IN:** formerly widespread and locally fairly common; now rare in most areas except in Gujarat and Punjab, where locally fairly common. **BD:** locally common winter visitor. **REFERENCES** Crosby (1995), Perennou *et al.* (1994), WWF India and AWB (1993).

GULLS Tribe Larini

Medium-sized to large birds with relatively long, narrow wings, usually a stout bill, moderately long legs and webbed feet. Immatures are brownish and cryptically patterned. In flight, gulls are graceful and soar easily in updraughts. All species swim buoyantly and well. Most gulls in the region are mainly coastal, although some species occur out at sea and some are found inland. They are highly adaptable, and most species are opportunistic feeders with a varied diet. Many feed on marine invertebrates and fish and have learned to scavenge refuse and fish offal from harbours, fishing boats and ships. Some species forage along the shoreline for invertebrates or other material washed up by the waves. Some eat freshwater or terrestrial invertebrates, or eggs and chicks at seabird colonies, or, like skuas, pursue smaller gulls and terns in flight, forcing them to disgorge food. Most species are gregarious, often feeding in flocks and forming breeding colonies and communal roosts. Where gulls are common, they make regular movements to and from roosts at dawn and dusk. A few gull species are resident and breed in the region; most are winter visitors. The main references specific to gulls are Cramp and Simmons (1983), Grant (1986) and Perennou *et al.* (1994).

WHITE-EYED GULL *Larus leucophthalmus* Plate 54

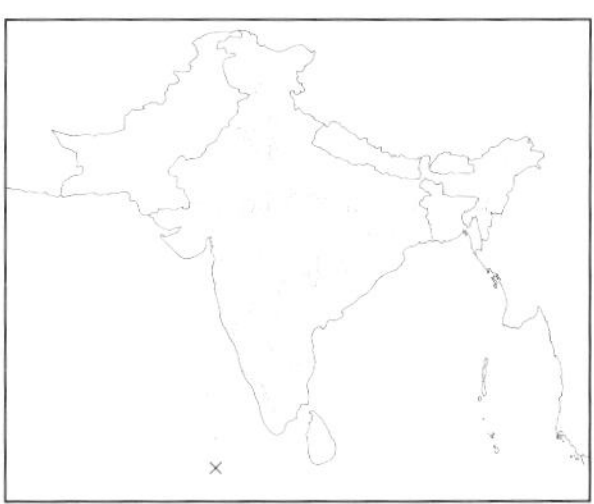

IDENTIFICATION 39 cm. Similar to Sooty Gull (p.504), with dark mantle and wings, blackish underwing contrasting with white underbody, and dark head and neck. Best told from that species by slimmer, all-dark bill (broader and distinctly two-toned on Sooty Gull). In all plumages, shows prominent white crescents above and below eye (crescent below eye is absent or indistinct on Sooty), and has more clear-cut hood. Further, it is smaller and has slightly narrower and more pointed wings than Sooty. **Adult breeding** distinguished from adult breeding Sooty Gull by bright red bill with black tip, bright yellow legs, black (rather than dark brown) hood and bib, and purer grey (rather than brownish-grey) mantle, upperwing and, especially, neck-collar and breast-band. In non-breeding plumage has white tips to feathers of black hood, especially on face. **Juvenile** has pale fringes to grey-brown mantle and scapulars, grey-brown upperwing, and whitish face and throat, reducing hooded appearance. Rather similar to juvenile Sooty, and best told by blackish bill and white eye-crescents. **First-winter/first-summer** as juvenile, but has uniform grey-brown mantle. Further differences from Sooty are darker nape and ear-coverts, resulting in more hooded appearance, with fine dark streaking on crown (Sooty's head is rather plain), greyer breast-band and flanks, and greenish (rather than greyish) legs. **Second-winter/second-summer** similar to adult, but has variable dark terminal tail-band. **VOICE** Similar in structure to that of Black-headed Gull (p.507), with hollow 'chicken-like' quality, including a *kook* and a drawn-out *krooo* (M. Elliot). **HABITS** Details not recorded in the region. Frequently associates with Sooty Gull in its normal range in the Red Sea, Gulf of Aden and Gulf of Suez. **HABITAT** Fishing ports, harbours and coastal settlements. **DISTRIBUTION AND STATUS** Globally threatened. **MV:** one collected in 19th century and one photographed recently; fishermen report capturing one or two almost every year, and sailors sometimes bring them in. **REFERENCES** Ash and Shafeeg (1995), Grant (1986), Harris *et al.* (1996), Hollom *et al.* (1988), Porter *et al.* (1996).

SOOTY GULL *Larus hemprichii* — Plate 54

Hemprich's Gull (R)

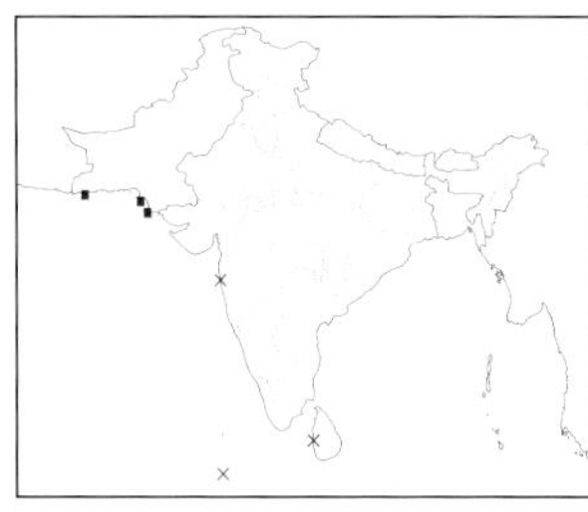

IDENTIFICATION 45 cm. Considerably darker in appearance than other medium-sized gulls regularly occurring in the subcontinent. Has heavy, two-toned bill, brown head and breast, brown mantle and wings, with broad white trailing edge to secondaries, and very dark underwing contrasting with white belly and vent. At close range, likely to be confused only with the vagrant White-eyed Gull (p.503); see that species for main differences. Long wings, powerful flight action and 'barrel-chest' give it a rather skua-like appearance at a distance; bill is distinctly longer, belly, rear flanks and vent are always white and unbarred, and shows white trailing edge to wing. **Adult breeding** has dark brown hood and bib, whitish half-collar on hindneck, brown breast-band, and greyish-brown mantle and upperwing. Bill is yellowish with black subterminal band and red tip, and legs are dull greenish-yellow. In non-breeding plumage, white half-collar is diffuse or lacking and head is paler. **Juvenile** has pale brown head and breast contrasting with white belly; also brown mantle and wing-coverts with pale fringes forming scaly pattern, broad black terminal band to tail, and pale grey bill with black tip. **First-winter/first-summer** as juvenile, but with grey-brown mantle and scapulars lacking pale fringes, paler head, and grey-brown breast-band and flanks. **Second-winter/second-summer** has whiter tail with variable dark terminal band; by second summer, head and bill can be similar to adult breeding. **VOICE** Generally silent. **HABITS** Similar to those of other gulls. Feeds by scavenging for scraps and fish offal in harbours or around fishing boats; also frequently robs smaller gulls and terns by aerial pursuit. **HABITAT** Found only on the coast; often in harbours and around fishing boats. **BREEDING** End June–end August. Mainly colonial. Nest is a hollow, scantily lined with vegetation, in the shelter of bushes or boulders. **DISTRIBUTION AND STATUS** Breeds in Pakistan; a rare visitor to coasts elsewhere in the subcontinent. **PK:** common in summer, breeds mainly on Astola Is; chiefly a non-breeding summer visitor to the rest of Sind and Makran coasts. **IN, LK:** vagrant. **MV:** one photographed recently, locality and date of capture unknown; one or two are reported in some years, and sailors sometimes bring them in. **REFERENCES** Ash and Shafeeg (1995), Grant (1986), Harris *et al.* (1996), Porter *et al.* (1996).

MEW GULL *Larus canus* — Plate 54

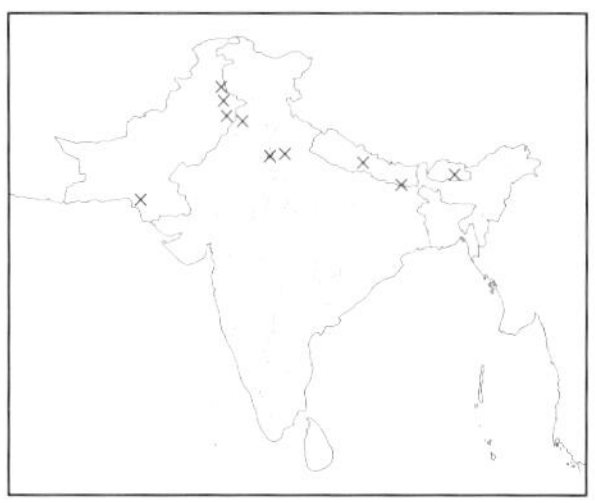

IDENTIFICATION 43 cm. Most likely to be confused with Yellow-legged Gull (p.505), but is noticeably smaller and daintier, with slimmer body and more rounded head, and shorter, finer bill. In flight, wings are proportionately longer and slimmer. At rest, has rather long and slim body and slim neck compared with Yellow-legged. **Adult** has medium-grey mantle and upperwing (darker than Yellow-legged), with black wing-tips and white 'mirrors' at tip. Black at wing-tips is more extensive than on Yellow-legged (which has pale on inner webs of primaries). In breeding plumage, head is white and bill yellowish-green; in non-breeding plumage, has paler bill with dark subterminal mark or band, and has dark markings on head (which are much more extensive and prominent than on non-breeding Yellow-legged). Compared with adult Yellow-legged, lacks red spot on bill and has dark iris. **Juvenile** has grey-brown mantle and wing-coverts with pale fringes, dark-streaked crown and ear-coverts, and mottled grey-brown breast-band. **First-winter/first-summer** has uniform grey mantle and scapulars, and is best told from second-winter/second-summer Yellow-legged by above-mentioned size and structural differences, plus unbarred greyish greater coverts forming prominent mid-wing panel, narrow black subterminal tail-band (tail of second-winter Yellow-legged is diffusely barred), dark iris, and well-defined dark tip to greyish or pinkish bill. Head, hindneck and sides of breast are well streaked (unlike on Yellow-legged), but become whiter following body moult into first-summer plumage, and upperwing pattern becomes paler through wear, with greater-covert bar appearing especially bleached. **Second-winter** resembles adult, but has black on primary coverts. **VOICE** Calls include a nasal *keow* and a drawn-out, shrill *glieeoo* (Jonsson 1992). **HABITS** Similar to those of other gulls. Feeds on invertebrates and fish. **HABITAT** Recorded in the region on lakes and large rivers, but also coastal in its normal range. **DISTRIBUTION AND STATUS PK:** rare winter visitor. **IN, NP, BT:** vagrant. **REFERENCES** Alström (1994), Grant (1986), Robson (1993a).

GREAT BLACK-BACKED GULL *Larus marinus* Not illustrated

Meinertzhagen (1900) shot an adult in Rajasthan, India, in 1899, but this was not preserved and the identification is now considered doubtful.

YELLOW-LEGGED GULL *Larus cachinnans* Plate 53

Herring Gull (P), *L. argentatus* (F,I,K,P,R)

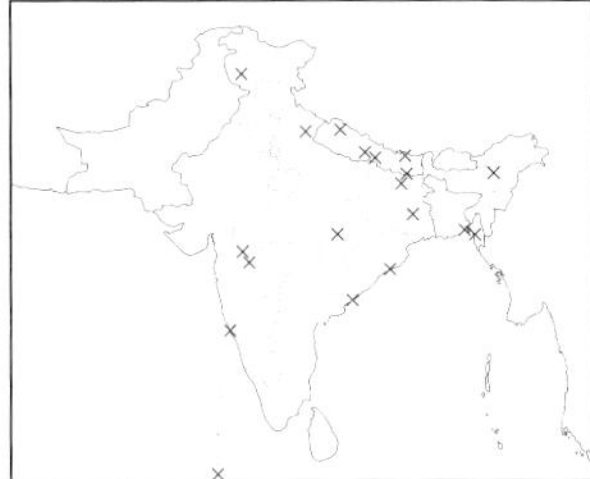

IDENTIFICATION 55–65 cm. A large gull, approaching Pallas's Gull (p.506) in size and structure, and similar to Heuglin's (p.506); clearly larger and broader-winged than Mew (p.504). Immatures are generally paler than Heuglin's, with second-winter and older having the palest upperparts of any large gull in the subcontinent. **Adult breeding** has grey upperparts, slightly paler than Pallas's. Outer six to eight primaries black with white tips when fresh. Black decreases inwards, often largely confined to outer webs, giving 'shutter' effect when fully spread (black parallel bars) but a solid black triangle when folded. White 'mirrors' are present on outer two primaries; outermost often with complete white tip, unlike Mew. Head, underparts and tail white. Bill yellow with red gonys spot; legs usually yellow, but occasionally pink. Iris darkish or pale, and with red orbital ring; looks 'beady'. **Adult non-breeding** as breeding. May show fine head streaking, especially around eyes, where can form faint mask, although this is usually apparent only during post-breeding moult (early winter); streaking on hindneck usually retained longer. Bill and legs can be duller or pinkish, former often with variable blackish subterminal band. Note that these bare-part changes are linked to post-breeding moult and are common to most large white-headed gulls. **Juvenile** is dark brownish above and on wings, with variable pale fringes and/or notches (more complex than on Mew or Pallas's). Outer greater coverts are mostly dark, these and secondaries forming double bar, and tail has a few narrow, inconspicuous bars and one broad subterminal band (again unlike those two). Underparts and head variably mottled dark, but become mostly white with moult. Best distinctions from Heuglin's are paler inner primaries and much paler underwing-coverts; latter are finely barred distally, forming narrow darkish lines (at long range like Mew or Pallas's). Bill and eye black; legs pale pinkish. **First-winter/first-summer** has underparts and head whiter, nearly pure white by summer, particularly head, central breast and belly. New scapulars variably barred/chequered and streaked dark on paler ground colour than Heuglin's, contrasting more with dark wing-coverts. Latter may wear to pale brownish by summer, when back even paler and often grey-tinged, not solid grey of Mew or Pallas's, and differing further in remnants of dark greater-covert bar and tail pattern. Bill may acquire pale base, up to half of length. **Second-winter/second-summer** extensively grey on back, but wings similar to first-winter. Easily separated from Heuglin's, but more like first-year Mew and Pallas's. However, tail-band still barred, greater coverts dark, and general impression still less tidy/more variegated. Bill ranges from mostly black to adult-patterned by summer; iris may become paler and legs yellowish (never grey). **Third-winter/third-summer** as adult, except more black and less white on primaries, variable dark marks on coverts, secondaries and tail, and can have dark eyes and some black on bill. Very similar to second-winter Mew, but averages paler grey, usually has red on gonys, and iris sometimes pale. Structure best distinction. **VOICE** Typical long-call is a braying *ka - yaow-owowow-ow-ow ow* etc, which is similar to that of most other large white-headed gulls and probably indistinguishable from Heuglin's in field. Other calls include guttural *ag-ag-ag* and higher *gliu(u)* alarm (M. Elliot). **Racial variation** *L. (c.) barabensis* may occur in the subcontinent, though taxonomy and identification poorly understood. It is smaller, and has darker upperparts, than *L. c. cachinnans*, and usually has more black and less white on primaries when adult; has greyer inner webs to primaries, brighter bare parts, is usually dark-eyed, and frequently shows bill-band. **HABITS** Similar to those of other gulls. Frequently scavenges for fish offal and refuse in harbours and around fishing boats and ships; seeks invertebrates on mudflats and by wading in surf; takes eggs and chicks at seabird colonies. Occasionally piratical on smaller gulls and terns. Roosts communally on rocks and sand bars. Flight is graceful and buoyant. **HABITAT** Coasts, harbours, offshore waters (at fishing boats); also inland lakes and rivers. **DISTRIBUTION AND STATUS** Widespread winter visitor; status uncertain. **PK:** common winter visitor to the coast; also a winter visitor and passage migrant to inland lakes. **IN:** uncommon. **NP:** probably an uncommon passage migrant and winter visitor, recorded mainly below 915 m; immatures found at up to 4725 m on passage (although some reports may be referable to Heuglin's Gull). **BD:** scarce winter visitor. **LK:** uncommon winter visitor to W and NW coasts. **MV:** a few confirmed records. **REFERENCES** Garner (1997), Gruber (1995), Klein (1994).

LESSER BLACK-BACKED GULL *Larus fuscus* Not illustrated

No confirmed records of this species for the subcontinent. Published records, e.g. Ali and Ripley (1987) and Ash and Shafeeg (1995), are now regarded as unacceptable. Confusion with Heuglin's Gull is the most likely explanation for most of the reports of this species.

HEUGLIN'S GULL *Larus heuglini* Plate 53

Herring Gull (I) *L. argentatus* (F,I,P,R)

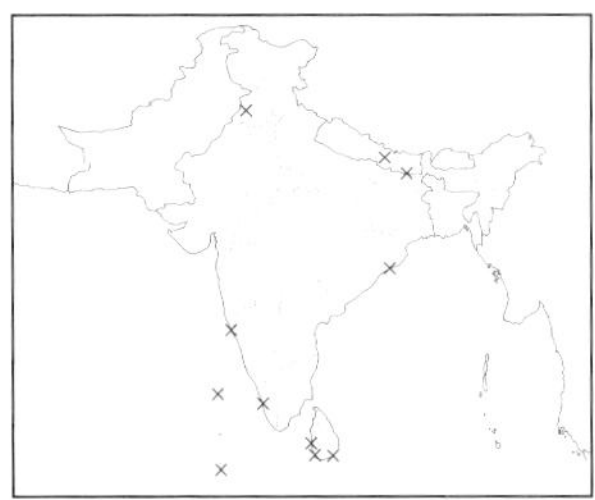

IDENTIFICATION 58–65 cm. Darkest large gull of region; *L. h. heuglini* averages smaller and darker. Second-years and older easily separable from congeners in region owing to dark grey upperparts, but younger birds similar to Yellow-legged (p.505). **Adult breeding** Dark grey above, tinged bluish when fresh, but becoming browner with wear, clearly contrasting with black outer primaries, and broad white trailing/narrow leading edges to wings. Underwing shows dusky bar along flight feathers. Head, underparts and tail white. Iris pale; bill/legs as Yellow-legged. **Adult non-breeding** becomes more heavily streaked on head than Yellow-legged, and streaking is retained longer. Wings still in active moult (suspended in *L. h. heuglini*?). Legs are more commonly pink. **Juvenile** Very similar to juvenile Yellow-legged but darker, especially below and on underwing-coverts. Inner primaries darker (but *L. h. taimyrensis* intermediate?), and usually has broader, complex, dark-barred tail-band making pale rump/uppertail-coverts very conspicuous. *L. h. taimyrensis* may be more pale-barred/notched on upperparts. This plumage retained mid- to late winter. Differs from Mew/Pallas's in same way as does Yellow-legged, but distinctions even more pronounced. Bare parts as Yellow-legged. **First-winter/first-summer** has new mantle/scapular feathers marked on darker grey-brown ground colour than Yellow-legged; unmoulted feathers become very worn and brown. Head and underparts whiter than juvenile, but probably always darker than first-year Yellow-legged until midsummer. **Second-winter and older**, owing to later timing of moult, may show more signs of immaturity than same-aged congeners, but general appearance still darker, and new dark grey areas on mantle are diagnostic. **Racial variation** *L. h. taimyrensis* (which is perhaps unlikely to occur in region) is bulkier (overlapping with some Pallas's), broader-winged, heavier-billed and paler, with slightly less black on primaries. **VOICE** Probably inseparable from that of Yellow-legged (M. Elliot). **HABITS** Similar to those of Yellow-legged. Sometimes seen with that species. **HABITAT** Similar to that of Yellow-legged. **DISTRIBUTION AND STATUS** Winter visitor to the subcontinent; status uncertain. **PK:** common winter visitor to coasts, seen inland only on passage. **NP:** probably a rare passage migrant. **IN:** winter visitor, mainly to W coast. **LK:** regular winter visitor to N and NW coasts, rare in south. **MV:** vagrant. **REFERENCES** Garner (1997), Jonsson (1996).

PALLAS'S GULL *Larus ichthyaetus* Plate 53

Great Black-headed Gull (F,I,P,R)

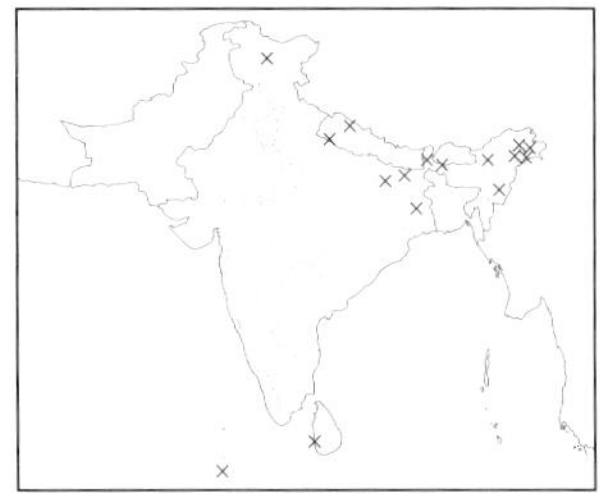

IDENTIFICATION 69 cm. Larger than Yellow-legged and Heuglin's Gulls (p.505 and above) and looks longer- and slimmer-winged, with deeper wingbeats. At all ages, head is more angular, with gently sloping forehead, and crown peaks behind eye; bill is longer and 'dark-tipped', with bulging gonys. Eye is always dark. **Adult breeding** has black hood with bold white eye-crescents, and yellow bill with red tip and black subterminal band. Has distinctive wing pattern, with broad white primary tips contrasting with black subterminal marks across outer primaries, and white primary coverts and base of outer primaries forming wedge-shaped patch on outer wing that contrasts with pale grey coverts. **Adult non-breeding** as adult breeding, but has largely white head with variable black mask (although retains white eye-crescents) and band of dark streaking across hindcrown. Head pattern varies, however, and dark markings can be rather indistinct. **Juvenile** has brown mantle and scapulars with pale fringes, resulting in scaly pattern. Distinguished from immature Yellow-legged by combination of more pronounced dark mottling on hindneck and sides of breast contrasting with whitish underbody, absence of dark bar across greater coverts, and stronger, more clearly defined, single black tail-bar; dark mask is more pronounced. **First-winter/first-summer** has grey mantle and scapulars (unlike respective plumage of Yellow-legged). Wing pattern as juvenile, but worn paler by first summer. Told from second-winter Yellow-legged by dark mask and streaking across hindcrown (as adult non-breeding), more pronounced brown mottling on hindneck and sides of breast (creating impression of brown shawl), more contrasting upperwing and underwing patterns (see comments under juvenile), and more pronounced dark tail-band; tail-band and mask are the best long-range features. Has pink bill with well-defined dark tip, although second-year Yellow-legged may show similar bill pattern. May acquire partial hood in first summer. **Second-winter/second-summer** has dark mask and mottling on hindneck, and more broken tail-band. Shows dark secondary bar and some dark lesser coverts, and extensive black on primaries and primary coverts. Can have largely black hood in summer. Legs are often greyish or greenish on second-year and younger (yellowish or pinkish on Yellow-legged). **Third-winter/third-summer** as adult non-breeding/breeding, but has more black on primaries and smaller 'mirrors' (showing as black wing-tips at a distance), and can have faint suggestion of dark tail-band. In third winter is most similar to Yellow-legged, when head-and-bill shape and dark mask are the most important features. **VOICE** A corvid-like *kra-ah*. **HABITS** Often solitary, although sometimes found in flocks. Feeds by scavenging and piracy, like other large gulls. Has a steady purposeful flight with deep wingbeats. Sits high on the water when swimming. **HABITAT** Mainly coasts and around fishing boats at sea, but rarely enters harbours; also inland lakes, large rivers and river-barrage head ponds. **DISTRIBUTION AND STATUS** Widespread winter visitor to coasts and large rivers of the subcontinent. **PK:** frequent winter visitor and passage migrant to the coast;

small numbers inland. **NP:** locally fairly common winter visitor and passage migrant; mainly in lowlands (–3050 m on passage). **IN:** widespread and locally frequent winter visitor. **BT:** uncommon passage migrant. **BD:** locally common winter visitor on coast and along large rivers. **LK:** regular winter visitor to N and NW coasts, rare in south. **MV:** vagrant. **REFERENCES** Grant (1986).

BROWN-HEADED GULL *Larus brunnicephalus* Plate 54

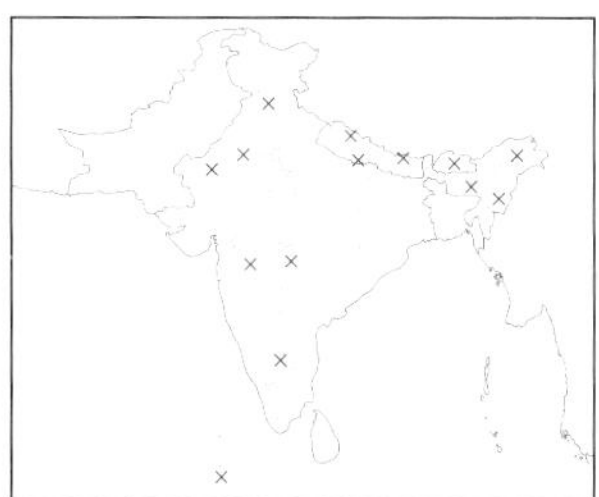

IDENTIFICATION 42 cm. Slightly larger than Black-headed Gull (below), with stockier appearance, and larger and broader bill which is dark-tipped at all ages. At rest, legs are longer. In flight, wings are broader and wing-tips more rounded. **Adult** is best distinguished from Black-headed by broad black wing-tips (broken by large white 'mirrors' on outer three primaries) which reduce white 'flash' on outer primaries and primary coverts to oval-shaped patch. In addition, upperwing is a shade darker grey, underside of primaries is largely black except for small white 'mirror' on outer primaries, and underwing-coverts are greyer. Iris is pale yellow (rather than brown). Hood is a paler brown, especially on face, and red bill has a dark tip. In non-breeding plumage, bill has black tip, and head is largely white with dark patch on ear-coverts. **Juvenile** has brownish-grey crown and nape, and greyish-brown mantle with paler buff fringes. Wing pattern much as first winter and is best feature for separation from juvenile Black-headed. **First-winter/first-summer** told from Black-headed by broad black wing-tips (lacking that species' white 'flash' on outer primaries) contrasting with largely white primary coverts and base of outer primaries, which form distinctive white patch on upperwing. As Black-headed, has black tail-band and trailing edge to wing, brown bar across wing-coverts, and orange legs; by first summer some have well-defined brown hood. **VOICE** As Black-headed's, but deeper and gruffer (M. Elliot). **HABITS** Similar to those of other gulls. Often feeds and roosts with other gulls, especially Black-headed. Frequently feeds by scavenging in harbours and from fishing boats and ships, which it often follows in and out of port, and by piracy; also feeds on terrestrial invertebrates inland and by hawking winged insects. **HABITAT** Coasts, fishing villages, tidal creeks, and large inland rivers and lakes. **BREEDING** June and July. Colonial. Nest is a mound of grass built on boggy ground near high plateau lakes. **DISTRIBUTION AND STATUS** Breeds in Ladakh at 3000–4500 m; widespread winter visitor and passage migrant to coasts and inland waters. **PK:** common on the coast, with small numbers on fresh waters inland. **NP:** fairly common at Kosi Barrage, uncommon elsewhere; mainly in lowlands (–5490 m on passage). **IN:** locally common on breeding grounds in Ladakh; in winter, common and widespread on coasts, especially in the south, also locally common inland. **BT:** vagrant. **BD:** common. **LK:** common winter visitor to coasts, especially in the north; occasionally oversummers in dry zone. **MV:** vagrant. **REFERENCES** Pfister (1997).

BLACK-HEADED GULL *Larus ridibundus* Plate 54

Common Black-headed Gull

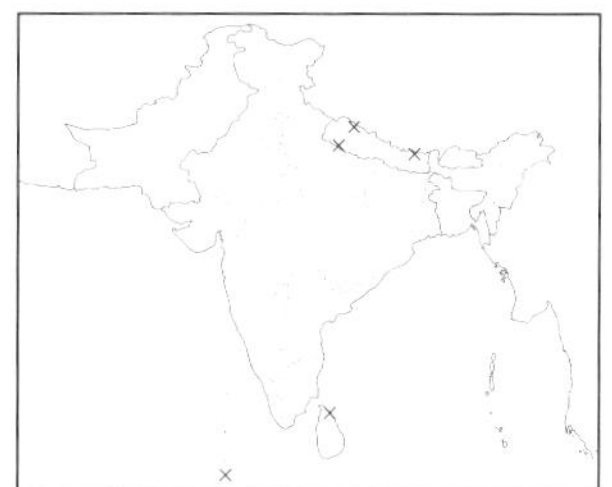

IDENTIFICATION 38 cm. Smaller than Brown-headed Gull (above), and with finer bill and narrower and more pointed wings. Wing patterns of adult and immatures are different from Brown-headed's (see below). Well-proportioned head, neck and bill, and dark eye, are best features for separation from Slender-billed Gull (below); for further differences, see that species. **Adult** has largely white outer primary coverts and primaries, forming triangular-shaped 'flash' on upperwing. Black on upperwing is restricted to primary tips, forming narrow rear band on wing-tip. Compared with Brown-headed, bill is blackish-red, and hood is a darker and more uniform brown in breeding plumage. In non-breeding plumage, bill has black tip, and head is largely white with dark patch on ear-coverts. **Juvenile** has brown crown and nape, and brown mantle and coverts with pale fringes. **First-winter/first-summer** has grey mantle; retains juvenile black tail-band and dark secondary and covert bars, which are faded by first summer. Wing pattern is otherwise essentially as adult, although with more black on outer primaries reducing extent and clarity of white 'flash' on upper- and underwing (never shows all-black outer primaries of immature Brown-headed). By first summer, head and bill are similar to adult breeding. **VOICE** A nasal *kyaaar*, short *keck* and deeper *kuk*, especially from flocks (M. Elliot). **HABITS** Similar to those of Brown-headed, and often associates with that species; in Pakistan also with Slender-billed. **HABITAT** Coasts, harbours, fishing villages, estuaries, large rivers and inland lakes. **DISTRIBUTION AND STATUS** Widespread winter visitor and passage migrant to coasts and inland waters. **PK:** common. **NP:** fairly common at Kosi Barrage, uncommon elsewhere; mainly in lowlands (–5490 m on passage). **IN:** locally common, especially on the W coast. **BD:** locally common throughout. **LK:** regular winter visitor to E and W coasts. **MV:** vagrant. **REFERENCES** Grant (1986).

SLENDER-BILLED GULL *Larus genei* Plate 54

IDENTIFICATION 43 cm. In plumage, closely resembles Black-headed Gull (above), although head is white throughout year. Best told from that species by elongated head (with gently sloping forehead), longer neck and larger bill. In flight, both neck and tail typically appear longer than Black-headed's. Has slightly longer legs. Neck

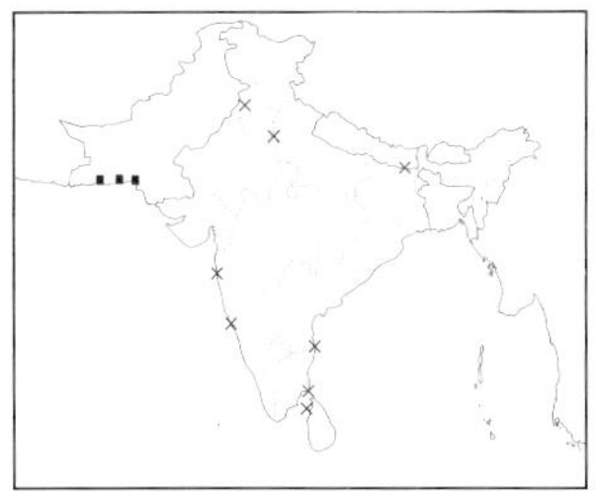

forms 'crop bulge' when hunched, and also in flight when neck retracted (when also looks hunchbacked). Unlike Black-headed, has pale iris in all plumages except juvenile (although iris of some breeding birds can look black). **Adult** has white head and variable pink flush on underparts. Bill is deep red (at a distance can look black); paler in non-breeding plumage. In latter plumage, can show faint grey ear spot and wash on hindneck. **Juvenile** has grey-brown mantle and scapulars, with pale fringes (generally paler and lacking ginger-brown coloration of juvenile Black-headed). **First-winter/first-summer** told from respective plumages of Black-headed by paler and less distinct dark eye-crescent and ear spot (sometimes completely lacking), pale iris, paler orange bill (with dark tip smaller or absent), paler legs, less prominent dark trailing edge to inner primaries, and more extensive white on outer primaries resulting in more prominent white 'flash' on wing. Shows brown bar across secondaries and another across greater coverts, but by first summer these can be very indistinct. **VOICE** Slightly deeper than that of Black-headed. **HABITS** Flocks frequently feed on shoals of small fish in the open sea; also scavenges from fishing boats, but in inner harbours. **HABITAT** Coastal waters, lagoons, estuaries, large tidal creeks and saltpans; also offshore, and in Pakistan small numbers on inland lakes in post-monsoon period. **BREEDING** April–June. Colonial, nesting with Caspian Terns. Nest is a pad of vegetation on ground on an island. **DISTRIBUTION AND STATUS** Breeding resident in Pakistan; widespread winter visitor to India and Nepal, mainly on coasts. **PK:** common resident on the coast, but only small numbers breed. **NP:** rare and irregular winter visitor, recorded only at Kosi Barrage. **IN:** probably under-recorded; a regular winter visitor to the W coast, common in Gujarat. **LK:** vagrant. **REFERENCES** Grant (1986), Mundkur *et al.* (1988).

LITTLE GULL *Larus minutus* — Plate 54

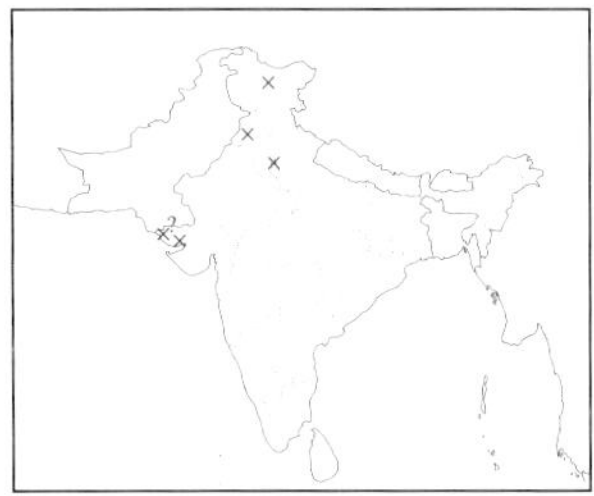

IDENTIFICATION 27 cm. A small gull with short legs and blackish bill. Buoyant flight is very similar to that of Whiskered Tern (p.516), as is feeding behaviour. Adult has rather rounded wings, but wing shape of immatures is similar to Whiskered Tern's. Best told from that species by dark grey underwing in adult plumages and by black M-shaped pattern across upperwing in immature plumages. Smaller size, daintier appearance, and patterning of upperwing and underwing separate it from Black-headed Gull (p.507). In all winter plumages, has greyish cap or black across rear crown, dark ear-covert spot and eye-crescent, and distinctive grey hindneck and sides of breast. **Adult** has pale grey mantle and upperwing lacking any black on wing-tips. Underwing is dark grey, with contrasting white tips of primaries and secondaries forming distinctive trailing edge. Has black hood in breeding plumage, and often with pink flush on underparts. **Juvenile** has black crown and ear-covert spot, blackish mantle and scapulars with whitish fringes, black M-mark across upperwing (created by largely black outer primary coverts and primaries, and blackish band across secondary coverts), and black band across tail. **First-winter/first-summer** has grey mantle and scapulars, but retains black M across wings. Dark markings on wings and tail become very pale and broken through moult and wear by first summer, when birds can have dark hood. **Second-winter/second-summer** are similar to adult winter and adult summer, respectively, but can show black subterminal tips to primaries, and paler grey underwing-coverts. **VOICE** A dry, short *kek* or *kik* (M. Elliot). **HABITS** A dainty gull which flies lightly and swims buoyantly, sitting high in the water. Feeds on insects by picking them from the water surface or by hawking. **HABITAT** Coastal and inland waters. **DISTRIBUTION AND STATUS IN:** vagrant. **REFERENCES** Grant (1986).

TERNS Tribe Sternini

Small to medium-sized aerial birds with a gull-like body, but, with the exception of the largest species, more delicately built. The wings are long and pointed, typically narrower than those of the gulls, and the flight is buoyant and graceful. There are three main groups of terns, namely the *Sterna* terns, the *Chlidonias* terns (or 'marsh terns') and the noddies of the genus *Anous*, plus the unique White Tern of the monotypic genus *Gygis*.

Sterna terns have a deeply forked tail, and are generally larger than other terns; most are black-capped. They inhabit inshore coastal waters, estuaries, tidal creeks, large rivers and other inland fresh waters. The black-capped *Sterna* species feed by hovering and then plunge-diving from the air to seize prey, often submerging completely, although at inland waters they will also pick prey from the surface like marsh terns. The dark-winged *Sterna* terns (Sooty and Bridled) hover above the water before swooping down to snatch prey from the surface; they feed offshore or far out to sea. Marine *Sterna* terns feed chiefly on fish, squid and crustaceans; freshwater species also eat tadpoles and crabs, as well as small fish. The nest of *Sterna* terns is usually an unlined or scantily lined hollow on open, flat, almost bare ground.

Marsh terns lack a prominent tail-fork and, compared with *Sterna* terns, are smaller, more compact and short-tailed, and have a more erratic and rather stiff-winged flight. They frequent marshes, lakes and rivers. Typically, marsh terns hawk insects or swoop down to pick small prey from the water surface. Their nest is small and flimsy, built of vegetation, and sited in marshes or lakes.

Noddies are pelagic terns, dark brown or black in colour, with a whitish cap, and with a distinctive wedge-shaped and slightly forked tail. Their normal flight is swift and with rapid wingbeats about 3 m above the sea, never high above it like Sooty and Bridled Terns. Noddies feed chiefly on small fish, squid, crustaceans and plankton, which they usually catch far out at sea, often feeding on bright moonlit nights. Typically, noddies gather in large flocks where predators drive shoals of small fish to the surface; they hover near the water, dart down, and pause momentarily to snatch small fry which are swimming near the surface or skipping above it. Noddies do not submerge, although they sometimes dive through wave crests and make shallow belly-flops. They can swim quite well, but prefer to perch above water, where they use any available resting place such as buoys, driftwood and ships' rigging.

Terns are very vocal birds, especially when breeding. Most species are highly gregarious, breeding in colonies – often with other terns, pratincoles or the Indian Skimmer – which they boldly defend against predators. They frequently roost in mixed flocks containing several tern species and gulls, often on sand bars on the coast or on river islands or lakeshores inland.

Most terns are migratory. Marsh terns move overland and the majority of *Sterna* species migrate by sea, although a few will undertake inland movements. Migratory species mature slowly, first breeding at two to five years of age, and when immature spending the breeding season in non-breeding areas.

These accounts have drawn extensively on Malling Olsen and Larsson (1995); calls are taken from that publication unless otherwise stated.

GULL-BILLED TERN *Gelochelidon nilotica* — Plate 55

Sterna nilotica

IDENTIFICATION 35–38 cm. Distinguished from Sandwich Tern (p.511) by shorter and stouter gull-like bill, broader-based, less pointed wings, and shorter, stockier body. Flight is steady and more gull-like, less graceful, with shallower wingbeats and with wings not so sharply angled. Lacks the yellow tip to bill and crested appearance of Sandwich. Rump and tail are grey (white on Sandwich) and concolorous with back in all plumages. When foraging, does not plunge-dive like Sandwich. **Adult breeding** has black cap, and darker grey upperparts than in other plumages. **Adult non-breeding** and **first-winter/first-summer** have distinctive black half-mask behind eye, with white crown and nape which may show some dark streaking (but lack black U-shaped crest of non-breeding Sandwich). By first summer, has darker, worn (juvenile) outer primaries which show as dark wedge owing to contrast with new inner primaries (although not so contrasting as on first-summer Sandwich). **Juvenile** has head pattern similar to adult non-breeding, although mask can be less well defined. Has sandy tinge to crown and mantle when fresh, and greyish-brown subterminal markings to tertials and some wing-coverts (markings are only exceptionally as bold or extensive as on juvenile Sandwich, and lacks the dark nape of that species). Tail has faintly darker terminal band, and bill has pale orange at base when very young. **VOICE** A guttural *gek-gek-gek* or *gir-vit*. **HABITS** Forages singly or in small flocks, often with marsh terns. Frequently feeds by hawking over open sand- and mudflats, swooping or dipping to pick up food and often skimming close to the surface, or seizing insects in mid-air. Sometimes hawks inland over marshes and fields. **HABITAT** Coastal mudflats, saltpans, tidal creeks, brackish lakes, large inland lakes and rivers, marshes and cultivation. **BREEDING** End April–end June. Nests on sandbanks in rivers and on islands in lakes or jheels. **DISTRIBUTION AND STATUS** Breeds locally in Pakistan, West Bengal, and Chilka Lake, Orissa; widespread in winter. **PK:** common winter visitor to the coast, major rivers and lakes; small numbers occasionally breed on islands in rivers and brackish lakes; also a passage migrant. **NP:** fairly common winter visitor and passage migrant to Kosi Barrage; rare on passage elsewhere (–3050 m). **IN:** widespread and locally common, mainly as a winter visitor. **BD:** common winter visitor throughout on rivers and coast; non-breeders oversummer. **LK:** regular winter visitor to lowlands, common in the dry zone, some birds oversummer; possibly a breeding resident in the northwest. **MV:** small numbers occur; reported to breed. **REFERENCES** Warakagoda (1994).

CASPIAN TERN *Sterna caspia* — Plate 55

***Hydroprogne caspia* (F,I,K)**

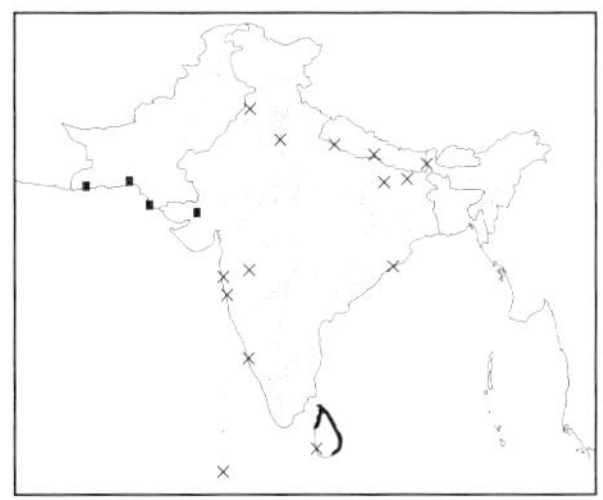

IDENTIFICATION 47–54 cm. Distinguished from Great Crested and Lesser Crested Terns (p.511 and p.510) by huge, stout red bill, broader-based and less angular wings, stockier, short-tailed appearance, paler upperparts, and striking blackish underside to primaries showing as dark patch on underwing in all plumages. Flight is powerful and swift, with deep, slow and elastic wingbeats. **Adult breeding** has complete black cap and short crest. **Adult non-breeding** has black-streaked crown and black mask; bill is duller, with more black at tip than in breeding plumage. **Juvenile** has narrow dark subterminal bars to scapulars and wing-coverts, and orange-red bill; forehead and crown are more heavily marked, almost forming dark cap. **First-winter** and **first-summer** are very similar to adult non-breeding, but show faint dark lesser-covert and secondary bars and dark-tipped tail; has dark, heavily worn outer primaries and primary coverts by first summer. In immature plumages, upperwing pattern is considerably less contrasting than on immature Great Crested and Lesser Crested Terns. **VOICE** A loud and far-carrying, hoarse *kretch* (E. Hirschfeld). **HABITS** Gregarious when nesting and roosting, but otherwise usually found singly or in twos or threes. Fishes by patrolling high above water, bill pointing downwards, hovering occasionally before plunging to seize prey, often disappearing entirely below the surface. Eats mostly fish, also crabs. **HABITAT** Coastal waters, estuaries, mudflats, mangroves and larger lakes and rivers. **BREEDING** May–September. Nests on bare open sand on islands and on lakes. **DISTRIBUTION AND STATUS** Breeds in Pakistan, Gujarat and Sri Lanka; winter visitor to the subcontinent, mainly on coasts, also on large inland waters. **PK:** common resident, subject to local movements; breeds occasionally on the coast, spreading inland in winter. **NP:** winter visitor and passage migrant; fairly common at Kosi Barrage, rare elsewhere. **IN:** common winter visitor to NW and SE coasts, frequent and widespread on large inland rivers; uncommon elsewhere. **BD:** local winter visitor to the coast. **LK:** winter visitor, common in dry-zone coastal areas, infrequent in wet zone; also a breeding resident on NW islets. **MV:** uncommon visitor. **REFERENCES** Ranjitsinh (1992).

RIVER TERN *Sterna aurantia* — Plate 55

Indian River Tern (F,I)

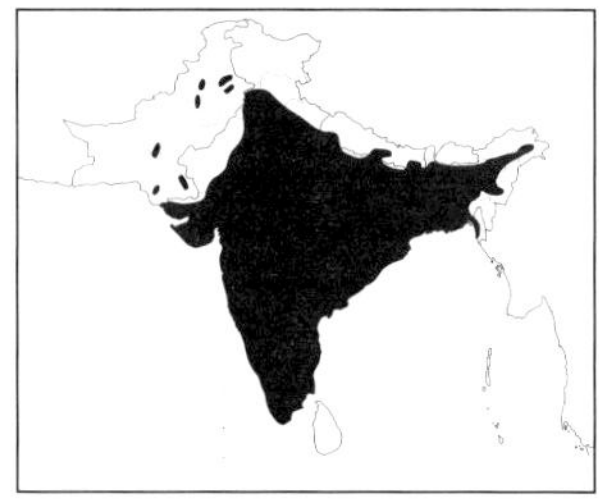

IDENTIFICATION 38–46 cm. A freshwater tern and likely to be confused only with Black-bellied Tern (p.515). Larger size (noticeably larger than Common Tern, p.513), longer and stouter bill, and stronger, more purposeful flight separate it from Black-bellied in all plumages. Head pattern of non-breeding and immature birds is also usually different. Flight is purposeful and often jerky. **Adult breeding** has large orange-yellow bill, black cap and nape, and red legs and feet. Fresh greyish-white primaries and primary coverts contrast with darker grey wing-coverts and secondaries to form striking 'flash' on outer wing in flight (although contrast is less when primaries become worn), and grey rump and centre of tail contrast with very long greyish-white outer tail feathers. Pale greyish-white underparts (some birds showing noticeable white cheek-stripe) separate it from breeding-plumaged Black-bellied. Birds can be seen in this plumage throughout the year. **Adult non-breeding** lacks long tail-streamers, and bill is yellower with variable dark tip. Shows blackish mask and nape, with variable amounts of black streaking on grey crown; dark mask merges into greyer ear-coverts and neck sides. **Juvenile** has black streaking on crown and nape, whitish supercilium, and dark mask extending as dark streaking onto ear-coverts and sides of throat. Also has brownish-black fringes to mantle, scapulars, tertials and coverts; uniform grey secondaries and primaries, with paler primary coverts; and brownish-black subterminal bars to tail feathers. Bill is yellow with black tip. **First-winter** and **first-summer** are similar to adult non-breeding, but retain brown-fringed juvenile tertials and tail feathers, as well as juvenile primaries, the latter being gradually replaced by paler greyish-white feathers. Head pattern as adult non-breeding, but can show largely white head with dark mask (recalling Gull-billed Tern, p.509, but has dark-tipped yellow rather than black bill). **VOICE** Contact calls in flight consist of fairly short, shrill, staccato notes, *kiuk-kiuk*, quite high-pitched and melodious, not grating. During display, a more extended, rapidly repeated disyllabic call is given, *kierr-wick kyerrwick-kierr-wick*, often accelerating in a crescendo (Roberts 1991). **HABITS** Typically as other black-capped *Sterna* terns. Feeds in noisy flocks, mainly by plunge-diving from the air; also by dipping to the surface and picking up prey. **HABITAT** Frequents larger rivers, lakes, tanks and canals. **BREEDING** November–August, varying locally. In colonies with Indian Skimmer, Little Tern and Small Pratincole. Nests on bare sand on spits and islets in rivers, also in reservoirs. **DISTRIBUTION AND STATUS** Resident. Throughout much of the subcontinent except Himalayas, parts of the northwest, northeast and Sri Lanka. **PK:** common resident; breeds on major rivers, and wanders widely on inland waters in winter. **NP:** locally common resident and partial migrant, mainly below 610 m (–1310 m). **IN:** widespread, locally common in the north, uncommon in south; chiefly in plains. **BT:** rare passage migrant. **BD:** local resident throughout.

LESSER CRESTED TERN *Sterna bengalensis* — Plate 55

Indian Lesser Crested Tern (I), Smaller Crested Tern

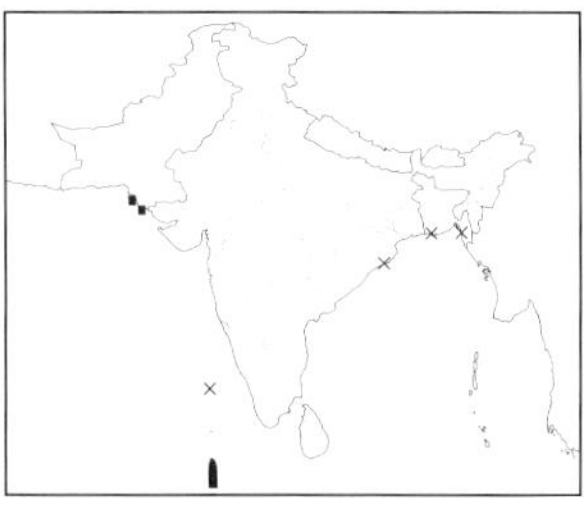

IDENTIFICATION 35–37 cm. Distinguished from Great Crested Tern (p.511) by smaller and slimmer yellowish-orange to orange bill, smaller size and lighter build (recalling Sandwich Tern, p.511), and paler grey coloration to upperparts. From Sandwich Tern by bill colour and grey rump and tail. **Adult breeding** has black crown and crest including forehead, although black of latter is quickly lost (forehead is never black on Great Crested). **Adult non-breeding** has black nape band (blacker and more clearly defined than on Great Crested); bill is paler yellowish-orange than in breeding plumage. **Juvenile** has brownish-grey centres to lesser and greater coverts and secondaries, which show as diffuse dark bars across wing, and has dark centres to feathers of mantle, scapulars and tertials. Upperwing pattern is similar to Great Crested's, but dark bars are typically paler and less contrasting. In **first-winter** plumage, juvenile body feathers, and median and greater coverts, are gradually replaced by paler grey feathers and is then similar to adult non-breeding, but shows darker grey primaries and primary coverts and dark lesser-covert and secondary bars. **First-summer** as adult non-breeding, but retains dark secondary bar and marks in outer tail feathers (as first-winter), and worn outer primaries contrast with fresh, paler grey inner primaries. **VOICE** An upward-inflected *kree-it,* much as Sandwich Tern's. **HABITS** As those of other black-capped *Sterna* terns. Feeds by plunge-diving from a considerable height. **HABITAT** A marine tern, usually found in offshore waters and often far out to sea; also tidal creeks and harbours; roosts on saltpans. **BREEDING** Little available information on season; mid August–mid September. Nests on bare sandy islands. **DISTRIBUTION AND STATUS** Occurs in offshore coastal waters almost all year; breeds in Pakistan, and may breed on the Maldives and Lakshadweep. **PK:** common, irregular year-round visitor; occasionally breeds on islands in the Indus delta; most often seen in spring, summer and autumn. **IN:** common off E and W coasts. **BD:** scarce winter visitor. **LK:** common winter visitor; stragglers oversummer. **MV:** resident in moderate numbers.

GREAT CRESTED TERN *Sterna bergii* — Plate 55

Large Crested Tern (I,P), Swift Tern (R)

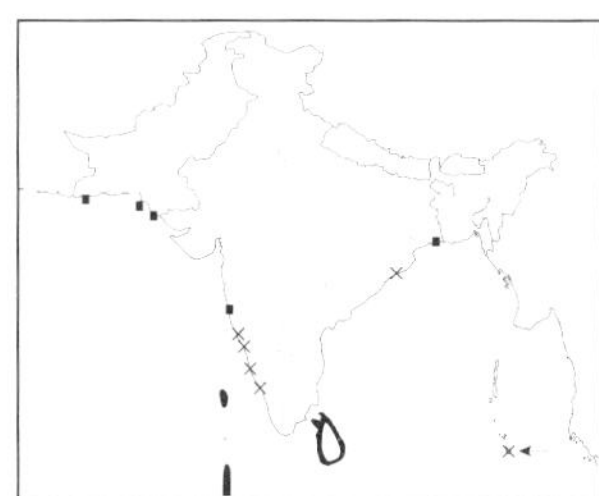

IDENTIFICATION 46–49 cm. Told from Lesser Crested Tern (p.510) by broader, slightly drooping, cold yellow to lime-green bill, and by larger size and stockier build. In adult plumage, shows well-defined whitish fringes to tertials, and has darker grey coloration to upperparts than Lesser Crested. Immature plumages are generally more strongly patterned than in Lesser Crested. Lighter build, slimmer and more angular wings, and bill colour readily separate it from Caspian Tern (p.510). **Adult breeding** shows black crown and shaggy crest, with white band across forehead. Bill is a shade brighter, and can even appear slightly orangey at onset of breeding season. **Adult non-breeding** has streaked nape band (more diffuse than on Lesser Crested); upperparts can appear patchy owing to mixture of worn grey-brown and fresh dark grey coverts. **Juvenile** shows four dark bars across upperwing (created by dark brownish-grey centres to lesser, median and greater coverts, and secondaries), and mantle, back and tertials are brownish-grey with pale fringes. Appears darker than juvenile Lesser Crested, with more strongly patterned upperwing. **First-winter** is similar to juvenile, but has uniform grey mantle and scapulars. Juvenile coverts are mostly replaced during first winter and first summer, resulting in untidy banding across upperwing, and by second winter is similar to adult non-breeding but still with dark secondary and lesser-covert bars, juvenile outer primaries and their coverts, and dark sides to tail. **Racial variation** *S. b. cristata,* with paler grey upperparts, has not yet been recorded, but may well be the race occurring in the Nicobar Islands. **VOICE** A harsh *kerrer* or *kerrak.* **HABITS** Similar to those of Lesser Crested. Often fishes with that species and with Sandwich Tern. **HABITAT** Mainly offshore waters and often at considerable distances out to sea; uncommonly on larger tidal creeks and channels. **BREEDING** April–August. Nests on bare sand, rock or coral on islands off the coast. **DISTRIBUTION AND STATUS** Resident. Breeds on coasts of Pakistan, W India, West Bengal, Lakshadweep, Sri Lanka, and possibly the Maldives; disperses along all coasts of the subcontinent after breeding. **PK:** common resident; occasionally breeds on offshore islands. **IN:** resident; breeds on offshore islands, and recorded along E and W coasts in the non-breeding season. **BD:** local winter visitor. **LK:** common resident. **MV:** widespread and resident in small numbers; reported to breed.

SANDWICH TERN *Sterna sandvicensis* — Plate 55

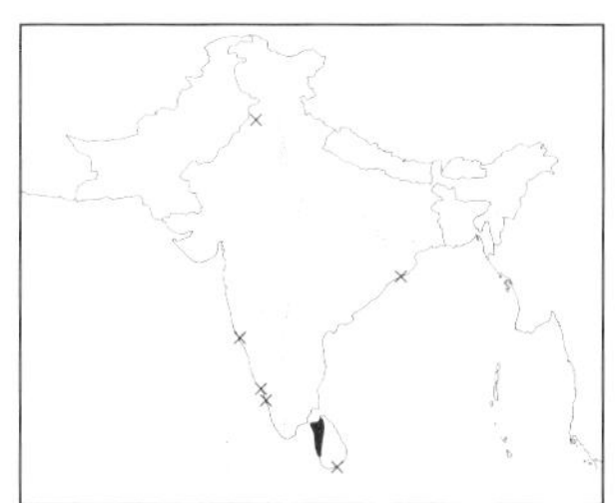

IDENTIFICATION 36–41 cm. Distinguished from Gull-billed Tern (p.509) by longer and thinner, dagger-like black bill with yellow tip, narrower, more pointed wings which appear set forward and sharply angled, and longer, tapering body. Has more jerky flight than Gull-billed, with rather quick, deep wingbeats, and bill typically directed downwards. Unlike Gull-billed, crest is usually apparent. Rump and tail are white (grey on Gull-billed) and contrast slightly with back in all plumages. Black bill and white rump and tail separate it from Lesser Crested Tern (p.510). **Adult breeding** has black cap with crest. **Adult non-breeding** has white forehead and crown, and black crest forming U-shaped patch. Upperwing is very pale grey, and darker worn outer primaries show as distinct wedge until midwinter. **Juvenile** has sandy tinge to mantle when fresh, and dark subterminal bars to wing-coverts and mantle, and dark patterning to tertials (markings are bolder and more extensive compared with Gull-billed). Juvenile mantle and covert feathers are largely replaced by grey first-winter feathers by August/September. **First-winter** as adult non-breeding, but has darker grey primaries and primary coverts, darker lesser-covert and secondary bars, and dark corners to tail. Upperwing pattern is more contrasting than first-winter Gull-billed, but less so than first-winter Lesser Crested. **First-summer** as first-winter, but has darker, heavily worn outer primaries which show as dark wedge (which is more contrasting than on Gull-billed). **VOICE** An upward-inflected, hoarse *kree-it.* **HABITS** As those of other black-capped *Sterna* terns. Plunge-dives for fish; often forages in flocks with Lesser Crested Tern, but flies closer to the water surface and usually does not dive so deeply as that species. **HABITAT** A marine tern; frequents coasts, tidal creeks and the open sea. **DISTRIBUTION AND STATUS** Non-breeding visitor mainly to W coasts of the subcontinent. **PK:** common non-breeding visitor, except during monsoon; may occur irregularly all year. **IN:** regular, locally common winter visitor to W coast. **LK:** regular, uncommon winter visitor to W and NW coasts.

ROSEATE TERN *Sterna dougallii* Plate 56

Rosy Tern

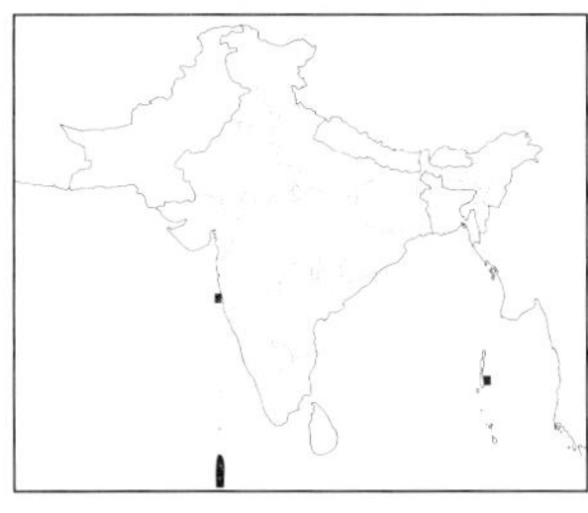

IDENTIFICATION 33–38 cm. In all plumages except juvenile, features which help to separate this species from Common Tern (p.513) are longer, slender bill (which can appear slightly downcurved); slimmer build and daintier appearance; longer tail, with all-white outer feathers which (unless broken off, and except for some immatures) project well beyond wings at rest; paler grey upperparts lacking any contrast between back and rump/tail; and distinctive call. In flight, wings appear comparatively short and angled and tail very long, and flight action, with wingbeats usually shallower, stiffer and faster than Common Tern's, recalls that of Little Tern (p.514); wings flutter more rapidly when hovering, again recalling Little. When primaries are fresh, their white inner webs form prominent broad white inner edge to wing at rest, which is not apparent on Common Tern. Has broader white trailing edge to secondaries, and lacks the prominent dark trailing edge to underside of primaries visible on Common. For differences from Black-naped Tern (below), see that species. **Adult breeding** has variable red base to black bill, and pinkish wash to underparts. Always shows more black at bill-tip than Common Tern, with black most extensive on lower mandible. **Adult non-breeding** has all-black bill and white forehead and forecrown, and may show faint dark lesser-covert bar (typically less prominent than on Common). May show pinkish tinge to underparts. Above-mentioned features, especially longer tail with white outer feathers, paler grey upperparts and broad white trailing edge to wing, help separate it from very similar Common Tern in non-breeding plumage. **Juvenile** told from juvenile Common Tern by long all-black bill (lacking orange at base), blackish legs, more extensive dark cap (wholly dark when young, with forehead and lores becoming whiter with age), and blackish subterminal bars to mantle, scapulars and tertials (on some, tertials are almost wholly black). **First-winter** and **first-summer** as adult non-breeding, but show dark lesser-covert and secondary bars. Can have long tail from midwinter. Worn outer primaries and primary coverts increasingly contrast with rest of wing. **VOICE** A disyllabic *chu-vee*, recalling Spotted Redshank (p.476), and a straight *aaahrk* (Jonsson 1992). **HABITS** Similar to those of other black-capped *Sterna* terns. Fishes by plunge-diving in shallow water in a very similar fashion to Common Tern. **HABITAT** Coastal waters and offshore islands and islets. **BREEDING** April–June. Nests among grass tufts on rocky islets or on sand. **DISTRIBUTION AND STATUS** Resident and breeding summer visitor. India, Sri Lanka and Maldives. **IN:** breeds on islets off SE and W coasts; resident on Nicobars? and Andamans. **LK:** resident and summer visitor, breeds on E and SW offshore islands. **MV:** frequently seen, and reported to breed. **REFERENCES** Carey and Leader (1994), Harris *et al.* (1989).

BLACK-NAPED TERN *Sterna sumatrana* Plate 56

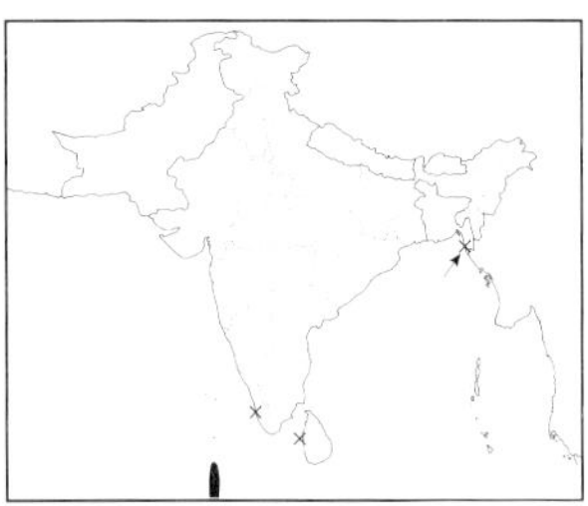

IDENTIFICATION 35 cm. **Adult** is most likely to be confused with Roseate Tern (above), but has all-black bill (lacks red at base, although can show pale tip), well-defined and narrow black bands running through each eye to join as broad band across nape, and black legs and feet. Has whiter mantle and wings, with distinct black outer edge to outermost primary, and lacks obvious white trailing edge to upperwing. At long range, appears strikingly white and much paler than Roseate. At rest, since primaries are almost white, inner webs do not form well-defined white edge to wing as on Roseate. Call is also different. Can show pink flush to underparts in breeding plumage, as on Roseate. Appears to show little seasonal variation, although nape band is paler and not so well defined in non-breeding plumage. **Juvenile** has blackish subterminal bars to mantle, scapulars, tertials and wing-coverts. Primaries and secondaries are grey, and white inner webs of primaries form white upper edge to closed wing, as on Roseate Tern. Bill is black (although can be dusky yellow when newly fledged, becoming black with age). Black legs and patterning of upperparts result in appearance similar to juvenile Roseate Tern, but head pattern is usually different: shows adult-like black stripe through eye and across nape, which is lightly marked with white but is usually well demarcated from forehead and crown; forehead and lores are white, and has variable amounts of dark streaking on crown (but this is not usually so heavily marked as on Roseate). The dark crescentic marks on the scapulars are not so V-shaped as on Roseate, nor are they so broad and distinct. **First-immature** is similar to adult, but has duskier black head patch, dark lesser-covert bar, darker grey (juvenile) primaries, and darker grey centres to tertials and markings on tail. **VOICE** A short, sharp *tsii-chee-ch-chip* and a hurried *chit-chit-chit-er* (Harrison 1985). **HABITS** Forages in flocks and prefers shallow inshore waters. Feeds like the noddies, picking prey from the surface while hovering, but will also submerge. **HABITAT** Inshore waters around islands and islets; favours lagoons. **BREEDING** May–July. Scattered colonies on rocky islets and coral banks. **DISTRIBUTION AND STATUS** Partly resident. **IN:** Andaman and Nicobar Is, status uncertain. **MV:** resident; the most common and widespread tern. **BD, LK:** vagrant. **REFERENCES** Carey and Leader (1994), Harrison (1983), Hoffmann (1996).

COMMON TERN *Sterna hirundo* Plate 56

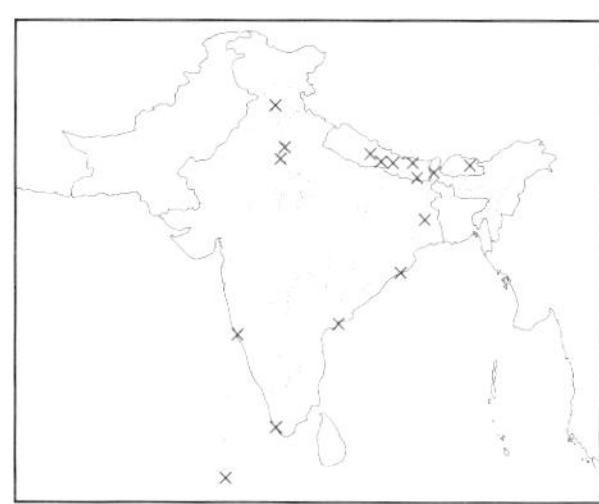

IDENTIFICATION 31–35 cm. Most likely to be confused in the subcontinent with Roseate and White-cheeked Terns (p.512 and p.515). Following features are for nominate race (see also racial variation). **Adult breeding** has orange-red bill with black tip, and orange-red legs. For differences from the vagrant Arctic Tern (below), see that species. Main differences from adult breeding Roseate Tern are shorter tail-streamers (which do not extend beyond tail at rest), darker grey upperparts contrasting with white rump and uppertail-coverts, dark trailing edge to underside of primaries and broader dark outer wedge to upperside, grey wash to underparts, and different flight action and call. Typically, shows less black at tip of bill than Roseate. Main differences from White-cheeked are paler grey upperparts and underparts, white rump and uppertail-coverts (with white inner webs to tail feathers), lack of well-defined white cheek-stripe, and paler and more uniform underwing. **Adult non-breeding** and **first-winter/first-summer** have black bill, black hood contrasting with white forehead, white underparts, and dark lesser-covert bar. Through wear, first-summer birds show contrastingly dark outer primaries, and darker bar on secondaries. Best told from Roseate Tern by darker grey upperparts (although back often does not contrast with rump as in breeding plumage), shorter and stouter bill, larger and stockier appearance, shorter tail (with noticeable grey outer webs to feathers), narrow and indistinct white trailing edge to secondaries and primaries, and more prominent lesser-covert bar; for further differences, see Roseate Tern. For differences from White-cheeked Tern (p.515), see that species. **Juvenile** is very different from juvenile Roseate. Has extensive orange at base of bill when newly fledged, bill becoming black with age, and has orange legs. Mantle and scapulars are initially fringed with buff and subterminally with dark brown, and forehead is also buff. With wear, forehead becomes white and upperparts lose buff and brown fringes (when mantle appears grey and white). **Racial variation** Adult breeding *S. h. tibetana* has darker grey upperparts than the nominate race, with a shorter bill that has a more extensive black tip. *S. h. longipennis* probably also occurs (R. Grimmett) and may even occur widely, with intermediates very likely. In breeding plumage, it has a mostly black bill, with greyer upperparts and underparts than the nominate race and a more distinct white cheek-stripe; legs are dark reddish-brown. Differences in bare-part coloration also hold for juvenile. White rump and uppertail-coverts are best distinctions from White-cheeked. **VOICE** A drawn-out and harsh *krri-aaah*, and a short *kik*. **HABITS** Typical of black-capped *Sterna* terns. Fishes mainly by plunge-diving from the air. **HABITAT** Mainly estuaries, tidal creeks and other coastal waters; also large inland lakes, jheels and rivers. **BREEDING** June and July. Usually colonial. In Ladakh, nests by high-altitude lakes, among dried vegetation or pebbles or on a grassy mound in the middle of a bog. **DISTRIBUTION AND STATUS** Breeds in Ladakh at 3500 m, and reported breeding in Sri Lanka; widespread but local winter visitor, mainly to coasts of subcontinent. **PK:** non-breeding visitor to the coast, passage migrant in Himalayas; scarce except in early summer, when frequent on coasts. **NP:** uncommon passage migrant; recorded 75–4000 m. **IN:** locally common on breeding grounds in Ladakh, recorded up to 4700 m; widespread in winter, mainly on the coast. **BT:** rare passage migrant. **BD:** local winter visitor; non-breeders oversummer. **LK:** common winter visitor to coastal waters; some birds oversummer, and reported breeding locally on islets off E coast. **MV:** status uncertain; recorded mostly in winter, possibly an irregular visitor. **REFERENCES** Pfister (1997), Warakagoda (1994).

ARCTIC TERN *Sterna paradisaea* Plate 56

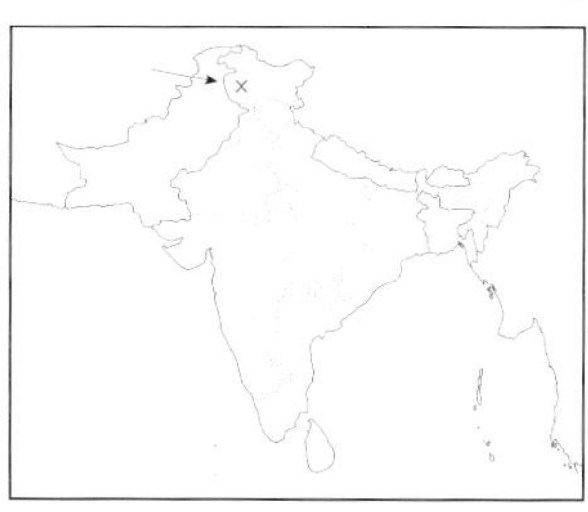

IDENTIFICATION 33–35 cm. Very similar in appearance to Common Tern (above). Arctic Tern always shows uniform primaries, since all are moulted in quick succession (and therefore no contrast between fresh and worn primaries to form the dark wedge that is often apparent on Common Tern, especially in late summer). Uniform, translucent primaries with well-defined dark trailing edge, short legs, and lack of dark secondary bar are further good features for separation from Common Tern at all ages. **Adult breeding** differs from adult breeding Common in having shorter, dark red bill (normally lacking black tip) and translucent primaries. In flight, appears shorter-winged and longer-tailed, with deeper and stronger wingbeats; wings appear to be set farther forward. Breast is typically greyer than Common Tern's, highlighting white cheeks. **Adult non-breeding**, **first-winter** and **first-summer** have black bill and legs, white forehead, and dark hood. Immatures show dark lesser-covert bar as on other immature *Sterna* terns. **Juvenile** is readily told from juvenile Common by white secondaries and inner primaries, which form a diffuse white triangle on wing. Mantle and wing-coverts have sandy-coloured tinge, and bill is initially red at base; these features are quickly lost, however, and bill becomes all black and mantle and coverts appear uniform grey (lesser coverts slightly darker). **VOICE** A *kriii-a*, clearer and shorter than Common Tern's. **HABITS** Very similar to those of Common Tern. **HABITAT** Normally a coastal species, but the only record in the region was well inland. **DISTRIBUTION AND STATUS IN:** vagrant to Kashmir.

LITTLE TERN *Sterna albifrons* Plate 57

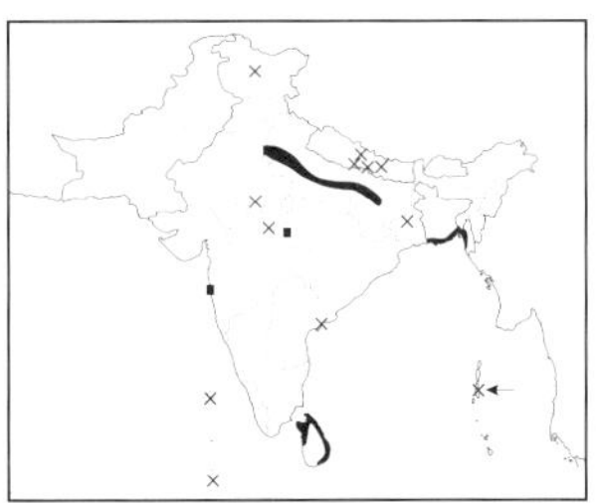

IDENTIFICATION 22–24 cm. A small tern with a long and pointed bill. Has fast flight, with quicker wingbeats than all other terns except Saunders's (below), and with wings held forward and sharply angled at carpal joint. Feeding behaviour is distinctive, with rapid hovering followed by a plunge-dive. The wings appear narrow and the tail rather short. For differences from the very similar Saunders's Tern, see that species. **Adult breeding** has yellow bill with black tip, white forehead contrasting with black loral stripe and hood, orange legs and feet, and black outer primaries which contrast with pale grey rest of wing. **Adult non-breeding** and **first-winter** have white forehead contrasting with black mask and nape band, and dark lesser-covert bar. The bill is black (sometimes with yellowish-olive base), and legs are black, grey or brown. Much smaller size and very different flight action separate them from adult non-breeding and first-winter Common Tern (p.513). Compared with adult non-breeding and first-winter Whiskered and White-winged Terns (p.516 and p.517), Little has a proportionately longer bill, narrower and more pointed wings, narrower body, and different flight action and feeding behaviour; dark outer primaries and lesser coverts and pale trailing edge of wing result in a wing pattern rather different from those species. **Juvenile** has dark subterminal bars to grey or yellowish-brown feathers of mantle, scapulars, tertials and wing-coverts. Darker grey outer primaries and inner coverts contrast with whitish secondaries and inner primaries, which form a broad pale trailing edge to the wing (although can show darker grey secondaries and inner primaries which are concolorous with outer primaries). When newly fledged, has more rounded wings and weaker, rather flapping flight, and yellowish-brown wash to forehead and breast, while bill is dark with yellowish at base. **Racial variation** Compared with the widespread nominate race, *S. a. sinensis*, which breeds on W coast of peninsula and Sri Lanka, has paler grey upperparts, longer tail-streamers, and white (rather than dark) primary shafts. **VOICE** Call is a monosyllabic *ket* or *ket-ket*. **HABITS** Forages singly or in small scattered flocks. Hovers more frequently and for longer periods than other terns (and with faster-fluttering beats than medium-sized *Sterna* species) before plunge-diving steeply after prey; has a habit of making a short sudden drop and then hovering again. Also feeds by dipping steeply to the surface and skimming prey from the water, and by taking insects in aerial pursuit. **HABITAT** Mainly freshwater lakes and rivers; also coastal waters and lagoons, tidal creeks, saltpans and reservoirs. **BREEDING** March–August, varying locally. Nests, sometimes with other species, on sandbanks or shingle of rivers, or islets in jheels, or on bare rock or shingle on islets off coast. **DISTRIBUTION AND STATUS** Resident. Breeds locally in the subcontinent; in the non-breeding season, disperses widely on inland and coastal waters and mixes, confusingly, with Saunders's Tern. **PK:** frequent resident; winters on the coast, and small flocks seen there all year; breeds inland on rivers. **NP:** locally common summer visitor; recorded chiefly below 120 m (–1280 m). **IN:** widespread but rather local resident. **BD:** uncommon resident. **LK:** common resident on coasts in dry lowlands, visitor to wet-zone coasts. **MV:** vagrant. **REFERENCES** Mundkur (1991).

SAUNDERS'S TERN *Sterna saundersi* Plate 57

Saunders's Little Tern (I)

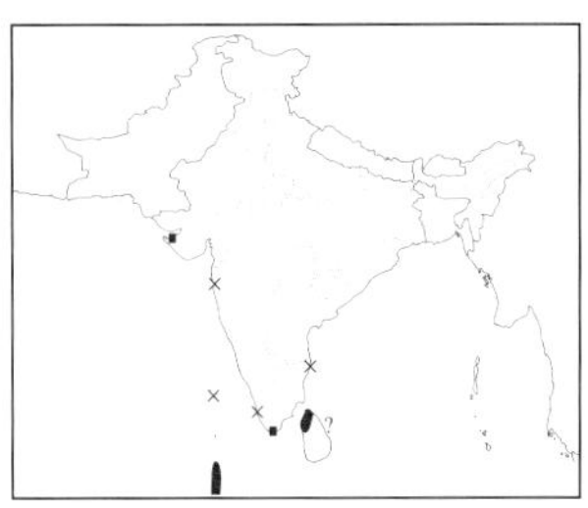

IDENTIFICATION 23 cm. Likely to be separable from Little Tern (above) only in breeding plumage, and identification is complicated by occurrence of intermediate birds. **Adult breeding** is identified by combination of following features: shorter and more rounded white forehead patch and broader black loral stripe (forehead patch does not extend over eye, and lacks short white supercilium of Little); shorter, reddish-brown to brown legs (orange on Little); purer and broader black outer edge to primaries (due to black outer three primaries, including black shafts, contrasting with paler grey upperwing); grey rump and centre of tail concolorous with paler grey mantle; and shorter tail-streamers. Note, however, that Little Tern with worn outer three primaries can show dark wedge (but normally with paler shafts), and that rump and centre of tail of some Little Terns (e.g. *S. a. sinensis*, which occurs in the subcontinent) can be grey. **Other plumages** There are no known features for safely separating adult non-breeding, first-winter and juvenile from respective plumages of Little Tern. Upperparts, including rump, are possibly darker grey, and a dark bar on secondaries might prove to be a useful feature. **VOICE** A *kit-kit* or *kit-ir-kit*, as Little Tern, but possibly less sharp. **HABITS** No recorded differences from Little Tern. **HABITAT** Coastal waters and lagoons and large tidal creeks; unlike Little, not found on fresh waters inland. **BREEDING** April–August. Forms small scattered colonies. Nests on mudflats above the high-water mark. **DISTRIBUTION AND STATUS** Breeds in Pakistan, Gujarat, Sri Lanka and possibly the Maldives; non-breeding birds collected on coasts of Maharashtra, Kerala and Tamil Nadu. **PK:** common in summer around Karachi and Lasbela coast; some birds are resident. **IN:** breeds; other status details uncertain because of confusion with Little. **LK:** uncommon resident in coastal areas of dry zone, straggler to wet-zone coasts. **MV:** common resident, reported breeding. **REFERENCES** Warakagoda (1994).

WHITE-CHEEKED TERN *Sterna repressa* Plate 56

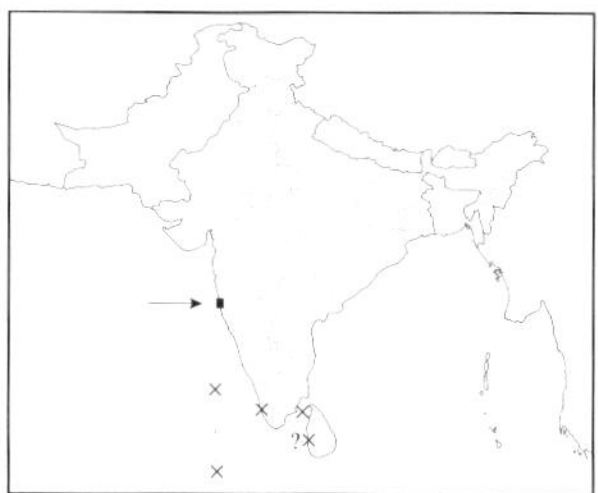

IDENTIFICATION 32–34 cm. Closely resembles Common Tern (p.513) in all plumages, although has proportionately slightly longer bill (which appears to droop at tip), and always shows grey rump and tail which are concolorous with back. At rest, tail-streamers are usually longer than closed wing, unlike on any Common. Is slightly smaller, with shorter and narrower wings and stronger flight action, with faster and deeper wingbeats. Has slightly different underwing pattern, with dark edge to primaries and secondaries, and grey lesser underwing-coverts, which contrast with paler central wing panel. **Adult breeding** is similar to Common Tern but has darker grey upperparts (with concolorous rump and tail); well-defined white cheek-stripe contrasting with grey throat and neck, and darker grey underparts. From adult breeding Whiskered Tern (p.516) by longer bill (typically brighter red with black tip); paler grey underparts; larger size and longer tail streamers. Bill is largely red with black tip but can be mainly black (especially in second summer). **Adult non-breeding** is very similar to adult non-breeding Common. Main plumage differences are darker grey upperparts and concolorous rump and grey tail (which lacks white inner webs of Common, and therefore appears uniformly grey from above and below). Adult non-breeding and first-winter/first-summer Common often show pale grey rump and uppertail-coverts, but grey areas appear patchy and slightly paler than mantle. White-cheeked also has slightly broader black hood, and dark trailing edge to underwing. When fresh, silvery-grey primaries are paler than coverts, but become darker when worn. **Juvenile** is much as juvenile Common Tern, but upperparts are darker, shows darker grey rump and tail, and has broader black hood, more prominent lesser-covert and secondary bars, darker primaries and secondaries, and pronounced dark subterminal bars to tertials. **First-summer** and **first-winter** as adult non-breeding, but with dark bar on lesser coverts and on secondaries; owing to wear, first-summer birds show contrastingly dark outer primaries. By first summer, may show grey on underparts. **VOICE** As that of Common Tern, although has diagnostic hoarse *kee-err kerrit* or *kee-ceek* (Britton 1982). **HABITS** As those of other black-capped *Sterna* terns. Fishes in flocks; plunges into the sea in steep dives. **HABITAT** Coastal waters, often far from land; not normally found in main creeks or lagoons. **BREEDING** May and June. Nest site is undescribed from the region; elsewhere, nests on open sandflats. **DISTRIBUTION AND STATUS** Breeds on Vengurla Rocks off Maharashtra coast; non-breeding summer visitor to offshore waters of Pakistan. Few records in non-breeding season, when found in offshore waters of Pakistan, W India, Lakshadweep and Maldives; possibly overlooked because of confusion in non-breeding plumages with Roseate and Common Terns. **PK:** common visitor March–June, also recorded October–December; flocks can be seen just beyond the surf. **IN:** full status uncertain. **LK:** possibly recorded. **MV:** a few records. **REFERENCES** De Silva (1990), Harris *et al.* (1996).

BLACK-BELLIED TERN *Sterna acuticauda* Plate 57

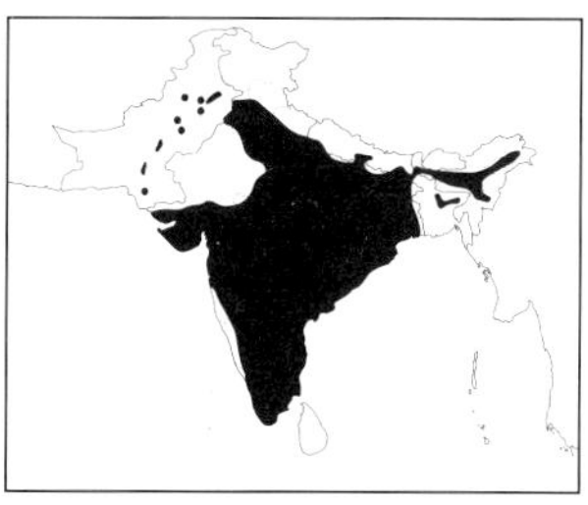

IDENTIFICATION 33 cm. Like River Tern (p.510), frequents freshwater habitats, and likely to be confused only with that species. Distinguished by much smaller size (noticeably smaller than Common Tern, p.513) and slimmer appearance, proportionately longer and slimmer bill, which is orange-coloured, and more rapid flight with faster wingbeats. Head pattern of adult non-breeding and immature birds appears to be different from that of River. **Adult breeding** has orange bill, black cap and nape, and orange-red legs and feet. Has dark grey breast and blackish belly and vent, contrasting with white throat and cheeks, which is the best feature for separation from River Tern. Upperparts and upperwing are similar to latter's, with fresh greyish-white primaries and primary coverts contrasting with dark grey of rest of wing to form striking 'flash' on outer wing in flight. Long orange bill and deeply forked tail separate it from Whiskered Tern (p.516). **Adult non-breeding** has white underparts and lacks tail-streamers. Has dark mask and dark streaking on crown; orange bill has dark tip. Confusingly, can occur with black cap and white underparts, when most similar to River, but structural differences and orange bill are diagnostic. **First-winter** is presumably as adult non-breeding, but with juvenile tertials, tail feathers and primaries. **Juvenile** has dark mask and streaking on crown and nape, sandy coloration to head and mantle, brown fringes to mantle, back and tertials, brown subterminal bars to tail, and grey primaries with broad buff tips to inner ones. **VOICE** Call is a clear piping *peuo*. **HABITS** Feeds by plunge-diving like other black-capped *Sterna* terns; also by dipping to the surface and picking up prey. Often hawks insects, sometimes flying over land adjacent to fresh waters. **HABITAT** Breeds on large rivers; disperses on to lakes, jheels and other inland waters in winter. Not found on the coast. **BREEDING** February–May, varying locally. Nests on bare sandy islands in major rivers. **DISTRIBUTION AND STATUS** Resident throughout much of the subcontinent, except parts of the northwest, northeast, Himalayas and Sri Lanka. Globally threatened. **PK:** frequent, most common in N Sind and throughout Punjab; rare in lower Sind, and almost absent from Baluchistan and NW Pakistan. **NP:** locally fairly common resident and partial summer visitor; below 730 m. **IN:** widespread and locally fairly common. **BD:** very local.

BRIDLED TERN *Sterna anaethetus* Plate 58

Brown-winged Tern (I)

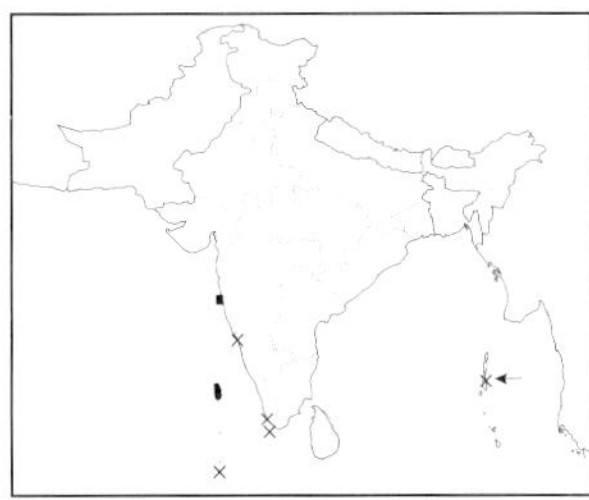

IDENTIFICATION 30–32 cm. Likely to be confused only with Sooty Tern (below), but is smaller and more elegant. Immature and juvenile plumages are quite different from those of Sooty. Flight is particularly buoyant, with elastic wingbeats and a marked lift of the body on each downstroke. **Adult breeding** differs from adult breeding Sooty in shape of white forehead patch (which extends over eye to form broad white supercilium), and in paler brownish-grey mantle and wings which are noticeably paler than black crown and nape. Often shows contrasting dark lesser coverts (with leading edge of wing contrasting with paler mid wing). Rump and tail are brownish-grey, tail not appearing strikingly black-and-white as on Sooty. Has subtly different underwing pattern, with dark underside to primaries less extensive and not so dark. **Adult non-breeding** and **immature** have less distinct dark loral stripe and crown/nape as these are streaked white, and have pale fringes to upperparts; upperparts may appear patchy owing to white feather bases being visible. **Juvenile** has greyish-white crown and dark mask, with white forehead and supercilium (shadow-pattern of adult), buffish fringes to mantle and wing-coverts, and brownish patch on sides of breast. **VOICE** Typical call is a yapping *wep-wep*, similar to the call of Black-winged Stilt (p.490). **HABITS** Frequently gathers in flocks with other seabirds over shoals of fish in deep water. Hovers over the water and dips down to pick fish and plankton from the surface. Often rests on buoys, ships' rigging or floating driftwood. **HABITAT** Entirely maritime; usually offshore waters, sometimes far out to sea. **BREEDING** June and July. Nests on sand on offshore islands and atolls. **DISTRIBUTION AND STATUS** Breeds on Vengurla Rocks off Maharashtra coast, has bred on Lakshadweep, probably breeds on Maldives; disperses in non-breeding season to offshore coastal waters of Pakistan, W India and Sri Lanka. **PK:** rare winter visitor to coastal waters. **IN:** occurs off W coastal waters all year, and also breeds. **LK:** regular passage migrant in summer; also a winter visitor. **MV:** reported to breed; also recorded in November. **REFERENCES** Mathew and Ambedkar (1964), Mathew *et al.* (1996), Warakagoda (1994).

SOOTY TERN *Sterna fuscata* Plate 58

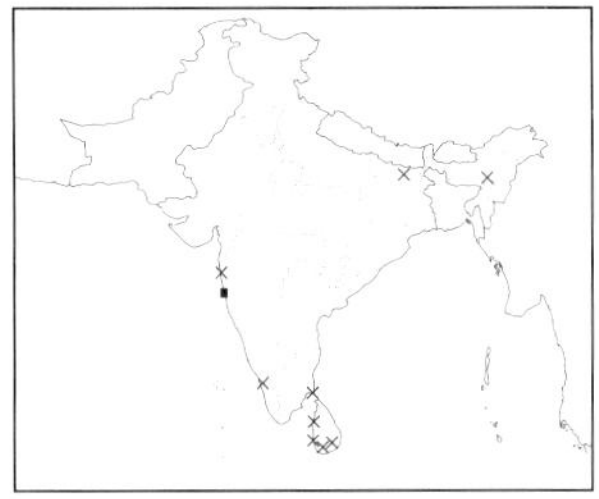

IDENTIFICATION 33–36 cm. Larger and more powerful than Bridled Tern (above), with blacker upperparts and more extensive blackish underside to primaries, which contrast with white underwing-coverts. **Adult breeding** differs from adult breeding Bridled in blackish mantle and wings which are concolorous with black crown and nape, and oval-shaped white forehead patch which does not extend over eye. White outer tail feathers contrast strongly with rest of tail, which is black. **Adult non-breeding** as adult breeding, but may show white spotting on crown and white fringes to upperparts; upperparts may appear brownish, and also patchy owing to white feather bases sometimes being visible. **Juvenile** is very distinctive, and has sooty-black head and breast contrasting with whitish lower belly, bold white spotting on mantle, scapulars and wing-coverts, and pale central panel along underwing-coverts. **Immature** is initially similar to juvenile, but after one year black of underparts is mixed with white; thereafter, resembles adult non-breeding, but with variable dark mottling on underparts. **VOICE** Call is a loud and piercing *wide-a-wake*. **HABITS** Pursues shoals of small fish and deftly scoops them from the surface; also catches flying fish as they leap above the surface. Capable of continuous flight for long periods without settling. Spends much time in aerial manoeuvres: diving, wheeling and soaring, sometimes high above the sea. **HABITAT** Normally occurs well out to sea and avoids coastal or shallow waters, except when breeding or storm-driven. **BREEDING** December–September, varying locally. Eggs are laid on bare soil or in a slight depression. **DISTRIBUTION AND STATUS** Breeds on Vengurla Rocks off Maharashtra, in Lakshadweep and probably in Maldives; in the non-breeding season, mainly disperses over seas adjacent to its breeding islands; vagrant inland, presumably storm-driven. **IN:** common on Lakshadweep in breeding season. **LK:** regular, uncommon summer passage migrant to W coastal waters. **MV:** reported breeding; also several November records.

WHISKERED TERN *Chlidonias hybridus* Plate 57

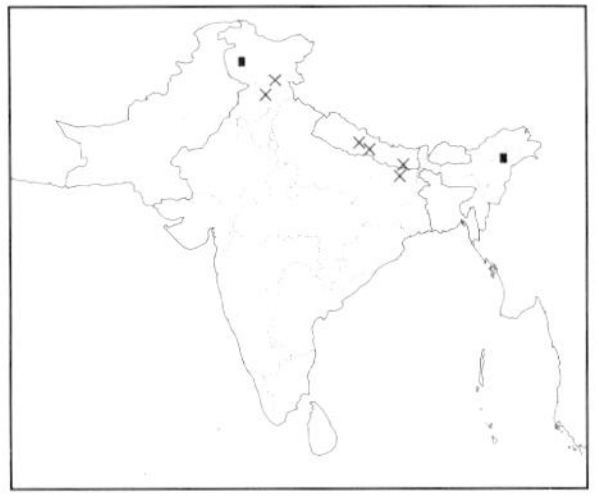

IDENTIFICATION 23–25 cm. Similar to White-winged Tern (p.517), but is slightly larger, stockier and broader-winged, and flight is more purposeful and less buoyant; bill usually appears larger, but there is some overlap. Flight is less direct than that of *Sterna* terns, but slower and less erratic, with deeper wingbeats, than flight of other marsh terns **Adult breeding** is very distinctive, with white cheeks contrasting with black cap, dark grey underparts contrasting with white vent, and with white underwing-coverts in flight, silvery-grey upperwing, and dark red bill and legs. Smaller size, broader wings, and short tail lacking streamers (with wings extending noticeably beyond tail at rest) result in appearance that is quite different from adult breeding *Sterna* terns.

Adult moulting into winter plumage can show black bill and patchy grey underparts. **Adult non-breeding** and **first-winter/first-summer** have pale grey and rather uniform mantle and wings (can show darker lesser-covert bar, secondary bar and primaries, but these are not very striking). Has different head pattern from White-winged (with dark bands behind eyes joining across nape), and pale grey rump and tail which are concolorous with back. Head markings can be limited to dark ear-covert patch, as on Gull-billed Tern (p.509). **Juvenile** has fawn-brown mantle and scapulars (with black subterminal bars and buff fringes) forming well-defined 'saddle', which contrasts with uniform pale grey wings. Compared with juvenile White-winged, saddle appears chequered (rather than uniformly dark), lacks well-defined lesser-covert and secondary bars of that species, and has uniform grey rump and tail. The dark patch behind ear-coverts and across hindcrown is more extensive and better defined than in adult/first-winter. **VOICE** A hoarse *eirchk* or *kreerp*. **HABITS** Often forages in flocks. Feeds mainly on insects in typical marsh tern fashion, by hawking or picking from the surface, but, unlike other marsh terns, will occasionally plunge for fish like *Sterna* terns. **HABITAT** Inland lakes, jheels, rivers, flooded paddy-fields, coastal lagoons, mudflats and tidal creeks. **BREEDING** Mid May–August. Nest is a small untidy pad of stems woven onto floating vegetation in freshwater lakes. **DISTRIBUTION AND STATUS** Breeds in Kashmir and Assam; winters throughout much of the subcontinent, except parts of the northwest, northeast and Himalayas. **PK:** common; mainly a spring and autumn passage migrant, also an irregular year-round visitor. **NP:** irregular and uncommon winter visitor and spring passage migrant to Kosi Barrage; rare passage migrant elsewhere. **IN:** widespread and locally common in winter and on passage. **BD:** common winter visitor throughout; non-breeders oversummer. **LK:** common winter visitor and scarce in summer in lowlands and lower hills.

WHITE-WINGED TERN *Chlidonias leucopterus* — Plate 57

White-winged Black Tern (F,I,P,R)

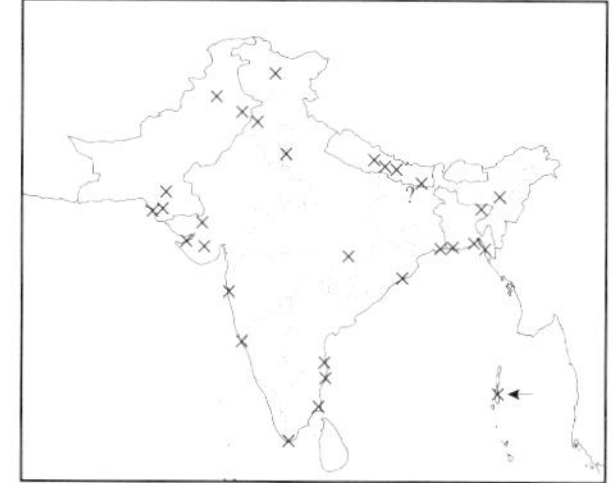

IDENTIFICATION 20–23 cm. Very distinctive in breeding plumage. Otherwise similar to Whiskered Tern (p.516), but is more finely built, with more rounded head and smaller bill, flight is more buoyant, and wings appear slimmer and more rounded at tip. For differences from Black Tern (below), see that species. **Adult breeding** is very distinctive, with black head and body contrasting with greyish-white upperwing-coverts and white rump, vent and tail. In flight, black underwing-coverts contrast with pale greyish underside to flight feathers. Black underwing-coverts are last part of plumage to be lost during moult into non-breeding plumage. **Adult non-breeding** and **first-winter/first-summer** have different head pattern from respective plumages of Whiskered, and a white rump which can contrast with grey back and tail (although rump can appear grey when worn). Black ear-covert patch is bold and drops below eye, and has well-defined black line down nape which is separated from ear-coverts by white crescent at sides of head (note, however, that some birds have a whiter head, with black restricted to ear-covert patch). First-year birds show dark lesser-covert and secondary bars, and by late winter these contrast strongly with pale (worn) median and greater coverts, which form pale panel in wing, while mantle also can appear noticeably darker than pale coverts, giving rise to 'saddled' appearance as with juvenile; birds in this plumage are very distinct from non-breeding and first-year Whiskered. **Juvenile** mantle is brownish-black and contrasts with paler greyish median and greater coverts. Mantle and scapular feathers lack black barring of juvenile Whiskered, and compared with that species shows well-defined dark lesser-covert bar and darker grey secondaries (which contrast with pale panel in centre of wing) and white rump (which contrasts with grey tail). Head pattern is similar to adult non-breeding, although more pronounced. **VOICE** A hoarse, dry *kersch*. **HABITS** A typical marsh tern. Gregarious; often feeds with Whiskered Terns in winter. Flies with great agility, turning this way and that to catch insects in the air, and swooping to pick them delicately from the water's surface. **HABITAT** Marshes, flooded paddy-fields, pools, lakes and lagoons; also coasts in Bangladesh and India. **DISTRIBUTION AND STATUS** Widespread winter visitor to the subcontinent, possibly overlooked because of similarity to Whiskered Tern in non-breeding plumage. **PK:** rare, but regular spring passage migrant. **NP:** rare spring passage migrant; below 1350 m. **IN:** locally common passage migrant and non-breeding migrant. **BD:** scarce passage migrant. **LK:** locally common winter visitor to lowlands. **MV:** fairly regular winter visitor.

BLACK TERN *Chlidonias niger* — Plate 57

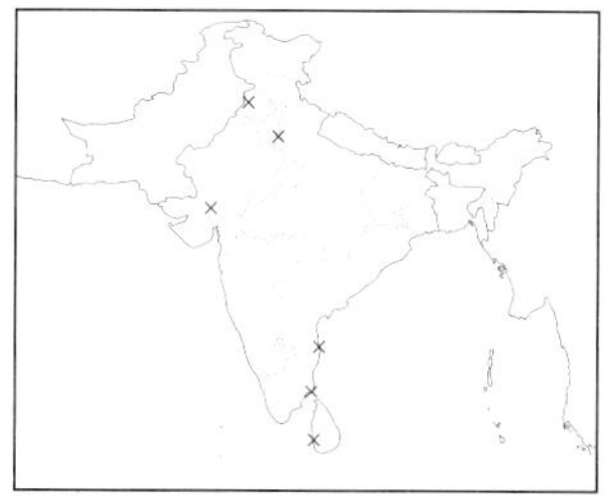

IDENTIFICATION 22–24 cm. Most likely to be confused with White-winged Tern (above). Has slightly larger-looking bill. **Adult breeding** differs from adult breeding White-winged in having pale grey underwing-coverts which contrast with black underbody, darker grey upperwing-coverts which hardly contrast with mantle, dark grey (rather than black) upperparts and underparts, grey rump and tail which are concolorous with back, and blackish (rather than red) and slightly shorter legs. **Adult winter** and **first-winter/first-summer** are similar to respective plumages of White-winged, but show well-defined dark patch on sides of breast, darker grey mantle and wings, lacking paler panel in centre of wing and 'saddled' appearance of worn White-winged, and with grey rump which is concolorous with back and tail. Darker grey upperparts and black patch on breast sides readily separate them from Whiskered Tern (p.516). **Juvenile** differs from juvenile White-winged in showing less contrast between greyish-brown mantle and grey median and greater coverts, prominent dark patch on sides of breast, and grey rump which is only slightly paler than back and is concolorous with tail. **VOICE** A short and sharp, nasal *kja*. **HABITS** Similar to those of White-winged. **HABITAT** Marshes, flooded paddy-fields, pools and lakes. **DISTRIBUTION AND STATUS** Passage migrant; possibly overlooked because of confusion with other marsh terns. **IN:** rare visitor. **LK:** vagrant. **REFERENCES** Mohapatra and Rao (1994), Robson (1996a), Tatu (1992a, 1992b).

BROWN NODDY *Anous stolidus* — Plate 58

Noddy Tern (I), Common Noddy (P)

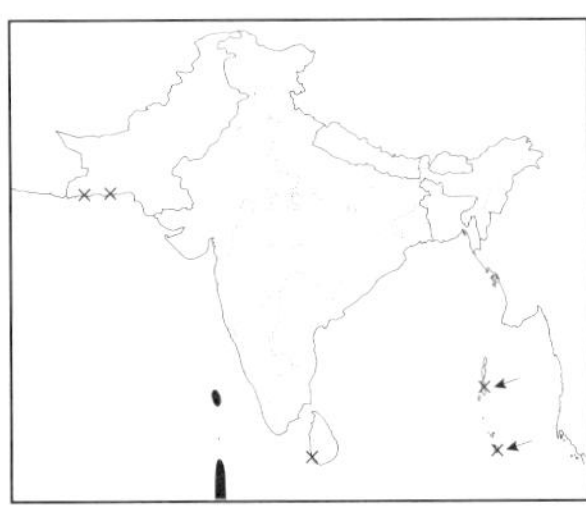

IDENTIFICATION 42 cm. An all-dark, tern-like bird with long wedge-shaped tail (showing slight central notch when spread). Told from juvenile Sooty Tern (p.516) by tail shape, dark underwing, dark lower belly and vent, and lack of white leading edge to wing. Flight is also different, with more flapping and less buoyancy than Sooty Tern. Extremely similar to the rarer Black and Lesser Noddies (below), though wingbeats are somewhat slower; for differences, see those species. **Adult** is dark chocolate-brown with pale grey forehead and crown. In flight, shows distinct pale diagonal bar across upperwing-coverts, contrasting with darker brownish-black flight feathers, and tail is a slightly darker brownish-black than upper body. Underwing light greyish-brown, paler than underbody. **Juvenile** is similar to adult, but has indistinct pale buff fringes to mantle, scapulars and coverts, and has browner forehead and crown. Scaling on coverts makes pale bar across wing more prominent than on adult. **VOICE** A *karrk*, or *kwok kuok* (Slater *et al.* 1986). **HABITS** A typical noddy. **HABITAT** Normally far out to sea, but storm-driven birds occur rarely on the coast. **BREEDING** Season poorly known; recorded in February, June and July. Nest is a small untidy pad of sticks and straw placed on a palm or bush, or sometimes on the ground. **DISTRIBUTION AND STATUS** Breeds in Lakshadweep and Maldives; also recorded off coasts of Pakistan, Andaman and Nicobar Is and Sri Lanka. **PK:** vagrant. **IN:** common on Lakshadweep; resident? on Andamans and Nicobars. **LK:** regular visitor, especially during bad weather. **MV:** common throughout year; bred once. **REFERENCES** Higgins and Davies (1996).

BLACK NODDY *Anous minutus* — Plate 58

White-capped Noddy (I), *A. tenuirostris* (I,V)

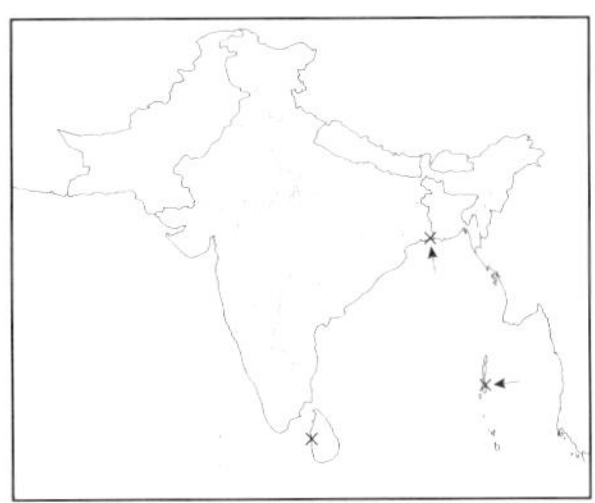

IDENTIFICATION 34 cm. Extremely similar to Brown and Lesser Noddies (above and below). **Adult** told from adult Brown by smaller and slimmer appearance, faster, more fluttering flight, darker brownish-black plumage, and slimmer and straighter, longer-looking bill (noticeably longer than head). Wings are slightly broader and shorter, often appearing straighter and more rounded at tip. Tail is shorter, falling level with wing-tips at rest (beyond wing-tips on Brown). Typically, appears whiter on forehead and crown, and border between forehead and black lores is usually straighter (noticeably curved on most Brown Noddies). In flight, shows all-dark upperwing and underwing, lacking paler bar across upperwing-coverts and any paleness on underwing-coverts; centre of uppertail is paler and greyer and often contrasts strongly with blackish rest of upperparts. Distinguished from adult Lesser Noddy by black lores with well-defined white forehead and crown; see that species for further details. **Juvenile** has faint pale fringes to upperparts and is whiter on head than adult. Told from juvenile Brown by bill shape and slimmer appearance, all-dark underwing, darker brown coloration, and whiter forehead and crown. Becomes paler brown with wear, and some Brown Noddies have similar head pattern to juvenile Black, so best separated by bill shape. **VOICE** A querulous *krrrk*, and a rapid laughing *k-k-k-k* (Slater *et al.* 1986). **HABITS** A typical noddy. Details not recorded in the region's waters. **HABITAT** Like that of Brown Noddy. **DISTRIBUTION AND STATUS IN, LK:** vagrant. **REFERENCES** Higgins and Davies (1996).

LESSER NODDY *Anous tenuirostris* — Plate 58

IDENTIFICATION 32 cm. **Adult** is very similar to Black Noddy (above), but has pale greyish lores contrasting with black patch in front of eye (white forehead is not strongly demarcated from black lores), and paler grey nape and neck (lacking well-defined white cap of Black). Some birds, however, including some (possibly all) juveniles, have a sharper demarcation between mostly dark grey lores and white forehead and are much as Black. Has grey cast to neck, upper mantle and breast (uniform blackish on Black). Upperwing-coverts are slightly paler than remiges (uniform on Black), and underwing-coverts are uniform with remiges (slightly darker than remiges on Black). Above features also help separate it from Brown Noddy (above). In addition, is smaller and slimmer than Brown, with longer and slimmer bill, and a proportionately shorter tail (falls level with wing-tips at rest); further, centre of tail is pale blue-grey, contrasting with dark brown outer tail and rest of upperparts (although this feature is not apparent on worn birds), and underwing-coverts are slightly paler than underbody but do not contrast with remiges. Has faster

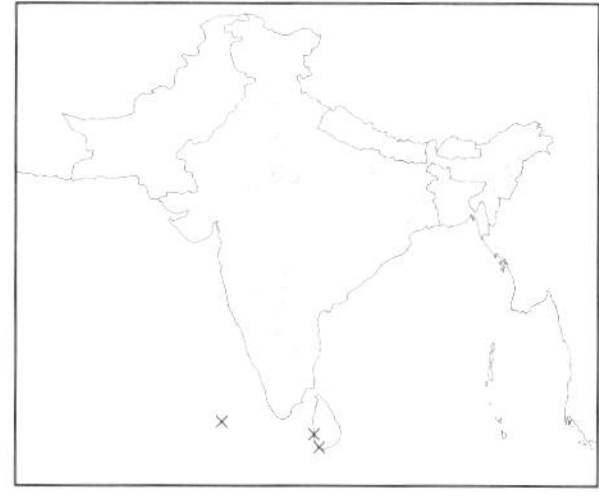

wingbeats than Brown. **Juvenile** is similar to adult, although typically with paler cap which is more sharply demarcated from nape; lores are dark grey and contrast more with forehead (although still showing contrast with black patch in front of eye as on adult). Upperwing-coverts are browner than adult, with pale fringes to mantle and scapulars. Cap is never as striking as on juvenile Black, further distinctions from which are paler plumage and uniform underwing. **VOICE** A soft *churr* (Slater *et al.* 1986). **HABITS** A typical noddy. Details not recorded in the region. **HABITAT** Like that of Brown. **BREEDING** Details unknown in the region. In Australia, nest is a platform of seaweed cemented to a branch with excreta. **DISTRIBUTION AND STATUS IN:** vagrant to Lakshadweep. **MV:** widespread, and breeds. **LK:** vagrant. **REFERENCES** Higgins and Davies (1996).

WHITE TERN *Gygis alba* — Plate 58

Common White Tern, Indian Ocean White Tern (I)

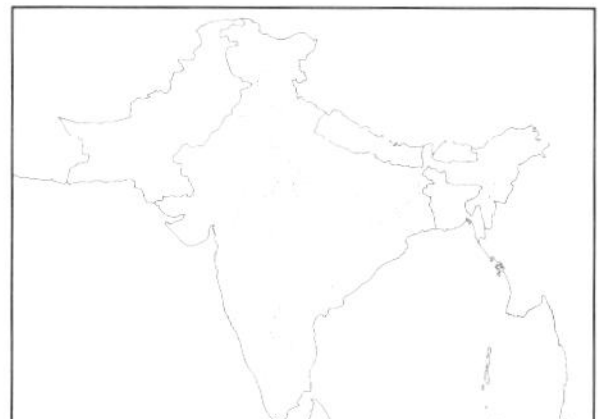

IDENTIFICATION 30 cm. A small tern with huge dark eye and broad-based, slightly upturned black bill. Flight is light and airy. **Adult** is entirely white except for narrow black eye-ring and dark shafts to primaries. **Juvenile** is similar to adult, but has dark flecking on crown and nape, brown and buff barring on mantle, back and coverts, and brownish tips to tail feathers. On plumage alone possibly confusable with juvenile Little and Saunders's Terns (p.514), but is much larger, is whiter in appearance, with white flight feathers, and has different bill shape and more buoyant flight action compared with those species. **VOICE** Calls include a guttural *heech, heech* (Higgins and Davies 1996). **HABITS** Tame and inquisitive. Feeds in a similar manner to the noddies; flutters over the water and catches small fish in mid-air as they leap out. **HABITAT** Pelagic when not breeding. **BREEDING** Throughout the year. Single egg is balanced precariously in a slight hollow of a branch, on a palm frond or on a banana leaf. **DISTRIBUTION AND STATUS MV:** breeds commonly on Seenu Atoll; also recorded on other islands.

OSPREY, HAWKS, EAGLES, HARRIERS AND VULTURES etc Accipitridae

This is a large and varied family of raptors, ranging from the Besra to the huge Himalayan Griffon. It comprises the Osprey, bazas, Oriental Honey-buzzard, kites, fish eagles, Old World vultures, harriers, true hawks and eagles, buzzards and hawk eagles. In most species, the vultures being an exception, the female is larger than the male and is often duller and brownish. The Accipitridae feed on mammals, birds, reptiles, amphibians, fish, crabs, molluscs and insects – dead or alive. All have a hooked, pointed bill and very acute sight, and all except the vultures have powerful feet with long curved claws. Apart from the vultures, which are colonial, the members of this family maintain home ranges which include feeding ranges. Their large stick nests are usually built in trees, but sometimes on cliffs or on the ground. They frequent all habitat types, ranging from dense forest, deserts and mountains to fresh waters and coasts. Many species in the region have declined because of habitat loss and probably also through pesticide poisoning. The main references specific to the Accipitridae are Brown and Amadon (1968) and Cramp and Simmons (1980).

OSPREY *Pandion haliaetus* — Plate 59

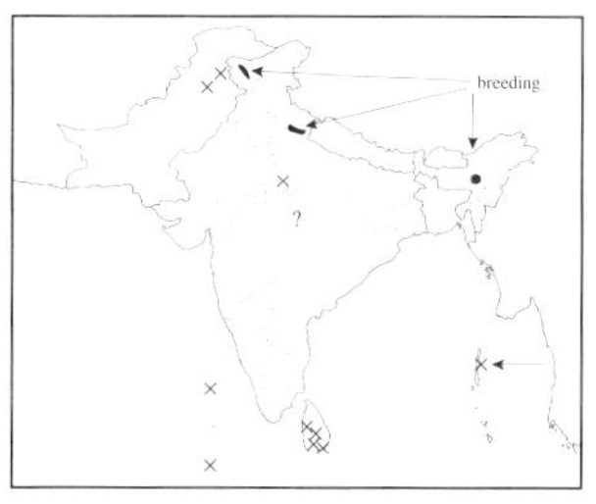

IDENTIFICATION 55–58 cm. Unlikely to be confused with any other raptor. Has long, rather thin wings and comparatively short tail, with wings typically angled at carpal joints. Rather fine head is often held downwards, and when soaring and gliding wings are sharply bowed. In direct flight, series of usually rather loose and shallow wingbeats are interspersed with long glides. At long range can be mistaken for a large gull. **Adult** has mainly white head with black stripe through eye, white underbody and underwing-coverts, the latter contrasting with black carpal patches and band across greater coverts, paler base to underside of primaries contrasting with black tips, and uniformly dark upperparts with paler barring on tail. **Juvenile** is similar to adult, but has buff tips to upperparts, including coverts; rusty breast-band (prominent on adult) is poorly defined, and has black streaking on white crown. **VOICE** Call is a shrill cheeping whistle, but mostly silent away from the nest (Cramp and Simmons 1980). **HABITS** Usually solitary. Frequently perches on stakes, dead trees or prominent rocks standing in or near water. Feeds entirely on fish, captured in a powerful shallow dive with feet first to grasp prey, sometimes submerging completely. Typically, plunges into water after flying over the surface at height of 20–30 m, hovering occasionally on sighting a fish. **HABITAT** Major rivers, lakes, large reservoirs, jheels, coastal lagoons and estuaries. **BREEDING** March and April. Builds a large stick nest 12–14 m up in a treetop, in or near water. **DISTRIBUTION AND STATUS** Breeds in Himalayas in Ladakh,

Kashmir, N Uttar Pradesh and Assam; winters throughout much of the subcontinent except C India. **PK:** common and widespread winter visitor throughout the Indus Basin and on coast; regularly visits Punjab Salt Range lakes. **NP:** fairly common and widespread winter visitor, resident and passage migrant; below 915 m (–3965 m on passage). **IN:** breeds in small numbers, 2000–3000 m; widespread and uncommon winter visitor below 1800 m. **BT:** frequent resident, winter visitor and passage migrant; 250–2460 m. **BD:** scarce winter visitor. **LK:** infrequent winter visitor to dry lowlands, vagrant elsewhere. **MV:** vagrant.

JERDON'S BAZA *Aviceda jerdoni* Plate 59

Blyth's Baza (I), Brown Baza

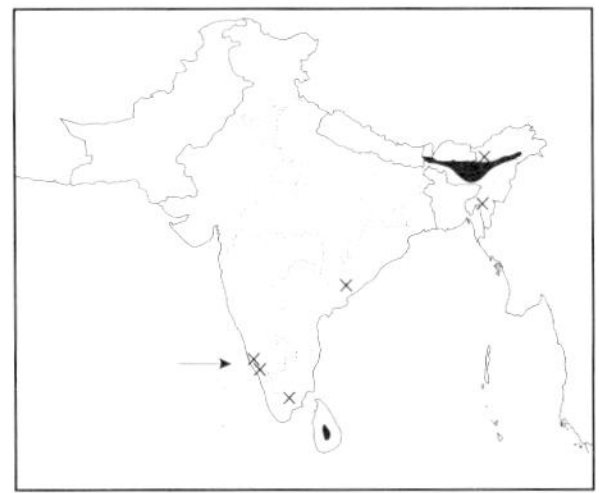

IDENTIFICATION 46 cm. A crested raptor with rather long and broad wings (pinched in at base) and fairly long tail. In flight, has strong wingbeats, interspersed with short glides on slightly raised wings, and soars with wings held flat. Possibly confusable with Crested Goshawk (p.533), but has much longer white-tipped crest (held erect when perched), blue-grey (rather than yellow) cere, rather pale head with pale cheeks and crown, and indistinct gular stripe. At rest, closed wings extend well down tail; in flight, wings are proportionately larger and longer than on Crested Goshawk, and has different flight action. Patterning of underwing is also different, with rufous-barred underwing-coverts (as belly), and strong dark barring across tips of primaries and pale patch at base. Undertail-coverts are barred with rufous (white on Crested Goshawk and frequently splayed in flight). **Adult** has three dark bands on tail (including broad subterminal band). **Juvenile** has whitish head with black streaking, and more even dark banding on tail. **VOICE** A *kip-kip-kip* or *kikiya, kikiya* uttered in display flight; also a plaintive mewing *pee-ow* (Ali and Ripley 1987). **HABITS** Crepuscular and elusive, keeping mostly within cover. Sometimes seen in family parties of up to five birds. Rather sluggish and slow on the wing. Spends long periods perched in a tree on the lookout for lizards, frogs and large insects, which are captured on the ground. At the onset of the breeding season, pairs often soar at height over forest. **HABITAT** Tropical and subtropical broadleaved evergreen forest. **BREEDING** November–June, varying locally. Builds a small compact nest of leafy twigs 7–20 m up in a tree in forest, sometimes in a tea plantation. **DISTRIBUTION AND STATUS** Resident. From Darjeeling, West Bengal and Sikkim east to E Assam; Bangladesh; hills of Karnataka, Kerala, S Tamil Nadu, Eastern Ghats, Andhra Pradesh; Sri Lanka. **IN:** rare; 350–1800 m in the northeast, 150–900 m in the south. **BD:** local in the northeast. **LK:** rare in the hills. **REFERENCES** Ferguson-Lees (in prep.).

BLACK BAZA *Aviceda leuphotes* Plate 59

Indian Black-crested Baza (I), Black-crested Baza (F,P)

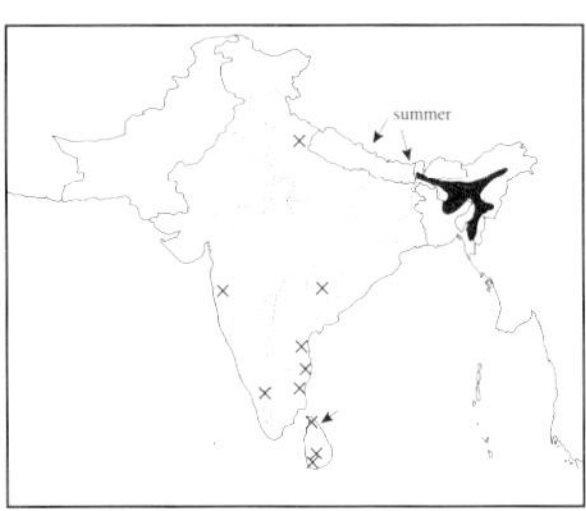

IDENTIFICATION 33 cm. **Adult** is largely black with long crest, and with broad white band across upper breast. Upperparts are variably marked with chestnut and white. Wings are broad and rounded, and tail moderately long. In flight, has flexible corvid-like wingbeats interspersed with short glides on flat wings; soars on level wings. From below, has light grey underside to primaries which contrasts with dark primary tips and black underwing-coverts, and grey underside to tail which contrasts with black thighs and undertail coverts. **Juvenile** very similar to adult, but has duller brownish-black upperparts showing more white; fine white streaking on throat, and brown streaking across white breast-band. **VOICE** Loud, shrill, high-pitched *tcheeoua*, often repeated (C. Robson). **HABITS** Rather crepuscular. Usually seen singly or in small parties of up to five birds, circling over forest; sometimes in larger flocks. Takes insects, small lizards, frogs, small birds and mammals, captured on the ground in short flights; flies to a nearby perch to eat prey. **HABITAT** Tropical broadleaved evergreen forest with glades or broad streams running through. **BREEDING** February–July. Nest is a platform of sticks usually 18–21 m up in a forest tree. **DISTRIBUTION AND STATUS** Resident. Mainly Himalayan foothills in N Uttar Pradesh and from C and E Nepal (summer visitor) east to NE India and Bangladesh; Kerala; Sri Lanka. **NP:** scarce and local summer visitor; 245–450 m (–1280 m). **IN:** uncommon in the northeast in plains and hills up to 1000 m; very rare visitor in foothills in Uttar Pradesh and Kerala; a few scattered records elsewhere in the peninsula, presumably migrants. **BD:** local resident. **LK:** rare, irregular winter visitor to lowlands. **REFERENCES** Ferguson-Lees (in prep.).

ORIENTAL HONEY-BUZZARD *Pernis ptilorhyncus* Plate 68

Honey Buzzard (I), Eurasian Honey-Buzzard, Crested Honey-Buzzard (P,R), Honey Kite (F)

IDENTIFICATION 57–60 cm. Has distinctive flight profile. Wings and tail are long and broad, and has narrow neck and small and rather pointed cuckoo-like head. Wings appear proportionately narrower and tail shorter than in the hawk eagles. Soars with wings held flat (and slightly arched when gliding), rather than in shallow V or with wing-tips upturned (as in the *Buteo* buzzards and hawk eagles). Flies with steady wingbeats alternating with short glides. At rest, has small crest, but bill is finer and legs and feet much weaker than those of the hawk

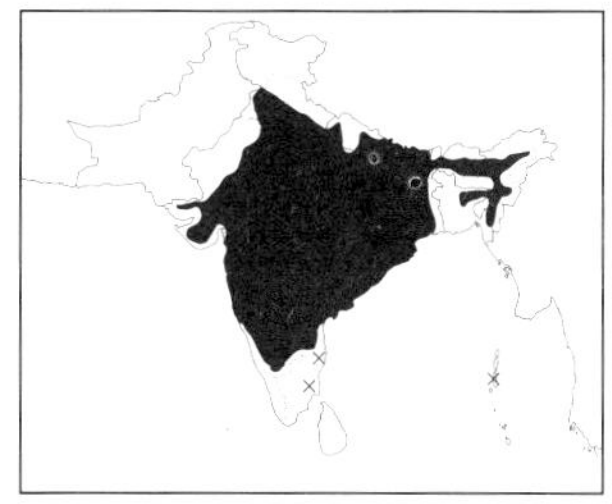

eagles (and tarsus is unfeathered). **Adult** is extremely variable in plumage, with underparts and underwing-coverts ranging from dark brown through rufous to white in general coloration; underparts may be unmarked, streaked or barred. Often shows a dark moustachial stripe and gular stripe, and a gorget of streaking across lower throat which can extend onto breast (this distinctive W pattern may, however, be absent). Broad dark barring across remiges and broad black subterminal band to tail are together often a good pointer, although variable (see below for details). Lacks a dark carpal patch on underwing which is evident in many *Buteo* plumages. **Male** has grey face, greyish-brown upperparts, two black bands on tail (tail appears black with broad white central band), usually three black bands across primaries/outer secondaries, and a dark brown iris. The dark trailing edge to the wing and the dark barring across the remiges are visible from above (upperwing appears uniform on female). **Female** has browner face, browner upperparts, three black bands on tail, four narrower black bands across primaries/outer secondaries, and a yellow iris. **Juvenile** is also very variable: underparts and underwing-coverts can be dark brown, rufous or white. Has finer and less distinct banding across underside of remiges than adult, and three or more black bands across tail. Scapulars and wing-coverts are fringed with buff, and has extensive dark tips to primaries. Cere is strikingly yellow (grey on adult), and has dark iris. **VOICE** A single high-pitched screaming whistle, *wheeew* (Ali and Ripley 1987). **HABITS** Normally found singly. Eats mainly honey and larvae of bees (and is protected from stings by a dense covering of scale-like feathers on the lores). Spends long periods perched within foliage of trees. Usually seen in flight over trees, either soaring or in active flight. **HABITAT** Well-wooded country; also groves in villages, towns and cultivation. **BREEDING** February–July, varying locally. Nest is a compact stick platform built 6–20 m up in a large leafy tree. **DISTRIBUTION AND STATUS** Resident, subject to local movements. Throughout most of the subcontinent, except parts of the northwest and northeast, W Himalayas and SE India. **PK:** frequent and irregular year-round visitor, mainly to Punjab and Sind; only a summer visitor to the north. **NP:** fairly common and widespread resident and passage migrant; below 1700 m (–3050 m on passage). **IN:** locally common and widespread resident; plains and hills, up to 1800 m in Himalayas. **BT:** frequent resident and passage migrant; 250–3050 m. **BD:** local resident. **LK:** regular resident in all zones, also a winter visitor. **MV:** regular winter visitor; some oversummer. **REFERENCES** Forsman (1994), Morioka *et al.* (1995).

BLACK-SHOULDERED KITE *Elanus caeruleus* — Plate 59

Black-winged Kite (F,I,N,R)

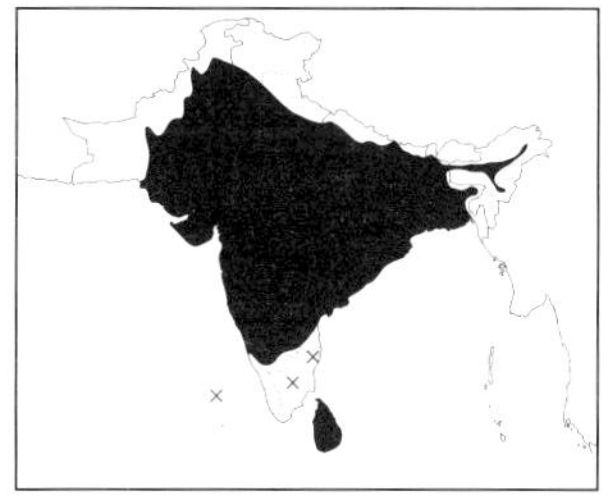

IDENTIFICATION 31–35 cm. A small, long- and broad-winged raptor with protruding head and short tail. Glides and soars with wings raised lke a harrier's. Active flight is buoyant, with soft rapid beats of angled wings alternating with long glides, and interspersed with much hovering. Flight silhouette and hovering action are characteristic. **Adult** has grey upperparts and upperwing, with black lesser and median coverts forming prominent patch on forewing, whitish head and underparts, and white underwing except for black underside to primaries. Has striking red iris and fine black line through eye. **Juvenile** is similar to adult, with black patch on forewing, but has dark streaking on crown, brownish-grey upperparts with pale fringes, pale fringes to wing-coverts, and rufous wash to ear-coverts and breast. **VOICE** Weak whistling notes (Cramp and Simmons 1980). **HABITS** Usually found singly or in widely separated pairs according to the season, and in the same area day after day. Often crepuscular. Spends much time perched on prominent vantage points such as telegraph wires or isolated trees; has a frequent habit of raising and lowering its tail. Hunts by quartering open ground at height of 15–60 m, hovering at intervals with wings held high over back and beaten rather slowly and with feet often trailing. Eats mainly large insects and reptiles. **HABITAT** Grassland interspersed with cultivation or with scattered trees, open dry scrub and scrub desert. **BREEDING** Nearly all year, varying locally. Builds a small untidy nest of twigs, usually below 9 m in a small tree. **DISTRIBUTION AND STATUS** Resident. Throughout much of the subcontinent, except N and W Pakistan and parts of NE and SE India, Bhutan and N Himalayas. **PK:** common and widespread resident in Indus plains; summer visitor to NW Pakistan below 1400 m. **NP:** fairly common and widespread resident, mainly in the terai; summer visitor to Kathmandu valley (1370–1550 m). **IN:** widespread, but patchily distributed, mainly resident, but possibly only a winter visitor to S Western Ghats; locally common in plains and hills, up to 1600 m in Himalayas, to 1200 m in peninsular hills. **BD:** resident, occurs throughout. **LK:** resident in all zones, infrequent in wet lowlands, common elsewhere.

RED KITE *Milvus milvus* — Plate 59

Kite (I)

IDENTIFICATION 60–66 cm. Has a distinctive, very buoyant flight; frequently manoeuvres its tail, and when increasing speed its wingbeats are deep and body movements noticeable (like a *Sterna* tern). Soars with wings typically held forward and slightly arched. Occasionally hovers briefly. When perched, has an upright posture with tail held down. Likely to be confused only with Black Kite (p.522), which has similar posture and flight

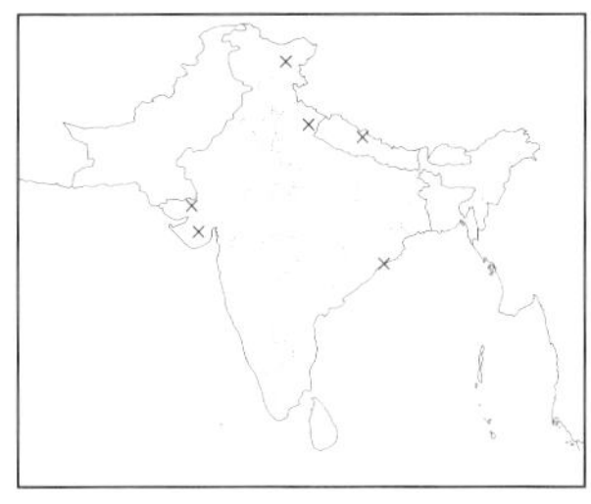

action. Is larger and more finely built than that species, with longer and more deeply forked tail (noticeably forked even when spread) and longer and more angular wings. Main plumage differences of **adult** are rufous-orange uppertail with dark corners, rufous underparts and underwing-coverts, whiter head, and broader and more prominent pale band across upperwing-coverts. Has large whitish patches at base of underside of primaries (contrasting with black carpal patches), but this feature can be equally prominent on Black Kite (especially *M. m. lineatus*); caution is required also because some Black Kites can appear very rufous on underparts. **Juvenile** has shallower tail-fork than adult; also darker head, streaked with white, white tips to greater and primary coverts, whitish patch on uppertail-coverts, and paler, more rufous-brown underparts and rufous-brown tail. Is, therefore, more similar to Black Kite, although combination of above-mentioned features still holds. **VOICE** A shrill, high-pitched mew (Cramp and Simmons 1980). **HABITS** Little known in the region, but well described from Europe. Flocks gather at carrion and rubbish dumps. Often soars for long periods and at considerable heights. Can hover briefly, and is agile when pursuing birds in flight. **HABITAT** Recorded in the region in lightly wooded semi-desert. **DISTRIBUTION AND STATUS NP, IN:** winter vagrant.

BLACK KITE *Milvus migrans* — Plate 59

Pariah Kite (I), Dark Kite (F), Black-eared Kite *M. lineatus*

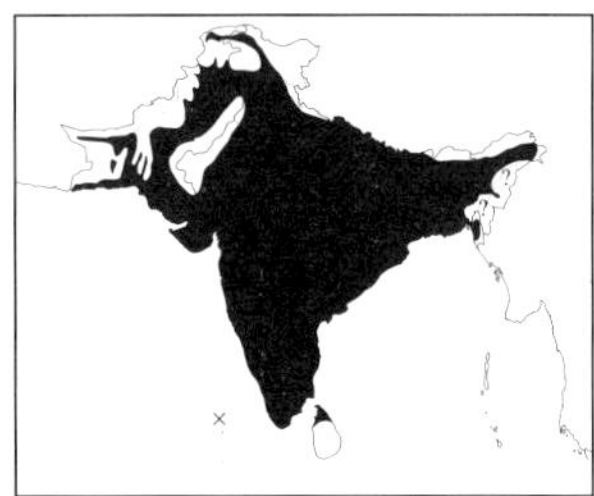

IDENTIFICATION 55–68.5 cm. A mainly dark brown raptor with shallow fork to tail. Agile and buoyant in flight, with much independent manoeuvring of wings and twisting of tail; when soaring and gliding, wings are usually slightly arched, with carpal joints held forward. Tail shape and flight action are best way of separating it from Eurasian Marsh Harrier (p.530) at a distance. See Red Kite (p.521) for differences from that species. **Adult** is fairly uniform dark rufous-brown. Shows variable pale crescent at base of primaries on underwing, and pale band across median coverts on upperwing. **Juvenile** has broad whitish or buffish streaking on head and underparts. **Racial variation** *M. m. lineatus*, which breeds in NW and NE subcontinent and winters to the south, is larger and broader-winged than *M. m. govinda*, and generally shows more prominent whitish patch at base of underside of primaries. **VOICE** A shrill, almost musical whistle, *ewe-wir-r-r-r-r* (Ali and Ripley 1987). **HABITS** Gregarious throughout the year, birds often soaring together and roosting communally in large numbers. Closely associated with human habitation. Feeds mainly on refuse and offal, but is omnivorous. A bold scavenger, snatching food from market stalls and even from human hand, swooping and turning with amazing dexterity and avoiding fast-moving traffic in busy streets. **HABITAT** Around human habitation, mainly in cities, towns and villages; also mountains. **BREEDING** September–May, varying locally. Nest is an untidy platform of sticks and rubbish, placed 7–30 m up in a large tree. **DISTRIBUTION AND STATUS** Resident and altitudinal migrant; also a winter visitor to the north, south to 18°N. Occurs throughout most of the subcontinent. **PK:** common and widespread resident and winter visitor in Indus plains; mainly a summer visitor to Baluchistan, NW Pakistan, Chitral, Gilgit and Baltistan. **NP:** common and widespread; resident and winter visitor below 2300 m, summer visitor up to 4900 m, also a passage migrant. **IN:** common and widespread resident, an altitudinal migrant in Himalayas, breeding in plains and hills (up to 3000 m in Himalayas); also a winter visitor to the Himalayan foothills and the N peninsula. **BT:** probably resident, winter visitor and passage migrant; frequent, 150–2400 m (–3800 m). **BD:** common resident and winter visitor throughout. **LK:** common resident in N coastal belt, rare inland and in other coastal areas.

BRAHMINY KITE *Haliastur indus* — Plate 59

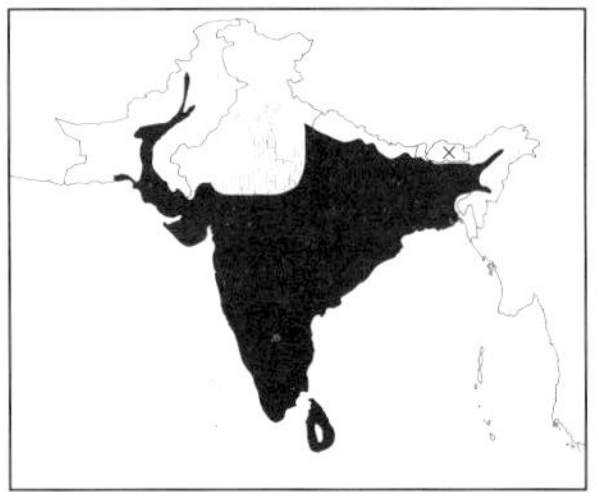

IDENTIFICATION 48 cm. Kite-like in flight, gliding and soaring with carpal joints pressed forward and wings often angled downwards, with much twisting of rounded tail. Active flight buoyant, slow and flapping, occasionally swooping down to pick up a food item. **Adult** is mainly chestnut, with white head, neck and most of underparts (with black shaft streaks visible at close range), and black wing-tips. In flight, underside of remiges is mainly pale cinnamon (as is tail), contrasting with black wing-tips and chestnut underwing-coverts. **Juvenile** is mainly brown, with pale streaking on head, mantle and breast. Underwing-coverts are brown, and has large whitish patches at base of primaries contrasting with dark wing-tips. Tail is cinnamon-brown. Possibly confusable with dark-morph Booted Eagle (p.543), but that species is larger, and has more uniform underwing (except for paler inner primaries), white 'shoulder' patches and pale crescent on uppertail-coverts. **VOICE** A nasal, drawn-out, slightly undulating *kyerrh* (Boonsong and Round 1991). **HABITS** Often found singly or in pairs, but gregarious where common, and roosts communally. Frequently perches on a tall tree overlooking water. Eats fish, frogs, crabs, lizards, young birds and insects; also refuse from ships at sea ports. **HABITAT** Neighbourhood of water, fresh or salt: marshes, flooded rice fields, tanks, estuaries, harbours, coastal lagoons, mangroves, fishing villages, reservoirs, rivers and jheels. **BREEDING** December–June, varying locally. Builds a stick nest, usually 6–15 m up in a large isolated tree near water, often close to a village. **DISTRIBUTION AND STATUS** Resident, subject to local movements depending on water conditions. Throughout most of the subcontinent, except parts of the northwest, northeast and N Himalayas. **PK:** common in Thatta district, Sind; elsewhere rare, and confined to the Indus R system. **NP:** uncommon and widespread; mainly below 360 m, sometimes wanders up to 1370 m. **IN:** widespread and locally fairly common; up to 1800 m in Himalayas. **BD:** common throughout. **LK:** common in lowlands.

WHITE-BELLIED SEA EAGLE *Haliaeetus leucogaster* Plate 60

White-bellied Fish-Eagle (I,K,P)

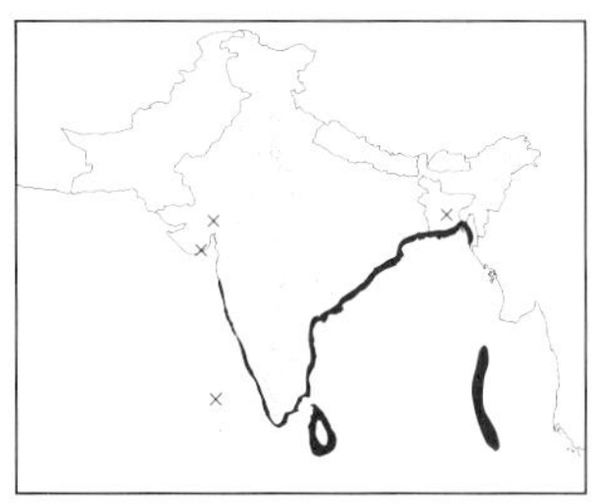

IDENTIFICATION 66–71 cm. In flight, soars and glides with wings pressed forward and raised in pronounced V. Long neck and slim head, bulging secondaries which are pinched in at base, rather narrow and pointed hand, and short wedge-shaped tail further contribute to distinctive profile in all plumages. In direct flight, powerful flaps are interspersed with long glides. **Adult** is unmistakable, with white head, neck and underparts, grey upperparts, white underwing-coverts contrasting with black remiges, and mainly white tail. **Juvenile** is mainly brown, with paler head. Tail is whitish with broad and diffuse brownish subterminal band. Upperwing shows pale panel across median coverts, and pale wedge on inner primaries. Underwing-coverts are rufous-buff, with pale band along greater coverts offset by dark tips to these feathers which form second band across underwing; has prominent white patch on underside of primaries, and variable white patch on axillaries. By second year, has whitish-buff underparts with rufous-buff breast and thighs, paler underwing-coverts with more pronounced dark band across greater coverts, and whiter tail with narrower greyish subterminal band. Older **immature** birds have whiter head and underbody, and mainly white tail with some dark at base. **VOICE** Loud, far-carrying and somewhat goose-like honking, *ank...ank...ank...*, and still faster and more duck-like nasal *ka..ka..kaa...* **HABITS** Usually keeps singly or in pairs. Frequently soars, circling at great heights. Also spends much time perched on a prominent rock or dead tree, usually near water. Feeds mainly on sea snakes (Hydrophiinae) and fish, seized close to the water surface after stooping from a perch or from soaring flight. **HABITAT** Coast and offshore islands, tidal creeks, mangroves, lagoons, estuaries; occasionally inland on tidal rivers and freshwater lakes. **BREEDING** October–March. Nest is a huge platform of sticks and twigs, placed 10–50 m up in a large tree on the coast or on a small island or rocky promontory. **DISTRIBUTION AND STATUS** Resident. Chiefly coasts and offshore islands from Bombay south down the W coast and up the E coast north to Bangladesh; Sri Lanka. Rarely on inland waters. **IN:** generally uncommon. **BD:** local and common. **LK:** regular in dry lowlands, occasionally recorded elsewhere.

PALLAS'S FISH EAGLE *Haliaeetus leucoryphus* Plate 60

Pallas's Fishing Eagle (F,I), Pallas's Sea-Eagle

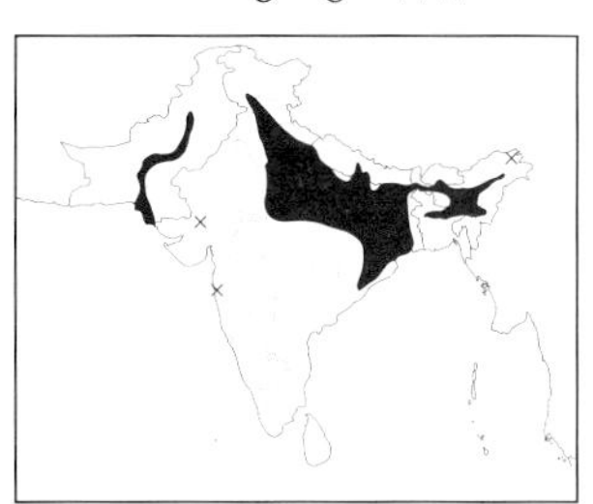

IDENTIFICATION 76–84 cm. In flight, soars and glides with wings held level; has long, comparatively narrow wings, fairly long tail, and noticeably protruding head and neck. Flight is lighter than that of White-tailed Eagle (p.524), and often perches in less upright posture than that species. **Adult** is unmistakable, with rufous-buff crown, hindneck and mantle (with whiter throat and foreneck), dark brown upper- and underwings, rufous-brown underparts, and mainly white tail with broad black terminal band. **Juvenile** is different in shape, with broader arm and longer tail. Most likely to be confused with immature White-tailed Eagle, but is less bulky and looks slimmer-winged, longer-tailed and smaller-billed. Has paler grey-brown body and upperwing-coverts, dark face mask, broad and more prominent pale band across underwing-coverts, large pale patch on underside of inner primaries, all-dark tail (lacking the pale inner webs of White-tailed), and pale crescent on uppertail-coverts. Older **immatures** have less strongly patterned underwing (lacking white at base of primaries), but show mottled tail-band with whitish base. **VOICE** Commonest call is a hoarse bark, *kvo kvok kvok* (Cramp and Simmons 1980). **HABITS** Rather sluggish, perching for long periods on a tree or post close to water, or on a sandbank. Feeds mainly on fish snatched near the surface; also on waterbirds such as Common Coot (p.467), which it hunts by gliding low over the water surface, and snakes, frogs and carrion. **HABITAT** Mainly larger rivers and lakes, also tidal creeks and mangroves. **BREEDING** September–April, varying locally. Nest is an enormous stick platform built 15–35 m up in an isolated large tree in or near water. **DISTRIBUTION AND STATUS** Resident and winter visitor. Mainly Pakistan and from Kashmir east to NE India and south to SE Rajasthan, N Madhya Pradesh, SE Orissa and C Bangladesh; Gujarat. Globally threatened. **PK:** scarce resident, found mainly along Indus R system, also over Salt Range lakes. **NP:** now scarce; recorded in all months, but mainly a winter visitor (below 305 m) and passage migrant (–2745 m). **IN:** resident, now generally scarce. **BT:** breeding resident, possibly also a passage migrant and winter visitor; uncommon; 150–1400 m (–2800 m). **BD:** rare breeding resident. **REFERENCES** Alström *et al.* (1991), Ferguson-Lees (in prep.).

WHITE-TAILED EAGLE *Haliaeetus albicilla* Plate 60

White-tailed Sea Eagle (F)

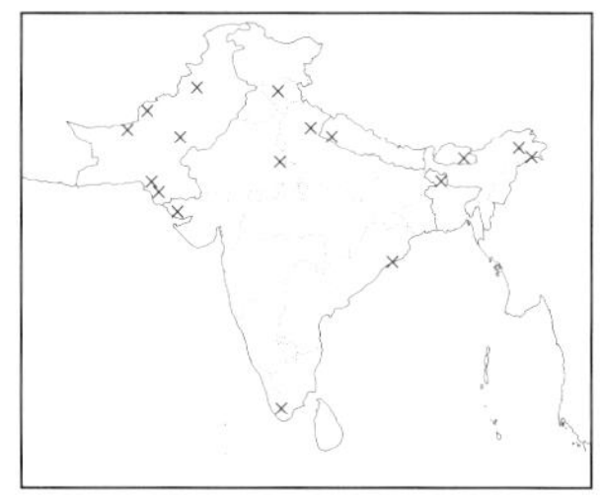

IDENTIFICATION 70–90 cm. A huge eagle with long, broad parallel-edged wings, short wedge-shaped tail, and protruding head and neck (which extend as far beyond wings as tail does behind). In direct flight, has shallow steady wingbeats interspersed sporadically with short glides. Soars with wings held perpendicular to body and level or very slightly raised; when gliding, holds wings horizontal or with hand slightly depressed. Perches upright. **Adult** is unmistakable, with huge yellow bill, pale yellowish-brown to creamy-white head, white tail, and yellowish-brown upperwing-coverts contrasting with darker remiges. **Juvenile** is mainly blackish-brown, with whitish centres to tail feathers, pale patch on axillaries, and variable pale band across underwing-coverts. Bill becomes yellow with age. These plumage features, combined with larger size and more protruding head, help separate it from adult Greater Spotted Eagle (p.540). Broader wings, shorter tail marked with white, and absence of large pale patch on underside of inner primaries are best features for separation from immature Pallas's (p.523); for further details, see that species. **VOICE** Rather vocal; normal call is quick series of metallic yapping notes (Cramp and Simmons 1980). **HABITS** Spends most of the time perched on a stump or on the ground near water. Catches fish, its main prey, by flying low over the water and seizing them near the surface; also hunts ducks and small mammals by flying low along lakeshores or coasts. **HABITAT** Coast, large rivers and lakes. **DISTRIBUTION AND STATUS** Winter visitor. Pakistan, Nepal, India and Bhutan. **PK:** rare winter visitor. **NP:** scarce but regular winter visitor; below 915 m (–1370 m on passage). **IN:** rare and widespread winter visitor. **BT:** vagrant or rare passage migrant. **BD:** vagrant. **REFERENCES** Alström *et al.* (1991), Jonsson (1992), Porter *et al.* (1974), Robson (1996b).

LESSER FISH EAGLE *Ichthyophaga humilis* Plate 60

Himalayan Grey-headed Fishing Eagle (F,I), Lesser Fishing Eagle (N), *I. nana*

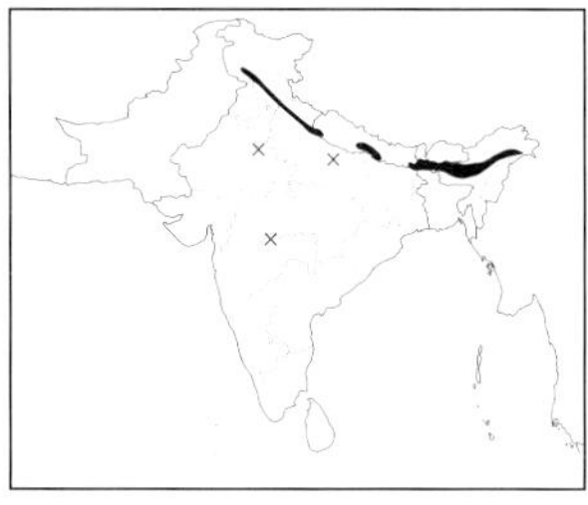

IDENTIFICATION 64 cm. A small, mainly grey fish eagle, with white belly, thighs and undertail-coverts clearly demarcated from breast. Has small head and longish neck, short and broad wings, and shortish tail. Glides and soars on level wings. **Adult** is best told from adult Grey-headed Fish Eagle (below) by grey tail with a slightly darker subterminal band (tail typically appears rather uniform). Further differences are paler grey upperparts, whitish patch at base of underside of outer primaries, and lack of rufous-brown coloration on breast. **Juvenile** is similarly patterned to adult, but has browner head and neck, browner upperparts, pale mottling on underwing-coverts, diffuse dark barring and trailing edge to underside of pale remiges, and paler base to tail. Best told from juvenile Grey-headed by darker head which lacks pale supercilium, lack of prominent pale streaking on neck and breast (streaking present but very indistinct), clear-cut white belly and vent, darker tail, and darker underwing. **Immatures** more similar to Grey-headed, and best told by tail and underwing differences. **VOICE** Loud, eerie, excitable shrieks include a wavering *kleeeuee* and an intensifying *kleeeu-kleee-kleeuee* (P. Holt). **HABITS** Found singly or in pairs. Usually seen perched low down on trees or rocks overlooking water, and has regular perches. Usually flies only short distances, and rarely soars. Hunts mainly from a perch, also occasionally in flight. Feeds almost entirely on fish seized near the surface. **HABITAT** Forested streams and lakes in the terai and foothills. **BREEDING** March–May. Nest is a large pile of sticks and twigs built in a tall forest tree, usually near water. **DISTRIBUTION AND STATUS** Resident. Mainly Himalayas from Kashmir east to Arunachal Pradesh. **NP:** now rare and local; below 250 m. **IN:** now rare; formerly recorded from foothills up to 2400 m in the west, to 1100 m in the east; in Uttar Pradesh, now restricted to 300–1300 m because of habitat loss and probably pesticide use. **BT:** very rare. **REFERENCES** Ferguson-Lees (in prep.), Naoroji (1995).

GREY-HEADED FISH EAGLE *Ichthyophaga ichthyaetus* Plate 60

Grey-headed Fishing Eagle (F,I,N)

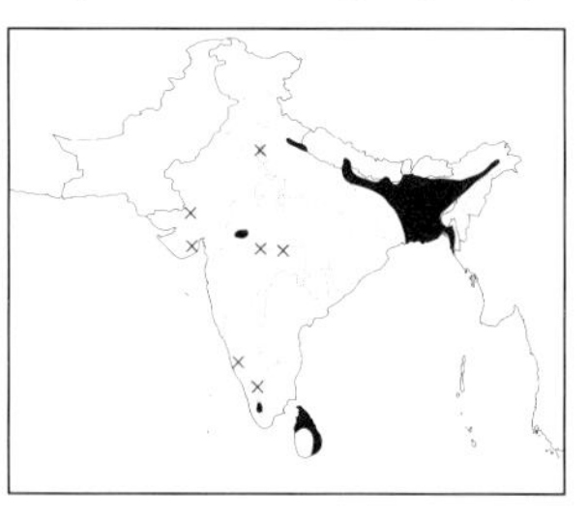

IDENTIFICATION 69–74 cm. A medium-sized, mainly grey-brown fish eagle with striking white belly, thighs and undertail-coverts. Glides and soars with short, broad wings held level; neck projects noticeably and head appears rather small. Has a very upright posture when perched. Compared with Lesser Fish Eagle (above), is larger, with relatively shorter wings and longer tail. **Adult** is told from Lesser by largely white tail with broad black subterminal band, darker and browner upperparts, lack of pale patch at base of underside to outer primaries, and rufous-brown breast. **Juvenile** is distinct from juvenile Lesser. Useful features when perched are pale supercilium, bold pale streaking on head, neck and breast, brown streaking on belly and thighs, and diffuse brown barring across pale tail. In flight, shows whitish underside to remiges (much paler than on Lesser) with pronounced dark trailing edge to wing. Older birds are more similar to immature Lesser and are best told by patterning of underwing or, if older, by adult-like tail pattern. **VOICE** In display flight, gives an eerie series of far-carrying, dreamy *tiu-weeeu* notes (P. Holt from A. Lewis recording). **HABITS** Very similar to those of Lesser Fish Eagle. Sluggish, and perches for most of the day in regularly used trees above water. Very noisy during breeding season. **HABITAT** Near slow-moving rivers and streams, lakes, reservoirs and tidal lagoons in wooded country. **BREEDING** November–March. Nest is a huge platform of sticks, built 10–30 m up in the top of a large tree in forest, or near a swamp or large tank. **DISTRIBUTION AND STATUS** Resident. India, S Nepal, Bangladesh and Sri Lanka. **NP:** now rare and local; mainly below 250 m (–915 m). **IN:** widespread; locally frequent in the northeast, scarce and very local in the peninsula. **BD:** uncommon and local, occurs throughout. **LK:** rare in dry lowlands. **REFERENCES** Ferguson-Lees (in prep.).

LAMMERGEIER *Gypaetus barbatus* — Plate 61

Bearded Vulture (F,I)

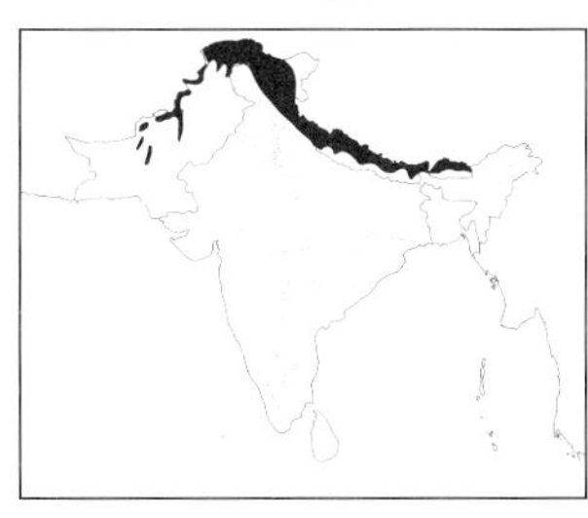

IDENTIFICATION 100–115 cm. Huge size, long (and relatively narrow) pointed wings, small but well protruding head, and large wedge-shaped tail result in an appearance quite unlike that of any other raptor. Wings are held flat when soaring, and slightly bowed at carpal joints when gliding. **Adult** has yellowish or white head with black mask and 'beard', greyish-black upperparts, wings and tail, cream or rufous-orange underparts contrasting with black underwing-coverts, and grey underside to remiges with slightly darker trailing edge. **Juvenile** has blackish head and neck, pale grey-brown underparts, and blackish-brown upperparts, wings and tail. Possibly confusable with juvenile Egyptian Vulture (below), but is considerably larger, has proportionately longer and narrower wings, and pale grey-brown underparts contrast with darker head and underside to tail. Older **immatures** (in third/fourth year) show more white on head, and have cream or rusty-yellow underparts with brown mottling on breast. **VOICE** Generally silent, but thin screams and whistles in display (Cramp and Simmons 1980). **HABITS** Spends long periods soaring majestically and gracefully around mountainsides. Highly manoeuvrable in flight, rarely flaps wings, and often glides close to the ground following the curve of mountain slopes. Has a unique habit of splitting bones by dropping them on to rock slabs. Eats bone fragments; also carrion, and scavenges at rubbish heaps around mountain villages. Perches on crags. **HABITAT** Mountains. **BREEDING** December–June. Nest is an enormous platform of sticks, draped with sheep's or goats' wool, dry skin or bones, and placed on a cliff ledge, often under a rock overhang. **DISTRIBUTION AND STATUS** Resident. Mountains of Pakistan and Himalayas from N Pakistan east to Arunachal Pradesh. **PK:** scarce. **NP:** common and widespread; mainly 1200–4100 m (305–7500 m). **IN:** common and widespread; found above 1500 m, most frequent at high altitudes. **BT:** frequent. **REFERENCES** Naoroji (1995), Porter *et al.* (1981).

EGYPTIAN VULTURE *Neophron percnopterus* — Plate 61

Scavenger-Vulture (P)

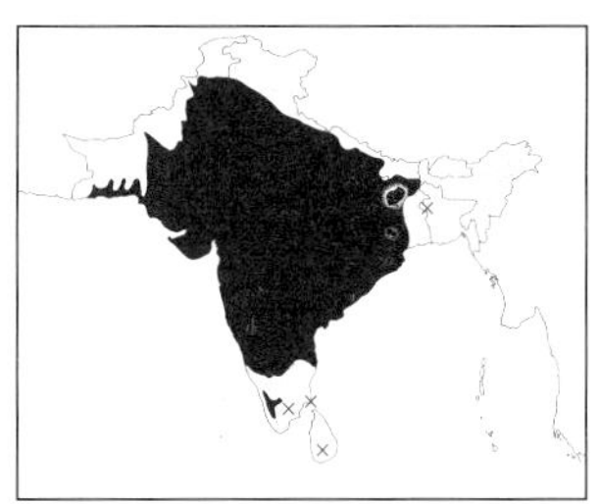

IDENTIFICATION 60–70 cm. A small vulture with distinctive profile. Has long pointed wings, small and pointed (but well protruding) head, and wedge-shaped tail. Buoyant in flight. Wings are held flat or slightly bowed when soaring, and bowed when gliding. **Adult** is unmistakable, with bare yellowish face, dirty white neck ruff, body, wing-coverts and tail, and black flight feathers (with whitish outer webs to secondaries apparent on upperwing). **Juvenile** is mainly blackish-brown with bare grey face. With maturity, tail, body and wing-coverts become whiter (although can look very mottled and untidy) and face becomes yellower. Much smaller size and proportionately broader wings should readily distinguish it from immature Lammergeier (above). **VOICE** Practically silent, but can emit mewing sounds, hisses and low grunts in excitement or anger (Brown and Amadon 1968). **HABITS** Usually seen singly or in twos or threes, but gathers in larger numbers at good food sources. A scavenger closely associated with human habitation. Spends the day soaring and gliding about in search of food, and perched around villages and rubbish dumps. Feeds chiefly on refuse and carrion; occasionally eats frogs and invertebrates. Gathers at carcases and rubbish dumps with other larger vultures; stays on the outside of the throng, and feeds when they are squabbling or after they have finished. **HABITAT** Towns, villages and city outskirts, especially around rubbish dumps and slaughterhouses. **BREEDING** February–May. Nest is a platform of twigs placed on the ledge of a cliff or ruin, sometimes 4–6 m up in a large tree. **DISTRIBUTION AND STATUS** Widespread resident, subject to altitudinal movements. Mainly Pakistan, Nepal, and India except the northeast and parts of southeast. **PK:** locally common and widespread; resident in the plains, summer visitor to mountain regions. **NP:** fairly common and widespread resident, also a passage migrant; up to 915 m all year, in summer regularly to 2000 m (–3810 m). **IN:** widespread and locally common; plains and hills, up to 2500 m (–3600 m) in Himalayas and to 2000 m in peninsular hills. **BD:** vagrant. **LK:** winter vagrant to dry lowlands and hills.

WHITE-RUMPED VULTURE *Gyps bengalensis* Plate 61

Indian White-backed Vulture (I), Oriental White-backed Vulture (N,R), White-backed Vulture (F)

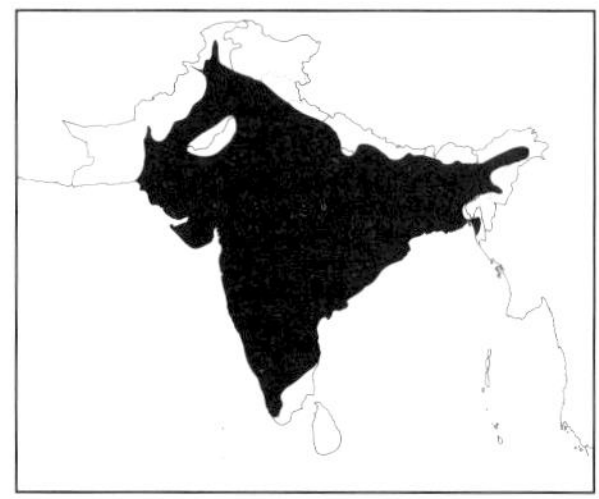

IDENTIFICATION 75–85 cm. Smallest of the *Gyps* vultures. Soars with wings held in a shallow V. **Adult** is distinctive. From below, mainly white underwing-coverts contrast with blackish underparts and black leading edge to underwing. From above, has blackish mantle and wing-coverts (becoming paler with bleaching), and white rump and back. Both at rest and in flight, white neck ruff stands out against blackish body and grey head and neck. Upper mandible is pale bluish-grey. **Juvenile** is dark brown, with whitish streaking on underparts and inner and median upperwing-coverts; lacks white rump and back, and has whitish head and neck. Bill is blackish. At rest, told from immature Long-billed Vulture (below) by darker lesser and median coverts which contrast less with remiges, lack of distinct pale streaking on mantle and scapulars, darker underparts with more pronounced pale streaking, and generally stouter and all-dark bill. In flight, the underbody and lesser underwing-coverts are distinctly darker than on Long-billed, and the greater underwing-coverts are uniform (rather pale) brownish-grey; more easily identified from above, by darker upperwing-coverts and brown rump and back. From below, immature can be rather similar to sub-adult and adult Eurasian Griffon (p.527) in coloration (especially when worn and bleached), but never shows more than two white panels on underwing-coverts (often up to four on Eurasian) and never shows a dark bar along greater underwing-coverts; from above, is usually much darker on wing-coverts, rump and back. Also very similar in plumage to juvenile Himalayan Griffon (p.527), but is much smaller and less heavily built, with narrower-looking wings and shorter tail, and generally soars on slightly raised wings with fingers only slightly upward-bent; further, underparts are less heavily streaked, and lacks streaking on mantle and scapulars. **VOICE** Croaks, grunts, hisses and squeals at nest colonies, roosts and carcases (Ali and Ripley 1987). **HABITS** A typical vulture. Gregarious all year. Groups perch for long periods in a hunched posture on treetops or buildings around slaughterhouses and rubbish dumps, often with other vultures. Roosts communally at traditional sites in groves. Feeds almost entirely on carrion, mainly by scavenging at rubbish dumps and slaughterhouses or by seeking dead animals. Uses thermal upcurrents to gain altitude, and then often soars for hours at great heights. When one bird spots a carcase, it descends rapidly; neighbouring birds see the descent and follow it, to be followed in turn by more distant birds. In this way large numbers of vultures gather quickly in a jostling rabble, and can rapidly devour a carcase. Gorged birds sit around near the carcase for several hours before flying off. **HABITAT** Cities, towns and villages near cultivation. **BREEDING** September–March, varying locally. Colonial at traditionally used sites. Nest is a large untidy platform of sticks and twigs, often with green leaves attached, built 10–18 m up in the top of a large tree, often near a village or along a road or canal bank. **DISTRIBUTION AND STATUS** Resident. Throughout most of the subcontinent, except W Pakistan, N Himalayas, parts of NE, NW and SE India and Sri Lanka. **PK:** common throughout the Indus plains. **NP:** common and widespread resident below 1000 m, summers up to 1800 m (–3100 m). **IN:** common and widespread; plains and hills up to 2500 m. **BT:** locally frequent; 250–1200 m. **BD:** common throughout. **REFERENCES** Alström (1997).

LONG-BILLED VULTURE *Gyps indicus* Plate 61

Indian Long-billed Vulture (I), Indian Griffon (F)

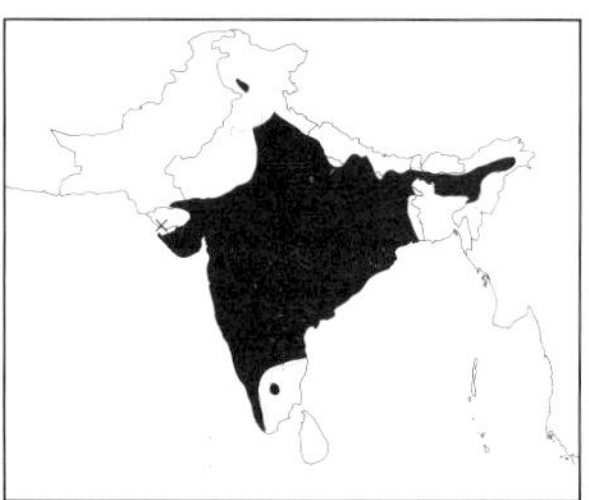

IDENTIFICATION 80–95 cm. **Adult** is very similar to the larger and more heavily built Eurasian Griffon (p.527) and has sandy-brown body and wing-coverts contrasting with black flight feathers and tail. Is generally a paler sandy-brown in coloration compared with adult of that species, and lacks pale streaking on underparts. Blackish head and neck have some white down, mainly on nape (but see racial variation), but look darker than on Eurasian Griffon, which has a more even covering of whitish down over crown and nape. Further differences include slimmer bill and pale pinkish, yellowish or greyish cere, as well as, in flight, lack of broad and pronounced whitish band across median underwing-coverts, and generally whiter rump and back. Can be rather similar to adult Himalayan Griffon (p.527) in appearance, but is much smaller and less heavily built, with slimmer bill; also, upperparts are slightly darker and browner, head and neck blacker, neck ruff is white, downy and more prominent, and legs and feet are grey with pale claws. **Juvenile** has darker brown (prominently buff-streaked) upperparts than adult, and more prominently streaked underparts and underwing-coverts. Further differences from adult include largely blackish bill (yellowish or greenish on adult) and blackish cere, lack of broad pale tips to median and greater coverts, brown, feathery neck ruff, and some whitish down covering head and neck. Told from juvenile Eurasian Griffon by structural differences (see above), darker brown upperparts with more pronounced pale streaking, paler, less rufescent underparts with less distinct pale streaking, generally blacker and less feathered head and neck (especially in race *tenuirostris*), and pale pinkish culmen to bill (although possibly not shown by very young birds, and juvenile *tenuirostris* has an all-dark bill). Distinguished from immature White-rumped (above) by paler and less distinctly streaked underparts, paler underwing-coverts, paler lesser and median upperwing-coverts (owing to heavy streaking) which contrast more with remiges, and whitish rump and back; see that species for further differences.

Racial variation *G. i. tenuirostris*, which occurs north of the Gangetic Plain, differs from the nominate race of the peninsula, described above, in completely lacking (or almost so) white down on grey head and neck (in both adult and immature). Bill appears longer and slimmer, and on adult and sub-adult birds the bill and cere are blackish with a pinkish culmen (i.e. like juvenile of nominate). In addition, the lateral tibia feathers are mainly downy (rather than long and firm) and the upperparts are darker brown. **VOICE** Hissing and cackling sounds (Brown and Amadon 1968). **HABITS** Like those of White-rumped, and often associates with that species. **HABITAT** Like that of White-rumped. **BREEDING** November–March. Usually in a small colony. Nest is a platform of twigs, sometimes with green leaves attached, at a traditional site on the ledge of a steep cliff or rocky outcrop or 7–14 m up in a large leafy tree, often near a village. **DISTRIBUTION AND STATUS** Resident, subject to altitudinal movements. SE Sindh, Pakistan, S Nepal and N Bangladesh and most of India, except parts of the northwest, northeast and southeast. **PK:** rare. **NP:** common and widespread resident; mainly below 350 m, in summer up to 1525 m. **IN:** widespread; fairly common in some areas at least, probably under-recorded. **BD:** scarce? winter visitor. **REFERENCES** Alström (1997).

HIMALAYAN GRIFFON *Gyps himalayensis* — Plate 62

Himalayan Griffon Vulture (N,R)

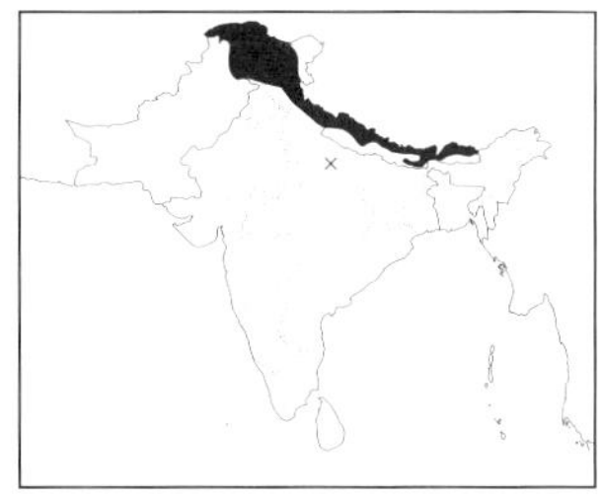

IDENTIFICATION 115–125 cm. **Adult** is very similar to Eurasian Griffon (below), but is larger and has broader body and slightly longer tail. Wing-coverts and body are a paler whitish-buff in coloration, and contrast more strongly with dark flight feathers and tail. Underparts lack pronounced streaking. Further, legs and feet are pinkish with dark claws, and has yellowish cere. In flight, wings are held flatter, with markedly upturned fingers when soaring, and underwing-coverts are almost entirely whitish with narrow dark leading edge to wing (resulting in quite different underwing pattern from that of adult Eurasian). **Immature** differs from adult in having brown feathered ruff; bill and cere are initially black (yellowish in adult). Differs from immature Eurasian in having darker brown body and wing-coverts which are boldly and prominently streaked with buff; wing-coverts are almost concolorous with flight feathers, and back and rump are also dark brown, and show much less contrast than on Eurasian. From Cinereous Vulture (p.528) by streaked upperparts and underparts and pronounced white banding across underwing-coverts. Very similar in plumage to juvenile White-rumped Vulture (p.526), but is much larger and more heavily built, with broader wings and longer tail, and has more heavily streaked underparts and streaking on mantle and scapulars. **VOICE** A variety of grunts and hisses, as other large vultures (Brown and Amadon 1968). **HABITS** Roosts gregariously on crags, and when air currents are suitable takes to the air and soars over the mountains at great heights and often for long distances. Aggressive when feeding, and dominates over all other vultures except Cinereous. **HABITAT** Mountains, especially along routes well used by pack animals. **BREEDING** January–June. Nests singly or in small colonies. Nest is a large platform of sticks and rubbish placed on a cliff ledge. **DISTRIBUTION AND STATUS** Resident. Himalayas from N Pakistan east to W Arunachal Pradesh. **PK:** frequent to common. **NP:** widespread and locally common; usually 900–4000 m (75–6100 m). **IN:** common; above 600 m, foraging to over 5000 m. **BT:** frequent; 2135–4500 m. **REFERENCES** Alström (1997).

EURASIAN GRIFFON *Gyps fulvus* — Plate 62

Griffon Vulture (I), Eurasian Griffon Vulture (N,R)

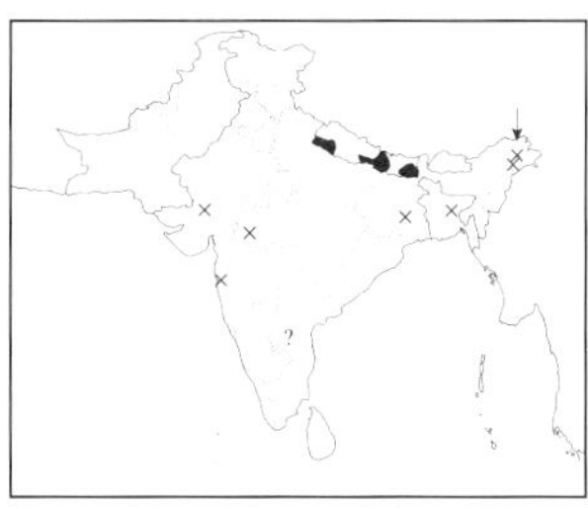

IDENTIFICATION 95–105 cm. **Adult** Distinguished from adult Long-billed Vulture (p.526) by larger size and stouter bill with blackish cere, warmer, more rufescent-buff upperparts, darker, more rufous-brown underparts and thighs with prominent pale streaking, and whiter head and neck (due to more extensive covering of down). Further differences in flight are prominent whitish band across median underwing-coverts, and generally deeper buff rump and back. From adult Himalayan Griffon (above) by smaller size, darker, more rufescent-buff upperparts, darker, more rufous-brown underparts with more pronounced white streaking, blackish cere, and dark grey legs and feet. In flight, compared with Himalayan, head appears proportionately larger and tail longer, body is less broad, and wings are slightly raised when soaring; underwing pattern is also different, with rufous-brown banding across underwing-coverts. **Immature** has richer rufous-brown upperparts and upperwing-coverts (with prominent pale streaking) than adult and lacks pale tips to greater coverts. Has rufous-brown feathered neck ruff, more whitish down covering grey head and neck, blackish bill (yellowish on adult), and dark iris (adult's pale yellowish-brown). Rufous coloration of wing-coverts and body separates it from immature Long-billed and Himalayan; see those species for further differences. **VOICE** Normally rather silent, but can emit a variety of grunting, whistling, hissing and sobbing sounds (Brown and Amadon 1968). **HABITS** Small numbers gather at a carcase with White-rumped and Long-billed Vultures, and dominates over both. Regularly makes long journeys in search of carcases. **HABITAT** Semi-desert, dry open plains and hills. **BREEDING** January–April. Nests singly or in small colonies. Nest is a large platform of sticks, leafy twigs and rubbish, placed on a cliff ledge. **DISTRIBUTION AND STATUS** Resident. Tends to replace

Himalayan Griffon at lower levels, although the two species overlap altitudinally. Breeds chiefly in hills of Pakistan, Kashmir and Nepal, spreading in winter to plains of Pakistan and mainly to N and NW India south to Gujarat and east to C Uttar Pradesh. **PK:** common in Baluchistan, NW Pakistan and Salt Range, frequent in Sind; resident and breeds in the drier lower hills, widespread winter visitor to the plains. **NP:** widespread resident; frequent below 915 m, summers locally up to 3050 m. **IN:** locally fairly common in winter in the northwest. **BD:** vagrant. **REFERENCES** Alström (1997).

CINEREOUS VULTURE *Aegypius monachus* — Plate 62

Black Vulture (I)

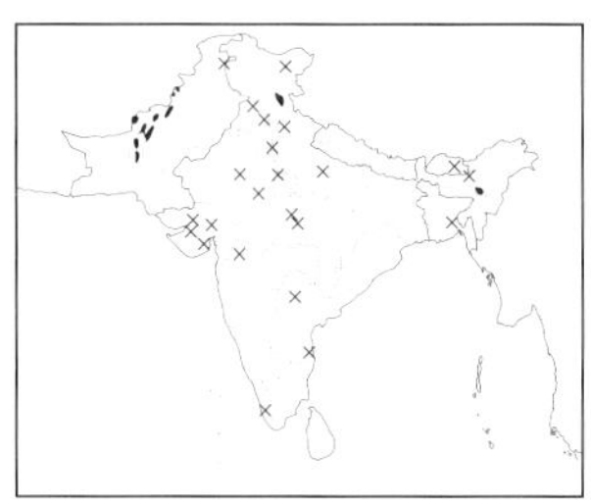

IDENTIFICATION 100–110 cm. A very large vulture. Has uniformly broad, almost parallel-edged wings (lacking bulging secondaries of similar species). Soars with wings held flat (not in a shallow V or with tips upturned). At a distance, appears uniformly blackish except for pale areas on head and bill. **Adult** is blackish-brown with paler brown ruff. May show paler band across greater underwing-coverts, but underwing is darker and more uniform than on *Gyps* species. **Juvenile** is blacker and more uniform in coloration than adult, with head darker brown (paler with blackish mask on adult). **VOICE** Usually silent (Cramp and Simmons 1980). **HABITS** Very similar to those of *Gyps* vultures. Normally solitary during the day. Usually roosts communally on the ground, often on an open escarpment close to a steep slope in readiness for suitable thermals the next morning. Dominates all other vultures at a carcase. **HABITAT** Forages over a wide range of habitats, including bare mountains, semi-desert, along river courses and savanna grassland. Breeds in mountains. **BREEDING** March and April. Nest is a huge mass of sticks and twigs, draped with animal skins and dung, placed 8–12 m up in a juniper growing out of a steep cliff. **DISTRIBUTION AND STATUS** Breeds in Baluchistan and NW Pakistan, and has bred in Himachal Pradesh and Cachar, Assam; winter visitor mainly to Pakistan and Himalayas from N Pakistan east to Nepal. **PK:** scarce resident; breeds above 3050 m, some birds winter in the plains. **NP:** mainly an uncommon winter visitor; below 2900 m (–4900 m on passage). **IN:** bred at 1800 m in Assam; widespread and rare winter visitor. **BT:** rare. **BD:** vagrant. **REFERENCES** Harris *et al.* (1996), Jonsson (1992).

RED-HEADED VULTURE *Sarcogyps calvus* — Plate 62

King Vulture (I), Black Vulture (F), *Torgos calvus* (F)

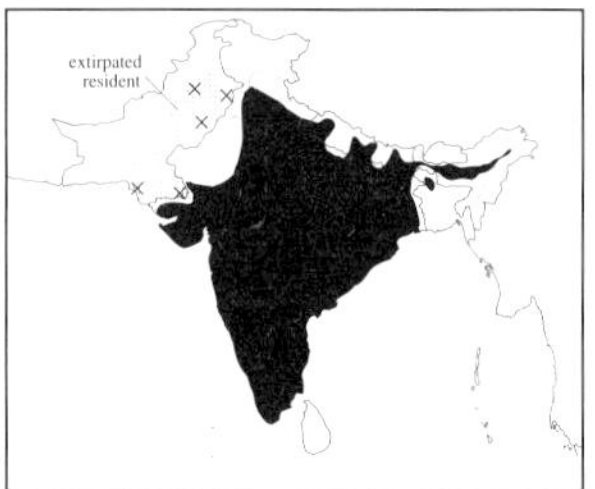

IDENTIFICATION 85 cm. Similar in size to White-rumped Vulture (p.526), but with longer, slimmer and more pointed wings. Graceful in flight, holding wings slightly above the horizontal. **Adult** is mainly black, with bare pinkish or reddish head and cere and broad black bill, white patches at base of neck and upper thighs, and reddish legs and feet. In flight, has greyish-white bases to secondaries which show as broad panel (particularly across underwing). Male has yellowish eyes, which are dark red in female. **Juvenile** has dark brown upperparts and wing-coverts (with narrow pale fringes), and paler brown underparts with buff shaft streaking; head is partly covered with white down. Superficially resembles juvenile White-rumped, but has pinkish coloration to head and cere, pinkish legs and feet, white patch on upper thighs, and whitish undertail-coverts. **VOICE** Mostly silent. Squeaks, hisses and grunts like other vultures (Brown and Amadon 1968). **HABITS** Has rather similar habits to those of other large vultures, but usually keeps singly or in pairs. Frequently feeds on carcases of small animals, such as rodents, which are overlooked by other large vultures. Also feeds timidly with other vultures at carcases of larger animals, but usually on isolated bones at the edge of the main feeding area. **HABITAT** Open country near human habitation; also well-wooded hills. **BREEDING** December–April. Nest is a large platform of sticks and twigs placed 9–12 m up in the top of a large tree, often near a village. **DISTRIBUTION AND STATUS** Widespread resident, subject to altitudinal movements. Throughout much of Nepal, India (except parts of the northwest and northeast), and NW Bangladesh. **PK:** now a rare straggler. **NP:** now uncommon; usually below 2000 m (–3100 m). **IN:** generally sparsely distributed, now rare in some areas (e.g. Kutch, Saurashtra and the northeast), but still common in forested W Himalayan foothills; plains and hills, up to 2500 m in Himalayas. **BD:** rare in the northwest. **REFERENCES** Naoroji (1995).

SHORT-TOED SNAKE EAGLE *Circaetus gallicus* — Plate 63

Short-toed Eagle (F,I,K,R)

IDENTIFICATION 62–67 cm. A medium-sized eagle with long and broad wings, which are distinctly pinched in at base, and rather long tail. Head is broad and rounded. When perched, appears big-headed, with wing-tips reaching tail-end, and shows long unfeathered tarsus. Soars with wings held forward and flat or slightly raised. Frequently hovers. **Adult** is variable in plumage, but usually distinctive. Often with dark head and breast, barred underbody, narrow barring across underwing with dark trailing edge, and three bands across underside of tail (subterminal band broadest). Can be very pale on underbody and underwing, but barring still apparent across under-

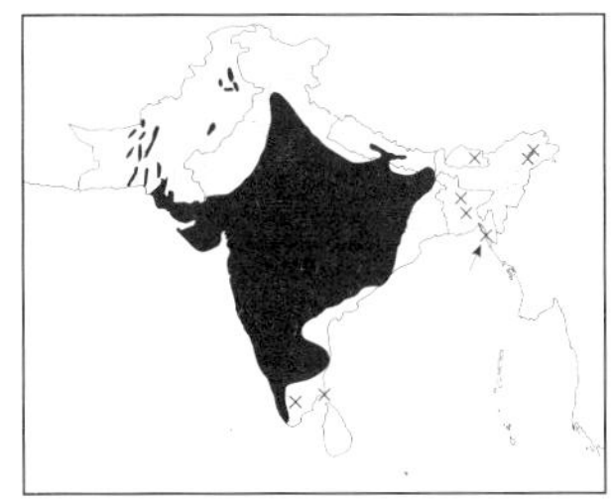

wing and undertail. On upperside, pale brown inner wing-coverts contrast with dark greater coverts and flight feathers. **Juvenile** apparently not distinguishable in field. **VOICE** Calls of breeding birds include *Buteo*-like mews, and ringing gull-like *quo-quo-quo* (Cramp and Simmons 1980). **HABITS** Usually found singly or in pairs. Spends most of the day soaring, actively searching for prey. Typically hunts 15–30 m above ground, occasionally higher, frequently hovering with gently beating wings; on spotting prey, plummets down almost vertically. Feeds mainly on snakes, also lizards, frogs, young birds, rats and large insects. **HABITAT** Open country, cultivation, semi-desert, and dry stony and scrub-covered hills. **BREEDING** December–March. Nest is relatively small, made of twigs and sticks, and concealed in a moderate-sized leafy tree. **DISTRIBUTION AND STATUS** Resident. Pakistan, S Nepal, and much of India except parts of the northwest and northeast and most of the Himalayas. **PK:** frequent, widespread but very local resident; an irregular year-round visitor in many areas; plains and low hills (–2485 m). **NP:** scarce; possibly a passage migrant, may also breed; mainly in the terai (–2130 m). **IN:** locally fairly common and widespread resident; plains and hills up to 2300 m. **BT:** rare. **BD:** vagrant. **REFERENCES** Cramp and Simmons (1980).

CRESTED SERPENT EAGLE *Spilornis cheela* — Plate 63

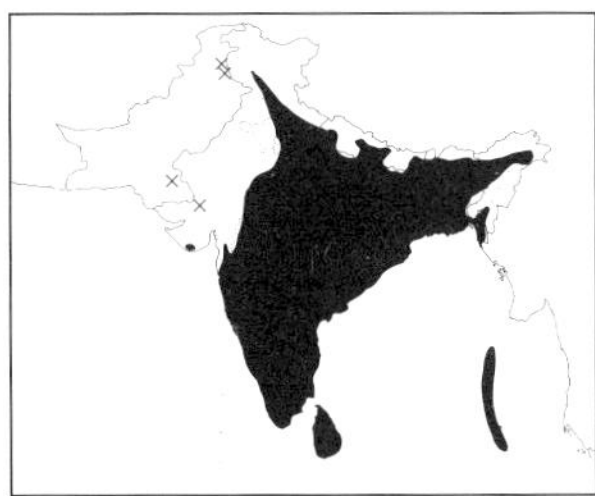

IDENTIFICATION 56–74 cm. **Adult** has distinctive appearance in flight, with broad white band across underside of remiges contrasting with broad black trailing edge to wing, broad white banding across upperside and underside of black tail, and white spotting on rufous-brown underwing-coverts. Has broad, rounded wings and soars with wings held forward and in pronounced V. At rest, combination of yellow cere and lores, hooded appearance, white spotting on brown underparts, black-and-white banded tail, and unfeathered yellow tarsus readily distinguishes this species from the hawk eagles. **Juvenile** is very different, with white underparts streaked black on breast, white fringes to mantle and upperwing-coverts, narrower dark bands across tail, and largely white underwing with fine dark barring and darker tips to remiges. More likely to be confused with one of the hawk eagles; best told by combination of yellow cere and lores contrasting with blackish ear-coverts, hooded appearance with black tips to mainly whitish crown and nape, broad pale banding on uppertail, and unfeathered yellow tarsus. When soaring, holds wings in more pronounced V than the hawk eagles. **Racial variation** Birds of peninsular India *S. c. melanotis*, and especially Sri Lanka *S. c. spilogaster*, are smaller than the nominate race, described above, and have grey ear-coverts and throat contrasting with blackish crown, and unbarred breast; adults have two greyish-white tail-bands. *S. c. davisoni*, of the Andaman and Nicobar Is, is also smaller than the nominate race, and has paler buff underparts and underwing-coverts, narrower white subterminal band along underwing, and two white bands across tail. **VOICE** A variety of loud, clear, ringing and musical whistling or screaming calls in flight (Brown and Amadon 1968). **HABITS** Usually found singly or in pairs. Often quite tame. Has a characteristic habit of soaring over forest in pairs, the birds screaming to each other and sometimes rising to great heights. Spends hours perched very upright on a forest tree, and raises its crest if alarmed. Usually hunts by dropping almost vertically on to prey from a perch. Eats mainly snakes, but also frogs, lizards, rodents and weak birds. **HABITAT** Forest and well-wooded country in quite high-rainfall areas. **BREEDING** December–June, varying with altitude. Nest is made of sticks and twigs and built high in a tree in or near a forest clearing, often near a stream. **DISTRIBUTION AND STATUS** Resident, subject to altitudinal movements. Throughout much of the subcontinent, except most of the northwest, N Himalayas and parts of NE India. **PK:** vagrant. **NP:** fairly common and widespread; usually summers below 2100 m (–3350 m) and winters below 915 m. **IN:** widespread in plains and hills; up to 2135 m in Himalayas, where fairly common, but less frequent in the peninsula. **BT:** fairly common; 250–2285 m. **BD:** common throughout. **LK:** common in all zones, especially in the dry zone, less common in wet zone. **REFERENCES** Naoroji (1995).

SMALL SERPENT EAGLE *Spilornis minimus* — Plate 63

***S. cheela* (I), *S. klossi*, Great Nicobar Serpent Eagle (I)**

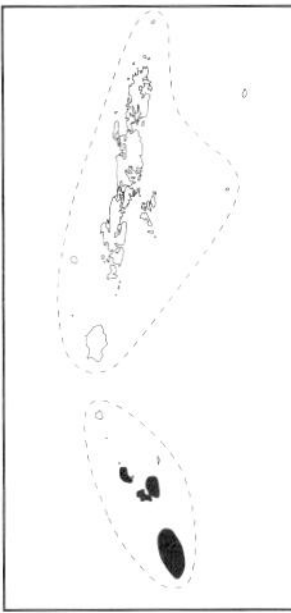

IDENTIFICATION 46–48 cm. Considerably smaller than Crested Serpent Eagle (above), which also occurs in the Nicobar Is (race *davisoni*). Has bare yellow lores and bushy crest typical of genus, which help separation from *Accipiter* species. See below for main differences from Crested. **Racial variation** Two distinct subspecies are recognised. *S. m. minimus*, of the central Nicobar Is, has white scaling on black crown and crest, and greyish sides of head and underparts (becoming more cinnamon on belly and thighs, which are finely barred with white); uppertail has broad grey central band, and undertail has broad white central band and some white at base. By comparison, Crested is larger, is more buffish below (with fine dark barring on breast), and has more pronounced white band at base of tail. Juvenile *minimus* has buff tips to crown, crest and upperparts, and full second pale band across tail. *S. m. klossi*, of Great Nicobar, is even smaller. Has cinnamon scaling to black crown and crest, grey sides of head with dark grey malar, whitish throat with black mesial stripe, and cinnamon collar and underparts (latter without barring or spotting); black uppertail has two broad brown bands and narrow white tip; undertail is more narrowly banded with black than on other serpent eagles. Very small size, dark throat stripe, narrower banding across undertail, and unmarked cinnamon underparts are best distinctions from Crested. Juvenile *klossi* has buff tips to crown and upperparts; underwing and undertail lack broad black banding. **VOICE** Undescribed. **HABITS** Very little known; presumably similar to those of Crested Serpent Eagle. Wild and shy. Eats lizards, rats and birds. **HABITAT** Forest near rivers. **BREEDING** Unknown. **DISTRIBUTION AND STATUS IN:** resident, endemic to Nicobar Is (Great Nicobar, Little Nicobar, Camorta, Nancowry, Teressa, Menchal, Katchall, Trinkat). **REFERENCES** Ferguson-Lees (in prep.), Sankaran (1997; 1998).

ANDAMAN SERPENT EAGLE *Spilornis elgini* — Plate 63

Andaman Dark Serpent Eagle (I)

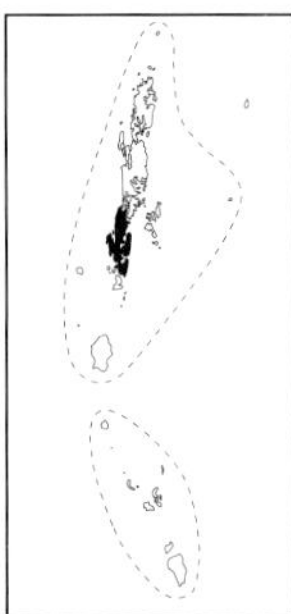

IDENTIFICATION 50 cm. **Adult** superficially resembles Crested Serpent Eagle (p.529), which also occurs in the Andaman Is (race *davisoni*), but has dark brown underparts (concolorous with upperparts) which are spotted with white, and narrower brownish-grey banding to uppertail. In flight, shows narrow greyish-white banding to underside of remiges, dark brown underwing-coverts profusely spotted with white, and two narrow greyish-white bands across tail, resulting in an appearance from below that is quite different from that of Crested. **Juvenile** is similar, although paler brown in coloration, with white fringes to feathers of crown and nape, darker ear-covert patch, and paler throat, and has more prominent banding on underside of remiges and tail (with three pale tail-bands). Much darker on underparts than juvenile Crested, and with narrower tail-bands. **VOICE** Clear whistles, quite different from the shrill ringing screams of Crested (Ferguson-Lees in prep.). **HABITS** Little known, but mainly like those of Crested Serpent Eagle. **HABITAT** Inland forest clearings and hillsides with scattered trees. Seems to be ecologically separated from Crested Serpent Eagle, which inhabits coastal forest in areas where the two species overlap in distribution. **BREEDING** Unknown. **DISTRIBUTION AND STATUS IN:** common resident, endemic to S Andaman Is. **REFERENCES** Davidar *et al.* (1997), Ferguson-Lees (in prep.).

EURASIAN MARSH HARRIER *Circus aeruginosus* — Plate 64

Western Marsh Harrier, Eastern Marsh Harrier, Marsh Harrier (F,I,P,R), *C. spilonotus*

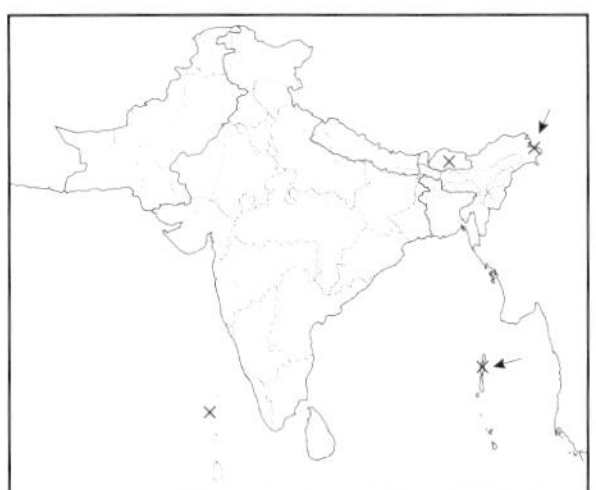

IDENTIFICATION 48–58 cm. A broad-winged, stout-bodied harrier; in common with other harriers, glides and soars with wings held in noticeable V, which helps to separate it from Booted Eagle (p.543) and Black Kite (p.522). **Adult male** is distinguished from other male harriers by combination of chestnut-brown mantle and upperwing-coverts contrasting with grey secondaries/inner primaries and black outer primaries, pale head (variably streaked with brown) and pale leading edge to wing, and brown streaking on breast and belly, becoming uniformly brown on lower belly and vent. Shows variable amount of brown on underwing-coverts, with rest of underwing being white except for black ends to primaries. All-dark melanistic morphs occur which are sooty-grey above and blackish below, with grey patch at base of underside of primaries. **Adult female** is mainly dark brown except for creamy crown, nape and throat, creamy leading edge to wing, and paler patch at base of underside of primaries. Melanistic female (and juvenile) much as melanistic male, but with grey or whitish colour extending across underside of all flight feathers (not just on primaries). **Juvenile** is similar to female, but head and wing-coverts may be entirely dark. **Racial variation** The eastern race *C. a. spilonotus*, which has been recorded in the NE subcontinent, differs markedly from the nominate race, described above, and in some plumages could be confused with Pied and Hen Harriers (p.532 and p.531). Compared with Pied Harrier, it is larger, has broader wings and tail, and is stouter-bodied with more prominent head. **Adult male** *spilonotus* has black streaking on whitish head and breast, and has black mantle and median coverts with feathers boldly edged with white. Head and mantle can appear mainly black on some, and is then not unlike adult male Pied Harrier, but is never as clean-cut in appearance as that species (i.e. breast is streaked, mantle and back show some white markings, and lacks clear-cut black bar across median coverts and broad white leading edge to wing). Less heavily marked birds can appear similar to female Pied; small size and finer build, prominent barring across tail, and more uniform mantle and coverts are useful features for Pied. **Adult female** has white uppertail-coverts, greyish flight feathers and tail with dark barring, cream head and breast with dark streaking, and broad diffuse rufous streaking on underparts. Structural differences and heavily marked underbody and underwing are best features for separation from female Pied. White 'rump' band recalls female Hen or Pallid Harriers (p.531), but is otherwise rather different in general appearance. **Juvenile** is rather dark, with cream breast-band and pale patch at base of underside of primaries; head usually mainly cream, with variable dark streaking, and some with pronounced cream streaking on mantle; lacks prominent white band across uppertail-coverts. **VOICE** Usually silent outside breeding season. **HABITS** Like other harriers, has a characteristic method of hunting (although its flight is heavier than that of most): systematically quarters the ground a few metres above it, gliding slowly on raised wings and occasionally flapping rather heavily several times; on locating prey, drops quickly with claws held out to catch it. Eats frogs, fish, weak birds, small mammals, small snakes and lizards, and large insects. Often perches for long periods on the ground or on a low perch such as a post, mound or bush. Roosts communally on the ground in favoured spots in marshes or fields. **HABITAT** Reedbeds, marshes, lakes, flooded paddy-fields; also coastal lagoons in Bangladesh. **DISTRIBUTION AND STATUS** Possibly bred in Baluchistan, Pakistan; mainly a winter visitor throughout much of the subcontinent, except parts of W Pakistan, N Himalayas and NE India, arriving from mid September, with most leaving by mid April. **PK:** common and widespread winter visitor to the plains; a few over-summer in Baluchistan. **NP:** fairly common and widespread winter visitor and passage migrant; usually winters below 915 m (–3050 m on passage). **IN:** widespread and locally common winter visitor; recorded up to 2000 m, mainly in plains. **BT:** rare. **BD:** common throughout, except in the southeast. **LK:** frequent in lowlands and lower hills. **MV:** regular winter visitor. **REFERENCES** Bakewell *et al.* (1988), Morioka *et al.* (1995).

HEN HARRIER *Circus cyaneus* — Plate 65

Northern Harrier

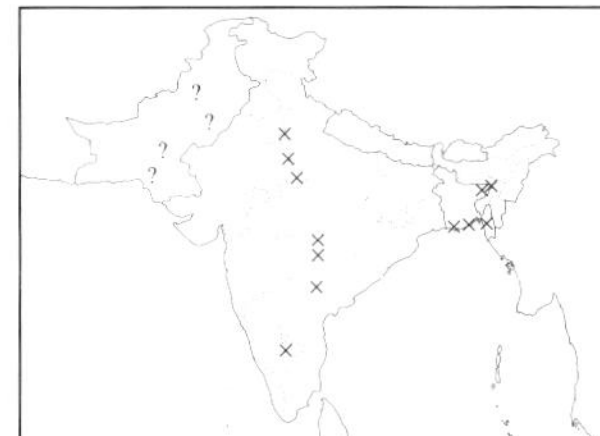

IDENTIFICATION 44–52 cm. Compared with Pallid and Montagu's Harriers (below and p.532), has slower and more laboured flight and is stockier, with broader wings and more rounded hand, normally with five (rather than four) visible primaries at tip. **Adult male** told from male Pallid and Montagu's by combination of dark grey upperparts with extensive black at tips of wings, prominent white uppertail-covert patch, absence of black banding across secondaries (although has variable dark trailing edge to underwing), and dark grey head and breast contrasting with white belly. **Adult female** has boldly streaked underparts. White band across uppertail-coverts is broader than on Pallid and Montagu's. Has narrow pale neck-collar, but otherwise head pattern is typically rather plain compared with those species, usually lacking dark ear-covert patch. **Juvenile** recalls female but has rufous-brown underparts and underwing-coverts, although these are noticeably streaked with dark brown (unlike on juvenile Pallid and Montagu's). **VOICE** Usually silent except near the nest (Brown and Amadon 1968). **HABITS** Flight and hunting behaviour are like those of Eurasian Marsh Harrier, but it is more graceful on the wing. Roosts gregariously on the ground in fields and marshes, often in large numbers and with other harriers. **HABITAT** Open country, grassland and cultivation in plains and foothills. **DISTRIBUTION AND STATUS** Winter visitor. Mainly Pakistan and Himalayas from N Pakistan east to Arunachal Pradesh; Punjab and Gujarat, India. **PK:** scarce, mainly in Himalayan outer foothills. **NP:** fairly common and widespread winter visitor and passage migrant; often up to 3000 m in winter (–5400 m on passage). **IN:** rather uncommon; plains and hills up to 2500 m. **BT:** frequent; 1400–3100 m. **BD:** rare. **REFERENCES** Cramp and Simmons (1980), Forsman (1995), Harris *et al* (1996).

PALLID HARRIER *Circus macrourus* — Plate 65

Pale Harrier (F,I,P)

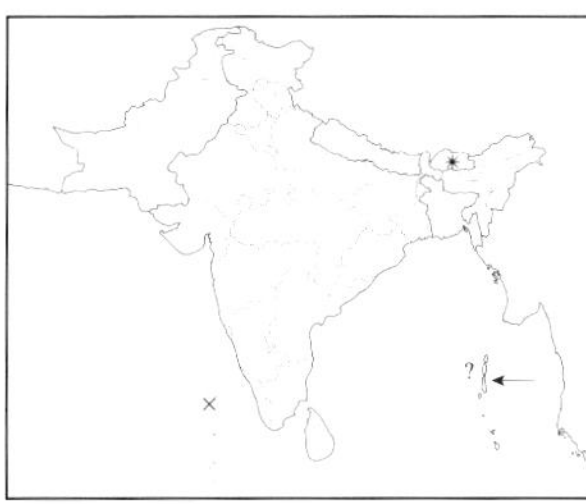

IDENTIFICATION 40–48 cm. A slim-winged, slender-bodied harrier, most likely to be confused with Montagu's (p.532). Like that species, soars and glides with wings in V-shape, and has buoyant flight, the males of these two species being the most buoyant and agile of all harriers. Folded wings fall short of tail-tip, and legs are longer than on Montagu's. **Adult male** told from adult male Montagu's by pale grey upperwing and underwing with dark wedge on primaries, very pale grey head and underbody, absence of black banding across secondaries, and absence of distinct white uppertail-coverts (these are finely barred with grey). **Immature male** has darker brownish-grey upperparts, and may show rusty breast-band and juvenile facial markings. **Adult female** is best told from female Montagu's by patterning of underwing: underside of primaries is pale and lacks a distinct dark trailing edge, with barring irregular and often absent towards tip and at base (often showing characteristic pale crescent at base of primaries, contrasting with dark primary coverts); also, pale primaries contrast with darker underside to secondaries, which typically show only one prominent pale band (may show more pale bands, but these are narrower than on Montagu's and taper towards body); lesser coverts are paler than median and greater coverts, forming pale leading edge to underwing, with dark (diffusely patterned) greater coverts merging into dark secondaries, and has dark, diffusely marked axillaries. Head pattern is also usually different, although there is variation: normally has more pronounced pale collar than Montagu's, contrasting with more prominent dark ear-coverts, while dark eye-stripe usually separates narrow white supercilium from white cheek patch. Typically, also shows contrast between heavily streaked upper breast and paler belly; darker upperwing lacking (or with only very indistinct) pale banding; and outer tail feathers lack rufous-brown barring. Further, appears stockier and broader-winged, with shorter tail, compared with female Montagu's. Confusion is possible with first-summer Montagu's, which has dark underside to secondaries, and best told by patterning of underside of primaries, coverts and axillaries. Best distinguished from female Hen Harrier (above) by narrower wings with more pointed hand and four (rather than five) visible primaries at tip, more pronounced pale banding across underside of secondaries, and irregularly barred primaries which lack dark trailing edge (although differences in underwing pattern do not hold in comparison with juvenile Hen). **Juvenile** differs from female in having orange-buff underparts and underwing-coverts. Best told from juvenile Montagu's by patterning of underside of primaries and by head pattern. Has evenly barred primaries, lacking pronounced dark fingers, lacks dark trailing edge to hand, and can (as adult female) show pale crescent at base of primaries which, when present, is characteristic. Head pattern is similar to juvenile Montagu's, but typically shows narrower white supercilium and smaller white patch below eye, and has more extensive dark ear-covert patch, resulting in darker face and smaller area of white on throat; further, has broader pale collar which is equally wide from nape to throat, appears to continue across throat, and contrasts strongly with dark neck sides. **VOICE** Silent, except in display at nesting grounds (Brown and Amadon 1968). **HABITS** Like those of Hen Harrier, but lighter on the wing. **HABITAT** Open country in plains and foothills: semi-desert, grassy slopes, cultivation, scrub-covered plains, and edges of marshes. **DISTRIBUTION AND STATUS** Winter visitor. Throughout most of the subcontinent, except parts of the northeast, Nepal and W Pakistan; arrives in late August, leaves in March/April. **PK:** widespread and common to frequent winter visitor to Sindh and Punjab, also a passage migrant to Baluchistan. **NP:** uncommon winter visitor and passage migrant; mainly below 2200 m (–3050 m). **IN:** widespread and locally fairly common winter visitor; plains and hills, up to 3000 m in Himalayas, to 2600 m in peninsular hills. **BT:** collected once in 19th century. **BD:** scarce winter visitor. **LK:** common winter visitor throughout; rarely oversummers. **MV:** regular winter visitor. **REFERENCES** Forsman (1995), Jonsson (1992), Harris *et al* (1996).

PIED HARRIER *Circus melanoleucos* Plate 64

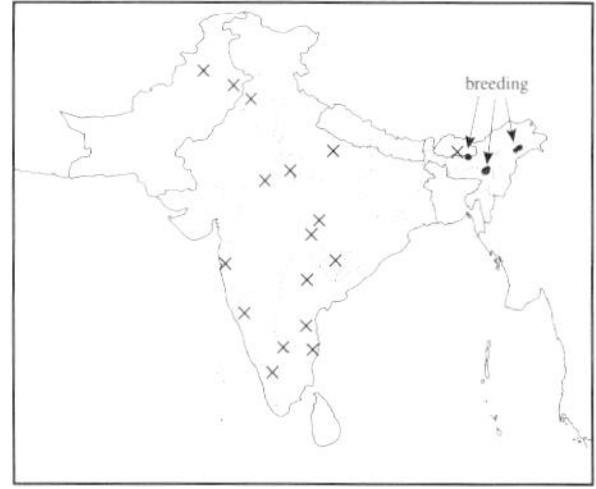

IDENTIFICATION 41–46.5 cm. Usually looks broader in wing and body than Pallid and Montagu's Harriers (p.531 and below), and slightly heavier in flight, although male can appear dainty and buoyant. Most likely to be confused with eastern race of Eurasian Marsh Harrier (p.530); see that species for details. **Adult male** is distinctive, with black head and breast contrasting with white underbody, black upperbody, median coverts and primaries contrasting with grey of rest of wing, and white leading edge to wing. Yellow cere and iris are especially striking against black of head. **Adult female** superficially resembles female Pallid and Montagu's, but has paler underwing with narrow dark barring on flight feathers and sparse streaking on coverts, brown upperwing-coverts (with pale leading edge to wing) contrasting with greyer primaries and secondaries, which have dark barring, and grey tail also with dark barring. **Juvenile** has dark brown head and upperparts, with white supercilium and patch below eye (but lacking pronounced white collar of juvenile Pallid and Montagu's), white uppertail-coverts, rufous-brown underbody and underwing-coverts, and pale underside to primaries (with dark fingers) contrasting with dark underside of secondaries. **VOICE** Male in display calls *keee-veeee*, and female utters a rapid *kee-kee-kee* or a rapid chattering *chak-chak-chak-chak-chak-chak*; usually silent in winter quarters, but rarely utters a rapid *wek-wek-wek* (Brown and Amadon 1968). **HABITS** Like those of Hen Harrier. **HABITAT** Open grassland and cultivation in plains and hills. **BREEDING** April–July? Nest is a rough pad of grasses built close to the ground in open grassland. **DISTRIBUTION AND STATUS** Breeds in Assam hills; mainly a winter visitor, chiefly to the northeast of the subcontinent from Nepal south to C Orissa and eastwards, Western Ghats and Sri Lanka. **PK:** vagrant. **NP:** widespread and uncommon; mainly below 350 m (–3810 m on passage). **IN:** locally frequent in northeast, rare elsewhere. **BT:** rare. **BD:** local. **LK:** scarce, in all zones. **REFERENCES** Bakewell *et al.* (1988), Clark and Khan (1995), Morioka *et al.* (1995).

MONTAGU'S HARRIER *Circus pygargus* Plate 65

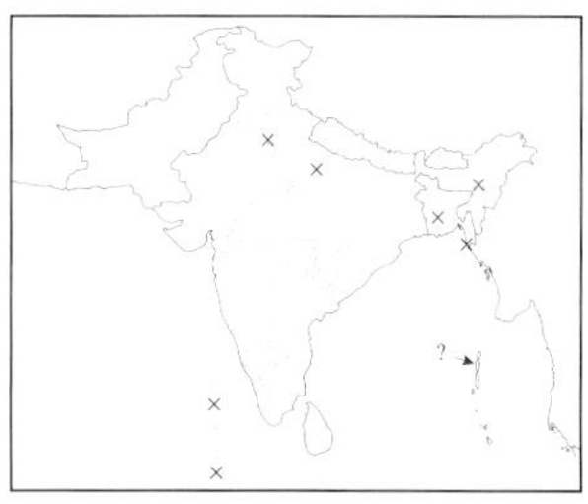

IDENTIFICATION 43–47 cm. Flight is lighter than that of Hen Harrier (p.531) and noticeably buoyant, very like that of Pallid Harrier (p.531), although perhaps not quite so light as the male of that species. **Adult male** told from adult male Pallid and Hen Harriers by contrast between grey lesser/median coverts and paler grey primary coverts and secondaries, single black band across secondaries of upperwing, with two bands visible on underwing, more extensive black on underside of primaries, grey head and breast, becoming whiter on belly, and rufous streaking on belly and underwing-coverts. Rarely, all-dark melanistic forms occur, which are all blackish but for sooty-grey secondaries. **Adult female** best told from female Pallid by patterning of underwing: primaries are distinctly and evenly barred and hand has a dark trailing edge, and patterning is continuous with secondaries, which show broader and more pronounced pale bands (these not narrowing towards body); further, has rufous-brown and white barring on underwing-coverts and axillaries. Pale collar and dark ear-coverts are usually less apparent than on Pallid, and usually has broader white supercilium which joins white cheek patch to form rather extensive pale area around eye. Typically, has more uniformly streaked underparts, and shows distinct dark banding on upperside of remiges, especially secondaries, which is lacking on female Pallid (although this latter feature may not be apparent on immature females). Outer tail feathers are barred with rufous-brown. Appears small-bodied, slim-winged and long-tailed compared with female Pallid. Folded wings reach tail-tip, and legs are shorter than Pallid's. Best told from female Hen Harrier by narrower wings with more pointed hand and four (rather than five) visible primaries at tip, and rufous-brown and white barring on underwing-coverts and axillaries. Rare melanistic female (and juvenile) Montagu's are all blackish except for paler greyish barring on flight feathers and tail. **Juvenile** differs from female in having rufous underparts and underwing-coverts, and darker secondaries. Best told from juvenile Pallid by patterning of underside of primaries and by head pattern. Has broad dark tips to primaries (fingers are entirely dark) and dark trailing edge to hand, typically showing no barring at base of outer primaries. Head pattern is similar, but typically shows more white around eye and smaller dark ear-covert patch, resulting in whiter face and more extensive white throat, and has narrower pale collar which is crescent-shaped (tapering at nape and throat), does not appear to continue across throat, and contrasts less with streaked neck sides. Birds which are dark copper-brown on the underparts and/or have faint streaking on breast and flanks are likely to be juvenile Montagu's. **VOICE** Silent except at breeding grounds and possibly at communal roosts (Brown and Amadon 1968). **HABITS** Like those of Hen Harrier, but lighter on the wing. **HABITAT** A variety of open habitats in the plains and foothills, including cultivation, scrub-covered plains, grassland and edges of marshes. **DISTRIBUTION AND STATUS** Widespread winter visitor. Although status uncertain, because of possible confusion with Pallid Harrier, its distribution is likely to be more patchy than that of Pallid, because, unlike that species, it prefers to feed on locusts and concentrates where locust density is high. **PK:** scarce winter visitor. **NP:** scarce winter visitor; below 250 m (–2650 m on passage). **IN:** scattered records throughout most of the country; probably under-recorded. **BD:** vagrant. **LK:** rare winter visitor throughout, more frequent in N coastal areas; also oversummers. **MV:** apparently common winter visitor. **REFERENCES** Clarke (1996), Cramp and Simmons (1980), Forsman (1995), Jonsson (1992), Harris *et al* (1996).

CRESTED GOSHAWK *Accipiter trivirgatus* — Plate 66

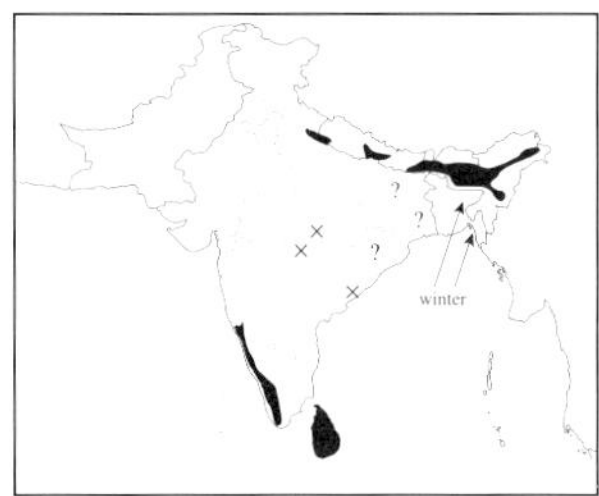

IDENTIFICATION 30–46 cm. Relatively large *Accipiter* with proportionately short, broad and very rounded wings, pinched in at base, and moderate-length tail compared with other species occurring in region. At rest, wing-tips barely extend beyond tail-base. Compared with other *Accipiter* species, has short stoutish legs and toes. Typically seen soaring low above the canopy in fluttering display flight, with white undertail-coverts prominently splayed. Otherwise, rapid stiff wingbeats are interspersed with gliding on level wings. Narrow white line along uppertail-coverts is diagnostic if present. The only crested *Accipiter* occurring in the subcontinent, but see Jerdon's Baza (p.520) for differences from that species. Larger size and crest are best distinctions from Besra (p.535). **Adult male** has dark grey crown and crest, paler grey ear-coverts, prominent black submoustachial and gular stripes, grey-brown upperparts, and rufous-brown streaking on breast and barring on belly and flanks. **Adult female** is similar, although larger in size, but has browner crown and ear-coverts and browner streaking and barring on underparts. **Juvenile** has paler brown upperparts with pale fringes, rufous or buffish fringes to crown, crest and nape feathers, streaked ear-coverts, and buff or rufous wash to underparts, which are mainly streaked with brown (with barring restricted to lower flanks and thighs). **Racial variation** Birds of SW India, and especially *A. t. layardi* of Sri Lanka, are much smaller than *A. t. indicus* of the N subcontinent. *A. t. layardi* has darker brown and sparser streaking and barring on underparts; juvenile is especially distinctive, with unmarked rufous-buff underparts and underwing-coverts (except for spotting on flanks and undertail-coverts). **VOICE** A shrill scream, *he, he, hehehehe*, recorded from Sri Lanka (Henry 1971). **HABITS** Similar to those of Shikra (below). Often frequents the same patch of forest day after day. Adept at catching prey in thick forest; perches hidden among the foliage of a forest tree, and dashes out swiftly to pounce on birds and small mammals on the ground. **HABITAT** Dense deciduous and evergreen broadleaved tropical and subtropical forest; also wooded gardens in Sri Lanka. **BREEDING** February–July, varying locally. Builds a huge untidy nest of sticks 9–13 m up in a thickly foliaged forest tree. **DISTRIBUTION AND STATUS** Resident. Mainly in Himalayas from N Uttar Pradesh east to Arunachal Pradesh; NE and SW India, Bangladesh and Sri Lanka. **NP:** uncommon, mainly from WC areas and eastwards; below 1370 m (–2100 m). **IN:** uncommon in Himalayas up to 2000 m; very rare in the southwest up to 1100 m. **BT:** frequent; 400–1830 m. **BD:** scarce. **LK:** regular in all zones, more frequent in wet lowlands, infrequent elsewhere.

SHIKRA *Accipiter badius* — Plate 66

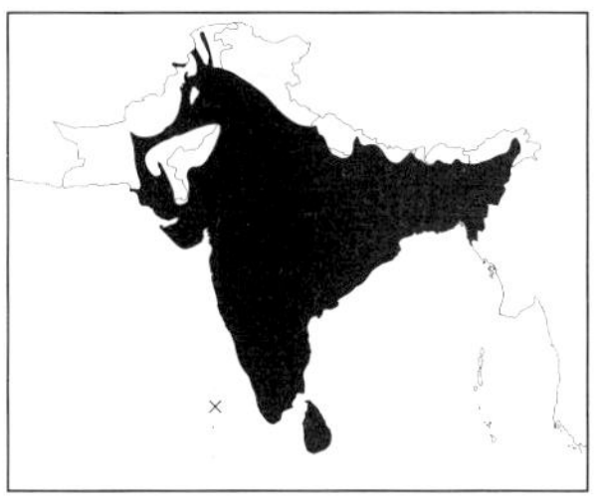

IDENTIFICATION 30–36 cm. Adults are paler in coloration than Besra and Eurasian Sparrowhawk (p.535); underwing is pale, with fine barring on remiges and slightly darker wing-tips. Head is rather cuckoo-like compared with other *Accipiter* species. Active flight is typical of the genus: swift and direct, with fast wingbeats followed by a glide. **Adult male** told from Besra and Eurasian Sparrowhawk by pale blue-grey upperparts with contrasting dark grey primaries, fine and rather indistinct grey gular stripe, pale and fine brownish-orange barring on underparts, unbarred white thighs, and unbarred or only lightly barred central tail feathers. **Adult female** is similar, but upperparts are pale brownish-grey. **Juvenile** is medium or pale brown above, with more prominent gular stripe and streaked underparts. Told from immature Besra by paler upperparts and narrower tail barring, and from Eurasian Sparrowhawk by streaked underparts. **Racial variation** The nominate race from Sri Lanka and *A. b. poliopsis* of the NE subcontinent are smaller and darker grey above than other races in the region, and have underparts more closely barred with darker rufous. **VOICE** Normal call is a loud, harsh *titu-titu*, similar to call of Black Drongo (p.610); also long, drawn-out screams, *iheeya, iheeya*, and a constantly repeated *ti-tui* in display (Ali and Ripley 1987). **HABITS** Usually found singly or in pairs according to the season. Frequently soars in small circles at considerable heights, especially in the breeding season. A bold and aggressive predator like other *Accipiter* species, sharing the same hunting techniques as the rest of the genus. Perches concealed in the foliage of a tree, scanning the surroundings, and captures prey in a short swift dash, relying on surprise tactics. Also seeks prey by swift low flight between trees, patches of cover or behind a hedge, darting over the top to take prey by surprise. Eats small mammals, birds, lizards, frogs and large insects. **HABITAT** Open wooded country and groves around villages and cultivation. **BREEDING** January–June, varying locally. Builds an untidy nest of twigs 7–15 m up in a leafy tree. **DISTRIBUTION AND STATUS** Resident. Throughout most of the subcontinent, except parts of W Pakistan, NW India and N Himalayas. **PK:** common resident throughout the Indus plains, uncommon summer visitor to Baluchistan and plains of NW Pakistan. **NP:** fairly common and widespread; usually below 1370 m (–2250 m). **IN:** common and widespread; plains and hills up to 1400 m in Himalayas, to 1500 m in peninsular hills. **BT:** uncommon. **BD:** common throughout. **LK:** common in all zones.

NICOBAR SPARROWHAWK *Accipiter butleri* — Plate 66

***A. badius* (I)**

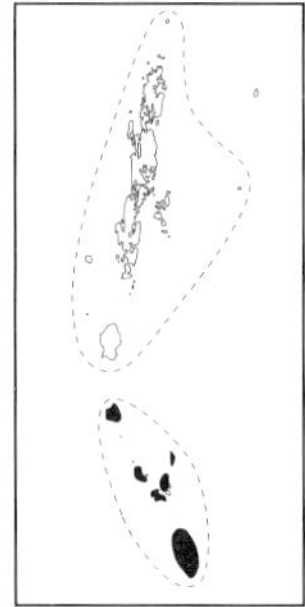

IDENTIFICATION 30–34 cm. Given its range, likely to be confused only with Japanese Sparrowhawk (p.535), Besra (p.535) and Chinese Sparrowhawk (below). Has very short primary projection (see other species for comparison). **Adult male** told from those species by pale blue-grey upperparts with paler head and contrasting dark grey primaries, white underparts with indistinct gular stripe and pale rufous vermiculations on breast, unbarred tail with narrow diffuse terminal band, and lack of barring on underwing, with white underwing-coverts. **Adult female** is similar, but upperparts are slightly browner, and has very slightly stronger barring on breast. **Juvenile** is typically distinctive, with rufous upperparts with dark brown feather centres, rufous-buff underparts with rufous-brown streaking on breast and blotching on belly and flanks, dark banding on rufous-cinnamon secondaries and tail, and whitish iris. (A single immature from Great Nicobar, however, has much browner and darker upperparts and may represent an undescribed race.) **VOICE** A shrill double note, described as *kee-wick*, similar to that of Shikra. **HABITS** Little known. Rather shy and difficult to observe. **HABITAT** Tops of tall trees. **BREEDING** Little known. February to March and October. One nest found 13 m up in a tree. **DISTRIBUTION AND STATUS IN:** resident, endemic to Nicobar Is (has been recorded on Katchall, Camorta, Car Nicobar and Great Nicobar; no recent records from Car Nicobar). **REFERENCES** Butler (1899), Ferguson-Lees (in prep.), Sankaran (1997; 1998).

CHINESE SPARROWHAWK *Accipiter soloensis* — Plate 66

Horsfield's Goshawk (I), Chinese Goshawk

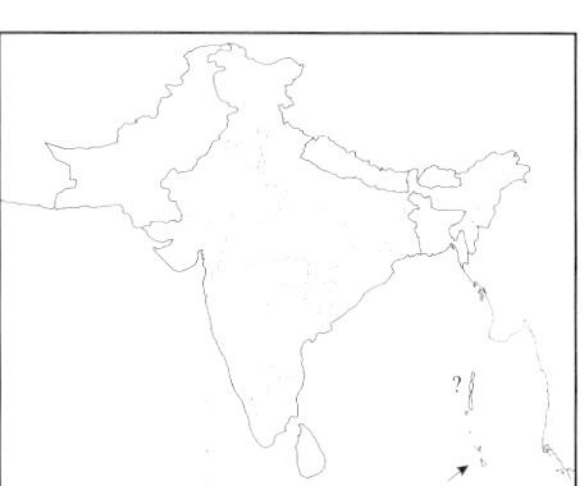

IDENTIFICATION 25–30 cm. A distinctive *Accipiter* with comparatively long, narrow and pointed wings. At rest, shows very long primary projection (extending nearly halfway down tail). **Adult** has blue-grey head and upperparts (with blue-grey coverts contrasting with blackish primaries), indistinct grey gular stripe, and rufous-orange breast. Sexes similar, and there is little difference in size, although breast coloration of male is paler and can be whitish or pale greyish-purple, while breast of female can show bars of darker grey and upperparts are a shade browner; central tail feathers are usually without bars on male and sometimes without bars on female; iris is dark crimson in male and yellow in female. Shows distinctive underwing pattern in flight: has unbarred flight feathers with blackish wing-tips and dark grey trailing edge to wing, and unbarred coverts. Sub-adult birds show some dark barring on underside of flight feathers. **Juvenile** has dark brown upperparts with rufous fringes to mantle and coverts, more pronounced dark gular stripe, rufous-brown heart-shaped spotting on breast and belly, and broad rufous-brown barring on flanks. Compared with juvenile Japanese Sparrowhawk (p.535), crown is a darker slate-grey than mantle, face is bluish-grey, lacks distinct supercilium, and has blackish orbital ring. Underwing pattern is also distinctive, with dark grey wing-tips and trailing edge and largely unmarked greyish-brown to pale rufous wing-coverts; underside of flight feathers is distinctly barred (although less heavily so than on juvenile Japanese, with three rather than four dark bars across secondaries in addition to grey band along trailing edge). **VOICE** Silent except when breeding, when gives shrill nasal piping notes in a rapid and accelerating series, descending in pitch, *kee..pe-pe-pe-petu-petu*, reminiscent of Eurasian Wryneck (p.380) (P. Holt). **HABITS** Not described from the region. Elsewhere in its range, it is unusual in not using swift, dashing, surprise attacks typical of the genus. Hunts mainly on open ground, taking frogs in short stoops from a perch or from flight. **HABITAT** Not described from the region. In the rest of its winter range, frequents forest or wooded country in the lowlands and hunts in rice fields. **DISTRIBUTION AND STATUS IN:** winter visitor to Nicobar Is (Car Nicobar, Katchall, Great and Little Nicobars). **REFERENCES** Mees (1981), Morioka *et al.* (1995).

JAPANESE SPARROWHAWK *Accipiter gularis* — Plate 67

***A. virgatus* (I)**

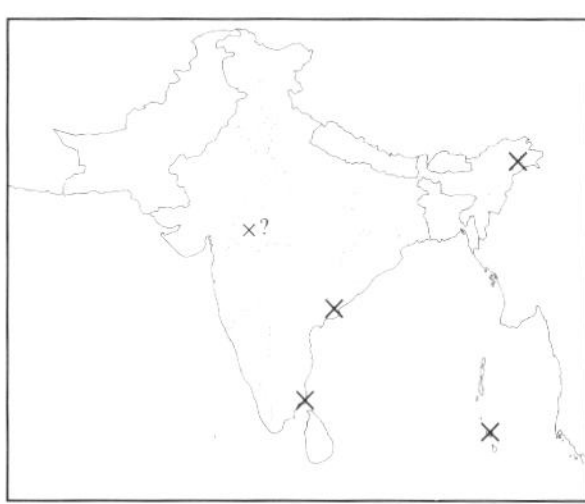

IDENTIFICATION 25–31.5 cm. Much as Eurasian Sparrowhawk (below), although smaller. Underside of flight feathers and underwing-coverts are distinctly barred as on that species and Besra (below). At rest, shows long primary projection (extending nearly halfway down tail) that is longer than on Besra (roughly one-third down tail). In all plumages, pale bars across tail are generally broader than the dark bars (reverse on Besra). In flight, wings are a shade narrower and more pointed than on Eurasian and Besra. Underpart patterning of adults rather different from Besra; juveniles rather similar. **Adult male** has dark bluish-grey upperparts, pale rufous to pale grey underparts, some with fine grey barring, and dark crimson iris. Has very indistinct gular stripe (often not visible in field). **Adult female** has browner upperparts, whitish underparts with grey-brown barring, and often narrow white supercilium; gular stripe is more prominent, and has yellow iris. **Juvenile** has dark greyish-brown upperparts with narrow rufous fringes, white supercilium, and brown to rufous streaking on breast, heart-shaped spots on lower breast and belly and barring on flanks and thighs. Iris and eye-ring are yellowish. Head coloration, flight profile and underwing pattern are best distinctions from juvenile Chinese Sparrowhawk (p.534; see that species). **VOICE** Undescribed. **HABITS** Very like those of Besra. **HABITAT** Not described from the region; probably forest. **DISTRIBUTION AND STATUS IN:** winter visitor, recorded from E Assam, NE Andhra Pradesh, E Tamil Nadu, Andamans, Nicobars and Madhya Pradesh?; possibly occurs more widely. **REFERENCES** Leader and Carey (1985), Mees (1981), Morioka *et al.* (1995).

BESRA *Accipiter virgatus* — Plate 67

Besra Sparrow-hawk (F,I,P)

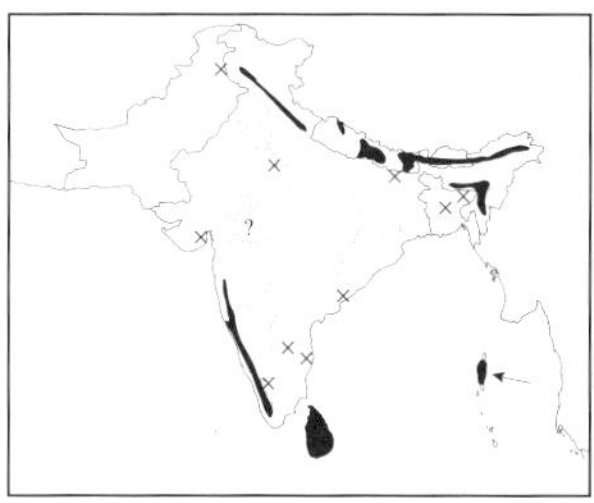

IDENTIFICATION 29–36 cm. Small *Accipiter*. Primary projection is comparatively short (less than one-third down tail). Upperparts are darker in coloration and underwing is strongly barred compared with Shikra (p.533), while prominent gular stripe and streaked breast should separate it from Eurasian Sparrowhawk (below). In all plumages resembles Crested Goshawk (p.533), but is considerably smaller, lacks crest, and has longer and finer legs. **Adult male** told from Shikra by dark slate-grey upperparts lacking strong contrast with primaries, broad blackish gular stripe, bold rufous streaking on breast and barring on belly, flanks and thighs, and pronounced and broad dark tail barring. **Adult female** is similar, but upperparts are browner, with blackish crown and nape. **Juvenile** has brown upperparts with rufous fringes, prominent gular stripe, and streaked/spotted breast and belly and barred flanks. Told from immature Shikra by darker, richer brown upperparts, broader gular stripe, and broader tail barring. From Eurasian Sparrowhawk by streaked underparts. **Racial variation** Male *A. v. abdulalii*, from the Andaman Is, is quite different from those from the rest of the subcontinent: the breast is greyish-tawny, the belly dull tawny and the thighs light grey, the entire underparts lacking streaking or barring. Female *abdulalii* is as in other races. **VOICE** A loud squealing *ki-weeer*, or a rapidly repeated *tchew-tchew-tchew*. Noisy, pairs often calling to each other (Brown and Amadon 1968). **HABITS** Very similar to those of Shikra. Expert at dodging and twisting at speed through the dense forest understorey. Eats mainly small birds. **HABITAT** Breeds in dense broadleaved forest; also in more open wooded country in winter and in gardens in Sri Lanka. **BREEDING** March–June, varying locally. Nest is a platform of sticks placed 15–25 m up in a forest tree; often uses old nests of crows and other birds. **DISTRIBUTION AND STATUS** Resident, subject to altitudinal movements. Mainly in Himalayas from Kashmir east to Arunachal Pradesh; NE India and Bangladesh; Western Ghats and Sri Lanka. **PK:** vagrant. **NP:** frequent; summers 1350–2800 m (–3440 m), winters down to 250 m (to 75 m). **IN:** uncommon; in Himalayas, breeds up to 3000 m and winters down to foothills and adjacent plains; 600–1200 m in Western Ghats. **BT:** frequent; 1130–2895 m. **BD:** possibly a scarce winter visitor, but Japanese Sparrowhawk cannot be ruled out. **LK:** occurs in all zones, infrequent, prefers the wet lowlands. **REFERENCES** Giri and Choudhary (1996), Leader and Carey (1985), Mees (1981).

EURASIAN SPARROWHAWK *Accipiter nisus* — Plate 67

Sparrow-hawk (F,I), Northern Sparrowhawk (K)

IDENTIFICATION 31–36 cm. Upperparts are darker in coloration than Shikra's (p.533), with prominent tail barring, and underwing is more strongly barred, while uniform barring on underparts and absence of prominent gular stripe should separate it from Besra (above). Female and immature are possibly confusable with Northern Goshawk (p.536), but are considerably smaller and slimmer-bodied, have proportionately shorter and more rounded wings and longer tail, and fly with more rapid wingbeats. **Adult male** told from Shikra by darker slate-grey upperparts lacking strong contrast with primaries, stronger reddish-orange barring to underparts, absence of gular stripe, and more prominent tail barring. **Adult female** has dark brown upperparts, white supercilium, and dark brown barring on underparts and underwing-coverts. **Juvenile** is dark brown above, with rufous fringes (which can result in warm orange-brown appearance); underparts usually look barred, but at close range breast of immature male may show

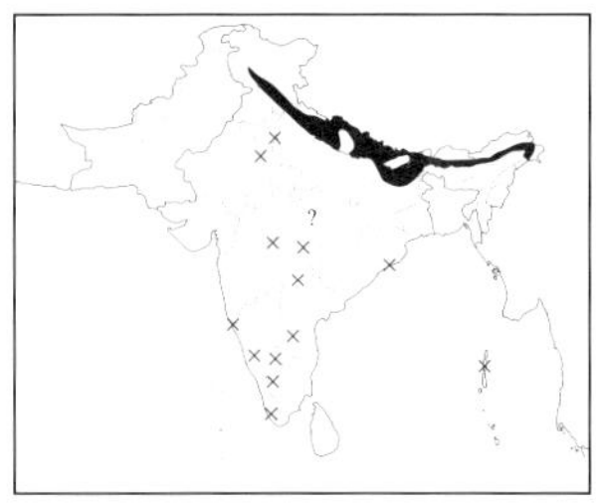

streaking or spotting (but always lacks gular stripe of immature Shikra and Besra). **Racial variation** Male of the resident Himalayan race, *A. n. melaschistos,* has darker grey upperparts, with almost black crown and mantle, and stronger rufous barring to underparts, compared with wintering race *A. n. nisosimilis.* **VOICE** Two long notes followed by three or four very short notes, *tiu-tiu-tititi* (Ali and Ripley 1987). **HABITS** Very similar to those of Shikra. Feeds chiefly on birds. **HABITAT** Well-wooded country, open forest, scrub forest, and groves in cultivation. **BREEDING** April–June. Nest is a stick platform built in a tree; often uses old nests of crows or other birds; sometimes nests on a cliff ledge. **DISTRIBUTION AND STATUS** Resident, subject to altitudinal movements, and winter visitor. Breeds in mountains of Baluchistan, Pakistan, and Himalayas from Pakistan east to Arunachal Pradesh; winters in Himalayan foothills and in plains south to Bangladesh and S Kerala. **PK:** in summer frequent in Baluchistan, less common in Himalayas; frequent winter visitor to the Indus plains. **NP:** fairly common; summers mainly at 2440–4200 m (–5180 m on passage), winters 250–1450 m (down to 75 m). **IN:** fairly common; in Himalayas, breeds 1400–3500 m and winters in foothills and plains; rare south of the Himalayas. **BT:** fairly common; 855–4300 m. **BD:** scarce winter visitor.

NORTHERN GOSHAWK *Accipiter gentilis* — Plate 67

Goshawk (F,I)

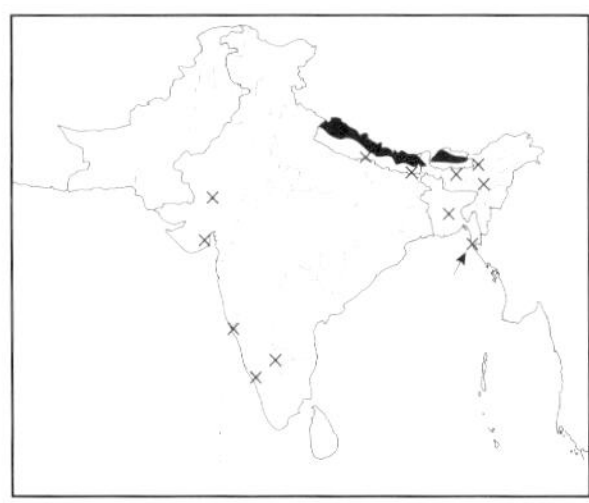

IDENTIFICATION 50–61 cm. Confusable really only with Eurasian Sparrowhawk (p.535), but usually appears considerably larger (although small males may not look that much bigger than large female Northern Sparrowhawk). In flight, appears stouter-bodied, with bulging breast, and with proportionately longer and narrower wings and shorter tail. Flies with slower, heavier and more deliberate wingbeats and with longer-sustained glides, and wings can appear quite narrow at tip, with bulging secondaries forming S-shaped curve to trailing edge. Above features also hold for separation from Crested Goshawk (p.533), in addition to plumage differences. **Adult male** has grey-brown upperparts, with darker crown and ear-coverts (and white supercilium), and has whitish underparts which are closely barred with dark brown. Upperparts are greyer than on female Eurasian Sparrowhawk, undertail-coverts are conspicuously white, and often grey ear-coverts give it a hooded appearance lacking on that species. **Adult female** is similar, but with browner upperparts, and is considerably larger in size. **Juvenile** has heavy streaking on buff-coloured underparts, and is browner above, with more uniform head and more prominent tail barring. **VOICE** Most common call is a shrill chatter, and female has a disyllabic *hee-aa* (Cramp and Simmons 1980). **HABITS** Very similar to those of Shikra (p.533), but much more powerful. Above the treeline in the Himalayas, perches on rocks and makes surprise attacks on prey coming to feed on open slopes. Eats birds and small mammals. **HABITAT** Oak and high-altitude coniferous forest, sometimes hunting above the treeline in Himalayas. **BREEDING** Poorly known in the region. Probably March and April. Nest is poorly described; one was built 12 m up a tree. **DISTRIBUTION AND STATUS** Winter visitor, probably also resident. Mainly Pakistan and Himalayas from N Pakistan east to Arunachal Pradesh; scattered records south to Kerala. **PK:** rare passage migrant, possibly also a winter visitor; recorded chiefly along the Indus R system. **NP:** widespread and presumably resident in the north; frequent; 1370–4880 m (250–6100 m). **IN:** status uncertain; rare winter visitor, possibly breeds in W Himalayas. **BT:** frequent. **BD:** vagrant. **REFERENCES** Porter *et al.* (1974).

WHITE-EYED BUZZARD *Butastur teesa* — Plate 68

White-eyed Buzzard-Eagle (I), White-eyed Hawk (F)

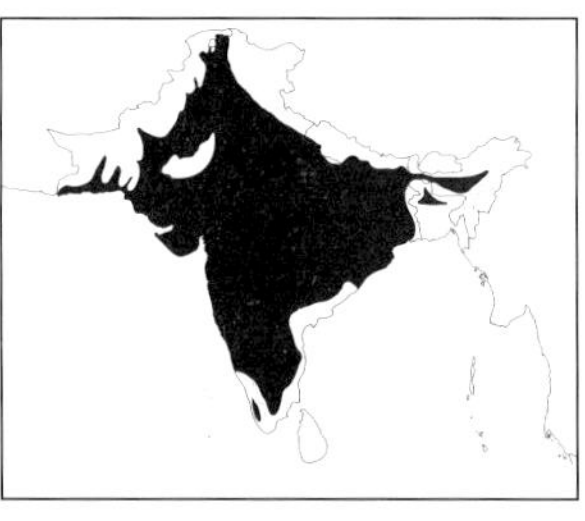

IDENTIFICATION 43 cm. Longish, rather slim wings, long tail and buzzard-like head give rise to distinctive appearance in flight. Flight is rather *Accipiter*-like and direct; often flies close to ground, with few fast wingbeats interspersed with short glides, and ending with an upward swoop to a perch. At rest, long wings almost reach tail-tip and has long unfeathered tarsus. **Adult** is largely brown, and has a white throat bordered with dark brown and with a dark brown mesial stripe, a white patch on nape, and rufous rump/uppertail-coverts and tail (with narrow black subterminal band). Underparts are barred. Iris is yellow. In flight, rufous uppertail and pale panel across median coverts are striking features from above; from below, remiges appear pale (with dark primary tips and whiter patch at base of primaries), and tail appears greyish (with outer feathers translucent when spread). **Juvenile** has buffish head and breast streaked with dark brown, with malar and throat stripes indistinct or absent, and has buff markings on coverts. Rufous uppertail has stronger dark band. Iris is brown. **VOICE** Noisy early in breeding season. Plaintive mewing *pit-weer, pit-weer...* uttered constantly, both when perched and when soaring. **HABITS** Found singly or in pairs. Sluggish; spends long periods perched very upright on a vantage point such as an isolated tree, telegraph pole or wires, or a mound. Hunts chiefly by dropping to the ground to seize small reptiles, rodents, frogs or large insects. Occasionally walks about on open ground seeking prey, especially after a recent fire. **HABITAT** Dry open country: cultivation, scrub, open deciduous and coniferous forest, scrub desert. **BREEDING**

February–June, varying locally. Builds a nest of twigs 9–12 m up in a thickly foliaged tree. **DISTRIBUTION AND STATUS** Resident. Throughout most of the subcontinent, except parts of W Pakistan, Bangladesh, NW, NE and S India, N Himalayas and Sri Lanka. **PK:** common and widespread resident in Indus plains; in summer, spreads into Chir Pine forests in foothills up to 1065 m. **NP:** widespread and fairly common; mainly below 300 m (–1500 m). **IN:** widespread resident, but summer visitor in Punjab and possibly elsewhere; locally frequent in the north, uncommon in the south; plains and hills, up to 1200 m in Himalayas. **BD:** local in the centre and northwest.

COMMON BUZZARD *Buteo buteo* — Plate 68

Buzzard (I), Eurasian Buteo (F)

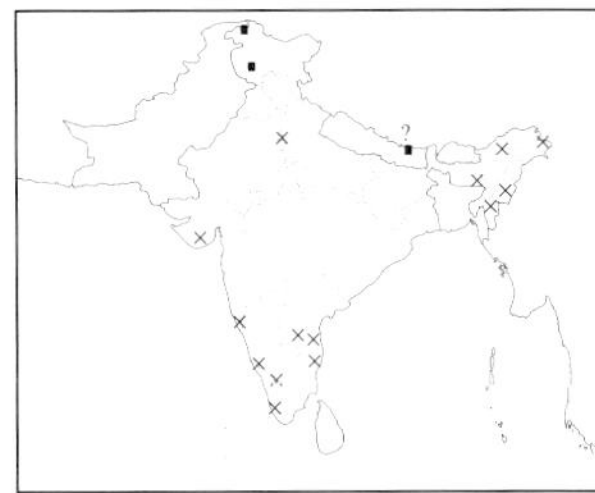

IDENTIFICATION 51–56 cm. Extremely variable in appearance, with some plumages giving rise to considerable danger of confusion with Long-legged and Upland Buzzards (below and p.538). See those species for main differences. Soars with wings held in a shallow V and tail well spread; glides on flat wings. **Racial variation** Poorly understood. *B. b. japonicus*, considered to be a winter visitor to the Himalayas, typically has rather pale head and underparts, with variable dark streaking on breast and brown patch on belly/thighs; tail is grey-brown with dark barring (although base colour may be paler greyish-white); dark carpal patch is often prominent. *B. b. refectus*, a resident in the Himalayas, is dark brown to rufous-brown, with variable amounts of white on underparts; tail is dull brown with some dark barring or uniform sandy-brown; has prominent white patch on underside of primaries. *B. b. vulpinus*, which has occurred as a winter visitor, is extremely variable in plumage, although usually shows rufous coloration to tail (see Long-legged Buzzard for details). **Adult** shows broad dark trailing edge to underwing, and tail has well-defined dark subterminal band. **Juvenile** has narrower, paler and more diffuse trailing edge to wing, and evenly barred tail (lacking broad subterminal band). **VOICE** A loud, clear mew, *peee-oo*, uttered repeatedly, especially in display; a repeated *mah* by pairs answering one another. *B. b. vulpinus* and *B. b. japonicus* are practically silent in winter quarters (Brown and Amadon 1968). **HABITS** Found singly or in pairs. Rather sluggish; spends much time perched on prominent positions such as trees, posts and rocks. Takes to the air with laboured wingbeats, but buoyant when at height. Soars for long periods with ease. Hunts by pouncing on prey from a vantage point, or by soaring over open country and at times actively hovering with gently fanning wing-tips before dropping onto prey, or by walking or standing on the ground. Eats rodents, reptiles, small birds and invertebrates. **HABITAT** Variety of habitats in open country, including cultivation, grassland and scrub desert. **BREEDING** Very little known in the region. Possibly late April–June. Builds a large stick nest on a cliff ledge. **DISTRIBUTION AND STATUS** Status uncertain because of confusion with other buzzards. Breeds in small numbers in Himalayas in Pakistan, Kashmir ?and Nepal; winter visitor to Pakistan and Himalayas from N Pakistan east to Arunachal Pradesh, also N, NE, NW and S India, Bangladesh and Sri Lanka. **PK:** frequent and widespread winter visitor. **NP:** fairly common and widespread winter visitor and passage migrant, mainly 1000–4300 m (down to 250 m); small numbers summer from 3350 m up to at least 3800 m. **IN:** locally fairly common winter visitor to the north; rare in the south. **BT:** common winter visitor and passage migrant, also probably resident; 150-3050 m. **BD:** rare winter visitor. **LK:** regular, rare winter visitor throughout. **REFERENCES** Voous and Bijleveld (1964).

LONG-LEGGED BUZZARD *Buteo rufinus* — Plate 68

Long-legged Buteo (F)

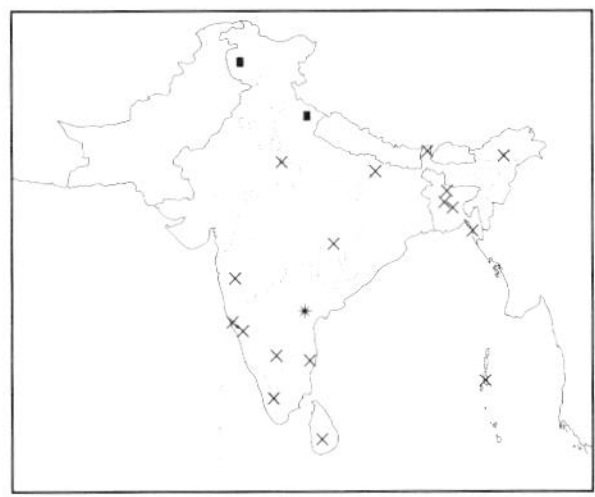

IDENTIFICATION 61 cm. Like Common Buzzard (above), is variable in plumage, and some birds are best told by differences in structure and flight action. For differences from Upland Buzzard (p.538), see that species. Compared with Common Buzzard, Long-legged is larger and appears longer-necked with larger head; wings are longer (and more eagle-like), tail looks longer, and in active flight looks heavier; glides with arms slightly raised; soars and circles with wings held in a deeper V, recalling Eurasian Marsh Harrier (p.530). Occasionally hovers like Common. **Adult** shows broad black trailing edge to underwing contrasting with otherwise whitish remiges, and tail is usually unbarred (although not in 'dark morphs'). Confusion is most likely with the so-called 'fox-red morph' of *vulpinus* race of Common Buzzard (= Steppe Buzzard), but most Long-legged differ in having a paler head and upper breast (with dark eye-stripe and moustache) which are sharply demarcated from rufous-brown lower breast and belly (rather than rufous head and breast, often with pale breast-band and/or distinct barring on breast and belly); more uniform rufous underwing-coverts (rather than showing noticeable contrast between darkish greater, pale median and rusty lesser underwing-coverts); more extensive black carpal patches (rather than usually limited to greater underwing-coverts); larger and more distinct pale patch at base of upperside of primaries; and unbarred pale orange upperside to tail, usually with some white at base (on 'fox-red' Steppe Buzzard, tail is usually more rufous and distinctly barred, with broader subterminal band). Long-legged may show barred uppertail, so combination of remaining features mentioned above is required. Some rufous Long-legged Buzzards are extremely similar in plumage to 'fox-red morph' of Steppe Buzzard (e.g. with head and breast rufous), and some may be separable only by uppertail differences. Also occurs as a 'blackish morph', which has blackish body and coverts, greyish underside to remiges with dark trailing edge, and dark band across tail; the only plumage difference from 'blackish morph' of *vulpinus* Common Buzzard is the broad and prominent dark barring on remiges of underwing and on uppertail of Long-legged. **Juvenile** is generally less rufous, has narrower, paler and more diffuse trailing edge to wing, and has lightly barred tail which on many birds is pale greyish-brown. Best separated from Common by larger size and different structure, and more prominent carpal patches and dark belly. **VOICE** Rather silent. In anxiety a high-pitched mew, like that of Common Buzzard but shorter and sharper (Brown and Amadon (1968). **HABITS** Similar to those of Common Buzzard. Feeds on small mammals, weak birds, carrion, reptiles and large insects. **HABITAT** Breeds in forested hills and mountains; winters in a variety of habitats in open country, especially desert and stony plains and sandbanks in main rivers, also semi-desert and cultivation. **BREEDING** Little known in the region. March–May. Builds a large stick nest on a crag or tall tree on a forested slope. **DISTRIBUTION AND STATUS** Status uncertain because of confusion with other buzzards. Breeds in Himalayas in N Pakistan, Kashmir and N Uttar Pradesh; widespread winter visitor, but recorded mainly in Pakistan, Himalayas from N Pakistan east to Bhutan, also in Assam, NW India and Bangladesh. **PK:** common and widespread winter visitor, less frequent in the mountains, arriving from mid August, with most leaving by mid March; small numbers breed in the north (2895 m, 3355 m). **NP:** widespread winter visitor and passage migrant, frequent below 2755 m (–5000 m on passage). **IN:** frequent in Kashmir, breeds 1830–3900 m; locally fairly common in winter in lower Himalayas and N plains. **BT:** frequent winter visitor and passage migrant. **BD:** scarce winter visitor. **LK:** winter vagrant to hills. **REFERENCES** Alström and Colston (1991), Shirihai and Forsman (1991).

UPLAND BUZZARD *Buteo hemilasius* Plate 68

Upland Buteo (F)

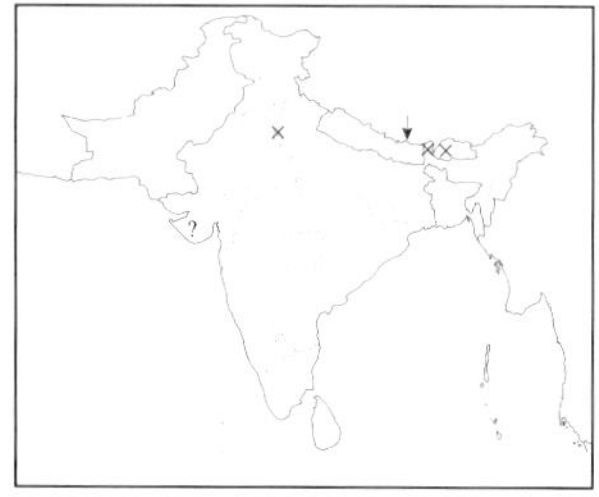

IDENTIFICATION 71 cm. Always has tarsus at least three-quarters feathered (often entirely feathered), whereas tarsus is normally half feathered (or less) on Long-legged and Common Buzzards (p.537). In flight, structure and appearance are much as Long-legged, and therefore looks larger, longer-winged and longer-tailed than Common (appearing more eagle-like), and in active flight looks heavier; soars with wings held in a deeper V, recalling Golden Eagle (p.542). Frequently hovers. **Adult** shows dark trailing edge to underwing contrasting with otherwise whitish remiges, and tail is only lightly barred towards tip (except in 'dark morph'). Dimorphic, although pale morph is variable (especially in patterning of underparts). 'Classic' pale-morph Upland shows combination of large white patch at base of upperside of primaries (more prominent and extensive than on other *Buteo* species); greyish-white tail, paler towards base and with two or three fine bars towards tip (although at a distance appearing uniformly pale); whitish head with bold dark brown streaking and streaked moustachial stripe; whitish underparts with dark brown streaking on breast, and brown thighs which form dark U when seen from below; and pale buff and only faintly marked underwing-coverts, with extensive black carpal patches. Race *japonicus* of Common Buzzard can, however, be very similar in general appearance of upperparts and underparts, although tail is typically darker grey and more extensively barred, has less prominent pale primary patches, and is structurally rather different (smaller and more compact, with shorter wings and less eagle-like appearance). Upland Buzzard never has rufous coloration to tail or rufous thighs shown by Long-legged. Also occurs as a 'blackish morph', which has blackish body and coverts, and dark-barred greyish tail with broader dark subterminal band; may show pale U on breast. Not safely separable from 'blackish morphs' of Common (*vulpinus*) and Long-legged Buzzards. **Juvenile** has narrower and more diffuse trailing edge to wing, with more evenly barred secondaries, and evenly and more prominently barred tail; pale morph has more heavily streaked underparts and underwing-coverts. Pale morph is probably not separable by plumage from *japonicus* race of Common and some juvenile Long-legged. **VOICE** A mewing call, more nasal and prolonged, not so clear as, but otherwise similar to, that of Common Buzzard; noisy in the breeding season, but otherwise rather silent (Brown and Amadon 1968). **HABITS** Similar to those of Common Buzzard. Diet is not recorded from the region; elsewhere, eats mainly small mammals, also some ground birds. **HABITAT** Open country, including grasslands and cultivation in hills and mountains. **BREEDING** Very little known in the region. Nests possibly of this species found in Nepal in June and July. Nest is a pile of twigs built on a rocky cliff ledge or tree. **DISTRIBUTION AND STATUS** Status uncertain because of confusion with other buzzard species. Possibly breeds in NC Nepal; winter visitor to Himalayas from Kashmir east to Bhutan, and to Punjab, India. **NP:** winter visitor, possibly also a resident breeder; winters down to 250 m, summers up to 4420 m. **IN, BT:** rare. **REFERENCES** Ferguson-Lees (in prep.).

ROUGH-LEGGED BUZZARD *Buteo lagopus* Plate 68

IDENTIFICATION 50–60 cm. Long wings and long tail, as well as profile when soaring, recall Long-legged and Upland Buzzards (p.537 and above). Frequently hovers like Upland. Typically, has whitish head and underparts, with variable (sometimes heavy) dark brown streaking on head and breast (with most heavily marked birds showing pale U on upper breast), and in plumage most closely resembles Upland. **Adult** is readily distinguished from Upland (and other *Buteo* buzzards) by broad black subterminal band to white tail (visible from above and below). Typically also has all-dark (or black-barred) belly, and whitish underwing-coverts (variably streaked with blackish, and with large black carpal patches). **Juvenile** lacks black subterminal band to tail (as well as black trailing edge to underwing) of adult; tail is white at base and gradually darkens to become brownish towards tip (and appearing especially pale from below). Patterning of tail more closely resembles that of Upland, but immature Rough-legged has extensive black belly and whiter head, combined with largely white underwing-coverts and black carpal patches, with resulting appearance quite different from any Upland. **DISTRIBUTION AND STATUS** One sight record from

BLACK EAGLE *Ictinaetus malayensis* — Plate 63

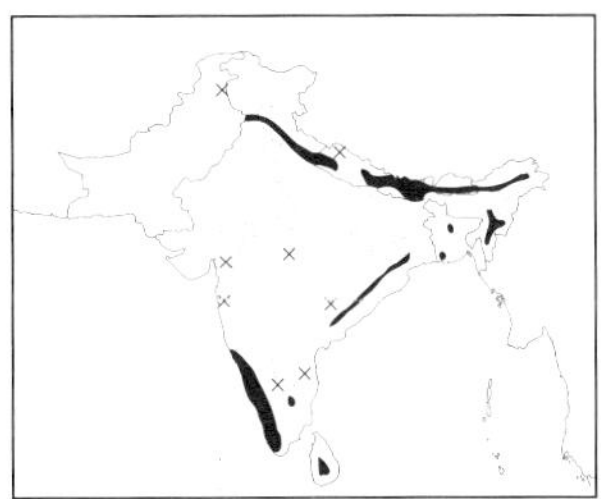

IDENTIFICATION 69–81 cm. A striking eagle: long wings have broad, rounded hands with pronounced fingers, and narrower arms which are pinched in at base, and tail is long and broad. Flies with wings raised to form V, with primaries upturned. At rest, long wings extend beyond tip of tail. **Adult** is dark brownish-black, with striking yellow cere and feet, and in flight shows whitish barring on uppertail-coverts and faint greyish barring on tail and underside of remiges. Confusable really only with dark morph of Changeable Hawk Eagle (p.544), and is best told by differences in wing shape (especially much broader hand) and patterning to underside of wings and tail: adult Changeable shows unbarred greyish underside to tail, with diffuse dark terminal band, and extensive greyish bases to underside of flight feathers which contrast with darker underwing-coverts and wing-tips (pale bases to remiges and rectrices may be barred on juvenile dark-morph Changeable, adding to potential for confusion). At rest, note also that Changeable's wing-tips fall well short of tail-tip. **Juvenile** has buffish head, with blackish crown and dark streaking on sides of head and neck, and buffish underparts and underwing-coverts also with blackish streaking (especially on breast); upperparts and underside to remiges and tail are much as adult (although pale barring on underside of remiges and tail is more prominent). Told from the hawk eagle by combination of distinctive shape, almost black upperparts, buffish underparts and underwing-coverts, and dark appearance to underside of remiges and tail. **Sub-adult** resembles adult, but has paler head, and browner underparts and underwing-coverts which are streaked with dark brown. **VOICE** Normally silent, although utters shrill yelping cries in aerial courtship (Ali and Ripley 1987). **HABITS** Invariably seen on the wing. Frequently soars over forest, often reaching considerable heights. Hunts by sailing buoyantly and slowly very low over the forest canopy, seldom flapping its wings and sometimes weaving in and out of treetops. Eats mainly birds' eggs and nestlings; also frogs, lizards, small mammals, birds and large insects. **HABITAT** Broadleaved forest in hills and mountains; also mangroves in Bangladesh. **BREEDING** November–April, varying locally. Nest is a compact platform of sticks and twigs concealed in foliage of a tall tree. **DISTRIBUTION AND STATUS** Resident. Mainly Himalayas from Punjab, India, east to Arunachal Pradesh; NE India and Bangladesh; hills of the peninsula and Sri Lanka. **PK:** rare and irregular straggler. **NP:** fairly common from WC areas eastwards, frequent in the west; usually 1000–3100 m (75–4000 m). **IN:** patchily distributed, locally fairly common in Himalayas from the foothills up to 2700 m, to 2000 m in peninsular hills. **BT:** common; 150–3250 m. **BD:** rare in the centre and south. **LK:** rare at mid to low altitudes, rare in the wet zone. **REFERENCES** Ferguson-Lees (in prep.).

LESSER SPOTTED EAGLE *Aquila pomarina* — Plate 69

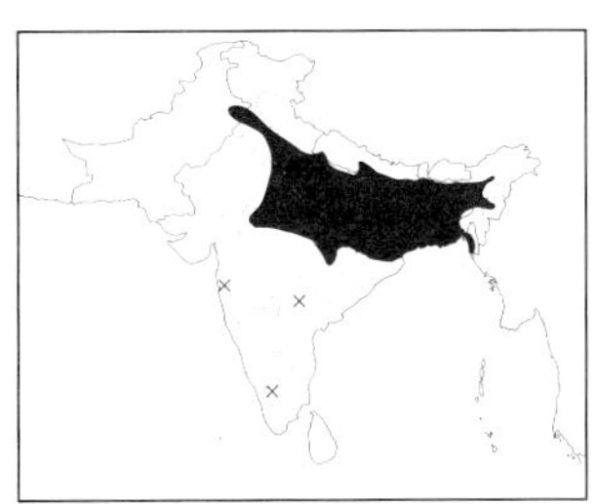

IDENTIFICATION 60–65 cm. A stocky, medium-sized eagle with rather short and broad wings, comparatively stocky and buzzard-like head and smallish bill, and rather short tail. Slightly less bulky than Greater Spotted (p.540), and does not appear so heavy in flight; wings are more rounded at tip (with very short 7th primary) and do not appear so broad, while tail appears marginally longer. Flies and soars with wings held flat or with primaries held in a characteristic droop. When gliding and soaring, wings held flattish or very slightly raised, and angled down at carpals, although this is usually slightly less pronounced than on Greater Spotted. In some plumages can be rather similar to Steppe Eagle (p.541), but Lesser Spotted is smaller in size and has a less protruding head and smaller bill, shorter wings, with shorter arm and less ample, less deep-fingered wing-tips, quicker wingbeats, and, at rest, smaller trousers exposing long, thin-looking feathered tarsi. Nostril is rounded (elongated on Steppe), but note that Indian race of Lesser Spotted has gape extending to rear of eye as on Steppe. **Adult** can usually be told from Greater Spotted by combination of structural differences, pale, buff-brown upperwing- and underwing-coverts contrasting with dark brown flight feathers, double whitish carpal crescent on underwing, and more extensive white patch at base of primaries on upperwing. Often shows darker mantle/scapulars than coverts, resulting in 'saddle' effect. Note, however, that some can be very similar in coloration of coverts to some Greater Spotted, when other features need to be applied. Can be rather similar to adult Steppe, and best told by patterning of underwing (see that species for further details). **Juvenile** has prominent whitish tips to greater and (on some) median coverts. **Older immature** can look very similar in plumage to immature Steppe Eagle, when both can show narrow but rather distinct pale greater-covert band on underwing; best told by combination of structural differences, prominence of double whitish carpal crescents, absence of barring on underside of primaries, and dark chin. Similar in plumage to some Tawny, but can be distinguished by double whitish carpal crescents, darker body and wing-coverts, lack of white rump V, and pale wedge on inner primaries. **VOICE** A very high-pitched cackling laugh (Baker). **HABITS** Like other *Aquila* eagles, an aggressive and powerful predator which can soar well, often at considerable heights. Hunts by quartering with slow glides over areas within and near forest, usually flying above treetop level; seizes most prey on the ground. Eats rodents, frogs and birds. **HABITAT** Wooded areas interspersed with cultivation in lowlands. **BREEDING** April–July. Nest is a large platform of sticks and twigs, some with leaves attached, placed 10–25 m up in a large tree, either isolated or in a grove. **DISTRIBUTION AND STATUS** Resident. Mainly from SE Punjab, India, east through S Nepal to NE India and south to S Madhya Pradesh, N Orissa and Bangladesh; S Gujarat. **PK:** status uncertain; several confirmed records, possibly under-recorded. **NP:** scarce; recorded below 915 m, mainly in the terai. **IN:** rare, chiefly in Gangetic plains. **BD:** local, occurs throughout. **REFERENCES** Clark and Khan (1995), Harris *et al.* (1996), Hirschfeld (1988).

GREATER SPOTTED EAGLE *Aquila clanga* — Plate 69

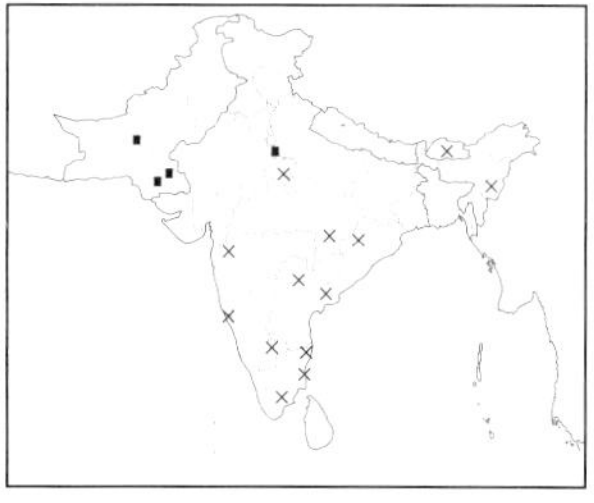

IDENTIFICATION 65–72 cm. A stocky, medium-sized eagle with rather short and broad wings, comparatively stocky head and smallish bill, and rather short tail. Heavier than Lesser Spotted Eagle (p.539); wings are broader with squarer hand, and tail appears shorter. Wings are distinctly angled down at carpals when gliding (more pronounced than on Lesser Spotted); when soaring, wings are almost flat. Compared with Steppe Eagle (p.541), has less protruding head and smaller bill, shorter wings, with shorter arm, and less deep-fingered wing-tips; at rest, trousers are less baggy, nostril is rounded (elongated on Steppe), and gape does not extend to rear of eye as on Steppe. **Adult** can usually be told from Lesser Spotted by combination of structural differences, dark brown upperwing- and underwing-coverts which show little contrast with flight feathers, lack (typically) of second whitish carpal crescent on underwing (at base of greater primary coverts), and less extensive white patch at base of primaries on upperwing. Note that some can be very similar in coloration of coverts to some Lesser Spotted, when other features need to be applied. Absence of barring on underside of flight and tail feathers, lack of dark trailing edge to wing, and dark chin are useful distinctions from adult Steppe. Also occurs as a pale morph, '*fulvescens*', with intermediates. Pale '*fulvescens*' is similar in appearance to juvenile Imperial Eagle (p.541), and best told by structural differences, lack of pale wedge on inner primaries, and lack of dark streaking on underparts. From pale juvenile Steppe by lack of white band on underwing and lack of barring on underside of flight feathers. Very similar in general coloration to pale-morph Tawny Eagle (below) but different shape and underwing pattern (often completely blackish greater underwing-coverts, usually plain-looking dark remiges and more distinct pale carpal arc). **Juvenile** has bold whitish tips to dark brown coverts, resulting in striking and distinctive pattern to upperwing; underwing-coverts are darker than underside of flight feathers. **VOICE** A barking *kluck-kluck* or *tyuck-tyuck*, rather lower-pitched and more ringing than that of Lesser Spotted Eagle (Brown and Amadon 1968). **HABITS** Often seen perched on a treetop, bush or bank near water. Hunts on the wing or on the ground, generally taking slow-moving prey, especially frogs. Also takes faster-moving waterbirds by swooping low and scattering flock, so isolating an individual. **HABITAT** Large lakes, jheels, canals, marshes; also mangroves. **BREEDING** April–June and November–January (Pakistan). Nest is a large platform of sticks placed in a tree in well-wooded areas. **DISTRIBUTION AND STATUS** Breeds in S Pakistan and Rajasthan; winter visitor, chiefly to Pakistan and N India from Punjab east through Nepal to NE India and Bangladesh, also Gujarat, and scattered records south through the peninsula. Globally threatened. **PK:** common winter visitor to Sindh and Punjab; a few pairs breed. **NP:** uncommon winter visitor, mainly below 250 m; passage migrant up to 3840 m. **IN:** mainly an uncommon winter visitor to the north, rare in the peninsula; rare and very local breeder. **BT:** rare. **BD:** local winter visitor. **REFERENCES** Harris *et al.* (1996).

TAWNY EAGLE *Aquila rapax* — Plate 70

Eurasian Tawny Eagle, *A. vindhiana*

IDENTIFICATION 63–71 cm. In flight, protruding head and neck are more pronounced than on the spotted eagles (p.539 and above) as well as Steppe Eagle (p.541). Compared with Steppe, hand of wing does not appear so long and broad, and tail appears slightly shorter. When perched, differences from Steppe include smaller and weaker build, and sits more erect, when does not look so elongated. At very close range, gape-line normally appears to end level with centre of eye (reaching rear of eye on Steppe), and adult has yellowish (rather than brown) iris. Baggy trousers, all the way to the feet, yellow iris, and oval nostril are distinctions from the spotted eagles. **Adult** is extremely variable, from dark brown, through rufous to pale cream, and may be unstreaked or streaked with rufous or dark brown. Dark morph is similar to adult Steppe (which shows much less variation in adult plumage). Subtle differences include less pronounced barring and dark trailing edge on underside of flight feathers, and dark nape, with pale feather tips when fresh (Steppe has rufous nape patch), and also lacks that

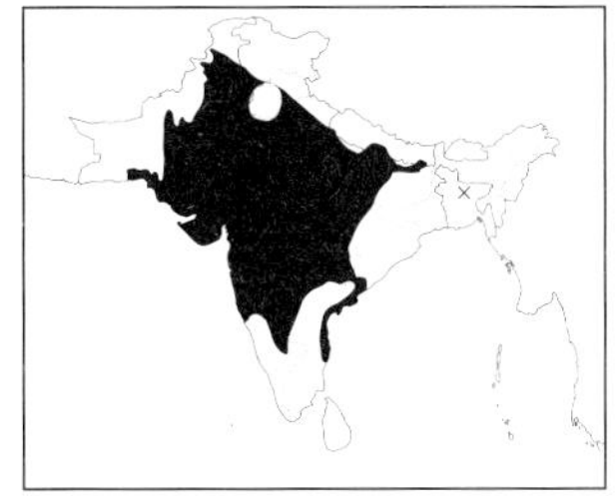

species' pale throat and its solid dark carpal on underwing. Possibly confusable with adult Greater Spotted Eagle (p.540); lacks whitish crescent at base of primaries on underwing often shown by that species, and structural differences are usually apparent (especially protruding neck of Tawny). Rufous to pale cream birds show strong contrast between coverts and dark flight and tail feathers. These birds have uniformly pale area from uppertail-coverts to back (Steppe and the spotted eagles show well-defined whitish uppertail-covert crescent which contrasts with darker rump), and undertail-coverts are same colour as belly (contrast often apparent on similar species); they also lack prominent whitish trailing edge to wing, tip to tail and greater-covert bar (all shown by immatures of similar species). Characteristic, if present, is distinct pale wedge on inner primaries of underwing (a feature shared with Imperial Eagle, below); also, dark-centred mantle and/or scapular feathers often contrast with paler coverts. **Juvenile** also shows a wide variety of plumages (from dark brown to pale cream), all with narrow white tips to unbarred secondaries. Features otherwise as described for similar-plumaged adult; in particular, lacks the white band across underwing of juvenile and immature Steppe. Many, possibly all, non-dark Tawny have a distinctive **immature/subadult** plumage, with dark throat and breast contrasting with pale belly, and can show dark banding across underwing-coverts; whole head and breast may be dark on some. **VOICE** A variety of loud, raucous cackles; a distinctive guttural *kra* while in pursuit; a harsh grating *kekeke* in display flight (Ali and Ripley 1987). **HABITS** Spends much time perched on treetops in cultivation or near village rubbish dumps or slaughterhouses. Feeds on carrion and refuse; also on small mammals, birds and reptiles, mainly stolen from other small birds of prey, but also catches mammals by pouncing on them from a low bush. Roosts communally in groves, on the ground or on power pylons. **HABITAT** Desert, semi-desert and cultivation in lowlands. **BREEDING** November–April, varying locally. Nest is a large platform made of sticks and twigs and placed in the top of a large isolated tree, often near a village. **DISTRIBUTION AND STATUS** Resident. Mainly from Pakistan east through S Nepal to Assam, and south through much of the peninsula (except parts of the east) to N Tamil Nadu. **PK:** widespread in the remoter, less settled parts of Punjab, Sindh and lowland areas of Baluchistan and NW Pakistan. **NP:** widespread and rare; below 250 m. **IN:** widespread; locally common in the northwest. **BD:** vagrant. **REFERENCES** Barua (1995a), Clark (1992), Harris *et al.* (1996), Inskipp and Inskipp (1991).

STEPPE EAGLE *Aquila nipalensis* — Plate 70

***A. rapax* (I,K,R)**

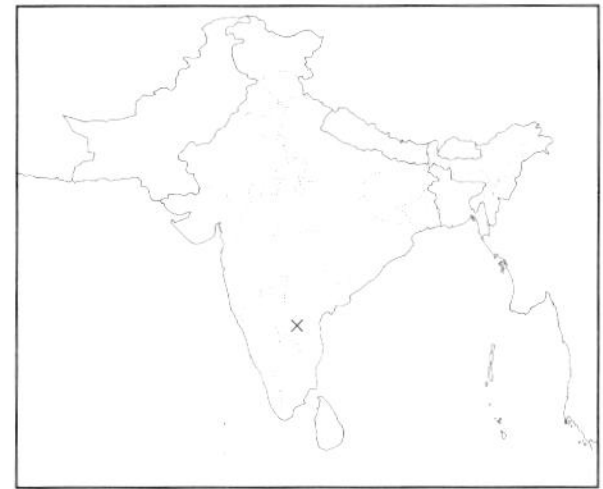

IDENTIFICATION 76–80 cm. Rather similar in shape and flight profile to Greater and Lesser Spotted Eagles (p.540 and p.539). Appears heavier in body than those species. Wings are broader and longer (owing to longer arm) and primary tips more pronounced and spread; wings are held flatter when soaring, and less distinctly angled down at carpals when gliding. In flight, tail appears slightly longer, and protruding head and neck are more pronounced than on the spotted eagles, but less so than on Imperial (below), and hand of wing does not appear so long and broad as on latter species. When perched, is clearly bigger and heavier than the spotted eagles, with heavier bill, and trousers are baggy all the way to the feet. See Tawny Eagle (p.540) for differences from that species. **Adult** can be rather similar in appearance to some adult spotted eagles. Features to look for are dark trailing edge to underwing; distinct barring on underside of remiges (on underwing of the spotted eagles, primaries are unbarred while secondaries are only lightly barred); indistinct or non-existent pale crescents in carpal region of underwing; diffuse but pronounced greyish patch at base of primaries on upperwing; pale rufous nape patch; and pale chin. **Juvenile** is very distinct, with broad white tips to greater and primary coverts of underwing showing as white band; upperwing has broad white tips to median and greater coverts which show as double wing-bar, and has white crescent across uppertail-coverts. Prominence of wing-bars both above and below is much reduced on **old immature** birds, and these are very similar to some Lesser Spotted Eagles; best told from that species by structural differences and by adult-like plumage differences, especially patterning of underwing, which are usually apparent (note that any dark-tipped adult-like secondaries would indicate Steppe). **VOICE** Undescribed in the region. **HABITS** Similar to those of Tawny Eagle. **HABITAT** Wooded hills, large lakes and open country. **DISTRIBUTION AND STATUS** Winter visitor. Mainly from Pakistan east to NE India and south to Bangladesh, C Maharashtra, S Madhya Pradesh and S Orissa. **PK:** common winter visitor. **NP:** widespread and common winter visitor and passage migrant; mainly below 2200 m (–7925 m on passage). **IN:** widespread and locally common winter visitor. **BT:** uncommon passage migrant. **BD:** rare winter visitor. **REFERENCES** Harris *et al.* (1996).

IMPERIAL EAGLE *Aquila heliaca* — Plate 70

IDENTIFICATION 72–83 cm. A large, stout-bodied eagle with long and broad wings, longish tail, and distinctly protruding head and neck. Wings are held flat (with tips of primaries slightly raised) when soaring and gliding, which is a good distinction from Golden Eagle (p.542). **Adult** has almost uniform upperwing, and small but usually visible white scapular patches, which are good features for separation from Golden. Has golden-buff

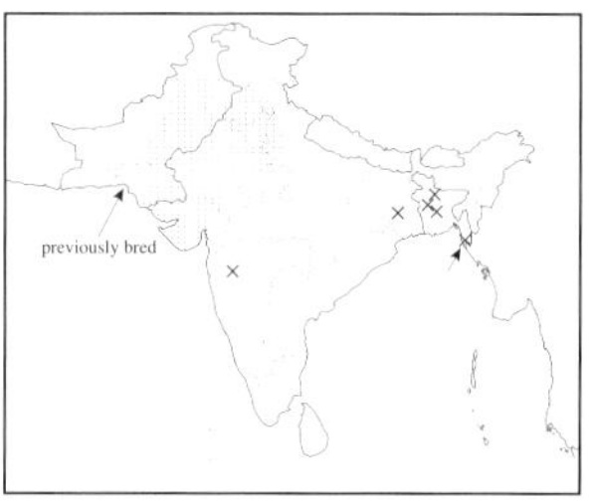

crown and nape, and two-toned tail with greyish base and darker terminal band, which are useful plumage differences from adult Steppe Eagle (p.541). Shape is similar to that of Golden, but wings are parallel-edged (lacking curved trailing edge to secondaries), and tail appears slightly shorter and more square-ended. **Juvenile** has pronounced curve to trailing edge of wing. Best told from other *Aquila* eagles by combination of following features: pale wedge on inner primaries; yellowish-buff body and wing-coverts contrasting with dark flight feathers and tail; distinct pale streaking on scapulars and inner coverts; uniform pale rump and back (lacking distinct pale crescent shown by other species); dark streaking on head, neck and breast (with pronounced streaked breast-band); and white tips to median and greater upper-wing-coverts, which form white bars across wing. Bulk and shape, especially protruding head and neck, are further useful distinctions from Tawny (p.540), Steppe and the two spotted eagles (p.539 and p.540). **Older immatures** can be rather similar to Steppe and Tawny, but those species show distinct barring on flight feathers and tail and pronounced pale base to primaries on upperwing, and they lack pale crown and nape which are usually apparent on Imperial. **VOICE** A sonorous barking *owk-owk-owk*; rather silent except in the breeding season (Brown and Amadon 1968). **HABITS** A solitary, majestic eagle. Rather inactive, typically spending most of the day perched on a good vantage point such as a tree or often on the ground in very open country. In the subcontinent feeds mainly by robbing other birds of prey in flight; also eats carrion and rodents, reptiles and birds taken on the ground. Soars high overhead, and can fly at great speeds. **HABITAT** Open country in plains, deserts and around major lakes and wetlands. **BREEDING** Little information from the region, and no recent records. November–April. Builds a large nest of twigs and sticks, 6–9 m up in a tree. **DISTRIBUTION AND STATUS** Formerly bred Pakistan, but no recent confirmed records; winter visitor mainly to Pakistan and NW India (from Punjab east to W Uttar Pradesh and south to Gujarat), Nepal and Bangladesh. **PK:** now mainly a scarce winter visitor. **NP:** mainly a scarce passage migrant, below 3900 m; a few winter records, below 1370 m. **IN:** uncommon. **BD:** rare winter visitor. **REFERENCES** Harris *et al.* (1996).

GOLDEN EAGLE *Aquila chrysaetos* — Plate 69

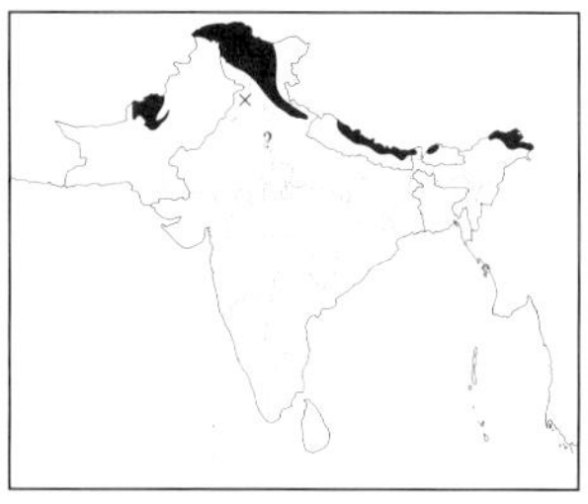

IDENTIFICATION 75–88 cm. A large eagle with long and broad wings, long tail, and distinctly protruding head and neck. When soaring, wings are clearly raised and pressed forward (with upturned fingers) in pronounced V, which is best distinction from other *Aquila* eagles; when gliding, wings are raised less and may be held horizontal. In direct flight, wingbeats are deep and powerful, with several strokes followed by a glide. **Adult** has distinct pale panel across upperwing-coverts which is absent on adult Imperial (p.541), and lacks white scapular patches of that species; brownish-gold crown and nape, and two-toned tail with greyish base and darker terminal band, are useful plumage differences from adult Steppe Eagle (p.541). Shape is most similar to that of Imperial, but has pronounced curve to trailing edge of wings and more rounded corners to tail. **Juvenile** is very distinct, with white base to tail and white patch at base of flight feathers; bulging secondaries result in stronger curve to trailing edge of wings. White patches on wings and tail are gradually lost with age. **VOICE** Generally very silent. Occasionally utters a loud, clear yelping *weee-o* in display; otherwise a thin, shrill *pleek* (Brown and Amadon 1968). **HABITS** Found singly or in pairs. Soars for hours over mountain ridges. Usually hunts by quartering a slope, flying low and then striking with talons in a swift dash; occasionally pounces from a perch. Feeds chiefly on gamebirds and mammals. **HABITAT** High rugged mountains, usually well above the treeline. **BREEDING** January–April. Nest is an enormous platform of sticks, placed on a cliff ledge, or in a tree overhanging or growing out of a cliff. **DISTRIBUTION AND STATUS** Resident. Mainly N Baluchistan, Pakistan, and Himalayas from N Pakistan east to Arunachal Pradesh. **PK:** generally scarce, locally fairly common. **NP:** widespread and uncommon; mainly 2745–4575 m (75–6190 m). **IN:** uncommon; mainly above 1700 m. **BT:** uncommon. **REFERENCES** Harris *et al.* (1996), Naoroji (1995).

BONELLI'S EAGLE *Hieraaetus fasciatus* — Plate 71

Bonelli's Hawk Eagle (P)

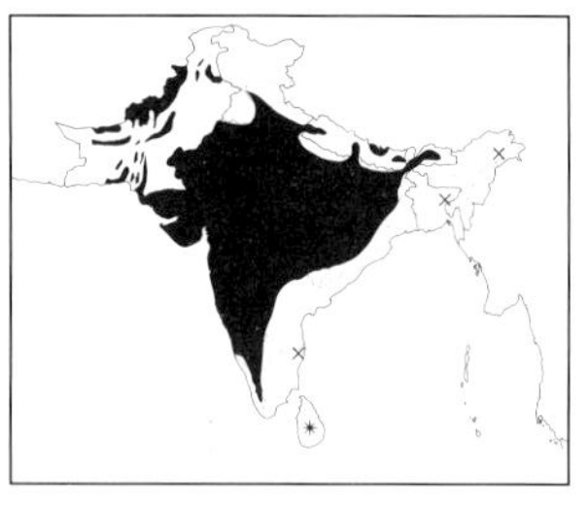

IDENTIFICATION 65–72 cm. A medium-sized eagle with long and broad wings, distinctly protruding head, and long square-ended tail. Often appears like a large Oriental Honey-buzzard (p.520). Soars with wings held flat (or just above the horizontal). Direct flight is fast and graceful, with loose wingbeats interspersed with glides on flat wings. **Adult** is very distinctive, with pale underbody and forewing, blackish carpals and band along underwing-coverts, greyish underside to flight feathers with diffuse dark trailing edge, whitish patch on mantle, and pale greyish tail with broad dark terminal band. **Juvenile** has pronounced curve to trailing edge of wing. Is best told by combination of distinctive shape (especially long tail), ginger-buff to reddish-brown underbody and underwing-coverts (with variable dark band along greater coverts), and narrow greyish barring on underside of wings and tail, which both lack dark trailing edge. Also shows pale inner primaries and base to outer primaries on underwing, comparatively uniform upperwing, and pale crescent across uppertail-coverts and patch on back. **Older immatures** show more pronounced dark band along greater underwing-coverts and dark terminal band on wings and tail. **VOICE** Usually rather silent, but in display and near nest emits mellow fluting calls, *klu-klu-klu-kluee* or *kluu-klu-klu-klu-klu*, associated with alarm (Brown and Amadon 1968). **HABITS** Found singly or in pairs. A bold predator, usually seen in flight, although soars far less than other large birds of prey. Normally hunts by perching concealed in a tree and making a quick dash; also quarters slopes, or stoops when soaring, and may hunt cooperatively. Takes most prey on the ground. Eats birds and small mammals. **HABITAT** Well-wooded country in hills and plains; also edges of desert and around large lakes in Pakistan. **BREEDING** Mainly December–May. Nest is a huge platform of sticks with a central depression; in S India usually built in tall trees, elsewhere on cliff ledges. **DISTRIBUTION AND STATUS** Resident and winter visitor. Throughout much of the subcontinent, except most of the northeast, W Himalayas, E India and Sri Lanka. **PK:** widespread but scarce resident and winter visitor; occurs mainly in S Baluchistan, NW Pakistan and Punjab Salt Range. **NP:** frequent but local resident; 1400–2600 m (915–3050 m). **IN:** widespread and uncommon resident and winter visitor; plains and hills, up to 2400 m in Himalayas. **BT:** uncommon (–3750 m). **BD, LK:** vagrant. **REFERENCES** Cramp and Simmons (1980), Harris *et al.* (1996), Inskipp and Inskipp (1996).

BOOTED EAGLE *Hieraaetus pennatus* — Plate 71

Booted Hawk Eagle (I,P)

IDENTIFICATION 45–53 cm. A smallish eagle which can be rather kite-like in appearance. Wings are comparatively long and narrow, with ample hand, and tail is long and square-ended. When gliding and soaring, wings are held slightly forward and are flat or slightly angled down at carpal. Twists tail in kite-like fashion. In direct flight, rather loose and deep wingbeats are interspersed with glides. **Adult** occurs as pale, dark and rufous morphs. In all plumages, shows small white shoulder patches (at base of leading edge of wing), pale panel across median coverts, pale wedge on inner primaries, pale scapulars, white crescent across uppertail-coverts, and greyish underside to tail with darker centre and tip. Head, underbody and underwing-coverts are whitish, brown or rufous respectively in pale, dark and rufous morphs. Dark and rufous morphs confusable with Black Kite (p.522), but have square-ended tail, show white shoulder patches and white crescent on uppertail-coverts, and have unbarred outer tail feathers. Also confusable with immature Brahminy Kite (p.522), but are larger, with longer wings and squarer tail, show white shoulder patches, and lack the large pale patch at base of primaries (and dark wing-tips) shown by that species. **Juvenile** plumage is much as adult, but shows broad white trailing edge to wings and tail when fresh. **VOICE** A high-pitched double whistle, *ki-keee*. In display very noisy, calling *pi-peee, pi-pi-pi-pi-peee* etc; also at times a longer scream, *kleeek-kleeek* (Brown and Amadon 1968). **HABITS** An active, swift and agile hunter, feeding on small mammals, birds and reptiles. Captures prey in trees by swift dive from above into foliage, followed by pursuit through branches; also soars at considerable heights over open country, and stoops at great speed on prey on the ground. Pairs often hunt cooperatively. **HABITAT** Well-wooded country in hills and plains, also semi-desert with plantations and groves around cultivation and villages. **BREEDING** March–June. Nest is a platform of sticks, placed 25–35 m up in a tall tree in forest or a tree growing out of a cliff. **DISTRIBUTION AND STATUS** Breeds in N Baluchistan, Pakistan, and in Himalayas from N Pakistan east to N Uttar Pradesh, NC Nepal, and possibly breeds in the peninsula; winter visitor throughout most of the subcontinent, except parts of the northeast, W Pakistan and NW and E India. **PK:** frequent winter visitor to Indus plains; small numbers breed in higher mountains; 1525–3050 m. **NP:** mainly an uncommon winter visitor and passage migrant, 75–4000 m; also a rare resident, has bred at 3200 m and 3850 m. **IN:** widespread and frequent in winter, also breeds in Himalayas; plains and hills up to 2400 m. **BT:** rare; 250–3800 m. **BD:** scarce winter visitor or passage migrant. **LK:** regular winter visitor throughout in small numbers. **REFERENCES** Inskipp and Inskipp (1996), Martens and Eck (1995).

RUFOUS-BELLIED EAGLE *Hieraaetus kienerii* — Plate 71

Rufous-bellied Hawk Eagle (I,P)

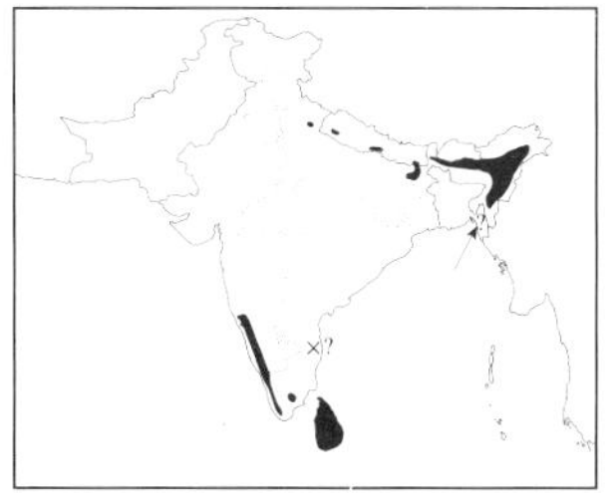

IDENTIFICATION 53–61 cm. A smallish eagle with buzzard-shaped wings and tail. At rest, wing-tips extend well down tail. Wings are narrower than on *Spizaetus* hawk eagles. Usually glides and soars with wings held flat and pressed slightly forward. Frequently dives, with wings folded, to catch prey. **Adult** is very distinctive, with blackish hood and upperparts, white throat and breast, and (black-streaked) rufous rest of underparts. Rufous coloration of underparts and underwing-coverts may not be apparent at a distance or in poor light. Greater underwing-coverts are tipped with black, forming blackish band, and has dark subterminal band to tail. Upperwing is uniformly dark except for pale patches at base of primaries. At rest, shows short crest. **Juvenile** is very different, with largely white underparts and underwing-coverts and browner upperparts. Has dark mask and white supercilium, dark patch on sides of upper breast, and dark patch on flanks. Undersides of flight feathers and tail are lightly barred (similar to adult), and secondaries appear darker than rest of underwing; when head-on, shows striking white leading edge to wing; upperwing appears uniformly dark but for paler base to primaries. Head pattern, comparatively uniform upperwing, very white underparts with dark breast and flank markings, and narrower wings are best distinctions from juvenile *Spizaetus*. Older immature birds show a range of intermediate plumages. **VOICE** Silent except in breeding season. Call usually described as piercing or plaintive scream. **HABITS** Most often seen soaring and circling high over forest, and often hunts from this position. Stoops very swiftly from the soar, with wings nearly closed (like a falcon), and seizes prey. Also catches prey on the ground by pouncing from a concealed perch in a treetop. Feeds mainly on birds, but also takes mammals. **HABITAT** Evergreen and moist deciduous broadleaved forest. **BREEDING** No data for N population. In Kerala and Sri Lanka breeds December–March. Nest is a large platform of sticks, often with green leaves attached, placed 24–30 m up in a tree in dense forest. **DISTRIBUTION AND STATUS** Resident. Mainly Himalayas from N Uttar Pradesh east to Arunachal Pradesh; NE India and Bangladesh; Western Ghats from Goa south to Kerala and S Tamil Nadu; Sri Lanka. **NP:** rare; 200–305 m. **IN:** rare in Himalayan foothills, up to 1000 m in the west, to 1500 m in the east; uncommon in Kerala hills up to 1200 m. **BT:** uncommon; 450–1740 m. **BD:** rare resident. **LK:** rare, mainly in the hills. **REFERENCES** Anon. (1994), Clark and Schmitt (1993), Ferguson-Lees (in prep.).

CHANGEABLE HAWK EAGLE *Spizaetus cirrhatus* — Plate 71

Crested Hawk Eagle (I,P)

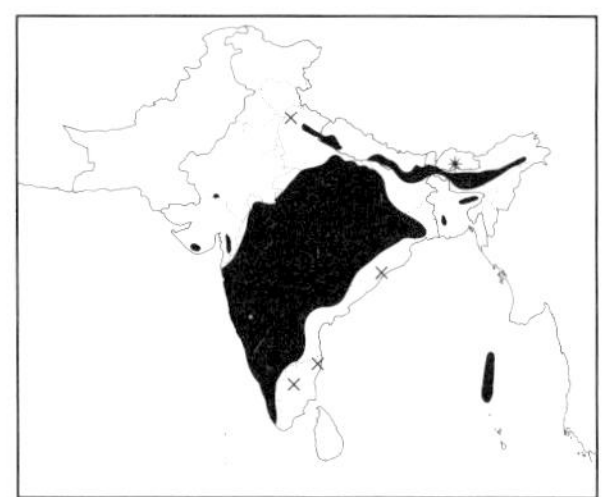

IDENTIFICATION 61–72 cm. A large, broad-winged eagle with long and broad tail. Wings are slightly narrower, and more parallel-edged, compared with Mountain Hawk Eagle (below), and has proportionately longer tail. Soars with wings held flat (except in display, when both wings and tail raised). **Adult** occurs in two morphs in northern subspecies. Where ranges overlap in Himalayas and NE India, pale morph is best told from Mountain by lack of prominent crest, boldly streaked underparts (with barring confined to flanks, thighs and undertail-coverts), lack of barring on rump, narrower tail barring (three to four bars, plus subterminal band; sometimes only subterminal band is prominent), and clearer white patches at base of underside of primaries. Note, however, that Changeable in the peninsula has prominent crest (see racial variation). Dark morph is easily confusable with Black Eagle (p.539), and is best told by structural differences (see that species), greyish underside to tail with diffuse dark terminal band, and extensive greyish bases to underside of flight feathers which contrast with darker underwing-coverts and wing-tips (note that greyish bases to remiges and rectrices may be barred on juvenile dark morph, adding to potential confusion). **Juvenile** has pale fringes to upperparts (some with largely white forewing), pale buff underparts and underwing-coverts, and narrower and more numerous tail-bands than adult. Is generally whiter on head than juvenile Mountain, and lacks crest where ranges overlap in N subcontinent. **Racial variation** Compared with *S. c. limnaetus*, described above, nominate *cirrhatus* of peninsular India and Sri Lanka has prominent crest and does not occur as a dark morph; underside of tail is more strongly barred, and underwing-coverts are darker and more heavily marked; juvenile *cirrhatus* has buff head with white-tipped black crest. Wing shape, patterning of breast and underwing-coverts, and dark vent and undertail-coverts are best distinctions from Mountain Hawk Eagle where ranges overlap. *S. c. andamanensis* of Andaman Is is much smaller and darker, with shorter crest. **VOICE** Silent except in breeding season. An ascending series of shrill whistles, *kri-kri-kri-kri-kree-ah*, and a *kreeee-krit* (nominate); a loud high-pitched *ki-ki-ki-ki-ki-ki-ki-ki-ki-kee*, which rises in crescendo and ends in long-drawn scream (Ali and Ripley 1987; Boonsong and Round 1991). **HABITS** Keeps singly or in pairs. Spends much of the day perched in an upright posture in a forest tree, often at the edge of a clearing, from where it makes a short dash and pounces on prey on the ground. Feeds on gamebirds, small mammals and lizards. Soars less frequently than many other raptors. **HABITAT** Broadleaved forest, open well-wooded country, and villages and cultivation in or near forest in foothills and lowlands. **BREEDING** November–June, varying locally. Nest is a large platform of sticks and twigs, placed 12–30 m up in a tree on a slope or at a ravine edge. **DISTRIBUTION AND STATUS** Resident. Himalayas from N Uttar Pradesh east to Arunachal Pradesh; NE India and Bangladesh; also India from S Gujarat, Mt Abu (Rajasthan), Madhya Pradesh and C Uttar Pradesh east to West Bengal and south through the peninsula except the E coastal strip; Andaman Is and Sri Lanka. **NP:** scarce; 75–1050 m, usually below 360 m. **IN:** uncommon and widespread; foothills and up to 1900 m in Himalayas. **BT:** once collected in 19th century. **BD:** local. **LK:** common in lowlands and lower hills, less frequent in wet zone. **REFERENCES** Boonsong and Round (1991), Ferguson-Lees (in prep.).

MOUNTAIN HAWK EAGLE *Spizaetus nipalensis* — Plate 71

Hodgson's Hawk Eagle (I), Legge's Hawk Eagle (P)

IDENTIFICATION 70–72 cm. A large, broad-winged eagle with long and broad tail. Shows prominent crest at rest. In flight, compared with Changeable Hawk Eagle (above), wings are broader, with more pronounced curve to trailing edge (and indent at base), and has proportionately shorter tail. Glides with wings held in shallow V and pressed slightly forward (held flat in Changeable). Where ranges overlap in N subcontinent, **adult** best told from pale morph of Changeable by prominent crest, extensively barred underparts (with sparse dark streaking on

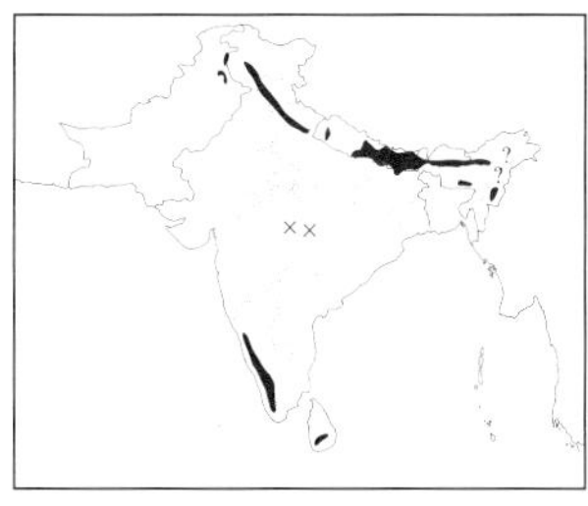

breast), whitish-barred rump, and strong dark barring on tail (with two or three broad bars and a broad subterminal band). Note, however, that the race of Changeable south of the Himalayas has prominent crest and stronger tail barring (see racial variation). As Changeable, shows paler band along median coverts in flight. **Juvenile** has pale fringes to upperparts, pale buff underparts and underwing-coverts, and narrower and more numerous tail-bands than adult. Distinguished from juvenile Changeable by more extensive dark streaking on crown and sides of head, white-tipped black crest, buff-barred rump, fewer and more prominent tail-bars, and broader wings. **Racial variation** *S. n. kelaarti*, of Sri Lanka and SW India, is smaller and has paler rufous barring on underparts compared with the nominate form of Himalayas and NE India; underwing-coverts are buff and almost unmarked, and median throat stripe is almost lacking (broad and prominent in nominate). Patterning of underparts and tail, comparatively unmarked underwing-coverts, and structural differences help separate from Changeable. **VOICE** Noisy in breeding season only. Three shrill notes, *tlueet-weet-weet*, reminiscent of Common Green Magpie (p.592); in display, has rapid bubbling call (Brown and Amadon 1968; Boonsong and Round 1991). **HABITS** Very similar to those of Changeable, but frequently seen soaring above forest, singly or in pairs. **HABITAT** Forest in hills and mountains. **BREEDING** December–May. Nest is a large platform of sticks, placed 12–25 m up in a large forest tree at the edge of a nullah or ravine. **DISTRIBUTION AND STATUS** Resident, subject to altitudinal movements. Himalayas from N Pakistan east to Arunachal Pradesh; NE, C and SW India and Sri Lanka. **PK:** rare and very local, now only in lower Neelum and Jhelum valleys and Murree hills; probably only an irregular visitor. **NP:** locally frequent; mainly 1500–2835 m, scarce below 250 m in winter. **IN:** locally frequent, rare in the southwest; 120–2400 m in Himalayas and NE hills. **BT:** common; 800–3100 m. **LK:** rare in hills. **REFERENCES** Boonsong and Round (1991), Ferguson-Lees (in prep.).

FALCONS Falconidae

Small to medium-sized birds of prey which resemble the Accipitridae in having hooked a beak, sharp curved talons, and remarkable powers of sight and flight. Like other raptors they are mainly diurnal, although a few are crepuscular. Females are larger than males. Two genera occur in the region: the *Microhierax* falconets and the *Falco* falcons. The small *Microhierax* species prey mainly on insects. Some *Falco* falcons kill flying birds in a surprise attack, often by stooping at great speed (e.g. Peregrine); others hover and then swoop on prey on the ground (e.g. Common Kestrel), and several species hawk insects in flight (e.g. Eurasian Hobby). Most do not build their own nests, and either lay their eggs on a cliff ledge or use abandoned nests of other birds. Some species have undergone declines because of habitat loss and probably also pesticide poisoning. The main references specific to the Falconidae are Brown and Amadon (1968) and Cramp and Simmons (1980).

COLLARED FALCONET *Microhierax caerulescens* Plate 72

Red-breasted Falconet (I), Red-thighed Falconet (F)

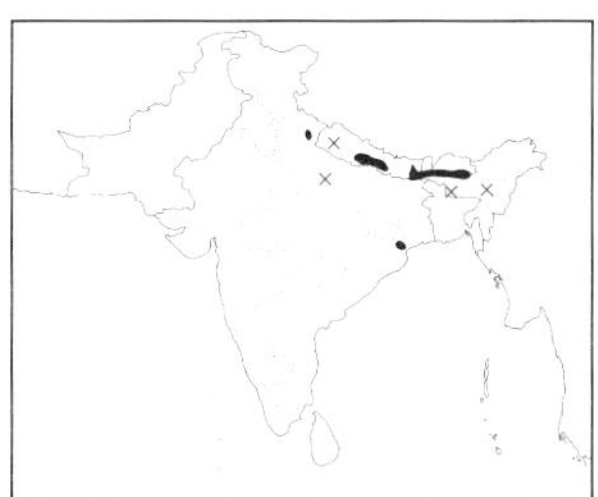

IDENTIFICATION 18 cm. A tiny raptor with rather long, broad and square-ended tail and shortish, rounded wings. Usually seen perched in open, when looks rather shrike-like. Flight is rapid, interspersed with long glides. **Adult** has largely white head, with black crown and nape (with white collar) and black stripe through eye. Upperparts are blackish and underparts are rufous-orange, with some white across breast. In flight, shows dark barring on underside of flight feathers, white barring on underside of dark tail, and rather uniform underwing-coverts; also a small area of white spotting at base of outer secondaries on upperwing. Sexes alike, although female is larger. **Juvenile** is very similar to adult, but shows rufous-orange on forehead and supercilium (and collar on some) and has white throat; underparts are otherwise generally whiter. In fresh plumage, shows narrow rufous edges to back and coverts. **VOICE** A high *kli-kli-kli* or *killi-killi-killi* (Brown and Amadon 1968). **HABITS** Found singly, in pairs or in small parties, which sometimes huddle together on a branch. Rather crepuscular. Perches on dead branches of a forest tree and makes short, swift darting sorties with rapidly beating wings; seizes flying insects with its talons and returns to its perch with a swooping glide. Occasionally takes insects on the ground. As well as large insects, occasionally takes small birds. Has a habit of slowly pumping its tail and bobbing its head when perched. **HABITAT** Edges and clearings of broadleaved tropical forest. **BREEDING** Poorly known in the region. Copulation and incubation observed in March/April, when apparently nesting in a barbet hole; elsewhere, also uses woodpecker holes. **DISTRIBUTION AND STATUS** Resident. Mainly Himalayan foothills from N Uttar Pradesh east to Bhutan; NE Orissa. **NP:** uncommon, mainly from WC areas and eastwards; below 915 m. **IN:** generally rare, locally frequent; mainly below 650 m, recorded up to 2000 m. **BT:** uncommon; below 760 m. **REFERENCES** Ferguson-Lees (in prep.), Ganguli-Lachungpa (1996), Naoroji (1996).

PIED FALCONET *Microhierax melanoleucos* Plate 72

White-legged Falconet (I)

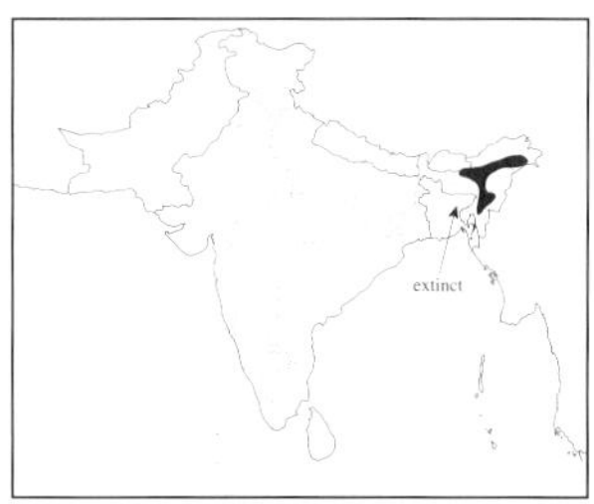

IDENTIFICATION 20 cm. Distinctly larger than Collared Falconet (p.545), with longer tail. Flight is similar to Collared's. **Adult** superficially resembles that species, but lacks rufous-orange on underparts, has narrower supercilium, and does not have white hindcollar. Crown, nape, mask and upperparts are blackish, and underparts are white. Has white forehead and white supercilium which curves down to outline dark mask. In flight, shows dark barring on underside of flight feathers and unbarred white underwing-coverts. Underside of tail has narrow white barring, which may be apparent on uppertail when spread. **Juvenile** is undescribed. **VOICE** A shrill scream and a low chattering call (Ferguson-Lees in prep.). **HABITS** Similar to those of Collared Falconet, but a more powerful predator. Eats mainly insects, but also takes birds, some much larger than itself, by stooping on them like a *Falco* falcon. **HABITAT** Forest clearings, tea plantations and wooded foothills. **BREEDING** Little known in the region. March–May. Nests in old barbet or woodpecker holes. **DISTRIBUTION AND STATUS** Resident. E Bhutan, NE India (Arunachal Pradesh, Assam, Manipur, Mizoram, Tripura) and Bangladesh. **IN:** locally fairly common; plains and foothills up to 1500 m, most frequent below 915 m. **BT:** rare. **BD:** ?former resident; no recent records, but could still occur in Chittagong Hill Tracts. **REFERENCES** Ferguson-Lees (in prep.).

LESSER KESTREL *Falco naumanni* Plate 72

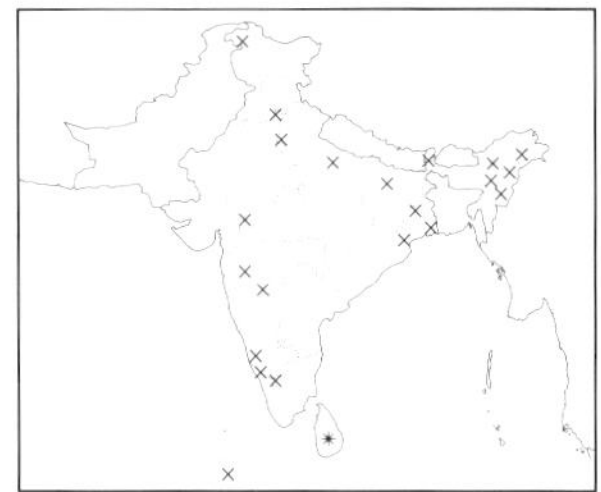

IDENTIFICATION 29–32 cm. Slightly smaller and slimmer than Common Kestrel (below), with more rounded head. In flight, wing-tips are more rounded, and flapping is shallower and stiffer. Frequently hovers like Common. When perched, wing-tips reach black subterminal tail-band. Claws are whitish (black on Common). **Male** is distinct from male Common. Has more uniform blue-grey head (lacking dark moustachial stripe), unmarked rufous mantle, scapulars and wing-coverts (heavily spotted on Common), blue-grey greater coverts, and almost unmarked orange-buff underparts with some spotting on flanks. In flight, underwing is whiter, with more clearly pronounced darker tips to primaries; underside of primaries is only faintly barred, and underwing-coverts are usually only sparsely spotted. Tail often looks more wedge-shaped owing to slightly projecting central feathers. **First-year male** is more like Common, with spotted and barred wing-coverts and lacking blue-grey panel across greater coverts; may also show suggestion of darker moustachial. Best distinguished by structural differences and unmarked rufous mantle and scapular feathers. **Female** and **juvenile** are very similar to female Common. There are subtle differences in head pattern: Lesser has a less distinct moustachial stripe than Common and lacks any suggestion of a dark eye-stripe, has paler cheeks, and head is more finely streaked. Underwing tends to be cleaner and whiter, with primary bases unbarred or only lightly barred, and underwing-coverts are less heavily spotted; dark primary tips tend to be more pronounced. Further, barring on upperparts tends to be more V-shaped, tail barring narrower, and underparts more finely and more neatly streaked, but these features are subject to variation. **VOICE** A *kee-chee-chee* or *chet-che-che*, which is less piercing and more slurred than that of Common (Harris *et al.* 1996). **HABITS** Hunts in open country in a similar manner to Common Kestrel, but usually in small parties or larger flocks, and is generally more graceful and agile on the wing. Mainly insectivorous. Flies 10–15 m above the ground, repeatedly hovering briefly, and swoops to seize prey on the ground. Generally hovers less often, for shorter periods and with less wing-flapping than Common Kestrel. Also hawks flying insects. Roosts communally, sometimes with Amur Falcons (p.547). **HABITAT** Open grassland and cultivation. **DISTRIBUTION AND STATUS** Status uncertain. Chiefly a passage migrant to and from its principal wintering grounds in Africa. Mainly Nepal, India and Maldives. Globally threatened. **PK:** vagrant. **NP:** mainly an uncommon autumn passage migrant, recorded below 2745 m; a few spring and several winter records, noted at 3700 m in February. **IN:** widespread and rare winter visitor and passage migrant. **LK:** vagrant. **MV:** probably an annual visitor in small numbers. **REFERENCES** Harris *et al.* (1996), Robson (1996a).

COMMON KESTREL *Falco tinnunculus* Plate 72

Kestrel (I,P), Eurasian Kestrel (F)

IDENTIFICATION 32–35 cm. Medium-sized falcon with relatively long wings and long, rather broad tail. Flight is a combination of rather fast shallow flapping, interspersed with glides, and frequent hovering. Soars frequently, with tail spread. Rufous coloration to upperparts helps separate it from all but Lesser Kestrel (above); see that species for main differences. In flight, wings appear longer and wing-tips are more rounded compared with Merlin (p.548), Eurasian Hobby (p.549) or Peregrine (p.551), and flapping is shallower, stiffer and less powerful. When perched, wing-tips fall well short of tail. **Male** has greyish head with diffuse dark moustachial stripe, rufous mantle, scapulars and wing-coverts which are heavily marked with black, buffish underparts with bold streaking, and grey tail with black subterminal band and whitish tip. In flight, rufous coverts contrast with blackish

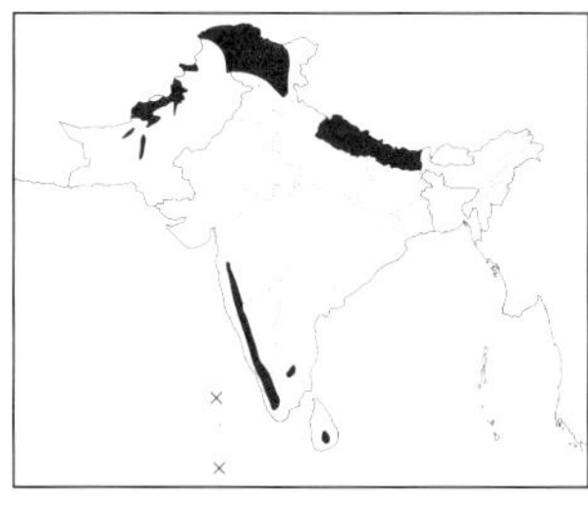

flight feathers; underside of primaries is lightly barred, and underwing-coverts are spotted. **First-year male** resembles female, but head and body feathers are similar to adult male and has grey feathers in tail. **Female** and **juvenile** have rufous crown and nape streaked with black, diffuse and narrow dark moustachial stripe, rufous upperparts which are heavily barred and spotted with black, and dark barring on rufous tail. Underwing is more heavily barred than male's. **VOICE** A high-pitched, shrill *kee-kee-kee.* **HABITS** Usually found singly or in pairs. Characteristically hovers in open country, with rapidly beating wings and fanned tail, while scanning the ground for prey; often drops in a series of gentle swoops before finally pouncing. Eats insects, frogs, lizards, small rodents and small birds. Perches conspicuously, with very upright stance, on trees, posts and telegraph wires. **HABITAT** Open country, cultivation, grassland and semi-desert in hills and plains, and open subalpine and alpine slopes. **BREEDING** January–June. Nest is usually in a cliff hole or on a cliff ledge, sometimes with a small flimsy collection of straw, twigs and rubbish added. **DISTRIBUTION AND STATUS** Breeding resident in mountains of W Pakistan and Himalayas from N Pakistan east to Bhutan and probably Manipur, also Western Ghats, Tamil Nadu and Sri Lanka; winter visitor throughout most of the subcontinent. **PK:** common and widespread resident in the mountains, nest found at 2135 m; some winter in the plains, where they are joined by other winter visitors. **NP:** common and widespread resident, winter visitor and passage migrant; recorded up to 5200 m. **IN:** widespread in Himalayas, 305–5000 m; uncommon in Western Ghats, breeds 1200–2500 m; widespread and locally common in winter in the peninsula. **BT:** common resident and winter visitor; 305–4500 m. **BD:** scarce winter visitor, locally common in the northeast. **LK:** rare resident in hills, common winter visitor to all zones. **MV:** annual visitor in moderate numbers. **REFERENCES** Cramp and Simmons (1980).

RED-NECKED FALCON *Falco chicquera* Plate 72

Red-headed Merlin (F,I), Red-headed Falcon

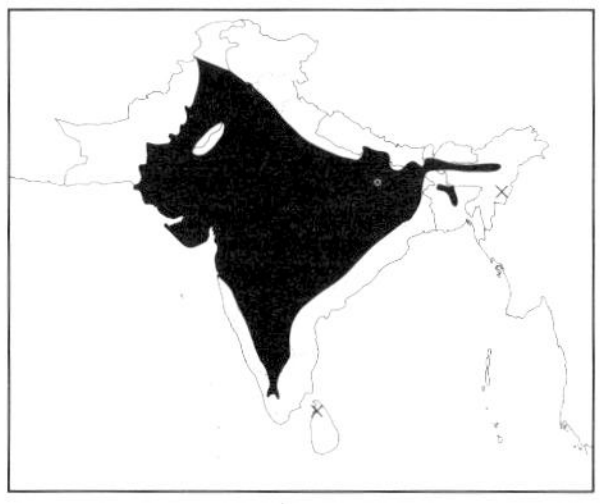

IDENTIFICATION 31–36 cm. A powerful falcon with pointed wings and longish tail. Flight is fast and dashing, with rapid wingbeats, often low over the ground; unlike Merlin (p.548), wings are not closed in glides. Most similar to Merlin in appearance and behaviour, but in all plumages readily told from that species, and from other small to medium-sized falcons, by rufous crown and nape contrasting with pale blue-grey upperparts. See Peregrine Falcon (p.551) for differences from 'Barbary Falcon'. **Adult** has rufous crown, nape and moustachial stripe contrasting with white cheeks and throat, pale blue-grey upperparts with faint dark barring and streaking, white underparts finely barred with black, and grey tail with broad black subterminal band and whitish tip. At rest and in flight, blackish primaries contrast with rest of upperwing; underwing is white, with underside of primaries lightly barred and coverts lightly spotted. Sexes are alike, although female is larger. **Juvenile** is similar to adult, but darker and with smaller white cheek patches. Darker rufous crown and nape are lightly streaked with black; mantle and inner wing-coverts are darker grey with narrow rufous fringes and more extensive dark barring; and underparts, especially flanks and thighs, are more strongly barred. **VOICE** A shrill *ki-ki-ki-ki-ki*, rasping *yak, yak, yak* and screaming *tiririri, tirirrrireee* recorded from Africa (Ferguson-Lees in prep.). **HABITS** A dashing falcon. Usually hunts cooperatively in pairs, one bird pursuing prey and the other cutting off its escape. Feeds mainly on small birds, taken on the wing. **HABITAT** Cultivation with groves, groves at edges of desert, and open country with trees. **BREEDING** January–May. Lays in old stick nest of corvid or other raptor, 5–10 m up in a thickly foliaged tree in open country, often near a village; also date palms in Pakistan. **DISTRIBUTION AND STATUS** Resident and partial migrant. Throughout much of the subcontinent, except parts of the northeast, W Pakistan, N Himalayas, coastal strip of E and SW India and Sri Lanka. **PK:** scarce; very widespread in Indus plains and outer foothills of NW Pakistan and Baluchistan. **NP:** now rare; 75–1370 m. **IN:** widespread, but now rare. **BD:** local in the centre and northwest. **LK:** vagrant to N dry lowlands. **REFERENCES** Ferguson-Lees (in prep.).

AMUR FALCON *Falco amurensis* Plate 73

Eastern Red-legged Falcon (P), Red-legged Falcon (F), *F. vespertinus* (F,I)

IDENTIFICATION 28–31 cm. In all plumages, red to pale orange base of bill, cere, eye-ring, legs and feet separate this from all other falcons occurring in region. Similar in shape and flight action to Eurasian Hobby (p.549), but wings are shorter and slightly more rounded at tip, and tail appears slightly longer. Frequently hovers, with deeper wingbeats than Common Kestrel (p.546). When perched, wing-tips reach beyond tail. **Male** is almost entirely dark grey, with slightly paler cheeks and underparts; thighs, vent and undertail-coverts are rufous. In flight, white underwing-coverts contrast with dark grey flight feathers and underbody. **First-year male** shows mixture of adult male and juvenile characters. Upperparts and underparts are typically mainly grey with some streaking, and has rufous undertail-coverts; shows dark moustachial, with paler throat and cheeks; has barred wing-coverts and tail (except for central tail feathers, which are grey); and underwing is whitish with dark barring. **Female** has dark grey crown, nape and moustachial, whitish cheeks and throat, grey upperparts with diffuse dark

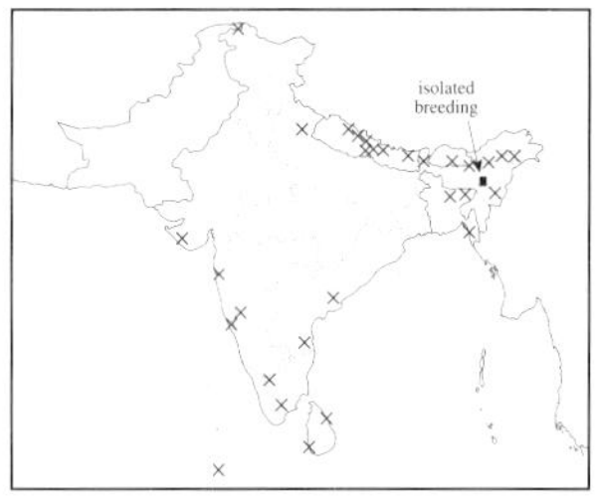

barring, whitish underparts with variable broad dark barring and some breast spotting, and orange-buff on centre of belly, thighs and undertail-coverts. In flight, underwing is white with strong dark barring, and has broad dark trailing edge. Main plumage differences from Eurasian Hobby are barred uppertail, more extensive grey nape and shorter and finer dark moustachial, dark markings on upperparts, coloration and patterning of underparts (lacking rufous thighs and vent of that species), and white ground coloration to underwing. **Juvenile** is similar to female, but feathers of mantle, scapulars and coverts are boldly fringed with rufous-buff, crown is streaked with rufous-buff, has whitish forehead and narrow supercilium, and underparts are boldly streaked. **VOICE** A shrill, screaming *kew-kew-kew...* when settling in to roost, continuing more or less throughout the night (Ali and Ripley 1987). **HABITS** A highly gregarious and crepuscular falcon; forms communal roosts, often with Lesser Kestrels (p.546). Hunts by hawking insects and also by hovering like a Common Kestrel, although does so less persistently; drops on to or beside prey, sometimes running and hopping along the ground to catch it. Feeds on large insects, such as locusts and beetles. **HABITAT** Open country. **BREEDING** Bred in the region in April and May. Lays in a disused stick nest of corvid or of another raptor, or sometimes in a tree hole, in open country, often near a village. **DISTRIBUTION AND STATUS** Widespread in subcontinent. Mainly an autumn passage migrant, few spring records, also recorded in winter in Nepal, Assam and Manipur; has bred in Cachar, Assam. **NP:** chiefly an uncommon autumn passage migrant; 915–2900 m (from 250 m in winter, to 4420 m in summer). **IN:** mainly a rare autumn passage migrant. **BT:** uncommon autumn passage migrant. **BD:** scarce passage migrant. **LK:** winter vagrant to lowlands. **MV:** winter visitor in small numbers. **REFERENCES** Morioka *et al.* (1995).

SOOTY FALCON *Falco concolor* — Plate 73

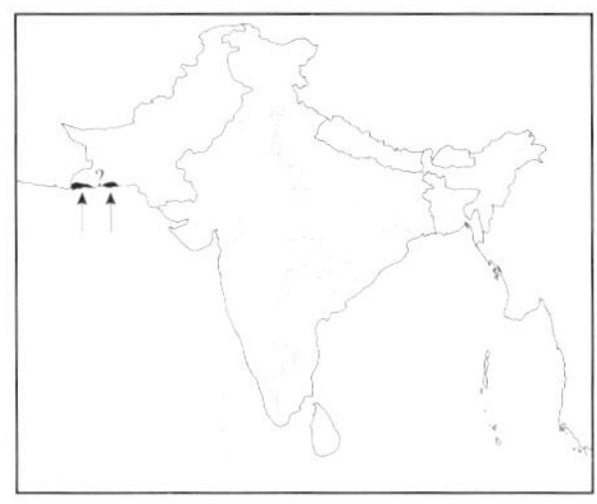

IDENTIFICATION 33–36 cm. A slim, very long-winged and long-tailed falcon, quite different in shape from Eurasian Hobby (p.549) or 'Barbary Falcon' (p.551). Tail often looks wedge-shaped, with slightly protruding central tail feathers. Flight is swift, with strong deep wingbeats interspersed with gliding and soaring. Does not hover. When perched, wing-tips reach tip of tail. **Adult** is entirely pale blue-grey, with blackish flight feathers and rear of tail. Older males are darker and can be almost black, showing no contrast between wing-coverts and flight feathers. Yellow cere is very prominent. **First-year** shows mixture of mainly adult-like head and body feathers and mainly juvenile wings and tail. **Juvenile** has pale grey upperparts with narrow buff fringes, yellowish-brown underparts which are diffusely streaked, buffish throat and cheeks, streaked crown, and dark mask and short moustachial; cere is bluish. In flight, underwing-coverts are yellowish-brown and diffusely streaked, has diffuse barring on underside of flight feathers, with darker trailing edge, and undertail is narrowly barred dark on outer feathers, with broader subterminal band; on upperwing, dark grey primaries contrast with pale grey coverts. Pale coloration of upperparts, diffusely streaked underparts, less heavily marked underwing, and structural differences are best distinctions from juvenile Eurasian Hobby. Possibly confusable with juvenile 'Barbary Falcon', but note structural differences and unbarred uppertail of Sooty. **VOICE** Alarm call near nest is a plaintive chatter similar to that of Common Kestrel (p.546); also a shrill, loud *kreeee-ah kreeee-ah* (Cramp and Simmons 1980). **HABITS** Most often seen hunting flying prey at dusk. Very swift and agile in pursuit, resembling Eurasian Hobby; usually catches prey on the wing by gliding just above the victim; also stoops on prey on the ground. Feeds chiefly on migrant birds, also insects and bats. **HABITAT** Not described from the region. Elsewhere, occurs in rocky areas and sand and stony desert, and on coral islands. **BREEDING** Little known in the region. Probably July and August. Nests on bare ground, in a hollow sheltered under a rock overhang or shrub (or cactus). **DISTRIBUTION AND STATUS PK:** rare and local summer visitor, confined to the Makran coast. **REFERENCES** Cramp and Simmons (1980), Harris *et al.* (1996).

MERLIN *Falco columbarius* — Plate 73

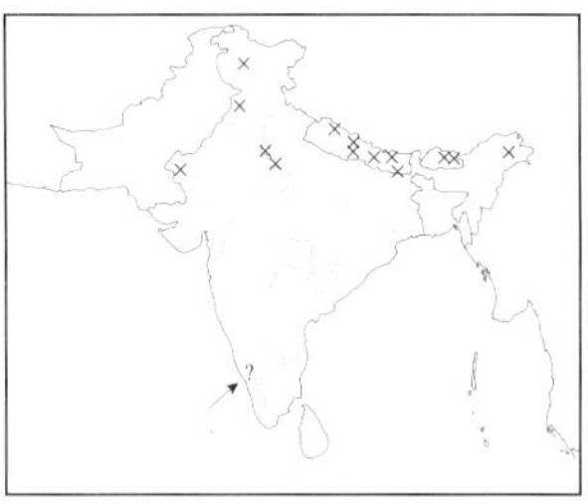

IDENTIFICATION 25-30 cm. A small and compact falcon with comparatively short, pointed wings and medium-length tail. Flight is swift, with rapid wingbeats interspersed with short dashing glides, when wings often closed into body. When perched, wing-tips fall short of tail-tip. Distinguished from Red-necked Falcon in all plumages by lack of rufous crown, by heavily streaked underparts, and by strongly barred underwing. **Male** is blue-grey above, with blackish flight feathers and broad black subterminal band to tail; underparts are cream to rufous-orange with dark streaking. Has weak moustachial stripe and has diffuse patch of rufous-orange on nape. Distinctly smaller than female. **Female** and **juvenile** have brown upperparts with variable rufous or buff fringes and spotting, and strongly barred uppertail; underparts are buffish and heavily streaked. Have weak moustachial stripe and fine whitish supercilium; juvenile typically shows whitish patch on nape. **VOICE** Usually silent away from breeding grounds. **HABITS** A bold and dashing falcon, normally found singly. Usually hunts in low flight with fast wingbeats and short glides, catching prey in a surprise attack; will also pursue birds in a long persistent chase, often climbing steeply and making sudden turns. Takes mainly small birds. Will perch in trees, but usually uses a low perch in the open with a good view. **HABITAT** A variety of open-country habitats, including cultivation and scrub and scrub desert. **DISTRIBUTION AND STATUS** Winter visitor. Pakistan, Nepal and N India (from Jammu and Kashmir east to Arunachal Pradesh). **PK:** rare winter visitor, reported quite widely. **NP:** rare winter visitor and possibly also a passage migrant; 75–4000 m. **IN, BT:** rare.

EURASIAN HOBBY *Falco subbuteo* — Plate 73

Hobby (I), Northern Hobby (K,R)

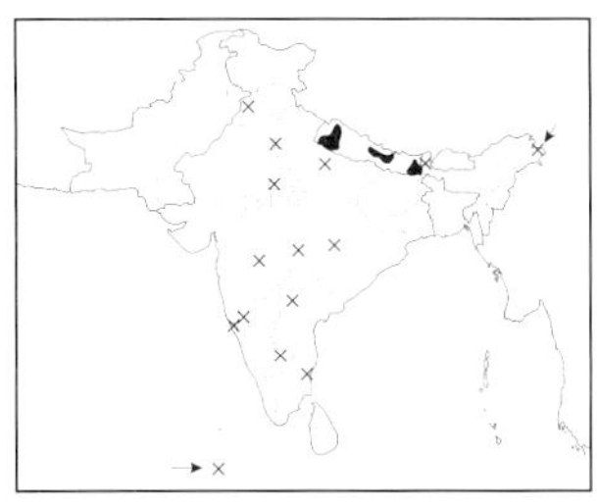

IDENTIFICATION 30–36 cm. A medium-sized falcon with long, pointed wings and medium-length tail. Slimmer in wings and body than Peregrine Falcon (p.551). Hunting flight is swift and powerful, with stiff wingbeats interspersed with short glides. When hawking insects, action is slower, with flatter wingbeats, and regularly soars with wings horizontal and tail spread. Only very rarely hovers. When perched, wing-tips reach tail-tip. See Amur and Sooty Falcons (p.547 and p.548) for differences from those species. **Adult** has dark slate cap and broad blackish moustachial stripe contrasting with white cheeks, slate-grey upperparts, cream underparts with bold blackish streaking, and rufous thighs and undertail coverts. Blackish primaries contrast slightly with rest of wing, and uppertail is unbarred; from below, underwing is heavily barred. White cheeks, streaked underparts and rufous thighs are main distinctions from Oriental Hobby (below). **Juvenile** is similar to adult, with broad black moustachial and pale cheeks, but crown is paler with diffuse buffish fringes, upperparts are dark brown with buffish fringes, pale buffish underparts are more heavily streaked, and lacks rufous thighs and undertail-coverts. Head pattern and coloration of underparts are best distinctions from juvenile Oriental. **VOICE** Call at nest site is a *kew-kew-kew* or *ki-ki-ki* (Jonsson 1992). **HABITS** Usually seen singly, but sometimes a few birds hunt together at good food sources. Often perches on isolated trees or on trees in clearings. Markedly crepuscular. A graceful falcon, capable of high speed in acrobatic pursuit of flying prey, usually birds and insects and occasionally bats; seizes victims with the feet. In slower hawking flight wheels and turns adeptly to catch insects, and will repeatedly fly back and forth through a swarm. Occasionally catches insects in sallies from a perch. Consumes insect prey on the wing, holding them with its feet. **HABITAT** Well-wooded areas, also open country and cultivation in winter. **BREEDING** May–July. Usually occupies the disused nest of a crow high in a tree at the forest edge. **DISTRIBUTION AND STATUS** Breeds in Himalayas from N Pakistan east to Nepal; winters widely in the subcontinent (except Sri Lanka). **PK:** frequent summer visitor to Himalayas; an uncommon, irregular but widespread winter visitor. **NP:** widespread resident, partial migrant, winter visitor and passage migrant; recorded up to 4200 m. **IN:** resident and partial migrant in Himalayas, breeding from 1200 m up to the treeline; widespread and rare in winter in the peninsula. **BT:** frequent, status uncertain; 1900–3015 m. **BD:** scarce winter visitor. **MV:** regular visitor.

ORIENTAL HOBBY *Falco severus* — Plate 73

Indian Hobby (P)

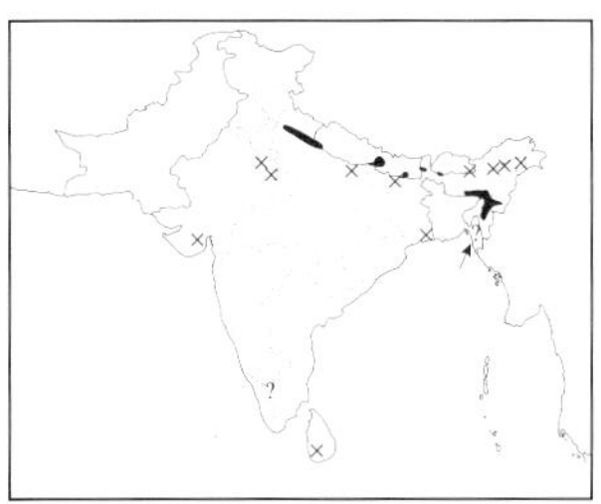

IDENTIFICATION 27–30 cm. Has long, pointed wings and shortish tail. Structure, flight action and appearance are similar to those of Eurasian Hobby (above), although slightly stockier, with shorter tail. Much slimmer in wings and body than Peregrine Falcon (p.551). **Adult** has complete blackish hood, lacking white cheeks of Eurasian Hobby. Further, has darker bluish-black upperparts than that species, and has rufous underparts which are unstreaked. In flight, underwing-coverts are rufous and unbarred, while underside of flight feathers is strongly barred. Superficially resembles *peregrinator* race of Peregrine (p.551) (which also has a dark hood and rufous underparts); distinguished from that form by slimmer build, no indication of moustachial stripe, deeper and more uniformly rufous underparts, including throat and sides of neck, absence of barring on thighs, flanks and undertail-coverts, and darker and more uniform upperparts. **Juvenile** is similar to adult, with full hood, but upperparts are browner with narrow rufous feather fringes, underparts are paler rufous-buff and sparsely but heavily streaked, and underwing-coverts are also streaked. **VOICE** A rapid *ki-ki-ki-ki* (Ali and Ripley 1987). **HABITS** Very similar to those of Eurasian Hobby. Feeds mainly on large flying insects; also small birds and bats. **HABITAT** Open or lightly wooded hills. **BREEDING** Little information. Probably late May–August. Normally uses an old crow nest in a tree growing from the side of a cliff. **DISTRIBUTION AND STATUS** Resident and partial migrant. Mainly Himalayas from N Uttar Pradesh east to Arunachal Pradesh; NE India and Bangladesh. **NP:** now rare, status uncertain; formerly bred in Kathmandu valley, recorded up to 1525 m. **IN:** now rare; breeds 1800–2400 m. **BT:** rare. **BD:** ?former resident; no recent records, but could still occur in Chittagong Hill Tracts. **LK:** rare winter visitor to all zones.

LAGGAR FALCON *Falco jugger* **Plate 74**

***F. biarmicus*, Lanner Falcon (I)**

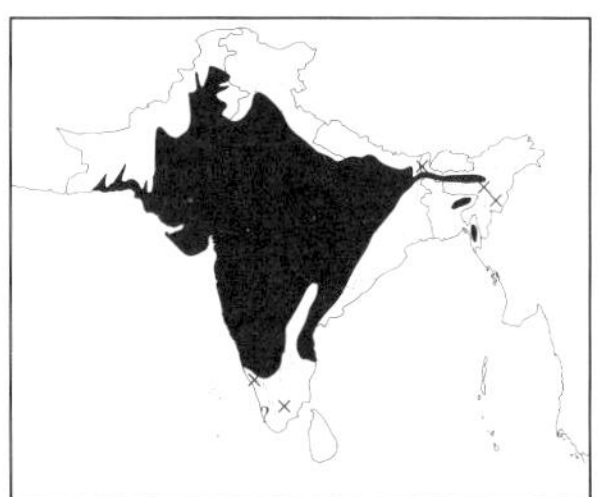

IDENTIFICATION 43–46 cm. A large falcon with long, pointed wings and longish tail. Slimmer in wings and body than Peregrine Falcon (p.551). Smaller, slimmer-winged and less powerful than Saker Falcon (below); for plumage differences, see that species. In direct flight, has fast, powerful wing-beats interspersed with glides and swoops. **Adult** has rufous-white to rufous crown with dark streaking, and narrow but rather prominent white supercilium; dark moustachial stripe is fairly prominent, but is less clearly defined than on Peregrine. Upperparts are dark brown with fine buff fringes. Tail is rather uniform, with narrow pale barring on inner webs of outer feathers, and has buff tip. Underparts vary: breast and belly can be unmarked or heavily streaked, although lower flanks and thighs are usually wholly dark brown. In flight, underwing-coverts are typically heavily spotted and streaked, particularly greater coverts, which may form dark panel across centre of wing and merging with dark patch on flanks and thighs; underside of flight feathers is also strongly barred. Cere, and legs and feet, are yellow. Sexes are alike, but female is larger. **Juvenile** has greyish cere, and greyish legs and feet. Similar to adult, but crown is duller and head pattern less well defined; underparts are more heavily streaked, and may appear entirely brown except for whitish throat and upper breast and odd white feather tips and bases elsewhere on underparts. Possibly confusable with juvenile Peregrine, but has paler crown, finer moustachial stripe and unbarred uppertail. **VOICE** Usually silent. A shrill *whi-ee-ee*, seldom heard except in breeding season (Ali and Ripley 1987). **HABITS** Often in pairs throughout the year. Usually seen perched on a regularly used vantage point, such as treetop or post. Also circles high overhead. Hunts mainly by flying rapidly and low, and seizing prey on the ground; less frequently stoops on prey from a height, like a Peregrine Falcon. Feeds on reptiles, rodents, small birds and large insects. **HABITAT** Open arid country, cultivation, thorn scrub, scrub desert, rocky escarpments and sand dunes in plains and low hills. **BREEDING** January–April. Lays in old stick nest of another bird of prey or crow 10–15 m up in a large tree, lower down in semi-desert and sometimes on a ledge of a cliff or building. **DISTRIBUTION AND STATUS** Resident, subject to local movements. Throughout most of the subcontinent, except parts of the northeast, W Pakistan, Himalayas, E and SE India, Western Ghats and Sri Lanka. **PK:** now scarce and becoming rare; throughout drier, less intensively cultivated areas of Indus plains. **NP:** rare; recorded up to 1980 m, mainly in the terai. **IN:** widespread, now rare in most areas, but locally fairly common in the northwest; plains and hills, up to 1000 m in Himalayas. **BD:** scarce? resident.

SAKER FALCON *Falco cherrug* **Plate 74**

***F. biarmicus*, Lanner Falcon (I)**

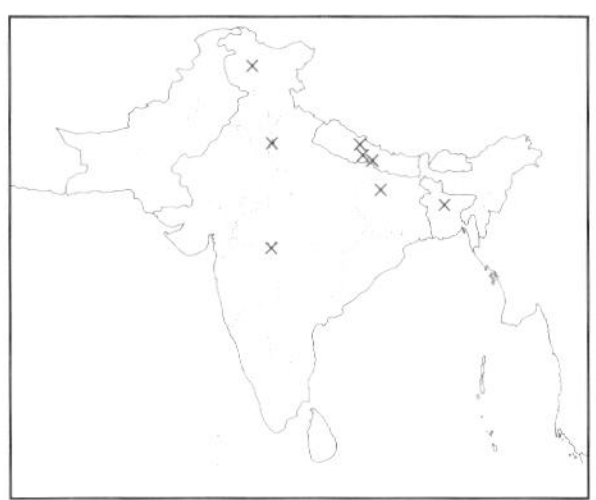

IDENTIFICATION 50–58 cm. A large falcon with long wings and long tail. Although fast and powerful when hunting, wingbeats are slow in level flight, with lazier action than Peregrine Falcon (p.551). Larger, and with longer wings and tail than that species, although wing-tips more rounded, and with more elongated body. Larger and broader-winged and more powerful than Laggar Falcon (above). At rest, tail extends noticeably beyond closed wings (wings fall just short of tail-tip on Laggar and are equal to tail on Peregrine). Best told from Laggar by differences in head pattern and coloration of upperparts. *F. c. milvipes* (see below) is more distinct in plumage and should not cause confusion. Soars like other falcons, and can hover with heavily beating wings. **Adult** has paler crown than Laggar, although can be rather similar; dark crescent at rear of ear-coverts is usually less pronounced than on Laggar; and moustachial stripe is less clearly defined, and is typically fine, diffuse and separated from eye. Upperparts are a paler rufous-brown, while underparts are generally not so heavily marked as on Laggar, with flanks and thighs usually clearly streaked and not appearing wholly brown (although there is some overlap). Underwing-coverts are also less heavily marked than Laggar's and underside of primaries less strongly barred, although again there is some overlap. Outer tail feathers are more prominently barred. Cere, and legs and feet, are yellow. Sexes are alike, but female is larger. **Juvenile** has greyish cere, and greyish legs and feet. Similar to adult, but crown is more heavily marked and moustachial is stronger; underparts are more heavily streaked, and upperparts are a darker brown. **Racial variation** *F. c. milvipes*, which is a rare winter visitor (and the race recorded in Nepal), is quite distinctive, having broad orange-buff barring on upperparts (including wing-coverts, tertials and secondaries), with patterning not unlike that of female Common Kestrel (p.546). **VOICE** Normally silent away from breeding grounds. **HABITS** Usually seen singly, sometimes in pairs. Spends long periods perched on rocks. Often scans from a prominent vantage point before launching attack. When hunting, flies fast and low and swiftly strikes its prey on the ground from behind; also stoops on aerial prey like a Peregrine Falcon. Feeds on lizards, small mammals and birds. **HABITAT** Desert and semi-desert, mainly in the mountains and foothills, also in the Indus plains. **DISTRIBUTION AND STATUS** Winter visitor. Mainly Pakistan, Gujarat and Nepal. **PK:** winter visitor, scarce and becoming rare; now mainly in Baluchistan and NW Pakistan. **NP:** rare and local winter visitor and passage migrant; 1525–3795 m. **IN:** rare. **BD:** vagrant.

PEREGRINE FALCON *Falco peregrinus* Plate 74

Red-capped Falcon (R), Barbary Falcon (N) *F. pelegrinoides*

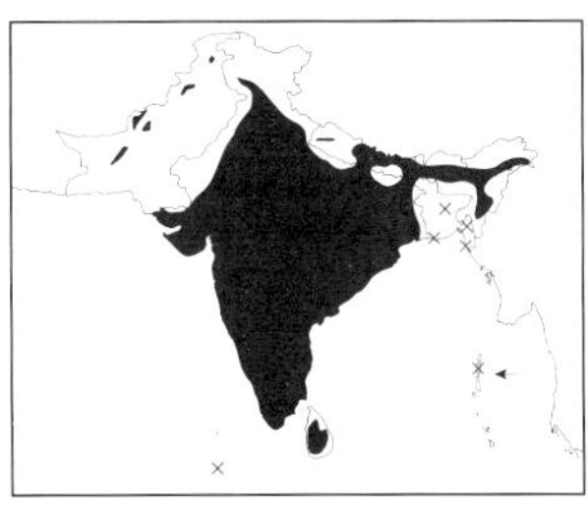

IDENTIFICATION 38–48 cm. A large, heavy-looking falcon with broad-based and pointed wings and short, broad-based tail. Flight is strong, with stiff, shallow wingbeats and occasional short glides; becomes dashing, with fast, deep and powerful beats, when hunting. Soars on level wings like other falcons, and can hover. Stockier, with shorter tail and shorter, broader-based wings, compared with other large and medium-sized falcons occurring in region. **Adult** has grey upperparts and usually barred underparts, these areas being respectively browner and streaked on **juvenile**. See below for other features. **Racial variation** *F. p. calidus*, a winter visitor throughout the subcontinent, is readily told from other falcons by combination of slate-grey upperparts, broad, clean-cut black moustachial stripe, and whitish underparts with narrow blackish barring. Juvenile *calidus* has browner upperparts with narrower rufous or buff fringes, and has heavily streaked underparts; may show narrow pale supercilium, but moustachial is broad and well defined. Broader moustachial (with clearly defined white cheek patch), dark crown and barred uppertail are best distinctions from juvenile Laggar Falcon (p.550). *F. p. peregrinator*, resident throughout the subcontinent, has darker upperparts than *calidus*, with more extensive black hood (and less pronounced moustachial); underparts are rufous, with dark barring on belly and thighs. Larger size, stockier and more powerful appearance, pale throat and lower cheek patch, and barring on underparts are main differences from Oriental Hobby (p.549). Juvenile *peregrinator* has darker brownish-black upperparts than adult, and paler underparts with heavy streaking. Compared with *calidus*, adult *F. p. babylonicus* ('Barbary Falcon'), confined as a breeder to N and W Pakistan and wintering west to NW India, has paler blue-grey upperparts contrasting with darker wing-tips, buffish underparts with only sparse streaking and barring, rufous on crown and nape, and a narrower dark moustachial; in flight, underwing appears pale, with dark wing-tips and dark crescent-shaped carpal patch, and dark barring towards tip of tail is more pronounced. Possibly confusable with Red-necked Falcon (p.547), but is larger and stockier, has dark markings on head (moustachial, eye-stripe, and patch on side of nape), and has more uniformly barred tail (subterminal dark band broader and more pronounced on Red-necked); at rest, wing-tips reach tail-tip (short of tip on Red-necked). Juvenile *babylonicus* has darker brown upperparts with narrow rufous-buff fringes, has heavily streaked underparts and underwing-coverts, and shows only a trace of rufous on head (forehead and supercilium). **VOICE** Voice of *peregrinator* is unrecorded, except for *chir-r-r-r* uttered close to nest (Ali and Ripley 1987). Generally silent away from breeding area. **HABITS** Generally seen singly or in pairs. A bold, aggressive and powerful falcon, highly skilful in flight. Feeds on waterfowl, pigeons, partridges and other birds, usually taken on the wing and over open country or water. Scans for prey by circling high overhead, and usually higher than other falcons, or from an elevated vantage point. Typically, pursues flying prey rapidly, and adept at following its every twist and turn; finally rises above it and stoops with terrific force, with wings almost closed, to seize or strike the victim. Occasionally catches prey without stooping. Hunts more actively at dawn and dusk. **HABITAT** Breeds in rugged hills and mountains; winters around large lakes, rivers, marshes, sea cliffs, coastal lagoons and mangroves; also resident in dry rocky hills and stony semi-desert in Pakistan. **BREEDING** December–May. Nests on a cliff ledge at traditional sites, laying either in disused stick platform of another raptor or corvid, or often directly on to the ledge. **DISTRIBUTION AND STATUS** Resident, subject to altitudinal movements, and winter visitor. Resident in Baluchistan and NW Pakistan; winters in Indus plains, Pakistan; resident and winter visitor throughout much of the rest of the subcontinent, except parts of the northeast and W Himalayas. **PK:** now scarce, recorded breeding at 650 m; widespread in winter in Indus plains. **NP:** frequent; usually summers 1500–3000 m (–4200 m), winters down to the terai. **IN:** widespread and uncommon; up to 2745 m in Himalayas. **BT:** uncommon. **BD:** scarce winter visitor. **LK:** rare resident in all zones, favouring rugged hills, occasionally in towns; scarce winter visitor throughout, more frequent in dry lowlands. **MV:** infrequent winter visitor. **REFERENCES** Clark and Shirihai (1995), Harris *et al.* (1996).

GREBES Podicipedidae

Aquatic birds adapted for diving from the surface and swimming under the water. Their strong legs are placed near the rear of their almost tailless body, and the feet are lobed. In flight, grebes have an elongated appearance, with the neck extended, and feet hanging lower than the humped back. They rise clumsily from the water, pattering over the surface, and fly with rapid beats of their relatively small wings. Although most species are migratory, they are generally reluctant to fly when settled on a particular water. Grebes feed mainly on fish and aquatic invertebrates, which are caught by diving. They usually feed singly, but may gather at concentrations of food and form loose congregations in the non-breeding season. When small, the chicks ride on their parents' backs or are kept in the nest. During the breeding season, grebes frequent fresh waters, especially shallow lakes and ponds. At other times, they may move nearer to the coast or to large inland waters. The main reference specific to grebes is Perennou *et al.* (1994). Measurements are taken from Jonsson (1992).

LITTLE GREBE *Tachybaptus ruficollis* Plate 75

Podiceps ruficollis **(F,I,K,P)**

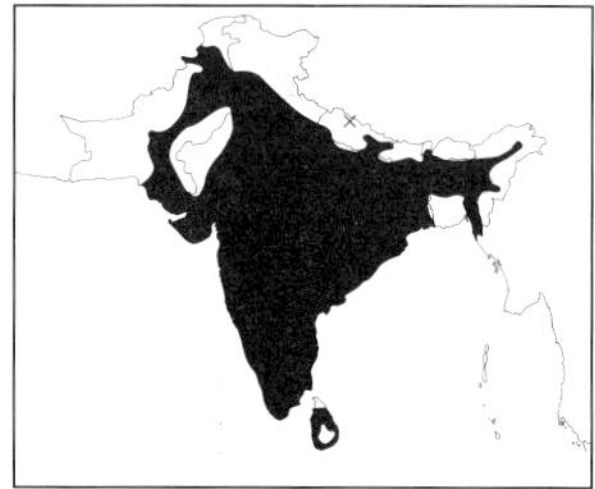

IDENTIFICATION 25–29 cm. A small, stocky grebe, often with puffed-up rear end. Shows whitish secondaries in flight. **Adult breeding** appears dark brown with paler flanks at a distance; cheeks and sides of neck are rufous, and has yellow patch at base of bill. **Non-breeding** has brown crown, hindneck and back contrasting with brownish-buff cheeks, foreneck and flanks; puffed-up rear end is often paler than flanks. **Juvenile** is similar to non-breeding, but has brown stripes across cheeks and is often tinged rufous on neck and breast. For differences from Black-necked Grebe (p.553), see that species. **VOICE** A drawn-out whinnying trill in breeding season, and a sharp *wit wit* in alarm. **HABITS** Often keeps singly or in pairs among aquatic vegetation when breeding; in the non-breeding season easily seen on open water, sometimes in small loose flocks. Can often be detected by its bubbling trill. Swims buoyantly. **HABITAT** Lakes, ponds, village tanks, reservoirs, ditches, and slow-moving rivers; rarely on coastal waters. **BREEDING** Throughout the year, varying locally. Nest is a mass of weeds and rushes, either floating or built on water weeds, and usually anchored to reeds or the bottom. **DISTRIBUTION AND STATUS** Resident, subject to local or long-distance movements depending on water conditions. Throughout much of the subcontinent, except parts of the northwest, northeast and Himalayas. **PK:** common and widespread resident. **NP:** fairly common resident, winter visitor and passage migrant; mainly below 1370 m (–3050 m). **IN:** widespread and locally common; from plains up to 1800 m (Kashmir). **BT:** rare. **BD:** locally common resident. **LK:** common and widespread resident in lowlands, occasionally visits hills.

RED-NECKED GREBE *Podiceps grisegena* Plate 75

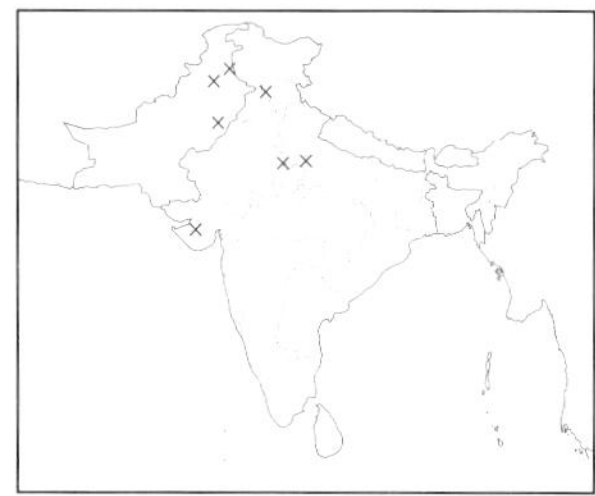

IDENTIFICATION 40–50 cm. Slightly smaller than Great Crested Grebe (below), with shorter, stouter neck, squarer head shape, stockier body which is often slightly puffed up at rear, and black-tipped yellow bill. In flight, appears less awkward and more compact, especially shorter-necked, than Great Crested, but with similar wing pattern. Unlike Great Crested, Red-necked often leaps clear of water when diving. **Non-breeding** is similar to Great Crested, but has more extensive and not so sharply defined black crown reaching to eye, and with black lores, dusky wash to pale cheeks, and dusky neck and flanks with prominent white flash at rear. Larger size, two-toned bill and dusky cheeks are best distinctions from Horned Grebe (p.553). **Adult breeding** has greyish-white cheeks contrasting with black crown and reddish foreneck. **Juvenile** is similar to non-breeding, but has brown striping on cheeks and rufous foreneck. **VOICE** Silent away from breeding areas. **HABITS** A typical grebe. Similar to those of Great Crested. **HABITAT** Recorded on lakes in the region; also occurs on coastal waters. **DISTRIBUTION AND STATUS** Winter visitor to N Pakistan, and N and NW India (Himachal Pradesh, Rajasthan, Gujarat and Uttar Pradesh). **PK:** small numbers winter. **IN:** locally common. **REFERENCES** Mundkur and Pravez (1990), Rahmani and Arora (1991).

GREAT CRESTED GREBE *Podiceps cristatus* Plate 75

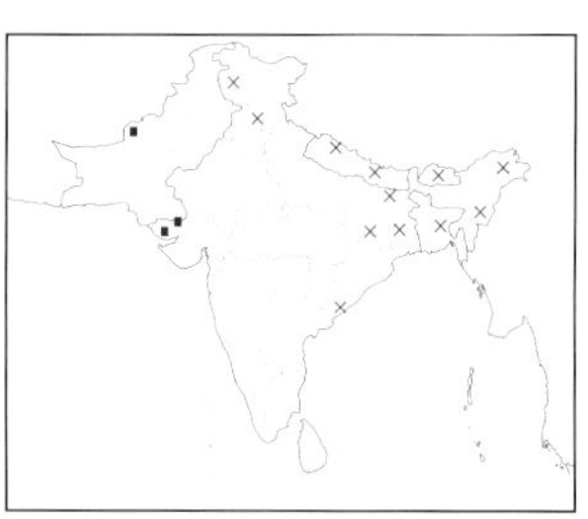

IDENTIFICATION 46–51 cm. Large grebe with slender body, long slender neck, and triangular-shaped head. In flight, appears very awkward, with arched back, large dangling feet, long thin neck, and rapid flight action; has two prominent white patches on wing. **Non-breeding** lacks ear-tufts. White cheeks and foreneck contrast strongly with dark crown and hindneck. Has pinkish bill. **Adult breeding** is striking, with broad, brown-edged rufous-orange ear-tufts, black crown and small crest contrasting with white cheeks, white foreneck, and rufous-orange flanks. **Juvenile** is similar to non-breeding, but has brown striping on cheeks. For differences from Red-necked Grebe (above), see that species. **VOICE** At breeding sites, a harsh rolling *aooorrr* and chattering *kek-kek....* **HABITS** A typical grebe. Swims with body low in the water and neck held erect. Both sexes perform striking, ritual courtship displays. **HABITAT** Favours open water: lakes, jheels and reservoirs, also coastal waters and saltpans. **BREEDING** June–August. Nest is a floating mass of piled-up weeds, loosely anchored to vegetation. **DISTRIBUTION AND STATUS** Breeds in Baluchistan, Pakistan, at 1750 m, in Ladakh at 4700–5200 m, and regularly in Gujarat; winter visitor to the N subcontinent from Pakistan east to NE India, and south to Maharashtra and NE Andhra Pradesh. **PK:** mainly a scarce winter visitor; occasionally breeds in small numbers. **NP:** locally frequent winter visitor, possibly breeds; mainly below 1370 m (–4800 m). **IN:** breeds in small numbers; in winter uncommon inland, more frequent on coast. **BT:** rare passage migrant. **BD:** scarce visitor. **REFERENCES** Mundkur and Pravez (1986).

HORNED GREBE *Podiceps auritus* Plate 75

Slavonian Grebe (R)

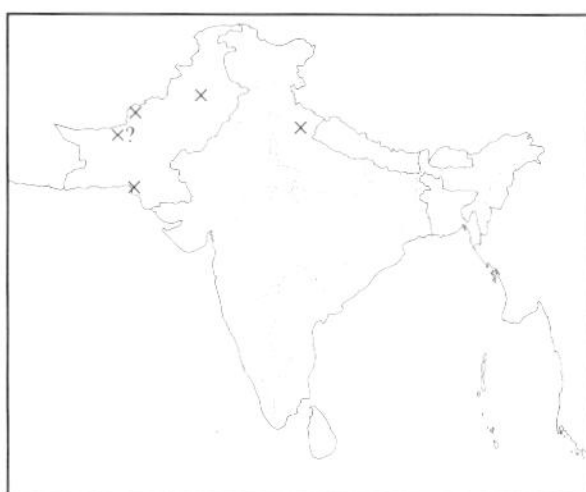

IDENTIFICATION 31–38 cm. **Non-breeding** is best told from Black-necked Grebe (below) by subtle differences in head shape, and whiter cheeks and neck. Head is larger and more triangular-shaped, with sloping forehead, and crown peaking at rear (forehead is typically higher and crown peaks at front or centre on Black-necked). White cheeks are more extensive and clearly defined from black crown (on Black-necked, black of crown extends below eye, ear-coverts are dusky grey, and white patch on side of head is crescent-shaped rather than triangular); and foreneck is typically whiter and contrasts more with black hindneck. In addition, bill is stouter and does not appear upturned. Has two white patches on upperwing, with white patch on fore wing-coverts which is usually lacking on Black-necked. **Adult breeding** has black head with yellow ear-tufts, and rufous neck and flanks. **Juvenile** as non-breeding, but may show faint dark stripes on cheeks and rufous on neck. **VOICE** Silent outside breeding season. **HABITS** A typical grebe. Usually swims with neck erect, in contrast to Black-necked. **HABITAT** Lakes and coastal waters. **DISTRIBUTION AND STATUS** Winter visitor to Pakistan and India. **PK:** rare, but possibly overlooked along the Makran coast. **IN:** vagrant. **REFERENCES** Drijvers (1995), Harris *et al.* (1989).

BLACK-NECKED GREBE *Podiceps nigricollis* Plate 75

***Podiceps caspicus* (F)**

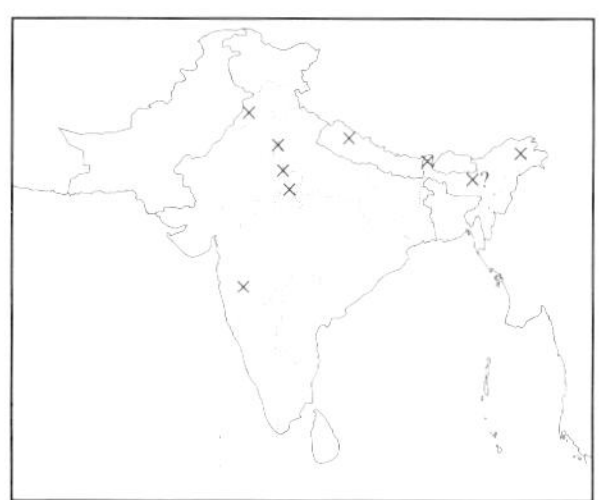

IDENTIFICATION 28–34 cm. Looks larger, slimmer and longer-necked than Little Grebe (p.552). Crown usually appears to peak at front or in centre, bill appears upturned and dark, and eye is bright red. In flight, white secondaries show as more striking wing-bar than on Little. **Non-breeding** is black and white rather than brown and buff, and white throat and sides of head contrast with blackish crown and dusky ear-coverts, forming striking white crescent which curves up behind eye. Has white centre to breast and rear flanks, which are more uniform brownish-buff on Little. Very similar in non-breeding plumage to Horned Grebe (above); see that species for main differences. **Adult breeding** is striking, with black head and neck, yellow ear-tufts, and rufous flanks. **Juvenile** as non-breeding, but may show buff wash to cheeks and foreneck and more closely resemble Little. **VOICE** Short whistles and trills at nesting site. **HABITS** Similar to those of Little. Typically swims with curved neck, in contrast to Horned. **HABITAT** Shallow, reed-edged lakes with emergent vegetation; also coastal waters in winter. **BREEDING** May–July, varying locally. Nest is a floating heap of plant stems concealed in sedges and anchored to reed stems. **DISTRIBUTION AND STATUS** Breeds in Baluchistan, Pakistan, at 1750 m, and India; winters mainly in Pakistan, NW India and Nepal. **PK:** frequent winter visitor to lakes and coast; a few breeding records. **NP:** scarce and local visitor, mainly in winter; recorded up to 3050 m. **IN:** frequent winter visitor to the northwest; breeds in small numbers.

TROPICBIRDS Phaethontidae

Aerial seabirds which range over tropical and subtropical waters. They nest mainly on oceanic and offshore islands. Between breeding seasons they wander far from land, and are probably under-recorded in coastal waters of the region. All three species are similar in appearance, resembling heavy-bodied terns, with mainly white plumage marked with black. The body is medium-sized, the wings are short, and the central tail feathers are greatly elongated. Tropicbirds have a graceful pigeon-like flight, with flapping and circling alternating with long glides. Usually they are solitary, but they may congregate with flocks of feeding terns and shearwaters. Fish and squid form their main diet. They feed by first hovering to locate prey, and then plunge-diving on half-closed wings. The main reference specific to tropicbirds is Harrison (1983).

RED-BILLED TROPICBIRD *Phaethon aethereus* Plate 76

Short-tailed Tropicbird (P)

IDENTIFICATION 48 cm. **Adult** told from White-tailed Tropicbird (p.554) by black barring on mantle, upperwing-coverts, scapulars and rump, and bright red bill. White tail-streamers, and black markings on upperbody and wings, separate it from Red-tailed Tropicbird (p.554). When soaring against bright light, usually shows dark barring on inner secondaries and tertials on underwing. **Juvenile** lacks tail-streamers, has more pronounced and extensive barring on upperparts than adult, and tail feathers have black tips. Differs from juvenile Red-tailed and White-tailed in having broader eye-stripes which join across nape; differs further from Red-tailed in yellow bill with black tip, larger size, and more black in primaries. **HABITS** A typical tropicbird. Occasionally follows ships.

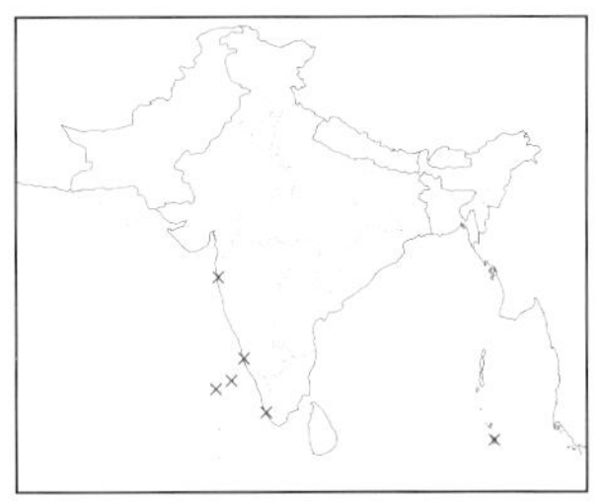

HABITAT Pelagic. **DISTRIBUTION AND STATUS** Visitor to coasts of the subcontinent, mainly off the W seaboard. **PK:** scarce visitor, January–May, mainly to the Makran coast. **IN:** rare winter visitor to W coasts, Lakshadweep and Andaman Is, February–July. **LK:** regular summer visitor to the SW coast. **REFERENCES** Harrison (1983).

RED-TAILED TROPICBIRD *Phaethon rubricauda* Plate 76

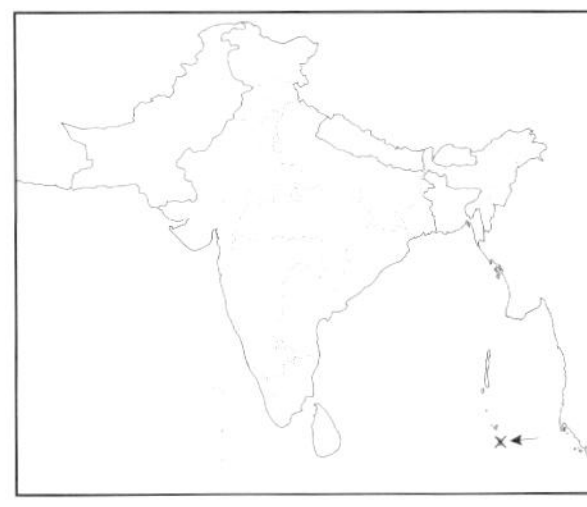

IDENTIFICATION 46 cm. Appears proportionately heavier-bodied and shorter-winged than other tropicbirds, with less graceful and rather heavy flight. **Adult** distinguished from Red-billed and White-tailed Tropicbirds (p.553 and below) by red tail-streamers and largely white upperwing (except for black primary shafts and markings on tertials). Has white mantle and rump (which are barred on Red-billed), and red bill (which is yellowish or orange on White-tailed). Often has pink wash to body and wings. Red tail-streamers can be difficult to see or be broken off. When soaring against bright light, shows few or no markings on underwing. **Juvenile** has grey or black bill (yellow with black tip on juveniles of other two species). Has much less black on primaries than White-tailed and Red-billed, and lacks nape band of Red-billed. **HABITS** A typical tropicbird. Rarely visits ships. **HABITAT** Pelagic. **BREEDING** Details unrecorded in the region. In Australia, nest is a scrape on the ground in the shade of a bush, under a rocky overhang or cliff. **DISTRIBUTION AND STATUS IN:** breeds on Nicobar Is; stragglers in the Bay of Bengal. **REFERENCES** Frith (1976), Harrison (1983), Marchant and Higgins (1990).

WHITE-TAILED TROPICBIRD *Phaethon lepturus* Plate 76

Long-tailed Tropic-bird (I,P), Yellow-billed Tropicbird

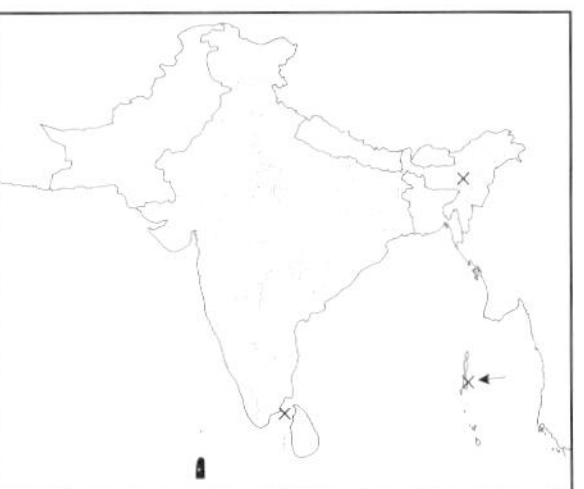

IDENTIFICATION 39 cm. Smallest tropicbird, with more graceful and buoyant flight than the other two species, and with comparatively long angular wings. Told from Red-billed Tropicbird (p.553) by white mantle and rump, black diagonal bar across inner upperwing, and yellow or orange bill; also has faster wingbeats. Bill colour, white tail-streamers and black markings on wing separate it from Red-tailed Tropicbird (above). Upperwing pattern can be visible from below when soaring overhead in strong light. **Juvenile** lacks dark nuchal collar and has coarser, more extensive barring on upperparts compared with Red-billed, and has more black on primaries compared with Red-tailed; yellow bill with dark tip is further difference from juvenile Red-tailed. **HABITS** A typical tropicbird. Often visits ships. **HABITAT** Pelagic. **BREEDING** Details unknown in the region. In Australia, nests in a tree fork or in a hollow or scrape on the ground. **DISTRIBUTION AND STATUS** Breeding resident on the Maldives; visitor to the coasts of India and Sri Lanka. **IN:** vagrant. **LK:** uncommon visitor to W and S coasts. **MV:** formerly plentiful throughout, but is now decreasing. **REFERENCES** Balachandran (1992), Frith (1976), Harrison (1983), Marchant and Higgins (1990).

BOOBIES Sulidae

Large seabirds with torpedo-shaped body, strong conical bill, long wings and long wedge-shaped tail. They forage on the wing, scanning the sea, and on sighting fish or squid they plunge-dive at an angle. Flying fish may also be caught on the wing. Their flight is direct, with alternating periods of flapping and gliding. Boobies may be found singly, in small groups, or in large flocks at profitable feeding areas. They breed colonially. Boobies are mainly rare or uncommon visitors to the coasts and coastal waters of the region, although some species possibly breed. They are undoubtedly under-recorded. The main references specific to boobies are Nelson (1978) and Harrison (1983).

MASKED BOOBY *Sula dactylatra* Plate 76

IDENTIFICATION 81–92 cm. Largest and most robust of the boobies occurring in the subcontinent. Flight is powerful and steady, usually fairly high above the water, and rarely shearing. **Adult** is largely white, with black flight feathers and tail. Bill varies from yellow to orange or greenish; legs and feet vary from lead-grey to dull orange, but are never red. Has blackish facial skin and gular pouch, resulting in masked appearance.

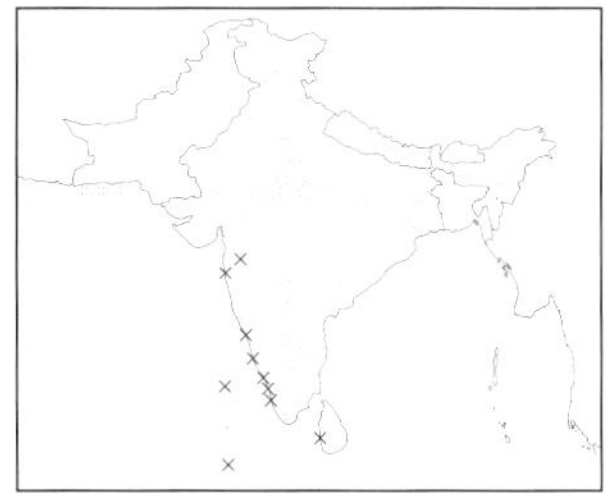

Distinguished from adult Red-footed Booby (below) by larger size, dark mask, coloration of bill and legs and feet, white head and neck lacking yellow on crown and hindneck, lack of black carpal patch on underwing, black tail, and black tertials (which complete black trailing edge of wing). **Juvenile** has brown head, neck and upperparts. Superficially resembles juveniles of Brown Booby (below) and Red-footed, but shows distinctive whitish collar creating hooded appearance, can show indistinct pale chin stripe (absent on some birds), and has narrow pale fringes to wing-coverts and upperbody, resulting in distinctly scaled appearance. Underbody and lesser and median underwing-coverts are white, with narrow dark bar across lesser coverts (underwing-coverts are dark brown on juvenile Red-footed, and dusky grey on juvenile Brown), and has white bases to greater primary coverts (all dark on Brown). Breast is white, whereas on Brown (in all plumages) brown of upper breast joins brown leading edge to wing. In **immature** plumage, head, upperbody and upperwing-coverts become increasingly white with age. Younger immatures can show dark head and neck, feathers of the upperbody mixed with brown and white, and have largely brown upperwing-coverts; older birds have largely white head, upperbody and upperwing-coverts, with variable brown mottling on back, scapulars and coverts. **HABITS** A typical booby. Seen in the region either singly or in small groups. **HABITAT** Pelagic, rarely coming within sight of land. **BREEDING** Details unknown in the region. In Australia, builds a nest of debris on the ground. **DISTRIBUTION AND STATUS** Possibly breeds on the Maldives and Lakshadweep; a rare visitor to W coastal waters of the subcontinent. **PK:** rare visitor to Makran coastal waters, probably only juveniles. **IN:** very rare visitor during monsoon gales; resident on Lakshadweep. **LK:** straggler. **MV:** rare visitor. **REFERENCES** Frith (1976), Harrison (1983), Marchant and Higgins (1990), Nelson (1978).

RED-FOOTED BOOBY *Sula sula* Plate 76

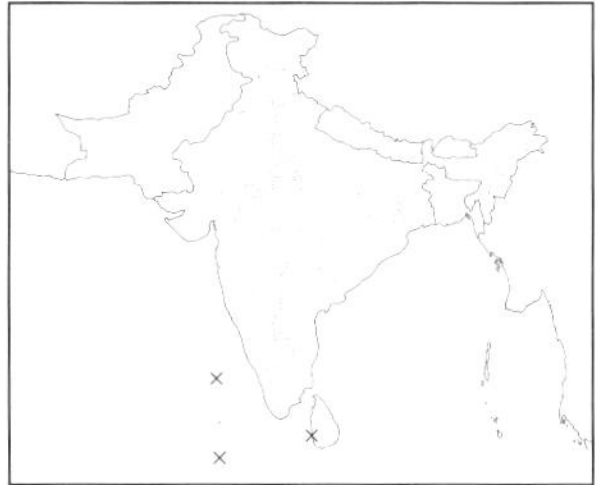

IDENTIFICATION 66–77 cm. Smallest of the boobies occurring in the subcontinent. Flight is more graceful and faster than that of other species; tends to shear above the waves and often glides for long distances. Polymorphic, occurring in white, brown and intermediate morphs; white morph most likely to be encountered in Indian Ocean. **Adult** white morph is largely white, with black flight feathers. Told from adult Masked Booby (p.554) by smaller size, variable yellow wash on crown and hindneck, bluish bill, lack of black mask (but does show black on chin), and red legs and feet; in flight, also by black carpal patch on underwing, white tail, and white tertials (black trailing edge does not reach body). Brown morph is similar in plumage to juvenile, but has red legs, blue-grey bill and pinkish facial skin. Other morphs occur which are brown and can have a white head and neck and/or white rump, tail and under-tail-coverts. **Juvenile** is largely dark grey-brown with paler grey-brown underbody. Superficially resembles juvenile Brown Booby (below), but has uniformly dark underwing (lacking pale panel across coverts) and has dark blackish-brown or greyish-black bill; has purplish facial skin and yellowish-grey legs and feet. **Immature** (white morph) is initially similar to juvenile, but has some white mottling on upperwing-coverts, and head and neck are paler, with diffuse dark breast-band; legs are brownish-red and bill is dull bluish. Older immatures show largely white head, neck and body, and variable brown mottling on upperbody, upperwing-coverts, scapulars and tertials. **HABITS** Similar to those of other boobies. Gregarious; occurs in small groups or flocks at good feeding areas. Attracted to ships, and perches on rigging or masts. Partly nocturnal. **HABITAT** Pelagic; often seen hundreds of kilometres from land. **BREEDING** Details unknown in the region. In Australia, builds a nest of sticks in a tree or bush. **DISTRIBUTION AND STATUS** Possibly breeds on the Maldives and Lakshadweep; an uncommon or rare visitor to coastal waters of the subcontinent. **IN:** resident on Lakshadweep, vagrant elsewhere. **LK:** vagrant. **MV:** uncommon visitor; may breed. **REFERENCES** Frith (1976), Harrison (1983), Marchant and Higgins (1990), Nelson (1978).

BROWN BOOBY *Sula leucogaster* Plate 76

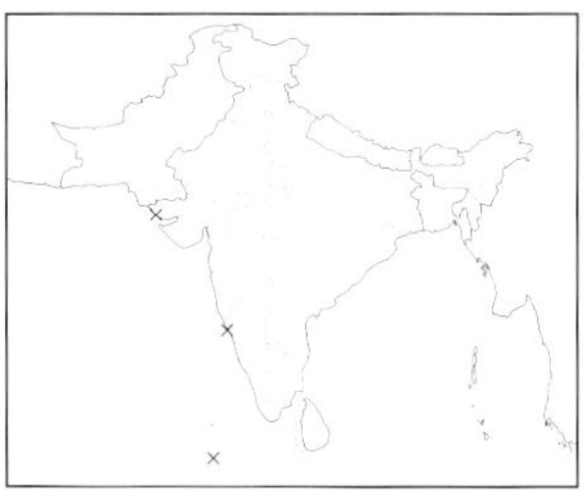

IDENTIFICATION 64–74 cm. **Adult** is readily separable from other adult boobies by dark chocolate-brown head, neck and upperparts contrasting with sharply demarcated white underbody and underwing-coverts. Bill is generally yellow, sometimes with green tinge. **Juvenile** is similar to adult, but has dusky brown underbody, which becomes paler on immatures. Possibly confusable with juvenile Red-footed Booby (above), but has pale panel across underwing-coverts and (on older birds) pale yellowish base to bill; immature Brown also shows contrast between upper and lower breast. Told from juvenile Masked Booby (p.554) by uniform upperwing and upperbody (lacking prominent pale feather fringes of Masked) and lack of whitish collar, and has brown upper breast, which joins brown leading edge of wings, and all-dark underside to primary coverts. **HABITS** A typical booby. In the region, generally solitary or in small groups. Feeds inshore, where often perches on rocks and buoys. **HABITAT** Pelagic; also found close to the shore. **BREEDING**

Details unknown in the region. In Australia, nest is a platform of sticks, leaves and debris placed on a cliff or on the ground. **DISTRIBUTION AND STATUS** Mainly a post-breeding visitor to the coasts and coastal waters of the subcontinent. **IN:** vagrant off the SW coast; resident, and possibly breeds, on Lakshadweep. **LK:** straggler. **MV:** fairly common visitor, most frequent December–February. **REFERENCES** Frith (1976).

ANHINGAS Anhingidae

Large aquatic birds adapted for hunting fish underwater. Anhingas have a long, slender neck and head, long wings and a very long tail.

DARTER *Anhinga melanogaster* — Plate 77

Indian Darter, Oriental Darter *A. rufa* (F,I,P)

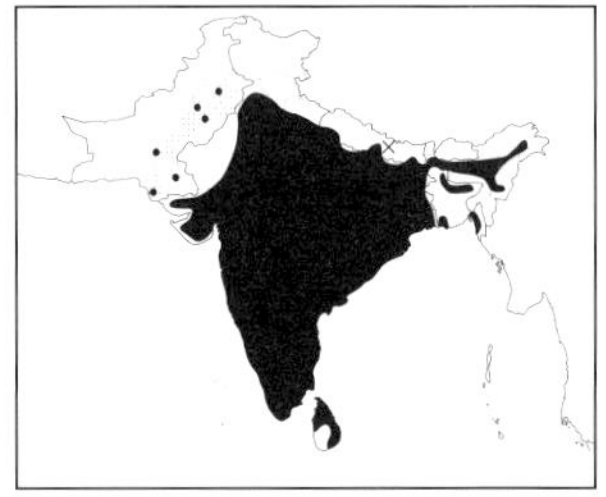

IDENTIFICATION 85–97 cm. Long, slim, heron-like head and neck, dagger-like bill, and long tail are the most striking features. Neck is typically held recoiled or with obvious kink. Has cormorant-like flight action, with prolonged gliding; outstretched neck with kink at base and long tail are especially evident. Often swims with most of body submerged. **Adult breeding** has blackish crown and hindneck, white stripe extending from behind eye down side of neck, and chestnut foreneck becoming blacker towards breast. Further, has lanceolate white scapular streaks and white streaking on upperwing-coverts. Head pattern is more striking on breeding male than on female. **Non-breeding** is similar, but has browner head, neck and upper mantle. **Juvenile** is brown above and buffish-white below, with contrasting brown flanks; has buff fringes to upperwing-coverts forming pale panel on wing. **VOICE** Usually silent except in vicinity of nest, when it utters a variety of harsh rattling and grunting calls (Cramp and Simmons 1977). **HABITS** Seen singly, in scattered pairs and sometimes in larger groups. Spends much time drying its spread wings and tail while sitting on a favoured perch. Often swims with head and neck above the water and body below, giving appearance of a swimming snake. Unlike cormorants, does not leap up before diving but slowly submerges, producing hardly a ripple. Pursues fish underwater, and catches them by spearing. **HABITAT** Lakes, jheels, ponds, reservoirs, rivers, marshes and other inland waters; also mangroves and coastal waters. **BREEDING** June–March, varying locally. Often nests colonially with cormorants, egrets, herons and ibises. Nest is an untidy platform of twigs, lined with weeds, and built on trees standing in or near water. **DISTRIBUTION AND STATUS** Resident, moving locally according to water conditions. Throughout much of the subcontinent, except parts of the northwest, northeast and Himalayas. **PK:** mainly an irregular year-round visitor, locally resident; fairly widespread on lowland rivers. **NP:** uncommon resident and non-breeding visitor; below 300 m (–1370 m). **IN:** widespread resident, locally common in Assam, current status elsewhere poorly known; probably declining. **BD:** local resident. **LK:** common resident in dry lowlands, visitor elsewhere. **REFERENCES** Cramp and Simmons (1977), Perennou *et al.* (1994), WWF India and AWB (1993).

CORMORANTS Phalacrocoracidae

Medium-sized to large aquatic birds found on both fresh and salt waters. They are long-necked, with a hooked bill of moderate length and a long, stiff tail. Cormorants are good swimmers, aided by their strong legs set far back on the body and by their large webbed feet, which are used for propulsion. The plumage is mainly dark. In flight, the neck is extended and the head is held slightly above the horizontal. Typically, they swim with the body low in the water, with the neck straight and the head and bill pointing a little upwards. They eat mainly fish, which are caught by underwater pursuit; normally they make a short upward leap before diving from the surface. In the region, cormorants breed colonially with storks, egrets, herons and ibises. The nest is a platform of sticks, lined with weeds, and is usually built in trees. Cormorants often perch for long periods in upright posture, with spread wings and tail, on trees, posts or rocks. The main references specific to cormorants are Johnsgard (1993) and Perennou *et al.* (1994).

PYGMY CORMORANT *Phalacrocorax pygmeus* — Plate 77

IDENTIFICATION 45–55 cm. Possibly overlooked owing to difficulty of separation from Little Cormorant (p.557). Similar in size and structure to Little, although on average is larger and bulkier. **Adult breeding** told from Little by chestnut head and upper neck; prior to breeding, however, head and neck are nearly black, although white filoplumes are more profusely scattered across head, neck and underparts than on breeding Little. Eyes are dark in Pygmy (green in Little). **Non-breeding** is very similar to Little, although tends to be browner on the body and to have more extensive whitish mottling on the breast and belly. The chin and throat are whitish, this gradually merging into the brown of foreneck (on Little, the white chin is clearly demarcated). **Immature** also

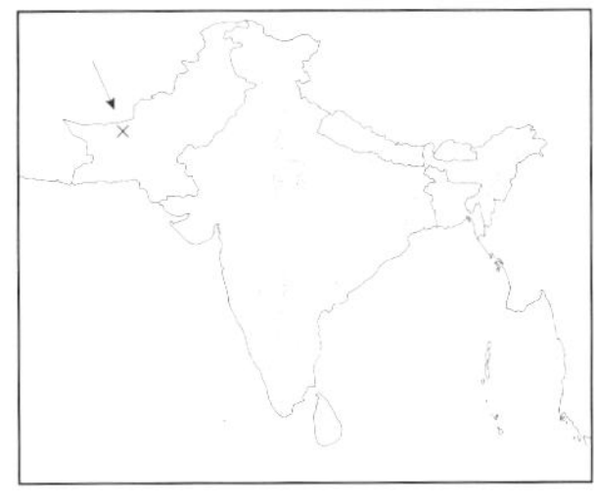

generally, but not always, has browner upperparts, and is more extensively white below (on Little, the underparts have a variable amount of whitish tips to breast and belly). **VOICE** Usually silent except in vicinity of nest. **HABITS** Similar to those of Little. **HABITAT** Similar to that of Little. **DISTRIBUTION AND STATUS PK:** vagrant.

LITTLE CORMORANT *Phalacrocorax niger* — Plate 77

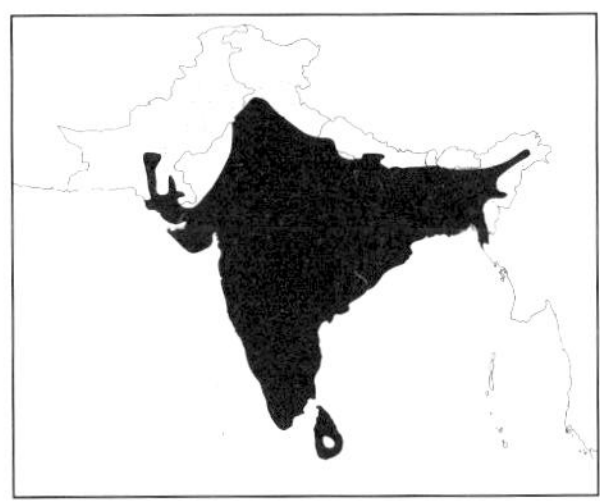

IDENTIFICATION 51 cm. Smaller than Indian Cormorant (below), with shorter and stouter bill, rectangular-shaped head (with steep forehead), shorter, thicker neck, and longer-looking tail. Lacks yellow gular pouch. Flies with regular, quite fast wingbeats. **Adult breeding** is virtually all black, glossed with bluish or greenish, with silvery-grey upperparts scalloped with black, a short crest, and a few white filoplumes on forecrown and sides of head. Bill is blacker than in non-breeding plumage. **Non-breeding** is similar to adult breeding, but head and neck have brownish cast (and head lacks white filoplumes), and has whitish chin. **Immature** has browner upperparts, with whitish chin, and foreneck and breast are a shade paler, with some pale fringes. For differences from Pygmy Cormorant (p.556), see that species. Underparts are darker than on immature Indian. **VOICE** Usually silent except in vicinity of nest. **HABITS** A typical cormorant. On smaller waters occurs singly or in small groups; on large inland waters or estuaries often gathers in great flocks. Frequently hunts in parties, often with Indian Cormorant, driving the fish towards shallower water. Feeds on fish, frogs, tadpoles and crustaceans. Has communal winter roosts. **HABITAT** Rivers, jheels, reservoirs, village tanks, marshes, canals, estuaries, saltpans and coastal waters. Prefers fresh waters in Pakistan. **BREEDING** July–May, varying locally. Builds a usual cormorant nest in mixed colonies; also singly and in small numbers in trees at village edges some distance from water. **DISTRIBUTION AND STATUS** Resident, subject to local movements depending on water conditions. Throughout much of the subcontinent, except parts of the northwest, northeast and Himalayas. **PK:** common resident in Sindh, a less common and irregular year-round visitor elsewhere. **NP:** recorded in all months below 250 m, but chiefly a winter visitor and passage migrant; common at Kosi Barrage, uncommon elsewhere. **IN:** widespread and common resident in the plains. **BT:** local and fairly common. **BD:** locally common resident throughout. **LK:** common resident in lowlands, visitor to the lower hills.

INDIAN CORMORANT *Phalacrocorax fuscicollis* — Plate 77

Indian Shag (I,K,P)

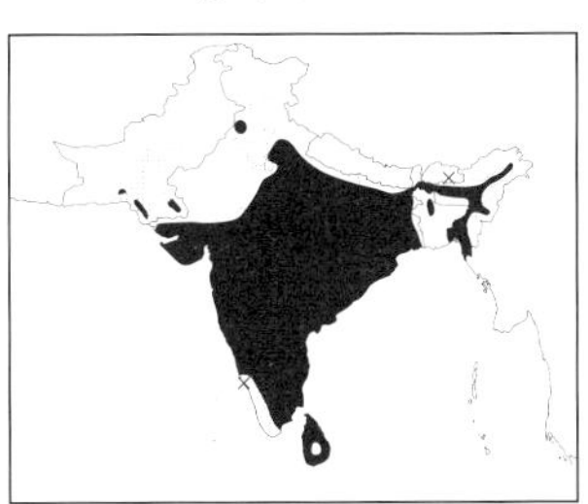

IDENTIFICATION 63 cm. Smaller and slimmer than Great Cormorant (p.558). Usually appears to have thinner neck, slimmer oval-shaped head, finer bill, and proportionately longer tail. In flight, looks slimmer, with quicker wing action. Larger than Little Cormorant (above), with longer, thinner neck, more oval-shaped head, and longer and thinner bill. In flight, looks more like Great than Little, with larger wings and shorter tail than latter. **Adult breeding** is all black, glossed with bronze and green on upperparts. Has tuft of white behind eye, scattering of white filoplumes on neck behind eye, bare purplish skin around eye, and purplish-black gular pouch edged with yellow. **Non-breeding** is similar to adult breeding, but lacks white head plumes, has whitish throat, and head, neck and underparts look browner. Is browner in coloration than non-breeding Great, with whitish throat less clearly marked than on that species. **Immature** has brown upperparts and brown-mottled whitish underparts. Is generally paler on underparts than immature Little, although not so pale as immature Great. **VOICE** Usually silent except in vicinity of nest. **HABITS** A typical cormorant. Gregarious, and often in larger flocks than Great. Frequently fishes with Little. **HABITAT** Fresh and salt waters: jheels, lakes, rivers, irrigation tanks, estuaries, and saltwater and mangrove creeks. **BREEDING** July–February, varying locally. Builds a usual cormorant nest in trees in large mixed colonies or in small colonies of its own. **DISTRIBUTION AND STATUS** Resident, subject to local movements depending on water conditions. Throughout much of the subcontinent, except parts of the northwest, northeast and Himalayas. **PK:** common and irregular year-round visitor, resident locally; most frequent in lower Sindh and estuarine waters. **IN:** widespread and locally common resident. **BT:** rare passage migrant or winter visitor. **BD:** scarce? resident. **LK:** common breeding resident in lowlands, less common in lower hills.

GREAT CORMORANT *Phalacrocorax carbo* Plate 77

Cormorant (I), Large Cormorant (F)

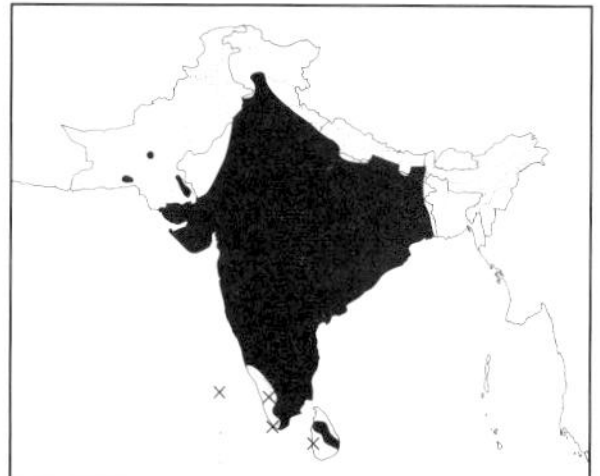

IDENTIFICATION 80–100 cm. Larger and bulkier than Indian Cormorant (p.557), with thicker neck, larger, more angular head, and stouter bill. In flight, looks heavier, with thicker neck, shorter tail, and slower wing action. **Adult breeding** is black, glossed with bottle-green on upperparts. Distinguished from Indian by bare orange skin around eye and across lores, white cheeks and throat, variable white streaking (head plumes) across sides of crown and neck, and white thigh patch. **Non-breeding** is similar to adult breeding, but lacks white head plumes and thigh patch, and lacks green gloss to upperparts. More blackish-brown in coloration than Indian, with more clearly marked and extensive white chin. **Immature** has dark brown to blackish upperparts and variable whitish or pale buff underparts. Underparts tend to be whiter than on immature Indian. **VOICE** Usually silent except in vicinity of nest, when it utters a variety of deep guttural calls (Cramp and Simmons 1977). **HABITS** A typical cormorant. Usually found singly or in small groups, although sometimes joins fishing flocks of other cormorants. Gathers in large numbers to breed, and often roosts communally in winter. **HABITAT** Coastal waters, saltpans, reservoirs, jheels, and large inland lakes and rivers in the Himalayas and lowlands. **BREEDING** September–February, depending on water conditions. Builds a usual cormorant nest in large colonies in trees. **DISTRIBUTION AND STATUS** Resident and winter visitor; locally migratory, depending on food supplies. Throughout most of the subcontinent, except parts of the northwest, northeast and Himalayas. **PK:** most birds breed and are local migrants, some are winter visitors; common in Sindh, less common elsewhere; mainly in the plains (–2750 m on passage). **NP:** fairly common non-breeding resident; mainly below 1000 m (–3960 m on passage). **IN:** widespread resident, locally frequent. **BT:** fairly common; 250–3100 m. **BD:** former resident, now local winter visitor in moderate numbers. **LK:** resident in N dry lowlands, uncommon in the south.

HERONS AND BITTERNS Ardeidae

Medium-sized to large fish-eating birds with long legs for wading. The diurnal herons have a slender body and long head and neck; the night herons and bitterns are more squat, with shorter neck and legs. They fly with leisurely flaps, with the legs outstretched and projecting beyond the tail, and nearly always with head and neck drawn back. The bitterns are characterised by their booming territorial calls. Bitterns and herons feed on a wide variety of aquatic prey, ranging from fish, amphibians and invertebrates to small mammals and young birds; herons also regularly eat shrimps and prawns on the coast. Bitterns usually skulk in reedbeds, although occasionally one may forage in the open, and they can clamber about reed stems with agility. Normally they are solitary and crepuscular and most often seen flying low over reedbeds with slow wingbeats, soon dropping into cover again. When in danger bitterns freeze, pointing the bill and neck upwards and compressing their feathers so that the whole body appears elongated. Herons frequent marshes and the shores of lakes and rivers, while many species also feed in shallow marine waters. Typically, herons feed by standing motionless at the water's edge, waiting for prey to swim within reach, or by slow stalking in shallow water or on land. Prey is normally grasped and killed by battering and is less often speared. The main references specific to herons and bitterns are Hancock and Kushlan (1984) and Perennou *et al.* (1994).

LITTLE EGRET *Egretta garzetta* Plate 78

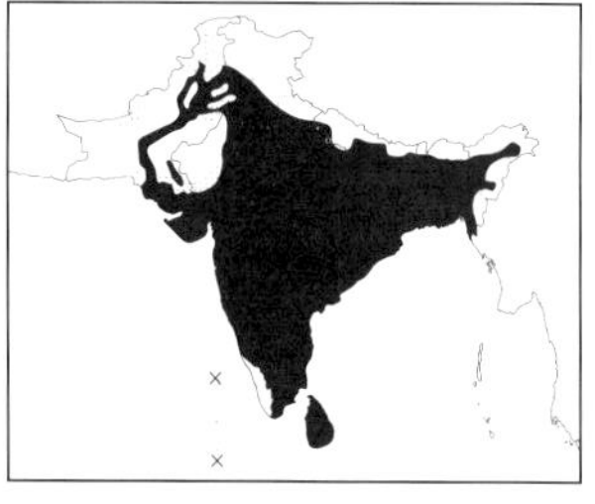

IDENTIFICATION 55–65 cm. A slim and graceful, medium-sized, white heron. Distinguished from Cattle Egret (p.563) in all plumages by thin black bill, longer black legs with prominent yellow feet, and longer and thinner neck. In flight, legs and feet extend well beyond tail, and appears less compact, with more pronounced neck bulge, compared with Cattle. Great care is needed when identifying Little at the coast, where confusion with the very similar Western Reef Egret (p.559) is very easy: for a summary of the differences, see that species. Adult breeding Intermediate Egret (p.562) can also cause confusion, since bill becomes black, but that species has black feet and lacks head plumes of breeding Little. Confusion is less likely with Great Egret (p.562), which also has a black bill in breeding plumage; Little is much smaller than that species, with finer bill and shorter-looking legs, and appears more compact in flight, with more buoyant flight action. **Adult breeding** has prominent plumes on nape, breast and mantle, and lores become reddish during courtship (and later, briefly, almost colourless, but otherwise lores as non-breeding). **Adult non-breeding** and **juvenile** lack plumes; legs and bill can be paler, and even yellowish on a few, and lores are generally blue-grey. **VOICE** Normally silent, except for throaty squawk when disturbed and various guttural calls at colonies. **HABITS** A typical heron. Often in flocks when foraging, and more sociable than the two larger egrets; also found singly. Roosts communally. **HABITAT** Lakes, rivers, marshes, flooded paddy-fields, also estuaries, tidal creeks and mangroves; prefers fresh waters. **BREEDING** November–September, varying locally. Breeds colonially with other herons and cormorants. Builds a flimsy nest of twigs 2–6 m up in a solitary tree, or in a grove, either standing in water or on dry land. **DISTRIBUTION AND STATUS** Resident, moving locally depending on water conditions. Throughout much of the subcontinent, except parts of the northwest, northeast and Himalayas. **PK:** common and widespread throughout Sindh and Punjab, and mainly resident; an irregular year-round visitor in some places. **NP:** fairly common and widespread resident; below 1525 m. **IN:** common and widespread resident; up to 900 m in peninsular hills. **BT:** local and fairly common. **BD:** common resident throughout. **LK:** common and widespread resident in the lowlands, visitor to foothills. **MV:** uncommon; winter visitor or migrant.

WESTERN REEF EGRET *Egretta gularis* Plate 78

Indian Reef Heron (I,P)

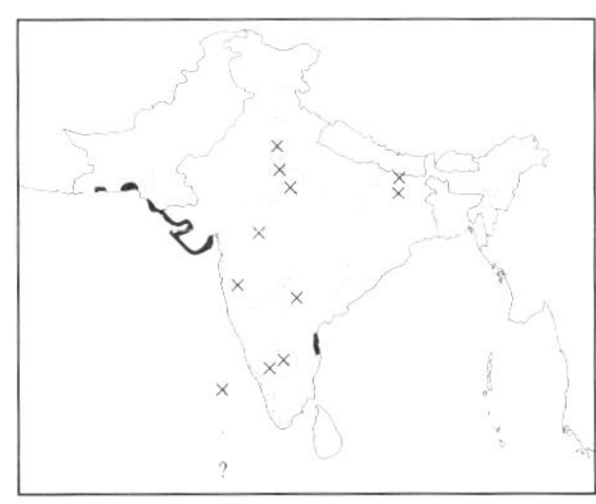

IDENTIFICATION 55–65 cm. A coastal-dwelling heron, occurring in dark grey, intermediate and white colour morphs. Intermediate morphs are very variable, but often have pale grey upperparts and whitish underparts. Separation from Little Egret (p.558) can be extremely difficult, with some birds not distinguishable in the field; dark-morph Little is, however, very rare, and Western Reef Egret is rarely found away from the coast. The two are sometimes considered conspecific (see Hancock and Kushlan 1984). Best told from Little by generally slightly longer, stouter bill with blunter tip, usually with a distinct curve to upper and lower mandibles (on Little, upper mandible is very slightly downcurved and lower is straight). Has a proportionately longer and thinner neck than Little, which it tends to hold in a more hooked or S-shaped pose, and a more angular head profile; further, has proportionately very slightly shorter and thicker-looking legs. In flight, wings appear more rounded and body more stocky. Bill colour is usually mainly yellowish or brownish-yellow, but may be black in breeding season (bill of Little is typically black, although in non-breeding/immature plumage can be paler and pinkish or greyish at base, tending to dull yellowish on a few individuals). Typically, has pale greenish or yellowish lores (although can be greyish as on Little, and that species can, exceptionally, appear to have yellowish tinge to lores). In breeding plumage, has black legs and yellow feet; in non-breeding plumage, legs are brownish or with some greenish or yellowish, with greenish or yellowish feet (on Little, legs are typically black throughout year, with contrasting yellow feet, although legs and feet can be paler and much as non-breeding Western Reef). For differences from Pacific Reef Egret (below), see that species. **Adult breeding** has prominent plumes on nape, breast and mantle, as on Little Egret; lores and feet turn orange during courtship. **Adult non-breeding** and **juvenile** lack plumes. Juveniles of dark morphs are brown or dark grey-brown. **VOICE** Normally silent, except for throaty squawk when disturbed and similar sounds at nest. **HABITS** Usually solitary when foraging, but occasionally in twos or threes; sometimes with Little Egrets. Roosts communally. Diurnal and partly crepuscular. More active than other egrets when hunting, often running about, jumping and turning rapidly. Frequently seeks prey by slow stalking; occasionally flicks its wings open and shut, disturbing prey by the sudden movement. At high water typically rests in hunched posture, waiting for the tide to ebb. **HABITAT** Seashores, estuaries, mangroves, and tidal lagoons and creeks; occasionally at fresh waters. **BREEDING** Late March–August, varying locally. Breeds in colonies of its own, or mixed with other waterbirds. Builds a flimsy nest of twigs in trees, usually in mangrove swamps, also in trees on dry ground. Interbreeds, or possibly does so, with Little Egret. **DISTRIBUTION AND STATUS** Resident and nomadic, occurring mainly on W and SE coasts; scattered records inland. **PK:** locally common resident on coast; straggles inland in the monsoon. **IN:** resident, common on the NW coast, occasionally recorded farther south on the W coast and a few kilometres inland; rare on E coast and far inland. **LK:** uncommon winter visitor to coastal areas; formerly a scarce breeding resident. **MV:** possibly recorded. **REFERENCES** Alström and Colston (1991), Dubois and Yésou (1995), Hancock and Kushlan (1984), Harris *et al.* (1996), Parasharya and Naik (1987, 1988).

PACIFIC REEF EGRET *Egretta sacra* Plate 78

Reef Heron (I)

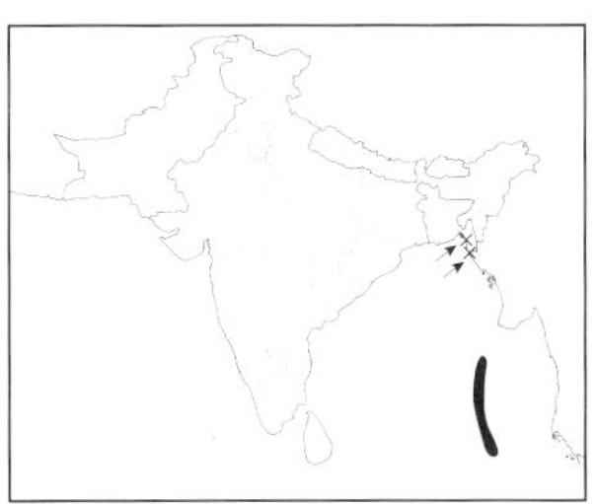

IDENTIFICATION 58 cm. A dimorphic, coastal-dwelling heron. The dark morph is slate-grey or brownish-black. Legs are stouter and shorter than on Western Reef Egret (above) (owing to shorter length of exposed tibia), and in flight it shows a shorter leg projection (with only feet projecting beyond tail). Is marginally stockier than Western Reef, with top-heavy appearance, and neck looks shorter and thicker. Also is often less 'elegant' when feeding (typically adopting a crouched posture, interspersed with quick walking or running). Bill usually appears blunt-tipped and stout (especially compared with that of Little Egret, p.558), and is generally shorter-looking than on Western Reef. Dark morph has an inconspicuous (occasionally non-existent) white chin and throat line (white chin and throat are very prominent on dark-morph Western Reef). There appear to be no constant differences from Western in coloration of bill, lores, legs and feet, and much variation exists: loral colour varies from yellowish-green to grey; bill from pinkish or yellowish to blackish; and legs and feet are generally greenish or yellowish, on some tending towards brown. **Adult breeding** has shortish plumes on nape, forming bushy tuft, and shorter plumes on breast and mantle than other white egrets. Bill and leg colours are generally yellower than on non-breeding birds (especially on dark morph), but can remain rather dull horn-brown. **Non-breeding** lacks plumes. **Juvenile** dark morph is pale smoky-grey. **VOICE** A grunted *ork* when feeding, and a harsh *squak* when disturbed (Hancock and Kushlan 1984). **HABITS** Very similar to those of Western Reef Egret. **HABITAT** Rocky coasts, coral beds and sandy shores. **BREEDING** May–September, depending on the monsoon. Breeds colonially. Builds a stick nest, usually in mangrove trees; sometimes among rocks. **DISTRIBUTION AND STATUS IN:** common resident on Andaman and Nicobar Is. **BD:** vagrant. **REFERENCES** Hancock and Kushlan (1984), Sankaran and Vijayan (1993), Sonobe and Usui (1993).

GREY HERON *Ardea cinerea* — Plate 79

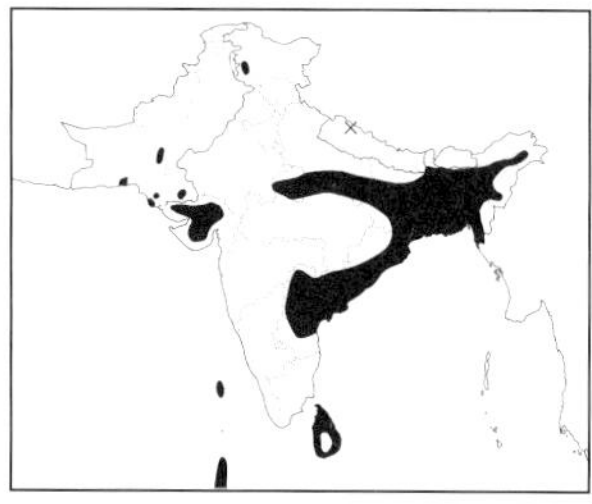

IDENTIFICATION 90–98 cm. A large whitish and grey heron, lacking any brown or rufous in its plumage, and in all plumages having greyish upperparts. In flight, grey upperwing-coverts contrast with greyish-black flight feathers, and shows a prominent white leading edge to wing when seen head-on. At a distance and in flight, compared with Purple Heron (p.561), kink of neck is less pronounced, protruding feet are smaller, and underwing-coverts are dark grey. For differences from White-bellied and Great-billed (p.561), see those species. **Adult** has bluish-grey upperparts with black patch at bend of wing, whitish head and neck with black head plumes, black streaking down centre of foreneck, white underparts with black and white breast plumes, and black patches on sides of belly. Bill is mainly yellow. In the breeding season, has whitish plumes extending from scapulars, and iris, bill and legs become orange or occasionally reddish. **Immature** is duller than adult, with grey crown, reduced black 'crest', greyer neck, less pronounced black patches on sides of belly, reduced breast and scapular plumes, and duller bill and legs. **Juvenile** has dark grey cap with slight crest, dirty grey neck and breast, lacks black patches on belly sides, lacks plumes, and has dark legs. **VOICE** Often calls in flight, a loud *frarnk*. **HABITS** A typical diurnal heron. Usually keeps singly when feeding; occasionally gathers in loose parties at good feeding areas. Roosts communally in winter. Prefers to hunt in the open, unlike Purple Heron. If flushed, it utters loud harsh croaks as it flaps off clumsily and heavily. Perches freely in trees. **HABITAT** Inland and coastal waters: rivers, jheels, lakes, marshes, estuaries, mangroves, tidal creeks, rocky offshore islands and coral reefs. **BREEDING** Throughout the year, varying locally. Usually nests in small colonies of its own species, but sometimes with other herons and egrets. Nest is a platform of sticks or plant stems built in trees or dense reedbeds. **DISTRIBUTION AND STATUS** Resident, passage migrant and winter visitor. Throughout much of the subcontinent, except parts of the northwest, northeast and Himalayas. **PK:** common and widespread; mainly a winter visitor, also a passage migrant and resident locally. **NP:** chiefly a winter visitor; widespread and frequent below 915 m (–3050 m on passage). **IN:** widespread and locally common resident and winter visitor; breeds up to 1750 m in Kashmir; recorded to 4500 m in Ladakh. **BT:** rare. **BD:** resident, occurs locally throughout. **LK:** resident in lowlands; frequent in the dry zone, uncommon in wet zone. **MV:** common resident. **REFERENCES** Pfister (1997).

GOLIATH HERON *Ardea goliath* — Plate 79

Giant Heron (I)

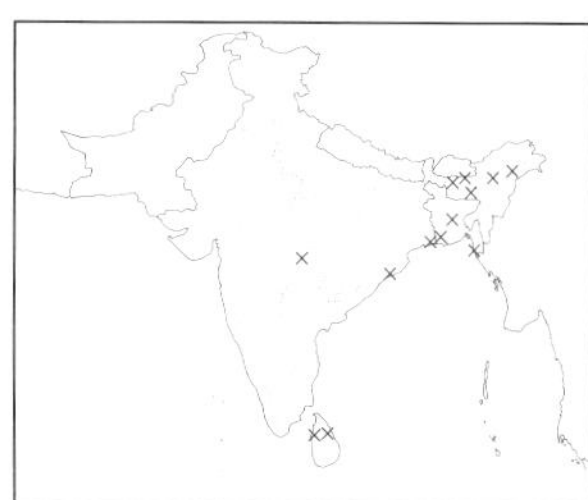

IDENTIFICATION 135–150 cm. A giant version of Purple Heron (p.561). In all plumages, distinguished from that species by much larger size, thicker head and neck, huge and thick dark bill, and black legs and feet. In flight, which is slow and heavy, with very deliberate wingbeats, looks more like a large, stocky Grey Heron (above) in shape, with less pronounced bulge to recoiled neck compared with Purple. Rufous coloration to head and neck distinguishes it from Great-billed and White-bellied Herons (p.561). **Adult** has chestnut crown and bushy crest (lacking the black head stripes of Purple Heron), rufous hindneck, white throat and foreneck, broken blackish stripes down foreneck, and deep purplish-chestnut underparts and underwing-coverts. **Immature** is similar to adult, but has dark grey forehead, chestnut underparts streaked with buff, dark grey flanks, and dark grey mottling on underwing-coverts. **Juvenile** has black forehead and crown, paler rufous hindneck and indistinct neck stripes (compared with adult), rufous fringes to feathers of mantle and upperwing-coverts, grey underparts streaked with pale chestnut, and dark grey underwing-coverts. **VOICE** Flight call has been described as a gargling rattle or like the bellowing of a calf (Cramp and Simmons 1977). **HABITS** A typical diurnal heron. Solitary and shy. Usually hunts in shallow water, but can wade well out from the shore because of its long legs; sometimes feeds from grass bunds. **HABITAT** In the region, recorded on rivers; elsewhere, also inhabits lakes, mangrove swamps, and tidal creeks and estuaries. **DISTRIBUTION AND STATUS** Visitor or possibly resident. Mainly NE India (Assam, Meghalaya, West Bengal). **IN:** rare. **BD, LK:** vagrant. **REFERENCES** Cramp and Simmons (1977), Jepson (1987), Madge (1995), Pandav (1997), Saikia and Bhattacharjee (1993).

WHITE-BELLIED HERON *Ardea insignis* Plate 79

Great White-bellied Heron (F,I), Imperial Heron (N), *A. imperialis* (F,N)

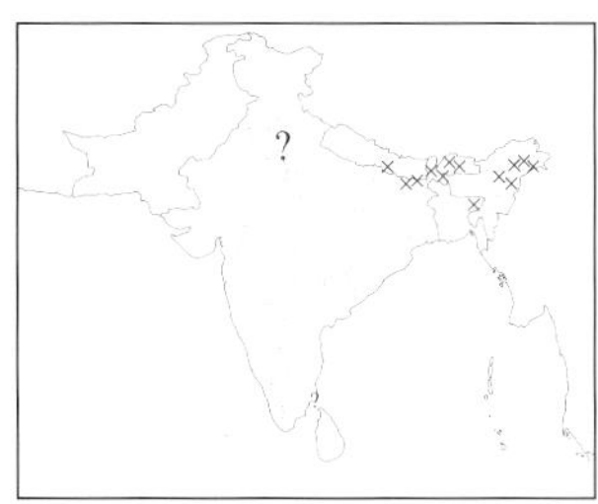

IDENTIFICATION 127 cm. A huge, mainly grey heron with very long, slender neck. In all plumages, differs from Grey Heron (p.560) in much larger size, much longer neck, and huge, thick bill. Upperparts are darker slate-grey, and grey foreneck and breast (streaked with white) contrast with white belly. Bill is blackish, and legs and feet grey. In flight, superficially resembles a large, stocky Grey, but has uniform dark-grey upperwing (with little or no contrast between wing-coverts and flight feathers), and white underwing-coverts contrast with grey of rest of underwing. More closely resembles Great-billed Heron (below), but that is generally a coastal bird; for differences, see that species. **Adult** has greyish-white nape plumes, elongate grey breast feathers with white centres (creating bold white streaks), and yellowish-green lores, orbital skin and base to lower mandible. White belly may show dark streaking and spotting. **Immature** is similar to adult, but has browner upperparts and unmarked white underparts. **VOICE** Has a loud, very deep, donkey-like croaking bray, *ock ock ock ock urrrrrr* (T. Inskipp from R. Pradhan recording). **HABITS** Shy and little known. Found singly or in pairs. Hunting methods are much as those of other diurnal herons. **HABITAT** Rivers, marshes and lakes in tropical and subtropical forest. **BREEDING** Details unknown in the region. Juvenile with two adults recorded in Bhutan in February. One nest located in Myanmar, a huge stick structure built in April in a tall tree. **DISTRIBUTION AND STATUS** Sedentary resident in E Himalayan foothills; formerly recorded from Nepal east to Bangladesh (sight records from Bihar, Delhi and Tamil Nadu require confirmation). Globally threatened. **NP:** recorded only in 19th century. **IN:** now very rare; recently recorded mainly from Assam and Arunachal Pradesh. **BT:** rare; 800–1400 m. **BD:** now a vagrant; only one recent record. **REFERENCES** Choudhury (1996c), Hancock and Kushlan (1984), Saikia and Bhattacharjee (1993), WWF India and AWB (1993).

GREAT-BILLED HERON *Ardea sumatrana* Plate 79

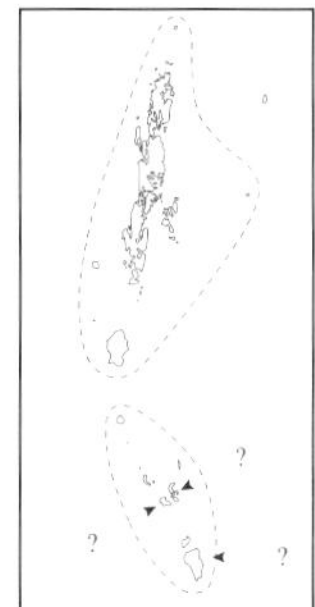

IDENTIFICATION 115 cm. A large, mainly dark-grey heron. In all plumages, told from Grey Heron (p.560) by larger size, huge and thick bill with sharply angled gonys, uniform grey head and neck (except for white throat), and grey underparts. In flight, superficially resembles a large Grey, but has uniform upperwing and underwing (with no contrast between wing-coverts and flight feathers). More closely resembles White-bellied Heron (above), but that is an inland, freshwater species; smaller size, grey belly and underwing-coverts, and pronounced white scapular plumes (on adult) are main differences shown by Great-billed. Bare-part coloration is variable: legs are pale yellowish to blackish-brown; loral and orbital skin is generally dull greenish, occasionally tinged yellow; and bill is blackish, with variable dull yellowish at base of lower mandible. **Adult breeding** has whitish plumes on nape, scapulars and breast. **Immature** is similar to adult, but has warmer brown upperparts (with rufous to buff tips to feathers), lacks whitish plumes, and has vinaceous tinge to neck (which is more strongly streaked with white). **VOICE** Various calls have been described, including a deep guttural roar (Hancock and Kushlan 1984). **HABITS** Usually shy and wary, hunting alone. When disturbed, flies to rest in trees overhanging water. **HABITAT** In normal range, from Burma to N Australia, inhabits coastal mangroves, mudflats and creeks. **DISTRIBUTION AND STATUS IN:** ?vagrant to Nicobar Is; reputedly seen on Trinkat, Katchall and Great Nicobar Is, but not collected. **REFERENCES** Hancock and Kushlan (1984), Richmond (1903).

PURPLE HERON *Ardea purpurea* Plate 79

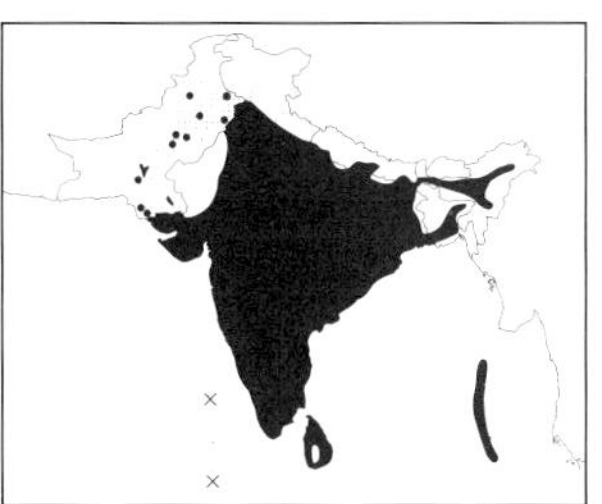

IDENTIFICATION 78–90 cm. A rather large, rakish and often secretive heron. At rest, neck appears very thin (often with pronounced kink), body rather small, and head very slim with long, rather slender bill. In flight, compared with Grey Heron (p.560), bulge of recoiled neck is very pronounced, protruding feet are very large, underwing-coverts are purplish or buff, and lacks white leading edge to wing. Bill is yellow (duller on immature). For differences from Goliath Heron (p.560), see that species. **Adult** has chestnut sides to head and neck, with black crown, cheek-stripe and head plumes, and black neck stripes (which can be lacking); also has slate-grey mantle and upperwing-coverts (with chestnut scapular plumes in breeding season), blackish-chestnut belly and flanks, and purplish-chestnut underwing-coverts. **Immature** is similar to adult, but head-and-neck colour is duller and patterning less well defined, wing-coverts are brownish, and lacks dark chestnut on belly. Takes three to five years to reach maturity, during which becomes progressively more like adult. **Juvenile** has buff neck, brownish mantle and wing-coverts with broad rufous-buff fringes, and buffish underparts; crown is blackish, but black streaking on neck is generally lacking. **VOICE** Flight call similar to Grey Heron's, a higher-pitched and not so loud *frarnk*. **HABITS** Active mainly in early mornings and evenings; sometimes also feeds by day. Shyer than Grey, normally feeding out of sight among dense aquatic vegetation. Most often seen in flight. Hunts alone, usually by standing motionless and waiting; less often by slow stalking in shallow water. **HABITAT** Lakes, jheels, rivers and marshes with plenty of tall cover, especially *Phragmites* reeds and *Typha* bulrushes; also mangroves in Bangladesh. **BREEDING** Almost all year, varying locally. Nest is a platform of sticks or rush stems, usually built in trees or reedbeds standing in water. **DISTRIBUTION AND STATUS** Resident and local migrant throughout the lowlands in much of the subcontinent, except parts of the northwest and northeast; possibly also a winter visitor. Probably under-recorded because of its secretive habits. **PK:** common and widespread in Sindh and Punjab; mainly an irregular year-round visitor, locally resident. **NP:** locally fairly common below 300 m (–1370 m); mainly resident, also a monsoon visitor. **IN:** widespread and locally fairly common resident. **BD:** local resident. **LK:** common and widespread resident in lowlands. **MV:** probably a frequent visitor. **REFERENCES** Harris *et al.* (1989).

GREAT EGRET *Casmerodius albus* — Plate 78

Large Egret (P), *Ardea alba* (I), *Egretta alba* (F,K,P,R)

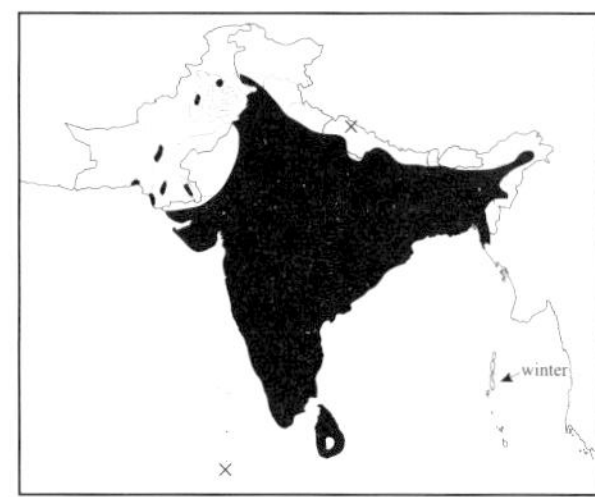

IDENTIFICATION 65–72 cm. A very large white heron which can be confused with Intermediate Egret (below), although typically appearing much larger. Often has a very upright posture, holding its long neck erect. Compared with Intermediate, usually looks smaller-headed and longer- and thinner-necked, with more angular and pronounced kink to neck when recoiled, and proportionately smaller-bodied; bill usually appears larger and longer. In flight, appears slower and heavier, with more pronounced neck kink. Black line of gape extends noticeably beyond (below and behind) eye (extends only to beneath eye on Intermediate). Bare-part coloration can provide further clues (see below). **Adult breeding** has prominent plumes on breast and mantle; the breast plumes are shorter and coarser than on Intermediate, while those extending from the mantle are generally longer. Initially, the lores are pale blue-green and the yellow bill has variable amounts of black; during courtship, lores become brighter blue, bill becomes black and the tibia become reddish. **Adult non-breeding** and **juvenile** lack plumes; lores are pale greenish, bill is yellow, and the tibia are yellowish (legs are uniformly dark on Intermediate). **VOICE** Normally silent, but occasionally utters low *kraak*; gives various deep guttural calls and softer notes during display. **HABITS** A typical diurnal heron. Generally less sociable than other egrets, and is often solitary when hunting, although will feed communally at concentrated food sources. Roosts communally. **HABITAT** Rivers, lakes, jheels, marshes, estuaries, mangroves and coral reefs. **BREEDING** November–May and July–September, varying locally. Nest and nest site are like those of Little Egret; also nests in mangroves and on islands. **DISTRIBUTION AND STATUS** Resident, moving locally according to water conditions. Throughout lowlands in much of the subcontinent, except parts of the northwest and northeast. **PK:** common; widespread and locally migratory in winter, also locally sedentary. **NP:** locally fairly common resident; mainly below 300 m (–3050 m on passage). **IN:** widespread and locally common resident. **BT:** local, fairly common resident. **BD:** resident, locally common throughout. **LK:** resident in lowlands, common in the dry zone, irregular in wet zone; visitor to hills. **MV:** recorded; status uncertain. **REFERENCES** Hancock and Kushlan (1984).

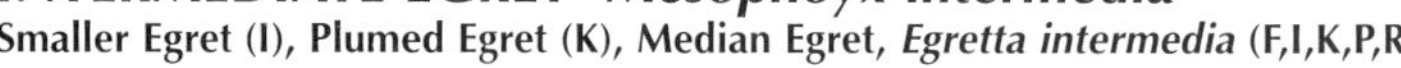

INTERMEDIATE EGRET *Mesophoyx intermedia* — Plate 78

Smaller Egret (I), Plumed Egret (K), Median Egret, *Egretta intermedia* (F,I,K,P,R)

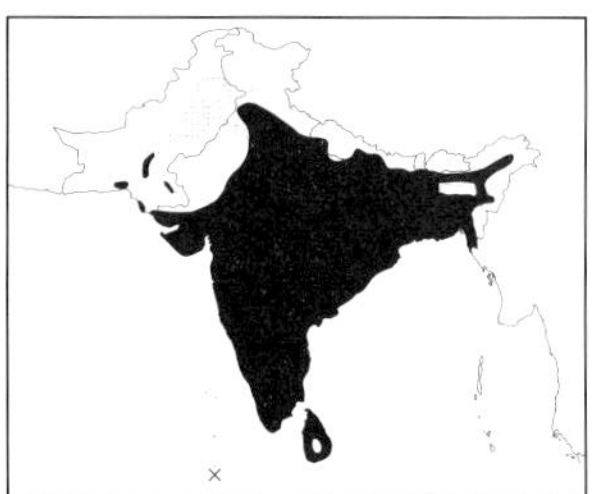

IDENTIFICATION 65–72 cm. A medium-sized to large white heron, easily confusable with Great Egret (above) since there is considerable variation in size within the two species (females averaging slightly smaller in both). In all plumages, told from Great by smaller size, while black line of gape does not extend beyond eye (ending beneath black pupil), and has a shorter bill. Bare-part coloration can provide further clues (see below). Usually appears more compact and well proportioned (typically appearing larger-headed and shorter- and stockier-necked, with less angular and less pronounced kink to neck when recoiled, and proportionately larger-bodied). Can look like a large and elongated Cattle Egret (p.563). In flight, appears more compact and neatly proportioned compared with Great. The potential for confusion with Cattle should not be underestimated, although Intermediate is larger, and has larger and longer bill, longer legs and longer and more serpentine neck. **Adult breeding** has prominent plumes on breast and mantle: the breast plumes are longer and finer than on Great, while those extending from the mantle are shorter. Has moderate crest to hindcrown and nape. The lores are initially yellow and the yellow bill has variable amounts of black; lores become yellow-green and bill black during courtship. **Adult non-breeding** and **juvenile** lack plumes; lores are pale yellow; bill is yellow, often with pronounced black tip. **VOICE** Normally silent; gives distinctive buzzing calls during display (Hancock and Kushlan 1984). **HABITS** A typical diurnal heron. Usually in small flocks, which separate when foraging. Hunts chiefly by slow stalking. Roosts communally. **HABITAT** Marshes, flooded grassland, well-vegetated pools; also shores of open jheels, lakes and reservoirs, and estuaries, mangrove swamps and tidal creeks. **BREEDING** As Great Egret. Also nests in mangrove forests. **DISTRIBUTION AND STATUS** Resident, moving locally according to water conditions. Throughout lowlands in much of the subcontinent, except parts of the northwest and northeast. **PK:** frequent, mainly an irregular year-round visitor, locally resident. **NP:** mainly resident; frequent throughout below 915 m (–1370 m). **IN:** widespread and locally common resident in plains. **BT:** rare and local. **BD:** resident, locally common throughout. **LK:** common resident in the lowlands, visitor to hills. **MV:** rare visitor. **REFERENCES** Hancock and Kushlan (1984).

CATTLE EGRET *Bubulcus ibis* — Plate 78

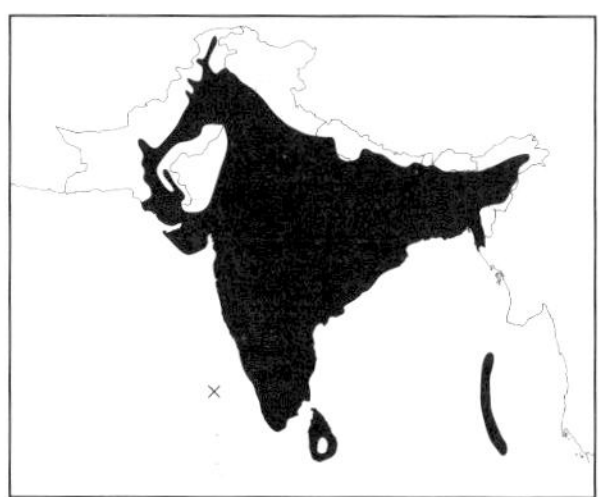

IDENTIFICATION 48–53 cm. A relatively small but stocky, predominantly white heron, often found well away from water. In all plumages, distinguished from Little Egret (p.558) by much shorter and stouter yellow bill, shorter legs (without prominent yellow feet), and shorter and stouter neck. From Intermediate Egret (p.562), which can be confusing with its yellow bill (except when breeding), by smaller size, shorter legs, and stocky appearance with much shorter neck. Has characteristic heavy-jowled expression, with chin feathering bulging forwards and extending along third to half of lower mandible. In flight, extension of legs and feet beyond tail is considerably shorter than on Little and Intermediate, and appears more compact, with less pronounced neck bulge. **Adult breeding** has orange-buff coloration to much of head, neck and breast, and elongated orange-buff mantle plumes. Bill, legs, iris and lores are yellow, but immediately prior to breeding turn pinkish-red. **Adult non-breeding** and **juvenile** are all white; juvenile can have blackish legs and bill, which become dark green and yellow respectively with age. **VOICE** Usually silent away from breeding colony. **HABITS** Gregarious when feeding and roosting. Typically seen in flocks around domestic stock, and also with Wild Buffalo, feeding on insects disturbed by the animals; often rides on the animals' backs, picking parasitic insects and flies from their hides. Also forages in flooded fields. Unlike other egrets, feeds mainly on insects; also takes tadpoles and lizards. **HABITAT** Damp grassland, paddy-fields, grass banks of village tanks, canals and lakes; also rubbish dumps (Sri Lanka) and forest clearings. **BREEDING** Almost all year, varying locally. Breeds colonially in large trees, not necessarily close to water; sometimes with other herons and egrets. **DISTRIBUTION AND STATUS** Resident, subject to local movements. Throughout much of the subcontinent, except parts of the northwest, northeast and Himalayas. **PK:** common and widespread throughout Sindh and Punjab. **NP:** common throughout; below 1525 m. **IN:** common and widespread; up to 2100 m in peninsular hills, to 1500 m in Himalayas. **BT:** local and fairly common. **BD:** occurs locally throughout. **LK:** very common in the lowlands, visitor to hills. **MV:** regular visitor, possibly breeds.

INDIAN POND HERON *Ardeola grayii* — Plate 78

Pond Heron (F,I)

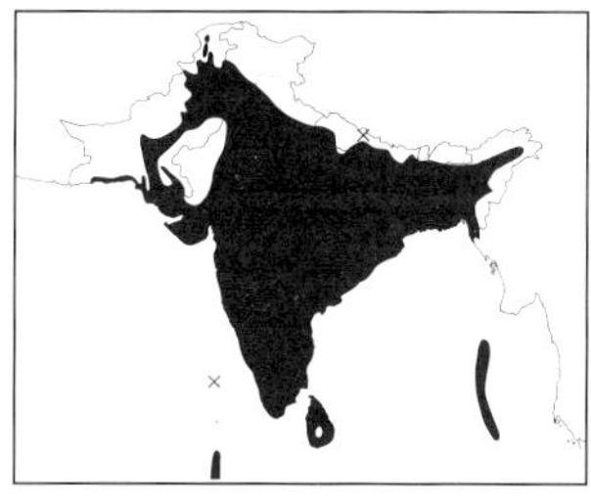

IDENTIFICATION 42–45 cm. A small, stocky, short-legged heron, in all plumages readily distinguished from all others, except from Chinese Pond Heron (below), by whitish wings and tail which contrast with dark 'saddle'. **Adult breeding** has yellow-buff head and neck with white nape plumes, maroon-brown mantle and scapulars, and white wings with buff wash across greater coverts. Bill can be bluish, yellow or orange, with dark tip, and legs can be bright yellow or even reddish. **Adult non-breeding** has buff head, neck and breast, boldly streaked with dark brown, and mid brown mantle and scapulars. Bill is dull yellowish with broad dark tip, and legs are dull yellowish-green. **Juvenile** is similar to adult non-breeding, but has breast spotted pale brown rather than streaked dark brown, buff shaft streaks on scapulars, faint brown mottling on tail, brown inner primaries, and grey wash to upperwing-coverts. **Immature** is very similar to adult non-breeding, but retains juvenile primaries and coverts. For differences from Chinese Pond Heron, see that species. **VOICE** A high, harsh squawk when flushed; birds at the nest constantly utter a human-like *wa-koo*. **HABITS** Usually solitary when hunting, but will gather in large numbers at drying-out pools to feed on stranded fish. Roosts communally. Hunts in typical heron fashion. Tame and inconspicuous when perched, but flies up with a startling flash of white wings. **HABITAT** Marshes, flooded paddy-fields, jheels, village tanks, ditches, borrow pits, lakes, mangrove creeks and tidal mudflats. **BREEDING** Almost all months, varying locally. Breeds in small groups in isolated large trees or clumps such as mangoes, often in the middle of a town or village, not necessarily close to water. **DISTRIBUTION AND STATUS** Resident, moving locally according to water conditions. Throughout much of the subcontinent, except parts of the northwest, northeast and Himalayas. **PK:** common and widespread resident throughout Sindh and Punjab; summer visitor to broader NW Pakistan valleys. **NP:** common throughout; below 1525 m (–2745 m). **IN:** common and widespread; up to 2150 m in Nilgiris, to 1500 m in Himalayas. **BT:** local and fairly common. **BD:** common, occurs throughout. **LK:** common in the lowlands and up to mid altitudes. **MV:** common in the south, a few records from the north.

CHINESE POND HERON *Ardeola bacchus* — Plate 78

IDENTIFICATION 52 cm. Very similar in plumage and structure to Indian Pond Heron (above), although generally slightly larger, with a marginally longer bill. Only adults in breeding plumage are separable with confidence from Indian Pond. **Adult breeding** differs from Indian Pond in having rich maroon-chestnut head and neck

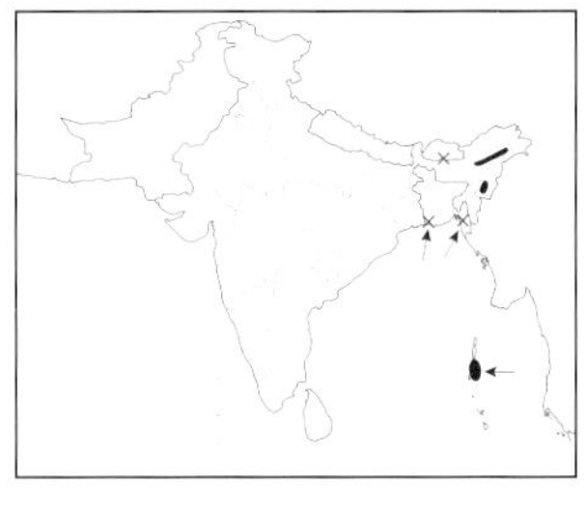

(with maroon-chestnut rather than white head plumes) and slaty-black mantle and scapulars. **Adult non-breeding**, **juvenile** and **immature** are much as respective plumages of Indian Pond, with streaked head, neck and breast. No constant differences between the two species in any plumage feature (e.g. in boldness of crown and nape streaking or in coloration of mantle and scapulars) have yet been determined. **VOICE** Presumably as that of Indian Pond. **HABITS** Like those of Indian Pond. **HABITAT** Like that of Indian Pond. **BREEDING** May–August. Nest is like that of Indian Pond Heron. **DISTRIBUTION AND STATUS** Resident, subject to local movements; also a migrant or winter visitor. Mainly NE India (Assam, Manipur) and Andamans. Probably under-recorded, since it is indistinguishable from Indian Pond Heron in winter plumage. **IN:** rare resident in the northeast; a few records from the Andamans. **BT, BD, LK:** vagrant.

LITTLE HERON *Butorides striatus* — Plate 80

Little Green Heron (F,I,P), Striated Heron

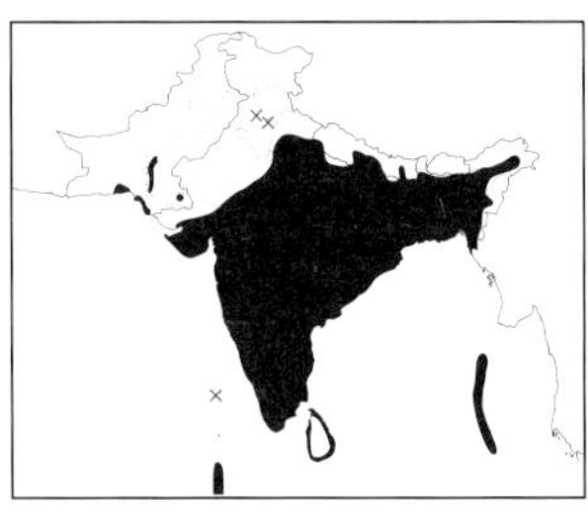

IDENTIFICATION 40–48 cm. A small, dark, stocky heron. **Adult** has black crown and long crest, and broad black line extending from bill-base to below and behind eye. Has dark greenish coloration to upperparts, with pale buff or white fringes to wing feathers giving rise to streaked appearance, and relatively uniform grey underparts. Bill is blackish, with yellow base to lower mandible; has bare yellow lores, and dull yellow legs and feet. Protruding yellowish feet and uniform dark mantle and wings are distinctive in flight. **Juvenile** has dark grey-brown crown and mantle with buff streaking, and prominent white or buffish spotting on wing-coverts; underparts are boldly streaked with dark brown. Possibly confusable with juvenile Little and Yellow Bitterns (p.000 and p.565), but habits and habitat are quite different, and is larger and stockier in appearance. **Immature** is similar to juvenile, but has uniform dark brown crown and mantle with variable dark green tinge. **VOICE** Usually silent, but gives a *k-yow k-yow* or *k-yek k-yek* call when flushed. **HABITS** Normally frequents the same area day after day. Hunts alone and in typical heron fashion. Often crepuscular, activity of coastal birds being dependent on the tidal cycle; sometimes active during the day, especially in overcast weather, but usually keeps to thick vegetation on banks of rivers and pools and often perches on branches overhanging water. Frequently stands hunchbacked when resting. If flushed, it flies low over the water and soon lands in cover nearby. **HABITAT** Pools, lakes, streams and rivers with dense shrubby vegetation on the banks; also mangrove swamps and creeks. **BREEDING** March–September, varying locally. Builds a small platform nest of sticks in a small tree in a mangrove swamp, or hidden in bushes at edge of a pond or stream; often near heron colonies. **DISTRIBUTION AND STATUS** Resident. Throughout much of the subcontinent, except parts of the northwest, northeast and Himalayas. Probably under-recorded because of its secretive habits. **PK:** resident and irregular year-round visitor; frequent in N Sindh, scarce elsewhere. **NP:** resident and summer visitor; frequent below 915 m. **IN:** widespread and frequent resident. **BT:** rare. **BD:** resident, occurring locally throughout. **LK:** resident in the lowlands, common in the coastal belt, irregular elsewhere. **MV:** common resident throughout, but probably decreasing.

BLACK-CROWNED NIGHT HERON *Nycticorax nycticorax* — Plate 80

Night Heron (F,I,P)

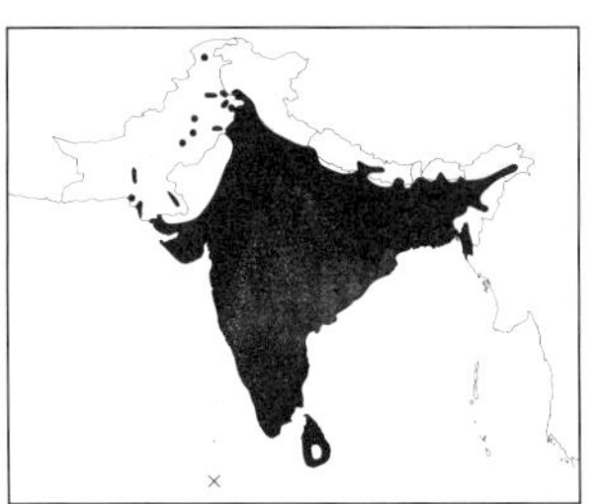

IDENTIFICATION 58–65 cm. A stocky, thick-necked heron with stout blackish bill. Essentially nocturnal, and most often seen when flushed from cover or during crepuscular flights. In flight, appears bulky and bull-headed, with broad rounded wings and slightly protruding feet. **Adult** has striking red eye, narrow white supercilium extending across forehead, black crown, mantle and scapulars, grey wings, and greyish-white underparts. Protruding yellow feet, and black 'saddle' contrasting with uniform grey wings and tail, are especially noticeable in flight. In breeding plumage, has elongated white nape feathers. **Juvenile** is brownish in coloration, and boldly spotted and streaked all over with white or buffish. In flight, shows uniform dark brown flight feathers and tail, with bold white or buffish spotting on upperwing-coverts. **Immature** by second year has dark brown crown, uniform dark grey-brown mantle and scapulars without the bold white spotting, and grey-streaked whitish underparts. By third year is a dull version of adult, with blackish-brown rather than glossy black crown, mantle and scapulars. **VOICE** Utters a distinctive, deep and rather abrupt *wouck* in flight. **HABITS** Nocturnal and crepuscular except when feeding young. Usually spends the day sitting hunched in a densely foliaged tree. Most often seen at dusk, flying singly or in small groups from its daytime roost. Usually forages singly, sometimes in a loose group. Feeds like a typical heron. **HABITAT** Ponds, tanks, jheels, streams, mangroves, estuaries, tidal creeks and coastal lagoons. **BREEDING** December–September, varying locally. Builds a rough stick platform in a tree or bush, not necessarily near water. **DISTRIBUTION AND STATUS** Resident, moving locally according to water conditions. Throughout much of the subcontinent, except parts of the northwest, northeast and Himalayas. **PK:** resident and breeding summer visitor, common and widespread, but local. **NP:** locally common below 1370 m; mainly a summer visitor, partly resident. **IN:** locally common and widespread, but rather patchily distributed. **BT:** rare. **BD:** resident, occurs locally throughout. **LK:** resident in lowlands and lower hills. **MV:** vagrant.

MALAYAN NIGHT HERON *Gorsachius melanolophus* Plate 80

Malay Bittern (I,P), Malay Night Heron (N), Tiger Bittern (F)

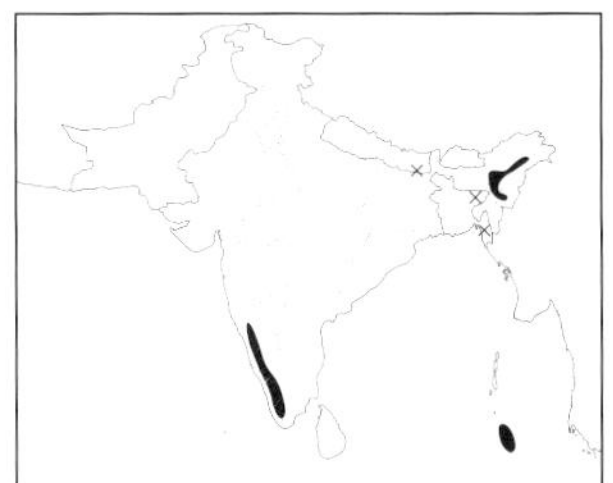

IDENTIFICATION 51 cm. A stocky, thick-necked, forest-dwelling, nocturnal heron with stout dark bill and hooded appearance. When flushed in forest, may possibly be mistaken for a fish owl, but has protruding feet, extended neck, and narrower and more boldly patterned wings. **Adult** has black crown and crest, blue facial skin, rufous sides to head and neck, black streaking down centre of foreneck and breast, and chestnut upperparts finely vermiculated with black. In flight, shows rufous secondaries with broad black subterminal band, and white tips to black primaries and rufous primary coverts; tail is black. **Juvenile** is rufous-buff, and barred and vermiculated all over with dark brown. **Immature** is dark brown in coloration, and vermiculated all over with white, grey and rufous-buff, with bold white spotting on blackish crown and crest. In flight, shows dark flight feathers which contrast with paler, finely vermiculated coverts; has whitish tips to primaries. **VOICE** Usually silent. Sequence of ten to eleven deep *oo* notes about 1.5 seconds apart (Boonsong and Round 1991). **HABITS** Shy and mainly nocturnal. Skulks in damp places in forest undergrowth during the day. If flushed, flies off silently into a nearby thickly foliaged tree. **HABITAT** Streams and marshes in dense evergreen broadleaved forest. **BREEDING** May–August, varying locally. Builds a flimsy stick nest in a small tree overhanging a stream or the side of a nullah in thick forest. **DISTRIBUTION AND STATUS** Resident and partial migrant in S Western Ghats, NE India and Nicobar Is; winter visitor mainly to Sri Lanka. Probably under-recorded because of its secretive and nocturnal habits. **NP:** vagrant. **IN:** scarce. **BD:** rare, local visitor. **LK:** rare winter visitor to all zones.

LITTLE BITTERN *Ixobrychus minutus* Plate 80

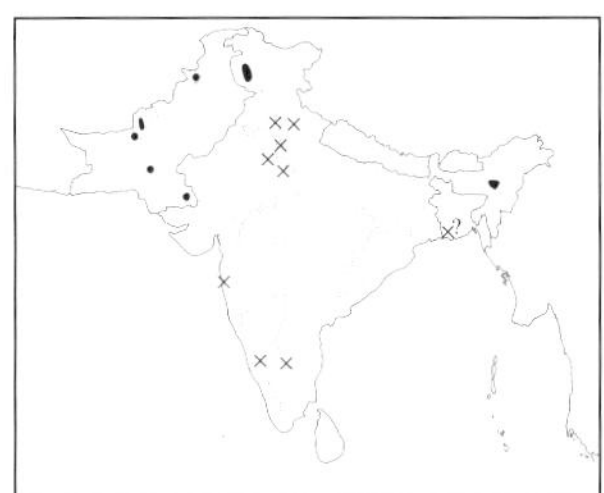

IDENTIFICATION 33–38 cm. A very small, thin-necked heron, closely resembling Yellow Bittern (below). Flies with fast, jerky wingbeats. **Adult male** differs from Yellow in having black (rather than pinkish-brown) upperparts including rump and uppertail-coverts, which contrast strongly with buffish-white wing-coverts; also, sides of head and neck are buff (rather than deep vinaceous), with faint greyish-vinaceous wash to hindneck. **Adult female** has black crown and brown upperparts (sometimes with distinct rufous tinge and variably streaked with buff), unlike female Yellow. Compared with male Little, has stronger greyish-vinaceous wash to face and neck, brownish-buff streaking on foreneck and breast, with streaking darker brown on belly and flanks, and has less striking upperwing pattern, with browner flight feathers and deeper greyish-buff coverts (becoming rufous-brown near bend of wing). **Juvenile** has broad buff fringes to dark brown upperparts and brown streaking on buff wing-coverts, and neck and underparts are more heavily streaked than on female. Juvenile is very similar to juvenile Yellow, but has broad dark brown shaft streaking on foreneck and breast, with diffuse rufous-buff edges to streaks (juvenile Yellow has rufous-orange streaking down foreneck and breast, although dark shaft streaking is apparent on some and general appearance of streaking can be very similar). **VOICE** Territorial call is a low-pitched, far-carrying and repeatedly uttered *woof..woof..woof*, and flight call is an abrupt *quer* or throaty *ker-ack* (Cramp and Simmons 1977). **HABITS** A typical bittern. Solitary. Most active at dusk; usually spends the day concealed in thick waterside vegetation, but may be seen in the daytime in cloudy weather. Forages by creeping through dense vegetation or by standing and waiting at the edges of cover. If disturbed, often freezes with head and bill pointing vertically skywards. **HABITAT** Tall reedbeds bordering jheels, lakes, marshes and streams. **BREEDING** May–September, varying locally. Nest is a pad of rushes, usually built in a dense reedbed. **DISTRIBUTION AND STATUS** Resident, subject to local movements. Pakistan, India and Bangladesh. **PK:** rare; mainly a winter visitor, very locally resident, also a passage migrant. **IN:** resident in Kashmir and Assam, scattered records elsewhere including some possibly breeding; mainly in the plains, up to 1800 m in Kashmir, where common. **BD:** former resident; no recent records.

YELLOW BITTERN *Ixobrychus sinensis* Plate 80

IDENTIFICATION 38 cm. A very small, slim, thin-necked heron. In flight, wings appear narrow and wingbeats are rapid (with occasional glides), while large feet usually hang clumsily. Most likely to be seen alongside Cinnamon Bittern (p.566), but readily distinguished from that species in all plumages by yellowish-buff wing-coverts contrasting with dark flight feathers, and blackish tail. Confusion most likely in the N subcontinent with Little Bittern (above); for differences, see that species. **Adult male** has warm pinkish-brown upperparts, including rump and uppertail-coverts, with noticeable black tail; face and neck (except foreneck) are deep vinaceous,

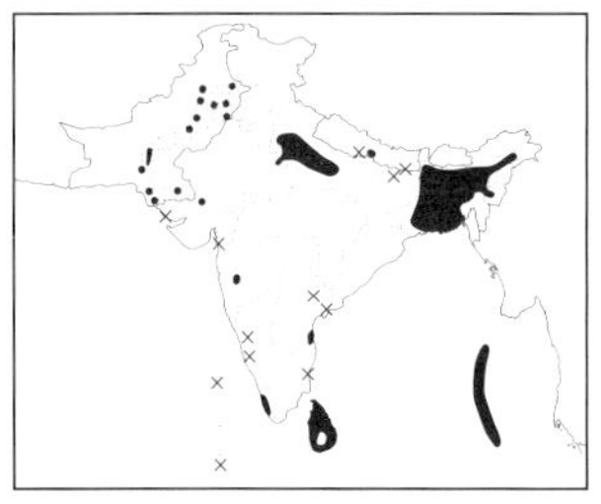

and foreneck and rest of underparts are unstreaked creamy-white. **Adult female** is similar to male, but has rufous streaking on black crown, variable rufous-orange streaking on foreneck and breast, and diffuse buff edges to rufous-brown mantle and scapulars resulting in streaked appearance. Sexing and ageing, however, appear not to be straightforward; some (older?) females would seem to be similar to males. **Juvenile** is similar to female. Mantle and scapulars are brown with broad buff fringes, and has brown streaking on buff wing-coverts; streaking on foreneck and breast is stronger, and feathers often have dark shafts. **VOICE** Territorial call is a low-pitched *ou-ou*. **HABITS** Very similar to those of Little Bittern. **HABITAT** Reeds and scrub in swamps, flooded paddy-fields; often in the same area as Cinnamon Bittern. **BREEDING** June–September. Nest is a small pad of reeds and sedges built in a reedbed or in bushes at the edge of a pond. **DISTRIBUTION AND STATUS** Resident, moving locally according to water conditions. Scattered distribution; absent from the Deccan plateau. **PK:** frequent; mainly an irregular year-round visitor, locally resident. **NP:** local and uncommon below 250 m; mainly a summer visitor, a few winter records. **IN:** widespread and uncommon resident; up to 900 m in peninsular hills. **BD:** local resident. **LK:** resident, irregular in dry zone, more frequent in the wet zone; visitor to hills. **MV:** rare visitor.

CINNAMON BITTERN *Ixobrychus cinnamomeus* — Plate 80

Chestnut Bittern (F,I,P)

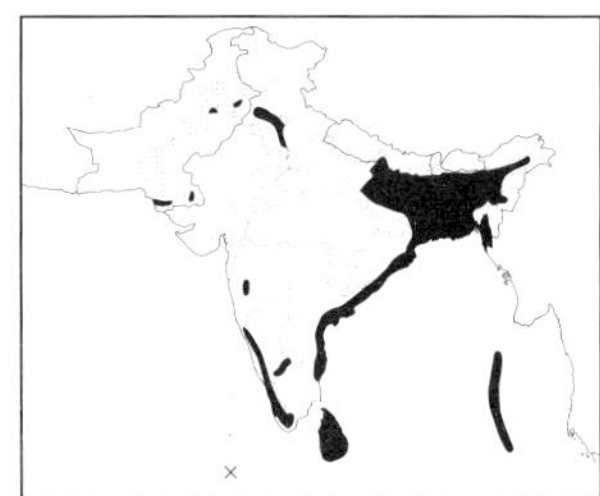

IDENTIFICATION 38 cm. Typically, appears slightly larger and stockier than Yellow Bittern (p.565), with more rounded wings. In flight, readily told from that species in all plumages by uniform-looking cinnamon-rufous flight feathers and tail (both are blackish on Yellow Bittern). **Adult male** is very distinctive, with uniform cinnamon-rufous crown, hindneck and upperparts and warm rufous-buff underparts, with variable dark stripe down foreneck (often inconspicuous or lacking). Often shows prominent white malar stripe, and has black streaking on sides of breast. **Adult female** has darker and browner crown, hindneck and mantle, dark brown streaking on foreneck and breast, and variable dark brown and buff mottling on scapulars and upperwing-coverts. **Juvenile** is similar to female; dark brown feathers of mantle, scapulars and wing-coverts are boldly marked with buff. Compared with juvenile Yellow Bittern, is darker brown above (appearing spotted and mottled rather than streaked), is more prominently streaked on the underparts (with blackish-brown rather than rufous-buff), and has cinnamon-rufous flight feathers and tail. **VOICE** Territorial call is a loud *kok-kok*. **HABITS** Very similar to those of Little Bittern (p.565). Often occurs at same locality and in same habitat as Yellow Bittern. **HABITAT** Reedbeds in jheels and marshes, and flooded paddy-fields. **BREEDING** May–September, varying locally. Nest is a small pad of leaves and reed stems built on bent-over reeds about 1 m above the water or mud. **DISTRIBUTION AND STATUS** Resident, moving locally according to water conditions. Scattered distribution; absent from the Deccan plateau. **PK:** frequent and irregular year-round visitor, locally resident; usually seen in summer. **NP:** frequent; mainly a summer visitor below 250 m, but found in all months; has bred at 1370 m. **IN:** widespread resident, occasionally recorded locally; up to 900 m in peninsular hills. **BD:** common resident throughout. **LK:** rare resident in the lowlands and foothills. **MV:** infrequent visitor.

BLACK BITTERN *Dupetor flavicollis* — Plate 80

Ixobrychus flavicollis

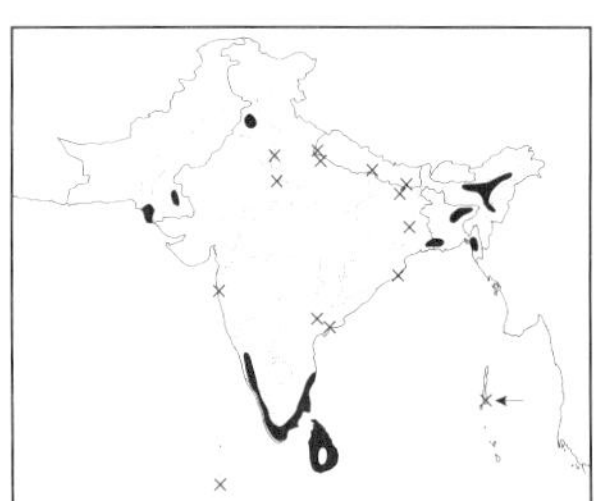

IDENTIFICATION 58 cm. Considerably larger than the *Ixobrychus* bitterns occurring in the subcontinent. Most likely to be seen in flight, when upperparts and well-rounded wings are uniform blackish, bill appears long, and always shows yellow-buff stripe down sides of neck (appearing as patch when neck recoiled). **Adult male** has blackish head, hindneck and upperparts, yellow-buff malar stripe extending down sides of neck, black-and-rufous streaking on whitish foreneck and breast, and dusky grey underparts. **Adult female** is similarly patterned, but upperparts are blackish-brown, foreneck and breast are more strongly streaked with rufous (and less so with black), and rest of underparts are dusky brown. **Juvenile** is similar to adult, but upperparts have narrow rufous feather fringes. **VOICE** Territorial call is a loud booming. **HABITS** A typical bittern. Chiefly nocturnal and crepuscular; skulks in dense swamps during the day. Most often seen flying at dusk and dawn, or in cloudy weather. **HABITAT** Reedbeds, and submerged bushes mixed with clumps of reeds and sedges. **BREEDING** May–September, varying locally. Nest is a pad of twigs and weeds placed in reeds or in a dense thicket in a marsh. **DISTRIBUTION AND STATUS** Resident, moving locally according to water conditions. Mainly Pakistan, S Nepal, Punjab, Gujarat, NE, SW and SE India, Bangladesh and Sri Lanka. **PK:** locally common; mainly a monsoon visitor to lower Sindh, a few may overwinter. **NP:** rare below 250 m; possibly resident. **IN:** widespread and uncommon, mainly in the south. **BD:** scarce, local resident. **LK:** rare resident in lowlands and lower hills, probably also a winter visitor. **MV:** infrequent visitor.

GREAT BITTERN *Botaurus stellaris* Plate 80

Bittern (I), Eurasian Bittern (F,P)

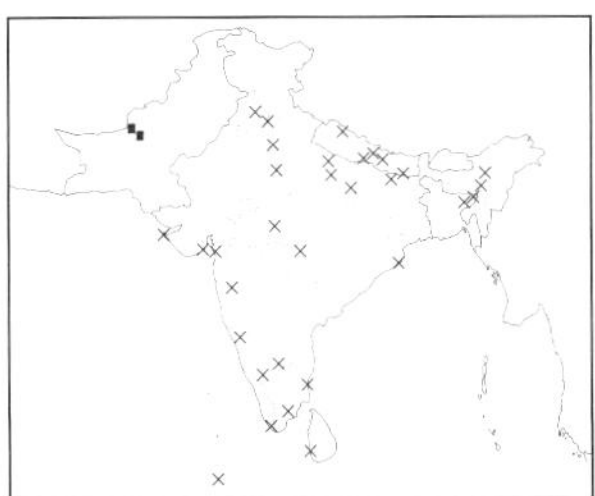

IDENTIFICATION 70–80 cm. Stocky, stout-necked, and cryptically patterned with golden-brown, blackish and tawny-buff. Has blackish crown and moustachial stripe separated by warm buff sides of head, and bold blackish streaking and barring on warm buff mantle and scapulars, with more intricate dark barring and mottling on buff upperwing-coverts. Usually well concealed in marsh vegetation, and most likely to be seen in flight, when retracted neck gives rise to stocky appearance (without neck bulge shown by most herons in flight) and wings are bowed, with rather quick wingbeats. Has blackish-brown remiges barred rufous-brown, contrasting slightly with paler wing-coverts. Can appear very owl-like in flight. Sexes are alike, and immature birds are not distinguishable in the field. **VOICE** Typically silent away from breeding areas, although calling has been recorded from Kashmir in summer. The territorial call is a booming *umphh...umphh...umphh*, often likened to the sound created by blowing across the opening of an empty bottle. **HABITS** A typical bittern. Usually remains hidden in reedbeds, and is most often seen flying low over the reed tops. Hunts alone, mainly by walking stealthily through the vegetation, often with intervals of standing motionless. **HABITAT** Dense tall beds of *Phragmites* reeds or *Typha* bulrushes growing in quite deep water in inland jheels, lakes and marshes. **BREEDING** Unknown in the subcontinent. Nest and nest site are similar to those of other bitterns. **DISTRIBUTION AND STATUS** Winter visitor, widespread in lowlands of subcontinent; also passage migrant in north. **PK:** scarce winter visitor, also a passage migrant; has possibly bred in Baluchistan. **NP:** rare winter visitor and passage migrant; mainly in the terai (–3050 m on passage). **IN:** rare, widespread winter visitor. **BD, LK, MV:** vagrant.

FLAMINGOS Phoenicopteridae

Large wading birds with long neck, very long legs, webbed feet and pink plumage. The bill is highly specialised for filter-feeding. Flamingos often occur in huge numbers and are found mainly on salt lakes and lagoons.

GREATER FLAMINGO *Phoenicopterus ruber* Plate 81

Flamingo *Phoenicopterus roseus* (F,I,K,P)

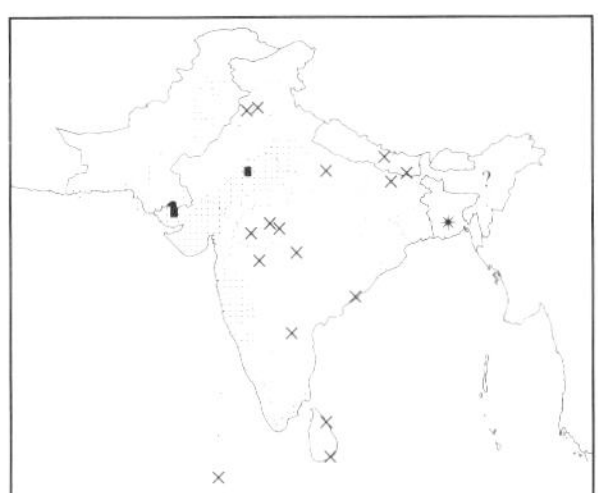

IDENTIFICATION 125–145 cm. Considerably larger than Lesser Flamingo (below); neck is proportionately longer and thinner, and in flight appears even more ludicrous, with very long, outstretched neck and legs and small wings, and with fairly rapid flight action. Bill is larger, less prominently kinked, and more banana-shaped than Lesser's. **Adult** differs from adult Lesser in pale pink bill with prominent dark tip, paler, pinkish-white coloration to head, neck and body, usually paler pink legs, and comparatively uniform crimson-pink upperwing-coverts which contrast in flight with much paler, whitish body. **Immature** has greyish-white head and neck, and body is white and lacks any pink; greater and primary coverts are white, mottled with brown, becoming pink with age. Best told from Lesser by pink-and-black bill (similar to adult). **Juvenile** has shorter neck and legs than adult and is brownish-grey, with black-tipped grey bill and generally grey legs; has dark streaking on lesser and median coverts and scapulars. Best told from juvenile Lesser by smaller size and different bill structure; also has paler brownish-grey plumage, with whitish band across greater coverts, although bleached juvenile Lesser can appear very similar in coloration. **VOICE** Flocks utter a goose-like *ka-ha* or *a-ha* (Cramp and Simmons 1977). **HABITS** Usually seen in small groups, large flocks or huge gatherings. Feeds in shallow water by immersing its head with the bill inverted, and filtering out small larvae, molluscs, crustaceans and seeds. **HABITAT** Shallow brackish lakes and lagoons, mudflats and saltpans. **BREEDING** July–April, varying according to water conditions. Forms densely packed colonies. Builds a conical nest mound of mud. **DISTRIBUTION AND STATUS** Mainly resident, but also a winter visitor; wanders erratically according to feeding conditions. Breeds in vast numbers in the Great Rann of Kutch, Gujarat. Widespread visitor to the plains; recently found mainly in the plains from Pakistan east to C Uttar Pradesh, W India, E Tamil Nadu and Sri Lanka. **PK:** common, mainly an irregular year-round visitor; has bred in the south on borders of the Great Rann. **NP:** vagrant. **IN:** frequent, but sporadic outside Kutch. **BD:** vagrant. **LK:** regular, local winter visitor to N and SE coastal areas; frequently oversummers. **MV:** sporadic visitor. **REFERENCES** Cramp and Simmons (1977), Perennou *et al.* (1994).

LESSER FLAMINGO *Phoenicopterus minor* Plate 81

***Phoeniconaias minor* (I)**

IDENTIFICATION 80–90 cm. Considerably smaller than Greater Flamingo (above), with shorter- and thicker-looking neck, and in flight appears more neatly proportioned. Bill is smaller and more prominently kinked

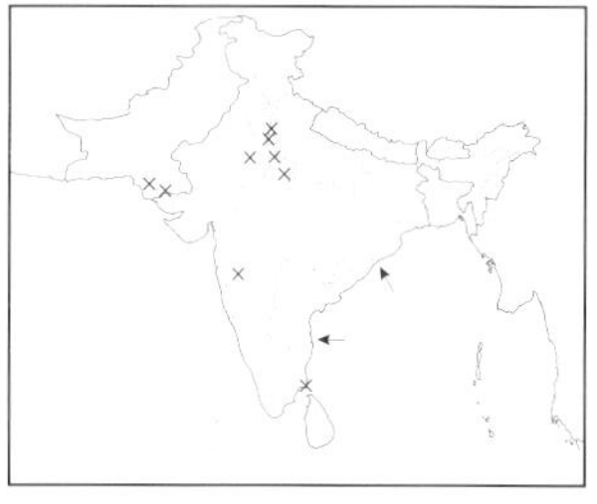

compared with Greater's. **Adult** differs from adult Greater in black-tipped dark red bill (which can appear all dark), dark red iris and facial skin, deeper rose-pink coloration to head, neck and body (although worn birds can be very pale), and usually darker pinkish-red legs. Has blood-red centres to lesser and median upperwing-coverts, contrasting with paler pink of rest of coverts. **Immature** has greyish-brown head and neck; body is pale pink, and wing-coverts are pink (with some brown on lesser coverts). Best told from immature Greater by structural differences and by bill shape and coloration (similar to adult). **Juvenile** is grey-brown, with darker streaking on wing-coverts and scapulars; has dark-tipped purplish-brown bill and dark grey legs. Best told from juvenile Greater by size, structure and bill shape, and is typically darker brown in coloration, with browner wing-coverts. **VOICE** The goose-like honking is higher-pitched than that of Greater Flamingo (Cramp and Simmons 1977). **HABITS** Similar to those of Greater Flamingo, and often found with that species. Does not compete, however, as it feeds on algae and diatoms. When foraging, it walks or swims while sweeping the head and neck to and fro, sieving micro-organisms from the surface waters; in very shallow water, it feeds in the same way as Greater Flamingo. **HABITAT** Salt and brackish lagoons, salt-pans; favours more saline waters than Greater Flamingo. **BREEDING** Mainly June and July, extending to January/February. Nest is like that of Greater Flamingo. **DISTRIBUTION AND STATUS** Breeds in the Great and Little Ranns of Kutch, Gujarat; in the non-breeding season partly disperses, with scattered records west to S Pakistan, east to E Orissa and south to Tamil Nadu. Moves erratically according to feeding conditions. **PK:** locally common in E Indus delta in winter. **IN:** recorded in all months; locally common in the northwest and west. **REFERENCES** Cramp and Simmons (1977), Mundkur *et al.* (1990), Perennou *et al.* (1994).

IBISES AND SPOONBILLS Threskiornithidae

Large birds with long neck and legs, partly webbed feet and long, broad wings. Ibises have a long decurved bill, and forage by probing in shallow water, mud and grass. Spoonbills have a long spatulate bill, and catch floating prey in shallow water. The main references specific to ibises and spoonbills are Hancock *et al.* (1992) and Perennou *et al.* (1994).

GLOSSY IBIS *Plegadis falcinellus* — Plate 81

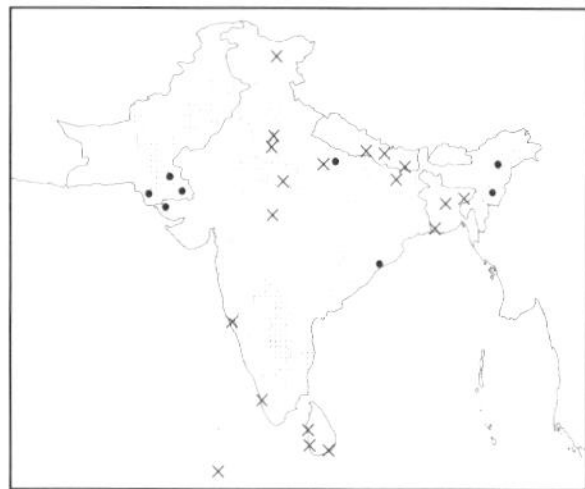

IDENTIFICATION 55–65 cm. A small, dark ibis with rather fine downcurved bill, and greenish to brownish legs. Graceful, but rather cormorant-like in flight, with extended slender neck, somewhat bulbous head, and legs and feet projecting well beyond tail. Flies with rapid wingbeats interspersed with short glides; flocks are often in V-formation. **Adult breeding** has dark olive-brown bill, deep chestnut head, neck and most of body glossed with purple and green, metallic green wings strongly glossed with purple, and narrow white surround to bare lores. **Adult non-breeding** has dark brown head and neck streaked with white, blackish-brown mantle and scapulars glossed with purple and green, and dark brown underparts with some chestnut mottling. **Immature** has head and neck like adult non-breeding; gradually acquires green-and-purple gloss to upperparts, and chestnut coloration to head, neck and underparts. **Juvenile** has dull brown head and neck mottled with white, whitish throat, dark brown upperparts and wings with faint greenish gloss, and brown underparts lacking any chestnut. **VOICE** Usually silent away from breeding colonies. **HABITS** Seen mainly in parties, sometimes of up to 50 birds. Forages in shallow water and marshes, often in well-scattered flocks; walks about or often wades belly-deep while probing rapidly into water and mud. Feeds chiefly on invertebrates; also fish and frogs. Readily perches and roosts in trees. **HABITAT** Freshwater marshes and large lakes, extensive areas of flooded grassland and paddy-fields. **BREEDING** May–July. Forms colonies with other large waterbirds. Builds a stick nest in trees standing in or near water. **DISTRIBUTION AND STATUS** Partly resident, partly a winter visitor; moves erratically, depending on water and feeding conditions. From Pakistan east to NE India and south through the peninsula and Sri Lanka; mainly in W and S subcontinent; has bred locally from Sind and Kutch east to Manipur and south to Orissa. **PK:** mainly an irregular year-round visitor, also a passage migrant, and has bred; locally common. **NP:** vagrant. **IN:** mainly a year-round visitor; locally frequent. **BD:** rare winter visitor. **LK:** now a rare and local winter visitor to the lowlands; formerly a breeding resident in dry zone. **MV:** rare local visitor. **REFERENCES** Cramp and Simmons (1977).

BLACK-HEADED IBIS *Threskiornis melanocephalus* — Plate 81

White Ibis (F,I,P), Oriental White Ibis (R), *T. aethiopicus* (I)

IDENTIFICATION 75 cm. A stocky, mainly white ibis with stout downcurved black bill, and black legs. **Adult breeding** has naked black head, variable yellow wash to white feathers of mantle and breast, grey on scapulars and elongated tertials, white plumes extending from lower neck, and all-white wings. In flight, shows stripe of

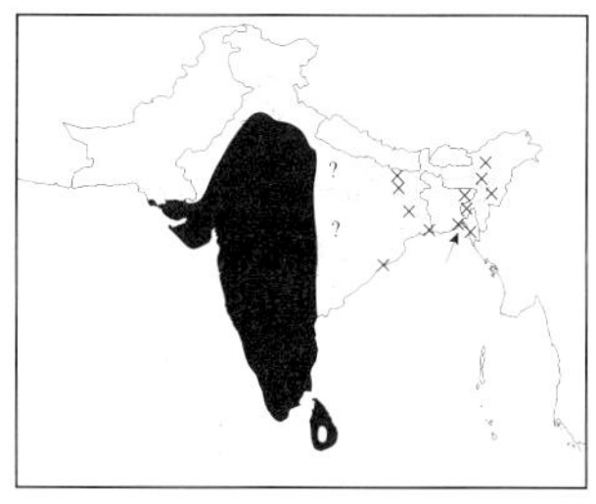

bare red skin on underside of white forewing and on flanks. **Adult non-breeding** has all-white body plumage, and lacks neck plumes. **Immature** has grey feathering on head and neck, and black fringes and tips to outer primaries. Bare skin on underwing is blackish. **VOICE** Usually silent away from breeding colonies. **HABITS** Similar to those of Glossy Ibis (p.568). Often forages in company with storks, egrets and spoonbills. **HABITAT** Freshwater marshes, tanks, jheels, rivers, flooded grassland, paddy-fields, tidal creeks and mudflats, saltmarshes and coastal lagoons. **BREEDING** June–March, varying according to monsoon and water conditions. Forms colonies with other large waterbirds. Nest is a small stick platform built in medium-sized trees or shrubs standing in or near water. **DISTRIBUTION AND STATUS** Resident and nomadic, depending on water and feeding conditions. Throughout much of the plains, except parts of NW subcontinent and E India. **PK:** mainly an irregular year-round visitor, locally resident; scarce, almost confined to the Indus delta and lower Sindh. **NP:** frequent resident and summer visitor; recorded mainly in the E terai. **IN:** widespread and locally common resident. **BD:** local visitor. **LK:** common resident in the lowlands, more frequent in the dry zone. **REFERENCES** Baral (1993).

BLACK IBIS *Pseudibis papillosa* — Plate 81

Red-naped Ibis (F,K)

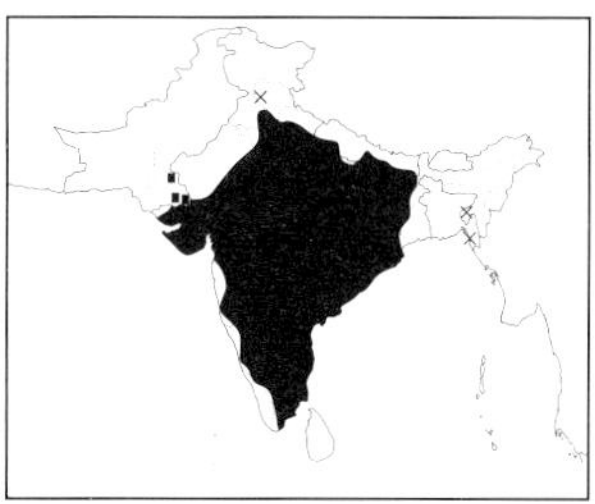

IDENTIFICATION 68 cm. A stocky, dark ibis with relatively stout down-curved bill, and reddish legs. Appears bulky and broad-winged in flight, with only the feet extending beyond tail. Told from Glossy Ibis (p.568) in all plumages by white shoulder patch and red legs. **Adult** has dark greenish bill, naked black head with red patch on rear crown and nape, dark brown neck and body glossed with green on scapulars, black wings strongly glossed with green and purple, and white inner wing-coverts (showing as prominent white wing patch in flight). **Immature** is dark brown, including feathered head, with white lesser wing-coverts (really visible only in flight) and blackish bill. At rest, told from immature Glossy Ibis by lack of white mottling on head and neck and by structural differences. **VOICE** Usually silent away from breeding colonies. **HABITS** Similar to those of Glossy Ibis, but prefers to feed in drier habitats and is less gregarious; usually found in small parties of up to ten birds. **HABITAT** Dry grassland and fallow fields, and drying edges of lakes and marshes; often near rubbish dumps in towns and villages. **BREEDING** March–October in N India; later farther south. Usually nests singly, but sometimes in small, unmixed colonies. Builds a large platform nest of sticks in a large tree; old nests of kites and vultures are often used. **DISTRIBUTION AND STATUS** Resident. Lowlands from S Pakistan east to West Bengal and south through most of the peninsula. **PK:** rare and irregular visitor, mainly in the monsoon, breeding occasionally; found in wetter parts of Sindh. **NP:** resident, frequent throughout; below 275 m (–915 m). **IN:** widespread and locally common resident in the plains. **BD:** vagrant. **REFERENCES** Baral (1993).

EURASIAN SPOONBILL *Platalea leucorodia* — Plate 81

Spoonbill (I,P), White Spoonbill (K,R)

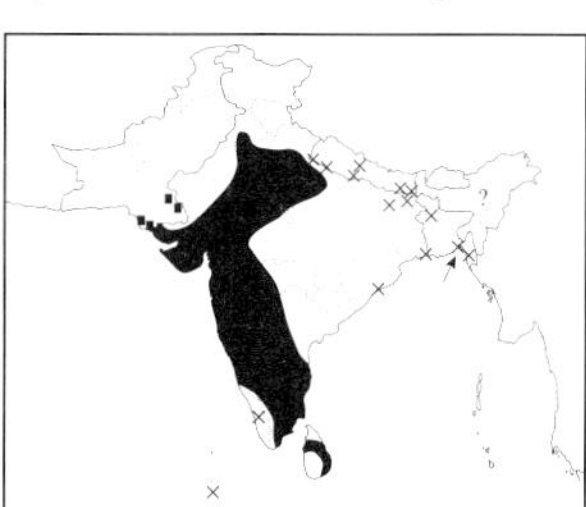

IDENTIFICATION 80–90 cm. Largely white, with extraordinary spatulate-ended bill, and stout black legs. In flight, neck is outstretched, and flapping is rather stiff and interspersed with gliding. **Adult breeding** has yellow tip to black bill, bare orange-yellow skin on throat, prominent crest, and yellow wash to breast. **Adult non-breeding** lacks crest and yellow wash to breast. **Immature** as adult non-breeding, but has black tips to primaries. **Juvenile** has pinkish bill and legs, black shafts to secondaries, and more extensive black tips to primaries than immature. **VOICE** Usually silent away from breeding colonies. **HABITS** Usually in small parties or flocks, often with other large waterbirds. Spends much of the day resting on one leg or sleeping with the bill tucked under the wing. Forages mainly in the mornings and evenings and at night. Wades actively in shallow water, making rhythmic side-to-side sweeps of its bill and sifting floating and swimming prey. Consumes aquatic invertebrates and small fish. **HABITAT** Chiefly larger lakes, lagoons, rivers and marshes; also tidal creeks and mangroves. **BREEDING** During the monsoon, July–January, varying locally. Forms colonies, usually with other large wading birds. Builds a platform nest of sticks in trees standing in water. **DISTRIBUTION AND STATUS** Resident and winter visitor; nomadic, depending on water conditions. Throughout much of the plains, except parts of NW and NE subcontinent and C and E India. **PK:** mainly a winter visitor and passage migrant, also a breeding resident; frequent along the Indus R and its main tributaries. **NP:** mainly a passage migrant and winter visitor, small numbers resident; flocks regularly recorded from Kosi marshes, rare elsewhere. **IN:** widespread and locally common resident. **BD:** vagrant. **LK:** rare and irregular resident in dry lowlands. **MV:** vagrant. **REFERENCES** Baral (1993).

PELICANS Pelecanidae

Large, aquatic, gregarious fish-eating birds. The wings are long and broad, and the tail is short and rounded. They have a characteristic long, straight, flattened bill, hooked at the tip, and with a large expandable pouch suspended beneath the lower mandible. Many pelicans often fish cooperatively by swimming forward in a semicircular formation, driving the fish into shallow waters; each bird then scoops up fish from the water into its pouch, before swallowing the food. Pelicans fly either in V-formation or in lines, and often soar for considerable periods in thermals. They are powerful fliers, proceeding by steady flaps and with the head drawn back between the shoulders. When swimming, the closed wings are typically held above the back. All frequent fresh and brackish lakes and coastal waters. The main references specific to pelicans are Johnsgard (1993) and Perennou *et al.* (1994).

GREAT WHITE PELICAN *Pelecanus onocrotalus* — Plate 82

White Pelican (F,I), Eastern White Pelican (K)

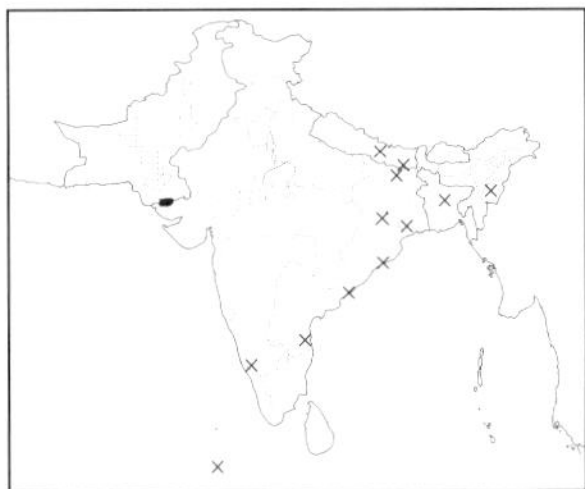

IDENTIFICATION 140–175 cm. Best told from Dalmatian and Spot-billed Pelicans (below and p.571) by patterning of underwing. Adult and immature birds have black undersides to primaries and secondaries which contrast strongly with white or largely white underwing-coverts. Upperwing also appears more contrasting, with blacker flight feathers. More difficult at rest, when bare-part coloration is more important (see below for details). Feathering of forehead is narrower than on Dalmatian and tapers to a point at bill-base (owing to more extensive area of orbital skin). Adult is generally cleaner and whiter than Dalmatian and Spot-billed. **Adult breeding** has white feathers of body and wing-coverts tinged with pink, bright yellow pouch and pinkish skin around eye, crimson tinge to pink legs and feet, and white crest. **Adult non-breeding** as adult breeding, but lacks pink tinge and crest, and bare parts are duller. **Immature** usually resembles adult non-breeding, but with variable amounts of brown on upperwing- and underwing-coverts and on scapulars. **Juvenile** has largely brown head, neck and upperparts, including upperwing-coverts, and dark brown flight feathers; upperwing appears more uniformly brown, and underwing shows pale central panel contrasting with dark inner wing-coverts and flight feathers. Greyish pouch becomes yellower with age. **VOICE** Usually silent away from breeding colonies. **HABITS** A typical pelican. May be found singly, in small flocks, or in huge concentrations on larger lakes and lagoons. Often hunts cooperatively. Roosts in flocks, usually on open sand bars. **HABITAT** Large lakes, lagoons and tidal creeks. **BREEDING** February–April. Colonial. Builds nest of white feathers on the ground. **DISTRIBUTION AND STATUS** Resident and winter visitor. Breeds in the Great Rann of Kutch, Gujarat. Mainly a winter visitor to S Pakistan and NW, N and NE India; scattered records south to S Karnataka. **PK:** a winter visitor, formerly very numerous in Sindh, but now common only in Thatta and Badin districts; also a passage migrant, mostly passing through the upper Kurram valley and across NW Baluchistan. **NP:** vagrant. **IN:** locally common in winter in Gujarat and Assam. **BD:** rare winter visitor. **MV:** vagrant. **REFERENCES** Cramp and Simmons (1977), Harris *et al.* (1996).

DALMATIAN PELICAN *Pelecanus crispus* — Plate 82

***P. philippinus* (I)**

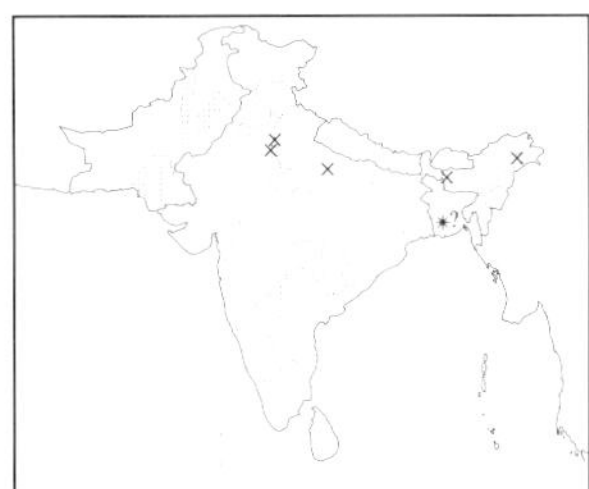

IDENTIFICATION 160–180 cm. Best told from Great White (above) by patterning of underwing. In all plumages, Dalmatian has greyish underside to secondaries and inner primaries (becoming darker grey on outer primaries), which do not contrast strongly with pale underwing-coverts, and often with whiter central panel. On most birds, especially immatures, upperwing also appears less contrasted, with greyer flight feathers. Feathering of forehead is broader across upper mandible owing to more restricted area of orbital skin than on Great White. Legs and feet are always dark grey (pinkish on Great White). Told from Spot-billed Pelican (p.571) by considerably larger size, cleaner, whiter appearance at all ages (whiter head, hindneck, mantle, and upperwing- and underwing-coverts), lack of ribbing on upper mandible, and typically darker bill than pouch. **Adult breeding** has silvery-grey tinge to upperparts and blue-grey tinge to underparts; also deep orange to red pouch and purple skin around eye, dark grey legs and feet, and curly, bushy crest. **Adult non-breeding** as adult breeding, but plumage is dirty white, has reduced crest, and has pale yellow pouch and skin around eye. **Immature** usually resembles adult non breeding, but is dingier, with some pale grey-brown on upperwing-coverts and scapulars. **Juvenile** has pale grey-brown mottling on hindneck and upperparts, including upperwing-coverts (much paler and less heavily marked than on juvenile Great White); pouch is greyish-yellow. **VOICE** Usually silent away from breeding colonies. **HABITS** A typical pelican. Found singly, in pairs and in flocks, but not in such large congregations as Great White Pelican. Fishes individually, or cooperatively in a flock. **HABITAT** Large lakes, rivers and coastal lagoons. **DISTRIBUTION AND STATUS** Winter visitor, formerly recorded from Pakistan east to Assam; now winters mainly in S Pakistan, Gujarat and Rajasthan. Globally threatened. **PK:** a passage migrant, using the same routes as Great White Pelican; also a winter visitor, common only in Tatta district. **IN:** locally common in winter in Gujarat. **BD:** vagrant? **REFERENCES** Cramp and Simmons (1977), Harris *et al.* (1996), WWF India and AWB (1993).

SPOT-BILLED PELICAN *Pelecanus philippensis* Plate 82

Grey Pelican (I)

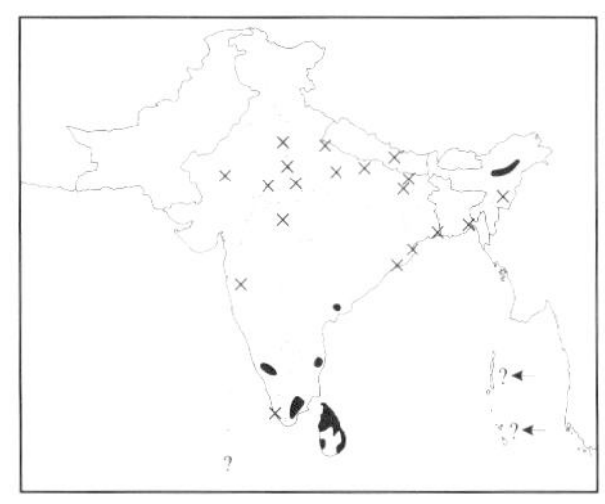

IDENTIFICATION 140 cm. Distinguished from Great White and Dalmatian Pelicans (p.570) by much smaller size, dingier appearance, rather uniform pinkish bill and pouch (except in breeding condition), and black spotting on upper mandible (except juveniles). Tufted crest and hindneck are usually apparent even on young birds. Patterning of underwing is similar to that of Dalmatian (and quite different from Great White), showing little contrast between wing-coverts and flight feathers but with paler greater coverts which show as distinct panel down centre of underwing. Pale circumorbital skin appears cut off from bill owing to dark greyish or purplish facial skin, resulting in facial appearance quite different from that of other two species (appears to be wearing goggles). **Adult breeding** has greyish-white upperparts and pinkish-white underparts, with cinnamon-pink rump, underwing-coverts and undertail-coverts. Head and neck appear greyish (owing to black bases to whitish feathers). Has purplish skin in front of eye, which offsets bulging pale yellow eye and orange-yellow circumorbital skin. Pouch is pink to dull purple, and blotched with black. Has blackish legs and feet. **Adult non-breeding** Upperparts and underparts are a dirtier greyish-white, pouch and circumorbital skin are pinkish, and facial skin between bill and eye is duller blue-grey. **Immature** resembles adult non breeding, but has variable grey-brown markings on upperparts (e.g. tertials, coverts and scapulars); crest and tufted hindneck feathering are well developed. **Juvenile** has brownish head and neck (with darker crown and hindneck), brown mantle and wing-coverts (fringed with pale buff), dark brown flight feathers, and brown streaking on underwing-coverts (with whitish greater coverts resulting in pale central panel). Spotting on the bill is initially lacking, and still indistinct at 12 months. **VOICE** Usually silent away from breeding colonies. **HABITS** A typical pelican. Gregarious, and fishes alone or cooperatively. **HABITAT** Large lakes, reservoirs and coastal lagoons and estuaries. **BREEDING** Mid September–April, varying locally. Forms colonies, often with other large waterbirds. Builds a huge nest of twigs, lined with straw, water weeds and reeds, in large tree. **DISTRIBUTION AND STATUS** Resident and local migrant. Breeds in S and SE India, Assam and Sri Lanka; widespread in the subcontinent in the non-breeding season. Declining. Globally threatened. **NP:** very local and uncommon non-breeding visitor, seen mainly March-May, all recent records being from Kosi. **IN:** locally common in the breeding season in Assam, Karnataka, Andhra Pradesh, and Tamil Nadu. **BD:** former resident, now vagrant. **LK:** regular breeding resident in the lowlands, locally common in dry zone. **MV:** possibly a rare visitor. **REFERENCES** Johnsgard (1993), Talukdar (1995), WWF India and AWB (1993).

STORKS Ciconiidae

Large or very large birds with long bill, neck and legs, long and broad wings and a short tail. In flight, the legs are extended behind and the neck is outstretched (except in the case of the two adjutant storks, which hold the neck retracted like the herons). They have a powerful slow-flapping flight and frequently soar for long periods, often at great heights. Most storks feed mainly on fish, frogs, snakes, lizards, large insects, crustaceans and molluscs, the exception being the Greater Adjutant, which also eats carrion. They capture prey while walking slowly in marshes, at edges of lakes and rivers and in grassland. Typically, storks build a large stick nest, lined with water weeds and leaves, high in trees. Most species also roost in trees. The main references specific to storks are Hancock *et al.* (1992) and Perennou *et al.* (1994).

PAINTED STORK *Mycteria leucocephala* Plate 84

***Ibis leucocephala* (F,K)**

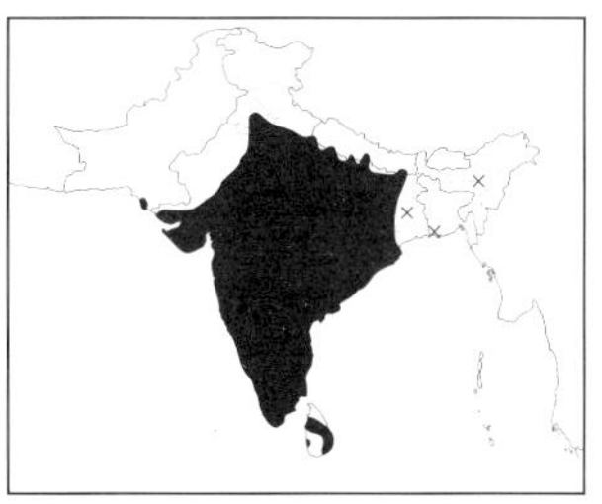

IDENTIFICATION 93–100 cm. **Adult** is mainly white, with large, downcurved yellow bill. Bare face is orange-yellow (red in the breeding season), and legs are red. Has black flight feathers, with white barring on mainly black coverts (on upperwing and underwing), largely pink tertials, and black barring across breast. Has distinctive appearance in flight, with extended drooping neck and downcurved bill, long wings with rather deep flapping beats, and long trailing legs. **Juvenile** is dirty greyish-white, with brownish (feathered) head and neck, and brown inner wing-coverts; as on adult, white rump and back contrast with black tail, and has black flight feathers. **VOICE** Largely silent away from the nesting colonies. **HABITS** Similar to those of other storks. Found singly, in small parties and sometimes in large flocks. Roosts gregariously, on trees if available, otherwise on open sandbanks, mud or saltpans. Forages by wading slowly in shallow water with the bill open and partly submerged, feeling for prey. Often stirs the water with its foot and occasionally flicks a wing to drive prey between its mandibles. **HABITAT** Freshwater marshes, lakes and reservoirs, flooded fields, river banks, intertidal mudflats and saltpans. **BREEDING** July–April, varying locally according to water conditions; starts in latter part of the monsoon. Forms colonies, often with other large waterbirds. Usually builds nest in trees standing in or near fresh water; also in mangroves, and in Gujarat on cactus on islands. **DISTRIBUTION AND STATUS** Resident, moving locally according to water conditions. Throughout the plains in much of the subcontinent, except parts of the northwest and northeast. **PK:** scarce; mainly confined to the Indus delta, where resident; occasionally wanders along major rivers after the monsoon and in early winter. **NP:** rare; mainly a summer visitor below 250 m, a few resident in the southwest. **IN:** widespread and locally common resident. **BD:** rare visitor to S coast; former resident. **LK:** resident in lowlands, more frequent in the dry zone. **REFERENCES** Baral (1993), Mundkur (1991b).

ASIAN OPENBILL *Anastomus oscitans* — Plate 84

Asian Openbill Stork (N,R), Openbill (P), Openbill Stork (I), Open-billed Stork (F)

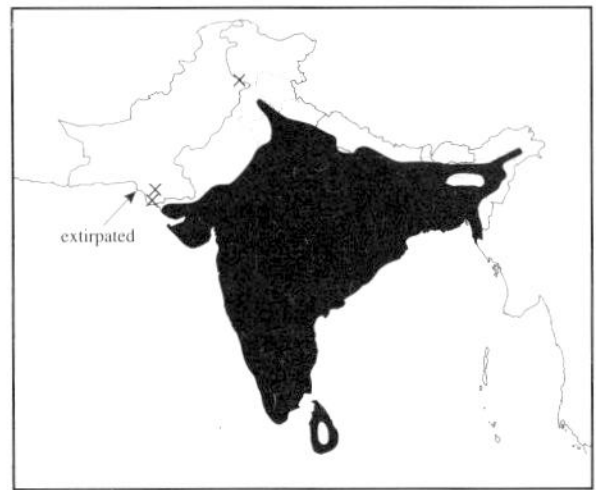

IDENTIFICATION 68 cm. Largely white or greyish-white, with stout 'open bill', and black flight feathers and tail. At a distance, and in flight, possibly confusable with White Stork (p.573), but is smaller and stockier, has stout-looking, dull-coloured bill, black tail and dull-coloured legs, and usually looks a dirtier, greyish white. **Adult breeding** has white body and wing-coverts, and reddish legs, although this plumage is retained for only a short period after the onset of the breeding season. **Adult non-breeding** has greyish-white body and wing-coverts (often looking very dusky), and dull pink legs. **Juvenile** has brownish-grey head, neck and breast, and brownish mantle and scapulars; as with adult, greyish-white back and rump contrast with black tail, and has black flight feathers. Has a smaller gap between mandibles than adult, and duller legs. **VOICE** Largely silent away from the nesting colonies. **HABITS** Similar to those of other storks. Forages singly or in small or medium-sized flocks. Usually seeks food by submerging its head and opened bill into shallow water and probing the bottom mud; the bill is quickly closed on any prey. Feeds mainly on molluscs; also eats crabs, frogs and fish. **HABITAT** Freshwater marshes, shallow lakes, reservoirs, jheels, tanks, lagoons and paddy-fields; rarely on river banks and mudflats. **BREEDING** July–April, depending on water conditions; starts at beginning of the monsoon. Forms large mixed colonies with other waterbirds. Nests in trees, often over water. **DISTRIBUTION AND STATUS** Resident, moving locally according to water conditions. In plains throughout much of the subcontinent, except parts of the northwest and northeast. **PK:** formerly a common resident in Sindh, now a rare non-breeding visitor. **NP:** widespread resident and summer visitor; below 250 m. **IN:** widespread and locally common resident. **BD:** local wandering resident, occurring throughout. **LK:** resident in the lowlands, more frequent in the dry zone. **REFERENCES** Baker (1929), Baral (1993), Hancock *et al.* (1992).

BLACK STORK *Ciconia nigra* — Plate 85

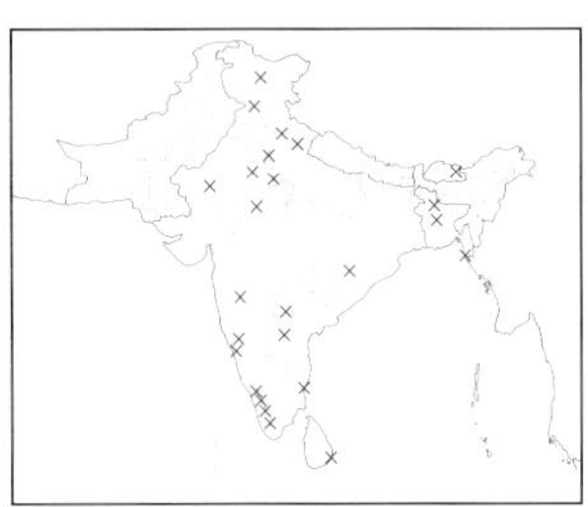

IDENTIFICATION 90–100 cm. **Adult** has red bill, glossy black head, neck, upperparts and wings, white lower breast and belly, and red legs. At close range, black is glossed with purple and metallic green. In flight, white underparts and axillaries contrast strongly with black neck and rest of underwing, head looks rather bulbous and neck slim, and red bill and legs are visible even at a distance: these features help to separate it easily from Woolly-necked Stork (below). **Juvenile** has brown head, neck and upperparts (with pale brown flecking on neck and breast, and pale brown tips to wing-coverts and scapulars), and bill and legs are greyish-green. In flight, patterning from below similar to adult. **VOICE** Largely silent away from the nest. **HABITS** Similar to those of other storks. Keeps in pairs or small parties. Very shy and wary. Forages by walking with measured strides in shallow water. **HABITAT** Marshes, rivers and inland fresh waters. **DISTRIBUTION AND STATUS** Winter visitor and passage migrant to much of the subcontinent, mainly in the north. **PK:** scarce. **NP:** frequent and widespread in winter; below 1000 m (–2925 m on passage). **IN:** widespread and uncommon, more frequent in the north. **BT:** uncommon and local. **BD:** rare. **LK:** vagrant. **REFERENCES** Baral (1993).

WOOLLY-NECKED STORK *Ciconia episcopus* — Plate 84

White-necked Stork (F,I,P)

IDENTIFICATION 75–92 cm. A stocky, largely blackish stork with 'woolly' white neck, black 'skullcap', and white vent and undertail-coverts. In flight, upperside and underside of wings are entirely dark and has forked black tail (with long white undertail-coverts extending beyond tail). **Adult** has black bill, with variable amounts of red. Black of body and wings is glossed with greenish-blue, purple and copper (and can appear brownish in colour). Bare skin of face is dull bluish- or lead-grey, and legs and feet are dull red. White neck contrasting with black breast is best feature for separation from Black Stork (above), even at a considerable distance. **Juvenile** is similarly patterned to adult, but has dull brown (instead of glossy black) upperparts, wings and breast, feathered forehead, and duller bill and legs. **VOICE** Largely silent away from the nest. **HABITS** Similar to those of other storks. Usually found singly or in pairs, occasionally in small parties. Hunts on dry or marshy ground and

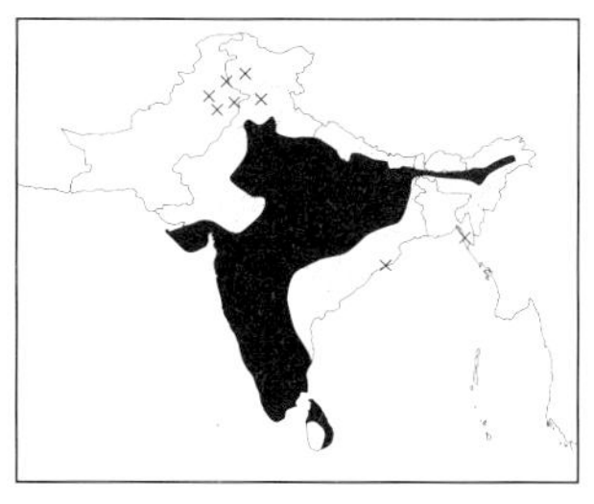

wet grasslands; rarely wades. Feeds on locusts and other large invertebrates; also amphibians and reptiles. **HABITAT** Flooded grassland, marshes, irrigated fields and riverain areas, usually in or near open forest or in open country with groves of trees. **BREEDING** July–April, varying locally with rainfall. Builds a solitary nest on a horizontal branch or near the top of a tree, usually 10–30 m above ground; sometimes on cliffs. **DISTRIBUTION AND STATUS** Widespread sedentary resident, except in parts of NW and NE subcontinent and E India. **PK:** probably once fairly widespread in N Punjab, has bred; now very rare, possibly extirpated. **NP:** widespread resident in small numbers; mainly below 915 m, occasionally up to 1800 m. **IN:** locally frequent and widespread resident in the plains, up to at least 650 m in peninsular hills. **BT:** rare. **BD:** rare winter visitor to the SE coast. **LK:** rare and irregular resident in the dry lowlands. **REFERENCES** Baral (1993), Hancock *et al.* (1992).

WHITE STORK *Ciconia ciconia* — Plate 84

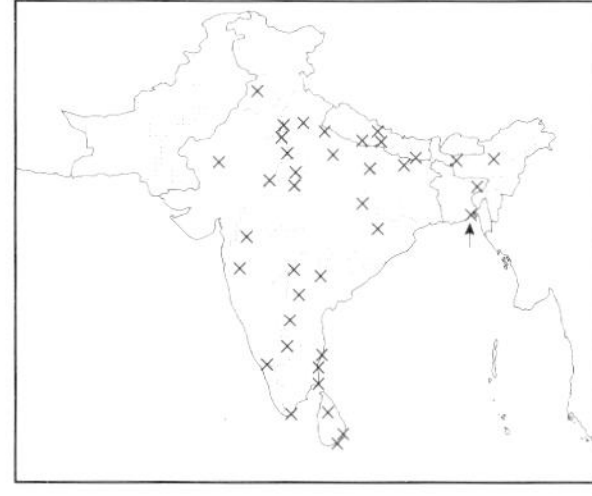

IDENTIFICATION 100–125 cm. **Adult** is mainly white, with black flight feathers, greater coverts and tertials, and striking red bill and legs. At a distance, and in flight, possibly confusable with Asian Openbill (p.572), but cleaner black-and-white appearance, white tail, finer red bill, and red legs are usually apparent. For differences from Oriental Stork (below), see that species. **Juvenile** is very similar to adult, but has brown greater coverts and duller brownish-red bill and legs. **VOICE** Largely silent away from the nest. **HABITS** Similar to those of other storks. Found singly and in flocks. Usually shy and difficult to approach. Stalks about deliberately on dry or moist ground in search of locusts and other large insects, frogs, reptiles and small rodents. **HABITAT** Dry and wet grassland, and damp ploughed or fallow fields. **DISTRIBUTION AND STATUS** Widespread winter visitor and passage migrant. From Pakistan east to Assam and south through the subcontinent. **PK:** scarce; winter visitor along the Rann of Kutch/Pakistan border and in Thatta district, also a passage migrant. **NP:** rare passage migrant, mainly in the lowlands (–915 m). **IN:** widespread winter visitor, locally fairly common in the northwest and south. **BD:** rare passage migrant. **LK:** vagrant to the lowlands; has bred once. **REFERENCES** Baral (1993).

ORIENTAL STORK *Ciconia boyciana* — Plate 84

Oriental White Stork, White Stork *C. ciconia* (I,K)

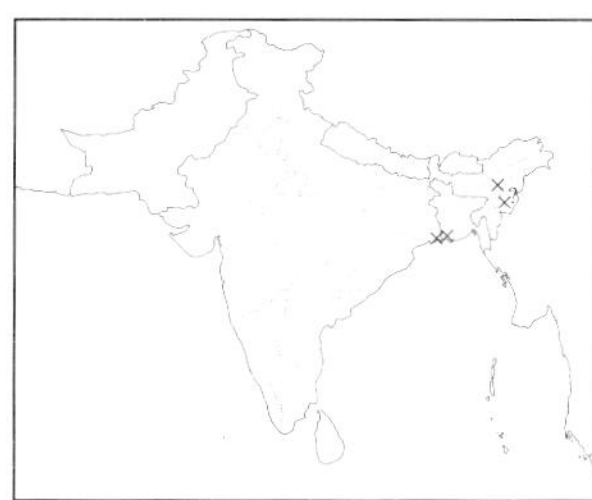

IDENTIFICATION 110–150 cm. Similar in plumage to White Stork (above). **Adult** distinguished from that species by larger size, larger, black bill (which appears slightly upturned towards tip), and prominent greyish-white outer webs to secondaries and inner primaries (forming panel on wing visible both at rest and flight) which are usually more apparent than on White. Further, has narrow band of purple or deep red at base of bill, and red (rather than black) orbital ring. **Juvenile** is very similar to adult, but has browner greater coverts and duller bill and legs. **VOICE** Largely silent away from the nest. **HABITS** Similar to those of White Stork. Wades in shallow or fairly deep water, seeking fish. **HABITAT** Details not recorded from the subcontinent. Elsewhere, feeds in wetter habitats than White Stork, in river valleys, wet meadows and marshes. **DISTRIBUTION AND STATUS** Globally threatened. **IN:** rare winter visitor to Assam, Manipur and West Bengal. **BD:** vagrant. **REFERENCES** Mitra (1996), WWF India and AWB (1993).

BLACK-NECKED STORK *Ephippiorhynchus asiaticus* — Plate 85

***Xenorhynchus asiaticus* (F,K)**

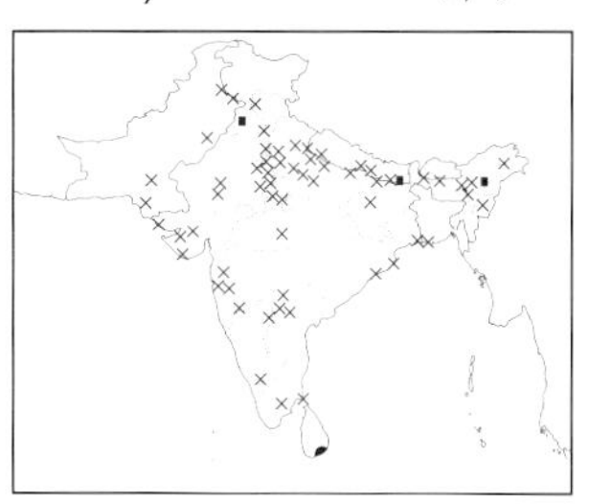

IDENTIFICATION 129–150 cm. **Adult male** is a large, black-and-white stork with long red legs and huge black bill. Black neck contrasts with white mantle and underparts, and at rest the white mantle and inner wing-coverts contrast with the long black scapulars and rest of coverts. At close range, black of plumage can be seen to be glossed with blue, purple and green. In flight, upperwing and underwing are largely white, except for broad black band across wing-coverts, and the tail is black. **Adult female** differs from adult male in having a yellow (rather than brown) iris, and is smaller in size. **Juvenile** has fawn-brown head, neck and mantle, brown-centred wing-coverts and scapulars, and dark legs and feet. In flight, shows whitish lower back and rump, and flight feathers are mainly blackish-brown. **VOICE** Largely silent away from the nest. **HABITS** Forages singly, in well-separated pairs within sight of each other, or in family parties after the breeding season. Usually very wary. Wades slowly and sedately while probing in shallow water and among aquatic vegetation with its bill open at the tip. **HABITAT** Freshwater marshes, lakes, jheels, tanks and large rivers; occasionally mangroves, rarely coastal mudflats. **BREEDING** September–December, varying according to the monsoon and water conditions; eggs are generally laid as the rains cease. Builds a solitary nest in a large tree 6–25 m above ground, not necessarily near water. **DISTRIBUTION AND STATUS** Resident. Throughout plains in much of the subcontinent; has declined steeply. **PK:** frequent in lower Sindh in early 20th century, now a straggler. **NP:** rare resident and winter visitor to the terai, only in protected areas. **IN:** still a widespread resident, but now rare, with its main strongholds in the north, northwest and northeast. **BD:** former resident, now vagrant. **LK:** rare resident in the dry lowlands, confined to the southeast. **REFERENCES** Baral (1993), Rahmani (1989b).

LESSER ADJUTANT *Leptoptilos javanicus* Plate 85

Lesser Adjutant Stork (F,N)

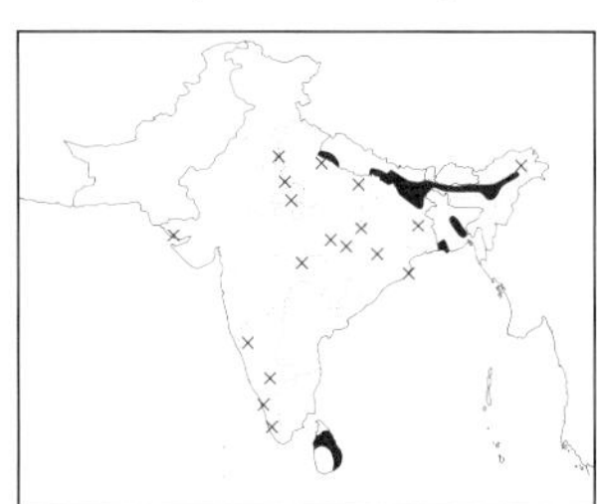

IDENTIFICATION 110–120 cm. Both this large stork and the even bigger Greater Adjutant (below) fly with neck retracted, giving rise to quite different profile compared with other storks. **Adult** has glossy black upperparts, white underparts, and naked orange-yellow head and neck. Told from adult breeding Greater Adjutant by smaller size, glossy black mantle and wings (lacking paler panel across greater coverts), largely black underwing (with white axillaries), and white undertail-coverts; neck ruff is largely black (appearing as black patch on sides of breast in flight). Further, bill is slimmer, with straighter ridge to culmen; and has pale greenish-brown or yellowish-tan frontal plate, denser hair-like feathering on back of head (forming small crest) and down hindneck, entirely black tibia, and much-reduced or non-existent neck pouch (which does not hang as pendent sack). **Adult breeding** has red tinge to face and neck, copper spots at tips of median coverts, and narrow white fringes to scapulars and inner greater coverts. **Juvenile** is similar to adult, but upperparts are dull black and head and neck are more densely feathered. **VOICE** Largely silent away from the nest. **HABITS** Similar to those of other storks. Usually found singly, and is very shy. Forages by walking slowly on dry ground or in shallow water, and grabs prey with its bill. **HABITAT** Marshes, forest pools, flooded fields, lakes and drying river beds. **BREEDING** July–January. Semi-colonial or colonial, usually in small numbers. Builds nest 12–30 m up in a large forest tree. **DISTRIBUTION AND STATUS** Resident and nomadic. Plains from NW Gujarat and Delhi east to Arunachal Pradesh; breeds mainly in Assam. Globally threatened. **NP:** frequent; below 250 m (–1350 m). **IN:** has declined; now locally common in Assam and widely distributed, but rare elsewhere. **BD:** local and declining. **LK:** scarce in dry lowlands. **REFERENCES** Baral (1993), Boonsong and Round (1991), Choudhury (1994), Hancock *et al.* (1992), WWF India and AWB (1993).

GREATER ADJUTANT *Leptoptilos dubius* Plate 85

Adjutant (I), Greater Adjutant Stork (N,R), Adjutant Stork (F)

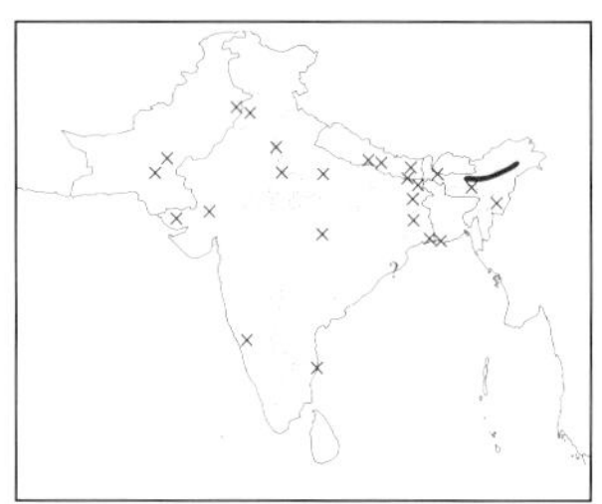

IDENTIFICATION 120–150 cm. **Adult breeding** told from adult Lesser Adjutant (above) by larger size, bluish-grey (rather than glossy black) mantle, prominent silvery-grey panel across greater coverts and tertials, greyish or brownish underwing-coverts, white neck ruff (and therefore lacks black patch on sides of breast in flight), and grey undertail-coverts. Further, has stouter, conical bill with convex ridge to culmen, blackish face and forehead (with appearance of dried blood), more sparsely feathered head and neck (lacking small crest), red at base of tibia, and larger neck pouch (visible only when inflated). **Adult non-breeding** has darker grey mantle and inner wing-coverts, and brown greater coverts (which barely contrast with rest of wing). **Immature** is similar to adult non-breeding, but has brownish (rather than white or yellowish-white) iris, and head and neck are more densely feathered. White neck ruff, larger size and larger conical bill are best distinctions from Lesser. **VOICE** Largely silent away from the nest. **HABITS** Similar to those of Lesser Adjutant, but less shy and, unlike that species, feeds partly on carrion. Gathers with others of the species, vultures and kites at carcases and refuse dumps. Also hunts small live animals in typical stork fashion, by walking slowly in marshes and shallow waters. **HABITAT** Marshes, jheels and agricultural land. Formerly very common around human habitations, when sanitation was much poorer than it is nowadays. **BREEDING** September–January, varying according to monsoon and water conditions. Breeds singly, semi-colonially or colonially, sometimes with other species. Nests in tall trees 12–30 m above ground, often near water. **DISTRIBUTION AND STATUS** Resident, nomadic and locally migratory. Recorded from S Pakistan east to Assam and south to Karnataka and NE Tamil Nadu; has bred in Assam, Orissa and Bangladesh. Has declined drastically; recent breeding records only from Assam. Globally threatened. **PK:** vagrant. **NP:** rare and erratic non-breeding visitor to the centre and east; below 250 m (–1500 m). **IN:** now locally common only in the Brahmaputra valley, Assam; a rare visitor elsewhere. **BD:** rare resident or winter visitor, formerly more common. **REFERENCES** Baral (1993), Bhattacharjee and Saikia (1995), Boonsong and Round (1991), Hancock *et al.* (1992), Rahmani *et al.* (1990), WWF India and AWB (1993).

FRIGATEBIRDS Fregatidae

Large aerial seabirds which rarely land on water and roost and nest in trees and bushes. They have a characteristic flight silhouette: long narrow wings, deeply forked tail, short neck, slender body and a long hooked bill. In flight, they can achieve skilful aerial manoeuvres and can soar for long periods with only occasional deep wingbeats. Fish, including flying fish, and squid form their main diet, supplemented by offal, seabird chicks, young turtles and eggs. Frigatebirds are noted for intercepting boobies, forcing them to disgorge fish and then catching the food in mid-air. They also capture their own prey by diving vertically to the water surface. Usually solitary when at sea, but hundreds may gather around fishing boats to scavenge offal. Frigatebirds are chiefly storm-driven visitors to the coasts of the subcontinent, often occurring in the monsoon. They have generally been rarely reported, but are undoubtedly under-recorded. The main reference specific to frigatebirds is Harrison (1983).

GREAT FRIGATEBIRD *Fregata minor* Plate 83

Lesser Frigate Bird

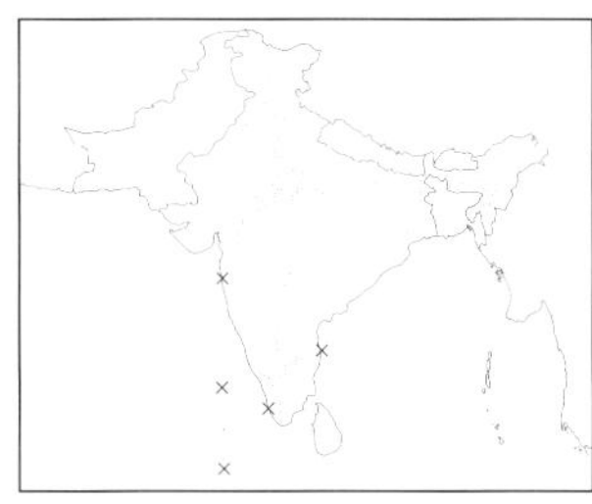

IDENTIFICATION 85–105 cm. Larger and heavier than Lesser (below). **Adult male** is the only all-black frigatebird, having entirely black underparts. As with other male frigatebirds, has red gular pouch. **Adult female** has white on breast which extends onto anterior flanks. Black cap and pink eye-ring separate it from all juvenile/immature frigatebirds. Differs from females of Christmas Island (p.576) and Lesser Frigatebirds in grey throat which is sharply demarcated from black cap, while white of breast does not extend onto sides of neck (almost forms collar on other two species), and lacks spur of white on inner underwing (on females of other two, white extends from breast onto axillaries). **Immature male** gradually loses breast-band of juvenile, and head and belly become black; sub-adult male has mottled black-and-white inverted U-shaped patch on breast and flanks, before underparts become entirely black. **Immature female** gradually loses breast-band, and cap and belly become black. **Juvenile** has white or rufous-coloured head, and largely white underparts with broad black breast-band. Juvenile and immature lack spur of white on inner underwing (shown by Lesser in all plumages and by some juvenile and immature Christmas Island), although may show white tips to axillaries. **HABITS** A typical frigatebird. **HABITAT** Pelagic. **DISTRIBUTION AND STATUS** Visitor to the coasts of India, Sri Lanka and the Maldives. **IN:** vagrant or rare visitor to W and E coasts and Lakshadweep. **LK:** visits W and S coasts and coastal waters in small numbers. **MV:** frequent visitor, recorded in January, May, June and December. **REFERENCES** Harrison (1983), Marchant and Higgins (1990), Rao and Mohapatra (1994), Warakagoda (1994).

LESSER FRIGATEBIRD *Fregata ariel* Plate 83

Least Frigate Bird (I), Small Frigatebird

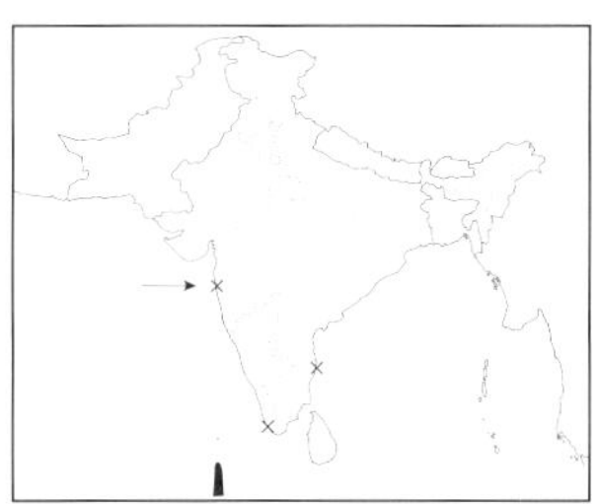

IDENTIFICATION 70–80 cm. Smaller and more finely structured than other two frigatebirds. Distinguished from Great (above) in all plumages by spur of white which extends from anterior flanks onto inner underwing (axillaries). Immature and juvenile are probably not safely separable on current knowledge from respective plumages of some Christmas Island (p.576), except by smaller size, although presumably any black on belly would indicate Lesser, and some immature/juvenile Christmas Island lack white spur. **Adult male** told from other frigatebirds by white spur extending from breast sides to axillaries on otherwise all-black underparts; on sub-adult male, these patches are more extensive and almost meet in centre of breast. As with other male frigatebirds, has red gular pouch. **Adult female** separated from all juvenile/immature frigatebirds by black head and red eye-ring. Has white breast and anterior flanks, with white of breast narrowing at centre owing to extension of black belly and to black of foreneck which projects as V-shape onto upper breast. Told from female Great by black throat, white of breast extending onto sides of neck and almost forming complete collar, and white of anterior flanks extending across axillaries. Lacks white belly of female Christmas Island Frigatebird; also lacks latter's black spur on side of breast (from base of forewing across breast side), although this feature may be apparent on immature females (as remnant of black breast-band). **Immature** gradually loses breast-band, and head and underparts darken until adult plumage attained. **Juvenile** has rufous head, variably mottled with white, broad black breast-band, and white lower breast, belly and flanks. **HABITS** A typical frigatebird. **HABITAT** Pelagic. **BREEDING** October and November in Maldives. No other details recorded for the region. In Australia, builds a nest of sticks, grass and debris in trees, bushes or occasionally on ground. **DISTRIBUTION AND STATUS** Visitor to the coasts of India, Sri Lanka and the Maldives; has bred. **IN:** vagrant or rare visitor to W and E coasts. **LK:** occasionally visits W and S coasts and coastal waters. **MV:** plentiful around most atolls; probably resident on some, and has bred. **REFERENCES** Harrison (1983), Marchant and Higgins (1990), Naoroji (1991), Neelakantan *et al.* (1993), Santharam (1983).

CHRISTMAS ISLAND FRIGATEBIRD *Fregata andrewsi* Plate 83

Christmas Frigatebird (K,P)

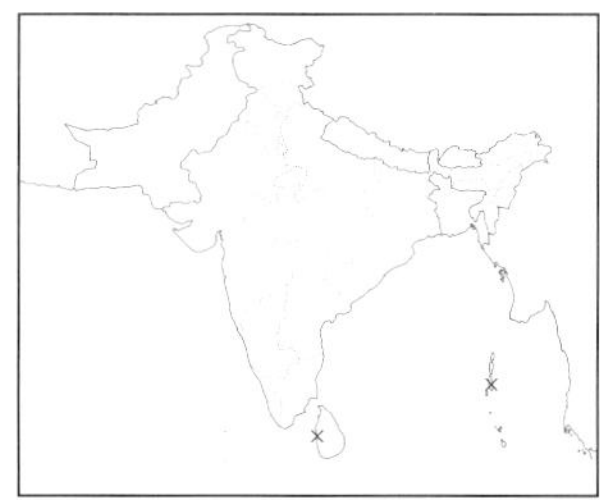

IDENTIFICATION 90–100 cm. Larger and heavier than Lesser (p.575). **Adult male** told from other frigatebirds in all plumages by combination of black head and breast and white patch on belly. Belly patch is more extensive on subadult male. As with other male frigatebirds, has red gular pouch. **Adult female** has black head and largely white underparts. Black head and pink eye-ring separate it from all immature and juvenile frigatebirds. Following features help separation from female Great (p.575): black throat; white sides of neck which almost join to form collar; black wedge extending onto side of breast from where forewing joins body; spur of white extending onto inner underwing; and white belly. Combination of larger size, black wedge on breast side and white (not black) belly are best distinctions from female Lesser. **Immature** has pale yellow and then white head, before this becomes black as adult; breast-band of juvenile is gradually lost. Extent of white on underparts is otherwise similar to female, and any black on belly is likely to indicate immature Great or Lesser rather than Christmas Island. Some immatures (perhaps females) differ from Great in having spur of white extending onto inner underwing. **Juvenile** has buffish head and rufous necklace, and broad black breast-band (often incomplete in centre). Probably not safely separable from juveniles of other frigatebirds. **HABITS** A typical frigatebird. **HABITAT** Pelagic. **DISTRIBUTION AND STATUS** Globally threatened. **IN:** vagrant. **LK:** rare visitor to W coast and coastal waters. **REFERENCES** Harrison (1983), Marchant and Higgins (1990), Saxena (1994).

LOONS (DIVERS) Gaviidae

Large aquatic birds with elongated body, thick neck and short tail. The legs are set well back on the body, and the feet are webbed. Fish form their main diet; aquatic invertebrates, frogs and plant material are also consumed. As their name implies, they are expert divers and catch their prey in underwater pursuit. Loons frequently swim with their body almost completely submerged. They fly directly, with legs trailing and with head and neck extended and inclined downwards, giving a humpbacked appearance.

RED-THROATED LOON *Gavia stellata* Plate 75

Red-throated Diver (I,K,R)

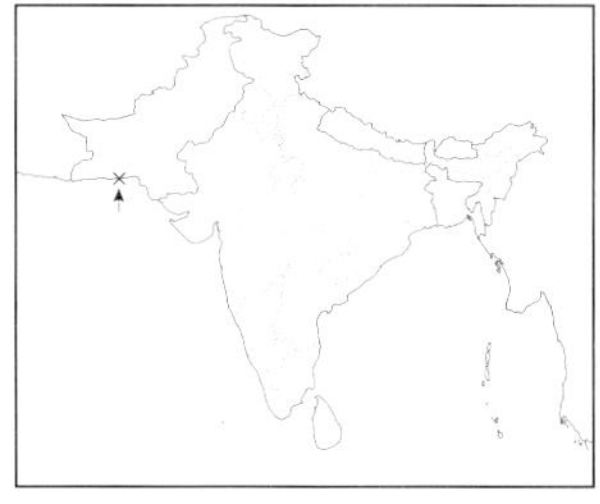

IDENTIFICATION 53–69 cm. In all plumages, told from Black-throated Loon (below) by upturned-looking bill (lower mandible is sharply angled, and head is usually uptilted), rounded head (with gently sloping forehead), and paler coloration. **Adult breeding** differs from Black-throated in red throat patch, comparatively uniform grey-brown upperparts, and fine black-and-white streaking on crown and hindneck. **Adult non-breeding**, compared with Black-throated, appears grey-and white rather than black-and-white, although on both species contrast between upperparts and underparts varies with light conditions. Grey of crown and hindneck is paler and less extensive (and does not contrast so strongly with white of ear-coverts and foreneck), and upperparts are paler brownish-grey. White of face generally extends above and around eye, and head and neck often look very pale. **Juvenile** initially has grey-brown head and neck, with pale throat, and may also show dark chestnut patch on upper foreneck. **HABITS** A typical loon. **HABITAT** Recorded on coastal waters in the region; elsewhere, also winters on lakes. **DISTRIBUTION AND STATUS PK:** winter vagrant. **REFERENCES** Harris *et al.* (1989), Jonsson (1992).

BLACK-THROATED LOON *Gavia arctica* Plate 75

Arctic Loon, Black-throated Diver (I)

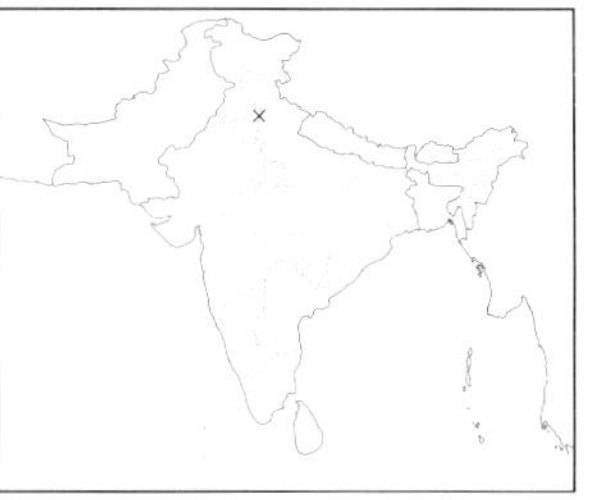

IDENTIFICATION 58–73 cm. In all plumages, distinguished from Red-throated Loon (above) by stouter, straighter-looking bill, squarer head, and black-and-white coloration. **Adult breeding** differs from Red-throated in having black throat patch, black-and-white chequered upperparts, uniform grey head and nape, and black-and-white streaking down sides of neck. **Adult non-breeding**, compared with Red-throated, appears black-and-white rather than grey-and-white; grey of crown and hindneck is darker and more extensive (and contrasts strongly with white of ear-coverts and foreneck), upperparts are blackish, and typically shows striking white flank patch. **Juvenile** is as adult non-breeding, although paler; has pale fringes to feathers of upperparts, and may show dusky foreneck. Can appear very similar in general coloration to juvenile Red-throated. **HABITS** A typical loon. **HABITAT** Recorded on flooded land in the region; elsewhere, usually winters on lakes and coastal waters. **DISTRIBUTION AND STATUS IN:** winter vagrant. **REFERENCES** Harris *et al.* (1989), Jonsson (1992).

PETRELS, SHEARWATERS AND STORM-PETRELS Procellariidae

The Procellariidae are often called tubenoses after their characteristic long, tubular external nostrils. The 'tube-nose' is used to excrete excess salt. It also seems to be related to a sense of smell, and is probably used to locate food some distance away at sea. All species are truly marine, spending the great majority of the time at sea, usually far from land, and coming ashore only to breed, although some species may visit their breeding sites occasionally throughout the year. Many species are difficult to identify, and are most easily distinguished by their flight behaviour. Most tubenoses are gregarious, often gathering in flocks at food concentrations and frequently following ships in their search for food. They feed on zooplankton, cephalopods, fish and offal, which are seized on or below the water surface. Typically, they breed in colonies on oceanic and offshore islands or on cliff headlands, nesting in long burrows or sometimes in holes among rocks, and usually coming ashore at night to avoid predators. The Procellariidae occurring in the region comprise the Cape Petrel, three or more gadfly petrels, shearwaters, and storm-petrels. Many species have been recorded only when forced to move to inshore waters by bad weather. Although most are reported only rarely, it seems likely that some species, at least, occur more regularly and that increased observations, particularly around the time of the SW monsoon, will produce more records. The main references specific to Procellariidae are Harrison (1983), Marchant and Higgins (1990) and Robertson (1995).

CAPE PETREL *Daption capense* — Plate 86

Cape Pigeon (I)

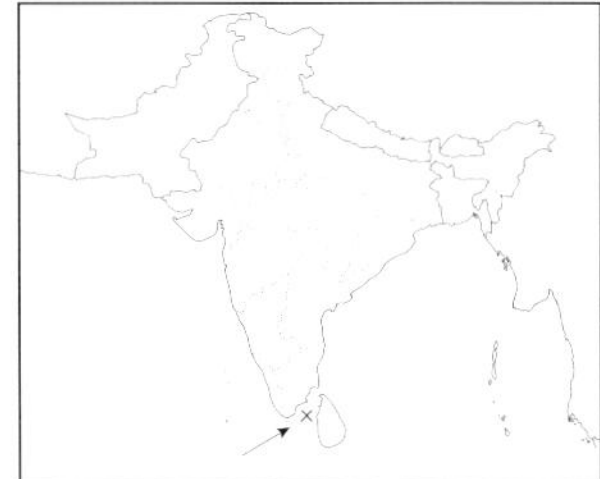

IDENTIFICATION 38–40 cm. A stocky, broad-winged, black-and-white petrel. Has black head, white upperbody untidily marked with black, black tail-band, black upperwings with bold white patches, mainly white underwings with broad black border, and white underparts. In calm conditions, quick stiff-winged flapping is interspersed with prolonged glides. In stormy conditions, birds can glide in strong sweeping arcs, often towering high above ocean. **HABITS** Typically feeds from the surface by picking up small food items while sitting buoyantly high in the water, and pecking busily ahead and to the sides rather like a pigeon. Also patters on the water surface like a storm-petrel, and occasionally makes shallow dives. **HABITAT** Pelagic. **DISTRIBUTION AND STATUS LK:** vagrant.

GADFLY PETRELS Genera *Pterodroma* and *Bulweria*

Medium-sized petrels with long wings and a short, stout and markedly grooved and hooked beak. Typically, they fly swiftly, with periods of rapid wingbeats interspersed with glides, and progressing on a zigzag course. Sometimes they fly low over the water, and frequently tower high above the waves. They normally feed on the wing, without diving, and rarely alight on the water.

MASCARENE PETREL *Pterodroma aterrima* — Not illustrated

Mascarene Black Petrel (I), *Bulweria aterrima* (I), *Pseudobulweria aterrima*

One caught in June 1940 off Bombay, W India, but the whereabouts of the specimen is unknown and there is doubt as to its identity since the subsequent discovery of Jouanin's Petrel.

BARAU'S PETREL *Pterodroma baraui* — Plate 86

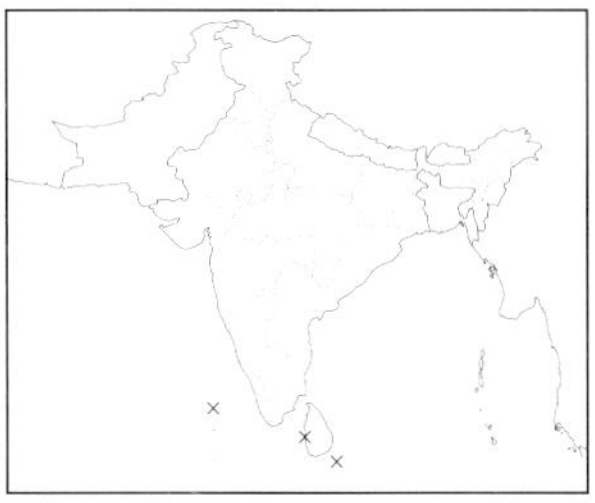

IDENTIFICATION 38 cm. Soft-plumaged Petrel (p.578) is the only other similar species that may occur in the region. Best distinguished from that species by following features: whitish forehead and dark grey cap; pronounced blackish M-mark across upperwings; dark rump and tail contrasting with grey lower mantle and back; dark patches on sides of breast, not forming complete breast-band; and largely white underwing, with black boomerang-shaped patch along leading edge and black trailing edge. **HABITS** Poorly known. Probably similar to those of other gadfly petrels. Often feeds with other seabirds, sometimes near fishing boats. Feeds by seizing prey from the surface or by dipping. **HABITAT** Pelagic. **DISTRIBUTION AND STATUS IN:** recorded in the Nine Degree Channel between the Maldives and Lakshadweep. **LK:** rare visitor. **REFERENCES** Harrison (1983), van den Berg *et al.* (1991).

SOFT-PLUMAGED PETREL *Pterodroma mollis* Plate 86

IDENTIFICATION 34 cm. Barau's Petrel (p.577) is the only similar species recorded in the region. Best distinguished from that species by pale grey crown, with slightly darker mask; generally darker upperwing, lacking (or with less prominent) dark M-mark; absence of contrasting darker rump and tail; complete (or almost complete) grey band across breast; and comparatively uniform dark underwing. Patterning of upperwing and underwing varies with light and viewing conditions: both may show reasonably pronounced dark M, with pale panel down centre of underwing and white wedge along leading edge of underwing-coverts, or can appear uniformly dark. In calm conditions, rapid wingbeats are interspersed with glides on slightly angled and bowed wings. In stormy conditions, can careen strongly, rising in high arcs above ocean with wings more angled. **HABITS** A typical gadfly petrel. Sometimes follows ships and cetaceans. Prey is taken mainly by seizing from the surface. **HABITAT** Pelagic. **DISTRIBUTION AND STATUS LK:** Possible vagrant recorded on 7 and 10 September 1988, but the record is not accepted by the Ceylon Bird Club.

BULWER'S PETREL *Bulweria bulwerii* Plate 86

Bulwer's Gadfly Petrel (I)

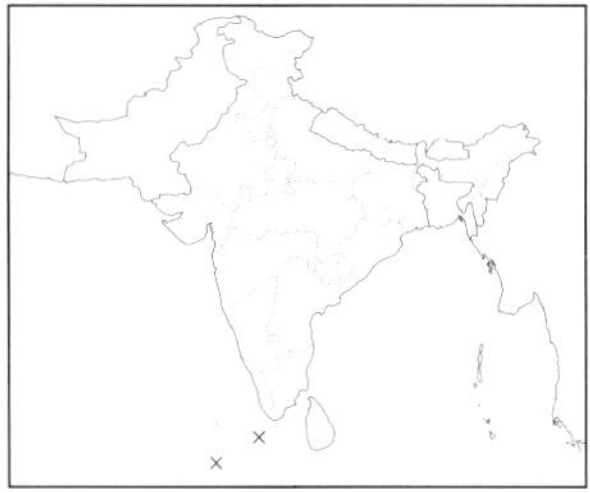

IDENTIFICATION 26–27 cm. All-dark, long-winged petrel with wedge-shaped tail and pale band across greater upperwing-coverts. Tail usually appears long, narrow and pointed in the field (may be briefly fanned). Considerably smaller than the all-dark *Puffinus* shearwaters, and has all-dark underwing. Told from the very similar Jouanin's Petrel (below) by smaller size, proportionately smaller, square-shaped head with finer bill, more prominent band across greater coverts (although Jouanin's in worn plumage may show this), and different flight action. Typically, flight is springy, erratic and close to the waves, with wings held forward and bowed; in calm conditions, rapid flapping is interspersed with short twisting glides. In strong winds, has faster wingbeats and glides in shallow arcs. **HABITS** Intermediate between a gadfly petrel and a storm-petrel, but more closely resembling a small lightweight gadfly petrel. Tail is often held slightly raised. Often circles and zigzags low over the surface when feeding. Usually does not follow ships. **HABITAT** Pelagic. **DISTRIBUTION AND STATUS IN:** vagrant off Cape Comorin, S Tamil Nadu. **LK, MV:** vagrant. **REFERENCES** Harrison (1983), Hoffmann (1996).

JOUANIN'S PETREL *Bulweria fallax* Plate 86

Jouanin's Gadfly Petrel (I)

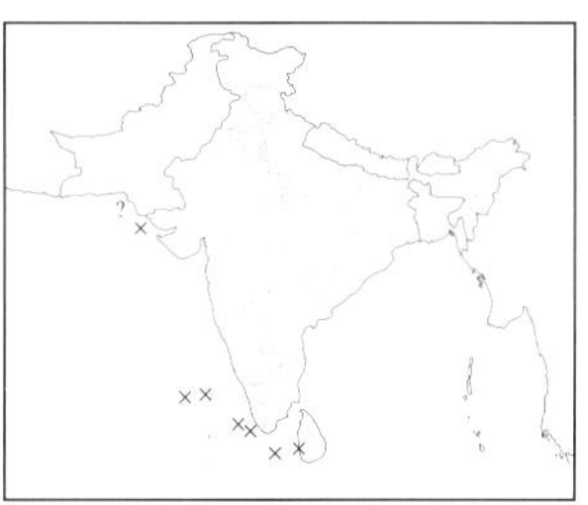

IDENTIFICATION 30–32 cm. All-dark, long-winged petrel with long pointed tail. Distinguished from the very similar Bulwer's Petrel (above) by much larger size and broader wings, larger head and larger, stouter bill, and different flight action; tail is broader and not so pointed and long, with midway 'step' formed by shorter outer feathers. Can show pale band across greater coverts, as on Bulwer's, perhaps through wear. Flight action differs from Bulwer's. In windy conditions, will rise 2–5 m or more above waves in long banking arcs, interspersed with short bouts of four or five rather leisurely flaps (usually when reaching the peak of the arcs). Otherwise, flies rather close to the sea surface, with a mix of steady beats and long glides as it moves through wave troughs. Confusable also with dark morph of Wedge-tailed Shearwater (p.579), but is smaller, with less languid flight, and has stouter all-dark bill which is held downwards at 45° angle. **HABITS** Similar to those of Bulwer's Petrel, but flies faster, more strongly and in higher broad arcs. **HABITAT** Pelagic. **DISTRIBUTION AND STATUS PK:** possibly recorded. **IN:** rare visitor, recorded off Cape Comorin, S Tamil Nadu, off S Kerala, in Lakshadweep and in Gulf of Kutch. **LK:** vagrant. **REFERENCES** Harrison (1983, 1987), Porter *et al.* (1996), van den Berg *et al.* (1991).

SHEARWATERS Genera *Calonectris* and *Puffinus*

Shearwaters have long, narrow wings for swift gliding flight. The bill is longish and slender, with a small hook at the tip. Typically, shearwaters glide low over the waves on stiff wings with occasional wingbeats, alternately rising and planing down. In strong winds, they bank from side to side, showing dark upperparts and then pale underparts. All species swim well, and some pursue prey underwater.

STREAKED SHEARWATER *Calonectris leucomelas* Plate 87

White-fronted Shearwater (I,P), *Procellaria leucomelaena* (I,P)

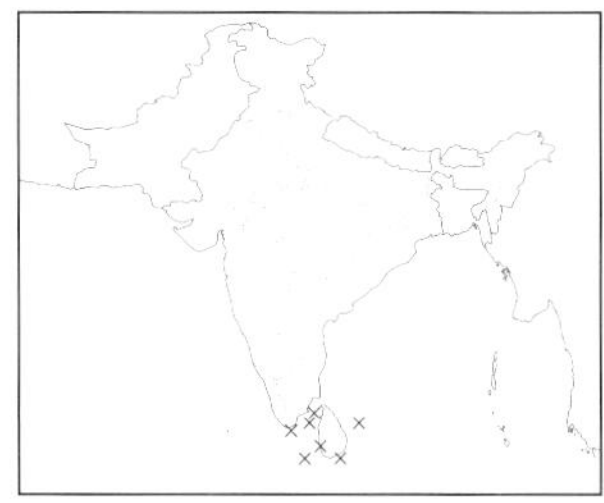

IDENTIFICATION 48 cm. A large shearwater with variable dark streaking on white head, pink or pale grey bill with dark tip, brown upperwing, and white underparts and underwing-coverts with variable dark patch on under primary coverts. Head can appear mainly white (with dark streaking restricted to hindcrown and nape), or forehead, crown and ear-coverts can be profusely streaked (in which case it has rather prominent white eye-ring). Nape and sides of breast always appear dark. Flight action rather relaxed and gull-like in calm conditions, with languid flapping (wings slightly angled at carpal joints) interspersed with gliding on bowed wings. Will rise high in strong winds, but wings still slightly angled and flapping relaxed. **HABITS** Frequently in flocks with other seabirds, and follows fishing boats. Seizes fish and squid from the surface; also makes shallow dives. **HABITAT** Partly pelagic, also occurring in offshore waters. **DISTRIBUTION AND STATUS IN:** rare visitor off Cape Comorin, S Tamil Nadu (and recorded also in the Gulf of Manaar, between Cape Comorin and Sri Lanka). **LK:** vagrant. **REFERENCES** Warakagoda (1994).

WEDGE-TAILED SHEARWATER *Puffinus pacificus* Plate 87

Green-billed Shearwater, *Procellaria pacifica* (I,P)

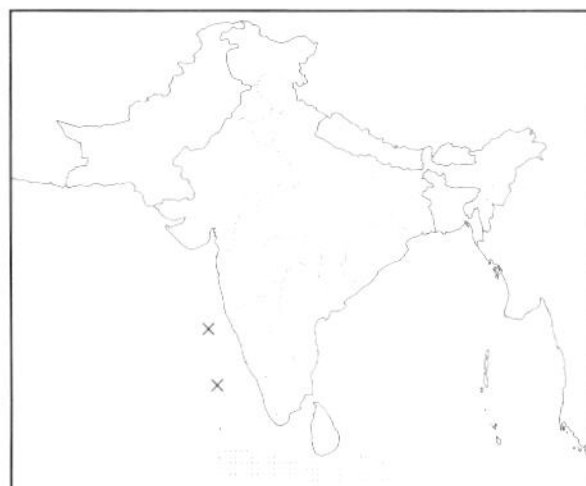

IDENTIFICATION 41–46 cm. A large, broad-winged shearwater with long tail, occurring in two colour morphs. Wedge shape to tail is often not apparent in the field (in normal flight the tail is folded, and so appears long and pointed). Dark morph closely resembles Flesh-footed Shearwater (below). Told from that species by finer greyish bill (with dark tip), longer and pointed or wedge-shaped tail, rather short, broad and rounded wing-tips, all-dark underwing (lacking pale patch at base of primaries), and different flight action and carriage of wings. Longer tail, broader wings, all-dark underwing, two-toned bill, and pale legs and feet help separate it from Sooty and Short-tailed Shearwaters (below and p.580). Dark morph is also confusable with Jouanin's Petrel (p.578), and is best told by broader-based wings with more languid flight action, pinkish feet, more protruding head, and long and finer dark-tipped bill which is held almost horizontally. Pale morph has paler brown upperparts than dark morph; underparts are mainly white, with brown mottling on sides of breast and flanks. Flight action is slow, with lazy flapping interspersed by short glides, with wings characteristically held forward and bowed; often circles. In stronger winds flight is erratic and bounding, often changing direction and soaring in low arcs between short bursts of flapping. **HABITS** Often follows fishing boats. Feeds mainly on the wing, by dipping to the surface; also by plunging head under water, but seldom completely submerges. **HABITAT** Pelagic. **DISTRIBUTION AND STATUS IN:** vagrant off Goa and Lakshadweep. **LK:** regular visitor. **MV:** frequent visitor, sometimes plentiful, March–July. **REFERENCES** Harrison (1983), Porter *et al.* (1996).

FLESH-FOOTED SHEARWATER *Puffinus carneipes* Plate 87

Pink-footed Shearwater (I,P), Pale-footed Shearwater, *Procellaria carneipes* (I,P)

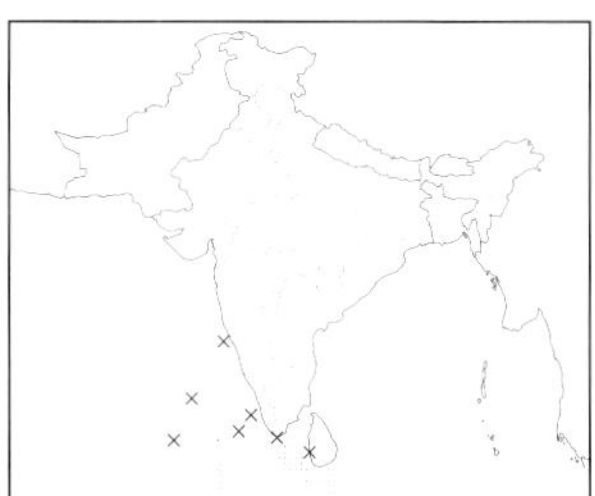

IDENTIFICATION 41–45 cm. A large, dark brown shearwater. Told from dark-morph Wedge-tailed (above) by stout pinkish bill with dark tip, silvery-grey patch at base to underside of primaries (not always apparent), shorter and rounded tail, different flight action, and by carriage of wings, which are held straight (not bowed and well forward). From Short-tailed Shearwater (p.580) by broad-winged, skua-like appearance, pink bill, pink legs and feet, dark underwing except for primary flash, and flight action. Flight typically relaxed and elegant, with slow, rather powerful, skua-like flapping interspersed with long, slow stiff-winged glides. In higher winds, banks and glides more, with less flapping. **HABITS** Catches food chiefly by plunge-diving and pursuing prey underwater; also by running along the surface between shallow belly-flop dives. **HABITAT** Mainly in offshore waters; also pelagic. **DISTRIBUTION AND STATUS IN:** regular visitor off S coast and Lakshadweep. **LK:** passage migrant. **MV:** small numbers, March–October. **REFERENCES** Harrison (1983), Warakagoda (1994).

SOOTY SHEARWATER *Puffinus griseus* Plate 87

IDENTIFICATION 40–46 cm. A sooty-brown shearwater, very similar to Short-tailed (p.580), but has longer bill, more sloping forehead, and silvery underwing-coverts which normally show as white wing flash. Distinguished from Flesh-footed and dark-morph Wedge-tailed Shearwaters (above) by slimmer, more pointed wings, whitish flash on underwing-coverts, all-dark bill, dark legs and feet which only just extend beyond tail, and different flight action. Flight is as Short-tailed's, powerful, fast and direct, with two to eight stiff wingbeats followed by low arcs and long glides. In

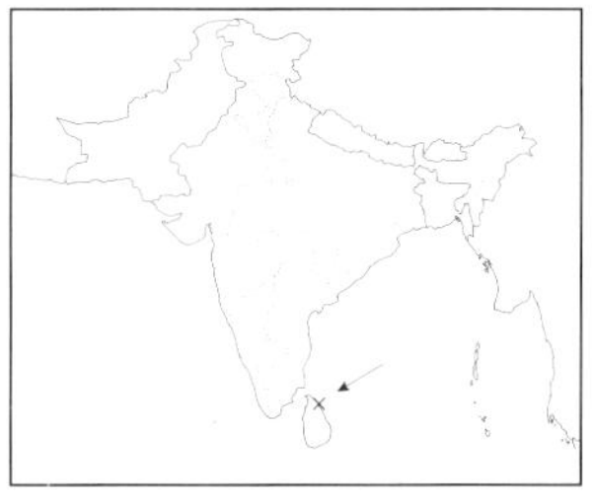

higher winds, flaps less and arcs higher. **HABITS** Often in large numbers with other seabirds; sometimes follows boats. Feeds mainly by shallow plunge-diving followed by underwater pursuit; sometimes by seizing prey from the surface while swimming. **HABITAT** Offshore and pelagic waters. **DISTRIBUTION AND STATUS LK:** vagrant to coastal waters. **REFERENCES** Harrison (1983, 1987).

SHORT-TAILED SHEARWATER *Puffinus tenuirostris* Plate 87

Slender-billed Shearwater (I,P), *Procellaria tenuirostris* (I,P)

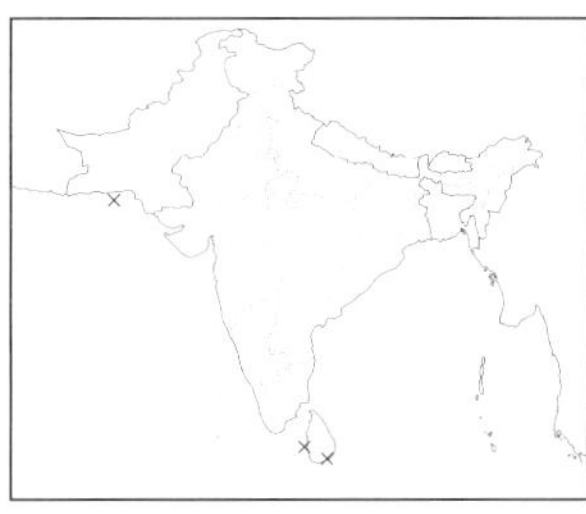

IDENTIFICATION 41–43 cm. A sooty-brown shearwater, very similar to Sooty (p.579), but with shorter bill, more steeply rising forehead, and shorter extension of rear body and tail behind wings, and underwing-coverts tend to be more uniformly pale brown or grey (although coverts may be whiter on some, more like Sooty). Also said to appear darker, more evenly coloured than Sooty, some with indistinct cap and whitish chin. Distinguished from Flesh-footed and Wedge-tailed (p.579) by slimmer, more pointed wings, noticeably paler underwing-coverts, all-dark bill, dark legs and feet which extend beyond tail, and different flight action; tail is shorter than Wedge-tailed's. Flight action is strong and deliberate, with comparatively fast stiff-winged flapping followed by long glides. In strong winds, banks high above ocean in steep arcs. **HABITS** Similar to those of Sooty Shearwater. **HABITAT** Inshore, offshore and pelagic waters. **DISTRIBUTION AND STATUS PK, LK:** vagrant. **REFERENCES** Harrison (1983, 1987).

AUDUBON'S SHEARWATER *Puffinus lherminieri* Plate 87

***Procellaria lherminieri* (I)**

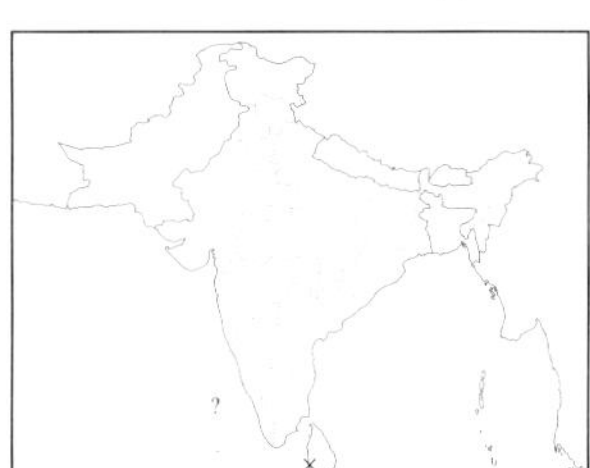

IDENTIFICATION 30 cm. A small, stocky shearwater with short, broad wings. Has dark brown upperparts, white underparts, and white wing-linings with broad dark margins to underwing. Flies with fairly fast wingbeats interspersed with short glides, low over sea, although often rises in low arcs in strong winds. **HABITS** Sometimes associates with other seabirds; occasionally follows fishing boats. Catches prey by plunge-diving followed by underwater pursuit, and by pattering across the surface with legs dangling. **HABITAT** Mainly offshore waters, also pelagic. **BREEDING** December–February, perhaps all year. No other details. Elsewhere, nests in burrows or in cavities in rocky sites. **DISTRIBUTION AND STATUS IN:** possibly resident on Lakshadweep. **LK:** vagrant. **MV:** frequent and widespread breeding visitor, sometimes in large numbers, but possibly decreasing. **REFERENCES** Harrison (1983, 1987), Porter *et al.* (1996).

PERSIAN SHEARWATER *Puffinus persicus* Plate 87

***Puffinus lherminieri* (I,R)**

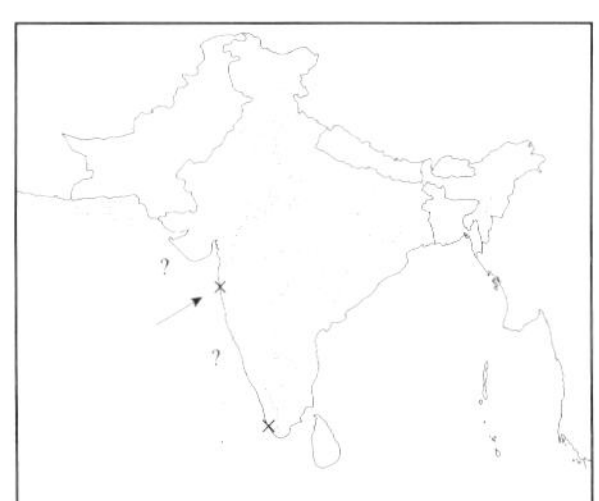

IDENTIFICATION 30.5–33.0 cm. Differs from Audubon's (above) in being slightly larger in size, with browner coloration to upperparts, longer bill, less prominent and less extensive white on underwing-coverts (with brownish leading edge), and brownish axillaries and flanks (white on Audubon's). Audubon's also has pronounced dark patch on side of breast. There may also be differences in leg and bill colours. **HABITS** Similar to those of Audubon's Shearwater. **HABITAT** Mainly offshore waters, also pelagic. **DISTRIBUTION AND STATUS PK:** regularly seen off Makran coast. **IN:** vagrant.

STORM-PETRELS Subfamily Hydrobatinae

Storm-petrels are small seabirds adapted to catch tiny marine animals while flying and usually far out to sea. Their wings are much shorter in relation to body length compared with other petrels. They spend almost all of their time on the wing except at the breeding grounds, although they can swim well. The flight is buoyant and erratic, resembling that of hirundines. They fly low over the water, with legs dangling, and seize prey from the surface with the bill.

WILSON'S STORM-PETREL *Oceanites oceanicus* Plate 86

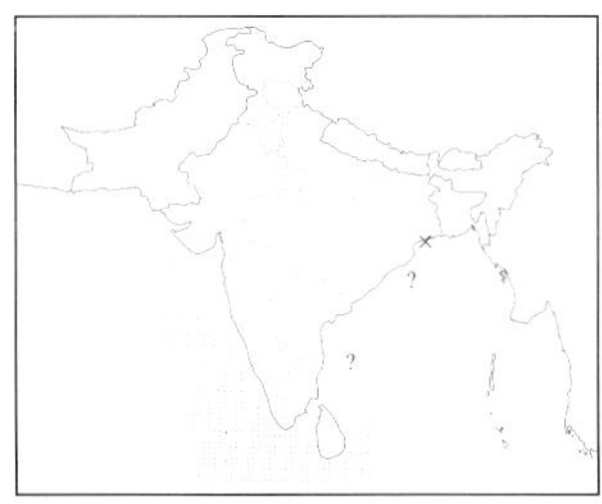

IDENTIFICATION 15–19 cm. The only storm-petrel with white rump and dark underparts recorded in the subcontinent. Has square-ended tail, pale band across greater upperwing-coverts, and uniformly dark underwing (although may show diffuse pale bar along greater coverts), and feet project noticeably beyond tail. When fluttering over water, dangling feet show yellow webbing. Wings are comparatively broad and rounded (without obvious angle to carpal or trailing edge). Flight is direct and swallow-like, with fast, shallow wingbeats and occasional brief gliding, and often higher above the water than other storm-petrels (at times up to 3 m above the waves). Feeding flight is much slower. **HABITS** Occurs singly or is gregarious, and often follows boats. Feeds by pattering, walking or jumping on the surface with wings held high over the back and legs dangling. **HABITAT** Pelagic. **DISTRIBUTION AND STATUS** Probably a widespread visitor to W and S coastal waters. **PK:** irregular year-round visitor to coast; large numbers seen near coast in monsoon. **IN:** mass southward migration noted off S coast, and common and widespread off Mumbai (Bombay) in September; the most northerly record is off West Bengal. **LK:** regular summer visitor to coastal waters, frequent from June to November in the west and south; mass southward migration noted. **MV:** large numbers April–October in adjacent seas. **REFERENCES** Harrison (1983), Warakagoda (1994).

WHITE-FACED STORM-PETREL *Pelagodroma marina* Plate 86

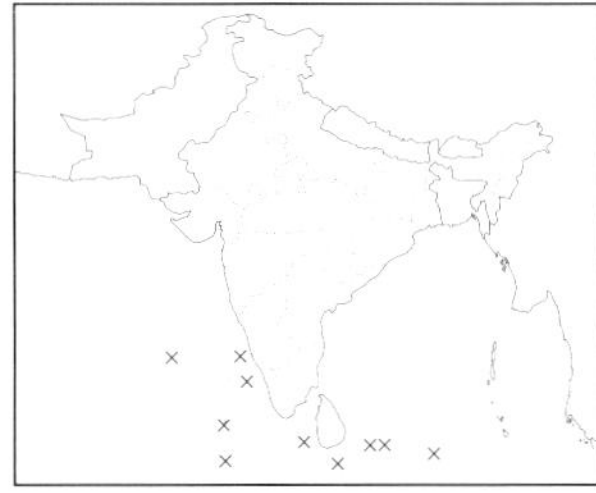

IDENTIFICATION 20 cm. **Adult** has white underparts and underwing-coverts, white supercilium contrasting with dark crown and ear-coverts, greyish-brown upperwing-coverts with paler grey greater-covert bar, and grey rump contrasting with slightly notched black tail. Feet project noticeably beyond tail, and wings appear broad and oval-shaped. **Juvenile** has paler head, whiter rump and more pronounced greater-covert bar. Flight action is peculiar and distinctive: rapid and jerky, with quick flapping followed by bounding glide (often seeming to 'leap' over waves). When feeding in calm conditions, glides on straight wings. **HABITS** Follows boats. Has a distinctive foraging flight: in light winds, glides slowly with wings held horizontally, legs dangling, and hopping on the surface every few seconds. Also feeds by dipping and pattering, and frequently flops down on its breast in the water. **HABITAT** Pelagic. **DISTRIBUTION AND STATUS** Vagrant or rare visitor in coastal waters off SW India near Sri Lanka and Maldives. **REFERENCES** Harrison (1983).

BLACK-BELLIED STORM-PETREL *Fregetta tropica* Plate 86

Dusky-vented Storm Petrel (I)

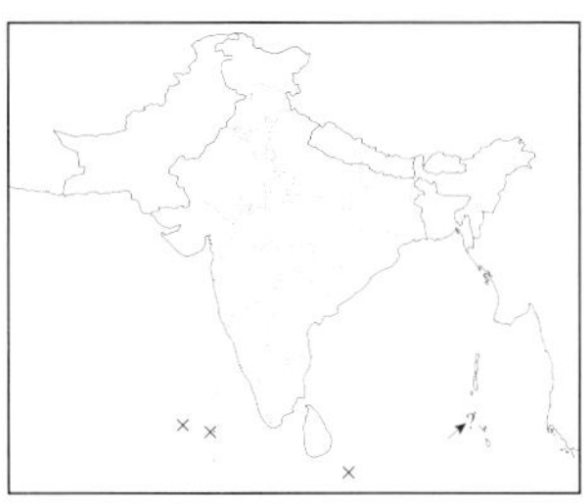

IDENTIFICATION 20 cm. Upperside resembles that of Wilson's Storm-petrel (above), with prominent white rump, and feet extending beyond tail. Upperwing-coverts are blacker, and upperwing can appear wholly dark. Underside is quite different from Wilson's, with largely white underwing-coverts and white flanks. For differences from White-bellied Storm-petrel (below), see that species. Flight is erratic, zigzagging from side to side, and closely following contours of ocean; often dangles feet and 'bounces' on to water. **HABITS** Attracted to ships, often flying ahead or to one side of the vessel. Feeds by skipping over the surface but does not patter, swinging wildly from side to side, with wings spread just above the horizontal. **HABITAT** Highly pelagic. **DISTRIBUTION AND STATUS IN:** vagrant in SW coastal waters and in Lakshadweep. **LK:** vagrant. **REFERENCES** Harrison (1983), Porter *et al.* (1996).

WHITE-BELLIED STORM-PETREL *Fregetta grallaria* Plate 86

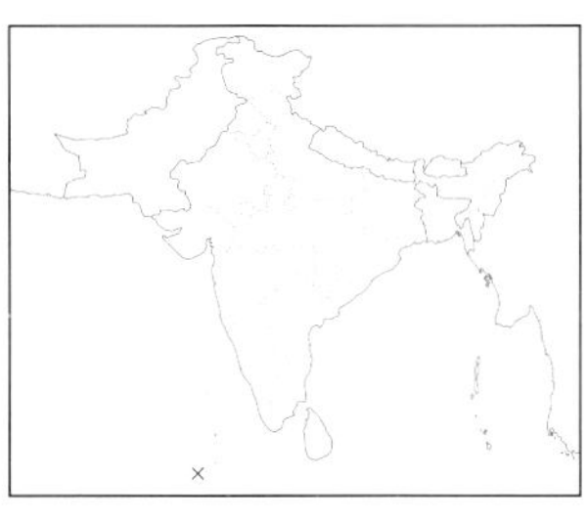

IDENTIFICATION 20 cm. Resembles Black-bellied Storm-petrel (above), with prominent white rump, white underwing-coverts, and diffuse pale bar across upperwing-coverts. Feet extend slightly beyond tail. Best told from that species by all-white underside to body (lacking black line down centre of belly), white undertail-coverts, and paler sooty-brown upperparts (owing to broader pale fringes to back). Pattern of underparts can, however, be difficult to see. Flight is similar to that of Black-bellied, but less erratic. In windy conditions, flies directly with wings upswept, body swinging from side to side, and one leg dangling and skipping from the surface. **HABITS** Feeds by pattering and dipping at the surface; often splashes breast into the water. **HABITAT** Highly pelagic. **DISTRIBUTION AND STATUS MV:** vagrant. **REFERENCES** Harrison (1983), Porter *et al.* (1996).

SWINHOE'S STORM-PETREL *Oceanodroma monorhis* Plate 86

Ashy Storm Petrel, Fork-tailed Storm Petrel (P), *O. leucorhoa* (I,P)

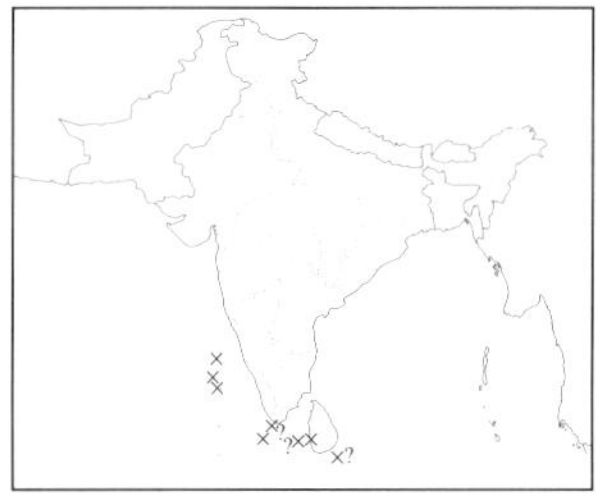

IDENTIFICATION 20 cm. The only all-dark storm-petrel (lacking white or pale rump band) recorded from the subcontinent. Has pale band across greater upperwing-coverts, angular wings (with pronounced carpal bend), and shallowly forked tail. Has fast, swooping flight with some bounding and gliding. (Matsudaira's Storm-petrel *Oceanodroma matsudairae*, which winters in the Indian Ocean but has not been recorded from waters of the subcontinent, is larger, has broad wings, slower flight action with lazy flapping interspersed with short glides, and has distinct white patch at base of primaries.) **HABITS** Feeds chiefly by dipping; does not patter. **HABITAT** Usually pelagic; also occurs in coastal waters. **DISTRIBUTION AND STATUS IN:** small numbers in Lakshadweep; also recorded in S and SW coastal waters. **LK:** summer straggler to W coastal waters. **REFERENCES** Harrison (1983), Porter *et al.* (1996).

PITTAS Pittidae

Brilliantly coloured, terrestrial forest passerines. They are of medium size, stocky and long-legged, with short square tail, stout bill and an erect carriage. Most of their time is spent foraging on the ground, flicking leaves and other vegetation, and probing with their strong bill into leaf litter and damp earth on the forest floor. Their diet consists of ants and other insects, worms and grubs. Pittas can fly quite well, their wings making a noisy whirring sound, but they usually progress on the ground by long hopping bounds. Typically, pittas are skulking and are often most easily located by their calls or songs, usually consisting of high-pitched whistles. They sing and roost in trees or bushes, sometimes high up. Pittas inhabit broadleaved evergreen or moist deciduous forest, dense secondary growth, mangroves and wooded ravines. They are usually seen singly or in separated pairs, except during migration, when large groups may be found. Their nests are large, oval, domed structures made of bamboo leaves (if available), twigs, roots and grass. The main reference specific to pittas is Lambert and Woodcock (1996).

BLUE-NAPED PITTA *Pitta nipalensis* Plate 88

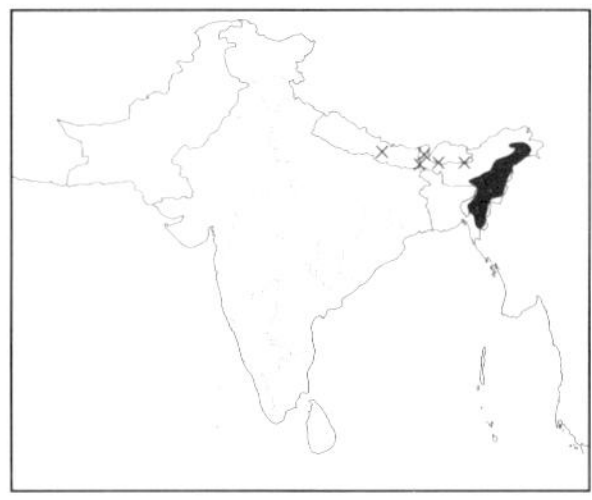

IDENTIFICATION 25 cm. A large, stocky pitta with fulvous sides of head and underparts, and uniform green upperparts. Wings are uniform brownish-green. **Adult male** has glistening blue hindcrown and nape, contrasting with fulvous forehead and ear-coverts. **Adult female** has rufous-brown crown and smaller, greenish-blue patch on nape. **Juvenile** has brown crown streaked with buff, brown upperparts and breast boldly spotted with buff, and brownish-green wings and tail (similar to adult); has dirty brownish-white supercilium, ear-coverts and throat. **VOICE** A powerful double whistle. **HABITS** A typical pitta. Very secretive. **HABITAT** Tropical and subtropical moist broadleaved evergreen forest; bamboo-dominated secondary growth in deserted forest clearings; damp shaded ravines in Nepal, and fairly dry ridge tops with dense cover in NE India. **BREEDING** April–August. Builds a typical pitta nest, usually on the ground or up to 2 m above, in bamboo or secondary growth, either at the bottom of a bamboo clump or dense bush or in the fork of a sapling. **DISTRIBUTION AND STATUS** Rather local resident. Himalayan foothills from Nepal east to Arunachal Pradesh; NE India and Bangladesh. **NP:** now rare and very local; possibly resident, all recent records are from the hills surrounding the Kathmandu valley, 1525 m. **IN:** formerly described as common, but very few recent records. **BT:** rare; 640–1000 m. **BD:** rare. **REFERENCES** Athreya *et al.* (1997), Barua (1995a), Ganguli-Lachungpa (1996), Raman (1995).

BLUE PITTA *Pitta cyanea* Plate 88

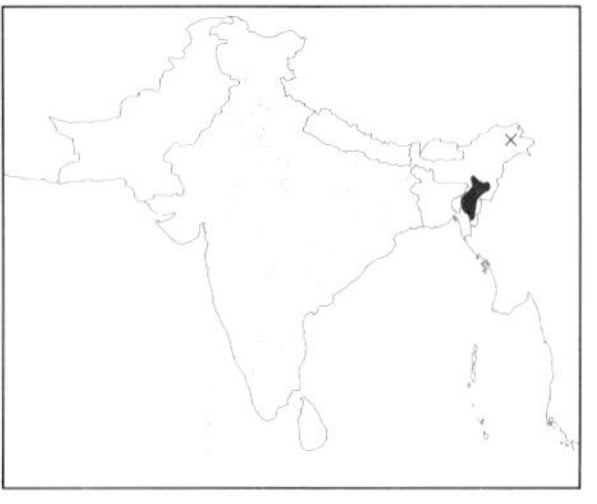

IDENTIFICATION 23 cm. A large pitta with pinkish-red on hindcrown, black stripe through eye and black moustachial stripe, and bold black spotting and barring on underparts. In flight, shows small white patch in wing. **Adult male** has blue upperparts and pale blue wash to underparts. **Adult female** has dark olive upperparts with variable blue tinge, and breast is washed with buff; occasionally lacks pinkish-red on hindcrown. **Juvenile** has prominent supercilium and dark eye-stripe, and is dark brown above, with bold rufous-buff spots on crown and duller rufous-buff streaks on mantle; throat is white, and rest of underparts are dark brown with bold rufous-buff spots. Bill is black with reddish base. **VOICE** Song is a liquid *pleoow-whit,* the first part falling, the second part sharp and short. In addition to the song, has a *skyeew* call-note (Thailand) (J. Scharringa). **HABITS** A typical pitta. **HABITAT** Damp ravines and bamboo and other dense undergrowth in broadleaved evergreen forest. **BREEDING** May–July. Builds a usual pitta nest on the top of a rock or tree stump or on the ground, mainly in moist evergreen forest, sometimes in bamboo and scrub, or in an overgrown ravine. **DISTRIBUTION AND STATUS** Resident, subject to local movements. NE India (Arunachal Pradesh, Assam, Manipur, Mizoram, Tripura) and Bangladesh. **IN:** status uncertain; very few recent records; plains and foothills up to 2000 m. **BD:** rare summer visitor. **REFERENCES** Raman (1995).

HOODED PITTA *Pitta sordida* — Plate 88

Green-breasted Pitta (F)

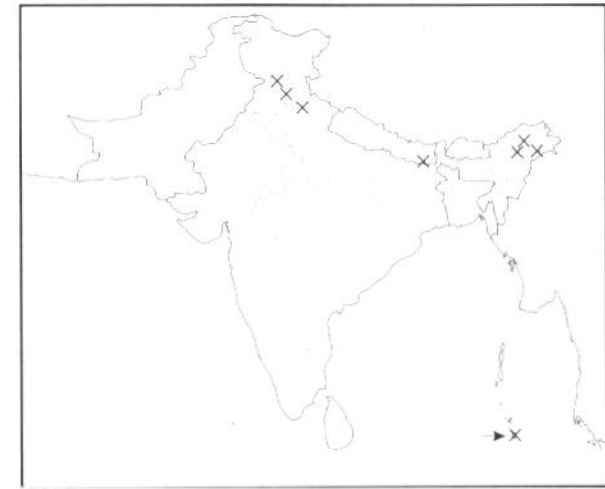

IDENTIFICATION 19 cm. A dark-hooded, mainly green pitta. Has largely black head with chestnut crown and nape, glistening blue forewing and uppertail-coverts, green breast and flanks, and scarlet belly and vent with black abdomen patch. Easily separated from Indian Pitta (below) by hooded appearance, green breast and flanks, and larger white patch in wing in flight. **Juvenile** has black scaling on crown, darker green upperparts, large white patch on median coverts, brownish chin and dirty white throat, and brownish underparts with dull pink belly and vent. **VOICE** Song is a loud, explosive double whistle, *wieuw-wieuw*; calls include the *skyeew* contact call and a bleating, whining note in distress (J. Scharringa). **HABITS** A typical pitta. **HABITAT** Tropical and subtropical broadleaved evergreen and moist deciduous forest and thick secondary scrub. **BREEDING** April–September. Builds a spherical nest, with a platform in front of the entrance, usually on the ground in thick cover. **DISTRIBUTION AND STATUS** Summer visitor or resident (with migratory movements?). Mainly in Himalayas from W Himachal Pradesh east to Arunachal Pradesh; NE India and Bangladesh. Birds from the Himalayan foothills possibly undertake an east–west migration, passing through NE India and spending the non-breeding season somewhere in Southeast Asia. **NP:** probably a summer visitor, very local below 305 m; common at Chitwan, rare elsewhere. **IN:** status uncertain; very few recent records; plains and foothills up to 2000 m. **BT:** rare. **BD:** local summer visitor. **REFERENCES** Mohan and Chellam (1991).

INDIAN PITTA *Pitta brachyura* — Plate 88

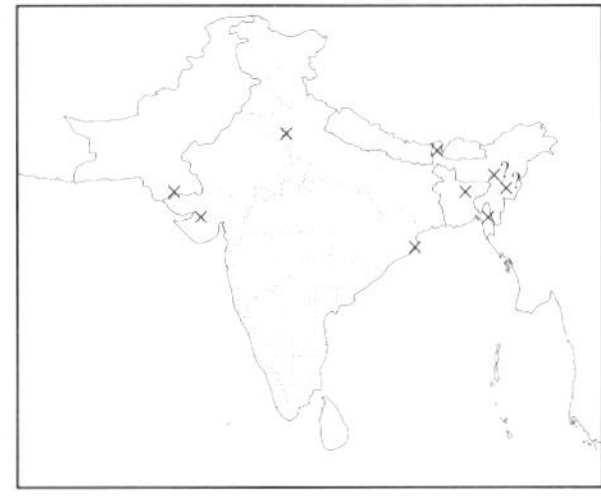

IDENTIFICATION 19 cm. Head pattern is striking. Has bold black stripe through eye contrasting with white throat and supercilium, and buff lateral crown-stripes separated by black centre to crown. Underparts are buff, with reddish-pink lower belly and vent; upperparts are green, with shining blue uppertail-coverts and forewing. In flight, shows small white patch on wing. Easily separated from Hooded Pitta (above) by head pattern, buff breast and flanks, and smaller white wing patch in flight. For differences from Mangrove Pitta (below), see that species. **Juvenile** is much duller: brownish-buff feathers on sides of crown are fringed with black, has darker olive-green upperparts with bluish coverts and edges to secondaries (but lacks shining blue shoulder patch), and underparts are a dirty brownish-buff with pale pink lower belly and vent. **VOICE** A sharp two-note whistle, second note descending, *pree–treer* (S. Connop from D. Michael recording). **HABITS** A typical pitta. **HABITAT** Breeds in broadleaved deciduous and evergreen forest with dense undergrowth, bamboo and scrub jungle, and thickly vegetated ravines. Winters in forested areas, forest patches, and occasionally in wooded gardens. **BREEDING** May–August. Builds a large globular nest, usually on a forked branch of a small tree up to 9 m above ground, sometimes on the ground. **DISTRIBUTION AND STATUS** Endemic to the subcontinent. Breeds in Himalayan foothills in the Margalla Hills, Pakistan, and from W Himachal Pradesh east to E Nepal and south to S Rajasthan and N Karnataka; status in NE is uncertain; winters in S India south of about 16.5°N and in Sri Lanka. **PK:** scarce and local, but regular summer visitor; 450–760 m. **NP:** local summer visitor below 245 m (–1360 m); common at Chitwan, rare elsewhere. **IN:** formerly common in some places, and large numbers were once recorded on migration in the peninsula, but has declined; now rather local and frequent; breeds locally up to 1200 m, winters up to 1700 m in the peninsular hills. **BD:** rare? summer visitor. **LK:** common winter visitor throughout. **REFERENCES** Gay (1996).

MANGROVE PITTA *Pitta megarhyncha* — Plate 88

P. moluccensis **Blue-winged Pitta (I,K)**

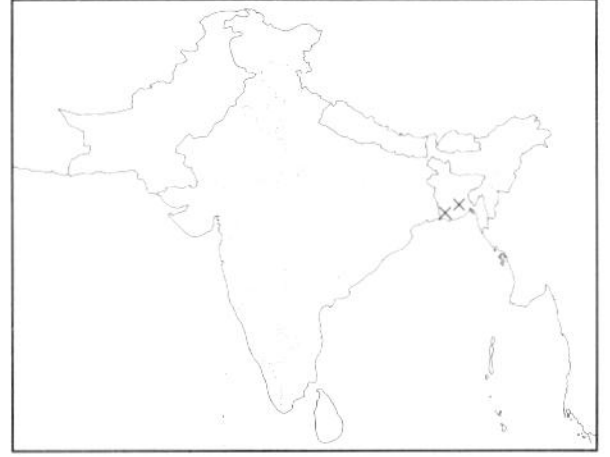

IDENTIFICATION 20 cm. Resembles Indian Pitta (above), with black stripe through eye, white throat, buff breast and flanks, and red centre to belly and vent. Is larger than Indian, with much larger and longer bill. Crown is uniform rufous-brown, lacking well-defined white supercilium and black crown-stripe, although does have buffish edge to crown side which may show as indistinct supercilium. Upperparts are darker green, and has deeper blue wing-coverts and rump/uppertail-coverts. Has larger white wing patch than Indian, and call is also different. **Juvenile** has darker brownish-green upperparts than adult, brown crown with black scaling, and dirty brownish-buff underparts with pale pink lower belly and vent. **VOICE** A loud, but slurred *tae-laew*, repeated regularly, and a *skyeew* alarm call (Boonsong and Round 1991). **HABITS** A typical pitta. **HABITAT** Mangroves. **BREEDING** Details not recorded in the region. Elsewhere, builds a large domed nest of twigs, leaves and grass, either on the ground or 1.5 m above. **DISTRIBUTION AND STATUS BD:** probably a very local resident in the Sunderbans; common at Khulna. **REFERENCES** Paynter (1970).

BROADBILLS Eurylaimidae

Small to medium-sized plump birds with rounded wings and short legs, most species having a distinctively broad bill. Typically, they inhabit the middle storey of forest and feed mainly on invertebrates gleaned from leaves and branches.

SILVER-BREASTED BROADBILL *Serilophus lunatus* — Plate 88

Hodgson's Broadbill (F,I)

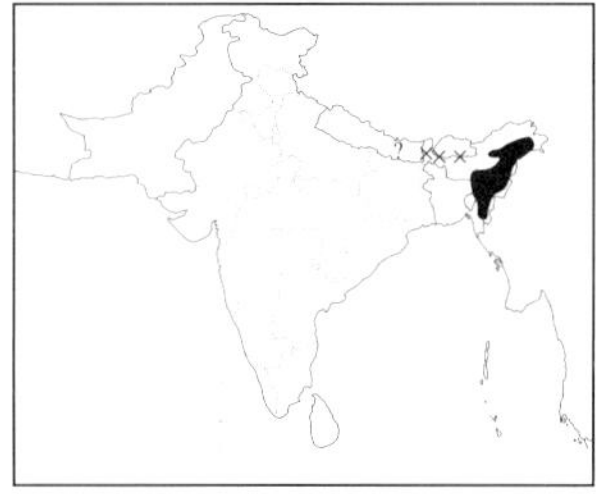

IDENTIFICATION 18 cm. Big head, crested appearance, large eye, stout bluish bill,'upright stance, and sluggish movements give rise to distinctive jizz. Has dusky supercilium, yellow eye-ring, brownish-grey upperparts and grey underparts, pale chestnut tertials and rump, complex white and blue patterning to black wings, and all-black tail. Shows white patch at base of primaries in flight. **Female** has a fine gorget across neck which is often broken in middle (lacking on male). **Juvenile** closely resembles adult, even when very young. **VOICE** Peculiar clicks and chirps, more like an insect or mouse (Athreya *et al.* 1997). A melancholy *ki-uu*, like a rusted hinge, and a thin, high-pitched *kitikitikit* trill in flight (Thailand) (Boonsong and Round 1991). **HABITS** Keeps in pairs or small groups in the lower canopy. Has a very upright posture when perched. Active in the early morning and evening, when it forages; often unobtrusive and lethargic at other times. Usually feeds by gleaning insects from foliage and branches while flying from one perch to another; occasionally makes sallies from a perch. **HABITAT** Tropical and subtropical broadleaved evergreen and semi-evergreen forest; also sal, secondary forest and bamboo jungle. **BREEDING** March–June. Nest is an untidy ball with a long hanging tail of loose material, normally suspended over an open space such as a ravine, path or pool. **DISTRIBUTION AND STATUS** Resident. Himalayas from Nepal east to Arunachal Pradesh; NE India and Bangladesh. **NP:** recorded only in the 19th century; now extirpated. **IN:** locally fairly common; plains and hills up to 1700 m. **BT:** rare. **BD:** scarce and local. **REFERENCES** Lambert and Woodcock (1996).

LONG-TAILED BROADBILL *Psarisomus dalhousiae* — Plate 88

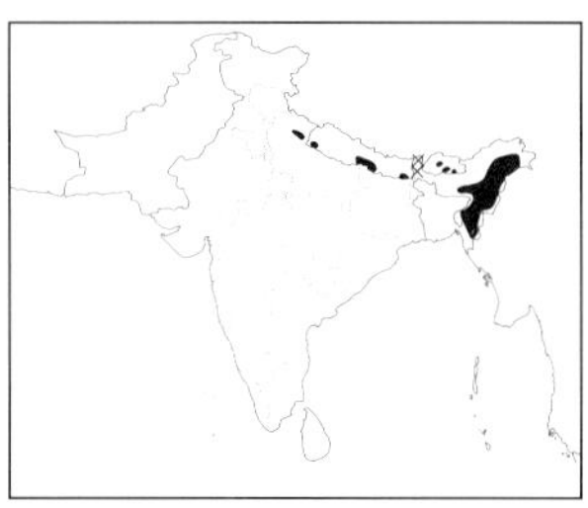

IDENTIFICATION 28 cm. A 'dopey-looking' bird with big head, large eye, stout lime-green bill, long and thin tail, and upright stance. Has black cap with blue spot on crown and yellow 'ear' spot; lores, throat and sides of neck are yellow. Has green upperparts and blue-green underparts, blue patch on primaries, and blue tail. Shows white patch at base of primaries in flight. **Juvenile** has black of head replaced by green (concolorous with mantle), and has paler greenish-yellow lores, throat, and sides of neck; lacks blue crown spot. **VOICE** Call is a loud, piercing *pieu-wieuw-wieuw-wieuw...*, usually five to eight notes on the same pitch (J. Scharringa). **HABITS** Similar to those of Silver-breasted Broadbill (above). Arboreal; keeps in the forest canopy or middle storey in flocks of up to 20 birds. **HABITAT** Tropical and subtropical broadleaved evergreen and semi-evergreen forest; also secondary growth dominated by bamboo. **BREEDING** April–June. Nest and nest site are similar to those of Silver-breasted Broadbill. **DISTRIBUTION AND STATUS** Resident, subject to local and altitudinal movements. Himalayan foothills from N Uttar Pradesh east to Arunachal Pradesh; NE India and Bangladesh. **NP:** now scarce and local; 275–1340 m. **IN:** locally fairly common; plains and hills up to 2000 m. **BT:** frequent; 245–1800 m. **BD:** ?former resident; no recent records, but may survive in Chittagong Hill Tracts. **REFERENCES** Lambert and Woodcock (1996).

FAIRY BLUEBIRDS AND LEAFBIRDS Irenidae

Small to medium-sized passerines having a fairly long, slender bill with the upper mandible decurved at the tip. All are arboreal, typically frequenting thick foliage in the canopy. They search leaves for insects and also feed on berries and nectar. Their flight is swift, usually over a short distance.

ASIAN FAIRY BLUEBIRD *Irena puella* Plate 88

Fairy Bluebird (F,I,P)

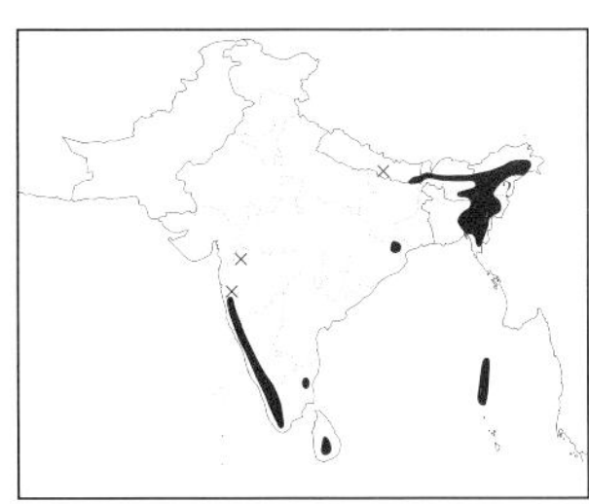

IDENTIFICATION 25 cm. **Male** is striking, with glistening violet-blue crown and upperparts contrasting with velvety-black face, underparts, wings and tail. **Female** is entirely dull blue-green, with dusky lores and blackish flight feathers. **First-year male** is like female. **Juvenile** is entirely dull brown. **VOICE** A liquid *tu-lip wae-waet-oo,* and various shorter liquid notes (Boonsong and Round 1991). **HABITS** Usually in flocks of up to eight birds when not breeding. Forages actively for fruit and nectar, usually in the tree canopy, but will descend to bushes. **HABITAT** Broadleaved evergreen and dense moist deciduous forest. **BREEDING** January–June. Nest is a flimsy shallow platform built from 5 m up in a fork of a large thick tree. **DISTRIBUTION AND STATUS** Resident, subject to seasonal movements. Himalayan foothills from EC Nepal east to Arunachal Pradesh; NE India and Bangladesh; hills of S India from W Maharashtra south to S Kerala and in E Tamil Nadu; Simlipal Hills, Orissa; Sri Lanka. **NP:** rare and local, mainly in the southeast; below 365 m. **IN:** locally fairly common in the Himalayas and northeast, from base of hills occasionally up to 1200 m; local and frequent in the south, from plains up to 1800 m. **BT:** frequent; from 250 m to at least 1065 m. **BD:** locally common. **LK:** status uncertain, probably extirpated.

BLUE-WINGED LEAFBIRD *Chloropsis cochinchinensis* Plate 88

Gold-mantled Chloropsis (I), Jerdon's Chloropsis (P)

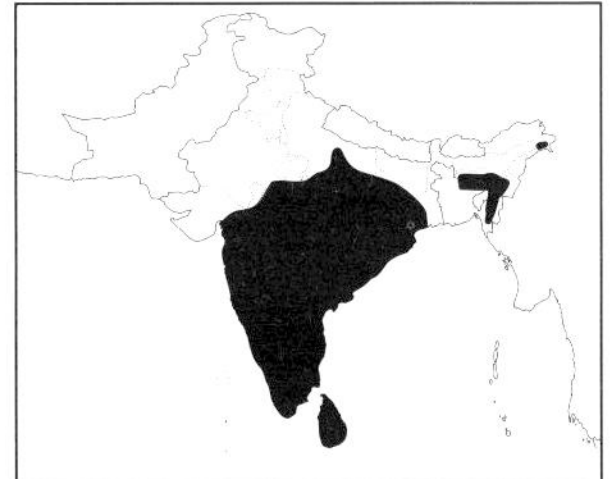

IDENTIFICATION 20 cm. In all plumages, including juvenile, nominate race is told from other leafbirds by blue edges to primary coverts and primaries which form panel in wing (duller on female and juvenile), and blue sides to tail. Further, both races in subcontinent lack well-defined golden-orange forehead which is usually present on adult Golden-fronted (below), and have uniform green underparts, lacking orange on belly shown by adult Orange-bellied (p.586). **Male** nominate has small violet-blue moustachial stripe, black lores and throat, diffuse yellow forehead and border to throat, golden cast to crown and nape, and bright blue shoulder patch. **Female** nominate is almost entirely green, with golden cast to crown and nape; throat is pale bluish-green, with brighter turquoise moustachial. **Juvenile** nominate has green head, with slight suggestion of turquoise moustachial. **Racial variation** *C. c. jerdoni* of peninsular India and Sri Lanka differs from the nominate race of NE subcontinent in lacking blue wing panel and sides to tail. **Male** lacks golden cast to nape, and diffuse yellow border to black throat is less extensive compared with nominate race. Yellowish forehead and forecrown merging with green of hindcrown and nape, and smaller black throat patch, are best distinctions from adult Golden-fronted. **Female** has broad diffuse yellow border to turquoise throat (female Golden-fronted has black throat). **Juvenile** has turquoise throat, brighter in moustachial region (throat is green on immature Golden-fronted). **VOICE** Typical song, with loud drongo-like chatty phrases, much mimicry plus varied whistles, chuckles and rattles, is difficult to separate from that of other leafbirds (P. Holt). **HABITS** A typical leafbird. Found singly, in pairs or in family parties. Pugnacious, and will drive other birds away from flowering trees. **HABITAT** Forest edges, groves, open forest, gardens, isolated large trees near villages or in cultivation. **BREEDING** Mainly November–May in the south of its range; May–September in the north. Nest is a small cup made of fine roots, grass and lichen, suspended between leaf stems or branching twigs at the end of a bough, usually 6–9 m above ground. **DISTRIBUTION AND STATUS** Resident. From S Gujarat north to C Uttar Pradesh, east to West Bengal and south through the peninsula and Sri Lanka; hills of NE India and Bangladesh. **IN:** fairly common in the hills, rather local in the plains; plains and hills up to 1000 m, locally to 1200 m in the peninsula; from foothills up to 1800 m in the northeast. **BD:** local winter visitor. **LK:** common resident in the lowlands and up to mid altitudes.

GOLDEN-FRONTED LEAFBIRD *Chloropsis aurifrons* Plate 88

Gold-fronted Chloropsis (I,P)

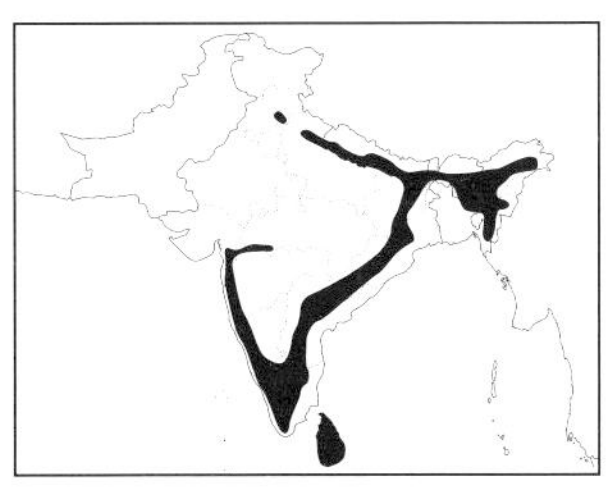

IDENTIFICATION 19 cm. **Adult** distinguished from Orange-bellied Leafbird (p.586) by lack of orange on belly, and by black of throat not extending onto breast. From nominate Blue-winged (above) by lack of blue panel on wings and on sides of tail, and from both races of that species by golden-orange forehead/forecrown which is clearly demarcated from green of crown (orange can, however, be rather dull on some birds, especially females). **Juvenile** is all green, with at best a diffuse yellowish patch on forecrown and a touch of blue in moustachial region on some birds. Probably inseparable from juvenile Orange-bellied, although never shows trace of orange on belly which may be apparent on some immatures of that species, and has finer bill. Lack of blue in wing, and green throat, separate it from juvenile nominate Blue-winged; and green throat separates it from juvenile *jerdoni* race of Blue-winged in peninsular India and Sri Lanka. **Racial variation** The nominate race of NE subcontinent (south to Orissa) has purplish-blue throat surrounded by black and with a golden-yellow border which is especially pronounced across upper breast. *C. a. frontalis* and *C. a. insularis*, from S India and Sri Lanka respectively, differ from the nominate race in having purplish-blue restricted to moustachial, and yellow border to black throat is less prominent or absent. **VOICE** A wide variety of harsh and whistling notes, and is a very good mimic of other birds. Song a cheery series of rising and falling liquid chirps, bulbul-like in tone: *chur-chee-dip-chur-chirpy-chirpy* (S. Madge). **HABITS** Very similar to those of Blue-winged. Usually found in pairs in the breeding season, and in small parties at other times. **HABITAT** Broadleaved deciduous and evergreen forest and secondary growth; found in more wooded habitats than Blue-winged Leafbird. **BREEDING** January–August, varying locally. Nest is like that of Blue-winged Leafbird, built in a tree 9–12 m above ground. **DISTRIBUTION AND STATUS** Resident, subject to local movements. Himalayas from N Uttar Pradesh east to Arunachal Pradesh and south to Bangladesh, through E India, also S and SW India and Sri Lanka. **NP:** fairly common below 365 m, uncommon up to 915 m (–2285 m). **IN:** locally common in the Himalayas; in the peninsula, common in the west but rare in the east; plains and hills up to 1800 m. **BT:** frequent; 250 m to at least 1000 m. **BD:** common. **LK:** rare in the lowlands and up to mid altitudes, mainly in the wet zone.

ORANGE-BELLIED LEAFBIRD *Chloropsis hardwickii* — Plate 88

Orange-bellied Chloropsis (I)

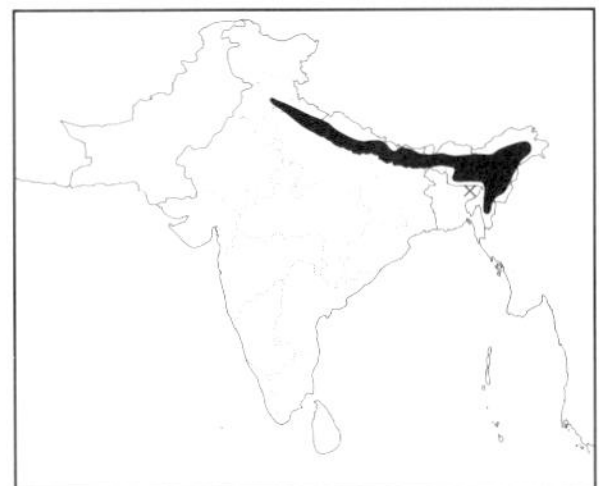

IDENTIFICATION 20 cm. **Male** told from other leafbirds by black of throat extending onto breast and by orange belly and vent. In addition, has large blue moustachial stripe, purplish-blue edges to primary coverts and primaries which form panel on wing (appearing black at distance), and also purplish-blue sides to tail. **Female** lacks black of throat and breast, and is largely green. Orange centre of belly and vent and large blue moustachial stripe are best distinctions from other leafbirds. **Juvenile** is all green and probably inseparable from immature Golden-fronted (p.585), except that some have touch of orange on belly, and has a stouter bill. Green wings and tail (although may show diffuse blue edges to some flight feathers) help separate it from juvenile Blue-winged (p.585) where ranges overlap. **VOICE** A wide variety of harsh and whistling notes, and is a very good mimic of other birds. **HABITS** A typical leafbird. Found singly or in pairs; often with other species in flowering trees. **HABITAT** Broadleaved evergreen and deciduous forest; favours the former more than do other leafbirds. **BREEDING** May–August. Nest and nest site are similar to those of Blue-winged Leafbird. **DISTRIBUTION AND STATUS** Resident, subject to altitudinal movements. Himalayas from W Himachal Pradesh east to Arunachal Pradesh; NE India and Bangladesh. **NP:** widespread and frequent; 250–2750 m, mainly 1300–2135 m. **IN:** locally common; favours zone around 1200 m, up to 2400 m in the Naga Hills. **BT:** common; 380–2645 m. **BD:** ?former resident; no recent records, but could still occur in remnant forest.

SHRIKES Laniidae

Medium-sized, predatory passerines with a strong stout bill, hooked at the tip of the upper mandible, strong legs and feet, a large head, and a long tail with graduated tip. The plumage is typically grey or brown, with a dark mask. Characteristically, shrikes search for prey from a vantage point, such the top of a bush or small tree, post, or telegraph wire. They swoop down to catch prey from the ground or in flight and carry large items back to a perch, where the food is dismembered before eating. Shrikes, especially the larger species, are bold and aggressive predators. Their diet consists of large insects, nestlings, and small reptiles, mammals and birds. Some species impale surplus dead prey on thorns. Over long distances their flight is typically undulating, but between close perches shrikes fly directly, dipping down from one perch and then swooping up to another. On the ground they progress by hopping. Their calls are harsh, but most have quite musical songs and are good mimics. Shrikes typically inhabit open country with scattered bushes or light scrub. Their nests are normally cup-shaped, made of twigs and grasses and lined with finer grasses, and placed in trees or bushes. The main reference used is Lefranc and Worfolk (1997).

RED-BACKED SHRIKE *Lanius collurio* — Plate 89

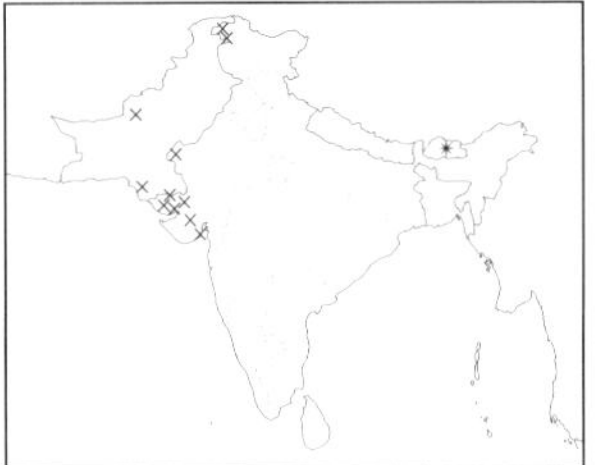

IDENTIFICATION 17 cm. **Adult male** is superficially similar to adult Bay-backed (p.588). Lacks broad black band on forehead of that species, has rufous (rather than deep maroon-chestnut) mantle and pink wash to underparts, and usually lacks white wing patch (at most, has small white patch at base of primaries). Tail is shorter and squarer, and terminal third of outer feathers is largely black, with narrow white tips (adult Bay-backed has a strongly graduated tail, with bold white tips to outer feathers). Immature Bay-backed frequently lacks black band across forehead, and can be very similar in appearance to male Red-backed, with similar mantle coloration. Tail shape and pattern, largely rufous coverts, and absence of prominent white patch at base of primaries are good features for male Red-backed. Red-backed also has a longer primary projection (longer than exposed tertials; shorter on Bay-backed). **Adult female** is more likely to be confused with female/first-winter Rufous-tailed or Brown (below), but has grey cast to head and especially nape, contrasting slightly with rufous-brown mantle; dark brown tail lacks any bright or warm rufous coloration, and has more prominent scaling on breast and flanks. **First-winter** is similar to female, but has pale fringes and dark subterminal lines to feathers of crown, mantle, scapulars and wing-coverts (giving rise to heavily barred appearance); tail is more rufous-brown, but does not contrast with mantle. First-winter Rufous-tailed has paler, more uniform sandy-brown upperparts (usually without prominent barring), and contrastingly pale rufous rump and tail. First-winter Brown has more uniform rufous-brown upperparts, without prominent barring, and stronger rufous cast to tail. **VOICE** Call is a typical shrike-like grating. **HABITS** A typical shrike. Conspicuous when feeding; more secretive at other times, when it often perches within the outer foliage of bushes. **HABITAT** Bushes and cultivation in dry country, and scrub desert. **DISTRIBUTION AND STATUS** Southward passage migrant, mainly through Pakistan, W Rajasthan and Gujarat. **PK:** scarce. **IN:** regular in small numbers. **BT:** vagrant.

RUFOUS-TAILED SHRIKE *Lanius isabellinus* — Plate 89

Isabelline Shrike (N), *L. collurio* (I)

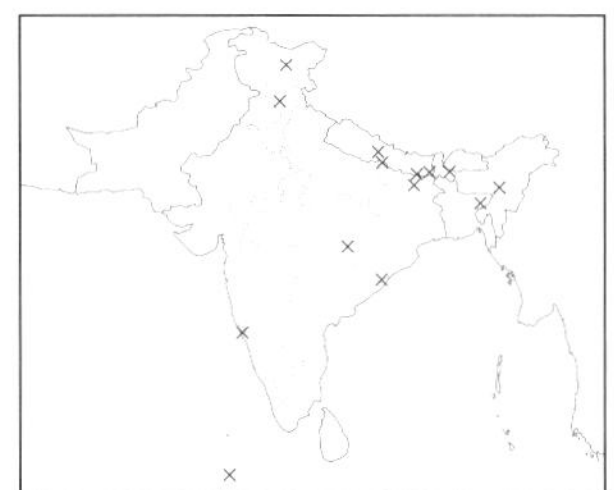

IDENTIFICATION 17 cm. Compared with Brown Shrike (below), Rufous-tailed typically has a paler sandy-brown or grey-brown mantle, with which warmer rufous rump and tail show noticeable contrast, and is smaller, with a slightly finer bill and less graduated tail. For differences from Red-backed (p.586), see that species. **Adult male** further differs from male Brown in having small white patch at base of primaries, and less prominent whitish forehead and supercilium. **Adult female** usually lacks white patch at base of primaries; has paler ear-coverts than male, and usually has faint dark scaling on breast and flanks. Grey-brown (rather than blackish) ear-coverts and buffish supercilium are further differences from female Brown. **First-winter** is similar to female, but has pale fringes and dark subterminal lines to scapulars, wing-coverts and tertials. **Racial variation** Two races occur in the subcontinent. Male *L. i. isabellinus* has uniform sandy greyish-brown crown and mantle, and paler rufous-orange rump and tail; male *L. i. phoenicuroides* has rufous cast to crown and nape, contrasting with darker grey-brown mantle, and deeper rufous-brown tail. These features are often apparent in female and first-winter plumages, although subspecific identification is less reliable. Male *phoenicuroides* has black lores (forming a complete black mask). **VOICE** Song is often a restrained chattering, but can be rich and varied; call is a typical shrike-like grating. **HABITS** A typical shrike, with habits very like those of Red-backed. **HABITAT** Breeds on open hillsides and in ravines with scattered bushes of wild almond and juniper. Winters in open dry scrub of tamarisk or babool, such as found along riverain tracts, major canals and edges of seasonal jheels. Favours uncultivated habitats. **BREEDING** Mid April–June. Builds a normal shrike nest in the fork of a juniper tree or large bush, 2–3 m above ground. **DISTRIBUTION AND STATUS** Breeds in Baluchistan, Pakistan; winters from Pakistan east to Assam and south to Goa, mainly in NW subcontinent. **PK:** frequent; breeds in C and N Baluchistan above 2135 m, winters in the plains of Punjab and Sindh. **NP:** very rare winter visitor; below 1340 m (–4050 m, presumably on passage). **IN:** winter visitor and passage migrant, regular in the northwest. **BD, MV:** vagrant. **REFERENCES** Alström and Colston (1991), Crosby (1995), Martens and Eck (1995).

BROWN SHRIKE *Lanius cristatus* — Plate 89

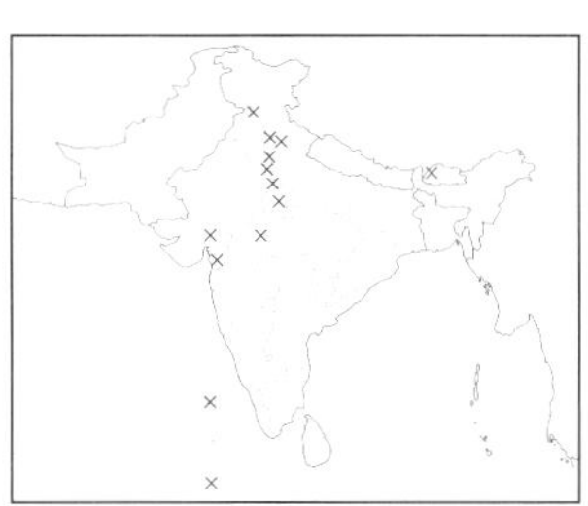

IDENTIFICATION 18–19 cm. Compared with Rufous-tailed (above), Brown Shrike typically has darker rufous-brown crown, mantle, rump and tail (lacking noticeable contrast between crown and mantle and mantle and tail). It is also slightly larger, with a thicker bill, and has a more graduated tail. For differences from Red-backed (p.586), see that species. **Adult male** further differs from male Rufous-tailed in lacking white patch at base of primaries, and in having more prominent whitish forehead and supercilium. **Adult female** is similar to male, but has paler lores and usually has faint dark scaling on breast and flanks. Blacker ear-coverts and prominent white forehead and supercilium are further differences from female Rufous-tailed. **First-winter** is similar to female, but has dark subterminal borders to scapulars, wing-coverts and tertials, browner mask (incomplete on lores), and more prominent scaling on breast and flanks. **Racial variation** *L. c. lucionensis*, occurring as a winter visitor to Sri Lanka and the Andamans/Nicobars, has greyish-white supercilium, grey cast to crown and nape, and more noticeable rufous rump and tail. **VOICE** Song is a rich and varied chattering; call is a typical shrike-like grating (Alström and Colston 1991). **HABITS** A typical shrike. Perhaps more crepuscular than the others. Territorial on winter grounds. **HABITAT** Forest edges and clearings, open secondary scrub, and hillsides with scattered bushes and small trees. **DISTRIBUTION AND STATUS** Widespread winter visitor, mainly to E, NE and S subcontinent; arrives mainly August/September, most leaving by mid April. **NP:** fairly common from C areas eastwards, uncommon farther west; mainly below 1525 m (–2700 m on passage). **IN:** locally common; the plains, and up to 2100 m in Himalayas and in peninsular hills. **BT:** uncommon; 250–2440 m (–3400 m on passage). **BD:** common visitor throughout. **LK:** common throughout. **MV:** rare. **REFERENCES** Inskipp and Inskipp (1996), Singh (1995).

BURMESE SHRIKE *Lanius collurioides* Plate 89

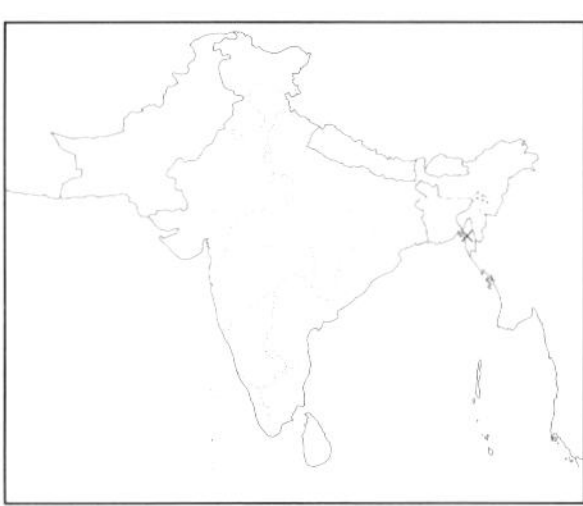

IDENTIFICATION 20 cm. **Adult male** Distinguished from Bay-backed (below) by darker grey crown and nape, lacking clearly defined black mask and band across forehead, and contrasting less with chestnut mantle. Also has chestnut (rather than whitish) rump and uppertail-coverts. From Long-tailed (below) by darker grey crown and nape, dark chestnut mantle, and white sides to shorter tail. **Adult female** has whitish forehead and supercilium in front of the eye, and paler chestnut mantle. In **first-winter** plumage, crown and nape are brownish-grey, with indistinct dark and buff barring, and mantle is rufous (also with some diffuse dark barring). **Juvenile** has two-toned upperparts, with buff barring on greyish or brown crown and nape, and rest of upperparts rufous with brown barring. Rufous coloration to rump and uppertail-coverts help separate juvenile and first-winter from respective plumages of Bay-backed. **VOICE** Alarm call consists of loud, rapid, harsh chattering, *chikachikachitchit, chekoochekoochitititititit, chetetetetet* etc, and a harsh single *jao* (C. Robson). Song is subdued, quiet, rapid and scratchy, including much repetition and varied mimicry. **HABITS** Very little known. Confiding and easy to detect. **HABITAT** Gardens, secondary growth, and bushes at edges of cultivation. **DISTRIBUTION AND STATUS IN:** locally common passage migrant, mainly in Assam and Manipur; reported breeding in S Assam requires confirmation. **BD:** vagrant.

BAY-BACKED SHRIKE *Lanius vittatus* Plate 89

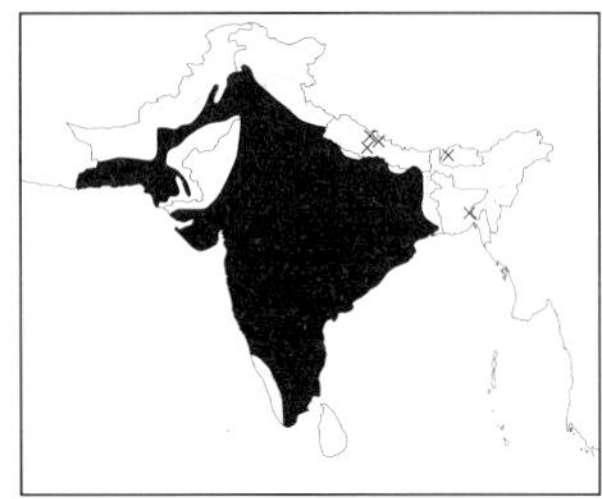

IDENTIFICATION 17 cm. **Adult** has black forehead and mask contrasting with pale grey crown and nape, deep maroon mantle contrasting with grey nape (and, in flight, with whitish rump), and rufous-buff wash to breast and flanks. Also has extensive white patch at base of primaries, and white sides and tip to black tail. For differences from Red-backed and Burmese Shrikes (p.586 and above), see those species. Sexes are alike, although frontal band is narrower on female. **Juvenile** has pale greyish to buffish upperparts with prominent dark barring, with slight rufescent cast to uppertail-coverts and greater coverts; tail is rufous-brown with buffish-white outer feathers, and has dark scaling on breast and flanks. Told from juvenile Long-tailed (below) by finer bill, smaller size and shorter tail, and more uniform greyish or buffish base coloration to upperparts (lacking Long-tailed's rufous-brown tone to scapulars, back and rump); coverts and tertials are more intricately patterned than on juvenile Long-tailed, with buff fringes and dark subterminal crescents and central marks, and primary coverts are prominently tipped with buff. Also shows a pale rump. **First-year** is very variable (and moult into adult plumage appears complex): crown and nape are brownish-grey, mantle and scapulars are rufous, and lacks adult's black on forehead; retains, to variable extent, juvenile tertials, primaries, secondaries and tail feathers. **VOICE** Song is a pleasant, rambling warble with much mimicry; call is a harsh churring. **HABITS** A typical shrike. Fairly conspicuous and quite tame. Quite territorial in winter and summer. **HABITAT** Dry country, open scrub and bushes at the edges of cultivation, and acacia groves; in Pakistan, also canal-bank tree plantations. **BREEDING** February–September. Builds a usual shrike nest in the fork of a thorn tree, 1.5–4 m above ground. **DISTRIBUTION AND STATUS** Resident, subject to local movements. Mainly from Pakistan east to West Bengal and south throughout most of the peninsula. **PK:** common; widespread resident in the Indus basin, summer visitor to Baluchistan and NW Pakistan. **NP:** mainly an uncommon winter visitor and passage migrant, below 335 m (–3965 m on passage); also recorded in summer. **IN:** resident, mainly in the plains, locally up to 2000 m in Himalayas; locally common in the N peninsula. **BT:** vagrant; 3760 m. **BD:** vagrant. **REFERENCES** Inskipp and Inskipp (1996).

LONG-TAILED SHRIKE *Lanius schach* Plate 89

Rufous-backed Shrike (I), Rufous-rumped Shrike (P), Black-headed/Rufous-backed Shrike (F)

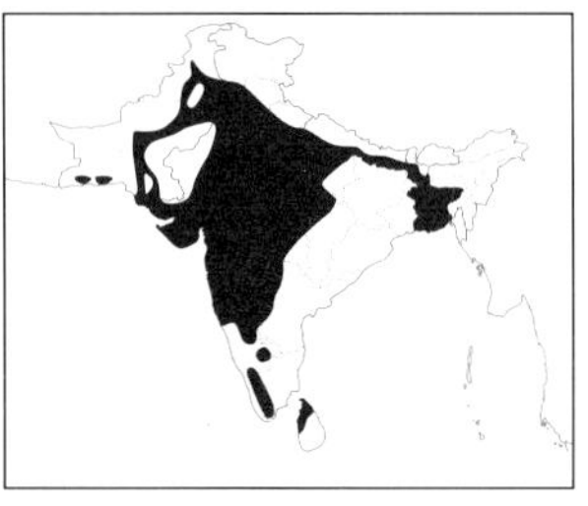

IDENTIFICATION 25 cm. A large, long-tailed shrike, similar to Grey-backed (p.589). **Adult** distinguished from that species by rufous scapulars and upper back contrasting with paler grey mantle (although see description of *L. s. caniceps* below), more extensive black forehead (although some overlap occurs), rufous sides to black tail, and more conspicuous white flash at base of primaries (although this may be lacking on some birds). **Juvenile** has greyish to buffish crown and mantle with dark barring, becoming (dark-barred) rufous-brown on scapulars, back and rump; greater coverts and tertials are typically brown to blackish, with rufous fringes. Told from juvenile Bay-backed (above) by stouter bill, larger size and longer tail, two-toned appearance to upperparts (with rufous base coloration to back etc), and patterning of coverts and tertials. See Grey-backed for differences from juvenile of that species. **First-winter** is similar to adult, but retains juvenile tertials, coverts and tail feathers (see above), and has variable brown cast to mantle and scaling on underparts. **Racial variation** *L. s. tricolor* of the Himalayas and NE subcontinent differs from *L. s.*

erythronotus in having black head (black crown, ear-coverts and nape), and is deeper rufous on lower mantle. *L. s. caniceps* of peninsular India and Sri Lanka has grey scapulars and back. **VOICE** Song is a pleasant, subdued, rambling warble with much mimicry; call is a harsh grating. **HABITS** A typical shrike. Conspicuous. Rather noisy in the mornings and evenings. Highly territorial. **HABITAT** Bushes in cultivation, gardens, canalside and roadside tree plantations, orchards, open forest, and tall grassland with scattered trees. Avoids dry country. **BREEDING** December–July, varying locally. Builds a bulky, untidy nest in trees or bushes, 3–6 m above ground. **DISTRIBUTION AND STATUS** Resident, subject to altitudinal and local movements, and partly migratory. Throughout much of the subcontinent, except parts of the northwest and northeast. **PK:** common; very widespread resident in the wetter parts of the Indus plains, summer visitor to Baluchistan and up to 3050 m in Himalayas. **NP:** common and widespread, mainly resident; summers 300–3100 m, chiefly 1500–2700 m, sometimes winters in the foothills and terai. **IN:** locally common and very widespread resident; breeds in the plains and Himalayas, from the base up to 3000 m, winters below 2200 m. **BT:** common resident; from 600 m to at least 2285 m. **BD:** common resident throughout. **LK:** common resident in the dry N and NW coastal lowlands, occasionally inland.

GREY-BACKED SHRIKE *Lanius tephronotus* — Plate 89

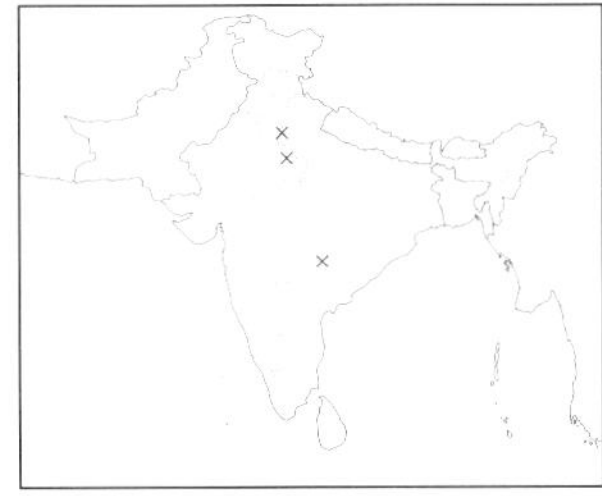

IDENTIFICATION 25 cm. A large, long-tailed shrike, similar to Long-tailed (p.588). **Adult** distinguished from that species by uniform, darker grey upperparts, with rufous on uppertail-coverts, but lacking rufous on scapulars and upper back. Also lacks or has very narrow black forehead band, and lacks (or has only very indistinct) white patch at base of primaries. **Juvenile** has brown ear-coverts; cold grey upperparts (except for rufous-brown uppertail-coverts), with indistinct black subterminal crescents and buff fringes to feathers; rufous fringes and indistinct black subterminal borders to coverts and tertials; and dark scaling on breast and flanks. Uniform cold grey base coloration to upperparts is best distinction from juvenile Long-tailed. **First-winter** is similar to adult, but retains juvenile wings and tail and mask is brown; mantle can be slightly paler, with brownish cast, and has variable dark scaling on underparts. **VOICE** Call is a harsh grating; also mimics other birds. **HABITS** A typical shrike. Noisy and conspicuous. Highly territorial all year. **HABITAT** Bushes on hillsides and at cultivation edges, open scrub and secondary growth, orchards and gardens; in Sikkim, occupies Tibetan steppe habitat. **BREEDING** June and July. Builds a bulky, untidy nest in a thorn bush or small tree, 1.5–3 m above ground. **DISTRIBUTION AND STATUS** Breeds in Himalayas from Ladakh east to Arunachal Pradesh; winters at lower altitudes and in adjacent plains in N and NE India and Bangladesh. **NP:** fairly common and widespread; summers 2200–4000 m (–4575 m), winters from 275 m to at least 2560 m. **IN:** locally common; breeds 2700–3600 m in W Himalayas, 2700–4575 in E Himalayas, and winters in foothills and adjoining plains. **BT:** common; 240–4060 m. **BD:** local winter visitor. **REFERENCES** Martens and Eck (1995).

LESSER GREY SHRIKE *Lanius minor* — Plate 89

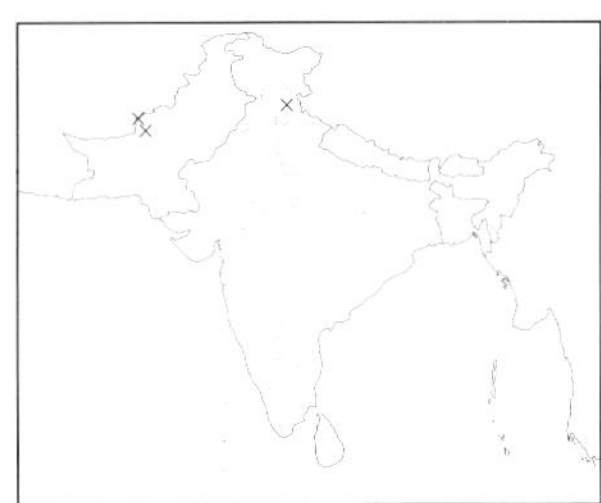

IDENTIFICATION 20 cm. **Adult** told from Southern Grey Shrike (p.590) by combination of extensive black on forehead (much more so than on *lahtora* race of Southern Grey), strong pink flush to breast, and structural differences given below. Female is similar to male, but has less black on forehead; lores are often tinged brown, and underparts are less strongly tinged pink. **First-winter** is similar to adult, but lacks black forehead and is therefore more similar to Southern Grey (especially *L. m. pallidirostris*), as well as to Great Grey Shrike (below). Distinguished from those species by combination of smaller size, shorter and stouter bill, little or no white in scapulars, shorter and squarer tail with less white at sides, all-black secondaries except for white at tips, and longer extension of primaries beyond tertials (although primary projection of *L. m. pallidirostris* is rather similar). Juvenile has fine scaling on upperparts. **VOICE** Call is a harsh grating. **HABITS** A typical shrike, but has a more upright posture, with tail often held down, and less undulating flight than other shrikes, especially Southern Grey. **HABITAT** Open country with bushes and tree clumps. **DISTRIBUTION AND STATUS PK, IN:** vagrant. **REFERENCES** Chakravaty *et al.* (1981).

GREAT GREY SHRIKE *Lanius excubitor* — Plate 89

IDENTIFICATION 25 cm. *L. e. homeyeri*, a vagrant to the subcontinent, is very similar to *pallidirostris* race of Southern Grey (p.590). Like that form, it differs from the widely distributed *lahtora* race of Southern Grey in lacking black on forehead, and in having a more restricted dark mask (including dusky to pale lores) and a paler grey mantle. Great Grey is best told from *pallidirostris* race of Southern Grey by white outer webs to basal half of secondaries (resulting in a more extensive white patch on wing at rest and in flight), and has distinct white rump and uppertail-coverts. **VOICE** Calls include a clear, ringing *schrreea* and a drawn-out nasal *eeh* (Europe) (Jonsson 1992). **HABITS** Similar to those of Southern Grey. **HABITAT** Similar to that of Southern Grey. **DISTRIBUTION AND STATUS PK:** winter vagrant. **IN:** winter vagrant to Kashmir. **REFERENCES** Clement and Worfolk (1995), Lefranc and Worfolk (1997).

SOUTHERN GREY SHRIKE *Lanius meridionalis* Plate 89

Grey Shrike, *L. excubitor* (F,I)

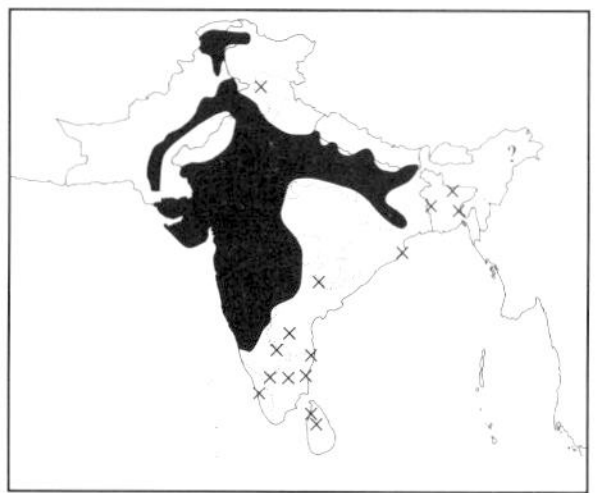

IDENTIFICATION 24 cm. A large, long-tailed shrike. Has a faster and more powerful flight than others of the genus, and often at a fair height. Throughout most of range, likely to be confused only with Grey-backed and Long-tailed Shrikes (p.589 and p.588). **Adult** told from those species by paler grey mantle and white scapulars, bold white markings on black wings and tail, greyish rump, and white breast and flanks. Black of mask extends over forehead and down sides of neck. Has extensive white patch at base of primaries and, with inner webs of secondaries and tips of outer webs also largely white, shows much white in wing at rest and in flight. **Juvenile** has sandy cast to grey crown and mantle, with very indistinct barring on crown, buff tips to tertials and median and greater coverts, and faint buffish wash to underparts; mask is grey, and does not extend over forehead as on adult. **Racial variation** *L. m. pallidirostris*, which breeds in extreme W Pakistan and winters east to Rajasthan, differs from the widely distributed *L. m. lahtora*, described above, in lacking black on forehead and having a more restricted dark mask (including dusky to whitish lores, typically strikingly pale in first-winter plumage); also has a paler grey mantle, generally a horn-coloured (rather than black) bill, and often shows a pink wash on breast; white on secondaries is confined to tips and basal half of inner webs, and therefore shows less white on wing, both at rest and in flight, than that race. *L. m. aucheri*, a vagrant, is very similar to *lahtora*, but has narrower black band on forehead, grey wash to breast, and secondaries largely black but for bold white tips (and therefore also shows less white on wing than *lahtora*). **VOICE** Song is a subdued low chattering or melodious warble, interspersed with harsh notes and mimicked songs and calls of other birds; call is a drawn-out whistle, *kwiet*. **HABITS** A typical shrike, but, unlike others in the region, it is wary and difficult to approach. **HABITAT** Dry country, open scrub desert, open thorn and dry deciduous forest and scrub; avoids cultivation in Pakistan, but occurs at cultivation edges in India and Nepal. **BREEDING** January–October. Builds a bulky, untidy nest in a babool tree or a thorn bush, 1.5–4 m above ground. Old nests of crows and babblers are often used. **DISTRIBUTION AND STATUS** Resident, subject to local movements, and winter vagrant. Mainly in N, NW and W subcontinent. **PK:** common; widespread resident in the Indus plains of Sind and Punjab, also occurring in Kohistan, Lasbela and the Salt Range; summer visitor to Baluchistan and NW Pakistan; breeds up to 2100 m. **NP:** locally and mainly uncommon resident in the terai. **IN:** locally common in the north; mainly resident, also a winter visitor. **BD:** rare winter visitor. **LK:** rare winter visitor to all zones, more frequent in N dry lowlands. **REFERENCES** Clement and Worfolk (1995), Lefranc and Worfolk (1997).

CORVIDS AND RELATED SPECIES Corvidae

This is a very large family, represented in the region by five subfamilies (in some cases, further subdivided into tribes).

WHISTLERS Subfamily Pachycephalinae

Whistlers have a robust body, a thick rounded head and a strong bill. They feed mainly on insects, gleaned from foliage, branches, trunks or the ground.

MANGROVE WHISTLER *Pachycephala grisola* Plate 90

Grey Thickhead *P. cinerea*

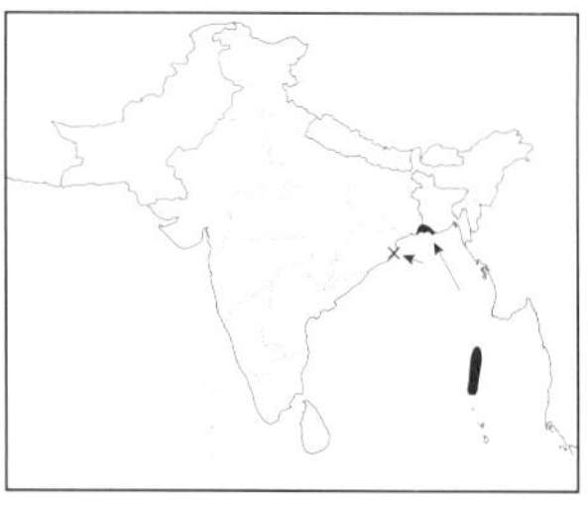

IDENTIFICATION 17 cm. A rather drab, woodshrike-like bird. Has thick black bill, uniform grey-brown crown and ear-coverts (lacking supercilium and eye-stripe), olive-brown mantle, rump and tail, and greyish-white throat and breast merging into silvery-white of rest of underparts (some with whiter throat). **VOICE** Variable phrase, with two to four short introductory notes and last note louder, shriller and more explosive: *tit.tit..phew-whiu-whit*; *chi.chi.chi.wit-phew-chew*; *tit.tit.tit..too-whit* etc. Also, similar phrases with undulating notes at end: *tit.....tit..tit.chewy-chi-chewy* etc (C. Robson). **HABITS** Solitary outside the breeding season, in pairs when breeding. Forages unobtrusively in trees, from the roots up to the canopy. Gleans insects from the branches, trunk and foliage. **HABITAT** Mangroves. **BREEDING** April–July. Builds a frail cup-shaped nest 1–4 m above ground in a small tree. **DISTRIBUTION AND STATUS** Resident. Sunderbans of West Bengal and Bangladesh, Orissa and Andaman Is. **IN:** local and fairly common. **BD:** very local.

JAYS, MAGPIES, TREEPIES, CHOUGHS, NUTCRACKERS, CROWS, RAVENS Subfamily Corvinae, tribe Corvini

These are all robust perching birds which differ considerably from each other in appearance, but which have a number of features in common: a fairly long straight bill, very strong feet and legs, and a tuft of nasal bristles extending over the base of the upper mandible. The sexes are alike or almost alike in plumage. They are strong fliers. Most are gregarious, especially when feeding and roosting. Typically, they are noisy birds, uttering loud and discordant squawks, croaks or screeches. Their behaviour suggests that they are very intelligent birds; they are highly adaptable, and some species have a complex social organisation. Many species, including the jays, magpies and nutcrackers, hide excess food to be consumed later in times of scarcity. Characteristically, members of the Corvini are inquisitive; sometimes bold and at other times cautiously wary, as the situation dictates. They build untidy nests of twigs and sticks, lined with grass or hair. Most species are sedentary, although those breeding at higher elevations move altitudinally with the seasons. Some may undergo movements in autumn, probably because of food shortages. The main reference specific to this tribe is Madge and Burn (1993).

EURASIAN JAY *Garrulus glandarius* Plate 90

Jay (I)

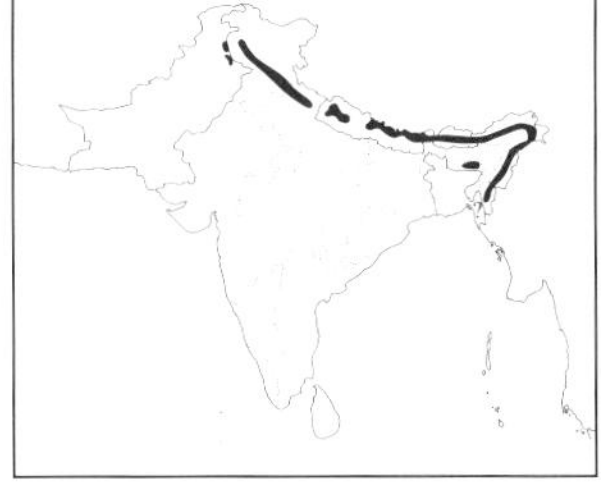

IDENTIFICATION 32–36 cm. Has pinkish- to reddish-brown body, with beady eye, stout black bill and black moustachial stripe. Wings and tail are mainly black, with cobalt-blue barring on wing-coverts and on bases of some secondaries. In flight, shows prominent white rump which contrasts with black tail. Flight action is slow and laboured, with rather jerky beats of its rounded wings. **Racial variation** *G. g. bispecularis* of the W Himalayas has vinaceous-fawn body; *G. g. interstinctus* of the E Himalayas has a darker reddish-brown body. **VOICE** Alarm call is a loud, rasping *skaaaak-skaaaak*, and also has a crow-like *kraah* (Madge and Burn 1993). **HABITS** Usually found singly, in pairs or in family parties in the breeding season; in autumn and winter, gathers in flocks of up to 30 and often associated with blue magpies and Black-headed Jays (below). Feeds on the ground and in bushes and trees; also forages by digging with the bill in soft soil, among dead leaves or in crevices. Acorns are important in the diet. **HABITAT** Dense, moist temperate forest, mainly of broadleaves and usually in oaks. **BREEDING** March–June. Builds a cup-shaped nest about 8 m above ground in a small tree or shrub. **DISTRIBUTION AND STATUS** Resident, subject to some altitudinal movements. Himalayas, mainly in N Pakistan (Kagan valley and Murree hills) and from Himachal Pradesh east to Arunachal Pradesh; NE India and Bangladesh. Chiefly 1800–2440 m (–2750 m) in C and W Himalayas, occasionally lower in winter; 1200–3660 m (down to 500 m) in E Himalayas. **PK:** frequent, but very local. **NP:** widespread, but local; fairly common in some places. **IN:** locally fairly common. **BT:** common.

BLACK-HEADED JAY *Garrulus lanceolatus* Plate 90

Black-throated Jay (F,I), Lanceolated Jay (N,R)

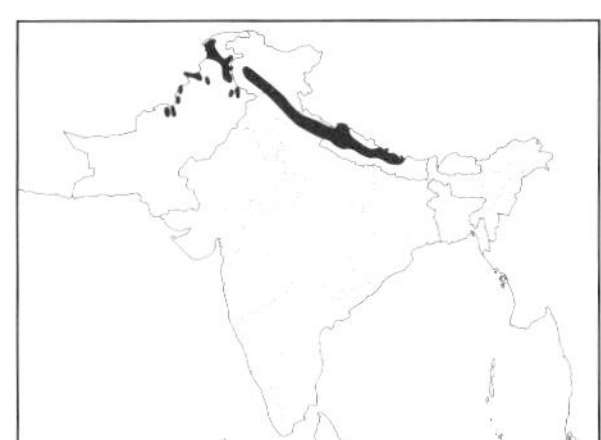

IDENTIFICATION 33 cm. Readily distinguished from Eurasian Jay (above) by black crest and ear-coverts, white-streaked black throat, pinkish-fawn upperparts and underparts variably washed with blue-grey, and white patches on mostly black wings. Wings also have patches of blue barring, similar to Eurasian Jay. In flight, show pinkish-fawn (rather than white) rump, and has longer tail which is mainly blue with black cross-bars and white tip. Flight action and rounded wings are similar to those of Eurasian Jay, but tail is noticeably longer and graduated. **Juvenile** is similar, but duller: has browner body, has paler throat with less extensive streaking, and lacks white tips to secondaries and tertials. **VOICE** Alarm call is a loud, rasping *skaaaak*, similar to that of Eurasian Jay but flatter, and usually given singly; also utters a soft *kraah* (Madge and Burn 1993). **HABITS** Similar to those of Eurasian Jay. In autumn and winter, often forages in loose parties with that species or Yellow-billed Blue Magpie (p.592). **HABITAT** Mixed temperate forest, mainly of oaks; often in more open forest than Eurasian Jay. **BREEDING** April–June. Builds a cup-shaped nest in the top of a small tree, 5–6 m above ground. **DISTRIBUTION AND STATUS** Resident, subject to limited altitudinal movements. NW mountains of Pakistan, and in Himalayas in N Pakistan and from Kashmir east to EC Nepal; 915–2500 m (rarely, descends to the plains in Pakistan in bad weather). **PK:** frequent. **NP:** common in the far west, uncommon farther east. **IN:** locally common.

SRI LANKA BLUE MAGPIE *Urocissa ornata* Plate 90

Ceylon Magpie (I), Ceylon Blue Magpie (P), Sri Lanka Magpie, *Cissa ornata* (I).

IDENTIFICATION 42–47 cm. Very distinctive, with red bill, eye-ring and legs/feet, chestnut head, breast and flight feathers, blue body, and long white-tipped blue tail. Has a rather weak flight. **Juvenile** is duller, with brown eye-ring, and grey wash to blue body (especially on underparts). **VOICE** Very varied, including a far-carrying loud

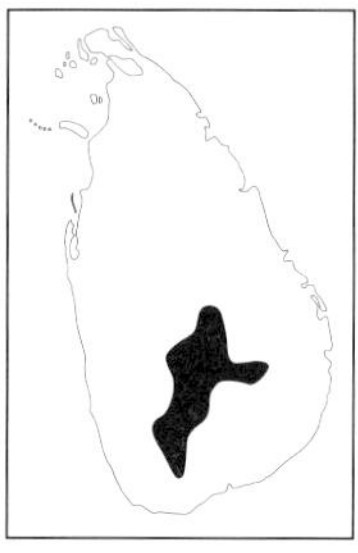

jingle, *chink-chink*, a rasping *crakrakrakrak* and a loud *whee-whee* (Madge and Burn 1993). Also high-pitched, noisy, squeaky *creeik* (S. Buckton). **HABITS** Usually keeps in groups of about six birds; sometimes singly or in pairs. Agile and lively when feeding; forages at all levels, from the ground to the tops of tall trees. Eats large invertebrates, tree-frogs and lizards. **HABITAT** Dense evergreen broadleaved forest. **BREEDING** January–March. Few nests found; one described as resembling that of a small crow, lined with lichen, and placed in the top of a small jungle tree. **DISTRIBUTION AND STATUS** Globally threatened. **LK:** rare endemic resident; up to 2100 m in the SW hill zone and down to 50 m in adjacent parts of the wet-zone foothills.

YELLOW-BILLED BLUE MAGPIE *Urocissa flavirostris* Plate 90

Gold-billed Magpie (K), *Cissa flavirostris* (E,I)

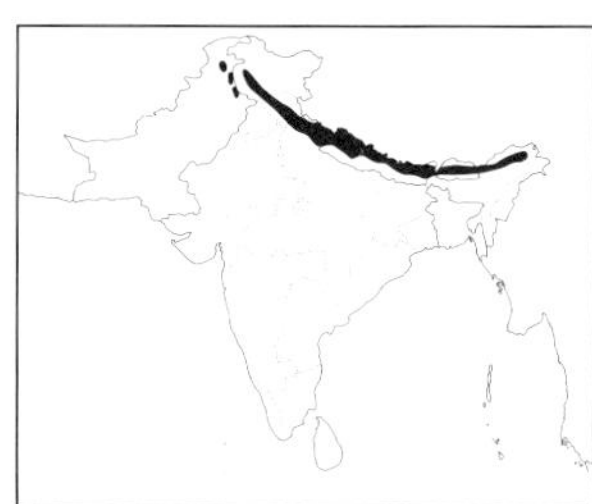

IDENTIFICATION 61–66 cm. Similar to Red-billed Blue Magpie (below), with mainly black head, 'blue' upperparts, and extremely long, graduated, black-and-white-tipped blue tail. Flies with a few rapid wingbeats, followed by a glide with tail feathers spread. **Adult** told from that species by yellow or orange-yellow bill, small white crescent on nape, and duller blue-grey mantle and wings. **Juvenile** is similar to adult, but has duller head and upperparts and dull olive-yellow bill. **Racial variation** *U. f. cucullata* of the W Himalayas has white underparts and bluer mantle and wings compared with *U. f. flavirostris* of the E Himalayas, which has greyer mantle and wings and primrose-yellow wash to the underparts. **VOICE** A wheezy *bu-zeep-peck-peck-peck, pop-upclea, pu-pu-weer* and a high *clear-clear* (Fleming *et al.* 1984). **HABITS** Usually found in pairs or flocks of up to 10 birds. Parties fly across clearings in single file, but when moving over long distances they usually fly low over the treetops. Forages in trees and bushes, hopping with agility from branch to branch; also feeds on the ground, progressing by long hops with its long tail held high. Eats insects, small animals, birds' eggs, carrion, fruit, berries and human food scraps. **HABITAT** Moist, temperate broadleaved and coniferous forest. **BREEDING** Late April–early July. Builds a flimsy cup-shaped nest in dense tree foliage, 5–6 m above ground. **DISTRIBUTION AND STATUS** Resident, subject to altitudinal movements. Himalayas in N Pakistan and from Kashmir east to Arunachal Pradesh; NE India. **PK:** frequent, but local; summers 1900–3350 m, winters down to 900 m. **NP:** common and widespread; mainly above 2440 m all year, summers up to 3660 m, sometimes winters down to 1850 m (1300 m). **IN:** locally fairly common; breeds 1800–3300 m, winters down to 1000 m. **BT:** fairly common; 1830–3390 m.

RED-BILLED BLUE MAGPIE *Urocissa erythrorhyncha* Plate 90

Red-billed Magpie, *Cissa erythrorhyncha* (I)

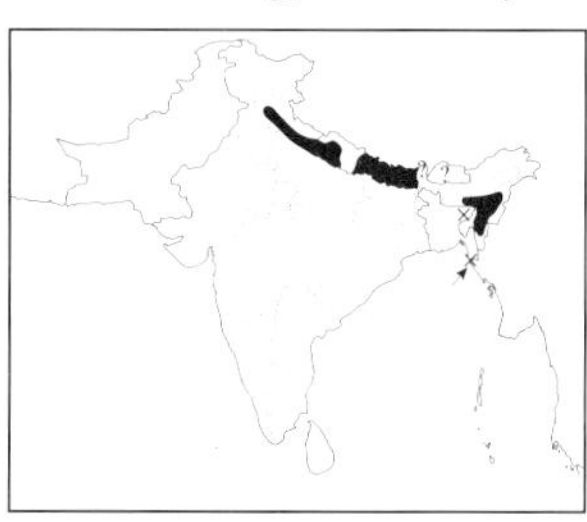

IDENTIFICATION 65–68 cm. Similar to Yellow-billed Blue Magpie (above), with mainly black head, 'blue' upperparts, and extremely long, graduated, black-and-white-tipped blue tail. **Adult** differs from that species in having red or orange-red bill, white hindcrown and nape, and brighter turquoise-blue mantle and wings. **Juvenile** is similar to adult, but has duller blue-grey upperparts, dull brownish-red bill, and a more extensive white crown. **Racial variation** *U. e. magnirostris* of the E subcontinent has darker purplish-blue mantle and wings, and larger bill, compared with *U. e. occipitalis* of the C Himalayas. **VOICE** A piercing *quiv-pig-pig*, a softer *beeee-trik*, a subdued *kluk*, and a sharp *chwenk-chwenk* (Fleming *et al.* 1984). **HABITS** Similar to those of Yellow-billed Blue Magpie. **HABITAT** Occupies a lower altitudinal zone than Yellow-billed Blue Magpie. Tropical and subtropical broadleaved forest, also near villages and at field edges; sometimes in lower temperate forest in summer. **BREEDING** April–June in Himalayas. Builds a flimsy cup-shaped nest 6–8 m up in a tree. **DISTRIBUTION AND STATUS** Resident, subject to some altitudinal movements. Himalayas from W Himachal Pradesh east to Nepal; NE India and Bangladesh. **NP:** common and widespread; mainly 365–1525 m, sometimes summers up to 2200 m (–3050 m). **IN:** locally fairly common, from 300 m (winter) up to 1800 m; in NE hills 1500–1600 m; rare in Assam. **BD:** rare winter visitor.

COMMON GREEN MAGPIE *Cissa chinensis* Plate 90

IDENTIFICATION 37–39 cm. Mainly lurid green, with red bill and legs, black mask, rufous-chestnut wings, black-and-white-tipped tertials and secondaries, and long, graduated black-and-white-tipped green tail. In worn plumage, green coloration can bleach to pale blue and chestnut wings can fade to olive-brown. **Juvenile** is similar to adult, but has dull yellow bill and legs, shorter crest, and paler underparts. **VOICE** Highly variable. Harsh *chakakakakakak* or *chakakak-wi*; high-pitched *wi-chi-chi, jao..wichitchit..wi-chi-chi, jao*, with harsher, shriller *jao* notes and rapid middle section; high-pitched *weeer-wit* and *wi* notes, rising whistled *wieeee* etc, and complex high shrill whistles combined with avian mimicry (C. Robson). **HABITS**

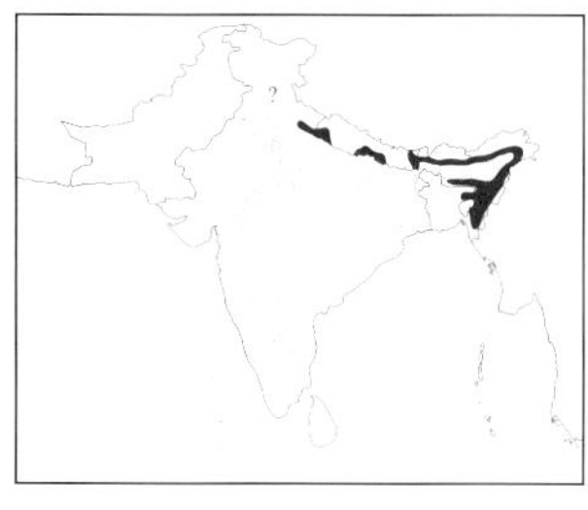

Keeps in pairs or small parties, often associated with roaming feeding flocks of other species. Usually remains among foliage, and often most easily detected by its calls. Forages in the forest understorey, or on the ground under thick vegetation. Feeds chiefly on large insects, small reptiles, amphibians and birds. **HABITAT** Tropical and subtropical broadleaved evergreen and moist deciduous forest; favours dense thickets at edges of streams and in ravines. **BREEDING** April–June. Builds a cup-shaped nest in a small tree or bamboo clump in dense forest. **DISTRIBUTION AND STATUS** Resident. Himalayas from N Uttar Pradesh east to Arunachal Pradesh; NE India and Bangladesh. **NP:** locally fairly common in WC areas and in the east; 245–1830 m, mainly below 1200 m (–2300 m). **IN:** locally fairly common; from base of hills up to 1200 m, locally to 1900 m. **BT:** fairly common; from foothills up to 1700 m. **BD:** local. **REFERENCES** Choudhary (1996).

RUFOUS TREEPIE *Dendrocitta vagabunda* Plate 90

Indian Treepie (F,I)

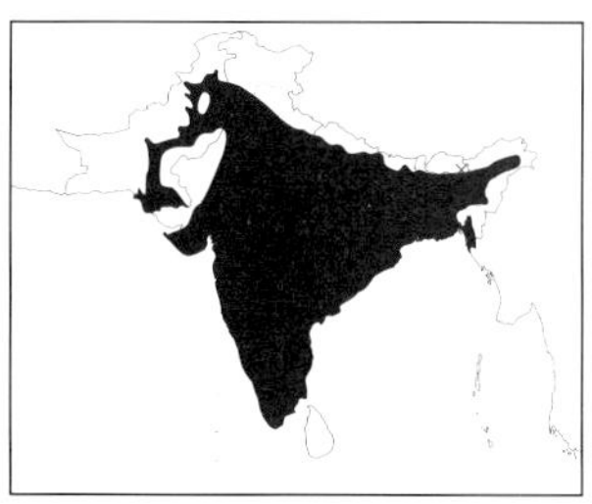

IDENTIFICATION 46–50 cm. **Adult** distinguished from other treepies by combination of uniform slate-grey hood (extending to breast and hindneck), rufous-brown mantle and scapulars, pale grey wing-coverts and band across tertials contrasting with black of rest of wing, fulvous-buff underparts, and black-tipped silvery-grey tail. Has a jerky, undulating flight typical of the treepies, alternately flapping several times and then gliding with wings spread. In flight, pale grey panel on wing, whitish subterminal tail-band and fulvous-buff rump help separate it from Grey Treepie (below). **Juvenile** resembles adult (with similar wing and tail patterns), but has browner hood (less well demarcated from mantle) and buffish wash to wing-coverts, and tail feathers have pale buffish tips. **Racial variation** Five races are recognised in the subcontinent; they are similarly patterned, and vary in size and length of tail and in richness of mantle and underpart coloration. **VOICE** Has a wide variety of harsh, metallic and mewing notes, the most distinctive of which is a loud, flute-like *ko-ki-la*, often mixed with a harsh rattling cry (Madge and Burn 1993). **HABITS** Usually in pairs or family parties, sometimes in larger gatherings at rich food sources; a frequent member of mixed hunting parties of insectivorous species, or joins flocks of barbets and green pigeons in fruiting trees. Chiefly arboreal, and climbs about trunks and branches with ease; often rather shy, keeping among thicker foliage near the treetops. Sometimes feeds on the ground. Omnivorous: eats fruit, nectar, invertebrates, small animals, birds' eggs and young, and carrion. **HABITAT** Open wooded country, gardens with trees and bushes, village groves, roadside avenues; also canalside plantations and scrub forest in Pakistan. **BREEDING** March–July. Builds a cup-shaped nest 6–8 m up in a tree. **DISTRIBUTION AND STATUS** Resident, subject to some local movements. Throughout much of the subcontinent, except parts of the northwest, northeast, Himalayas and Sri Lanka. **PK:** common in the more wooded plains and foothills; up to 900 m in Murree hills. **NP:** widespread and common below 1050 m, uncommon up to 1370 m (–1800 m). **IN:** widespread and locally common; up to 2000 m in Himalayas and peninsular hills. **BT:** uncommon. **BD:** common throughout.

GREY TREEPIE *Dendrocitta formosae* Plate 90

Himalayan Tree Pie (F,I)

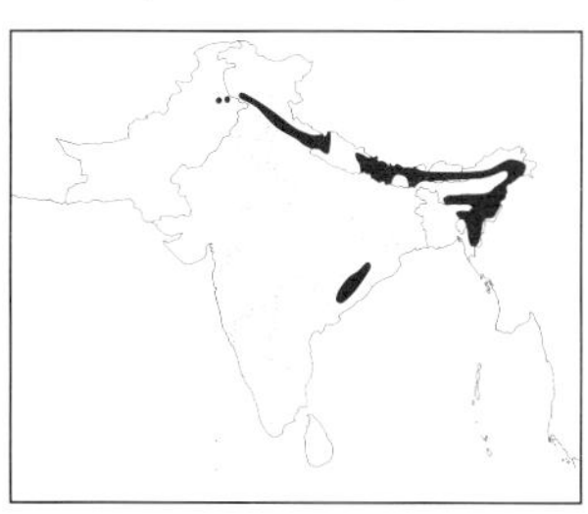

IDENTIFICATION 36–40 cm. Dullest of the treepies. **Adult** told from other treepies by dull black forehead, ear-coverts and throat, grey crown, nape and underparts, dull brown mantle, black wings with white patch at base of primaries, grey rump, and rufous undertail-coverts. In flight, black wings with small white wing patch, absence of whitish subterminal band to tail, and grey rump help separate it from Rufous Treepie (above). **Juvenile** is similar to adult, but has narrower black forehead, dusky throat concolorous with upper breast, browner crown and nape, whitish belly, and rufous tips to wing-coverts. **VOICE** Has a wide variety of calls, the most frequent of which is a loud, metallic, undulating *klok-kli-klok-kli-kli* (Madge and Burn 1993). **HABITS** Similar to those of Rufous Treepie. Typically, found in flocks of up to 20 birds; often forages in company with other forest species, especially drongos. Mainly arboreal, and keeps high in trees; occasionally forages on the ground, hopping about with its tail cocked high. **HABITAT** Broadleaved forest and secondary growth in the tropical, subtropical and lower temperate zones; in Pakistan, found in dry areas with deciduous trees and dense bushy ground cover. Less associated with human habitation and cultivation than Rufous Treepie. **BREEDING** April–July. Builds a cup-shaped nest 3–7 m up in a bush or small tree in forest or in a bush-covered ravine. **DISTRIBUTION AND STATUS** Resident, subject to altitudinal movements. Himalayas in N Pakistan (Margalla and Murree hills) and mainly from Himachal Pradesh east to Arunachal Pradesh; NE India, Eastern Ghats and Bangladesh. **PK:** scarce and very local; 460–1060 m. **NP:** common and widespread; summers chiefly 1050–2150 m (–2590 m), winters 915–1525 m (down to 80 m). **IN:** locally common; 600–1500 m, occasionally to 2100 m in the west and to 2300 m in the east. **BT:** common; 380–2135 m. **BD:** locally common. **REFERENCES** Lama (1994a).

WHITE-BELLIED TREEPIE *Dendrocitta leucogastra* — Plate 90

Southern Tree Pie (I)

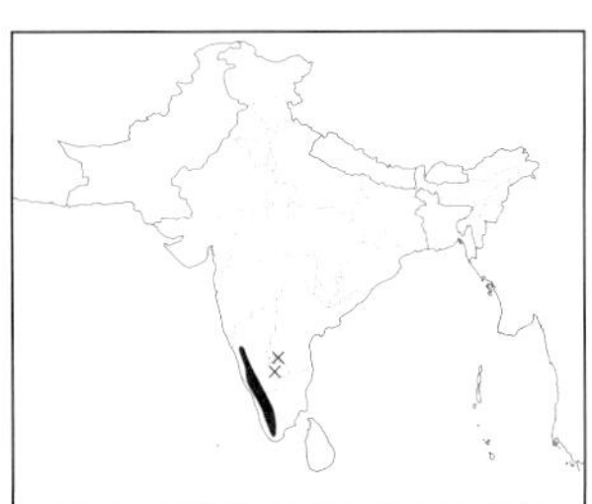

IDENTIFICATION 48 cm. A white, black and rufous treepie. **Adult** told from Rufous Treepie (p.593) by black forecrown, ear-coverts and throat which contrast with white hindcrown, nape and underparts. Additional features are largely black wings with white patch at base of primaries, white rump, bright rufous undertail-coverts, and longer tail with more black at tip. In flight, black wings with small white patch, and white rump, help separate it from Rufous Treepie, even in poor views. **Juvenile** is similar to adult, but has narrower and shorter central tail feathers, buff fringes to white body feathers, and diffuse demarcation between black throat and white underparts. **VOICE** Has a wide variety of calls, similar to those of Rufous Treepie but harsher and more metallic, and frequently mimics Greater Racket-tailed Drongo (p.614); calls include a distinctive rattling *kt-kt-kt-kt-kt* and a throaty *chuff-chuff-chuff* (Ali and Ripley 1987). **HABITS** Similar to those of Rufous and Grey Treepies (p.593), but usually keeps to the middle or lower storey of trees, sometimes in low shrubs or on the ground close to cover. Frequently follows roving bands of insectivorous birds, especially Greater Racket-tailed Drongos. **HABITAT** Humid, broadleaved evergreen hill forest and associated secondary growth, sholas and overgrown rubber plantations. Replaced by Rufous Treepie in deciduous woodland, but where evergreen and deciduous woodland are intermixed the two species may occur side by side. **BREEDING** February–April. Builds a cup-shaped nest in a tall shrub or sapling in dense forest. **DISTRIBUTION AND STATUS IN:** endemic resident in Western Ghats from N Karnataka south to S Kerala, and east to W Tamil Nadu, S Andhra Pradesh and E Karnataka; uncommon to common; 60–1500 m. **REFERENCES** Gaston and Zacharias (1996).

COLLARED TREEPIE *Dendrocitta frontalis* — Plate 90

Black-browed Treepie (I)

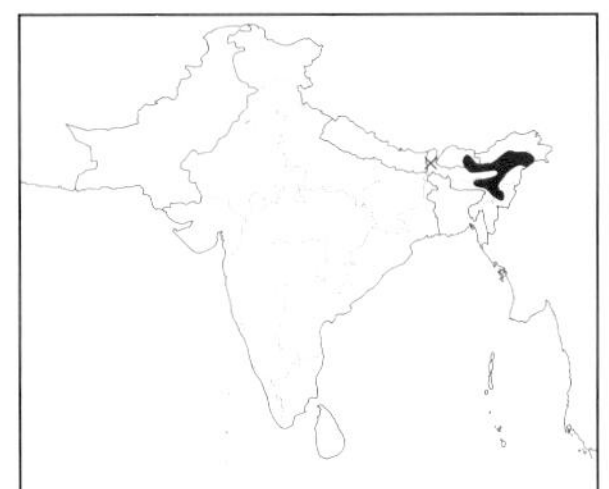

IDENTIFICATION 38 cm. A grey, black and rufous treepie. **Adult** distinguished from Rufous Treepie (p.593) by black forecrown, ear-coverts and throat contrasting with pale grey hindcrown, nape, breast and belly. Additional features are smaller size, black tertials, rufous rump concolorous with mantle, rufous lower belly and vent, and black tail. In flight, black tail and rufous rump help separate it from Rufous Treepie, even in poor views. **Juvenile** is similar to adult, but is duller, with brownish fringes to grey of head and breast. **VOICE** Poorly described, but has a wide variety of calls similar to those of other treepies (Ali and Ripley 1987). **HABITS** Similar to those of Rufous and Grey Treepies (p.593), but is quieter. **HABITAT** Dense, humid broadleaved evergreen forest with bamboo thickets in the tropical, subtropical and lower temperate zones. **BREEDING** April–July. Builds a cup-shaped nest in a bamboo clump or thorny bush near forest edge. **DISTRIBUTION AND STATUS** Resident. Himalayas from Nepal?, Darjeeling, West Bengal, Sikkim and E Bhutan east to Arunachal Pradesh; NE India. **NP:** possibly recorded in 19th century, but the specimen may have originated in India. **IN:** locally frequent in Arunachal Pradesh, very few recent records from elsewhere; foothills up to 2100 m. **BT:** uncommon; 510 m up to at least 1700 m. **REFERENCES** Ganguli-Lachungpa (1996), Katti *et al.* (1992), Singh (1995).

ANDAMAN TREEPIE *Dendrocitta bayleyi* — Plate 90

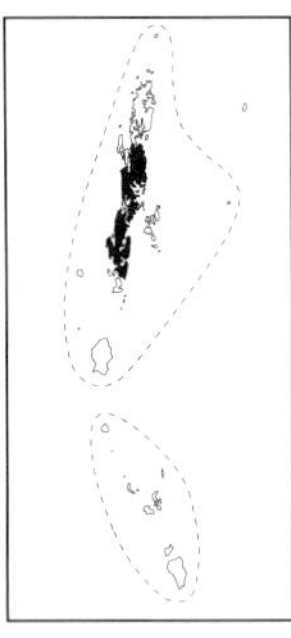

IDENTIFICATION 32 cm. A small treepie. **Adult** has blue-grey head and neck (with blacker face) merging into dull rufous-brown mantle and bright rufous underparts; also blackish wings with white patch at base of remiges, and blackish tail. Iris is strikingly yellow. **Juvenile** has browner hood, brownish fringes to wing-coverts, and shorter and greyer tail. **VOICE** Calls include a loud, fluty, oriole-like whistle, *kiu-duu*, regularly repeated, and a harsh rasping *kyow* or *kiayow*. Like other treepies, probably has a large repertoire of harsh as well as melodious notes (P. Holt). **HABITS** Similar to those of Rufous and Grey Treepies (p.593). Usually found in pairs, family parties, or flocks of up to 20 birds in tall trees. Often with feeding parties of other forest birds, especially the Andaman Drongo (p.612). **HABITAT** Dense broadleaved evergreen forest. **BREEDING** March–May. Builds a flimsy nest 5 m above ground in a small thickly foliaged forest tree. **DISTRIBUTION AND STATUS IN:** locally fairly common resident, endemic to the Andaman Is. **REFERENCES** Davidar *et al.* (1997).

BLACK-BILLED MAGPIE *Pica pica* Plate 91

Magpie (I)

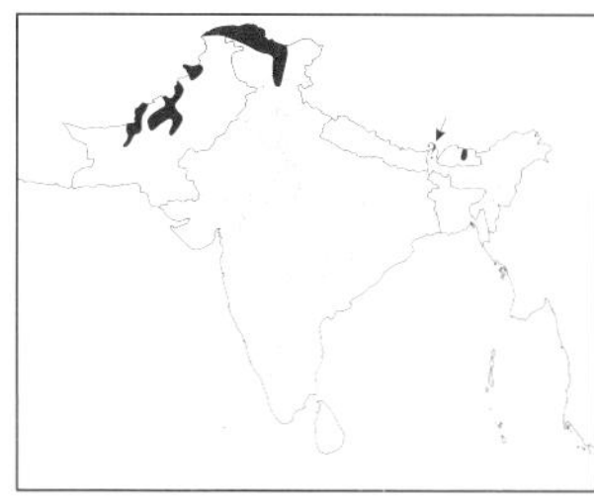

IDENTIFICATION 43–50 cm. Body is mainly black (with weak purple-and-green sheen), with white scapulars, flanks and belly. Has metallic blue-black wings, with white inner webs to primaries showing as a white flash in flight. Tail is long, graduated, and metallic bronze-green and purple. Has undulating and weak-looking flight, with rather rapid wingbeats interspersed with short glides. **Juvenile** resembles adult, but has greyish-black head and breast. **Racial variation** *P. p. bactriana* of the W Himalayas has a white rump, which is black in *P. p. bottanensis* of N Bhutan. **VOICE** A staccato *chack-chack-chack-chack...* etc, uttered in bursts of eight or more notes; also an enquiring *ch'chack* and a squealing *keee-uck* (Madge and Burn 1993). **HABITS** Usually found in pairs, sometimes in loose flocks of up to 20 or more birds. Forms communal roosts. Bold and conspicuous, often seen in the open, resting on walls and rooftops or feeding on the ground. Struts about, carrying the tail a little elevated; frequently hops to catch prey, and flicks its wings and tail when excited. Omnivorous: diet includes small mammals, birds' eggs, invertebrates, cereal grains, fruits and human food scraps. **HABITAT** Open cultivated upland valleys, around villages with orchards; also scrub forest in Pakistan. **BREEDING** March–May. Builds a large domed nest 2–3 m up in a tree or in a thorn bush. **DISTRIBUTION AND STATUS** Resident, subject to altitudinal movements. W and N Pakistan, Ladakh, Himachal Pradesh, Sikkim? and Bhutan. **PK:** common, but rather thinly distributed, in drier mountains; 1300–3200 m. **IN:** locally common in Ladakh; 2000–4500 m. **BT:** locally common, mainly in Bumthang; 3100–4600 m. **REFERENCES** Pfister (1997).

HUME'S GROUNDPECKER *Pseudopodoces humilis* Plate 91

Hume's Ground Chough (I), Hume's Ground Jay (N), Tibetan Ground Jay, *Podoces humilis* (I)

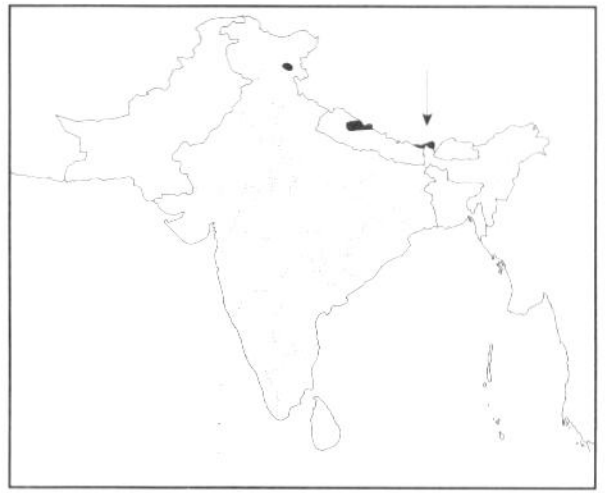

IDENTIFICATION 19 cm. A small, upright and fluffy-looking, ground-dwelling bird with downcurved black bill. Bears a passing resemblance to Isabelline Wheatear (p.667). Bounces along on the ground, and has weak, fluttering flight on rounded wings low over the ground. **Adult** has much of head and upperparts sandy-brown, and underparts off-white, with buffish sides to head, throat and breast. Has largely buffish-white tail with brown central feathers, black lores, whitish nape, and broad white tips to alula. **Juvenile** has shorter, straighter bill, which is browner in coloration, and lacks black lores. **VOICE** A feeble munia-like *cheep,* and a plaintive whistling *chip* followed by a quick-repeated *cheep-cheep-cheep-cheep* (Ali and Ripley 1987). **HABITS** Often tame around human habitation. Terrestrial. Prefers to escape by hopping away. Seeks invertebrates by using its long strong bill to peck vigorously into short turf and yak dung, and to probe crevices. Very active; makes long bounding hops and flicks its wings. Often rests on walls and rocks, bobbing up and down and flicking its tail. **HABITAT** Tibetan steppe country with scattered dwarf bushes or stony slopes. **BREEDING** Poorly known in region. Nest with eggs found in mid April: made of dry plant material and animal hairs, and built at end of a tunnel at least 1.85 m long excavated in a small, steep earth bank. **DISTRIBUTION AND STATUS** Resident, with little seasonal movement. N Nepal and extreme N Sikkim. **NP:** frequent in the trans-Himalayan region; 3965–5335 m. **IN:** rare in Ladakh, recorded 4200–5500 m; fairly common in Sikkim near human habitations, 4450 m. **REFERENCES** Martens and Eck (1995), Pfister (1997), Robson (1994).

SPOTTED NUTCRACKER *Nucifraga caryocatactes* Plate 91

Nutcracker (F,I), Eurasian Nutcracker

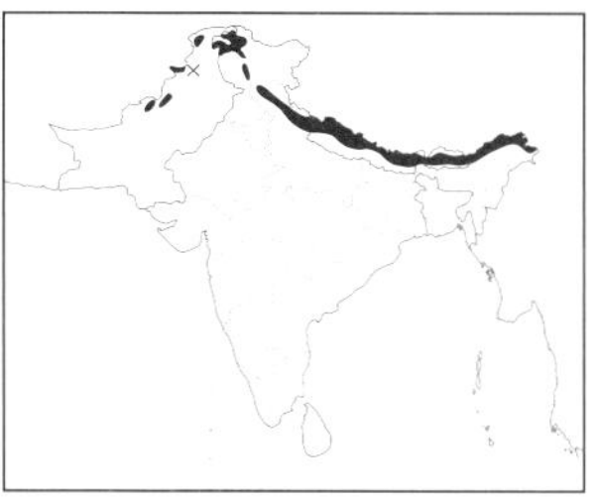

IDENTIFICATION 32–35 cm. **Adult** is largely brown, with bold white spotting on head and body. Further, has pointed black bill, unmarked brown crown, white vent, comparatively unmarked glossy brownish-black wings, and white sides and tip to outer tail feathers. In silhouette, has larger bill and shorter tail than Eurasian Jay (p.591). Flight is rather heavy and laboured. **Juvenile** is duller, with unglossed wings, and is less cleanly spotted owing in part to paler brown body coloration. **Racial variation** Three subspecies occur in the subcontinent. *N. c. multipunctata* of the W Himalayas is distinctive, with large, dense white spots on body; has white spotting on throat, scapulars, lower back to uppertail-coverts, flanks, greater and primary coverts and tertials which is typically lacking in *N. c. hemispila* and *N. c. macella,* which occur from Himachal Pradesh eastward; bill of *multipunctata* is also finer (on some, strikingly long and thin). Note that *multipunctata* is treated as possibly a separate species ('Larger-spotted Nutcracker') by Madge and Burn (1993). Spotting on *hemispila* and *macella* is most profuse on ear-coverts and sides of neck, and is comparatively sparse on mantle and breast; flanks and lower belly of these two races are almost unspotted, and contrast strongly with white vent, while background colour of body is a warmer chocolate-brown (more blackish-brown in *multipunctata*). **VOICE** Call is a far-carrying, dry and harsh *kraaaak*, sometimes shortened to a weaker *zhree*; also has a quiet, musical song of various piping, clicking, squeaking, whistling and whining notes (Madge and Burn 1993). **HABITS** Usually in pairs or family parties. Sedentary and mainly territorial all year. Frequently perches on tops of tall conifers and often flicks its tail, revealing the white sides. Also easily located by its distinctive grating calls. Feeds mainly on pine and spruce seeds, using its sharp pointed bill to extract seeds from cones; also eats hazelnuts, walnuts, acorns and invertebrates. **HABITAT** Dry coniferous forest of pine, fir and spruce. **BREEDING** March–June. Builds a cup-shaped nest 6–18 m above ground and close to the main trunk of a tall conifer. **DISTRIBUTION AND STATUS** Resident, subject to some altitudinal movements. Mountains of NW Pakistan, and in Himalayas from N Pakistan east to Arunachal Pradesh. Mainly 2000–3000 m in W Himalayas, 1500–3660 m in the east (305–4000 m). **PK:** frequent but local in W mountains and valleys and in inner valleys of the Himalayas. **NP, IN, BT:** common and widespread.

RED-BILLED CHOUGH *Pyrrhocorax pyrrhocorax* — Plate 91

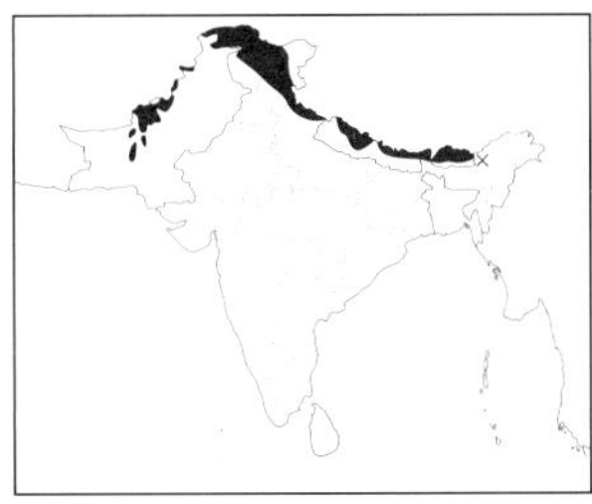

IDENTIFICATION 36–40 cm. **Adult** differs from Yellow-billed Chough (below) in longer and thinner, more downcurved, red bill. Call is also distinctive. In flight, has broader wing-tips (and more rectangular wing shape) with more pronounced fingered primaries, and square-ended tail which equals width of wing-base. At distance, vigorous digging with downcurved bill can aid identification. As with Yellow-billed, flight is distinctive and different from that of other corvids, with bounding buoyant flight action; often engages in spectacular aerobatics, diving with closed wings and sweeping up again, and characteristically soars with spread primaries curved upwards at tips. **Juvenile** lacks metallic gloss of adult, has pinkish-brown or blackish (rather than red) legs, and has shorter pinkish-brown to orange-brown bill which is closer in shape to Yellow-billed's (but is still slimmer, and more noticeably – although only very slightly – downcurved). **VOICE** Call is a far-carrying, penetrating and nasal *chaow..chaow*. **HABITS** Gregarious throughout the year; often in flocks of several hundred in winter. Roosts communally. Feeds chiefly on invertebrates, which it seeks by methodically probing and digging into the ground and by turning over stones and animal dung. Walks and runs actively. Frequently perches on cliffs, rocks, walls and buildings. **HABITAT** High mountains with cliffs and adjacent pastures of short turf; also upland cultivation in winter. **BREEDING** March–May. Builds a bulky nest in a cave, or a hole in an inaccessible cliff face or wall. **DISTRIBUTION AND STATUS** Resident, subject to altitudinal movements. Higher mountain ranges of W Pakistan and in Himalayas from N Pakistan east to Arunachal Pradesh. **PK:** common in the north; up to at least 4875 m in the breeding season. **NP:** common and widespread; mainly above 2400 m, summers up to 5490 m (–7950 m), sometimes winters down to 2135 m (1450 m). **IN:** locally common; 3000–4500 m, foraging up to 6000 m in summer, in winter locally down to 1800 m. **BT:** common; above 2200 m.

YELLOW-BILLED CHOUGH *Pyrrhocorax graculus* — Plate 91

Alpine Chough (N)

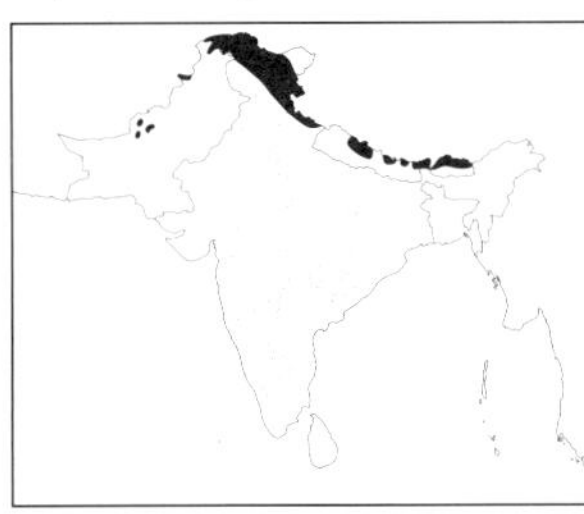

IDENTIFICATION 37–39 cm. **Adult** told from Red-billed Chough (above) by shorter and straighter, yellow bill. Call is also distinctive. In flight, has narrower wing-tips with less pronounced fingered primaries, more pronounced curve to trailing edge of wing, and rounded tail which is greater in length than width of wing-base. As Red-billed Chough, has distinctive flight, with bounding and buoyant flight action, and indulges in similar aerobatics. **Juvenile** lacks metallic gloss of adult, and has brown or blackish (rather than red) legs, and duller olive-yellow bill. Bill is shorter and stouter than that of juvenile Red-billed. **VOICE** Call is a far-carrying, sweet, rippling *preeep*, and a descending whistled *sweeeoo*; also has a rolling *churrr* (Madge and Burn 1993). **HABITS** Similar to those of Red-billed Chough, but more confiding and will scavenge around settlements for kitchen scraps. **HABITAT** High mountains with cliffs, alpine pastures and cultivation. Generally occurs at higher altitudes than Red-billed Chough, but mixes with that species in overlap zones. **BREEDING** May and June. Sometimes breeds colonially. Builds a bulky nest in a hole in an inaccessible cliff face or a cave. **DISTRIBUTION AND STATUS** Resident, subject to some altitudinal movements. Mountains of W Pakistan and in Himalayas from N Pakistan east to Arunachal Pradesh. **PK:** common and widespread in higher Himalayas; local and in small numbers in W mountains. **NP:** common and widespread; chiefly above 3500 m and up to at least 6250 m (2350–8235 m). **IN:** locally common; from the treeline up to 8600 m, winters locally down to 1500 m. **BT:** fairly common.

EURASIAN JACKDAW *Corvus monedula* — Plate 91

Jackdaw (I), Common Jackdaw (R)

IDENTIFICATION 34–39 cm. A small, stocky corvid with small bill, grey nape and hindneck, and pale iris. In flight, looks blunt-headed, and wings appear oval-shaped and tail comparatively long. Flight is fast and direct,

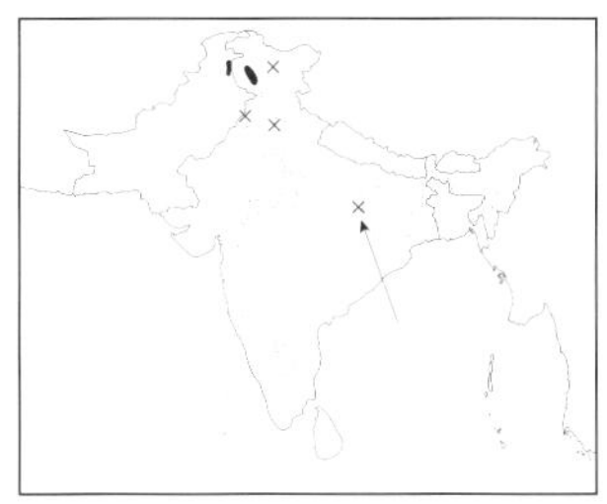

with quicker wingbeats, compared with that of other corvids; frequently performs aerobatics, but is less agile than the choughs. **Adult** has silky-grey nape and hindneck which contrast with glossy black face and cap; also slate-grey underparts, and pale grey iris. Hindneck is almost white where it adjoins mantle, forming half-collar. **Juvenile** is duller, with darker grey nape and hindneck (lacking whitish collar) which contrasts less with dull black face and cap, and has brownish-black underparts and darker grey iris. **VOICE** Call is an abrupt, oft-repeated *chjack...chjack...*; other calls include a low, drawn-out *chaairurr*, and a high, slurred *kyow* (Madge and Burn 1993). **HABITS** Sociable and usually keeps in flocks, frequently in huge numbers in winter. Roosts communally throughout the year, often with other corvids. Bold and inquisitive. Usually feeds on the ground in open country. When foraging, walks about briskly and sometimes hops and runs; digs and probes in the ground and picks from the surface. Feeds chiefly on invertebrates and seeds, also birds' eggs and nestlings and human food scraps. **HABITAT** Open cultivated valleys and damp pastures. **BREEDING** April–June. Builds an untidy nest in the roof of a house, hole in a wall or ruin, or tree hollow. **DISTRIBUTION AND STATUS** Resident. Mainly N Pakistan and Kashmir; also winters from W and N Pakistan east to Uttar Pradesh, numbers varying from year to year. **PK:** frequent but very local resident; breeds mainly 1200–1500 m in Hazara district and in the lower Neelum and Kunhar valleys, winters locally in the foothills. **IN:** breeds commonly in Kashmir, 1500–2100 m, with post-breeding dispersal up to 3600 m; occasionally winters down to the plains. **REFERENCES** Baker (1922).

HOUSE CROW *Corvus splendens* — Plate 91

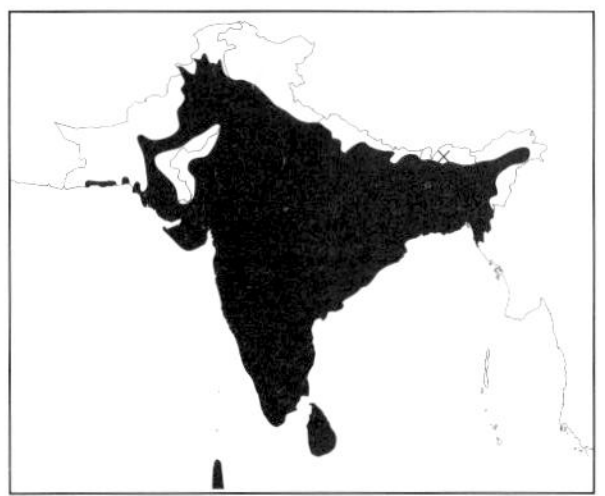

IDENTIFICATION 40 cm. A two-toned corvid. Throughout its range in the subcontinent, has black crown, face and throat contrasting with paler nape, neck and breast, giving rise to collared appearance. See Carrion Crow (p.598) for differences from the 'hooded' form of that species, which occurs as a winter visitor to the NW subcontinent. Direct flight is steady, with shallow wingbeats. **Adult** has gloss to black of plumage, and 'collar' is well defined and becomes paler with wear. **Juvenile** lacks gloss, and 'collar' is duskier and less well defined. **Racial variation** Four races are recognised from the subcontinent. The northwesternmost *C. s. zugmayeri* has a paler smoky-white 'collar' (dull sandy-white when worn), strongly contrasting with black of plumage. 'Collar' is darker and greyer in the widely distributed nominate race, and is less well defined in the two races occurring in S India/Sri Lanka and the Maldives. Southern races are closer in coloration to Large-billed Crow (p.598), but retain 'two-toned' appearance (with contrast between black crown and throat and dark grey mantle and breast). **VOICE** Main call is a flat, dry *kaaa-kaaa*, weaker than that of Large-billed (Madge and Burn 1993). **HABITS** Gregarious when feeding and roosting. Adapted to exploit human activity. Bold and cunning, omnivorous and an opportunistic feeder. Scavenges at rubbish dumps, in streets and on banks of rivers, lakes and the seashore, takes nestlings and birds' eggs from urban gardens, seeks invertebrates and grain in cultivation near villages, and attracted to carrion. On the ground, moves with confident strides and occasional sideways hops. Gathers in enormous roosts throughout the year at traditional sites of favoured stands of trees, often with Large-billed Crows, mynas and parakeets; indulges in spectacular aerobatics in pre-roost gatherings. Flocks make regular morning and evening flights from and to roosts. **HABITAT** Closely associated with human activity: occurs in villages, towns, cities, gardens and nearby cultivation. **BREEDING** January–September, varying locally. Builds an untidy stick nest, usually 3–4 m up in a tree; also at times on a ledge of a building or on a power pylon. **DISTRIBUTION AND STATUS** Resident, subject to altitudinal and seasonal movements. Throughout much of the subcontinent, except parts of the northwest, northeast and Himalayas. **PK:** common, widespread and sedentary; below 600 m. **NP:** common and widespread; below 1525 m (–2100 m). **IN:** widespread and common; from plains up to 2100 m. **BT:** locally fairly common; up to 2500 m in summer. **BD:** common and widespread. **LK:** common in coastal lowlands and locally inland. **MV:** common.

ROOK *Corvus frugilegus* — Plate 91

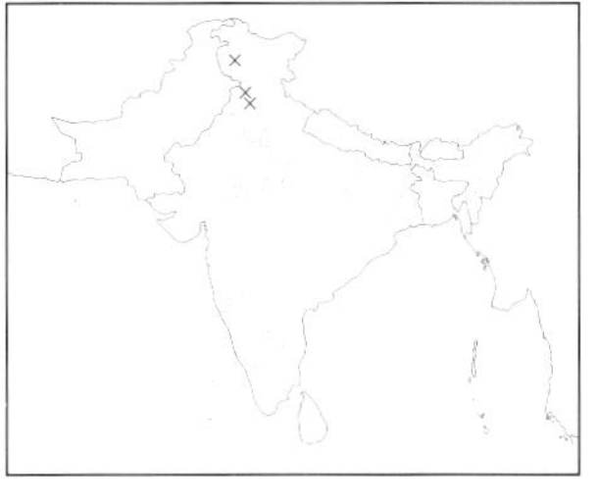

IDENTIFICATION 47 cm. **Adult** readily told from Carrion and Large-billed Crows (p.598) by bare whitish skin around base of bill and throat. **Juvenile** has black feathering on face and throat, and lacks gloss to black plumage. More closely resembles Carrion and Large-billed Crows, and best told by the following subtle differences (which are also shown by adult birds): has thinner and more pointed bill, with straighter ridge to culmen; steeply rising forehead and peaked crown; and shaggy 'trousered' thighs. In flight, trailing edge to wing is straighter, has narrower, more prominently fingered wing-tips, and tail is more rounded or wedge-shaped compared with Carrion Crow's. **VOICE** Call is a drier and flatter *kaah* compared with that of Carrion Crow; also has a high-pitched *kraa-a* (Madge and Burn 1993). **HABITS** Highly gregarious; keeps in large flocks, often with other corvids and starlings. Struts about on the ground in open country, stopping to dig and probe in search of invertebrates, seeds and shoots. Gathers in communal roosts in trees, often with Eurasian Jackdaws and House Crows (p.595 and p.597). **HABITAT** Cultivation and short pastures near habitation in open country. **DISTRIBUTION AND STATUS PK:** locally frequent winter visitor to plains and broad valleys adjacent to N mountains; also in NW Pakistan and Baluchistan; arrives in mid October, leaves by end March. **IN:** rare visitor to Punjab in 19th century. **REFERENCES** Harris *et al.* (1989).

CARRION CROW *Corvus corone* — Plate 91

Hooded Crow

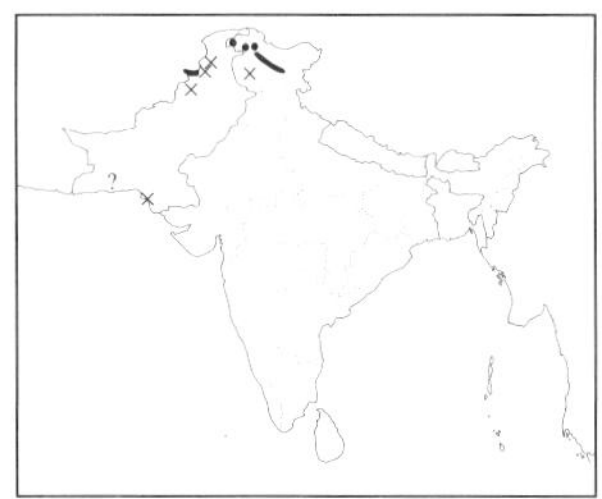

IDENTIFICATION 48–56 cm. Confusion is most likely with Large-billed Crow (below). Distinguished from that species by smaller bill with straighter culmen (distinctly arched on Large-billed), and flatter forehead and crown (Large-billed has a domed or rather short, square-shaped head). For differences from juvenile Rook (p.597), see that species. Has a steady flight, with slower wingbeats than Rook. **Adult** has glossy black plumage, which is dull blackish-brown in **juvenile**. **Racial variation** 'Hooded Crow' *C. c. sharpii* occurs as a winter visitor to the region, and differs markedly from *C. c. orientalis,* described above, in having grey hindneck and mantle and mainly grey underparts. Patterning similar to House Crow (p.597), but whole of head and most of breast is black, and mantle is grey, not black. **VOICE** Call is stronger and more resonant than that of Large-billed Crow, a confident *kraa.* **HABITS** Usually keeps singly or in pairs; often associates with Rooks or House Crows. Quite shy and wary. Forages in cultivation and pastures; also scavenges at refuse tips, and readily takes carrion. Feeds by picking, probing, and turning over stones and other objects. Omnivorous. **HABITAT** Open country with patches of cultivation, often near upland villages. **BREEDING** April and May. Builds nest in the fork of a tree 8–10 m above ground, usually near habitation. **DISTRIBUTION AND STATUS** N Pakistan, Ladakh and Kashmir. Eastern Carrion Crow *C. c. orientalis* is resident. **PK:** scarce and local; breeds at 2600 m. **IN:** small numbers; 2700–3600 m. Hooded Crow *C. c. sharpii* is a winter visitor. **PK:** uncommon and local. **IN:** common in Ladakh, rare in Kashmir; 2500–4000 m. **REFERENCES** Pfister (1997).

LARGE-BILLED CROW *Corvus macrorhynchos* — Plate 91

Jungle Crow (F,I,N), Black Crow (P), *C. levaillantii*

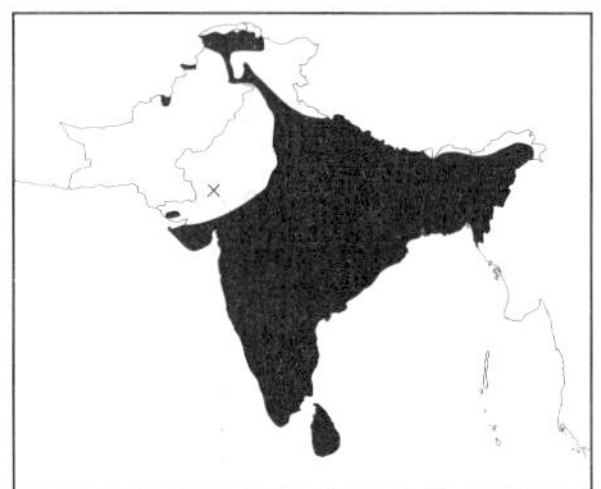

IDENTIFICATION 46–59 cm. All-black plumage separates this species from House Crow (p.597). Lacks any of the contrast between head and neck/breast which is shown by even the darkest races of House Crow (from S India and Sri Lanka). Bill is stouter, and has more pronounced curve to culmen. Direct flight is steady, with shallow wingbeats, like that of House Crow. For differences from the desert-dwelling Brown-necked Raven (below), Carrion Crow (above) and juvenile Rook (p.597), see those species. **Adult** has glossy black plumage, which is dull black in **juvenile**. **Racial variation** The two Himalayan races, *C. m. intermedius* and especially *C. m. tibetosinensis,* are more raven-like than *C. m. culminatus* and *C. m. levaillantii* of the 'plains' – which are sometimes treated as a separate species, 'Jungle Crow' (see Madge and Burn 1993) – and have a bigger and heavier bill, wedge-shaped tail, and harsher calls. In flight, Himalayan races are best told from Common Raven (p.599) by shorter neck, shorter and broader (less angled) wings, and less strongly wedge-shaped tail. On the ground, further differences are slighter appearance, absence of prominent throat hackles, squarer or domed crown, and longer tail extension beyond closed wings. Call is also different. **VOICE** Call of Himalayan races is rather loud, dry *kaaa-kaaa,* different from the deep resonant call of Common Raven; call of the other two races is weaker and higher-pitched. **HABITS** Similar to those of other *Corvus* species. Usually keeps singly, in pairs or in small groups, but roosts communally in large numbers, often with House Crows and mynas. Inquisitive, bold and omnivorous. Frequently scavenges and eats carrion; follows herds of goats and sheep in mountain pastures. Himalayan birds indulge in aerial gambolling. **HABITAT** Around human habitation in well-wooded country and at forest edges and clearings, alpine pastures above the treeline, also villages, towns and cities; avoids deserts and semi-deserts. **BREEDING** November–September, varying locally. Builds nest 7–18 m up in a tree at forest edges (Himalayas) or at the edges of cultivation (peninsula). **DISTRIBUTION AND STATUS** Resident, subject to some altitudinal movements. N Baluchistan, Pakistan; Himalayas from N Pakistan east to Arunachal Pradesh; NE India, Bangladesh, peninsular India and Sri Lanka. **PK:** common in the Himalayan forest zone up to 3600 m. **NP:** widespread, common; from plains up to 4900 m (–5790 m). **IN:** widespread and common; from plains up to 4500 m in Himalayas, to 2300 m in peninsular hills. **BT:** common. **BD, LK** common throughout.

BROWN-NECKED RAVEN *Corvus ruficollis* — Plate 91

IDENTIFICATION 52–56 cm. Best told from Large-billed Crow (above) by brown cast to head, neck and breast (especially pronounced in fresh plumage, when glossed with copper and purple). In bright light, or when worn,

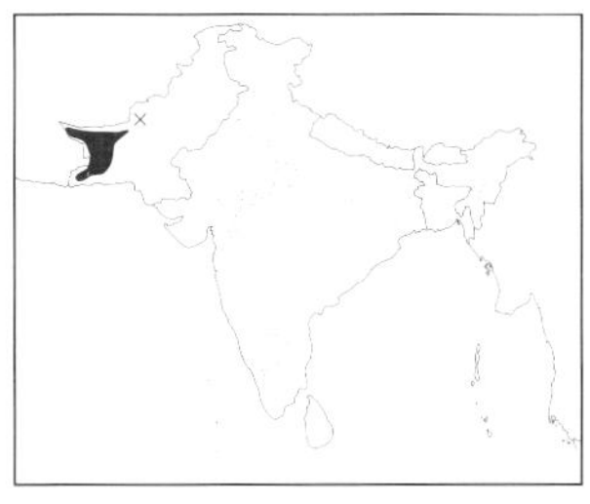

brown of neck is often not apparent. Compared with Large-billed Crow, has raven-like appearance, with longer and more angled wings showing more pronounced fingered primaries, and more markedly wedge-shaped tail. Although very similar to Common Raven (below) in structure and in flight behaviour, differences from that species include distinctive call, thinner bill, less shaggy throat owing to shorter throat hackles, and slimmer build; and at rest folded wings reach tail-tip (falling slightly short of tail on Common). Caution is needed, since *subcorax* race of Common Raven can have brown cast to head and neck. **Juvenile** is similar in plumage to adult. **VOICE** A dry rising *aarg-aarg-aarg* (Madge and Burn 1993). **HABITS** Very similar to those of Common Raven. Usually keeps in pairs or small parties; gathers in larger numbers at good food sources and at communal roosts. Generally shy and wary, but quite bold where not persecuted. Particularly favours carrion. **HABITAT** Desert. **BREEDING** Little known in the subcontinent; recorded in December, January and March. Nests in cliffs and sides of narrow gorges. **DISTRIBUTION AND STATUS PK:** resident along the Makran coast, where frequent, and in S Baluchistan; spreads north in winter, occasionally to Quetta, and west to Chagai.

COMMON RAVEN *Corvus corax* Plate 91

Raven (F,I)

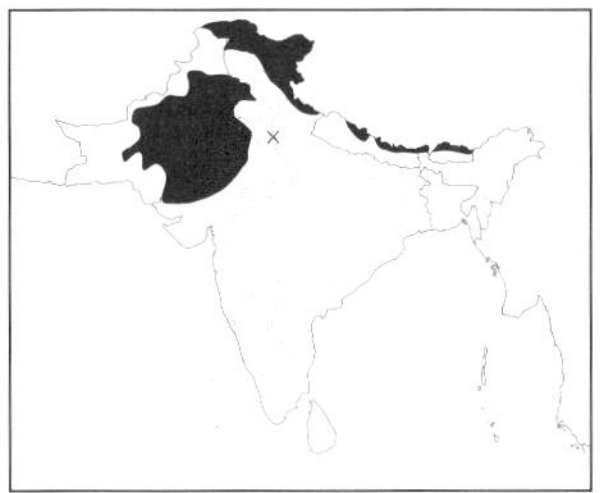

IDENTIFICATION 58–69 cm. Confusion is possible with Large-billed Crow (p.598) and Brown-necked Raven (p.598). Large-billed occurring in the Himalayas are more raven-like compared with those of the plains, and are often mistaken for Common Raven. In flight, latter best told from Large-billed by longer neck, longer and more angled wings with more pronounced fingered primaries, and more markedly wedge-shaped tail. On the ground, further differences are larger appearance, with more rugged and shaggy look, prominent throat hackles and flatter crown, and wing-tips fall just short of tail (noticeably short on Himalayan Large-billed). Call is also different. For differences from the desert-dwelling Brown-necked Raven, see that species. Powerful and agile in flight, and can soar and glide well; performs impressive aerobatics, often tumbling, diving with closed wings and rolling on to the back in mid-air. **Adult** has glossy black plumage, which is dull black in **juvenile**. **Racial variation** The Himalayan race, *C. c. tibetanus*, differs from *C. c. subcorax* of the W plains and foothills in being larger, with longer throat hackles. **VOICE** Typical call is a loud, deep, resonant, croaking *wock..wock*, quite different from that of other corvids; also has a high, knocking *toc-toc-toc*. **HABITS** Found singly, in pairs or in family parties in the breeding season, although has communal roosts and may gather in flocks at carcases or other rich food sources. Forms pair-bonds for life, and keeps the same breeding territory each year. Wanders in small flocks in winter. Walks with a waddling gait, and hops occasionally. **HABITAT** *C. corax subcorax* occurs around villages, towns and nomadic settlements in desert and semi-desert in lowlands and foothills. *C. corax tibetanus* inhabits high-altitude trans-Himalayan country: dry, rocky desert above the treeline. **BREEDING** *C. corax subcorax* December–March. Nests in the top of a solitary tree or on an earth cliff. *C. corax tibetanus* February–early April. Nests on a cliff ledge or in a rock crevice. **DISTRIBUTION AND STATUS** *C. c. subcorax* Pakistan and NW India. Resident, subject to local movements, from the plains up to 600 m, occasionally higher. **PK:** thinly distributed, occurs widely in Baluchistan and NW Pakistan, now rare in Punjab and confined to the northwest; also in extreme SE Sindh; rapidly declining and range reduced because of the spread of irrigation and cultivation. **IN:** locally common. *C. c. tibetanus* Himalayas from N Pakistan east to Arunachal Pradesh. Resident, subject to some altitudinal movements. **PK:** only in extreme N drier mountains, where thinly distributed. **NP:** fairly common in the trans-Himalayas; mainly from 3500 m up to at least 5000 m (2500–8235 m). **IN:** trans-Himalayas; 4000–5500 m, foraging to over 6000 m, wintering down to 2500 m. **BT:** fairly common.

WOODSWALLOWS Tribe Artamini

Plump birds with long, pointed wings, short tail and legs, and a wide gape. They feed on insects, usually captured in flight. Characteristically, they spend prolonged periods on the wing. They perch close together on a bare branch or wire, and often waggle the tail from side to side.

ASHY WOODSWALLOW *Artamus fuscus* Plate 92

Ashy Swallow-shrike (I,P)

IDENTIFICATION 19 cm. At rest, looks top-heavy, with large head and full breast and slim tapering body with long, pointed wings. In flight, long glides are broken by short bouts of rapid wing-flapping; broad-based, pointed wings, held stiff and flat, and broad, well-rounded tail are distinctive. **Adult** has stout blue-grey bill, uniform slate-grey head (with slightly darker mask), greyish-maroon mantle, and pinkish-grey underparts. In flight,

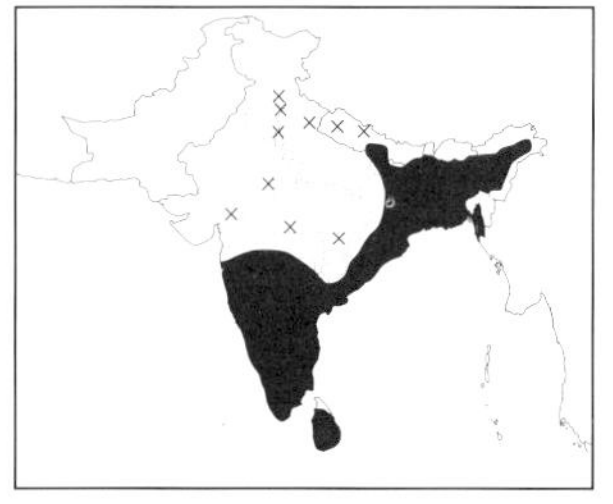

features include whitish underwing, white-tipped tail, and narrow greyish-white 'horseshoe' band across uppertail-coverts. **Juvenile** differs from adult in having browner upperparts, with buff fringes to mantle, wing-coverts and remiges, and paler grey throat which is almost concolorous with pale buffish-grey underparts (with indistinct brownish barring). **VOICE** Has a harsh *chek-chek-chek* call; song is a drawn-out pleasant twittering, starting and finishing with harsh *chack* notes (Ali and Ripley 1987). **HABITS** Sometimes in flocks of up to 30 birds. Chiefly insectivorous, and spends much time hawking prey on the wing. Perches on dead branches near treetops, telegraph wires or other vantage points and makes frequent aerial sallies. Flies in a wide circle with rapid wingbeats alternating with glides, often returning to the same perch. Between feeding forays, several individuals may be seen lining a branch, often huddled together. Has a distinctive habit of wagging its stumpy tail when perched. Calls frequently, both when perched and in flight. **HABITAT** Open wooded country, often with palm trees. **BREEDING** January–July, varying locally. Nest is a shallow cup of fine fibres, placed on a horizontal bough of a palm tree. **DISTRIBUTION AND STATUS** Resident, subject to local movements. Mainly in the E, NE and S subcontinent. **NP:** local, mainly below 365 m (–2560 m); common in the east, fairly common in C areas, uncommon elsewhere. **IN:** locally common and patchily distributed; up to 1700 m in Himalayas, to 2100 m in peninsular hills. **BT:** locally common. **BD:** common throughout. **LK:** locally frequent in the lowlands and lower hills.

WHITE-BREASTED WOODSWALLOW *Artamus leucorynchus* Plate 92

White-rumped Wood Swallow (I)

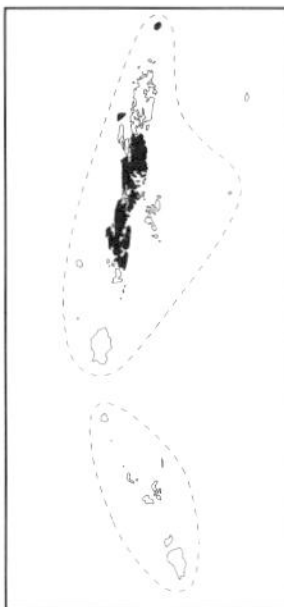

IDENTIFICATION 19 cm. The only woodswallow occurring in the Andaman Is. Structure and behaviour as Ashy Woodswallow (p.599). Similar in appearance to that species, but has broad white band across lower rump and uppertail-coverts, and white lower breast, belly and vent (contrasting with dark grey head). **Juvenile** is similar to adult, but has uniform brown upperparts with buff fringes, buff tips to wing-coverts and remiges, and greyish-white throat which merges into white underparts. **VOICE** Calls and song as those of Ashy Woodswallow. **HABITS** Similar to those of Ashy Woodswallow. **HABITAT** Forest clearings. **BREEDING** April and May. Has similar nest to that of Ashy Woodswallow. **DISTRIBUTION AND STATUS IN:** found in the subcontinent only on the Andaman Is, where common. **REFERENCES** Sankaran and Vijayan (1993).

ORIOLES, CUCKOOSHRIKES, TRILLERS, MINIVETS, FLYCATCHER-SHRIKES Tribe Oriolini

ORIOLES Genus *Oriolus*

Medium-sized arboreal passerines which usually keep hidden in the leafy canopy. Characteristically, orioles have beautiful, fluty, whistling songs and harsh grating calls. They are usually seen singly, in pairs or in family parties. Their flight is powerful and undulating, with fast wingbeats. They feed mainly on insects and fruit. The typical nest is a neat, deep cup woven with grasses and other fibres, and suspended like a hammock from a forked branch in a large tree.

EURASIAN GOLDEN ORIOLE *Oriolus oriolus* Plate 92

Golden Oriole (F,I,P)

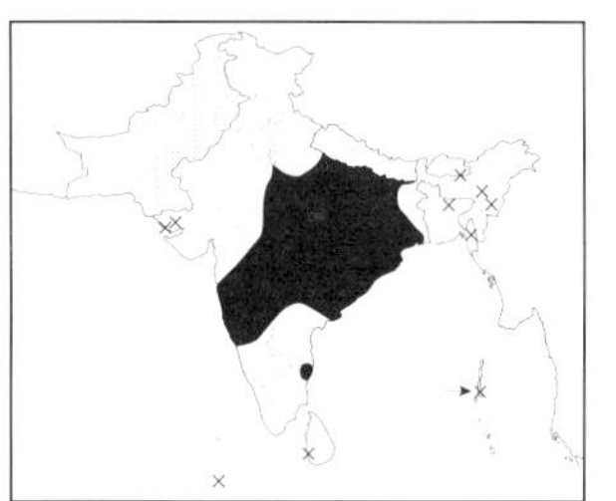

IDENTIFICATION 25 cm. **Adult male** has small black eye-patch, golden-yellow head and body, largely black wings with yellow primary coverts and tips to tertials/secondaries, and yellow-and-black tail. **Adult female** has yellowish-green upperparts, blackish streaking on whitish underparts (with variable amounts of yellow on sides of breast), brownish-olive wings, yellow rump, and brownish-olive tail with yellow corners. Some older females have unstreaked (or faintly streaked) yellow underparts and brighter yellow upperparts, and wings and tail are similar to male's; mantle, wing-coverts and tertials, however, usually have an olive cast. **Immature** is similar to adult female, but is initially duller on upperparts and more heavily streaked on underparts. Older immature males resemble older females, with (streaked) yellow underparts. **Racial variation** Male *O. o. oriolus*, a vagrant to the subcontinent, differs from *O. o. kundoo*, described above, in having largely black wings (with indistinct pale tips to tertials and secondaries), less yellow on sides of tail (two-thirds, rather than one-third, of outer feathers are black), and smaller yellow patch on primary coverts, and black mask does not extend behind eye. **VOICE** Song is a loud, fluty *weela-whee-oh*; call is a harsh, nasal *kaach*. **HABITS** A typical oriole. **HABITAT** Open deciduous woodland, groves, orchards, and trees at the edge of cultivation. **BREEDING** April–August. Builds a usual oriole nest in a tree, 6–20 m above ground. **DISTRIBUTION AND STATUS** Resident, partial migrant and passage migrant. Summer visitor to W Pakistan and Himalayas from Pakistan east to Nepal and N plains of subcontinent; resident from E Rajasthan and N Maharashtra east to West Bengal and south to Karnataka and N Tamil Nadu; winter visitor farther south; status in NE India uncertain. **PK:** summer visitor from plains up to 2600 m, mainly in the north, where common. **NP:** widespread summer visitor below 1830 m (–2600 m); common at Chitwan, frequent elsewhere. **IN:** locally common; usually summers in the plains and up to 1800 m in Himalayas (–4400 m), widespread in the peninsula in winter in plains and up to 1800 m in hills. **BT:** uncommon summer visitor; 300–1280 m. **BD:** local passage migrant. **LK:** winter visitor, scarce in the N dry lowlands, rare in S lowlands and in S lower hills. **MV:** rare passage migrant. **REFERENCES** Martens and Eck (1995).

BLACK-NAPED ORIOLE *Oriolus chinensis* — Plate 92

(= *O. chinensis diffusus, O. c. andamanensis, O. c. macrourus* Ripley)

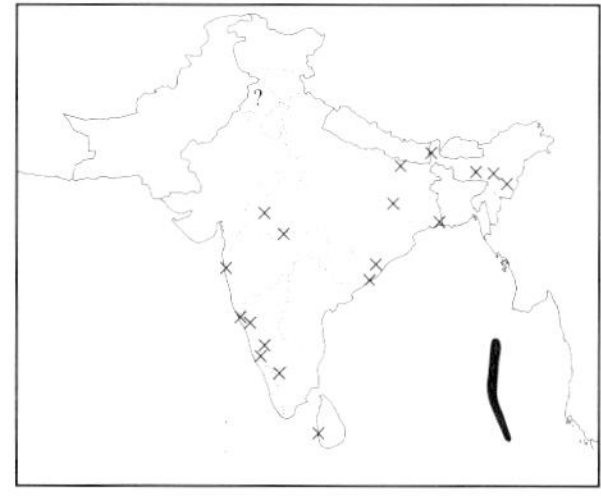

IDENTIFICATION 27 cm. Very similar to Slender-billed Oriole (below), and adult female and immature birds can probably be safely distinguished from that species only by stouter bill and call. **Adult male** is best told by stouter bill, broader dark stripe through eye and across nape (although this is somewhat variable, and on some width of band is very similar to that of Slender-billed), bright yellow mantle (concolorous with head and underparts), golden-yellow wing-coverts and panel across tertials/secondaries, and distinctive call. **Adult female** similar to male, but mantle, wing-coverts and panel across tertials/secondaries are more yellowish-green (and much as Slender-billed). **Immature** is as immature Slender-billed in plumage. Diffuse mask and band across nape (if present), and larger and stouter bill, are best features for separation from immature Eurasian Golden (p.660). **VOICE** A cat- or jay-like squeal and fluted, yodelling whistled song like those of Eurasian Golden Oriole, but song is more repetitive and lacks jumps in pitch (P. Holt). **HABITS** A typical oriole. **HABITAT** Mixed broadleaved secondary forest, rubber plantations and well-wooded gardens. **BREEDING** April–June. Builds a usual oriole nest, 3–7 m above ground. **DISTRIBUTION AND STATUS** Winter visitor to Kerala and Bangladesh; resident on Andaman and Nicobar Is; widely scattered records from elsewhere. **IN:** occasionally recorded on mainland in winter; common on Andaman and Nicobar Is. **BD:** local. **LK:** vagrant.

SLENDER-BILLED ORIOLE *Oriolus tenuirostris* — Plate 92

***O. chinensis* (F,I)**

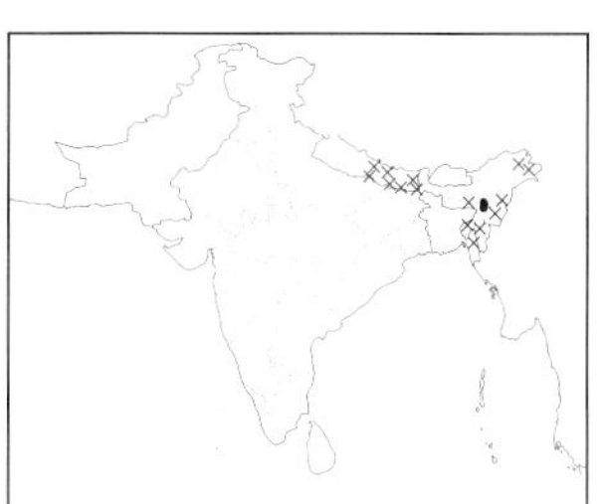

IDENTIFICATION 27 cm. Very like Black-naped Oriole (above), from which female and immature are not safely separable except by bill shape and call. **Adult male** distinguished from Eurasian Golden Oriole (p.600) by dark stripes behind eye which join at nape, longer and more downcurved bill, and olive-yellow wing-coverts and panel across tertials/secondaries. Safely told from female Black-naped only by slimmer, longer-looking bill, typically narrower dark stripe through eye and across nape (although there is some variation in the width of this band on both species), and distinctive call. For differences from male Black-naped, see account for that species. **Adult female** similar to male, but has dull black head stripe, duller yellow head and underparts, and duller olive-yellow mantle. **Immature** initially has yellowish-green upperparts including crown and nape, dark bill and eye, more uniformly olive wings (with yellowish edges to coverts and remiges), and whitish underparts with black streaking; nape patch and stripe behind eye can be very diffuse, and prominence of streaking and extent of yellow on underparts vary (presumably with age). Diffuse mask and band across nape (if apparent), and longer bill, are best features for separation from immature Eurasian Golden. **VOICE** Utters mellow fluty notes, *wheeow* or *chuck,tarry-you* (Ali and Ripley 1987); call is a diagnostic, high-pitched, woodpecker-like *kick* (Boonsong and Round 1991). **HABITS** A typical oriole. **HABITAT** Well-wooded areas, groves, large trees in open country. **BREEDING** May and June in NE India. Nest and nest site are like those of Eurasian Golden Oriole. **DISTRIBUTION AND STATUS** Breeds in Himalayas from Bhutan east to Arunachal Pradesh, and NE India; winters west to C Nepal and Bihar. **NP:** scarce, probably a winter visitor; recorded below 2285 m. **IN:** uncommon; breeds in the northeast, 1500–2100 m, winters in adjacent hills and plains. **BT:** probably breeds; locally fairly common in late spring, 1125–2135 m.

BLACK-HOODED ORIOLE *Oriolus xanthornus* — Plate 92

Black-headed Oriole (F,I,P)

IDENTIFICATION 25 cm. In all plumages, distinguished from other orioles by blackish crown and nape contrasting with yellow to olive-yellow mantle. **Adult male** has glossy black head and neck contrasting with

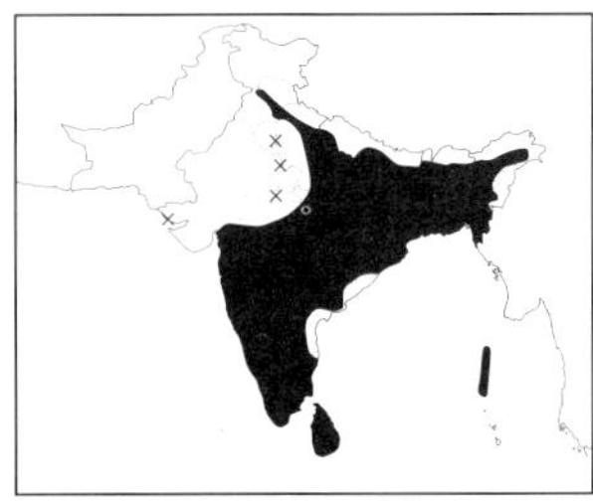

golden-yellow body, bold yellow outer edges to black tertials and secondaries, and mainly yellow tail. **Adult female** similar, but has olive-yellow mantle. **Immature** is similar to adult female, but has blackish (rather than red) bill, yellow forehead, yellow streaking on crown and sides of head, black streaking on white throat, diffuse black streaking on yellow breast, and duller wings with narrow yellowish edges to tertials/secondaries and narrower yellow tips to primary coverts. **VOICE** Song is a mixture of mellow fluty notes, *wye-you* or *wye-you-you*, and harsh *cheeah* and *kwaak* notes; call is a harsh, nasal *kwaak* (Ali and Ripley 1987). **HABITS** A typical oriole, but not shy. Frequently seen flying from tree to tree. Sometimes with itinerant bands of insectivorous birds. **HABITAT** Open broadleaved forest, groves, well-wooded country, and wooded gardens. **BREEDING** Throughout the year, varying locally. Builds a usual oriole nest, 4–10 m above ground in a large tree. **DISTRIBUTION AND STATUS** Resident, subject to local movements. From Punjab, Gujarat and E Rajasthan east through the Himalayan foothills to Arunachal Pradesh, and south through most of the subcontinent. **NP:** widespread and common below 365 m, uncommon up to 915 m, rare to 1370 m. **IN:** locally common in plains and hills; up to 1200 m in Himalayas, rarely to 1700 m in peninsular hills. **BT:** frequent; 245–450 m (–1800 m). **BD:** common throughout. **LK:** common in lowlands and up to middle altitudes.

MAROON ORIOLE *Oriolus traillii* — Plate 92

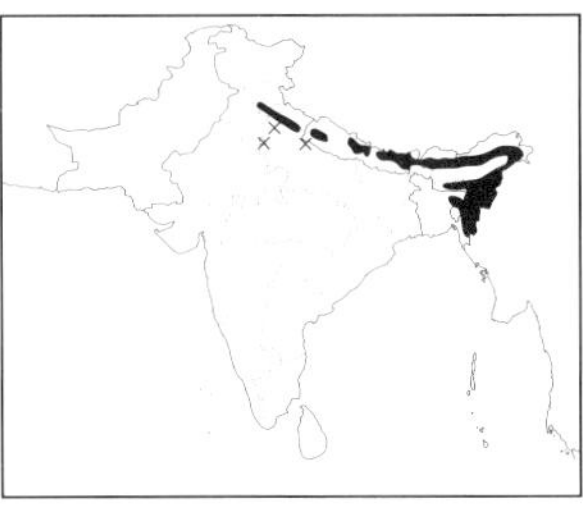

IDENTIFICATION 27 cm. In all plumages, has maroon rump, undertail-coverts, and upperside and underside to tail. **Adult male** has black head, breast and wings contrasting with glossy maroon body. Like female, has blue-grey bill and pale yellow iris. **Adult female** is similar to male, with blackish head and wings, but has duller maroon mantle, and whitish belly and flanks with diffuse maroon-grey streaking. **Immature** is similar to adult female, but has more uniformly brown upperparts, including wings, whitish underparts streaked with dark brown, and brown iris. **Juvenile** has orange-buff fringes to mantle and back and tips to coverts. **VOICE** Song is a rich fluty *pi-io-io*; has nasal, squawking call, less harsh than that of Black-naped Oriole (p.601) (Boonsong and Round 1991). **HABITS** A typical oriole. Rather shy, and usually keeps among the foliage of tall trees. Often with mixed hunting flocks of other species. **HABITAT** Dense, moist, broadleaved deciduous and evergreen forest. **BREEDING** April and May. Builds a usual oriole nest, 4–20 m above ground in a tree fork in thick forest. **DISTRIBUTION AND STATUS** Resident, subject to local and altitudinal movements. Mainly Himalayas from Himachal Pradesh east to Arunachal Pradesh; NE India and Bangladesh. **NP:** locally fairly common; summers mainly 1500–2440 m, winters 1200–1800 m (down to 75 m). **IN:** locally fairly common in hills up to 3100 m and adjacent plains. **BT:** fairly common; 250–2440 m. **BD:** local winter visitor. **REFERENCES** Lama (1995a).

CUCKOOSHRIKES Genus *Coracina*

Arboreal, insectivorous birds which usually keep high in the trees. They are of medium size, with long pointed wings, a moderately long rounded tail, and an upright carriage when perched. Their plumage is drably coloured in grey, black and white. The nest is a shallow saucer-shaped cup made of grasses, small twigs and cobwebs.

LARGE CUCKOOSHRIKE *Coracina macei* — Plate 92

C. novaehollandiae **(F,I,K,R)**

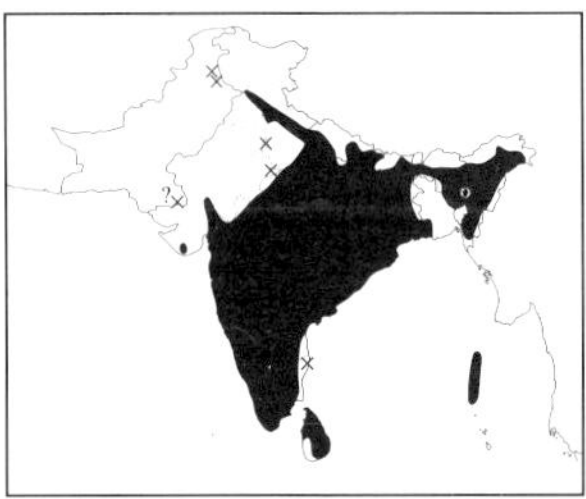

IDENTIFICATION 30 cm. A large cuckooshrike with pale grey upperparts, wings and tail, and greyish-white underparts with variable amounts of faint grey barring. For differences from Bar-bellied Cuckooshrike (p.603), see that species. **Male** has black lores and dark grey ear-coverts, and throat and breast are uniformly grey, with rest of underparts barred. **Female** has paler lores, and underparts are almost entirely barred; has pale barring on rump and uppertail-coverts. **Juvenile** is heavily scaled with brown and white above and below (except belly and vent), and has whitish rump; wing-coverts and remiges have broad greyish-white fringes and tips (former with dark subterminal marks). **First-year** is similar to adult female, but retains some juvenile coverts and tertials. **Racial variation** Compared with *C. m. macei* of the peninsula, described above, *C. m. nipalensis* of the Himalayan foothills and E subcontinent has broader whitish fringes to greater coverts, tertials and secondaries (forming obvious pale wing panel) (not shown on plate, fig 8a); further, male of this race has uniform grey underparts (without barring), while female has barring on belly and flanks (and is similar to adult male of nominate race). *C. m. andamanensis* of Andaman Is is similar to *nipalensis*, but slightly paler. **VOICE** A loud, wheezy *jee-eet* (R. Grimmett). **HABITS** Found singly, in scattered pairs or in loose flocks. A noisy bird which usually perches in the topmost branches of trees, although sometimes descends to bushes or the ground to feed. Eats large insects and their larvae. Has a distinctive habit of flicking each wing slightly, one after the other, when it alights. Flies from tree to tree with an undulating flight. **HABITAT** Light woodland, secondary forest, groves, trees at cultivation edges and in gardens, and edges of forest clearings; also scrub in Assam and on the Andaman Is. **BREEDING** January–October, varying locally. Builds a usual cuckooshrike nest on a horizontal branch, up to 18 m above ground. **DISTRIBUTION AND STATUS** Resident, subject to local and altitudinal movements. Himalayan foothills from E Pakistan, east to Arunachal Pradesh; Punjab, S Gujarat and E Rajasthan east to Bangladesh and south through most of the subcontinent. **PK:** former resident around Murree and Islamabad; now a rare straggler. **NP:** common and widespread resident; summers up to 2135 m (–2440 m), winters up to at least 1525 m. **IN:** widespread and locally fairly common; plains and hills, up to 1200 m in the peninsula. **BT:** uncommon. **BD:** locally common. **LK:** common in the dry lowlands and lower hills.

BAR-BELLIED CUCKOOSHRIKE *Coracina striata* — Plate 92

Barred Cuckooshrike (I)

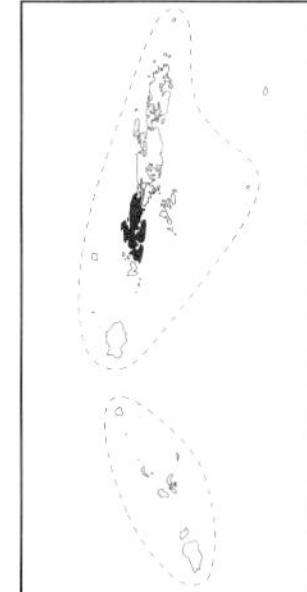

IDENTIFICATION 26 cm. Occurs in the subcontinent only in the Andaman Is, and very different from populations of same species in Malay peninsula. Told from Large Cuckooshrike (p.602), which also occurs in the Andamans, by smaller size, much darker grey upperparts and tail, and crimson iris. Is forest-dwelling and, unlike Large Cuckooshrike, does not occur in 'open' habitats. **Male** has dark grey throat and breast, and broad blackish barring on rest of underparts. By comparison, male Large in Andamans has uniform grey underparts, while female has pale grey throat/breast and lightly barred rest of underparts. **Female** lacks grey breast and is entirely barred below. **Juvenile** is very scaly above; has pale rufous tips and fringes to greater coverts and tertials (former with dark subterminal marks), and barred underparts, with distinctive rufous cast to throat and breast **First-year** has adult-like (dark and uniform) upperparts, barred underparts with distinctive rufous cast to throat and breast, and retains some juvenile coverts and tertials. Has pale horn base to bill (as juvenile) **VOICE** In Thailand, gives clear whinnying whistles, *kliu-kliu-kliu-kliu* (Boonsong and Round 1991). Also has a loud, harsh, grating *gree-ew...gree-ew*, similar to call given singly by Large Cuckooshrike; usually calls in flight (C. Robson). **HABITS** Similar to those of other cuckooshrikes. Keeps to the treetops, often in pairs and with foraging flocks of other species, such as minivets and drongos. **HABITAT** Forest. **BREEDING** Not definitely recorded in the subcontinent. **DISTRIBUTION AND STATUS IN:** found in the subcontinent only on the Andaman Is, where resident.

BLACK-WINGED CUCKOOSHRIKE *Coracina melaschistos* — Plate 92

Smaller Grey Cuckooshrike (I), Dark Cuckooshrike (F)

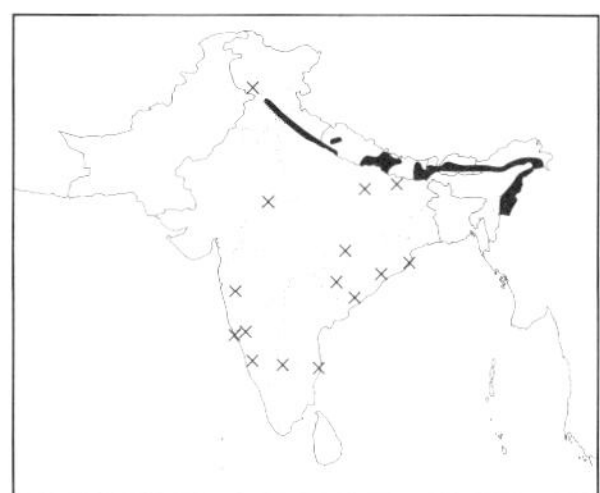

IDENTIFICATION 24 cm. **Male** differs from other cuckooshrikes occurring in the region in having dark slate-grey head and body, black wings, fine white tips to undertail-coverts, and bold white tips to tail feathers. **Female** is similar, but paler grey above and below, with wings not so contrastingly black, and has faint barring on underparts (usually most pronounced on belly and vent). Underparts are never as strongly barred as on female/immature Black-headed (p.604); also lacks latter's whitish supercilium, upperparts are darker, showing little contrast between rump/uppertail-coverts and tail, and has indistinct pale fringes to wing-coverts and tertials. Further, has more graduated tail, with several large white tips visible on underside (Black-headed also has white tips to tail, but these form single white patch on underside because tail is less graduated). **Juvenile** has bold white tips to upperparts, and underparts are heavily barred with white; wing-coverts and tertials are broadly tipped with white. **First-year** appears to be similar to adult of respective sex, but retains some pale-tipped juvenile tertials, greater coverts and primary coverts. **VOICE** A descending, monotonous *pity-to-be*. **HABITS** Similar to those of other cuckooshrikes. Generally keeps singly or in pairs, and often associates with minivets, drongos and other insectivorous birds. Gleans insects from the foliage, usually high up in trees, but sometimes in undergrowth. Has an undulating flight. **HABITAT** Open forest, forest edges and groves; prefers deciduous rather than coniferous trees. **BREEDING** April–June. Builds a usual cuckooshrike nest in a tree fork, 3–8 m above ground. **DISTRIBUTION AND STATUS** Resident, subject to altitudinal and seasonal movements. Breeds in Himalayas from Murree, Pakistan, east to Arunachal Pradesh, and NE Indian hills; winters mainly in Himalayan foothills and in plains and hills of E and NE India and Bangladesh, with scattered winter records west to W Maharashtra and south to N Tamil Nadu. **PK:** rare and very local summer visitor; 1800–2000 m. **NP:** resident; frequent up to 915 m all year, to 2400 m in summer. **IN:** locally fairly common resident and winter visitor; summers from foothills up to 2100 m, winters in plains and foothills. **BT:** common resident; 400–2440 m. **BD:** local winter visitor. **REFERENCES** Martens and Eck (1995).

BLACK-HEADED CUCKOOSHRIKE *Coracina melanoptera* Plate 92

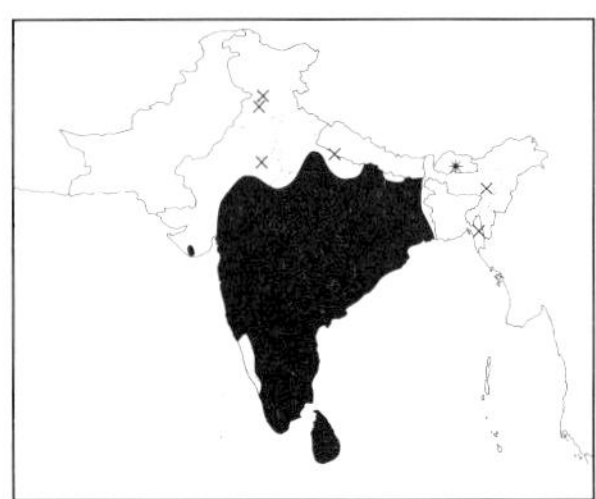

IDENTIFICATION 18 cm. **Male** differs from other cuckooshrikes occurring in the region in having dark slate-grey head, neck and upper breast, contrasting with pale-grey mantle and rest of underparts; wings are darker grey than mantle, and have broad pale fringes to coverts and tertials. **Female** has fine whitish supercilium, uniform brownish-grey crown, nape and mantle, and buffish-white underparts, barred with dark brown on throat, breast and belly. Underparts are more clearly barred dark grey and white than on female Black-winged (p.603), pale grey back and rump contrast noticeably with blackish tail, and has broader white fringes to coverts and tertials. See that species for further differences. **Juvenile** is similar to female, but upperparts are barred with white; tertials and wing-coverts have dark subterminal marks. **First-year** appears to be similar to adult of respective sex, but retains a few juvenile coverts and tertials. **VOICE** Song comprises clear, mellow whistling notes, followed by a quick-repeated *pit-pit-pit* (Ali and Ripley 1987). **HABITS** Similar to those of Black-winged. **HABITAT** Light broadleaved forest, secondary growth and groves. **BREEDING** March–September, varying locally. Builds a small nest similar to that of other cuckooshrikes, 2–8 m above ground on a branch of a large tree. **DISTRIBUTION AND STATUS** Resident, endemic to the subcontinent. Mainly Himalayan foothills from Himachal Pradesh east to West Bengal and south throughout much of the peninsula and Sri Lanka; summer visitor to Himalayas. **NP:** scarce; recorded mainly in spring and summer, below 275 m (–1430 m). **IN:** generally uncommon; summer visitor to Himalayas up to 1000 m; resident and winter visitor to the peninsula, mainly in the plains, also up to 1500 m in the hills, to 2100 m in Nilgiris. **BT:** vagrant; collected once in 19th century. **BD:** local. **LK:** rare resident in lowlands and hills.

PIED TRILLER *Lalage nigra* Plate 92

Pied Cuckooshrike (I)

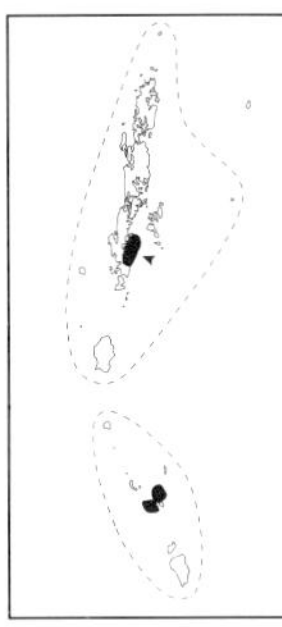

IDENTIFICATION 18 cm. **Male** has white supercilium and black eye-stripe, black crown, nape and mantle, broad white fringes to black wing-coverts, tertials and secondaries, grey rump, black tail with prominent white tips, and white underparts with grey wash to breast. **Female** has black of upperparts replaced by slate-grey; has slight buffish wash to underparts, which are faintly barred, and narrower white fringes to wing-coverts. **Juvenile** is similar to female, but has browner upperparts with faint buff barring. **VOICE** A disyllabic whistle, the second note lower, and a descending series of nasal *chack* notes (Boonsong and Round 1991). **HABITS** Usually found in pairs or scattered parties. Forages for insects in undergrowth, close to the ground. **HABITAT** Forest edges and secondary growth. **BREEDING** Season uncertain; eggs found in May. Builds a cup-shaped nest of twigs, covered with lichens, in dense forest. **DISTRIBUTION AND STATUS IN:** uncommon or rare resident; occurs in the subcontinent only on Nicobar Is (Camorta, Katchall, Trinkat). **REFERENCES** Sankaran (1997; 1998).

MINIVETS Genus *Pericrocotus*

Small to medium-sized, brightly coloured passerines with a moderately long tail and an upright stance when perched. They are arboreal, and feed on insects by flitting about in the foliage to glean prey from leaves, buds and bark, sometimes hovering in front of a sprig or making short aerial sallies. They usually keep in pairs in the breeding season, and in small parties when not breeding. Minivets are frequently members of roving mixed parties of insectivorous species in forest. When feeding and in flight, they continually utter contact calls. Typically, the nest is a neat cup made of roots, small twigs and grass stems, covered on the outside with cobwebs and lichen; it is usually placed on the horizontal branch of a tree where it is well camouflaged against the bark.

ROSY MINIVET *Pericrocotus roseus* Plate 93

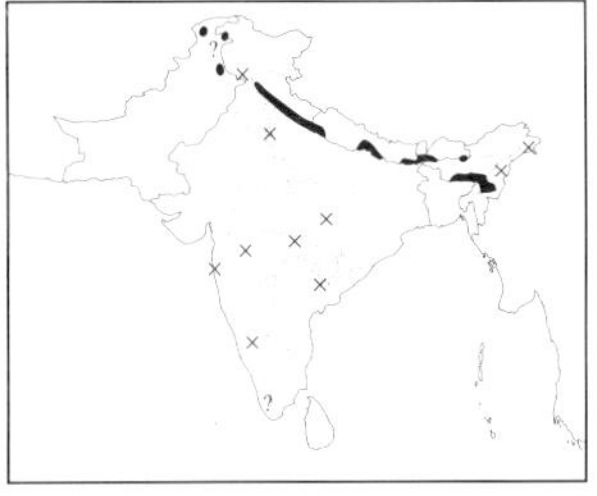

IDENTIFICATION 20 cm. **Male** told from other minivets by combination of grey to grey-brown upperparts, pinkish-white throat and pink underparts, pinkish-red edges to tertials, and dull pinkish rump with variable scarlet uppertail-coverts. Has scarlet wing patch and outer tail feathers. **Female** has 'pink' in plumage of male replaced by pale yellow. Distinguished from other female minivets by combination of grey to grey-brown upperparts, with indistinct greyish-white forehead and supercilium, dull and indistinct olive-yellow rump, whitish throat, and pale yellow underparts. Most closely resembles female Small Minivet (p.605), but is larger in size, and Small has flame-orange rump and/or uppertail-coverts. Paler underparts and dull rump help separate Rosy from female Grey-chinned (p.606). **Juvenile** similar to female, but upperparts (crown, nape, mantle, back and coverts) have distinct pale yellow tips, giving a scaly appearance.

Immature male like female, but shows traces of pink on underparts, and traces of scarlet in wings and uppertail-coverts and tail. **VOICE** A whirring trill. **HABITS** Similar to those of other minivets, but rather less active. Seeks insects from foliage high up and in middle branches of trees and in bushes. **HABITAT** Broadleaved deciduous and evergreen forest, open woodland and gardens; in Pakistan, usually in Chir Pine forest. **BREEDING** Mainly May and June. Builds a usual minivet nest on a moss- or lichen-covered branch, 3–10 m above ground. **DISTRIBUTION AND STATUS** Resident and partial migrant. Breeds, and possibly resident, in Himalayas from N Pakistan east to Arunachal Pradesh, and NE India; winters in NE and E India and Bangladesh, with scattered non-breeding-season records south to Karnataka. **PK:** rare and very local resident or summer visitor; 1500 m. **NP:** local, possibly resident, mainly below 245 m (–1370 m); frequent at Chitwan, uncommon elsewhere. **IN:** resident, generally uncommon; breeds in Himalayas from the base up to 1800 m, winters in the plains and foothills. **BT:** rare. **BD:** local winter visitor.

ASHY MINIVET *Pericrocotus divaricatus* — Plate 93

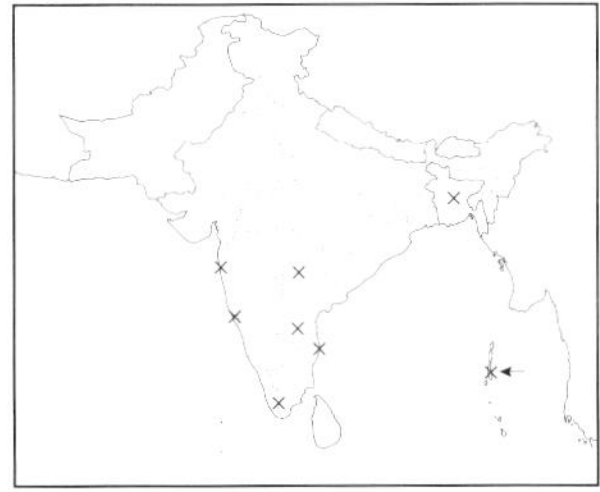

IDENTIFICATION 20 cm. Both sexes differ from most other minivets in being predominantly grey and white in coloration, without any red or yellow in plumage. In flight, shows whitish wing-bar, which is especially prominent on underwing. **Male** has white forehead and forecrown contrasting with black ear-coverts, rear crown and nape, cold grey upperparts including rump, dark grey wings with greyish-white edges to flight feathers, white underparts, and dark grey tail (contrasting with uppertail-coverts) with white outer feathers. **Female** is similar to male, but lacks black 'cap'; has narrow white forehead and short supercilium, black lores, and pale grey crown, ear-coverts and nape. Possibly confusable with female Black-headed Cuckooshrike (p.604), but is longer-tailed and lacks barring on underparts. **Immature** has little or no white on head, and has brownish-grey upperparts, white tips to tertials and greater coverts, and faint brownish scaling on neck sides and breast. **VOICE** A whirring trill. Flight call coarser and more rasping than that of other minivets: an unmelodious, and somewhat hesitant, *tchue-de....tchue-dee-dee....tchue-dee-dee,* slightly ascending (P. Holt). **HABITS** Similar to those of other minivets. Very active and restless; usually seen on the topmost branches of trees, especially in bare, caterpillar-infested ones. **HABITAT** Canopy of light forest. **DISTRIBUTION AND STATUS IN:** winter visitor; regular but scarce near Madras, Tamil Nadu, rarely recorded in Maharashtra, Andhra Pradesh, Goa, Kerala and Andaman Is. **BD:** vagrant. **REFERENCES** Anon. (1994), Neelakantan *et al.* (1993), Robertson and Jackson (1992), Uddin (1995).

SMALL MINIVET *Pericrocotus cinnamomeus* — Plate 93

Little Minivet (P)

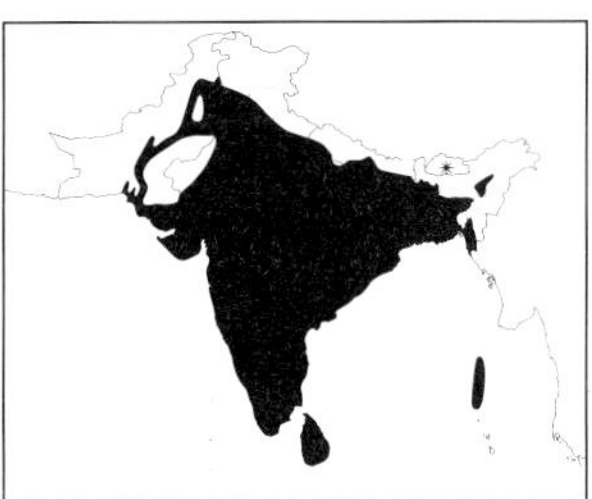

IDENTIFICATION 16 cm. A small minivet which varies considerably in coloration according to race. **Male** distinguished from other minivets by combination of small size, dark grey to black face and throat, grey crown, nape and mantle, and orange breast, wing patch and rump. **Female** from other minivets by combination of small size, grey upperparts, orange wing patch, and orange rump and/or uppertail-coverts. **Immature male** is similar to adult female, but shows traces of black on throat and orange on breast. **Juvenile** similar to female, but upperparts are scaled with buff. **Racial variation** Five races are described from the subcontinent. *P. c. pallidus* of NW subcontinent is strikingly pale, male having pale grey upperparts and dark grey throat, orange of underparts restricted to narrow band across breast, and wing patch and sides of tail pale orange to pale buff. Female *pallidus* is also extremely pale, with sandy-grey upperparts, white underparts with at best a trace of yellow, and orange-buff patch on wing; flame-orange of uppertail-coverts is only bright colour in plumage. For differences from female White-bellied (p.606), see that species. *P. c. peregrinus* of NC subcontinent is darker grey above: male has darker throat and more extensive orange on underparts, and female has stronger yellow wash to underparts, compared with *pallidus*. *P. c. malabaricus* of SW peninsula is brightest of the races: male has blackish throat, dark slate-grey upperparts, and blackish wings and tail with orange patch on wing and orange outer tail feathers, while breast and flanks are deep orange, becoming orange-yellow on belly; female has yellow-buff throat and breast, becoming orange-yellow on belly and flanks. *P. c. cinnamomeus,* which occupies the rest of peninsula, and *P. c. vividus,* of NE subcontinent and Andaman Is, are intermediate between *malabaricus* and *peregrinus.* **VOICE** A continuous high-pitched *swee-swee...* etc. **HABITS** A typical minivet. Forages actively in the tree canopy. **HABITAT** More open wooded areas than those preferred by most other minivets. Light forest, groves, plantations, scrub with scattered small trees, orchards, trees at cultivation edges, gardens and roadside avenues. **BREEDING** February–October, varying locally. Nest is a tiny cup, usually built high up in a tree. **DISTRIBUTION AND STATUS** Resident throughout much of the subcontinent, except parts of the northwest, northeast and Himalayas. **PK:** widespread but local, common only in Punjab and N Sind. **NP:** frequent throughout; below 290 m (–915 m). **IN:** widespread and locally common in plains and hills; up to 1500 m in the peninsula, to 1600 m in Himalayas. **BT:** rare. **BD:** locally common throughout. **LK:** common in the lowlands and hills.

WHITE-BELLIED MINIVET *Pericrocotus erythropygius* Plate 93

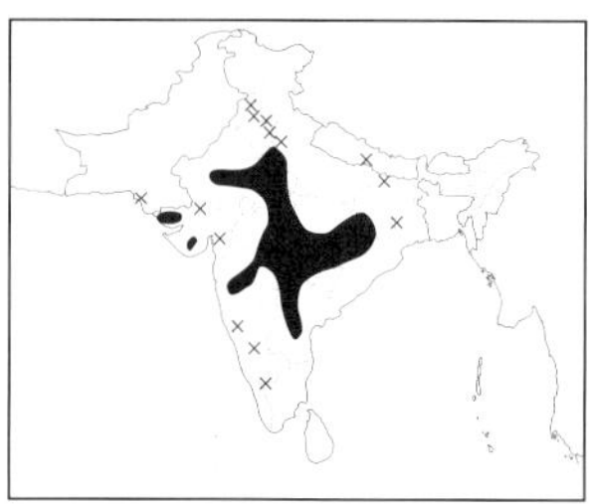

IDENTIFICATION 15 cm. A small minivet, both sexes with white wing patch. Male bears a passing resemblance to a male Common Stonechat (p.661). Flight is direct and dipping, rather like that of a wagtail. **Male** is the only black, white and orange minivet. Readily distinguished by combination of black head and mantle (with blue gloss), white underparts with pale orange or pink breast patch, white patch on black wings, orange and white rump, and white sides to tail. **Female** told from other minivets by combination of small size, grey-brown ear-coverts, crown and upperparts, white throat and underparts (without any yellow), white wing patch, pale orange and white rump, and white sides to black tail. Most similar to *pallidus* race of Small Minivet (p.605), and best told by browner upperparts, broader white wing-bar (lacking any trace of orange), longer tail with pure white on outer feathers, orange and white rump, and brown uppertail-coverts (rather than sandy-grey rump and flame-orange uppertail-coverts). **Juvenile** as female, but with white scaling on upperparts. **VOICE** Flight call is a *tsip-i-tsip*; song a stumbling medley of disjointed *chup* and *tsip* notes, plus higher thin wheezes and fine whistles (P. Holt). **HABITS** Similar to those of other minivets, but less arboreal. Often feeds in small bushes, seldom on the ground, but has been recorded perching on grass stalks and picking up grasshoppers by flying close to the ground. **HABITAT** Scattered dry scrub with grassy ground cover, thorn bushes in semi-desert, and sparse dry deciduous forest. **BREEDING** June–October. Nest is a small cup covered with cobwebs and down, and placed on a branch in thorn scrub or deciduous forest. **DISTRIBUTION AND STATUS** Resident, subject to erratic movements in winter. Mainly Gujarat and from C Rajasthan east to Bihar and south to C Maharashtra and Andhra Pradesh. **PK, NP:** vagrant. **IN:** local and uncommon resident. **REFERENCES** Giri and Choudhary (1996), Dhindsa *et al.* (1991).

GREY-CHINNED MINIVET *Pericrocotus solaris* Plate 93

Yellow-throated Minivet (F,I)

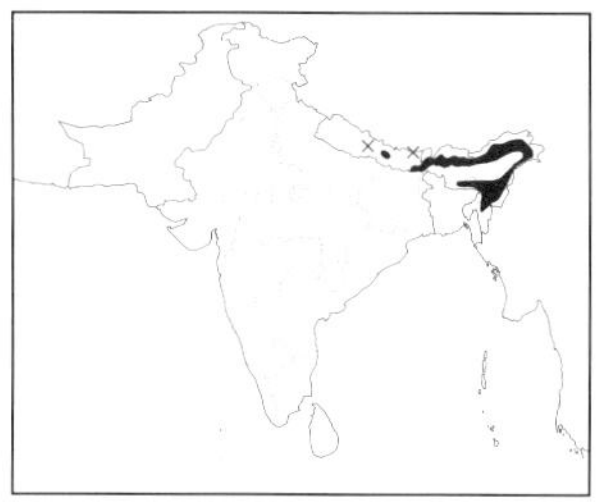

IDENTIFICATION 18 cm. **Male** distinguished from other minivets by greyish chin and pale orange throat, grey ear-coverts, slate-grey crown, nape and mantle, orange-red underparts, and orange-red rump, wing patch and outer tail feathers. **Female** is similar to several other female minivets, having grey crown and nape, becoming olive on mantle and back, yellow-green rump and uppertail-coverts, and yellow underparts and wing patch. Best told by combination of absence of yellow on forehead and supercilium, with whitish chin and sides to (yellow) throat, and grey ear-coverts. Most likely to be confused with female Long-tailed (below), especially *P. e. laetus* of E Himalayas, but that species always shows at least a trace of yellow on forehead and supercilium (in front of eye). Told from female Rosy (p.604) by brighter yellow underparts and yellow-green rump. **Juvenile** has pale yellow fringes to feathers of upperparts. **VOICE** A distinctive, rasping *tsee-sip*, recalling Vernal Hanging Parrot (p.418) (Boonsong and Round 1991). **HABITS** A typical minivet. Forages in the canopy and middle storey of forest. **HABITAT** Moist deciduous and evergreen broadleaved subtropical and lower temperate forest. **BREEDING** Little known. June. Has a similar nest to that of other minivets. **DISTRIBUTION AND STATUS** Resident, subject to altitudinal movements. Himalayas from WC Nepal east to Arunachal Pradesh; NE India. **NP:** scarce; 250–2075 m. **IN:** locally frequent; 120–2500 m (–3000 m). **BT:** fairly common; 245–2300 m (–3050 m).

LONG-TAILED MINIVET *Pericrocotus ethologus* Plate 93

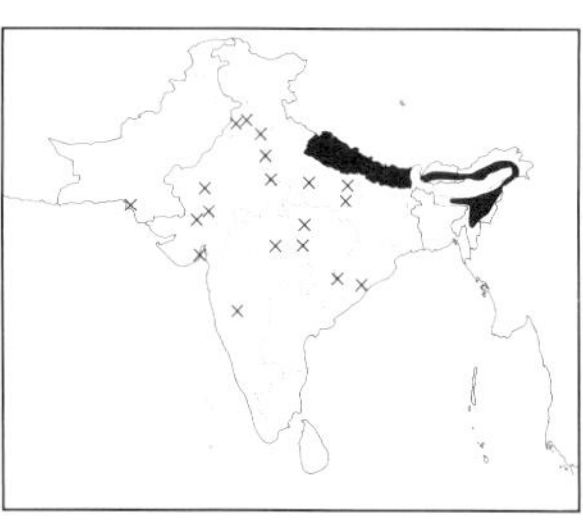

IDENTIFICATION 20 cm. **Male** is one of three 'red-and-black' minivets in the subcontinent. Distinguished from Scarlet (p.607) by smaller size, slimmer build with longer tail, shape of red wing patch, deeper red underparts, and call. More likely to be confused with the more local Short-billed (p.607), from which it differs in shape of red wing patch (with red extending as narrow panel along tertials and secondaries) and in call; additional subtle distinctions are deeper-coloured, more scarlet-red, underparts and rump, and less extensive and duller black throat, and more often has pale centre to belly (although these differences are variable and extremely difficult to detect in field). **Female** is very similar to several other female minivets, with greyish upperparts, yellow underparts and yellow wing patch. Best told by narrow area of yellow on forehead and supercilium, which is absent on female Grey-chinned (above) and much more extensive on female Scarlet and Short-billed. Ear-coverts are more uniformly grey than on female Short-billed, compared with which generally has distinctly paler yellow throat (than breast) and duller rump and uppertail-coverts. **Juvenile** is similar to female, but is browner above, with whitish tips to feathers of upperparts, coverts and tertials giving scaly effect, and paler below, with brown barring on throat and breast. **Racial variation:** Three races occur, the males becoming deeper red from *P. e. favillaceus* in the west to *P. c. mariae* in the east, and the females are correspondingly more richly coloured. **VOICE** Has a distinctive, sweet, double whistle, *pi-ru*, the second note lower than the first (Boonsong and Round 1991). **HABITS** A typical minivet. Highly gregarious throughout the year, except when nesting; sometimes in flocks of 30 or more. Forages chiefly in the treetops. **HABITAT** Open broadleaved and coniferous forest; in winter, also in trees at cultivation edges, groves, plantations and roadside avenues. **BREEDING** April–June. Builds a usual minivet nest near the end of a horizontal branch, 15–24 m above ground. **DISTRIBUTION AND STATUS** Resident, subject to altitudinal movements. Breeds in N Baluchistan, Pakistan, Himalayas from N Pakistan east to Arunachal Pradesh, and NE India and Bangladesh; winters south to Maharashtra and Orissa. **PK:** common; most nests found 1800–2400 m; winters in adjacent plains. **NP:** common and widespread; summers 1200–3500 m (–3965 m), winters 245–2135 m. **IN:** common in Himalayas; summers 1200–3400 m, mainly 1800–2400 m; in NE hills summers up to at least 1800 m; winters in N plains and hills up to 1500 m. **BT:** common; 1100–3800 m. **BD:** scarce, local winter visitor.

SHORT-BILLED MINIVET *Pericrocotus brevirostris* — Plate 93

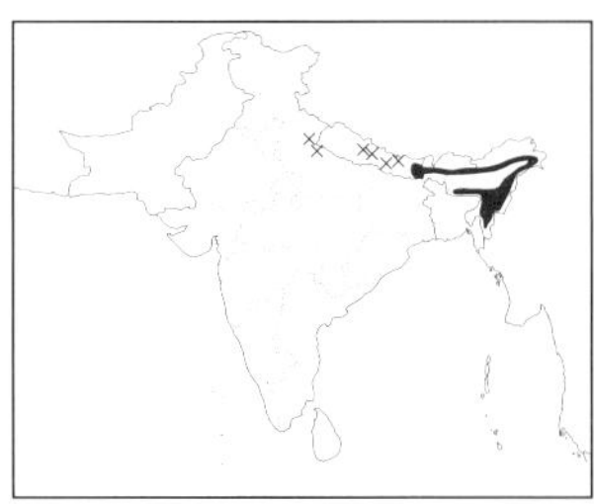

IDENTIFICATION 20 cm. **Male** is one of three 'red-and-black' minivets in the subcontinent. Told from Scarlet (below) by smaller size, slimmer build, and absence of red spots on tips of tertials and inner secondaries. More likely to be confused with Long-tailed (p.606), and is best told by all-black secondaries (lacking extension of red wing patch along tertials and secondaries) and different call. Further finer differences, which are variable and difficult to detect in field, are crimson-red (rather than scarlet-red) underparts and rump, more extensive glossy black throat (which can extend onto breast), and glossy black upperparts. **Female** has greyish upperparts, yellow underparts and yellow wing patch. Resembles female Scarlet, which also has extensive area of yellow on forehead; differs from that species in smaller size and slimmer build, and absence of spots on tertials and inner secondaries. Yellow forehead and forecrown (extending back to above eye) and yellow cast to ear-coverts are best features for separation from female Long-tailed; except where range overlaps with that of *mariae* race of Long-tailed (in NE subcontinent), further differences are deeper yellow throat (concolorous with rest of underparts) and brighter yellow rump and uppertail-coverts. **Juvenile** as female, but has slightly browner upperparts with white tips to feathers, resulting in scaly effect. **First-winter male** is similar to female, but has orange-yellow underparts and orange on wings and tail. **VOICE** Distinctive loud, high-pitched, monotone whistle, often coupled with dry *tup* contact notes (P. Holt). **HABITS** A typical minivet. **HABITAT** Open subtropical and temperate broadleaved forest and forest edges. **BREEDING** Very poorly known. One nest under construction in Nepal was built of moss and lichen and placed in the fork of a large tree, 10 m above ground. **DISTRIBUTION AND STATUS** Status of this species is relatively little known because of confusion with Long-tailed Minivet, especially in the past. Resident, subject to altitudinal movements. Himalayas from N Uttar Pradesh east to Arunachal Pradesh; NE India. **NP:** scarce from WC areas eastwards; 1005–2745 m. **IN:** 1800–2400 m; descends to foothills in winter. **BT:** common; 710–2620 m. **REFERENCES** Heath (1989).

SCARLET MINIVET *Pericrocotus flammeus* — Plate 93

Orange Minivet (P)

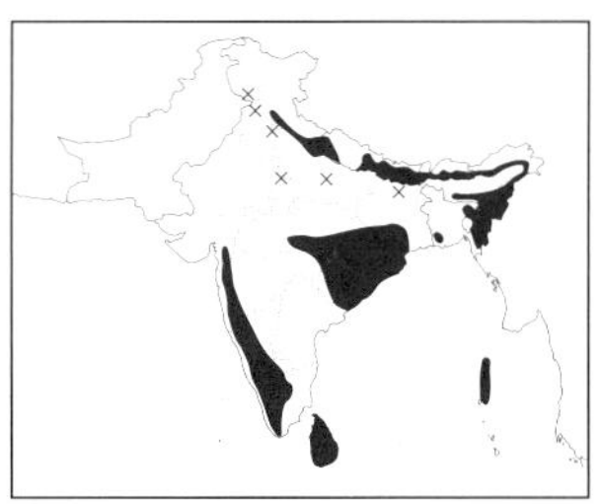

IDENTIFICATION 20–22 cm. **Male** is one of three 'red-and-black' minivets in the subcontinent, although the only one occurring in the peninsula. Told from Long-tailed and Short-billed Minivets (p.606 and above) by larger size, stockier build with larger head, orange-red underparts, and circular red patch at tips of tertials and inner secondaries. **Female** has greyish upperparts, yellow underparts and yellow wing patch. Resembles female Short-billed, which also has extensive area of yellow on forehead and ear-coverts; best separated by structural differences, and by yellow patch at tips of tertials and inner secondaries. Yellowish forehead and forecrown and yellow ear-coverts are further differences from female Long-tailed. **First-winter male** is similar to female, but underparts, rump and wing patches are orange-yellow. **VOICE** A piercing, whistled *sweep-sweep* (Boonsong and Round 1991). **HABITS** A typical minivet. Highly gregarious in the non-breeding season; often in flocks of up to 30 birds. **HABITAT** Open tropical, subtropical and lower temperate forest, usually of broadleaves, also conifers. **BREEDING** February–September, varying locally. Builds a usual minivet nest on a branch, 6–18 m above ground. **DISTRIBUTION AND STATUS** Resident, subject to seasonal and possibly altitudinal movements. Mainly Himalayas, from Jammu and Kashmir east to Arunachal Pradesh; locally in hills of India, Bangladesh and Sri Lanka. **NP:** common and widespread; below 2200 m. **IN:** locally common up to 1800 m; may descend to plains in winter. **BT:** common; 245–1880 m. **BD:** locally common. **LK:** common throughout, more frequent in the hills.

BAR-WINGED FLYCATCHER-SHRIKE *Hemipus picatus* — Plate 93

Pied Flycatcher-shrike (I,P), Pied Shrike, Pied Wood-Shrike (F)

IDENTIFICATION 15 cm. Minivet-like bird with flycatcher-like behaviour, perching with upright stance. Has dark crown, ear-coverts and nape with contrasting white sides of throat, longitudinal white wing patches

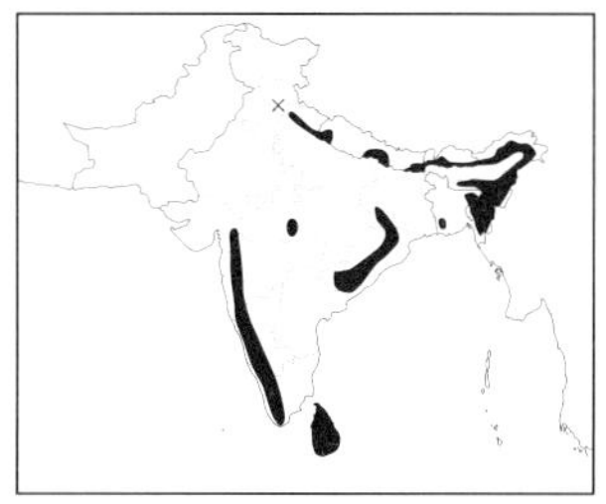

(appearing as a white V on back when bird facing away), white rump, white sides to black tail, and vinaceous-grey breast. **Male** has black crown, ear-coverts and nape, and brown mantle. **Female** has black of head replaced by brown (and therefore concolorous with mantle). **Juvenile** has buffish tips to feathers of upperparts and rufous wash to underparts. **Racial variation** Male *H. p. picatus* of the peninsula differs from male *H. p. capitalis* of the Himalayas, described above, in having a black mantle; both male and female *H. p. leggei*, occupying SW India and Sri Lanka, have black mantle. **VOICE** A continuous *tsit-it-it-it-it-it* or *whiriri-whiriri-whiriri*; a high-pitched trilling *sisisisisisi*, and insistent tit-like *chip* (Ali and Ripley 1987). **HABITS** Found in the tree canopy, usually in pairs or small parties; often members of itinerant hunting flocks of mixed insectivorous species. Hunts insects among the foliage, and by making frequent aerial sallies like a flycatcher. **HABITAT** Open tropical and subtropical broadleaved forest, also forest clearings and edges and mangroves. **BREEDING** February–August, varying locally. Nest is a small, neat, shallow cup made of roots, small twigs, moss and cobwebs, placed 3–9 m above ground near the end of a horizontal branch and well camouflaged against the bark. **DISTRIBUTION AND STATUS** Resident, subject to some altitudinal and local movements. Himalayan foothills from Himachal Pradesh east to Arunachal Pradesh, and south through the subcontinent in the hills. **NP:** common and widespread; below 1830 m. **IN:** fairly common; in Himalayas and NE hills breeds 600–1800 m, locally to 2100 m, wintering in foothills and adjacent plains; from the base to the summit of peninsular hills. **BT:** common; from 245 m up to at least 1445 m. **BD:** local. **LK:** common throughout, more frequent in the hills.

FANTAILS, DRONGOS AND MONARCHS Subfamily Dicrurinae

FANTAILS Tribe Rhipidurini

Small, confiding, arboreal birds, perpetually on the move in search of insects. Characteristically, they erect and spread the tail like a fan, and droop the wings, while pirouetting and turning from side to side with jerky, restless movements. When foraging, they flit from branch to branch, making frequent aerial sallies after winged insects, often rising vertically and tumbling, twisting or looping in the air, before returning to a perch. They call continually. Fantails are usually found singly or in pairs, and often join mixed hunting parties with other insectivorous birds.

YELLOW-BELLIED FANTAIL *Rhipidura hypoxantha* — Plate 93

Yellow-bellied Fantail Flycatcher (F,I)

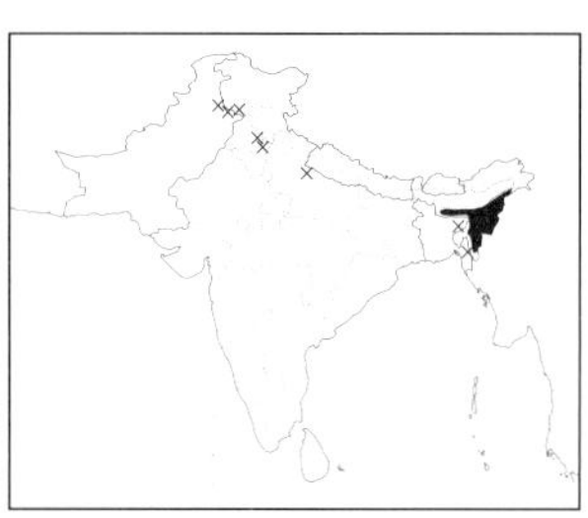

IDENTIFICATION 13 cm. Distinguished from other fantails by yellow forehead and supercilium, dark mask, yellow underparts, greyish-olive upperparts, and blackish tail which is boldly tipped with white. Like other fantails, hops about with tail erect and fanned, and wings drooped. Long, fanned tail separates it from Black-faced Warbler (p.737). **Male** has black mask, which is dark olive-brown on **female**. **Juvenile** resembles female, but lacks yellow on forehead and has duller and paler supercilium and underparts, and greyer upperparts. **VOICE** A constantly uttered *sip, sip,* these notes being strung together to comprise a trilling song. **HABITS** A typical fantail, although even more lively and active than the larger species. Forages mainly in the middle storey of forest, but also in bushes and the canopy. **HABITAT** Temperate and subalpine broadleaved and mixed broadleaved–coniferous forest in summer; mainly tropical and subtropical broadleaved forest in winter. **BREEDING** May–July, varying locally. Nest is a neat, deep cup of moss, covered in lichen and spiders' webs, and built 3–6 m above ground on a thick horizontal branch. **DISTRIBUTION AND STATUS** Resident, subject to altitudinal movements. Himalayas from Pakistan east to Arunachal Pradesh; NE India. **PK:** rare and local winter visitor; in foothills and plains from Sialkot district west to the Margalla hills. **NP:** common and widespread resident; summers chiefly 2440–4000 m, and winters 1200–1800 m (245–2560 m). **IN:** common resident; in Himalayas breeds from 1800 m up to the treeline, down to 1000 m in Assam; winters from 1800 m down to foothills and adjacent plains. **BT:** common resident. **BD:** vagrant.

WHITE-THROATED FANTAIL *Rhipidura albicollis* — Plate 93

White-throated Fantail Flycatcher (F,I)

IDENTIFICATION 19 cm. A variable fantail with white supercilium and dark ear-coverts, olive-brown to slate-grey upperparts, and dark brown to blackish tail which is tipped with greyish-white. All races are separable from White-browed Fantail (p.609) by shorter and finer supercilia which do not join across forehead, white

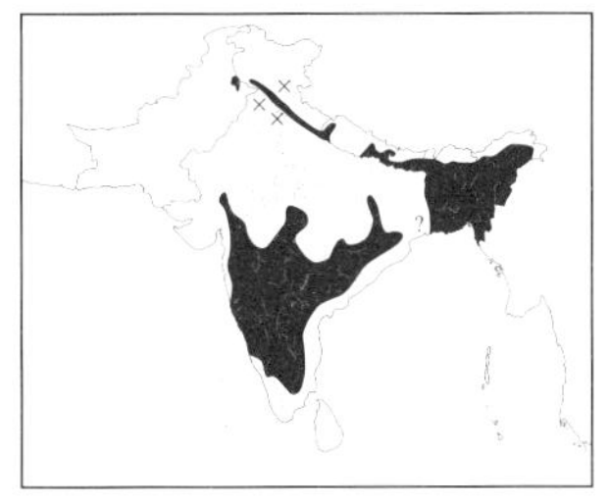

throat, absence of white spotting on wing-coverts, and less white at tip of tail. Further, Himalayan races have slate-grey underparts, while races in the peninsula have a white-spotted grey breast (see below). **Juvenile** is browner, with body feathers, wing-coverts and tertials tipped with rufous; throat is either pale (but less well defined than on adult) or dark. **Racial variation** Six races are recognised in the subcontinent. Three from the Himalayas and NE subcontinent have uniform slate-grey crown and mantle, and slate-grey breast and belly; and two races in the peninsula have uniform dark olive-brown crown and mantle, white-spotted grey breast, and buff belly. These are linked by an intermediate race, *R. a. orissae* from the NE peninsula, which has a dark grey crown contrasting with olive-brown mantle, unspotted grey breast and flanks, and buff belly. **VOICE** Song is a descending series of weak whistles, *tri..riri..riri..riri..riri*; call is a squeaky *cheek*. **HABITS** A typical fantail. Usually forages in the middle storey of forest, and often near the main trunk of trees. **HABITAT** Ravines and other shady areas in forest; also groves, secondary growth and gardens in winter. **BREEDING** March–August. Nest is a neat cone of fine grass stems, covered with spiders' webs and often with strips of nest material dangling below, built in a horizontal fork within 3 m of the ground. **DISTRIBUTION AND STATUS** Resident, subject to altitudinal and local movements. Himalayas from Margalla hills, Pakistan, east to Arunachal Pradesh; NE India and Bangladesh, and from S Rajasthan east to Orissa and south through most of the peninsula. **PK:** scarce and very local; breeds at 460 m, occasionally recorded up to 1800 m. **NP:** fairly common and widespread up to 1500 m, sometimes to 2440 m; usually withdraws from higher altitudes in winter. **IN:** fairly common; breeds up to 2700 m in E Himalayas, to 1500 m south of Brahmaputra R and to 2000 m in peninsular hills. **BT:** common; 305–2745 m. **BD:** local.

WHITE-BROWED FANTAIL *Rhipidura aureola* — Plate 93

White-browed Fantail Flycatcher (I,P), White-breasted Fantail Flycatcher (F)

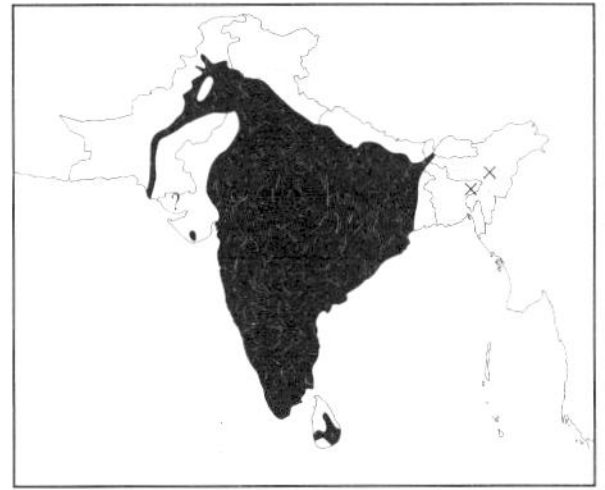

IDENTIFICATION 18 cm. Like White-throated Fantail (p.608), has white supercilium and dark ear-coverts, greyish-brown upperparts, and blackish tail which is boldly tipped with white. Separable from all races of that species by broader white supercilia which meet across forehead and extend farther back to reach nape, by blackish throat which is spotted with variable amounts of white or grey (and can sometimes appear almost white, as on White-throated), and by white submoustachial stripe, white-spotted wing-coverts, uniform white breast, belly and flanks, and more extensive white tips to tail. **Juvenile** similar to adult, but has browner upperparts, with rufous tips to body feathers, tertials and coverts. **Racial variation** Three races are recognised in the subcontinent, varying in amount of white at tip of tail, darkness of upperparts, and whether or not crown is blacker than mantle. **VOICE** Song is an ascending and then descending series of clear whistles, *chee-chee-cheweechee-vi*; call is a harsh *chuck* (Ali and Ripley 1987). **HABITS** A typical fantail. Frequents the lower and middle storeys of forest. **HABITAT** More open and drier forest than that occupied by White-throated Fantail; also groves, gardens, and bushes and trees alongside roads and canals. **BREEDING** January–August, varying locally. Nest is a tiny cup of fine grasses and plant fibres, covered with spiders' webs, built on a horizontal branch, often in a fork 1.5–4 m above ground. **DISTRIBUTION AND STATUS** Resident, subject to local movements. Mainly Indus plains, Pakistan, and Himalayan foothills from E Pakistan, east to West Bengal; and south through most of the subcontinent. **PK:** widespread in the Indus plains, common in Punjab, less common in Sindh, a few around Islamabad. **NP:** uncommon in most areas below 275 m. **IN:** common and widespread; locally up to 1000 m in Himalayas and peninsular hills, and to 1500 m in NE hills. **BD:** ?former resident; no recent records. **LK:** common throughout, more frequent in the east.

DRONGOS Tribe Dicrurini

Medium-sized passerines with characteristic black and often glossy plumage, long, often deeply forked tail, and a very upright stance when perched. They are mainly arboreal and insectivorous, catching larger winged insects by aerial sallies from a perch. Nectar and occasionally small birds, reptiles and mammals supplement their diet. When in pursuit of insects, drongos are very agile, twisting and turning adroitly in mid-air. Although usually solitary, they gather in flocks at good food sources, such as flowering trees, or when chasing fleeing insects in the smoke of forest fires. Their direct flight is swift, strong and undulating. Drongos are bold and pugnacious, and will fearlessly drive away larger predatory birds which threaten their nests. They are typically rather noisy, and have a varied repertoire of harsh calls and pleasant whistles; some species are good mimics. The usual drongo nest is a flimsy cup made of twigs, grasses and other plant fibres, bound together with cobwebs, and built between twigs of a horizontal fork near the end of a branch.

BLACK DRONGO *Dicrurus macrocercus* Plate 94

***D. adsimilis* (F,I)**

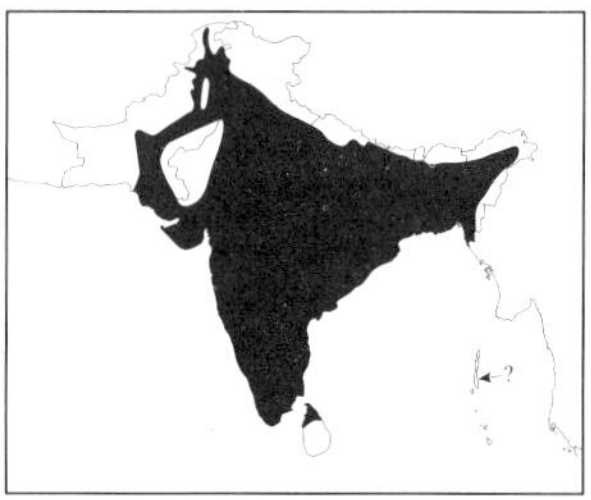

IDENTIFICATION 28 cm. **Adult** is glossy blue-black, with deeply forked tail (although tail-fork usually lost during moult); usually shows white rictal spot, which is not shown by other species. Told from Ashy Drongo (below), which can also appear very dark and glossy, by shiny blue-black throat and breast, merging into black of rest of underparts. From White-bellied Drongo (p.611) by black belly, flanks and undertail-coverts. For differences from Crow-billed Drongo (p.611), see that species. **First-winter** birds have diffuse whitish fringes to dull black breast, belly and undertail- and uppertail-coverts; upperparts and breast have a glossy sheen. They are similar to first-winter Ashy, but underparts are blacker, with more prominent and extensive whitish fringes (which can merge to form whitish patches in centre of belly). **Juvenile** has uniform dark brown upperparts and underparts, lacking glossy sheen, and may show white fringes to secondaries; tail is short, with only a slight fork, when young. **VOICE** Less varied than that of Ashy Drongo. A harsh *ti-tiu*, and a harsh *cheece-cheece-chichuk*; pairs duet during breeding season. **HABITS** Usually found singly or in pairs, but may gather in loose flocks in winter; often associates with grazing cattle. Crepuscular, often hunting insects after dusk. Typically, perches singly on a telegraph wire, post, bare treetop, earth bank or other vantage point in open country. Makes frequent sallies to seize insects in mid-air or from the ground. **HABITAT** Found in more open country than other drongos: open cultivation, around villages and suburbs of towns and cities. **BREEDING** February–August, varying locally. Builds a usual drongo nest in an isolated tree, 4–12 m above ground. **DISTRIBUTION AND STATUS** Resident, subject to local and altitudinal movements. Throughout much of the subcontinent, except parts of the northwest, northeast and Himalayas. **PK:** common; a summer visitor to the far north, resident and winter visitor farther south. **NP:** common and widespread; from the terai up to at least 1525 m all year, in summer sometimes to 2000 m. **IN:** common and widespread in plains and hills; up to 1500 m in the Himalayas, where mainly a summer visitor. **BT:** uncommon. **BD:** common throughout. **LK:** common in dry N and NW coastal belt, occasional inland and farther south.

ASHY DRONGO *Dicrurus leucophaeus* Plate 94

Grey Drongo (I,P)

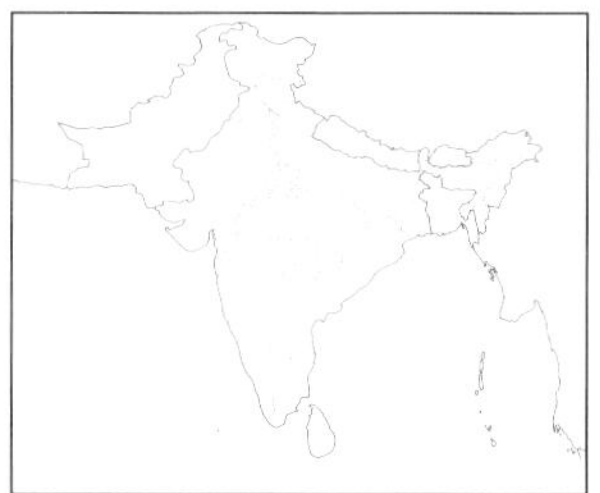

IDENTIFICATION 29 cm. **Adult** told from Black Drongo (above) by dark grey (rather than black) underparts, this difference in coloration especially apparent on throat, breast and flanks. Has blue-grey gloss on sides of neck and breast, but gloss is not so extensive as on Black. Upperparts are slate-grey with strong blue-grey gloss, although can appear almost black and much as Black Drongo. Often appears slimmer, with longer, more deeply forked tail (although tail-fork can be lost during moult), and has more striking red iris. Does not show white rictal spot which is often apparent at close range on Black Drongo. From White-bellied Drongo (p.611) by uniform grey underparts (although care is needed in Sri Lanka, where one race of that species has all-dark belly). **First-winter** birds have uniform brownish-grey underparts, with diffuse (and typically very indistinct) whitish fringes to belly and whitish tips to undertail-coverts, and blue-grey gloss to upperparts. Distinguished from first-winter Black by duller and greyer underparts, which also have much less prominent and extensive fringes, and appears to lack distinct pale fringes to uppertail-coverts shown by first-winter Black. From first-winter White-bellied by brownish-grey underparts (lacking well-defined white belly and flanks always shown by that species except in Sri Lanka). **Juvenile** has shorter tail when young (with only a shallow fork), and uniform brownish-black upperparts and underparts which lack glossy sheen. Probably not safely distinguishable in the field from juvenile Black. **Racial variation** Birds breeding in the E Himalayas (*D. l. hopwoodi*) are paler and greyer than those breeding in the W Himalayas (*D. l. longicaudatus*), and are more easily separable from Black Drongo. *D. l. salangensis*, which is much paler grey and has white lores and ear-coverts, has been recorded in Nagaland and possibly the Andamans; this form has grey wing-coverts and secondaries which contrast with black alula and primaries, and often has a blackish forehead. **VOICE** More varied than Black Drongo's, and a good mimic. Has a harsh *cheece-cheece-chichuk* (like Black), often followed by a pleasant whistling *kil-kil-kil-kil*; other calls include a distinctive *drangh-gip, gip-drangh-gip* (Ali and Ripley 1987). **HABITS** Very similar to those of other drongos. When hunting, usually perches on bare branches near the top of a tall tree. Crepuscular. **HABITAT** Broadleaved and coniferous forest in the breeding season, preferring more open rather than dense forest; well-wooded areas in winter, such as groves, plantations, secondary growth and wooded gardens. **BREEDING** April–June. Builds a usual drongo nest, 15–20 m above ground in a tall tree. **DISTRIBUTION AND STATUS** Breeds in Himalayas from N Pakistan east to Arunachal Pradesh, and NE Indian hills; winters in the plains from E Punjab and S Gujarat eastwards, and south through most of the peninsula and Sri Lanka. **PK:** frequent summer visitor to the more wooded Himalayan valleys; 900–3000 m. **NP:** common; summers 1220–2745 m, winters 1065–1525 m; also a locally common resident in the lowlands. **IN:** locally common; summers in Himalayas from foothills up to 3000 m, winters in the plains. **BT:** common resident; 250–3300 m. **BD:** uncommon winter visitor throughout. **LK:** winter visitor to the lowlands, more frequent in the E dry zone.

WHITE-BELLIED DRONGO *Dicrurus caerulescens* Plate 94

White-vented Drongo (P)

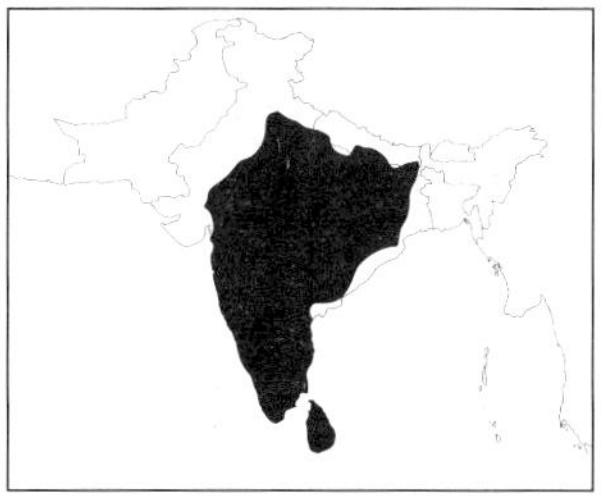

IDENTIFICATION 24 cm. **Adult** differs from Black and Ashy Drongos (p.610) in having brownish-grey throat and breast (lacking glossy sheen) and white belly and undertail-coverts. Some birds have blue-grey cast to breast. Tail is shorter and fork is typically shallower than on those two species. Upperparts are glossy slate-grey, much as Ashy (and therefore less black than Black Drongo). Care is needed in Sri Lanka, where one race has all-dark belly. **First-winter** is similar to adult, but throat and breast are browner and border between breast and white belly is less clearly defined. **Juvenile** as first-winter, but upperparts are dark brown, lacking slate-grey gloss. **Racial variation** Two races occurring in Sri Lanka have less white on underparts than the nominate race of the peninsula; *D. c. leucopygialis*, of the wet zone, has uniform dark grey underparts with slight gloss to breast, and has white restricted to vent and undertail-coverts. Easily confusable with Ashy Drongo (especially first-winter birds), which is a winter visitor to Sri Lanka; shorter tail with shallower fork, blacker throat and breast (of adult) and all-white undertail-coverts are helpful features for distinguishing White-bellied. **VOICE** Typical drongo song, with melodious and jarring notes, frequent changes of tempo and much talented mimicry all interwoven. Similar to that of Black Drongo, but typically more continuous, richer and with fewer harsher notes (P. Holt). **HABITS** Very similar to those of other drongos. Hawks insects from exposed perches. Highly crepuscular. **HABITAT** Clearings and edges of light forest, well-wooded country, gardens, and tea and rubber plantations. **BREEDING** February–June, Builds a usual drongo nest in open forest. **DISTRIBUTION AND STATUS** Resident, subject to local movements. From E Haryana and S Gujarat east through S Nepal to West Bengal, and south through the subcontinent. **NP:** locally common; below 305 m. **IN:** widespread, but generally uncommon; plains and foothills up to 1800 m. **LK:** common in the lowlands and adjacent lower hills.

CROW-BILLED DRONGO *Dicrurus annectans* Plate 94

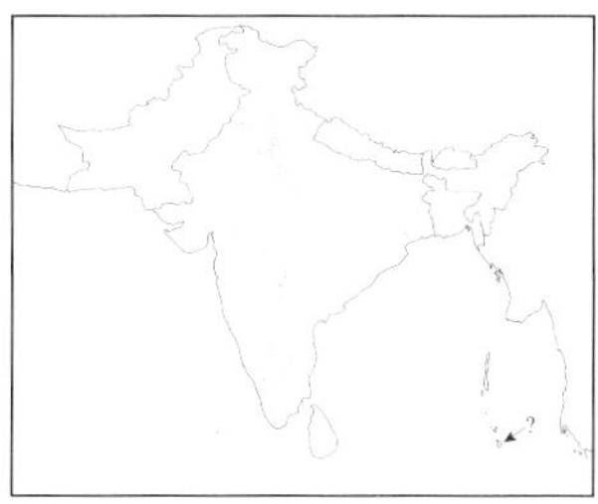

IDENTIFICATION 28 cm. Most likely to be confused with Black Drongo (p.610), although that species is not found in dense forest. **Adult** told from Black by much stouter bill, more extensive area of rictal bristles (resulting in tufted forehead not unlike that of Lesser Racket-tailed Drongo, p.612), and shorter, broader tail which is widely splayed at tip but not deeply forked (with outer feathers more noticeably curving outwards). **First-winter** birds have white spotting on breast, belly and flanks, and undertail-coverts, and are quite different from other first-winter drongos (except Greater Racket-tailed, p.614). Has less pronounced tail-fork than adult. **Juvenile** has uniform brownish-black upperparts and underparts which lack gloss. Spotted feathers of first-winter plumage quickly appear. **VOICE** Loud, musical whistles and churrs, and a characteristic descending series of harp-like notes (Boonsong and Round 1991). **HABITS** Usually hunts from the middle storey of forest or lower canopy, rather than from an exposed perch in the treetops. Associates in loose flocks on migration. **HABITAT** Dense broadleaved evergreen and moist deciduous forest. **BREEDING** April–June. Builds a usual drongo nest in a tree, 5–12 m above ground. **DISTRIBUTION AND STATUS** Status is uncertain because of confusion with Black Drongo. Summer visitor, or resident subject to seasonal movements, in Himalayan foothills from N Uttar Pradesh east to Arunachal Pradesh, and NE India; winters in NE India and Bangladesh, but rest of wintering range is unknown. **NP:** probably a local and uncommon summer visitor; below 250 m. **IN:** locally frequent; recorded in foothills up to 800 m, occasionally higher, and in adjacent plains. **BT:** fairly common, probably a summer visitor; 300–1450 m. **BD:** status uncertain, local summer or winter visitor.

BRONZED DRONGO *Dicrurus aeneus* Plate 94

Little Bronzed Drongo (F)

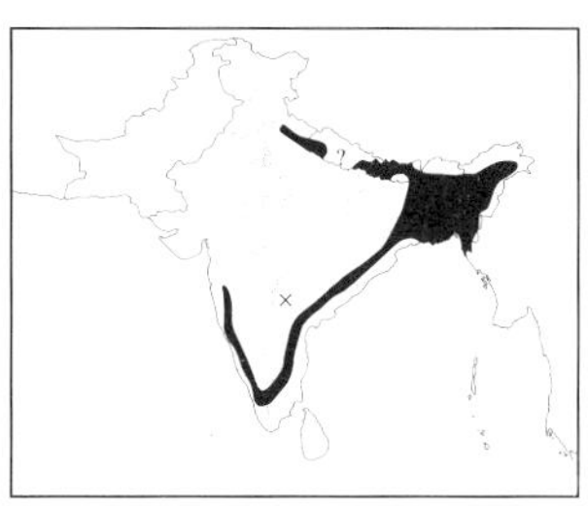

IDENTIFICATION 24 cm. A small, hyperactive, forest-dwelling drongo. **Adult** is black and strongly glossed with metallic blue-green. Told from Black Drongo (p.610) by smaller size, spangled appearance (especially to crown, nape, mantle and breast), flatter bill, and shorter, less deeply forked tail (which can be almost square-ended on moulting or juvenile birds). **Juvenile**'s underparts are uniform sooty-brown and initially lack spangling, and upperparts are duller and less heavily spangled compared with adult. **VOICE** Loud, varied, musical whistles and churrs. **HABITS** Usually found singly or in pairs; a regular member of mixed feeding parties of insectivorous species. Hunts in shaded areas in forest, in overgrown forest clearings and along forest paths. **HABITAT** Broadleaved evergreen and moist deciduous forest and coffee and rubber plantations. **BREEDING** March–July. Builds a usual drongo nest in a horizontal fork of a small tree.

DISTRIBUTION AND STATUS Resident, subject to seasonal movements. Himalayan foothills from N Uttar Pradesh east to Arunachal Pradesh, and south through the hills of NE India and Bangladesh; Eastern and Western Ghats. **NP:** fairly common; summers mainly below 1600 m, sometimes to 2000 m, usually winters below 1220 m. **IN:** fairly common in Himalayas, common in Western Ghats; summers up to 2000 m. **BT:** fairly common; 250–1500 m. **BD:** locally common.

LESSER RACKET-TAILED DRONGO *Dicrurus remifer* Plate 94

Small Racquet-tailed Drongo (F)

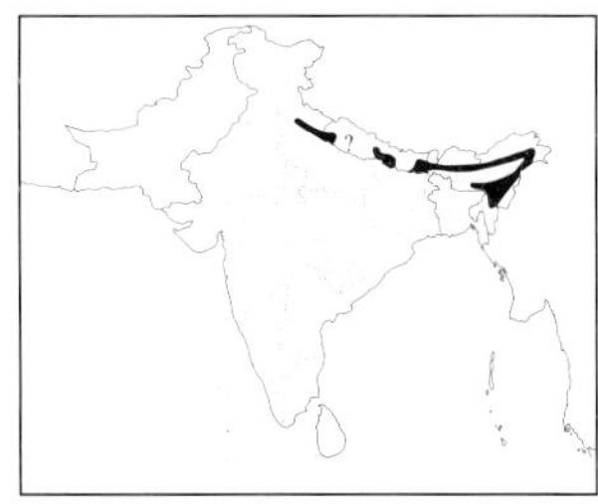

IDENTIFICATION 25 cm. **Adult** distinguished from Greater Racket-tailed (p.614) by smaller size, smaller bill, tufted forehead (giving rise to rectangular head shape), square-ended tail, and smaller, flattened, oval rackets (which are fully webbed on both sides of shaft). Tail-streamers and rackets can be missing or broken. **Immature** lacks tail-streamers and rackets, and is less heavily spangled on upperparts and underparts than adult. Tail can appear very slightly forked, and is best told from immature Greater Racket-tailed by smaller size, tufted forehead (and absence of any form of crest), and smaller bill. **VOICE** Loud, varied, musical whistling, screeching and churring, with much mimicry. **HABITS** Found singly or in pairs, often associated with roving mixed flocks of other forest species. Normally keeps to the leafy canopy in dense forest, shaded clearings, at forest edges and along streams. **HABITAT** Dense broadleaved evergreen and moist deciduous forest. **BREEDING** April–June. Builds a usual drongo nest up to 7 m above ground, sometimes higher. **DISTRIBUTION AND STATUS** Resident. Himalayan foothills from N Uttar Pradesh east to Arunachal Pradesh; hills of NE India and Bangladesh. **NP:** local and frequent; 915–1800 m (–2440 m); possibly withdraws from higher levels in winter. **IN:** locally fairly common; from foothills up to 2000 m. **BT:** fairly common; from foothills up to 1900 m. **BD:** local winter visitor.

SPANGLED DRONGO *Dicrurus hottentottus* Plate 94

Hair-crested Drongo

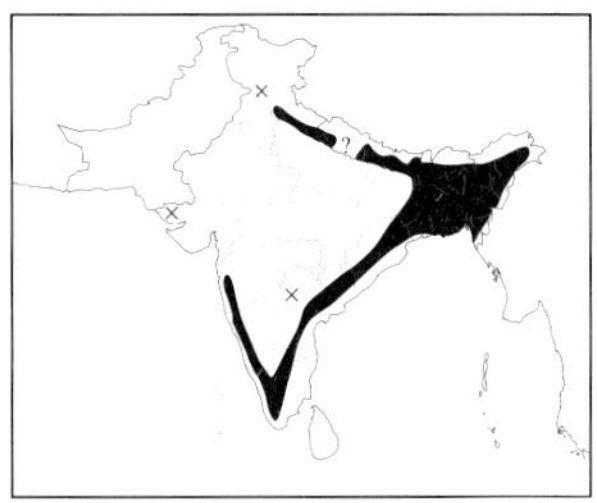

IDENTIFICATION 32 cm. A large, stocky, forest-dwelling drongo. **Adult** told from other drongos by hair-like crest, broad tail with shallow, outward- and upward-twisted fork (appearing almost square-ended in field), long down-curved bill, metallic spangling on crown, sides of neck, throat and breast, and highly glossed wings and tail. **Juvenile** is browner and lacks spangling of adult; lacks crest, and has square-ended tail with less pronounced upward twist to outer feathers. **VOICE** A loud *chit-wiii*, the first note stressed and the second rising, or sometimes the *wiii* note given singly (C. Robson from H. S. Baral recording). **HABITS** Found singly or in small parties, in winter sometimes in larger flocks; frequently joins mixed foraging flocks of insectivorous birds. Feeds mainly on flower nectar; also eats insects, which are located chiefly by searching flowers, leaves and trunks, although it will sometimes catch them on the wing. **HABITAT** Broadleaved evergreen and moist deciduous forest; associates with flowering trees, especially silk cotton. **BREEDING** March–June, varying locally. Builds a usual drongo nest, often untidy, 5–10 m above ground. **DISTRIBUTION AND STATUS** Resident, subject to seasonal movements depending on nectar supplies. Himalayan foothills from Punjab east to Arunachal Pradesh; south through the NE Indian hills and Bangladesh; Eastern Ghats, and Western Ghats north to N Maharashtra and south to S Kerala. **NP:** fairly common below 1050 m, uncommon up to 1525 m (–4115 m). **IN:** locally common in Himalayas, uncommon in Western Ghats; from plains up to 1400 m, occasionally to 2000 m. **BT:** fairly common; 250–1850 m. **BD:** locally common; from plains up to 1400 m, occasionally to 2000 m.

ANDAMAN DRONGO *Dicrurus andamanensis* Plate 94

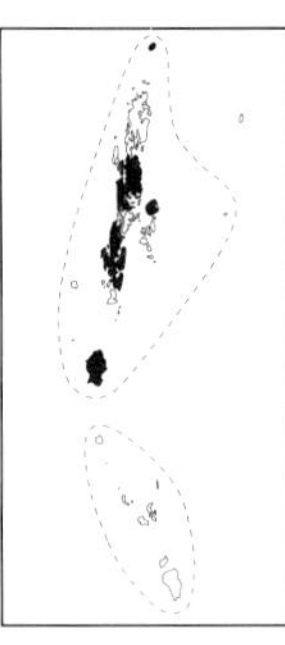

IDENTIFICATION 32 cm. **Adult** superficially resembles Black Drongo (p.610), being all black with blue-black gloss. Has much larger and longer bill than that species, and long, broad tail with shallow fork and outer feathers twisting inwards at tip. Has several hair-like filaments on forehead, resulting in a crest reminiscent of (although less distinct than) that of Spangled Drongo (above). **Juvenile** is browner and less glossed, and initially has square-ended tail. **VOICE** A variety of sharp, metallic notes, and a long *tseep* (Ali and Ripley 1987). **HABITS** Gregarious, often in flocks of a dozen to 20 together, sometimes with mixed flocks of other species. Hawks flying insects in typical drongo fashion. **HABITAT** Forest. **BREEDING** April and May. Builds a usual drongo nest, high up in a leafless tree. **DISTRIBUTION AND STATUS** Common resident, endemic to the Andaman Is (Little and South Andaman), India, and also Coco Is (Myanmar). **REFERENCES** Davidar *et al.* (1997).

Greater Racket-tailed Drongo D. p. paradiseus *(southern India) (left-hand bird) and* D. p. lophorhinus *(wet zone) (Drawing by Nigel Bean)*

GREATER RACKET-TAILED DRONGO *Dicrurus paradiseus* Plate 94

Ceylon Crested Drongo (P), Racket-tailed Drongo (P), Large Racquet-tailed Drongo (F)

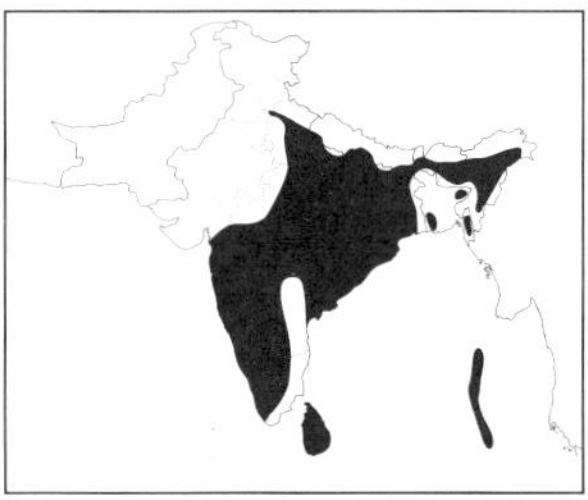

IDENTIFICATION 32 cm. A forest-dwelling drongo, most races of which are pendant-tailed. Unlike Lesser Racket-tailed (p.612), occurs widely throughout the peninsula. **Adult** told from Lesser Racket-tailed (where ranges overlap) by larger size and less tidy appearance, larger bill, crested head, forked tail, and larger, longer, twisted tail-rackets (which are webbed on only one side of shaft). Tail-streamers and rackets can be missing or broken, and tail can appear almost square-ended when in moult (or in juvenile plumage). **Juvenile** initially lacks rackets; is less heavily glossed than adult, and has much-reduced crest. Has white fringes to belly and vent in first-winter plumage. Best told from Lesser Racket-tailed by larger size, presence of some form of crest, longer and heavier bill, more pronounced fork to tail, and, if present, white fringes to underparts. **Racial variation** Six races are recognised from the subcontinent, varying in size, length of tail-streamers and size of crest. Races in S India, Sri Lanka and Andaman and Nicobar Is have much-reduced or almost non-existent frontal crest and can look very like Lesser Racket-tailed (but note that that species does not occur in the peninsula or in these islands). *D. p. lophorhinus* of the wet zone in Sri Lanka has a long and deeply forked tail, slightly twisted at the tips, and lacks the terminal rackets of other subspecies. **VOICE** Loud, varied, musical whistling, screeching and churring, with much mimicry, and much as that of Lesser Racket-tailed. **HABITS** Very similar to those of other drongos, but more sociable, often in small groups, and joins mixed hunting parties of other species in forest. Frequently crepuscular. Forages in the lower and middle storeys of forest. **HABITAT** Broadleaved forest and bamboo jungle. **BREEDING** February–July, varying locally. Builds a usual drongo nest, 5–15 m above ground in a forest tree. **DISTRIBUTION AND STATUS** Resident, subject to seasonal wanderings. From S Gujarat and NE Haryana east through S Nepal to NE India and Bangladesh, and south through the subcontinent. **NP:** locally common; mainly below 150 m, uncommon up to 365 m (–1370 m). **IN:** widespread and locally common; from plains up to 1500 m. **BT:** uncommon; 250–1000 m. **BD:** local. **LK:** lowlands and adjacent lower hills; common in the wet zone, infrequent in the dry zone.

MONARCHS Tribe Monarchini

Most species are small to medium-sized, with long, pointed wings and a medium-length to long tail. They feed mainly on insects.

BLACK-NAPED MONARCH *Hypothymis azurea* Plate 95

Black-naped Flycatcher (F,I,P), Azure Flycatcher, *Monarcha azurea* (F,P)

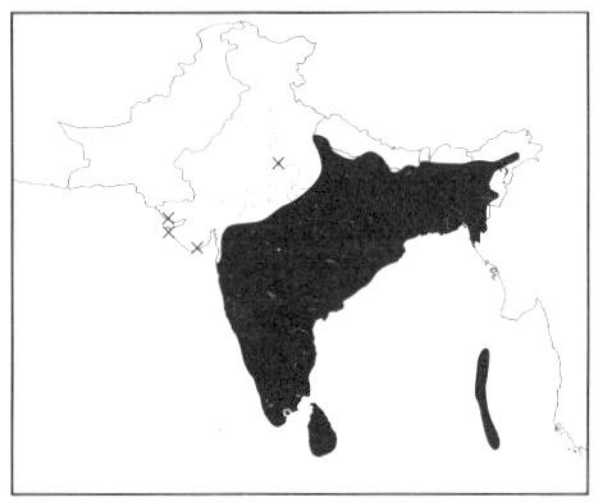

IDENTIFICATION 16 cm. **Male** is almost entirely azure-blue, with black nape patch, black gorget across upper breast (except in Sri Lanka), beady black eye, and black feathering at base of bill. **Female** has duller blue head, lacks black nape patch and breast gorget, and has blue-grey breast and grey-brown mantle, wings and tail. **Racial variation** Five races are recognised in the subcontinent. Of the three confined to the Andaman and Nicobar Is, two have blue, or mainly blue (rather than white), belly. Male *H. a. ceylonensis* of Sri Lanka lacks, or has very indistinct, breast gorget, has a less extensive black nape patch, and is more purplish-blue than *H. a. styani* which occurs throughout the peninsula; female *ceylonensis*, compared with female *styani*, is brighter blue on head, neck and breast and has blue wash to browner mantle. **VOICE** Has a high-pitched rasping *sweech-which* and a ringing *pwee-pwee-pwee-pwee* (Ali and Ripley 1987; Boonsong and Round 1991). **HABITS** Usually occurs singly or in pairs, and often associates with mixed foraging flocks of other species. Arboreal, often found in the canopy, but also in bushes in the forest understorey. Flits actively about the foliage and branches. Captures flying insects by making aerial sorties from a perch; also hovers in front of leaves to disturb insects. Noisy even in winter. **HABITAT** Tropical broadleaved forest, well-wooded areas, secondary growth, coffee and cardamom plantations; favours bamboo. **BREEDING** March–September, varying locally. Builds a neat cone-shaped nest, covered with cobwebs and spiders' egg cases and with nest material often trailing from the bottom, 3–5 m above ground in a tree, bush or bamboo clump. **DISTRIBUTION AND STATUS** Resident, subject to local movements. Mainly from Gujarat and C Uttar Pradesh east through S Nepal to Arunachal Pradesh, and south to Bangladesh and through the subcontinent. **PK:** vagrant. **NP:** local and frequent; below 365 m. **IN:** widespread and locally common; subject to erratic movements; plains and hills up to 1050 m (–1300 m). **BT:** frequent; 250–1000 m. **BD:** locally common throughout. **LK:** common resident in lowlands and up to middle altitudes.

ASIAN PARADISE-FLYCATCHER *Terpsiphone paradisi* Plate 95

Paradise Flycatcher (F,I,P)

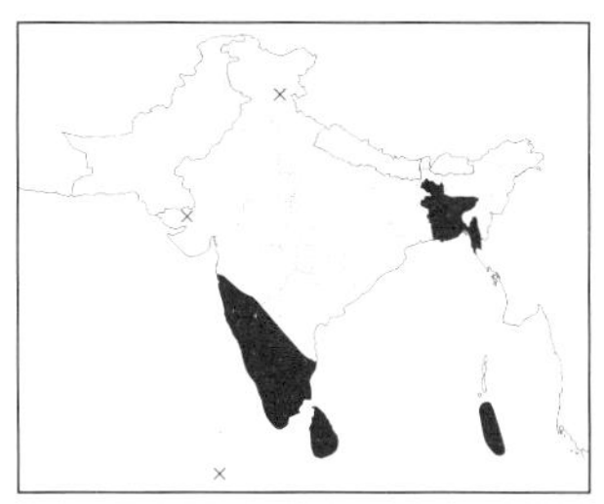

IDENTIFICATION 20 cm (with tail-streamers up to additional 35 cm). **Male** occurs in two colour morphs: both have prominent crest on glossy black head, blue eye-ring, blue-grey bill, and very long tail-streamers. The white morph has rest of plumage almost entirely white but for mainly black primaries and secondaries, black on tertials and outer tail feathers, and black shafts to central tail feathers. The rufous morph has rufous mantle, wings and tail, and white to greyish underparts merging into glossy black to greyish-black throat. Intermediate birds, showing rufous and white in plumage, do occur. **Female** and **immature** are similar to rufous male, but have shorter crest and short square-ended tail; throat and lower ear-coverts are greyer. **Juvenile** is similar to female, but shows indistinct pale centres and dark fringes to breast feathers. **VOICE** Song is a slow warble, *peety-to-whit*, repeated in quick succession; calls and alarm include a nasal *chechwe*, and a harsh *wee poor willie weep-poor willie* (Ali and Ripley 1987). **HABITS** Keeps singly or in pairs; sometimes joins roving hunting parties of other species. Perches with an upright stance, often high up in trees, then darts out to catch flying insects in mid-air. Active and graceful, with an undulating flight. Male often whisks his long tail-streamers about. **HABITAT** Shady areas, often near water, in forest, plantations, groves and gardens; also orchards in Pakistan. **BREEDING** March–August, varying locally. Builds a deep, neat cone-shaped nest, often with loose material dangling below and covered with cobwebs and spiders' egg cases, 1–15 m above ground in a tree fork. **DISTRIBUTION AND STATUS** Resident and partial migrant. Himalayan foothills from N Pakistan east to Arunachal Pradesh and NE India, and south through much of the subcontinent except parts of N and NW India; Himalayan and N and C Indian birds winter farther south in the peninsula. **PK:** locally common summer visitor in N foothills, adjacent plains and broader Himalayan valleys; also a passage migrant over most of Sind and Punjab. **NP:** summer visitor below 1525 m; common at Chitwan, now uncommon elsewhere. **IN:** locally fairly common summer visitor to the north, breeds mainly in the foothills, locally up to 2400 m, uncommon in plains; fairly common but local resident and summer visitor in the peninsula, breeds mainly in the hills. **BT:** rare. **BD:** local. **LK:** common resident in dry lowlands and E foothills, common winter visitor throughout, more frequent in the lowlands. **MV:** vagrant.

IORAS Subfamily Aegithininae

Small, fairly lively passerines which feed in trees, mainly on insects and especially caterpillars.

COMMON IORA *Aegithina tiphia* Plate 95

Iora (F)

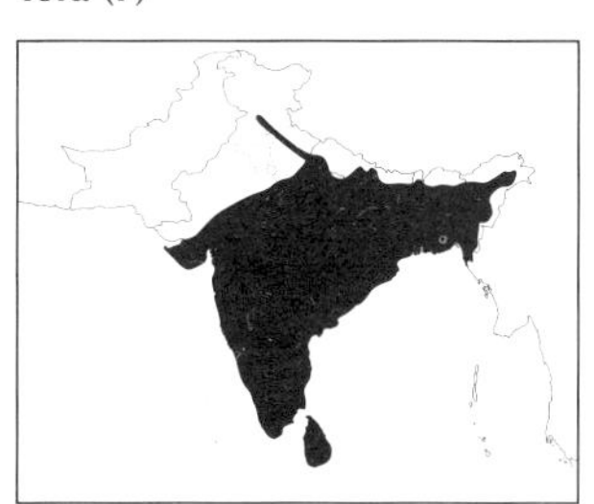

IDENTIFICATION 14 cm. Told from Marshall's Iora (p.616) in all plumages by uniform black or green tail (without any white). Very variable, but always has blackish wings with white median-covert bar, yellowish-green rump, and yellow underparts. **Male breeding** has black tail; crown, nape and mantle vary from entirely black to yellowish-green (depending on race). **Male non-breeding** is similar to female, but has black tail in some races. **Female** has yellowish to greenish upperparts, as non-breeding male, but always has green tail. **Racial variation** Five races are recognised in the subcontinent, giving rise to considerable plumage variation. Breeding male *A. t. multicolor* of S India and Sri Lanka typically has uniform black upperparts and wings (except for single white median-covert bar). Breeding male *A. t. deignani* and *A. t. humei*, which occupy much of peninsular India, have black crown, yellowish-green mantle which is variably marked with black, white greater- and median-covert wing-bars, and pale yellow edges to secondaries and tertials. Breeding male *A. t. tiphia* and *A. t. septentrionalis*, of the Himalayas and NE subcontinent, have green crown, nape and mantle (with some black markings on crown and nape), and often closely resemble non-breeding males of other races, but always have black tail. **VOICE** Song is a long, drawn-out (two-toned) whistle, *wheee-teooo*; call is a *chee-chit-chit-chit* (Ali and Ripley 1987; Boonsong and Round 1991). See also Marshall's Iora. **HABITS** Keeps singly or in pairs, each bird calling to the other frequently. Arboreal. Searches methodically among foliage of trees and bushes for insects and caterpillars; hops about branches and sometimes hangs upside-down. **HABITAT** Broadleaved trees in open forest, forest edges, secondary growth, scrub, groves, roadside avenues, and large trees in open country and gardens. **BREEDING** January–September, varying locally. Builds a shallow cup-shaped nest, covered with cobwebs, 1–9 m above ground in trees or bushes. **DISTRIBUTION AND STATUS** Resident. Himalayas from Himachal Pradesh east to Arunachal Pradesh; NE India, and south through most of the subcontinent except the northwest. **NP:** common and widespread below 365 m, frequent up to 1900 m; a summer visitor at higher altitudes. **IN:** widespread and locally common; subject to local movements; plains and hills up to 1500 m, locally to 2000 m in Himalayas, to 1000 m in the peninsula. **BT:** frequent; recorded up to at least 450 m. **BD:** common throughout. **LK:** common in lowlands and lower hills.

MARSHALL'S IORA *Aegithina nigrolutea* Plate 95

White-tailed Iora

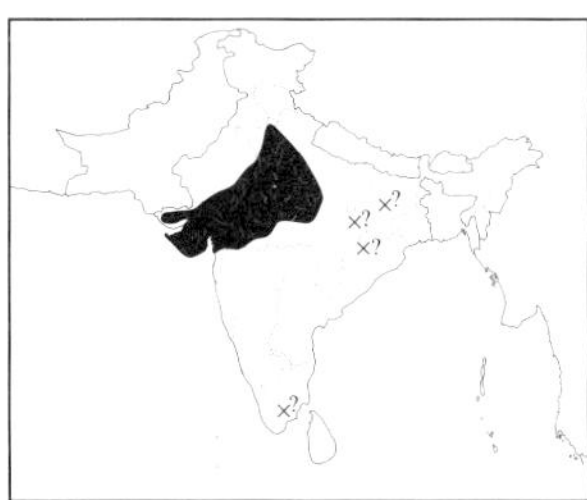

IDENTIFICATION 14 cm. Distinguished from Common Iora (p.615) in all plumages by extensive white in black tail, with central feathers varying from black with a white tip to largely white to greyish-white with irregular black bases. Otherwise is generally similar to Common Iora, having blackish wings with white wing-bars, and yellow underparts. **Male breeding** has black crown and nape, yellow hindcollar (not usually shown by any race of Common Iora), and black mantle with variable yellowish-green mottling. **Male non-breeding** has yellowish-green upperparts, and is similar to **female**. **VOICE** Both Common and Marshall's Ioras have a wide repertoire, including individually variable sweet whistled songs, often repeating two phrases of two to six clear whistled notes. Each species, however, has diagnostic phrases or notes: Marshall's an ascending nasal wheeze, often followed by a more Common Iora-like but less sputtered and scolding note_*dzwee-chrrrt*; and Common Iora a diagnostic flat piping *tu-tu-tu-tu* (P. Holt). **HABITS** Very similar to those of Common Iora. **HABITAT** Scrub and groves. **BREEDING** June–August. Nest is very similar to that of Common Iora, and built 1–2 m above ground in bushes. **DISTRIBUTION AND STATUS IN:** uncommon endemic resident, occurring from Gujarat, Rajasthan and Haryana east to S Uttar Pradesh and Orissa and south to Maharashtra; replaces Common Iora in the northwest. Specimens intermediate between this and Common Iora have been found elsewhere in India and in Sri Lanka. Note: Ali and Ripley (1987) state that Marshall's Iora is not confirmed as a true species. **REFERENCES** Hall (1957).

WOODSHRIKES Subfamily Malaconotinae

Medium-sized arboreal passerines with mainly grey or brown plumage and a dark band through the eye. The bill is stout and hooked, the wings are rounded, and the tail is short.

LARGE WOODSHRIKE *Tephrodornis gularis* Plate 95

***T. virgatus* (I,K)**

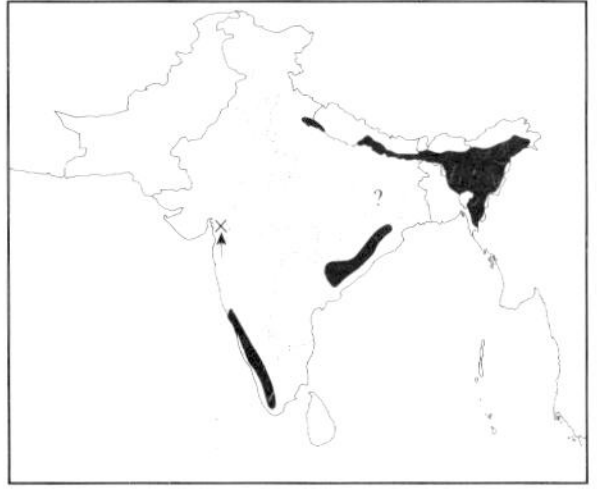

IDENTIFICATION 23 cm. **Male** is a shrike-like bird with stout black bill, dark mask, grey-brown upperparts, white rump, and pale pinkish-grey underparts. Told from Common Woodshrike (below) by larger size, absence of white supercilium, and uniform grey-brown tail (not dark with white sides). **Female** differs from male in having poorly defined brown mask, paler bill, and brown (rather than grey) crown and nape which is concolorous with mantle. **Juvenile** has a scaly appearance and superficially resembles a juvenile shrike, with buffish-white spots on crown, buffish fringes and dark subterminal crescents to mantle and scapulars, and buff fringes, dark subterminal crescents and diffuse dark bars on tertials and tail feathers, the latter being more pointed than on adults. **Racial variation** Male *T. g. pelvica* of the Himalayan foothills and E subcontinent differs from *T. g. sylvicola* of SW India in having paler, browner mantle and noticeably distinct pale grey crown and nape (uniform in *sylvicola*), and paler pinkish-grey breast and flanks. **VOICE** Call of *T. g. pelvica* is a musical *kew-kew-kew-kew*; call of *T. g. sylvicola* is a quick-repeated *witoo-witoo-witoo-witoo*; also has harsh shrike-like calls (Ali and Ripley 1987). **HABITS** Usually keeps in pairs or small parties, in winter sometimes in larger flocks of up to 30 birds; often joins other insectivorous birds. Quiet and unobtrusive. Seeks insects in foliage, on trunks and on branches, usually high in trees, but will sometimes descend to the ground; occasionally hawks from a perch. Birds follow one another in flight through the trees. **HABITAT** Broadleaved forest and well-wooded areas; prefers moister habitats than those used by Common Woodshrike. **BREEDING** December–June, varying locally. Builds a shallow saucer-shaped nest, covered with cobwebs, 3–8 m above ground in a medium-sized forest tree. **DISTRIBUTION AND STATUS** Resident, subject to local movements. Himalayan foothills from N Uttar Pradesh east to Arunachal Pradesh; NE, E and SW India, and Bangladesh. **NP:** locally fairly common below 365 m, uncommon up to 1450 m. **IN:** locally common; plains and hills up to 1000 m; to 1300 m, locally to 1800 m, in Western Ghats; locally to 1500 m in Himalayas and NE Indian hills. **BT:** frequent; below 1130 m. **BD:** local.

COMMON WOODSHRIKE *Tephrodornis pondicerianus* Plate 95

Woodshrike (P), Lesser Wood-shrike (F)

IDENTIFICATION 18 cm. **Adult** superficially resembles Large Woodshrike (above), with dark mask, grey-brown upperparts and whitish underparts, and small white band across rump. Differs from that species in smaller size, white supercilium above dark mask, and dark brown tail with white sides. **Juvenile** has buffish-white supercilium, buffish-white tips to crown, mantle and coverts, pale fringes and dark subterminal crescents to tertials and

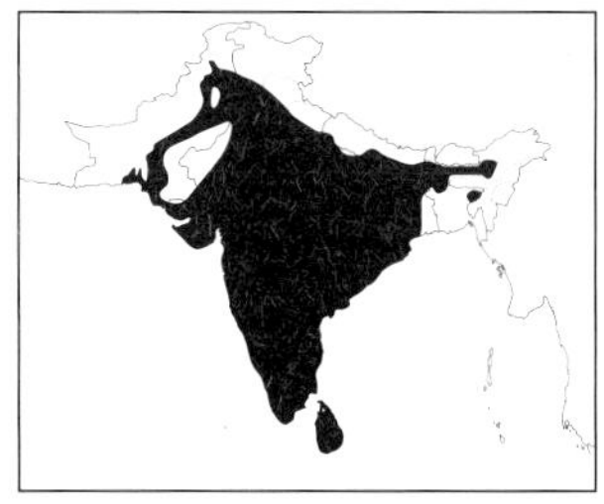

greater coverts, and indistinct brown streaking on breast and sides of throat. **VOICE** Described as a plaintive whistling *weet-weet*, followed by a quick interrogative *whi-whi-whi-whee?* (Ali and Ripley 1987), and an accelerating trill *pi-pi-i-i-i-i*, which is similar to the song of Large Woodshrike but more rapid (Boonsong and Round 1991). **HABITS** Similar to those of Large Woodshrike. **HABITAT** Dry country, where it replaces Large Woodshrike: open broadleaved forest, secondary growth, avenues alongside canals and roads, wooded gardens and forest plantations. **BREEDING** January–August, varying locally. Nest is a small neat cup, covered with soft bark or lichen, built 2–9 m above ground in a horizontal forked branch of a tree. **DISTRIBUTION AND STATUS** Sedentary resident throughout most of the subcontinent, except parts of the northwest, northeast and Himalayas. Replaces Large Woodshrike in drier habitats. **PK:** common and widespread in the more wooded plains. **NP:** locally fairly common; below 455 m. **IN:** widespread and generally common; usually below 200 m, but up to 900 m, locally 1200 m, in NW Himalayas and to 450 m in C and E Himalayas, locally to 1000 m in peninsular hills. **BD:** common. **LK:** common in lowlands and lower hills, most frequent in the dry zone.

WAXWINGS Bombycillidae

Have soft plumage, crested head, short broad-based bill, and short, strong legs and feet. Outside the breeding season, they are found wherever fruits are available.

BOHEMIAN WAXWING *Bombycilla garrulus* — Plate 95

Waxwing (I)

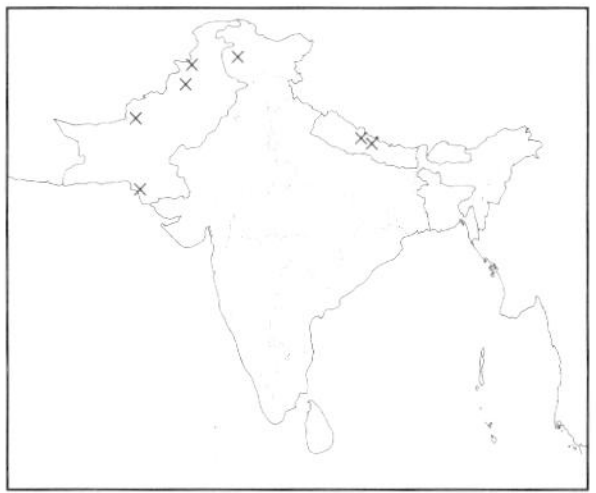

IDENTIFICATION 18 cm. Mainly fawn-brown in coloration, with swept-back crest, black mask and throat, grey rump and uppertail-coverts contrasting with blackish tail that has broad yellow tip, yellow and red waxy markings on wings, prominent white patch at base of primaries, and chestnut undertail-coverts. Flight is direct and rapid. In flight, recalls starling, and when catching insects in air can recall Ashy Woodswallow (p.599). **First-winter** lacks white margins to inner webs of primaries. **VOICE** Call is a sibilant trill which has a soft ringing quality, especially when heard from a flock in flight. **HABITS** Gregarious and remarkably tame. Typically, perches inactively and quietly in upright posture on an exposed branch for quite long periods. Forages in trees and bushes, and in winter feeds on berries. **HABITAT** Open country with fruiting trees and bushes. **DISTRIBUTION AND STATUS PK, NP, IN:** vagrant.

DIPPERS Cinclidae

Have short wings and tail, and are adapted for feeding in or under running water. Typically, they inhabit fast-flowing rivers and streams in hilly or mountainous country.

WHITE-THROATED DIPPER *Cinclus cinclus* — Plate 95

Dipper (I), White-breasted Dipper (F,N)

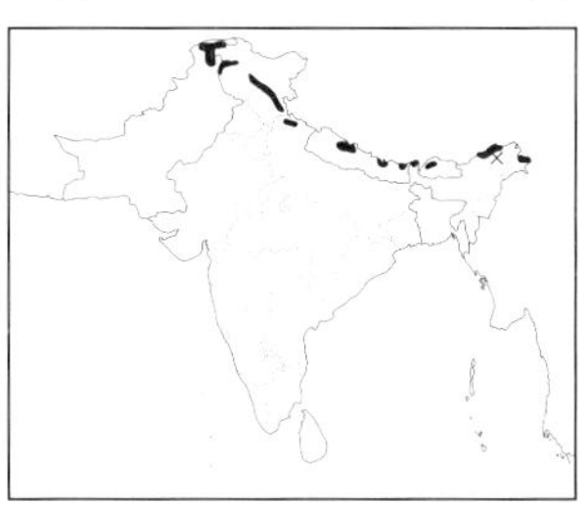

IDENTIFICATION 20 cm. **Adult** is readily separated from Brown Dipper (p.618) by white throat and breast contrasting with brown belly; also has brown head and nape merging into blackish-slate of mantle, wings and tail. Note, however, that a rare colour phase, with brown throat and breast, has been recorded in Ladakh. **Juvenile** has grey upperparts boldly scaled with black, narrow whitish fringes to greater coverts and tertials, white throat, and white underparts (becoming greyer on belly and flanks) scaled with grey brown. Told from juvenile Brown Dipper by greyer coloration to upperparts, without prominent spotting, and by whiter underparts. **Racial variation** *C. c. leucogaster*, which has an all-white belly, has been recorded in N Pakistan. **VOICE** Call is an abrupt, rasping *jeeet*; song is a quiet mixture of grating and twittering notes. **HABITS** Aquatic; usually seen perched on a rock in mid-stream, bobbing up and down. Generally occurs singly, in widely separated pairs or in scattered family parties. Highly territorial in winter and summer. Regularly submerges to swim underwater or walk on the stream bed in search of invertebrates; after popping to the surface, often floats downstream on half-spread wings before getting out of the water. Flies low over the water surface on rapidly whirring wings. **HABITAT** Fast-flowing mountain streams. **BREEDING**

April–July. Nest is a large ball of moss, built in a bank overhanging water, in a rock crevice or among a pile of rocks. **DISTRIBUTION AND STATUS** Resident. Himalayas from N Pakistan east to Arunachal Pradesh. Replaces Brown Dipper at higher elevations, but altitudinal ranges overlap and both species may be seen on the same streams. **PK:** scarce and sedentary; 3000–4250 m. **NP:** fairly common in the trans-Himalayan region, 3500–4800 m (–2590 m); subject to some altitudinal movements. **IN:** common north of the main Himalayan range, scarce to the south; breeds 3000–4800 m (2000?–5000 m); may descend in winter, rare below 2400 m; **BT:** frequent throughout; above 3660 m in summer. **REFERENCES** Pfister (1997).

BROWN DIPPER *Cinclus pallasii* Plate 95

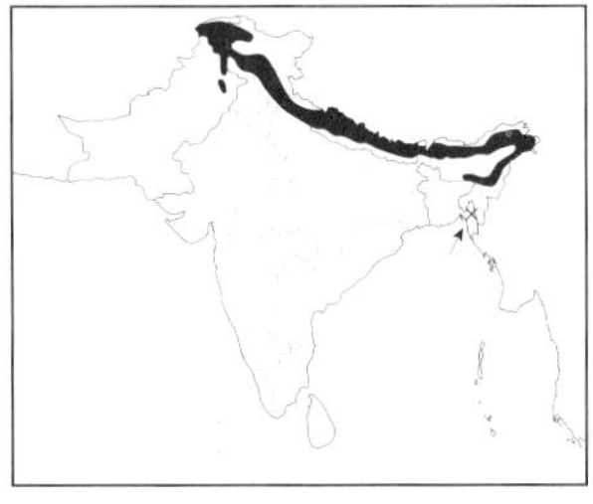

IDENTIFICATION 20 cm. **Adult** is entirely brown and therefore readily distinguished from White-throated Dipper (p.617), which has a white throat and breast. **Juvenile** has grey-brown upperparts boldly spotted with white, broad whitish fringes and tips to wing feathers, and grey-brown underparts boldly spotted with white. Told from juvenile White-throated Dipper by browner coloration with conspicuous spotting on upperparts and underparts, and more prominent pale fringes to wing feathers. **Racial variation** Adults of eastern race *C. p. dorje* are slightly darker than *C. p. tenuirostris*; and juvenile *dorje* has pale rufous spotting on darker blackish-brown upperparts and underparts, and less prominent pale fringes to wings compared with juvenile *tenuirostris*, which is described above. **VOICE** Call is an abrupt, rasping *dzit-dzit*, less harsh than White-throated's; song is stronger and richer. **HABITS** Very similar to those of White-throated Dipper. **HABITAT** Fast-flowing mountain streams and small mountain lakes. **BREEDING** December–early August. Nest is similar to that of White-throated Dipper; built behind a waterfall, in the structure of a bridge or in a rock crevice. **DISTRIBUTION AND STATUS** Resident, subject to some altitudinal movements. Himalayas from N Pakistan east to Arunachal Pradesh; NE India and Bangladesh. Generally at lower altitudes than White-throated Dipper. **PK:** common, widespread and mainly sedentary in N mountains; noted up to 3900 m and in winter down to 600 m. **NP:** common and widespread; 800–3100 m, frequent up to 4960 m in summer (455 m to nearly 5000 m). **IN:** common; breeds 450–3900 m in W Himalayas, 1000–4200 m in the east. **BT:** common; 610–4245 m. **BD:** former? resident in south-east; no recent records, but may still occur in hill tracts. **REFERENCES** Martens and Eck (1995).

THRUSHES, SHORTWINGS, OLD WORLD FLYCATCHERS AND CHATS Muscicapidae

A large and varied family, represented in the region by two distinct subfamilies, the second of which is subdivided into two tribes.

THRUSHES AND SHORTWINGS Subfamily Turdinae

THRUSHES Genera *Monticola, Myophonus, Zoothera* and *Turdus*

Medium-sized passerines with rather long, strong legs, a slender bill and fairly long wings. On the ground they progress by hopping. All are insectivorous, and many eat fruit as well. Some species are chiefly terrestrial and others arboreal. Most thrushes have loud and varied songs, which are used to proclaim and defend their territories when breeding. Many species gather in flocks outside the breeding season. Typically, the nest is cup-shaped and well built of grasses, moss etc, and is sometimes strengthened with mud. Nest sites are varied.

RUFOUS-TAILED ROCK THRUSH *Monticola saxatilis* Plate 96

Rock Thrush (I)

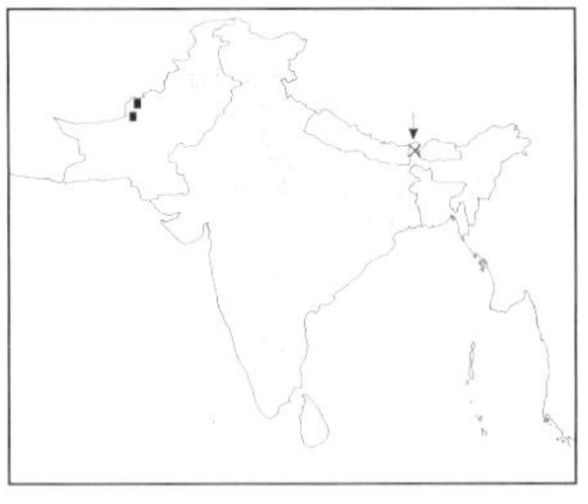

IDENTIFICATION 20 cm. The only rock thrush with orange-red tail. **Male breeding** has blue head and mantle, brownish-black wings, orange-red underparts and tail, and white back. Red tail and white on back separate it from other male rock thrushes. **Female** has grey-brown upperparts which are spotted with white and barred with black (upperparts are more uniform in worn plumage), orange wash to underparts, which are boldly scaled and barred with brown, and rufous tail. **First-winter/non-breeding male** resembles female, but has bluish cast to upperparts; in fresh plumage, has broad buff fringes to upperparts and wing feathers. **Juvenile** is similar to female, but looks more washed out, with greyer ground colour to upperparts, which also appear more mottled, and colder buff ground colour to underparts, which are more strongly barred. **VOICE** Softer and more flowing than that of Blue Rock Thrush (p.620), with much mimicry and variety, e.g. *chip chip chip chip tell r-r-r-r-r tu tu wechoo tu whechoo*; calls include a clear *diu*, a *chak* and a rattling *kschrrr* (Jonsson 1992; Cramp 1988). **HABITS** Usually found in pairs in the breeding season; otherwise singly, but may gather in loose flocks on passage. When perched, has an upright stance and slowly wags its tail up and down, like other rock thrushes. Often perches conspicuously on rocks or ridges. Forages mainly by hopping on the ground in search of insects; also eats berries. **HABITAT** Open rocky hillsides. **BREEDING** May and June. Builds nest in a rock crevice within 3 m of ground. **DISTRIBUTION AND STATUS** Breeds in N Baluchistan, Pakistan; passage migrant in Pakistan and Ladakh, mainly in autumn, very rare in spring. **PK:** rare on passage, 2100–3000 m; breeds infrequently, nest found at 3000 m. **IN:** current status uncertain; mainly above 2100 m.

BLUE-CAPPED ROCK THRUSH *Monticola cinclorhynchus* — Plate 96

Blue-headed Rock Thrush (F,I)

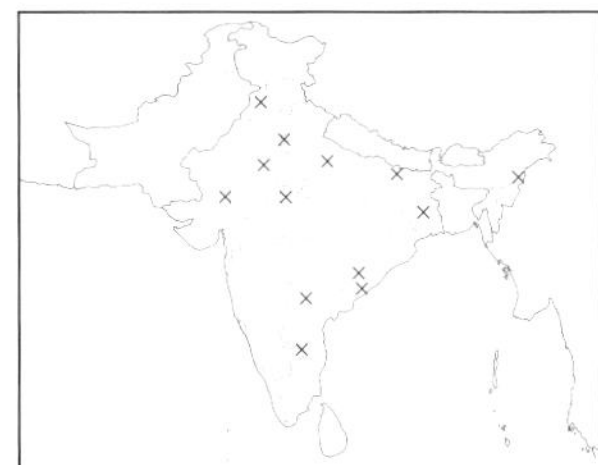

IDENTIFICATION 17 cm. **Male breeding** is only rock thrush with white patch on wing and rufous-orange rump and uppertail-coverts. Blue-black tail eliminates possible confusion with male redstarts. Further differences from Chestnut-bellied Rock Thrush (below) are smaller size and shorter tail, blackish ear-coverts contrasting with cobalt-blue throat, bluish-black mantle, and paler, more reddish-orange underparts. **Female** has olive-brown upperparts, barred with dark brown, and whitish underparts which are boldly scaled and barred with brown; has buff barring on rump and more rufescent-buff barring on uppertail-coverts, but otherwise upperparts are unbarred. Distinguished from female Chestnut-bellied by smaller size, absence of buffish neck patch, paler, more uniform olive-brown coloration to upperparts, and rufous-buff barring on uppertail-coverts. From female Blue Rock Thrush (p.620) by paler olive-brown coloration, and absence of blue cast to upperparts. **First-winter/non-breeding male** resembles breeding male, but has brownish-buff fringes to head, mantle and wings, and whitish fringes to orange of underparts. Fringes are very broad and, on some, largely obscure head pattern. **Juvenile** resembles female, but has buff spotting on crown and mantle, and buff fringes to coverts and tertials. Juvenile male has white wing patch. **VOICE** Short and monotonous, undulating and fluty *tree-deear-tree-deear...* or *trili dee-trili dee-trili dee-wheet-whi*. Calls include a *trigoink* (Roberts 1992). **HABITS** Found singly or in pairs in the breeding season; sometimes gathers in mixed flocks in winter. Chiefly arboreal. In spring, males often perch conspicuously in treetops. Has a very erect posture, and often wags its tail up and down. Feeds mainly on insects, which it seeks on trunks and branches; occasionally descends to the ground to forage among leaves on the forest floor, or flies out from a branch to catch flying insects. **HABITAT** Summers in open dry forest, often of pines, or on dry rocky slopes with scattered trees; winters in moist deciduous forest, coffee and cardamom plantations, secondary evergreen growth and mango groves. **BREEDING** April–July. Builds nest on sloping ground, under a rock or grass tuft, among tree roots or in a rock crevice. **DISTRIBUTION AND STATUS** Summer visitor to Himalayas from N Pakistan east to Arunachal Pradesh, and NE India; winters mainly in Western Ghats, also in Assam hills. **PK:** common in summer; 900–3000 m. **NP:** frequent in summer; 1200–2135 m (down to 275 m on passage). **IN:** common in summer; breeds from 1000 m up to at least 3000 m (–3600 m), mainly 1200–2200 m. **BT:** fairly common summer visitor; 715–2285 m.

CHESTNUT-BELLIED ROCK THRUSH *Monticola rufiventris* — Plate 96

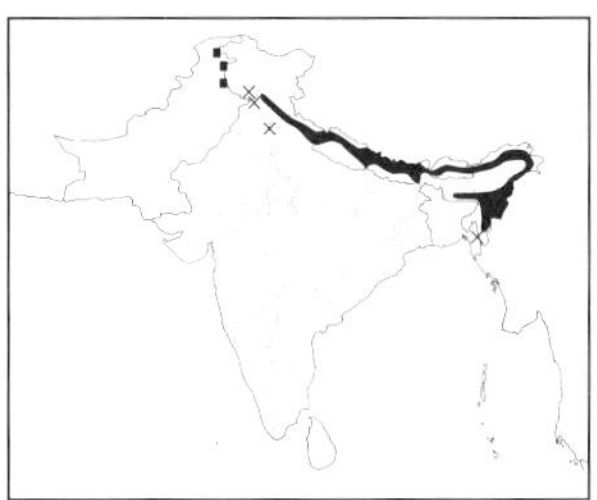

IDENTIFICATION 23 cm. Largest of the rock thrushes. **Adult male** is best told from Blue-capped Rock Thrush (above) by larger size, blue rump and uppertail-coverts (concolorous with rest of upperparts), absence of white wing patch, bluish-black throat concolorous with ear-coverts, and chestnut-red underparts. **Female** from female Blue-capped by larger size, prominent orange-buff eye-ring and throat, orange-buff patch on sides of neck, dark malar stripe, darker slaty olive-brown coloration to upperparts (which are barred with dark brown), and white to orange-buff underparts which are heavily dark-scaled. **Male non-breeding** and **first-winter male** are similar to breeding male, but have fine buff fringes to mantle, scapulars and throat. **Juvenile** resembles female (with buff neck patch), but has bold whitish or buff spotting and brown fringes to crown and mantle, and more prominent buff spotting on underparts. Juvenile male has blue on wings and tail. **VOICE** Rather soft and subdued compared with Blue-capped, an undulating and fluty *twew-twi-er trew-twi teedle-desh*. Calls include rasping jay-like notes (Roberts 1992). **HABITS** Usually seen perched high up in tall forest trees, slowly jerking its tail up and down from time to time. Forages mainly on the ground, seeking insects; sometimes makes aerial sallies after flying insects. Also eats berries. **HABITAT** Open coniferous and broadleaved forest on rocky slopes. **BREEDING** April–July. Builds nest on the ground, usually well hidden in a crevice, under a rock or tree roots or in a hole in a cliff face. **DISTRIBUTION AND STATUS** Resident, subject to altitudinal movements. Himalayas from Murree, Pakistan, east to Arunachal Pradesh, and NE India; winters in foothills, rarely in adjacent plains. **PK:** locally frequent summer visitor, mainly to the Murree hills; 2100–3000 m. **NP:** fairly common resident; summers mainly 1800–3400 m (–4460 m), winters 915–2380 m. **IN:** fairly common resident; breeds from 1200 m up to at least 3300 m, mainly 1800–2400 m; winters from 2300 m down to foothills, rarely in adjacent plains. **BT:** fairly common resident; 610–3350 m. **BD:** ?former winter visitor to the southeast; no recent records, but could still occur in hill tracts.

BLUE ROCK THRUSH *Monticola solitarius* Plate 96

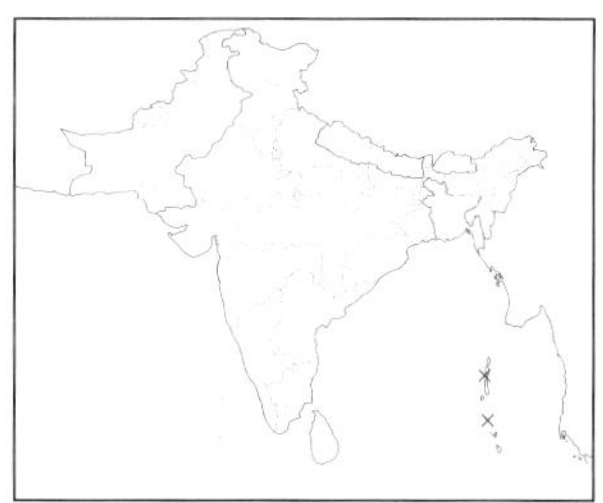

IDENTIFICATION 20 cm. **Adult male** is almost entirely indigo-blue, with blacker wings and tail. In fresh plumage, has narrow buff fringes to upperparts, white tips to wing-coverts, and brown and white fringes to underparts. **Female** told from other female rock thrushes by dark slate-brown upperparts (with bluish tinge and diffuse dark barring), dark brown wings and tail, and rather darker-coloured underparts (with buff spotting and scaling, but lacking prominent pale throat). **First-winter male** has blue of body plumage heavily marked with brownish-buff fringes. **Juvenile** resembles female, but lacks any blue, and has buff spotting and brown fringes to crown and mantle, and buff fringes to wing-coverts and tertials. **Racial variation** *M. s. philippensis*, from E Asia, has been recorded as a vagrant: males in all plumages (except juvenile) have rufous breast and belly (scaled with buff except in worn plumage). Some birds wintering in NE subcontinent show a variable amount of red on vent, and are presumably intergrades. **VOICE** Short and repetitive song, with fluty phrases, e.g. *chu sree, churr teetee...*, often with long pauses. Calls include a *chak*, a *veeht veeht* and high *tsee* (Jonsson 1992). **HABITS** Keeps singly in the non-breeding season and in pairs when breeding. Typically, perches very upright on a boulder, frequently wagging its tail up and down. Seeks insects chiefly on the ground among boulders and grass tufts, progressing by long hops; sometimes catches them in the air. Also eats banyan and peepul figs, berries and small lizards. **HABITAT** Breeds on open rocky slopes; winters in dry rocky areas, cliffs and rocks by the seashore, rocky gorges, quarries, rocky stream beds, ruins, and sometimes inhabited buildings. **BREEDING** April–July. Builds nest in a rock crevice, hole in a wall of building or field embankment. **DISTRIBUTION AND STATUS** Resident and winter visitor. Breeds in Baluchistan, Pakistan, and Himalayas from N Pakistan east to WC Nepal; winters throughout the Himalayan foothills and much of the rest of the subcontinent. **PK:** common; very widespread in summer in drier mountain areas, 1500–1800 m (–3800 m); winters from the lower hills down to the coast; occasionally seen on passage in Indus plains. **NP:** widespread; frequently summers in trans-Himalayan region, recorded 2590–4880 m; winters below 1400 m. **IN:** common in W Himalayas in summer, 1200–4500 m; locally fairly common in winter. **BT:** fairly common; 610–4200 m. **BD:** local winter visitor, occurs throughout. **LK:** rare winter visitor to dry lowlands and hills.

SRI LANKA WHISTLING THRUSH *Myophonus blighi* Plate 96

Ceylon Whistling Thrush (I,P)

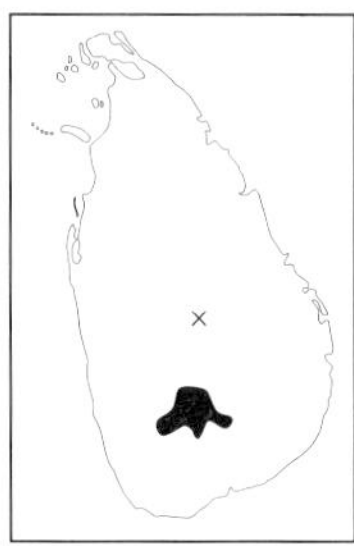

IDENTIFICATION 20 cm. Considerably smaller than Malabar Whistling Thrush (below) of the peninsula. **Male** is brownish-black and spangled with glistening blue (especially pronounced on forehead, supercilium and inner wing-coverts). **Female** is brown, with blue shoulder patch; has rufescent cast to lores, throat and breast. **Juvenile** is similar to female, but has more rusty-brown underparts, with ochre shaft streaks on head, neck and breast. **VOICE** Call is a shrill whistle, *sreee* (Henry 1971). **HABITS** Similar to those of Blue Whistling Thrush (p.621), but unlike that species it is shy, and the female is even more retiring than her mate and is rarely seen. **HABITAT** Mountain streams running through dense, damp montane forest in fern-clad gorges. **BREEDING** January–May. Nest is similar to that of Blue Whistling Thrush; usually placed in a rock crevice or ledge behind a waterfall, occasionally in a tree fork or on a stump, and always in forest. **DISTRIBUTION AND STATUS** Globally threatened. **LK:** endemic resident; rare and local, above 900 m, probably now confined to the Horton Plains National Park, 1300–2300 m.

MALABAR WHISTLING THRUSH *Myophonus horsfieldii* Plate 96

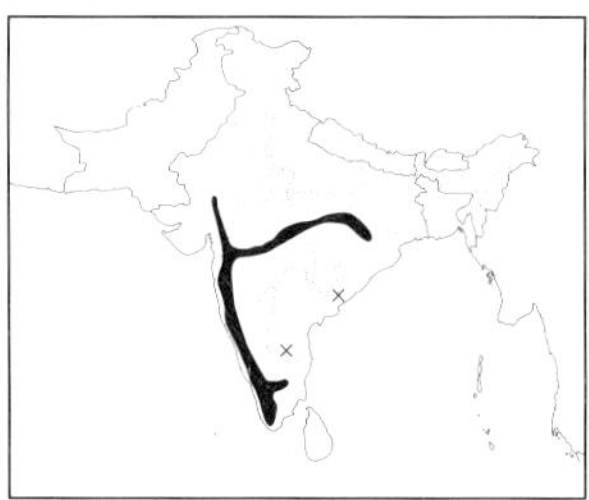

IDENTIFICATION 20 cm. **Adult** has cobalt-blue forehead and shoulder patch, black rest of head and breast, and glistening blue-black rest of body and, especially, wings and tail. Bill is black. **Juvenile** lacks blue forehead; head and body are sooty-brown, with dull blue wings and tail. **VOICE** Haunting song of slow, clear whistles meandering aimlessly up and down the scale; slower and mellower than, and superior to, that of Blue Whistling Thrush (p.621). Call is intense penetrating *schree*, purer and less harsh than that of Blue Whistling Thrush, and also usually given in flight (P. Holt). **HABITS** Similar to those of Blue Whistling Thrush, except for its shy behaviour. **HABITAT** Damp situations along fast-flowing, rocky hill streams running through forest, secondary growth and cardamom plantations. **BREEDING** February–September, varying locally. Nest and nest site are similar to those of Blue Whistling Thrush. **DISTRIBUTION AND STATUS IN:** endemic resident, from the hills of S Rajasthan, Surat Dangs and Satpura range east to NW Orissa, and in Western Ghats complex south to Kerala and east to W Tamil Nadu; locally fairly common from foothills up to 2200 m; disperses into adjacent plains during monsoon.

BLUE WHISTLING THRUSH *Myophonus caeruleus* Plate 96

Whistling Thrush (F)

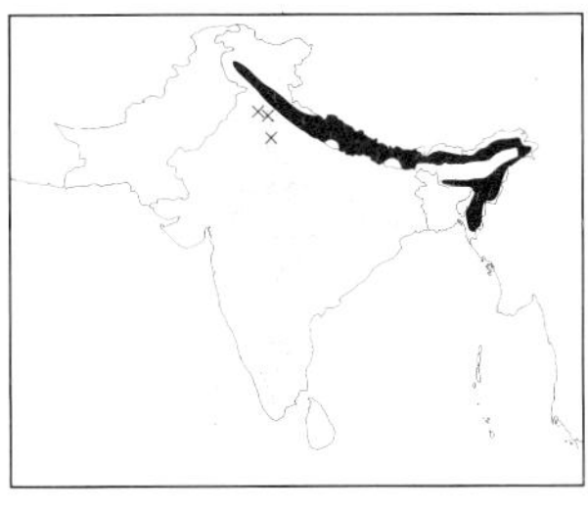

IDENTIFICATION 33 cm. A large, blackish thrush with stout yellow bill. **Adult** is dark blue-black, with head and body spangled with glistening silvery-blue. Forehead, shoulders, and fringes to wings and tail are brighter blue. **Juvenile** is similar to adult, but body plumage is browner, and lacks blue spangling; breast is indistinctly streaked or spotted with grey. Wings and tail are duller blue than adult's. **VOICE** Song is a melodic, rambling whistling with human-like qualities. Calls include a shrill, rasping *tzet* or shrill *kree* (Ali and Ripley 1987). **HABITS** Often in pairs in the breeding season; otherwise solitary. Crepuscular, typically starting to sing before dawn and foraging until dark. Often perches in trees, and when alighting raises and lowers the tail several times, spreading the feathers as tail is lowered. Forages on the ground, where it proceeds by long hops or by running rapidly for short distances; turns over leaves and digs in soft ground, or perches on stones in mid-stream and snatches food items as they float past. Feeds on invertebrates, berries, small frogs and nestlings. **HABITAT** Forest and wooded areas, often along streams and rivers, usually close to water; favours wooded gorges and ravines. **BREEDING** April–August. Builds a large cup-shaped nest of moss and roots, nearly always near running water, on a ledge behind a waterfall, among boulders or roots on a stream bank, or occasionally in a roof of a building. **DISTRIBUTION AND STATUS** Resident, subject to altitudinal movements. Breeds in N Baluchistan, Pakistan, Himalayas from N Pakistan east to Arunachal Pradesh, and NE India; winters in foothills, rarely in adjacent plains. **PK:** common and very widespread in N mountains; breeds 1200–3000 m. **NP:** common and very widespread; summers from 1500 m up to the treeline (470–4800 m), most frequent up to 3100 m, winters below 2745 m. **IN:** common; breeds from 1000 m up to the treeline, winters mainly from 2745 m down to foothills. **BT:** common and widespread; 150–4125 m. **BD:** local winter visitor. **REFERENCES** Martens and Eck (1995).

PIED THRUSH *Zoothera wardii* Plate 97

Pied Ground Thrush (F,I,N,P)

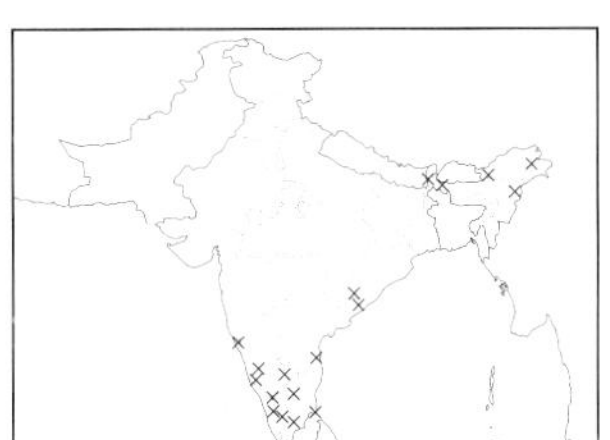

IDENTIFICATION 22 cm. **Adult male** is black and white, with yellowish bill and legs. Has white supercilium, white median- and greater-covert wing-bars, white-tipped tertials and secondaries, white barring on rump, and white belly and flanks (latter barred with black). **Female** has buff supercilium, olive-brown upperparts, buff median- and greater-covert bars, buff tips to tertials, buff spotting on olive-brown breast, and white belly and flanks (with prominent dark scaling). Possibly confusable in winter (in Sri Lanka) with Spot-winged Thrush (p.622); distinguished from that species by white supercilium, coloration and patterning of underparts (especially buff spotting on breast and barred flanks), and buff coloration to wing-bars; in flight, shows white corners to tail, which are lacking on Spot-winged. For differences from Siberian Thrush (p.622), see that species. **First-winter male** is similar to adult male, but black of head/body is duller (mixed with dark olive-brown); throat is almost white, mottled with black, and shows dark malar, black breast is spotted with white, and supercilium is buffish-white with feathers tipped black. Has fine buff greater-covert bar (median coverts as adult male: black, broadly tipped white). **Juvenile** resembles female, but has buff streaking on mantle and breast. Tail is blackish on juvenile male and olive-brown on juvenile female. Prominent buff supercilium separates juvenile from those of other thrushes occurring in Himalayan region. **VOICE** Alarm call is a spitting *ptz-ptz-ptz-ptz* (Fleming *et al.* 1984). Song is a phrase of two to four sweet and relatively high-pitched, quite short notes, the last often consisting of a short rattle, *tsrrrii*, or short *si* or *tzit*; different phrases are repeated after short intervals to form the song (C. Robson from E. Vercruysse recording). **HABITS** Found singly or in pairs. Usually keeps to the ground or in undergrowth; if disturbed, flies up into lower branches and remains motionless and quiet. Forages mainly by hopping about on the ground and by rummaging among leaf litter, searching for insects; also eats berries. **HABITAT** Open broadleaved forest, forest edges, secondary scrub with scattered trees, thickly vegetated ravines, undergrowth alongside streams, and well-wooded gardens. **BREEDING** May–July. Builds a broad, cup-shaped nest, strengthened with mud, 1–5 m above the ground in a small tree. **DISTRIBUTION AND STATUS** Resident, endemic to the subcontinent. Breeds in Himalayas from Himachal Pradesh east to Arunachal Pradesh, and NE India; migrates through India to winter in Sri Lanka and Tamil Nadu. **NP:** widespread but uncommon summer visitor; mainly 1500–2400 m (–3050 m). **IN:** uncommon summer visitor to Himalayas, 1200–2400 m; rare winter visitor to the south. **LK:** frequent winter visitor to middle altitudes and higher hills. **REFERENCES** Karthikeyan (1996), Kazmierczak (1991), Sugathan (1983).

ORANGE-HEADED THRUSH *Zoothera citrina* Plate 97

Orange-headed Ground Thrush (F,I,N,P,R)

IDENTIFICATION 21 cm. Shows white banding on underwing. **Adult male** has orange crown, nape, breast and belly, blue-grey mantle, rump and tail, and white vent and undertail-coverts. **Female** is similar to male, but has

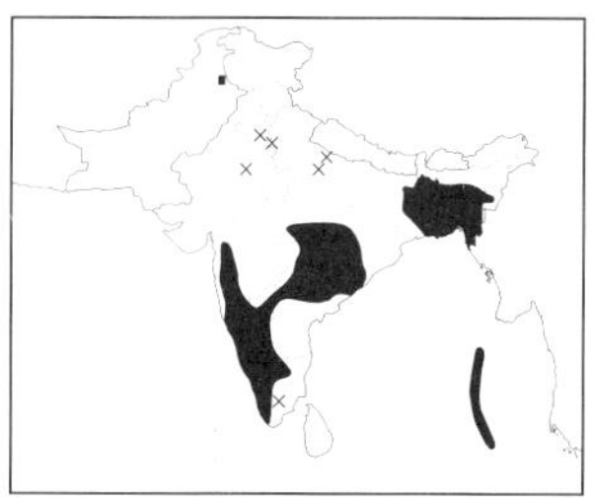

strong olive-brown wash to mantle, tertials and secondaries. **Juvenile** has buffish-orange streaking on crown and mantle, orange-buff tips to wing-coverts, and diffuse brownish mottling and barring on underparts (with buff shaft streaking). **Racial variation** *Z. c. citrina* of the Himalayas and NE subcontinent, wintering south to peninsular India and Sri Lanka, has head entirely orange (although may show diffuse dark vertical bar at rear of ear-coverts). *Z. c. cyanotus* of the peninsula has vertical black stripes across white ear-coverts, and white throat. *Z. c. andamanensis* and *Z. c. albogularis* of the Andaman and Nicobar Is lack the white shoulder patch shown by the two continental races, and also lack black head stripes. **VOICE** A rich, sweet and variable song of short, frequently repeated strophes, and a thin *tzzeet* in flight (Boonsong and Round 1991). **HABITS** Keeps singly or in pairs. Crepuscular, often coming on to forest paths and roads at dusk. Shy, quiet and terrestrial. Seeks insects and worms by turning over leaves and debris and probing into soft ground on the forest floor. When disturbed, flies up into a nearby tree and remains silent and still, often concealed from view. **HABITAT** Damp and shady places, often near water, in forest, ravines, plantations, bamboo thickets, thick secondary scrub and well-wooded areas. **BREEDING** May–September, varying locally. Builds a shallow cup-shaped nest, covered in moss, 1–5 m up in the fork of a tree or bush. **DISTRIBUTION AND STATUS** Resident and partial migrant. Himalayas in Margalla hills, N Pakistan, and from Himachal Pradesh east to Arunachal Pradesh, NE India and Bangladesh; also from S Gujarat east to West Bengal and south through much of the subcontinent. PK: scarce and very local summer visitor; 460 m. NP: widespread and fairly common partial migrant, mainly a summer visitor; 250–1830 m, rare in winter below 250 m (–915 m). IN: resident and partial migrant; fairly common, but local; breeds from foothills up to 1600 m, locally to 2300 m, in Himalayas and NE hills, and in plains and peninsular hills up to 1200 m, locally to 1500 m; winters in plains and foothills. BT: frequent; 510–1220 m. BD: local resident, subject to local movements; occurs throughout. LK: rare winter visitor to lowlands, mainly in the south, centre and west.

SIBERIAN THRUSH *Zoothera sibirica* — Plate 97

Siberian Ground Thrush (I)

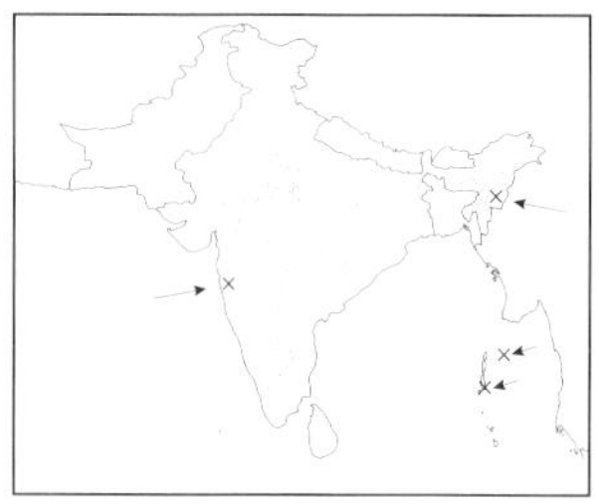

IDENTIFICATION 22 cm. **Adult male** is almost entirely slate-grey, with striking white supercilium, and broad white fringes to undertail-coverts. In flight, shows white banding across underwing and white corners to tail. Uniform slate-grey wings and underparts are best features to separate it from male Pied Thrush (p.621). **Female** has buff supercilium (often curving down behind ear-coverts), dark malar stripe, dark olive-brown upperparts, and whitish underparts (variably washed buff) with extensive dark spotting and scaling. Best told from female Pied Thrush by lack of buff tips to tertials (although these can, through wear, be narrow or lacking on Pied) and less prominent (or non-existent) buff tips to median and greater coverts, while scaling on flanks is partly obscured by olive-brown (belly and flanks of Pied whiter, with clearer and darker brown scaling). **First-winter male** resembles adult male, but is paler slate-grey, and typically has buff wash to supercilium, buff markings on throat, buff greater-covert bar, and pale mottling on underparts. **VOICE** Call is a soft *stit*. **HABITS** Similar to those of other *Zoothera* thrushes. Usually in small parties; gathers in larger flocks before departing in spring. **HABITAT** Forest. **DISTRIBUTION AND STATUS IN:** current status uncertain, and no recent published records; recorded in W Maharashtra, Manipur hills up to at least 1800 m, and Andamans.

SPOT-WINGED THRUSH *Zoothera spiloptera* — Plate 97

Spotted-winged Ground Thrush (I), Spotted-winged Thrush (P)

IDENTIFICATION 27 cm. **Adult** is a distinctive thrush, with olive-brown upperparts and white underparts. Has diffuse black crescent behind ear-coverts and patch below eye, bold (but sparse) black spotting on white breast and flanks, and prominent white tips to median and greater coverts. These features, as well as absence of supercilium and of pale tips to tertials, separate it from female Pied Thrush. **Juvenile** is less boldly patterned than adult, with dark head markings less prominent (although still apparent); has fine buff streaking and diffuse dark scaling on upperparts, buff tips to median and greater coverts (wing-bars are therefore much less prominent than on adult), and diffuse dark scaling on buffish breast and flanks. **VOICE** Typical, rich thrush-like song, usually delivered as a series of short (c. 2 seconds), often repeated phrases; each phrase consists of clear and sweet whistling notes, with differing, often abrupt endings. Call is a quiet, rapid, high-pitched *tsit-sit-sit* (P. Morris). **HABITS** Rather shy. In early mornings and evenings, calls frequently from a low perch and often comes into the open. **HABITAT** Dense, damp forest, well-wooded areas, and occasionally in gardens near forest. **BREEDING** March and April, August–November. Builds nest 1.5–3.5 m above ground in the fork of a sapling or crown of a tree fern, or on a bank. **DISTRIBUTION AND STATUS LK:** endemic resident, frequent in lowlands and hills of the wet zone, 305–1220 m; also in adjacent areas of the dry zone, but no recent records.

PLAIN-BACKED THRUSH *Zoothera mollissima* Plate 97

Plain-backed Mountain Thrush (F,I,N,R)

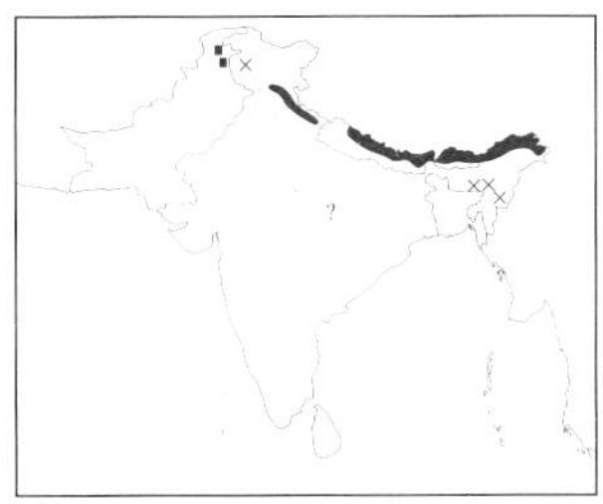

IDENTIFICATION 27 cm. Very similar to Long-tailed Thrush (below), with olive-brown upperparts and heavily scaled underparts. In flight, shows broad whitish banding across underwing. Best told from Long-tailed by indistinct (or complete lack of) median- and greater-covert wing-bars (at their most prominent, can show as small buff tips or narrow and crescent-shaped fringes to median coverts, with buff tips to greater coverts uniformly narrow and forming only a very fine bar); in addition, belly and flanks are generally more heavily scaled with black (this scaling distinctly crescentic in shape), and breast and belly are usually more strongly washed with buff. Further, has more rufescent coloration to upperparts, especially to uppertail-coverts/rump and tail (valid in C and E Himalayas only), less pronounced pale wing panel, and shorter tail. **Juvenile** has upperparts finely streaked with buff and diffusely scaled with dark brown; tips of median and greater coverts are slightly broader than on adult (but still narrower than on Long-tailed), and underparts are more heavily marked with broader and more intensive black barring and scaling (different from juvenile Long-tailed, which has underparts much as on adult of that species). **VOICE** Song begins with a *plee-too,* a *plee-chu* or a *ti-ti-ti,* and usually ends with a descending *chup-ple-oop* (Fleming *et al.* 1984); has Eurasian Blackbird-like phrases (J. Scharringa). **HABITS** Keeps singly, in pairs or in family parties in the breeding season; often in loose flocks in winter. Secretive and shy. Male often sings from treetops, and keeps well hidden in the foliage. Feeds mainly on the ground, in typical thrush manner, and flies up into bushes and trees when disturbed. **HABITAT** Summers on open grassy hillsides and rocky and grassy slopes with dense bushes near the treeline; winters in forest and open country with bushes. **BREEDING** May–July. Builds a large cup-shaped nest on a rock ledge or among rhododendron roots. **DISTRIBUTION AND STATUS** Resident, subject to altitudinal movements. Mainly Himalayas, from N Pakistan east to Arunachal Pradesh; NE India. **PK:** very rare and local; breeds 3600–4500 m. **NP:** fairly common; summers 3000–4000 m, winters 1500–2400 m (–2700 m). **IN:** locally fairly common in east, rather scarce in west; breeds 2700–4300 m, winters 600–3600 m, mainly 1500–2400 m. **BT:** fairly common; 1450–4265 m.

LONG-TAILED THRUSH *Zoothera dixoni* Plate 97

Long-tailed Mountain Thrush (F,I,N)

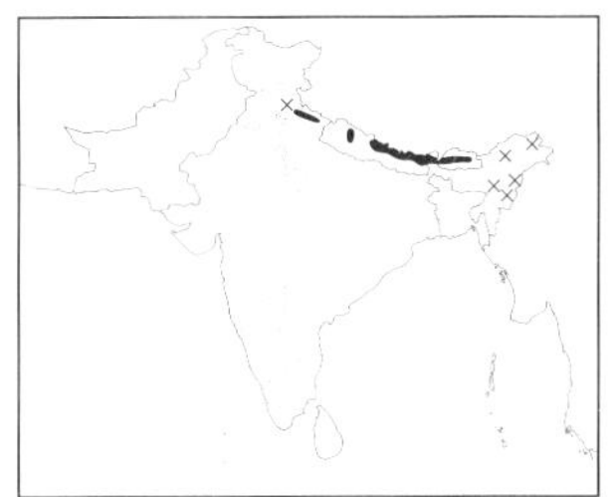

IDENTIFICATION 27 cm. Very similar to Plain-backed Thrush (above), with olive-brown upperparts and heavily scaled underparts. In flight, shows broad whitish banding across underwing. Best told from Plain-backed by comparatively broad and prominent median- and greater-covert wing-bars (buff tips to median coverts form distinct spotting); belly and flanks are more sparsely marked with black, and flank markings appear more bar-like in shape (on some, almost spotted), and less crescentic, than on Plain-backed. Further, has greyer coloration to upperparts (valid in C and E Himalayas only), whiter ground colour to breast and belly, more pronounced pale panel on wing, and longer tail. **Juvenile** has upperparts finely streaked with buff and diffusely scaled with dark brown; wing-bars, and coloration and patterning of underparts, are much as on adult, and are good distinctions from juvenile Plain-backed. **VOICE** A long-sustained, rambling series of mainly harsh notes, e.g. *zwheer* and *zwit,* interspersed occasionally with a tremulous *yowowoit* or a pure, ringing *preet* (T. Inskipp). **HABITS** Similar to those of Plain-backed Thrush. **HABITAT** Undergrowth and bushes in birch–rhododendron, fir and juniper forest in summer; at other times dense forest, secondary growth, especially near streams, and open country with bushes. **BREEDING** May–July. Builds a cup-shaped nest in a tree, 3 m from the ground. **DISTRIBUTION AND STATUS** Resident, subject to altitudinal movements. Himalayas from Himachal Pradesh east to Arunachal Pradesh; NE India. **NP:** frequent in summer, 2100–4520 m; winters 1500–2700 m. **IN:** scarce; breeds 2100–4200 m, winters 450–2700 m. **BT:** frequent; 2135–4330 m. **REFERENCES** Athreya *et al.* (1997).

SCALY THRUSH *Zoothera dauma* Plate 97

Golden Mountain Thrush (I), White's Thrush, Speckled Mountain Thrush (F)

IDENTIFICATION 26–27 cm. A boldly scaled thrush with pale face and large black eye. Distinguished from other *Zoothera* thrushes by bold black scaling on golden-olive upperparts, and golden-olive panels across wing, with dark bar at tip of primary coverts. In flight, shows dark tail with white corners and pale centre, quite different from tail of Plain-backed and Long-tailed Thrushes (above). **Juvenile** is similar to adult, but upperparts are more barred than scaled, and breast is distinctly spotted. **Racial variation** *Z. d. neilgherriensis* of the Western Ghats differs from the nominate race, described above, in having darker, browner and more uniform upperparts (mantle and scapulars lack the golden-olive subterminal spots/fringes which give *Z. d. dauma,* of N and NE subcontinent, its spangled appearance); bill is bigger, and face is plainer and more regularly marked with black (lacking dark patches). *Z. d. imbricata* of Sri Lanka is strikingly different from nominate: is smaller, with shorter tail, and bill is proportionately much longer; upperparts are darker olive-brown; has rufous-buff ground colour to

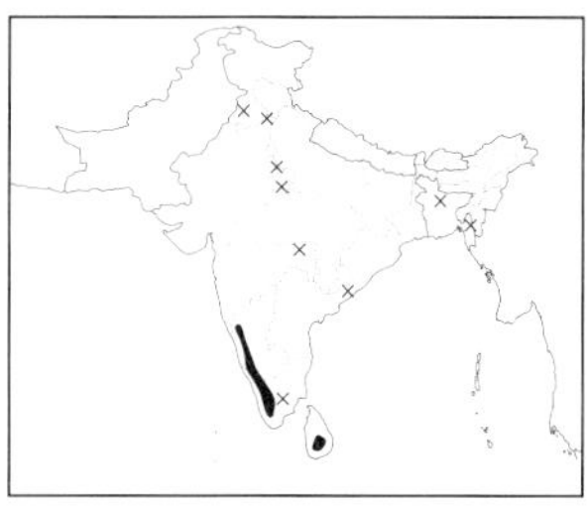

underparts, with narrower black scaling; and head is more uniformly marked. **VOICE** Song of nominate race is a slow, broken *chirrup...chwee...chueu...we ep..chirrol..chup...* etc (Ali and Ripley 1987); call is a grating *tsshhh* (R. Grimmett). **HABITS** Found singly or in pairs. Shy, retiring and quiet. Forages on the forest floor by searching among leaf litter; progresses on the ground by walking and running. Flies up into thick foliage at the slightest disturbance, sweeping up to a perch in a characteristic glide. Has a bounding flight, deep wingbeats alternating with closed-wing glides. **HABITAT** Summers in broadleaved, mixed broadleaved–coniferous and moist coniferous forest with a well-developed understorey; winters in dense forest and well-wooded areas, often near water. **BREEDING** March–October, varying locally. Builds nest in the fork of a tree or bush, 1–6 m above ground; occasionally on a bank. **DISTRIBUTION AND STATUS** Breeds in Himalayas from N Pakistan (Neelum valley, Kaghan valley and Murree hills) east to Arunachal Pradesh, also NE India, Western Ghats from N Karnataka south to Kerala and W Tamil Nadu, and Sri Lanka; N birds are partially migratory, some wintering south to Andhra Pradesh and Orissa. **PK:** scarce and local resident; 2100–3000 m. **NP:** widespread partial migrant, fairly common; summers 2320–3300 (–3540 m), winters 275–1500 m (down to 120 m). **IN:** fairly common in Himalayas and NE hills, breeds 2100–3600 m, wintering from foothills up to 1800 m (–2650 m) and sparsely in plains; uncommon resident in Western Ghats, 600–2100 m. **BT:** fairly common; 610–3385 m. **BD:** winter vagrant. **LK:** rare resident, 600–1500 m, more frequent above 900 m. **REFERENCES** Kaul *et al.* (1995).

LONG-BILLED THRUSH *Zoothera monticola* — Plate 97

Large Brown Thrush (I), Large Long-billed Thrush (F)

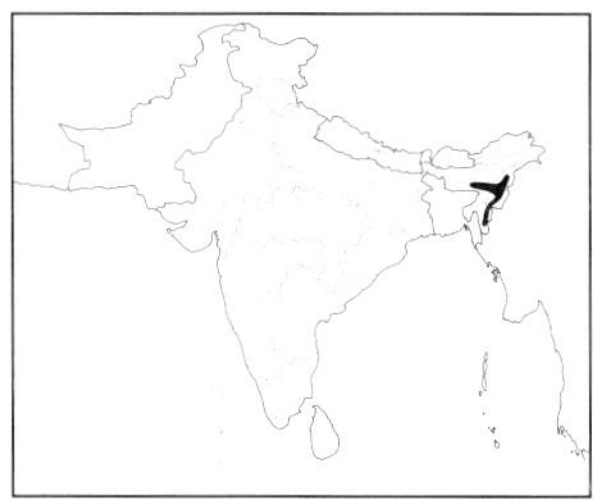

IDENTIFICATION 28 cm. A stocky, short-tailed, very dark thrush with huge, black bill (with pronounced curve to culmen and hooked tip). Distinguished from Dark-sided Thrush (below) by larger size, larger bill with prominent hooked tip, dark lores, very dark slaty-olive upperparts, darker and more uniform sides of head (with diffuse dark malar stripe and well-defined narrow white throat patch), darker and more uniform breast and flanks (both with diffuse dark spotting), and dark spotting on whitish belly. Shows white banding on underwing in flight. **Juvenile** has pale shaft streaks on upperparts, prominent buff tips to wing-coverts, and buffish underparts with bold dark spotting. Spotted (rather than scaled) underparts and darker olive coloration are the best distinctions from juvenile Dark-sided. **VOICE** Song is a loud, slow, plaintive whistle of two to three notes, *te-e-uw* or *tew-tew-tew*; alarm is a loud *zaaaaaaaa* (Fleming *et al.* 1984). **HABITS** Solitary and shy. Crepuscular. Skulks on the ground under dense undergrowth in forest. Probes damp soil, tosses aside leaves, and turns over stones with its long bill. Flight is strong and rapid, but prefers to escape by hopping into dense undergrowth. **HABITAT** Floors of dense, shady moist forest, with thick undergrowth, especially near streams; also swampy ground in dense, damp forest. **BREEDING** May–July. Nest is a deep cup of green moss, built in a fork or branch or on a stump 2–7 m above ground in dense forest. **DISTRIBUTION AND STATUS** Resident, subject to altitudinal movements. Himalayas from Himachal Pradesh east to Arunachal Pradesh; NE India. **NP:** frequent in winter, 915–2500 m (down to 75 m); summers 2285–3850 m. **IN:** uncommon; breeds 2000–3000 m in Himalayas, down to 900 m south of the Brahmaputra; winters from 2400 m down to foothills. **BT:** uncommon. **BD:** vagrant.

DARK-SIDED THRUSH *Zoothera marginata* — Plate 97

Lesser Brown Thrush (I), Lesser Long-billed Thrush (F)

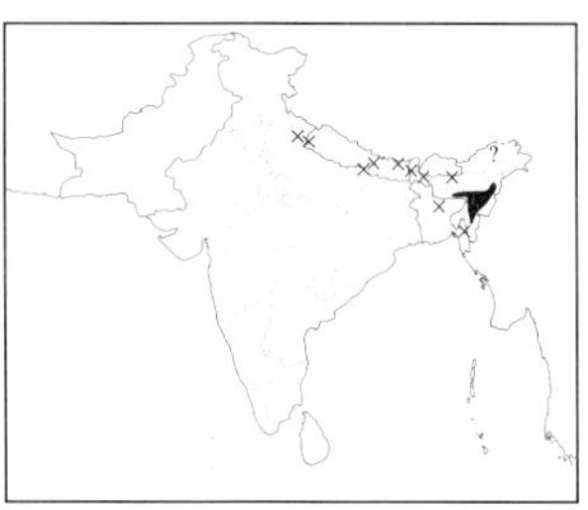

IDENTIFICATION 25 cm. A stocky, short-tailed thrush with large, black bill. Told from Long-billed Thrush (above) by smaller size, smaller bill, rufescent-brown upperparts, pale lores and paler and more patterned sides of head (paler ear-coverts with dark patch at rear and pale crescent behind, more prominent dark malar stripe), rufous edges to tertials and secondaries forming panel on wing, and paler underparts with prominent scaling on breast and flanks. **Juvenile** has pale shaft streaks on upperparts, and prominent buff tips to wing-coverts; underparts, especially belly and flanks, are similar to adult's (although more heavily marked), and are scaled (rather than spotted as on juvenile Long-billed). **VOICE** Song is a thin whistle, like that of Scaly Thrush but softer and shorter; call a soft, deep, guttural *tchuck* (Boonsong and Round 1991). **HABITS** Very similar to those of Long-billed. **HABITAT** Forest floor in damp, dense forest near streams; in winter, also in dense reeds along slow-moving streams in broadleaved evergreen forest. **BREEDING** May–August. Nest is like that of Long-billed Thrush; built in a tall bush or small tree near water in dense forest. **DISTRIBUTION AND STATUS** Resident. Himalayas from N Uttar Pradesh east to Arunachal Pradesh; NE India. **NP:** rare, possibly resident; 275–2440 m. **IN:** uncommon resident, most frequent south of the Brahmaputra, where it breeds 750–2100 m; in Sikkim, winters from foothills up to 1900 m (winter range elsewhere uncertain). **BD:** winter vagrant.

TICKELL'S THRUSH *Turdus unicolor* Plate 98

Indian Grey Thrush

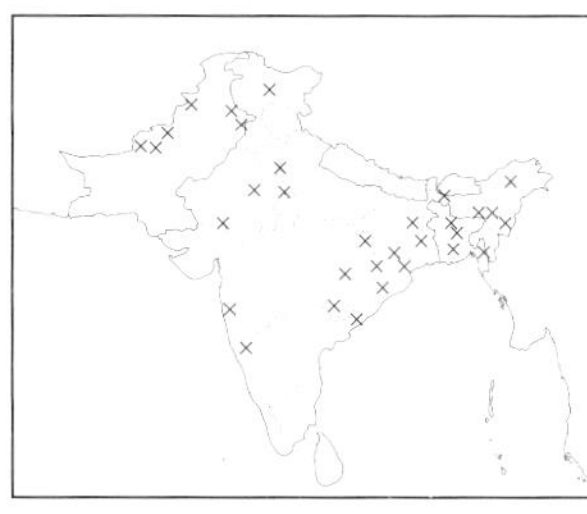

IDENTIFICATION 21 cm. A small, compact thrush with rather plain face, small yellowish or pale brown bill, and pale legs. Possibly confusable outside the breeding season with races of Eurasian Blackbird (p.626) from the peninsula and Sri Lanka, although is much smaller (see below for differences). **Adult male** is almost entirely pale bluish-grey, with whitish belly and undertail-coverts, and has yellow bill and fine yellow eye-ring. Paler and more uniformly grey on head, upperparts and breast than any race of Eurasian Blackbird, lacking any suggestion of darker cap. **Female** has olive-brown upperparts, plain olive-brown face (lacking supercilium), prominent dark (streaked) malar stripe, whitish throat and submoustachial stripe, pale grey-brown to olive-brown breast-band and flanks (with variable orange-buff wash), and white belly and undertail-coverts; mantle can have bluish-grey cast, and breast usually shows diffuse spotting. Females of some races of Eurasian Blackbird are quite similar; smaller size and finer bill, whiter throat, dark malar stripe, spotting on breast (if present), and orange-buff wash to breast and flanks are good features for Tickell's. **First-winter male** superficially resembles female, but has distinct grey cast to upperparts (especially rump and uppertail-coverts) and breast; new greyish wing-coverts contrast with old buff-tipped brown ones. **Juvenile** has dark olive-brown upperparts with fine orange-buff shaft streaks, orange-buff tips to coverts, and heavily barred and spotted breast and flanks. **VOICE** Song is typical of thrushes, although comparatively weak and monotonous, with repeated disyllabic or trisyllabic phrases, e.g. *chilliyah-chilliyah, tirlee-tirlee-chelia-chelia* or *trilooo trilooo tru-tu-leee*, but shows much variation throughout range. Call is a soft *juk-juk* (Ali and Ripley 1987; Roberts 1992). **HABITS** Keeps in pairs in the breeding season, and in small loose flocks on passage and in winter. Gait and feeding behaviour are typical of *Turdus* thrushes. Often stops with head cocked on one side, listening intently for earthworms or insect larvae. Also eats fruit and berries; favours apples, plums and apricots in orchards. If disturbed, flies up into the nearby tree canopy. **HABITAT** Summers in open forest, groves, wooded gardens, terraced cultivation with deciduous trees and orchards; also in heavy forest in Kashmir. Winters in groves and well-wooded areas. **BREEDING** April–August. Builds a typical thrush nest, usually in a tree fork 2–7 m above ground, sometimes lower down in bushes or in a hollow in a bank. **DISTRIBUTION AND STATUS** Resident, endemic to the subcontinent. Summer visitor to Himalayas from N Pakistan east to Bhutan; winters chiefly east and south of its main breeding range, east to Arunachal Pradesh and Manipur and south to N Andhra Pradesh. **PK:** mainly a summer visitor to Himalayas, locally frequent, breeds 1200–2400 m; a few winter records. **NP:** mainly a fairly common summer visitor, 1500–2450 m (–2745 m); several winter reports, 150–1280 m. **IN:** fairly common summer visitor to Himalayas, breeds 1200–2200 m; winters in foothills and plains. **BT:** rare summer visitor. **BD:** vagrant.

BLACK-BREASTED THRUSH *Turdus dissimilis* Plate 98

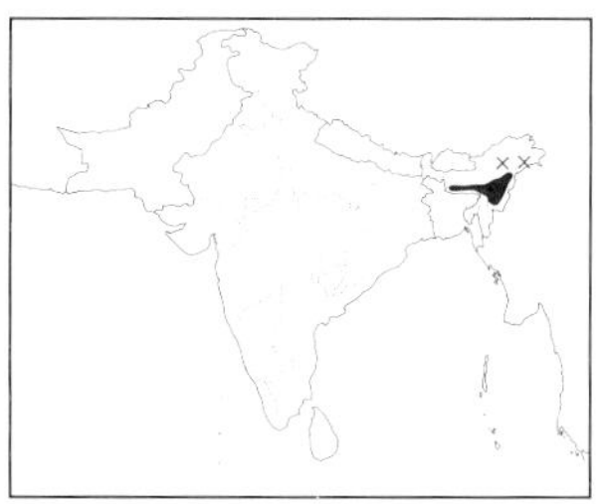

IDENTIFICATION 22 cm. A small, compact thrush. **Adult male** has black head and breast, grey upperparts, orange upper belly and flanks, and white centre to belly and vent. **Female** has dark olive-grey upperparts, plain face (lacking supercilium), prominent dark (streaked) malar stripe and dark spotting across olive-grey upper breast, whitish throat (with variable dark streaking) and submoustachial stripe, and orange lower breast and flanks. Absence of supercilium and boldly spotted breast separate it from Eyebrowed Thrush (p.628). **Juvenile** superficially similar to female, but has buff streaking on upperparts, and heavily barred and spotted throat, breast and flanks with ochraceous wash. **VOICE** Song is sweet and mellow, typical of the genus, consisting of three to eight varied, spaced notes per phrase. Calls are a resounding *tup-tup....tup-tup-tup-tup-tup-tup....* etc (C. Robson) and a thin *seee* (R. Grimmett). **HABITS** Very secretive and shy. Forages on the forest floor, among leaf litter and mossy boulders. **HABITAT** Breeds in moist, shady broadleaved evergreen forest; in winter, also found in scrub jungle and mangroves in Bangladesh. **BREEDING** April–July. Builds a typical thrush nest 1–6 m above ground in the fork of a tree or high bush, occasionally on the ground. **DISTRIBUTION AND STATUS** Resident, subject to some altitudinal and local movements, in NE India south of the Brahmaputra (Assam, Manipur, Meghalaya, Nagaland); winters south to Tripura and Bangladesh. **IN:** current status uncertain, very few recent records; in hills from 1200 m to summits (Meghalaya), up to at least 2400 m (Nagaland), winters in neighbouring plains and foothills. **BD:** rare winter visitor. **REFERENCES** Athreya *et al.* (1997).

WHITE-COLLARED BLACKBIRD *Turdus albocinctus* Plate 98

IDENTIFICATION 27 cm. A large, dark, long-tailed thrush with striking whitish collar. **Adult male** is mainly black, with white throat and broad white collar; bill and legs are yellow. **Female** has pale collar, and rest of plumage is rufous-brown with pale feather fringes on underparts; extent, coloration and prominence of collar varies, on some being broad and greyish-white to pale greyish-buff, while on others it is rather narrow and pale. **Juvenile** lacks collar; has orange-buff streaking on upperparts, orange-buff tips to coverts (forming double wing-bar), and orange-buff underparts with dark brown spotting and barring. Coloration and patterning of underparts help separate it from juve-

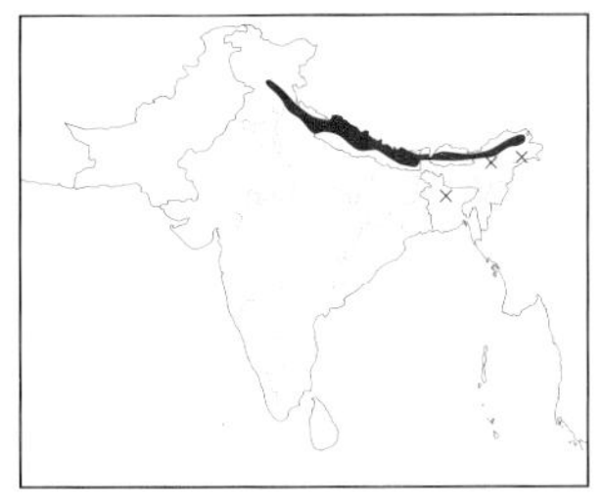

nile Eurasian Blackbird (below). Absence of pale panelling on wing separates it from juvenile Grey-winged Blackbird (below). **VOICE** Calls like Dark-throated Thrush (p.628): a coarse, chuckling chatter, *tjuk*, often doubled or in an explosive sequence. Song is rather melancholy, a broken and simple series of soft descending whistles, *hoo-ee, hoo-ou, hoo-uu*, repeated five to seven times per minute and occasionally interwoven with hissing and squeaking notes (P. Holt). **HABITS** Rather shy in the breeding season, when found singly or in pairs; sometimes in flocks and with other thrushes in autumn and winter. Often feeds in trees; also on the ground in forest, and sometimes in more open areas in winter. **HABITAT** Broadleaved, coniferous and mixed broadleaved–coniferous forest, forest edges and clearings. **BREEDING** March–July. Builds a typical thrush nest 1–3 m above ground in a high bush or sapling; occasionally among roots of a fallen tree on a steep bank. **DISTRIBUTION AND STATUS** Resident, subject to altitudinal movements. Himalayas from Himachal Pradesh east to Arunachal Pradesh; NE India. **NP:** fairly common; summers chiefly 2400–3445 m (–3750 m), and winters 1525–3000 m, mainly above 2100 m (down to 80 m). **IN:** fairly common; breeds 2100–4000 m or up to the treeline, winters from foothills up to 3000 m. **BT:** common; 2135–4060 m. **BD:** vagrant. **REFERENCES** Lama (1995b).

GREY-WINGED BLACKBIRD *Turdus boulboul* — Plate 98

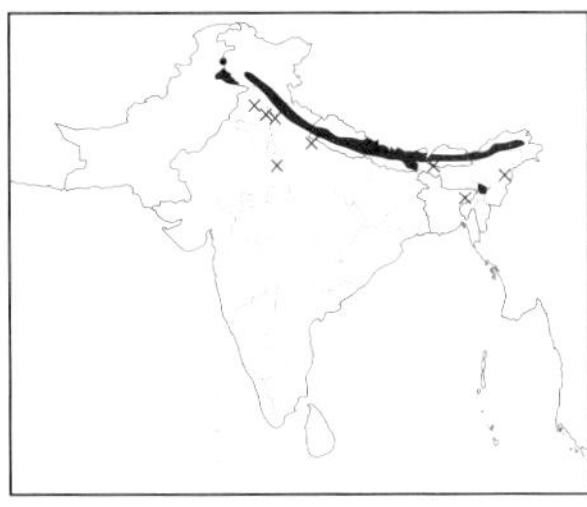

IDENTIFICATION 28 cm. A large, slim, long-tailed thrush with contrastingly pale wing panel. **Adult male** is black, with pale grey panel on wing (created by grey on greater and median coverts, tertials and secondaries). In fresh plumage, has prominent whitish fringes to belly and vent. Bill is orange and legs are yellowish. **Female** is olive-brown; has paler rufous-brown panel on wing (with greater coverts becoming paler buffish or greyish towards tips, contrasting with dark brown primary coverts). **Juvenile male** has blackish-brown upperparts with fine and indistinct orange-buff streaking, and orange-buff tips to median coverts; strength of wing panel varies, from much as adult male's on some to a darker grey on others; underparts, too, vary, some birds being mainly dark brown, with orange-buff throat, and fine orange-buff streaking on breast and diffuse barring on belly, while others have pale orange-buff underparts with dark brown barring. **Juvenile female** is similar to female, with similar wing panel, but with fine and indistinct orange-buff shaft streaking on upperparts and diffuse brown barring on orange-buff underparts. **VOICE** A rich and melodious song, with repeated two-noted whistles, e.g. *twee-toooh twee-toooh chuiyui-twit weear-twit weear-trtrtrtt-whih-whih-which wheeeyar-wheeyar*; call is a *chook-chook-chook* (Roberts 1992). **HABITS** Solitary or in pairs in the breeding season; in small loose flocks, sometimes with other thrushes, in autumn and winter. Rather shy. Movements and feeding behaviour are similar to those of other *Turdus* thrushes (see Tickell's Thrush, p.626). Often perches in trees. **HABITAT** Summers in moist broadleaved and mixed broadleaved–coniferous forest; favours oaks. Winters in open forest, forest clearings and edges. **BREEDING** March–August. Builds a typical thrush nest in the fork of a tree, 2–5 m above ground, or sometimes in a bank or among tree roots. **DISTRIBUTION AND STATUS** Resident, subject to altitudinal movements. Himalayas from Murree and Kagan valley, N Pakistan, east to Arunachal Pradesh, and NE India; winters down to the foothills and, rarely, in adjacent plains. **PK:** common, but very local; breeds 1500–2100 m, winters in adjacent foothills and plains. **NP:** common and widespread; summers chiefly 2100–2745 m (1850–3300 m), winters 1400–1980 m, sometimes down to the terai. **IN:** fairly common; breeds from 1800 m up to at least 2700 m in Himalayas, 1200–1400 m in NE India; winters from 2600 m down to the foothills, rarely to plains. **BT:** common; 1370–2900 m. **BD:** vagrant. **REFERENCES** Martens and Eck (1995).

EURASIAN BLACKBIRD *Turdus merula* — Plate 98

Blackbird (I,P), Common Blackbird (K)

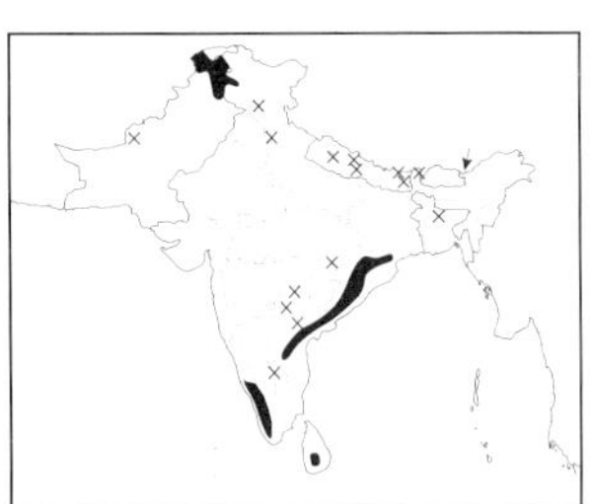

IDENTIFICATION 25–28 cm. Very variable, with seven subspecies occurring in the subcontinent (deserving taxonomic examination, since separate species likely to be involved). Races occurring in the peninsula and Sri Lanka are confusable with Tickell's Thrush (p.625); see that species for main differences. **Racial variation** *T. m. intermedius/maximus*, former a winter visitor to NW subcontinent and latter a Himalayan resident, are larger than other races (27–28 cm), and told from White-collared and Grey-winged Blackbirds (p.625 and above) by absence of pale collar and by all-dark wings: **adult males** are black or brownish-black, with yellow bill; **females** are dark brown, with brown bill, female *intermedius* having whitish throat, streaked dark brown, with diffuse dark brown spotting on breast, while female *maximus* is more uniform dark brown on underparts; **juvenile** *maximus* has rufous-buff underparts with diffuse dark brown barring and spotting, back and rump are variably spotted and barred with rufous-buff, and crown and mantle tend to be rather uniform dark brown (male) or pale brown (female). *T. m. nigropileus/spencei/simillimus* of peninsular India are smaller than Himalayan race (25 cm): **adult males** have brownish slate-grey upperparts, with darker brown to blackish crown and ear-coverts resulting in capped effect (especially in *nigropileus*), all have distinct patch of orange post-orbital skin, and underparts are paler brownish-grey, with whitish lower belly and undertail-coverts in *spencei*; **females** are more uniform brown, with paler underparts; **juveniles** have buffish underparts with broad dark barring and spotting, and indistinct buff shaft streaking. **Males** of *T. m. bourdilloni* of SW peninsula and *T. m. kinnisii* of Sri Lanka are uniform slate-grey (purer bluish-grey in *kinnisii*); **female** *bourdilloni* is fairly uniform olive-brown, with warmer buffish olive-brown on breast and a slightly paler (and diffusely streaked) throat, whereas female *kinnisii* is similar to male, but duller and browner. **VOICE** Song of *maximus* is a mournful, repeated whistle, *piew-piew* or *tieuw-quoit*; call is a rattling *chak-chak-chak* (Roberts 1992). Birds in peninsula have a loud melodious song resembling that of Oriental Magpie Robin (p.651), with much mimicry of other species (Ali and Ripley 1987). **HABITS** Keeps in pairs or family parties in summer, and in flocks, often with other thrushes, in autumn and winter. Gait and feeding behaviour are similar to those of other *Turdus* thrushes (see Tickell's Thrush, p.625), but stance is less upright, with the tail often held horizontal. Males sing in early morning or at dusk, from a treetop, ridge top or boulder. Mainly terrestrial. Himalayan subspecies feed on grassy slopes in search of insects, hopping about with agility on rocks and occasionally perching in trees and bushes; in autumn and winter they also feed on berries, especially of juniper. Usually shy and wary, flying off rapidly if alarmed, often hurtling downhill. Peninsular Indian and Sri Lankan subspecies rummage among leaf litter in forest, looking for insects and fruit. **HABITAT** Himalayan subspecies summer on grassy and rocky slopes with juniper scrub or in rocky alpine meadows; winter in shrubberies or stands of juniper. Peninsular Indian and Sri Lankan subspecies inhabit moist deciduous and evergreen broadleaved forest, sholas, wooded ravines; also well-wooded gardens and plantations in Sri Lanka and in winter in the peninsula. **BREEDING** Himalayan subspecies: May–July; builds nest in a low bush under an overhanging bank, among tree roots or on ground against a boulder. Peninsular and Sri Lankan subspecies: February–November, varying locally; builds nest in the fork of a small tree or bush 1–7 m above ground, or on the ledge of a bank. **DISTRIBUTION AND STATUS** Resident in Himalayas from N Pakistan east to N Uttar Pradesh; breeds in Arunachal Pradesh; status in Nepal is uncertain; resident in hills of peninsular India and Sri Lanka. **PK:** sedentary resident, with small altitudinal movements; scarce but locally frequent in N Himalayas; breeds 3200–3900 m. **NP:** an erratic visitor, mainly in winter and spring, a few summer records; 3305–4800 m (down to 75 m). **IN:** locally common resident in W Himalayas, breeds mainly 3300–4500 m and winters below 3000 m; locally common resident in peninsular hills, breeds from 900 m to summits in the west, from 700 m to summits in Eastern Ghats, and winters from low country up to 1000 m. **BD:** vagrant. **LK:** common resident in higher hills.

CHESTNUT THRUSH *Turdus rubrocanus* — Plate 98

Grey-headed Thrush (F,I)

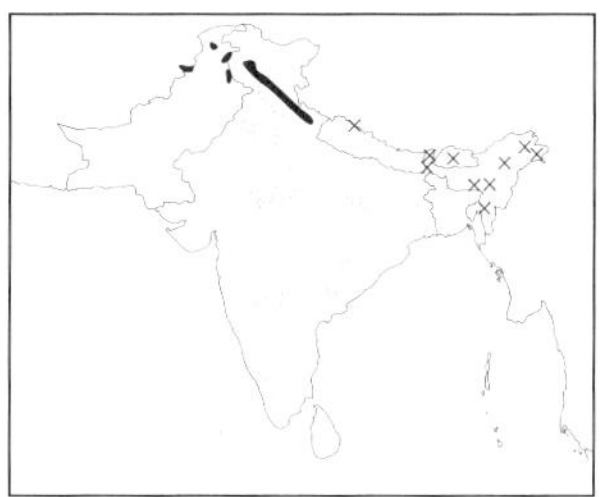

IDENTIFICATION 27 cm. A large chestnut-and-grey thrush with brown or blackish wings. **Adult male** has grey head, becoming pale buffish-grey on throat, neck and upper breast (forming distinct collar); rest of body is mainly chestnut, and has blackish wings and tail. **Female** is very similar, but duller; head and hindneck are pale brownish-grey (lacking distinct collar), and wings and tail are brown. **Juvenile** has buff shaft streaking on upperparts and dark spotting and barring on underparts; back, rump and uppertail-coverts have distinct chestnut cast. Upperparts of juvenile male are darker, and wings and tail more blackish-brown, compared with female. **Racial variation** *T. r. gouldii*, a rare winter visitor to the E Himalayas and NE subcontinent, differs in all plumages from the nominate race of the W Himalayas in having a darker head and neck (darker rather than paler than body); male has slate-grey head and neck, lacking collared effect of nominate race, and female has dark, brownish-grey head. **VOICE** Song comprises a series of short phrases, repeated three to eight times, e.g. *yee-bre yee-bre yee-bre-diddiyit diddiyit-yip bru yipbru-yip-bru*; has a *kwik-kwik* alarm call (Roberts 1992). **HABITS** Solitary or in pairs when breeding; at other times in small flocks, sometimes with other thrushes. Rather shy and retiring, but sings from treetops in the breeding season. Gait and feeding behaviour are similar to those of other *Turdus* thrushes (see Tickell's Thrush, p.625). Mainly terrestrial. Feeds in forest undergrowth in spring and summer; eats mainly berries and seeds in winter. **HABITAT** Summers in shady, moist coniferous forest, often of firs, and mixed coniferous–broadleaved forest; winters in open wooded areas with fruiting trees and orchards. **BREEDING** April–July. Builds a typical thrush nest, 2–3 m above ground in a sapling on a bank, or among tree roots. **DISTRIBUTION AND STATUS** Resident, subject to some altitudinal movements. Himalayas from N Pakistan east to N Uttar Pradesh; winters in Himalayas from Nepal east to Arunachal Pradesh, NE India. **PK:** common, but local; summers 2300–3300 m, winters down to 450 m. **NP:** uncommon and erratic winter visitor; mainly 2000–2745 m (915–3100 m). **IN:** fairly common resident in W Himalayas, breeds 2100–3200 m, winters 1200–3050 m, occasionally down to foothills; rare winter visitor to Sikkim, locally common winter visitor to NE hills. **BT:** rare.

KESSLER'S THRUSH *Turdus kessleri* — Plate 98

White-backed Thrush (I,N)

IDENTIFICATION 27 cm. Following features distinguish Kessler's from Chestnut Thrush (above). **Adult male** has black head, neck and upper breast, and creamy-white mantle and lower breast separate black of head and breast from chestnut of rest of body. **Female** mirrors patterning of male: head, neck and breast are greyish-brown, mantle is variably pale grey-brown to greyish-cream but always shows contrast with hindneck, and shows variable,

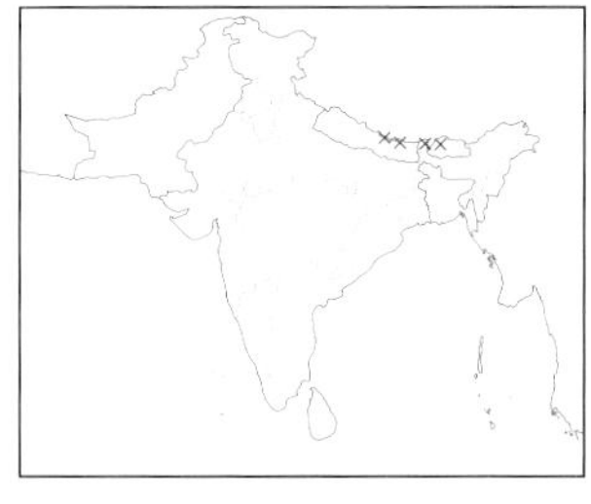

diffuse buffish division between brown of upper breast and ginger-brown of rest of underparts; rump and uppertail-coverts have distinct ginger cast. **VOICE** Call is a soft *dug dug* (Ali and Ripley 1987). **HABITS** Gregarious in winter, often with Dark-throated (p.628) or Dusky Thrushes (p.629) or Eurasian Blackbird (p.626). Feeds mainly on juniper berries, also berberis berries. **HABITAT** Shrubberies and stands of juniper; also berberis bushes and potato fields. **DISTRIBUTION AND STATUS** Winter visitor. E Himalayas from EC Nepal east to Bhutan. **NP:** scarce and erratic, mainly at Khumbu; 3440–4330 m. **IN:** rare and irregular; 3960 m. **BT:** vagrant. **REFERENCES** Jepson (1991).

GREY-SIDED THRUSH *Turdus feae* — Plate 98

Fea's Thrush (I)

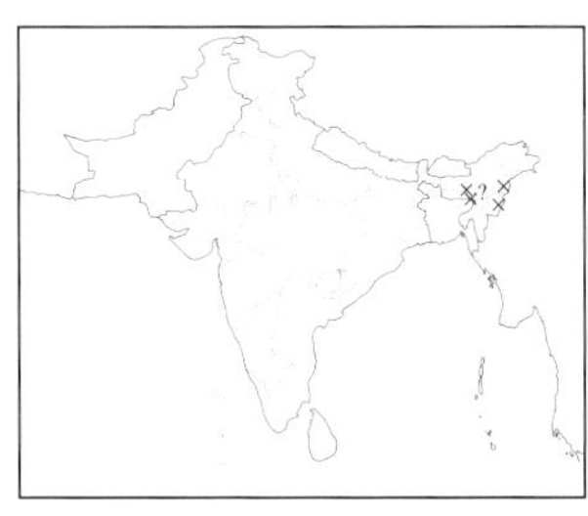

IDENTIFICATION 24 cm. Superficially resembles Eyebrowed Thrush (below), with white supercilium and white crescent below eye. **Adult male** has rufescent-olive upperparts, including crown and ear-coverts, and grey underparts, becoming paler on belly and vent. **Female** is similar to male, but has white throat, and centre to breast and belly are whiter; has brown-streaked malar stripe; grey of breast and flanks is variably washed with orange-buff, and coloration of underparts can approach that of the dullest Eyebrowed. Best told by rufescent coloration to crown, ear-coverts and sides of neck (these areas have distinct greyish cast on Eyebrowed). **First-winter** similar to female, but with pale tips to greater coverts. **VOICE** Unreported in region. **HABITS** Wary, and gregarious in winter, often in flocks with Eyebrowed Thrushes. **HABITAT** Details unknown in the region; winters in evergreen forest in Thailand. **DISTRIBUTION AND STATUS** Globally threatened. **IN:** winter visitor to the northeast (Assam?, Manipur, Meghalaya and Nagaland), in hills above 1500 m; described as not rare in 19th century, but no recent published records.

EYEBROWED THRUSH *Turdus obscurus* — Plate 98

Dark Thrush (F,I)

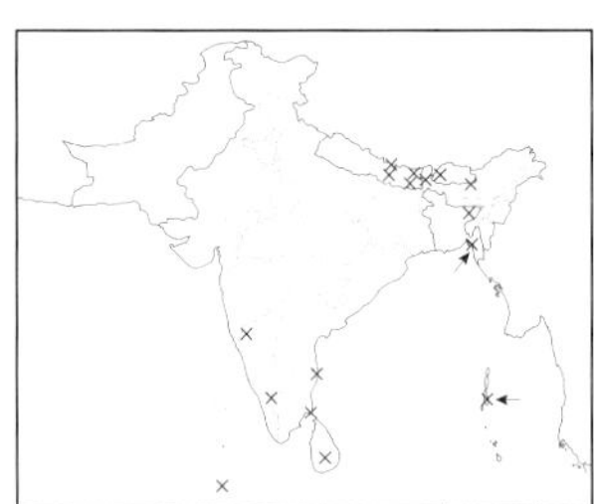

IDENTIFICATION 23 cm. Distinguished from Grey-sided Thrush (above) in all plumages by peachy-orange flanks contrasting with white belly. Other striking features are white supercilium and white crescent below eye, contrasting with dark lores. **Adult male** has blue-grey head, including throat, with just a small area of white on chin. **Female** is similar to male, but has olive-brown crown and nape, browner ear-coverts, white throat and submoustachial stripe, dark malar stripe, narrow grey gorget across upper breast, and duller orange breast and flanks. **First-winter** similar to female, but has fine greater-covert wing-bar; first-winter males are brighter, with more grey on ear-coverts and upper breast. **VOICE** Call is a thin drawn-out *tseep* (Boonsong and Round 1991). **HABITS** Gregarious in winter and on passage, sometimes with Dark-throated Thrushes (below). Gait and feeding behaviour are similar to those of other *Turdus* thrushes (see Tickell's Thrush, p.626). Escapes into the canopy if alarmed; flight is fast and direct. **HABITAT** Open forest. **DISTRIBUTION AND STATUS** Winter visitor. Mainly Himalayas from EC Nepal east to Arunachal Pradesh; NE India. **NP:** scarce in the east; 1500–2300 m. **IN:** common in the NE hills, rare in E Himalayas, vagrant elsewhere. **BT:** rare. **BD, LK, MV:** vagrant. **REFERENCES** Alström and Colston (1991), Hoffmann (1996), Jakobsen (1995).

DARK-THROATED THRUSH *Turdus ruficollis* — Plate 99

Red-throated/Black-throated Thrush (F,I)

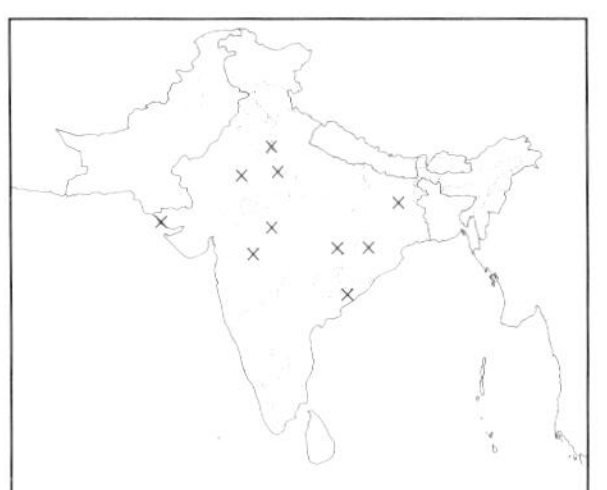

IDENTIFICATION 25 cm. Two distinct subspecies occur, *T. r. atrogularis* ('Black-throated Thrush') and *T. r. ruficollis* ('Red-throated Thrush'). Red-throated always shows reddish-orange at sides of tail, which can be very prominent in flight (and, from below, undertail can appear entirely orange). **Adult male** has black or red supercilium, throat and breast (with narrow white fringes in fresh plumage), grey upperparts, and whitish underparts. **Female** is similar to male, but typically has white or buffish throat and black-streaked malar stripe, and black or red of breast is a gorget of spotting. Female Black-throated often show white 'spot' between a band of black streaking across lower throat and mottling across upper breast. Some birds more closely resemble adult male. **First-winter** has white tips to greater coverts and pale-fringed tertials. First-winter male resembles adult female. First-winter female is less heavily marked, and has finely streaked breast and flanks: Red-throated usually shows rufous wash to supercilium and throat and/or breast; Black-throated can show fairly prominent whitish supercilium (as on first-winter male). First-winter birds can be similar to very dull examples of Dusky Thrush (below), which can lack chestnut on wing; for differences, see that species. **VOICE** Calls include a thin *see* and a hard *tack-tack*. **HABITS** Highly gregarious in winter, often with other thrushes. Movements and feeding behaviour are similar to those of other *Turdus* thrushes (see Tickell's Thrush, p.626). Feeds on the ground and in berried shrubs and trees. Spends much time in trees and, if disturbed when on the ground, flies up into the canopy. **HABITAT** Forest, forest edges, grassy slopes, cultivation and pastures with scattered trees. **DISTRIBUTION AND STATUS** Winter visitor, numbers varying from year to year; most arrive in October and leave at end April. Baluchistan, Pakistan, and Himalayas from N Pakistan east to Arunachal Pradesh and south to Sindh, Pakistan, NE India and Bangladesh, straggling south to Maharashtra and Andhra Pradesh; may occur fairly frequently in N Indian plains depending on the severity of the winter. **PK:** locally common. **NP:** common below 4200 m. **IN:** common and widespread in the far north and northeast. **BT:** common; from 610 m up to at least 3200 m. **BD:** local.

DUSKY THRUSH *Turdus naumanni* — Plate 99

Rufous-tailed Thrush, Naumann's Thrush (R)

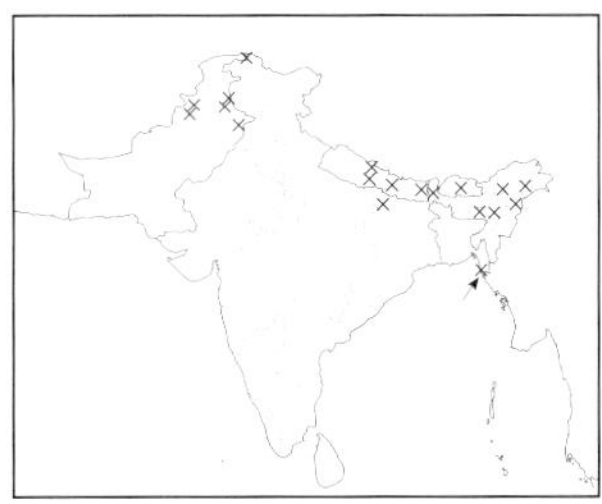

IDENTIFICATION 24 cm. Variable, but race *eunomus* described here always shows broad white supercilium, and usually has double gorget of spotting across breast and chestnut panelling on wing. **Adult male** has white supercilium and throat contrasting with dark crown and ear-coverts, broad chestnut fringes to coverts and remiges forming bright panels on wing, rufous-brown mantle with dark feather centres, double gorget of blackish spotting across breast, and bold spotting on flanks contrasting with white of underparts. **Female** is similar to male, but is usually duller and less strikingly patterned, and usually shows a more distinct black-streaked malar stripe. **First-winter** is variable, and some can be very dull compared with adult: crown and ear-coverts can be greyer and supercilium less pronounced, double gorget of spotting less distinct, upperparts greyer, and chestnut in wing can be less extensive. Some very dull birds can appear to lack rufous on upperparts and chestnut on wing, and can closely resemble first-winter Dark-throated Thrush (p.628); they are best told by broader supercilium contrasting with dark ear-coverts, and dark spotting (rather than fine streaking) on flanks. Dull birds usually show dark feather centres and some rufous on upperparts (upperparts are uniform grey on Dark-throated) and show at least some chestnut on wing (reduced to narrow, dull fringes to greater coverts and tertials), which are further differences from Dark-throated. **VOICE** Calls include a shrill *shrree* and a harsh *chack-chack*. **HABITS** Often found in flocks in winter. Feeds chiefly on the ground in the manner of other *Turdus* thrushes. When on the ground, holds bill noticeably uptilted at times. **HABITAT** Open cultivation and pastures with thinly scattered trees. **DISTRIBUTION AND STATUS** Winter visitor. Mainly Himalayas from WC Nepal east to Arunachal Pradesh; NE India. **PK:** vagrant. **NP:** scarce; 75–3175 m. **IN:** irregular and rare in Himalayas; 900–3000 m. **BT:** rare. **BD:** vagrant. **REFERENCES** Alström and Colston (1991), Lama (1995b).

FIELDFARE *Turdus pilaris* — Plate 99

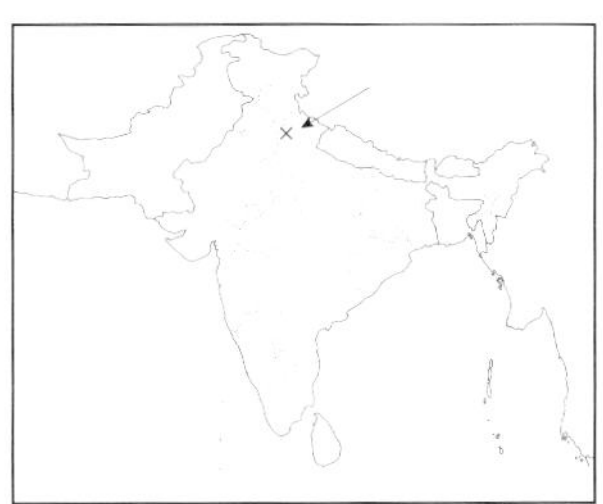

IDENTIFICATION 25 cm. **Adult** has blue-grey crown, ear-coverts and nape, chestnut-brown mantle and much of wing, blue-grey rump and uppertail-coverts contrasting with black tail, black streaking on throat and crescent-shaped spotting on breast and flanks, and orange-buff wash to throat and breast. Shows white underwing in flight. **First-winter** is very similar to adult but duller, especially on upperparts. **VOICE** Calls include a hard *chack-chack-chack* and a strident *see*. **HABITS** Details not recorded in the region. Gregarious and noisy. Feeds on the ground, and on berries of trees and bushes, in similar fashion to other *Turdus* thrushes. Flight has pronounced undulations. **HABITAT** Details not recorded in the region. Elsewhere, winters in open fields, pastures and orchards. **DISTRIBUTION AND STATUS IN:** vagrant.

REDWING *Turdus iliacus* — Not illustrated

Status uncertain; two records from Pakistan (in Kohat and near Drosh), but specimens have not been located and occurrence is doubted by Roberts (1992) and omitted from the Pakistan checklist.

SONG THRUSH *Turdus philomelos* — Plate 99

IDENTIFICATION 23 cm. A small, compact thrush. **Adult** superficially resembles Mistle Thrush (p.630), with bold black spotting on underparts. Best told by much smaller size and more compact shape, darker olive-brown upperparts, uniform wings and tail (lacking prominent pale fringes to coverts and tertials and white sides to tail of Mistle Thrush), orange-buff (rather than white) underwing-coverts, and very different flight call. Smaller size, more upright

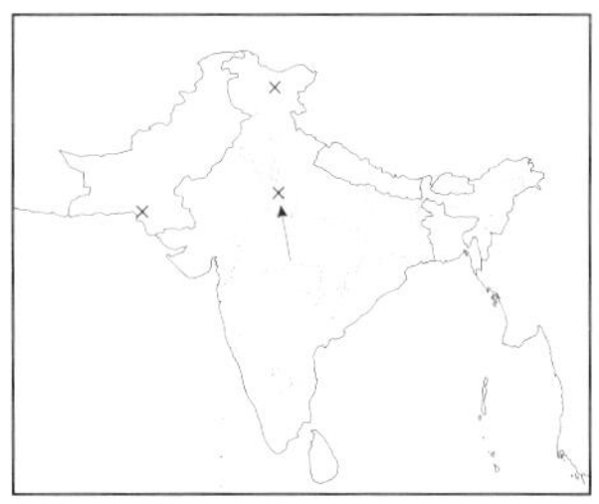

stance, and evenly spotted (rather than barred) underparts help separate it from Plain-backed and Long-tailed Thrushes (p.623). **First-winter** is as adult, but shows buff tips to greater coverts. **VOICE** Calls include a quiet, but penetrating *siit*, a soft *tit* and a hard *tchuk*. **HABITS** Gait and feeding behaviour similar to those of other *Turdus* thrushes. Feeds mainly on the ground, often close to cover. Flight is fast, with slight undulations. **HABITAT** Thorn scrub in Pakistan. **DISTRIBUTION AND STATUS PK, IN:** vagrant.

MISTLE THRUSH *Turdus viscivorus* Plate 99

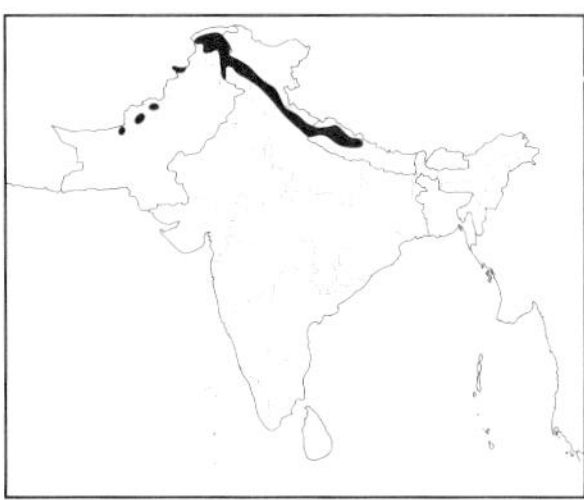

IDENTIFICATION 27 cm. A large, pale thrush with boldly spotted underparts. Shows prominent white underwing in flight. **Adult** distinguished from Plain-backed and Long-tailed Thrushes (p.623) by sparse, bold, black spotting on creamy-white underparts, paler grey-brown upperparts, prominent whitish-buff edges to wing feathers, and white sides and corners to tail. **Juvenile** is similar to adult, but has buffish-white spotting and diffuse dark tips to feathers of upperparts. Possibly confusable with juvenile (and even adult) Scaly Thrush (p.623), but has colder grey-brown coloration to upperparts, lacks golden-buff banding on wing of that species, and has very different habits. **VOICE** Song is loud, ringing and rather melancholy, with short repeated phrases and long pauses, e.g. *tree-twee wooh...... tree-twee-wooh.....tree-tili-terooh tree-tili-terooh*. Calls include a characteristic loud rattle, and a staccato *tuck-tuck-tuck* (Roberts 1992). **HABITS** Similar to those of other *Turdus* thrushes (see Tickell's Thrush, p.626). Solitary or in pairs when breeding, and in loose flocks in autumn and winter. Shy and wary. Sings from treetops in spring and summer. Flight is powerful and undulating, and often at a considerable height. **HABITAT** Summers in open coniferous forest, sometimes mixed with broadleaves, and in juniper shrubberies above the treeline, also in open rocky areas with stunted junipers and in orchards in higher montane valleys; winters on open grassy slopes and at forest edges. **BREEDING** April–July. Builds a typical thrush nest in a sapling or juniper, 2–5 m above ground. **DISTRIBUTION AND STATUS** Resident, subject to altitudinal movements. W and N Baluchistan, Pakistan, and Himalayas from N Pakistan east to WC Nepal. **PK:** locally common and widespread in the drier inner mountain ranges; breeds 1800–3600 m, winters mainly in lower valleys. **NP:** fairly common and widespread in the west; summers mainly 2400–3800 m, winters 2135–3050 m (down to 1525 m). **IN:** fairly common; breeds from 1800 m to the treeline, mainly 2400–3600 m, winters 1200–3000 m.

SHORTWINGS Genus *Brachypteryx*

Small, chat-like thrushes with short rounded wings, almost square tail, and strong legs. They are mainly terrestrial, and inhabit low bushes, undergrowth or thickets. Chiefly insectivorous. Found singly or in pairs.

GOULD'S SHORTWING *Brachypteryx stellata* Plate 99

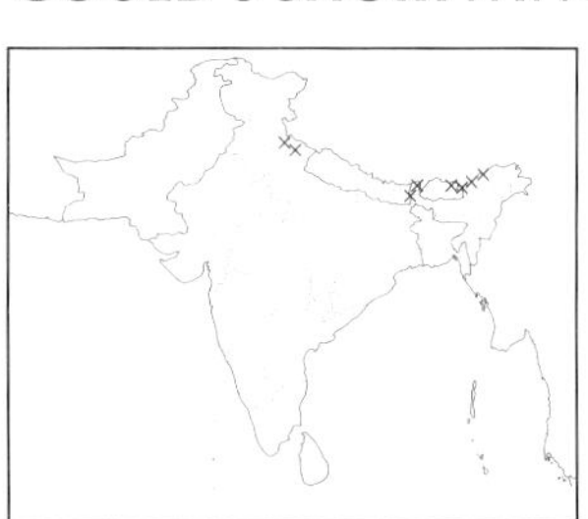

IDENTIFICATION 13 cm. **Adult** is striking, with chestnut upperparts, slate-grey underparts (blacker around face), with white star-shaped spotting on belly and flanks, and fine greyish-white supercilium extending to eye. **Juvenile** has rufous streaking on head, mantle and breast, and greyish-black belly and flanks with broad whitish V-shaped spots. **VOICE** Song begins with series of very high-pitched notes, which gradually become louder and more closely spaced and immediately run into a series of 26–34 very high-frequency piercing notes in a slightly undulating pattern, *tsitsitssiutssiutssiutssi-utsitsi* etc (C. Robson from E. Vercruysse recording). **HABITS** Often very confiding, and comes out in the open more than other shortwings. Sometimes perches on tops of bushes. Hops about on the ground like a mouse among fallen branches and roots. **HABITAT** Breeds in dense rhododendron and bamboo growth, juniper shrubberies, thick undergrowth in fir and rhododendron forest near damp ravines, also among boulders in the alpine zone far from shrub growth; winter habitat is poorly known, but has been recorded in a damp stream bed with ferns and mosses. **BREEDING** End May–July. Nest unknown. **DISTRIBUTION AND STATUS** Resident. Himalayas from N Uttar Pradesh east to Arunachal Pradesh. **NP:** scarce and very local, possibly resident; summers 3250–3900 m (450 m on passage). **IN:** very local resident, with very few recent records; breeds 3300–4200 m, winters 2000–3600 m (down to 540 m). **BT:** possibly resident; locally common, 2745–4265 m. **REFERENCES** Giri and Choudhary (1997), Mohan (1990).

RUSTY-BELLIED SHORTWING *Brachypteryx hyperythra* Plate 99

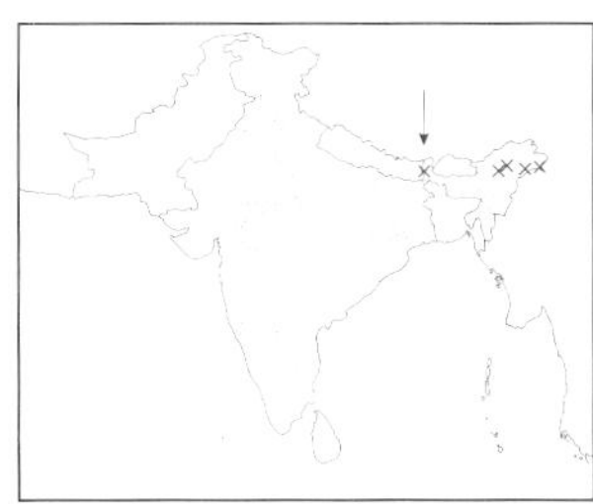

IDENTIFICATION 13 cm. **Male** has short, fine white supercilium and black lores, blue upperparts including wings and tail, and rufous-orange underparts. Possibly confusable with males of White-browed Bush Robin (p.650) or Indian Blue Robin (p.648), but has much shorter tail, and supercilium is much less prominent. Terrestrial habits, orange chin and undertail-coverts, shorter tail and longer legs would distinguish this species from Snowy-browed Flycatcher (p.637). **Female** has olive-brown upperparts, paler rufous-orange underparts with whitish centre to belly, and lacks white supercilium. Told from female Lesser and White-browed Shortwings (below and p.632) by rufous-orange underparts. **Juvenile** and **immature male** are undescribed. **VOICE** Song is similar to that of Lesser Shortwing, but faster and longer and more musical: a high-speed warble consisting of a rather slurred series of notes, distinctly introduced (as is Lesser's) by two spaced notes, *tu-tiu* or *wi-tu*; the space between the first and second introductory notes is greater than that between the second introductory note and the fast warble; ends abruptly (as Lesser) (C. Robson from E. Vercruysse recording). **HABITS** Very poorly known. Quite fearless. One bird seen with tail half-cocked and wings drooping. **HABITAT** Winters in undergrowth in forest, thick secondary scrub and dense thickets of reeds or bamboo. **BREEDING** Unknown. **DISTRIBUTION AND STATUS** Resident. Himalayas in Nepal? and from Darjeeling, West Bengal and Sikkim to Arunachal Pradesh and Assam. Globally threatened. **NP:** possibly recorded. **IN:** very scarce or very local resident; in Darjeeling and Sikkim, where possibly resident, base of hills, 450 m and 1000–1150 m in December–February (–3000 m in January), 2050 m in April, 1100 m in May. **REFERENCES** Athreya *et al.* (1997), Heath (1988), Kaul *et al.* (1995), Ripley *et al.* (1991), Stevens (1915, 1925).

WHITE-BELLIED SHORTWING *Brachypteryx major* Plate 99

Rufous-bellied Shortwing (I)

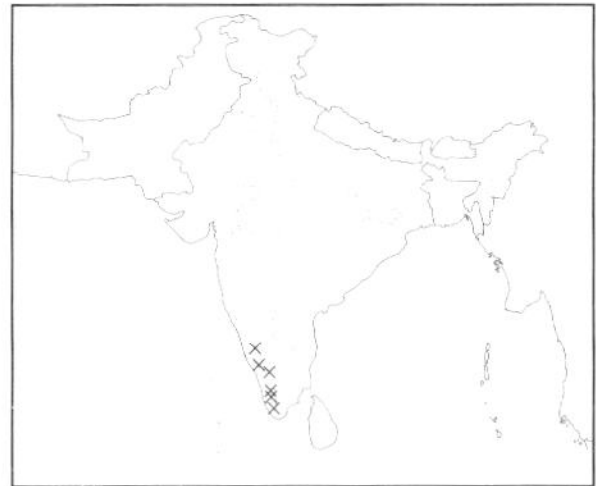

IDENTIFICATION 15 cm. The only shortwing occurring in the Western Ghats. **Adult** has bright blue forehead and supercilium, slaty-blue head, breast and upperparts, and striking white belly. **Juvenile** is said to be spotted. **Racial variation** *B. m. major* has rufous-brown flanks and undertail-coverts. *B. m. albiventris* has slaty-blue flanks, and the undertail-coverts are slaty-blue, fringed with white. **VOICE** Song is a rather simple medley of powerful high-pitched penetrating whistles, often introduced by slower disyllabic notes, last usually descending, *tsee-du...ts-tsee-du-du-du* (possibly some regional variation, some birds having more varied thrush-like songs). Calls include a scolding 'electric' rattle and a penetrating, indrawn, whistled *hweeep*, the two often given in combination (P. Holt). **HABITS** Retiring. Keeps on the ground under shady cover, or in low bushes. **HABITAT** Thick undergrowth in dense evergreen forest, including sholas and damp thickly vegetated ravines. **BREEDING** March–June. Builds a cup-shaped nest of green moss in a hollow in a tree or bank, within 1 m of ground. **DISTRIBUTION AND STATUS IN:** rare endemic resident; hills of S Karnataka and Nilgiris, 1300–1900 m, and hills of Kerala and W Tamil Nadu from 900 m to the summits. **REFERENCES** Gaston and Zacharias (1996).

LESSER SHORTWING *Brachypteryx leucophrys* Plate 99

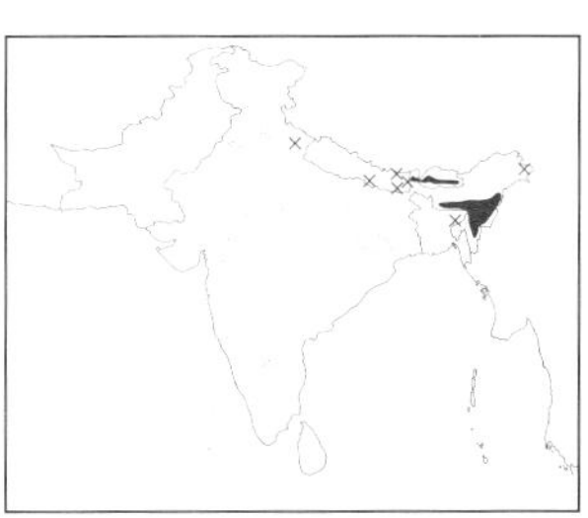

IDENTIFICATION 13 cm. Smaller than White-browed Shortwing (p.632), with shorter tail, and pale pinkish (rather than dark) legs. **Male** has short, fine white supercilium, slaty-blue upperparts including wings and tail, blue-grey breast-band and flanks, and white throat and centre of belly. Immature male has variable slate-blue coloration to upperparts, with rufous-brown wings, and blue-grey wash to breast. **Female** has rufous-brown upperparts, white throat and belly, and rufous-brown wash and diffuse scaling on breast and flanks; has buff eye-ring, and like male has short white supercilium (although this is often concealed). White throat and belly, diffuse scaling on breast, and lack of rufous-orange forehead and lores are main plumage differences from White-browed. **Juvenile** is as White-browed. **VOICE** A brief, melodious warbling song of about ten to twelve notes, with the first notes alternating up and down and then accelerating into a rapid jumble (Boonsong and Round 1991). Calls include a hard *tock-tock* and a plaintive whistle. **HABITS** Very skulking. Keeps mostly to the forest floor among thick undergrowth. Seeks insects by hopping about on the ground among leaf litter, or by working through low stems and branches. **HABITAT** Thick undergrowth in damp broadleaved forest and secondary growth. **BREEDING** April–July. Builds a ball-shaped nest of moss, roots, leaves and grass, placed low down in thick bushes, among moss growing on tree trunks or rocks. **DISTRIBUTION AND STATUS** Resident, subject to altitudinal movements. Himalayas from N Uttar Pradesh and EC Nepal east to Arunachal Pradesh; NE India. **NP:** rare, possibly resident; 250–2135 m in January–April. **IN:** resident; rare in Himalayas, 1500–3900 m, more common in hills south of the Brahmaputra from 900 m to the summits, winters in foothills. **BT:** frequent; 1500–3150 m in April and May. **BD:** vagrant.

WHITE-BROWED SHORTWING *Brachypteryx montana* Plate 99

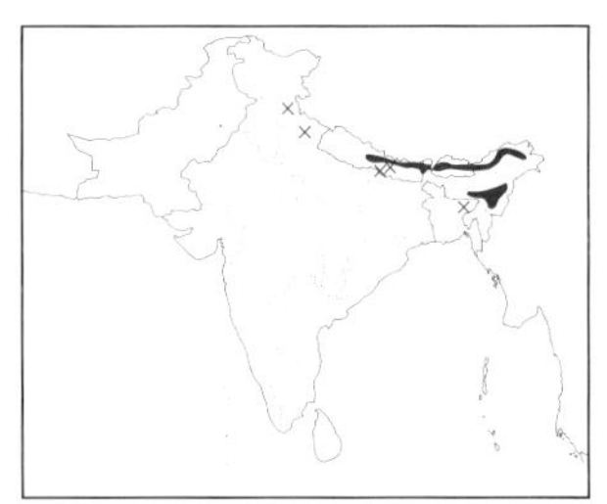

IDENTIFICATION 15 cm. Larger than Lesser Shortwing (p.631), with longer tail, and dark legs. **Adult male** is entirely dark slaty-blue, with black lores and fine white supercilium which extends well beyond eye. **Female** has rufous-orange forehead, lores and eye-ring, brown upperparts with more rufescent wings, and brownish underparts with paler belly. **Immature male** is similar to female, but has fine white supercilium. Rufous-orange lores and more uniform brownish underparts (lacking striking white throat and belly) are useful features for separating female and immature male from Lesser. For differences from Rusty-bellied Shortwing (p.631), see that species. **Juvenile** is similar to female, but with pale orange spotting on crown and nape, orange-buff spotting on underparts, and rufous uppertail-coverts. **VOICE** A rich, loud, explosive warbling song, usually introduced by one to three whistled *wheez* notes (Boonsong and Round 1991). Call is a hard *tock toc*. **HABITS** Very secretive. Skulks on the ground under dense low cover in forest. Progresses on the ground like a chat; alternately hops rapidly in short spurts and then pauses briefly. **HABITAT** Undergrowth in damp oak and rhododendron or fir and rhododendron forest near streams, also in moist thickets in ravines. **BREEDING** May–July. Builds an oval nest of moss among living moss on a rock face or tree trunk. **DISTRIBUTION AND STATUS** Resident, subject to altitudinal movements. Himalayas, mainly from C Nepal east to Arunachal Pradesh; NE India. **NP:** very uncommon resident; breeds 2560–3660 m, found 245–2375 m in non-breeding season. **IN:** locally fairly common resident; breeds 1500–3300 m, mainly above 2000 m, winters 300–2400 m. **BT:** common resident; breeds 2135–3620 m; 610 m and 1830 m in November. **BD:** vagrant. **REFERENCES** Crosby (1995).

OLD WORLD FLYCATCHERS Tribe Muscicapini

Small insectivorous birds with a small flattened bill, and bristles at the gape which help in the capture of flying insects. The legs are short and weak. They normally have a very upright stance when perched. Many species frequently flick the tail and hold the wings slightly drooped. Generally, flycatchers frequent trees and bushes. Some species regularly perch on a vantage point, from which they catch insects in mid-air in short aerial sallies or by dropping to the ground, often returning to the same perch. Other species capture insects while flitting among branches or by picking them from foliage. Flycatchers are usually found singly or in pairs; a few join mixed hunting parties of other insectivorous birds. Most are territorial in the breeding season.

BROWN-CHESTED JUNGLE FLYCATCHER *Rhinomyias brunneata* Plate 100

Olive Flycatcher (I), Brown-chested Flycatcher, *R. nicobarica*

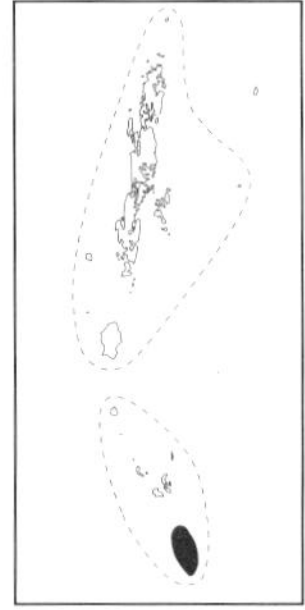

IDENTIFICATION 15 cm. The only *Rhinomyias* flycatcher recorded in the subcontinent. **Adult** is a large, mainly brown flycatcher with more rufescent-brown tail. Has long bill (with yellowish lower mandible), dark scaling on whitish throat, brownish breast, and pale fleshy-coloured legs. **First-winter** has dark tip to lower mandible, and rufous-buff tips to greater coverts and tertials. **VOICE** Unknown. **HABITS** Keeps in bushes or low down in small trees. Catches winged insects in typical flycatcher fashion, in aerial forays from a perch. **HABITAT** Mainly forest, sometimes gardens. **DISTRIBUTION AND STATUS** Globally threatened. **IN:** common winter visitor or resident on Great and Little Nicobar Is; vagrant to Andaman Is. **REFERENCES** Boonsong and Round (1991), Collar and Andrew (1988), Sankaran and Vijayan (1993).

SPOTTED FLYCATCHER *Muscicapa striata* Plate 100

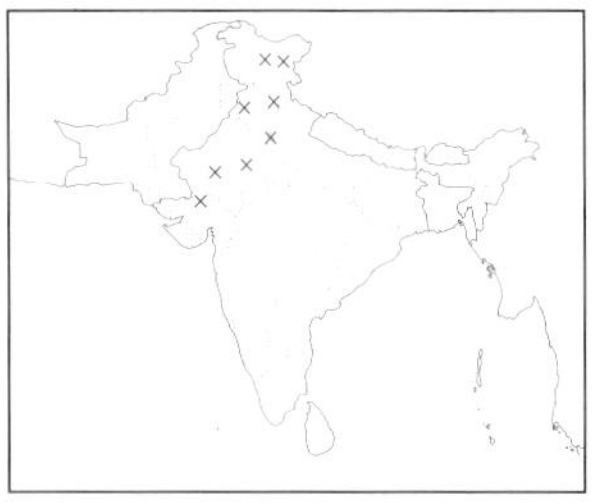

IDENTIFICATION 13 cm. A grey-brown and white flycatcher with lightly streaked breast. **Adult** distinguished from Dark-sided Flycatcher (p.633) by larger size, flatter forehead and longer bill, paler grey-brown upperparts, faint dark streaking on forehead and crown, poorly defined eye-ring, and diffuse grey-brown streaking on throat and breast. Extent and intensity of streaking on underparts vary, but sides of breast and flanks are never uniformly dark as on Dark-sided. Further, breast can be washed with buff and flanks warm brownish on Spotted. **Juvenile** superficially resembles adult, but has buffish-white spotting on head, mantle and wing-coverts and dark scaling on underparts. **VOICE** Calls include thin, scratchy *ptsirr, tseeht* or *tseet...chup, chup*; song consists of a few call-like squeaks, well separated and drawn back and forth (Jonsson 1992). **HABITS** Mainly solitary. Perches upright, characteristically with the head partly sunk between the shoulders. Often flicks wings and tail, but far less so than *Ficedula* flycatchers. Usually hunts from a low perch, sometimes hidden in foliage, at other times in the open. Hunts in a similar manner to most other brown flycatchers. Catches insects in aerial sallies; very agile on the wing, twisting and turning in mid-air after prey; also drops to the ground to seize insects. **HABITAT** Breeds in juniper forest, scrub forest, ravines with scattered trees and open pine forest. **BREEDING** May and June. Builds a neat cup-shaped nest 2 m above ground on the branch of a tree, against the trunk or in a crevice. **DISTRIBUTION AND STATUS** Summer visitor to Pakistan, breeding in Baluchistan, Chitral, Gilgit and Baltistan; passage migrant in S Pakistan and NW India (from Jammu and Kashmir south to Gujarat). **PK:** locally common in summer, 1500–2400 m; regular on passage. **IN:** regular autumn passage migrant. **REFERENCES** Alström and Hirschfeld (1991).

DARK-SIDED FLYCATCHER *Muscicapa sibirica* — Plate 100

Sooty Flycatcher (F,I), Asian Sooty Flycatcher (N)

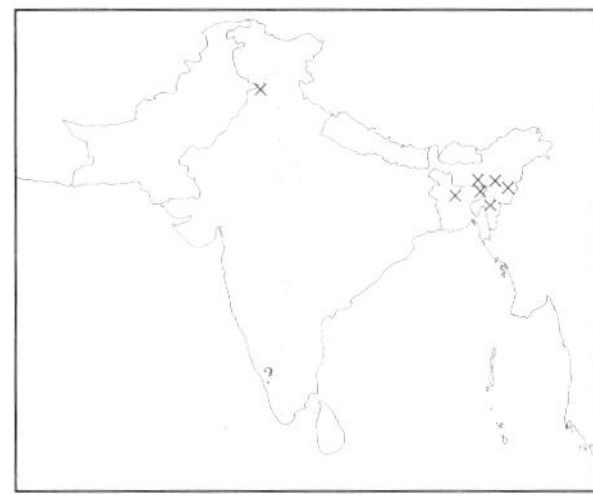

IDENTIFICATION 13 cm. A slim, long-winged flycatcher with large eyes and prominent eye-ring. Typically seen perched upright on high, exposed branches, and at times can recall a small hirundine. **Adult** most likely to be confused with Asian Brown Flycatcher (below), but has smaller head, slimmer shape and longer primary projection (exposed primaries are equal to or distinctly longer – usually by 15–20% – than the tertials). Compared with Asian Brown, has darker sooty-brown upperparts, and breast and flanks are more heavily marked with diffuse sooty-brown streaking (resulting in prominent white throat, white crescent on sides of neck, and narrow white centre to belly); breast sides and flanks can be uniformly dark and concolorous with upperparts. Also has smaller, mainly dark bill (any orange or yellow visible at base of lower mandible does not extend beyond nostril), and, seen from below, bill has very broad base and is short, with pointed tip, and with edges straight or slightly concave. Lores are less extensively pale, and are often washed brown, and eye-ring is typically less prominent (often apparent only behind eye). For differences from Spotted Flycatcher (p.632), see that species. **Juvenile** told from juvenile Asian Brown by fine buff streaking on upperparts (especially apparent on scapulars), heavy dark mottling on breast and flanks, orange-buff tips to greater coverts (forming wing-bar) and fringes to tertials, less distinct pale lores, and differences in primary projection and bill mentioned above. **VOICE** Song is very soft and weak, a complicated pattern of thin, high-pitched, repetitive phrases, including sibilant *tsee-tsee-tsee* notes, followed by quite melodious trills and whistles (Roberts 1992). **HABITS** Similar to those of Spotted Flycatcher (p.632). Often active in late afternoon and at dusk. Usually hunts from a favoured prominent vantage point, such as a dead branch or stump near the tops of tall trees, or from telegraph wires; occasionally hunts near the ground. **HABITAT** Clearings and edges in temperate and subalpine coniferous, broadleaved or mixed broadleaved–coniferous forest. **BREEDING** May–July. Builds a compact cup-shaped nest 2–18 m above ground on a horizontal branch of a large tree, sometimes in a tree hole. **DISTRIBUTION AND STATUS** Breeds in Himalayas from N Pakistan east to Arunachal Pradesh, and NE India, arriving on breeding grounds in April (Nepal) or May (Pakistan), leaving in September/October; winter quarters poorly known, but a few records from NE India and once in Nepal. **PK:** fairly common and widespread; breeds 2660–3350 m. **NP:** fairly common and widespread; breeds 2000–3300 m (down to 275 m on passage); one winter record, at 915 m. **IN:** fairly common; in W Himalayas breeds chiefly from 2100 m to the treeline, locally to 1500 m, in E Himalayas breeds from 2400 m to at least 3600 m. **BT:** common; up to 3800 m. **BD:** vagrant. **REFERENCES** Alström and Hirschfeld (1991).

ASIAN BROWN FLYCATCHER *Muscicapa dauurica* — Plate 100

Brown Flycatcher (F,I,P), *M. latirostris* (F,I,K,R)

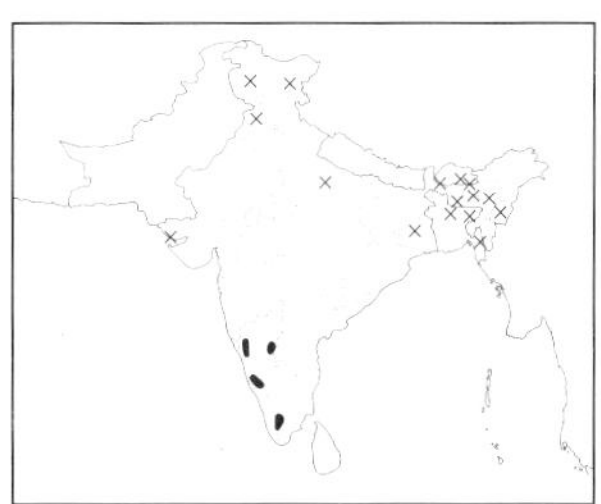

IDENTIFICATION 13 cm. A grey-brown flycatcher with short tail, large head, and huge eye with prominent eye-ring. **Adult** best told from Dark-sided Flycatcher (above) by paler underparts, typically with just a light grey-brown wash to breast and flanks (may show blurred streaking on breast, but underparts are never as heavily marked as on Dark-sided). Further differences are larger bill with more extensive orange base to lower mandible, larger head and stockier appearance, more extensive pale lores, shorter primary projection (shorter than tertials – usually 80–90% the length of latter), and paler olive- to grey-brown upperparts. Compared with Dark-sided, orange or yellow at base of lower mandible extends beyond nostril, and, seen from below, the bill is more evenly broad, with broader tip, and with slightly convex edges. In fresh plumage, shows distinct whitish (orange-buff on Dark-sided) wing-bar and fringes to tertials; wing-bar is lacking in worn plumage. Possibly confusable with Rusty-tailed Flycatcher (p.634), but that species has rufous uppertail-coverts and tail. For differences from Brown-breasted Flycatcher (p.634), see that species. **Juvenile** told from juvenile Dark-sided by prominent buffish spotting on upperparts (especially prominent on scapulars), whiter underparts with fine dark scaling on breast, creamy-white tips to greater coverts (forming wing-bar) and fringes to tertials, more extensive pale lores, and differences in primary projection and bill mentioned above. **VOICE** Song consists of short trills interspersed with two- or three-noted whistling phrases, and is louder than that of Dark-sided (Roberts 1992); call is a weak trilling *sit-it-it-it.* **HABITS** Usually found singly. A partly crepuscular, rather quiet flycatcher. Perches in the lower branches of trees. Behaviour is similar to that of Spotted Flycatcher (p.632), but hunting sallies are shorter. **HABITAT** Open subtropical broadleaved forest, plantations, village groves, wooded gardens, edges of sholas; in Pakistan, damp ravines in mixed Chir Pine–deciduous forest. **BREEDING** April–July, varying locally. Builds a neat cup-shaped nest, mainly of moss, on a thick branch of a tree 2–9 m above ground. **DISTRIBUTION AND STATUS** Breeds in Himalayan foothills from Murree, Pakistan, east to Bhutan, also in Vindhya Range, Madhya Pradesh, in Gujarat, and in Western Ghats and Sandur, E Karnataka; winters in SC and E India and Sri Lanka. **PK:** rare and local summer visitor in Murree hills, 1200 m. **NP:** mainly an uncommon passage migrant and summer visitor, breeds 1000–1550 m; rare in winter. **IN:** summer visitor to Himalayas, 900–1900 m, locally to 2230 m, common in the west, scarce in the east; summer visitor to Vindhya Range; locally common resident in Western Ghats; scarce winter visitor to most of the peninsula, but mainly in the Western Ghats below 1500 m. **BT:** rare. **BD:** scarce passage migrant. **LK:** common winter visitor to the lowlands and lower hills. **REFERENCES** Alström and Hirschfeld (1991), Ghorpade (1974), Mahabal (1992), Mundkur (1990).

RUSTY-TAILED FLYCATCHER *Muscicapa ruficauda* — Plate 100

Rufous-tailed Flycatcher (F,I,N,R)

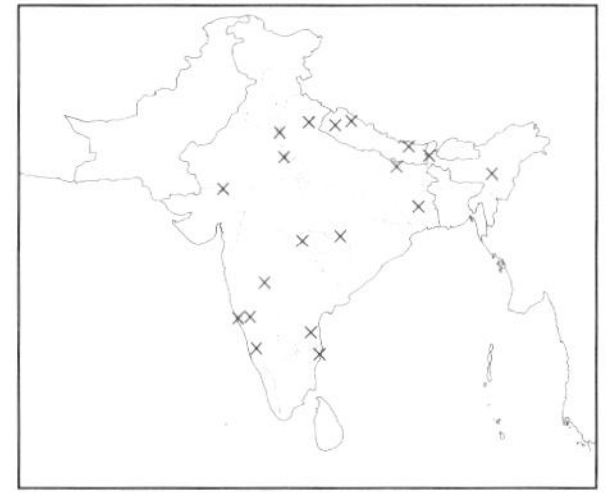

IDENTIFICATION 14 cm. **Adult** is most likely to be confused with Asian Brown Flycatcher (p.633), but has rufous uppertail-coverts and tail, resulting in (female) redstart-like appearance. It appears larger than Asian Brown, with flatter forehead, and crown feathers are often slightly raised, giving crested appearance to nape. Further, it has a rather plain face, with only a faint supercilium (back to eye) and indistinct eye-ring, and has entirely orange lower mandible and cutting edges to upper mandible. Could be confused with female redstart, but has larger bill with pale lower mandible, shorter tarsus, and flycatcher-like stance and behaviour (and, unlike redstarts, does not vibrate tail). **Juvenile** superficially resembles adult, with rufous uppertail-coverts and tail, but has buff spotting on upperparts and dark scaling on underparts. **VOICE** Song is comparatively loud and melodious, comprising a drawn-out, rising and falling, mournful whistle followed by a rapid (but variable) warbling, e.g. *phiee-u-u-h-chee-chwy-chwy tuh-tuh-tu-tu* (Roberts 1992). Calls include a bullfinch-like *peu peu*, and a short, deep churring. **HABITS** Usually solitary. Unobtrusive, and most easily located by its alarm calls, especially in the breeding season. Has a chat-like habit of bobbing forward and at the same time flicking its wings. Hunts insects by flitting among the foliage and from perch to perch; seldom by aerial sallies. **HABITAT** Favours forest clearings and edges, breeding in open mixed coniferous–deciduous forest, also in open coniferous and broadleaved forest; winters in evergreen broadleaved forest. **BREEDING** May–July. Builds a compact cup-shaped nest, mainly of moss, in varied sites: 1–2 m above ground in bushes, up to 9 m high in trees, and also on the ground. **DISTRIBUTION AND STATUS** Breeds in Himalayas from N Pakistan east to E Nepal; winters mainly in Kerala and W Tamil Nadu, with widespread records from elsewhere in India. **PK:** local, frequent summer visitor; breeds 1500–3000 m. **NP:** uncommon summer visitor and passage migrant; summers 2440–3655 m (down to 250 m on passage). **IN:** summer visitor to W Himalayas, common in the far west, scarce farther east; breeds 2100–3600 m; locally common winter visitor to the southwest. **REFERENCES** Lama (1994c).

BROWN-BREASTED FLYCATCHER *Muscicapa muttui* — Plate 100

Layard's Flycatcher

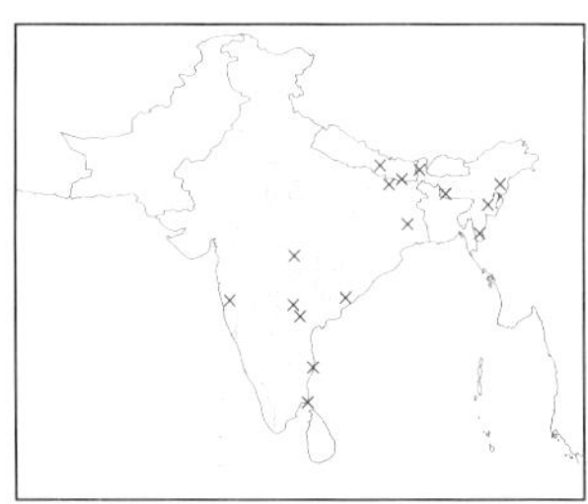

IDENTIFICATION 14 cm. A nondescript, olive-brown flycatcher with large head and huge eye with prominent eye-ring. **Adult** is most likely to be confused with Asian Brown Flycatcher (p.633), but has longer and broader-based bill with entirely pale lower mandible (lacking dark tip), pale, yellowish-pink legs and feet (blackish on Asian Brown), more prominent whitish submoustachial stripe and darker malar stripe, warm rufous-buff (rather than whitish) tips to greater coverts and fringes to tertials, warmer (slightly rufescent) tone to rump and tail, more pronounced brown or grey-brown breast-band, and warmer brownish-buff flanks. Underparts may appear entirely warm buff, lacking breast-band and white throat, when also has broad brownish-orange greater-covert bar (first-year birds?). **VOICE** A pleasant, feeble song; call a thin *sit* (Ali and Ripley 1987; Boonsong and Round 1991). **HABITS** Usually solitary. Quiet and retiring, and partly crepuscular. Perches on the lowest branches of trees or thickets in dense forest or bamboo. Hawks insects in the typical manner of other brown flycatchers (see Spotted Flycatcher, p.632). Territorial in winter as well as in the breeding season, and often seen in the same spot day after day. **HABITAT** Dense thickets and tangles of vegetation in broadleaved evergreen forest; also along banks of forest rivers in Sri Lanka. **BREEDING** May and June. Builds a cup-shaped nest of moss in a tree or bank or in thick cover. **DISTRIBUTION AND STATUS** Breeds in NE India (Assam, Manipur, Meghalaya, Mizoram, Nagaland?); winters mainly in SW India and Sri Lanka. **NP:** vagrant. **IN:** breeds above 1200 m; uncommon in winter, mainly 300–1000 m. **LK:** rare winter visitor to the lowlands and lower hills.

FERRUGINOUS FLYCATCHER *Muscicapa ferruginea* Plate 100

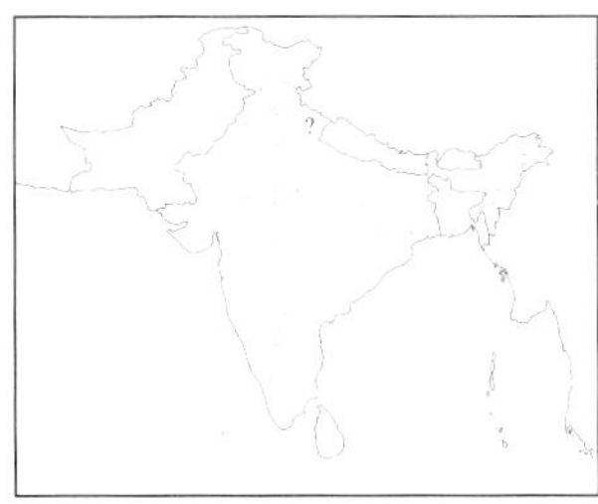

IDENTIFICATION 13 cm. A rather compact, large-headed flycatcher with large eye and prominent white eye-ring. **Adult** differs from other *Muscicapa* flycatchers in having blue-grey cast to head (with darker malar stripe), rufous-brown mantle, rufous-orange rump, uppertail-coverts and tail sides, rufous-orange lower breast, flanks and undertail-coverts, and prominent rufous fringes to greater coverts and tertials. **Juvenile** superficially resembles adult, but has orange-buff spotting on upperparts, rufous-orange greater-covert wing-bar and fringes to tertials, and dark scaling on breast. **VOICE** Call is a quiet accentor-like trill. Probable song: very high-pitched silvery notes introduced by harsher, shriller notes, *tsit-tittu-tittu*, the first note sharp, short and high-pitched; also three-note phrase, sometimes repeated (C. Robson from E. Vercruysse recording). **HABITS** Normally found singly. Partly crepuscular. Unobtrusive and very quiet, usually keeping to the middle or lower storey of forest. Hawks insects from a branch in similar fashion to other brown flycatchers (see Spotted Flycatcher, p.632). **HABITAT** Humid broadleaved forest, especially oaks, also firs (Himalayas); dense mixed jungle (Assam). **BREEDING** June and July. Builds a neat cup-shaped nest of moss and lichen 3–15 m above ground in a tree, usually among moss. **DISTRIBUTION AND STATUS** Probably a summer visitor; only two winter records. Breeds in Himalayas from WC Nepal east to Arunachal Pradesh; NE India. **NP:** scarce; breeds 2000–3300 m (down to 1200 m on passage). **IN:** generally uncommon; breeds 1800–3300 m in Himalayas, above 1200 m in NE hills. **BT:** frequent; from 1650 m up to at least 2950 m.

YELLOW-RUMPED FLYCATCHER *Ficedula zanthopygia* Plate 100

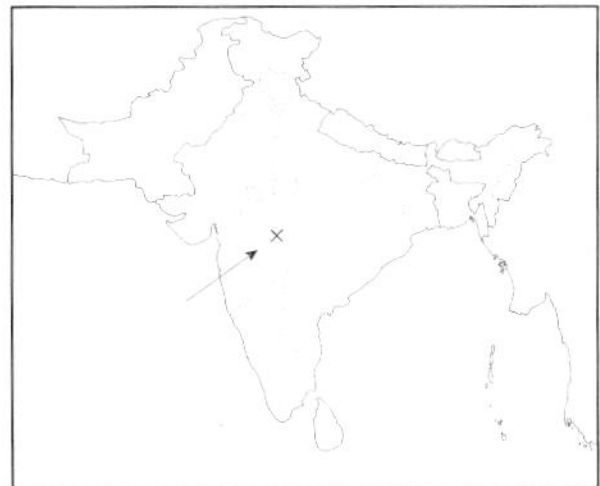

IDENTIFICATION 13 cm. In all plumages shows yellow rump, which separates it from all other flycatchers recorded in the subcontinent. **Male** has black upperparts, with white supercilium and wing patch, yellow back/rump and underparts, and white undertail-coverts. **Female** and **first-winter male** have greyish-olive upperparts and pale yellow wash to underparts, with variable amounts of dark scaling on breast; white on wing can be reduced to white tips to inner greater and median coverts and narrow white edge to outermost tertial. **VOICE** Call is a slow, unobtrusive, dry rattled *tr-r-r-t*, lower-pitched than that of Red-throated Flycatcher (p.636). **HABITS** Mainly arboreal, keeping just below the canopy. **HABITAT** Luxuriant vegetation and dense undergrowth along rivers and streams. **DISTRIBUTION AND STATUS IN:** vagrant. **REFERENCES** Haribal (1992), Harrap (1993).

SLATY-BACKED FLYCATCHER *Ficedula hodgsonii* Plate 100

Rusty-breasted Blue Flycatcher (F,I), ***Muscicapa hodgsonii***

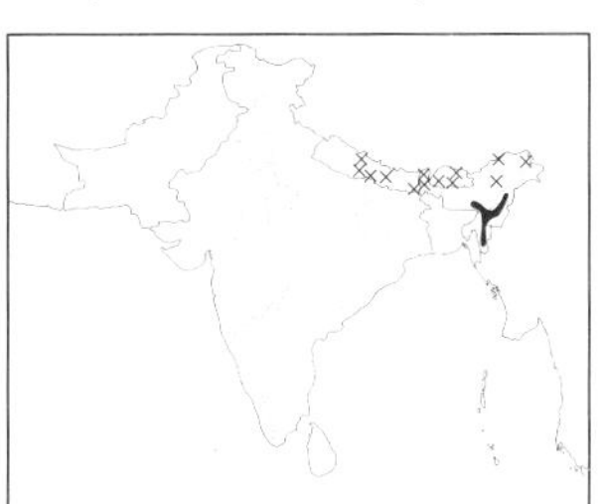

IDENTIFICATION 13 cm. A small, slim, long-tailed flycatcher with very short bill. **Male** has deep blue upperparts and bright orange underparts (becoming whiter on belly), and has black tail with white patches at base. Lack of glistening blue in plumage, and black tail with white at base, are best features for separation from male *Cyornis* flycatchers. **Female** is rather nondescript, having olive-brown upperparts and greyish-olive underparts, with poorly defined whitish throat, lores and eye-ring. Lack of well-defined whitish or buff throat, and olive-brown uppertail-coverts and tail, help separate it from female Slaty-blue (p.638). Possibly confusable with female Pale Blue (p.644), but is smaller and lacks that species' rufous coloration to tail (although may show slight rufescent tinge to rump and uppertail-coverts). **Juvenile** has buff spotting on upperparts and dark scaling on buff underparts, with whitish throat. **First-winter** resembles adult female, and often breeds in this plumage. **VOICE** Short and abrupt, flute-like meandering song of whistled notes in a rapid, generally descending series: *per-ip-it-u-or-per-ip-it-tu*. Calls with a particularly deep rattle, *terrht* (P. Holt). **HABITS** Quiet. Frequents the middle storey and understorey of forest. Frequently makes aerial sallies like other flycatchers. **HABITAT** Breeds in oak–rhododendron, fir and pine forest; winters in damp broadleaved forest, shrubberies and bamboo. **BREEDING** Mid April–July. Builds a cup-shaped nest, mainly of moss, in a hollow between rocks or on a steep moss- and fern-covered bank. **DISTRIBUTION AND STATUS** Resident, subject to altitudinal movements. Himalayas from WC Nepal east to Arunachal Pradesh; NE India. **NP:** scarce and local; once at 3450 m in summer, all other records at 245–2000 m in winter and early spring. **IN:** rare; breeds 2100–3900 m in Himalayas, down to 1200 m south of the Brahmaputra R; winters in foothills up to 2000 m. **BT:** scarce; 610–2225 m.

RUFOUS-GORGETED FLYCATCHER *Ficedula strophiata* Plate 100

Orange-gorgeted Flycatcher (F,I,N)

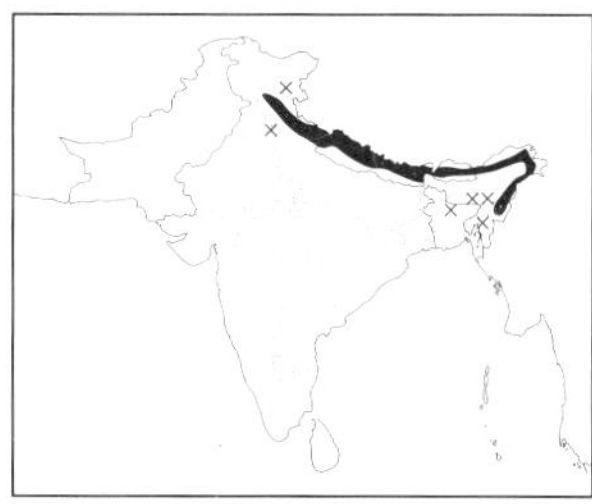

IDENTIFICATION 14 cm. **Male** has dark olive-brown upperparts, blackish face and throat, prominent white forehead and eyebrow, small rufous patch in centre of grey breast (can be difficult to see), and large white patches at sides of tail. **Female** is similar, but has less distinct eyebrow, duller and less distinct rufous 'gorget', and paler grey face and throat. **Juvenile** has tail pattern as adult, but otherwise has dark brown upperparts spotted with orange-buff, and orange-buff throat and breast and whiter belly and flanks all scaled with dark brown. **VOICE** Song is a thin *zreet-creet-creet-chirt-chirt*; calls include a *pee-tweet*, a metallic *pink*, and a harsh *trrt* (deeper than similar call of Red-throated Flycatcher, below) (Fleming *et al.* 1984; Boonsong and Round 1991). **HABITS** Inconspicuous. Keeps to the middle storey and undergrowth of forest, sometimes dropping to the ground to feed. Frequently jerks and spreads its tail, showing the black-and-white pattern. Makes frequent aerial sallies. **HABITAT** Dense or open forest and forest clearings. **BREEDING** April–June. Builds a cup-shaped nest of moss and rootlets on the ground or in a tree hole 3–6 m up. **DISTRIBUTION AND STATUS** Altitudinal migrant. Breeds in Himalayas, mainly from Himachal Pradesh east to Arunachal Pradesh, and NE India; winters in foothills. **NP:** common and widespread; summers mainly 2440–3800 m, winters 915–1830 m (245–2135 m). **IN:** locally common in the east, uncommon in the west; breeds from 2400 m to over 3700 m; winters from foothills up to 2400 m. **BT:** common; summers 2745–3810 m, down to 335 m in winter. **BD:** vagrant.

RED-THROATED FLYCATCHER *Ficedula parva* Plate 101

Red-breasted Flycatcher, *Muscicapa parva* (F,I)

IDENTIFICATION 11.5–12.5 cm. Combination of long, white-sided blackish tail, which is frequently cocked, and dry rattling call help distinguish this from all other flycatchers except Kashmir (below). **Male** told from that species by paler orange throat and upper breast which lack black border (and orange does not extend onto lower breast and flanks). Many males are without red throat until second or third year, and resemble females. **Female** lacks grey cast to crown and face of male, and underparts are creamy-white, suffused with buff on breast. **First-winter** male and female are similar to adult female, but have orange-buff greater-covert wing-bar. **Racial variation** Two races winter in the subcontinent: the nominate, described above, and *F. p. albicilla*. Male of the latter has less orange on the underparts than the nominate race, with orange throat bordered below by grey breast-band; female and first-winter *albicilla* have colder grey-brown upperparts, with pronounced black uppertail-coverts, and underparts are whiter with grey across breast. Bill of *albicilla* is mainly dark (prominent pale base in nominate). **VOICE** Calls include a sharp *chack* and a rattling *purrr*. **HABITS** Partly crepuscular. Unobtrusive, but active and with an alert posture. Frequently droops wings and flicks tail while calling simultaneously; sometimes cocks tail well over the back. Forages in the understorey or in bushes, often dropping to the ground to pick up prey. Catches insects in typical flycatcher fashion in aerial forays and when flitting from one perch to another among foliage; sometimes hovers in front of leaves. **HABITAT** Bushes, groves, open forest, scrub at edges of cultivation, orchards, plantations, suburban gardens and roadside trees. **BREEDING** Very poorly known in the region. Builds a tiny cup nest of green moss in a hollow in a stone wall. **DISTRIBUTION AND STATUS** Winter visitor and passage migrant throughout most of the subcontinent, except parts of the northwest, northeast, Himalayas, S India and Sri Lanka; has bred in Kashmir at 3000 m and in Ladakh at 3660 m. **PK:** common and widespread passage migrant, mid March–late April and mid September–end October; small numbers overwinter. **NP:** common and widespread winter visitor; below 1830 m (–2590 m on passage). **IN:** common and widespread winter visitor and passage migrant; in plains and hills. **BT:** fairly common winter visitor. **BD:** common winter visitor throughout.

KASHMIR FLYCATCHER *Ficedula subrubra* Plate 101

Kashmir Red-breasted Flycatcher (F,I,P), *Muscicapa parva* (P), *Muscicapa subrubra* (F,I)

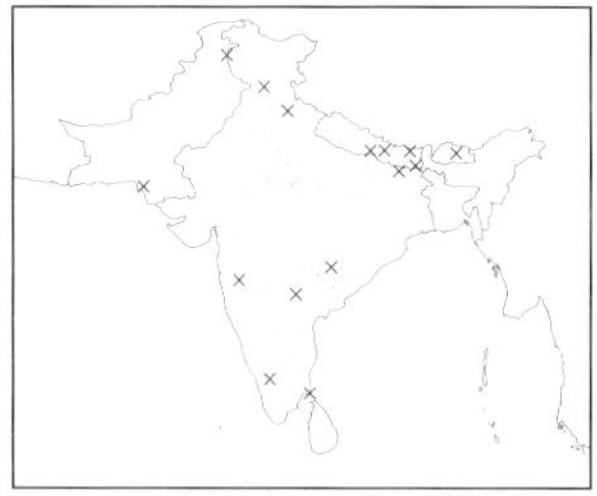

IDENTIFICATION 13 cm. Very similar to Red-throated Flycatcher (above), with white-sided black tail which is frequently cocked. **Male** told from that species by deep rufous throat, breast/upper belly and flanks, diffuse black border to throat and breast, and darker grey-brown upperparts. **Female** and **first-winter male** are variable, but usually with some rufous-orange on throat and breast (washed out on some), and with pronounced grey sides to neck and breast. Can rather resemble male Red-throated, but coloration on throat and breast is rufous, is often more pronounced on breast than on throat, and often continues as a wash onto belly and/or flanks; upperparts are also a slightly darker grey-brown. **First-winter female** lacks 'orange' on underparts. Darker grey-brown upperparts and grey wash to sides of neck and across breast are best distinctions from female nominate Red-throated; pale base to bill helps separate it from *albicilla* race of that species. **Juvenile** has tail pattern as adult, but otherwise has dark brown upperparts spotted with buff, and buffish underparts scaled with dark brown. **VOICE** Song is a short, sweet phrase, *sweet-eat, sweet-eat-did-he?*. Call is a staccato rolled twitter (S. Madge); also calls with a sharp *chack* and a rattling *purr* similar to calls of Red-throated. **HABITS** Similar to those of Red-throated. **HABITAT** Breeds in deciduous forest; winters in gardens, tea estates and forest edges. **BREEDING** May and June. Builds an untidy nest of dried leaves and moss, up to 3 m above ground in a hole in a tree trunk. **DISTRIBUTION AND STATUS** Endemic to the subcontinent. Breeds in NW Himalayas in Neelum valley, Pakistan, Kashmir and Pir Panjal Range, India; winters in Sri Lanka and S Western Ghats. Globally threatened. **PK:** probably a rare and very local, but regular breeding summer visitor, 2100 m; also a very rare passage migrant. **NP:** scarce passage migrant, mainly in spring; recorded below 2135 m. **IN:** formerly common summer visitor to Himalayas, 1800–2700 m, but has apparently declined; rare winter visitor to Western Ghats. **BT:** vagrant. **LK:** common winter visitor to higher hills. **REFERENCES** Harrap and Redman (1990), Karthikeyan and Athreya (1993), Robson (1985).

WHITE-GORGETED FLYCATCHER *Ficedula monileger* — Plate 101

***Muscicapa monileger* (F,I)**

IDENTIFICATION 13 cm. A compact flycatcher with large domed head and large bill, typically found close to the ground. **Adult** is mainly olive-brown, but has large white throat patch enclosed by black moustachial stripe and neck gorget. **Juvenile** lacks black-bordered white throat of adult; has dark brown upperparts streaked with warm buff, buff tips to greater coverts, and buffish underparts diffusely streaked with dark brown. Like adult, and unlike many other *Ficedula* flycatchers, has pinkish legs and feet. **Racial variation** *F. m. monileger* of the E Himalayas has an orange-buff supercilium, which is white in *F. m. leucops* of the NE subcontinent east and south of Brahmaputra R. **VOICE** A thin, high-pitched whistling song; calls include a metallic *dik*, a metallic scolding rattle, and a short, plaintive whistle (Boonsong and Round 1991). **HABITS** Shy and secretive. Keeps under cover in dense undergrowth or small trees close to the ground in forest. Captures insects in short aerial sallies or sometimes on the ground. Flicks and spreads tail when perched. **HABITAT** Undergrowth in moist broadleaved forest, thick bushes and bamboo. **BREEDING** Timing unknown in Himalayas; end April and May in NE India. Nest is a ball of grass and leaves, placed on an overgrown bank or in a dense bush. **DISTRIBUTION AND STATUS** Resident, subject to altitudinal movements. Himalayas from WC Nepal east to Arunachal Pradesh; NE India. **NP:** rare, presumably resident; 915–3000 m, but altitudinal movements are poorly known. **IN:** scarce in Himalayas, from foothills up to 2000 m; uncommon in NE hills, 750–1800 m. **BT:** uncommon; 610 m up to at least 1830 m.

SNOWY-BROWED FLYCATCHER *Ficedula hyperythra* — Plate 101

Rufous-breasted Blue Flycatcher (F,I), *Muscicapa hyperythra* (F,I)

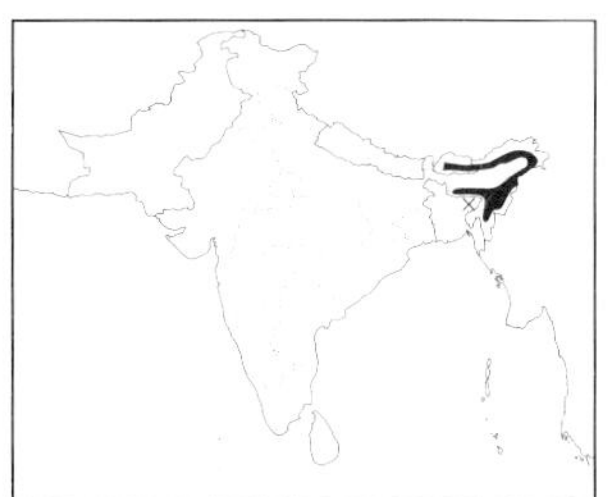

IDENTIFICATION 11 cm. A small, compact, short-tailed flycatcher, typically found close to the ground. **Male** has short, broad white supercilium, dark slaty-blue upperparts with rufous-brown wings, rufous-orange throat and breast, dusky flanks, and white patches at base of tail (which can be difficult to see). **Female** told from other small flycatchers by combination of small size and compact shape, dark olive-brown upperparts, orange-buff supercilium and eye-ring, and faint rufous panel on wing; underparts are variable, some having orange-buff on throat and breast, others having orange-buff pectoral band. Like male, and unlike many other *Ficedula* flycatchers, has pinkish legs and feet. **Juvenile** resembles female, but has orange-buff streaking on upperparts, orange-buff greater-covert wing-bar, and diffuse dark streaking on dull orange-buff underparts. Juvenile male has slate-blue tail. **VOICE** A quiet, high-pitched wheezy song, *tsit-sit-si-sii*; call a thin, repeated *sip* (Boonsong and Round 1991). **HABITS** Rather unobtrusive. Flits among undergrowth and bushes close to the forest floor; occasionally sallies after insects. **HABITAT** Humid broadleaved forest with dense undergrowth; favours bamboo and ravines. **BREEDING** April–June. Builds a deep cup-shaped nest low down in a hole in a mossy bank, tree trunk, between boulders or among tree roots. **DISTRIBUTION AND STATUS** Altitudinal migrant. Himalayas from N Uttar Pradesh east to Arunachal Pradesh; NE India. **NP:** frequent; summers 2000–2440 m, sometimes up to 3000 m, winters 275–1525 m. **IN:** rather uncommon; breeds 1900–3000 m in Himalayas, almost to the base of hills south of the Brahmaputra R; winters from foothills up to 1700 m. **BT:** uncommon; 610–3320 m. **BD:** winter vagrant.

LITTLE PIED FLYCATCHER *Ficedula westermanni* — Plate 101

Westermann's Flycatcher, *Muscicapa westermanni* (F,I)

IDENTIFICATION 10 cm. A small, compact, bull-headed flycatcher. **Male** is striking, with mainly black upperparts and white underparts, long and broad white supercilium, white patch on wing, and white sides to base of

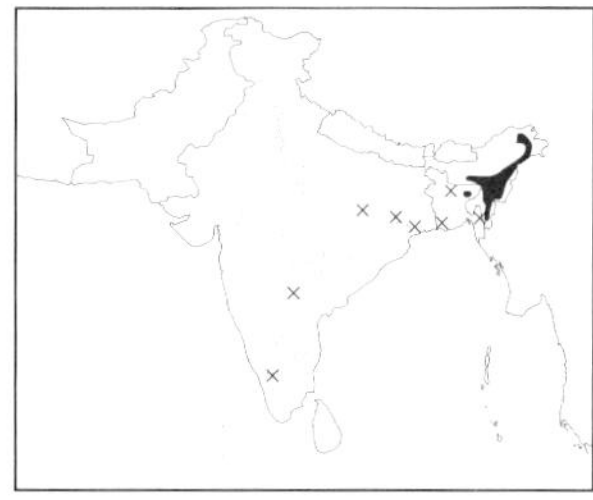

tail. **Female** has brownish-grey upperparts (tinged with warm brown on forehead, lores and around eye), and whitish underparts with brownish-grey wash to breast and flanks. Most likely to be confused with female Ultramarine (below), but has rufous cast to rump and uppertail-coverts, and lacks well-defined patches on sides of breast. Smaller size, rufous rump, and small, all-dark bill help separate it from Asian Brown (p.633). Superficially resembles female Slaty-blue (below), but shorter tail, greyish coloration to upperparts and to breast/flanks (with white belly), different call, and more arboreal habits are good pointers. **Juvenile** has buff spotting on upperparts and tips to coverts, and whitish underparts with dark scaling on breast. Juvenile male has white on wings and tail (similar to adult male), while juvenile female has rufous-brown uppertail-coverts and base of tail; white underparts and spotted (rather than streaked) scapulars help separate latter from juvenile Slaty-blue. **Racial variation** Female of the E race, *F. w. australorientis*, has brighter rufous rump, uppertail-coverts and edges to tail compared with the western race, described above. **VOICE** Song is a series of thin, high-pitched notes followed by a low rattle, *pi-pi-pi-pi-churr-r-r-r-r*; call is a mellow *tweet* (Ali and Ripley 1987). Also has a low *chur*. **HABITS** Keeps in pairs in the breeding season; otherwise singly or in pairs, and often within flocks of other insectivorous species. Flits actively about the canopy, moving from one tree to another. Hunts insects mainly while fluttering from branch to branch; also by gleaning from leaves and bark. **HABITAT** Breeds in broadleaved deciduous and evergreen forest; winters also in open wooded country, orchards and trees around cultivation. **BREEDING** April–June. Builds a cup-shaped nest of moss and fern stems, placed between stones, among tree roots, or under a rock on a steep slope. **DISTRIBUTION AND STATUS** Resident, subject to altitudinal movements, and short-range migrant. Breeds in Himalayas from Himachal Pradesh east to Arunachal Pradesh, and in NE India and Bangladesh; winters in the foothills and plains south to Bangladesh and Tamil Nadu. **NP:** uncommon; summers 1200–3000 m, winters from 275 m up to at least 915 m. **IN:** locally fairly common in Himalayas, locally common in NE hills; breeds 1200–2700 m, winters in the plains and foothills up to 1800 m and in south. **BT:** frequent. **BD:** scarce resident and local winter visitor; has bred at 30 m.

ULTRAMARINE FLYCATCHER *Ficedula superciliaris* — Plate 101

White-browed Blue Flycatcher (F,I), *Muscicapa superciliaris* (F,I)

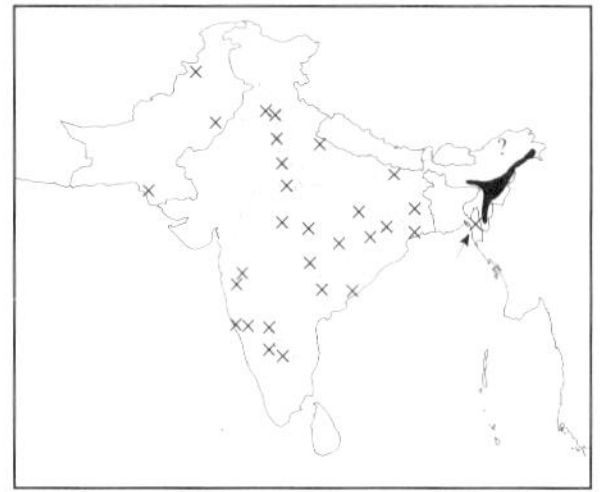

IDENTIFICATION 12 cm. A small, compact, arboreal flycatcher. **Male** has deep blue upperparts (with brighter crown), sides of neck and breast sides, contrasting with white of rest of underparts. **Female** has greyish-brown upperparts and whitish underparts, with greyish patches on sides of breast (patterning of underparts mirrors male's); some have blue cast to uppertail-coverts and tail. Most likely to be confused with female Little Pied (p.637), but has dark grey (or bluish, rather than rufous) rump, uppertail-coverts and tail, and well-defined grey patches on breast sides. Possibly confusable with Asian Brown (p.633), but is smaller, with smaller, all-dark bill. **First-winter/first-summer male** resembles female, but has blue cast to mantle and blue rump/uppertail-coverts, wings and tail; has buff greater-covert wing-bar and whitish fringes to tertials. **Juvenile** has buffish-white spotting on upperparts, and dark scaling on whitish underparts. Juvenile male has blue tail and blue edges to flight feathers; bold buffish-white spotting on scapulars and rump, and whitish underparts, help separate it from juvenile male Slaty-blue (below). Juvenile female has grey wings and tail; colder buffish-white coloration of scapular spotting and coloration of uppertail-coverts help separate it from juvenile Little Pied. **Racial variation** Male in W Himalayas (*F. s. superciliaris*) has white supercilium and white patches at base of tail, which are typically lacking in E populations (*F. s. aestigma*), although there is much overlap. **VOICE** Song is feeble, high-pitched and rather disjointed, with short trills and chirps, e.g. *tseep-te-e-te-e-te-e te-tih...... tseep.......tse-e-ep* etc; calls include a short, rising squeak, followed by a rapid trill, *chee-tr-r-r-r*, or low, rattling *t-r-r-r-t* (Boonsong and Round 1991; Roberts 1992). **HABITS** Arboreal, found in the middle and upper storeys. Sallies after flying insects; also searches for prey among foliage and branches. **HABITAT** Breeds in temperate broadleaved or pine forest; winters in open deciduous woodland, groves, gardens and orchards. **BREEDING** Mid April–early July. Builds nest up to 7 m above ground, in a hole in a tree or bank. **DISTRIBUTION AND STATUS** Resident and short-range migrant. Breeds in Himalayas from N Pakistan east to Arunachal Pradesh, and NE India; winters south to Bangladesh and Karnataka. **PK:** common summer visitor to moist temperate forest, mainly 1800–2700 m (–3200 m); a few winter records in plains. **NP:** common and widespread; mainly a summer visitor, 1800–3200 m; a few winter records below 1500 m. **IN:** common in the west, breeds 1800–3000 m; uncommon in the east, breeds 2000–3200 m in Himalayas, above 1500 m in NE hills; winter status unknown. **BT:** fairly common; 610–3045 m. **BD:** very rare winter visitor.

SLATY-BLUE FLYCATCHER *Ficedula tricolor* — Plate 101

***Muscicapa leucomelanura* (F,I)**

IDENTIFICATION 13 cm. A small, slim, long-tailed flycatcher which typically feeds close to (or on) the ground and frequently cocks tail. **Male** has dark blue upperparts with brighter blue forehead, blue-black sides of head

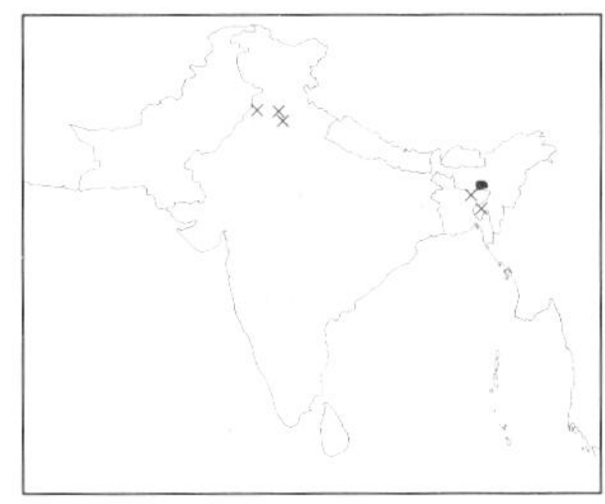

and breast contrasting with whitish throat, and blue-black tail with white patches at base. **Female** has warm brown upperparts, well-defined buffish-white throat contrasting with brownish-buff breast and flanks, and rufous uppertail-coverts and tail. Combination of well-defined whitish throat (except in *cerviniventris*: see below) and rufous tail help separate it from female Slaty-backed (p.635). Longer tail, warm brown upperparts, and brownish-buff (not greyish) breast and flanks help separate it from female Little Pied (p.637). Possibly confusable with female redstarts, but is smaller and typically flycatcher-like in behaviour and appearance. **Juvenile** has warm buff streaking on upperparts and dark scaling on buff underparts; tail is as female's. Streaked scapulars and buff coloration to underparts separate it from juvenile Little Pied. **First-winter** of both sexes resembles adult female, but has buff greater-covert wing-bar. **Racial variation** Male of the nominate race has greyish-white belly and flanks, which are strongly tinged with orange-buff in *F. l. cerviniventris* of NE subcontinent; in latter race, underparts (including throat) of female are entirely warm orange-buff. **VOICE** Song is three or four high-pitched whistles, the first drawn out, the second short and emphasised and the third a lower rapid trill, *chreet-chrr-whit-tit*; calls include a rapid *tic-tic* or *tek-tek-tek* (Roberts 1992). **HABITS** Keeps close to the ground in bushes and undergrowth. Rather chat-like; often droops its wings and jerks its tail over the back; has a less upright stance than most other flycatchers. Forages actively, mainly by dropping to the ground to pick up insects, also by short aerial sallies. **HABITAT** Breeds in subalpine shrubberies, thick bushes and forest edges in the Himalayas, and in undergrowth in dense moist oak–rhododendron or pine forests in Khasi Hills; winters in dense bush-covered ravines, reedbeds, sugarcane fields, tall grass, and forest undergrowth. **BREEDING** April–July. Builds a cup-shaped nest of moss, up to 2 m above ground in a hole in a bank or tree trunk, or crevice in wall or among boulders. **DISTRIBUTION AND STATUS** Resident, subject to altitudinal movements. Himalayas from N Pakistan east to Arunachal Pradesh, and NE India; very rare in adjacent plains (Punjab and Bihar, India) in winter. **PK:** frequent; summers in moister, more forested regions, 2600–3300 m; winters in adjacent foothills, 460–1500 m. **NP:** common and widespread; summers mainly 3050–3400 m (–4000 m) and winters 160–2135 m. **IN:** common in W Himalayas, breeds 1800–3300 m, winters in foothills below 1200 m; locally common in the east, breeds 2700–4000 m in Himalayas, at 1500 m in NE hills, winters mainly in foothills. **BT:** common; from 245 m up to at least 3810 m. **BD:** vagrant. **REFERENCES** Robson (1996b).

SAPPHIRE FLYCATCHER *Ficedula sapphira* — Plate 102

Sapphire-headed Flycatcher (F,I), *Muscicapa sapphira* (F,I)

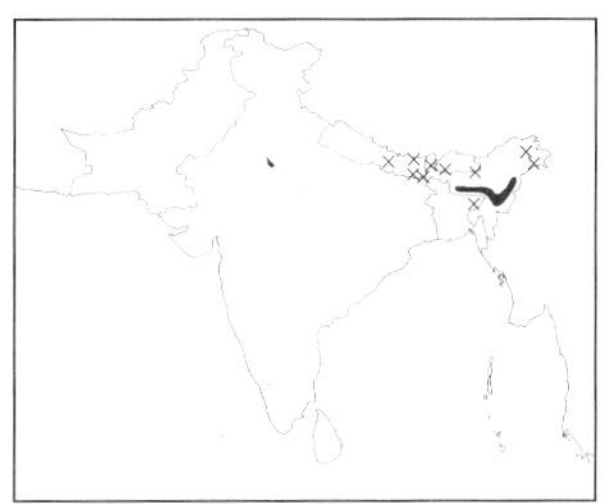

IDENTIFICATION 11 cm. Small size, slim appearance and tiny bill help separate this from the *Cyornis* blue flycatchers. **Male** has glistening blue crown and rump/uppertail-coverts, bright blue upperparts and sides of head, neck and breast, orange throat and centre to breast, and white belly and undertail-coverts. Many males (including immatures) have brown crown and mantle, and brownish sides of head, neck and breast (with orange throat and breast centre). **Female** has olive-brown upperparts and orange throat and breast. Distinguished from female Slaty-backed and Slaty-blue (p.635 and p.638) by shorter tail, orange throat and breast (latter with brownish sides), and white belly and vent; and from Slaty-backed additionally by rufous-brown uppertail-coverts and tail. **Juvenile** has orange-buff spotting on brown upperparts, and dark-scaled orange-buff breast which contrasts with white belly and flanks (latter with fine barring). Juvenile male has blue tail and wings (brown and rufous respectively on juvenile female; contrast on underparts helps separate it from juvenile female Little Pied, p.637). **VOICE** Call is a low *tit-it-it-it* rattle, deeper than that of other small flycatchers except Ultramarine (p.638) (Boonsong and Round 1991); dry rattled call, *trrrt* (P. Holt from P. Round recording). **HABITS** Arboreal, frequenting the middle and lower storeys. Pursues insects in extended aerial forays, usually returning to the same perch. **HABITAT** Moist evergreen broadleaved forest. **BREEDING** End April–June. Builds a cup-shaped nest of moss in a hollow of a steep bank, or hole in a tree or dead stump. **DISTRIBUTION AND STATUS** Resident, subject to altitudinal movements. Himalayas from EC Nepal east to Arunachal Pradesh; NE India. **NP:** rare, possibly resident; recorded mainly in the east, 2135–2800 m in April and May and 150 m in winter. **IN:** uncommon; breeds 2100–2600 m, in NE hills locally down to 1400 m; winters in foothills below 1700 m, mainly below 800 m. **BT:** uncommon. **BD:** winter vagrant; once at 35 m.

BLACK-AND-ORANGE FLYCATCHER *Ficedula nigrorufa* — Plate 102

Black-and-rufous Flycatcher (I), *Muscicapa nigrorufa* (I)

IDENTIFICATION 11 cm. A small, compact, orange-and-black flycatcher. **Male** is almost entirely rufous-orange, with black hood (crown, nape and ear-coverts) and black wings. **Female** is similar, but has dark olive-brown hood, orange-buff lores, and brownish-black wings. **Juvenile** has wings and tail as adult, but rest of plumage is dark brown, speckled with light brownish. **VOICE** Song is a high-pitched, metallic and insect-like *chiki-riki-chiki* or *chee-ri-ri-ri*; call is a low *pee*, and alarm a *zit-zit* (Ali and Ripley 1987). **HABITS** Tame. Forages in dense undergrowth or by making short aerial sallies from low branches; sometimes drops to the

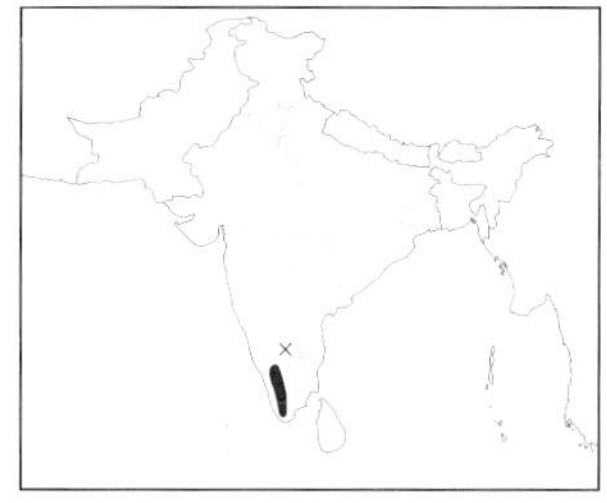

ground to pick up insects. **HABITAT** Evergreen sholas with dense undergrowth and plenty of leaf litter, cardamom and coffee plantations, often moist thickets in ravines near streams. **BREEDING** March–July. Nest is a ball of leaves and ferns, built in a dense bush or among ferns. **DISTRIBUTION AND STATUS IN:** endemic resident to Western Ghats; uncommon to common, but patchily distributed, in Kerala, Karnataka and W Tamil Nadu, from 700 m up to the summits. **REFERENCES** Gaston and Zacharias (1996).

VERDITER FLYCATCHER *Eumyias thalassina* Plate 102

***Muscicapa thalassina* (F,I,K,R)**

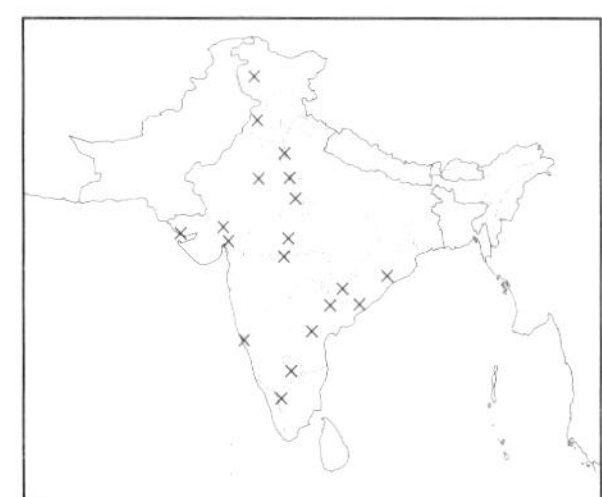

IDENTIFICATION 15 cm. **Male** is entirely greenish-blue, with brighter forehead and throat, and black lores. Not really confusable with any other flycatcher. **Female** is similar, but duller and greyer, and has dusky lores. Can be confused with male (but not female) Pale Blue Flycatcher (p.644), but has shorter bill, turquoise-blue upperparts and uniform greyish turquoise-blue underparts (lacking contrast between breast and belly), and whitish fringes to undertail-coverts. For differences from Nilgiri Flycatcher (below), see that species. **Juvenile** has turquoise cast to grey-brown upperparts, with fine orange-buff spotting, and bold orange-buff spotting on brown underparts; wings and tail are as adult, but has buff tips to coverts. **VOICE** Call is a *tze-ju-jui* (Ali and Ripley 1987); song is a series of rapid undulating notes, strident but musical, gradually descending the scale (J. Scharringa). **HABITS** Conspicuous and confiding. Hunts mainly by sallying forth from an exposed perch in treetops or from telegraph wires; sometimes gleans insects from branches or leaves. **HABITAT** Open forest, forest clearings and edges, tall trees in open areas, groves and gardens; mangroves in winter in Bangladesh. **BREEDING** April–August. Builds a cup-shaped nest of moss in a hole in a tree, wall or bank, or under the eaves of a house. **DISTRIBUTION AND STATUS** Partial migrant. Breeds in Himalayas from N Pakistan (Murree hills, lower Neelum and lower Kagan valleys) east to Arunachal Pradesh, and NE India; winters in Himalayan foothills and south to Bangladesh, also in Western Ghats, with widespread records from elsewhere in India. **PK:** common, local summer visitor; 1500–2800 m. **NP:** partial migrant; common and widespread in summer, 1200–2625 m, uncommon up to 3200 m and down to 1000 m; occasionally recorded in winter below 350 m. **IN:** common; breeds in Himalayas, 1200–3000 m, mainly below 2400 m; up to 750 m in Himalayan foothills in winter. **BT:** common; 710–2930 m. **BD:** common winter visitor throughout. **REFERENCES** Martens and Eck (1995).

DULL-BLUE FLYCATCHER *Eumyias sordida* Plate 102

Dusky-blue Flycatcher (I,P), *Muscicapa sordida* (I,P)

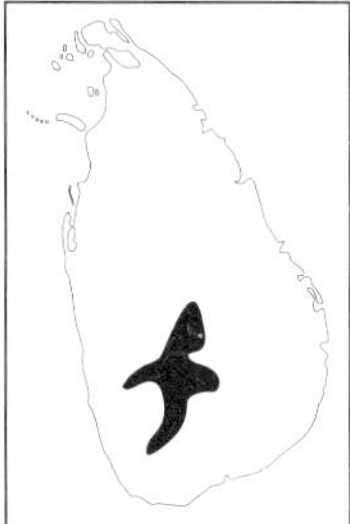

IDENTIFICATION 15 cm. The only all-'blue' flycatcher occurring in Sri Lanka. **Adult** is dull ashy-blue, with greyish-white belly, flanks and vent. Has black lores and chin, which are bordered above and below by bright cobalt-blue (especially noticeable on forehead). Sexes are similar, although female is slightly duller. **Juvenile** has buff spotting and diffuse black scaling on brown upperparts, and buffish throat and breast with black scaling; wings and tail are as adult, but has buff tips to coverts. **VOICE** Song is a sweet phrase of six to eight notes, often with a slide in each note which gives a mournful effect; call is a series of four or five *chip* notes (Ali and Ripley 1987). **HABITS** A quiet bird, not shy, and less active than most flycatchers. Frequently uses low perches such as fallen trees and low stumps. **HABITAT** Edges of forest and well-wooded areas, and shady wooded gardens. **BREEDING** Mid March–May, August and September. Builds a cup-shaped nest of moss, usually 1–3 m above ground on a ledge or in a crevice of a moss-covered bank or rock face, or in a hole of a trunk or branch, in forest. **DISTRIBUTION AND STATUS LK:** endemic resident, common in higher hills, 1220–1830 m, infrequent at middle altitudes, and occasionally in wet lowlands.

NILGIRI FLYCATCHER *Eumyias albicaudata* Plate 102

***Muscicapa albicaudata* (I)**

IDENTIFICATION 15 cm. **Male** is almost entirely dark indigo-blue, with brighter blue forehead and supercilium and black lores. Told from male White-bellied (p.643) by blue-grey belly and flanks (on White-bellied, blue breast contrasts with white belly), diffuse whitish fringes to blue-grey undertail-coverts, and presence of white at base of tail (although this can be difficult to see). Darker and bluer coloration and white in tail are best features for separation from Verditer Flycatcher (above). **Female** is distinctive, with dusky blue-grey upperparts and paler underparts, white fringes to undertail-coverts, and white at base of tail. Coloration of upperparts and underparts

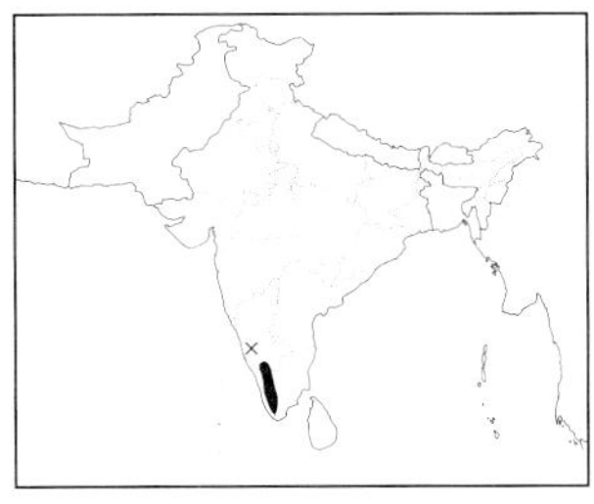

and white in tail help separate it from female Verditer. **Juvenile** has buff spotting and diffuse black scaling on brown upperparts, and white underparts with black scaling; wings and tail are as adult, but has buff tips to coverts. Coloration and patterning of underparts, and white in tail, help separate it from juvenile White-bellied. **VOICE** Call is a series of four or five *chip* notes (Ali and Ripley 1987). Hesitant melancholy warble of eight to twelve notes, *dwe te-te dtwe de-twe he-te-te dwe (te)*, slower, lower and less intense than that of Verditer Flycatcher (P. Holt). **HABITS** Hunts mainly by making short aerial forays from the canopy; also found lower down. **HABITAT** Evergreen biotope in the hills, thick vegetation near streams, forest edges and clearings, cardamom plantations and sholas. **BREEDING** February–June. Builds a cup-shaped nest of moss in a hole in a bank or wall, among hanging roots or under a bridge. **DISTRIBUTION AND STATUS IN:** resident, endemic to Western Ghats; common in Karnataka, Kerala and W Tamil Nadu, from 600 m up to the summits.

LARGE NILTAVA *Niltava grandis* — Plate 102

***Muscicapa grandis* (F,I)**

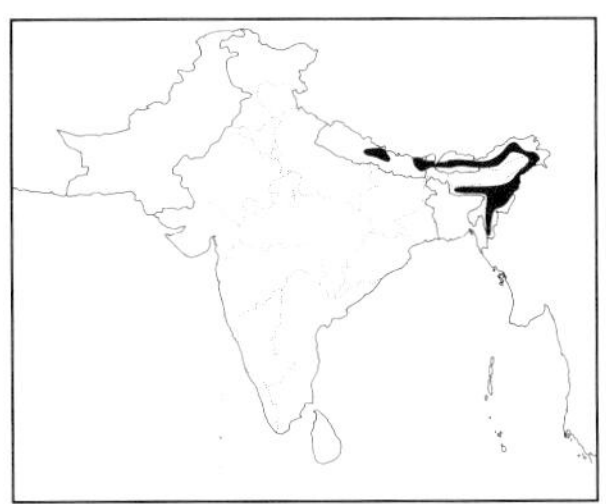

IDENTIFICATION 20 cm. A very large, stocky niltava. **Male** is dark blue (often appearing entirely black in poor light), with blackish face and tufted forehead. Has brilliant blue crown, neck patch, shoulder patches and rump. **Female** has blue patch on side of neck (which can be obscured), dark olive-brown upperparts with rufescent wings and tail, clearly defined (narrow) buff throat, and rufous-buff forecrown and lores. Told from female Rufous-bellied Niltava (p.642) by larger size, streaked ear-coverts and underparts, and absence of oval white patch on lower throat. **Juvenile** has rufous-brown upperparts with orange-buff streaking and diffuse blackish scaling, and rufous underparts with profuse blackish scaling and barring. Juvenile male has bluish wings (with orange-buff tips to greater coverts) and tail. Deep rufous coloration to underparts, and lack of oval buff throat patch, help separation from juvenile Rufous-bellied. **VOICE** Simple melancholy song of three to four ascending whistles, *do ray me*, repeated slowly. Harsh rattle and unobtrusive nasal *dju-ee* (P. Holt). **HABITS** Less active than most other flycatchers; often sits on one perch for long periods, occasionally flicking wings and tail. Usually frequents the middle storey of forests. Eats insects and berries. **HABITAT** Dense moist broadleaved forest, especially near streams. **BREEDING** April–July. Builds a cup-shaped nest of moss among moss on boulders, against a large trunk or in a hole in a dead stump. **DISTRIBUTION AND STATUS** Resident, subject to altitudinal movements. Himalayas from WC Nepal east to Arunachal Pradesh; NE India. **NP:** local and uncommon; 1525–2850 m. **IN:** locally frequent; breeds 1800–2700 m in Himalayas, down to 900 m in NE hills; winters from foothills up to at least 2000 m. **BT:** uncommon; from 600 m up to at least 2710 m.

SMALL NILTAVA *Niltava macgrigoriae* — Plate 102

***Muscicapa macgrigoriae* (F,I)**

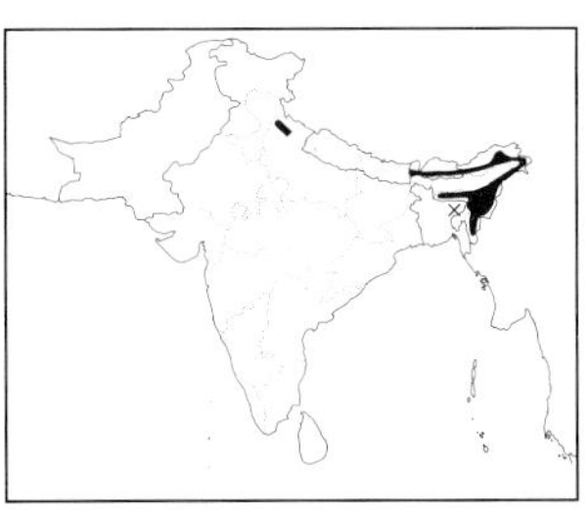

IDENTIFICATION 11 cm. A miniature version of Large Niltava (above). **Male** has brilliant blue forehead, neck patch and rump, blackish face, throat and breast, and dusky grey belly and vent (underparts paler, with whitish belly, in W and C Himalayan populations). **Female** has small blue patch on side of neck (often difficult to see), dark olive-brown upperparts and underparts (with paler belly and vent), and rufescent wings and tail; is paler and warmer brown on forehead, throat and around eye. Told from female Rufous-bellied Niltava (p.642) by smaller size and absence of oval white patch on lower throat. **Juvenile** has orange-buff shaft streaking on brown upperparts, and buffish breast with diffuse brown streaking; wings and tail are as adult, but has buff tips to coverts. **VOICE** A very thin, high-pitched song, *twee-twee-ee-twee*, which rises and then falls; calls include a high-pitched (second note lower) *see-see* and metallic scolding and churring notes (Ali and Ripley 1987; Boonsong and Round 1991). **HABITS** Active, but rather shy and elusive, especially when breeding. Partly crepuscular. Keeps to shady undergrowth and bushes, flying out from time to time to catch insects. Eats insects and berries. **HABITAT** Shrubberies along streams and bushes at the edges of tracks and clearings in broadleaved forest; in winter, also dense reed and grass jungle with scattered trees in the plains. **BREEDING** End April–early July. Builds a nest of moss in a hollow between boulders or in a stream bank. **DISTRIBUTION AND STATUS** Resident, subject to altitudinal movements. Himalayas from N Uttar Pradesh east to Arunachal Pradesh; NE India. **NP:** fairly common; winters 270–1400 m, summers up to 2200 m. **IN:** fairly common; breeds 1000–2100 m in Himalayas, down to 900 m in the east; winters in plains and foothills up to 1400 m. **BT:** common; 305–2180 m. **BD:** winter vagrant.

RUFOUS-BELLIED NILTAVA *Niltava sundara* Plate 102

Beautiful Niltava (F), *Muscicapa sundara* (F,I)

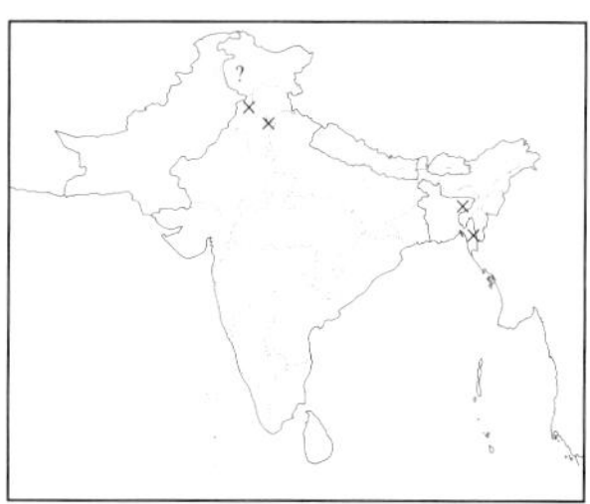

IDENTIFICATION 18 cm. **Male** has dark blue upperparts and orange underparts, with brilliant blue crown, neck patch, shoulder patch and rump. Distinguished from similarly plumaged Blue-throated Flycatcher (p.644) by larger size, niltava shape (especially large, rectangular-shaped head), well-defined patches of brilliant blue against darker blue upperparts, and orange underparts extending to vent. For differences from male Vivid Niltava (below), see that species. **Female** has well-defined oval-shaped throat patch (which separates it from other female niltavas), small blue patch on side of neck (often difficult to see), olive-brown upperparts with rufescent wings and tail, orange-buff forehead and lores, and grey-brown underparts. For differences from female Vivid, see that species. **Juvenile** has oval-shaped buff throat patch, which separates it from other juvenile niltavas, and background colour of underparts is whiter than on juvenile Large (p.641). Juvenile male has blue wings and tail. **VOICE** Includes a raspy *z-i-i-i-f-cha-chuk* (perhaps song), a hard *tic*, a thin *see*, and a low, soft *cha...cha* (Fleming *et al.* 1984; Ali and Ripley 1987). **HABITS** Usually sits quietly in a bush or on a branch low down in the forest, occasionally darting out or dropping to the ground to catch insects. **HABITAT** Bushes and undergrowth in broadleaved or mixed coniferous–broadleaved forest; also secondary growth. **BREEDING** April–July. Builds nest, mainly of moss, close to the ground in a hole in a bank or tree stump, or a rock crevice. **DISTRIBUTION AND STATUS** Resident, subject to altitudinal movements. Himalayas from N Pakistan (Murree hills, Kagan valley and Palas valley, Indus Kohistan) east to Arunachal Pradesh; NE India. **PK:** scarce and local; breeds 1800–2600 m, some wintering in foothills. **NP:** common and widespread; winters chiefly 800–1830 m, summers 2135–3200 m. **IN:** fairly common; breeds 1800–3200 m in Himalayas, down to 900 m in NE hills; winters from 2300 m down to foothills. **BT:** fairly common; from 245 m up to at least 2930 m (–3540 m). **BD:** winter vagrant. **REFERENCES** Inskipp and Inskipp (1996).

VIVID NILTAVA *Niltava vivida* Plate 102

Rufous-bellied Blue Flycatcher (I), *Muscicapa vivida* (E,I)

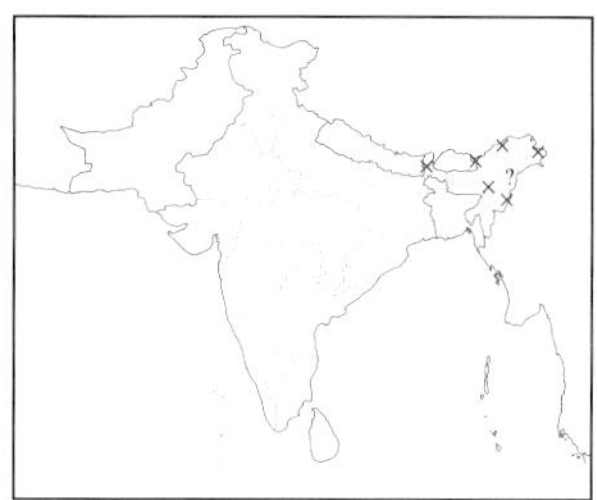

IDENTIFICATION 18 cm. Superficially resembles Rufous-bellied Niltava (above), but is larger and more chat-like in appearance and behaviour, has longer wings, often has peaked crown, and is typically more arboreal and found away from dense cover. **Male** has blue head and upperparts and orange underparts, with brighter blue forecrown, rump and tail. Compared with Rufous-bellied, lacks bright glistening blue crown and nape (which contrast with black ear-coverts and mantle on that species), has blue (rather than black) sides of throat, and blue shoulder patch and rump are less striking. Further, orange of breast extends as a variable wedge onto lower throat (throat of Rufous-bellied is entirely black, with horizontal demarcation from orange breast). **Female** lacks well-defined oval-shaped patch on lower throat shown by female Rufous-bellied, and typically has peaked crown. Resembles female Large (p.641) in coloration, with narrow buffish throat, but is smaller and lacks blue neck patch, and wings and tail are nowhere near as rufescent as on that species. **Juvenile** as Rufous-bellied, but lacks buff throat patch. **VOICE** Simple slow song of up to ten mellow whistles, usually interspersed with scratchier notes, *heu wee riu.. chrt-trrt...heu wee tiu-wee-u* (P. Holt from D. Farrow recording). **HABITS** Usually keeps to the middle storey and canopy. **HABITAT** Broadleaved evergreen and mixed forest. **BREEDING** Details unknown in the subcontinent. **DISTRIBUTION AND STATUS IN:** resident, subject to altitudinal movements; rare, but range and status are poorly known; NE hills (Arunachal Pradesh, Assam, Manipur, Nagaland?, West Bengal); 2000–2700 m in summer, altitudinal range in winter unknown. **REFERENCES** Boonsong and Round (1991).

WHITE-TAILED FLYCATCHER *Cyornis concretus* Plate 103

White-tailed Blue-Flycatcher (I), *Muscicapa concreta* (I)

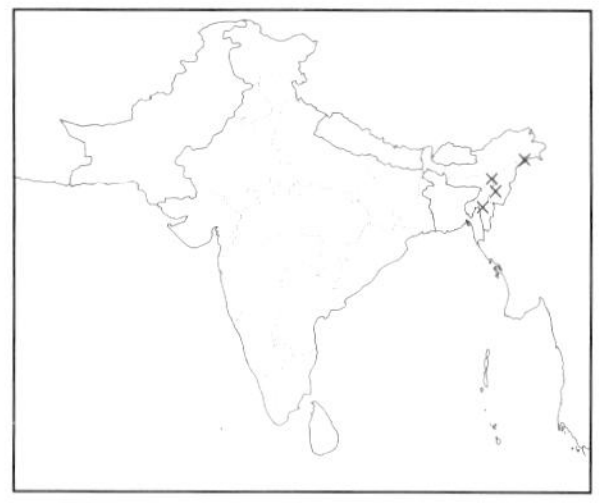

IDENTIFICATION 18 cm. Told from other flycatchers by large size, and by white in tail which is frequently revealed as tail is flicked open. **Male** bears some resemblance to Large Niltava (p.641), but is mainly slaty-blue and lacks brilliant blue neck patch, shoulder patch and rump. Further, has longer and slimmer bill, and whitish belly and undertail-coverts. Superficially resembles White-tailed Robin (p.657), and best separated by flycatcher-like stance and proportionately shorter tail; also has shorter tarsus, white belly and undertail-coverts, and habit of quickly flicking open tail (rather like Little Forktail, p.658). **Female** has prominent oval white patch on lower throat, and superficially resembles female Rufous-bellied Niltava (above); longer and slimmer bill, blue cast to crown, lack of rufous-orange forehead and lores, and white-sided dark tail separate it from that species. **VOICE** Variable, piercing, sibilant whistles, *tii-tuu-tii-tuu-tii, huiiee*

and *tuu-tii*, and a harsh *scree* in alarm (Boonsong and Round 1991). **HABITS** Slower-moving and less active than most flycatchers; often spreads its tail. Inhabits the lower storey of forest. Gleans insects from foliage and branches; also captures them in flight. **HABITAT** Dense forest, often close to streams. **BREEDING** Only one nest known: found in June, made of moss and placed in the hole of a rocky bank of a ravine. **DISTRIBUTION AND STATUS IN:** resident, subject to altitudinal movements; current status uncertain, very few recent records; breeds at 1500 m in the Patkai Range in Arunachal Pradesh, winters in Assam and Mizoram. **REFERENCES** Raman (1995).

WHITE-BELLIED BLUE FLYCATCHER *Cyornis pallipes* Plate 103

***Muscicapa pallipes* (I)**

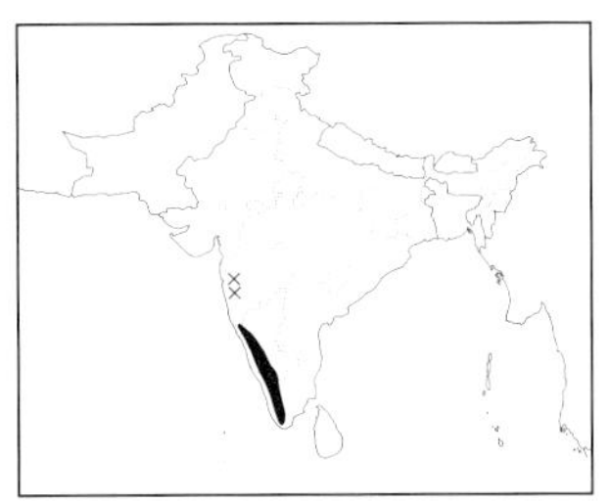

IDENTIFICATION 15 cm. Has striking habit of lifting and fanning tail. **Male** is almost entirely blue, blacker around face, with brighter blue forehead and supercilium. Distinguished from male Nilgiri Flycatcher (p.640) by larger and longer bill, dark indigo-blue coloration, white belly and undertail-coverts (latter lacking blue-grey scaling), and absence of white at base of tail. **Female** is similar to female Blue-throated Flycatcher (p.644), but has striking orange-red throat and breast (with cream chin), strong grey cast to head, more extensive cream on lores and forehead, brighter, chestnut tail, and is larger, with much longer bill. Note that rather similar Pale-chinned Flycatcher (below) does not occur in the Western Ghats. **Juvenile** has olive-brown upperparts with diffuse buff spotting and black scaling, and warm buff breast with brown scaling contrasting with unmarked buff throat and white belly and flanks; wings and tail are as those of respective adult, but has buff tips to coverts. Buff throat and unmarked white belly (and chestnut tail of juvenile female) help separate it from juvenile Nilgiri. **VOICE** Song is a lengthy, faltering series of unmelodious high-pitched, squeaky slurring and sliding notes, rambling erratically, and often audible only at close range (P. Holt from A. Lewis recording). Call is a low *tsk-tsk* (Ali and Ripley 1987). **HABITS** Rather lethargic and inconspicuous. Frequents the undergrowth and lower storey of forest. Hunts among the foliage, also by pursuing insects in flight, and sometimes by descending to the ground. **HABITAT** Undergrowth in dense broadleaved evergreen forest, sholas, *Strobilanthes* and *Channa* patches on hillsides. **BREEDING** February–September. Builds an untidy nest of moss on a rock ledge or in a hole in a tree stump or bank, quite close to the ground. **DISTRIBUTION AND STATUS IN:** uncommon endemic resident, mainly in Western Ghats from Maharashtra south to Kerala and adjacent hills of Tamil Nadu; from foothills up to 1700 m. **REFERENCES** Gaston and Zacharias (1996).

PALE-CHINNED FLYCATCHER *Cyornis poliogenys* Plate 103

Brooks's Flycatcher (F,I), Pale-chinned Blue Flycatcher, *Muscicapa poliogenys* (F,I)

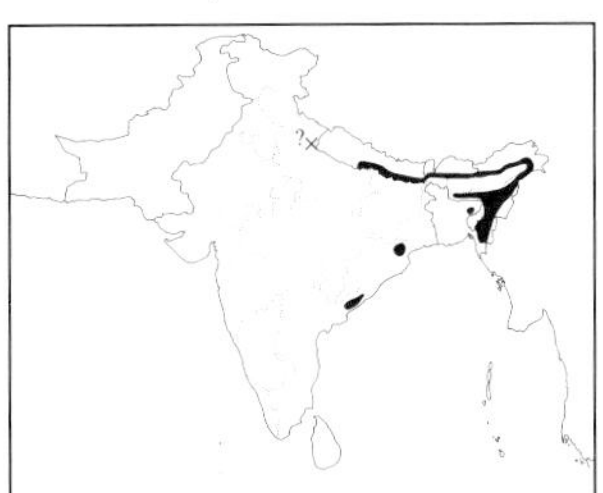

IDENTIFICATION 18 cm. A rather nondescript flycatcher with prominent buffish eye-ring and lores, olive-brown upperparts, whitish or pale buff throat, pale orange breast and flanks, and rufous-brown tail. Indicative features for separation from females of Blue-throated and Hill Blue Flycatchers (p.644) (although see comments below) are grey cast to head, fairly clear-cut pale throat, pale creamy-orange breast and flanks which merge with white of lower belly, and cream undertail-coverts. Pale lores of Pale-chinned are a further difference from female Hill Blue. **Racial variation** Some birds in NE subcontinent, *C. p. cachariensis*, differ from the nominate race, described above, in lacking grey cast to head and in having pale orange throat which is concolorous with breast, and are therefore more similar to female Blue-throated and Hill Blue. Male *C. p. vernayi* of the Eastern Ghats has variable bluish-slate coloration to upperparts: most have bluish head and edges to remiges and rectrices, others almost no blue except on head; bluest birds resemble female Tickell's Blue (p.645), and are best told by more uniform creamy-orange underparts (especially throat and lower breast and flanks, which are whiter on Tickell's), narrow whitish eye-ring, and paler pinkish legs. Female *vernayi* is much as nominate race. **Juvenile** has olive-brown upperparts with diffuse buff spotting and black scaling, and buff underparts with brown scaling on breast and flanks. Told from juvenile females of other *Cyornis* flycatchers by combination of well-defined (and unmarked) buff throat, diffusely marked upperparts, and well-marked underparts, especially barring on flanks. **VOICE** Call is a repeated *tik* (Fleming *et al.* 1984). The song is well structured and quite even: a high-pitched series of four to eleven notes, slightly rising and falling in its overall pattern, sometimes interspersed with harsh *tchut-tchut* call-notes (C. Robson from H. S. Baral tape). **HABITS** A typical flycatcher. Forages in bushes and undergrowth in forest, also higher in trees, and sometimes on the ground, where it resembles a chat. **HABITAT** Bushes and undergrowth in open broadleaved forest; more open areas in winter. **BREEDING** Mid April–end June. Builds nest of moss in a hollow in a bank, among boulders or up to 1 m above ground in a hole of a dead stump. **DISTRIBUTION AND STATUS** Resident. Himalayan foothills in N Uttar Pradesh and from WC Nepal east to Arunachal Pradesh; NE India and Bangladesh; also Eastern Ghats in Orissa and Andhra Pradesh, but no recent published records from there. **NP:** locally common; below 455 m. **IN:** locally fairly common; from edge of the plains up to 1500 m in Himalayas and NE hills, to 1000 m in Eastern Ghats. **BT:** uncommon; 270–1335 m. **BD:** common and local. **REFERENCES** Ripley *et al.* (1988).

PALE BLUE FLYCATCHER *Cyornis unicolor* Plate 103

***Muscicapa unicolor* (F,I)**

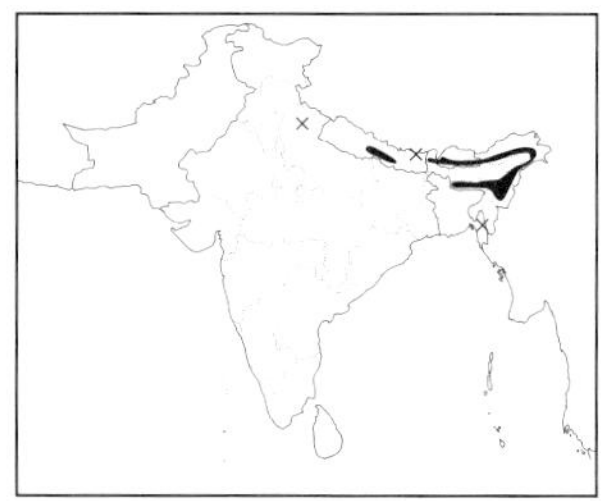

IDENTIFICATION 18 cm. **Male** is most likely to be confused with Verditer Flycatcher (p.640), but has longer bill and is pale blue in coloration (lacking greenish cast), with distinctly greyer belly. Has shining blue forecrown and dusky lores. **Female** is very different, and not confusable with Verditer. Like other *Cyornis* flycatchers, has rufous-brown uppertail-coverts and tail. Best distinguished by combination of larger size, slimmer appearance and longer tail, brownish-grey upperparts, and uniform greyish underparts (lacking paler throat) with greyish-white centre of belly and dark buff undertail-coverts. **Juvenile** has olive-brown upperparts with prominent orange-buff spotting and diffuse black scaling, and buffish throat and breast with profuse brown scaling; wings and tail are as adult, but has buff tips to coverts. Lack of blue-green cast to upperparts and bluer wings and tail separate juvenile male from juvenile Verditer. Combination of bold spotting on scapulars and well-marked underparts (especially throat, flanks and belly) separate juvenile of both sexes from juveniles of other *Cyornis* flycatchers. **VOICE** Song is rich and melodious, loud and 'thrush-like' (and different in quality from that of other *Cyornis*), with descending sequences, *chi, chuchichu-chuchichu-chucchi*, usually ending with harsh *chizz* (Boonsong and Round 1991). **HABITS** Usually frequents the middle and upper storeys in forest; sometimes also near the ground. Pursues insects like a typical flycatcher; usually moves from one perch to another, instead of returning to the same one. **HABITAT** Moist, dense broadleaved forest, bamboo and secondary growth. **BREEDING** Poorly known. April–June. Builds a nest of moss in a hole in a tree stump or between stones in a bank. **DISTRIBUTION AND STATUS** Resident. Himalayas in N Uttar Pradesh and from WC Nepal east to Arunachal Pradesh; NE India. **NP:** rare and local; 275–1525 m. **IN:** no recent published records from the west, uncommon in the east; from foothills in winter up to at least 1800 m in summer, breeds mainly at around 1500 m. **BT:** frequent; 1320–2180 m. **BD:** ?former winter visitor, but could still occur in hill tracts.

BLUE-THROATED FLYCATCHER *Cyornis rubeculoides* Plate 103

***Muscicapa rubeculoides* (F,I)**

IDENTIFICATION 14 cm. **Male** has blue upperparts, orange breast, and white belly and vent. Distinguished from other blue flycatchers by blue throat (sometimes with narrow orange wedge), and from Tickell's (p.645) additionally by darker blue upperparts and slight extension of orange of breast onto flanks. **Female** has olive-brown head and upperparts, rufous-brown rump and tail, narrow (and poorly defined) creamy-orange throat and orange breast, and white belly and undertail-coverts. Coloration of upperparts (especially tail) separates it from female Tickell's Blue (bluish on that species). Safest distinction from Pale-chinned (p.643) is deeper orange coloration of breast, which is also well demarcated from white belly (and well-defined white throat of Pale-chinned is also distinctive; see that species for further details). For differences from female White-bellied and Hill Blue Flycatchers (p.643 and p.644), see those species. **Juvenile** has olive-brown upperparts with orange-buff spotting and diffuse blackish scaling, and buffish breast with black scaling; wings and tail are as adult, but has buff tips to coverts. Very similar to juvenile Tickell's Blue; upperparts are more prominently spotted and breast more distinctly barred, and juvenile male has cobalt-blue (rather than cerulean-blue) wings and tail. Neatly spotted upperparts, poorly defined and slightly marked pale throat, and whiter belly and flanks (and blue wings and tail of juvenile male) are best features for separation from juvenile Pale-chinned. **VOICE** Short, sweet song, phrases of which recall Tickell's Blue, but delivery is more rapid and is higher-pitched, with more trilling notes; calls include a hard *tac* and a *trrt-trrt* (Boonsong and Round 1991). **HABITS** Frequents bushes and low branches close to the ground. Sallies after insects, but does not use a regular perch. **HABITAT** Open forest, groves and well-wooded gardens. **BREEDING** April–August. Builds nest of moss in a hollow of a bank, tree, rock or dead stump. **DISTRIBUTION AND STATUS** Breeds in Himalayan foothills from Pakistan (Margalla hills) east to Arunachal Pradesh, and NE India; winters in E Himalayan foothills and south to Bangladesh, SW India and Sri Lanka, with scattered records from elsewhere in India. **PK:** scarce and very local summer visitor; 460–900 m. **NP:** mainly a summer visitor, frequent 365–1500 m (–2135 m); rare in winter in lower foothills. **IN:** locally frequent in summer from the foothills up to 1500 m, locally to 1800 m; widely scattered in winter in hills up to 1000 m (–1145 m). **BT:** fairly common; 350–2090 m (–3045 m). **BD:** rare winter visitor. **LK:** rare winter visitor to dry lowlands and lower hills. **REFERENCES** Inskipp and Inskipp (1996).

HILL BLUE FLYCATCHER *Cyornis banyumas* Plate 103

Large-billed Blue Flycatcher (F,I), *Muscicapa banyumas* (F,I)

IDENTIFICATION 14 cm. **Male** distinguished from male Tickell's Blue (p.645) by deeper cobalt-blue upperparts, blackish ear-coverts, orange chin (dark blue of ear-coverts meets under bill on most Tickell's), and ill-defined border between orange of breast and white of belly, with orange extending to upper belly and flanks (although there is some variation in sharpness of border on both species). Further, has longer and larger bill, paler pinkish legs,

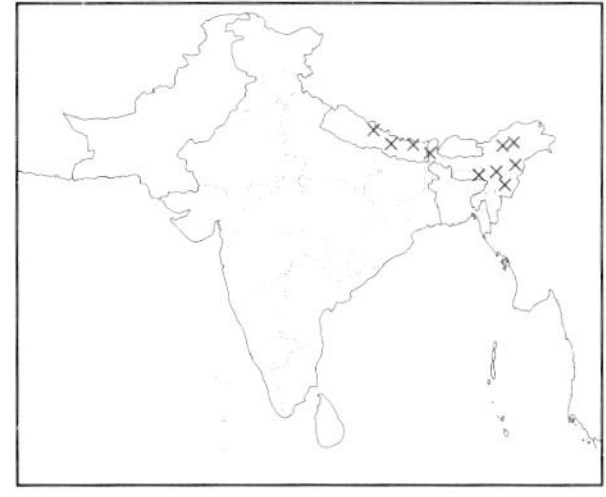

and longer primary projection compared with Tickell's. **Female**'s olive-brown coloration to upperparts and rufous-brown uppertail-coverts and tail are best distinctions from female Tickell's. From female Blue-throated (p.644) by dark lores, and by sharp demarcation between grey-brown sides of head and creamy-orange throat. Dark lores, less grey on forehead, crown and ear-coverts, and less distinct pale throat help separate it from Pale-chinned (p.643). Longer bill and longer primary projection are further differences from last two species. **Juvenile** has olive-brown upperparts with orange-buff spotting and diffuse black scaling, and buffish breast with dark scaling (which is possibly more prominent than on other juvenile *Cyornis* flycatchers). **VOICE** Sweet, melancholy, warbling song, with longer and more complex phrases than Tickell's, but delivery is more rapid; both sexes give brief, simplified version in alarm; calls include a hard *tac* and a scolding *trrt-trrt-trrt* (Boonsong and Round 1991). **HABITS** Details not recorded in the region. Presumably similar to those of other *Cyornis* flycatchers. **HABITAT** Dense moist broadleaved forest; favours ravines. **BREEDING** End April–June. Builds nest of moss in a hole in a bank, among tree roots or low down against a moss-covered trunk. **DISTRIBUTION AND STATUS** Resident, subject to altitudinal movements. Himalayas from WC Nepal east to Arunachal Pradesh; NE India. **NP:** rare; a few records from the centre and east in May and August, 1250–3350 m, and from C middle hills in winter. **IN:** rare, but distribution and status are poorly known; in Assam, breeds 750–1800 m, mainly above 1200 m, also recorded at 300 m in summer; 1900 m in June in Arunachal Pradesh.

TICKELL'S BLUE FLYCATCHER *Cyornis tickelliae* — Plate 103

Orange-breasted Blue Flycatcher, *Muscicapa tickelliae* (F,I,P)

IDENTIFICATION 14 cm. **Male** has blue upperparts, and orange breast which is cleanly demarcated from white belly and flanks. Told from Blue-throated Flycatcher (p.644) by paler cerulean-blue upperparts, orange throat, and often clear division between orange of breast and white of belly/flanks (although orange can diffuse onto belly and flanks on some). For differences from Hill Blue Flycatcher (p.644), see that species. **Female** has blue-grey cast to upperparts (especially rump and tail), orange breast, and white belly, flanks and undertail-coverts. Coloration of upperparts (especially tail) separates it from female Blue-throated and Hill Blue. In Eastern Ghats, possibly confusable with Pale-chinned (p.643) (subspecies *vernayi* of latter can have blue-grey wash to upperparts), but upperparts are strongly suffused with cerulean-blue, lacks eye-ring, and has whiter throat, white belly and undertail-coverts (orange usually more concentrated on upper breast), and paler, pinkish legs. **Juvenile** is very similar to juvenile Blue-throated, but upperparts are generally less prominently spotted and breast less distinctly barred; further, has duller (cerulean-, rather than cobalt-) blue wings and tail than juvenile male Blue-throated. **Racial variation** Male *C. t. jerdoni* of Sri Lanka differs from male of the nominate race in having darker, deeper blue upperparts, and longer bill; orange of breast extends onto upper belly (and flanks on some), lacking clear division from white of rest of underparts. **VOICE** Song is a short, metallic trill of six to ten notes, the first half descending and the second half ascending; both sexes sing in alarm; calls include a hard *tac* and a *trrt-trrt* (Ali and Ripley 1987; Boonsong and Round 1991). **HABITS** Flits actively around bushes, undergrowth and low branches, hawking insects in mid-air. **HABITAT** Occurs in drier habitats than Blue-throated Flycatcher: open dry forest, bushes in forest or along streams, groves, wooded gardens, scrub and bamboo. **BREEDING** May–August, varying locally. Builds nest of moss in a crevice in a rock ledge, tree hole or among aerial roots, up to 2 m above ground. **DISTRIBUTION AND STATUS** Resident. Mainly from Gujarat and N Uttar Pradesh east to West Bengal and south through the peninsula and Sri Lanka; also NE India, Bangladesh. **NP:** scarce, status uncertain; below 305 m. **IN:** locally common, subject to local movements; breeds mainly in broken country and hills up to 1500 m in the south; disperses into plains in winter. **BD:** rare winter visitor. **LK:** common resident in the lowlands and up to middle altitudes.

PYGMY BLUE FLYCATCHER *Muscicapella hodgsoni* — Plate 103

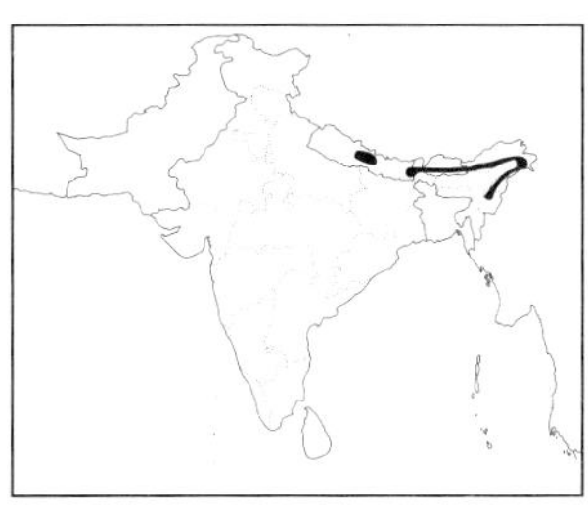

IDENTIFICATION 10 cm. A very small flycatcher with short tail and tiny bill, giving rise to flowerpecker-like appearance. Tends to be more arboreal than Snowy-browed (p.637), and often found high in trees and tangled vines. Has curious habit of stretching head forward, dropping and spreading wings and fanning tail. **Male** has blue upperparts (with bright blue forecrown), and underparts almost entirely orange. **Female** has olive-brown upperparts and orange-buff underparts. Told from female Snowy-browed by shorter tail, absence of orange-buff forehead and supercilium, and brighter orange underparts (without dusky flanks). **Juvenile** is undescribed. **VOICE** Song is a short, weak *tzzit-che-che-che-heeee* (Fleming *et al.* 1984); call is a low *churr.* **HABITS** Found in the canopy, as well as in dense bushes in the lower forest storey. Very active. Hunts insects by making short sallies, searching leaves, hovering before flowers like a warbler, and also by dropping to the ground. **HABITAT** Dense, damp broadleaved forest. **BREEDING** Only one nest known, taken in July; built of moss and placed among creeper stems growing over an old stump. **DISTRIBUTION AND STATUS** Resident, subject to altitudinal movements. Himalayas from WC Nepal east to Arunachal Pradesh; NE India. **NP:** scarce and local; 2100–3500 m in breeding season, down to 75 m in winter. **IN:** uncommon; above 2135 m in breeding season, winters 300–750 m. **BT:** uncommon; 245–2400 m and probably higher. **REFERENCES** Athreya *et al.* (1997), Lama (1995a).

GREY-HEADED CANARY FLYCATCHER *Culicicapa ceylonensis* Plate 103

Grey-headed Flycatcher (F,I,K,N,R)

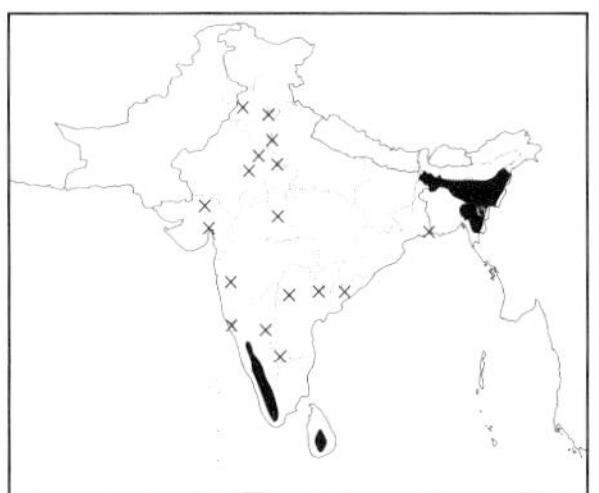

IDENTIFICATION 13 cm. A flycatcher with grey head and breast, greenish mantle, and yellow belly, flanks and vent. Upright stance, crested appearance, and flycatcher behaviour serve to distinguish it from the similarly plumaged *Seicercus* and *Abroscopus* warblers. **VOICE** Song is a loud, high-pitched, interrogative *chik...whichee-whicheee,* which can be regularly repeated; a clear *kitwik...kitwik,* and a soft *pit...pit...pit* when foraging (Ali and Ripley 1987). **HABITS** Found singly in winter, often with mixed foraging flocks of other insectivorous species; in pairs or family parties in the breeding season. Conspicuous, confiding and noisy throughout the year. Always on the move, sallying forth to pursue insects acrobatically in flight like a typical flycatcher, and frequently turning head and jerking tail. Inhabits the lower and middle storeys of forest, also often perches on telegraph wires. **HABITAT** Forest, groves, and open wooded country; in S India, broadleaved evergreen forest, sholas, coffee plantations, wooded ravines, bamboo and gardens. **BREEDING** February–early July, varying locally. Builds a half-cone nest of moss, lichens and cobwebs, bound to a moss- or lichen-covered trunk or rock, up to 12 m above ground. **DISTRIBUTION AND STATUS** Breeds in Himalayas from N Pakistan east to Arunachal Pradesh, also hills of NE, E, C and SW India, Bangladesh and Sri Lanka; winters in Himalayan foothills and south in plains in Pakistan and E and NE India. **PK:** frequent, local summer visitor in moist temperate deciduous forest, breeds mainly 1200–1800 m (–2400 m); scarce in winter in Punjab and Sindh. **NP:** very common and widespread partial migrant; summers 1200–3100 m, mainly 1500–2400 m; some birds remain to winter below 1800 m. **IN:** common on breeding grounds, widely dispersed in winter; breeds 1500–2400 m in Himalayas, down to foothills in the northeast and above 900 m in peninsular hills; winters in plains and hills, up to 1800 m in Himalayas. **BT:** common and widespread; from 245 m up to at least 2875 m. **BD:** locally common resident. **LK:** common resident in wet-zone hills.

CHATS Tribe Saxicolini

A diverse group of small/medium-sized passerines that including the chats, bush robins, magpie robins, redstarts, forktails, cochoas and wheatears. Most are terrestrial or partly terrestrial, some are arboreal, and some are closely associated with water. Their main diet is insects, and they also consume fruits, especially berries. They forage mainly by hopping about on the ground in search of prey, or by perching on a low vantage point and then dropping to the ground on to insects or making short sallies to catch them in the air. Typically, they are solitary except in the breeding season, when they often keep in pairs. Most species defend breeding territories.

COMMON NIGHTINGALE *Luscinia megarhynchos* Plate 104

Nightingale (I), *Erithacus megarhynchos* (I)

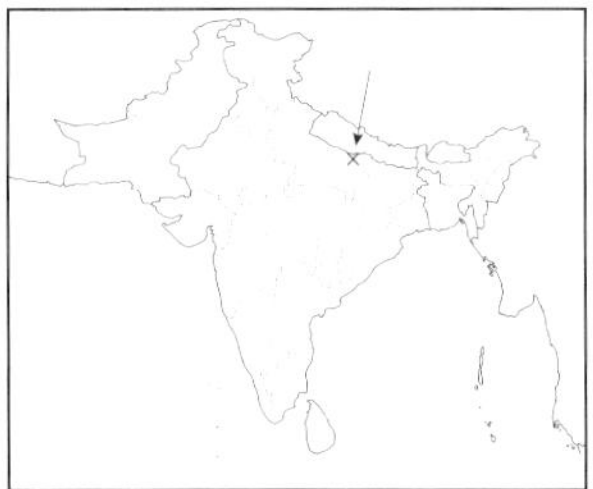

IDENTIFICATION 16 cm. Much as Bluethroat (p.647) in shape and behaviour, although has longer tail. **Adult** distinguished from other 'chats' by combination of uniform greyish olive-brown upperparts, greyish-white underparts with whiter throat, rufous uppertail-coverts and tail (lacking darker central rectrices), and pale fringes to wing-coverts and remiges. Has fairly prominent supercilium, but lacks dark eye-stripe, malar stripe or moustachial stripe. **First-winter** as adult, but retains juvenile buff tips to tertials and some greater coverts. **VOICE** Calls include a *hweet,* a hard *chack,* and a deep, throaty *crrer.* **HABITS** Skulks low down in bushes or on the ground beneath. Feeds chiefly on the ground. **HABITAT** Bushes; favours damp places. **DISTRIBUTION AND STATUS PK, IN:** vagrant.

SIBERIAN RUBYTHROAT *Luscinia calliope* Plate 104

Rubythroat (I), Eurasian Rubythroat (F), *Erithacus calliope* (F,I,K)

IDENTIFICATION 14 cm. Skulking, with bold upright carriage and tail often erect, as Bluethroat (p.647) and White-tailed Rubythroat (p.647). **Male** has brilliant ruby-red throat and striking white supercilium and moustachial stripe. Told from male White-tailed by absence of broad black breast-band, and by olive-brown (rather

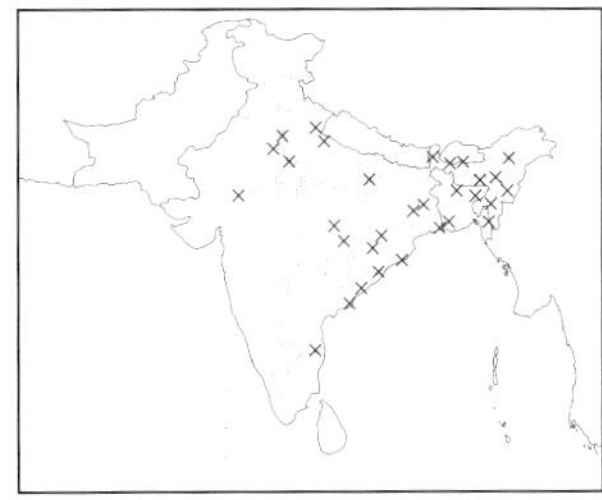

than slate-grey) upperparts and uniform olive-brown tail (lacking white at sides and tip). Breast is olive-brown in fresh plumage, and greyer when worn (in spring). **Female** can show some red or pink on throat, but typically throat is white and has short white supercilium and moustachial stripe and indistinct dark submoustachial stripe. Very similar to female White-tailed Rubythroat, but has olive-brown (rather than grey-brown) upperparts, olive-buff wash (rather than dark grey) to breast and flanks, lacks white tip to tail, and has pale brown or pinkish legs. Uniform olive-brown tail and lack of banding across breast readily separate this species from Bluethroat. **First-winter** as adult (i.e. male has red throat), with retained juvenile buff tips to greater coverts and tertials. **VOICE** Calls include a loud, clear double whistle, *ee-uh*, and a hard *schak* (Alström and Colston 1991). The song is a long, pleasant scratchy warble, often given during spring migration. In alarm, gives a deep quiet *chuck* (P. Morris). **HABITS** Shy, and skulks in cover. Feeds on the ground or low down in bushes and undergrowth. Wings are often drooped, and when alert the tail is fanned or cocked, and sometimes flicked over the back. Moves on the ground by hops and fast short runs. **HABITAT** Bushes and thick undergrowth, long grass and reeds; often near water, sometimes along roadsides and the edges of cultivation; favours damp ravines in the Himalayas. **DISTRIBUTION AND STATUS** Winter visitor and passage migrant. From S Rajasthan and Punjab east to Manipur and south to Andhra Pradesh. **NP:** winter visitor and passage migrant; frequent below 1370 m. **IN:** locally fairly common in the north in the plains and foothills (–4500 m on passage). **BT:** rare. **BD:** uncommon. **REFERENCES** Alström and Colston (1991).

WHITE-TAILED RUBYTHROAT *Luscinia pectoralis* **Plate 104**

Himalayan Rubythroat (F,I), *Erithacus pectoralis* (F,I,K)

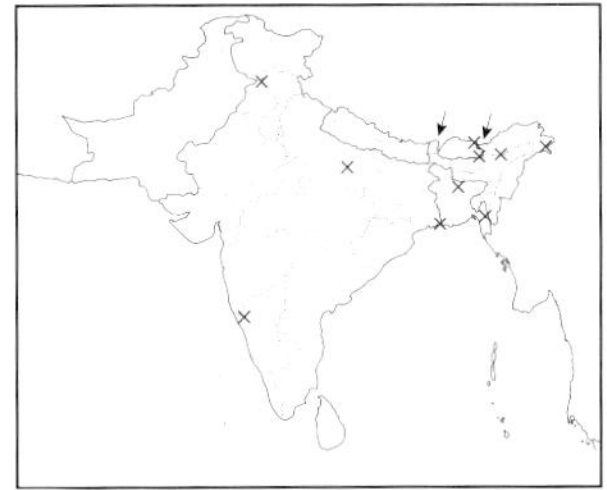

IDENTIFICATION 14 cm. Skulking, with bold upright carriage and long tail which is typically held upright. **Male** has brilliant scarlet throat, and striking white supercilium contrasting with blackish ear-coverts. Told from male Siberian Rubythroat (p.646) by broad black breast-band, slate-grey upperparts, and blackish tail with white at sides and tip. In fresh plumage, black feathers of breast are fringed with white. Some first-summer males have female-like (i.e. browner) upperparts. **Female** has white throat and short white supercilium. Very similar to female Siberian Rubythroat, but has grey-brown (rather than olive-brown) upperparts, grey breast and flanks contrasting with white belly, white tip to tail, and black legs. Lack of rufous on tail and absence of multiple banding across breast readily separate this species from Bluethroat (below). **First-winter** as adult female, with retained juvenile buff tips to greater coverts and tertials. Male has white sides to tail, and usually acquires scarlet throat and black breast by first summer. **Juvenile** has dark brown upperparts and coverts with bold fulvous streaking, and fulvous breast and flanks with black scaling; male has white at base of tail (as adult male). **Racial variation** Male *L. p. tschebaiewi* differs from other two races occurring in the subcontinent in having a broad white moustachial stripe; female of this race shows indistinct white moustachial and dark submoustachial stripe. **VOICE** Song is a long, complicated series of rising and falling warbling trills and twitters (although can be uttered in short bursts); call is a harsh *ke* (Ali and Ripley 1987; Roberts 1992). **HABITS** Similar to those of Siberian Rubythroat, but often conspicuous in the breeding season, when males regularly sing from the top of a large boulder or bush. **HABITAT** Breeds in dwarf rhododendron and juniper scrub and *Caragana* scrub interspersed with scree and boulder-strewn grassy slopes above the treeline; winters in the lowlands in dense bushes, hedges and thickets and tall grass in marshes. **BREEDING** End May–August. Usually builds a domed nest, well hidden and close to or on the ground in scrub, among rocks or grass tufts. **DISTRIBUTION AND STATUS** Altitudinal migrant. Breeds in Himalayas from N Pakistan east to Arunachal Pradesh; winters mainly in Himalayan foothills and NE India. **PK:** locally fairly common; breeds in moister regions of Chitral, Gilgit, Hazara district and Baltistan, 2700–4500 m (–2600 m); some winter in adjoining valleys. **NP:** frequent resident, breeds 3300–4800 m, winters 275–1340 m; also a rare passage migrant and winter visitor. **IN:** locally fairly common; summers 2700–4800 m, winters in the foothills. **BT:** rare. **BD:** vagrant. **REFERENCES** Kaul *et al.* (1995), Pfister (1997), Robson (1996b).

BLUETHROAT *Luscinia svecica* **Plate 104**

***Erithacus svecicus* (F,I,K,P)**

IDENTIFICATION 15 cm. In all plumages, has white supercilium and shows rufous sides to dark tail, which is especially prominent in flight. Like the rubythroats, usually skulking, although moves boldly with tail typically held cocked. **Male** has multicoloured throat and breast. In breeding plumage, throat is glistening blue and breast is variably patterned with blue, black, red and white; central breast 'star' can be red, white or both. In non-breeding plumage (autumn and winter), throat is whitish and patterning of breast is duller and obscured by whitish fringes. **Female** is less brightly coloured than male on throat and breast; main features are black submoustachial stripe, patchy black band across breast (usually mixed with blue), and a poorly defined rufous band below this. **First-winter** is similar to adult non-breeding, but has retained juvenile buff tips to greater coverts and tertials; female lacks blue on breast, which also shows very little rufous. **Juvenile** has dark brown upperparts and breast

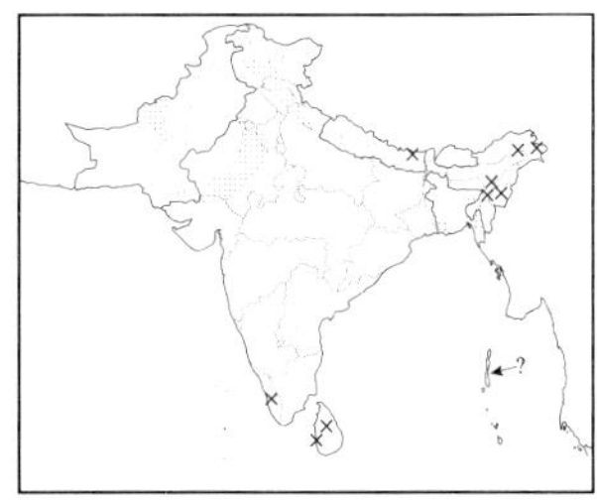

with bold fulvous streaking, and fulvous tips to wing-coverts; tail has rufous sides (as adult). **VOICE** Song is long and varied, with characteristic accelerating bell-like notes, such as *tree tree tree tree* or *ting ting ting*; call is a deep *chack* or *chack-chack* (Jonsson 1992). **HABITS** Secretive. Forages on the ground, often under thick cover, sometimes in the open. Moves by long hops and fast running spurts, keeping a bold upright posture. Often cocks and fans the tail and flashes the rufous basal patches. Flies close to the ground and soon dives into cover. **HABITAT** Summers in scrub along banks of streams and lakes; winters in scrub and tall grass, often near water, reedbeds, crops, bushes at the edges of cultivation and in damp ravines, and saltmarshes. **BREEDING** May–August. Builds a cup-shaped nest, well hidden in a grass clump, in a hollow on the ground or at the base of a bush. **DISTRIBUTION AND STATUS** Summer visitor to Baltistan, Pakistan, Ladakh, N Kashmir and Spiti, Himachal Pradesh; winters throughout much of the subcontinent, except parts of the northwest, northeast, Himalayas, S India and Sri Lanka. **PK:** frequent and widespread winter visitor throughout the Indus plains from N Punjab to Karachi; common on passage in Baluchistan and NW Pakistan; small numbers breed in Baltistan, around 3000 m. **NP:** fairly common and widespread winter visitor and passage migrant; below 1370 m (–3445 m on passage). **IN:** locally common summer visitor, 2600–3800 m; locally common and widespread in winter in plains and foothills. **BT:** rare passage migrant, 4060–4570 m; possibly also a winter visitor. **BD:** locally common passage migrant. **LK:** vagrant.

FIRETHROAT *Luscinia pectardens* — Plate 104

Erithacus pectardens **(I,K)**

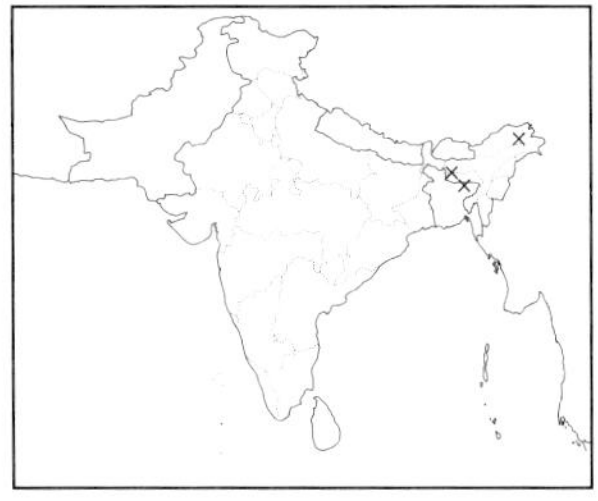

IDENTIFICATION 15 cm. In profile and behaviour is much like Indian and Siberian Blue Robins (below and p.649); very skulking, with short tail, and rather horizontal stance. **Male breeding** is striking, with slaty-blue upperparts, black forehead and face, white patch on side of neck, flame-orange throat and breast bordered at sides with black, white belly with buff wash, and white sides to base of blackish tail. **Male non-breeding** has upperparts and tail as breeding male, but underparts are similar to female's. **First-winter male** has olive-brown upperparts, with slaty-blue back and wing-coverts; tail is as adult male, and underparts as adult female. **Female** has olive-brown upperparts, with a rufous cast to uppertail-coverts, and buffish underparts; tail is brown. Very similar to female Indian Blue Robin, and possibly told by orange-buff vent and undertail-coverts and darker legs and feet. **VOICE** Call is like that of Orange-flanked Bush Robin (p.649) (Ali and Ripley 1987). Masterful, lengthy song, reminiscent of that of Bluethroat or *Acrocephalus* warbler, is loud, sweet, varied and highly mimetic: each note is often repeated two to four times, with sweet musical notes interspersed with harsher, more discordant ones, each separated by distinct pause (P. Holt from D. Farrow recording). **HABITS** Skulks in dense thickets. **HABITAT** Dense bushes and dense woodland. **DISTRIBUTION AND STATUS IN:** single records from Arunachal Pradesh and Meghalaya; possibly a rare and local winter visitor. **BD:** vagrant. **REFERENCES** Goodwin (1956).

INDIAN BLUE ROBIN *Luscinia brunnea* — Plate 104

Blue Chat (F,I,P), ***Erithacus brunneus*** **(F,I,K,P)**

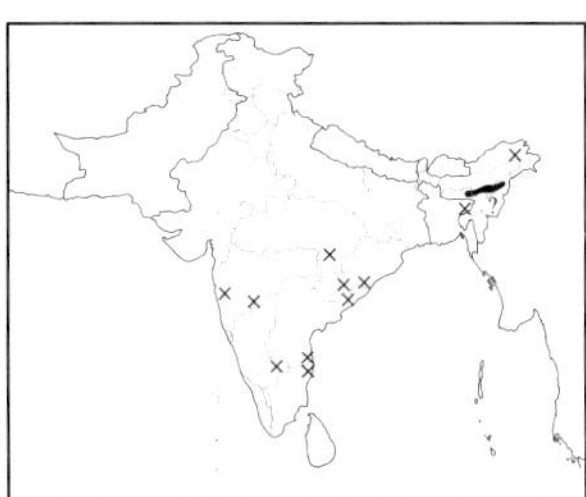

IDENTIFICATION 15 cm. Carriage and profile, with short tail and horizontal stance, differ from those of the bush robins; has long pale legs and large feet, and frequently bobs and fans tail. **Male** has slaty-blue upperparts, white supercilium, and rufous-orange underparts. Told from male White-browed Bush Robin (p.650), in addition to features noted above, by shorter and broader white supercilium (not extending beyond ear-coverts), (usually) black ear-coverts, and whitish centre to belly and vent. **Female** has olive-brown upperparts, and orange-buff to brownish-buff underparts with striking white throat, belly and vent. Distinguished from female White-browed Bush Robin by absence of buffish-white supercilium, and differences in carriage and profile mentioned above. For differences from female Siberian Blue Robin (p.650) and Firethroat (above), see those species. **First-winter male** varies: some are as adult male, but have retained juvenile rufous-buff tips to greater coverts and brown remiges; others are more different from adult male, having buffish supercilium, duller blue upperparts mixed with olive-brown, and duller orange breast and flanks. **Juvenile** is mainly brown, streaked with fulvous. Juvenile male has blue tail. **VOICE** Song is short and stereotyped, comprising three or four piercing whistles, immediately followed by a rapid, tumbling *tit-tit-titwit-tichu-tichu-chuchu-cheeeh*; alarm call is a hard *tek-tek-tek* (Roberts 1992). **HABITS** Secretive. Found on or close to the ground within bushes or thickets, often turning over leaves or hopping about lower branches. Even in the breeding season the male prefers to keep out of sight, usually singing from the middle of a bush. Often moves the tail up and down. **HABITAT** Summers in dense undergrowth in moist oak, mixed deciduous or coniferous forest or in forest clearings; winters in evergreen forest, and tea and coffee plantations. **BREEDING** May–July. Builds a cup-shaped nest, usually well hidden on a bank, between roots, among stones or under an overhang. **DISTRIBUTION AND STATUS** Resident. Breeds in Himalayas from N Pakistan east to Arunachal Pradesh, and NE Indian hills; winters in Sri Lanka, hills of NE and SW India, and occasionally in E Himalayan foothills. **PK:** local summer visitor; locally common in Himalayas. **NP:** fairly common and widespread summer visitor, breeds 2135–3445 m, mainly 2440–3355 m; two winter records, from foothills and at 3505 m. **IN:** locally common in summer, breeds 1600–3300 m; locally fairly common in winter, 610–1525 m and probably higher. **BT:** fairly common summer visitor. **BD:** vagrant. **LK:** widespread winter visitor, more frequent in wet lowlands and hills.

SIBERIAN BLUE ROBIN *Luscinia cyane* — Plate 104

Siberian Blue Chat (I), ***Erithacus cyane*** **(I,K)**

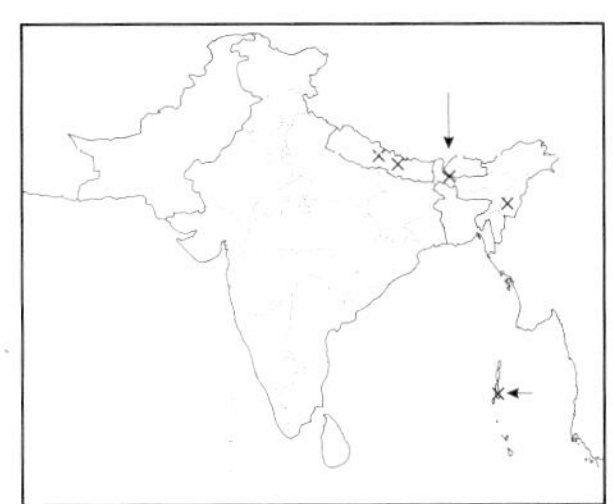

IDENTIFICATION 15 cm. Short tail, which is constantly quivered, horizontal stance, with much bobbing when alarmed, and long pink legs and large pink feet are similar to those of Indian Blue Robin (p.648) and help differentiate Siberian Blue from the bush robins and rubythroats. **Male** is striking, with dark blue upperparts, black sides to throat and breast, and brilliant white underparts. **Female** has olive-brown upperparts and pale buff throat and breast, latter faintly scaled with darker brown (on some, appearing as narrow breast-band), and usually shows blue on rump; on some, tail is also blue. Similar to female Indian Blue Robin, but that species has orange-buff across breast and on flanks. See Firethroat (p.648) for differences from female of that species. **First-winter** male is similar to female, but usually has variable amounts of blue on scapulars and mantle (although some look like blue-tailed females); first-winter female is as adult female, but more often lacks blue on uppertail-coverts and tail; both have retained juvenile buff tips to greater coverts and tertials. **VOICE** Call is a quiet, hard *tuck* and a loud *se-ic* (Boonsong and Round 1991). **HABITS** Shy and skulking. Forages under dense vegetation; runs and hops about on the ground with frequent pauses, rarely leaving cover. **HABITAT** Dense bushes. **DISTRIBUTION AND STATUS NP, IN:** vagrant. **REFERENCES** Alström and Colston (1991).

ORANGE-FLANKED BUSH ROBIN *Tarsiger cyanurus* — Plate 105

Red-flanked Bluetail, ***Erithacus cyanurus*** **(F,I)**

IDENTIFICATION 14 cm. Shows white throat, bright orange flash on flanks, and blue uppertail-coverts and tail. Combination of longish tail, redstart-like stance and behaviour, and fine dark legs and feet helps differentiate it from the blue robins and rubythroats. For differences from Rufous-breasted Bush Robin (p.650), see that species. **Male** has bright blue upperparts and breast sides, white throat, centre of breast and belly, and orange flanks. **Female** has olive-brown upperparts, sides of head and breast-band, well-defined white throat patch, orange flanks, and bright blue uppertail-coverts and tail. **First-winter** is as female, but may show juvenile buff tips to greater coverts and tertials. First-summer male also resembles female, and often breeds in this plumage. **Juvenile** has blue uppertail-coverts and tail; upperparts are brown, spotted with buff, and underparts are scaled with brown. **VOICE** Call is a deep croaking *tock-tock*; song is rather soft and weak, short and stereotyped, *churrrh-chee* or *dirrh-tu-tu-dirrrh* (Roberts 1992). **HABITS** Mainly frequents bushes; also found high up in trees. Feeds by dropping to the ground from a perch to pick up prey, by making swooping fly-catching sallies, by searching foliage for insects, by hopping about on the ground, and sometimes by clinging to tree trunks. Male often sings in the open from the top of a bush or branch in the middle storey of forest. Like other bush robins, continually flicks wings and fans tail and has a fairly upright stance. **HABITAT** Forest understorey and dense bushes in forest clearings. **BREEDING** April–July. Builds a cup-shaped nest, well concealed on a bank, in a hollow, under a log or among tree roots. **DISTRIBUTION AND STATUS** Altitudinal migrant. Breeds in Himalayas from N Pakistan east to Arunachal Pradesh; winters in Himalayas and south to the NE Indian hills. **PK:** locally common; breeds up to the treeline, 2400–3400 m; winters chiefly in the foothills and lower valleys, down to 610 m. **NP:** common and widespread; summers mainly 3000–4000 m, winters 1370–2745 m. **IN:** locally common; breeds 2700–4400 m, winters 150–3000 m. **BT:** common from 4120 m down to at least 1450 m.

GOLDEN BUSH ROBIN *Tarsiger chrysaeus* — Plate 105

Erithacus chrysaeus **(F,I)**

IDENTIFICATION 15 cm. Orange to orange-buff underparts and orange sides to dark tail readily separate this from other bush robins. Has pale legs and bill (with contrasting black ridge to culmen). **Male** has blackish mask, orange supercilium and underparts, orange scapular line, rump and sides to black tail, and burnt-umber crown and mantle. **Female** has duller buffish-orange supercilium and underparts, uniform golden-olive upperparts, and pale orange uppertail-coverts and sides to olive-brown tail; supercilium is less distinct than male's and curves down behind olive ear-coverts. **Juvenile** has tail as respective adult; upperparts are brown, streaked with

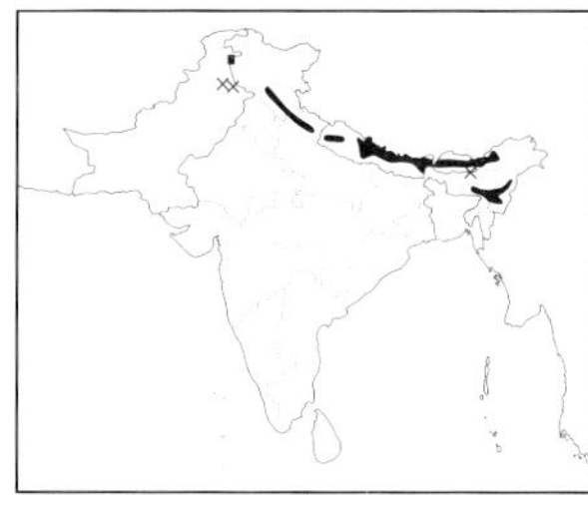

golden-buff, and underparts are boldly spotted with golden-buff. **VOICE** Call is a purring croak, *trr-trr*; also a harder *tcheck-tcheck*. Song is a high, wispy *tze-du-tee-tse*, ending in a lower *chur-r-r-r* (Fleming *et al.* 1984). **HABITS** Very skulking in winter, when it usually keeps hidden in bushes; easier to see in its more open breeding grounds of dwarf scrub and scree. Feeds on the ground, in low bushes, and by making short aerial sallies. **HABITAT** Summers in dwarf rhododendron, juniper and birch near the treeline, in clearings and edges of coniferous forest, on rocky slopes with sparse scrub or scattered dense bushes; also in dense rhododendrons in open conifer forest in Arunachal Pradesh. Winters in thick undergrowth in forest and in dense secondary scrub. **BREEDING** April–July. Builds a cup-shaped nest, well hidden on a bank, under tree roots or under a stone. **DISTRIBUTION AND STATUS** Altitudinal migrant. Himalayas from N Pakistan east to Arunachal Pradesh; NE India hills. **PK:** very rare and local; found breeding at 3350 m in the Kagan valley, and in winter in the Margalla hills. **NP:** frequent, locally fairly common; summers mainly 3500–4200 m, winters 1700–2800 m. **IN:** locally fairly common; breeds 3000–3600 m in the west, 3000–4600 m in the east; winters mainly 1400–2000 m, occasionally up to 3000 m, rarely down to the foothills. **BT:** common; 610–4265 m.

WHITE-BROWED BUSH ROBIN *Tarsiger indicus* Plate 105

***Erithacus indicus* (F,I)**

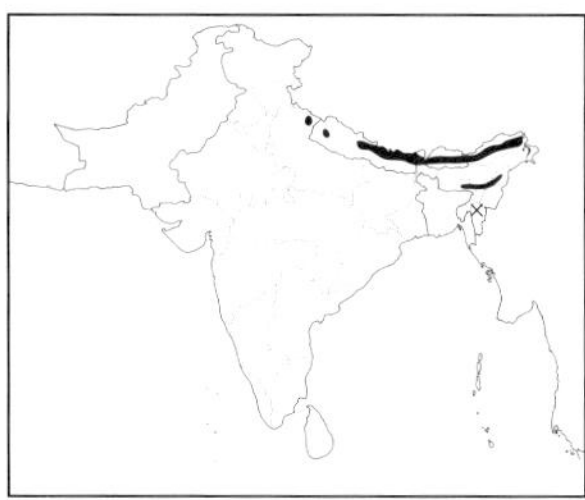

IDENTIFICATION 15 cm. Superficially resembles Indian Blue Robin (p.648). Carriage and profile, however, are very different, with longer tail, more upright stance, and rounded head. Has dark legs and feet. Cocks tail with rapid jerks. **Male** has slaty-blue upperparts, white supercilium, and rufous-orange underparts. Distinguished from male Indian Blue Robin, in addition to above-mentioned features, by longer and finer white supercilium (extending beyond, and curving down behind, ear-coverts), slate-blue (rather than black) ear-coverts which are concolorous with nape, and entirely rufous-orange belly and vent. Some males show white moustachial stripe. **Female** has dark olive-brown upperparts and dirty orange-buff underparts. Told from female Indian Blue Robin by carriage and behaviour, long (sometimes partly concealed) buffish-white supercilium which curves down behind eye, and orange-buff throat which is concolorous with underparts. **First-summer male** can breed in female-like plumage. **Juvenile** has brown upperparts streaked with orange-buff, and orange-buff underparts are boldly scaled with brown; has indistinct supercilium. **VOICE** Call is a repeated *trrrrr*; song is a bubbling, double-phrased *shri-de-de-dew.......shri-de-de-dew* (Fleming *et al.* 1984). **HABITS** Feeds mainly on the ground under dense bushes; also by searching foliage, and by sallying after flying insects before diving back into cover. **HABITAT** Summers mainly in subalpine forest of fir, birch, rhododendron and juniper with dense undergrowth, and favours bamboo; in the Khasi Hills, found in steep ravines running through open pine, oak and rhododendron forest. Winters in damp places in the understorey of dense forest. **BREEDING** April–July, varying locally. Builds a cup-shaped nest in the hollow of a bank. **DISTRIBUTION AND STATUS** Resident and altitudinal migrant. Himalayas from N Uttar Pradesh east to Arunachal Pradesh; NE Indian hills. **NP:** frequent in the centre and east, very uncommon in the west; summers 3000–4000 m, winters 2100–3050 m (down to 915 m). **IN:** generally uncommon; breeds 3000–4200 m, winters mainly 2000–3000 m, uncommonly in the foothills. **BT:** common; from 1700 m up to at least 3750 m. **REFERENCES** Kaul *et al.* (1995).

RUFOUS-BREASTED BUSH ROBIN *Tarsiger hyperythrus* Plate 105

Rufous-bellied Bush Robin (F,I), *Erithacus hyperythrus* (F,I)

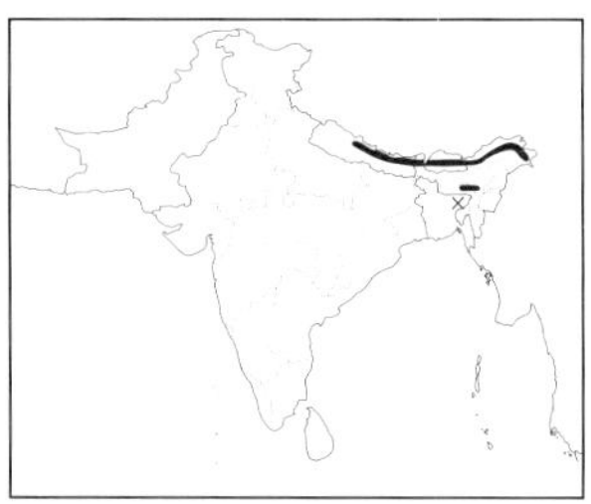

IDENTIFICATION 15 cm. In carriage and profile resembles Orange-flanked Bush Robin (p.649), with comparatively long tail, redstart-like stance and behaviour, and fine dark legs. Long legs help separate it from blue flycatchers. **Male** has blue upperparts, with glistening blue supercilium, 'shoulders' (lesser coverts) and uppertail-coverts, and rufous-orange throat, breast and belly; blackish of ear-coverts and sides of throat is sharply cut off at rear from orange of breast sides. Absence of white supercilium readily separates it from Indian Blue Robin (p.648) and White-browed Bush Robin (above). **Female** superficially resembles Orange-flanked Bush Robin, with (darker) olive-brown upperparts and bright blue uppertail-coverts and tail; has orange-buff throat, and browner breast and flanks (lacking clearly demarcated white throat and orange flank patch of female Orange-flanked). **Juvenile** has blue uppertail-coverts and tail; upperparts are brown with buffish streaks, and underparts are orange-buff, scaled with brown. Finely streaked scapulars and ultramarine (rather than cerulean) uppertail-coverts and tail are best distinctions from juvenile Orange-flanked. **VOICE** Call is a *duk-duk-duk-squeak*; song is a lisping warble, *zeew..zee.. zwee..zwee* (Fleming *et al.* 1984). **HABITS** Similar to Orange-flanked Bush Robin in most respects. Mostly frequents the lower forest storey. Not shy; sometimes perches quietly and still in the open for short periods. **HABITAT** Summers in bushes at edges and clearings of dwarf rhododendron and birch forest and in fir–rhododendron forest; winters in moist undergrowth of oak–rhododendron forest; favours the edges of streams. **BREEDING** In C Nepal, seen feeding young in nest in May and young just able to fly in early June. Nest and eggs are undescribed. **DISTRIBUTION AND STATUS** Resident and altitudinal migrant. Himalayas from WC Nepal east to Arunachal Pradesh; winters south to NE Indian hills. **NP:** locally frequent; summers 3200–4200 m, winters 2135–3050 m (down to 1500 m). **IN:** locally frequent; breeds 3400–3800 m, winters 150–3500 m. **BT:** frequent. **BD:** vagrant.

RUFOUS-TAILED SCRUB ROBIN *Cercotrichas galactotes* Plate 104

Rufous Chat (I), Rufous-tailed Bush Chat (R), Rufous Bush Robin (P), *Erythropygia galactotes* (I,P)

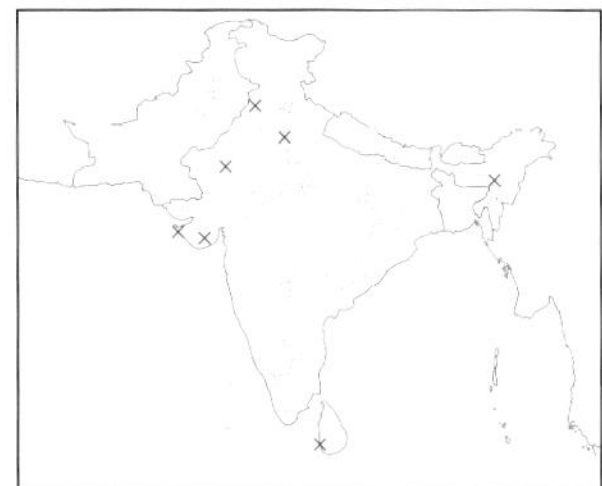

IDENTIFICATION 15 cm. In carriage and profile resembles Common Nightingale (p.646), but with longer, fan-shaped tail. Has bright rufous rump and tail, the latter frequently held acutely cocked. Outer rectrices are tipped with white and subterminally marked with black. Flight action resembles that of a large warbler rather than a chat. **Adult** has creamy-white supercilium with black eye-stripe, blackish moustachial line bordering pale area below eye, sandy-grey upperparts with pale fringes to wing-coverts and tertials/secondaries, and creamy-white underparts. **Juvenile** resembles adult, but has faint mottling on throat and breast. **VOICE** Call is a hard *teck teck* or *chack chack*; song is rich and varied, with mixture of loud ringing and pulsing notes and murmuring phrases (Cramp 1988). **HABITS** Fairly tame. Feeds in the open by hopping along in short spurts; also forages in low bushes. Has a distinctive habit of cocking the tail right over the back; also bobs head and turns body. Droops and flicks wings and fans and jerks tail. Males sing from exposed perches, such as the top of a bush. **HABITAT** Dry scrub jungle, areas with scattered tamarisks, *Saccharum*, cane grass and thorny bushes; in Pakistan, breeds in scrub-dotted run-off channels and dry stream beds. **BREEDING** April–July. Builds an untidy nest, well hidden in dense thickets, within 1.5 m of the ground. **DISTRIBUTION AND STATUS** Mainly a southward passage migrant through Pakistan (lower Sind and Punjab Salt Range) and NW India (Gujarat, Rajasthan, Punjab and Delhi); breeds in Pakistan (W Baluchistan and NW Pakistan). **PK:** scarce; passage migrant in September, and local breeder. **IN:** uncommon passage migrant. **LK:** vagrant.

ORIENTAL MAGPIE ROBIN *Copsychus saularis* Plate 105

Magpie Robin (I,K,P,R), Asian Magpie Robin (N), Robin Dayal (F)

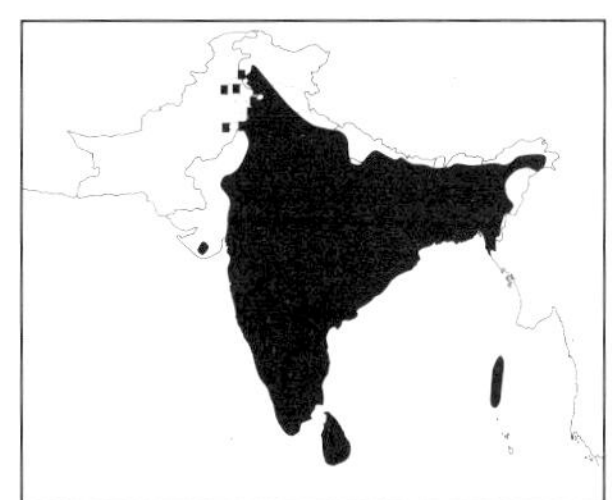

IDENTIFICATION 23 cm. Blackish or slate-grey and white, and with long, frequently cocked tail with white at sides. **Male** has glossy blue-black upperparts, head and breast, white rest of underparts, and white patch on wing. **Female** is similarly patterned, but head, breast and mantle are bluish slate-grey. **Juvenile** resembles adult female, but has indistinct orange-buff spotting on upperparts, rufous-orange tips to wing-coverts and edges to remiges, and orange-buff wash and diffuse dark scaling on throat and breast. **Racial variation** In Sri Lanka, female *C. s. ceylonensis* has darker, glossy blue upperparts. In Andamans, female *C. s. andamanensis* also has slight gloss to upperparts and has underparts sullied with rufous. **VOICE** Call is a plaintive *swee-ee* or *swee-swee*; alarm is a harsh *chr-r*; song is a spirited, clear and varied whistling, divided into short, repetitive phrases; subsong is an endless, quiet and intricate tune, interrupted by loud bursts of *chee-which-which... chee-chee-witch-chee-chi* (Ali and Ripley 1987). **HABITS** Confiding and conspicuous. Partly crepuscular. Forages chiefly on the ground in the open; hops about on lawns and around habitation in sheltered areas, often under trees. Frequently perches on buildings and quite high in trees. Tail is usually held cocked and is frequently lowered and fanned, then closed and jerked up, while wings are often drooped and flicked. Has an undulating flight, showing the white outer tail feathers. **HABITAT** Mainly gardens and groves in villages and towns; also in open dry broadleaved forest and secondary growth. **BREEDING** February–September, varying locally. Builds an untidy nest in a hole in a bank, wall or tree, or under eaves, or in a nestbox, usually 1–10 m above ground. **DISTRIBUTION AND STATUS** Resident, subject to some local movements. Throughout the subcontinent, except most of the northwest and parts of the northeast and Himalayas. **PK:** very local and scarce; partly resident. **NP:** common and widespread resident below 1525 m, frequent up to 2000 m (–3050 m in summer). **IN:** locally common and widespread in plains and hills and up to 2000 m in Himalayas; mainly a summer visitor above 1500 m. **BT:** fairly common; 245–1980 m. **BD:** common throughout. **LK:** common throughout.

WHITE-RUMPED SHAMA *Copsychus malabaricus* Plate 105

Shama (F,I)

IDENTIFICATION 22 cm. Has white rump and uppertail-coverts, and extremely long, graduated tail which has white at sides and is frequently cocked. **Male** has glossy blue-black head, breast, mantle and wings, and rest of

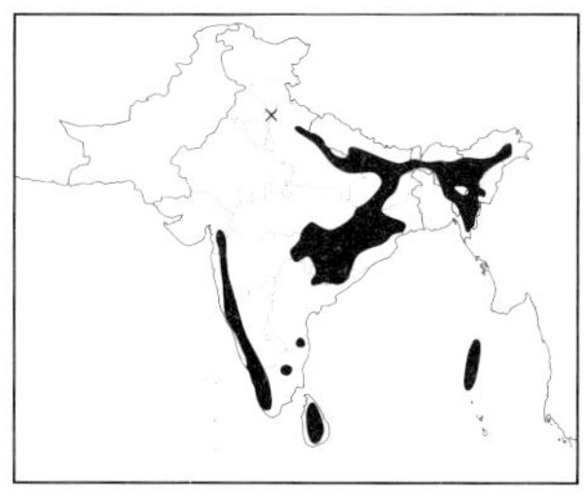

underparts are rufous-orange. **Female** is similarly patterned, but has shorter, squarer tail, and has black of plumage replaced by brownish-grey and underparts duller and paler orange. **Juvenile** resembles adult female, but has orange-buff spotting on dark brown head and mantle, orange-buff throat and breast with fine blackish scaling, orange-buff tips to wing-coverts and tertials, and creamy-white belly. **Racial variation** Female *C. m. leggei* of Sri Lanka is similar to male, with blue-black head, breast and mantle. Male *C. m. albiventris* of the Andamans has white rather than rufous belly; female of this race is similar to male, but with less gloss on throat and upperparts. **VOICE** Call is a musical *chir-chur* and *chur-chi-churr*; alarm is a harsh scolding; song comprises spasmodic, rich melodious phrases, *oi-o-lee-nou* (Ali and Ripley 1987). **HABITS** Keeps close to the ground in forest undergrowth and in low trees; heard more often than seen. **HABITAT** Undergrowth in broadleaved forest; favours bamboo. **BREEDING** January–September, varying locally. Nest is a pad of rootlets and leaves built in a tree hollow or bamboo clump, usually within 2 m of ground. **DISTRIBUTION AND STATUS** Resident. Himalayan foothills from N Uttar Pradesh east to Arunachal Pradesh; NE India and Bangladesh, and south to E Madhya Pradesh and Eastern Ghats; W India from the Surat Dangs, Gujarat, south to S Kerala; also Tamil Nadu, Andhra Pradesh and Sri Lanka. **NP:** locally fairly common throughout; below 365 m. **IN:** local and frequent; up to 700 m in the peninsula. **BT:** frequent; 245–650 m. **BD:** locally common. **LK:** common in lowlands and up to middle altitudes in the dry zone, rare in the wet zone.

INDIAN ROBIN *Saxicoloides fulicata* — Plate 105

Black Robin (P), Indian Chat (H)

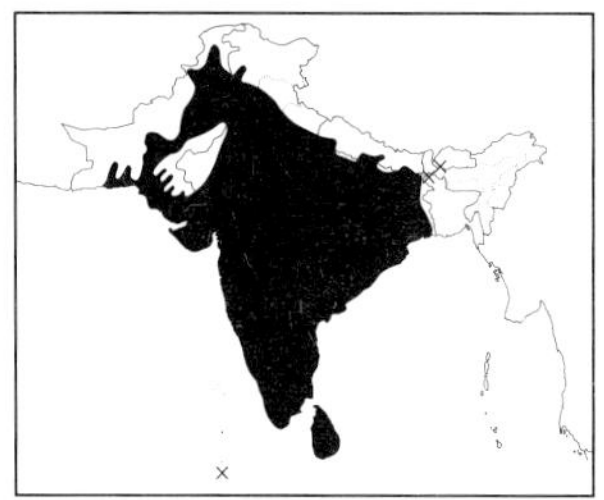

IDENTIFICATION 19 cm. Graduated black tail, which is frequently held cocked, and reddish vent and undertail-coverts are apparent in all plumages. **Adult male** has glossy black underparts and white shoulder patch. **Adult female** has greyish-brown upperparts and purer grey underparts, and lacks white shoulder patch; wings are uniform grey-brown, and has rather plain head. **Juvenile** is similar to female, but is darker brown; lacks spotting and scaling which is typical of juvenile chats, but throat is lightly mottled. **Racial variation** *S. f. cambaiensis* and *S. f. erythrura* of N subcontinent have brown upperparts, whereas *S. f. leucoptera* and *S. f. fulicata* of Sri Lanka and S India, respectively, have glossy blue-black upperparts which are concolorous with underparts (becoming browner with wear), while *S. f. intermedia* of C India has black upperparts washed with dark brown. **VOICE** Song is a very short, high-pitched warble of four to five whistles which glide into each other; the warning call is a clear two-toned whistle *pi-peear* (Roberts 1992). **HABITS** Often tame around villages. Bold, sprightly and terrestrial. Hops and runs about over open stony ground, sometimes perching low down in bushes or on top of stones. Frequently flips the tail and has a habit of holding it vertically over the back, or even farther forward almost to touch the head. **HABITAT** Dry, stony areas with sparse scrub, arid stony ridges, low rocky hill outcrops, edges of cultivation and deserted buildings, and gardens and groves in villages. **BREEDING** December–September, varying locally. Builds a shallow cup-shaped nest in a hole in a wall, earth bank or tree, under a boulder or in a rock crevice. **DISTRIBUTION AND STATUS** Resident, endemic to the subcontinent. Occurs throughout, except the northeast, the Himalayas and parts of the northwest. **PK:** common, widespread and sedentary; mainly in the plains, locally up to 900 m. **NP:** local, uncommon in the west, rare in the centre and east; below 760 m. **IN:** locally common and widespread; in plains and hills up to 1000 m, locally to 1500 m in Himalayas, to 900 m and locally to 1800 m in peninsular hills. **BT:** rare. **BD:** ?former resident in the northwest; no recent records, but could still occur. **LK:** resident in lowlands and medium-level hills, more frequent in dry zone. **MV:** vagrant.

RUFOUS-BACKED REDSTART *Phoenicurus erythronota* — Plate 106

Eversmann's Redstart (F,I,R)

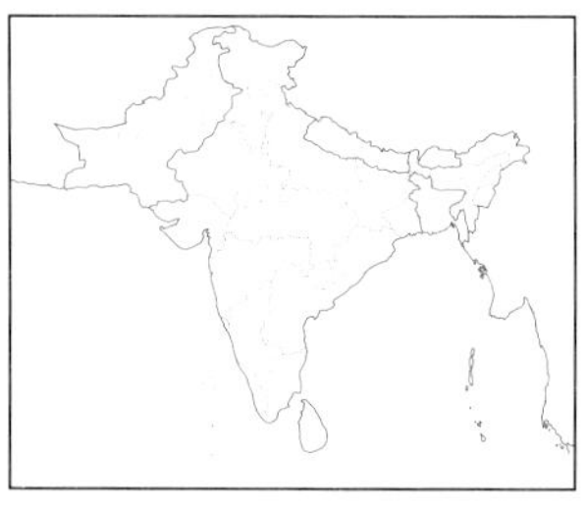

IDENTIFICATION 16 cm. Larger than other redstarts except White-winged (p.655). Can appear rather shrike-like, tail can be held slightly cocked, and flicks tail and droops wings in a flycatcher-like manner. **Adult male (worn)** has blackish ear-coverts contrasting with grey crown and nape, rufous-orange mantle with blackish scapulars, blackish wings with white patch on coverts and white primary coverts, and rufous-orange throat, breast and flanks. **Adult male (fresh)** and **first-winter male** are duller owing to extensive pale fringes to body plumage (especially on first-winter); dark mask and grey crown/nape are largely obscured. **Adult female** is pale brown above and buff below. Possibly confusable with female White-winged, but has prominent buff greater- and median-covert wing-bars, broad buff fringes to tertials, and darker brown centre to tail. Larger size and above plumage features separate it from female Black Redstart (p.653). **VOICE** Call is a soft croaking *gre-er* (Cramp 1988). **HABITS** Flicks tail vigorously upwards, but does not vibrate it like most other redstarts. Frequently perches on rocks and bushes; has an erect posture. Feeds mainly by picking insects from the ground or by flying on to prey from a low perch. **HABITAT** Dry country: hills, ravines and valleys with scattered bushes, scrub forest, olive groves, stone walls and hedges bordering fields. **DISTRIBUTION AND STATUS** Winter visitor to Pakistan and W Himalayas from N Pakistan east to WC Nepal. **PK:** locally frequent; mainly in hills and valleys, from 2400 m down to plains. **NP:** locally fairly common in some years in the northwest; 2300–3300 m. **IN:** numbers vary from year to year, generally not common; from base of hills up to 2100 m.

BLUE-CAPPED REDSTART *Phoenicurus coeruleocephalus* Plate 106

Blue-headed Redstart (F,I,R)

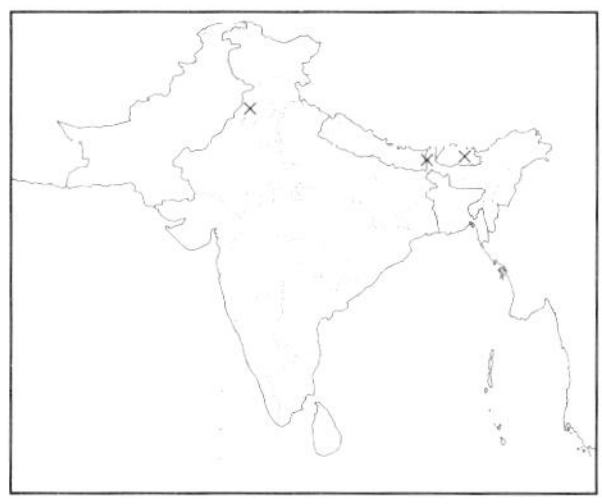

IDENTIFICATION 15 cm. **Adult male (worn)** differs from other redstarts in lacking any rufous in plumage. Has blue-grey crown and nape, black upperparts and tail, blackish wings with white patch on coverts and fringes to tertials, black throat and breast, and white rest of underparts. **Adult male (fresh)** and **first-winter male** have black of plumage duller owing to extensive brown fringes to body plumage, and grey of crown/nape is largely obscured and is brown. **Adult female** superficially resembles other female redstarts, although is duskier on underparts, with whitish belly and undertail-coverts, and has prominent greater- and median-covert wing-bars; dark tail contrasts with chestnut uppertail-coverts and rump. **Juvenile** is similar to adult female, with dark brown barring on upperparts and underparts; juvenile male has broad white edges to tertials. **VOICE** Song consists of pleasant, repetitive warbling phrases, *trrri-trrru-trrri-trrru-trrri-trrru-trruwhit-trruwhit*; call is a rapid *tit-tit-tit* or *tik-tik-tik* (Roberts 1992). **HABITS** Generally frequents bushes and lower branches of trees. Occasionally drops from a perch to pick up prey from the ground, or sometimes sallies after flying insects. Vibrates tail, and when on the ground sometimes raises and lowers it slowly. Flight is slightly undulating. **HABITAT** Summers on rocky slopes in juniper and open forest; winters in open forest and secondary growth. **BREEDING** May–August. Builds a cup-shaped nest in a hollow in the ground or under a stone or fallen tree. **DISTRIBUTION AND STATUS** Resident and altitudinal migrant. Himalayas from N Pakistan east to Bhutan. **PK:** locally common and widespread breeder in inner, drier mountain ranges, 2300–3700 m; winters in outer foothills and inner N valleys. **NP:** fairly common on breeding grounds in the northwest, 2900–3700 m (–4270 m); in non-breeding season, frequent in the west and centre, rare in the east, 1370–2900 m (down to 150 m). **IN:** locally fairly common in the west, rare in the east; breeds 2400–3900 m, winters from foothills up to 3500 m, mainly 1200–2600 m. **BT:** very rare. **REFERENCES** Giri and Choudhary (1997).

BLACK REDSTART *Phoenicurus ochruros* Plate 106

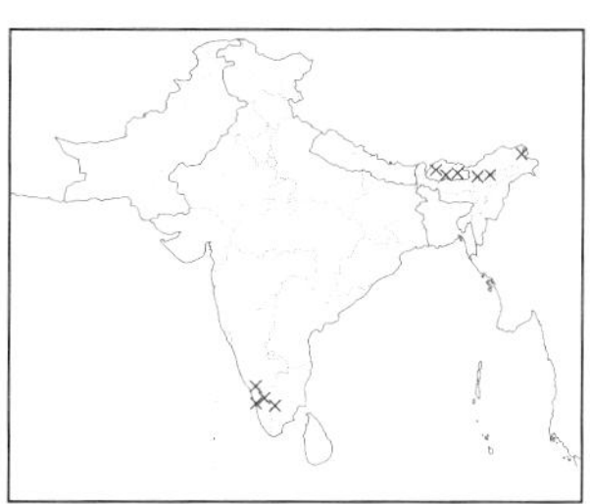

IDENTIFICATION 15 cm. **Adult male (worn)** has largely black or dark grey upperparts with browner wings, black throat and breast, and rufous-orange rest of underparts. Some can show narrow whitish band across forecrown and extending as line to above eye. Likely to be confused only with Hodgson's Redstart (p.654), but is darker above and lacks white patch on wing. **Adult male (fresh)** has black of plumage duller owing to extensive brownish-grey fringes to body plumage. **Adult female** and **first-year male** are almost entirely dusky brown. Distinguished from female Hodgson's by rufous-orange wash on lower flanks and belly. From female Blue-capped Redstart (above) by rufous-orange tail which is concolorous with rump/uppertail-coverts, and by absence of broad buffish-white greater- and median-covert wing-bars. Lack of black terminal band to tail separates it from female Blue-fronted (p.655). **Juvenile** is similar to adult female, but has diffuse dark scaling on upperparts and underparts, and fine buff greater-covert bar. **Racial variation** Male *P. o. phoenicuroides* of W Himalayas has grey crown, nape and lower back in fresh plumage; these areas are much blacker in *P. o. rufiventris* of the C and E Himalayas. **VOICE** Song is a scratchy trill, followed by a short wheezy jingle; calls include a short *tsip*, a scolding *tucc-tucc*, and a rapid rattle, *tititicc* (Cramp 1988). **HABITS** Vibrates its tail like most redstarts, but more frequently than any of the others except Common Redstart (p.654). Has an upright alert stance. Mainly terrestrial; perches on rocks, bushes or other low vantage points and flies to the ground to pick up insects; also hops and runs about on the ground seeking prey. Territorial in winter, as well as in summer. **HABITAT** Breeds in Tibetan steppe habitat in meadows and scree above the treeline, stony ground with *Caragana* scrub, dwarf juniper forest and subalpine scrub; winters in cultivation, gardens, plantations by roadsides and canals, and riverain forest. **BREEDING** May–early August. Builds an untidy nest, hidden under stones on the ground, in a stone wall or in a rock crevice. **DISTRIBUTION AND STATUS** Altitudinal migrant. Breeds in W Pakistan and Himalayas from N Pakistan east to Sikkim; winters in Himalayas and south through much of the subcontinent, except Sri Lanka. **PK:** common; mainly breeds 2750–3900 m (–4250 m); very widespread in winter throughout the Indus plains. **NP:** common in summer in the northwest and frequent in Khumbu, 2560–5200 m (–5700 m); fairly common below 700 m in winter. **IN:** locally common on breeding grounds, 2400–5100 m in the west, 3300–5200 m in the east; winters widely in plains and hills, up to 1700 m in Himalayas. **BT:** uncommon. **BD:** scarce winter visitor throughout.

COMMON REDSTART *Phoenicurus phoenicurus* Plate 106

Redstart (I)

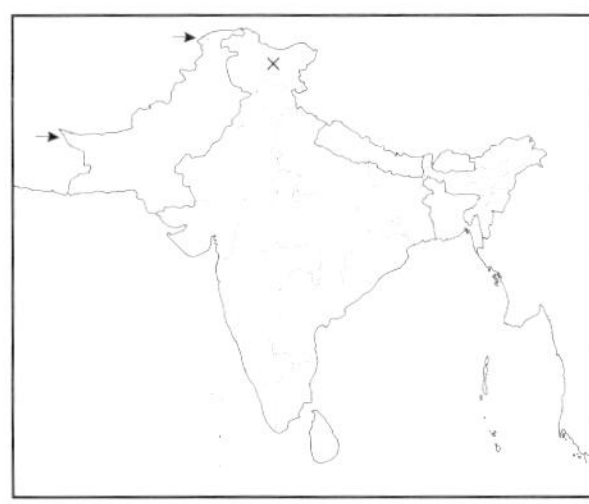

IDENTIFICATION 15 cm. Closely resembles Hodgson's Redstart (below), but unlikely to occur within the winter range of that species. **Adult male (worn)** distinguished from male Black Redstart (p.653) by paler grey crown, nape and mantle, generally more prominent white band across forehead and line to above eye, and rufous-orange (rather than black) breast. From Hodgson's by lack of prominent white patch on wing; black of throat does not extend onto breast. **Adult male (fresh)** and **first-winter male** have black of throat and rufous of breast and flanks partly obscured by white fringes, and grey of upperparts is duller owing to olive-brown fringes. Hodgson's does not have a distinct fresh plumage, and first-winter male of that species is as female. **Adult female** similar to female Black and Hodgson's, but has warmer brown upperparts and buffish underparts, with whiter throat and belly, and variable orange wash to breast and flanks. **VOICE** Calls include a distinctive *hweet* (not uttered by Black Redstart), often followed by a loud *tit-tit.* **HABITS** Posture and manner are similar to those of Black Redstart. Frequents trees and bushes. Forages by gleaning insects from branches and leaves, flying to the ground from a perch to take prey, hopping about on the ground, and in short aerial sallies. **HABITAT** Usually inhabits forest; recorded in the subcontinent in arid areas. **DISTRIBUTION AND STATUS PK:** very local and rare spring passage migrant to W borders. **IN:** vagrant. **REFERENCES** Cramp (1988).

HODGSON'S REDSTART *Phoenicurus hodgsoni* Plate 106

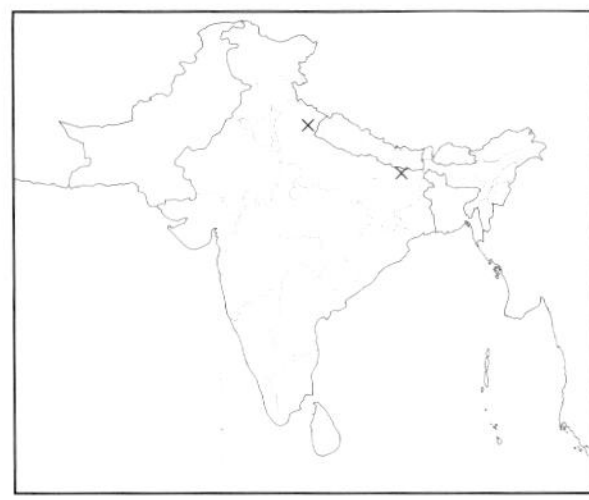

IDENTIFICATION 15 cm. For differences from Common Redstart (above), see that species. **Adult male** told from male Black Redstart (p.653) by uniform pale grey crown, nape and mantle, and white patch on wing. In fresh plumage, has grey fringes to breast and foreneck, but these soon wear off. **Adult female** and **first-year male** are very similar to female Black Redstart, but has whitish area on belly (and lacks rufous-orange wash to lower flanks and belly). Distinguished from female Blue-capped Redstart (p.653) by rufous-orange tail concolorous with rump/uppertail-coverts, and by absence of double wing-bar. Lack of black terminal band to tail separates it from female Blue-fronted (p.655). **VOICE** Calls include a single rattling *prit,* and alarm is a rattling *trr* or *tschrrr* (Ali and Ripley 1987). **HABITS** Stance and movements are typical of the genus (see Black Redstart), but vibrates tail less often. Frequently catches insects by making sallies in the air; also forages by hopping about on the ground in search of prey. **HABITAT** Winters on stony river beds with trees or bushes on the banks; also in open grassy areas, cultivation with scattered bushes, open forest and forest edge. **DISTRIBUTION AND STATUS** Winters in Himalayas from N Uttar Pradesh east to Arunachal Pradesh; NE Indian hills. **NP:** frequent throughout, locally common; mainly 760–2800 m (down to 150 m; to 5030 m on passage). **IN:** locally common; mainly in the plains and foothills, locally up to 2800 m. **BT:** common; 610–3335 m.

WHITE-THROATED REDSTART *Phoenicurus schisticeps* Plate 106

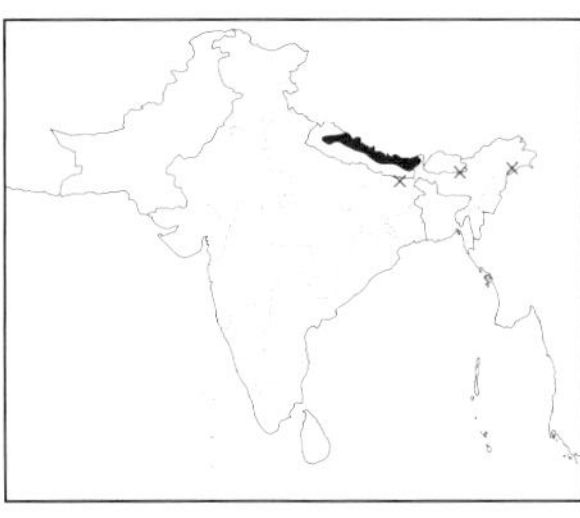

IDENTIFICATION 15 cm. Both sexes are best distinguished by clearly defined white throat patch, white patch on wing-coverts and edges to tertials, and rufous-orange rump, uppertail-coverts and sides to tail-base which contrast with otherwise blackish tail. **Adult male (worn)** has blue crown and nape (with brighter blue forehead), black chin, ear-coverts and mantle, and rufous on scapulars, breast and belly. In fresh plumage, has rufous fringes to head and upperparts and buff fringes to underparts, although these would appear to wear off rather quickly. **Adult female** has grey-brown head and mantle and paler grey-brown breast, becoming more buffish on belly. **Juvenile** is similar to adult female, with distinctive rump/tail and white patch on wing, but has buff spotting and dark scaling on upperparts and underparts. Similar to juvenile male Blue-capped (p.653), but is more boldly marked and has a larger white wing patch. **VOICE** Calls include a drawn-out *zieh,* followed by a rattling note; song is undescribed (Ali and Ripley 1987). **HABITS** Fairly shy, but often perches conspicuously on posts and the tops of bushes. Feeds mainly in bushes; also on the ground. **HABITAT** Summers in open shrubberies on rocky slopes and ridges; also bushes at edges and in clearings of open conifer and birch forest. Winters in meadows and fallow cultivation and on rocky, bush-covered slopes. **BREEDING** Poorly known in the region. Young found in June and July in Nepal. In Tibet, builds a cup-shaped nest in a tree hollow or stream bank within 2 m of the ground. **DISTRIBUTION AND STATUS** Resident, subject to some altitudinal movements, and winter visitor. Mainly Himalayas from W Nepal east to Bhutan. **NP:** frequent; 3050–4400 m in summer, 2500 m up to at least 3150 m in winter (2200–3965 m). **IN:** locally fairly common; summers 2700–4570 m, winters 1400–4200 m. **BT:** common winter visitor, rare in summer. **REFERENCES** Martens and Eck (1995).

DAURIAN REDSTART *Phoenicurus auroreus* Plate 106

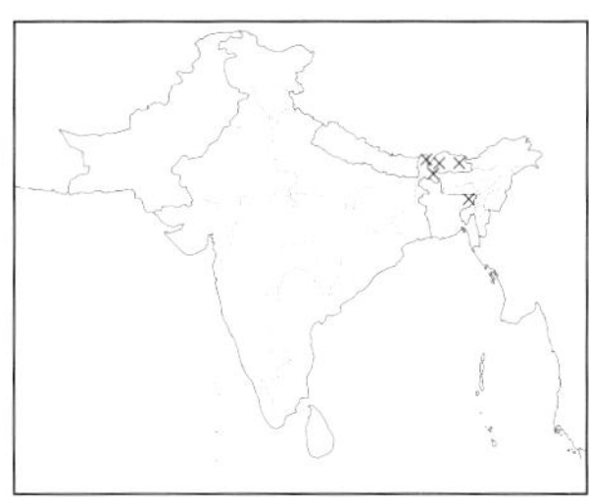

IDENTIFICATION 15 cm. **Adult male (worn)** superficially resembles Hodgson's (p.654), but has large white patch at base of secondaries, has blackish wing-coverts and mantle, and black of throat does not extend onto breast. **Adult male (fresh)** and **first-winter male** have black of mantle and coverts partly obscured by brown fringes (mantle appears brown, diffusely streaked with black), and grey of crown and black of throat are duller owing to dark grey fringes. **Adult female** is similar to female Black (p.653), but has prominent white patch at base of secondaries and darker centre to rufous tail. **VOICE** Calls include a short, penetrating, monosyllabic indrawn whistle, *eehp* – as from an unoiled bicycle – and a hard deep *gak*, the two often combined (P. Holt). **HABITS** Posture and manner are typical of the genus (see Black Redstart). Frequents bushes and lower branches of trees. **HABITAT** Summers in open forest, trees around villages and cultivation at high altitude; winters in bushes near villages and along streams and roads, in tea estates and in secondary growth. **BREEDING** May–August. Builds a cup-shaped nest in a hole in a bank or wall or under tree roots. **DISTRIBUTION AND STATUS** Summer visitor to Himalayas from Sikkim east to Arunachal Pradesh, and NE Indian hills; winters in foothills. **IN:** summers 2800–3300 m; locally fairly common in foothills in winter. **BT:** uncommon winter visitor. **BD:** former winter visitor; no records in 20th century.

WHITE-WINGED REDSTART *Phoenicurus erythrogaster* Plate 106

Güldenstädt's Redstart (F,I,N,R)

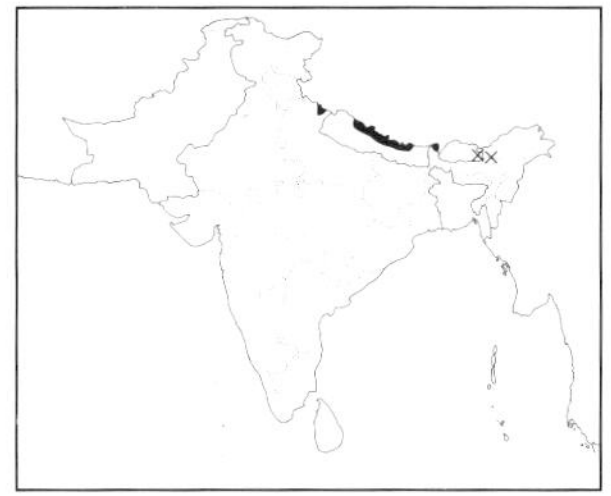

IDENTIFICATION 18 cm. A large redstart. **Adult male** has white crown and nape, black face, throat and mantle, black wings with large white patch at base of flight feathers, and rufous-orange underparts and tail. In fresh plumage, crown is greyish-white, and black of upperparts/breast and red of underparts are slightly duller owing to narrow (usually indistinct) grey fringes. **Adult female** resembles a large female Black Redstart (p.653), but has warmer brown upperparts, buffish underparts, and more uniform rufous-orange tail. Uniform wings, larger and stockier appearance and different behaviour help separate it from Rufous-backed Redstart (p.652). **First-winter** as respective adult. **Juvenile** has brown head and body with diffuse buff spotting and brown scaling, and rufous-buff tips to median and greater coverts. Juvenile male has white wing patch, and blacker coverts and flight feathers. **VOICE** Calls include a weak *lik* and a harder *tek*. Song comprises a short, but pleasant, whistling phrase, *teet-teet-teet* or *tit-tit-titer*, followed by a wheezy burst of short notes (Cramp 1988; Roberts 1992). **HABITS** Movements and carriage are typical of the genus (see Black Redstart). Frequently perches on boulders, walls and low bushes. Forages by hopping or running about on the ground and picking up insects; also by flying on to prey from a low perch, or taking insects in the air in brief flight. **HABITAT** Breeds in the dry alpine zone among glacial moraine and boulder-strewn meadows; winters on stony pastures, in patches of *Hippophae* and along river beds. **BREEDING** May–August. Builds nest in a hollow between stones on the ground or in a wall or rock crevice. **DISTRIBUTION AND STATUS** Resident, subject to altitudinal movements, and winter visitor. Himalayas from N Pakistan east to Arunachal Pradesh. **PK:** local and common; breeds in inner, drier mountain ranges of the far north, 3900–5000 m; winters 1750–2400 m on lower slopes of main N Himalayan valleys. **NP:** uncommon in summer, recorded 4900–5600 m; locally fairly common in some years in winter, 2650–3965 m and probably higher. **IN:** locally common; breeds mainly on N Himalayan slopes, 3600–5200 m; winters 1525–4800 m (down to 900 m). **BT:** uncommon.

BLUE-FRONTED REDSTART *Phoenicurus frontalis* Plate 107

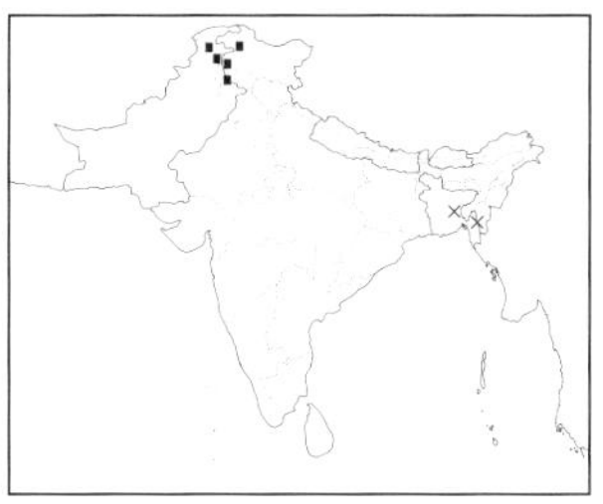

IDENTIFICATION 15 cm. **Adult male (worn)** is readily told from other redstarts by blue head, mantle and breast (with brighter blue supercilium), chestnut-orange underparts, and orange-red rump and tail sides with strongly contrasting black centre and tip to tail. **Adult male (fresh)** and **first-winter** have blue and orange of body duller owing to extensive rufous-brown fringes, and have buff fringes to wing-coverts and tertials. **Adult female** told from other female redstarts by combination of dark brown upperparts and underparts, with orange wash to centre of belly and vent, and orange-red rump and tail sides with strongly contrasting black centre and tip to tail. **Juvenile** is similar to juveniles of other redstarts, but separated by distinctive adult-like tail pattern, and is also dimorphic: spotting on head and body, panel on wing and tips to coverts are either white or orange-buff, as is unspotted belly and vent. **VOICE** Song consists of one or two harsh trilling warbles and then short whistling phrases, this being repeated with minor variations; calls include an *ee-tit* (Roberts 1992). **HABITS** Usually found singly, or in loose flocks on migration. Normally perches on bushes, rocks or lower tree branches; has an upright alert stance, but, unlike most redstarts, flicks tail up and down and does not vibrate it. Flies from a perch to pick up insects from the ground, and also catches them on the wing; also eats berries in winter. **HABITAT** Summers in subalpine birch, rhododendron and juniper shrubberies, on stony slopes or broken ground interspersed with bushes above the treeline; in winter, occurs in bushes and on walls around fields and in open forest. **BREEDING** May–August. Builds a cup-shaped nest, usually in a hollow in a bank, between stones or in a wall or tree. **DISTRIBUTION AND STATUS** Altitudinal migrant. Breeds in Himalayas from N Pakistan east to Arunachal Pradesh; winters in Himalayan foothills, and NE India. **PK:** locally frequent in N mountains; summers 3350–4260 m, winters in mountain valleys. **NP:** common and widespread; summers chiefly 3350–4900 m, winters 1000–3050 m (down to 455 m). **IN:** common; breeds 2700–4500 m, locally down to 2000 m, winters 1000–2700 m. **BT:** common; 1450 m up to at least 4265 m. **BD:** vagrant.

WHITE-CAPPED WATER REDSTART *Chaimarrornis leucocephalus* Plate 107

White-capped Redstart (I,N,R), River Chat (K), White-capped River Chat (F), *Thamnolaea leucocephala* (K)

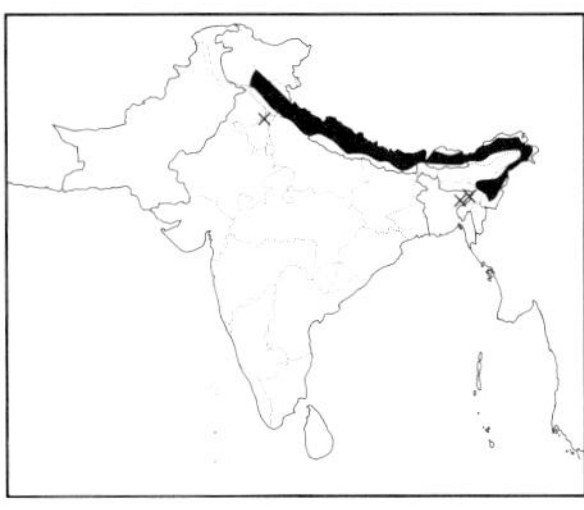

IDENTIFICATION 19 cm. **Adult** is striking, with white cap contrasting with blue-black rest of head, mantle and breast, rufous belly and rump, and rufous tail with broad black terminal band. Black tail-band and lack of white on wing separate it from White-winged Redstart (p.655). Sexes are alike. **Juvenile** has rump and tail as adult, but has black fringes to white crown, brownish-black upperparts, and blackish underparts with rufous fringes. **VOICE** Song is a weak, drawn-out undulating whistle, *tieu-yieu-yieu-yieu*; main call is a far-carrying, upward-inflected *tseeit tseeit* (Roberts 1992). **HABITS** Flies actively from stone to stone in mountain streams. Has a distinctive habit of pumping and fanning its tail, and sometimes tilting it right over the back, often accompanied by a deep curtsey. Feeds mainly on insects, which are caught in erratic flight or picked from the surface at the water's edge; also eats berries. In summer, will also forage some distance from water in alpine meadows. **HABITAT** Mountain streams and rivers; in winter, also along low-altitude canals; in summer, also in alpine meadows and rocky areas far from water. **BREEDING** May–August. Builds a large cup-shaped nest, close to water in a hole in a bank or broken stump, in a rock crevice, or under a boulder. **DISTRIBUTION AND STATUS** Altitudinal migrant. Breeds in Himalayas from N Pakistan east to Arunachal Pradesh, and NE Indian hills; winters south to Baluchistan, Pakistan, and Bangladesh. **PK:** locally common in Himalayas; rare as high as 3300–3600 m in summer, winters mainly in N valleys (–2400 m). **NP:** common and very widespread; summers 1830–5000 m (–5100 m); winters 915–1525 m, sometimes up to 2590 m and down to 245 m (even 75 m). **IN:** common; overall breeds 1830–4880 m, varying locally; winters mainly from foothills up to 1500 m (–2100 m). **BT:** common; 250 m up to at least 4510 m. **BD:** rare, regular, but very local winter visitor to the northeast, 100 m. **REFERENCES** Choudhary (1996a).

PLUMBEOUS WATER REDSTART *Rhyacornis fuliginosus* Plate 107

Plumbeous Redstart (F,I,K,N,R)

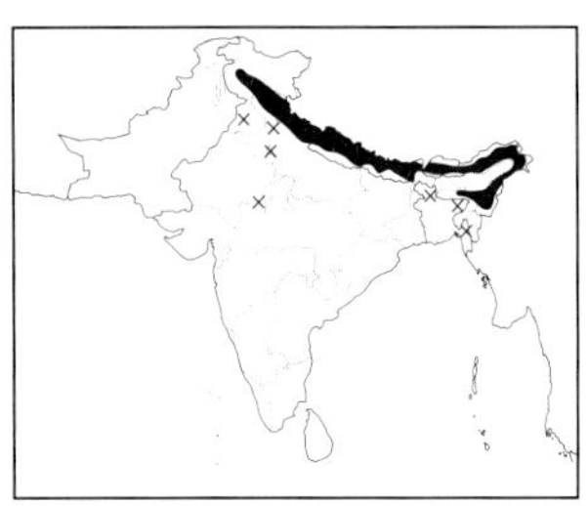

IDENTIFICATION 12 cm. A small, stocky 'redstart' which constantly flicks open its short, broad tail while moving it up and down. **Adult male** is almost entirely dark slaty-blue, with rufous-chestnut uppertail-coverts and tail. **Adult female** and **first-year male** are very different, with slate-grey upperparts, paler grey underparts with white spotting and scaling, white tips to wing-coverts, white rump and vent, and white sides to black tail. **Juvenile** resembles female (with same tail pattern), but has buff spotting on browner upperparts, buff tips to wing-coverts, and buffish underparts with black scaling (becoming whiter on lower belly and vent). **VOICE** Alarm call is a strident *peet-peet*; song is a rapidly repeated, insect-like *streee-treee-tree-treeeh* (Roberts 1992). **HABITS** Confiding and energetic. Flits restlessly between rocks in mountain streams; frequently makes flycatcher-like aerial sallies after insects, and picks up insects among stones and shallows; also eats berries. Partly crepuscular. **HABITAT** Fast-flowing mountain streams and rivers. **BREEDING** April–early August. Builds a cup-shaped nest on a rock ledge, in a hole in a stream bank or under a bridge. **DISTRIBUTION AND STATUS** Altitudinal migrant. Breeds in Himalayas from N Pakistan east to Arunachal Pradesh, and NE Indian hills; winters south to Bangladesh. **PK:** locally common; usually summers 1800–2700 m, down to adjacent foothills in winter. **NP:** common and very widespread; summers mainly 1525–3750 m (down to 600 m), uncommon up to 4420 m; winters 75–2560 m. **IN:** common; breeds 1200–4300 m, varying locally; winters from 2400 m down to foothills, locally to plains. **BT:** common; from 305 m up to at least 3810 m. **BD:** rare, local winter visitor. **REFERENCES** Tyler and Ormerod (1994).

WHITE-BELLIED REDSTART *Hodgsonius phaenicuroides* Plate 107

Hodgson's Shortwing (I)

IDENTIFICATION 18 cm. In behaviour and profile recalls White-tailed Rubythroat (p.647), but is slimmer and has much longer, graduated tail which is frequently acutely cocked and fanned, with wings dropped. **Adult male** is almost entirely dark slaty-blue, with white belly and vent and rufous sides to base of bluish-black tail; has two

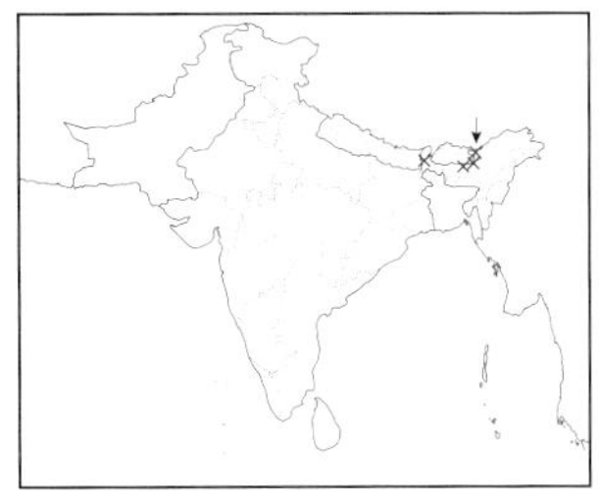

white spots on the alula. White belly, rufous tail sides and white spots on wing separate it from Blue-fronted Robin (below). **Adult female** has olive-brown upperparts, chestnut sides to tail (with darker brown centre), creamy-white throat and centre of belly, and rufous brown flanks and vent. Told from female Blue-fronted Robin by chestnut on tail, white throat and belly, and dark fringes to undertail-coverts. **First-year male** resembles female, but is darker brown in coloration; head, mantle and breast have some blue, and tail has blue cast. **Juvenile** is similar to female, but has pale chestnut spotting on upperparts and dark scaling on underparts. **VOICE** Song comprises three or four whistling notes, of which the second is a drawn-out whistle which rises and then falls, followed by a briefer, lower-pitched note, the whole rendered as *teuuh-tiyou-tuh*; call is a grating croak, *chack-chack-chack* (Roberts 1992). **HABITS** Shy; skulks in dense undergrowth, on or close to the ground. Feeds by running about on the ground, usually under cover. Males sing within thick bushes. **HABITAT** Summers in subalpine dwarf birch, rhododendron and juniper; thickets of *Viburnum* and beds of dense tall herbs in Pakistan, and thorny undergrowth under cypress and juniper shrubs in the trans-Himalayan zone of Nepal; favours undergrowth immediately bordering the forest edge. Winters in thick undergrowth and at forest edges. **BREEDING** May–August. Builds a deep cup-shaped nest, close to the ground in bushes or on the ground among tall herbs. **DISTRIBUTION AND STATUS** Altitudinal and short-range migrant. Himalayas from N Pakistan (Azad Kashmir and Kagan valley) east to Arunachal Pradesh. **PK:** scarce and local summer visitor; from the upper limit of the treeline down to 3350 m. **NP:** frequent summer visitor, mainly 2900–4270 m (down to 2450 m); rare winter visitor to foothills, 915 m. **IN:** locally common; breeds 2440–3900 m, winters from 1500 m down to foothills. **BT:** uncommon; summers 2440–3960 m, winters 305–610 m.

WHITE-TAILED ROBIN *Myiomela leucura* — Plate 107

White-tailed Blue Robin (F,I), *Cinclidium leucurum*

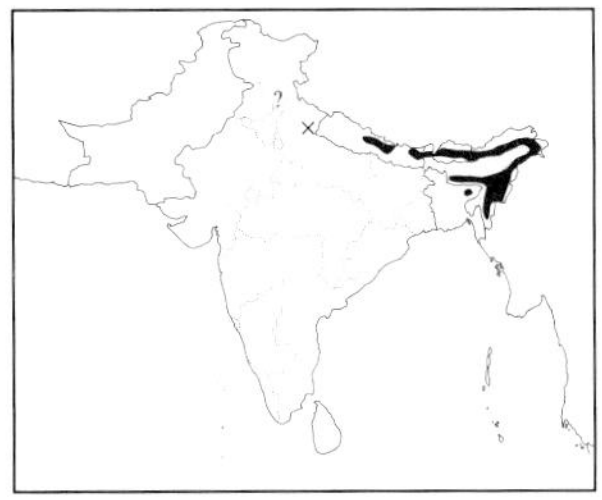

IDENTIFICATION 18 cm. Has long, broad tail which is frequently dipped and spread. White patches on tail often reveal bird as it perches in dense cover. **Adult male** is almost entirely blue-black, with glistening blue forehead, supercilium and bend of wing, and oval-shaped white patches on tail contrasting strongly with black of rest of tail; has white patch on side of neck, but this is usually concealed. Confusable really only with White-tailed Flycatcher (p.642), although flycatcher-like stance, short tarsus and different habits distinguish that species. **Adult female** is almost entirely olive-brown, with slightly paler underparts, and with whitish or buff patch on lower throat; has white patches on tail, as male. **Juvenile** is similar to female (juvenile male is darker brown), with same distinctive tail pattern, but has orange-buff spotting on upperparts and underparts. **First-year** birds are similar to female, but with buff tips to wing-coverts; first-year male has darker tail than female and blue on uppertail-coverts. **VOICE** Song is a loud, clear, rather hurried jangling whistling of seven or eight notes; calls include a thin one- or two-note whistle and a low *tuc* (Boonsong and Round 1991). **HABITS** Retiring. Usually keeps under cover among dense vegetation close to the ground, where it usually feeds. Flies up into bushes and lower branches of trees if disturbed. **HABITAT** Undergrowth in dense moist broadleaved forest; often near streams or in watered ravines; favours bamboo. **BREEDING** April–August. Nest is a deep cup, often domed or semi-domed, usually built in a rock crevice near a stream or in a hole in a bank, sometimes among boulders or tree roots. **DISTRIBUTION AND STATUS** Altitudinal migrant. Himalayas from N Uttar Pradesh east to Arunachal Pradesh; hills of NE India and Bangladesh. **NP:** generally uncommon, locally fairly common; summers 1900–2745 m, winters mainly below 915 m. **IN:** locally fairly common; breeds 1200–2700 m, winters from 1500 m down to foothills and locally in adjacent plains. **BT:** frequent. **BD:** rare, very local resident in the northeast at the unusually low altitude of 35 m.

BLUE-FRONTED ROBIN *Cinclidium frontale* — Plate 107

Blue-fronted Long-tailed Robin (F)

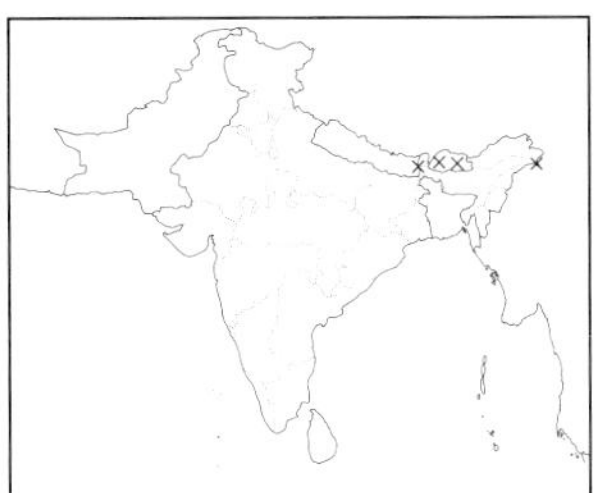

IDENTIFICATION 19 cm. Superficially resembles White-tailed Robin (above), but has a longer, strongly graduated, all-dark tail which is frequently slowly fanned. In addition, is larger, with more horizontal stance, and has longer legs and more terrestrial behaviour. **Adult male** is almost entirely deep blue, with glistening blue forehead, supercilium and bend of wing, and blackish lores; some individuals have whitish mottling on belly. Lacks rufous on tail, white spots on alula and contrasting white belly of White-bellied Redstart (p.656). **Adult female** is almost entirely dark brown, with slightly paler underparts. Lacks white tail patches of female White-tailed Robin. Told from female White-bellied Redstart by absence of chestnut on tail. **First-year male** has blue on forehead, and dark throat, lores and shoulders. **Juvenile** is dark brown and virtually featureless but for buff streaks on throat and buff tips to belly feathers. **VOICE** Song is a series of short melodic phrases, clearer and less watery than that of White-tailed Robin, e.g. *tuuee-be-tue* and *tuu-buudy-doo*. Gives a harsh, buzzy *zshwick* call in alarm (P. Morris). **HABITS** Poorly known. Has been observed close to or on the ground among dense forest undergrowth; also in the open at the forest edge. Seldom flies, and then not more than a few metres. Feeds by hopping about on the ground, and has an almost horizontal posture when perched and when feeding. As well as its habit of slowly fanning its tail, occasionally bobs and curtsies. **HABITAT** Dark, densely vegetated gullies and dense undergrowth in humid subtropical and temperate forest; also in the open at forest edge between clumps of tall herbaceous vegetation in bamboo thickets, and once in a spinach crop in a small garden adjacent to a thickly vegetated gully. **BREEDING** Details unknown. **DISTRIBUTION AND STATUS** Altitudinal migrant. Himalayas in Nepal?, Darjeeling in West Bengal, Sikkim, Bhutan and E Arunachal Pradesh. **NP:** possibly collected in 19th century, but the specimen may have originated in India. **IN:** generally rare; recorded mainly 1350 m (February) to 2340 m (July), 700–800 m (January–March). **BT:** rare; 1850 m in March and April, 2300 m in March, 2100–2345 m and 3130 m in May. **REFERENCES** Alström (1997), Athreya *et al.* (1997), Inskipp and Inskipp (1994), Redman (1992).

GRANDALA *Grandala coelicolor* — Plate 107

Hodgson's Grandala (I)

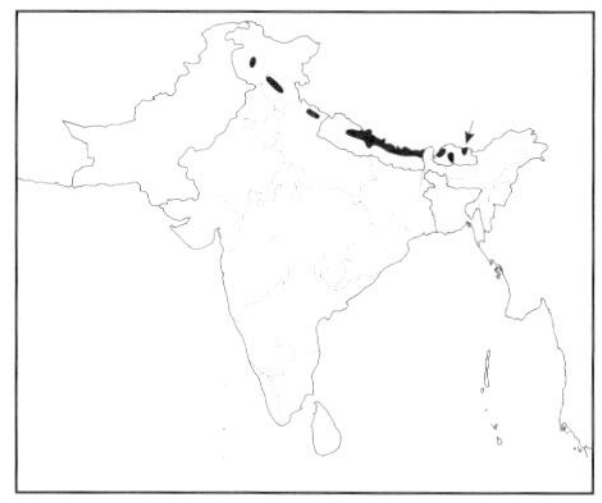

IDENTIFICATION 23 cm. A slim, long-winged, starling-like chat. A strong, streamlined flier, often in large flocks; on the ground, flicks open wings and tail. **Adult male** is almost entirely purple-blue with glistening sheen, but with black lores, wings and tail. **Adult female** and **immature male** are dark brown, with blue wash to rump and uppertail-coverts, and with whitish streaking on head, mantle and underparts, white tips to tertials and coverts, and white patches on wing (prominent in flight). **Juvenile** is said to be similar to female, but is darker brown and more boldly streaked, with streaking on throat and breast becoming broad triangular spots; lacks blue on rump and uppertail-coverts. **VOICE** Flight call is a *tew-wee*; song is a repeated *galeb-che-chew-de-dew* (Fleming *et al.* 1984). **HABITS** Found chiefly in flocks, consisting of several hundred birds in the non-breeding season; even in summer, 50 or more congregate to feed. Flocks circle buoyantly for long periods high over valleys and ridges, catching insects on the wing; also seeks insects on the ground, hopping about on alpine meadows and stony slopes. Often perches on rocks with an upright posture, recalling a rock thrush; in winter also perches in trees and bushes. **HABITAT** Summers on rocky slopes and ridges and stony meadows in the alpine zone; winters in similar habitat at lower altitude, and in severe weather may descend to below treeline. **BREEDING** Mid June–July. Builds a large cup-shaped nest on a rock ledge. **DISTRIBUTION AND STATUS** Altitudinal migrant. Himalayas from Kishenganga valley in Pakistan? and Kashmir east to Arunachal Pradesh. Summers 3900–5500 m; winters mainly 3000–4300 m (down to 1950 m in Nepal). **PK:** possibly recorded. **NP, IN, BT:** local and fairly common.

LITTLE FORKTAIL *Enicurus scouleri* — Plate 107

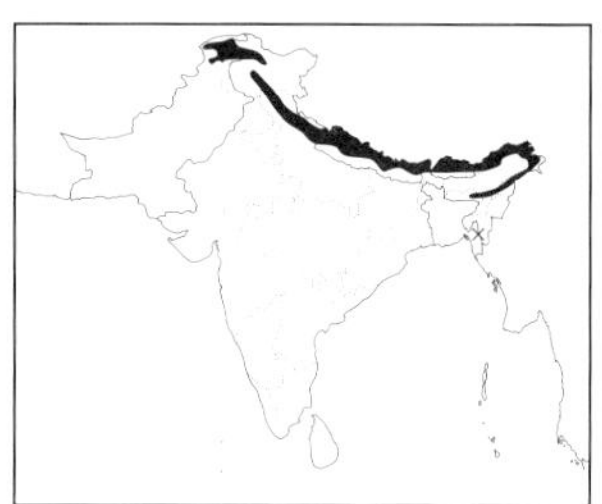

IDENTIFICATION 12 cm. **Adult** readily distinguished from other forktails by combination of small size, more rounded body and upright stance, short black tail with prominent white sides, black band across white rump, and prominent white forehead. Tail is constantly wagged and flicked open. **Juvenile** superficially resembles adult, but lacks white forehead; has brownish-black upperparts, and white underparts with dark scaling on throat and breast. **VOICE** Generally silent; song has been described as a loud *ts-youeee* (Flint *et al.* 1984). **HABITS** Always keeps close to water. Continually fans and closes its tail while simultaneously moving it slowly up and down. Feeds by standing on or running over partly submerged rocks and picking up aquatic invertebrates from the water as it flows past; often makes dashes under the spray of falling water. Flight is low over the water. Less active and restless than the other forktails, often sitting almost still for short periods. **HABITAT** Rushing rocky mountain streams, often near waterfalls, and, unlike other forktails, is not dependent on tree cover; in winter, also on larger slower-moving rivers. **BREEDING** April–June. Nest is similar to that of Spotted Forktail (p.659), often built behind a waterfall or in a hole in a moss-covered bank. **DISTRIBUTION AND STATUS** Resident, subject to altitudinal movements. Himalayas from N Pakistan east to Arunachal Pradesh; hills of NE India and Bangladesh. **PK:** widespread in Himalayas, locally frequent but generally rather uncommon; breeds 2100–2400 m, winters 760–2700 m. **NP:** fairly common and widespread; summers chiefly 1830–4000 m (1150–4240 m), winters 900–1830 m. **IN:** locally fairly common; breeds 1800–3700 m (uncommonly down to 1000 m); winters mainly from 1000 m up to at least 2000 m, locally down to 300 m. **BT:** fairly common. **BD:** ?former winter visitor; no recent records, but could still occur in hill tracts. **REFERENCES** Martens and Eck (1995).

BLACK-BACKED FORKTAIL *Enicurus immaculatus* — Plate 107

IDENTIFICATION 25 cm. **Adult** resembles Slaty-backed Forktail (p.659), with long, forked black-and-white tail and white band across wing. Differs from that species in having black (rather than slate-grey) crown and mantle, generally smaller bill, and more white on forehead. See White-crowned Forktail (p.659) for differences from that

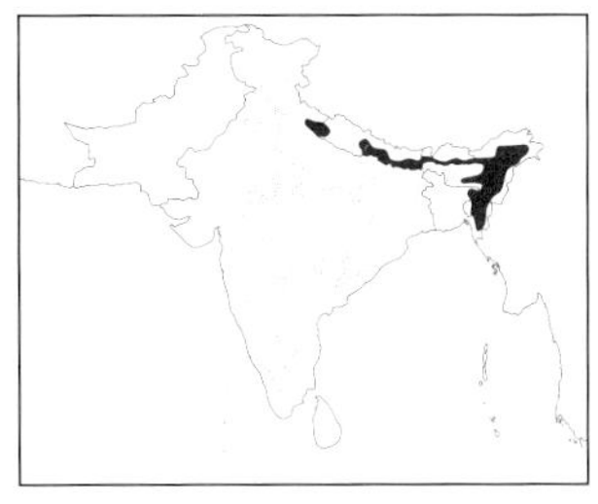

species. **Juvenile** superficially resembles adult, but has shorter tail, lacks white forehead and supercilium, and has brownish-black upperparts and dark scaling on white breast. **VOICE** Call is a Grey Bushchat-like hollow *huu*, often followed by a shrill *zeee*, the second note slightly higher-pitched than similar whistle of Slaty-backed Forktail (P. Holt from R. Drijvers recording). **HABITS** Similar to those of Spotted Forktail (below). **HABITAT** Fast-flowing streams in damp broadleaved tropical and subtropical forest. **BREEDING** End March–May. Nest is similar to that of Spotted Forktail, usually built on a ledge, in a rock crevice or in a hollow in a fallen tree or stream bank. **DISTRIBUTION AND STATUS** Resident. Himalayan foothills from N Uttar Pradesh east to Arunachal Pradesh; NE India and Bangladesh. **NP:** frequent below 1370 m from WC areas eastwards, very uncommon in the west. **IN:** locally fairly common in the east, rare west of Sikkim; Himalayan foothills from 1450 m down to adjacent plains; below 900 m in NE hills. **BT:** fairly common. **BD:** local.

SLATY-BACKED FORKTAIL *Enicurus schistaceus* — Plate 107

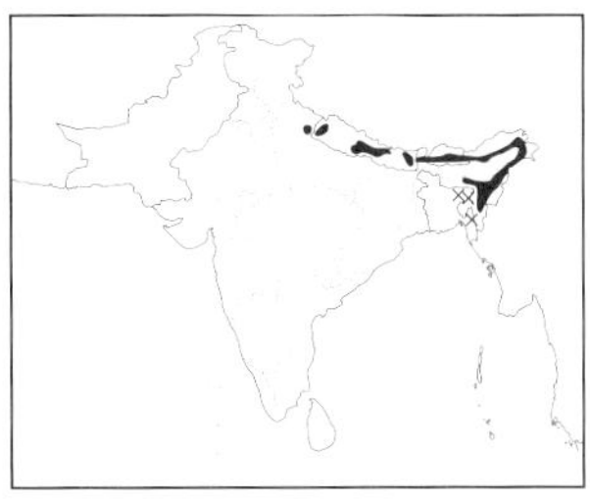

IDENTIFICATION 25 cm. **Adult** resembles Black-backed Forktail (p.658), with long, forked, black-and-white tail. Distinguished from that species by slate-grey (rather than black) crown and mantle, contrasting with black throat and wing-coverts; bill is generally larger, and shows less white on forehead than Black-backed. **Juvenile** superficially resembles adult, but has shorter tail, lacks white forehead and supercilium, has brown upperparts, and has dark scaling on breast. **VOICE** A mellow *cheet* (Fleming *et al.* 1984), or sharp metallic *teenk* (Boonsong and Round 1991). **HABITS** Similar to those of Spotted Forktail (below). **HABITAT** Large fast-flowing rocky streams in the tropical and subtropical zones, usually through forest; also wooded lake margins, and nullahs in cultivation. **BREEDING** April–June. Nest is similar to that of Spotted Forktail, built among boulders or tree roots, or on a ledge in a rock crevice or hollow in a bank. **DISTRIBUTION AND STATUS** Resident, subject to some altitudinal movements. Himalayas from N Uttar Pradesh east to Arunachal Pradesh; NE India. **NP:** generally uncommon, but fairly common locally; 900–1675 m (down to 450 m). **IN:** locally fairly common in the east, rare west of Nepal; breeds 300–1600 m, winters down to the base of the hills and adjacent plains. **BT:** frequent; 250–2375 m. **BD:** vagrant. **REFERENCES** Lama (1995a).

WHITE-CROWNED FORKTAIL *Enicurus leschenaulti* — Plate 107

Leschenault's Forktail

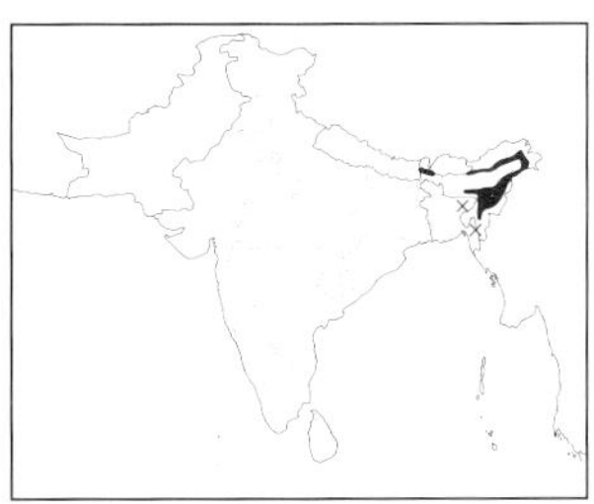

IDENTIFICATION 25 cm. A large forktail. **Adult** superficially resembles Black-backed (p.658), but is larger, with longer tail, has prominent white forehead and forecrown, and black of throat extends to breast. Unspotted black mantle separates it from Spotted (below). **Juvenile** lacks white forehead, and has brownish-black upperparts, brownish-black throat and breast with white streaking, brown mottling on upper belly, and brown flanks. **VOICE** A harsh *scree* or *scree, chit chit*; also has an elaborate, high-pitched whistling song (Boonsong and Round 1991). **HABITS** Similar to those of Spotted Forktail. Very shy, and flies off immediately if disturbed. **HABITAT** Fast-flowing streams and rivers in dense tropical broadleaved evergreen forest. **BREEDING** April–June. Nest is similar to that of Spotted Forktail, built in a steep bank covered with vegetation, or in a tree hollow or rock crevice or between boulders, usually in damp situations. **DISTRIBUTION AND STATUS** Resident, subject to seasonal movements. Himalayan foothills from Darjeeling, West Bengal, east to Arunachal Pradesh; NE Indian hills. **IN:** uncommon; breeds from the base of the hills up to 800 m, spreading into adjacent plains in winter. **BT:** rare. **BD:** vagrant.

SPOTTED FORKTAIL *Enicurus maculatus* — Plate 107

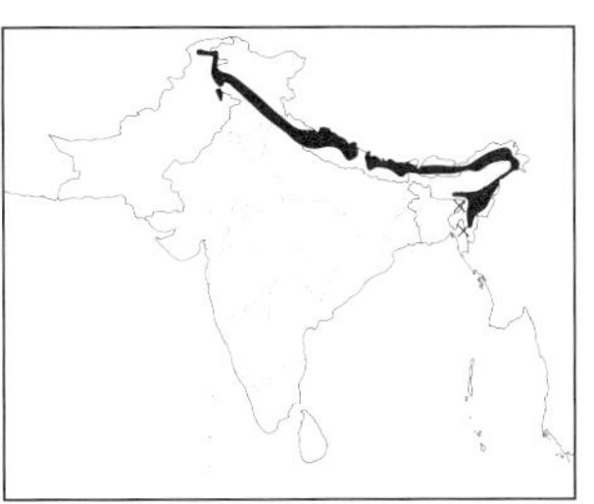

IDENTIFICATION 25 cm. **Adult** distinguished from other forktails by combination of large size and very long tail, white spotting on black mantle (forming white collar towards nape), prominent white forehead, and black of throat extending to breast. White-spotted mantle separates it from White-crowned Forktail (above). **Juvenile** lacks white forehead, and has brownish-black upperparts, paler brownish-black throat and breast with white streaking, brown mottling on upper belly, and brown flanks. **Racial variation** *E. m. guttatus* of the E Himalayas and NE India differs from *E. m. maculatus* of the W and C Himalayas in being smaller, lacking white scaling on black breast, and having fewer and smaller white spots on mantle. **VOICE** A shrill, rasping *kreee* or *tseek*; also a creaky *cheek-chik-chik-chik-chik* (Ali and Ripley 1987). **HABITS**

Occurs singly or in separated pairs, always keeping close to water. Like all forktails, has a characteristic habit of constantly swaying its tail slowly up and down, and usually holds it above the horizontal. Very restless, and frequently turns from side to side, facing in one direction and then another. Walks daintily over stones at the water's edge or hops from stone to stone in mid-stream, picking aquatic invertebrates from the water or the ground; sometimes enters the water. Has a graceful, undulating flight low over the water. Shy; if disturbed, flies off, calling, and following the line of the watercourse. **HABITAT** Rocky streams in forest and shady wooded ravines; avoids larger rivers, lakes and open country. **BREEDING** April–July. Builds a cup-shaped nest in a hole in a stream bank, in a rock crevice, on a rock ledge or between boulders, usually in a damp situation. **DISTRIBUTION AND STATUS** Resident, subject to altitudinal movements. Himalayas from N Pakistan east to Arunachal Pradesh; hills of NE India and Bangladesh. **PK:** locally frequent and sedentary on Himalayan streams in moist temperate forest zone; recorded breeding at 1500 m, winters 460–2100 m. **NP:** fairly common and widespread; summers mainly 1370–3100 m, winters from 290 m up to at least 2745 m. **IN:** locally fairly common; breeds from 3000 m down to 600 m in the east, from 3000 m down to 1000 m in the west (extremes 3600 m and 900 m); winters down to the base of the hills in the east, and from 600 m up to at least 2300 m in west. **BT:** fairly common; 3125 m down to at least 1270 m. **BD:** ?former resident; no recent records, but could still occur in hill tracts.

PURPLE COCHOA *Cochoa purpurea* — Plate 108

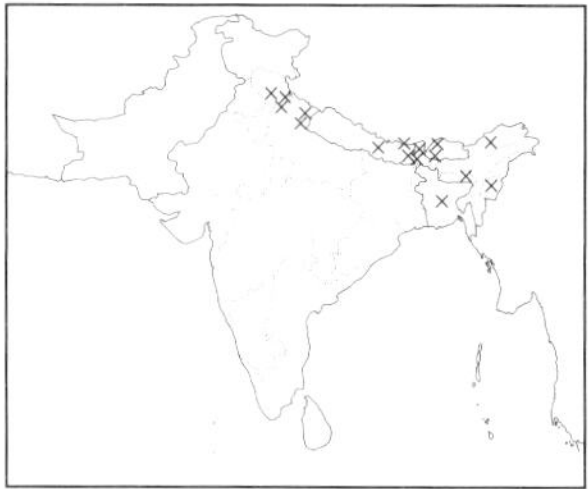

IDENTIFICATION 30 cm. An unobtrusive, slow-moving and stocky, arboreal thrush. **Adult male** has lilac-blue crown, black mask, lilac panelling on wing, and lilac tail with black tip. Body is dull purplish-grey. **Adult female** resembles male, but has rusty-brown mantle, wing-coverts and base of secondaries and tertials; underparts are brownish-orange. **Juvenile male** has wing and tail patterns similar to adult male's; has white crown scaled with black, blackish upperparts with indistinct buff streaking and spotting, orange-buff underparts with bold black barring, and buff tips to wing-coverts. Lilac panelling on wing, lilac tail, and dusky-brown vent and undertail-coverts are main differences from juvenile Green Cochoa (below). **Juvenile female** resembles juvenile male, but has brown mask, browner upperparts, and brown (rather than purplish) wing-coverts and base of secondaries. **VOICE** A low chuckle (Ali and Ripley 1987). Song is a broad flute-like *peeeeee*; also *peeee-you-peeee* like the music of a shepherd's bamboo flute (the pitch drops one note in the middle of the phrase) (Fleming *et al.* 1984). **HABITS** Quiet and unobtrusive, usually keeping well hidden among tree foliage. Seen most often in spring, when males sing from the tops of tall trees. Rather lethargic; sits still for long periods in the canopy and middle storey of forest; sometimes drops to the ground to feed. Eats mostly berries, also insects. **HABITAT** Mainly dense moist broadleaved evergreen forest; undergrowth in ravines through pine forest in Khasi Hills. **BREEDING** Early May–mid July. Builds a shallow cup-shaped nest, usually 2–6 m above ground in the fork of a small tree. **DISTRIBUTION AND STATUS** Resident. Himalayas from Himachal Pradesh east to Arunachal Pradesh; NE Indian hills. Poorly known. **NP:** rare, possibly resident; recorded only from the centre and east, 915–2255 m, May–early November. **IN:** rare; 1000–3000 m. **BT:** rare; 1830 m, 2200 m, 3000 m. **BD:** winter vagrant, recorded at less than 5 m.

GREEN COCHOA *Cochoa viridis* — Plate 108

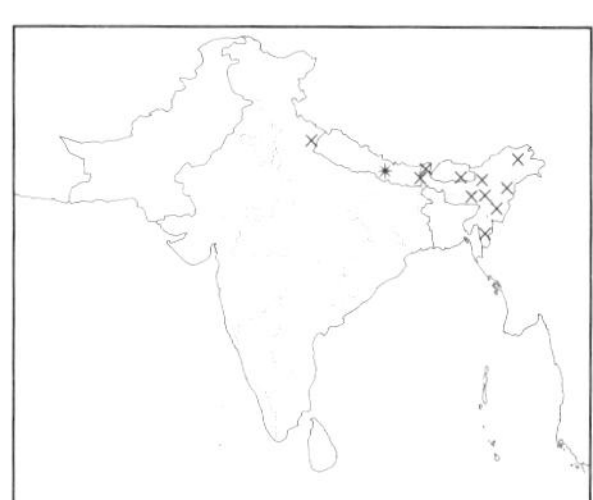

IDENTIFICATION 28 cm. Similar in behaviour and habits to Purple Cochoa (above). **Adult** distinguished from that species by blue crown and nape (with blackish mask), green body faintly scaled with black on mantle, pale blue panelling across wing, and pale blue tail with black tip. As on Purple, tail is wholly black from below. Sexes are similar, but female has green at base of secondaries. **Juvenile** has wing and tail patterns as respective adult, but has white crown with black scaling, orange-buff spotting and dark scaling on upperparts and underparts, and buff tips to wing-coverts. Adult-like flight feathers and tail and heavily spotted upperparts are main differences from juvenile Purple. **First-winter** resembles adult, but with dark shaft streaking on body; first-winter male is darker brownish-green above than adult male, and first-winter female has yellowish-green underparts. **VOICE** A pure, drawn-out monotone whistle (Boonsong and Round 1991), which is thinner and weaker than that of Purple Cochoa (C. Robson). **HABITS** Solitary, with similar habits to those of Purple Cochoa. **HABITAT** Dense moist broadleaved evergreen forest, usually on steep ground. **BREEDING** May–July. Nest and nest site are similar to those of Purple Cochoa, but usually near water. **DISTRIBUTION AND STATUS** Resident. Himalayas from N Uttar Pradesh east to Arunachal Pradesh; NE India. **NP:** extirpated; recorded only in the 19th century. **IN:** rare; breeds 700–1830 m; 300–1600 m in non-breeding season in Arunachal Pradesh. **BT:** rare. **REFERENCES** Singh (1995).

STOLICZKA'S BUSHCHAT *Saxicola macrorhyncha* — Plate 108

White-browed Bushchat, Stoliczka's Whin-chat (R)

IDENTIFICATION 17 cm. Slimmer than other bushchats and with longer wings, tail and bill (recalling Desert Wheatear, p.666, in shape). **Adult male (worn)** is readily told from other bushchats by combination of

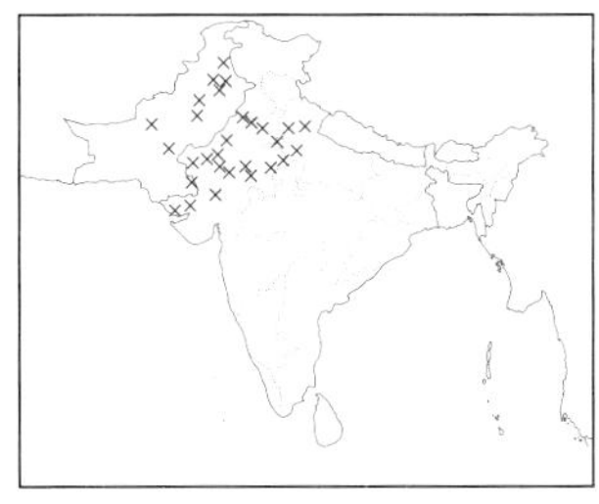

prominent white supercilium contrasting with blackish crown and ear-coverts, blackish mantle, blackish wings with white patch on inner coverts, largely white primary coverts, whitish underparts with buff wash to breast, whitish uppertail-coverts, and much white on tail (all but central pair of rectrices have mainly white inner webs). **Adult male (fresh)** has black of crown and mantle obscured by buffish fringes (giving rise to streaked appearance), and has broad buff fringes to tertials, secondaries and coverts; uppertail-coverts are strongly washed with rufous-buff, and dark ear-coverts are also partly obscured by rufous-buff tips (head pattern may appear much as female). **Adult female** as fresh male, but lacks white on tail and lacks darker ear-coverts; uppertail-coverts are rufous-buff, as are edges and narrow tips to rectrices, the white on inner wing-coverts is reduced or lacking, and primary coverts are brownish-black. Female can closely resemble female Common Stonechat (below); above-mentioned structural differences, more prominent supercilium, more uniform creamy-white underparts (Common Stonechat usually shows pronounced pale orange wash to breast), and broad buffish edges and tips to rectrices (when fresh) are best features. **First-winter male** is like (fresh) adult male, but with white on tail less extensive and strongly tinged with buff; primary coverts are brownish-black. **Juvenile** is similar to adult female, but has darker brown upperparts, which are streaked and spotted with buff, and whitish underparts with indistinct brown mottling on throat and breast. **VOICE** Low musical song, *twitch-chhe chee chee* (Rahmani 1997); a sharp *chip-chip* (Hume 1878). **HABITS** Usually solitary outside the breeding season. Frequently perches on tops of exposed bushes; very parochial, using favourite bushes from which to forage, either by descending to the ground to pick up food items or by making aerial sallies to catch small flying insects. When on the ground has a curious habit, not shared by other bushchats, of puffing up its breast and swaying sideways, making the whitish breast and belly conspicuous; the significance of this behaviour is unknown. **HABITAT** Dry, sandy desert plains with low herbs and very scattered bushes and dominated by *Capparis decidua*. **BREEDING** Details unknown. **DISTRIBUTION AND STATUS** Resident. Formerly occurred in Pakistan and NW India (Punjab, Haryana, W Uttar Pradesh, Rajasthan and Gujarat); now endemic solely to India, and in the last 20 years recorded mainly in Rajasthan. Globally threatened. **PK:** formerly very rare and local; now apparently extirpated. **IN:** locally fairly common in the Thar desert. **REFERENCES** Rahmani (1993, 1997), Whistler (1922).

HODGSON'S BUSHCHAT *Saxicola insignis* — Plate 108

White-throated Bushchat

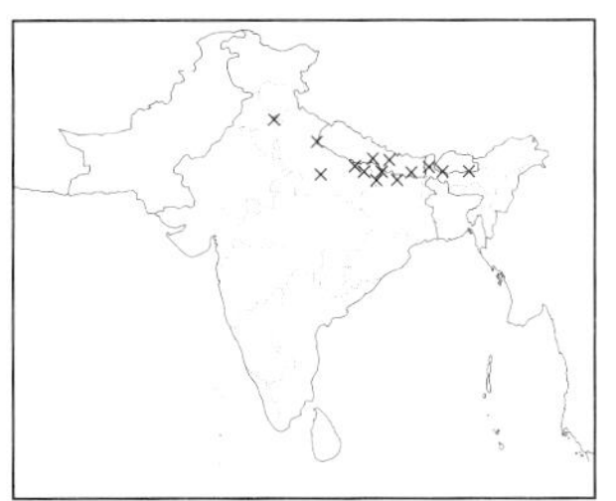

IDENTIFICATION 17 cm. Distinctly larger than Common Stonechat (below), with longer-looking tail. Head looks larger and more bulbous and bill proportionately bigger, and is noticeably less agile (feeding mainly by dropping ponderously to the ground). **Adult male (fresh)** and **first-winter male** superficially resemble Common Stonechat, but with white throat which joins white sides of neck to form almost complete broad white collar, and more extensive white on wing. Have white primary coverts and patch at base of primaries, lacking on Common; also show much white on inner median and greater coverts, and at base of tertials and secondaries. As on male Common Stonechat, black of crown, ear-coverts and especially mantle is obscured by rufous-brown fringes (giving rise to streaked appearance). Underparts are rufous-orange, becoming paler on belly (as Common). Uppertail-coverts are white, with rufous-orange tips. **Adult male (worn)** has black crown, ear-coverts and mantle. **Adult female** is similar to female Common, but upperparts are a shade greyer and head more uniform, with less distinct supercilium; also has broad buffish-white wing-bars and tips to primary coverts, and small whitish patch at base of primaries. **VOICE** A metallic *teck-teck* (Ali and Ripley 1987). **HABITS** Similar to those of Common Stonechat. Solitary and rather shy. Feeds mainly on the ground, by dropping from a perch to pick up insects. **HABITAT** Tall grass, reeds and tamarisks along river beds; also cane fields. **DISTRIBUTION AND STATUS** Winter visitor. From Haryana east through the Nepal terai to Assam. Globally threatened. **NP:** rare and very local; below 150 m (–1380 m). **IN:** rare and very local. **REFERENCES** Anon. (1992).

COMMON STONECHAT *Saxicola torquata* — Plate 108

Stonechat (I), Collared Bush Chat (F), Siberian Stonechat, *S. maura*

IDENTIFICATION 17 cm. Variable, although in all plumages distinguished from White-tailed Stonechat (p.662) by blackish tail. For differences from Hodgson's and Stoliczka's Bushchats (above and p.660), see those species. **Adult male (worn)** has black crown, ear-coverts and throat contrasting with white patch on side of neck, rusty-orange breast, blackish mantle (often with rufous-buff edges still apparent), large white patch on wing (created by white inner coverts), and white uppertail-coverts contrasting with largely dark tail. **Adult male (fresh)** and **first-winter** have black of crown and mantle obscured to a variable extent by rufous-buff fringes (giving mottled appearance to upperparts), and have buff fringes to tertials and secondaries; ear-coverts and throat are mainly black, but can be partly obscured by buff fringes. **Adult female** has buffish supercilium and white throat, brownish-buff crown and mantle, rufous-orange to orange-buff uppertail-coverts contrasting with dark tail, and buffish

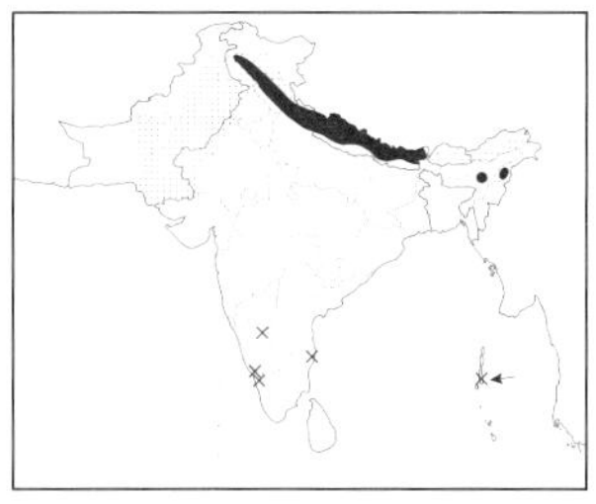

underparts with orange wash across breast. **Juvenile** has brownish-black upperparts, streaked and spotted with buff, and buff underparts which are streaked and spotted with black. **Racial variation** Four rather similar races are recognised from the subcontinent. *S. t. przevalskii*, a winter visitor to N and NE subcontinent, is perhaps the most distinctive, being larger and having underparts almost entirely deep rufous-orange on both sexes. **VOICE** Song is a variable, rather melancholy warbling; main calls are a *hweet* and a hard *tsak tsak*, which are often run together. **HABITS** Usually keeps in pairs. Perches prominently on tops of bushes, tall herbaceous plants, rocks or posts; has an alert upright stance. Frequently flicks wings and jerks tail up and down, simultaneously fanning tail rapidly. Flies or hops to the ground, picks up prey and returns to the same perch or a new one; also catches insects by aerial sallying. **HABITAT** Summers in open country, cultivation with scattered bushes, grassy slopes with bushes, and in trans-Himalayan Nepal high-altitude semi-desert with *Caragana* bushes; winters in stony scrub, reedbeds bordering tanks, tamarisk bushes beside rivers and lakes, fallow cultivation, bushes along tidal creeks and on sand dunes. **BREEDING** March–July. Builds a cup-shaped nest in a hollow at the base of a bush or other plants, under a stone, or in a hole in a grass bank or stone wall. **DISTRIBUTION AND STATUS** Resident and winter visitor. Breeds in Baluchistan, Pakistan, and Himalayas from N Pakistan east to Nepal; winters throughout much of the subcontinent, except most of S India and Sri Lanka. **PK:** common; breeds widely in N Baluchistan, NW Pakistan and N Himalayas, 1500–3500 m (–3880 m); on passage throughout the Indus plains; small numbers overwinter. **NP:** common resident, winter visitor and passage migrant; summers 365–4880 m, winters below 1500 m. **IN:** common on breeding grounds, locally common in winter; breeds mainly 1500–2500 m, locally to 3300 m; winters in plains and hills, up to 2200 m in Himalayas. **BT:** fairly common; 250–4265 m. **BD:** common winter visitor throughout.

WHITE-TAILED STONECHAT *Saxicola leucura* — Plate 108

White-tailed Bushchat (F,K)

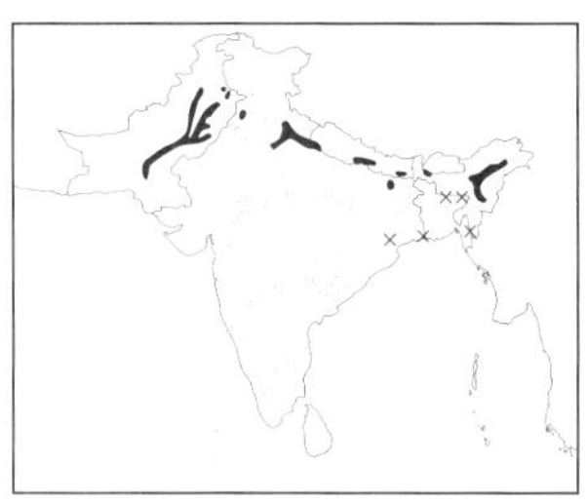

IDENTIFICATION 12.5–13 cm. **Adult male (worn)** is very similar to Common Stonechat (p.661), but inner webs of all but central tail feathers are largely white; as a result, shows much white in tail in flight, although this feature is not usually apparent at rest. Also tends to show more restricted area of rusty-orange on breast, although some Common can be very similar. Upperparts are black. **Adult male (fresh)** has black of crown and mantle largely obscured by buff fringes. **Adult female** is similar to female Common, but upperparts are greyer and streaking is diffuse and less distinct (especially in fresh plumage), while underparts are also paler and with light orange-buff wash (although Common can be very similar in overall coloration); tail is paler grey-brown (blacker on Common), with diffuse pale tips and edges to feathers, and rump is generally a paler dirty buff. Birds from Manipur are darker and browner on the upperparts (and may represent a distinct race), and are more similar in coloration to Common, although tail is still paler grey-brown. **Juvenile** plumage does not seem to have been described. **VOICE** Differences from Common Stonechat are poorly described. Alarm note is a *peep-chaaa* (Ali and Ripley 1987). **HABITS** Very similar to those of Common Stonechat. **HABITAT** Reeds and tall grassland, often in wet areas and near large rivers. **BREEDING** March–May. Builds a cup-shaped nest, well hidden on the ground among leaf litter or in tamarisk roots or a grass tussock. **DISTRIBUTION AND STATUS** Resident, subject to local movements. Indus R system in Pakistan, and from Punjab, India, east through the Nepal terai to Assam and south to N Orissa. **PK:** scarce and sedentary. **NP:** local and fairly common; below 275 m (–915 m). **IN:** locally fairly common, mainly in terai (–700 m). **BD:** former resident?; now vagrant. **REFERENCES** Choudhary (1996b).

PIED BUSHCHAT *Saxicola caprata* — Plate 108

Pied Stone-chat (R)

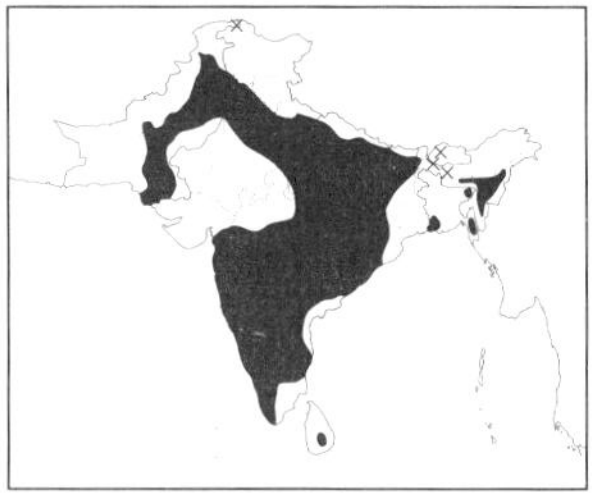

IDENTIFICATION 13.5 cm. Similar in shape to Common Stonechat (p.661), but is much darker. **Adult male (worn)** is entirely black except for white rump, belly/vent and patch on wing. **Adult male (fresh)** and **first-winter male** have diffuse rufous-buff fringes to mantle and underparts. **Adult female** has dark brown upperparts and paler rufous-brown underparts, with paler throat and centre of belly and vent; lacks prominent supercilium. Possibly confusable with female White-tailed Stonechat (above), but is darker, with rufous-orange rump and black tail. **Juvenile** is similar to female, but has buffish spotting on upperparts, and buffish underparts with dark scaling. **Racial variation** *S. c. bicolor* of N and NW subcontinent has white belly and lower breast (although extent of white is variable), which are black in the other three races occurring in the region. **VOICE** Song is a brisk and whistling *chip-chepee-chewee chu*; calls include a plaintive *chep chep-hee* or *chek chek trweet* (Cramp 1988). **HABITS** Very similar to those of Common Stonechat. Territorial throughout the year. **HABITAT** Cultivation and open ground with scattered bushes or clumps of tall

Saccharum grass; tamarisks, reeds and tall grass around canals and tanks; in Pakistan, also juniper forest, subtropical pine forest and saline flats. **BREEDING** February–August. Builds a cup-shaped nest on the ground under a grass tuft, or in a hole in a wall or bank. **DISTRIBUTION AND STATUS** Resident and partial migrant. Throughout much of the subcontinent. **PK:** common; subject to local winter movements; widespread throughout the Indus plains, up to 1800 m, locally to 2400 m in summer. **NP:** common and very widespread below 915 m, fairly common up to 1400 m, sometimes summers up to 2400 m (–2850 m). **IN:** common and widespread in plains and hills; breeds up to 1500 m (–2440 m) in Himalayas, to 2100 m in Nagaland and to 1200 m in Eastern Ghats, mainly above 900 m in S hills. **BT:** rare. **BD:** local. **LK:** common in hills.

JERDON'S BUSHCHAT *Saxicola jerdoni* — Plate 108

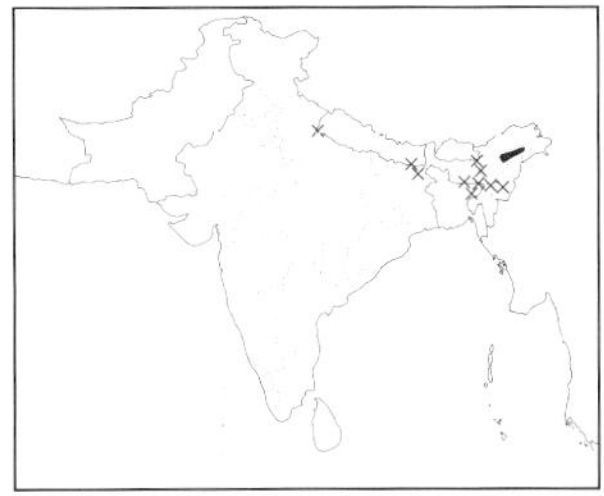

IDENTIFICATION 15 cm. Similar in shape to Grey Bushchat (below), but with longer tail. **Adult male** is very distinctive, with glossy blue-black upperparts, including rump and tail, and white underparts with white throat clearly demarcated from black ear-coverts. **Adult female** resembles female Grey Bushchat, with rufous-brown upperparts, rufous rump and uppertail-coverts, and pale brownish-buff underparts with white throat. Lacks supercilium and darker mask of Grey (although some may show slight suggestion of supercilium in front of eye), and has longer, more rounded tail which lacks rufous at sides. **Juvenile** male is said to be like female, but darker and more broadly marked above and on the breast, with dark edges to the feathers. **VOICE** Calls described include a short, plaintive whistle which is higher-pitched than that of other chats (Boonsong and Round 1991), and a low *chit-churr, chit-churr* (although is generally rather silent) (Baker 1924). **HABITS** Similar to those of Common Stonechat (p.661), but less active on the wing. Sometimes also forages on the ground, at the bottom of reeds and grass, like a babbler. **HABITAT** Large areas of elephant grass, grass and reeds along river or channel banks. **BREEDING** February–May. Builds a cup-shaped nest on the ground among roots or in a grass tuft, or in a hollow in a bank. **DISTRIBUTION AND STATUS** Resident, subject to seasonal movements. Mainly NE India and Bangladesh. **NP:** very rare and local breeding visitor. **IN:** formerly locally common, but very few recent records; plains and foothills up to 700 m. **BD:** rare winter visitor. **REFERENCES** Baker (1924), Choudhary (1996b), Choudhury (1994), Giri and Choudhary (1997).

GREY BUSHCHAT *Saxicola ferrea* — Plate 108

Dark-grey Bush Chat (F,I)

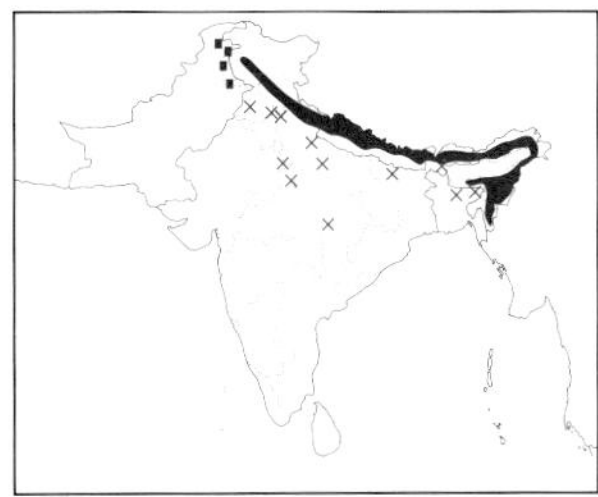

IDENTIFICATION 15 cm. Larger and longer-tailed than Common Stonechat (p.661). **Adult male (worn)** is distinctive, with broad white supercilium contrasting with black ear-coverts, almost black crown and mantle (mixed with some grey), and whitish underparts with grey breast and flanks. Rump and uppertail-coverts are grey, and tail is brownish-black with white outer feathers. **Adult male (fresh)** has grey upperparts (with rufous-brown cast when very fresh) with some dark streaking, and has greyish breast-band. **Adult female** has broad buff supercilium contrasting with dark brown ear-coverts, rufous-brown upperparts which are faintly streaked with dark brown, rufous rump and sides to tail, and whitish underparts with brownish-buff breast and flanks. Confusable really only with female Jerdon's Bushchat (above); for differences, see that species. **Juvenile** is similar to female, but has rufous-buff spotting on upperparts, and buffish underparts with indistinct dark scaling; can be sexed by tail, which is as adult. **VOICE** Song is brief but repeated, starting with two or three emphatic notes and ending with a trill, *tree-toooh tu-treeeh-t-t-t-tuhr* (Roberts 1992); calls include a *zee-chunk*, a sharp *tak-tak*, and a *tic-tic-brzeeee* (Ali and Ripley 1987). **HABITS** Similar to those of Common Stonechat. Territorial on its breeding and wintering grounds. Perches low down on bushes, also high up on telegraph wires. **HABITAT** Bushes at edges and in clearings of forest, scrub-covered hillsides, terraced cultivation with some bushes or secondary growth, and open country with clumps of bushes. **BREEDING** February–July, varying locally. Builds a cup-shaped nest in a hollow on the ground among grass, under a stone or clod of earth, or among tree roots, or in a hole in a wall. **DISTRIBUTION AND STATUS** Resident, subject to altitudinal and local movements. Breeds in Himalayas from N Pakistan east to Arunachal Pradesh, and NE Indian hills; winters south to N Indian plains (Madhya Pradesh). **PK:** common resident in rather restricted range; breeds in outer Himalayas, 1980–2900 m, some wintering in adjacent lower valleys and a few on outer hills and edge of plains. **NP:** common and widespread resident; summers 1500–3355 m, most frequent above 1800 m, winters chiefly 915–2135 m (down to 75 m). **IN:** common resident; breeds 1500–3300 m, winters from 2400 m down to foothills and plains. **BT:** common resident; from 600 m up to 3350 m. **BD:** scarce passage migrant.

HOODED WHEATEAR *Oenanthe monacha* — Plate 109

Hooded Chat (I)

IDENTIFICATION 17.5 cm. Appears elongated, with long bill, but has relatively short legs which give it a less upright stance than most wheatears. Flight can be rather buoyant and hoopoe-like, resembling that of a large

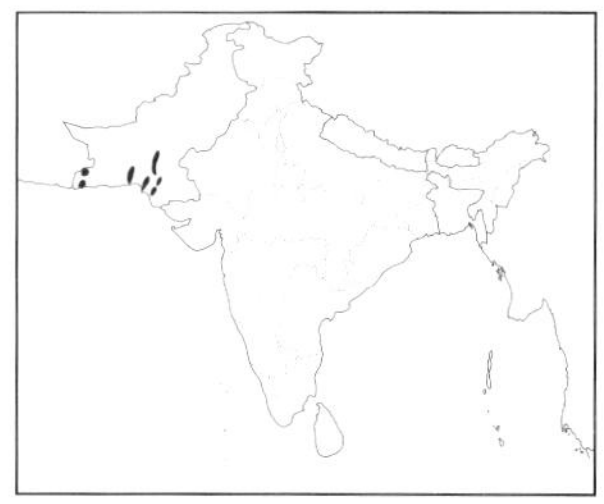

redstart. **Adult male breeding** has white crown contrasting with black mantle, and black throat and upper breast contrasting with white of rest of underparts. Possibly confusable with *capistrata* race of Variable Wheatear (p.665) and Pied Wheatear (p.665), but is larger, with longer bill, has black extending farther onto breast, and has largely white outer tail feathers (although tips may have small black spots or be shaded greyish or blackish). **Adult male winter** is similar to adult male summer, but has buffish or greyish wash to crown and whitish or buffish fringes to black of mantle, wings and breast. **Adult and first-winter female** is distinctive, with sandy to rufous-buff rump and tail with brown central tail feathers, and rather plain-faced appearance (lacking bold eye-stripe or prominent supercilium). In autumn, underparts are rich orange or reddish-brown. **First-winter male** is similar to adult male, but has rump and tail like adult female; also has buff crown and buff wash to underparts, buff fringes to black of mantle and throat/breast, and buff tips/fringes to wing-coverts and flight feathers. **VOICE** Song has short, melodious phrases mixed with stone-clacking notes; a brief thrush-like warble is infrequently given (Porter *et al.* 1996). **HABITS** Similar to those of other wheatears (see Northern Wheatear, below). Shy; has a long escape flight, and sometimes hides after landing. Seeks insects from a low perch, such as a stone, and flies after prey on the ground; also catches insects in aerial sallies, more so than other wheatears. **HABITAT** Barren desert. **BREEDING** Poorly known. Old nests were once found in June, in holes in limestone cliffs. **DISTRIBUTION AND STATUS PK:** rare and local resident in S Baluchistan. **REFERENCES** Clement (1987).

HUME'S WHEATEAR *Oenanthe alboniger* — Plate 109

Hume's Chat (I)

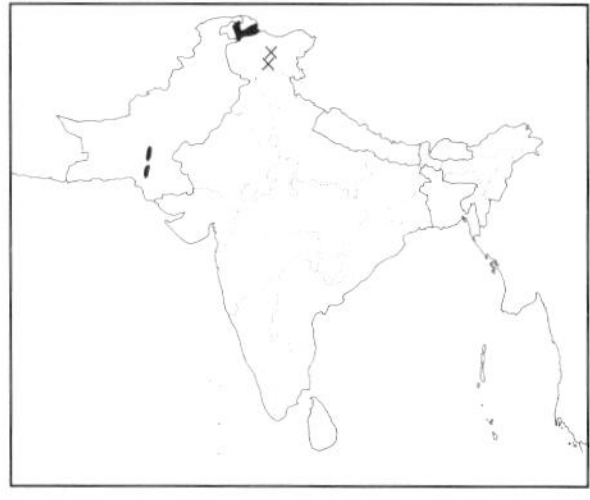

IDENTIFICATION 17 cm. All-black head and largely white underparts separate this from all other wheatears occurring in the subcontinent except *picata* race of Variable Wheatear (p.665). Is larger and stockier than that species, with distinctly domed head, and has larger bill. **Adult** has black head and upper breast contrasting with white of rest of underparts; almost identical in plumage to *picata* race of Variable, but has glossy sheen to black feathering (although absent in worn plumage), white of rump extends farther up lower back, and black of throat does not extend so far onto breast. **First-winter** is similar to adult, but plumage is duller and browner (lacking any sheen) and has buff tips/fringes to wing-coverts. **VOICE** Song is a loud and cheerful *chew-de-dew-twit* and lacks discordant notes of most wheatears; calls include a short, sharp whistle and a harsh quiet *chit-tit-tit* (Cramp 1988). **HABITS** Typical of the genus (see Northern Wheatear, below). Has quite a short escape flight, often landing on a rock or ridge afterwards. Forages by making quick dashes along the ground or by launching aerial sallies from a low perch. **HABITAT** Very barren stony slopes, often with scattered huge boulders and at foot of steep cliffs. **BREEDING** April–June. Builds a cup-shaped nest in a hole in rocks or in a cliff face, sometimes with a rampart of stones and mud. **DISTRIBUTION AND STATUS PK:** resident in Gilgit and locally in Sindh; recorded in winter in NW Baluchistan and S Makran. **IN:** vagrant. **REFERENCES** Clement (1987), Pfister (1997).

NORTHERN WHEATEAR *Oenanthe oenanthe* — Plate 109

Wheatear (I)

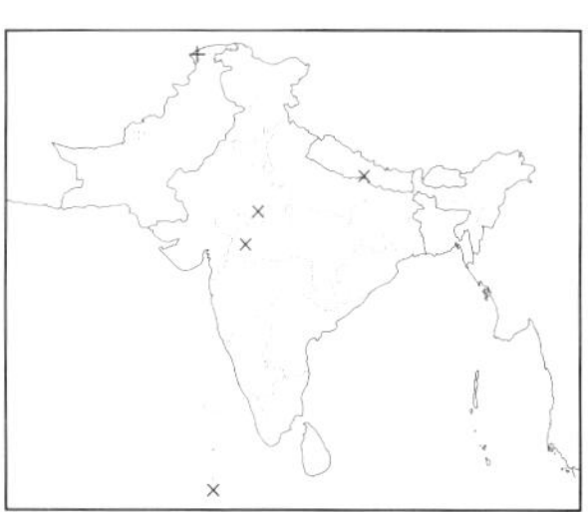

IDENTIFICATION 15 cm. A stocky, comparatively short-tailed wheatear which is very variable in appearance. **Adult male breeding** is distinctive, with blue-grey upperparts, white supercilium and black mask, pale peachy-orange wash to breast, and worn blackish wings. **Adult female breeding** has greyish to olive-brown upperparts with dull black wings; lacks the black mask of male, and has whiter underparts. Easily confusable with female Finsch's Wheatear (p.665), although typically has darker and greyer upperparts, and is best told by more prominent white supercilium (especially behind eye) and lack of rufous on ear-coverts (although rufous can be lacking on Finsch's when worn); never shows dark grey or black on throat and sides of neck which is often apparent on Finsch's (especially when worn). Females with browner upperparts and wings are easily confusable with Isabelline Wheatear (p.667); see below for differences. **Adult winter** and **first-winter** have warm brownish-buff upperparts and a warm buff wash to underparts. Easily confusable with Isabelline, but have slighter bill, look shorter-legged and longer-tailed, have slightly darker, more olive-brown upperparts and blackish centres to wing-coverts and tertials (fringes when fresh are brighter and more rufous), and show more white at sides of tail. **VOICE** Call is a hard *chack*. **HABITS** Like other wheatears, frequently bows whole body and bobs head and forebody, often flicks wings and tail, and at times spreads tail and moves it slowly up and down. Usually has a half-upright carriage, and is fully erect when alert. Forages chiefly by running or hopping on the ground a short distance, then stopping to pick up prey, or drops on to prey from a low perch such as a stone or bush. Usually has a short escape flight and lands on a prominent perch.

HABITAT Open stony ground and cultivation. **BREEDING** No details for the subcontinent. In Europe, nest is an untidy mass, usually built in a burrow, sometimes under a stone. **DISTRIBUTION AND STATUS PK:** passage migrant, mainly in the west and north; has possibly bred in the northwest, at 1280 m. **NP, IN, MV:** vagrant. **REFERENCES** Clement (1987), Vyas (1992b).

FINSCH'S WHEATEAR *Oenanthe finschii* — Plate 109

Barnes's Chat (I)

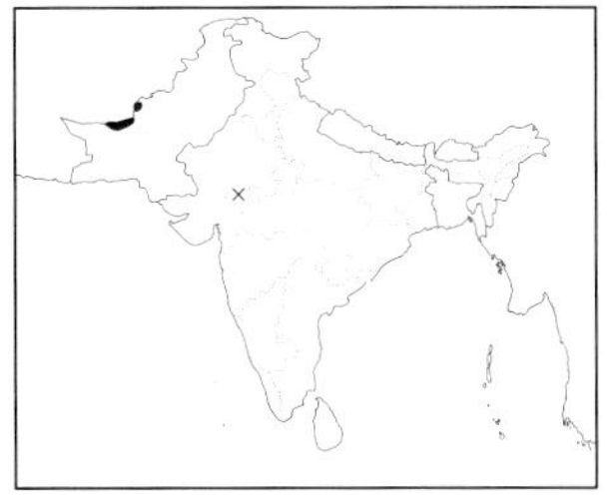

IDENTIFICATION 14 cm. Flight is often darting and somewhat erratic. **Adult male** is similar throughout the year. Superficially resembles male *capistrata* race of Variable Wheatear (below) and male Pied Wheatear (below), but has creamy-buff mantle and upper back (which become white with wear by spring). Further, shows broader black terminal band on tail than most Pied. **Adult female** and **first-winter** have warmer rufous ear-coverts and paler grey-brown upperparts than female Variable and Pied Wheatears, with noticeable contrast between mantle and coverts. In fresh plumage in autumn, throat and breast are paler than on Variable and Pied; adult female, when worn in spring/summer, can show blackish on lower throat. For differences from female Northern Wheatear, see that species (p.664). **VOICE** Song is a scratchy warble, but including some rich fluty whistles; calls include a *zik* and *chek* (Cramp 1988). **HABITS** Typical of the genus (see Northern Wheatear) apart from its flight, which is often darting, with sudden rises or falls and changes of direction. Conspicuous, often perching on telegraph wires. Hunts by making short dashes along the ground and by fluttering to the ground from a perch. Territorial in its breeding and winter quarters. **HABITAT** Desolate dry stony hills and valleys. **BREEDING** April–June. Builds a flat saucer-shaped nest in a hole in a bank or rock face, or under a heap of stones. **DISTRIBUTION AND STATUS PK:** locally frequent and widespread winter visitor to Baluchistan, mainly early October–early March; breeds occasionally. **IN:** vagrant. **REFERENCES** Buckton and Morris (1990), Clement (1987).

VARIABLE WHEATEAR *Oenanthe picata* — Plate 109

Pied Chat (I), Pied Wheatear (F)

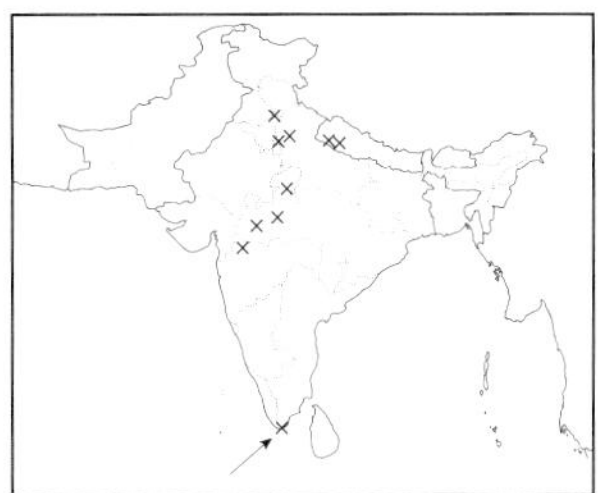

IDENTIFICATION 14.5 cm. Very variable, with three races. **Adult male** *O. p. capistrata* has white to pale grey crown and nape, and white lower breast and belly; for differences from male Pied Wheatear (below), see that species. *O. p. picata* has all-black head and white lower breast and belly, and is extremely similar to Hume's Wheatear (p.664); for main differences, see that species. Intergrades between *capistrata* and *picata* are known from Pakistan. *O. p. opistholeuca* is the most distinctive of the races, being almost entirely black or dark grey, with whitish undertail-coverts. **Adult female** is very variable, with much intergradation. Typical female *capistrata* has grey upperparts and greyish-white underparts (often with some buff); confusion is possible with female Finsch's Wheatear (above; see that species for details). Typical female *picata* has darker grey upperparts, dark grey throat and upper breast, and pale fulvous-white lower breast. Female *O. p. opistholeuca* is similar to male, although is a duller sooty-brown. Females can show rufous-brown on ear-coverts and/or throat and breast. In worn (spring/summer) plumage, many females are not separable from female Pied Wheatear, but in fresh plumage Variable does not show Pied's prominent pale fringes to mantle/scapulars and wing feathers. **VOICE** Song is a long and complicated mixture of low-pitched whistles, chirrups and trills, with much mimicry; calls include a *chek-chek* (Roberts 1992). Calls also include agitated indrawn whistles, a single *pluw* and double *plew-wit*, both very similar to those of Isabelline Wheatear (p.667) (P. Holt from R. Drijvers recording). **HABITS** Typical of the genus (see Northern Wheatear, p.664). Often perches conspicuously on bushes and walls. Forages by flying to the ground from an elevated perch, by hopping on the ground, or in aerial sallies. Territorial on its breeding and wintering grounds. **HABITAT** Breeds in barren open country in valleys and low hills, around villages and old buildings; winters in plains and stony desert foothills, eroded gullies, fallow cultivation, village edges, and sand-dune desert with sparse scrub. **BREEDING** March–August. Builds a saucer-shaped nest, well hidden inside a hole, usually under a rock or in a bank or wall. **DISTRIBUTION AND STATUS** Breeds in Baluchistan and the higher hill ranges of Chitral, NW Pakistan, Gilgit and Baltistan, Pakistan; a winter visitor mainly to Pakistan and NW India (from Jammu and Kashmir south to Gujarat and N Maharashtra and east to W Madhya Pradesh). **PK:** common and widespread; winters in plains and lower hills and valleys. **NP:** very rare and very local winter visitor. **IN:** locally common in the northwest. **REFERENCES** Clement (1987).

PIED WHEATEAR *Oenanthe pleschanka* — Plate 109

Pleschanka's Pied Chat (I)

IDENTIFICATION 14.5 cm. Very similar to Variable Wheatear (above), although is slightly smaller and has different tail pattern. While tail pattern is variable, always shows black edge to outer feathers (lacking on

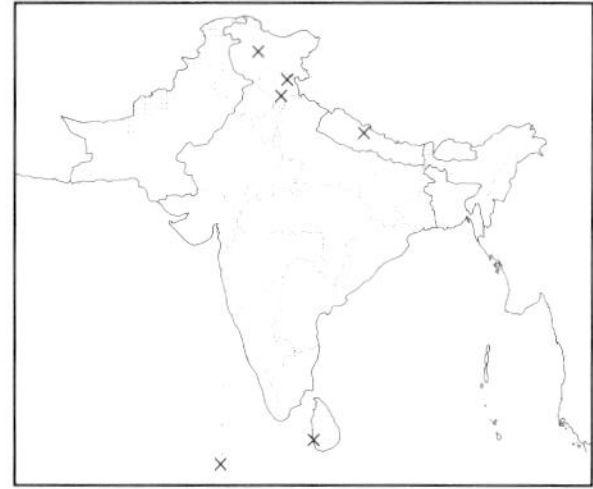

Variable) and often has only a narrow and broken terminal black band (always broad and even on Variable). **Adult male breeding** has white crown and nape and white breast and belly, and is almost identical to *capistrata* race of Variable Wheatear; on Pied, however, white of nape extends onto mantle, black of throat does not extend onto upper breast, and breast is washed with buff. **Adult male non-breeding** and **first-winter male** have black of face and throat partly obscured by whitish fringes, and have grey-brown crown and mantle with broad buff fringes, and broad whitish or buff fringes to wing-coverts and tertials. These plumages are distinct from Variable, which retains a well-defined pale crown and nape and lacks prominent pale fringes to body and wing feathers in fresh plumage (in autumn and early winter). **Adult female breeding** has cold grey-brown upperparts and greyish to blackish throat, and some show orange-buff wash to breast. Probably not separable from female Variable, except by tail pattern. **Adult female non-breeding** and **first-winter female** are similar, but lack black on face and throat; separable from Variable by prominent pale fringes to body and wing feathers. **VOICE** Song is highly variable, consisting of lark-like fluting and whistling, with much mimicry; call is a harsh *zack-zack* (Cramp 1988). **HABITS** Typical of the genus (see Northern Wheatear, p.664). Often perches conspicuously on boulders and buildings. Usually captures insects by flying to the ground from a perch; also by hopping on the ground, and in aerial sallies. **HABITAT** Open stony ground with scattered boulders and no bushes. **BREEDING** May–July. Builds a cup-shaped nest in a hole in a dry bank or under stones. **DISTRIBUTION AND STATUS** Breeds from Gilgit, Baltistan and the Kurram valley, N Pakistan, east to Lahul, Himachal Pradesh; also a passage migrant in Pakistan. **PK:** frequent summer visitor to far N hills, 2700–4100 m, generally replacing Variable Wheatear above 3000 m; scarce passage migrant elsewhere. **IN:** status uncertain. **NP, LK:** vagrant. **MV:** irregular winter visitor. **REFERENCES** Clement (1987).

RUFOUS-TAILED WHEATEAR *Oenanthe xanthoprymna* — Plate 109

Red-tailed Chat (I), Red-tailed Wheatear (R)

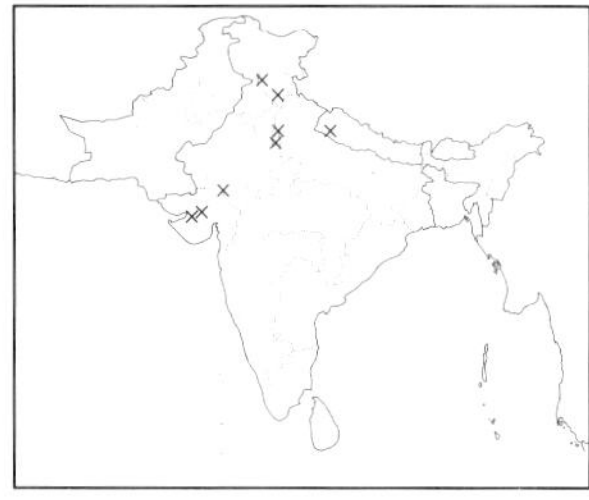

IDENTIFICATION 14.5 cm. Distinguished in all plumages from other wheatears occurring in the subcontinent by rufous-orange lower back and rump and rufous sides to tail. **Adult male** has grey-brown crown and mantle, indistinct pale supercilium and black lores, and warm brown ear-coverts; has broad buff fringes to wing feathers when fresh (autumn), with wings appearing uniform grey-brown when worn (spring). **Female** is similar to male, but lacks black lores and has more sandy-brown upperparts. **First-winter** is similar to adult winter female. **VOICE** Song is a loud warbling, with considerable mimicry; has a low grating call (Roberts 1992). **HABITS** Typical of the genus (see Northern Wheatear, p.664). Forages by making dashes on the ground, often running after prey, and by flying down from an elevated perch, such as a bush or telegraph wire. Sometimes hides in holes. **HABITAT** Summers on dry rocky slopes; winters in semi-desert, on stony or sandy ground with scattered bushes, on low rocky hills and ravines, and at the foot of rocky hillsides. **BREEDING** April–June. Builds a shallow saucer-shaped nest in a small hollow in a cliff or wall, or under stones. **DISTRIBUTION AND STATUS** Breeds in Baluchistan, Pakistan; winter visitor to Pakistan and NW India (from Himachal Pradesh south to Gujarat). **PK:** widespread and locally common winter visitor, commoner on passage in most areas; scarce breeder in Baluchistan. **NP:** vagrant. **IN:** uncommon. **REFERENCES** Clement (1987), Giri and Choudhary (1997).

DESERT WHEATEAR *Oenanthe deserti* — Plate 109

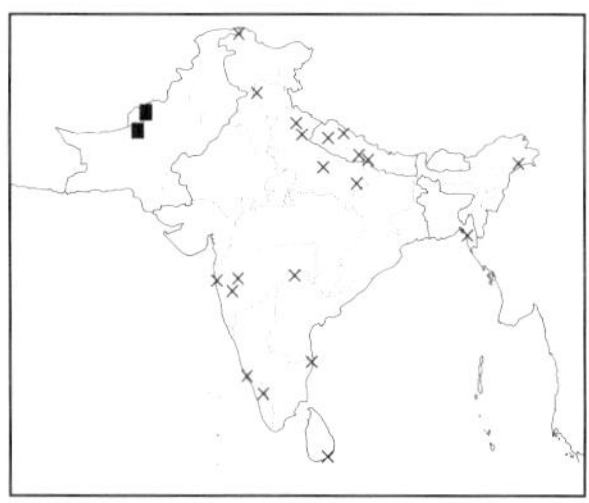

IDENTIFICATION 14–15 cm. A comparatively small and well-proportioned wheatear, distinguished in all plumages from other wheatears occurring in the subcontinent by largely black tail contrasting with white rump. Female is possibly confusable with Isabelline Wheatear (p.667), which can appear to have a largely black tail, but Desert is smaller and more rounded, with a smaller bill, and shows blackish centres to wing-coverts and tertials in fresh plumage and largely black wings when worn. **Adult male breeding** is distinctive, with sandy-brown upperparts, black face and throat (with black extending down sides of neck to reach shoulders), and largely black wings. **Adult female breeding** lacks black throat of male (although may show some black on ear-coverts and lower throat), and has colder grey-brown crown and mantle. **Adult male non-breeding** and **first-winter male** have black of face and throat partly obscured by whitish fringes and have broad whitish or buff fringes to coverts and tertials (especially first-winter). **Adult female non-breeding** and **first-winter female** are similar, but lack black on face and throat. **VOICE** Call is a hard *check-check*. **HABITS** Typical of the genus (see Northern Wheatear, p.664). Has a long escape flight, often hiding behind a plant or rock after landing. Usually feeds by dropping to the ground from a low perch; also by rapidly hopping after prey on the ground, and by aerial sallies. **HABITAT** Breeds on rock or sandy plateaux with scattered *Caragana* bushes; winters in barren semi-desert and on gravel slopes, eroded earth cliffs or sand dunes with scattered scrub. **BREEDING** May–July. Builds a cup-shaped nest in a hollow under a rock on the ground, or in a wall. **DISTRIBUTION AND STATUS** Has bred in Baluchistan, possibly breeds in N Hunza, Pakistan, and also breeds from Kashmir east to NC Nepal; winter visitor mainly to Pakistan and NW India (from Punjab south to Gujarat and east to W Madhya Pradesh). **PK:** common and widespread winter visitor. **NP:** scarce but regular summer visitor and passage migrant in the northwest; summers up to 4880 m, down to 150 m on passage. **IN:** locally common in summer in the west, 3000–5100 m; widespread in the plains in winter. **BD, LK:** vagrant. **REFERENCES** Clement (1987), Sangha (1995).

ISABELLINE WHEATEAR *Oenanthe isabellina* — Plate 109

Isabelline Chat (I)

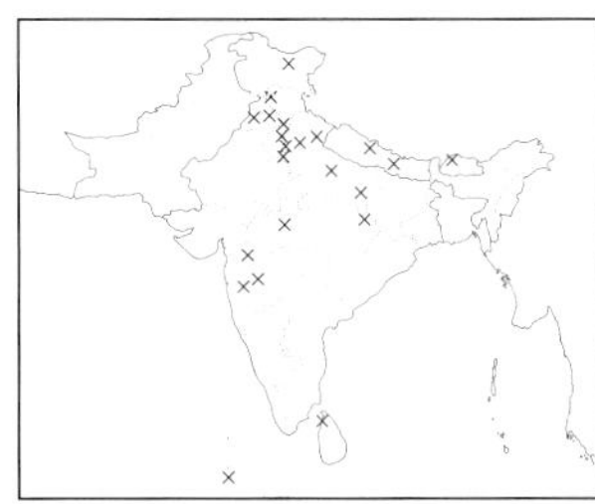

IDENTIFICATION 16.5 cm. A plain sandy-brown and buff wheatear. Stance is typically upright, and head and bill look rather large and tail short. In the subcontinent most likely to be confused with female Desert Wheatear (p.666), and is best told by larger size and larger bill, longer-legged appearance and more upright stance, shorter tail with more white at sides (indented black at base of tail), paler sandy-brown wings with contrastingly dark alula (lacking black centres to coverts and tertials/secondaries), and whitish (rather than black) underwing-coverts giving rise to pale underwing in flight. For differences from Northern Wheatear (p.664), which can appear very similar in adult non-breeding and first-winter plumages, see that species. **Adults** of the two sexes are alike, although male typically has darker lores and more prominent supercilium. In spring/summer has worn wings, which appear browner and more uniform compared with autumn/winter, when wings appear sandier-brown owing to broad sandy-buff fringes to coverts and tertials/secondaries. **Juvenile** is similar to female, but has faint mottling on upperparts and dark markings on breast. **VOICE** Song is very variable, with dramatic speed changes, and comprises a mixture of hard and harsh notes and clear whistles (Alström and Colston 1991); call is a hard *chack*. **HABITS** Typical of the genus (see Northern Wheatear). Typically, feeds by making rapid dashes after prey on the ground; also by dropping to the ground from a perch. **HABITAT** Breeds on stony plateaux or in valleys and eroded gullies; winters in sandy semi-desert with scattered bushes, preferring more sandy ground to that frequented by Desert Wheatear. **BREEDING** March–June. Builds a shallow cup-shaped nest in a deep hole, usually that of a rodent. **DISTRIBUTION AND STATUS** Breeds in C and N Baluchistan and NW Pakistan; winters in Pakistan and mainly NW India (Rajasthan and Gujarat). **PK:** widespread and locally common; winters throughout the uncultivated parts of Indus plains and in lower foothills; breeds 900–1500 m; also a passage migrant in the far north. **NP:** rare spring passage migrant; 1370–2590 m. **IN:** fairly common winter visitor to NW plains; passage migrant elsewhere in the north. **BT, LK:** vagrant. **MV:** fairly regular autumn passage migrant. **REFERENCES** Alström and Colston (1991), Clement (1987), Murphy (1994).

BROWN ROCK-CHAT *Cercomela fusca* — Plate 108

Indian Chat

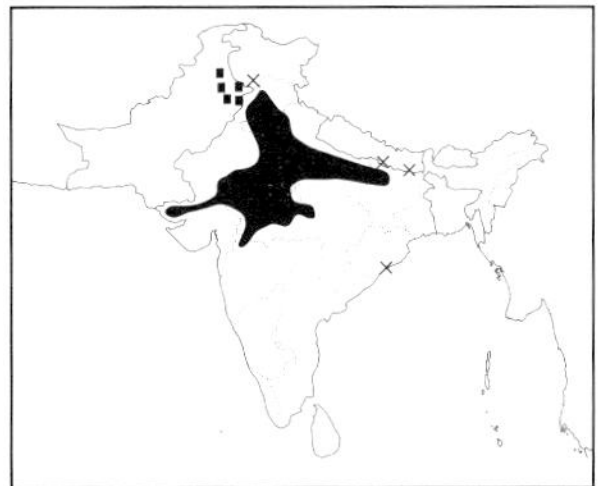

IDENTIFICATION 17 cm. Similar in behaviour and habits to Blue Rock Thrush (p.620). Is smaller and longer-tailed; tail is frequently (slowly) cocked and spread, and body frequently bobbed. **Adult** is uniform rufous-brown, with darker wings and blackish tail. Distinguished from female Blue Rock Thrush by absence of pale spotting and scaling on underparts. From female Indian Robin (p.652) by larger size, stockier appearance, and absence of chestnut vent. **Juvenile** is similar to adult, but is darker brown, without rufous coloration. **VOICE** Song is sweet and thrush-like, although can include much mimicry; calls include a short, whistling *chee* and a harsh *check-check* (Ali and Ripley 1987). **HABITS** Confiding; often perches on roofs and walls, and even enters occupied buildings. Territorial, and frequently found in the same locality throughout the year. Feeds on insects, captured mainly by flying to the ground from a perch or by picking from a crevice. **HABITAT** Rocky hills, cliffs and ravines, old forts and tombs, ruins in urban areas, quarries, and walls and houses in towns and cities. **BREEDING** February–August. Builds a rough, shallow cup-shaped nest in a rock crevice, in a hollow in a wall or on a ledge of a building; usually has a rampart of small pebbles and earth lumps. **DISTRIBUTION AND STATUS** Resident, endemic to the subcontinent. Mainly N Pakistan and from Jammu and Kashmir east to C Bihar and south to N Maharashtra and C Madhya Pradesh. **PK:** scarce and very local in the north. **NP:** rare and very local in the terai. **IN:** local, common in some areas and uncommon or absent in other apparently similar areas; plains and hills up to 1000 m, locally to 1300 m in Himalayas and to 1800 m in peninsular hills. **LK:** common in lowlands and up to middle altitudes, more frequent in dry zone.

STARLINGS AND MYNAS Sturnidae

Robust, medium-sized passerines with strong legs and bill, moderately long wings and a square tail. The flight is direct; strong and fast in the more pointed-winged species (*Sturnus*), and rather slower with more deliberate flapping in the more rounded-winged ones. Most species walk with an upright stance in a characteristic, purposeful jaunty fashion, broken by occasional short runs and hops. Typically, starlings are noisy and garrulous. Their calls are often loud, harsh and grating, and the song of many species is a variety of whistles; mimicry is common. Most are highly gregarious at times, especially when feeding and roosting, and many form loose breeding colonies. Some starlings in the region are mainly arboreal and feed on fruits, often of *Ficus* figs, nectar (favouring *Bombax*, *Erythrina* and *Salmalia* species) and insects; others are chiefly ground-feeders, and are omnivorous. Many are closely associated with human cultivation and habitation. The nest is usually an untidy collection of plant material, and, with the exception of the Bank Myna, is placed in a natural hole or one excavated by another species, such as a barbet or woodpecker.

ASIAN GLOSSY STARLING *Aplonis panayensis* — Plate 110

Glossy Stare (I), Philippine Glossy Starling (K)

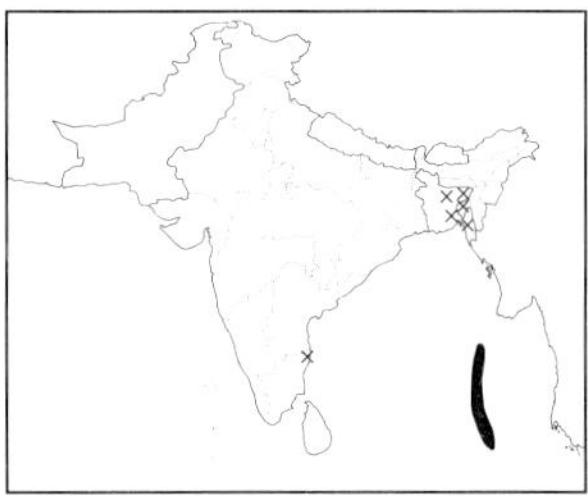

IDENTIFICATION 20 cm. A slim, dark starling with stout black bill. **Adult** is entirely glossy greenish-black, with bright red iris. **Juvenile** has blackish-brown upperparts with variable greenish gloss, buffy-white underparts which are heavily streaked with blackish-brown (streaking also with variable greenish gloss), and yellowish-white iris. **VOICE** Call consists of sharp ringing whistles, *tseu...tseu* etc (C. Robson). **HABITS** A typical starling. Chiefly arboreal. Feeds on insects, nectar and small figs, often with other starlings in flowering and fruiting trees. **HABITAT** Coconut groves, forest edges and clearings with large fig trees. **BREEDING** March–May. Nest is in a tree hole, usually high up. **DISTRIBUTION AND STATUS** Partly resident. Breeding visitor to Assam (Cachar hills), resident on Andaman and Nicobar Is, also recorded in Meghalaya, Tripura and Bangladesh. **IN:** common on Andaman and Nicobar Is; elsewhere, status is uncertain. **BD:** rare passage migrant.

SPOT-WINGED STARLING *Saroglossa spiloptera* — Plate 110

Spotted-winged Stare (I), Spot-winged Stare (F)

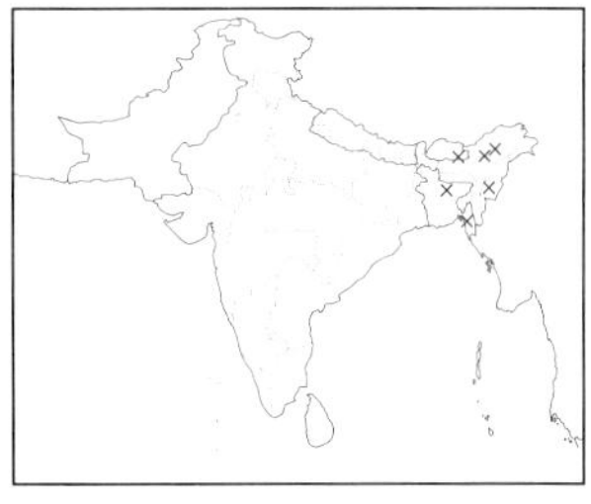

IDENTIFICATION 19 cm. A slim starling with a white wing patch (at base of primaries) and whitish iris. **Adult male** has blackish mask extending through ear-coverts to sides of neck, reddish-chestnut throat, whitish underparts with variable pale rusty-orange on breast and flanks, greyish upperparts scalloped with blackish on crown and brown on mantle (resulting in marbled effect), and rufous-brown uppertail-coverts. **Adult female** has brown upperparts with greyer centres to feathers (resulting in patterning similar to male's), slightly darker brown ear-coverts, whitish throat spotted and streaked with greyish-brown, and more diffuse brownish-grey mottling on breast. **Juvenile** is similar to female, but (at least on some) has buff tips to median and greater coverts forming double wing-bar, has dull rufous-brown rump, and upperparts are more uniform. Juvenile male shows faint blotches of rufous on throat. **VOICE** Song similar to that of Rosy Starling (p.670), a continuous harsh, unmusical jumble of dry, discordant notes and a few melodious warbles; calls include an explosive scolding *kwerrh* and a grating nasal *schaik* (P. Holt). **HABITS** A typical starling. Prefers to feed on flower nectar, using its specially adapted bill; also eats insects, figs and berries. Keeps in noisy flocks, often with mynas and drongos on flowering and fruiting trees, rarely on the ground. Has a bullying manner when feeding. Occasionally, and for no apparent reason, the flock will dive into the air and circle rapidly once or twice before resettling and carrying on feeding as before. **HABITAT** Open broadleaved forest and forest edges and clearings, and cultivation with groves or scattered trees of *Bombax*, *Erythrina* and *Salmalia* trees, which it favours. **BREEDING** April–June. Builds nest in a tree hole, 6–10 m above ground. **DISTRIBUTION AND STATUS** Status uncertain; an east-west migrant, probably resident. Himalayan foothills from W Himachal Pradesh east to Arunachal Pradesh; NE India and Bangladesh. **NP:** passage migrant and breeder, recorded in most months; frequent throughout below 915 m, uncommon up to 1830 m. **IN:** passage migrant and breeder; foothills up to 2000 m in summer; summers in W Himalayas, winters in NE hills; common in winter in Assam. **BT:** rare. **BD:** rare visitor, no recent records.

WHITE-FACED STARLING *Sturnus senex* — Plate 110

Ceylon White-headed Myna (I), Ceylon White-headed Starling (P)

IDENTIFICATION 22 cm. **Adult** has dirty white forehead and face, dark lavender-grey upperparts with slight green gloss, and pale lavender-grey underparts with fine white shaft streaking. On some birds, most of head is white. Bill is bluish-brown, with plumbeous blue at base of lower mandible. **Juvenile** has whitish supercilium,

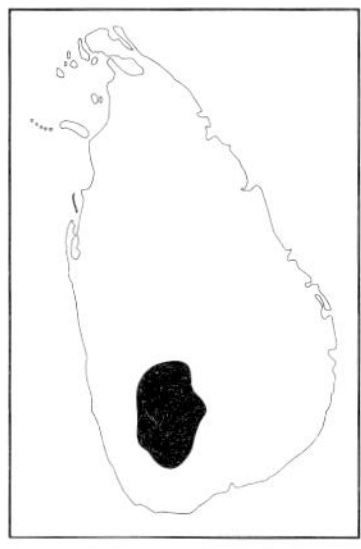

ear-coverts and throat; upperparts are dull brown, and underparts are dark grey (lacking shaft streaking of adult). **VOICE** A starling-type *chirp*, but generally rather silent (Legge 1880). **HABITS** Arboreal, and spends most of the time in the treetops. Commonly found in small flocks. Feeds on fruits and insects, taken by walking gracefully along branches. **HABITAT** Tall natural forest. **BREEDING** Little known. One nest in a tree hole in April. **DISTRIBUTION AND STATUS LK:** endemic resident, rare in wet zone from foothills up to middle altitudes.

CHESTNUT-TAILED STARLING *Sturnus malabaricus* — Plate 110

Grey-headed Myna (F,I,P)

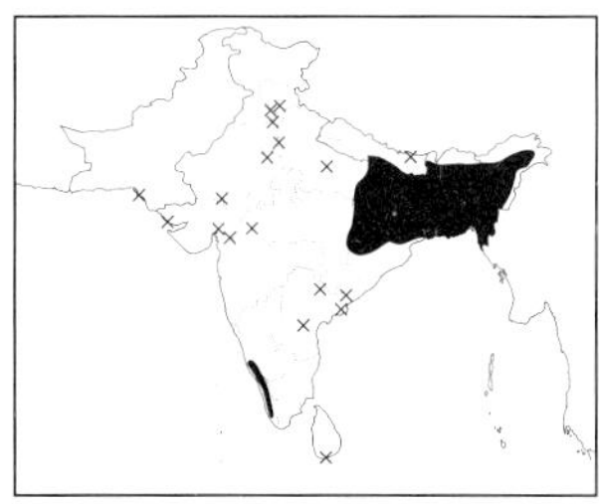

IDENTIFICATION 20 cm. **Adult** has grey head and upperparts, with whitish forehead and throat and whitish lanceolate feathers across crown, nape, sides of neck and breast; underparts are typically rufous, and tail is mainly chestnut with grey central feathers. There is much variation, with whitish lanceolate feathers less apparent on some birds (particularly females), when head appears more uniformly pale grey, and underparts can be pale rufous-buff. **Juvenile** has pale sandy-grey upperparts and greyish-white underparts, with darker brownish-grey wings and tail. Rufous sides and tips to outer tail feathers are best distinction from other juvenile starlings. **Racial variation** Male *S. m. blythii* of SW peninsula and Western Ghats differs from adult of the widespread nominate race, described above, in having white head and breast which contrast strongly with grey of mantle and with rufous on belly and flanks. Female *blythii* has white of head confined to forehead and forecrown, and underparts are paler rufous. **VOICE** A sharp, disyllabic metallic note, and a mild, tremulous single whistle (Ali and Ripley 1987). **HABITS** A typical starling. Chiefly arboreal, although will descend to flowering bushes and sometimes to the ground. Usually feeds in flocks, often with other starlings and mynas, the birds constantly chattering and squabbling. Forages by hopping about branches, seeking nectar, berries and figs; also captures insects, often by clinging acrobatically to flower clusters, twigs and fruits. From time to time the flock dives into the air, wheels around a couple of times, and then settles and carries on as before. **HABITAT** Lightly wooded country, groves, young forest plantations, sometimes around villages and towns. **BREEDING** February–July, varying locally. Builds nest in a barbet or woodpecker hole, 3–12 m above ground. **DISTRIBUTION AND STATUS** Resident in NE subcontinent and SW Indian hills; winter visitor to C and W India, with scattered records elsewhere. Subject to marked seasonal movements during the SW monsoon and in winter. **PK:** vagrant to SE Sindh. **NP:** recorded in all months, but has poorly understood migratory movements; fairly common and widespread below 1370 m. **IN:** locally common; plains and hills up to 1500 m, locally to 2000 m in Himalayas, to 1200 m in NE and peninsular hills. **BT:** frequent. **BD:** common throughout. **LK:** rare, irregular visitor.

WHITE-HEADED STARLING *Sturnus erythropygius* — Plate 110

White-headed Myna (I)

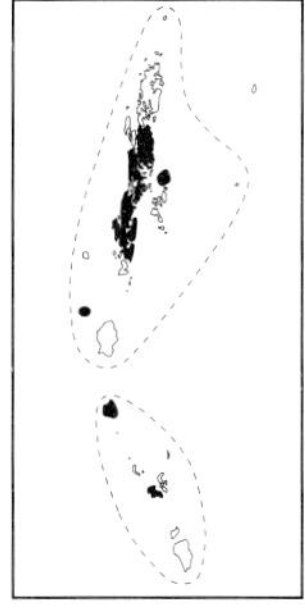

IDENTIFICATION 21 cm. **Adult** readily identified by combination of creamy-white head and underparts, grey mantle and back, and glossy greenish-black wings and tail. Has greenish-yellow bill with blue base, and yellowish legs. **Juvenile** is said to be similar to adult, but has brownish-grey shaft streaking on crown and rufous fringes to feathers of wings. **Racial variation** *S. e. erythropygius* of Car Nicobar has rufous rump, uppertail- and undertail-coverts and sides/tip of tail. *S. e. andamanensis* of the Andaman Is has rump pale grey, with white sides and tip of tail and creamy-white to buff undertail-coverts. **VOICE** Noisy, metallic bulbul-like chatter of four to six notes (P. Holt). **HABITS** Very similar to those of Chestnut-tailed (above). **HABITAT** Forest clearings, cultivation and grassland. **BREEDING** March–May. Builds nest in a tree hole, 2–10 m above ground. **DISTRIBUTION AND STATUS IN:** endemic to Andaman and Nicobar Is (Car Nicobar and Katchall, introduced to Camorta), where common. **REFERENCES** Davidar *et al.* (1997).

BRAHMINY STARLING *Sturnus pagodarum* — Plate 110

Black-headed Myna (I), Brahminy Mynah (F,P)

IDENTIFICATION 21 cm. A thick-necked, stout-billed starling with rounded wings, giving rise to myna-like profile. In flight, which is less rapid than that of other *Sturnus* starlings, combination of smaller size, white sides and tip to dark tail, and uniform wings without white wing patch separates this species from mynas. **Adult** has black on crown and crest which extends across nape, with rest of head, neck and underparts rufous-orange (with paler shaft streaking); and has grey upperparts and wings with darker flight feathers, yellowish bill with blue base, and

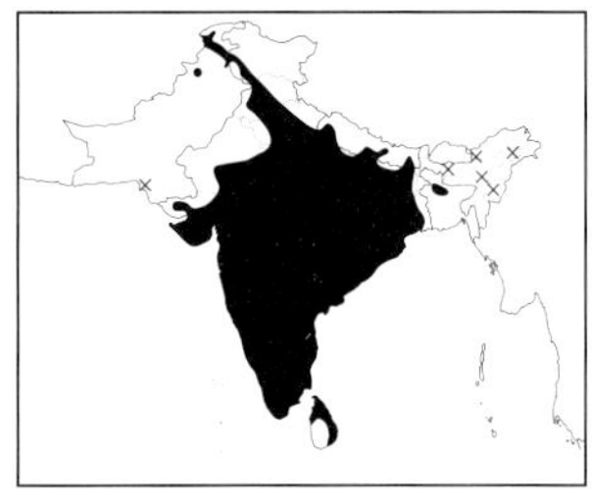

blue or yellow skin behind eye. **Juvenile** lacks crest, but has grey-brown cap, paler orange-buff underparts (lacking shaft streaking of adult), buffish wash to grey upperparts and buff fringes to wing-coverts and tertials/secondaries, and duller bill, with olive-coloured patch behind eye. **VOICE** Territorial song is rather short, comprising a gurgling drawn-out cry followed by a louder, more vehement bubbling yodel, rendered as *gu-u-weerh-kwurti-kwee-ah* (Roberts 1992). **HABITS** A typical starling. Forages on the ground for insects in a sprightly manner; also takes fruits, berries and nectar in trees. Less gregarious than most species, often occurring singly, in pairs or in small groups, but gathers in large flocks at rich food sources and at communal roosts, often with parakeets and mynas. **HABITAT** Cultivation with groves and scattered trees, open dry deciduous forest, grassland and dry thorny scrub. **BREEDING** February–September. Nests in a hole, usually with a small entrance, in a trunk, branch, wall or roof. **DISTRIBUTION AND STATUS** Resident and partial migrant. Throughout much of the subcontinent, except the more arid parts of the northwest and moist evergreen biotope in the northeast. **PK:** rather local and erratically distributed; a frequent summer visitor to Himalayan foothills and border valleys, mainly 900–1800 m. **NP:** frequent in the west, uncommon in the centre and east; mainly below 915 m (–3050 m); has poorly understood seasonal movements. **IN:** locally common and widespread; plains and hills, up to 1800 m in Himalayas (–3000 m), summer visitor to W Himalayas. **BD:** local. **LK:** rare; resident in dry lowlands, more frequent in dry coastal areas.

PURPLE-BACKED STARLING *Sturnus sturninus* — Plate 110

Daurian Myna (I), Daurian Starling

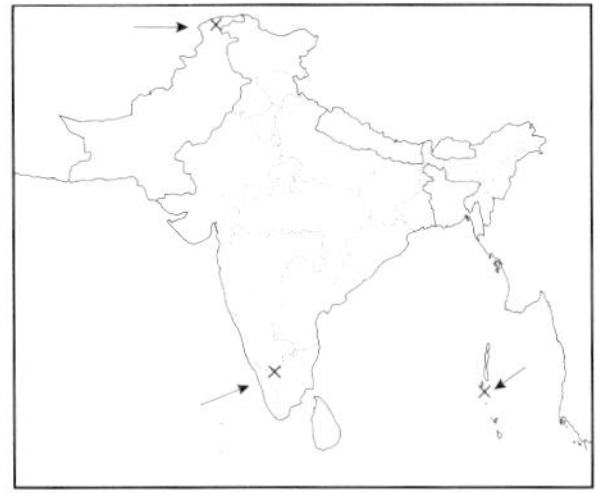

IDENTIFICATION 19 cm. A comparatively small, stocky starling with short tail and stout bill. **Adult male** is striking, with pale grey head, nape and underparts, purplish-black patch on hindcrown, purplish-black mantle, broad white tips to median coverts and rear scapulars forming prominent white V from behind, and glossy greenish-black wings with greyish-white tips to inner greater coverts and tertials. **Female** is similarly patterned to male, but duller, with grey-brown mantle and duller wings and tail. Combination of indistinct dark patch on hindcrown (not always apparent), distinctive wing pattern (white tips to median coverts and rear scapulars, as well as pale grey panel on secondaries), greyish-white to buffish uppertail-coverts, and blackish tail with greyish-white at sides (but not tip) are best features for separation from other starlings. **Juvenile** is similar to female, but duller, with browner wings, less white on scapulars, and only narrow grey tips to median coverts. **VOICE** Call when flushed a slow, soft, drawn-out *chirrup*, resembling similar call of Common Starling (p.671) (Riddiford *et al.* 1989). **HABITS** A typical starling. Has the jaunty walk and short bounding run of Common Starling. Feeds on insects, berries and fruits. **HABITAT** Undescribed in the region. Lightly wooded country in breeding areas. **DISTRIBUTION AND STATUS PK, IN:** vagrant.

WHITE-SHOULDERED STARLING *Sturnus sinensis* — Plate 110

Chinese Myna (I)

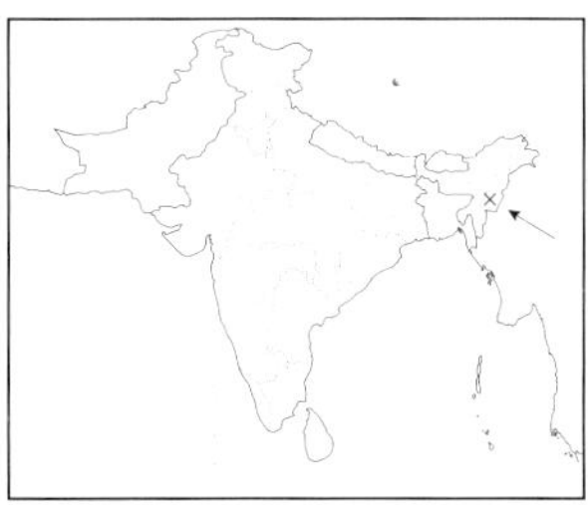

IDENTIFICATION 20 cm. **Adult male** has silky-grey head and body with white forehead and throat, and white scapulars and wing-coverts forming large white patch and contrasting with black of rest of wing. In flight, pale grey uppertail-coverts contrast with black base of tail, which has greyish-white sides and tip. Many birds throughout year have (variable) pale rusty-orange wash to forehead, lores, flanks, greater coverts, uppertail-coverts and tail sides/tip. **Adult female** is brownish-grey, with faint gloss to blackish wings; has variable but less extensive area of white on wing than male (typically, white is confined to inner greater coverts, although is lacking on some). Pale grey uppertail-coverts and black tail with greyish-white sides and tip help separate birds lacking white on wing from Chestnut-tailed (p.669). As on male, white on greater coverts, as well as uppertail-coverts and sides/tip to tail, can be washed with pale rusty-orange. **Juvenile** resembles female, although upperparts and underparts are paler, and wings are browner and without gloss; fringes to coverts and tertials are sandy-grey, and usually lacks white on wing, while greyish-white sides and tip to tail are much narrower and less distinct. **VOICE** Unknown in the region. **HABITS** A typical starling. Described as gregarious, cheerful and noisy, feeding in trees as well as on the ground. **HABITAT** Undescribed in the region. **DISTRIBUTION AND STATUS IN:** vagrant to the northeast.

ROSY STARLING *Sturnus roseus* — Plate 110

Rosy Pastor (F,I), Rose-coloured Starling (R)

IDENTIFICATION 21 cm. **Adult summer** has purple-black head with shaggy crest, pink bill with black base, clear pink mantle and underparts, and blue-green gloss to wings. **Adult winter** has pink of plumage duller owing to

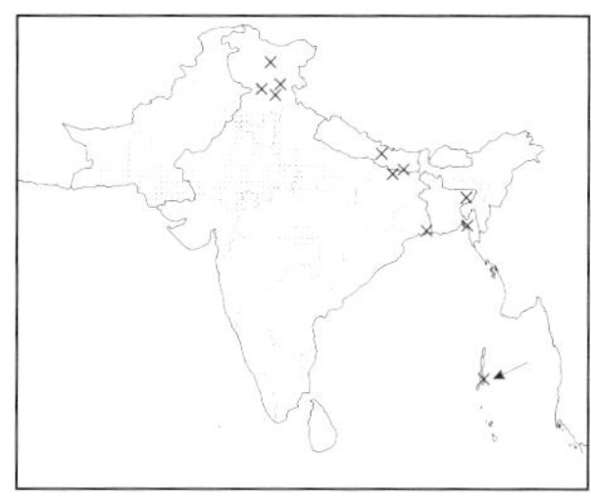

brownish-buff fringes; has greyish fringes to black of head, nape and breast, and dull brownish-pink bill. **First-winter** resembles adult winter, but is generally duller (especially female); head, nape and breast have broad brownish-buff fringes, mantle is fawn-brown with pink hardly apparent, has buffish fringes to coverts and tertials, and underparts are pinkish-buff. **Juvenile** is mainly sandy-brown. Stout yellowish bill, pale rump contrasting with dark tail, paler coloration, with diffuse streaking on breast, pale lores, and broad pale fringes to wing feathers separate it from juvenile Common Starling (below). **VOICE** Flight call is a loud, clear *ki-ki-ki*; also has a *shrr* like Common Starling, and a rattling *chik-ik-ik-ik* when feeding (Jonsson 1992). **HABITS** Similar to those of Common Starling, but more gregarious and often forms huge flocks at rich feeding sources. Follows locust swarms and helps to control this pest; runs about, actively chasing locusts, sometimes springing into the air to catch them. Causes extensive damage to cereal crops by feeding on grain. Attracted to flowering and fruiting trees, and then feeds like Chestnut-tailed Starling (p.669). Follows grazing livestock to catch insects they disturb, and probes for insects in damp grassland like Common Starling. Flocks often suddenly take flight for no apparent reason, and turn and wheel in unison before settling and carrying on feeding as before. Roosts communally in enormous noisy flocks, often with other species. **HABITAT** Cultivation, damp grassland, thorn scrub and mulberry groves. **DISTRIBUTION AND STATUS** Winter visitor to Gujarat and peninsular India and Sri Lanka; passage migrant in NW subcontinent. **PK:** common passage migrant, passing through in SE direction in autumn and NW in spring. **NP:** vagrant. **IN:** common winter visitor to Gujarat and the Deccan, becoming less frequent farther south. **BD:** vagrant. **LK:** irregular winter visitor to dry lowlands, more frequent in the north.

COMMON STARLING *Sturnus vulgaris* — Plate 110

Starling (I), Eurasian Starling (F)

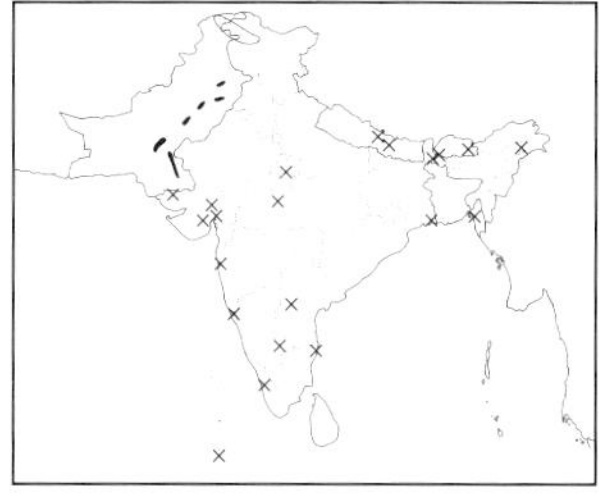

IDENTIFICATION 21 cm. **Adult breeding** is metallic green and purple, with fine golden-buff tips to feathers of mantle. Bill is yellow and legs and feet dull red. **Adult non-breeding** has dark bill; upperparts are heavily spangled with buff, wing feathers have broad buff fringes, and underparts are boldly spotted with white. **Juvenile** is entirely dusky brown, with whiter throat, and buff fringes to wing-coverts and flight feathers. **VOICE** Song is a varied combination of chirps, twitters, clicks and drawn-out clear whistles, with much mimicry; flocking birds utter a slurred *scree-scree*. **HABITS** A typical starling. Forms large feeding flocks, in which the birds are energetic, restless, quarrelsome and constantly alert; often the whole flock will take off and wheel around together, like Rosy Starlings (p.670). Forages mainly on the ground with a confident waddling walk, feeding chiefly on insects, by pecking and probing at the ground; often stalks around grazing livestock or follows the plough. Also eats fruits and berries. Congregates in huge noisy roosts, often with other species. **HABITAT** Cultivation, mulberry groves, damp grassland and irrigated lawns. **BREEDING** March–June, varying locally. Builds a typical starling nest, usually in a hole in a tree, bank or wall or under eaves of village houses. **DISTRIBUTION AND STATUS** Sedentary resident close to the Indus R system, Pakistan; summer visitor to Kashmir; winter visitor mainly to N subcontinent from C Pakistan east to E Nepal; scattered records farther south. **PK:** very local resident; common and widespread in winter. **NP:** uncommon and widespread in winter and on passage; mainly below 1500 m (–2805 m). **IN:** 1500–2500 m in Kashmir in summer; common in winter in the north, becoming less frequent in the northeast and south. **BT, BD, MV:** vagrant.

ASIAN PIED STARLING *Sturnus contra* — Plate 110

Pied Myna (F,I)

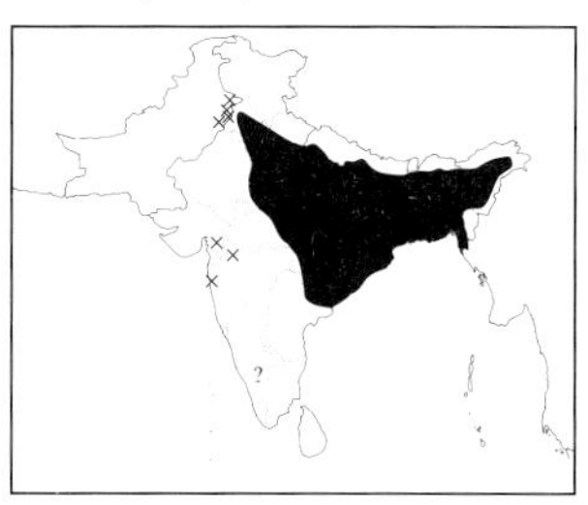

IDENTIFICATION 23 cm. **Adult** is black and white, with orange orbital skin and large, pointed yellowish bill. Has white ear-coverts, black throat and breast contrasting with pale grey to dirty white underparts, and white scapular line and inner wing-coverts contrasting with black wings. In flight, white uppertail-coverts contrast with black tail. **Juvenile** superficially resembles adult, but black of plumage is replaced by dark brown; has brown wash to white ear-coverts, which (when young) are not clearly demarcated from sides of neck, while dark brown of throat and breast is marked with white or buff, and breast-band is not clearly defined. **Racial variation** *S. c. superciliaris*, occurring in Manipur, differs from other races in subcontinent in having white streaking on forehead and forecrown. **VOICE** Assortment of high-pitched musical liquid notes. **HABITS** A typical starling. Mainly terrestrial. Seeks insects by digging in damp ground; also eats cereal grain, ripe fruit and flower nectar. Usually in small parties in the non-breeding season and forms noisy communal roosts, sometimes of up to a few hundred birds. **HABITAT** Open cultivation, damp grassland, refuse dumps and sewage farms; often near habitation or grazing animals. **BREEDING** March–October. Builds a large untidy nest in outer branches of trees, 5–10 m above ground, usually near habitation. **DISTRIBUTION AND STATUS** Resident, subject to local movements. Mainly from NE Pakistan east to NE India and south to Bangladesh, and N Andhra Pradesh; absent from more arid areas. **PK:** rare and local. **NP:** fairly common and widespread; below 305 m (–1370 m, possibly escaped birds). **IN:** locally common in plains and hills up to 800 m; patchily distributed in some areas. **BT:** locally common. **BD:** common throughout.

COMMON MYNA *Acridotheres tristis* — Plate 111

Common Mynah

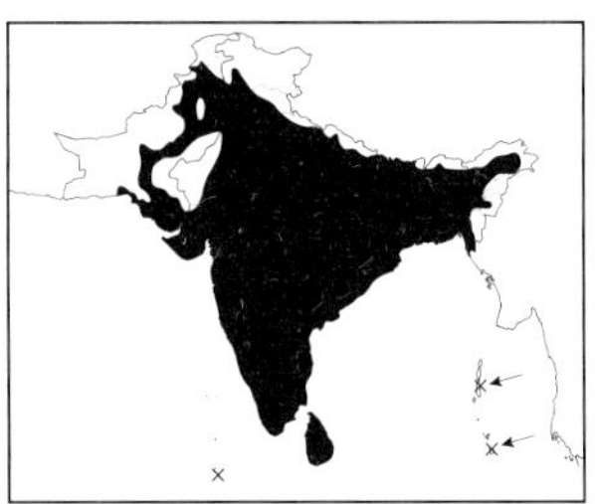

IDENTIFICATION 25 cm. A large myna with yellow orbital skin, and one of the most familiar birds in villages, towns and cities in the region, frequently seen scavenging in streets and bazaars. Has a strong direct flight, more flapping than that of *Sturnus* species. **Adult** has glossy black on head and breast merging into maroon-brown of rest of body. Has large white patch at base of primaries, white tip to tail, and white vent. **Juvenile** is duller than adult, with brownish-black rather than glossy black head and paler brown throat and breast. Combination of yellow orbital skin, white patch on wing and white tip to tail separate it from other juvenile mynas. **Racial variation** Birds in Sri Lanka are race *melanosternus*, but nominate race occurs throughout the rest of the subcontinent. **VOICE** Most distinctive is the harsh *chake-chake* call when alarmed; when flushed, utters a rather weak *kweerh*. Song is disjointed, noisy and tuneless, with gurgling and whistling, and much repetition. **HABITS** Usually in pairs or small parties. Bold, tame and pugnacious. Commonly scavenges in built-up areas, and flocks often follow grazing cattle or the plough, or feed in cultivation. Feeds chiefly on the ground; strides jauntily along with rapid determined steps, occasionally stopping to pick up an item of food or probe the ground. Omnivorous, diet includes insects, ripe fruits and berries, flowers, nectar and food refuse. Perches readily in trees. Forms large noisy communal roosts, often with other species. **HABITAT** Cultivation, villages, towns, cities, also isolated houses in forest or desert. **BREEDING** February–December, varying locally. Builds an untidy nest in a rock face, earth bank, wall or under eaves. **DISTRIBUTION AND STATUS** Resident throughout much of the subcontinent, except parts of the northwest and northeast. **PK:** common and widespread. **NP:** common and widespread; regular up to at least 1830 m all year, occasionally summers up to 3050 m and winters to 2135 m. **IN:** common and widespread; in plains and hills up to 3000 m, descends from higher altitudes in winter. **BT:** common; 150–2800 m (–3370 m). **BD:** common throughout. **LK:** common in lowlands and lower hills. **MV:** introduced, but has since died out. **REFERENCES** Inskipp and Inskipp (1996).

BANK MYNA *Acridotheres ginginianus* — Plate 111

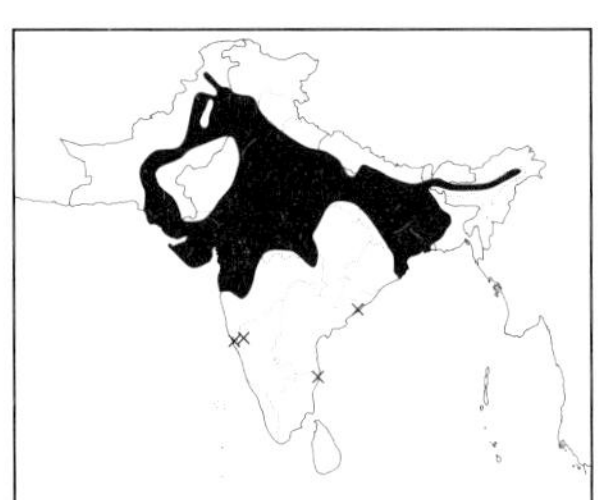

IDENTIFICATION 23 cm. Similar to Common Myna (above) and, like that species, also occurs locally in cities. **Adult** distinguished from Common by smaller size, orange-red orbital patch, orange-yellow bill, orange-buff patch at base of primaries and on underwing-coverts, and orange-buff tip to tail. Further, has glossy black crown and ear-coverts contrasting with bluish-grey body (throat and breast are concolorous with rest of underparts, and has capped appearance rather than the hooded appearance of Common); also, usually shows short but prominent tuft on forehead, and buff vent and undertail-coverts. Orange-red orbital skin and orange-buff on wings and tail are best distinctions from Jungle Myna (below). **Juvenile** is duller than adult, having dark brown crown and ear-coverts, browner upperparts and underparts, and brown wings with narrow rufous tips to greater coverts and tertials. Wing patch and underwing-coverts are paler buffish-white than on adult, and rufous-buff tips to tail feathers are narrower and less well defined, but these features help to separate it from juvenile Common; smaller size, orangish orbital patch and buffish vent and undertail-coverts are additional useful features. **VOICE** Calls and song are similar to those of Common Myna, but generally not so loud and strident. **HABITS** Similar to those of Common Myna, but rather more gregarious, usually keeping in small flocks in breeding season and in large flocks in winter. Roosts in huge numbers with other species. Feeds chiefly on the ground; also regularly rides on backs of grazing animals, seeking invertebrates. **HABITAT** Irrigated cultivation, sewage farms and damp grassland, often with livestock and around villages; also in towns and cities in India, where, like Common Myna, is often seen around railway stations and in busy bazaars. **BREEDING** March–August. Nests colonially, often up to 50 birds together. Builds nest in a tunnel excavated by the birds in a steep earth bank; sometimes in a hole in a river or canal bank or road cutting. **DISTRIBUTION AND STATUS** Endemic to the subcontinent, where resident, subject to seasonal movements. Mainly from Pakistan east to Assam and Bangladesh and south to C Maharashtra and N Orissa. **PK:** widespread in Sindh and Punjab, common in rice-growing areas of the plains. **NP:** fairly common and widespread but local, mainly in the terai (–1370 m, possibly escaped birds). **IN:** locally common and patchily distributed; plains and hills, locally up to 800 m. **BT:** local and uncommon. **BD:** local.

JUNGLE MYNA *Acridotheres fuscus* — Plate 111

IDENTIFICATION 23 cm. **Adult** superficially resembles Bank Myna (above), but has more prominent tuft of feathers at base of bill, white patch at base of primaries and white tip to tail, and lacks bare orbital skin. Grey

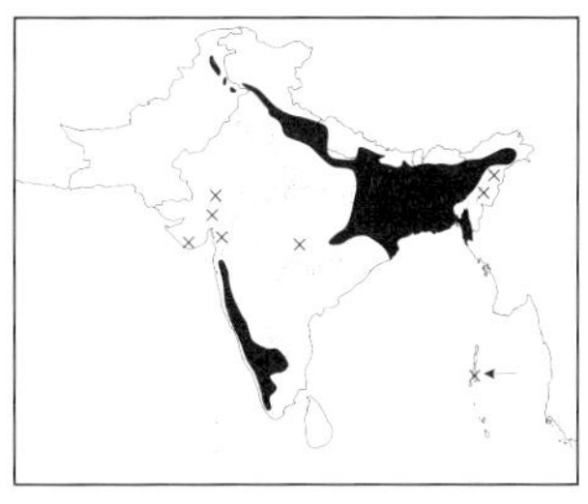

coloration to body, tufted forehead, and absence of yellow orbital skin separate it from Common Myna (p.672). Black of crown and ear-coverts merges into grey or grey-brown of upperparts (with 'cap' much less clearly demarcated from mantle than on Bank), and grey of throat merges into pinkish-grey of rest of underparts, with (variable) buffish lower belly and white undertail-coverts. Bill is orange, with dark blue base to lower mandible. See White-vented (below) for differences from that species. **Juvenile** is browner, with darker brown head; has pale shafts on ear-coverts, pale mottling on throat, and all-yellow bill, and tuft on forehead is much reduced. Absence of bare orbital patch is best distinction from juvenile Common and Bank. **Racial variation** *A. f. mahrattensis* of peninsular India is browner (less slate-grey) on upperparts compared with the nominate race of N and NE subcontinent, and has grey or bluish-white (rather than lemon-yellow) iris. Birds in extreme northeast (*A. f. fumidus*) are darker, more sooty, on the upperparts and underparts. **VOICE** Song is loud, discordant and jumbled, similar to that of Common Myna, although distinguishable: disyllabic notes and drawn-out liquid calls, *trrreech-trrreech-truper tireeper traper tiricht tiricht,* varied with plaintive whistles, *teeya teeyar teeya* (Roberts 1992). **HABITS** Similar to those of Common Myna, but not so bold, less of a scavenger, and not so commensal with humans. Keeps in pairs or family parties, or in flocks in winter. **HABITAT** Cultivation near well-wooded areas, tea and coffee plantations, edges of towns and villages, and forest edges and scrub, rarely in dense forest. **BREEDING** February–July, varying locally. Forms large nesting colonies, unlike Common Myna. Builds nest in a tree hole, in a crevice in a wall or bridge, or under a roof. **DISTRIBUTION AND STATUS** Resident, subject to local movements. Mainly Himalayas from N Pakistan east to Arunachal Pradesh, south to Bangladesh and N Orissa; W India. **PK:** very local; frequent in the main valleys of Indus Kohistan and in N Hazara. **NP:** common and widespread; below 1525 m (–2200 m). **IN:** locally common and patchily distributed; mainly in foothills, up to 2100 m in Himalayas, to 2400 m in peninsula, from plains up to 550 m in the northeast. **BT:** local and frequent. **BD:** common throughout.

WHITE-VENTED MYNA *Acridotheres cinereus* — Plate 111

Orange-billed Jungle Myna (I), *A. grandis, A. javanicus* (I,K)

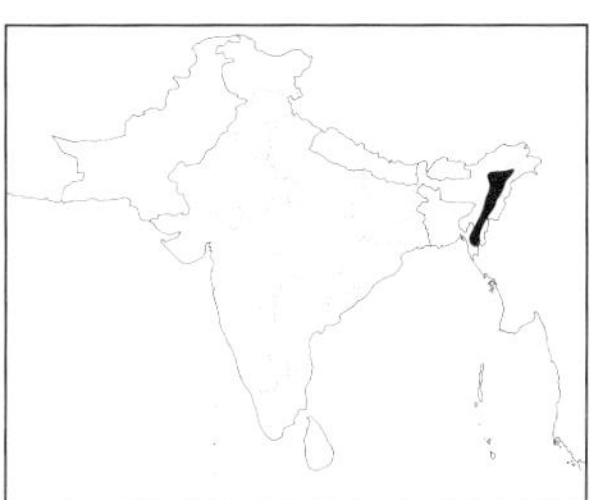

IDENTIFICATION 25 cm. **Adult** is similar to Jungle Myna (p.672), with tufted forehead and lacking yellow orbital skin, and has white patch on wing and white tip to tail. Distinguished from that species by more uniform, blackish-grey upperparts (showing little contrast between crown and mantle and rump and tail), and uniform dark grey underparts, including belly and flanks, strongly contrasting with white undertail-coverts. Further, has all-yellow bill, and reddish to orange-brown iris. For differences from Collared Myna (below), see that species. **Juvenile** has browner upperparts and underparts, and, like moulting adult, lacks tuft on forehead; throat is diffusely mottled with white on some birds. Brown belly and flanks (former with diffuse brownish-white margins, latter concolorous with breast) and broad whitish tips to brown undertail-coverts are best distinctions from juvenile Jungle. **VOICE** Song is a disjointed jumble of repeated tuneless phrases, very similar to that of Common Myna but perhaps coarser and harsher (Thailand) (P. Holt from U. Treesucon recording). **HABITS** Very similar to those of Jungle Myna. Often feeds and roosts with Collared Myna. **HABITAT** Open country with elephant grass, cultivation and villages. **BREEDING** April–July. Builds nest in a hole in a tree or in earth bank of a river. **DISTRIBUTION AND STATUS** Resident. NE India (Arunachal Pradesh, Assam, Manipur, Mizoram and Nagaland) and Bangladesh. **IN:** locally fairly common; from foothills up to 1300 m. **BD:** very local. **REFERENCES** Choudhury (1994).

COLLARED MYNA *Acridotheres albocinctus* — Plate 111

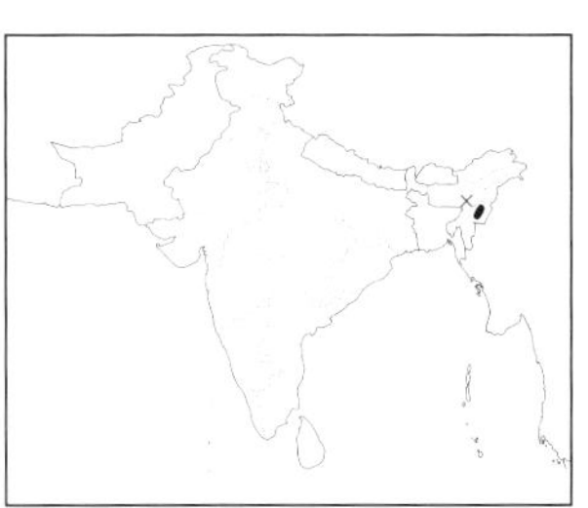

IDENTIFICATION 23 cm. **Adult** is mainly dark grey, with tufted forehead, and with white patch on wing and white tip to tail. Told from White-vented (above) by large whitish patches on sides of neck which join as white streaking across hindneck, and has white tips to dark grey undertail-coverts. Neck patch is strongly washed with buff on some birds. **Juvenile** is dark brown, with paler throat and belly. Has diffuse brownish-white patch on side of neck (smaller than adult's), which helps separate it from juvenile White-vented. **VOICE** Undescribed. **HABITS** Very similar to those of Jungle Myna (672). Often feeds and roosts with White-vented Myna. **HABITAT** Open country with elephant grass, cultivation and villages. **BREEDING** Similar to that of Jungle Myna, but details not recorded in the region. **DISTRIBUTION AND STATUS IN:** resident, subject to local movements, in the Manipur Valley, 800–1200 m; vagrant to Assam.

GOLDEN-CRESTED MYNA *Ampeliceps coronatus* Plate 111

Gold-crested Myna (I), *Mino coronatus* (I)

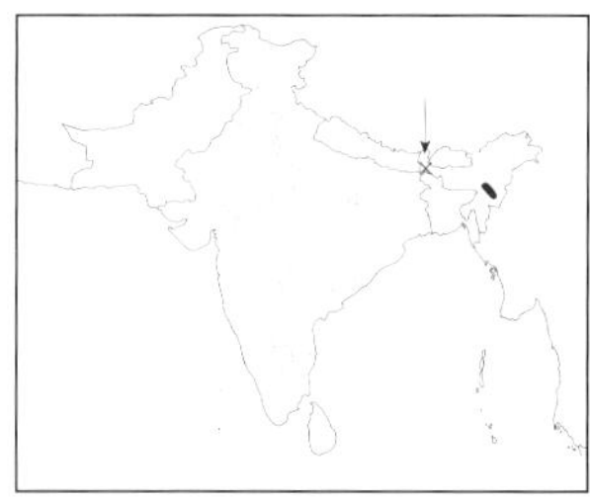

IDENTIFICATION 22 cm. A small, stout-billed myna. **Male** is largely glossy black, with bushy, golden-yellow forehead and crown; has yellow throat, naked orange-yellow orbital patch, and yellow patch at base of primaries. **Female** is similar, but has less extensive yellow crown and smaller yellow throat patch. **Juvenile** is dark brown, slightly paler below, with pale yellow lores and throat, and pale yellow patch on wing. **VOICE** A higher-pitched, more metallic whistle than that of Hill Myna (below), and a bell-like note (Boonsong and Round 1991). **HABITS** Very similar to those of Hill Myna. Usually in small parties, occasionally in pairs. Arboreal; feeds mainly on fruits, also insects. **HABITAT** Open, moist, broadleaved deciduous and evergreen forest and tall trees in cultivated forest clearings. **BREEDING** April–May. Builds nest in a tree hole, 5–10 m above ground. **DISTRIBUTION AND STATUS IN:** resident in Assam, Manipur and West Bengal, from plains up to 900 m, mainly below 500 m; current status uncertain, no recent published records.

SRI LANKA MYNA *Gracula ptilogenys* Plate 111

Ceylon Hill Myna (I,P), Ceylon Myna

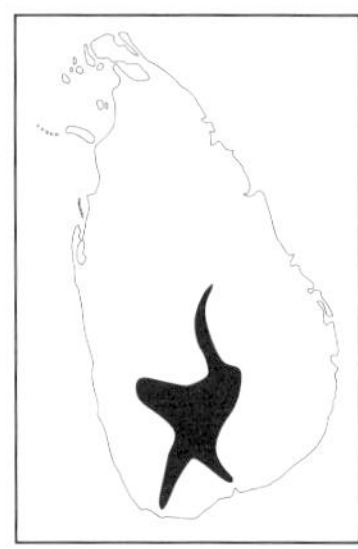

IDENTIFICATION 25 cm. **Adult** is similar to Hill Myna (below), with purple-and-green gloss to black plumage, and white patch on wing. Main differences are larger, stouter orange-red bill (compared with *indica* race of Hill occurring in Sri Lanka) with dark blue base, and different shape and position of wattles on head. Lacks bare patch on side of head, but has two oval-shaped wattles which extend from nape. **Juvenile** has duller bill, much smaller and paler yellow wattles, and less gloss to plumage, with unglossed brownish-black underparts. **VOICE** Similar to that of Hill Myna, with varied squeaks and loud whistles, including *piau, peeoo* and a twanging *chionk* (S. Buckton); also other croaking and guttural notes (Ali and Ripley 1987). **HABITS** Similar to those of Hill Myna. Keeps in the canopy. In the non-breeding season, often in small groups of four to six birds. Collects in large numbers at fruiting trees. **HABITAT** Natural forest and well-wooded country; also plantations and gardens if forest cover is nearby. **BREEDING** March–May and August/September. Nests in a tree hole, usually above 15 m, sometimes 7–12 m above ground. **DISTRIBUTION AND STATUS LK:** endemic resident; common in lowlands and hills of wet zone.

HILL MYNA *Gracula religiosa* Plate 111

Grackle (I), Common Hill Myna (P), Talking Myna (F)

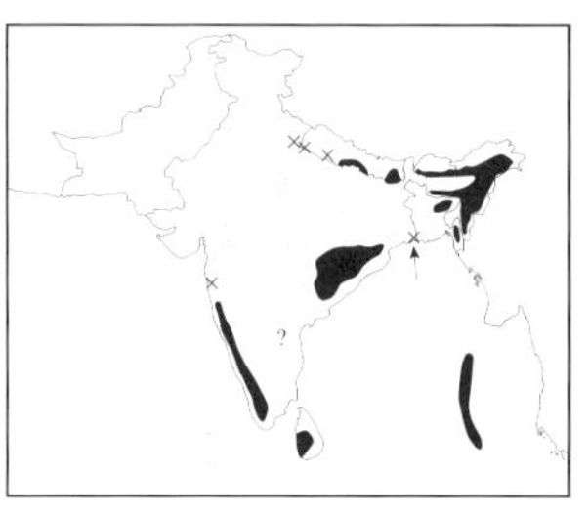

IDENTIFICATION 25–29 cm. Large myna with yellow wattles and with large orange to yellow bill. Plumage is entirely black except for white patches on wing, which are very prominent. Flight is strong and direct, with rapid wingbeats, producing a hum audible at some distance. See Sri Lanka Myna (above), which is similar and occurs alongside Hill Myna in Sri Lanka. **Adult** has purple-and-green gloss to plumage and bright orange bill. **Juvenile** has duller yellowish-orange bill, paler yellow wattles, and less gloss to plumage, with unglossed brownish-black underparts. **Racial variation** Three races are recognised from the subcontinent, these varying in size of bill and shape of wattles. *G. r. indica* of the Western Ghats and Sri Lanka is smaller and has finer bill compared with *intermedia* of N, E and NE subcontinent, and has the eye wattles distinctly separated from the nape wattles, with the latter extending up sides of crown. **VOICE** Extremely varied, with loud piercing whistles, as well as screeches, croaks and wheezes. Marked geographic variation: NE birds higher-pitched, accomplished mimics, and with much broader vocabulary; well-known piercing *ti-ong* restricted to northeast (and Andamans?) (P. Holt). **HABITS** Active and noisy. Strictly arboreal; forages in trees, sometimes in fruiting bushes, hopping about branches in search of food. Usually seen in small flocks in the treetops; will gather in large flocks at fruiting trees, along with barbets, hornbills and green pigeons. Feeds mainly on fruits and berries, especially figs; also takes flower buds, nectar and insects. Roosts alone, in pairs or in small parties. **HABITAT** Tropical moist broadleaved deciduous and evergreen forest, and cardamom and coffee plantations. **BREEDING** February–August, varying locally. Builds nest in a tree hole, 10–15 m above ground, at the forest edge or in an isolated tree in a clearing. **DISTRIBUTION AND STATUS** Resident, subject to local movements. Himalayan foothills from N Uttar Pradesh east to Arunachal Pradesh; hills of NE India and Bangladesh; Eastern and Western Ghats and Sri Lanka. **NP:** frequent in the centre and east, rare in the west; mainly below 455 m (–1280 m). **IN:** locally fairly common; from base of hills locally to 2000 m in Himalayas, mainly in lower foothills; from plains up to 1700 m in Western Ghats. **BT:** fairly common. **BD:** local. **LK:** lower hills of wet and dry zones and S lowlands; frequent at middle altitudes, infrequent elsewhere.

NUTHATCHES AND WALLCREEPER Sittidae

Nuthatches and the Wallcreeper are small, energetic passerines with a compact body, short tail, large strong feet and a long bill. The Wallcreeper is an atypical member of the family, and is adept at clambering over rock faces. Nuthatches are also agile climbers, mainly on trees, a few species on rocks. They can move with ease upwards, downwards, sideways and upside-down over trunks, branches or rocks, progressing by a series of jerky hops. Unlike woodpeckers and treecreepers, they usually begin near the top of a tree and work down the main trunk or larger branches, often head-first, and do not use the tail as a prop. They can also perch on a branch like other passerines. Their flight is direct over short distances, and undulating over longer ones. Nuthatches capture insects and spiders which hide in bark crevices; in mountain areas, in winter, they also eat seeds and nuts, which they wedge into cracks and break into small pieces by hammering with the bill. They are often found singly or in pairs; outside the breeding season, most forest species will associate with foraging flocks of other insectivorous birds. Nuthatches are territorial, and some species defend winter and summer territories. Most species nest in natural holes in trees or those made by other birds, usually plastering mud around the entrance hole. The main reference specific to nuthatches and the Wallcreeper is Harrap and Quinn (1995).

CHESTNUT-VENTED NUTHATCH *Sitta nagaensis* — Plate 112

Eurasian Nuthatch, *S. europaea* (I), Common Nuthatch (I)

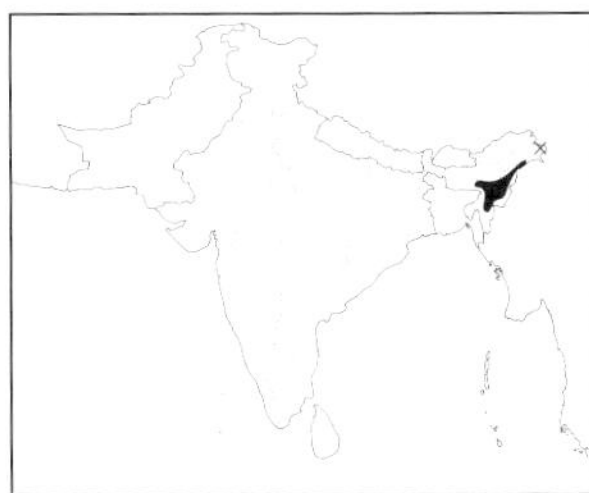

IDENTIFICATION 12 cm. **Male** is similar to female Chestnut-bellied (p.676), and also White-tailed (p.676), but has uniform whitish throat, breast and belly (with cheeks and throat concolorous with rest of underparts) which contrast with chestnut rear flanks, and chestnut undertail-coverts with tear-shaped white spots. Underparts are variably washed with buff, and some may approach female Chestnut-bellied in coloration, although upperparts are a slightly darker and duller blue. Lacks white at base of central tail feathers present on White-tailed (although this is difficult to determine in the field), and note that White-tailed has uniform undertail-coverts. **Female** is similar to male, but flanks and undertail-coverts are a paler rufous. **VOICE** Song is a level and vibrating trill (bubbling), *duiduiduiduiduidui*, and call is a distinctive nasal *djeeeep* or *chuueep* (Thailand) (J. Scharringa). **HABITS** A typical nuthatch. Habits very similar to those of Kashmir Nuthatch (below). Feeds in the middle and lower forest storeys; frequently also on the ground. **HABITAT** Open forest of deciduous, broadleaved evergreen and coniferous trees. **BREEDING** March–June. Builds nest of moss, lined with fur, in a tree hole. **DISTRIBUTION AND STATUS IN:** common resident in NE Indian hills (Patkai range in Arunachal Pradesh and Assam, also Manipur, Meghalaya, Mizoram and Nagaland); breeds 1400–2600 m, occasionally up to 3200 m.

KASHMIR NUTHATCH *Sitta cashmirensis* — Plate 112

European Nuthatch, *S. europaea* (F,I,R), Common Nuthatch (I)

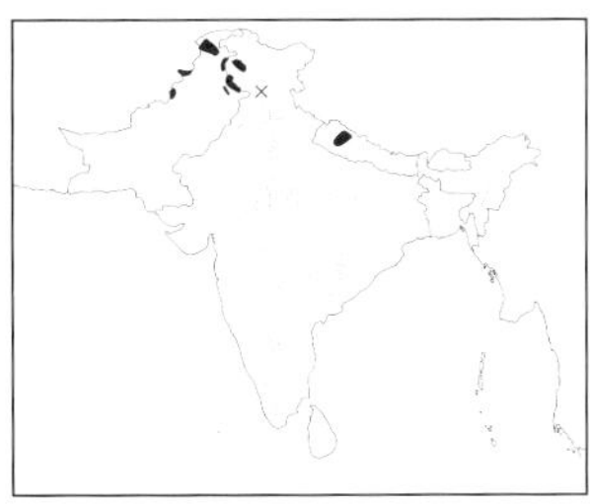

IDENTIFICATION 12 cm. At all times, distinguished from Chestnut-bellied (p.676) by uniform undertail-coverts (rather than scalloped with white). Upperparts are a shade darker and greyer. Compared with White-tailed (p.676), is larger (with a relatively longer bill) and lacks white at base of central tail feathers (although this is difficult to determine in the field). Different calls are a useful guide to identification. **Male** is otherwise very similar to female Chestnut-bellied and both sexes of White-tailed, although there are subtle differences in coloration of underparts. Chin, cheeks and ear-coverts are whitish, throat is buff, becoming more cinnamon on breast, and flanks, vent and undertail-coverts are rufous. Whitish cheek patch is less well defined than on female Chestnut-bellied, and that species has darker and more uniform underparts. Cheek patch is more clearly defined than on White-tailed (with rear ear-coverts white, rather than usually pale orange), and underparts are a shade darker and more pinkish-cinnamon. **Female** is similar to male, but underparts are paler, with flanks and undertail-coverts more deep cinnamon, and whitish cheek patch is less clearly defined. Very similar to White-tailed, but ear-coverts are whiter and underparts more pinkish-cinnamon. **VOICE** Song is a series of rapidly repeated, high-pitched squeaky whistles, *pee-pee-pee-pee-pee*. Call is a rasping jay-like note, which is loud and far-carrying; also utters squeaky *tsi-tsi* contact notes (Roberts 1992). **HABITS** A typical nuthatch, and a frequent member of feeding flocks of tits, warblers and other birds. Forages at lower levels than White-cheeked Nuthatch (p.676), often in the understorey and occasionally on the ground. Feeds chiefly on small invertebrates in summer; also on nuts in winter. **HABITAT** Deciduous and mixed broadleaved–coniferous forest and well-wooded country; more likely at slightly lower altitudes and in deciduous trees than White-cheeked Nuthatch. **BREEDING** End April–July. Nests in a tree hole scantily lined with bark, dried leaves and seed husks. **DISTRIBUTION AND STATUS** Endemic to the subcontinent, where resident, subject to altitudinal movements. N Baluchistan and NW Pakistan, and in Himalayas from N Pakistan east to Kashmir and in NW Nepal. **PK:** locally frequent; summers up to 3350 m, winters down to 1800 m. **NP:** locally fairly common in the northwest; 2400–3505 m. **IN:** locally common; breeds 2100–3000 m, locally down to 1800 m.

CHESTNUT-BELLIED NUTHATCH *Sitta castanea* **Plate 112**

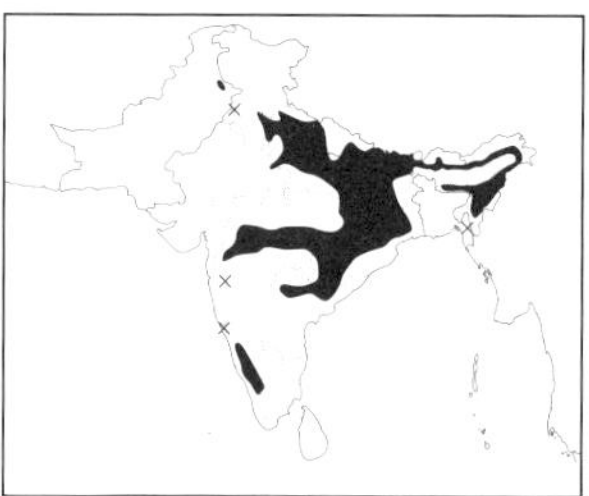

IDENTIFICATION 12 cm. At all times, separated from Kashmir and White-tailed Nuthatches (p.675 and below) by whitish or grey scalloping on undertail-coverts. **Male** always shows striking white cheek patch contrasting with rather uniform dark reddish-chestnut to orange-brown underparts. **Female** is similar, but underparts are paler. In W Himalayas confusion is most likely with Kashmir, but underparts are richer, darker and more uniform cinnamon-brown, with more clearly defined white chin and cheeks. Lacks white at base of central tail feathers of White-tailed, underparts are darker and more uniform, and cheek patch is more prominent. For differences from Chestnut-vented (p.675), see that species. **Racial variation** Four races are recognised from the subcontinent. *S. c. castanea* of N and C Indian plains is relatively small, with short, slender bill; scalloping on undertail-coverts is grey (same colour as mantle), and crown/nape are distinctly paler than mantle, while underparts of male are a dark reddish-chestnut. *S. c. almorae/cinnamoventris/koelzi* of the Himalayan foothills and NE subcontinent are larger, with much larger bill; have white scalloping on undertail-coverts, and lack strong contrast between crown/nape and mantle, while male's underparts are paler and more orange-brown. **VOICE** Varied. Song is a single pure whistle, repeated every few seconds, which may change to a rippling whistle or quavering trill. Calls include an explosive rattle, *sidititit* (Harrap and Quinn 1996). **HABITS** A typical nuthatch. Often with mixed feeding parties. Usually forages in the upper half of trees, occasionally on the ground. Feeds on small invertebrates, seeds and nuts. **HABITAT** Broadleaved forest, groves and roadside trees, especially deciduous; also mixed pine–deciduous forest in Pakistan. **BREEDING** February–September, varying locally. Builds nest of moss, small pieces of bark and a thick layer of fur, usually in a tree hole, sometimes in a wall. **DISTRIBUTION AND STATUS** Resident. Himalayas in Murree foothills, Pakistan, and from N Uttar Pradesh east to Arunachal Pradesh; NE India and Bangladesh; locally south to N Andhra Pradesh; Western Ghats. **PK:** rare and very local. **NP:** common and widespread; below 1830 m. **IN:** common; from the plains edge up to 1800 m in Himalayas, 900–1000 m in Eastern Ghats, locally in plateaux and foothills in the peninsula. **BT:** common. **BD:** ?former resident; no recent records, but could still occur in hill tracts.

WHITE-TAILED NUTHATCH *Sitta himalayensis* **Plate 112**

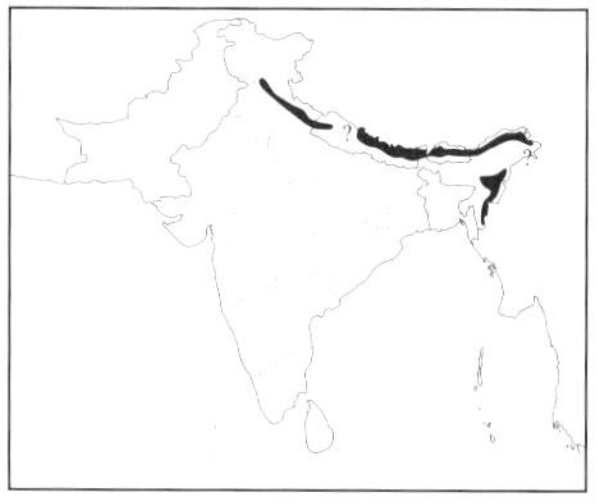

IDENTIFICATION 12 cm. Very similar to Kashmir Nuthatch (p.675). Distinguished from that species by white at base of central tail feathers (although this feature can be very difficult to see in the field). Further, is smaller, with relatively shorter bill, and calls are different. Sexes are similar. White-tailed has less distinct cheek patch compared with Kashmir (cheeks are off-white or buff, and ear-coverts are more cinnamon-orange). Told from female Chestnut-bellied (above) by uniform undertail-coverts, while rest of underparts are paler and less uniform than on that species: throat is whitish, becoming more cinnamon-orange on breast, with coloration deepening on rear flanks and undertail-coverts. **VOICE** Song is a variable series of clear whistles, e.g. *dwi-dwi-dwi*; calls include a squeaky *nit* and a soft *chak*, a harder *chak'kak* which may rapidly repeated as monotonous rattle, and shrill *shree* (Harrap and Quinn 1996). **HABITS** A typical nuthatch. Frequently keeps in pairs, accompanying mixed hunting flocks. Frequents the upper half of trees, occasionally low bushes; often feeds on mossy branches. Eats small invertebrates, seeds and nuts. **HABITAT** Broadleaved and mixed broadleaved–coniferous forest. **BREEDING** Mid March–early May. Nests in a tree hole, lined with moss and rhododendron leaves, 1–15 m above ground. **DISTRIBUTION AND STATUS** Resident, subject to altitudinal movements. Himalayas from Himachal Pradesh east to Arunachal Pradesh; NE India. **NP:** common and widespread; summers chiefly 1800–3140 m (–3400 m), sometimes descending in winter (down to 915 m). **IN:** common in Himalayas, breeds 1500–3500 m, winters down to 950 m; fairly common in NE hills, breeds above 1700 m. **BT:** common.

WHITE-CHEEKED NUTHATCH *Sitta leucopsis* **Plate 112**

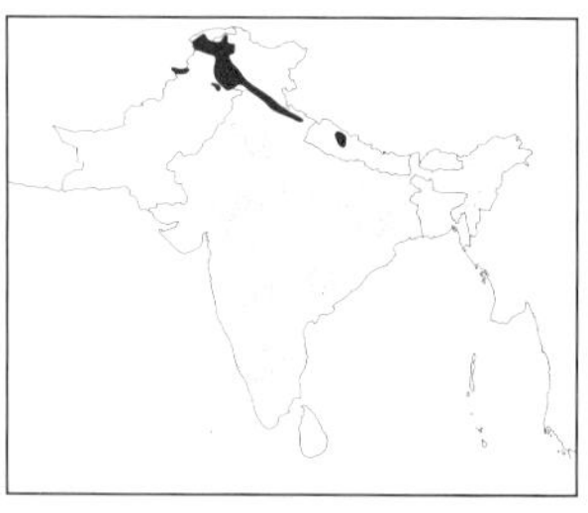

IDENTIFICATION 12 cm. **Adult** is a very distinctive nuthatch, with black crown and nape, white face and throat with beady eye, and whitish underparts with buffish wash and with rufous rear flanks and undertail-coverts. **Juvenile** is slightly duller, and has faint barring on underparts. **VOICE** Likened to the bleating of a young goat, song is a continuous, rapid series of low-pitched squeaks, *quee-queeh-quee-queeh*; call is similar but slower, and in shorter bursts, or in alarm is a series of single notes (Roberts 1992). **HABITS** A typical nuthatch. Feeds in the upper canopy, where most easily located by its distinctive call. In the breeding season, males sometimes perch conspicuously on the tops of tall trees, calling and flicking wings. **HABITAT** Coniferous forest and mixed coniferous–broadleaved forest. **BREEDING** End April–early

July. Nest is a pad of moss, lined with animal hairs or grass and bark, in a tree hole 6–30 m above ground; does not plaster mud around entrance hole as do other nuthatches. **DISTRIBUTION AND STATUS** Resident, subject to altitudinal movements. Himalayas from N Pakistan east to NW Nepal. **PK:** common and fairly sedentary; summers up to 3600 m, winters down to 2000 m. **NP:** locally fairly common in the northwest; 2745–3900 m. **IN:** frequent in Kashmir; breeds from 2100 m up to the treeline, winters locally down to 1800 m. **REFERENCES** Martens and Eck (1995).

EASTERN ROCK NUTHATCH *Sitta tephronota* Plate 112

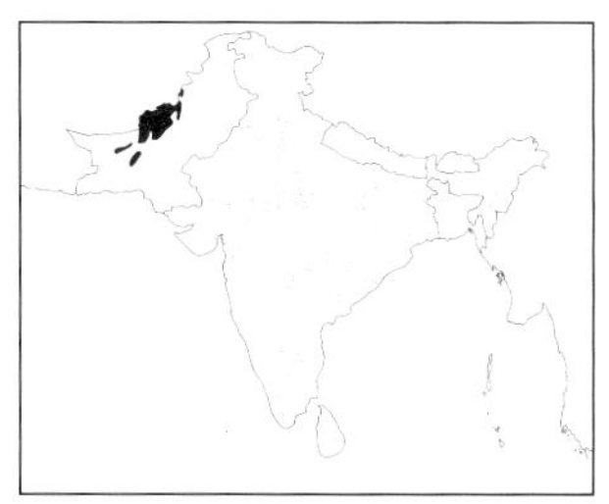

IDENTIFICATION 15 cm. Habits and habitat are quite different from those of other nuthatches in the subcontinent. Is comparatively large, with very large, slightly upturned-looking bill. Has long black eye-stripe, extending to side of mantle, pale blue-grey upperparts, and whitish underparts with orange-buff rear flanks and undertail-coverts. **VOICE** Song is a loud and far-carrying trill, with duetting by pair-members; also short single or double calls, *tsik* or *chik* (Cramp and Perrins 1993). **HABITS** Usually in pairs, and often keeps to the same locality throughout the year. Feeding behaviour is similar to that of other nuthatches, but forages chiefly on rock faces, cliffs and boulders, seeking insects in crevices. **HABITAT** Rocky mountains with scattered scrub and rock outcrops; favours rocky gorges or ridges. **BREEDING** February–June. Builds a most unusual nest: a hole in a rock face is lined with fur and feathers, and the entrance is heavily plastered with mud to close up the hole (often there is a projecting entrance tunnel of mud); the mud around the entrance is decorated with feathers and other bright objects. **DISTRIBUTION AND STATUS PK:** common and sedentary resident in Baluchistan; breeds 1800–2100 m in N and C areas, and up to 2700 m in the south.

VELVET-FRONTED NUTHATCH *Sitta frontalis* Plate 112

Velvet-fronted Blue Nuthatch

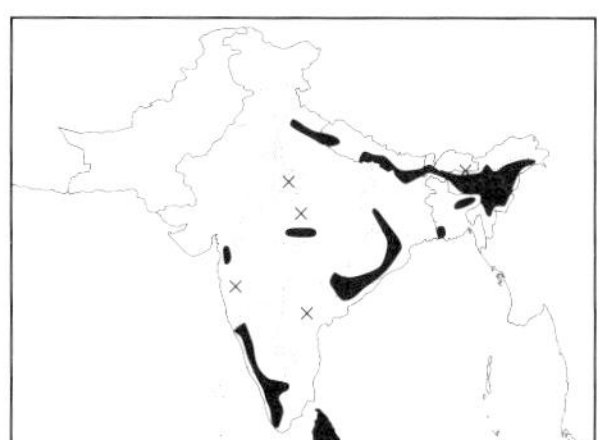

IDENTIFICATION 10 cm. A striking and beautiful nuthatch. Distinguished from other nuthatches by violet-blue upperparts, black forehead (and lores), black-tipped red bill, startling yellow iris and eye-ring, and lilac suffusion to ear-coverts and underparts. **Male** has black eye-stripe extending behind eye. **Female** lacks black eye-stripe, and underparts are suffused more with cinnamon and less with lilac. **Juvenile** has blackish bill and duller and greyer upperparts; underparts lack lilac suffusion and are washed with orange-buff. **VOICE** Common calls include a single hard *chat, chit, chlit* or *chip,* and a much thinner and more sibilant *sip, sit* or *tsit* (with many intermediate notes); song is a series of *sit* units, which may become a fast, hard rattle (Harrap and Quinn 1996). **HABITS** A typical nuthatch, more active than others in the region. Usually keeps in pairs with mixed foraging flocks, often with Chestnut-bellied Nuthatch (p.676). Forages from the canopy down to the undergrowth, but not on the ground. Feeds on insects and their larvae. **HABITAT** Open broadleaved forest and well-wooded areas, and tea, coffee and cardamom plantations; mangroves in the Sunderbans. **BREEDING** January–June, varying locally. Nests in a tree hole, lined with moss, fur and feathers, 1–12 above ground. **DISTRIBUTION AND STATUS** Resident. Himalayas from N Uttar Pradesh east to Arunachal Pradesh; NE India and Bangladesh; hills of the peninsula and Sri Lanka. **NP:** fairly common and widespread; below 2015 m, most frequent up to 1800 m. **IN:** common in Eastern and Western Ghats, locally fairly common elsewhere; from plains up to 1500 m, locally to 2200 m in Himalayas and in peninsular hills. **BT:** rare. **BD:** local. **LK:** common in the hills, infrequent in the lowlands.

BEAUTIFUL NUTHATCH *Sitta formosa* Plate 112

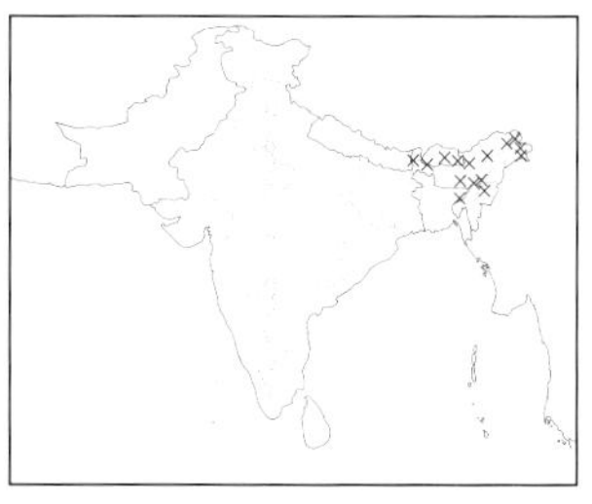

IDENTIFICATION 15 cm. A large nuthatch with black upperparts, streaked with blue, and rufous-orange underparts. Told from other nuthatches by much larger size, black crown and mantle with white and blue streaking, blue 'scapular lines', and broad bluish-white fringes to coverts and tertials. From underside, outer tail feathers show broad white tips and, in flight, white patch at base of primaries contrasts with blackish underwing-coverts. **VOICE** Poorly described. **HABITS** Poorly known. Apparently similar to those of other nuthatches, but actions on larger branches and trunks are rather slow and deliberate, reminiscent of Cutia (p.769). Flight is very swift. Usually keeps in pairs or small groups, and flock of 21 seen in Bhutan; often with mixed-species flocks. **HABITAT** Dense forest. **BREEDING** Little known. April–June. Nests in a tree hollow, lined with leaves, bark chips and fur, 2–8 m above ground. **DISTRIBUTION AND STATUS** Resident, subject to altitudinal movements. India in E Himalayas and NE hills (Sikkim, West Bengal, Arunachal Pradesh, Assam, Manipur, Meghalaya) and Bhutan. Globally threatened. **IN:** rare and local; summers 1500–2400 m, winters 330–2200 m. **BT:** rare; 1700 m, 1900 m. **BD:** vagrant? **REFERENCES** Athreya *et al.* (1997).

WALLCREEPER *Tichodroma muraria* Plate 112

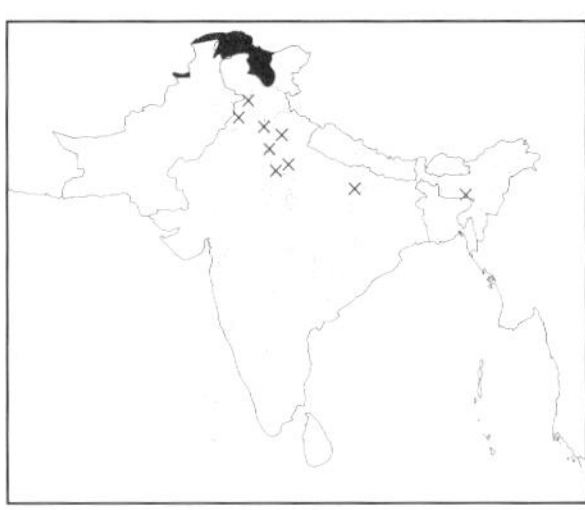

IDENTIFICATION cm. A rock and cliff-face dweller with long, downcurved, black bill. In flight, wings are rounded and reveal largely crimson wing-coverts and bases to black flight feathers, with two rows of white spots across primaries. Also shows white corners to tail. **Adult male breeding** has black throat and upper breast, and underparts are dusky grey. **Adult female breeding** has whitish chin, and variable blackish patch on lower throat and upper breast. **Adult non-breeding** has white throat and upper breast, and brown cast to crown. **Juvenile** has straighter bill, and underparts are paler and more uniform grey. **VOICE** Song is a variable, repeated sequence of high whistles, *ti-tiu treeh*, increasing in strength and speed; call is a thin piping and high whistles, e.g. *twee* or *tuweeht* (Jonsson 1992). **HABITS** Clings with ease to rock cliffs and walls, often on vertical faces, searching actively for insects and larvae. Progresses mainly in short jerky hops, sometimes creeping, and constantly flicks wings and tail when foraging; occasionally flutters into the air to capture insects and spiders it has disturbed. Frequently flies high over wide valleys when moving to new feeding areas; has an erratic, flitting, butterfly-like flight, reminiscent of a Common Hoopoe (p.399). Found in pairs in the breeding season and singly at other times. **HABITAT** Rock cliffs and gorges; in winter, also rocky roadside embankments, earth cliffs, bridges, ruins and boulders in river beds. **BREEDING** May–July. Nest, made of moss, roots, grass, wool and hairs, is usually built in an inaccessible rock crevice. **DISTRIBUTION AND STATUS** Resident, subject to altitudinal movements. Breeds in Himalayas from N Pakistan east to E Nepal; winters down to the foothills east to E Arunachal Pradesh, sometimes wandering to the plains south to Rajasthan. **PK:** common resident in the north; breeds mainly 3600–4600 m and winters in main N valleys, 1200–2400 m, sometimes in adjacent plains. **NP:** fairly common and widespread in winter, 245–5000 m (–5730 m); has bred at 3350 m, 4400 m. **IN:** fairly common, but local; breeds chiefly from 3300 m up to the snowline. **BT:** common winter visitor, from 230 m up to at least 2895 m; possibly resident. **REFERENCES** Martens and Eck (1995).

CREEPERS AND WRENS Certhiidae

A family of mostly small, rather similar-looking species, with two subfamilies.

TREECREEPERS AND SPOTTED CREEPER Subfamily Certhiinae

Small, quiet, arboreal passerines with a slender, decurved bill and, with the exception of the Spotted Creeper, a stiff tail which is used as a prop when climbing, like that of the woodpeckers. The plumage is streaky brown above and whitish below; juveniles are similar to adults, but tend to show faint dark scaling or mottling on underparts. Treecreepers forage by creeping up vertical trunks and along the underside of branches, spiralling upwards in a series of jerks, using the bill to probe bark cracks and crevices in search of insects and spiders; on reaching the top of a tree, they fly to the base of the next one. Occasionally they feed on the ground or on stone walls. They are very active and frequently flick their wings when creeping. Their flight is undulating and weak, and is usually only over short distances. Treecreepers are non-gregarious, but outside the nesting season they usually join mixed hunting parties of other insectivorous birds. They inhabit broadleaved and coniferous forest, woodland, groves, and gardens with trees. Except for the Spotted Creeper, all members of the subfamily normally build their nests behind loose bark or ivy stems or in deep cracks or crevices in the bark of trees, occasionally in wall crevices. The nest is an untidy structure of twigs, roots, grass, and mosses, lined with feathers and bark pieces. Thin high-pitched contact calls are used continually between birds of a foraging group. Their songs are rather weak. The main reference specific to treecreepers and Spotted Creeper is Harrap and Quinn (1995).

EURASIAN TREECREEPER *Certhia familiaris* Plate 112

Tree Creeper (I), Common Treecreeper (K), Northern Tree Creeper (F)

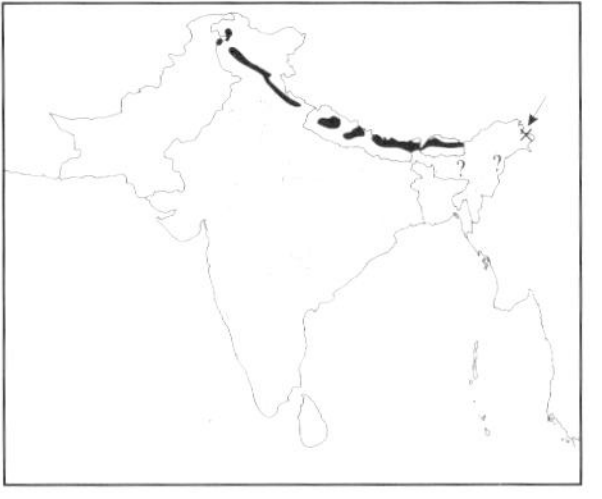

IDENTIFICATION 12 cm. Distinguished from Bar-tailed (p.679) by combination of (generally) shorter, less downcurved bill, uniform (unbarred) tail, and more prominent buff banding across wing. From Brown-throated (p.679) by whitish throat and breast, dull brown tail, and more pronounced white supercilium. From Rusty-flanked (p.679) by lack of (or less prominent) white border to rear of ear-coverts, more pronounced buff banding across wing, and duller buffish flanks. **Racial variation** Three races are described from the subcontinent. *C. f. hodgsoni* of W Himalayas is comparatively pale and grey above, with pronounced whitish streaking. *C. f. mandellii* and *C. f. khamensis* of C and E Himalayas are darker and browner above: former has indistinct rufescent streaking on upperparts, and buffish flanks; latter has paler, more buffish streaking on upperparts, and greyish flanks. **VOICE** Song is a high-pitched, rising and then descending *tzee, tzee, tze-tzizitzi* (Fleming *et al.* 1984); call is a thin, piercing *tsee-tsee-tsee.* **HABITS** A typical treecreeper. **HABITAT** Mainly coniferous forest mixed with birch; also conifers mixed with rhododendron or oak, and pure oak or birch forest. **BREEDING** Poorly known. May and June. In Nepal, nest found in a tree hole 0.5 m above ground and observed nest-building in a fir stump. **DISTRIBUTION AND STATUS** Resident, subject to some altitudinal movements. Himalayas from N Pakistan (NE Gilgit and in SE ranges of Kagan valley watershed) east to Arunachal Pradesh; NE India? **PK:** rare and local; 3350 m. **NP:** fairly common; summers mainly 3000–4100 m, winters from 2000 m up to at least 3655 m. **IN:** locally fairly common; breeds mainly from 2700 m up to the timberline. **BT:** frequent; 2435–4120 m. **REFERENCES** Martens and Eck (1995).

BAR-TAILED TREECREEPER *Certhia himalayana* — Plate 112

Himalayan Treecreeper (F,I)

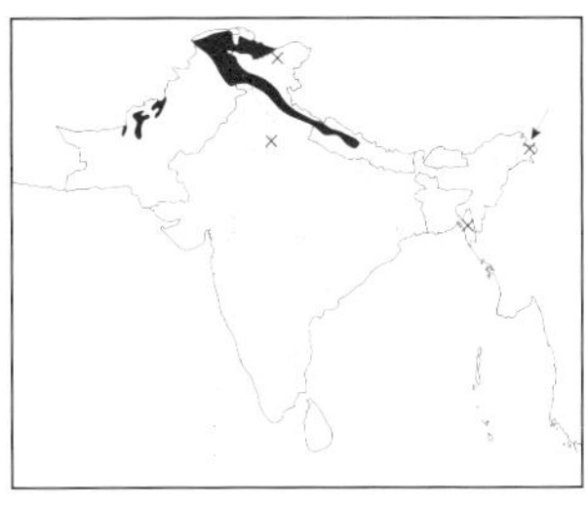

IDENTIFICATION 12 cm. Separated from other treecreepers by combination of (generally) longer, more downcurved bill and dark cross-barring on tail. Supercilium and pale banding across wings are less distinct than on Eurasian (p.678). White throat and dull whitish or dirty greyish-buff underparts are further differences from Brown-throated and Rusty-flanked (below). **Racial variation** Birds in W Himalayas have colder and browner upperparts compared with E Himalayan birds, which are more rufous, with more pronounced whitish streaking. **VOICE** Song is a high-pitched trill of seven to nine whistled notes, *chi-chi-chi-chiu-chiu-chiu-chu,* which rise slightly in tone and increase in speed at the start, and drop off slightly at the end; call is a weak, high-pitched, thin *tsi-tsi* (Roberts 1992). **HABITS** A typical treecreeper. **HABITAT** Breeds preferably in coniferous forest, such as spruce, pine and juniper, also rhododendron and birch; winters in forest, groves, roadside avenues, plantations, wooded gardens and orchards. **BREEDING** April–June. Has a usual treecreeper nest and nest site, from near the ground to 15 m above. **DISTRIBUTION AND STATUS** Resident, subject to altitudinal movements. Mountains of N and W Pakistan and Himalayas from N Pakistan east to WC Nepal; Arunachal Pradesh. **PK:** common to locally frequent; breeds in C and N Baluchistan and Himalayas, 2100–3350 m, most descending in winter, with stragglers down to the Punjab plains. **NP:** fairly common; summers 2200–3660 m, winters down to 1800 m, occasionally to 305 m. **IN:** common in Kashmir, fairly common farther east; breeds from 1500 m up to the timberline, winters from 2400 m down to the foothills. **BD:** vagrant. **REFERENCES** Martens and Eck (1995).

RUSTY-FLANKED TREECREEPER *Certhia nipalensis* — Plate 112

Nepal Tree Creeper (F,I)

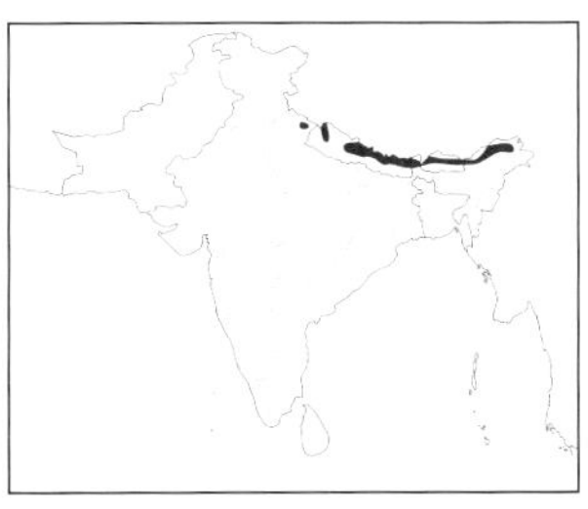

IDENTIFICATION 12 cm. Distinguished from other treecreepers by combination of shorter, straighter bill, well-defined buffish supercilium, which continues around (and contrasts with) dark ear-coverts, and creamy-buff breast and belly with warm rufous flanks. Supercilium of Eurasian (p.678) may extend, rather indistinctly, behind ear-coverts, but ear-covert patch is paler and smaller. Unbarred tail is an additional feature for separation from Bar-tailed (above), and white throat an additional distinction from Brown-throated (below). **VOICE** Distinctive song, with a couple of slow, clearly enunciated introductory notes followed by a rapid, penetrating, accelerating trill and ending abruptly, *si-si-sss-rt-rt-t.* Calls with a high, thin *sit,* often doubled, or an intense penetrating *zip,* reminiscent of Ashy-throated Warbler (p.728) (P. Holt). **HABITS** A typical treecreeper. **HABITAT** Breeds in oak, also in mixed oak–rhododendron–fir and hemlock forest; winters in broadleaved forest. **BREEDING** Poorly known. May and June. Seen in May repeatedly flying to an oak crevice 12 m above ground, and presumed feeding young. **DISTRIBUTION AND STATUS** Resident, subject to altitudinal movements. Himalayas from N Uttar Pradesh east to Arunachal Pradesh. Summers chiefly 2550–3660 m (–3805 m in Bhutan); winters from 1830 m, locally 1500 m, up to 3505 m. **NP:** fairly common. **IN:** locally frequent. **BT:** fairly common.

BROWN-THROATED TREECREEPER *Certhia discolor* — Plate 112

Sikkim Tree Creeper (F,I)

IDENTIFICATION 12 cm. Separated from other treecreepers, where ranges overlap, by brownish-buff throat and breast, becoming paler on belly and flanks. Unbarred tail is an additional distinction from Bar-tailed (above), and less distinct supercilium, which does not continue around ear-coverts, is an additional difference from Rusty-flanked (above). **Racial variation** *C. d. manipurensis* from S Manipur has cinnamon-orange throat and breast compared with brownish-buff of nominate race of Himalayas, described above. **VOICE** Call is an explosive *chit* or *tchip,* as well as a higher and thinner *tsit* or *seep;* song is a long, monotonous rattle comprising 6–37 *chit*-type notes, *chit-it-it-it-it-it-it-it-it-it* (Harrap and Quinn 1996). **HABITS** A typical treecreeper. **HABITAT** Mainly broadleaved forest, especially mossy oak forest; also in mixed coniferous–broadleaved forest. **BREEDING** Poorly known. Probably

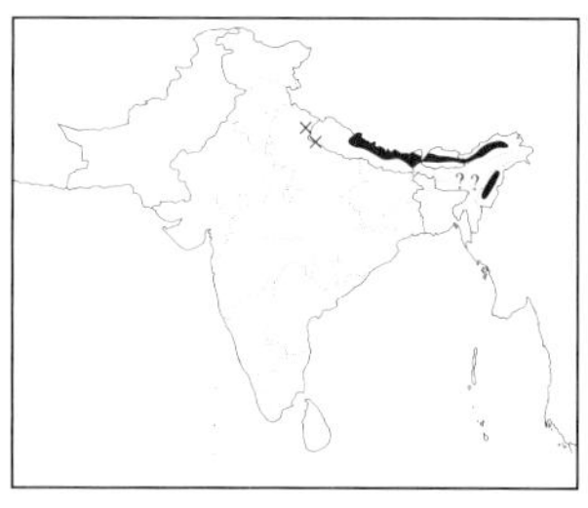

March–May. Details undescribed from Himalayas; in NE India, has a usual treecreeper nest in a hole 2–4 m up in a small tree. **DISTRIBUTION AND STATUS** Resident, subject to altitudinal movements. Himalayas in N Uttar Pradesh and from WC Nepal east to Arunachal Pradesh; NE India. In Himalayas, summers mainly from 2000 m (locally 1800 m) to 2750 m, occasionally up to 3050 m and in Bhutan to 3200 m; winters chiefly down to 1800 m, locally 1120 m (down to 305 m in Nepal). **NP:** locally fairly common. **IN:** locally fairly common in Himalayas, locally common in the northeast. **BT:** frequent.

SPOTTED CREEPER *Salpornis spilonotus* — Plate 112

Spotted Grey Creeper (I)

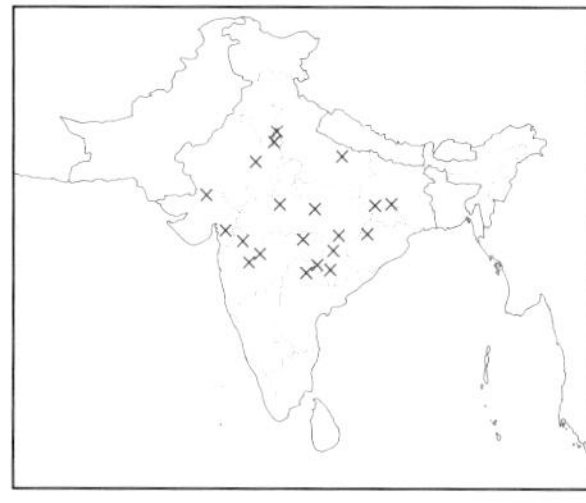

IDENTIFICATION 13 cm. Larger and stockier than the treecreepers, with shorter and broader, slightly rounded tail (which is not pressed against tree for support). Brown upperparts, including wings, are boldly spotted and barred with white, greyish-white tail is banded with dark brown, and underparts are washed with orange-buff and spotted with brown. Has prominent whitish supercilium and dark eye-stripe. **VOICE** Call is a faint *see-ee*, and an almost croaking *kek-kek-kek-kek-kek-kek* (Harrap and Quinn 1996). Song is a powerful series of descending plaintive whistles, *tchiu-tchuwu-tchuwu*; a second song type is a series of very high-pitched sunbird-like wispy notes (P. Holt). **HABITS** Usually found singly or in pairs; may associate in small flocks in winter. Flutters and clambers rapidly from the base of a tree to the upper branches, exploring bark fissures for invertebrates; does not spiral trunks like treecreepers. Clings upside-down to branches. Typically moves to new trunk or branch by 'tumbling' with open wings. **HABITAT** Open deciduous forest and mango groves. **BREEDING** March–May. Nest is a cup of leaves, lichen and bark, placed 3–5 m up in a thin tree, well camouflaged against the bark. **DISTRIBUTION AND STATUS IN:** scarce and local resident; from Gujarat and S Haryana east to Bihar and south to C Maharashtra and N Andhra Pradesh.

WRENS Subfamily Troglodytinae

Small, plump passerines with rather short, blunt wings, strong legs and the tail characteristically held erect.

WINTER WREN *Troglodytes troglodytes* — Plate 114

Wren (F,I), Northern Wren (K,N,R)

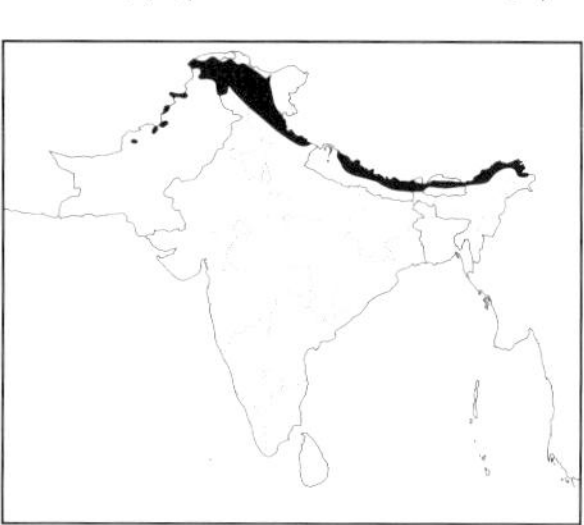

IDENTIFICATION 9.5 cm. Small and squat, with stubby tail, and rather long, pointed bill. Has buffish supercilium, brownish upperparts, wings and tail variably barred with darker brown, and brown barring on underparts. **Racial variation** *T. t. magrathi* from the far NW subcontinent has grey-brown upperparts with fine, dense (and indistinct) dark barring, and greyish underparts with paler throat. *T. t. neglectus* of the W Himalayas has darker brown upperparts with heavy blackish barring, and smoky-brown underparts. *T. t. nipalensis* of the C and E Himalayas is the darkest race, and is sooty-brown all over. **VOICE** Song is a powerful, rapidly delivered warbling and trilling; calls include a hard *chek* or *chet* and a rattling *churr*. **HABITS** Normally solitary; may roost communally in very cold weather. Sprightly, always on the move, creeping and flitting among rocks and low vegetation. Tail is usually carried erect, and is moved vigorously backwards and forwards in display. When excited, has a habit of swivelling and bobbing; when singing, its whole body vibrates. Feeds mainly on insects taken from the surface of leaves, leaf litter, and crevices in rocks, walls and bark. Flight is rapid, whirring and usually over short distances. **HABITAT** Breeds among rocks on moraines, screes and tumbled rock slopes above the treeline, and scattered bushes in alpine and subalpine zones; winters on stone walls around villages and fields, stony river beds, and on fallen tree trunks in coniferous forest. **BREEDING** May–July. Nest is a globe with a side entrance, made of moss, lichen, bark and dry leaves, and placed among tree roots, between boulders, in a wall or in the hollow of a bank. **DISTRIBUTION AND STATUS** Resident, subject to altitudinal movements. Baluchistan, Pakistan, and Himalayas from N Pakistan east to Arunachal Pradesh. **PK:** very widespread and locally common in inner Himalayan ranges, with small numbers in Baluchistan; breeds up to 3800 m, winters down to 1500 m. **NP:** fairly common and widespread; chiefly 2500–4725 m (2135–5300 m). **IN:** common; in the west, breeds 2400–3900 m and winters from 1200 m up to at least 3000 m; in the east, breeds 2700–5000 m and winters 3000–4700 m. **BT:** common; 2225–4875 m.

PENDULINE TITS AND TITS Paridae AND LONG-TAILED TITS Aegithalidae

Small, active (except for Sultan Tit), highly acrobatic passerines with a short bill and strong feet. Their flight over long distances is undulating. They are mainly insectivorous, although many species also depend on seeds, particularly from trees in winter, and some also eat fruit. They forage systematically, probing bark crevices, searching branches and leaves, and frequently hanging upside-down from twigs; sometimes they attack buds which contain small invertebrates. Tits are chiefly arboreal, but also descend to the ground to feed, hopping about and flicking aside leaves and other debris. They are very gregarious; in the non-breeding season most species join roving flocks of other tits, warblers and other insectivorous birds. Many species, including the *Parus* tits, are hole-nesters, and the others mostly build globular nests. The main reference specific to tits is Harrap and Quinn (1995), from which the measurements below are taken.

WHITE-CROWNED PENDULINE TIT *Remiz coronatus* — Plate 113

Penduline Tit (I), Eurasian Penduline Tit, *R. pendulinus* (I,R,V)

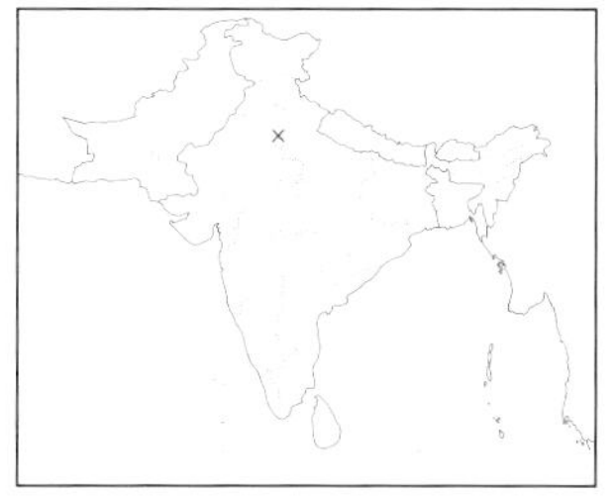

IDENTIFICATION 10 cm. **Adult male** has blackish mask through eye which extends as band across nape, whitish crown, and broad white collar. In worn plumage, hindcrown may also be black but forehead remains white. Has band of chestnut across mantle, prominent white fringes to tertials and secondaries, chestnut greater coverts forming dark band across wing, and whitish underparts with pinkish tinge and some chestnut spotting on breast. **Female** and **first-year male** are similar, but duller and paler; crown and collar are pale grey rather than white, and mask is browner and barely extends across nape. **Juvenile** has brownish-buff upperparts and buffish underparts, and lacks adult's dark mask and chestnut band across mantle; distinctive features are dark cinnamon panel across greater coverts, with buffish-white tips forming wing-bar. **VOICE** Utters a thin, high-pitched *tsee* or *tseeuh* or a repeated *tsee-tsee-tsee.* **HABITS** Similar to those of other tits. Even more acrobatic than the *Parus* tits, and able to climb upside-down along the underside of branches. **HABITAT** Reedbeds, acacia trees in riverain forest, and irrigated forest plantations. **BREEDING** Not proven in the region. Has a pendulous, domed nest of vegetable down, suspended from twigs, usually above water. **DISTRIBUTION AND STATUS** Winter visitor to Punjab and Sindh, Pakistan, and Punjab, India. **PK:** scarce, mainly along major river systems. **IN:** very local and fairly common in Punjab; one record of small parties at 4900 m in June in Ladakh (Meinertzhagen 1927) is now regarded as doubtful.

FIRE-CAPPED TIT *Cephalopyrus flammiceps* — Plate 113

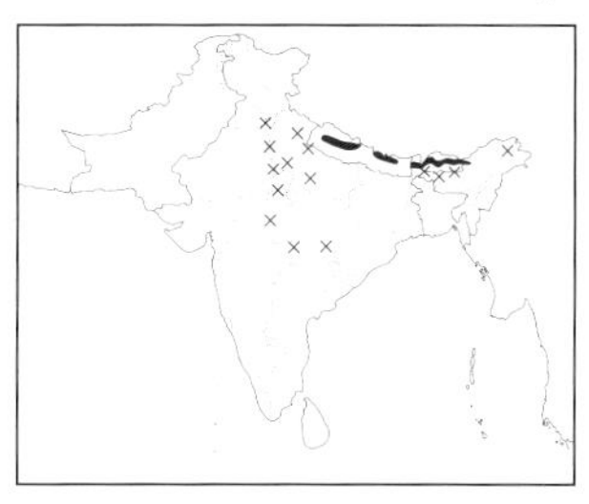

IDENTIFICATION 10 cm. Rather flowerpecker-like, with greenish upperparts and yellowish underparts. Separated from Yellow-browed Tit (p.686) at all times by fine, sharply pointed bill, paler yellowish or greenish rump contrasting with dark tail, and pale fringes to tertials and tips to greater and median coverts (which usually form indistinct wing-bars). Further, it lacks the crest which is frequently apparent on Yellow-browed, and is generally more yellowish on underparts. **Male breeding** has bright orange-scarlet forecrown, chin and throat, and golden-yellow breast. **Female breeding** has yellowish forecrown and olive-yellow throat and breast. **Adult non-breeding** is similar to breeding female, but throat is whitish, with female generally duller than male. **Juvenile** is similar to adult non-breeding, but has duller olive rump and pale grey underparts (with no trace of yellow). **Racial variation** *C. f. olivaceus* of the NE subcontinent differs from *C. f. flammiceps* of the W and C Himalayas, described above, in having darker olive-green upperparts; on breeding male, orange is restricted to forehead and centre of throat, and breast is greener. **VOICE** Calls include a high-pitched, repeated *tsit, tsit* etc, and a soft and weak *whitoo-whitoo*; song is composed of a series of thin, high-pitched motifs, with some sequences recalling Coal Tit (p.683) (Harrap and Quinn 1996). **HABITS** Similar to those of other tits. Quite gregarious in winter and on passage. Forages in the tops of tall trees, where unobtrusive and easily overlooked; also in bushes. Will fly high across hillsides between feeding grounds. Feeds chiefly on insects, also pollen and nectar, but not seeds. **HABITAT** Temperate deciduous broadleaved forest or mixed deciduous–coniferous forest. **BREEDING** March–early June. Nest is a cup of dry grass, rootlets and feathers, built near the ground or up to 15 m up in a hole in a tree trunk or branch. **DISTRIBUTION AND STATUS** Himalayas from N Pakistan east to Arunachal Pradesh. Summer visitor to far W Himalayas, probably resident farther east; winter distribution is uncertain, but records from Nepal and C India (from Delhi and W Rajasthan south to NE Maharashtra and S Madhya Pradesh). Resident in NE India. **NP:** uncommon; mainly 2135–3000 m (down to 1280 m). **IN:** generally distributed, but frequent in Kashmir, summers 2000–3500 m; rare in the far east, 300–2300 m. **BT:** frequent; 1800–3355 m.

RUFOUS-NAPED TIT *Parus rufonuchalis* Plate 113

Simla Black Tit (F,I), Dark-grey Tit

IDENTIFICATION 13 cm. A black-crested tit with white cheeks and black throat and breast. **Adult** has rufous undertail-coverts, and buff wash to whitish patch on nape. Very similar to Rufous-vented Tit (below) and, where ranges overlap in the W Himalayas, is best told from that species by larger size, more extensive black bib (extending onto upper belly), and grey (rather than rufous) lower belly. Purer grey underparts and more extensive black on breast should be sufficient to distinguish it from the eastern race of Rufous-vented, which is more similar, although there is no known overlap in range. Told from Spot-winged Tit (below) by larger size, uniform wings, and more extensive black bib. **Juvenile** is similar to adult, but with shorter crest; mantle and belly are suffused with brown, undertail-coverts are buff, and black bib is duller and less extensive, and not so clearly divided from grey belly as on adult. **VOICE** Song is a monotonous, repeated two-noted whistle, *whi-whee...whi-whee*; also a *tswi-tswi-tswi* followed by a rapid trill. Call is three-noted and repeated every few seconds: the first two notes are rather high metallic squeaks, followed by a louder downward-inflected whistle, *tsi-tsi-peeduw* (Roberts 1992). **HABITS** A typical tit. Forages in the canopy, in bushes and on the ground. Often in mixed foraging flocks with other species, including Spot-winged Tit, but feeds more on the ground than that species. Less active than other black tits. **HABITAT** Chiefly coniferous forest of fir, pine, deodar, spruce and juniper. **BREEDING** May–July. Builds nest of moss, wool and hair deep in a hole, usually in a steep bank, under a large stone or in tree roots. **DISTRIBUTION AND STATUS** Resident, subject to altitudinal movements. NC Baluchistan, Pakistan, and Himalayas from N Pakistan east to WC Nepal. Summers 2400–3600 m (–4000 m in Nepal), winters down to 1500 m (to foothills). **PK:** locally common. **NP:** fairly common. **IN:** common.

RUFOUS-VENTED TIT *Parus rubidiventris* Plate 113

Rufous-bellied Crested Tit (I), Rufous-breasted Black Tit (F)

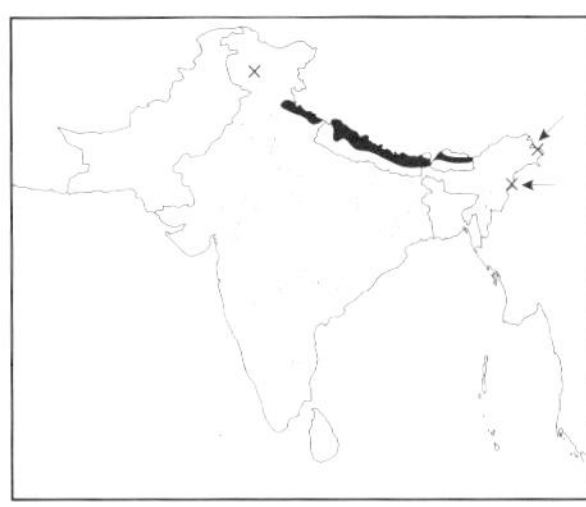

IDENTIFICATION 12 cm. **Adult** is very similar to Rufous-naped Tit (above), with black crest, white nape and cheeks, and black throat and breast. Where ranges overlap in the W Himalayas it is best told from that species by smaller size, rufous belly concolorous with undertail-coverts, and less extensive black bib (not reaching onto belly). Told from Spot-winged Tit (below) by absence of broad white tips to median and greater coverts. **Juvenile** is similar to adult, but with shorter crest and duller cap; cheeks are tinged with yellowish, and bib is less clearly defined. **Racial variation** *P. r. beavani* of the E Himalayas differs from *P. r. rubidiventris*, described above, in having greyish belly (washed buff, especially in fresh plumage), buff wash to cheeks, and purer blue-grey mantle (latter feature incorrectly depicted on plate). **VOICE** Gives a wide variety of calls, including a *seet*, *piu* and *chit*; song is a variable rattling, e.g. *chi-chi-chi-chi* (Harrap and Quinn 1996). **HABITS** A typical tit. Often in mixed flocks with other species throughout the year. Feeds very actively in the treetops, also on the ground and in bushes. Bold and noisy. **HABITAT** Coniferous, mixed coniferous–birch and oak–rhododendron forest, and rhododendron shrubberies; rhododendron forest in Nagaland. **BREEDING** April–June. Nest and nest site are similar to those of Rufous-naped Tit, or nest may be in a tree hole. **DISTRIBUTION AND STATUS** Resident, subject to limited altitudinal movements. Himalayas, mainly from SE Himachal Pradesh east to Bhutan; Nagaland. In Himalayas, summers from 2550 m up to the timberline; in winter may descend to 2135 m, but noted at 4270 m (Nepal). **NP, IN, BT:** common and widespread. **REFERENCES** Martens and Eck (1995).

SPOT-WINGED TIT *Parus melanolophus* Plate 113

Crested Black Tit (I), Black-crested Tit, Spot-winged Black Tit (F,R)

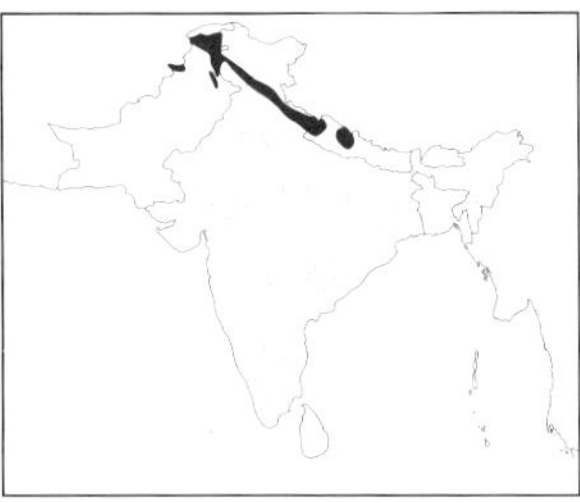

IDENTIFICATION 11 cm. **Adult** superficially resembles Rufous-naped and Rufous-vented Tits (above). with black crest, white nape patch and cheeks, and black throat and breast. Told from both by smaller size, and by broad white tips to median and greater coverts, forming prominent 'spotted' wing-bars in all plumages. Has less extensive black on breast compared with Rufous-naped, and belly is grey, rather than rufous as in W Himalayan race of Rufous-vented. Distinguished from Coal Tit (p.683) by rufous breast sides and flanks, dark grey belly, and darker blue-grey mantle. Nevertheless, hybridises frequently with Coal Tit in WC Nepal, and a variety of intergrades occurs; some hybrids, however, differ from either species in having band of cinnamon-orange down centre of underparts. **Juvenile** has duller black bib and (shorter) crest, faint yellow wash to cheeks, rusty-buff wing spots, greyish-olive upperparts and buffish-grey underparts. More closely resembles Coal Tit, but has rufous flanks and greyer belly. **VOICE** Calls similar to those of Coal Tit: include a *stit*, a *pip*, *pip-sziu*, and a plaintive *tsi-tsu-whichooh*. Song is a repeated *psip-iu*. **HABITS** A typical tit, very similar in behaviour to Rufous-vented and Coal Tits. Hunts in mixed bands of tits, warblers and other insectivorous species, even in summer. Forages chiefly in the upper half of trees, occasionally on the ground and in bushes. **HABITAT** Favours coniferous forest; also in mixed broadleaved–coniferous forest. **BREEDING** May and June. Builds nest of moss, fur and hair, usually in a tree hole within 2 m of ground or under stones. **DISTRIBUTION AND STATUS** Resident, subject to altitudinal movements. Himalayas from N Pakistan east to WC Nepal. **PK:** common; usually summers 1800–3000 m, winters from 2400 m down to the foothills, occasionally to adjacent plains. **NP:** common and widespread in the west; hybridises with Coal Tit in WC areas; summers 2800–4000 m (down to 2200 m). **IN:** common; breeds 2000–3300 m, winters down to 600 m. **REFERENCES** Martens and Eck (1995).

COAL TIT *Parus ater* — Plate 113

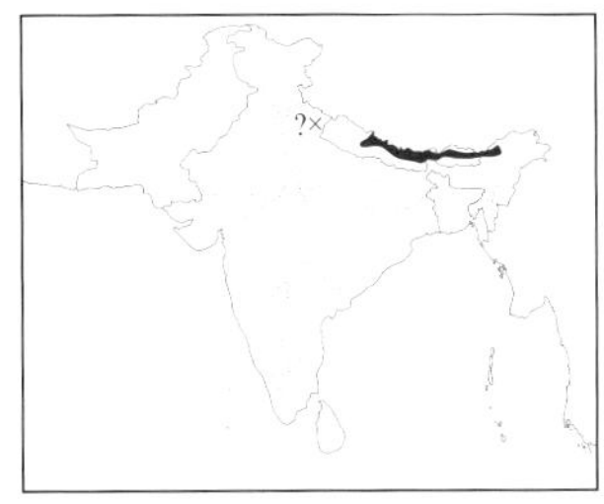

IDENTIFICATION 11 cm. **Adult** is similar to Spot-winged Tit (p.682), with black crest, white nape and cheeks, and black throat and breast. Like that species, it has whitish tips to median and greater coverts. Told from Spot-winged by olive-grey mantle and creamy-buff underparts. Small size and whitish wing spots separate it from other black-crested tits. Hybridises with Spot-winged Tit in WC Nepal. **Juvenile** lacks crest, and cap and bib are brownish, with bib very poorly defined; has stronger olive cast to mantle, and yellowish wash to cheeks and breast. **VOICE** Song is a low-pitched, slow *wee-tsee....wee-tsee....wee-tsee*; calls include a thin *tsi tsi*. **HABITS** A typical tit. Behaviour similar to that of Spot-winged Tit. **HABITAT** Mainly coniferous forest, also fir and birch forest. **BREEDING** End March–June. Poorly known in the region. Nest is a pad of fur in a tree hole. **DISTRIBUTION AND STATUS** Resident, subject to limited altitudinal movements. Himalayas, mainly from WC Nepal east to Arunachal Pradesh; claims from farther west in Uttar Pradesh require confirmation. **NP:** fairly common and widespread in the centre and east; hybridises with Spot-winged in WC areas; summers 2440–4000 m (–4250 m), winters from 2500 m up to at least 3050 m (1830–4270 m). **IN:** common; breeds 2500–3800 m, winters 1800–3810 m. **BT:** common; 2135–3940 m.

GREY-CRESTED TIT *Parus dichrous* — Plate 113

Brown Crested Tit (I), Crested Brown Tit (F)

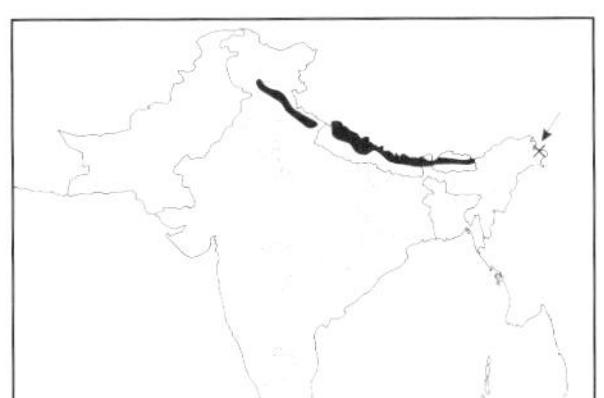

IDENTIFICATION 12 cm. Very different from other crested tits. **Adult** has greyish cap, crest and upperparts, buffish-white half-collar and submoustachial stripe, greyish-buff throat, and orange-buff underparts. **Juvenile** has shorter crest, and paler and less uniform underparts. **VOICE** Song is a *whee-whee-tz-tz-tz*; alarm is a rapid *cheea, cheea, a ti-ti-ti-ti-ti* (Fleming *et al.* 1984). **HABITS** A typical tit, but is rather quiet. Often joins mixed-species flocks of other tits and warblers. Forages in the middle and lower storeys, also on the ground. **HABITAT** Mainly oak and other broadleaved forest, also coniferous–rhododendron and coniferous forest. **BREEDING** April–June. Builds a nest of moss, fur and hair in a tree hole 3–6 m above ground. **DISTRIBUTION AND STATUS** Resident, subject to limited altitudinal movements. Himalayas, mainly from Jammu and Kashmir east to Bhutan. **NP:** fairly common and widespread; summers chiefly 2450–4000 m, winters 2000–3655 m (–4270 m). **IN:** uncommon in the west, breeds 2400–3300 m; fairly common in the east, breeds from 2700 m to the timberline, may winter down to 2200 m. **BT:** common; from 2745 m to the timberline. **REFERENCES** Martens and Eck (1995).

GREAT TIT *Parus major* — Plate 113

Grey Tit (F,I,P)

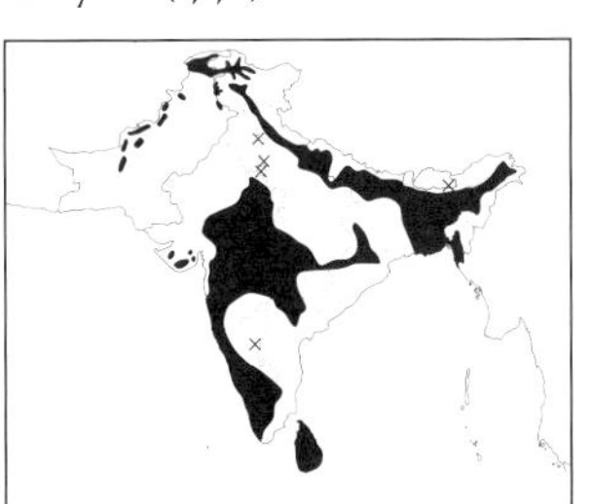

IDENTIFICATION 14 cm. A distinctive tit, with white cheeks and nape patch contrasting with black of rest of head, black centre of breast and line down belly, greyish mantle, and white greater-covert wing-bar and fringes to tertials. **Adult** told from Green-backed Tit (p.684) by greyish (rather than green) mantle, and greyish-white (rather than yellow) on underparts. See White-naped Tit (p.684) for differences from that species. **Juvenile** has brownish-black cap and throat, yellowish-white cheeks and underparts, yellowish-olive wash to mantle, and diffuse blackish line down centre of breast. **Racial variation** Seven races are known from the subcontinent. Six of these are in the *cinereus* group of subspecies, and vary subtly in coloration of upperparts and underparts and in the amount of white in rectrices: extremes are *P. m. ziaratensis* of NW subcontinent, which has pale blue-grey upperparts and is almost white on underparts, and *P. m. mahrattarum* of S India and Sri Lanka, which has darker grey upperparts and is smoky-grey on underparts. There is one record from Sikkim of *P. m. tibetanus*, which is one of the *minor* group of subspecies: this has a greenish-olive cast to the mantle. **VOICE** Extremely variable. Song phrases include loud, clear whistling *weeter-weeter-weeter, wreet-chee-chee*, and *witwit-seeee*; calls include a *tsee tsee tsee* and a harsh churring note.

HABITS A typical tit, although less gregarious than most species. Often keeps singly or in pairs; sometimes joins roving mixed parties in the non-breeding season. Confiding. Forages in the middle and especially the lower level of trees and bushes. **HABITAT** Open forest, groves, trees in cultivation and gardens; favours dry, broadleaved deciduous forest; juniper and pine forest in Baluchistan; wet deciduous and sal forest in NE India. **BREEDING** February–November, varying locally. Builds nest of moss, wool and hair in a hole in a wall, building, tree, stump or roadside bank. **DISTRIBUTION AND STATUS** Resident, subject to altitudinal movements in Himalayas and local movements in the peninsula. Baluchistan and NW Pakistan, and Himalayan foothills from N Pakistan east to Arunachal Pradesh; widespread in NE and peninsular India; Bangladesh and Sri Lanka. **PK:** common; breeds in mountainous regions, 1200–2400 m; locally migratory or nomadic in winter, some wander down to adjacent foothills, **NP:** widespread; common up to 1525 m, frequent up to 1800 m (–3050 m). **IN:** common; breeds mainly from the foothills up to 1800 m, locally to 2400 m in Himalayas, to 3600 m in Ladakh, to 900 m in the NE hills, and from the plains to hill summits in Kerala; winters in the foothills and spreads to the plains. **BT:** rare. **BD:** occurs locally throughout. **LK:** common throughout, more frequent in the hills. **REFERENCES** Pfister (1997).

GREEN-BACKED TIT *Parus monticolus* — Plate 113

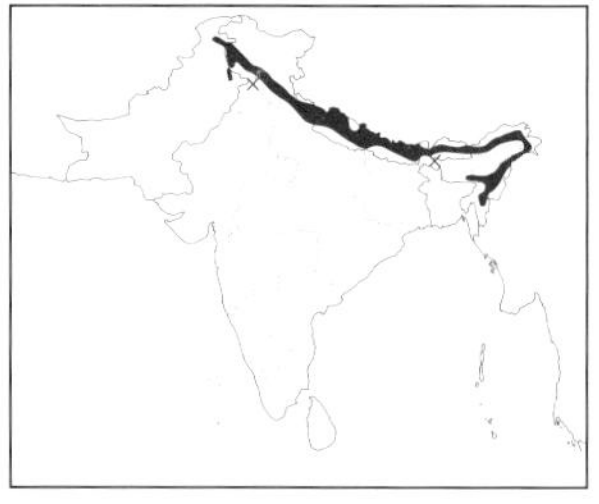

IDENTIFICATION 12.5 cm. **Adult** told from Great Tit (p.683) by bright green mantle and back, yellow on underparts, and white median-covert wing-bar. Further, wings look bluish owing to blue edges to remiges. Otherwise similar, with white cheeks and nape patch, contrasting with black of rest of head, and black breast and line down centre of belly. **Juvenile** as adult, but black of head and breast is duller, mantle is a duller green, and white cheeks and median- and greater-covert bars are washed with yellow. **VOICE** Song includes a loud, pleasant, ringing *whitee... whitee, whitee* etc; calls are similar to Great Tit's and include a ringing *te-te-whee, ti-ti-tee-ti* and *whit whit whit* etc (Ali and Ripley 1987). **HABITS** A typical tit. Forages chiefly in the lower storey, also in the middle storey and occasionally on the ground. **HABITAT** Both open and dense broadleaved forest, preferring moister habitats than those used by Great Tit; also mixed broadleaved–coniferous and spruce–deodar forest in Pakistan. **BREEDING** March–July. Builds nest of moss, fur, feathers and wool in a hole up to 7 m high in a tree trunk, stump, post, stone wall or under a roof. **DISTRIBUTION AND STATUS** Resident, subject to limited altitudinal movements. Himalayas from N Pakistan east to Arunachal Pradesh; NE India. **PK:** common; usually 1500–2700 m (down to 580 m). **NP:** widespread, common from 1370 m up to 3100 m, frequent up to 3660 m; replaces Great Tit altitudinally; breeds chiefly above 1525 m and winters below 2745 m. **IN:** locally common; breeds 1600–2800 m in Kashmir, 1200–3660 m in the east, and winters down to the foothills. **BT:** common; 100–3660 m.

WHITE-NAPED TIT *Parus nuchalis* — Plate 114

White-winged Black Tit (I)

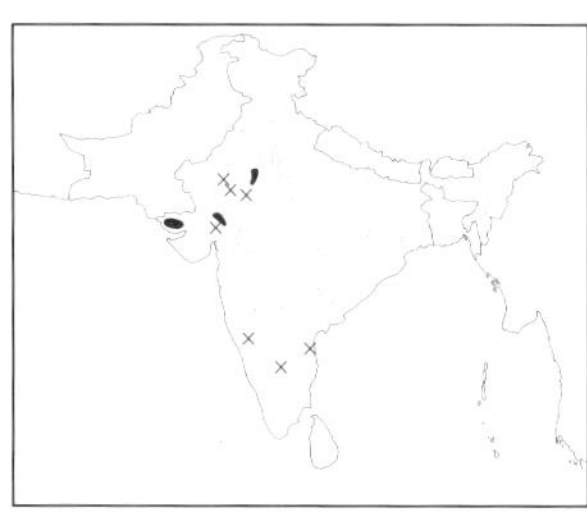

IDENTIFICATION 12 cm. **Adult** is strikingly different from Great Tit (p.683), although, as that species, has white cheeks and black line down centre of breast. Has black mantle and wing-coverts (grey on Great Tit) and large amounts of white on wing, with much white on tertials and at bases of secondaries and primaries. Has striking white nuchal patch, and shows variable yellow wash to underparts. In flight, white on wings and tail and black upperparts result in very different appearance from that of Great Tit. **Male** has glossy black (as opposed to dull black) mantle and more white on tertials and base of secondaries than **female**. **Juvenile** is similar to female, but has dull cap. **VOICE** Extensive vocabulary, very similar to Great Tit's: includes loud penetrating *pee-pee-pee-pee-pee* song; shrike-like scolding *tchrrr*, occasionally given in series; mellow *pit* and *chit* notes; *tink* like that of Chaffinch (p.830); and *tip-it*, recalling Barn Swallow (p.690) (P. Holt). **HABITS** Similar to those of Great Tit. Usually in pairs or family parties. Shy. Usually forages in trees, and roosts in tree hollows. Feeds chiefly on insects and spiders, also fruit and nectar. **HABITAT** Thin thorn-scrub forest, usually *Acacia nilotica*, on broken stony ground in the northwest; moist deciduous forest in Kerala. **BREEDING** May–August. Nest is a pad of soft fibres, wool and hair, placed 1–2.5 m up in a tree hole, often in an old nest of Yellow-crowned Woodpecker. **DISTRIBUTION AND STATUS** Globally threatened. **IN:** endemic resident, subject to local movements; occurs in the northwest (Kutch, C and SC Rajasthan and N Gujarat) and south (old records from S Andhra Pradesh and S Karnataka, recent record from Kerala now regarded as doubtful); fairly common but local in Kutch, local and uncommon elsewhere in the northwest. **REFERENCES** Hussain *et al.* (1992), Tiwari and Rahmani (1997), Zacharias and Gaston (1993).

BLACK-LORED TIT *Parus xanthogenys* — Plate 114

Yellow-cheeked Tit (F,I)

IDENTIFICATION 13 cm. A crested black-and-yellow tit with whitish or yellowish wing-bars. **Adult** told from Yellow-cheeked Tit (p.685) by black forehead and lores (which are yellow on Yellow-cheeked), and more uniform

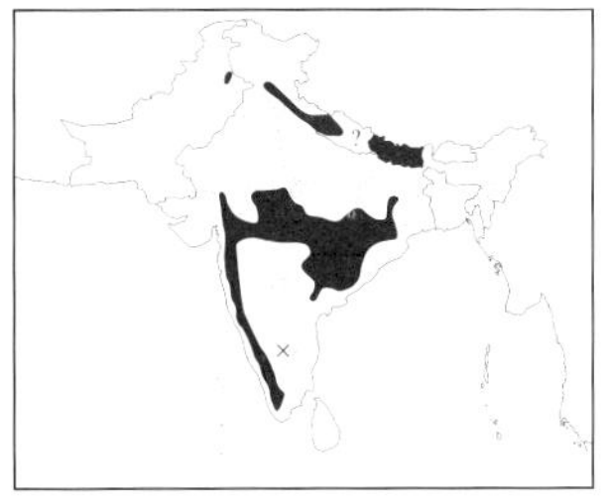

greenish upperparts, with black streaking confined to scapulars. Further, has olive rump and (where ranges overlap) wing-bars are yellowish. Unlike Yellow-cheeked, occurs widely in the C and W Himalayas and peninsular India. **Juvenile** virtually identical to adult, although black of head and ventral stripe is duller and crest is shorter. **Racial variation** *P. x. xanthogenys* of the Himalayas, described above, has yellow tips to wing-coverts, these being white on adults (although not juveniles) of the two races occurring in the peninsula. Sexes of the nominate race are practically identical. Male *P. x. aplonotus* of N and E peninsular India is similar to *xanthogenys*, although duller; female *aplonotus* has greyish-olive rather than black bib and ventral stripe, and paler yellow cheeks and underparts. Male *P. x. travancoreensis* of S India is similar to male *aplonotus*, although duller; female *travancoreensis* is similar to female *aplonotus*, but crest is also greyish-olive, while juvenile female has blackish crest and olive bib and ventral line (i.e. is similarly patterned to female *aplonotus*, but has dull black cap and bib, and ventral stripe contrasts less with underparts). **VOICE** Song comprises various stereotyped phrases, e.g. *pui-pui-tee, pui-pui-tee...*, *tsi-teuw, tsi-teuw...* or *tsi-wheeah-wheeah*; calls include a *tzee-tzee-wheep-wheep-wheep*, a *tsi-tsi-pit-tui*, and a rattled *ch-chi-chi-chi* (Harrap and Quinn 1996). **HABITS** A typical tit. Often joins mixed foraging flocks. Feeds mainly in the upper storey, occasionally lower down in trees. **HABITAT** Open forest, secondary forest, edges of dense forest and groves, mainly of broadleaves in N and C subcontinent; broadleaved evergreen forest, coffee plantations and cardamom sholas in SW India. **BREEDING** March–October, varying locally. Builds nest of moss and fur in a tree hole up to 6 m above ground. **DISTRIBUTION AND STATUS** Endemic to the subcontinent. Resident, subject to altitudinal movements. Himalayas from Murree, Pakistan, east to Darjeeling, West Bengal; peninsular hills. **PK:** now only a straggler. **NP:** widespread and common, except in the far east, where uncommon; summers 850–2300 m (–2925 m), winters 915–2135 m (down to 75 m). **IN:** common in Himalayas, breeds 1500–2100 m, occasionally winters down to 1200 m; widespread and fairly common in the peninsula. **REFERENCES** Martens and Eck (1995).

YELLOW-CHEEKED TIT *Parus spilonotus* — Plate 114

Black-spotted Yellow Tit (F,I)

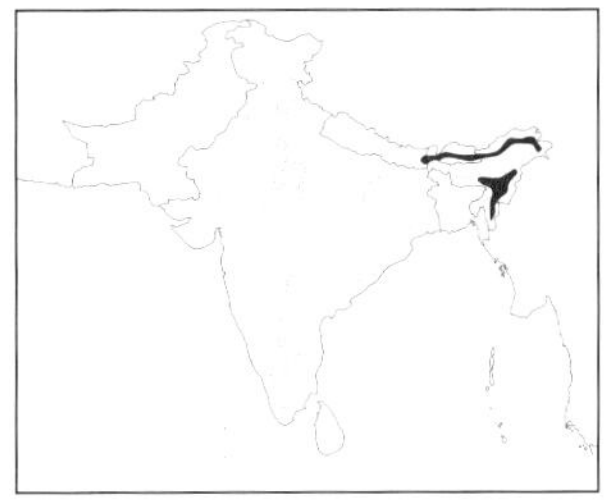

IDENTIFICATION 14 cm. A black-crested tit with yellow cheeks and black stripe behind eye. Most likely to be confused with Black-lored Tit (p.684), although has a more easterly distribution and does not occur in the peninsula. **Adult** told from Black-lored by yellow forehead and lores (which are black on Black-lored), and black streaking on greenish mantle; also has grey rump, and wing-bars are white where ranges overlap. Sexes are similar in the nominate race. **Juvenile** similar to adult, but duller, with shorter sooty-black crest; wing-coverts are browner, and has yellowish-white wing-bars, while yellow of underparts is also duller. **Racial variation** *P. s. subviridis* of E hill states south of the Brahmaputra R differs from nominate E Himalayan race: male has darker, more olive upperparts, and flanks are more extensively washed with greyish-olive; female has dull olive-yellow (rather than black) bib and ventral line, and mantle is less heavily marked with black. **VOICE** Song is a ringing three-note motif, rapidly repeated up to six times, *chee-chee-piu, chee-chee pui, chee-chee-pui...*; calls are rather like those of Great Tit (p.683) and include a *sit, si-si-si* and a *witch-a-witch-a-witch-a*, often combined with a harsh *churr-r-r-r-r* (Harrap and Quinn 1996). **HABITS** A typical tit. Frequently in mixed-species foraging flocks. Hunts chiefly in the lower forest canopy, also lower down in small trees and bushes. **HABITAT** Open forest, mainly of broadleaves. **BREEDING** End March–June. Nest is a pad of moss, fur, hair and wool, usually in a tree hole. **DISTRIBUTION AND STATUS** Resident, subject to altitudinal movements. Himalayas from E Nepal east to Arunachal Pradesh; NE Indian hills. **NP:** uncommon and very local in the far east; 1980–2440 m (down to 450 m). **IN:** in Himalayas locally fairly common in the far east, summers 1600–2400 m, winters down to 900 m (–3700 m?); in NE hills locally common, breeds above 1500 m. **BT:** frequent; 1130–2450 m.

AZURE TIT *Parus cyanus* — Plate 114

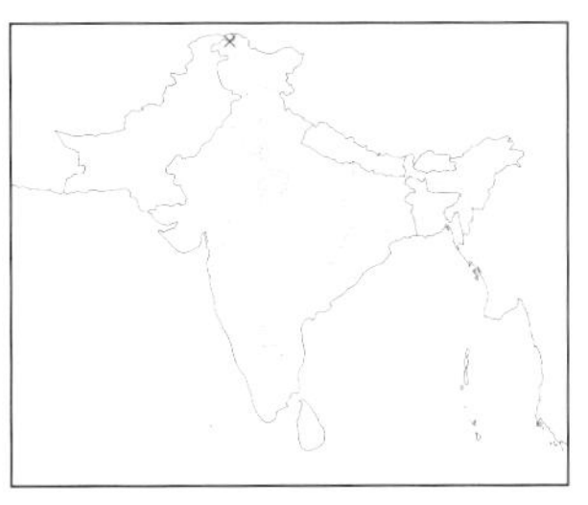

IDENTIFICATION 13.5 cm. **Adult** is a beautiful blue-grey, black and white tit which shows extensive white on the wings and tail. Very similar to Yellow-breasted Tit (p.686), but underparts are all white, lacking yellow on breast, and crown and ear-coverts are white. **Juvenile** shows grey (rather than bluish) lesser and median coverts, and grey edges to greater coverts; underparts may be washed with very pale yellow; crown and upperparts are greyer. **VOICE** Song includes a loud descending trill, *tii-tsi-dji-daa-daa-daa-daa*; calls include a quiet, slurred *tirr tirr* or *tsirrup*, and a hard, scolding *chr-r-r-r-rit* (Harrap and Quinn 1996). **HABITS** A typical tit. Often remains under cover; feeds in bushes, trees and on the ground. Has quite a strong, bounding, undulating flight. **HABITAT** In Pakistan, recorded in tamarisks along a river bed. **DISTRIBUTION AND STATUS PK:** one record from N Hunza; possibly a rare winter visitor.

YELLOW-BREASTED TIT *Parus flavipectus* **Plate 114**

Yellow-breasted Blue Tit (I), *P. cyanus* (I,R,V)

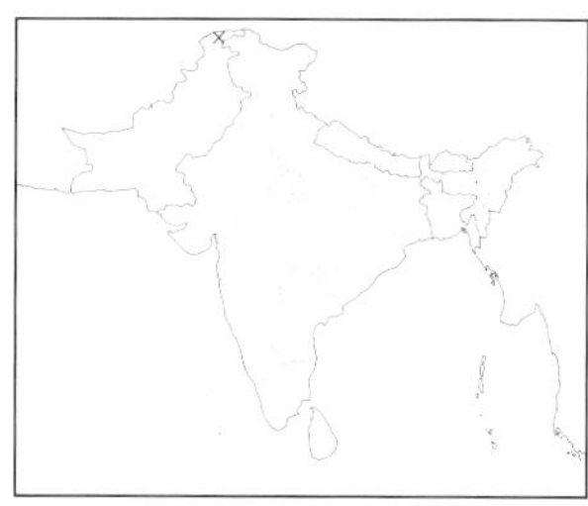

IDENTIFICATION 13 cm. **Adult** very similar to Azure Tit (p.685), with dark blue half-collar and blackish eye-stripe, blue-grey mantle, and extensive white on blue wings and tail. Told from that species by yellow breast and greyish head; chin and centre of throat are greyish and show as faint bib. Female is duller, and has paler, less blue upperparts and paler yellow breast than male. Hybridises with Azure Tit, offspring having yellow wash on entire underparts rather than clear breast-band. **Juvenile** has yellow wash to head and underparts and greenish wash to upperparts. **VOICE** Vocal, with most notes similar to those of Azure Tit: clear seesawing song, *tse-u-tsee-tsee-uw*; calls include peevish scolding *tchrrt* and finch-like *chink-chink-chink* (P. Holt). **HABITS** Similar to those of Azure Tit. **HABITAT** In Pakistan, recorded in dense thickets of willow, juniper and birch. **BREEDING** Unknown in the region. In CIS, nests in May in a rock crevice, natural tree hole, or hole in a clay bank. **DISTRIBUTION AND STATUS PK:** possibly a small resident population, or breeds sporadically; in July 1902, found to be numerous on the Yarkhan R, NE Chitral, at 3000 m.

YELLOW-BROWED TIT *Sylviparus modestus* **Plate 114**

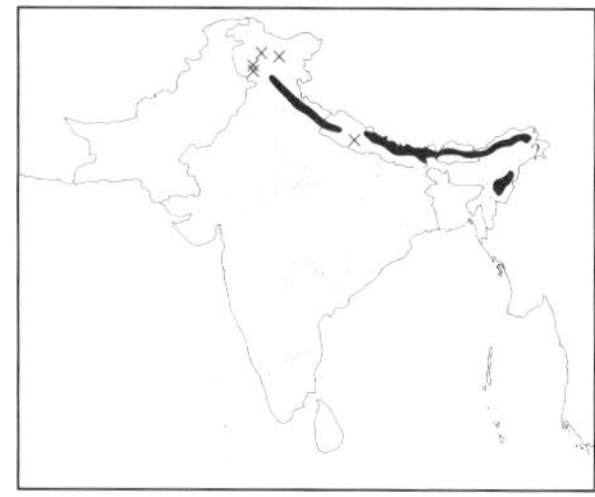

IDENTIFICATION 10 cm. A diminutive tit, sometimes overlooked as a leaf warbler because of its small size and greenish plumage, but easily distinguished by its behaviour and slightly raised crest. **Adult** has olive-green upperparts, yellowish eye-ring, short, fine yellow supercilium (sometimes not visible in field), and yellowish-buff underparts. In worn plumage, has duller greyish-olive upperparts and whiter underparts. **Juvenile** is much as adult. Told from Fire-capped Tit (p.681) by stouter bill, crested appearance, rather uniform wings with less distinct (olive-buff) greater-covert bar, and lack of pale rump or distinct pale tertial fringes. **Racial variation** *S. m. simlaensis* of the W Himalayas has brighter yellowish-olive upperparts and yellowish underparts compared with *S. m. modestus* of the C and E Himalayas. **VOICE** Sharp, very high-pitched, well-spaced *tis* notes (singly or *tis-tis-tis*), also combined with rapid series of very high-pitched thin *si* notes, *tis-tis-tis-sisisisisi*; the latter may well be the song, repeated at intervals of a few seconds (C. Robson). **HABITS** Very similar to those of other tits, but quiet and unobtrusive. Often in company with mixed-species flocks of other insectivorous birds. Forages mainly in the canopy, also lower down. Frequently flicks wings. **HABITAT** Mainly broadleaved forest, favouring oaks. **BREEDING** Little known. April and May. Builds nest of hair, fur and moss in a tree hole 0.5–6 m above ground. **DISTRIBUTION AND STATUS** Resident, subject to some altitudinal movements. Himalayas from Ladakh and W Kashmir east to Arunachal Pradesh; NE India. **NP:** fairly common in centre and east, uncommon in west; summers 2135–3250 m (–3660 m), winters 1500–2800 m. **IN:** fairly common; summers 2100–3600 m, winters from 1200 m (west) or 900 m (east) up to 2900 m. **BT:** common; 1700–3400 m.

SULTAN TIT *Melanochlora sultanea* **Plate 114**

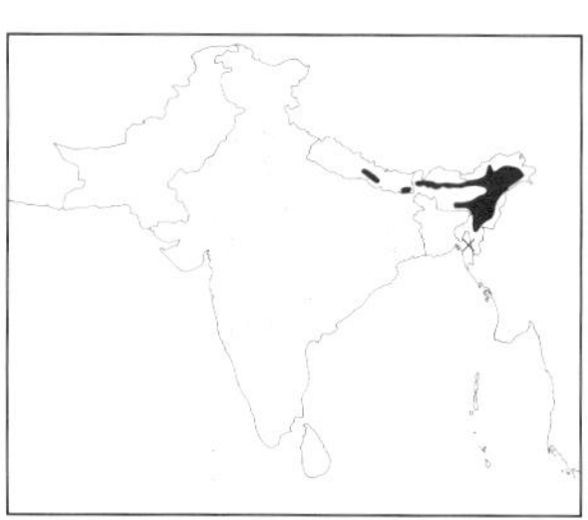

IDENTIFICATION 20.5 cm. A huge, bulbul-like tit. **Male** is largely glossy blue-black, with bright yellow crest and yellow underparts below black breast. **Female** is similar, but black of plumage is duller blackish-olive (especially pronounced on throat and breast). **Juvenile** as female, but with shorter crest, and with fine yellowish-white tips to greater coverts. **VOICE** Call is a loud, rapidly uttered, squeaky whistle, *tcheery-tcheery-tcheery*; also a rattling *tji-jup*. Song is a series of five loud, ringing *chew* notes (Boonsong and Round 1991). **HABITS** Similar to those of other tits, but is noticeably slower and more deliberate in its actions. Keeps to the treetops, singly, in pairs or in small parties. **HABITAT** Edges of broadleaved forest, also large trees near cultivation; favours evergreens. **BREEDING** Little known. April–July. Builds nest of moss and vegetable down in a tree crevice. **DISTRIBUTION AND STATUS** Resident. Himalayan foothills from C Nepal east to Arunachal Pradesh; NE India and Bangladesh. **NP:** rare and local in the centre and east; 275–1370 m. **IN:** locally common in Himalayas, common in the northeast; foothills up to 1600 m (–1900 m?). **BT:** frequent; 300–1800 m. **BD:** ?former resident; no recent records, but could still occur in hill tracts.

WHITE-CHEEKED TIT *Aegithalos leucogenys* **Plate 114**

IDENTIFICATION 11 cm. **Adult** superficially resembles Black-throated Tit (p.687), with dark mask and black throat. Told from that species by lack of white supercilium above a narrower and duller mask, duller cinnamon-coloured crown, black chin and black of throat extending farther onto breast, and duller grey-brown

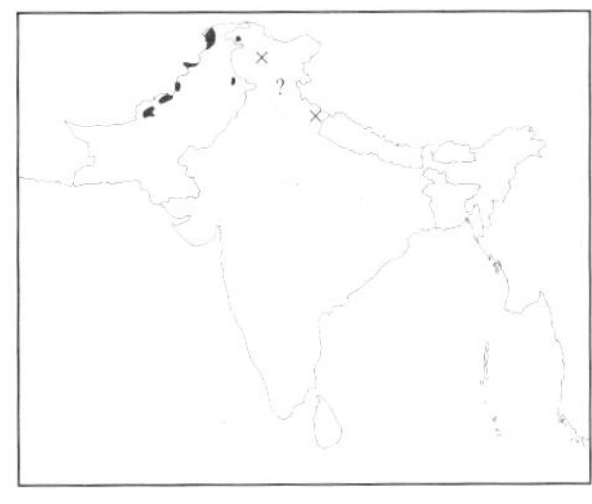

mantle and back. Readily told from White-throated Tit (p.687) by black throat, uniform cinnamon forehead and crown, and striking yellowish iris. **Juvenile** has paler, more buffish crown, browner upperparts, and buffish underparts with streaking on breast; cheeks and throat are buffish-white, although may show traces of dark bib. Told from adult and juvenile White-throated by narrower dark mask and uniform cinnamon-buff forehead and crown (White-throated has white forehead). **VOICE** All notes weak and typical of genus. Quiet, high-pitched contact calls, *see-see-see-sip*, dry *trrrp* and a mellow *tsup*; song slightly stronger and includes bubbling *ti-ti-tsup* etc, sunbird-like *sip-sip* and seesawing *we-ti..we-ti* (P. Holt). **HABITS** A typical tit. In the non-breeding season keeps in family groups, or small parties; sometimes associates with other tits and treecreepers. Forages mainly in bushes, occasionally in the treetops. Chiefly insectivorous. Makes a winter roost nest. **HABITAT** Prefers open scrub forest, including juniper forest and holly oak scrub; also tamarisk bushes along rivers. **BREEDING** End March–May. Nest is an oval ball with a side entrance, made of moss, fine grasses and cobwebs, usually 1–3.5 m up in a tree or bush. **DISTRIBUTION AND STATUS** Resident, subject to altitudinal movements. Mainly Baluchistan and NW Himalayas, Pakistan; isolated records from N Uttar Pradesh and Kashmir. **PK:** locally frequent resident; breeds 1500–3660 m, winters up to at least 2100 m, straggles down to 460 m. **IN:** current status uncertain, no recent published records; 1800 m.

BLACK-THROATED TIT *Aegithalos concinnus* Plate 114

Red-headed Tit (F,I)

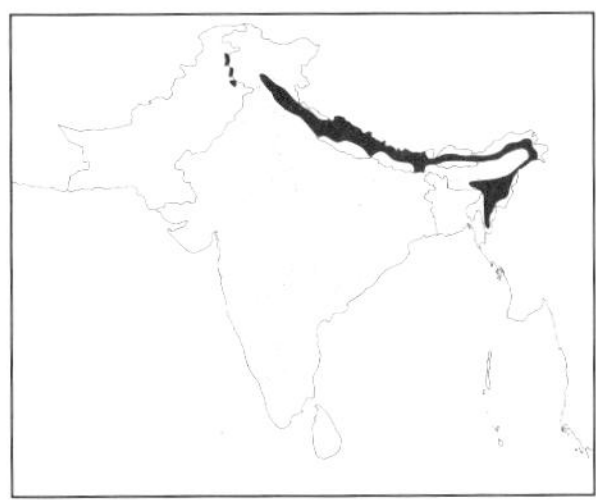

IDENTIFICATION 10.5 cm. **Adult** told from White-cheeked Tit (p.686) by white rear supercilium above broader, more clearly defined black mask, and by chestnut crown, white (rather than black) chin, and purer grey mantle and back. From Rufous-fronted Tit (p.688) by chestnut crown, white cheeks, clearly defined black throat, and paler buff underparts. **Juvenile** has paler rufous crown and white throat, paler underparts, and breast-band of indistinct black spots. Possibly confusable with White-throated Tit (below), but lacks white forehead and has narrower and clearly defined black mask, yellow iris, and paler buff breast and belly. **Racial variation** *A. c. manipurensis* of E hill states south of the Brahmaputra R has paler rufous-cinnamon crown, indistinct white supercilium (mixed with black), and white breast-band which separates black throat from rufous-cinnamon breast and flanks. **VOICE** Calls include a churring *trrrt trrrt* and a rapid, low-pitched twittering *tir-ir-ir-ir-ir* (also used in song), and alarm call is a drier *tzit-tzit-tzit* (Roberts 1992). **HABITS** A typical tit. Highly gregarious, usually in flocks of the same species and often in company with mixed hunting parties of insectivorous birds. Frequently forages in the middle and lower storeys, sometimes in the treetops. Feeds mainly on insects, also soft fruits. **HABITAT** Broadleaved or moist mixed broadleaved–coniferous forest, secondary growth, and bushes in open forest. **BREEDING** Late March–May. Nest is a ball of moss mixed with cobwebs, lichen and down, placed in a low bush or tree. **DISTRIBUTION AND STATUS** Resident, with short altitudinal movements. Himalayas from N Pakistan (Neelum valley, Murree hills and Kagan valley) east to Arunachal Pradesh; NE India. **PK:** local and frequent; 1375–2400 m. **NP:** common and widespread; mainly 1400–2700 m all year, but occasionally down to 1065 m (–3000 m). **IN:** common in Himalayas, breeds 1400–2400 m (west), to 3200 m (east), and in winter wanders down to 900 m and up to 2900 m; locally common in NE hills, breeds above 1500 m. **BT:** common.

WHITE-THROATED TIT *Aegithalos niveogularis* Plate 114

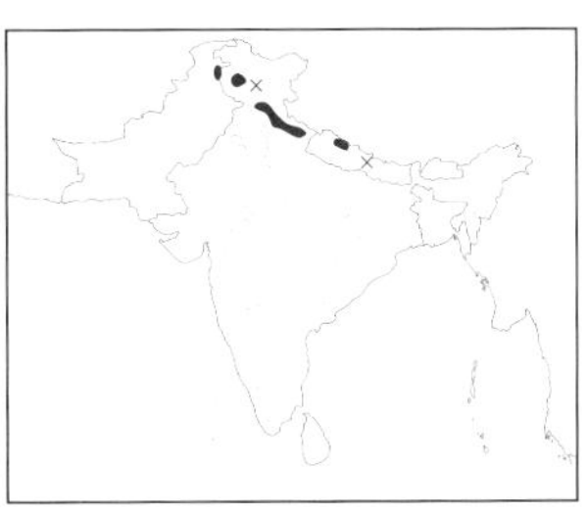

IDENTIFICATION 11 cm. **Adult** distinguished from other *Aegithalos* tits by white forehead and forecrown and whitish throat. Iris is brownish (not strikingly yellow as in others of genus). Has blackish mask and sides to crown which merge with cinnamon-brown hindcrown and ear-coverts. The underparts are warm cinnamon, becoming darker at border with white throat. Possibly confusable with juvenile Black-throated Tit (above), which also has white throat, but White-throated has white forehead, white of throat is well demarcated from cinnamon breast and belly, and has broader (but less clearly defined) mask. **Juvenile** is similar to adult, but throat is dull pinkish, breast-band is darker and more prominent (with paler lower breast and belly), and upperparts are brown. **VOICE** Song is longer and more elaborate than that of other *Aegithalos* tits: it has a rapid chattering *tweet-tweet* interspersed with high-pitched *tsi-tsi* notes and short warbling phrases. Calls include a frequently uttered *t-r-r-r-r-t* (Roberts 1992). **HABITS** A typical tit. In the non-breeding season keeps in small parties, often with leaf warblers and other tits. Usually forages fairly close to the ground. Feeds mainly on insects. **HABITAT** Bushes in mixed birch and coniferous forest and mixed deciduous forest, and at forest edges; dwarf shrubberies near the treeline. **BREEDING** May–early July. Nest is oval- or pear-shaped, made of moss, cobwebs and lichen, and placed 1–3 m up in a bush or suspended 10 m up in a tree.

DISTRIBUTION AND STATUS Resident, endemic to the subcontinent. Himalayas from Pakistan (Palas valley, Indus Kohistan, Neelum valley, Azad Kashmir, and Hazara district in Kagan valley) east to NW Nepal. **PK:** rare and local; usually 2400–3400 m in spring, 1750–2200 m in winter. **NP:** frequent and local in the northwest; 2800–3965 m. **IN:** rare; summers 2400–3600 m, winters down to 1800 m.

RUFOUS-FRONTED TIT *Aegithalos iouschistos* — Plate 114

Black-browed Tit (F,I)

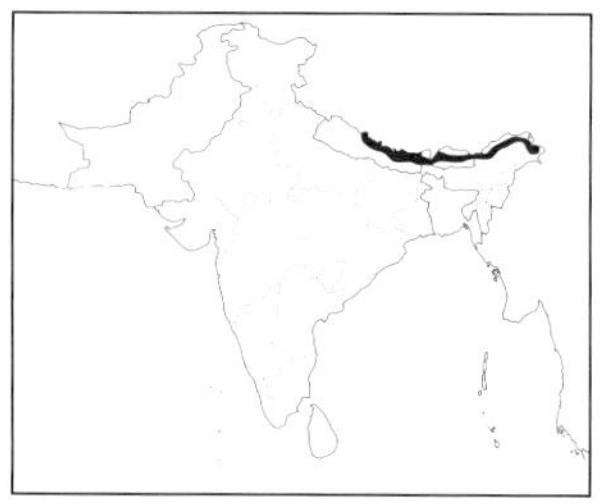

IDENTIFICATION 11 cm. **Adult** separated from other *Aegithalos* tits by combination of broad black mask through eye (covering sides of crown and reaching nape), rufous-buff forehead and centre of crown, rufous-buff cheeks and deeper cinnamon-rufous underparts, and silvery-white bib bordered by blackish chin and sides to throat. Iris is yellow (brown in White-throated, p.687). **Juvenile** is similar to adult, but crown-stripe, cheeks and underparts are paler buff. **VOICE** Variety of feeble purrs, mellow *tup* notes and squeaky notes, similar to calls of Black-throated Tit (p.687), continuously uttered from feeding flocks (P. Holt). **HABITS** A typical tit. Keeps in pairs in the breeding season; otherwise usually in parties of up to 30 birds, often not with other species. Forages at all levels, from the treetops down to bushes. **HABITAT** Broadleaved, coniferous and mixed coniferous–broadleaved forest; prefers drier habitats. **BREEDING** Little known. April–July. Only one nest described from the region, from Nepal in May: a ball, studded with lichens and lined with feathers, in an oak tree. **DISTRIBUTION AND STATUS** Resident. Himalayas from WC Nepal east to Arunachal Pradesh. **NP:** frequent; 2590–3700 m all year. **IN:** locally fairly common; 2745–3660 m all year (down to 1100 m). **BT:** common; 2600–3770 m.

SWALLOWS AND MARTINS Hirundinidae

Rather small passerines with a distinctive slender, streamlined body, long, pointed wings and a small bill. The long-tailed species are often called swallows, and the shorter-tailed species termed martins. All hawk day-flying insects in swift, agile, sustained flight, sometimes high in the air. Many species have a deeply forked tail, which affords better manoeuvrability. Hirundines catch most of their food while flying in the open, but in bad weather they may brush past or occasionally hover in front of vegetation to disturb insects. They perch readily on exposed branches and on telegraph wires, but are clumsy on the ground. The legs and feet are relatively weak, but the burrowing and cliff-dwelling species have strong claws. Most members of the family are gregarious and often feed in flocks, together with other hirundine and swift species, in places where their prey is concentrated. They also often roost and breed communally. The nest may be in a hole in a tree, rock face or building, or a tunnel which the birds have excavated in a bank, or built of mud and fixed to a branch, cliff or wall of a building. Many species undergo regular migrations. The main reference specific to hirundines is Turner and Rose (1989).

PALE MARTIN *Riparia diluta* — Plate 115

Collared Sand Martin (F,I,R), *R. riparia diluta*

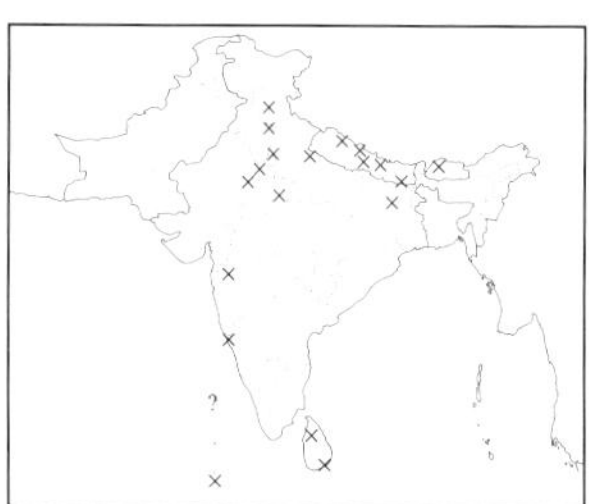

IDENTIFICATION 13 cm. **Adult** separated from Plain Martin (p.689) by brown breast-band. In addition, appears stockier and more purposeful in flight, and has a more prominently forked tail; upperparts are paler greyish-brown. Very similar to Sand Martin (p.689), but upperparts are paler and greyer, the breast-band is pale and weakly defined, the throat is greyish-white and grades into the pale greyish-brown ear-coverts, and the tail-fork is shallower. **Juvenile** has buff fringes to upperparts, including tertials and uppertail-coverts, and is probably indistinguishable in the field from Sand Martin. **VOICE** Different from Sand Martin's (sonagrams given in Goroshko 1993). **HABITS** A typical hirundine. Usually feeds over water, sometimes also over land, often in flocks with other hirundines and swifts; especially active at dusk. Frequently seen perched in rows on telegraph wires in the early morning. Forms large communal roosts in reedbeds. **HABITAT** Around large waterbodies. **BREEDING** November–May, varying locally. Breeds in small colonies (sometimes up to 150 nests), often far from water. **DISTRIBUTION AND STATUS** Recently split from Sand Martin (Goroshko 1993). The distribution and status of the two forms is poorly known. Breeds in Himalayas in Pakistan, and probably farther east; winters in Pakistan and probably farther east. **PK:** locally common in winter; locally frequent in summer in river valleys in drier mountain regions. **NP:** passage migrant; status uncertain. **IN:** resident, and possible winter visitor; status uncertain. **BT:** vagrant. **BD:** possibly recorded; status uncertain. **LK:** one sight report, but Sand Martin not excluded. **MV:** reported as regular winter visitor and passage migrant, but Sand Martin not excluded. **REFERENCES** Goroshko (1993).

SAND MARTIN *Riparia riparia* Plate 115

Collared Sand Martin (F,I,R), *R. riparia ijimae*

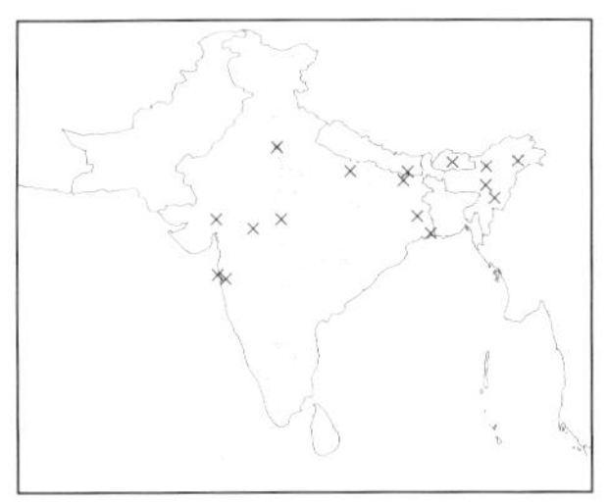

IDENTIFICATION 13 cm. **Adult** told from Plain Martin (below) by white throat and half-collar, and by brown breast-band which is generally well defined against whitish underparts. In addition, appears stockier and more purposeful in flight, and has a more prominently forked tail. Very similar to Pale Martin (p.688), but upperparts are slightly darker brown, the breast-band is dark and clearly defined, the throat is white and clearly demarcated from the dark brown ear-coverts, and the tail-fork is deeper. **Juvenile** has buff fringes to upperparts (most obvious on tertials and uppertail-coverts) and buff tinge to throat, and breast-band can be less clearly defined. **VOICE** Characteristic call is a dry rasp, drier and less rolling than similar call of Northern House Martin (p.693); song is a pleasant twittering intermixed with rasping call. **HABITS** Similar to those of Pale Martin. **HABITAT** Around large waterbodies; in summer, around streams and rivers with sandy or earth banks. **BREEDING** October–November in Assam. In large colonies of up to 1500 nests. Builds nest in a horizontal tunnel dug by the birds into a deep sandy bank near water. **DISTRIBUTION AND STATUS** Poorly known. Resident. Breeds in Assam; recorded also from Gujarat, Bihar, Manipur, Maharashtra, Nepal, Bangladesh and Maldives; possibly occurs more widely. **NP:** passage migrant; status uncertain. **IN:** resident; status uncertain. **BD:** local winter visitor and common passage migrant, but Pale Martin not excluded. **MV:** regular winter visitor and passage migrant. **REFERENCES** Abdulali (1976).

PLAIN MARTIN *Riparia paludicola* Plate 115

Plain Sand Martin (I), Brown-throated Sand Martin (R), Sand Martin (F)

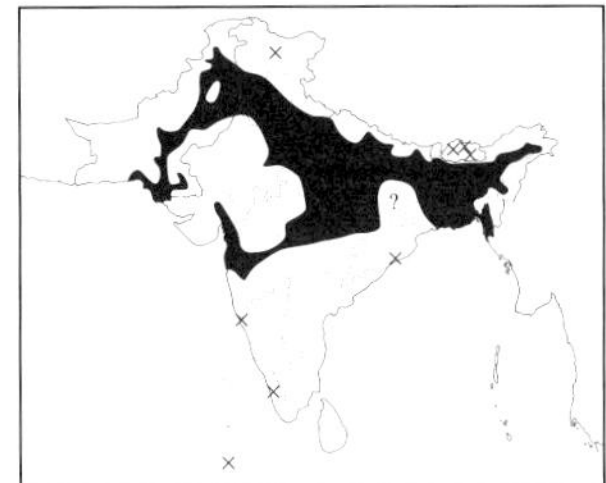

IDENTIFICATION 12 cm. **Adult** similar to Sand and Pale Martins (above and p.688), but has pale brownish-grey throat and breast, merging into dingy white of rest of underparts. On some, throat is paler than breast, and may show suggestion of breast-band. Underwing, especially coverts, is darker than on both other species. In addition, is smaller and slighter, with weaker and more fluttering flight on stiffer wings, and has squarer-shaped tail (with just a slight indentation when closed). Has slightly darker, richer brown upperparts than Pale Martin. **Juvenile** has rufous fringes to upperparts (especially tertials and rump/uppertail-coverts), and throat and breast are paler and washed with buff. **VOICE** Song is a weak, high-pitched twitter; call is a rasping *chrrr*, softer and not so grating as that of Sand Martin. **HABITS** Very similar to those of Sand Martin. **HABITAT** Around rivers and lakes; in summer around those with steep sandy banks. **BREEDING** Almost throughout the year, varying locally. Nest and nest site are very similar to those of Sand Martin. **DISTRIBUTION AND STATUS** Resident, subject to local movements. Mainly N and C subcontinent south to C Maharashtra. **PK:** common resident in Indus plains; those in N Punjab and NW Pakistan move south in winter. **NP:** widespread and common; below 1500 m (–2900 m). **IN:** widespread and locally common; plains and hills up to 1500 m. **BT:** rare. **BD:** occurs locally throughout. **MV:** vagrant. **REFERENCES** Leader (1995).

EURASIAN CRAG MARTIN *Hirundo rupestris* Plate 115

Crag Martin (F,I), Northern Crag Martin (N,R), *Ptyonoprogne rupestris* (R,V)

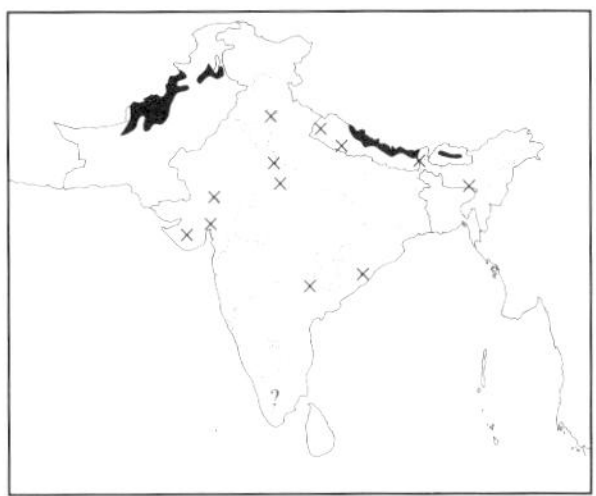

IDENTIFICATION 15 cm. As other crag martins, is stocky and broad-winged, and has white spots on tail which are apparent when tail is spread. Flight is strong and swift, with much gliding and stooping, although can appear rather slow for a hirundine. **Adult** told from Rock Martin (p.690) by larger size and darker coloration. Has darker brown upperparts, dusky, lightly flecked chin and throat, dusky brown flanks and vent, dark brown undertail-coverts with more distinct pale fringes, and blackish underwing-coverts which contrast more with rest of underwing. From Dusky Crag Martin (p.690) by larger size, paler brown upperparts, and paler underparts with throat and breast noticeably paler than belly and vent. Further, underwing appears strongly two-toned compared with that of Dusky. **Juvenile** has buff to rufous fringes to upperparts (particularly to tertials and uppertail-coverts); underparts are generally warmer, washed with buff or rufous, and chin/throat are less distinctly marked. **VOICE** Song is a series of soft twittering notes; calls include a commonly heard *prrrt*, a *zirr* alarm call, a plaintive *whee* and a descending *siu* whistle (Turner and Rose 1989). **HABITS** A typical hirundine. As other crag martins, hawks insects close to the contour of cliff faces. Keeps in small flocks in winter. **HABITAT** Rocky cliffs and gorges, ancient hill forts. **BREEDING** April–July. Nest is an oval saucer of mud attached to a rock face, usually sheltered by an overhang. **DISTRIBUTION AND STATUS** Resident, subject to migratory movements. Breeds in W and N Pakistan, and in Himalayas from N Pakistan east to Bhutan; winter visitor to Western Ghats. **PK:** frequent;

resident in the south of its range, locally migratory in the north. **NP:** widespread and locally fairly common resident; usually winters 915–2135 m, summers up to 4575 m. **IN:** locally fairly common; breeds 1200–4500 m, winters chiefly below 2000 m. **BT:** rare.

ROCK MARTIN *Hirundo fuligula* Plate 115

Pale Crag Martin (I), *Ptyonoprogne fuligula* (R,V), *Ptyonoprogne obsoleta, Hirundo obsoleta* (I)

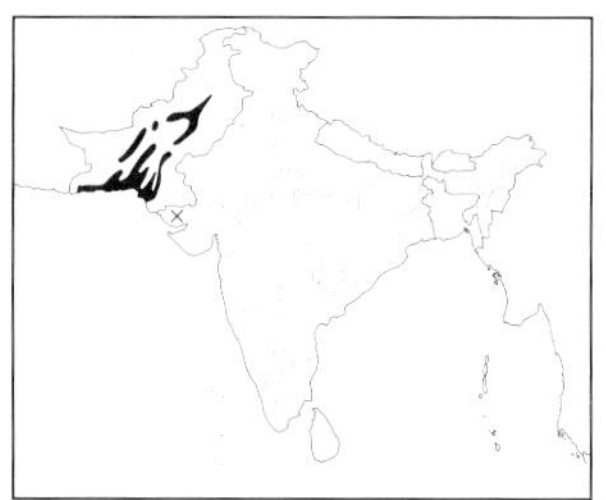

IDENTIFICATION 13 cm. Very similar to Eurasian Crag Martin (p.689), but is smaller, less robust and paler. Specifically, has dark lores and patch around eye, unmarked buffish-white throat, paler sandy-grey vent and undertail-coverts, and paler underwing-coverts which do not contrast so strongly with rest of underwing. Upperparts are a paler sandy-grey (much less brown), and rump can appear especially pale. **Juvenile** has pale fringes to upperparts, especially tertials and uppertail-coverts. **VOICE** Call is a clear *seep* or *seep-seep*, and a drier *ptrrr* (Jonsson 1992). **HABITS** A typical hirundine. Has very similar habits to those of Eurasian Crag Martin. A quiet bird. Sometimes in flocks with Red-rumped Swallow (p.691) or House Swift (p.428). **HABITAT** Rocky gorges and cliffs in arid hills. **BREEDING** April–June. Not colonial. Nest is a small half-cup of mud pellets strengthened with plant stems, attached to a rock face usually below a cliff overhang. **DISTRIBUTION AND STATUS PK:** scarce and sedentary resident, chiefly in S Baluchistan and W Sindh. **IN:** vagrant. **REFERENCES** Butler (1875).

DUSKY CRAG MARTIN *Hirundo concolor* Plate 115

***Ptyonoprogne concolor* (R)**

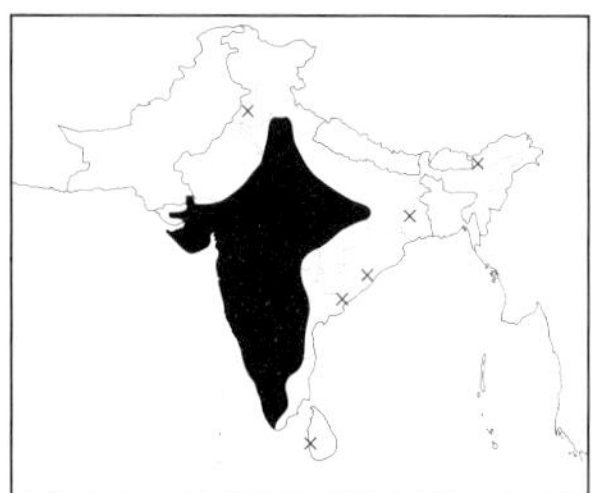

IDENTIFICATION 13 cm. Similar to Eurasian Crag Martin (p.689), but is smaller and more slightly built, and much darker and more uniformly coloured. Upperparts and underparts are darker brown, with breast and belly not noticeably paler than vent. Throat is a slightly warmer and paler buff-brown, with indistinct darker brown streaking. Underwing also appears more uniform, lacking strongly contrasting coverts of Eurasian Crag Martin. **VOICE** Song is a soft twittering, and has a soft *chit-chit* contact call. **HABITS** Very similar to those of Eurasian Crag Martin. Keeps in small parties outside the breeding season. **HABITAT** Hilly and mountainous areas with cliffs, gorges and caves; also in lowland areas around ancient forts and old buildings in towns and cities. **BREEDING** All year, varying with locality. Usually nests singly, sometimes in a loose colony. Nest is a half-cup of mud pellets strengthened with plant stems and attached to a rock face, usually under an overhang, or to eaves or an archway. **DISTRIBUTION AND STATUS** Resident, subject to local movements. From N Haryana, E Rajasthan, Gujarat and extreme SE Pakistan east to W Bihar and south through the peninsula. **PK:** rare and very local. **IN:** locally common; widely but patchily distributed. **LK:** winter vagrant to wet lowlands.

BARN SWALLOW *Hirundo rustica* Plate 115

Swallow (I), Common Swallow (P)

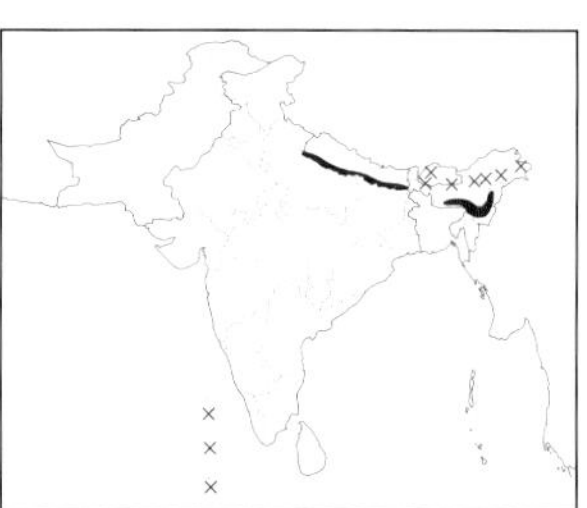

IDENTIFICATION 18 cm. **Adult** has bright red forehead and throat, bright blue cast to upperparts, and long tail-streamers. Underparts vary from white to rufous. Combination of uniform upperparts (except for red forehead band) and blue-black breast-band separates it from other swallows. **Immature** has duller orange to orange-buff forehead and throat, breast-band is browner and less well defined, upperparts are duller, and has shorter tail-streamers. For differences from juvenile Pacific Swallow (p.691), see that species. **Racial variation** *H. r. tytleri*, occurring as a winter visitor to NE subcontinent, has rufous breast, belly and vent, and narrower breast-band. **VOICE** Song is a varied and pleasant twittering and screeching; call is a clear *vit vit*, becoming a louder anxious *vheet vheet* when alarmed. **HABITS** A typical hirundine. Flight is swift and agile, with frequent banks and turns. Usually forages by skimming low over open ground or water in pursuit of insects, often in flocks with other hirundines; also hawks insects in busy streets of villages and towns. Highly gregarious in the non-breeding season, when often congregates on telegraph wires, the birds perched closely side by side. Roosts in huge numbers in reedbeds, tamarisks and mangroves, often with martins and wagtails. **HABITAT** Cultivation, towns, villages, lakes and rivers in open country; usually near water in winter. **BREEDING** March–July. Nest is a half-cup of mud pellets strengthened with plant stems, attached to a wall or beam inside a building or under a bridge arch. **DISTRIBUTION AND STATUS** Resident and partial migrant. Breeds in hills of W and N Pakistan, and in Himalayas from N Pakistan east to Arunachal Pradesh; NE India; widespread farther south in winter. **PK:** common and widespread altitudinal migrant; breeds in hills and valleys, winters in the plains. **NP:** widespread and common resident and summer visitor; mainly below 1830 m (–6400 m on passage). **IN:** locally common; breeds from foothills up to 3000 m, widespread in winter. **BT:** uncommon resident or summer visitor. **BD:** common winter visitor throughout; stragglers oversummer. **LK:** common winter visitor throughout. **MV:** annual winter visitor in small numbers.

PACIFIC SWALLOW *Hirundo tahitica* Plate 115

House Swallow (I,P), Hill Swallow, *H. domicola* (I,P)

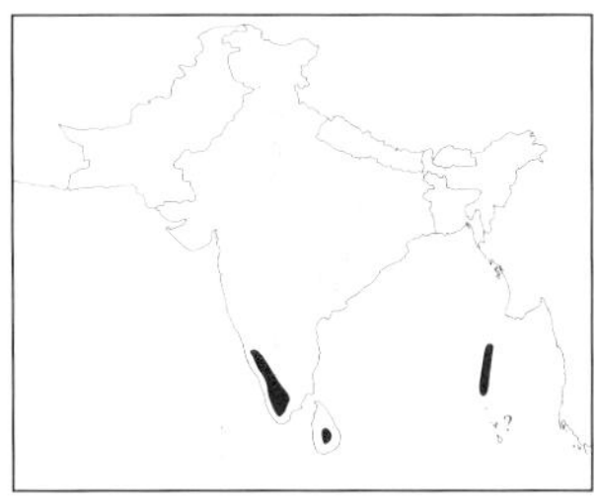

IDENTIFICATION 13 cm. **Adult** distinguished from Barn Swallow (p.690) by rufous on head extending to forecrown, more extensive rufous on throat and lack of blue-black breast-band, greyish-brown underparts (giving rise to rather dingy appearance), blackish undertail-coverts with crescentic whitish tips, and rather uniform dusky underwing (coverts not contrastingly paler as on Barn). Further, is smaller, lacks elongated tail-streamers of adult Barn, and flight appears weaker and more bat-like. **Juvenile** has browner (less glossy) upperparts, with very little rufous on forehead, and has paler rufous throat. Lack of blackish breast-band and greyish-brown underparts help separate it from juvenile Barn. **Racial variation** *H. t. domicola* of SW India and Sri Lanka has more of a metallic green gloss to upperparts. *H. t. javanica* of the Andaman Is has more of a purplish-blue gloss (close to coloration of Barn), and many have fine dark streaking on underparts. **VOICE** A *qwit* or *qwit-wit*, given singly or twice in rapid succession; similar to call of Barn Swallow, but huskier (P. Holt from R. Drijvers recording). **HABITS** Similar to those of Barn Swallow, but less dashing in flight. Frequently perches on telegraph wires, also on leafless twigs close to the ground and in the upper branches of dead trees. **HABITAT** Grassy hills around tea and coffee plantations, around bungalows and factory sheds; in Andaman Is, open country along the coast, rivers and around habitation. **BREEDING** Throughout the year, varying locally. Nest is a half-cup of mud pellets reinforced with straw, and attached to a wall under eaves or on a veranda, inside a room, or under the overhang of a bank, road culvert, or sea cliff. **DISTRIBUTION AND STATUS** Resident. SW Indian hills from Karnataka south through Kerala and W Tamil Nadu; Andaman Is and Sri Lanka. **IN:** uncommon; above 700 m in the peninsula. **LK:** common resident in hills, visitor to wet-zone foothills.

WIRE-TAILED SWALLOW *Hirundo smithii* Plate 115

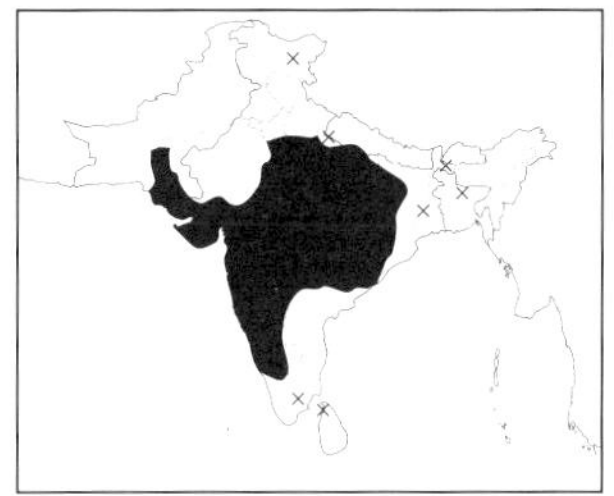

IDENTIFICATION 14 cm. **Adult** told from Barn Swallow (p.690) by chestnut crown, brighter blue upperparts, glistening white underparts, and fine filamentous projections to outer tail feathers. White underwing-coverts contrast more strongly with dark underside of flight feathers. Some birds have faint pinkish wash to breast, while others have indistinct buffish wash to underparts. Wire-like tail-streamers are frequently broken, entirely lost, or can be difficult to see, tail then appearing square-ended, with outer feathers projecting only slightly. **Juvenile** has brownish cast to blue upperparts and dull brownish crown. Possibly confusable with Streak-throated Swallow (p.692), but is larger and proportionately longer-winged/shorter-tailed, and has whiter, unstreaked underparts and underwing-coverts. White throat and breast (some with faint pinkish wash) and squarer tail help separate it from juvenile Barn. **VOICE** Has a twittering song. Calls include a double *chirrik-weet*, a *chit-chit* contact call, and a *chichip chichip* alarm call (Turner and Rose 1989). **HABITS** Similar to those of Barn Swallow, but more closely associated with water. Flight is swift; skims low over water, swoops, turns and banks adroitly. Usually feeds in pairs or loose flocks. Forms communal roosts with other hirundines and wagtails in reedbeds and tamarisks. **HABITAT** Open country and cultivation near lakes, rivers and canals; also wet paddy-fields in summer. **BREEDING** March–September, varying locally. Nest is like that of other swallows, and attached to a vertical wall, under a bridge or eaves, or under a rock overhang by a stream. **DISTRIBUTION AND STATUS** Resident and partial migrant. Widespread in the subcontinent, except parts of the northwest, northeast and southeast. **PK:** widespread and common summer visitor in the Indus plains and in foothills up to 1800 m; resident in S Sindh. **NP:** uncommon and local in the W terai, possibly resident. **IN:** locally common; summer visitor to the north, resident farther south; plains and foothills up to 1500 m (–2745 m). **BD, LK:** vagrant. **REFERENCES** Vaid (1965).

RED-RUMPED SWALLOW *Hirundo daurica* Plate 116

Striated Swallow (F,I,P)

IDENTIFICATION 16–17 cm. Differs from Barn Swallow (p.690) in having rufous-orange sides of neck (creating complete collar and dark-capped appearance in some races), rufous-orange rump, finely streaked uniformly buffish-white underparts, and black undertail-coverts resulting in distinctive appearance to rear end. Compared with Barn, is bulkier, and has slower and more buoyant flight, gliding strongly and for prolonged periods. **Juvenile** has less gloss to blue crown, mantle and wings, paler neck sides (and collar) and rump, buff tips to tertials, and shorter tail-streamers. For differences from Striated Swallow (p.692), see that species. **Racial variation** Six races are recognised from the subcontinent, differing mainly in strength of streaking on

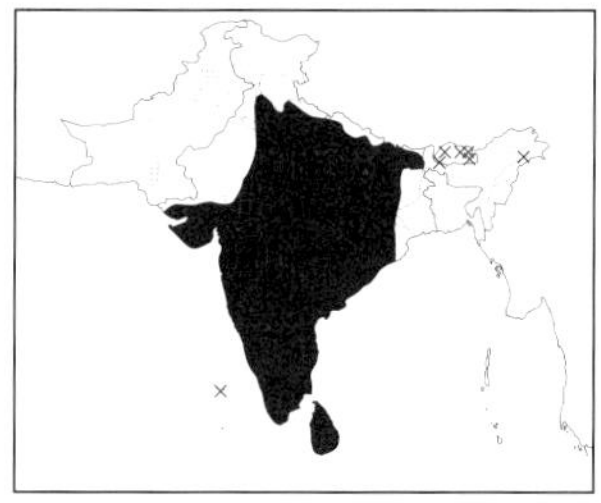

and coloration of underparts and rump, and prominence of collar. *H. d. rufula* of NW subcontinent is only faintly streaked on underparts, has a complete collar, and has whiter uppertail-coverts than rump. *H. d. japonica*, a winter visitor to N and NE subcontinent, and *H. d. nipalensis*, which breds in Himalayas, are the most heavily streaked on underparts; collar can be indistinct in these races. *H. d. hyperythra* of Sri Lanka is very distinctive, with deep chestnut underparts, non-existent or poorly defined chestnut collar, and dark chestnut rump. **VOICE** Has a distinctive *treep* call; twittering song, which sometimes ends in a trill, is shorter and quieter than Barn Swallow's. **HABITS** A typical hirundine. Gathers in huge numbers in winter and on migration, when frequently seen in close-packed flocks on telegraph wires and in communal roosts in reedbeds. **HABITAT** Summers in upland cultivation and on open grassy hill slopes; rocky gorges and cliffs in Baluchistan. Winters in open scrub country, cultivation and forest clearings. **BREEDING** March–September, varying locally. Nest is retort-shaped, with an entrance tunnel, made of mud pellets, and attached to an overhang of a cliff or cave, ceiling of a house, dome of an old building, or arch of a bridge or road culvert. **DISTRIBUTION AND STATUS** Resident, subject to altitudinal movements, and partial migrant. Throughout much of the subcontinent, except parts of the northwest and northeast. **PK:** common summer visitor to mountain regions up to 3300 m; also a passage migrant; strays to the plains in winter. **NP:** widespread and common resident; breeds below 2745 m, winters below 915 m; also a rare winter visitor. **IN:** widespread and locally common; summer visitor to W Himalayas, breeds 1000–3300 m; resident in plains and hills south of the Himalayas, up to 1600 m. **BT:** uncommon. **BD:** common passage migrant and scarce winter visitor; occurs throughout. **LK:** common resident from lowlands up to middle altitudes; also an irregular winter visitor to lowlands and lower hills.

STRIATED SWALLOW *Hirundo striolata* — Plate 116

Larger Striated Swallow (I), *H. daurica* (K)

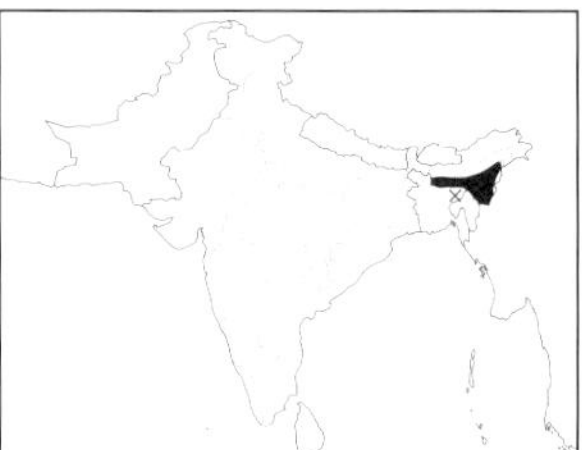

IDENTIFICATION 19 cm. Very similar to Red-rumped Swallow (p.691), occurring alongside that species in NE subcontinent. Distinguished from Red-rumped of the subspecies *nipalensis* and *japonica*, which both have well-streaked underparts, by larger size, stronger (broader and blacker) streaking on underparts and sides of neck, typically non-existent or sometimes poorly defined rufous collar, and broader and blacker shaft streaking on rump. Collar can, however, be incomplete in those races of Red-rumped. **Juvenile** is less glossy on crown, mantle and wings, and has paler rump, shorter tail-streamers, broader, browner and more diffuse streaking below, and buff fringes to coverts and tertials. **VOICE** Song is a soft twittering; calls include a *pin* or long drawn-out *quitsch*, and *chi-chi-chi* when alarmed (Turner and Rose 1989). **HABITS** Similar to those of Red-rumped Swallow. **HABITAT** Little information from the region; around steep cliffs in the hills. **BREEDING** April and May. Builds a retort-shaped nest in small colonies on steep cliffs. **DISTRIBUTION AND STATUS** Summer visitor, probably resident. Hills of NE India (Assam, Manipur, Meghalaya, Nagaland)) and Bangladesh. **IN:** current status uncertain, no recent published records; former irregular summer visitor to Assam. **BD:** rare in the northeast, resident?, probably overlooked among Red-rumped Swallows.

STREAK-THROATED SWALLOW *Hirundo fluvicola* — Plate 116

Indian Cliff Swallow (F,I,P,R)

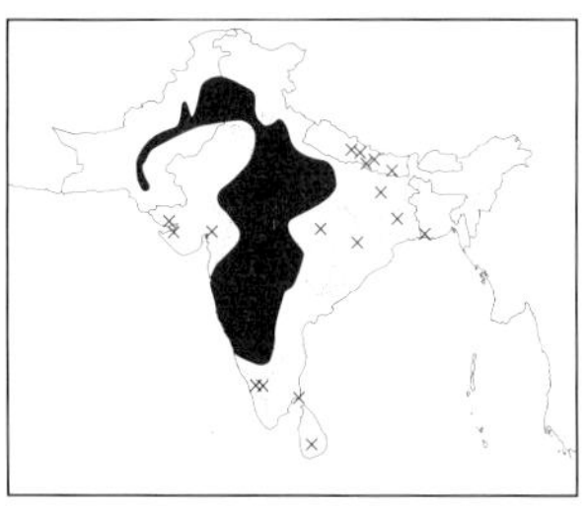

IDENTIFICATION 11 cm. A small, compact swallow with slight fork to long broad tail and a weak and fluttering flight. **Adult** told from other swallows by combination of lightly streaked chestnut crown and nape, dirty off-white underparts, with brown streaking on chin, throat and breast, narrow white streaks on mantle, and brownish rump. **Juvenile** has duller, browner crown, and brown-toned mantle and wings, with buff fringes (most obvious on scapulars and tertials). Separated from juvenile Plain Martin (p.689) by larger size, chestnut cast to crown, blue gloss to mantle, and heavily streaked throat. Streaked throat is best distinction from juvenile Wire-tailed Swallow (p.691). **VOICE** Has a twittering *chirp*, and a sharp *trr trr* uttered in flight (Ali and Ripley 1987). **HABITS** A typical hirundine. Highly gregarious throughout the year. Usually forages in flocks, often over water and with other swallows. **HABITAT** Cultivation and open country near water: rivers, canals, reservoirs and lakes. **BREEDING** Almost all year, varying locally. Colonial, the nests adjoining each other. Nest retort-shaped, with the entrance projecting outwards, and made of mud pellets; built under bridges or irrigation barrages, usually above or close to water, often in towns. **DISTRIBUTION AND STATUS** Resident and partial migrant. Mainly from Indus plains, Pakistan, east to E Uttar Pradesh and south to S Karnataka; scattered records elsewhere. **PK:** common resident. **NP:** scarce visitor below 1280 m. **IN:** locally common in N plains; breeds in plains and up to 700 m in Himalayas. **BD, LK:** vagrant.

NORTHERN HOUSE MARTIN *Delichon urbica* Plate 116

House Martin (I), Common House Martin (K,R), Eurasian House Martin (F)

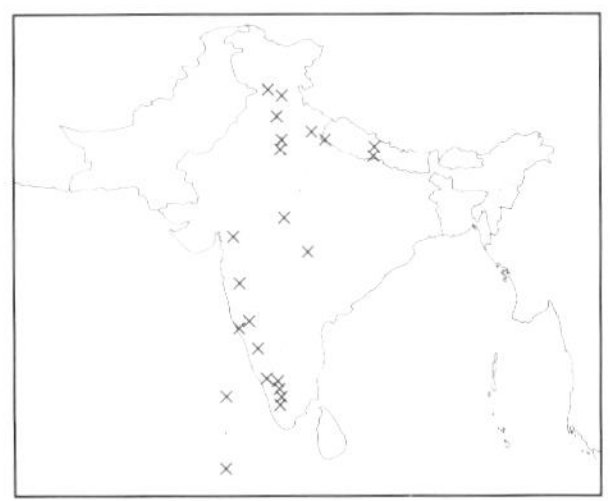

IDENTIFICATION 13 cm. **Adult** is very similar to Asian House Martin (below) and best distinguished by combination of whiter underparts (although, in winter, can have faint grey-brown wash to throat and rump), longer and more deeply forked tail (always appears forked, even when spread), and paler underwing-coverts (greyish-white, and contrasting with dark underside of flight feathers). Rarely, can have well-defined band across breast. **Juvenile** has browner (less glossy) upperparts, with whitish tips to tertials, and variable pale brownish-grey wash to underparts, often with darker sides of breast; also has brownish centres to some feathers of vent and uppertail- and undertail-coverts, and tail is less deeply forked. Separation from Asian, especially juvenile, is therefore considerably more difficult; underparts are less dusky than juvenile Asian's, and paler underwing-coverts and longer and more deeply forked tail are good pointers. **VOICE** Song is a soft twittering; flight call is a rolling, scratchy *prrit-prrit*, and alarm call is a *jeet-jeet.* **HABITS** A typical hirundine. Gregarious throughout the year; hunts in scattered parties, often with other hirundines and swifts. Flight is less swift and with much less swooping and twisting than Barn Swallow's (p.690), and usually feeds higher above the ground than that species. **HABITAT** Mountain valleys, with suitable cliffs and gorges, close to patches of terraced cultivation and villages. **BREEDING** June and July in Ladakh. Colonial. Nest is a deep cup of mud pellets attached under a rock ledge or overhang of a high cliff face. **DISTRIBUTION AND STATUS** Uncertain, because often considered conspecific with Asian House Martin. Summer visitor to Himalayas from N Pakistan (Hunza and Baltistan) east to Lahul and Spiti, Himachal Pradesh; passage migrant east to WC Nepal and south to Kerala and Tamil Nadu; may sometimes winter in S India. **PK:** locally common summer visitor to the innermost Himalayas. **NP:** probably a rare passage migrant; recorded below 1470 m. **IN:** breeds 3000–4500 m in Himalayas; widespread on passage in small numbers. **MV:** irregular winter visitor.

ASIAN HOUSE MARTIN *Delichon dasypus* Plate 116

Asian Martin, *D. urbica* (F,I)

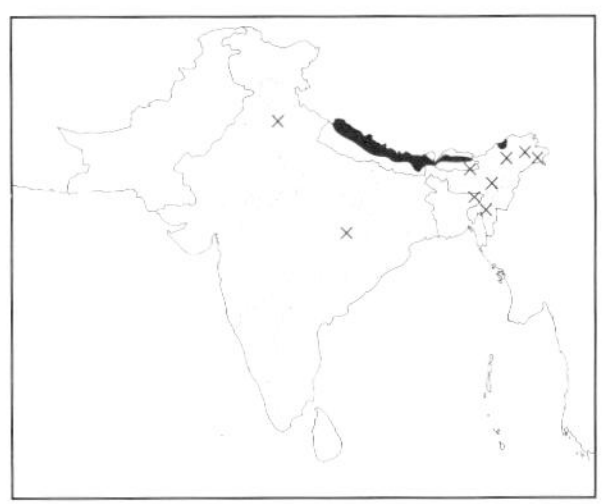

IDENTIFICATION 12 cm. **Adult** is very similar to Northern House Martin (above) and best distinguished by uniform pale dusky grey-brown wash to underparts, shallower fork to shorter tail, with tail appearing almost square-ended when spread, and darker underwing with dark grey coverts concolorous with underside of flight feathers. Most adult Asian have variable dusky brown centres to undertail-coverts, which are lacking on adult Northern but present on juvenile of that species. Rump patch often looks smaller, dirty white and with more pronounced black shaft streaking compared with Northern, but there is much overlap in this feature. **Juvenile** has browner upperparts (most obvious on crown), stronger dusky wash to underparts, broad white tips to tertials, and squarer-shaped tail. Caution is needed to avoid confusion with juvenile Northern, which has pale brownish-grey wash to underparts and less deeply forked tail; see that species for details. **VOICE** Apparently as that of Northern. **HABITS** Very similar to those of Northern House Martin. Forms loose flocks with other hirundines and swifts. Flies high above valleys, gorges and forests and low over alpine ridges. **HABITAT** High alpine slopes, grassy hill slopes with cliffs, and around mountain villages and over forest. **BREEDING** May–mid July. Nest and nest site are like those of Northern House Martin; also nests under house eaves in mountain villages. **DISTRIBUTION AND STATUS** Uncertain, because often considered conspecific with Northern House Martin. Resident, subject to altitudinal movements. Breeds in Himalayas from N Pakistan east to Arunachal Pradesh; winters mainly in foothills. **PK:** common and widespread summer visitor, often nests above 3000 m; a few winter records. **NP:** widespread and fairly common; recorded below 4575 m, has bred at 3500 m and 4000 m. **IN:** status uncertain; breeds 1800–4800 m, locally down to 1300 m in the west; winters at lower altitudes, rarely down to the plains. **BT:** common from 250 m up to at least 4265 m. **BD:** vagrant.

NEPAL HOUSE MARTIN *Delichon nipalensis* Plate 116

Nepal Martin

IDENTIFICATION 13 cm. Superficially resembles Northern and Asian House Martins (above), but is smaller and more compact, and has square-cut tail (lacking indentation even when closed), very dark, almost black, underwing-coverts, black undertail-coverts contrasting sharply with white vent and belly, and variably mottled blackish throat, giving rise to dark-headed appearance; on some birds, only chin is black. White rump band is narrower, sometimes with black fringes. **Juvenile** is apparently duller and browner on upperparts, has less black on throat, and has buffish wash to underparts. **VOICE** Call is a high-pitched *chi-i* (Lister 1954). **HABITS** Very similar to those of Northern House Martin. **HABITAT** Over forest, river valleys, mountain ridges with cliffs, and around villages. **BREEDING** March–September, varying locally. Colonial. Nest and nest site are

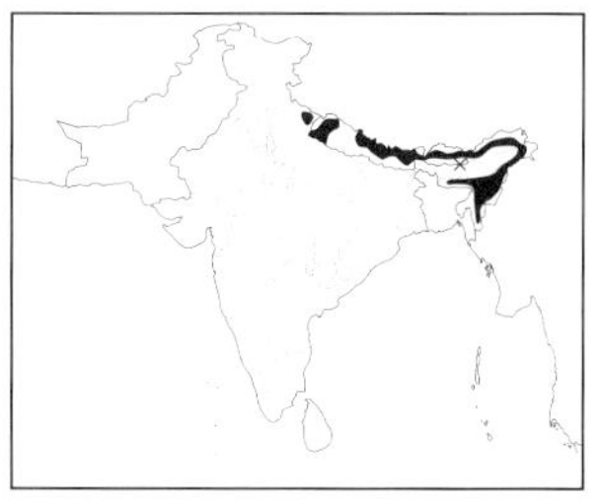

like those of Northern House Martin; not recorded nesting in houses. **DISTRIBUTION AND STATUS** Resident, subject to altitudinal movements. Himalayas from N Uttar Pradesh east to Arunachal Pradesh; NE Indian hills. **NP:** widespread and fairly common; summers up to 3500 m (–3865 m), winters 915–2135 m (down to 160 m). **IN:** locally fairly common; breeds 1000–4000 m, winters 300–2000 m. **BT:** common; from 150 m up to at least 3390 m.

KINGLETS Regulidae

Tiny passerines with bright crown feathers. Typically, they inhabit the canopy of coniferous forest and frequently hover as they forage for insects.

GOLDCREST *Regulus regulus* — Plate 127

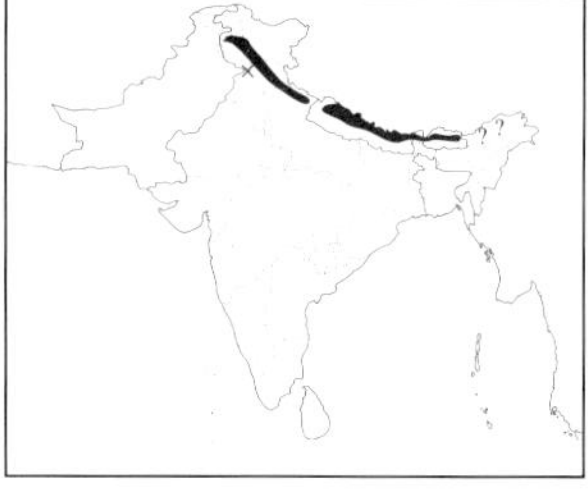

IDENTIFICATION 9 cm. Superficially resembles the smaller species of *Phylloscopus* warbler. Is small and plump, with greenish upperparts, and with yellowish-white greater-covert wing-bar and fringes to tertials and secondaries. Best distinguished by very plain face, which lacks supercilium and eye-stripe, by pale ring around large dark eye, and by brilliant yellow to orange crown bordered by black. **Juvenile** lacks crown patch of adult. **VOICE** Call is a high trisyllabic *see-see-see*; song is a similarly high-pitched *see-seesisyu-seesisyu-seesisyu-sweet.* **HABITS** Arboreal, often in mixed flocks with tits, treecreepers and leaf warblers. Forages actively among the foliage, usually in the forest canopy. Constantly flits from twig to twig in search of insects; frequently hovers, flutters and flicks wings; also clings upside-down to twigs. Keeps up high-pitched contact calls when feeding. **HABITAT** Mainly coniferous forest. **BREEDING** May–July. Builds a hammock-shaped nest of green moss, lichen, spiders' webs and rootlets, suspended from the end of a branch 2–12 m above ground and well concealed. **DISTRIBUTION AND STATUS** Resident, subject to altitudinal movements. Himalayas from N Pakistan east to Arunachal Pradesh. **PK:** scarce; summers 2400–3300 m, winters down to 760 m. **NP:** widespread and frequent; 2200–3050 m in winter, up to 4000 m in summer. **IN:** locally frequent; in the west, breeds from 2200 m up to upper limit of coniferous forest, winters from 1500 m up to at least 3000 m; in the east, winters 2600–3000 m, summers up to upper limit of coniferous forest; in NE hills, from 2000 m (winter) to upper limit of coniferous forest (summer).

BULBULS Pycnonotidae

Medium-sized passerines with soft, fluffy plumage, rather short and rounded wings, a medium-long to long tail, and short, weak legs. All except the genus *Spizixos* have a slender bill. Some are common and familiar birds in gardens and around human habitation; these species are generally bold and confiding. Other bulbuls frequent forest, and some of these are quite shy and skulking. Bulbuls in the region feed on berries and other fruits, often supplemented by insects, and sometimes also nectar and buds of trees and shrubs. Many species are noisy, especially when feeding. Typically, bulbuls have a variety of cheerful, loud, chattering, babbling and whistling calls. Most species are gregarious in the non-breeding season. The nest is usually cup-shaped and made of twigs and other plant materials, lined with fine rootlets and grasses, and built in bushes or trees. Most species are sedentary.

CRESTED FINCHBILL *Spizixos canifrons* — Plate 117

Finch-billed Bulbul (I)

IDENTIFICATION 22 cm. **Adult** told from other green-and-yellow bulbuls by stout, pale yellowish bill, erect blackish crest and blackish throat, grey forehead, ear-coverts and sides of neck, and broad blackish tip to green tail. **Juvenile** has pale brown ear-coverts, contrasting with blackish-brown crown and nape, and brown throat. **VOICE** A long, dry bubbling trill, *purr-purr-prruit-prruit-prruit* (Ali and Ripley 1987; Boonsong and Round 1991). Alarm call consists of gentle, scolding, bubbling trills or rattles: *pri pri-pri..prrrrrr, pri-pri,* etc (C. Robson). **HABITS** Keeps in flocks in the non-breeding season. Forages at all levels, from high up in trees down to bushes and undergrowth. Feeds on insects, fruit and seeds. **HABITAT** Broadleaved evergreen and deciduous forest, secondary growth and semi-cultivation. **BREEDING** April–July. Has a distinctive cup-shaped nest of creeper tendrils, usually placed low in a bush, sometimes in a small tree up to 3 m above ground.

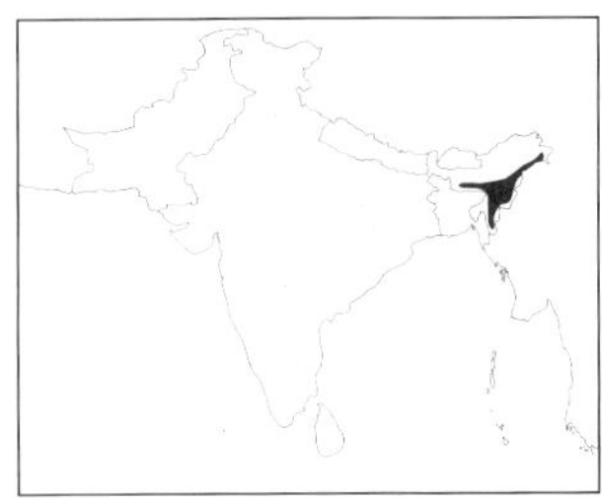

DISTRIBUTION AND STATUS IN: resident in NE hills (Arunachal Pradesh, Assam, Manipur, Meghalaya, Mizoram and Nagaland); 1400–2500 m, winters down to 900 m; current status uncertain, very few recent records. **REFERENCES** Singh (1995).

STRIATED BULBUL *Pycnonotus striatus* — Plate 117

Striated Green Bulbul (I)

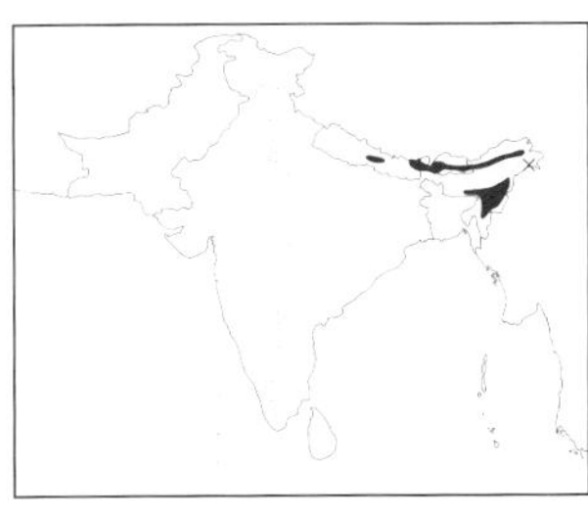

IDENTIFICATION 23 cm. A crested, green bulbul. Distinguished from other green bulbuls by bold yellowish-white streaking on breast and belly, fine white streaking on crest, ear-coverts, nape and mantle, bright yellow lores, eye-ring and throat, and yellow undertail-coverts. In flight, the olive-green tail has pale yellow tips to outer feathers. **VOICE** A distinctive, repeated, disyllabic *chi-chirp* (Boonsong and Round 1991). **HABITS** Found in small flocks in the non-breeding season. Less noisy than most other bulbuls. Forages chiefly in the treetops, often among the foliage. Feeds on berries; also catches insects in short aerial sallies. Has a strong, direct flight. **HABITAT** Mainly broadleaved evergreen forest, also moist oak–rhododendron forest; deciduous forest in NE India. **BREEDING** Little known. May and June. Builds nest low down and well hidden in a thick bush or bamboo clump. **DISTRIBUTION AND STATUS** Resident, subject to altitudinal movements. Himalayas from WC Nepal east to Arunachal Pradesh; NE India. **NP:** local and frequent; 1525–2690 m. **IN:** local and fairly common; breeds mainly 1200–2400 m, locally higher, winters down to the foothills. **BT:** common; from 335 m up to at least 2440 m.

GREY-HEADED BULBUL *Pycnonotus priocephalus* — Plate 117

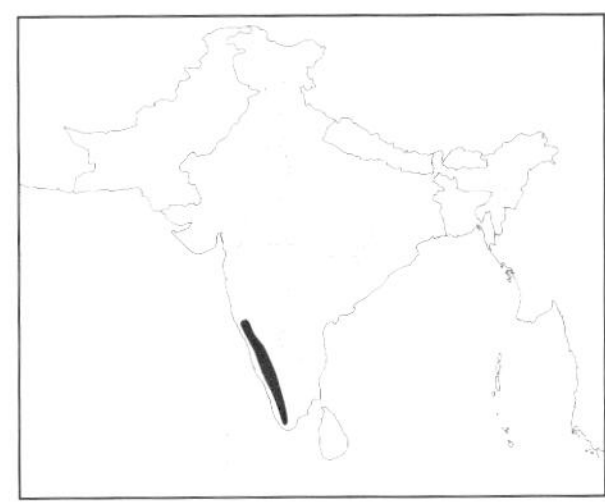

IDENTIFICATION 19 cm. A crestless, grey-and-green bulbul. Has greyish head, greenish-yellow forehead and black chin, striking yellowish bill and iris, olive-green mantle, underparts and wings, and uneven black barring on grey-green rump. At rest tail appears grey, but in flight shows blackish outer feathers with grey tips. Some birds have olive-green head, rather than grey, and greener coloration to rump, uppertail-coverts and tail. **VOICE** Distinctive explosive, unmusical *chaink*, repeated every 1.5 seconds or so (P. Holt). **HABITS** Keeps among foliage in the treetops or in thickets. Feeds on berries and fruits, often with frugivorous species such as other bulbuls, barbets and orioles. **HABITAT** Moist broadleaved evergreen forest with plenty of bamboo and other dense undergrowth; dense thickets in deserted forest clearings. **BREEDING** March–July. Builds nest low down in a bush in thick jungle. **DISTRIBUTION AND STATUS IN:** endemic resident in SW peninsula; local and fairly common from Goa and N Karnataka south through Kerala and adjacent hills of Tamil Nadu; from plains up to 1800 m, mainly 600–900 m.

BLACK-HEADED BULBUL *Pycnonotus atriceps* — Plate 117

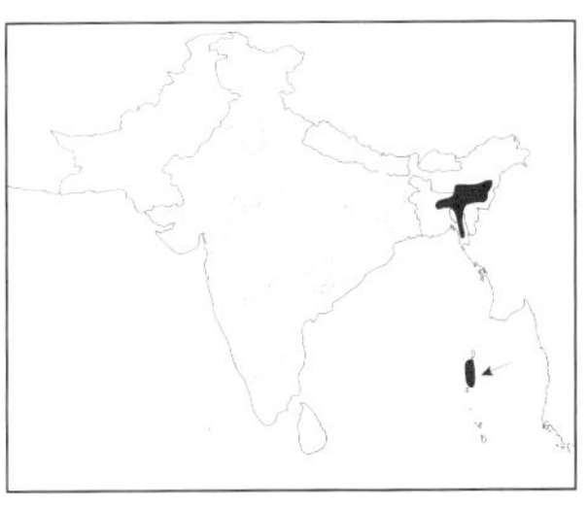

IDENTIFICATION 18 cm. A crestless, olive-green and yellow bulbul with black head. Told from Black-crested (p.696) by broad black subterminal band and yellow terminal band to tail, and striking yellow panel on wing (formed by yellow outer webs of tertials, which contrast with blackish primaries and inner webs of tertials). Lacks crest, which is erect and prominent in the NE race of Black-crested, and has pale blue iris. A rare grey morph occurs which has greyish nape and greyish underparts (except for yellow vent and undertail-coverts). **Juvenile** is darker and duller; chin and throat are more olive-green, and forehead is dark olive; upperparts are a darker olive, and primaries are browner, contrasting less with yellow panel on wing. **Racial variation** *P. a. fuscoflavescens* of the Andaman Is has dusky olive-green head, with blackish throat which contrasts with ear-coverts and breast. **VOICE** Song is a hesitant series of short, tuneless whistles; call is a ringing metallic *chewp* (Boonsong and Round 1991). In Andamans, song is a jolting series of unmelodious short piping whistles and call a penetrating *cherk* (P. Holt). **HABITS** Arboreal. Found at all forest levels, from the treetops down to the undergrowth. Keeps in pairs or small parties. Feeds on berries and insects. **HABITAT** Open forest, light jungle and gardens. **BREEDING** February–September, varying locally. Nest is well concealed, low down in a bush or small tree.

DISTRIBUTION AND STATUS Resident in NE India (Assam, Manipur, Meghalaya and Tripura), Andaman Is (South and Middle Andamans) and Bangladesh. **IN:** current status uncertain; very few recent records. **BD:** locally common. **REFERENCES** Gee (1995).

BLACK-CRESTED BULBUL *Pycnonotus melanicterus* **Plate 117**

Black-headed Yellow Bulbul (F,I), Black-capped Bulbul (P)

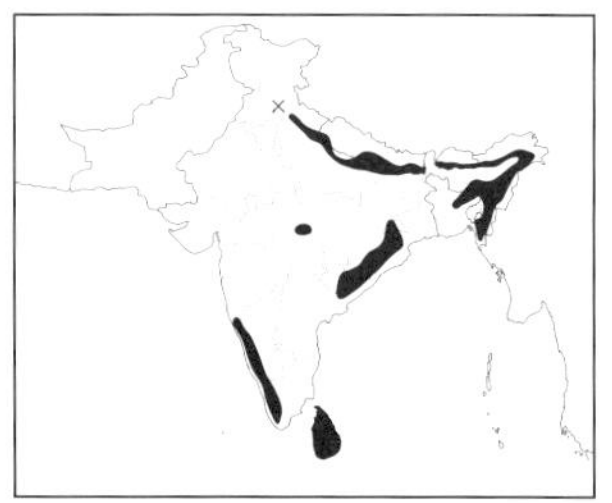

IDENTIFICATION 19 cm. A black-headed bulbul with olive-green upperparts and yellow underparts. Told from Black-headed (p.695) by uniform olive-brown tail, uniform olive-green wings, and yellow iris. Where ranges overlap in NE subcontinent, it has prominent, erect black crest, which is lacking on Black-headed. **Racial variation** The widely distributed *P. m. flaviventris* has prominent black crest, black throat, and olive-yellow breast merging into yellow of rest of underparts; juvenile has dull black head and shorter crest, and paler yellow underparts. *P. m. gularis* of the Western Ghats lacks crest, and has ruby-red throat and bright yellow breast and belly. *P. m. melanicterus* of Sri Lanka lacks crest, and has yellow throat which is concolorous with rest of underparts, dull red or brown iris, and bold white tips to outer tail feathers. **VOICE** Song of *P. m. flaviventris* is a *weet-tre-trippy-weet* (Ali and Ripley 1987), and that of *P. m. melanicterus* an ascending *yor, yer, ye* or *wer wer we we* (Henry 1971). **HABITS** Rather quiet and retiring for a bulbul. Found singly, in pairs or in small parties. **HABITAT** Moist broadleaved forest with dense undergrowth, thick secondary growth, and abandoned forest clearings overgrown with thickets. **BREEDING** January–September, varying locally. Builds nest 0.3–2.5 m up in a thick bush or sapling. **DISTRIBUTION AND STATUS** Resident. Himalayas from Himachal Pradesh east to Arunachal Pradesh; NE India and Bangladesh; E Madhya Pradesh, Orissa and NE Andhra Pradesh; SW India from Goa and N Karnataka south to Kerala and Tamil Nadu; Sri Lanka. **NP:** common in the far east, frequent elsewhere; widespread below 365 m, uncommon up to 915 m (–1525 m). **IN:** fairly common in Himalayas from the terai up to 1500 m (–2400 m); uncommon in the southwest from plains up to 1000 m, locally to 1200 m. **BT:** fairly common; 250–1125 m (–2545 m). **BD:** locally common. **LK:** common in the lowlands and lower hills.

RED-WHISKERED BULBUL *Pycnonotus jocosus* **Plate 117**

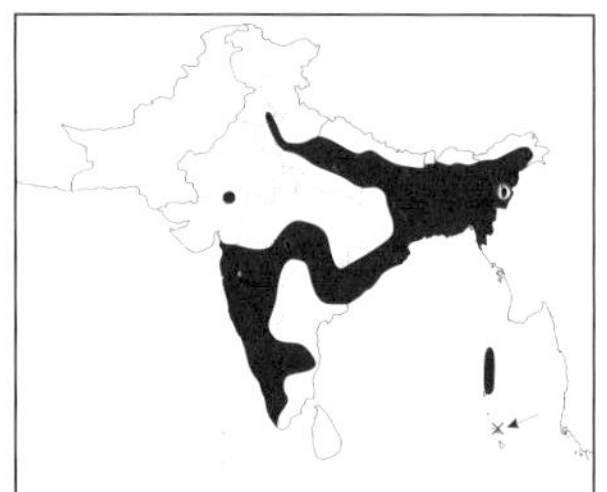

IDENTIFICATION 20 cm. A black-crested bulbul with brown upperparts and largely white underparts. **Adult** told from other brown-and-white bulbuls by combination of glossy black crown and erect crest, red patch behind eye, white patch on lower ear-coverts bordered below by black moustachial stripe, white underparts with complete or broken breast-band, and red vent. **Juvenile** lacks red 'whiskers'; crest and nape are a lighter brown compared with adult, and has paler, rufous-orange vent. **Racial variation** Six races have been described from the subcontinent. They vary in presence or absence of white tips to rectrices, in having a complete or broken breast-band, and in coloration of upperparts (from grey-brown to rufous-brown). **VOICE** Calls include a lively *pettigrew* or *kick-pettigrew* (Ali and Ripley 1987). **HABITS** Active, noisy and confiding. Often perches conspicuously on the tops of small bushes. Sometimes in flocks with other bulbuls outside the breeding season. Takes fruit, also insects, spiders, nectar and flower buds. Flight is strong, slow and jerky. **HABITAT** Open forest, scrub jungle, gardens, orchards, and bushes around villages and cultivation. **BREEDING** December–September, varying locally. Builds a neat nest in a low bush or creeper within 3 m of ground. **DISTRIBUTION AND STATUS** Resident. From Himachal Pradesh east to Arunachal Pradesh and Bangladesh, and throughout most of India except parts of the north and northwest. **NP:** widespread and locally common; below 455 m. **IN:** common and widespread; up to 1500 m in Himalayas, chiefly in the hills up to 1800 m in the W peninsula. **BT:** fairly common; 250–1710 m. **BD:** common throughout.

WHITE-EARED BULBUL *Pycnonotus leucotis* **Plate 117**

***P. leucogenys* (I,R)**

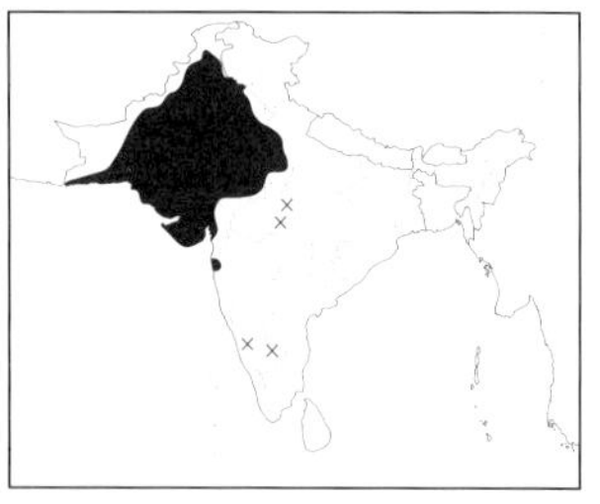

IDENTIFICATION 20 cm. A white-cheeked bulbul with brown upperparts, whitish underparts (with variable brownish-grey flanks), and yellow vent. Distinguished from Himalayan Bulbul (p.697) by black crown and nape, and short or non-existent crest. Hybridises with Red-vented (p.697); see that species for further details. **Racial variation** *P. l. humii* of NW part of range differs from the nominate race in having a short crest. **VOICE** Sings short, fast burbling melodies, repeated with small variations, *ghe-did, ghe-did* etc, very similar to those of Himalayan Bulbul; calls include a mellow *pip* or *pip-pip* (P. Holt). **HABITS** Bold, cheerful and confiding. Very lively and conspicuous, often sits on the tops of perches, posturing and flicking wings; keeps on the move, flying from bush to bush. Feeds on insects on the ground, and sometimes fly-catches in clumsy aerial sallies; also eats berries, seeds, buds and nectar. Flight is strong and undulating. **HABITAT** Dry habitats of semi-desert type: thorn scrub, dry open cultivation with thickets, gardens and orchards; favours *Capparis, Salvadora* and *Carissa* bushes. **BREEDING** March–September. Builds nest in low bushes. **DISTRIBUTION AND STATUS** Resident, subject to local movements. Pakistan and NW India (east to E Uttar Pradesh, Madhya Pradesh and NE Maharashtra). **PK:** widespread; formerly common in Sindh, has decreased and is now replaced by Red-vented Bulbul in well-irrigated tracts and urban areas; scarce in Baluchistan and more settled areas of Punjab. **IN:** locally common.

HIMALAYAN BULBUL *Pycnonotus leucogenys* Plate 117

White-cheeked Bulbul (F,I,R)

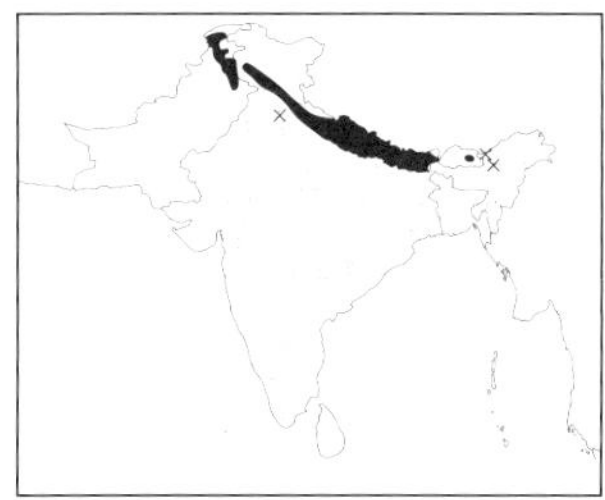

IDENTIFICATION 20 cm. A crested bulbul with white cheeks, brownish-grey upperparts, and yellow vent. Told from White-eared Bulbul (p.696) by prominent forward-pointing brown crest, brown nape, and black crescent at base of white ear-coverts. Frequently hybridises with Red-vented Bulbul (below); see that species for further information. **VOICE** Song is a variable combination of melodious phrases, e.g. *we-did-de-dear-up, whet-what,* and *who-lik-lik-leer*; also has a *plee-plee-plee* flight call, and a *wik-wik-wik-wiker* alarm call (Fleming *et al.* 1984). **HABITS** Like those of White-eared Bulbul. **HABITAT** Dry habitats: open scrub jungle, hillsides with scattered wild raspberry and *Berberis* bushes, hedgerows, bushes around towns and villages and secondary growth. **BREEDING** March–June. Nest and nest site are like those of White-eared Bulbul. **DISTRIBUTION AND STATUS** Endemic to the subcontinent. Resident, subject to local movements. N Pakistan, and Himalayas from N Pakistan east to Arunachal Pradesh. **PK:** common and widespread up to 1675 m (–2100 m); hybridises with Red-vented Bulbul around Mangla dam and the surrounding hills in Mansehra district of Abbottabad, around Kalabagh on the Indus, Nurpur Shahan in Margalla hills and around Bann and Kohat towns. **NP:** widespread and common; 350–2400 m (250–3050 m). **IN:** common; 300–2400 m. **BT:** uncommon in drier valleys. **REFERENCES** Roberts (1992).

RED-VENTED BULBUL *Pycnonotus cafer* Plate 117

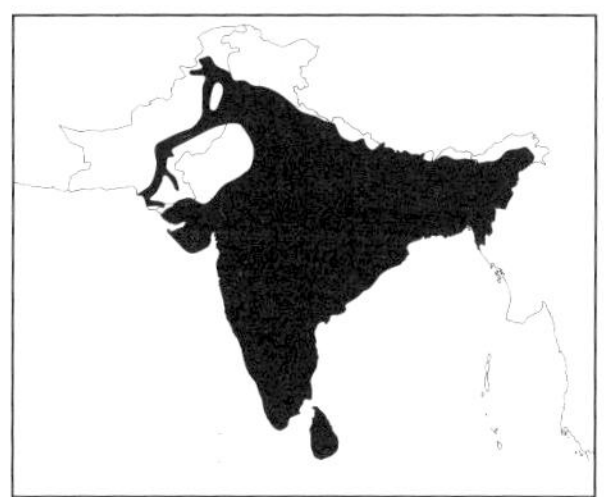

IDENTIFICATION 20 cm. A distinctive bulbul, with crested black head, white rump and uppertail-coverts, white-tipped black tail, and red vent. White rump is a good feature for separation from other bulbuls in flight. **Racial variation** Seven races have been described from the subcontinent, varying mainly in extent to which black of head reaches onto mantle and breast and in prominence of whitish fringes to feathers of mantle and breast. Extremes are *P. c. humayuni*, which has pale brown mantle and breast (with prominent pale fringes, and well demarcated from black of head), and *P. c. bengalensis*, which has black extending onto mantle and breast (which have indistinct pale fringes). **Hybridisation** In NW of range, frequently hybridises with White-eared and Himalayan Bulbuls (p.696 and above): hybrids resemble Red-vented, but have paler brownish-white ear-coverts and dirty orange or orange-red vent, and may show a noticeable crest where parentage is Himalayan. **VOICE** A cheery *be-care-ful* or *be quick-quick*; alarm is a sharp, repetitive *peep* (Ali and Ripley 1987). **HABITS** Bold, tame and quarrelsome. Keeps in pairs or in small loose flocks, according to the season. Feeds mainly on fruits and berries; also insects, which it catches on the ground or sometimes in aerial sallies, by flying vertically into the air from the top of a bush. **HABITAT** Deciduous rather than evergreen biotope: light deciduous forest, secondary growth, gardens, roadside avenues and light scrub; avoids barren or arid areas away from settlements. **BREEDING** Throughout the year, varying locally. Builds a compact nest 1–9 m above ground, often in a bush, also in trees, and sometimes in buildings. **DISTRIBUTION AND STATUS** Resident throughout much of the subcontinent. **PK:** common; occurs throughout the Indus plains, cultivated main valleys of NW Pakistan and Indus Kohistan, and Murree hills up to 1500 m. **NP:** widespread and common below 1500 m, uncommon up to 2135 m. **IN:** common and widespread in plains and hills, up to 1830 m in Himalayas and the northeast, to 1500 m in the peninsula. **BT:** common; mainly 250–1830 m, frequent up to 2285 m. **BD:** common throughout. **LK:** common and widespread, less frequent in wet-zone forest. **REFERENCES** Roberts (1992).

YELLOW-THROATED BULBUL *Pycnonotus xantholaemus* Plate 117

IDENTIFICATION 20 cm. A crestless, olive-green bulbul with plain yellow-green head, contrasting with bright yellow throat and upper breast. Has grey breast-band, whitish flanks and belly, yellow vent and undertail-coverts, and broad yellow tip to tail. Wing-coverts, remiges and outer rectrices are edged yellowish-green. **VOICE** Conversational explosive babble, similar to, but higher-pitched and less raucous than, that of White-browed Bulbul (p.698); pleasant nasal call, a mellow *rhid-tu-tu* (P. Holt). **HABITS** Keeps in pairs or in small groups of up to six birds. Shy, but often sits on large boulders in the open. Feeds on berries, especially those taken from shrubs; also on insects, frequently taken by fly-catching from vegetation. **HABITAT** Sparse thorn

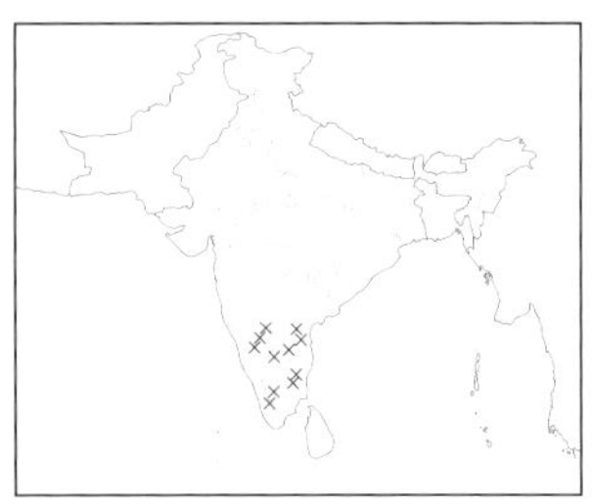

jungle interspersed with some large trees among broken stony hillocks; also moist deciduous habitats in the hills. **BREEDING** Little known. May–July. One nest found in a dwarf date palm, another among dead leaves between boulders on a sloping hillside. **DISTRIBUTION AND STATUS IN:** endemic resident; hills of S Andhra Pradesh, E Karnataka and N Tamil Nadu; common, but very local; 600–1200 m. **REFERENCES** Subramanya *et al.* (1995).

YELLOW-EARED BULBUL *Pycnonotus penicillatus* Plate 117

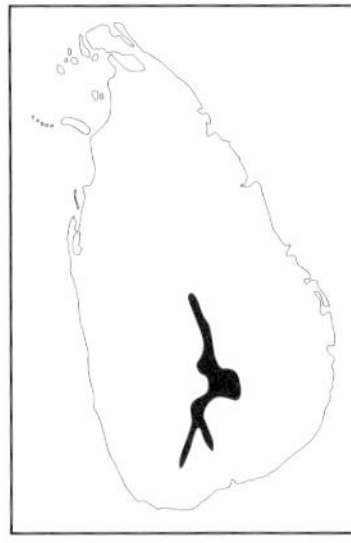

IDENTIFICATION 20 cm. A striking bulbul, with yellow tuft behind eye and yellow patch on ear-coverts, white tuft extending from lores, and black crown, eye-stripe and moustachial stripe. Further, has olive-green upperparts, white throat and yellow underparts. **VOICE** A loud sweet-toned whistle, *wheet wit wit,* usually uttered in flight; alarm note is a low *crr crr* (Henry 1971). **HABITS** Fairly shy. Gathers in large numbers when trees are fruiting. Prefers the middle canopy and low bushes, but also goes higher to eat fruit. **HABITAT** Forest; occasionally gardens close to forested patches. **BREEDING** March–May, August–October. Builds nest 3–5 m up in a sapling fork or at the end of a branch, often overhanging a stream. **DISTRIBUTION AND STATUS LK:** common endemic resident at middle and higher altitudes.

FLAVESCENT BULBUL *Pycnonotus flavescens* Plate 118

Blyth's Bulbul (I)

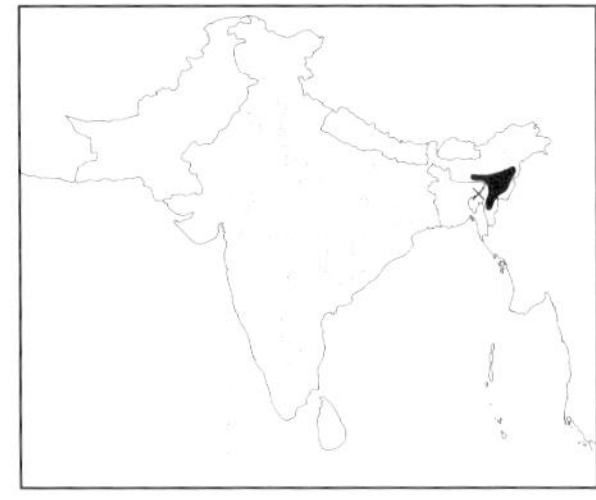

IDENTIFICATION 22 cm. A rather nondescript, smallish, olive bulbul. Likely to be confused only with Olive Bulbul (p.699), but is larger, with longer tail, and has shorter black bill. Has white supercilium back to eye contrasting with black lores, brownish-olive crown with slight crest, olive-brown upperparts with greenish cast, brownish-grey underparts (mixed with some yellow, and with lightly streaked appearance), yellow vent and undertail-coverts, and greenish uppertail-coverts and tail. As on Olive, remiges are edged with yellow, forming fairly prominent panel on wing. Possibly confusable with White-browed Bulbul (below) of the peninsula (although there is no overlap in ranges), but white supercilium does not extend beyond eye, lacks white on cheeks, and underparts are much dingier. **Juvenile** has yellower head with less prominent supercilium. **VOICE** Song is a jolly phrase of usually three to six notes: *joi..whiti-whiti-wit, ti-chi..whiti-whiti-whit-tu, chi..whiti-whiti-whi-tu.chitiwit, brr..whiti-chu* etc. Alarm call is harsh, rapid *djo.djo.drrrrrt, dreet.dreet.drrrr.dreet-dreet,* etc (C. Robson). **HABITS** Arboreal. Keeps in flocks of 6–30 birds. Rather quiet. Forages inside bushes and trees, rather than perching conspicuously on top. Feeds on berries and insects. **HABITAT** Forest with plenty of undergrowth, thick bushes in deserted cultivation and secondary growth. **BREEDING** April–July. Builds a neat nest low down in bushes. **DISTRIBUTION AND STATUS** Resident in NE India (Assam, Manipur, Meghalaya, Mizoram and Nagaland) and Bangladesh. **IN:** current status uncertain, and very few recent records; breeds 900–2100 m, winters down to 450 m. **BD:** former local resident, only one recent record.

WHITE-BROWED BULBUL *Pycnonotus luteolus* Plate 118

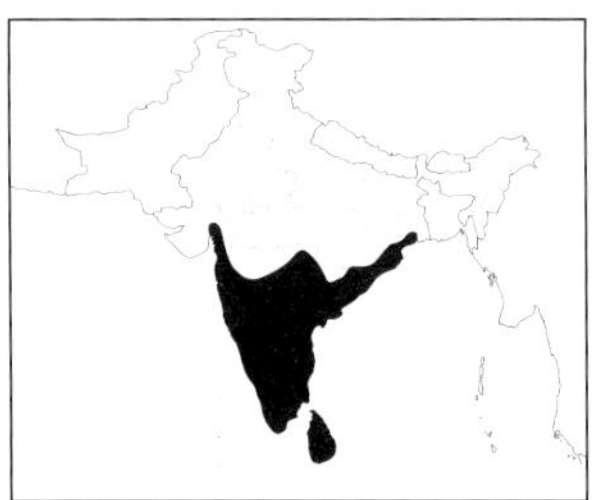

IDENTIFICATION 20 cm. A rather nondescript, olive bulbul. **Adult** has prominent white supercilium extending beyond eye, narrow dark eye-stripe, white crescent beneath eye and dark moustachial stripe, diffusely streaked ear-coverts, and yellowish chin and malar patch. Further, has pale greyish-olive breast merging into yellowish-white belly, and yellowish undertail-coverts. See Flavescent Bulbul (above) for differences from that species, although there is no overlap in ranges. **Juvenile** has duller, browner upperparts, less distinct supercilium, browner breast, and uniform olive-brown ear-coverts. **VOICE** Simple distinctive song is a quarrelsome cacophonous explosion of loud, discordant babbles, usually lasting 1–3 seconds; calls include a rasping *churrr* (P. Holt). **HABITS** Usually in pairs. A shy bulbul; skulks within bushes, and is heard more often than seen. Feeds mainly on berries, also on insects and nectar. **HABITAT** Dry light scrub jungle, thickets around villages, in gardens, grazing grounds, and forest edges. **BREEDING** Throughout the year, varying locally. Builds nest in thick bushes, usually within 1.5 m of ground. **DISTRIBUTION AND STATUS** Resident, endemic to the subcontinent. From Rajasthan and Delhi east through Madhya Pradesh to West Bengal and south through much of the peninsula, and Sri Lanka. **IN:** plains and hills, locally to 1200 m; local and fairly common in the east, rare in the west. **LK:** common in lowlands and lower hills.

WHITE-THROATED BULBUL *Alophoixus flaveolus* Plate 118

***Criniger flaveolus* (F,I,K)**

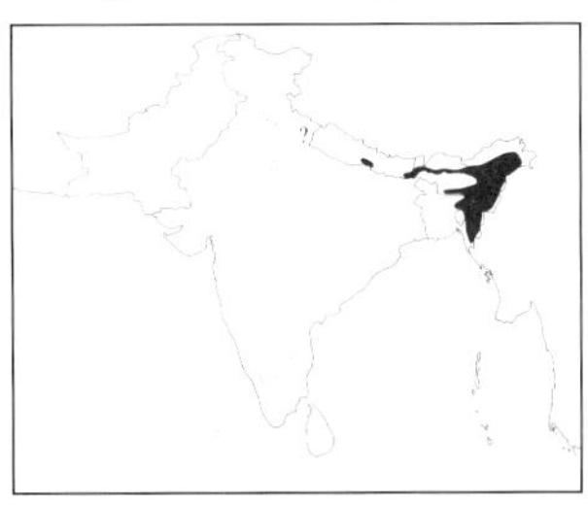

IDENTIFICATION 22 cm. A large, crested, olive bulbul. **Adult** readily distinguishable from other bulbuls occurring in the subcontinent by prominent brownish crest, whitish lores and grey ear-coverts (streaked with white), puffed-out white throat, yellow breast and belly, and olive-green upperparts with rufous-brown cast to wings and tail. **Juvenile** has browner crest and upperparts, more rufescent wings and tail, and brownish wash to underparts. **VOICE** A chacking *chi-chack chi-chack chi-chack,* and a nasal *cheer* (Boonsong and Round 1991). **HABITS** Noisy, and is heard more often than seen. Creeps and clambers about bushes and the lower storey of forest in flocks of up to 15 birds, rather like laughingthrushes; sometimes ascends into the canopy. Often puffs out its throat feathers. Feeds mainly on berries, also on insects. **HABITAT** Evergreen biotope: bushes and undergrowth in dense forest and secondary growth. **BREEDING** April–July. Builds nest low down in a thick tangle of vines or undergrowth or in a small bush, usually within 1 m of ground. **DISTRIBUTION AND STATUS** Resident, subject to altitudinal movements. Himalayas from C Nepal east to Arunachal Pradesh; NE India and Bangladesh. **NP:** local in the centre and east, mainly below 455 m; locally frequent in the far east, rare west to Chitwan. **IN:** common in the east; breeds mainly 600–1200 m, also up to 1800 m, winters in foothills and adjacent plains. **BT:** common; from 245 m up to at least 1130 m. **BD:** locally common.

OLIVE BULBUL *Iole virescens* Plate 118

***Hypsipetes viridescens* (I,K)**

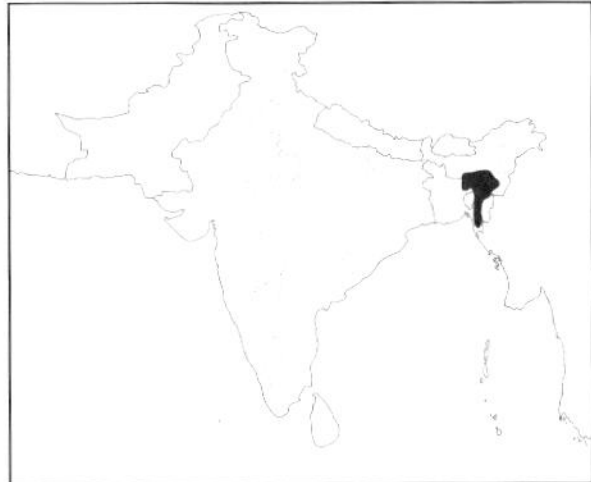

IDENTIFICATION 19 cm. A rather nondescript, olive bulbul. Likely to be confused only with Flavescent Bulbul (p.698), but is smaller, and has proportionately shorter tail and longer bill, which is brownish-horn with paler lower mandible. Further, has unstreaked pale olive-yellow underparts, pale rufous vent, and rufous-brown tail. Lores and ear-coverts can appear distinctly paler than crown. Legs and feet are brownish-pink (black on Flavescent). **VOICE** A disyllabic, musical *whe-ic* (Boonsong and Round 1991). **HABITS** Rather secretive and quiet. Feeds in the tops of higher bushes and treetops. **HABITAT** Dense moist broadleaved evergreen forest, and secondary growth in deserted cultivation in forest. **BREEDING** Poorly known. All nests found in May. Builds a compact nest in bushes, 1.5 m above ground. **DISTRIBUTION AND STATUS** Resident in NE India (Assam, Manipur, Meghalaya, Mizoram) and Bangladesh. **IN:** current status uncertain, very few recent records; from plains up to 900 m. **BD:** local. **REFERENCES** Raman (1995).

YELLOW-BROWED BULBUL *Iole indica* Plate 118

***Hypsipetes indicus* (I,P)**

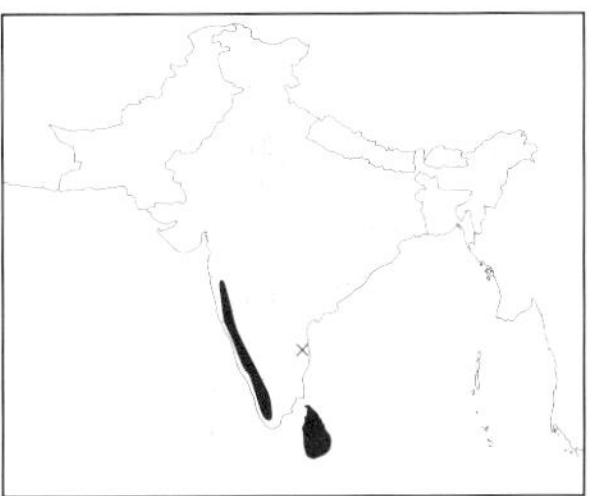

IDENTIFICATION 20 cm. An olive-green and yellow bulbul. **Adult** told from other olive bulbuls by bright yellow supercilium and broad eye-ring, yellow throat and underparts, and uniform olive-green upperparts. Black bill and dark eye are striking. Olive-green upperparts and ear-coverts (latter with some yellow streaking) and yellow underparts give distinctive two-tone appearance. **Juvenile** is duller than adult. **Racial variation** Three races are recognised from the subcontinent, varying in tone of greenish upperparts and brightness of yellow of underparts. **VOICE** Simple song is built around slow repetition of pleasant inflected nasal *pru-eep* or *pru-eehp-eehp* call-notes; peevish *chaink-chaink* in alarm (P. Holt). **HABITS** Keeps in pairs or small noisy flocks in the lower and middle forest storeys. Often associates with mixed hunting bands of other species. Feeds chiefly on berries, also on insects. **HABITAT** Humid broadleaved forest, sholas and secondary growth. **BREEDING** February–September, varying locally. Nest is suspended in a horizontal fork in a tall bush or small tree, within 1.5 m of ground. **DISTRIBUTION AND STATUS** Resident, endemic to the subcontinent. Western Ghats from Maharashtra south to Kerala and east to adjacent hills of Tamil Nadu and Andhra Pradesh; Sri Lanka. **IN:** locally common in the north, 600–1900 m; common from sea level to 1950 m, mainly 1000–1500 m, in the south. **LK:** frequent in wet lowlands, infrequent in dry lowlands and adjacent hills.

ASHY BULBUL *Hemixos flavala* Plate 118

Brown-eared Bulbul (F,I,K), *Hypsipetes flavala*

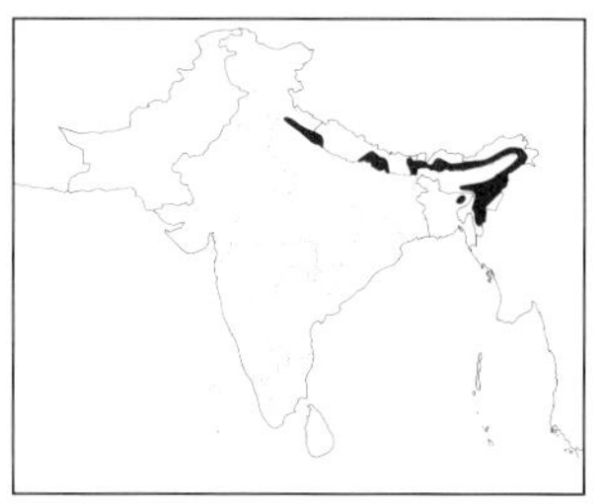

IDENTIFICATION 20 cm. A distinctive, crested bulbul, with black mask, tawny ear-coverts, grey upperparts and greyish-brown tail, olive-yellow patch on wings (formed by greater coverts and broad fringes to tertials and secondaries), white throat, and pale grey breast merging into whitish belly. **Juvenile** is similar to adult, but has browner upperparts. **VOICE** A loud, ringing call of four or five notes, the second or third highest, and the last two in descending sequence (Boonsong and Round 1991). **HABITS** Found in pairs in the breeding season; otherwise in noisy parties. Arboreal; forages in the middle and upper storeys. Feeds on berries, nectar and insects, the last sometimes caught in aerial sallies. **HABITAT** Broadleaved forest, sometimes plantations; in winter, also forest edges and cultivation. **BREEDING** May and June. Builds a deep cup nest, well hidden in a thick bush or tangle of creepers, within 2 m of ground or up to 12 m high in large tree. **DISTRIBUTION AND STATUS** Resident, subject to altitudinal movements. Himalayan foothills from N Uttar Pradesh east to Arunachal Pradesh; NE India and Bangladesh. **NP:** frequent; 305–1525 m. **IN:** common in the east; breeds 700–1600 m, winters down to the foothills and rarely to the plains. **BT:** fairly common. **BD:** locally common.

MOUNTAIN BULBUL *Hypsipetes mcclellandii* Plate 118

Rufous-bellied Bulbul (F,I), *H. virescens* (F)

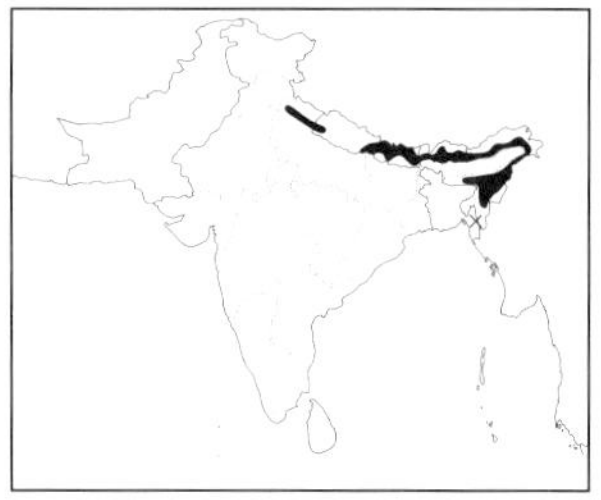

IDENTIFICATION 24 cm. A distinctive bulbul, with white streaking on shaggy brown crest, white-streaked greyish throat, and cinnamon-brown breast with buff streaking. Has greenish mantle, wings and tail, and yellowish vent. **Juvenile** has browner upperparts, including edges of wings, and shorter crest. **VOICE** A metallic, ringing or squawking *tsiuc, tsiuc* (Boonsong and Round 1991). **HABITS** Keeps in pairs or small parties, usually in the forest canopy, also in bushes. Rather shy. Often puffs out its throat feathers. Feeds chiefly on berries and fruits. **HABITAT** Forest and secondary growth, also deserted cultivation clearings with scattered trees. **BREEDING** April–July. Suspends nest in a fork, 6–12 m up in a tree, sometimes in bushes. **DISTRIBUTION AND STATUS** Resident, subject to altitudinal movements. Himalayas from N Uttar Pradesh east to Arunachal Pradesh; NE India and Bangladesh. **NP:** widespread and fairly common; most frequent 1830–2135 m (915–2285 m). **IN:** locally common; breeds 900–2700 m, mainly 1800–2100 m, winters down to the foothills and sometimes plains. **BT:** fairly common; 940–2000 m. **BD:** ?former resident; no recent records, but could still occur in hill tracts.

BLACK BULBUL *Hypsipetes leucocephalus* Plate 118

Gray Bulbul (F), *H. madagascariensis* (I,K,N,P,R)

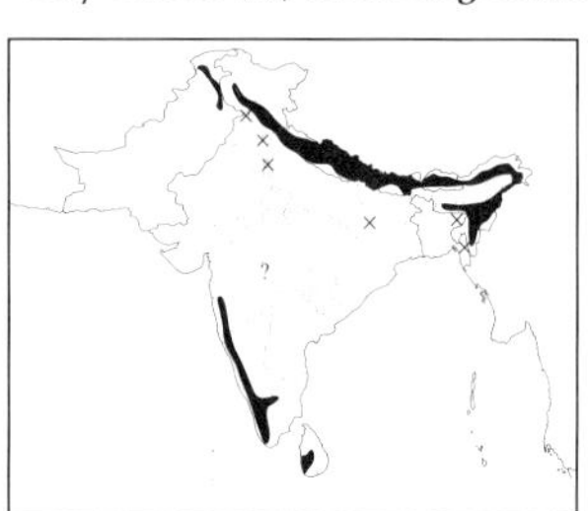

IDENTIFICATION 25 cm. **Adult** is a slate-grey to blackish bulbul, with slight crest. Has bright red bill, legs and feet, pale fringes to undertail-coverts, and shallow fork to tail (at times recalling a drongo). **Juvenile** lacks crest; has whitish throat, grey breast-band, brownish cast to upperparts, and brownish bill, legs and feet. **Racial variation** *H. l. nigrescens* of the NE subcontinent is dull black in coloration compared with the paler slate-grey of *H. l. psaroides*, which occupies most of the Himalayan range of the species. *H. l. ganeesa* and *H. l. humii* of the Western Ghats and Sri Lanka, respectively, are darker than *psaroides*, with less noticeable fork to tail, and lack grey patch above lores and black surround to ear-coverts of *psaroides*. **VOICE** Song is a monotonously repeated series of three or four rising and falling notes, *pa-chit-chit* or *pip-per-tree* (Roberts 1992), and a variety of loud, screeching and mewing notes. **HABITS** Gregarious and very noisy. When not breeding keeps in flocks, sometimes of up to 100 birds. Forages chiefly in the treetops, moving restlessly from tree to tree. Feeds mainly on berries, also insects; often fly-catches from the treetops in the evening. Flight is strong, swift and agile. **HABITAT** Tall forest, mainly of broadleaves; in S India, broadleaved evergreen forest, sholas and shade trees in plantations. **BREEDING** March–September, varying locally. Nest usually 7–10 m up in a forest tree. **DISTRIBUTION AND STATUS** Resident, subject to altitudinal movements in Himalayas and local movements in SW India. Himalayas from N Pakistan east to Arunachal Pradesh; NE India and Bangladesh; Western Ghats from Maharashtra south to Kerala and adjacent hills of W Tamil Nadu; Sri Lanka. **PK:** frequent; in lower valleys and foothills up to 1500 m, to 2100 m in Murree hills. **NP:** widespread and common; 75–3050 m, most frequent 1830–2135 m. **IN:** common; in Himalayas, breeds 1000–2400 m, locally to 3200 m in the west, to 3000 m in the east, mainly 1800–2100 m, and winters down to the foothills and locally in adjacent plains; in the NE hills, breeds from 700 m up to at least 2400 m, winters in foothills and plains; in the southwest, breeds from 1000 m up to the summits, winters down to the foothills. **BT:** common; 250–3210 m. **BD:** ?former resident; no recent records, but could still occur in hill tracts. **LK:** common in wet lowlands and adjacent mid-altitude hills, visitor to dry zone and higher hills. **REFERENCES** Mahabal (1992).

NICOBAR BULBUL *Hypsipetes nicobariensis* **Plate 118**

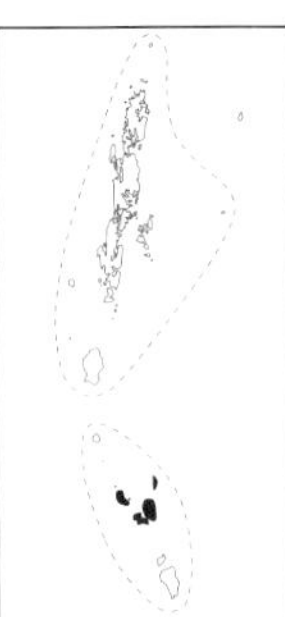

IDENTIFICATION 20 cm. A rather drab olive bulbul. Lacks crest, and has dark brown crown and nape, olive upperparts with browner wings and tail, and whitish underparts (faintly washed with yellow). **VOICE** Chattering notes, similar to those of Black Bulbul (p.700). **HABITS** Little described. Usually found singly, in pairs or in small parties, sometimes in flocks of nearly 100 birds. Food unknown. **HABITAT** Mainly forest; also gardens and secondary growth. **BREEDING** Details unrecorded. Very young birds collected in February. **DISTRIBUTION AND STATUS** Globally threatened. **IN:** resident, endemic to Nicobar Is (Nancowry subgroup: Camorta, Trinkat, Nancowry, Katchall, Teressa, Bompoka, Tillanchong); formerly common, has declined, but still fairly common on Katchall. **REFERENCES** Collar *et al.* (1994), Sankaran (1997; 1998).

GREY HYPOCOLIUS Hypocoliidae

The only member of the family.

GREY HYPOCOLIUS *Hypocolius ampelinus* **Plate 118**

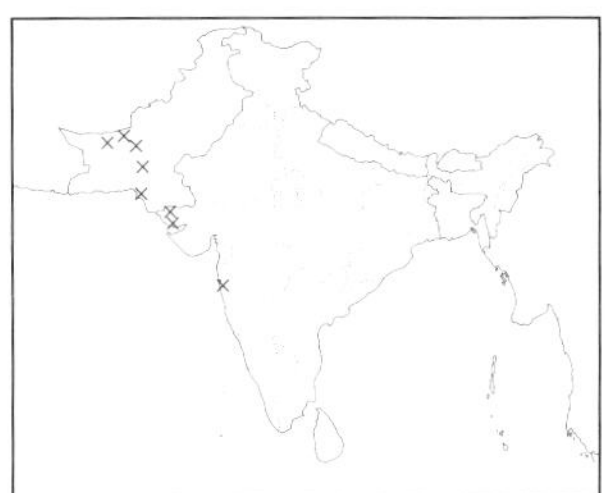

IDENTIFICATION Long-tailed and rather short-winged. Resembles a shrike or babbler if seen briefly. Often raises crown feathers. **Male** is mainly grey, with black mask and black tip to tail. In flight, shows black primaries with prominent white tips. **Female** and **immature** are browner, and lack black mask; have well-defined creamy-white throat, and diffuse dark tip to tail. **VOICE** A mellow, liquid *tre-tur-tur*, and a descending *whee-oo* (Porter *et al.* 1996). **HABITS** Gregarious in winter, when seen in flocks of up to 20 birds. Forages chiefly by hopping and clambering about within trees and bushes; sometimes descends to the ground to pick up insects. Feeds mainly on berries; also occasionally on insects. Flight is strong and direct, with rapid wingbeats and occasional swooping glides or circling; often high above the ground. Settles on the top of a bush and remains still for long periods. If excited, raises its ear-coverts and nape feathers. **HABITAT** Semi-desert with scattered thorn scrub of berried bushes or around oases and date palm groves. **DISTRIBUTION AND STATUS** Winter visitor and passage migrant. Mainly Pakistan (SW Baluchistan and S Sindh) and Gujarat. **PK:** rare and irregular. **IN:** regular winter visitor and passage migrant to parts of Kutch. **REFERENCES** Tiwari *et al.* (1996).

AFRICAN WARBLERS (CISTICOLAS, PRINIAS AND STREAKED SCRUB WARBLER) Cisticolidae

CISTICOLAS Cisticolas are tiny, short-tailed passerines, usually coloured in shades of brown, grey, buff and tawny. The tail is longer in winter than in summer. They are often found in grassy habitats, and many have aerial displays.

ZITTING CISTICOLA *Cisticola juncidis* **Plate 120**

Streaked Fantail Warbler (I,P)

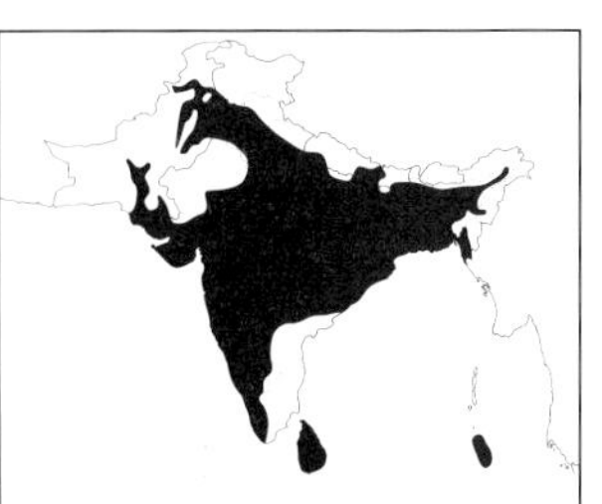

IDENTIFICATION 10 cm. A small warbler with boldly streaked buffish upperparts, whitish underparts (with variable buff wash to breast and flanks), indistinct whitish supercilium, and very pale legs. Most likely to be confused with Bright-headed Cisticola (p.702) and distinguished, in all plumages, by broad white tips to rectrices (except central pair), usually with more distinct dark subterminal markings; also has a very different song flight and song. For further differences, see that species. **Adult breeding** has diffusely streaked grey-brown crown, and often rather distinct buff or rufous rump. Never has unstreaked rufous or creamy-white crown as on breeding male Bright-headed. **Adult non-breeding** has more heavily streaked upperparts and often less distinct rump than adult breeding; some birds have brighter rufous-buff coloration to upperparts, but lack the more clearly defined rufous nape of Bright-headed. **First-winter** is similar to adult, but has sulphur-yellow wash to underparts and less heavily streaked upperparts. **VOICE** Song, uttered in distinctive display flight, is a repetition of a single note, e.g. *pip pip pip pip...*; call is a single or repeated *plit*. **HABITS** Found singly or in loose parties. Active and excitable; frequently flicks wings and cocks and spreads tail. Skulks in cover, and can move rapidly between plant stems. Seeks insects close to or on the ground among grass tussocks and other low vegetation. Sometimes perches on bushes and telegraph wires. Has a characteristic display flight, and displays frequently during the breeding season: circles widely over its territory with bouncing flight, beats the wings rapidly as it rises, drops a little, and then rises again, all the time repeating a short monotonous *pip* or *tzet*. Otherwise, normally flies only short distances with whirring wings and tail spread, before dropping into cover again. **HABITAT** Paddy-fields and other crops of cereals, sugarcane, lucerne etc, and dry and marshy grassland. **BREEDING** Throughout the year, varying locally. Often nests in loose colony. Builds a pear-shaped or bottle-shaped nest of grasses, woven around grass or reed stems, usually within 0.5 m of ground. **DISTRIBUTION AND STATUS** Resident, subject to local movements. Himalayan foothills and south throughout much of the subcontinent, except parts of the northwest, northeast, southeast and Himalayas. **PK:** common and widespread in Indus plains and adjacent foothills; patchily distributed. **NP:** widespread and fairly common resident; below 1350 m, summers locally up to 1900 m. **IN:** widespread and locally common; plains and hills up to 1800 m. **BD:** common throughout. **LK:** common in lowlands and hills.

BRIGHT-HEADED CISTICOLA *Cisticola exilis* — Plate 120

Fantail Warbler (I), Bright-capped Cisticola (K,N)

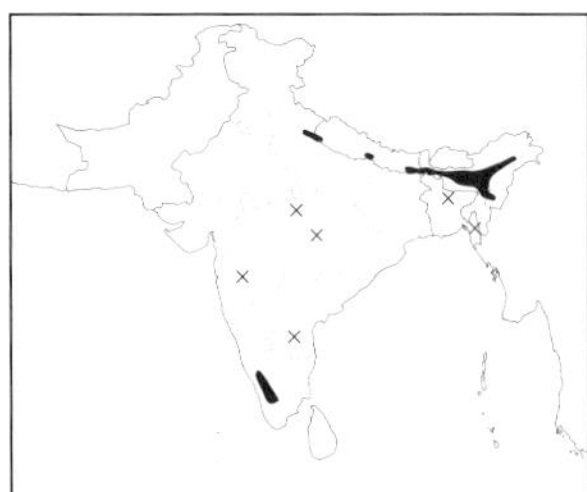

IDENTIFICATION 10 cm. Similar to Zitting Cisticola (p.701), with prominently streaked upperparts and unstreaked underparts. Differences from that species are best described with references to the two distinct races occurring in the subcontinent. **Racial variation** Breeding male *C. e. erythrocephala* of the Western Ghats differs markedly from breeding Zitting in having an unstreaked rufous crown, neck sides and nape, rufous-buff sides of throat, breast and flanks, and more uniform blackish tail with narrower buffish tips to feathers. Female and non-breeding male have streaked crown and more closely resemble Zitting: best told by unstreaked rufous nape and sides of neck, rufous (rather than whitish) supercilium, and rufous coloration to streaked crown and mantle; nape may be diffusely streaked on some birds, but much less heavily so than crown and mantle; further differences are deeper rufous-buff coloration to breast (often forming breast-band) and flanks, and longer, more uniform blackish tail with narrower buff tips. First-winter is similar to female, but has yellow wash to underparts; other features mentioned above (for separating females) should help separate it from first-winter Zitting. Breeding male *C. e. tytleri* of N and NE subcontinent is very distinctive, with unstreaked creamy-white crown and underparts, and rufous-brown wash to nape and sides of neck; further, has unstreaked olive-grey rump contrasting with short black tail, and a narrow band of black streaking across back. Female and non-breeding male have heavily streaked crown and mantle, and more closely resemble Zitting: best told by rufous coloration to supercilium, nape and neck sides (nape is unstreaked, and forms a distinct patch on some birds), blacker crown and mantle (streaking is less distinct owing to narrow pale edges to feathers), and longer, more uniform black tail with narrower greyish-white tips. **VOICE** A curious, comical song, given in display flight or from perch, usually with one or two jolly, doubled notes introduced by a long buzzy wheeze: *bzzeeee..joo-ee*, or *cheeezz..joo-ee.di-di*, or *bzzzeeee-dji-shiwi..joo-ee*, etc; sometimes shortened to *trrrt.joo-ee*. The wheeze is often repeated on its own (C. Robson). **HABITS** Similar to those of Zitting Cisticola, but its display flight is faster, less jerky, and ends in a nose-dive at high speed, and its normal flight is more direct. **HABITAT** Tall grassland; hillsides with tall grass and low *Strobilanthes* and bracken scrub in S India; open grassy areas in woodland in Bangladesh. **BREEDING** April–August. Builds nest of fine grass stems, either a frail cup sewn to the side of an upright broad leaf or an egg-shaped structure. **DISTRIBUTION AND STATUS** Local resident. Chiefly from N Uttar Pradesh and Nepal terai east to Arunachal Pradesh; NE India and Bangladesh; S Indian hills (Karnataka, Kerala, Tamil Nadu). **NP:** local and fairly common. **IN:** uncommon; plains up to 1200 m, breeds mainly in the foothills, disperses more over plains in winter. **BD:** rare; recently recorded only from Madhupur Forest.

STREAKED SCRUB WARBLER *Scotocerca inquieta* — Plate 120

Scrub Warbler (R)

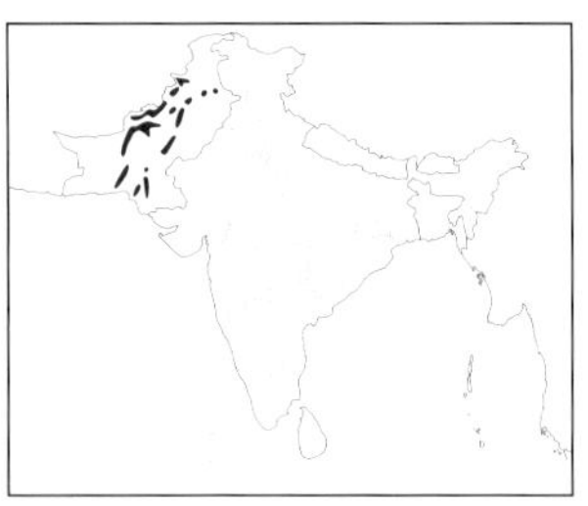

IDENTIFICATION 10 cm. A small, long-tailed, prinia-like bird. Superficially resembles Graceful Prinia (p.706), with streaking on crown and mantle, although is stockier, with blunter, broader and darker tail. Also has flatter crown and bigger head. Main differences are broad vinous-buff supercilium, blackish lores and eye-stripe, fine dark streaking on white throat, vinous-buff ear-coverts, breast sides and flanks, greyish cast to upperparts, with boldly streaked crown (and ill-defined streaking on mantle), and dark underside to tail (except for white tips). **VOICE** Calls include a *drzip*, rolling *tlyip-tlyip-tlyip*, and a piping *pip*; song is a thin *di-di-di-di-di*, followed by warbling *toodle toodle toodle* (Porter *et al.* 1996). **HABITS** Found in pairs or small parties. Rather wren-like and very active. Mainly terrestrial, sometimes skulking.

Rummages in plant debris under bushes, but often feeds in the open among stones; will also feed in the tops of bushes and small trees. Often cocks its tail when feeding, and calls frequently. Flight is whirring, usually over short distances and close to the ground. When escaping, flies directly into cover or lands and runs into cover. **HABITAT** Mainly dry, open stony slopes with thorn scrub, also dry juniper and *Pinus gerardiana* forest. **BREEDING** End March–August. Builds a domed nest of dry plant stems in a low bush, within 1.5 m of ground. **DISTRIBUTION AND STATUS PK:** frequent and widespread resident in dry lower hills, up to 2500 m in Baluchistan, to 700 m in Sindh and NW Pakistan.

PRINIAS Mainly dull-coloured warblers with a long, graduated tail. The tail is longer in winter than in summer. Most inhabit grassland, marsh vegetation or scrub. They forage by gleaning insects and spiders from vegetation, and some species also feed on the ground. They are adept at threading their way rapidly between plant stems. When perched, the tail is often held cocked and slightly fanned and is frequently jerked and sideswitched. Most prinias have a characteristic display flight: they rise vertically, beating the wings rapidly, snapping the wings together over the back and jerking and twisting the tail, resulting in an erratic flight; then they drop down, before rising again. Normal flight is weak and jerky and over only short distances. Their nests are variable.

RUFOUS-VENTED PRINIA *Prinia burnesii* — Plate 119

Long-tailed Grass Warbler (I), Long-tailed Prinia (R)

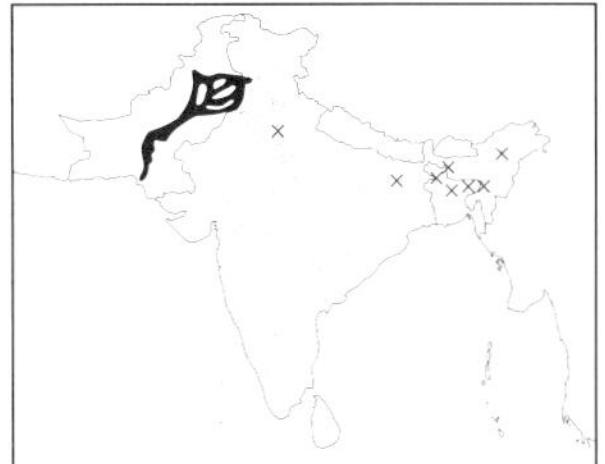

IDENTIFICATION 17 cm. A large, long-tailed prinia with dark streaking on upperparts, whitish throat and breast, conspicuous whitish lores and eye-ring, and rufous-chestnut undertail-coverts. Streaked upperparts have greyish cast to crown and warm rufous-brown cast to nape and upper mantle. Graceful Prinia (p.706) is the only other prinia with streaked upperparts likely to be found in similar habitat, but that species is considerably smaller, has uniform sandy grey-brown coloration to streaked upperparts, and lacks rufous vent. Upperparts are similar to those of *striatula* race of Striated Prinia (below) (although habitat of that species is usually quite different); compared with Striated, has broader babbler-like tail with rufous-buff tips when fresh (lacking well-defined pale tips and dark subterminal bands visible on underside of tail of Striated), and also has whiter throat and breast, greyish-olive (rather than buff) flanks, rufous undertail-coverts, and rather uniform wings (lacking rufous edges to remiges). **Juvenile** of the nominate race has more uniform sandy grey-brown upperparts (with indistinct streaking), and buffish wash to underparts, and is quite different in appearance from adult. Uniform wings, rufous (although paler than adult) undertail-coverts, and broad tail are best distinguishing features. **Racial variation** *P. b. cinerascens* of the plains of Brahmaputra and Ganges differs from the nominate race, described above, of the Indus plains in having cold olive-grey coloration to streaked upperparts, uniform greyish-white underparts, with grey flanks, and grey (rather than rufous) undertail-coverts. **VOICE** Alarm calls of the nominate race include a loud drawn-out, rising and falling, nasal *skeeow-skeeow-skeeow* and a more rapid twittering *szik-szik-szik*; song of nominate race is a rising and falling, clear, high-pitched warbling *tuweet-tiwittoo-tweeet-tu-wittoo-weeto-witoo*, which is very different from the songs of other prinias (Roberts 1992). Vocalisations of *P. b. cinerascens* are undescribed. **HABITS** Usually found singly or in pairs. Skulks in dense vegetation; most easily located by its frequent calls, and when it emerges to sing in the early mornings and evenings. Also feeds on the ground by hopping about and flicking over dead leaves, like a small babbler. Flies low over vegetation and soon drops into cover again. Unlike other prinias, does not have a display flight. **HABITAT** Large expanses of tall grass in pure stands or with scattered trees and extensive reedbeds; usually near rivers and in swamps. **BREEDING** February–September. Builds a deep cup-shaped nest of coarse grasses, woven around plant stems in a tall grass clump, within 1 m of ground. **DISTRIBUTION AND STATUS** Resident, endemic to India and Pakistan. Indus plains in Pakistan and NW India (Punjab and Delhi); Brahmaputra plains in Assam, Bihar and Bangladesh. Globally threatened. **PK:** frequent along the Indus R system, also around larger lakes and marshes. **IN:** very local and fairly common in Punjab; current status elsewhere uncertain, with few recent published records; formerly locally common in the east. **BD:** ?former resident; no recent records, but could still occur locally in northwest, centre and northeast. **REFERENCES** Barooah (1994), Barua (1995b), Choudhury (1994), Robson (1996a).

STRIATED PRINIA *Prinia criniger* — Plate 119

Brown Hill Warbler (I), Brown Hill Prinia (F)

IDENTIFICATION 16 cm. A large, long-tailed, hill-dwelling prinia with stout bill. **Adult breeding** has dark grey-brown (and very worn) upperparts with ill-defined blackish streaking, dark lores, buffish-white underparts with variable dark grey mottling (owing to bases of worn throat and breast feathers showing through), narrow rufous-brown edges to remiges, and black bill. **Adult non-breeding** has rufous-brown (and fresh) upperparts with prominent dark brown streaking, buff lores and eye-ring, warm buff on underparts, especially flanks, broad rufous-brown fringes to remiges, and orangish lower mandible; underside of tail has rufous-buff tips and dark subterminal bands. Possibly confusable with non-breeding Hill Prinia (p.704), but that species has whitish supercilium

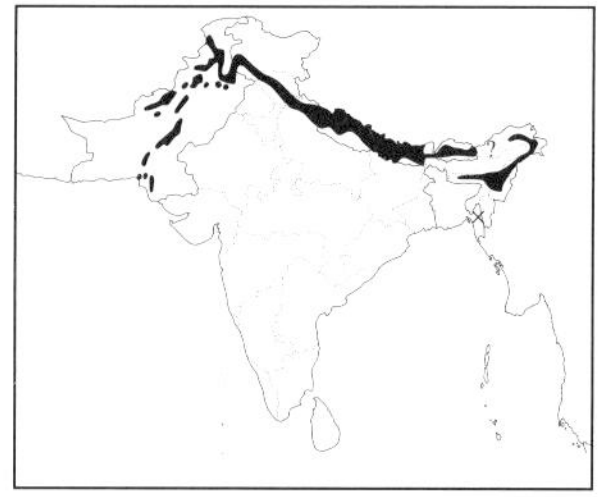

contrasting with dark lores, unstreaked upperparts, and finer bill. Confusion with Graceful Prinia (p.706) of the plains is very unlikely, since that species is much smaller, and has paler sandy grey-brown coloration to (less heavily streaked) upperparts, whiter underparts, and very fine bill. **Juvenile** has olive-brown coloration to upperparts, with indistinct streaking (streaking is really apparent only on crown), and warm buff or pale yellowish underparts. Streaking on crown, lack of supercilium, and stouter bill should help distinguish it from juvenile Hill Prinia. **Racial variation** Non-breeding *P. c. striatula* of the NW subcontinent has paler greyish coloration to streaked upperparts compared with the nominate race, described above. **VOICE** Song is a monotonous, wheezy *chitzereet-chitzereet-chitzereet*, and contact call is a *tchak-tchak* (Roberts 1992). **HABITS** Solitary or in pairs. Skulking; hops and clambers actively about within bushes and low vegetation. In the breeding season, males sing frequently in the open from the top of small bushes, fences and telegraph wires. **HABITAT** Open grass-covered hillsides with scattered bushes, terraced cultivation, long grass in open pine forests and dry thorn scrub forests. **BREEDING** April–October. Builds a domed oval nest within 0.5 m of ground in grass or a small bush. **DISTRIBUTION AND STATUS** Resident, with small altitudinal movements. Hills of Pakistan and Himalayas from Murree, Pakistan, east to Arunachal Pradesh; hills of NE India and Bangladesh. **PK:** frequent; 300–1800 m, locally to 2100 m. **NP:** widespread and common; summers chiefly 1220–2300 m (–3000 m), winters 915–2135 m (down to 75 m). **IN:** common; breeds 1200–2100 m, locally to 2800 m (–3100 m), in the west down to 600 m; winters 300–2100 m. **BT:** common; from 610 m up to at least 2200 m. **BD:** ?former resident in northeast and southeast; no recent records, but could still occur in hill tracts. **REFERENCES** Martens and Eck (1995).

HILL PRINIA *Prinia atrogularis* — Plate 119

Black-throated Hill Warbler (I), Black-throated Hill Prinia (F)

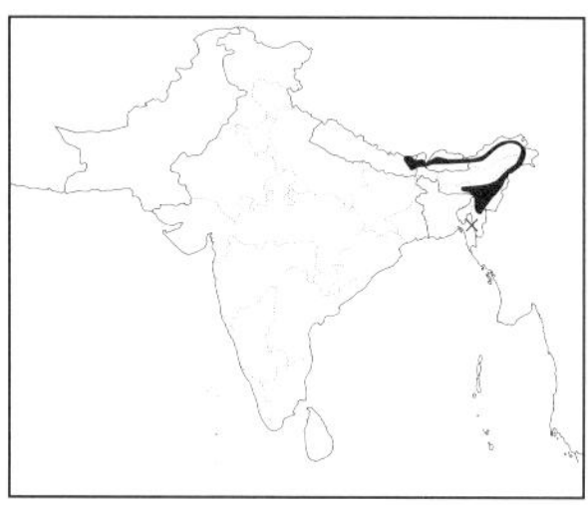

IDENTIFICATION 17 cm. A large, long-tailed, hill-dwelling prinia. **Adult breeding** is very distinctive, with black throat and breast, white moustachial stripe and breast spotting, greyish ear-coverts and breast sides, greyish olive-brown upperparts and tail, olive-buff fringes to remiges forming panel on wing, whitish belly, and olive-buff flanks. **Adult non-breeding** is very different, with white supercilium, buff underparts with variable dark mottling/streaking on sides of throat and breast (sometimes covering whole of throat and breast), and rufous-brown edges to remiges. In this plumage, possibly confusable with Striated Prinia (p.703), but has white supercilium contrasting with dark lores, unstreaked upperparts (although can appear to be very diffusely streaked, especially on lower back), and longer and finer bill. **Juvenile** is said to be similar to non-breeding adult, but with yellowish wash on underparts and darker olive breast-band. **Racial variation** *P. a. khasiana*, occurring east and south of Brahmaputra R, differs markedly from the nominate race, described above, in having rufous-brown upperparts (especially crown) and warmer buff flanks in both breeding and non-breeding plumages. **VOICE** Song is loud *tulip..tulip..tulip*; calls include a soft *tp-tp-tp-tp*, a soft, high-pitched *pri...pri*, and a *tyip...tyip* (Ali and Ripley 1987). **HABITS** Very similar to those of Striated Prinia. **HABITAT** Scrub and grass on hillsides, long grass in open pine forest, and bushes at the edges of forest and terraced cultivation. **BREEDING** May and June. Builds a globular nest of grasses in a grass clump or bush. **DISTRIBUTION AND STATUS** Resident. Himalayas from E Nepal east to Arunachal Pradesh; hills of NE India and Bangladesh. **NP:** frequent; 1400–2500 m. **IN:** locally frequent in Himalayas, 1000–2500 m; common in NE hills, 300 m up to at least 1800 m. **BT:** frequent; 610–2745 m. **BD:** ?former resident in southeast; no recent records, but could still occur in hill tracts. **REFERENCES** Athreya *et al.* (1997).

GREY-CROWNED PRINIA *Prinia cinereocapilla* — Plate 119

Hodgson's Wren-Warbler (I), Grey-capped Prinia (F,R)

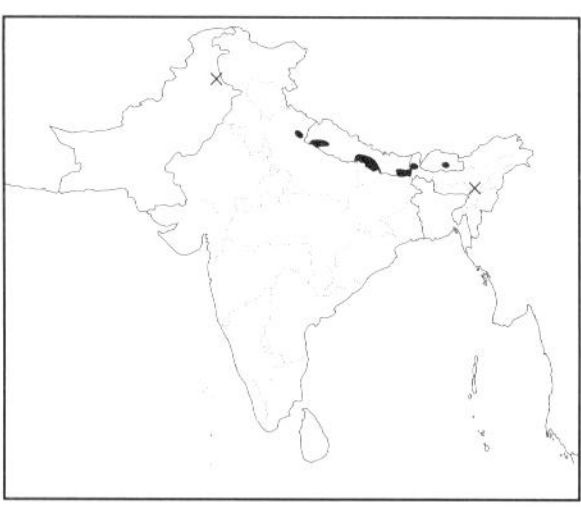

IDENTIFICATION 11 cm. **Adult** superficially resembles a small, short-tailed Ashy Prinia (p.707). Supercilium is orange-buff, contrasts with blackish lores and extends noticeably (and becomes whiter) beyond eye (on Ashy, supercilium is whitish and typically extends only to above eye), and has a touch of rufous-brown on forehead (absent on Ashy). Further, shows noticeable contrast between purer blue-grey crown and nape and more rufescent-brown mantle and back compared with Ashy. Above-mentioned features would help differentiate it from Rufescent Prinia (p.705) in breeding plumage; additional distinctions from that species include finer all-dark bill, and orange-buff wash to sides of throat and sides of breast. **Juvenile** is undescribed. **VOICE** Song is a squeezed-out *cheeeeeeeesum-zip-zip-zip*, also a rapid, repeated *tzit* (Fleming *et al.* 1984). **HABITS** Found in small flocks, often with other prinias. Forages low down in bushes. Very active, like other small prinias. **HABITAT** Grassland in forest clearings and at forest edges, and secondary growth. **BREEDING** Very poorly known. About June. Nest is very like that of Grey-breasted Prinia (p.705), and built in secondary growth.

DISTRIBUTION AND STATUS Resident, endemic to the subcontinent. Himalayan foothills in Margalla hills, Pakistan, and locally from N Uttar Pradesh east to Bhutan; Assam (N Cachar). **PK:** very local; 450–1000 m. **NP:** local and fairly common; below 1065 m (–1600 m). **IN:** current status uncertain, and very few recent published records; from edge of the plains up to 1350 m. **BT:** uncommon. **REFERENCES** Grewal and Sahgal (1995).

RUFOUS-FRONTED PRINIA *Prinia buchanani* — Plate 119

Rufous-fronted Wren-Warbler (I)

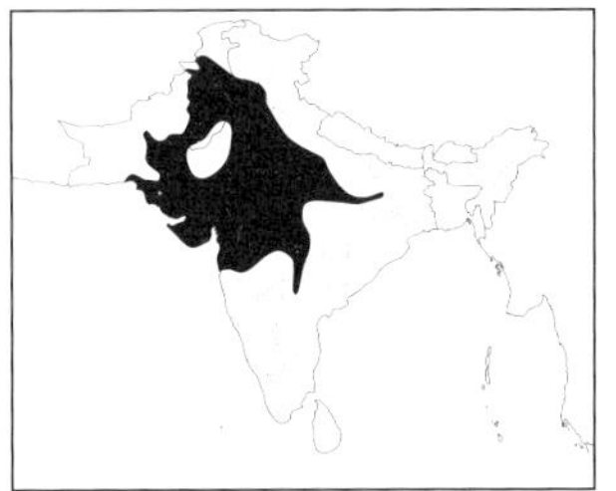

IDENTIFICATION 12 cm. Resembles Plain Prinia (p.708), with grey-brown mantle and whitish underparts, and greyish or white lores and diffuse supercilium. **Adult** told from that species in breeding plumage by rufous-brown forehead and crown, blending into sandy grey-brown of mantle, and broad white tips to all but central tail feathers (which are very prominent in flight). Underparts are white with variable greyish cast, and lack buff wash which is often apparent on Plain, and bill has pale yellowish on lower mandible (all black on breeding Plain). Has prominent pale fringes to tertials and greyish panel on secondaries, but these features can also be shown by Plain. Has distinctive trilling call. In worn plumage, crown becomes greyer-brown and almost concolorous with mantle, but prominent white tail-feather tips are nearly always apparent. On some birds, supercilium, ear-coverts and entire underparts are strongly washed with grey, and upperparts are a darker and more uniform greyish-brown. **Juvenile** is similar to adult, with white tips to tail, but has uniform pale rufous-brown upperparts (lacking distinct rufous crown) and buffer underparts. **VOICE** Call is a rippling trill; song is a *chid-le-weest* (the *weest* being upward-inflected) followed by a repetitive *chidle-ee..chidle-ee..* etc. **HABITS** Found in pairs in the breeding season and in small parties, often with Grey-breasted Prinia, in winter. More terrestrial and gregarious than Plain Prinia. Frequently forages on the ground; creeps actively around the base of bushes and grass tussocks. Males often sing from the tops of bushes. **HABITAT** Favours semi-desert: thorn scrub, stony semi-desert with scattered bushes, and drier parts of irrigated forest plantations. **BREEDING** Mainly end June–September. Nest varies from a cup to a domed oblong purse, made of fine grass, built in a thorn bush or grass tussock within 1 m of ground. **DISTRIBUTION AND STATUS** Endemic to the subcontinent. Resident, with some seasonal movements. Mainly from C Pakistan east to Bihar and south to C Maharashtra and N Andhra Pradesh. **PK:** widespread and common in Indus plains and adjacent lower hills, up to 460 m. **IN:** locally common.

RUFESCENT PRINIA *Prinia rufescens* — Plate 119

Beavan's Wren-Warbler (I), Rufous Prinia (N)

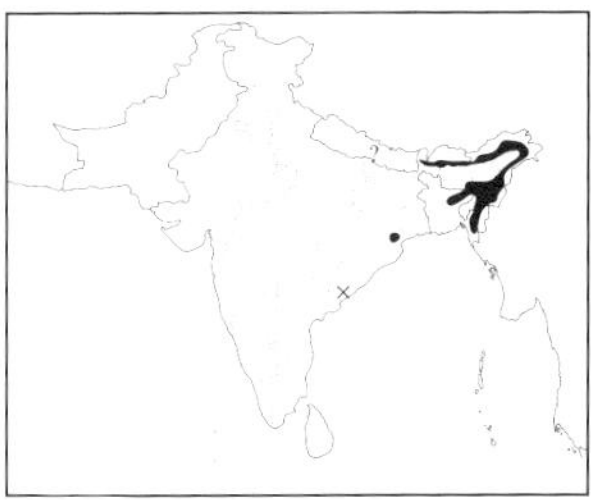

IDENTIFICATION 11 cm. A small, comparatively short-tailed prinia with prominent white supercilium. Closely resembles non-breeding Grey-breasted (below) where ranges overlap in NE subcontinent; distinguished in all plumages from that species by larger, stouter bill (usually with pale lower mandible), rufous-brown (rather than grey-brown) tail, more rufescent mantle and edgings to tertials, and nasal buzzing call. **Adult breeding** has grey cast to crown, nape and ear-coverts which further helps to separate it from non-breeding Grey-breasted. Possibly confusable with Grey-crowned (p.704), but has larger bill, whitish supercilium, paler grey crown and ear-coverts, browner upperparts, and whiter underparts. **Adult non-breeding** has rufous-brown crown and ear-coverts which are concolorous with mantle, and a longer tail. Separable from non-breeding Grey-breasted by features mentioned above, and also has stronger buff wash on throat and breast . **Juvenile** is similar to non-breeding adult, although crown has greyish-olive cast, but has yellowish wash to underparts. **VOICE** Call is a buzzing *peez-eez-eez-eez*; song is a rhythmic *chewp chewp chewp* (Boonsong and Round 1991). **HABITS** Like those of Grey-breasted Prinia. **HABITAT** Tall grassland, grass under deciduous forest, bushes around terraced cultivation, open wooded areas, secondary growth and forest edges. **BREEDING** April–September. Nest is like that of Grey-breasted Prinia; site is undescribed. **DISTRIBUTION AND STATUS** Resident. Himalayas in Nepal? and from Sikkim east to Arunachal Pradesh; hills of NE India and Bangladesh; Simlipal hills, Orissa, and Andhra Pradesh. **NP:** possibly collected in 19th century, but the specimen may have originated in India. **IN:** locally fairly common; breeds in foothills up to 1200 m (Sikkim), mainly 500–1200 m (–1800 m) in NE hills. **BT:** common in the east; from 380 m up to at least 1220 m. **BD:** local.

GREY-BREASTED PRINIA *Prinia hodgsonii* — Plate 119

Franklin's Wren-Warbler (I), Franklin's Prinia (P), Hodgson's Prinia (F)

IDENTIFICATION 11 cm. A small, comparatively short-tailed prinia. **Adult breeding** is readily identified by uniform brownish-grey to slate-grey upperparts, including ear-coverts (lacking white supercilium), and grey breast-band contrasting with white of rest of underparts. Breast-band is often very poorly defined, however, especially on birds in N and NE subcontinent. **Adult non-breeding** (except *P. h. pectoralis*) has white supercilium and dark lores, and olive-brown upperparts with rufescent cast (especially to lower back, rump and edges of remiges); col-

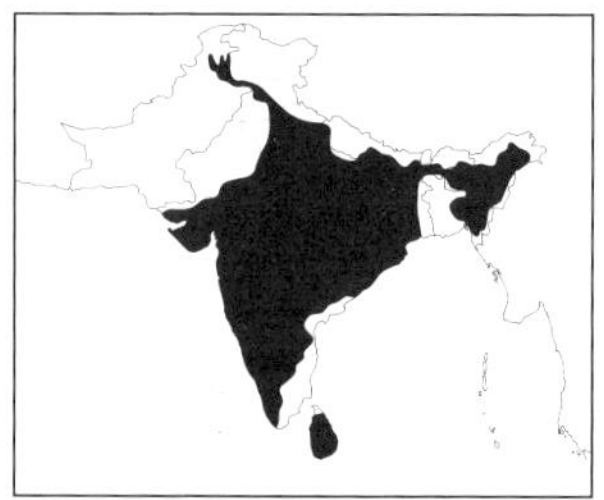

oration of underparts varies from being very white to being heavily sullied with grey on sides of breast and buff on lower belly and flanks. Closely resembles non-breeding Rufescent Prinia (p.705) where ranges overlap in NE subcontinent, and best distinguished by slimmer all-dark bill, grey-brown tail, and greyish wash to sides of neck and breast. **Juvenile** is much as non-breeding adult, but is said by some authors to have faint yellowish wash to underparts. **Racial variation** *P. h. pectoralis* of Sri Lanka has grey upperparts and breast throughout year, although the breast-band is incomplete on female. **VOICE** Call is a laughing, high-pitched *hee-hee-hee-hee*; song is a rhythmic, undulating *tirr-irr-irr-irr* (Boonsong and Round 1991). **HABITS** Gregarious in winter, when in flocks of up to 20 birds. Always on the move; creeps about in bushes and runs about like a mouse at their base. **HABITAT** Bushes in clearings and at forest edges, bushes around cultivation and villages; thorn scrub and dry deciduous scrub forest in Pakistan. **BREEDING** March–October, varying locally. Builds a rough cup-shaped nest of grass and fibres within 0.5 m of ground inside a broad hanging leaf, the edges of which are sewn together to form a cone. **DISTRIBUTION AND STATUS** Resident, with some local movements. N Pakistan and most of the rest of subcontinent, except parts of the northwest, northeast, southeast and Himalayas. **PK:** locally common in the north; mainly up to 1200 m in summer and down to 450 m in winter. **NP:** widespread and common below 400 m, frequent up to 1200 m, locally to 1750 m. **IN:** widespread and common; from base of the hills up to 1600 m in Himalayas, to 1500 m in peninsular hills. **BT:** locally fairly common. **BD:** common. **LK:** common in dry lowlands and adjacent foothills in east and southeast, rarely in wet zone.

GRACEFUL PRINIA *Prinia gracilis* — Plate 120

Streaked Wren-Warbler (I), Graceful Stripe-backed Prinia (R), Fulvous-streaked Prinia (F)

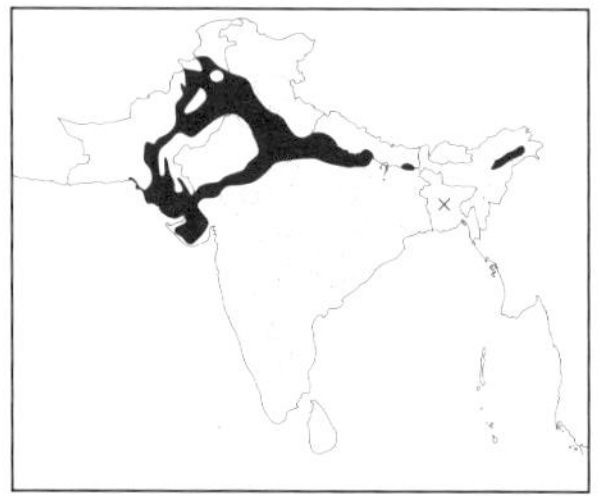

IDENTIFICATION 11 cm. A small prinia with streaked sandy grey-brown upperparts and white underparts, with buffish wash on flanks. Distinguished from all other prinias, except the much larger Striated and Rufous-vented (p.703), by dark streaking on crown and mantle. Is considerably smaller and has much finer bill than Striated and Rufous-vented, with paler sandy coloration to upperparts and whiter underparts. In the W subcontinent, possibly confusable with Streaked Scrub Warbler (p.702); see that species for main differences. **Racial variation** *P. g. stevensi* of the plains of the Brahmaputra and lower Ganges has darker and greyer upperparts and duller greyish-white underparts compared with the more widely distributed *P. g. lepida*. This race is very similar in coloration to the *cinerascens* race of Rufous-vented, but is considerably smaller, has a slimmer tail, and has prominent pale fringes to wing-coverts and remiges. **VOICE** Call is a nasal, buzzing *bzreep*; song is a fast, rhythmic wheezy warble, *ze-r witze-r wit* (Inskipp and Inskipp 1991). **HABITS** Found in pairs or small parties, depending on the season. Quite tame. Often perches on tops of bushes and reeds. Feeds actively in bushes, in grass and on the ground. **HABITAT** Tall grass, tamarisks and scrub, especially by rivers, canals, lakes, marshes and irrigation channels, and paddy-fields. **BREEDING** February–October. Nest is a dome or oval pouch made of dry grass, built in a bush or grass clump within 1 m of ground. **DISTRIBUTION AND STATUS** Resident. C Pakistan, parts of NW, N and NE India, S Nepal and Bangladesh. **PK:** common and very widespread. **NP:** very local and fairly common. **IN:** locally fairly common in the plains. **BD:** ?former resident; no recent records.

JUNGLE PRINIA *Prinia sylvatica* — Plate 120

Jungle Wren-Warbler (I), Large Prinia (P)

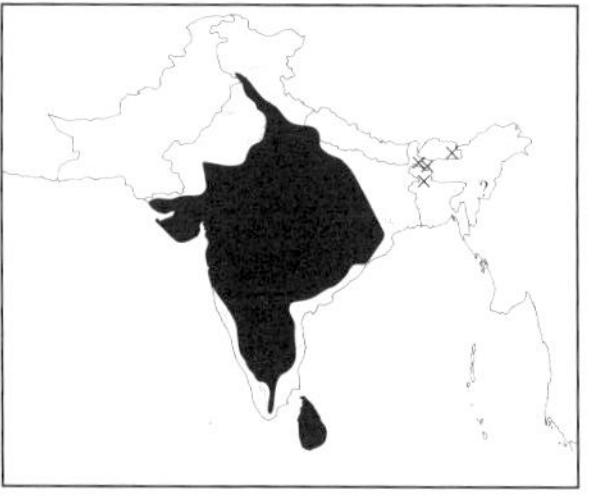

IDENTIFICATION 13 cm. Resembles Plain Prinia (p.708), although is usually noticeably larger-bodied and has stouter bill. Call and song are very different. There is much variation in size and in 'stoutness' of bill, with some birds differing only marginally from Plain. The tail does not look so proportionately long and so 'loosely attached' as on Plain. Given the variation in this and Plain Prinia across the subcontinent, however, caution is needed in applying identification features mentioned herein. **Adult breeding** has dark grey-brown upperparts and buffish-white underparts, and can show much white in outer rectrices. Tail is shorter than in non-breeding plumage, and bill is black. Tends to be a darker grey-brown on the upperparts than breeding Plain (although Plain from NE and S subcontinent are similar in coloration), supercilium does not usually extend beyond eye (or can be entirely absent, with dark lores), and lacks pale fringes to tertials and wing-coverts. **Adult non-breeding** is similar to adult breeding, but upperparts, especially crown and nape, are more rufescent-brown, has buffish or greyish-white lores and/or supercilium and pale orange-brown lower mandible, and white in outer rectrices is restricted to tips. Compared with adult non-breeding Plain, has darker brown upperparts and has more uniform wings (lacking prominent rufous edges to tertials). Can appear quite rufescent on forehead/crown, giving rise to possible confusion with Rufous-fronted; told from that species by habits, larger size and stouter bill, darker brown upperparts and buffish underparts, and lack of broad white tips to tail. **Juvenile** has paler, more olive-brown upperparts, with more rufescent edges to tertials, and can have yellowish wash to supercilium and underparts. **Racial variation** In Sri Lanka (*P. s. valida*), there is no difference between breeding and non-breeding plumages; birds have darker and greyer upperparts compared with the nominate race, as well as longer and stouter bill, and also lack a supercilium (at best, some show suggestion of supercilium in front of eye). Larger size and stouter bill, lack of supercilium above and behind eye, and more uniform wings are best distinctions from the Sri Lankan race of Plain. **VOICE** Loud pulsing song, *zee-chu*, repeated metronomically; calls include a sputtering dry rattle and a Common Tailorbird-like whistled *tiu* (P. Holt). **HABITS** Found in pairs in the breeding season; otherwise in small parties, often with Grey-breasted Prinia. Rather less active than the small prinias. Flits about bushes and grass; occasionally pops to the top of vegetation and then dives down again. Sings from an exposed perch. **HABITAT** Scrub and tall grass in open dry, stony, uncultivated areas with scattered bushes. **BREEDING** Throughout the year, varying locally. Nest is an untidy spherical or oval ball made of grass, built in a low bush or grass clump. **DISTRIBUTION AND STATUS** Resident, endemic to the subcontinent. Most of India except parts of the northwest, north and northeast; W Nepal, Bhutan, Bangladesh, and Sri Lanka. **NP:** frequent in the far west. **IN:** locally fairly common; plains and foothills up to 1000 m in the north, to 1500 m in the peninsula. **BT:** rare. **BD:** ?former resident in the northwest; no recent records. **LK:** rare in lowlands and medium hills.

YELLOW-BELLIED PRINIA *Prinia flaviventris* — Plate 120

Yellow-bellied Wren-Warbler (I)

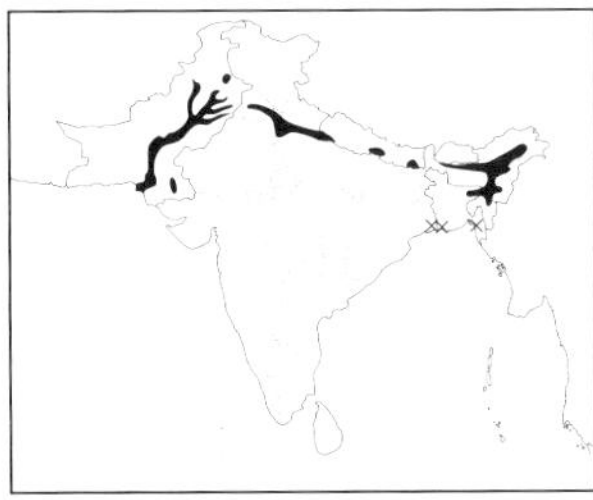

IDENTIFICATION 13 cm. A dainty prinia with greenish upperparts and yellow on underparts. **Adult** has fine white supercilium (sometimes lacking), white throat and breast, slate-grey forecrown and ear-coverts, dark olive-green upperparts, and yellowish belly and vent with orange-buff thighs. **Juvenile** has yellowish olive-brown upperparts (lacking blue-grey on head), and uniform pale yellow underparts. **Racial variation** Birds in NW subcontinent (*P. f. sindhiana*) are paler yellow on belly and flanks compared with those in NE subcontinent (*P. f. flaviventris*); on some, yellow is almost entirely lacking, and reduced to yellowish-buff flanks. **VOICE** Call is an incessant *chink-chink*; song is a sharp *chirp* followed by a trill of five notes. **HABITS** Solitary, or a few scattered in the same area. Very active; forages in tall grass, occasionally clambering to the top to look around; sometimes feeds on the ground. Not shy. **HABITAT** Tall grassland or tamarisks along rivers, and near lakes and marshes. **BREEDING** April–October. Builds an oval nest of fine grass, fixed to grass stems or placed in a bush, 0.5–1.5 m above ground. **DISTRIBUTION AND STATUS** Local resident. C Pakistan, N and NE India, S Nepal and Bangladesh. **PK:** locally common and widespread along the Indus R system, also around major canal systems. **NP:** local and fairly common. **IN:** local and fairly common; plains and foothills to 800 m, locally to 1200 m in the east. **BT:** rare; recorded only in 19th century. **BD:** rare resident.

ASHY PRINIA *Prinia socialis* — Plate 120

Ashy Wren-Warbler (I)

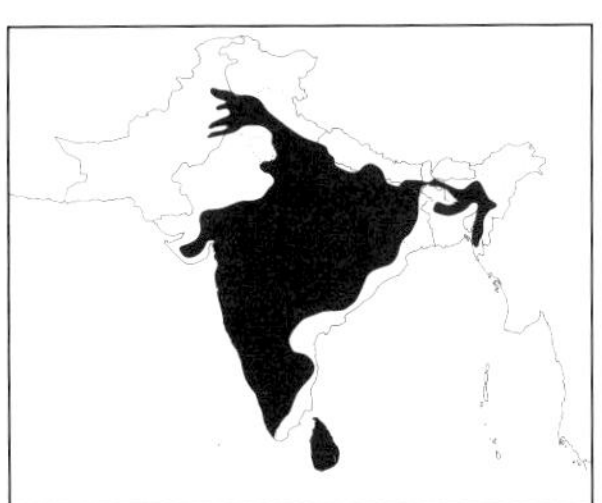

IDENTIFICATION 13 cm. **Adult** readily told from other prinias by combination of white supercilium (sometimes lacking), contrasting with slate-grey crown and ear-coverts, deep red eye, slate-grey (in breeding plumage) or rufous-brown (in non-breeding plumage) mantle, rufous-brown wings and tail, orange-buff wash on underparts (especially strong on flanks), and prominent black subterminal marks (and whitish tips) to tail feathers. Possibly confusable with Grey-crowned Prinia (p.704), but is larger, with longer tail, and has white (rather than orange-buff) supercilium in front of eye. **Juvenile** has greenish upperparts and buffish-yellow wash on underparts; has slightly darker ear-coverts, and short supercilium in front of eye. Wings and tail are rufous, latter with dark subterminal band on upperside and dark subterminal tips on underside, and these features help separate it from juvenile Yellow-bellied Prinia (above). **Racial variation** *P. s. inglisi* of the NE subcontinent and *P. s. brevicauda* from Sri Lanka differ from birds in the rest of the region in having slate-grey upperparts throughout the year. The latter race also has a much shorter tail, whiter underparts and brown iris, and juvenile has olive cast to upperparts. Blue-grey cast to upperparts and buff wash to underparts (and lack of grey breast-band) would help separate the Sri Lankan race from Grey-breasted (p.705). **VOICE** Call is a sharp nasal *near-near-near*; song is a wheezy *jimmy-jimmy-jimmy*. **HABITS** A typical small prinia. Very lively and quite tame. Non-gregarious; keeps in pairs in the breeding season and is otherwise solitary. Forages low down in grasses and bushes and on the ground. **HABITAT** Tall grass and scrub at the edges of cultivation and deciduous forest, open secondary growth, gardens, reedbeds along rivers and mangroves; also long grass or scrub in Sri Lanka, and canalside groves and irrigated forest plantations in Pakistan. **BREEDING** Throughout the year, varying locally. Nest is either a cup built in one or more leaves sewn together, or an oblong purse made of grass and fibres supported by and woven through grass stems, or a ball of grass supported by weed and grass stems. **DISTRIBUTION AND STATUS** Resident, endemic to the subcontinent. N Pakistan, and most of India except parts of the northwest, northeast and east; S Nepal, Bangladesh and Sri Lanka. **PK:** common in N Punjab plains. **NP:** widespread and fairly common below 305 m. **IN:** widespread and common; in plains and hills up to 1200 m in the north, to the summits in the peninsula. **BD:** local. **LK:** common and widespread.

PLAIN PRINIA *Prinia inornata* — Plate 120

Plain Wren-Warbler (I), White-browed Prinia (P), *P. subflava* (F,I,K)

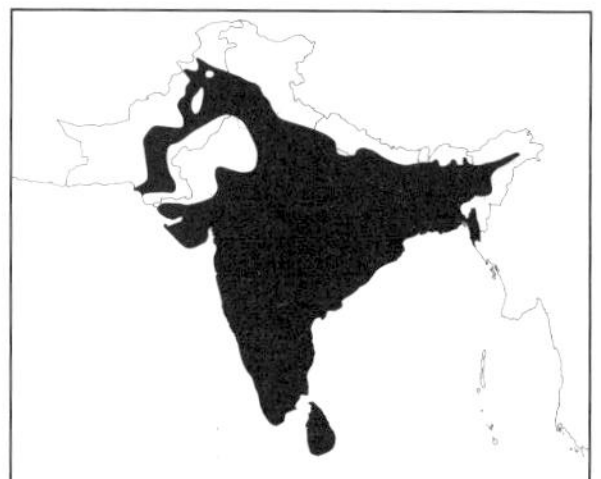

IDENTIFICATION 13 cm. Resembles Jungle Prinia (p.706), although is noticeably smaller-bodied, appears proportionately longer-tailed, and has finer bill. Song and calls are very different. Compared with Jungle, generally has more prominent supercilium which extends noticeably beyond eye (although, on some Jungle, supercilium can similarly extend beyond eye), and tends to have more distinct edges to wing feathers (especially apparent on tertials). In all plumages, told from Rufous-fronted (p.705) by brown or grey crown concolorous with nape and mantle (although some Plain can appear to have more rufescent crown), and lack of broad white tips to tail feathers (which are very prominent on Rufous-fronted, especially in flight). See those two species for further differences and cautionary remarks. **Adult breeding** has black bill, pale grey-brown upperparts and whitish underparts, with much white on outermost rectrices. Wing-coverts and tertials can be prominently fringed with greyish-white, and underparts usually have at least a faint buffish wash. **Adult non-breeding** is different from adult breeding, with longer tail (as on most prinias), warm brown upperparts, rufous fringes to feathers of wings and tail, buff tips and dark subterminal marks to rectrices, and warm buff wash to underparts, especially flanks; bill is brown, with yellowish base to lower mandible. **Juvenile** is more rufescent than adult breeding, although has similar-length tail. **Racial variation** Birds in the northeast (*P. i. fusca*) differ from the widely distributed nominate race, described above, in having darker, browner upperparts in breeding plumage and more rufescent-brown upperparts and warmer rufous-buff underparts in non-breeding plumage. Those in SW India (*P. i. franklinii*) and Sri Lanka (*P. i. insularis*) have darker and greyer upperparts (with little difference between breeding and non-breeding plumages), and latter race has larger bill. **VOICE** Calls include a plaintive *tee-tee-tee* and a nasal *beep*; song is a rapid wheezy trill, *tlick tlick tlick* (Inskipp and Inskipp 1991). **HABITS** A typical small prinia. Keeps in pairs or small parties, depending on the season. Feeds actively in low vegetation and is quite tame. **HABITAT** Tall crops, paddy-fields, reeds and tamarisks in marshy areas around canals, rivers, marshes, scrub mixed with tall grass, grassland, mixed bamboo and scrub jungle, mangroves and saltmarshes. **BREEDING** Throughout the year, varying locally. Nest is variable, often a pear-shaped pouch of grass, sometimes open at the top, attached to several upright grass stems, up to 1 m above ground; sometimes the nest is supported by two or more broad leaves stitched together, usually in a grass tussock or bush. **DISTRIBUTION AND STATUS** Resident throughout most of the subcontinent, except parts of the northwest, northeast and Himalayas. **PK:** common and widespread throughout the Indus plains; locally moves into adjacent foothills in summer. **NP:** frequent throughout; below 305 m. **IN:** widespread and fairly common; plains and hills up to 1200 m in the north, to 1800 m in the southwest. **BT:** rare. **BD:** local. **LK:** common throughout, except higher hills.

WHITE-EYES Zosteropidae

Small or very small passerines with a slightly decurved and pointed bill, a brush-tipped tongue, and a white ring around each eye. White-eyes frequent forest, forest edge, and bushes in gardens.

SRI LANKA WHITE-EYE *Zosterops ceylonensis* — Plate 120

Ceylon White-eye (I), Ceylon Hill White-eye (P)

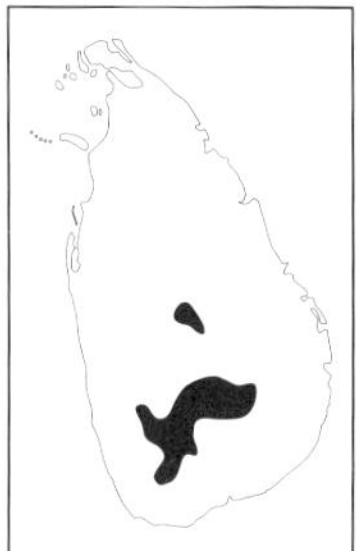

IDENTIFICATION 11 cm. Told from Oriental White-eye (p.709) by slightly larger size and longer bill, duller green upperparts (lacking bright yellow forehead), poorly defined greyish lores, with grey extending diffusely onto ear-coverts and sides of throat, and duller olive-yellow throat and breast. **VOICE** Call, constantly uttered, is a reedy *chirp*, very like that of Oriental White-eye but stronger and deeper in tone; has a jingling song, suggestive of shaking a bunch of keys repeatedly eight or nine times (Henry 1971). **HABITS** Similar to those of Oriental White-eye. Keeps in flocks of 10–15 birds, often with other species, in the non-breeding season. Favours the canopy. **HABITAT** Forest; also gardens and plantations close to natural forest. **BREEDING** March–September. Nest is similar to that of Oriental White-eye, often in a low tree or shrub growing in the open. **DISTRIBUTION AND STATUS LK:** common endemic resident in wet lowlands and hills, mainly above 1000 m.

ORIENTAL WHITE-EYE *Zosterops palpebrosus* — Plate 120

White-eye (F,I,P), Small White-eye

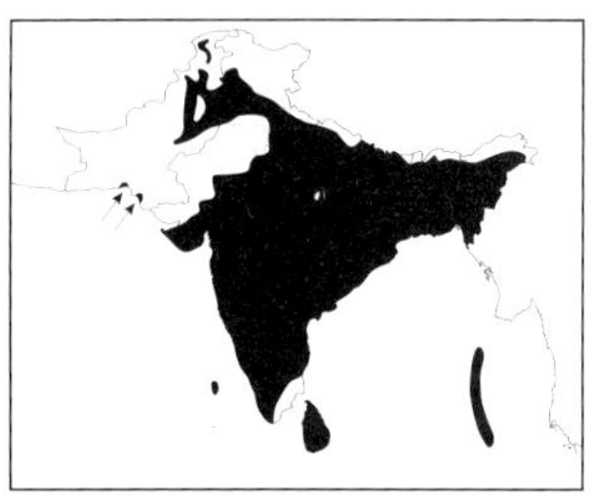

IDENTIFICATION 10 cm. Distinctive, with prominent white eye-ring, black bill and lores, green to yellowish-green upperparts, bright yellow throat and vent, and whitish rest of underparts with variable greyish wash. In Sri Lanka, is confusable with Sri Lanka White-eye (p.708); for differences, see that species. **VOICE** Very vocal, especially when in flocks. Call is plaintive *cheer* or *prree-u*; song is a tinkling jingle (Ali and Ripley 1987). **HABITS** Outside the breeding season, keeps in flocks of up to 50 birds which continually utter plaintive contact calls. Arboreal; favours flowering shrubs and trees. Forages actively among the foliage and flowers for insects, caterpillars, berries, seeds and nectar, often clinging upside-down. **HABITAT** Open broadleaved forest, groves, gardens, orchards, mangroves; also sholas and cardamom plantations in S India. **BREEDING** February–September, varying locally. Nest is a small cup slung like a hammock at the end of a branch, 1–6 m above ground. **DISTRIBUTION AND STATUS** Resident, with some altitudinal movements. Throughout most of the subcontinent, except parts of the northwest and Himalayas. **PK:** common and widespread in Punjab plains and NW Pakistan. **NP:** widespread and common resident below 1370 m, summers up to 2440 m. **IN:** widespread and generally common; plains and hills, up to 2100 m (–2700 m) in breeding season in Himalayas, to the summits in SW hills. **BT:** common; 245–2400 m. **BD:** locally common throughout. **LK:** common in lowlands and hills.

WARBLERS, GRASSBIRDS, LAUGHINGTHRUSHES AND BABBLERS Sylviidae

A huge and varied family of mostly small species, many brightly coloured but others rather drab. It is represented in the subcontinent by four subfamilies, one of which is further divided into two tribes.

WARBLERS Subfamily Acrocephalinae

A large group of small, active perching birds with a fine pointed bill. Their plumage colours are generally unobtrusive browns, greens, greys and yellows. Insects and spiders form their main diet; some species also consume berries, seeds and nectar. They usually capture their prey by gleaning from foliage, but sometimes also from the ground. Warblers inhabit all types of vegetation, often in dense habitats. Many species are under-recorded in the subcontinent.

TESIAS Tiny, active, almost tailless warblers inhabiting forest. Mainly terrestrial.

CHESTNUT-HEADED TESIA *Tesia castaneocoronata* — Plate 120

Chestnut-headed Ground Warbler (F,I)

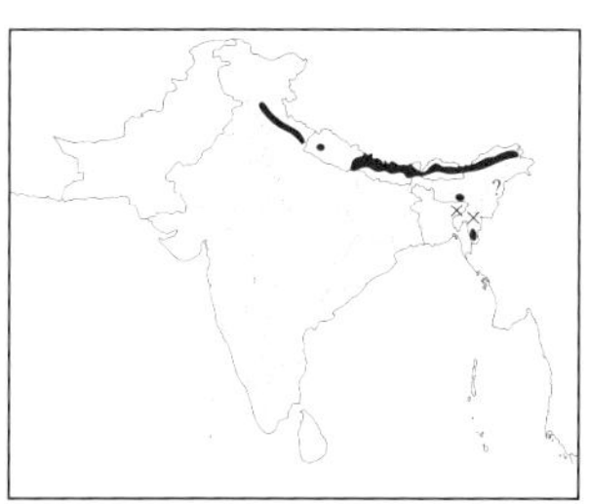

IDENTIFICATION 8 cm. Very small, and resembling a wren babbler in shape. **Adult** has bright chestnut 'hood' (crown, nape and ear-coverts), prominent white crescent behind eye, dark olive-green mantle and wings, and bright yellow underparts with olive-green sides of breast and flanks. **Juvenile** is very different, having dark olive upperparts with brownish cast (lacking chestnut head of adult), and dark rufous underparts. **VOICE** Has a loud and explosive *cheep-cheeu-chewit* song (S. Buckton); calls include a sharp, explosive *whit* or a high-pitched *pseet* (J. Scharringa). **HABITS** Usually found singly or in pairs. Skulks among forest undergrowth, usually within 1 m of the ground; singing males sometimes briefly emerge from cover. Active and inquisitive; bobs up and down when excited. Eats insects and spiders. Has a weak flight, and is very loath to fly. **HABITAT** Thick undergrowth of ferns, nettles and bamboo in broadleaved and mixed broadleaved–coniferous forest; favours damp forest ravines and streamsides. **BREEDING** April–July. Nest is a ball of moss suspended from a small branch, within 2 m of ground. **DISTRIBUTION AND STATUS** Altitudinal migrant. Himalayas from W Himachal Pradesh east to Arunachal Pradesh; NE Indian hills. **NP:** fairly common and widespread in the centre and east, rare in the west; summers 2135–4000 m, winters mainly 800–1830 m (down to 250 m). **IN:** fairly common; breeds 1800–3355 m, mainly above 2400 m, winters from 1800 m down to the foothills. **BT:** common; from 245 m up to at least 3770 m. **BD:** vagrant.

SLATY-BELLIED TESIA *Tesia olivea* — Plate 120

Slaty-bellied Ground Warbler (I)

IDENTIFICATION 9 cm. Very similar to Grey-bellied Tesia (p.710) in coloration, with olive-green upperparts and grey underparts. **Adult** is best told from adult Grey-bellied by uniform dark slate-grey underparts, and yellowish-

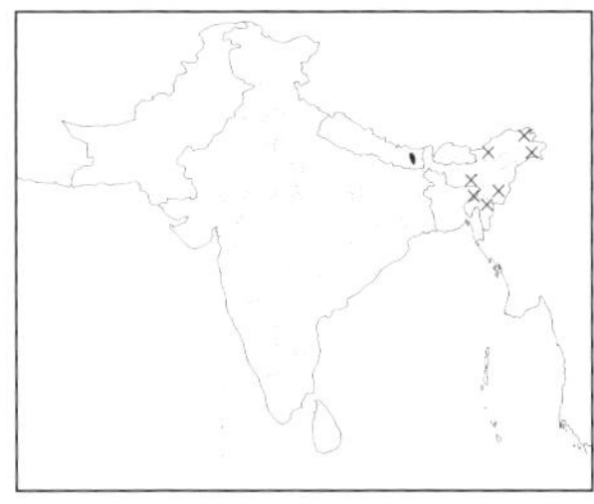

green crown which is distinctly brighter than mantle (although some birds have duller and less contrasting crown, and may show suggestion of brighter supercilium). Additional features are less prominent black stripe behind eye, and finer bill with brighter orange or orange-red lower mandible which lacks dark tip. Song is also different. **Juvenile** is said to be similar to juvenile Grey-bellied, but with darker olive-green underparts. **VOICE** Song is four to six measured whistles followed by sudden explosive, tuneless jumble of notes; calls include a sharp *tchirik* (Ali and Ripley 1987; Boonsong and Round 1991). **HABITS** Similar to those of Chestnut-headed Tesia (p.709), but even more active and skulking and keeping closer to the ground. Always on the move, but frequently hardly stirs the vegetation as it hops about. **HABITAT** Thick low undergrowth of ferns and nettles in dense moist tropical and subtropical forest; favours evergreen biotope. **BREEDING** Unknown, or confused with Grey-bellied Tesia. **DISTRIBUTION AND STATUS** Resident, subject to altitudinal movements. Himalayas from E Nepal east to Arunachal Pradesh; NE Indian hills. **NP:** rare, probably resident; recorded only in the Arun valley, 1000–1700 m, in August and September. **IN:** locally fairly common; winters 150–1000 m; 1500–1800 m in April. **BT:** generally uncommon, locally frequent; 1400–1960 m in April and May, down to 245 m in winter. **BD:** vagrant. **REFERENCES** Inskipp and Inskipp (1996).

GREY-BELLIED TESIA *Tesia cyaniventer* — Plate 120

Dull Slaty-bellied Ground Warbler (I), Slaty-bellied Ground Warbler (F)

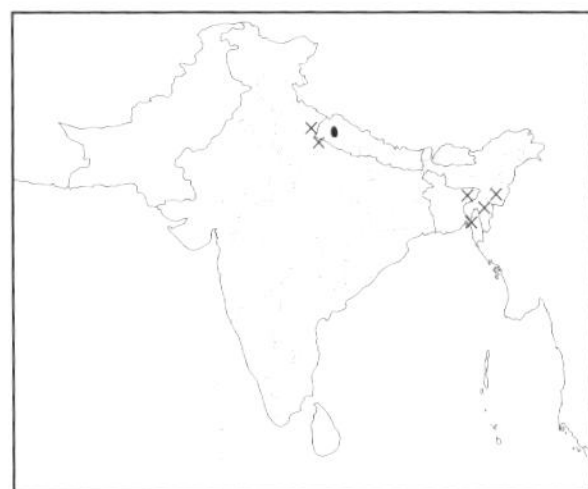

IDENTIFICATION 9 cm. Very similar to Slaty-bellied Tesia (p.709) in coloration, with bright olive-green upperparts and grey underparts. **Adult** is best told from that species by paler grey underparts, becoming almost whitish on throat and centre of belly, and by concolorous olive-green crown and mantle, with brighter lime-green supercilium. Further, has more prominent black stripe behind eye, and stouter bill with dark tip and yellow basal two-thirds to lower mandible. Song is also different. **Juvenile** has dark olive-brown upperparts and olive cast to grey of underparts; like adult, has brighter green supercilium and dark eye-stripe. **VOICE** Call is a loud and rattling *trrrrrk;* song is much slower than that of Slaty-bellied, and lacks its explosive, tuneless jumble of notes (R. Drijvers; Boonsong and Round 1991). **HABITS** Very similar to those of Slaty-bellied Tesia. **HABITAT** Summers in thick undergrowth of ferns, nettles and dwarf bamboo near small streams or moist ravines in dense broadleaved forest; winters in shady broadleaved forest and secondary growth. **BREEDING** May–July. Nest is a ball of moss built in a bush among creepers, or among moss against a tree trunk, c. 0.3 m above ground. **DISTRIBUTION AND STATUS** Resident, subject to altitudinal movements. Himalayas from N Uttar Pradesh east to Arunachal Pradesh; hills of NE India and Bangladesh. Breeds 1500–2550 m, mainly above 1800 m; winters from 1800 m down to the foothills (down to 75 m in Nepal). **NP:** frequent resident in the centre and east, uncommon in the west. **IN:** locally fairly common resident. **BT:** frequent resident. **BD:** local winter visitor.

BUSH WARBLERS Medium-sized warblers with dull brownish plumage and rounded wings and tail which inhabit marshes, grassland and forest undergrowth. They are usually found singly. Most species are probably under-recorded, as they are very skulking in the non-breeding season, although less so when breeding. They call frequently, and are usually heard more often than seen. *Cettia* species have surprisingly loud voices, and some can be identified by their distinctive melodious songs. Typically, bush warblers seek insects and spiders by actively flitting and hopping about in vegetation close to the ground. They are reluctant to fly, and usually cover only short distances at low level before dropping into dense cover again. When excited, they flick their wings and tail.

ASIAN STUBTAIL *Urosphena squameiceps* — Plate 121

Stub-tailed Bush-Warbler (K), *Cettia squameiceps* (K)

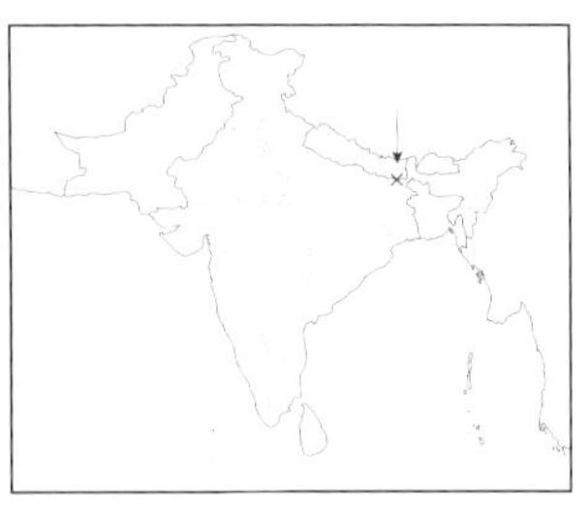

IDENTIFICATION 11 cm. Told from all other bush warblers by very short, rounded tail. Otherwise, is similar to Pale-footed Bush Warbler (p.711), but has more rufescent upperparts and longer and more prominent buffish supercilium and brownish-black eye-stripe (which almost reach hind-crown). Has gleaming white underparts, long, pale pinkish legs, and large feet. Has dark scaling on slightly brighter chestnut crown (usually difficult to see in the field), and brown mottling on ear-coverts and sides of throat. **VOICE** Call is a sharp *stit* (Boonsong and Round 1991). **HABITS** Feeds on the ground or among low vegetation in forest. Hops jerkily about on long flexed legs in characteristic bush warbler fashion. Not shy. **HABITAT** Tropical broadleaved forest. **DISTRIBUTION AND STATUS NP:** vagrant. **REFERENCES** Lewis (1994a).

PALE-FOOTED BUSH WARBLER *Cettia pallidipes* Plate 121

Blanford's Bush Warbler (F)

IDENTIFICATION 11 cm. Distinguished from Brownish-flanked Bush Warbler (below) by whiter throat, centre of breast and belly (contrasting more strongly with brownish-olive breast sides and flanks), shorter, square-ended tail, pale pinkish legs and feet, and different song and call. Upperparts are slightly more rufescent (especially compared with W Himalayan race of Brownish-flanked), and pale buff supercilium and dark brown eye-stripe are more prominent. Possibly confusable with Dusky Warbler (p.726); the very pale legs and feet of Pale-footed, as well as its shorter tail, more rounded wings with very short primary projection beyond closed tertials, and different call-note, are best features for separation. For differences from Cetti's Bush Warbler (p.713), see that species. **Racial variation** *C. p. osmastoni* of the Andaman Is has darker, richer brown upperparts and warmer buff breast sides and flanks compared with the nominate race, described above. **VOICE** Song is a loud, explosive *zip..zip-tschuk-o-tschuk*; call is a *chik-chik* or *chip-chip*. **HABITS** A typical bush warbler. **HABITAT** Tall grasses and bushes at forest edges and clearings. **BREEDING** May–July. Nest is a ball of grass placed in bushes, or a cup of bamboo leaves supported by plant stems near the ground. **DISTRIBUTION AND STATUS** Local resident. Mainly the Himalayas from N Uttar Pradesh east to Arunachal Pradesh; NE India and S Andaman Is. **NP:** local, fairly common at Chitwan, mainly single records from elsewhere; chiefly below 250 m (–1830 m). **IN:** uncommon; breeds 1000–1500 m, winters in foothills and adjacent plains. **BT:** uncommon; 1370–1830 m (–2255 m). **REFERENCES** Melville *et al.* (1991).

JAPANESE BUSH WARBLER *Cettia diphone* Plate 121

Chinese Bush Warbler (I), *C. diphone* (I)

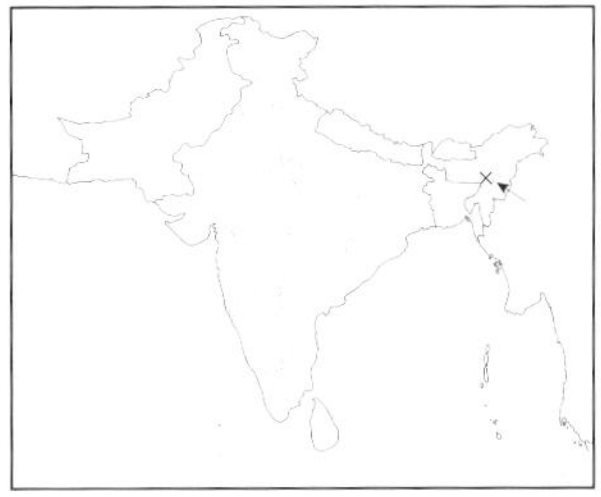

IDENTIFICATION Male 18 cm; female 15 cm. Male, which is considerably bigger than female, is the largest of all bush warblers recorded in the subcontinent (approaching Thick-billed Warbler, p.720, in size). Both sexes have olive-brown upperparts with rufous-brown forehead and forecrown, prominent whitish supercilium which is buffier in front of eye, large, stout bill, strong buff or olive-buff wash to underparts, with whiter belly, and rufous edges to remiges. Long tail is slightly notched, and usually held slightly cocked. Above-mentioned features, especially rufous crown and coloration of underparts, would help separate it from Cetti's Bush Warbler (p.713), although range and habitat are very different. **VOICE** Has a short song, usually introduced by a slurred liquid note, which rises in volume (similar to that of Brownish-flanked, below), culminating in a louder, short fluty warble: *wrrrrrr-whuchiuchi* etc. Call is a stony *tchet...tchet...tchet...* etc, sometimes interspersed with short rattling *trrrt* notes. (C. Robson) **HABITS** A typical bush warbler. **HABITAT** Scrub jungle and low bushes at forest edges. **DISTRIBUTION AND STATUS IN:** vagrant.

BROWNISH-FLANKED BUSH WARBLER *Cettia fortipes* Plate 121

Strong-footed Bush Warbler (F,I,R), Brown-flanked Bush Warbler (N), *C. montana* (I)

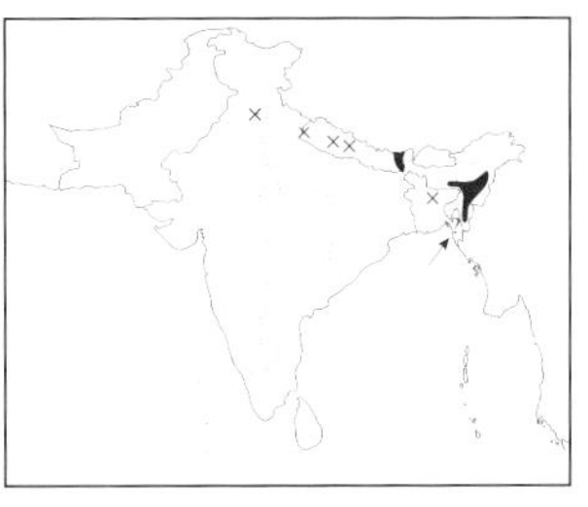

IDENTIFICATION 12 cm. Told from Pale-footed Bush Warbler (above) by duskier underparts, which are mainly pale buffish-grey with brownish-olive flanks and show only a small area of off-white on belly, giving less contrast between upperparts and underparts. Additional features are longer, rounded tail, brownish legs and feet, more olive coloration to upperparts, less prominent supercilium and more diffuse dark stripe through eye, and different song and call. **Racial variation** Compared with *C. f. pallidus* of the W Himalayas, *C. f. fortipes* of the E Himalayas and NE subcontinent has warmer, more rufous-brown upperparts, brownish-buff (rather than buffish-grey) coloration to throat and breast, stronger olive-buff flanks, and buffish (rather than greyish-white supercilium); upperparts of *C. f. fortipes* are closer in coloration to those of Pale-footed. Some (first-year?) *fortipes* have olive cast to upperparts and yellow wash on belly, when underparts are not dissimilar to those of some Yellowish-bellied (p.712), although Brownish-flanked is considerably larger and has more olive coloration to upperparts; such birds are easily confusable with dull Aberrant Bush Warbler (p.712), but that species is more uniform yellow below, and lacks strong buff tones to sides of breast and flanks. **VOICE** Song is a loud whistle, *weeee,* followed by an explosive *chiwiyou*; call of *C. f. pallidus* is a harsh *tchuk,* and that of *C. f. fortipes* is a *chuk* and a loud *tyit tyu-tyu* (Inskipp and Inskipp 1991). **HABITS** A typical bush warbler. **HABITAT** Open dry temperate forest, thickets in ravines, on hillsides and around ponds, bushes at the edges of cultivation, and tea gardens. **BREEDING** May–August. Nest is a deep purse or dome made of grass, built in dense low bushes or thick herbage within 0.5 m of ground. **DISTRIBUTION AND STATUS** Resident, subject to altitudinal movements. Himalayas from N Pakistan east to Arunachal Pradesh; NE Indian hills. **PK:** scarce to frequent resident; summers mainly 1200–1800 m, occasionally up to 2800 m, winters down to foothills and plains. **NP:** locally fairly common in far east, rare farther west; has uncertain seasonal movements, 1800–3200 m in summer, 1400–2135 m in December. **IN:** common; in the west, breeds from 1800 m up to at least 3000 m, winters from 1800 m down to foothills; in the east, breeds 2000–3300 m (Himalayas), 1200–2000 m (NE hills), winters from 2100 m down to the foothills and uncommonly in adjacent plains. **BT:** common; 305–3300 m. **BD:** vagrant.

CHESTNUT-CROWNED BUSH WARBLER *Cettia major* Plate 121

Large Bush Warbler (F,I)

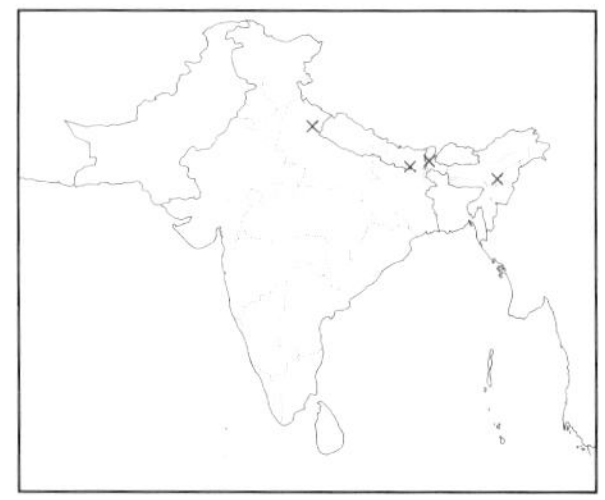

IDENTIFICATION 13 cm. Distinguished from other bush warblers (except Grey-sided, p.713) by combination of chestnut on forehead and crown, which often extends onto nape, dark brown upperparts, and whitish underparts with greyish-olive sides of breast and brownish-olive flanks. From Grey-sided by larger size and more robust appearance, larger bill, longer supercilium (which is indistinct and rufous-buff in front of eye, merging into chestnut of forehead, and buffish-white behind the eye), and whiter underparts, particularly throat and centre of breast. **Juvenile** lacks chestnut on crown, and has uniform dark olive-brown upperparts; has greyish-buff supercilium behind eye, dark greyish-olive breast sides and mottling on throat and centre of breast, and whitish belly with variable yellowish wash; gape and base of lower mandible are orange. Whiter throat and belly separate it from juvenile Grey-sided. **VOICE** Song comprises an introductory note followed by a three- or four-noted explosive warble; call is an explosive bunting-like *pseek*, very similar to call of Grey-sided Bush Warbler (J. Scharringa). **HABITS** A typical bush warbler. **HABITAT** Summers in rhododendron shrubberies, rhododendrons in fir forest, and thorny scrub at rhododendron forest edges near the treeline; winters in lowland reedbeds. **BREEDING** Poorly known. June. Nest is a ball made of grass, bamboo leaves and roots, built in a bush. **DISTRIBUTION AND STATUS** Altitudinal migrant. Locally in Himalayas from N Uttar Pradesh east to Arunachal Pradesh; NE Indian hills. **NP:** rare; breeds in C Himalayas, 3550–3680 m, winters very locally below 250 m. **IN:** status uncertain; in Himalayas, summers 3300–4000 m, but winter range is poorly known (recorded in the terai); in the NE hills, summers 1800 m. **BT:** uncommon; summers 3300–3900 m.

ABERRANT BUSH WARBLER *Cettia flavolivacea* Plate 121

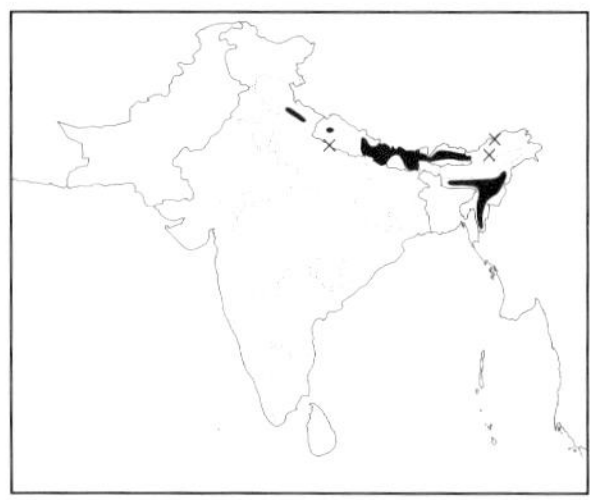

IDENTIFICATION 12 cm. Distinguished from other bush warblers by yellowish-green cast to olive upperparts, yellowish-white supercilium, and buffish-yellow to olive-yellow underparts which become darker olive on sides of breast and flanks. Intensity of yellow on underparts varies: a few (worn?) individuals have less yellow on throat and upper breast, are duller olive-yellow on rest of underparts, and also have a greyish-yellow supercilium, and such birds are possibly confusable with Yellowish-bellied Bush Warbler (below), but they have greenish cast to upperparts, including wings. See also remarks under Brownish-flanked Bush Warbler (p.711). Possibly confusable with Tickell's Leaf Warbler (p.726), but has longer, 'loosely attached' and rounded tail (with slight notch), usually held slightly cocked (with very short uppertail- and undertail-coverts), more rounded wings (with shorter primary projection), and distinctive, incessantly repeated, grating call accompanied by much wing-flicking. Underparts tend to be more olive-yellow, with strong olive-buff on breast sides and flanks. **Juvenile** is similar to adult, but has more uniform buffish-yellow underparts. **VOICE** Harsh grating alarm note (Ali and Ripley,1987). Call is similar to that of Yellowish-bellied, a soft, shivering *brrrt-brrrt* (J. Scharringa); also a sudden *chick*, softer than that of Grey-sided Bush Warbler (S. Madge). The song is a short sweet phrase consisting of a short warble followed by a long inflected whistle, *dir dir-tee teee-weee* (P. Morris). **HABITS** A typical bush warbler. **HABITAT** Bushes at forest edges and in clearings, scrub and long grass and bushes in pine forest. **BREEDING** May–August. Nest is a dome made of grass and bamboo leaves, built among grass clumps. **DISTRIBUTION AND STATUS** Resident, subject to altitudinal movements. Himalayas from N Uttar Pradesh east to Arunachal Pradesh; NE Indian hills. **NP:** common in the centre and east, rare in the west; summers mainly 2440–3950 m, winters 915–1830 m (down to 250 m). **IN:** fairly common; in Himalayas, breeds 2400–3600 m, winters 700–2700 m; in Meghalaya, summers from 1200 m to summits, winters down to the foothills; in other NE hills, recorded at 2900 m (summer) down to 1100 m (winter). **BT:** fairly common; from 3600 m down to at least 1220 m. **REFERENCES** Martens and Eck (1995).

YELLOWISH-BELLIED BUSH WARBLER *Cettia acanthizoides* Plate 121

Verreaux's Bush Warbler (I), Yellow-bellied Bush Warbler (N), Hume's Bush Warbler (F)

IDENTIFICATION 9.5 cm. Smallest of the bush warblers. Told from Pale-footed and Brownish-flanked Bush Warblers (p.711) by smaller and finer bill, paler rufous-brown upperparts with strong olive cast, especially to lower back and rump, noticeable rufous fringes to remiges (especially tertials), and paler underparts with yellowish belly and flanks. Yellow on underparts is sometimes much reduced, but underparts are always paler than on Brownish-

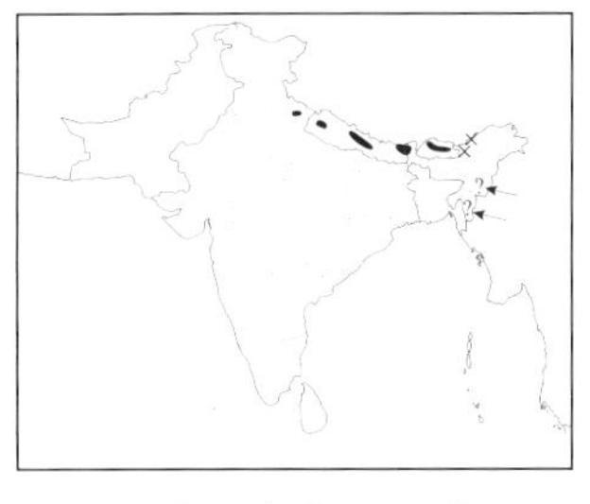

flanked, and lack any brownish-olive on flanks. Has paler legs and feet than Brownish-flanked. Possibly confusable with dull Aberrant Bush Warbler (p.712), but underparts are whiter and upperparts (especially crown, nape and wings) are pale rufous-brown (lacking strong greenish coloration of Aberrant). **VOICE** Typical song is an amazing series of four very thin, high-pitched notes, *see-saw see-saw see-saw* etc; variations of this song are given. Call is a typical *chrrt chrrt chrrt* (P. Morris). **HABITS** A typical bush warbler. **HABITAT** Mainly bamboo thickets, either pure stands or in forest. **BREEDING** May and June. Nest is a dome or a very deep cup made of grass and bamboo leaves, built low down in bushes. **DISTRIBUTION AND STATUS** Local resident, subject to poorly known altitudinal movements. Himalayas from N Uttar Pradesh east to Arunachal Pradesh; NE India. **NP:** scarce and local; 2000–3660 m in spring and summer. **IN:** scarce and local; summers 2400–3300 m, one winter record at 1350 m. **BT:** frequent; 2700–3400 m.

GREY-SIDED BUSH WARBLER *Cettia brunnifrons* Plate 121

Rufous-capped Bush Warbler (F,I)

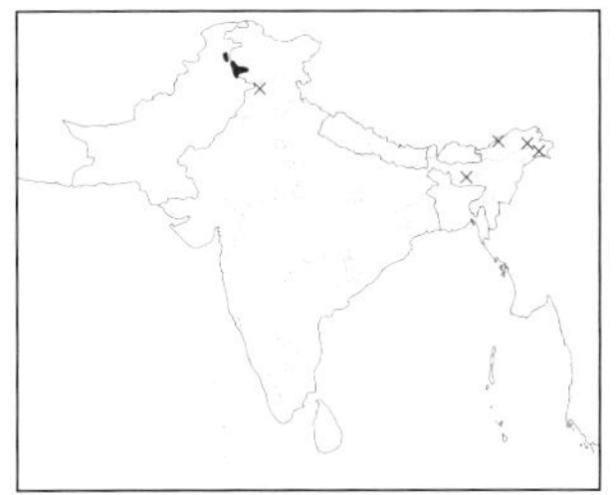

IDENTIFICATION 10 cm. Separated from other bush warblers (except Chestnut-crowned, p.712) by chestnut forehead and crown, and whitish underparts with grey sides of breast and brownish-olive flanks. From Chestnut-crowned by much smaller size and daintier appearance, smaller bill, shorter supercilium, which is well defined in front of eye and is entirely whitish-buff, and greyer underparts, with much less white on throat and belly than Chestnut-crowned. **Juvenile** lacks chestnut crown, and has uniform rufous-brown upperparts; supercilium is pale brown and less distinct, and has brownish-olive underparts, becoming more yellowish-olive on belly. Coloration of underparts separates it from juvenile Chestnut-crowned. **VOICE** Song is a loud wheezing *sip ti ti sip*, repeated continually, which is accompanied by curious nasal notes repeated twice immediately after the song; call is a bunting-like *pseek* (J. Scharringa). **HABITS** Similar to those of other bush warblers, but less skulking in the breeding season; males will emerge from cover to sing on top of a bush or rock. Quite tame. Feeds chiefly in bushes and low vegetation, sometimes also on the ground. **HABITAT** Summers in shrubberies above the treeline and bushes at forest edges and in clearings; winters in tall grass, on bush-covered hillsides, and in undergrowth in open forest and tea gardens. **BREEDING** April–August. Nest is a dome made of grass, moss and lichen, built c. 0.5 m above ground in a bush. **DISTRIBUTION AND STATUS** Altitudinal migrant. Breeds in Himalayas in N Pakistan (Neelum and Kagan valleys) and from Himachal Pradesh east to Arunachal Pradesh; winters down to the foothills and NE Indian plains. In W Himalayas, breeds 2900–3600 m, winters chiefly 1000–2100 m; in E Himalayas, breeds 2700–4000 m (–4115 m in Bhutan), winters from 2200 m down to the foothills (down to 75 m in Nepal). **PK:** very local. **NP:** common and widespread. **IN, BT:** common.

CETTI'S BUSH WARBLER *Cettia cetti* Plate 121

Cetti's Warbler (I)

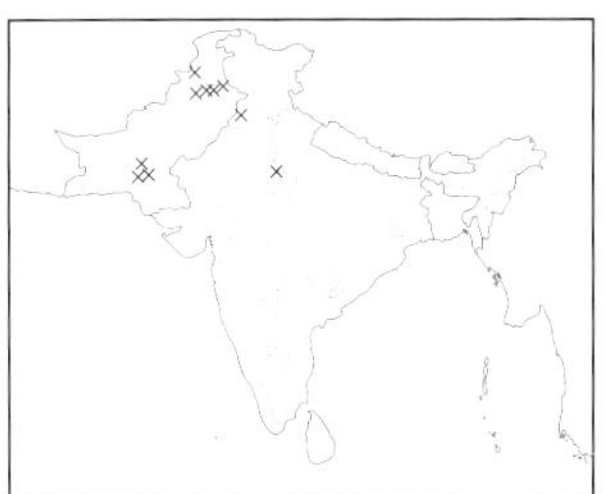

IDENTIFICATION 14 cm. Superficially resembles Pale-footed Bush Warbler (p.711), although typically frequents marshy lowland habitats. Is very white on breast and supercilium. Distinguished from Pale-footed by larger size, more robust appearance and larger tail, shorter and less prominent supercilium and absence of dark stripe through eye, greyish (rather than olive) breast sides and flanks, dull white tips to greyish-brown undertail-coverts, and loud, explosive call. See Japanese Bush Warbler (p.711) for differences from that species. **VOICE** Song is an explosive *chit..chit.. chitity-chit...chitity-chit*; call is an explosive *chit*. **HABITS** Very similar to those of other bush warblers. Can move rapidly up and down reed stems. **HABITAT** Dense reedbeds and tamarisks by streams and in marshes. **DISTRIBUTION AND STATUS** Winter visitor and passage migrant to Pakistan (mainly E Baluchistan and NW Pakistan), also Sindh and Punjab plains and NW India (Punjab and Rajasthan). **PK:** locally frequent. **IN:** very local and uncommon.

SPOTTED BUSH WARBLER *Bradypterus thoracicus* Plate 121

IDENTIFICATION 13 cm. As other *Bradypterus* bush warblers, is rather like a *Locustella* warbler in shape and behaviour, with long undertail-coverts, but has unstreaked upperparts. Confusion is possible with Long-billed, Chinese and Russet Bush Warblers (p.714 and p.715). Separated from Long-billed by much shorter bill, greyish and less distinct supercilium, dark olive-brown upperparts with rufescent cast, combination of grey ear-coverts, sides of neck and breast and olive-brown flanks, and boldly patterned undertail-coverts with dark brown centres and sharply defined white tips. Birds with bold spotting on throat and breast are readily distinguished from Chinese and Russet Bush Warblers. Some individuals, however, show only fine spotting, and some Chinese and Russet can be similarly marked: best distinctions from those two species are shorter tail, grey ear-coverts, sides of neck and

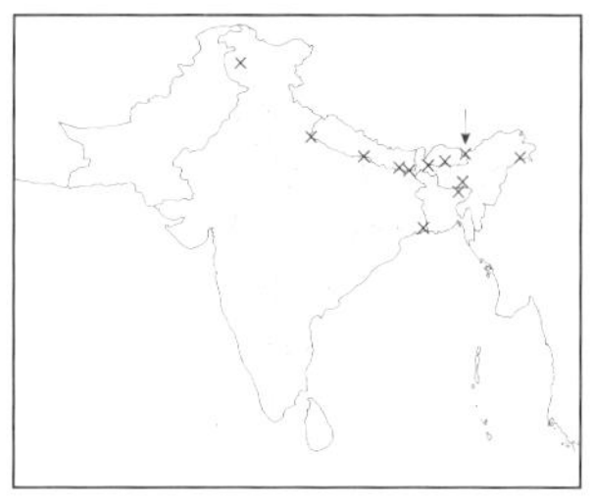

breast, and boldly patterned undertail-coverts, in addition to which upperparts are a darker brown compared with Chinese. **Juvenile** lacks grey on underparts, and has cloudy olive-brown spotting on throat and breast, merging into olive-brown sides of breast and flanks, and faint olive-yellow wash to underparts. **Racial variation** Three races are known from the subcontinent. *B. t. kashmirensis* and *B. t. thoracicus* have a Himalayan distribution (and are covered by the description above). *B. t. shanensis* (= *suschkini*), which has been recorded from NE India, may be better treated as a separate species (*B. davidi*): it differs from *thoracicus* in having paler brown upperparts, brownish wash on sides of neck and across breast (lacking grey band across breast shown by *thoracicus*), typically weaker and browner spotting on throat and breast, and whitish supercilium, as well as a pale lower mandible (bill all dark on *thoracicus*). Weakly 'spotted' birds are very similar to some Chinese in breeding plumage, but have shorter tail and more boldly patterned undertail-coverts. **VOICE** Song of *thoracicus* is a rhythmic *trick-i-di, tric-i-di* or *tri-tri-tri-tree* (sometimes *tri-tir-tree*); song of *shanensis* is a monotonous, buzzing *dzzzzzzr, dzzzzzzr...* (Round and Loskot 1994). Calls include a long, drawn-out, harsh *tzee-eenk*, as well as chacking and *pwit* notes (Boonsong and Round 1991). **HABITS** Very similar to those of other bush warblers. **HABITAT** Summers at or near the treeline in rhododendron and juniper shrubberies, open areas of rank grass and *Rumex*, areas of bracken, rank grass and bushes between forest patches, and shrubberies at the edge of grassland; winters in reedbeds and tall grass in the lowlands. **BREEDING** May–August. Nest is a dome or deep cup made of coarse grass, well hidden in a low bush or among grass tufts, up to 0.5 m above ground. **DISTRIBUTION AND STATUS** Altitudinal migrant. Breeds locally in Himalayas from Kashmir east to Arunachal Pradesh; winters in foothills, NE Indian plains. **NP:** rare; summers in C Himalayas, 3350–3850 m, winters locally below 250 m. **IN:** status uncertain; breeds 3000–4000 m in the west, 3300–4350 m in the east. **BT:** locally common; breeds 3355–4485 m. **BD:** vagrant. **REFERENCES** Round and Loskot (1994).

LONG-BILLED BUSH WARBLER *Bradypterus major* — Plate 121

Large-billed Bush Warbler (I,R)

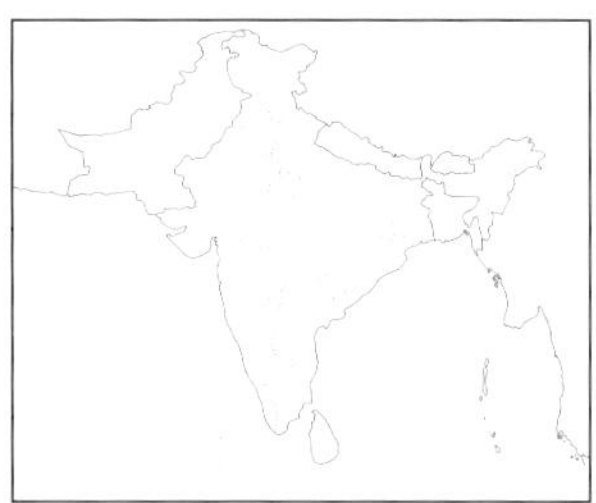

IDENTIFICATION 13 cm. Compared with Spotted Bush Warbler (p.713), has much longer and finer bill, whiter underparts, with whiter lower throat and breast, and olive-buff or buff flanks, longer tail, and unmarked undertail-coverts. Supercilium is white and more prominent behind the eye than on Spotted, and on most birds spotting is finer but more clearly defined against white base colour of breast. Extent and intensity of spotting vary considerably: on some it covers entire throat and upper breast, while on others it is almost, or completely, lacking except on ear-coverts and malar region. Upperparts vary from warm olive-brown (especially on edges to remiges) when fresh, to cold greyish-olive when worn; some birds are very white on underparts, lacking buff on flanks. **Juvenile** has cloudy and less distinct spotting on throat and breast, yellowish wash to underparts, and more extensive olive-brown on breast sides and flanks. **VOICE** Song is a monotonous metallic *pikha-pikha-pikha...* etc, the note repeated rapidly (up to 200 times without stopping); call is a grating *trr* (Ali and Ripley 1987; Roberts 1992). **HABITS** A typical bush warbler. Extremely secretive. **HABITAT** Slopes with bushes, rank grass and bracken at forest edges, weedy embankments between terraced cultivation, and thickets of wild gooseberry at the edges of spruce forest. **BREEDING** June and July. Nest is a deep cup made of grass, well concealed at the base of a low bush or among thick vegetation on or near the ground. **DISTRIBUTION AND STATUS** Presumed altitudinal migrant. Breeds in W Himalayas from N Pakistan east to Kashmir; presumed to winter in the foothills. Globally threatened. **PK:** distribution imperfectly known; summers in inner Himalayas, 2400–3300 m. **IN:** was locally fairly common but few recent records; breeds 2400–3600 m.

CHINESE BUSH WARBLER *Bradypterus tacsanowskius* — Plate 122

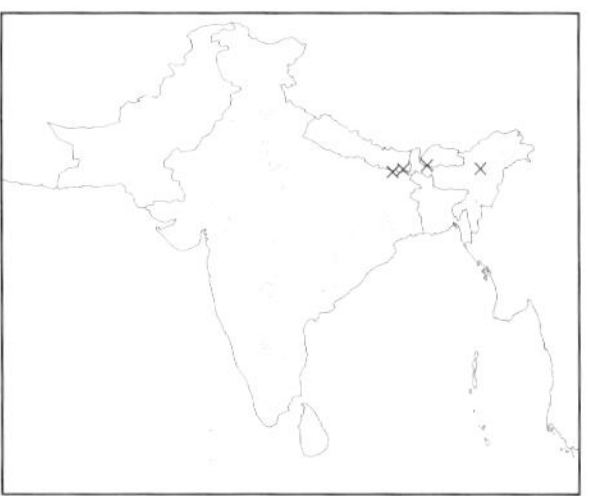

IDENTIFICATION 14 cm. Very similar to Brown Bush Warbler (p.715). Lacks that species' rufescent cast to upperparts and warm sandy-brown coloration to sides of breast and flanks. Specifically, has greyer-brown upperparts with olive cast (with slightly warmer brown edgings to remiges), olive grey-brown ear-coverts, sides of neck and breast (latter often with yellowish wash), olive-buff flanks, and pale tips to undertail-coverts (which are lacking or only just apparent on Brown). Supercilium is yellowish-white to buffish-white. Some birds have fine spotting on lower throat, and are confusable with lightly speckled *shanensis* (= *suschkini*) race of Spotted Bush Warbler (p.713); see that species for main differences. Presumed **first-winter** birds have strong yellowish wash to breast and flanks, yellowish-buff undertail-coverts, and stronger olive wash to upperparts. **VOICE** Call is a *chirr chirr* (Inskipp and Inskipp 1991); song is an insect-like rasping note, repeated, *dzzzeep-dzzeep-dzeep* (S. Madge). **HABITS** A typical bush warbler. Often feeds on the ground among vegetation. **HABITAT** Reedbeds, grass and bushes, standing paddy-fields, and stubbles. **DISTRIBUTION AND STATUS NP, IN:** vagrant. **REFERENCES** Kennerley and Leader (1993), Robson (1994).

BROWN BUSH WARBLER *Bradypterus luteoventris* Plate 122

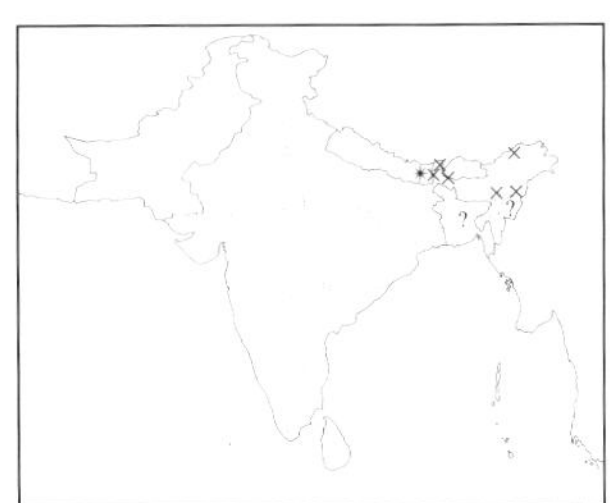

IDENTIFICATION 13.5 cm. Compared with the very similar Chinese Bush Warbler (p.714), has warmer brown upperparts (with slight rufescent cast), and warm rufous-buff ear-coverts, sides of neck and breast, and flanks, contrasting with silky-white of rest of underparts. The upperparts are a warmer, paler brown than those of Spotted and Russet Bush Warblers (p.713 and below). Additional features which help to differentiate it from other bush warblers include indistinct rufous-buff supercilium (which barely extends beyond eye and is concolorous with the lores), lack of prominent pale tips to undertail-coverts (feathers may be just slightly paler towards tip), and pale pinkish-orange lower mandible. Unlike other bush warblers, does not have spotting on throat and breast. **First-winter** is said to have yellowish wash to underparts. **VOICE** Song is a rather quiet, rapid, prolonged sewing-machine-like repetition of short notes, *tututututu-tutututututut...*; calls include *tchack..tchack..tchack* typical of the genus, a sharp high-pitched *tink.. tink..tink..tink...*, and harsh, grating *tchrrrrk..tchrrrrk...* (C. Robson). **HABITS** A typical bush warbler. **HABITAT** Grassy hills, tall grass and bracken-covered hillsides; in the Khasi Hills, inhabits undergrowth of bushes, bracken and grass in pine forest. **BREEDING** April–July. Nest is a deep cup, made mainly of grasses, built within 1 m of ground in a low bush or tangle of weeds and creepers. **DISTRIBUTION AND STATUS** Altitudinal migrant. Himalayas from Nepal east to Arunachal Pradesh; NE Indian hills. **NP:** recorded only in 19th century. **IN:** current status uncertain; breeds 2100–3300 m in Himalayas, 1200–1600 m in Meghalaya. **BT:** locally common; summers 2440–3355 m. **BD:** vagrant. **REFERENCES** Husain *et al.* (1974), Kennerley and Leader (1993), Khan (1986).

RUSSET BUSH WARBLER *Bradypterus seebohmi* Plate 122

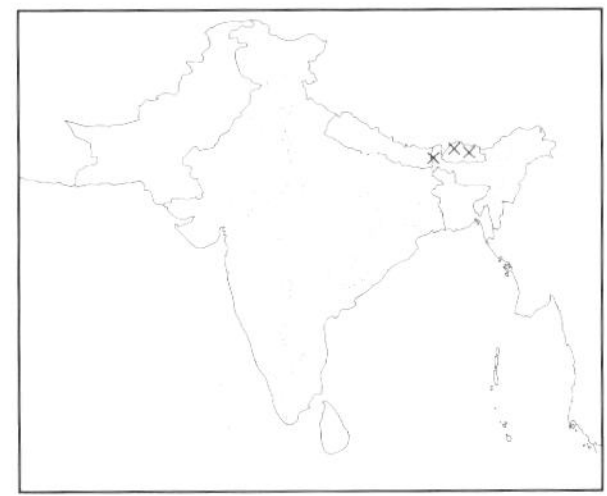

IDENTIFICATION 13.5 cm. Superficially resembles Spotted Bush Warbler (p.713), with rich brown upperparts. Best told by longer, broader tail, less boldly marked undertail-coverts (with diffuse pale tips), indistinct and off-white supercilium (which does not extend noticeably beyond eye as on Spotted), and brown ear-coverts, sides of breast and flanks which are concolorous with upperparts. Lacks or has only a faint trace of the grey on sides of neck and across breast shown by *thoracicus* race of Spotted. Some birds have brown spotting on lower throat and upper breast, although this is not so prominent as on most Spotted. Compared with Chinese and Brown Bush Warblers (p.714 and above), has darker and more rufescent-brown upperparts and warm brown flanks; in addition, has pale fringes to undertail-coverts and can have spotted breast, two features not shown by Brown. Bill is blackish. **First-winter** is undescribed. **VOICE** Song is a monotonous, metallic and buzzing *zree-ut zree-ut...*, uttered in a long series of notes; calls with an excited chacking and also an explosive *rink-tink-tink* (Boonsong and Round 1991). **HABITS** A typical bush warbler. **HABITAT** Edge of forest with bamboos, secondary growth with bushes and dense ferns, and along edges of tea plantations. **BREEDING** Details unknown in region; very poorly known elsewhere. **DISTRIBUTION AND STATUS** Resident and presumed altitudinal migrant. Recently recorded in West Bengal and C Bhutan; probably overlooked previously. **IN:** fairly common in West Bengal; 2050–2200 m (April). **BT:** status unknown; singing at 2200 m (late May). **REFERENCES** Kennerley and Leader (1993), Tymstra *et al.* (1997).

SRI LANKA BUSH WARBLER *Bradypterus palliseri* Plate 122

Palliser's Warbler (I,P), Ceylon Bush Warbler, Ceylon Warbler

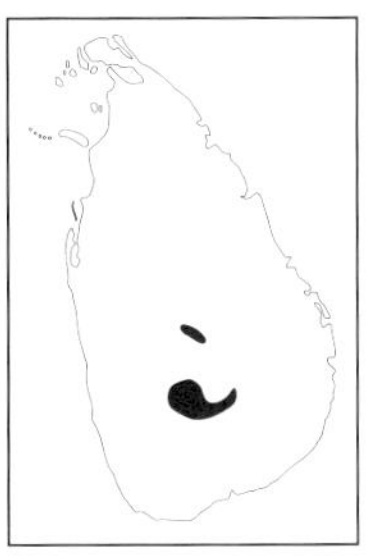

IDENTIFICATION 16 cm. A large, stocky *Bradypterus*. Has dark olive-brown upperparts with rufescent cast to wings and tail, greyer ear-coverts and indistinct paler grey supercilium, orange-buff throat, and olive-grey underparts with olive-yellow wash especially to belly. **Juvenile** is similar, but lacks orange-buff throat: throat is washed with olive-yellow and mottled with dark olive. **VOICE** Call is a sharp, often endlessly repeated, staccato *spik* or *squik* (P. Holt from A. Lewis recording); has an odd, rather squeaky little song (Henry 1971). **HABITS** A typical bush warbler, often in pairs. Skulks in moist undergrowth close to the ground. **HABITAT** Confined to forest with dense undergrowth, where it prefers vegetation along streams. **BREEDING** February–May, mid-August–September. Builds a deep cup-shaped nest of moss, twigs and leaves, well concealed on top of a shrub and close to the ground, often beside an opening or path. **DISTRIBUTION AND STATUS LK:** rare endemic resident, mainly in higher hills above 1500 m, but recorded also down to 350 m.

***LOCUSTELLA* WARBLERS** Very skulking, medium-sized warblers with a rounded tail, usually found singly. Characteristically, they keep low down or on the ground among dense vegetation, walking furtively and scurrying off when startled. Their plumage is dull brownish, and they differ from Spotted, Chinese and Brown Bush

Warblers, which are similar in behaviour and winter in the same habitat, in having noticeable streaking on the upperparts. They fly at low level, flitting between plants, or rather jerkily over longer distances, ending in a sudden dive into cover.

LANCEOLATED WARBLER *Locustella lanceolata* Plate 122

Streaked Grasshopper Warbler (F,I)

IDENTIFICATION 12 cm. Confusable really only with Grasshopper Warbler (below), but typically has bold, fine streaking (almost spotting) on throat, breast and flanks, and stronger and better defined streaking on upperparts. In addition, is smaller, with proportionately shorter tail, and has stouter bill. Has warmer brown upperparts and warmer buff flanks in fresh plumage, although both are colder greyish-olive when worn. Only rarely is there a yellow wash to underparts, whereas this is frequently shown by Grasshopper. Some individuals, especially juveniles (see below), are more lightly streaked on upperparts and underparts and can be very similar to heavily streaked Grasshopper. Streaking on undertail-coverts is typically less extensive and narrower, but blacker and more clear cut, or drop-shaped, compared with the more extensive and diffuse arrowhead-shaped markings of Grasshopper; largest undertail-coverts are usually unmarked (well marked on Grasshopper). Lanceolated also has blacker tertials with narrower and clearer pale edges than Grasshopper. **First-winter** is as adult, but **juvenile** (which could occur in the subcontinent) is less heavily streaked and plumage is looser and fluffier. **VOICE** Calls include a sharp metallic *pit*, a rather faint *tack*, and a scolding, slightly shrill *cheek-cheek-cheek-cheek* (Alström and Colston 1991). **HABITS** Very similar to those of other *Locustella* warblers, but even more skulking; sometimes inquisitive. Keeps well concealed in even very low vegetation and leaves it only for short flights or runs. Can run very rapidly on the ground, like a mouse. **HABITAT** Tall grassland, paddy stubbles, dense bush and grass. **DISTRIBUTION AND STATUS** Winter visitor, mainly to N India. **NP:** vagrant. **IN:** rare. **BD, LK:** vagrant. **REFERENCES** Alström and Colston (1991), Hoffmann (1996)

GRASSHOPPER WARBLER *Locustella naevia* Plate 122

Common Grasshopper Warbler

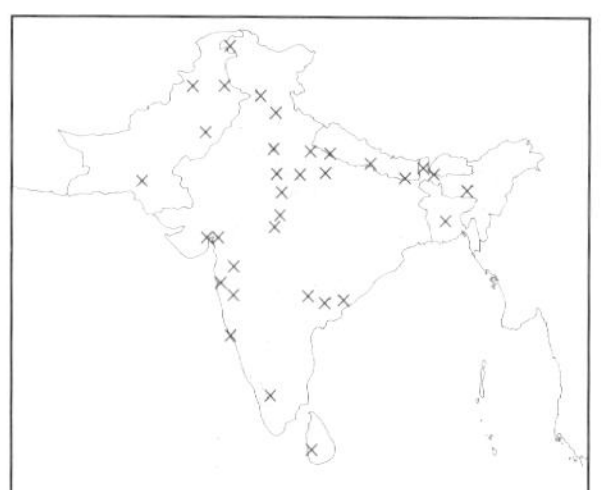

IDENTIFICATION 13 cm. Confusable with both Lanceolated and Rusty-rumped Warblers (above and below). Distinguished from Rusty-rumped by olive-brown coloration to crown and mantle, and less prominent supercilium; in flight, rump and uppertail-coverts are olive-brown (rather than rufous) and concolorous with mantle, and tail does not appear dark (and lacks white tip) as on Rusty-rumped. For further differences, see Rusty-rumped. From Lanceolated by (usually) unmarked or only lightly streaked throat and breast, and less heavily streaked upperparts (especially rump and uppertail-coverts). Some Grasshopper Warblers, however, are as heavily streaked as a lightly streaked Lanceolated: see Lanceolated for subtle differences. **First-winter** can have yellowish wash on underparts. **VOICE** Calls include a hard *sit.* **HABITS** Very similar to those of other *Locustella* warblers. Unobtrusive, and rather crepuscular. Creeps and hops about systematically low down among grass and reeds. **HABITAT** Tall grassland, reedbeds and sedges in marshes, alongside lakes, streams, and standing paddy-fields; in Kerala, also hillsides covered with coarse grass and reeds on hilltops. **DISTRIBUTION AND STATUS** Local winter visitor, mainly in Pakistan, Western Ghats and Bangladesh. **PK:** scarce winter visitor and passage migrant. **NP:** vagrant. **IN:** generally uncommon; plains and hills, up to 1800 m in the peninsula. **BD, LK:** vagrant.

RUSTY-RUMPED WARBLER *Locustella certhiola* Plate 122

Pallas's Warbler, Pallas's Grasshopper Warbler (F,I,P)

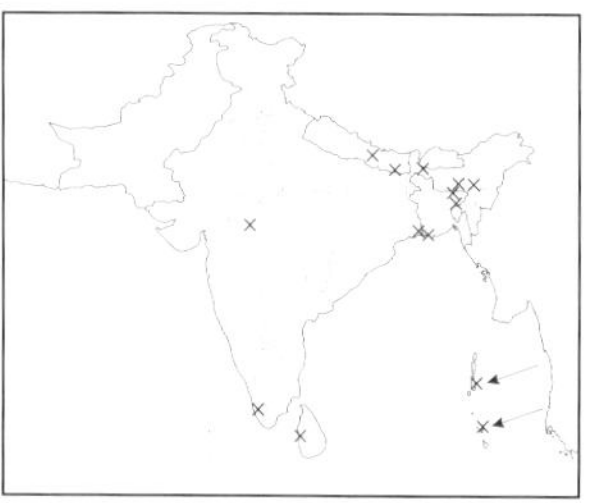

IDENTIFICATION 13.5 cm. Distinguished from the *Bradypterus* bush warblers by streaked upperparts. Most likely to be confused with Grasshopper Warbler (above), but is larger and fatter, and has more prominent supercilium contrasting with greyer crown, the latter with broader and more diffuse dark streaking. It also has more heavily streaked mantle with rufous tinge, rufous rump and uppertail-coverts, cleaner and narrower fringes to tertials (often with whiter tips), rufescent olive-brown breast sides and flanks (contrasting with white of rest of underparts), and unstreaked undertail-coverts. In flight, or when tail is spread, shows rather dark, white-tipped tail (white tips can be very difficult to see on uppertail) which contrasts with rufous of uppertail-coverts. **Juvenile** has yellowish wash to underparts and light spotting on breast. Some individuals can more closely resemble Grasshopper, with less distinct supercilium and more olive-brown and less heavily streaked crown and mantle; generally, they are best told by more rufescent and more heavily streaked rump and uppertail-coverts, well-defined narrower fringes to tertials, white tips to tail, and unmarked undertail-coverts. **VOICE** Calls include a sharp metallic *pit,* and a hard, drawn-out and descending rattle, *trrrrrrrrrr* (Alström and Colston 1991). **HABITS** Very similar to those of other *Locustella* warblers. **HABITAT** Reedbeds and standing paddy-fields. **DISTRIBUTION AND STATUS** Very local winter visitor in the subcontinent. **NP:** vagrant. **IN:** rare winter visitor in plains. **BD:** several records; uncommon passage migrant? **LK:** ?winter visitor to all zones. **REFERENCES** Alström and Colston (1991).

***ACROCEPHALUS* WARBLERS** Medium-sized to large warblers with prominent bill, brownish plumage and rounded tail. They usually occur singly. Many species are skulking, typically keeping low down in dense vegetation, and are probably under-recorded in the region. Most frequent marshy habitats, and are able to clamber about readily in reeds and other vertical stems of marsh plants. Their songs are harsh and often monotonous. The Large-billed Reed Warbler *A. orinus,* known from one specimen from Himachal Pradesh, India, was described as a separate species, but was considered by Ali and Ripley (1987) to be a subspecies of Clamorous Reed Warbler (p.720); a recent examination of the specimen, by C. Byers and R. Grimmett, concluded, however, that it fitted Blyth's Reed Warbler in all essential features (Inskipp *et al.* 1996), and this conclusion is followed here.

MOUSTACHED WARBLER *Acrocephalus melanopogon* — Plate 122

Moustached Sedge Warbler (I)

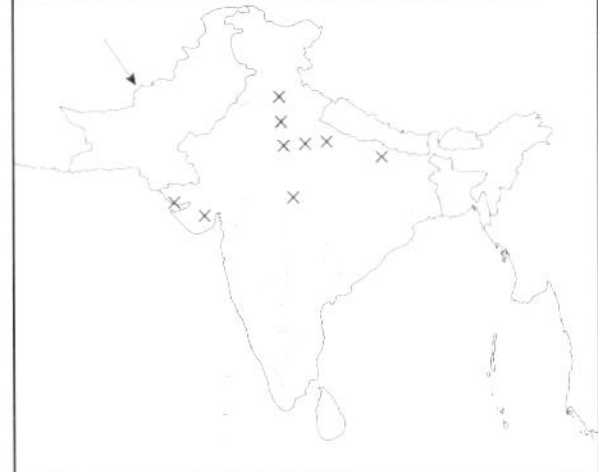

IDENTIFICATION 12.5 cm. Distinguished from other *Acrocephalus* warblers regularly recorded in the subcontinent by combination of broad white square-ended supercilium (which broadens behind eye, and contrasts with blackish sides of crown and blackish eye-stripe) and boldly streaked rufous-brown mantle. Has distinctive habit of cocking tail above back in chat-like fashion, although can spend long periods with tail held out in a straight line with body. See Sedge Warbler (below) for differences from that species. **VOICE** Calls include a harsh *trr-trr* and a hard *tcht;* song is varied and scratchy, although contains clear notes and trills, including a subdued, high *lu lu lu lu* (Jonsson 1992). **HABITS** Unobtrusive, but not shy, and less skulking than most other *Acrocephalus.* Moves about low down in partly submerged reeds, often clinging to vertical stems and stretching down to the water surface to pick up insects. Also often forages by hopping about on the ground. Frequently moves to the tops of reeds, and sometimes makes short aerial sallies after insects. When alarmed, often cocks, flicks and bobs the tail nervously; also cocks the tail at other times. **HABITAT** Tall reedbeds and seasonally flooded tamarisks and rushes around lakes and rivers. **BREEDING** Very poorly known in the region. Nests with eggs found in June; deep cup made of dried reed stalks, woven on to upright supporting sedges in shallow water. **DISTRIBUTION AND STATUS** Possibly breeds in Baluchistan, Pakistan, and in Punjab and Uttar Pradesh, India; winter visitor to N plains, Pakistan, and NW India (from Punjab south to Gujarat and east to C Uttar Pradesh and C Madhya Pradesh); passage migrant in Baluchistan and Kurram valley, NW Pakistan. **PK:** common winter visitor; widespread in Baluchistan on passage. **IN:** uncommon in the plains.

SEDGE WARBLER *Acrocephalus schoenobaenus* — Plate 122

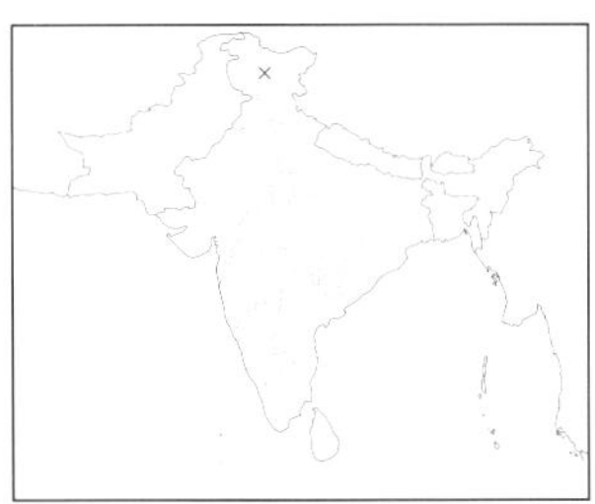

IDENTIFICATION 13 cm. Very similar to Moustached Warbler (above), with broad white supercilium and streaked mantle. Head pattern is less striking than that of Moustached: has paler but more cleanly streaked crown, and narrower (usually buffish) supercilium, and usually lacks the clear, narrow moustachial stripe found on that species. Further differences are buffish olive-brown coloration to upperparts (upperparts are darker, more rufescent-brown, on Moustached), more uniform buffish or yellowish-buff underparts (whiter, often contrasting with rufous-buff flanks, on Moustached, although worn individuals of both species have uniformly white underparts), and broad, well-defined buffy fringes to tertials and greater coverts. Sedge has a longer primary projection, typically around 75% of the length of exposed tertials (around 50% on Moustached), tail is less graduated, and bill is stronger and stouter. Rarely cocks tail, unlike Moustached, and has a more fluid flight, with tail often spread. Some worn birds (with more greyish-brown upperparts, more uniformly dark crown and whiter underparts) are virtually identical in plumage to worn Moustached. **First-winter** is more distinct from Moustached, with more yellowish-brown upperparts and more boldly streaked crown, often with suggestion of a pale crown-stripe, and often has a gorget of spotting across breast. **VOICE** Calls include a harsh *chek* and a fast, churring *trrr.* **HABITS** Details unknown in the subcontinent, although well studied in Europe. Habits very similar to those of Moustached Warbler. Spends much time creeping about in low tangled vegetation, but will also perch freely on exposed reed stems, bushes and tall plants. **HABITAT** Unknown in the region. In Europe, tall grasses, bushes and other rank vegetation at fringes of marshes, ditches, ponds and lakes. **DISTRIBUTION AND STATUS IN:** vagrant to Ladakh. **REFERENCES** Madge (1992).

BLACK-BROWED REED WARBLER *Acrocephalus bistrigiceps* Plate 122

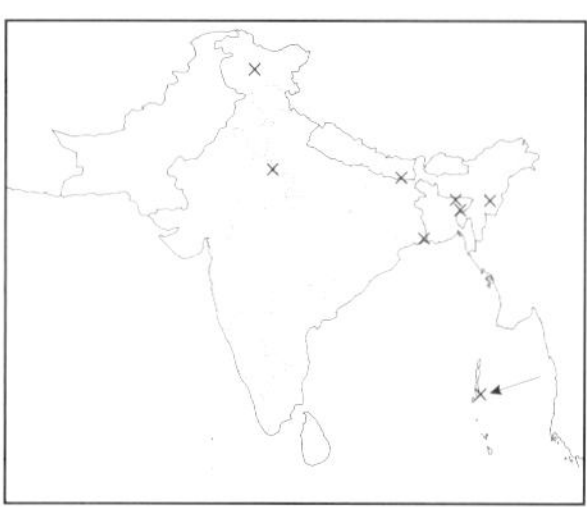

IDENTIFICATION 13 cm. Most likely to be confused with Paddyfield Warbler (below). Distinguished from that species by slightly broader and more prominent, square-ended buffish-white supercilium and, more significantly, by presence of broad black lateral crown-stripes. Paddyfield can have a dark border above the supercilium, but it is not so broad and well defined as on Black-browed, and the supercilium is not usually so prominent and broad behind eye. Black-browed has olive-brown upperparts in worn plumage; it is more rufescent above, with warm buff sides of breast and flanks, in fresh plumage. Paddyfield is usually more rufescent on upperparts (especially rump and uppertail-coverts) in fresh plumage, and even when worn rump and uppertail-coverts are contrastingly rufescent. In addition, Black-browed has shorter tail and longer primary projection beyond tertials, and in shape and appearance resembles an unstreaked Sedge Warbler (p.717). Further, it has dark grey (rather than yellowish-brown to pinkish-brown) legs and feet. **VOICE** Call is a soft, repeated *chuc* (Boonsong and Round 1991). **HABITS** A typical small unstreaked *Acrocephalus*; see Paddyfield Warbler. Shy, and skulks in dense cover. **HABITAT** Tall grass and paddy-fields. **DISTRIBUTION AND STATUS** Winter visitor. Mainly NE India (Assam, Manipur, West Bengal) and Bangladesh. **NP:** vagrant. **IN:** rare. **BD:** local winter visitor and passage migrant to the northeast. **REFERENCES** Gee (1995), Kennerley and Leader (1992), Majumdar *et al.* (1992), Robson (1991), Williamson (1968).

PADDYFIELD WARBLER *Acrocephalus agricola* Plate 122

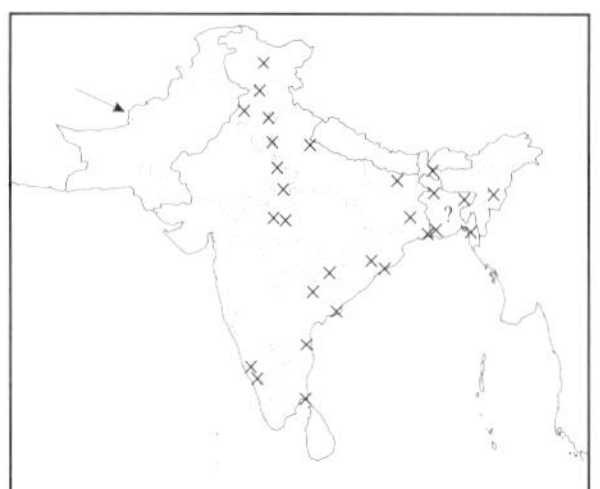

IDENTIFICATION 13 cm. Usually best told from Blyth's Reed Warbler (p719) by more rufescent upperparts and warm buff flanks, shorter bill, and more prominent white supercilium. Typically, looks longer-tailed than Blyth's Reed, with tail frequently held cocked, and often shows more angular, peaked hindcrown. Unlike on Blyth's Reed, supercilium often broadens behind eye, becoming almost square-ended, and is bordered above by diffuse (and often very indistinct) dark line and below by a dark eye-stripe. Some birds can have a less prominent supercilium which is less distinct behind eye, and/or lack darker lateral crown-stripes. Often shows whitish neck sides. Typically, shows dark centres and contrastingly paler edges to tertials, which are usually very uniform on Blyth's Reed. Shorter bill usually has well-defined dark tip to lower mandible, which is either entirely pale or has a diffuse dark smudge on Blyth's Reed. Paddyfield has noticeable rufous cast to mantle and rump in fresh plumage, when Blyth's Reed is distinctly more olive on upperparts. Breast sides and flanks are typically warm buff on Paddyfield, although underparts, when worn, become uniformly white. When worn, Paddyfield has greyer or sandier upperparts but usually retains rufous cast to rump, which is not apparent on Blyth's Reed. Further, has yellowish-brown to pinkish-brown (rather than dark grey) legs and feet. For differences from the very similar Blunt-winged Warbler (below), Black-browed Reed Warbler (above) and Booted Warbler (p.721), see those species. **VOICE** Call is a soft *dzak*. **HABITS** A typical small unstreaked *Acrocephalus*, although flicks and cocks its tail and raises crown feathers more frequently than most species. Lively, and adept at climbing up and down reed stems. Usually flies only for short distances, low over the reeds, and with tail slightly spread and depressed. **HABITAT** Reedbeds, tall damp grassland, marshes, mangroves, paddy-fields and sugarcane crops. **BREEDING** Very poorly known in the region. A loose colony of nests with eggs found in July; deep cup, woven around and supported by upright reed stems in shallow water, 0.5–1 m above the surface. **DISTRIBUTION AND STATUS** Has bred very locally in Baluchistan, Pakistan; winters mainly in S Pakistan, S Nepal, and W and NE India. **PK:** mainly a passage migrant in N plains; common winter visitor to S Sindh. **NP:** local; fairly common at Kosi, uncommon elsewhere. **IN:** widespread and locally fairly common in the plains. **BD:** status uncertain because of confusion with Blunt-winged Warbler; possibly a local winter visitor/passage migrant. **REFERENCES** Alström and Colston (1991), Kennerley and Leader (1992), Svensson (1992).

BLUNT-WINGED WARBLER *Acrocephalus concinens* Plate 122

Blunt-winged Paddyfield Warbler (F,I)

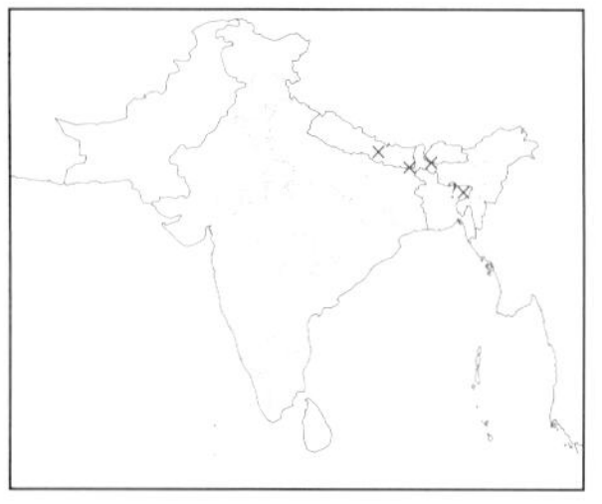

IDENTIFICATION 13 cm. Very similar to Paddyfield Warbler (above). Subtle differences from that species are shorter and less distinct supercilium, which typically barely extends beyond eye (on occasional worn birds it may be more extensive, but is never more than a thin and inconspicuous line over the ear-coverts); absence of dark border above supercilium (although this is often not apparent on Paddyfield) and lack of dark stripe behind eye (with rather uniform ear-coverts); longer and stouter bill, with uniformly pale lower mandible (occasionally has dark shadow towards tip, but lacks well-defined dark tip of most Paddyfield); and longer tail, accentuated by shorter primary projection. Upperparts are much as Paddyfield's, although slightly more olive-toned; breast and flanks are washed with warm buff (much as on Paddyfield). When worn, Blunt-winged has colder olive-brown upperparts, but retains more rufescent rump and uppertail-coverts. Confusable with Blyth's Reed Warbler (below) but, when fresh, has more rufous tones to plumage, with warm buff breast and flanks; in worn plumage, retains rufous coloration to rump. In addition, tends to appear shorter-billed than Blyth's Reed, has longer and more rounded tail, has more prominent fringes to tertials, and has a shorter and more rounded primary projection. **VOICE** Calls include a quiet *tcheck* and a soft drawn-out *churr.* **HABITS** Like those of Paddyfield Warbler. Skulking except in breeding season, when males sing from the tops of tall plants or bushes. **HABITAT** Breeds in tall grassy marshes and tall grass close to lakes and rivers; in Kashmir, also breeds some distance from water, in weeds on hillsides. Winters in reedbeds, grass and small bushes and willows along rivers. **BREEDING** April–July. Nest is a neat deep cup made of grass and reeds, woven on to and supported by several upright plant stems, within 1 m of ground; also nests in bush clumps on hillsides. **DISTRIBUTION AND STATUS** Breeds in W Himalayas from Hazara district, N Pakistan, east to Kashmir; resident in Assam, with some seasonal movements; other winter quarters are poorly known, but recorded from Nepal, West Bengal ?and Bangladesh. **PK:** rare summer visitor; breeds 2700–3000 m. **NP:** status uncertain; few confirmed records, 230 m, 1220 m. **IN:** locally fairly common in W Himalayas; breeds 1525–3000 m. **BD:** status uncertain because of confusion with Paddyfield Warbler; possibly a local winter visitor/passage migrant. **REFERENCES** Boonsong and Round (1991), Kennerley and Leader (1992).

EURASIAN REED WARBLER *Acrocephalus scirpaceus* — Not illustrated

Reed Warbler (I), European Reed Warbler (R)

Status uncertain, but is likely to occur in Pakistan; one possible record of nesting in N Baluchistan (Roberts 1992).

BLYTH'S REED WARBLER *Acrocephalus dumetorum* — Plate 122

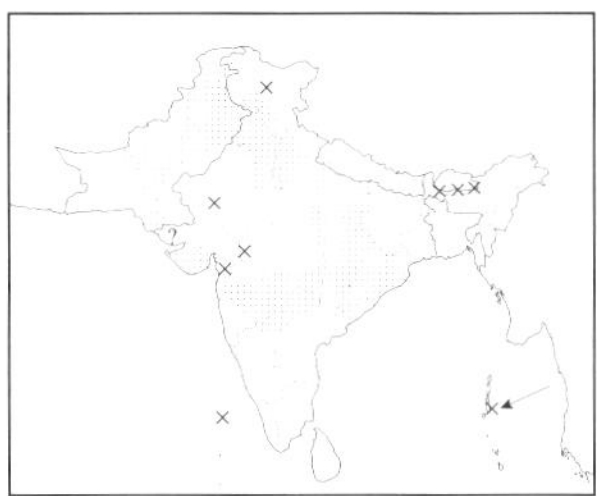

IDENTIFICATION 14 cm. Usually readily told from Paddyfield Warbler (p.718) by colder olive-grey to olive-brown upperparts (generally lacking rufous in plumage), longer bill, uniform wings, and comparatively indistinct supercilium. Supercilium often does not extend beyond eye on Blyth's Reed, or barely does so, and never reaches rear of ear-coverts, and is not bordered above by diffuse dark line and below by a noticeably dark eye-stripe (as on some Paddyfield). Longer bill almost always lacks well-defined dark tip to lower mandible which is typically apparent on Paddyfield. Wings are typically rather uniform, usually lacking paler or rufous fringes to tertials which are usually shown by Paddyfield. Has noticeable warm olive cast to upperparts and edges of remiges in fresh plumage, when Paddyfield is distinctly rufous-brown (especially on rump and uppertail-coverts); also in fresh plumage, has light buffish wash to flanks, but buff is not so bright and extensive as on Paddyfield. When worn, Blyth's Reed is colder and greyer in coloration, with whiter underparts. Birds in fresh first-winter plumage can have a slight rufous cast to the upperparts and are closer in coloration to Paddyfield. For differences from Blunt-winged Warbler (p.718), see that species. Is easily confusable with *rama* race of Booted Warbler (p.721); compared with that species, supercilium is less distinct behind eye, and upperparts are a darker olive-brown; lacks pale sides to tail, edges to tertials, and pale panel on secondaries, which are all good features for Booted (although are not always apparent). Additional indicative features distinguishing Blyth's Reed from Booted are shorter-looking, more rounded tail (although tail can appear square-ended), longer uppertail- and undertail-coverts (extending beyond closed wings, with undertail-coverts extending roughly two-thirds along length of undertail), stockier build, more skulking and lethargic behaviour, stouter bill, and harder and harsher calls. For differences from Upcher's Warbler (p.722), see that species. **VOICE** Song consists of various themes, repeated several times, a typical theme having two sections: one or two tongue-clicking sounds, followed by musical whistling, e.g. *trek-trek CHUEE* or *chrak-chrak CHU-EE-LOO.* Call is a fairly soft *chek* or grating *chek-tchr.* (Jonsson 1992) **HABITS** Similar to those of other unstreaked *Acrocephalus* warblers, but hops and creeps about within bushes and sometimes quite high in trees, as well as in ground cover. Frequently flicks, raises and fans the tail. Flight is usually flitting. **HABITAT** Dry habitats and near water: bushes and trees at the edges of cultivation and forest, and in gardens, groves, orchards and hedges. **DISTRIBUTION AND STATUS** Widespread winter visitor or passage migrant in the subcontinent, except in parts of the northwest and northeast. **PK:** common and widespread spring and autumn passage migrant. **NP:** fairly common and widespread winter visitor; below 1525 m (–2900 m on passage). **IN:** common winter visitor; plains and hills up to 2100 m. **BT:** frequent; 245–1460 m. **BD:** common and widespread winter visitor. **LK:** common and widespread winter visitor.

GREAT REED WARBLER *Acrocephalus arundinaceus* — Plate 123

Eurasian Great Reed Warbler (I)

IDENTIFICATION 19 cm. Very difficult to distinguish from Clamorous Reed Warbler (p.720). Best features in the field are shorter, stouter bill, longer primary projection, and shorter-looking tail, which is slightly less graduated or rounded, along with more prominent supercilium (especially behind eye). Primary projection is roughly equal to length of tertials (approximately two-thirds of tertial length on Clamorous Reed), with eight or nine exposed primary tips (rather than six or seven) visible beyond the tertials. Unlikely to occur within the wintering range of

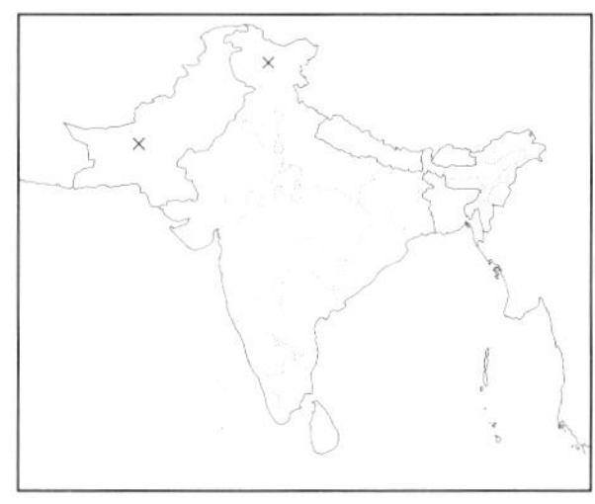

Oriental Reed Warbler (below), but can also, as that species, show faint streaking on sides of neck and breast: Great Reed is larger in size than Oriental Reed, generally has a longer primary projection (often visibly shorter than length of tertials on Oriental Reed), and lacks prominent whitish tips to outer rectrices which are often apparent on Oriental Reed. **VOICE** Song is not so loud and harsh as that of Clamorous Reed, being faster and more melodious, with many variations and longer phrases, *karra-karra-karra-keek* or *karre-karre-keet dree-dree-dree trr trr*; calls are much as those of Clamorous Reed. **HABITS** Similar to those of other *Acrocephalus* warblers, and very like Clamorous Reed Warbler. **HABITAT** Reedbeds. **DISTRIBUTION AND STATUS PK, IN:** vagrant. **REFERENCES** Anon. (1979), Shirihai *et al.* (1995).

ORIENTAL REED WARBLER *Acrocephalus orientalis* Plate 123

Eastern Great Reed Warbler (I), *A. arundinaceus* (K)

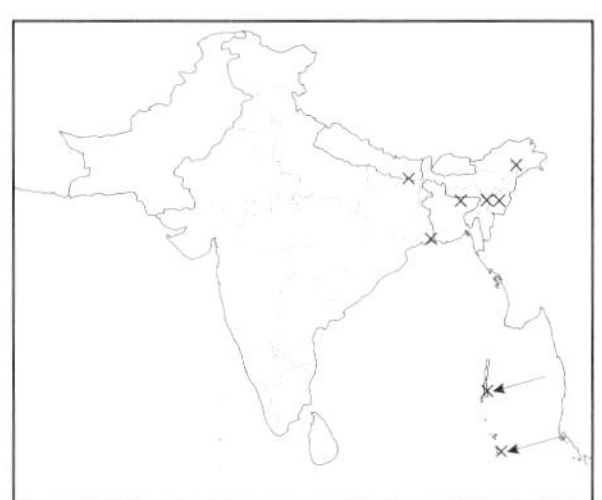

IDENTIFICATION 18 cm. Confusion is most likely with the very similar Clamorous Reed Warbler (below). Compared with that species, Oriental Reed is noticeably smaller, with shorter, squarer tail (and generally looks well proportioned compared with the slim and long-tailed appearance of Clamorous Reed). Often has streaking on sides of neck and breast, and well-defined whitish tips to outer rectrices. Streaking on underparts can, however, be lacking or not visible in the field, while a few Clamorous Reed can also show faint streaking. Primary projection is equal to or roughly two-thirds the length of tertials. For differences from Great Reed Warbler (p.719), see that species. **VOICE** Song is similar to that of Clamorous Reed, but is richer, softer and less rhythmic, consisting of a series of grating phrases, *kawa-kawa-kawa-gurk-gurk eek eek gurk kawa* or *char-char-chee*; calls are much as those of Clamorous Reed. **HABITS** Similar to those of other *Acrocephalus* warblers, and very like Clamorous Reed Warbler. **HABITAT** Reedbeds. **DISTRIBUTION AND STATUS** Winter visitor, mainly to NE India (Assam, Manipur, West Bengal). **NP:** vagrant. **IN:** rare. **BD:** vagrant. **REFERENCES** Majumdar *et al.* (1992), Robson (1996b), Shirihai *et al.* (1995).

CLAMOROUS REED WARBLER *Acrocephalus stentoreus* Plate 123

Indian Great Reed Warbler (I), Great Reed Warbler (P), Large-billed Reed Warbler (I), *A. orinus*

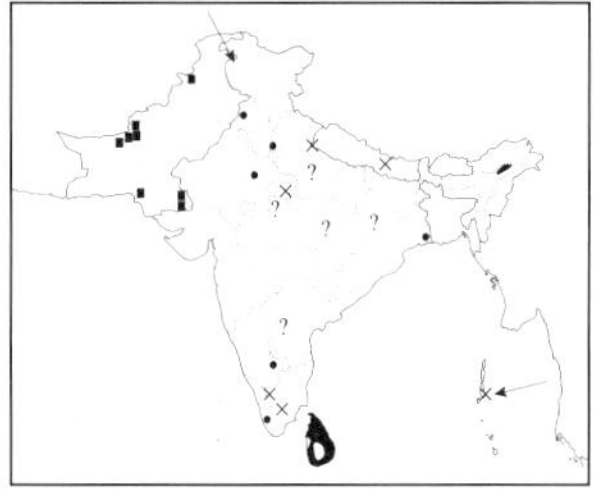

IDENTIFICATION 19 cm. Distinguished from Thick-billed Warbler (below), which is the only other large *Acrocephalus* warbler occurring widely in the subcontinent, by much longer bill (usually with dark tip to lower mandible), whitish supercilium, and dark lores and diffuse stripe behind eye (Thick-billed appears very plain-faced). From Blyth's Reed Warbler (p.719) by much larger size and larger, stouter bill. For differences from Oriental Reed and Great Reed Warblers (above and p.719), see those species. In fresh plumage, has greyish-olive upperparts and whitish underparts (with variable buff wash to breast and flanks). Worn birds have colder and greyer upperparts and whiter underparts. **Racial variation** Birds in Sri Lanka have darker brown upperparts, and can be distinctly smaller than those of the S Asian continent. **VOICE** Song is a very loud and rather melodious, repeated *karra-karra-karet-karet*, often introduced by *tek-tek-tek*; call is a loud and deep, hard *tak* or *chak*, or soft *karrk* (Shirihai *et al.* 1995). **HABITS** Similar to those of other *Acrocephalus* warblers, but not particularly shy; often forages in bushes, where seen more easily than in reeds. Occasionally males sing in the open, especially in the breeding season. Slower and less agile than the small *Acrocephalus*, causing more disturbance to leaves and stems when moving about. **HABITAT** Reedbeds and bushes around lakes, ponds and marshes; on passage, sometimes in dry habitats such as gardens and roadside plantations. **BREEDING** March–August. Nest is a large, deep cup made of dry reed leaves, woven between several reed stems standing in water, 0.3–1 m above the surface. **DISTRIBUTION AND STATUS** Breeds locally in Pakistan, Kashmir, the peninsula and Sri Lanka; winters widely in the subcontinent. **PK:** breeds widely and sporadically; common and widespread winter visitor. **NP:** local winter visitor and passage migrant, chiefly in the terai; frequent at Kosi, rare elsewhere. **IN:** common in summer in the Kashmir vale, breeds sporadically in the peninsula; widespread and locally common in winter in the plains and peninsular hills up to 1800 m. **BD:** common winter visitor throughout; sometimes oversummers. **LK:** resident in lowlands, frequent in the dry zone, uncommon in wet zone; also a rare winter visitor to lowlands.

THICK-BILLED WARBLER *Acrocephalus aedon* Plate 123

***Phragamaticola aedon* (F,K)**

IDENTIFICATION 19 cm. Distinguished from Clamorous Reed Warbler (above), which is the only other large *Acrocephalus* warbler occurring widely in the subcontinent, by short, stout bill, rounded head, and 'plain-faced' appearance. Has paler, often greyish-looking, ear-coverts and lores, but lacks prominent supercilium and any suggestion of a darker eye-stripe. Bill has sharply downcurved upper mandible, and can appear all pale, and always

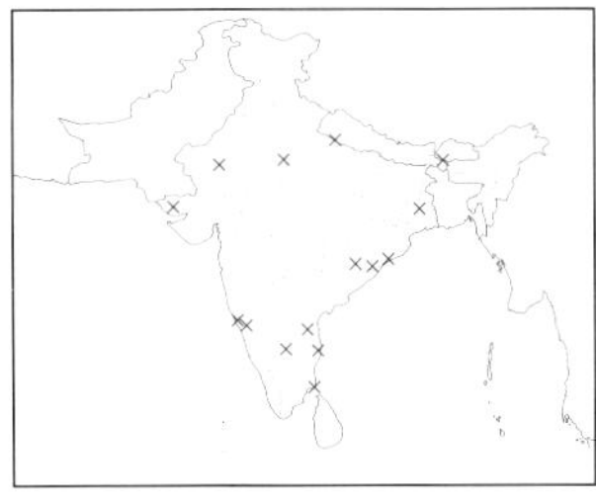

has entirely orange or pink lower mandible (lacking dark tip). Head usually appears dome-shaped, with crown feathers often raised, while tail appears long and graduated, and wings short. In fresh plumage, upperparts have rufous suffusion, especially to fringes of remiges, rump and uppertail-coverts (which is not apparent on Clamorous Reed), and is warmer buff on breast and flanks. The above features would also help in separation from Oriental Reed Warbler (p.720). **VOICE** Powerful song, with scratchy, staccato and unmusical notes interwoven in hurried repeated sequences, faster, less guttural and richer in mimicry than songs of other large *Acrocephalus*; hard *shak*, tongue-clicking *tuc* and louder chatter calls (P. Holt). **HABITS** Similar to those of other *Acrocephalus* warblers, but skulks in dense bushes, usually moving about with clumsy, heavy hops. **HABITAT** Tall grass and scrub along wooded streams, edges and clearings of forest, including mangroves, bushes in gardens and at the edges of cultivation, reeds, and bushes in marshes. **DISTRIBUTION AND STATUS** Winters mainly in S Nepal, NE and SW India and Bangladesh; scattered records elsewhere. **NP:** uncommon but regular in the centre and east; below 1500 m. **IN:** current status uncertain; found in plains and foothills. **BT:** rare. **BD:** local. **REFERENCES** Alström and Colston (1991), Shirihai *et al.* (1995).

***HIPPOLAIS* WARBLERS** Medium-sized warblers with a large bill, square-ended tail, and rather sloping forehead and peaked crown giving a distinctive domed head shape. Their songs are harsh and varied. They clamber about vegetation with a rather clumsy action.

BOOTED WARBLER *Hippolais caligata* — Plate 124

Booted Tree Warbler (F), Sykes's Warbler

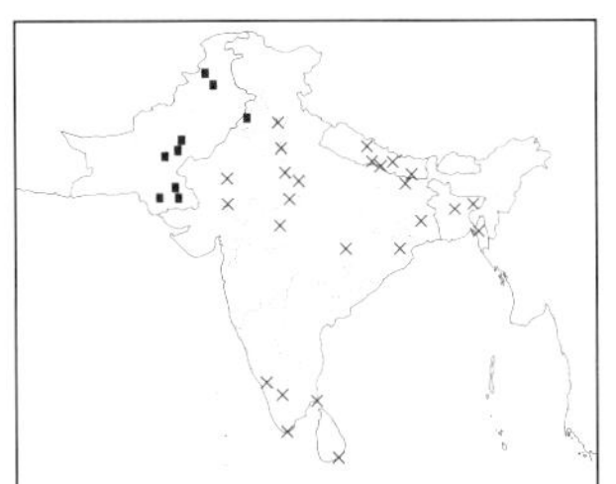

IDENTIFICATION 12 cm. A rather nondescript warbler with brown to grey-brown upperparts and off-white underparts, and a reasonably distinct supercilium. Often shows faint whitish edges and tips to outer tail feathers, and pale edges to tertials and secondaries which may appear as distinct panel on wing (although these features are frequently indistinct or not apparent, especially in worn plumage). Supercilium can be rather broad and square-ended behind the eye, and can be bordered above by a diffuse dark line, but dark border is often lacking or not apparent and prominence of supercilium is very variable. Wings look short and tail rather long owing to short uppertail- and undertail-coverts, and the bird can look rather pot-bellied. Head shape can appear *Acrocephalus*-like, especially when crown feathers are raised. Is rather *Phylloscopus*-like in feeding behaviour (being much more active and less skulking than e.g. Blyth's Reed Warbler, p.719), frequently foraging in outermost branches and with occasional fly-catching and even hovering, and also often on the ground. Two races winter widely in the subcontinent and, with much variation, confusion is possible with Common Chiffchaff (p.724), Blyth's Reed Warbler and also Blunt-winged and Paddyfield Warblers (p.718). Differences from those species are covered below. **Racial variation** The nominate race is typically shorter- and finer-billed than *H. c. rama*, with more prominent supercilium, and upperparts are warmer brown; it usually appears more *Phylloscopus*-like, owing to shorter bill, and more frequently feeds on the ground. Confusion is possible with Common Chiffchaff: in addition to above-mentioned plumage features, upperparts, especially edges to remiges and rectrices, lack any of the greenish or strong olive tones shown by Common Chiffchaff; bill is longer and is yellowish on lower mandible (at least at base), and legs are paler and browner; the supercilium is frequently no more distinct than on Common Chiffchaff, although Booted has less distinct pale crescent below eye; and Booted never shows yellow at bend of the wing. Possibly confusable with Paddyfield and Blunt-winged, especially those Booted with prominent supercilium and warm brown upperparts: helpful features distinguishing Booted are its less skulking, more *Phylloscopus*-like behaviour and appearance, squarer tail and short undertail-coverts, and presence of whitish fringes to remiges and edges to outer tail feathers (if apparent). In fresh plumage, Paddyfield and Blunt-winged are typically warmer rufescent-brown above, often with warm buff on breast sides and flanks, and when worn show brighter rufescent rump compared with Booted. *H. c. rama* is typically greyer and distinctly longer-billed than the nominate race, and more arboreal in its habits. It is easily confusable with Blyth's Reed: compared with that species, supercilium of *H. c. rama* is more distinct behind eye, lores can appear rather pale, and upperparts are a paler greyish-brown, while pale sides to tail and edges to remiges are good features if present; additional features are longer-looking, square-ended tail which can sometimes appear notched, despite being usually slightly rounded (although less so than on Blyth's Reed), shorter undertail- and uppertail-coverts, finer build, and *Phylloscopus*-like behaviour; bill of *rama* can appear as long as that of Blyth's Reed, but usually appears deeper throughout its length, broader at base and more extensively and obviously pale; legs and feet are paler and browner. For differences from Upcher's Warbler (p.722), see that species. **VOICE** The nominate race has a frequently uttered, hard *chur chur* call (recalling similar note of Common Stonechat, p.661); *H. c. rama* gives a rapidly repeated *tut-tut-tut...* call, which is softer, and is distinct from the harder *tack-tack* and harsh slow grating calls of Blyth's Reed. Both forms regularly sing while in India. **HABITS** Found singly or in loose parties, sometimes several foraging in the same tree. Moves restlessly about foliage and branches. Forages at all levels, from the tree canopy down to bushes, undergrowth and sometimes the ground. Captures insects mostly by gleaning, and also in the air by fluttering from the end of a branch. Unlike Olivaceous Warbler, does not persistently dip the tail. **HABITAT** Breeds near water in extensive areas of tamarisks and *Saccharum* reed-grass along rivers and canals, usually where subject to seasonal flooding. Winters in dry habitats and semi-desert: deciduous scrub and groves, bushes at the edges of cultivation and grass clumps; favours acacias. **BREEDING** May–July. Builds a cup-shaped nest of grasses and twigs, well concealed in a dense bush or grass clump, within 2 m of ground. **DISTRIBUTION AND STATUS** Breeds in Pakistan and very locally in Punjab, India; winters mainly in Pakistan, W, C and S India and Sri Lanka. **PK:** common; breeds widely in Baluchistan and occasionally elsewhere, especially in S Sindh; mainly a winter visitor or passage migrant, widespread in the Indus plains. **NP:** scarce winter visitor and passage migrant; 75–2810 m. **IN:** locally common winter visitor, and breeds in Punjab. **BD:** rare winter visitor. **LK:** winter visitor, mainly to N dry coastal areas. **REFERENCES** Shirihai *et al.* (1996), Svensson (1992).

OLIVACEOUS WARBLER *Hippolais pallida* — Not illustrated

Reported from India, but there are no confirmed records.

UPCHER'S WARBLER *Hippolais languida* — Plate 124

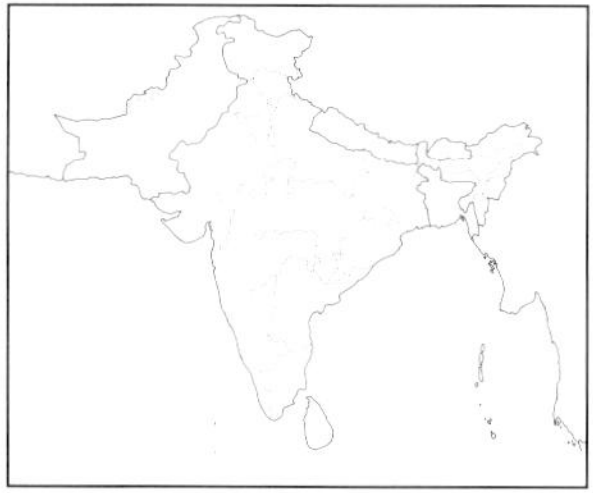

IDENTIFICATION 14 cm. Possibly confusable with Booted Warbler (p.721), especially of race *H. c. rama*. Distinguished from that species by larger size and heavier appearance, with broader and fuller tail and longer primary projection beyond tertials. Bill is stronger-looking. Upperparts are greyer (Booted is often more brownish, although can be very similar in coloration), and flight feathers, wing-coverts and tail often look noticeably darker than rest of upperparts (although this is variable, and may not be apparent as a result of light conditions, background and habitat, or wear). Supercilium is short and barely extends beyond eye. On breeding grounds has distinctive habit of waving and bobbing (often fanned) tail, while on passage it flicks tail downwards. Separated from Blyth's Reed (p.719) by paler and greyer upperparts, shorter extension of undertail-coverts, squarer-ended and darker tail, white edges and tips to outer rectrices which are usually conspicuous, blacker remiges and wing-coverts with prominent pale fringes in fresh plumage (especially apparent on tertials, and often forming pale panel on secondaries), and browner legs and feet. Much less skulking than Blyth's Reed, frequently perching out in open (on outermost branches and rocks, etc). **VOICE** Song is very variable, with much mimicry, and with rich, melodious quality; calls include a loud, deep *chuk* (Shirihai *et al.* 1996). **HABITS** Mostly keeps fairly low down in thick vegetation within grass clumps and bushes. Feeds chiefly by gleaning insects from leaves and branches; occasionally by making short aerial sallies to seize flying prey. Makes frequent tail movements. **HABITAT** Open stony hillsides covered in *Artemisia* bushes. **BREEDING** May. Builds a neat cup-shaped nest of grass and cobwebs 0.3–0.5 m above ground in a thorn bush in a ravine or gully with scattered bushes. **DISTRIBUTION AND STATUS PK:** rather uncommon summer visitor to Baluchistan; breeds 1800–2400 m.

TAILORBIRDS Have a long, decurved bill, short wings and a graduated tail, the latter held characteristically cocked. Tailorbirds are named for their habit of sewing a large leaf or several leaves together to form a cone, in which the nest is built.

MOUNTAIN TAILORBIRD *Orthotomus cuculatus* — Plate 125

Golden-headed Tailor Bird (I)

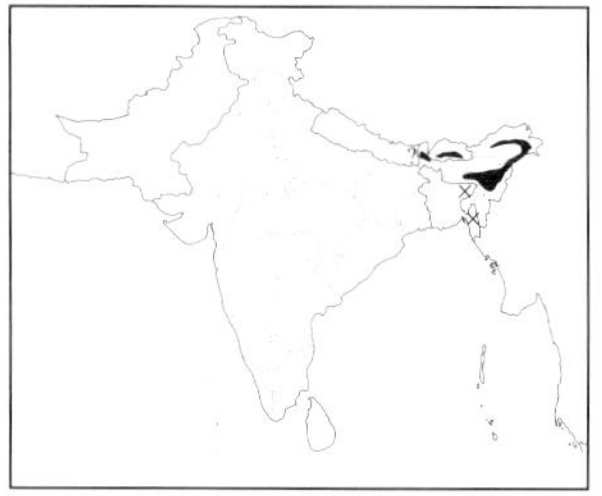

IDENTIFICATION 13 cm. Differs from Common and Dark-necked Tailorbirds (p.723) in brighter orange-rufous crown, yellowish supercilium contrasting with dark grey eye-stripe, grey ear-coverts, greyish throat and breast, and bright yellow belly and undertail-coverts. Possibly confusable with Broad-billed Warbler (p.737), but has long, slender bill, less extensive rufous on crown, dark grey nape and yellowish supercilium, and lacks white on tail. **Juvenile** is similar to adult, but has olive-green crown and nape (concolorous with mantle), and paler grey eye-stripe and supercilium. **VOICE** A thin, high-pitched and melodious whistle of four to six notes, glissading up and down the scale; call consists of dry *trrit* notes (Boonsong and Round 1991). **HABITS** Very similar to those of Common Tailorbird. Found in pairs or small parties. Skulking. Forages energetically within thickets of bushes and grass in the forest undergrowth; occasionally makes sallies after insects. **HABITAT** Evergreen biotope: forest, secondary growth, and mixed bush, grass and bamboo jungle. **BREEDING** May–July. Like Common Tailorbird, builds nest of grasses and moss inside sewn-up leaves, usually within 1 m of ground. **DISTRIBUTION AND STATUS** Resident. Himalayas in Nepal? and from Darjeeling, West Bengal, east to Arunachal Pradesh; NE India and Bangladesh. **NP:** possibly collected in 19th century, but the specimen may have originated in India. **IN:** uncommon; up to 1800 m. **BT:** uncommon; 305–1910 m. **BD:** resident or rare visitor to the northeast and southeast.

COMMON TAILORBIRD *Orthotomus sutorius* Plate 125

Tailor Bird (F,I,P)

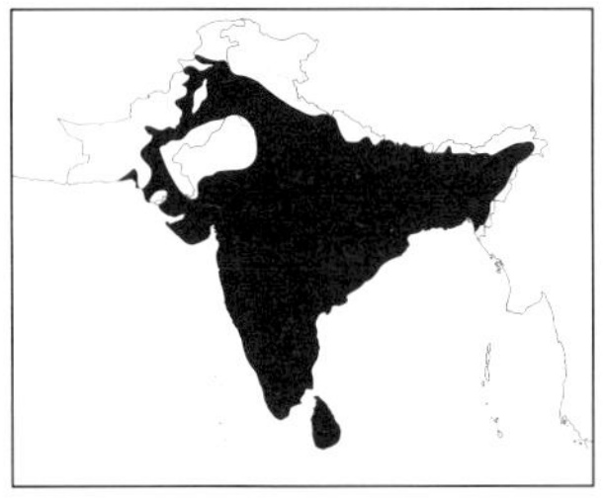

IDENTIFICATION 13 cm. Throughout most of its range, this is the only tailorbird and is readily identified by long, slightly downcurved pale bill, rufous forehead and forecrown, greenish upperparts, and dull whitish or buffish underparts. Frequently cocks tail. Breeding male has elongated central tail feathers. In NE subcontinent confusable with female Dark-necked Tailorbird (below); for differences, see that species. In same area, confusable also with the forest-dwelling Mountain Tailorbird (p.722), but is readily distinguishable by uniform whitish underparts. **Juvenile** is similar to adult, but lacks rufous on forehead and forecrown. **Racial variation** *O. s. sutorius* and *O. s. fernandonis* from Sri Lanka have darker and greener upperparts than birds from the rest of the subcontinent. **VOICE** Song is a loud *pitchik-pitchik-pitchik*; calls include a loud, quick-repeated *pit-pit-pit*, and a quick *cheep-cheep* (Ali and Ripley 1987). **HABITS** Generally found singly or in pairs. Usually keeps within bushes and plant clumps, but is confiding and will allow close approach. Hunts very actively, usually low down among herbaceous plants, bushes and on the ground; occasionally climbs quite high in trees. Feeds mainly on insects, also on flower nectar. Cocks tail constantly over the back. Flies weakly and only over short distances, still with tail cocked. **HABITAT** Bushes in gardens, edges of cultivation, deciduous scrub, forest edges, orchards, and irrigated forest plantations; also mangroves in Pakistan. **BREEDING** Throughout the year, varying locally, mainly in the monsoon. Builds a deep cup-shaped nest, usually within 1 m of ground, inside a large, broad, drooping leaf, the edges of which are sewn together to form a cone, with the top opening sheltered by the enclosing leaf. **DISTRIBUTION AND STATUS** Widespread resident in the subcontinent, except in parts of the northwest. **PK:** common and widespread in Indus plains and adjacent valleys; ascends Murree foothills up to 900 m. **NP:** common and widespread; below 1830 m. **IN:** common and widespread in plains and hills; up to 1800 m in Himalayas, to 1400 m (–2000 m) in peninsular hills. **BT:** common; below 1830 m. **BD:** common throughout. **LK:** common in lowlands and hills.

DARK-NECKED TAILORBIRD *Orthotomus atrogularis* Plate 125

Black-necked Tailor Bird (I)

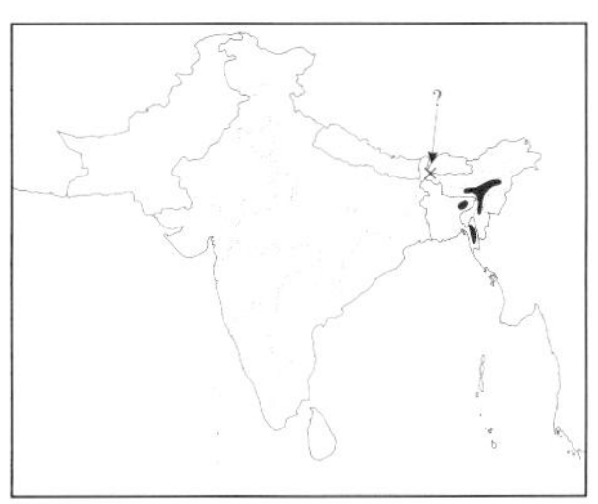

IDENTIFICATION 13 cm. **Adult** differs from Common Tailorbird (above) in having more extensive rufous on crown (extending onto hindcrown), yellow (rather than white or buffish-white) bend of wing, flanks and undertail-coverts, brighter yellow fringes to remiges, and different call. Readily distinguished from Mountain Tailorbird (p.722) by buffish-white underparts. **Male** has blackish lower throat and sides of breast, further distinguishing it from Common and Mountain (although Common, when calling or singing, reveals dark bases to feathers of neck). **Juvenile** is similar, but lacks rufous on forehead and forecrown. **VOICE** A nasal, staccato, high-pitched *kri-i-i-i-i*, a short *tew* and a dry *prrp-prrp* (Boonsong and Round 1991); song is a rather high, agitated, shivery *pirrah*, rapidly repeated 10–12 times (S. Madge). **HABITS** Similar to those of Common Tailorbird, but much more shy. Most easily located by its call. **HABITAT** Dense scrub, bamboo thickets and edges of broadleaved evergreen forest. **BREEDING** March–August. Nest and nest site are like those of Common Tailorbird. **DISTRIBUTION AND STATUS** Resident. West Bengal?, NE India (Assam, Meghalaya, Mizoram, Nagaland) and Bangladesh. **IN:** status uncertain, and very few recent published records; from base of the hills and adjacent plains up to 1800 m. **BD:** locally common in the northeast and southeast. **REFERENCES** Raman (1995).

TIT WARBLERS Small warblers with soft, copious plumage. Inhabit scrub or coniferous forest.

WHITE-BROWED TIT WARBLER *Leptopoecile sophiae* Plate 125

Stoliczka's Tit Warbler (F,I,N)

IDENTIFICATION 10 cm. Very distinctive, with white supercilium, rufous crown, greyish upperparts, white outer tail feathers, and bluish flanks and rump. **Male** has lilac wash to crown, violet-blue sides to head, throat and breast, and buffish belly. **Female** has pale grey-brown head sides and buffish-white underparts (except for lilac wash to flanks). **Racial variation** Male *L. s. obscura* of the C Himalayas differs from male *L. s. sophiae* of the W Himalayas, described above, in having darker upperparts and deeper purple coloration to underparts, lacking clearly defined buff belly. Female *obscura* has darker, deeper rufous crown, and greyer underparts. **VOICE** Slow, subdued *teet*;

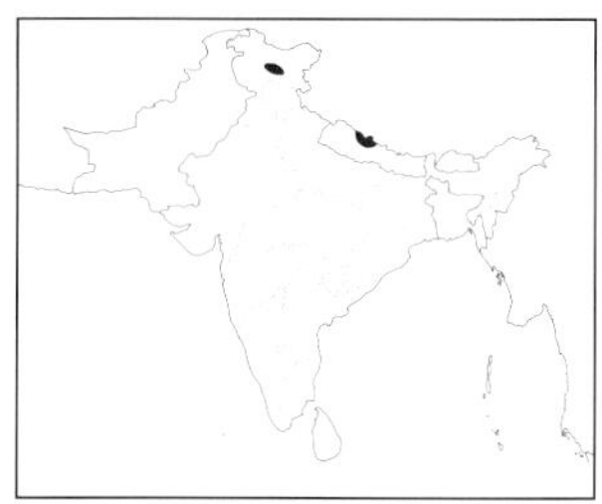

song is a sweet, loud chirping. **HABITS** Often in small parties, sometimes with other insectivorous birds. Quite shy. Forages very actively within bushes and undergrowth; flits and hops among branches and foliage, can hang upside-down like a tit, and sometimes flutters into the air to capture flying insects. Occasionally perches on top of a bush. Frequently cocks its tail. **HABITAT** Dwarf juniper, *Caragana* scrub or dwarf rhododendron above the treeline in Tibetan semi-desert; also winters in *Hippophae* thickets or willows along streams. **BREEDING** April–July. Nest is a ball or deep cup of moss, vegetable fibres and animal hair, built within 1 m of ground in a bush. **DISTRIBUTION AND STATUS** Resident, with some altitudinal movements. Baltistan and Gilgit, Pakistan, Ladakh and NW Nepal. **PK:** frequent in winter, 1800–3000 m; a few summer records above 3000 m. **NP:** frequent; 2700–4575 m all year, mainly above 3500 m. **IN:** common; breeds 3000–3900 m, winters down to 1800 m. **REFERENCES** Martens and Eck (1995).

***PHYLLOSCOPUS* WARBLERS** Rather small, slim and short-billed warblers, generally coloured in rather sombre greens or browns, and often referred to as leaf warblers. Useful identification features are voice, strength of supercilium, colour of underparts, rump, bill and legs, and presence or absence of wing-bars, of coronal bands or of white on the tail. The coloration of upperparts and underparts and the presence or prominence of wing-bars are affected by wear. Leaf warblers are fast-moving and restless, hopping and creeping about actively and often flicking the wings. They forage in vegetation at all levels, from the tree canopy down to the undergrowth, and a few species also feed on the ground. They mostly glean small insects and spiders from foliage, twigs and branches, often first disturbing prey by hovering and fluttering; they also make short fly-catching sallies.

WILLOW WARBLER *Phylloscopus trochilus* — Plate 125

IDENTIFICATION 11 cm. Very similar to Common Chiffchaff (below), subtle distinctions being different call, generally paler brown to orangish legs and feet (although can be dark grey-brown), larger-looking bill with orange basal two-thirds of lower mandible, and more prominent supercilium (and less noticeable pale crescent below eye, where crescent is often very apparent on Common Chiffchaff). In addition, appears more attenuated in shape, with more angular head, and has longer primary projection which is three-quarters of, or equal in length to, exposed tertials (on Common Chiffchaff, exposed primaries are a third to half of tertial length). Does not frequently bob tail as does Common Chiffchaff. Confusion is also possible with a worn Greenish Warbler (p.731) lacking wing-bar, but supercilium is shorter and less prominent, and has different call. In fresh plumage, fringes of wing-coverts are paler, and can give rise to suggestion of a wing-bar (but this is never white and well-defined as on Greenish). There is considerable variation in plumage: upperparts vary from olive-brown with yellowish-green tinge to brownish-grey and virtually lacking greenish tinge; and throat, breast and supercilium vary from being strongly washed with yellow to being entirely whitish. **VOICE** Call is a distinctly disyllabic *who-eet* (different from the plaintive monosyllabic *peu* of Common Chiffchaff, and recalling Mountain Chiffchaff, p.725, but more strongly disyllabic). **HABITS** Well studied in Europe. A typical *Phylloscopus.* Feeds from the tree canopy down to undergrowth. Usually has a horizontal carriage. Flight is fast and light, with a flitting action; agile when fly-catching or hovering. **HABITAT** Bushes and trees. **DISTRIBUTION AND STATUS** One recorded in Gujarat (Ali 1954), but subsequently reidentified as Greenish Warbler (Abdulali and Unnithan 1985); also in Nagaland (Meinertzhagen collection in Ali and Ripley 1987), but this record is considered doubtful. **REFERENCES** Harris *et al.* (1989).

COMMON CHIFFCHAFF *Phylloscopus collybita* — Plate 125

Brown Leaf Warbler (F,I), Chiffchaff (N)

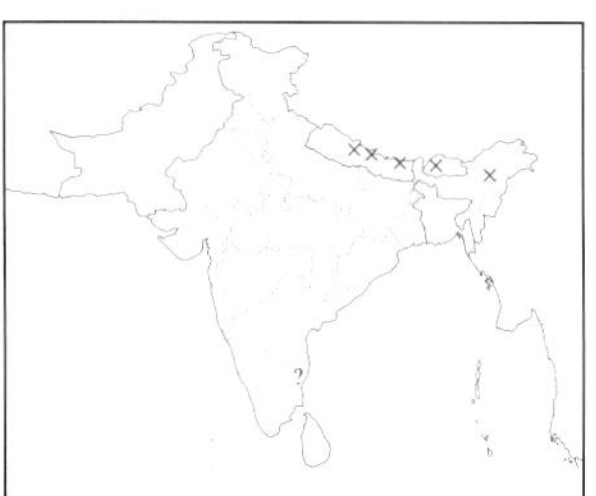

IDENTIFICATION 11 cm. A rather nondescript *Phylloscopus* warbler with whitish or buffish supercilium, and greyish to brownish upperparts with olive-green cast to rump and edges of remiges and rectrices. Underparts are whitish, with variable buffish or greyish wash to sides of breast and flanks. Very similar to Mountain Chiffchaff (p.724) and Plain Leaf Warbler (p.724) of the NW subcontinent, and main differences are given in accounts for those species. Elsewhere in the subcontinent, most likely to be confused with Greenish Warbler (p.731) or Dusky Warbler (p.726). Told from Greenish by smaller blackish bill and black legs, shorter and less prominent supercilium, and prominent whitish crescent below eye, lack of well-defined white or yellowish-white greater-covert wing-bar (although this can be missing on Greenish in worn plumage), and different call; in fresh plumage, upperparts are distinctly browner than on Greenish, while underparts generally appear dirtier and more heavily sullied with buff or grey than in *viridanus* race of that species. Appears slimmer and longer-tailed than Dusky, and is less skulking in habits; can be very similar in plumage, but generally has a shorter and less prominent supercilium (with distinct eye-crescent), usually has yellow at bend of wing, and in fresh plumage has olive-green edges to coverts, remiges and rectrices and sometimes also to back and scapulars (which are lacking on Dusky). Dark bill, legs and feet of Common Chiffchaff, and very different call, are also very distinctive. For differences from Willow Warbler (p.724), see that species. **Racial variation** *P. c. collybita* has been recorded once in the NW subcontinent. This differs from *P. c. tristis*, described above, in having variable greenish-olive upperparts, yellowish coloration to supercilium and eye-crescent, and varying amounts of yellow on underparts (especially on breast and undertail-coverts). **VOICE** Calls include a plaintive monosyllabic *peu* or more disyllabic *sie-u*, as well as a plaintive *hweet*; birds in E India have a very different *zit* call (T. Inskipp). Song is a *whichoo-weet-chu-whichoo-twuit-twit-tu-wichoo*, which is said to be a little more fluid and less disjointed in sequence than that of Mountain Chiffchaff (Roberts 1992). **HABITS** Found singly or in small parties. Forages actively at all levels, from the tops of tall trees down to bushes, undergrowth, standing crops and sometimes the ground. Feeds chiefly by gleaning, but will also hover and make short aerial sallies; often takes prey above water, sometimes picking from the surface. Has a horizontal carriage. Its flight is agile, but rather jerky and fluttering. **HABITAT** Forest, including mangroves, and groves, bushes, gardens, standing crops and reedbeds. **DISTRIBUTION AND STATUS** Winters in Pakistan, S Nepal, India south to N Karnataka and Orissa, and Bangladesh. **PK:** common throughout the plains, in N areas and main valleys. **NP:** frequent throughout; below 1370 m (–2800 m on passage). **IN:** common and widespread in the north; up to 2100 m in Himalayas. **BT:** uncommon. **BD:** common.

MOUNTAIN CHIFFCHAFF *Phylloscopus sindhianus* — Plate 125

***P. collybita* (I)**

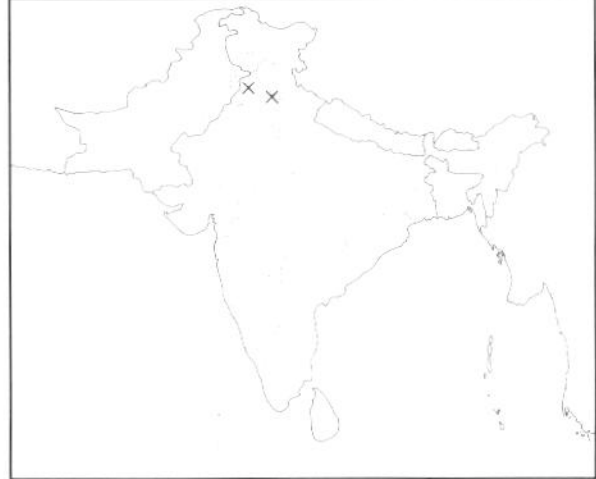

IDENTIFICATION 11 cm. Has brownish to greyish-brown upperparts and mainly whitish underparts. Lacks wing-bars and lacks any yellow on supercilium or underparts. Very similar to Common Chiffchaff (p.724), from which it is often indistinguishable on plumage in the field, although does seem to have different call. Generally lacks olive-green tinge to rump and edges of tail feathers, and usually shows buffish edges to wing-coverts and remiges (lacking the olive-green tones usually present on Common Chiffchaff), although these differences may not be apparent in worn plumage. In fresh plumage, shows warm buff coloration to ear-coverts, breast sides and flanks (although this is often also evident on Common). Bend of wing is often whitish (usually brighter yellow on Common, although there is some overlap). Differs from Plain Leaf Warbler (below) mainly in larger size, proportionately longer tail, and call. **VOICE** Call is a distinctly disyllabic *swe-eet*, or *tiss-yip* (sometimes almost three-noted, *tiss-yuitt*), different from the plaintive monosyllabic *peu* of Common Chiffchaff; song is similar to that of Common, although more disjointed and tinny-sounding, e.g. *chit-chiss-chyi-chiss-chit-chiss-chyi-chip-chit-chyi* (Roberts 1992). **HABITS** Very like those of Common Chiffchaff. **HABITAT** Breeds in subalpine shrubberies, also lower down on open hillsides with scattered bushes, poplar groves and willows; winters in riverain trees and bushes, trees along canal banks, and tamarisk bushes in seasonally flooded areas. **BREEDING** May–July. Nest is a dome, made of fine grass and reed stems, built in low thorny scrub within 0.5 m of ground. **DISTRIBUTION AND STATUS** Breeds in W Himalayas in Pakistan (NW Chitral, Gilgit and Baltistan) and NW India (Ladakh and Rupshu, Kashmir; Lahul and Spiti, Himachal Pradesh); winters mainly in plains and Himalayan foothills in S Pakistan. **PK:** locally frequent in summer, breeds from 2300 m up to over 3600 m; winters in the plains. **IN:** locally common on breeding grounds, 2500–4400 m. **REFERENCES** Roberts (1992), Williamson (1967).

PLAIN LEAF WARBLER *Phylloscopus neglectus* — Plate 125

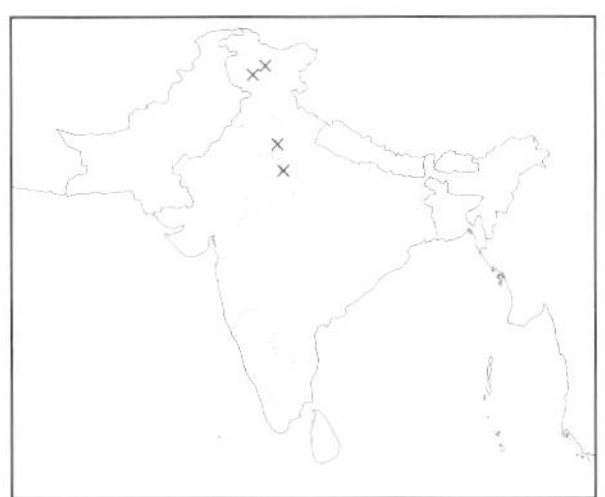

IDENTIFICATION 10 cm. A grey-brown and whitish *Phylloscopus* with whitish supercilium, similar in size to Hume's Warbler (p.730) but recalling a small Common Chiffchaff (p.724). Very similar to Common Chiffchaff and Mountain Chiffchaff (above), and best told by smaller size and proportionately larger head and shorter tail, and distinctive calls. Flicks wings, but does not seem to bob tail like Common Chiffchaff. Lacks yellowish or greenish on upperparts and wing (usually apparent at least on edges to rectrices and remiges and bend of wing of Common Chiffchaff), and in fresh plumage shows pale buffish edges to secondaries which form panel on wing. Further, upperparts tend to be paler and greyer, but can show yellow streaks on breast when fresh. Many are almost identical in plumage to Mountain Chiffchaff, although warm buff tones to cheeks, sides of breast and flanks are less apparent. **VOICE** Calls have been variously described as a hard *tak-tak* or Lesser Whitethroat-like *tshak-tshak*, a low-pitched *churr* or *chiip*, and a *twissa-twissa*; song is a thin, high-pitched warbling *chit-chuwich-chissa* or *chit-chu-chit chit-chu-twissa-twit*. **HABITS** Rather shy. Feeds mainly in the canopy within cover, sometimes making aerial sallies. Flight is more whirring and jerky than that of other *Phylloscopus*. **HABITAT** Summers in juniper forest and low bushes, also in Chighoza Pine forest; winters in tamarisks in damp riverain habitats, and also in dry habitats such as roadside trees and acacias. **BREEDING** Details unknown in the region. In Iran, nest is a half-sphere with a side entrance, built low down in a thorny bush. **DISTRIBUTION AND STATUS** Altitudinal migrant. Breeds in Baluchistan,

Pakistan and Kashmir; winters mainly in Pakistan. **PK:** common in summer in Baluchistan, above 2400 m; fairly common in winter throughout Sindh, also occurs in S Punjab. **IN:** current status uncertain. **REFERENCES** Eriksen (1988), Hirschfeld (1994), Roberts (1992), Robson (1985), Sangha (1995).

DUSKY WARBLER *Phylloscopus fuscatus* Plate 125

Dusky Leaf Warbler (F,I)

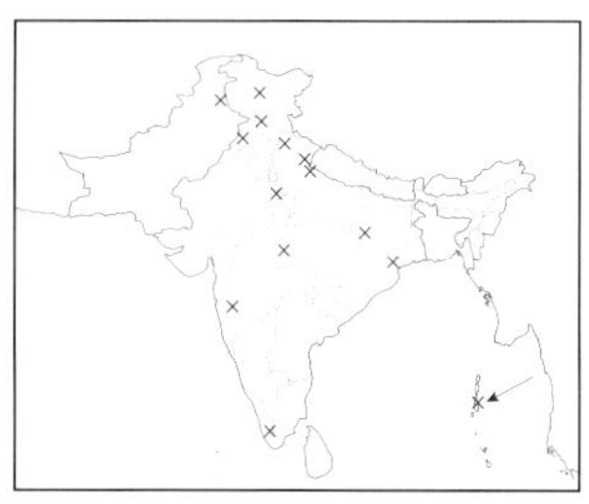

IDENTIFICATION 11 cm. A brown-and-whitish *Phylloscopus* warbler with broad buffish-white supercilium. Underparts are white to rather dirty greyish-white, often with buff on sides of breast and flanks. Upperparts vary from dark brown to paler greyish-brown. Lacks any yellow or green in plumage (except, rarely, for a slight trace of yellow on belly of some birds). Hard call is very different from calls of other similar *Phylloscopus* species. Most likely to be confused with Common Chiffchaff (p.724), which can be very similar in overall coloration: Dusky appears stockier and slightly shorter- but broader-tailed, and has a longer and broader supercilium offset against stronger dark eye-stripe, lacks olive-green edges to wing-coverts, remiges and rectrices (although olive-green can be lacking on worn Common Chiffchaff), lacks yellow at bend of wing, and has paler legs, and pale (orangish or pinkish) base to lower mandible. Unlike Common Chiffchaff, is typically very skulking. Distinguished from Smoky Warbler (below) by paler and browner upperparts, more prominent white or buffish supercilium, and whiter underparts. From Sulphur-bellied and Tickell's Leaf Warblers (p.727 and below) by coloration of upperparts, and whitish and buff coloration to supercilium and underparts. Possibly confusable with Pale-footed Bush Warbler (p.711), but has longer tail, longer primary projection, darker, brownish legs and feet, and different call. For differences from Radde's Warbler (p.728), see that species. **VOICE** Call is a hard *chack chack*. **HABITS** Usually solitary. Secretive; skulks in dense low cover, often on or close to the ground, sometimes in lower branches. Feeds mainly by gleaning; also makes darting flights after insects. **HABITAT** Bushes, hedges and long grass, especially near water. **DISTRIBUTION AND STATUS** Winters mainly in Himalayan foothills from W Nepal east to Arunachal Pradesh; NE India and Bangladesh. **NP:** widespread and frequent; below 1600 m. **IN:** locally common in plains and hills. **BT:** fairly common; 250–1830 m (–3810 m on passage). **BD:** common throughout.

SMOKY WARBLER *Phylloscopus fuligiventer* Plate 125

Smoky Willow Warbler (I), Smoky Leaf Warbler (F)

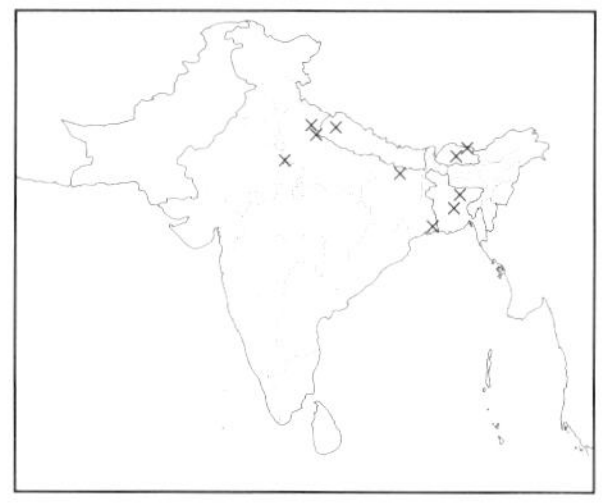

IDENTIFICATION 10 cm. A small, very dark *Phylloscopus* warbler with oily yellow on underparts. Separated from Dusky and Sulphur-bellied Warblers (above and p.727) and from Tickell's Leaf Warbler (below) by smaller size and short-looking tail, much darker, dark sooty-olive upperparts (with greenish tinge in fresh plumage), comparatively short and indistinct yellowish supercilium (with prominent white crescent below eye), and mainly dusky-olive underparts (almost concolorous with upperparts), with oily yellow centre to throat, breast and belly. **Racial variation** *P. f. tibetanus*, which occurs in NE subcontinent in winter, differs from the nominate race, described above, in lacking any yellow on the supercilium and underparts. **VOICE** Call is distinct from that of similar species, being a throaty *thrup thrup*; song is a monotonous *tsli-tsli-tsli-tsli-tsli* (Ali and Ripley 1987). **HABITS** Found singly or in pairs. Keeps on or close to the ground. In the breeding season, creeps about in low scrub and clambers among boulders; in winter, forages close to the water's edge, sometimes darting out and hovering briefly over water. **HABITAT** Summers in dwarf juniper shrubberies and other low bushes above the treeline, also in alpine meadows with scattered boulders; winters in dense undergrowth and tall grass near water. **BREEDING** Very poorly known. Probably May–August; fledged young found in Nepal in August. **DISTRIBUTION AND STATUS** Altitudinal migrant. Breeds in Nepal, Sikkim and Bhutan; winters in adjacent foothills and plains from N Uttar Pradesh east to NE India. **NP:** uncommon; summers 3900–5000 m, regular in winter below 915 m. **IN:** uncommon; summers from 3960 m up to at least 4270 m, winters in plains and foothills. **BT:** locally common; summers 4205–4265 m and probably higher. **BD:** vagrant. **REFERENCES** Martens and Eck (1995), Robson (1985, 1996a).

TICKELL'S LEAF WARBLER *Phylloscopus affinis* Plate 126

Tickell's Warbler (N)

IDENTIFICATION 11 cm. A greenish-and-yellow *Phylloscopus* with prominent yellow supercilium but without any wing-bars. Confusion is possible with Sulphur-bellied Warbler (p.727). Has dark greenish to greenish-brown upperparts, greenish edges to primaries and secondaries, and brighter lemon-yellow underparts (lacking strong buff tones to throat, breast and flanks). Supercilium is similar in coloration to throat, and eye-stripe is more clearly defined than on Sulphur-bellied, contrasting with yellowish ear-coverts. Greater care is needed with some worn individuals, when upperparts may lack greenish cast and underparts and supercilium may be paler yellow: compared with Sulphur-bellied, supercilium remains concolorous with throat, and underparts are paler and lack strong buff coloration to breast, flanks and undertail-coverts. Possibly confusable with Greenish Warbler (p.731) (especially *P. t. nitidus*), which may lack wing-bars in worn plumage, but Tickell's Leaf has darker upperparts, brighter yellow underparts (only a few very

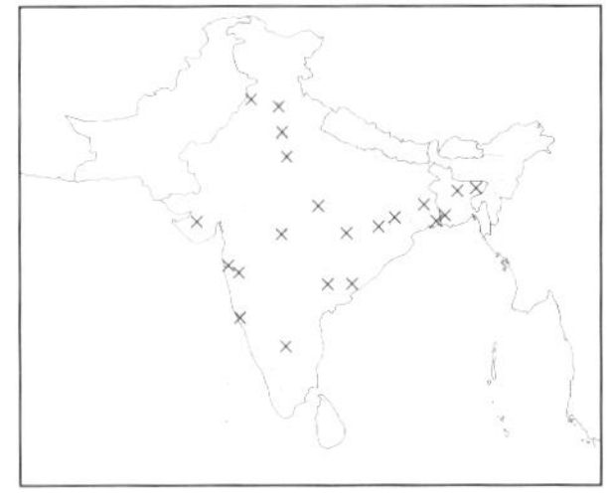

pale and worn individuals may approach Greenish in coloration of underparts), and different call. For differences from Aberrant Bush Warbler (p.712) and Buff-throated Warbler (below), see those species. **VOICE** Call is a *chit* or *sit*, not so hard and chacking as Dusky Warbler's (p.726); song is a short *chip....whi-whi-whi-whi*, similar to that of Sulphur-bellied, but hard introductory note is different from the thinner, drawn-out opening note of that species (Roberts 1992). **HABITS** Found singly, in pairs or in loose parties, depending on the season. Quite tame. Flits actively among low bushes, rocks and on the ground in the breeding season; in winter usually in bushes, also in trees. Occasionally makes aerial sallies after insects. **HABITAT** Summers in bushes in subalpine and alpine zones, in open country with bushes in temperate zone, and in forest clearings with bushes; winters in bushes and trees at edges of forest and cultivation, and in secondary growth. **BREEDING** May–August. Nest is a ball of grass, placed in a low bush. **DISTRIBUTION AND STATUS** Breeds in Himalayas from N Pakistan east to Bhutan; winters in Himalayan foothills and adjacent plains, NE and SW India and Bangladesh; widespread elsewhere in India, possibly on passage or wintering. **PK:** common summer visitor; 2700–4200 m. **NP:** common and widespread; summers mainly 2550–4880 m, winters chiefly in the terai, occasionally up to 1190 m. **IN:** common summer visitor to Himalayas, breeds 3300–4800 m; widespread in winter, chiefly in the hills, from the base up to 2100 m. **BT:** common. **BD:** scarce winter visitor. **REFERENCES** Alström and Olsson (1994), Martens and Eck (1995).

BUFF-THROATED WARBLER *Phylloscopus subaffinis* — Plate 126

***P. affinis* (I)**

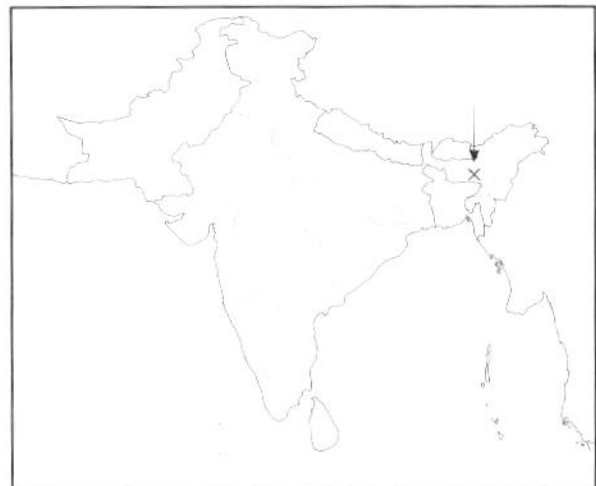

IDENTIFICATION 11 cm. Very similar in appearance to Tickell's Leaf Warbler (p.726), and is best told by subtle differences in coloration of underparts, head and bill patterns, structure, and calls and song. Compared with Tickell's Leaf, underparts of Buff-throated are more yellowish-buff (paler on centre of belly), the supercilium is less prominent and more buffish-yellow (only slightly more yellow in tone than underparts), and the eye-stripe is less distinct (contrasting less with rather dusky ear-coverts). Supercilium is usually uniform in colour on Buff-throated (often becomes paler towards rear on Tickell's). The tip of the lower mandible is extensively dark, while Tickell's has little or no dark at tip (although there is a slight overlap in this feature). Buff-throated is also slightly smaller, with proportionately longer tail. **VOICE** Call is a soft, rather weak *trrup* or *tripp*; song is slower and weaker than that of Tickell's Leaf Warbler and does not begin with the *chip* note, although sometimes introduced by a short, subdued *trr* or *trr-trr* (Alström and Olsson 1994). **HABITS** Unknown in the region. **HABITAT** Unknown in the region. **DISTRIBUTION AND STATUS IN:** one was collected in Meghalaya in winter; vagrant, or possibly overlooked and more regular. **REFERENCES** Alström and Olsson (1994), Rasmussen (1996).

SULPHUR-BELLIED WARBLER *Phylloscopus griseolus* — Plate 126

Olivaceous Leaf Warbler (F,I)

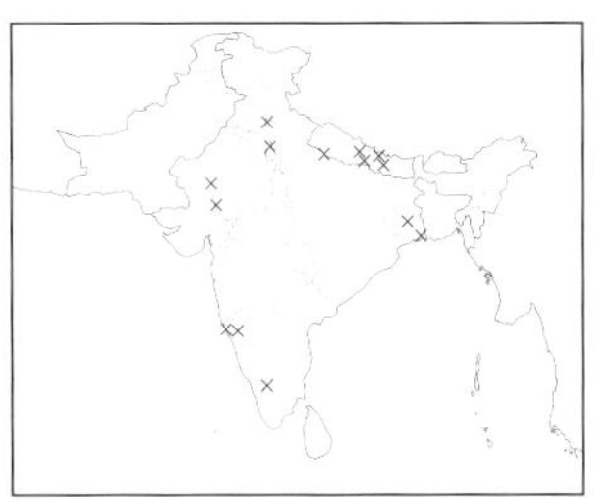

IDENTIFICATION 11 cm. A dark *Phylloscopus* warbler with yellow supercilium and yellowish-buff underparts. Most likely to be confused with Tickell's Leaf Warbler (p.726), but stockier appearance, different call and distinctive habits of Sulphur-bellied are often sufficient for identification. Further, has colder brown to brownish-grey upperparts lacking any greenish tones, greyish-white (rather than greenish) edges to remiges, and duller underparts. Has strong buff tones to breast, flanks and undertail-coverts, with yellow purest on belly. Supercilium is bright sulphur-yellow, and distinctly brighter than throat, and has grey-brown ear-coverts and sides of breast (which are yellower on Tickell's Leaf and contrast with more prominent dark eye-stripe). Possibly confusable with Smoky Warbler (p.726), but has more prominent supercilium, and is paler greyer-brown on the upperparts and paler and yellower on the underparts. In fresh first-winter plumage, has browner upperparts and more uniformly buff underparts. Yellowish supercilium and buffish throat and belly would separate it from Dusky Warbler (p.726). **VOICE** Call is a distinctive, soft *quip* or *dip*; song a high-pitched *tseep-tyi-tyi-tyi-tyi-tyi* (Roberts 1992). **HABITS** Behaviour is characteristic and is a good distinction from Tickell's Leaf Warbler. Climbs about rocks like Eastern Rock Nuthatch (p.677); when in wooded areas, frequently creeps on tree trunks and branches like a nuthatch. Forages on or close to the ground, often among rocks, also in low undergrowth and scrub; in wintering areas, frequently also hunts on walls of old buildings. **HABITAT** Summers in open dry, stony mountain slopes with scattered junipers and Blue Pine bushes and screes dotted with bushes; winters in rocky areas, steep-sided ravines or around ancient buildings, and in deciduous woodland. **BREEDING** June and July. Nest is a large ball of grass or juniper fibres, built in low bushes. **DISTRIBUTION AND STATUS** Breeds in hills of N and W Pakistan, and in Himalayas in N Pakistan and from Ladakh east to Lahul and Spiti, Himachal Pradesh; winters mainly in C and NW India; scattered records from elsewhere in India. **PK:** common; breeds 2300–3300 m, passage migrant in the plains, mainly in N Punjab and NW Pakistan. **NP:** scarce passage migrant and winter visitor; below 1500 m. **IN:** locally common; breeds 2400–4500 m, winters in plains and hills up to 1000 m, passage migrant in the northwest. **REFERENCES** Alström and Olsson (1994).

RADDE'S WARBLER *Phylloscopus schwarzi* Plate 125

Radde's Leaf Warbler (F)

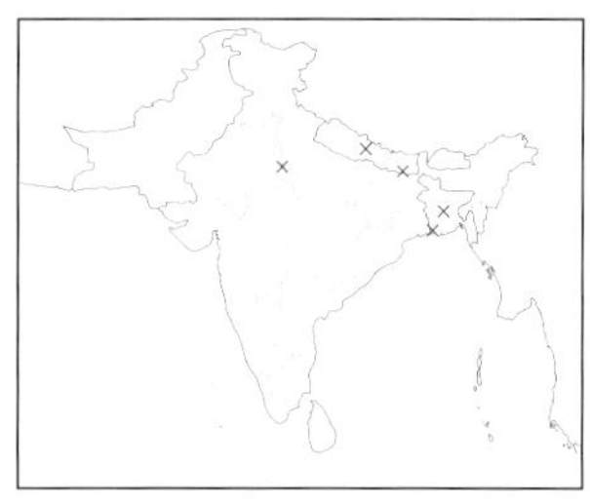

IDENTIFICATION 12 cm. Has olive-brown upperparts, long buffish-white supercilium, contrasting with dark eye-stripe, and whitish underparts with buff wash to sides of breast and flanks. Appears stockier than Dusky Warbler (p.726), with bigger head and with longer tail, which may be cocked and swayed when the bird is agitated. Bill is thicker, with more distinctly curved culmen, and typically looks rather pale. Has longer supercilium, which is broader and diffuse in front of eye (rather than narrow and sharply defined in front of eye as on Dusky), and often curves upwards towards nape (and is bordered above by diffuse dark margin), and in fresh plumage coloration of supercilium also tends to differ: on Radde's it is a deeper buff in front of the eye than it is behind, while on Dusky it is whitish in front of the eye, becoming buffish towards rear. Further, has thicker and stronger-looking, brighter orangish or yellowish legs and feet, and different call. In fresh plumage (especially first-winter), can show pronounced greenish-olive cast to upperparts, buffish-yellow cast to supercilium and underparts, and rufous-buff undertail-coverts, which are additional, more striking differences from Dusky. **VOICE** Call is different from Dusky's, a nervous, twittering *twit-twit* or *prit-prit* or a harsher *bit bit*; also a sharp *chuck chuck* or *tschak* (J. Scharringa). **HABITS** Skulks in low cover, keeping on or near the ground. Has similar habits to Dusky Warbler, but Dusky is more active, constantly flicking wings and tail and more likely to feed high in trees. Not recorded hovering or fly-catching. Flight is usually low and direct, often ending in a sudden dive into cover. **HABITAT** Undergrowth and bushes. **DISTRIBUTION AND STATUS NP, IN, BD:** vagrant. **REFERENCES** Alström and Colston (1991), Jepson (1987), Leader (1995).

BUFF-BARRED WARBLER *Phylloscopus pulcher* Plate 126

Orange-barred Leaf Warbler (F,I,N)

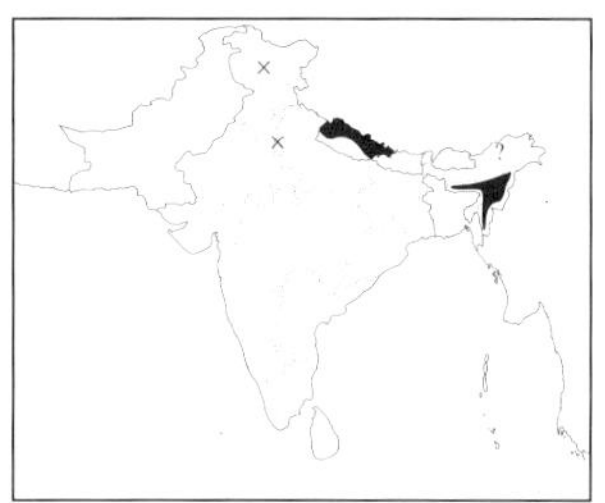

IDENTIFICATION 10 cm. Similar in shape and size to Hume's Warbler (p.730). Distinguished from that species by buffish-orange wing-bars, white on tail (apparent as tail is flicked open), and small yellowish rump patch. From below, tail appears largely white with dark border. Coloration of wing-bars can be difficult to determine, and may be paler and more buffish when worn, and median-covert wing-bar is often not apparent. Upperparts are dark olive-green, with greyer sides to crown (and paler and often very poorly defined dull yellowish centre to rear crown), and underparts are sullied with grey and can be noticeably washed with yellow (although generally appear rather dull). In overall coloration is very similar to *mandellii* race of Hume's, but is darker above and dirty yellow below compared with nominate Hume's. Above features also help separate it from Yellow-browed Warbler (p.730). Possibly confusable with Ashy-throated Warbler (below), which also has white on tail, but is slightly larger and less compact, and is readily told by orange-buff wing-bars, yellowish supercilium, and uniform underparts (lacking bright yellow belly and flanks of Ashy-throated). **Racial variation** *P. p. kangrae* of the NW Himalayas differs from the nominate race, described above, in having brighter, more yellowish-olive upperparts and cleaner yellow underparts. **VOICE** Call is a short, sharp *swit*; song is a high-pitched twitter, preceded by, or ending with, a drawn-out trill. **HABITS** Usually in mixed hunting parties of other insectivorous species in the non-breeding season. Arboreal; forages actively among foliage and twigs in the upper storey. Hovers less frequently than Ashy-throated and Lemon-rumped Warblers (p.728 and p.729). **HABITAT** Summers in subalpine shrubberies of birch, juniper or rhododendron, and forest of fir, birch or mixed conifers–rhododendron–birch; winters in oak and other broadleaved forest. **BREEDING** June and July. Nest is a ball of moss, grass and lichen, built in a thick bush, against a tree trunk or in a tree branch, 0.6–4 m above ground. **DISTRIBUTION AND STATUS** Resident, subject to altitudinal movements. Breeds in Himalayas from W Himachal Pradesh east to Bhutan, and in NE Indian hills; winters at lower altitudes in the same hills. **NP:** common and widespread; summers 3250–4300 m, winters 915–3050 m and possibly higher (down to 75 m). **IN:** common; breeds 2800–4300 m, winters 500–2800 m. **BT:** common; 610–4265 m. **REFERENCES** Alström and Olsson (1987), Martens and Eck (1995), Ticehurst (1938), Williamson (1967).

ASHY-THROATED WARBLER *Phylloscopus maculipennis* Plate 126

Grey-faced Leaf Warbler (F,I,N)

IDENTIFICATION 9 cm. Similar in shape and size to Lemon-rumped Warbler (p.729), with yellow rump and double yellowish wing-bars. Separated from that species by greyish-white supercilium and crown-stripe contrasting with dark grey lateral crown-stripes and eye-stripe, greyish ear-coverts, throat and breast, yellow belly, flanks and undertail-coverts, and white on tail (apparent as tail is flicked open). Possibly confusable with Buff-barred Warbler (above), which also has white on tail: is smaller and more compact than that species, with yellowish (rather than orange-buff) wing-bars, greyish-white supercilium and crown-stripe, and two-toned (grey and yellow) underparts, and has brighter, more clearly defined yellow rump. **VOICE** Call is a short *swit*; song is a *ti-ti–whee-tew* or *whee-teew–whee-teew* (Fleming *et al.* 1984). **HABITS** Usually seen singly or in foraging parties,

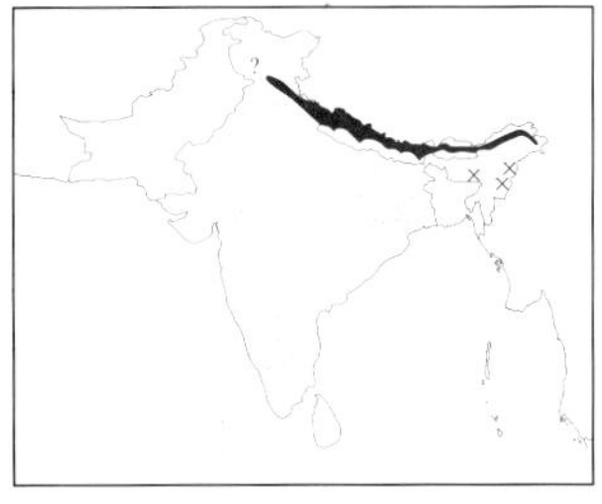

often mixed with other insectivorous species. Keeps mainly in trees; also frequents bushes. Very restless; flutters and hovers among foliage and twigs (yellow rump and white on outer tail feathers are then conspicuous). **HABITAT** Summers in oak–rhododendron and deciduous forest with a well-developed understorey, also coniferous–rhododendron forest; winters in broadleaved forest and secondary growth. **BREEDING** Little known. Mid April–July. Nest is a ball of moss, suspended from a branch about 5 m above ground. **DISTRIBUTION AND STATUS** Resident, subject to altitudinal movements. Breeds in Himalayas from W Himachal Pradesh east to Arunachal Pradesh, and probably NE Indian hills; winters at lower altitudes. **NP:** fairly common and widespread; summers chiefly 2440–3500 m, winters 1525–2900 m (down to 915 m). **IN:** locally fairly common; breeds 2500–3400 m, winters from 2900 m down to the foothills. **BT:** common; 1220–3530 m. **REFERENCES** Ticehurst (1938), Williamson (1967).

LEMON-RUMPED WARBLER *Phylloscopus chloronotus* — Plate 126

Pallas's Leaf Warbler (R), Yellow-rumped Leaf Warbler, Pale-rumped Warbler (F), *P. proregulus* (F,I,R)

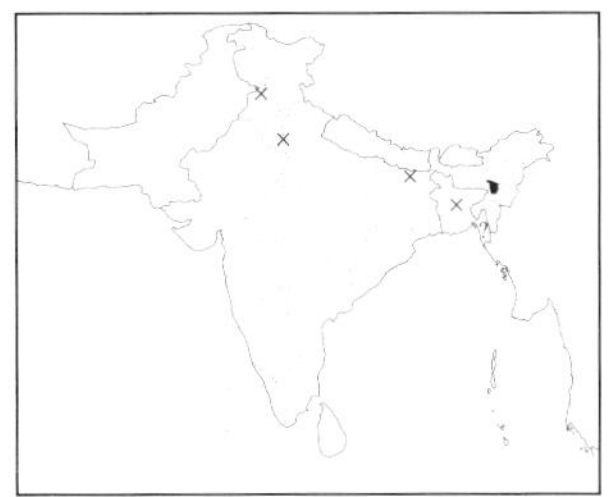

IDENTIFICATION 9 cm. Most likely to be confused with Hume's and Yellow-browed Warblers (p.730), having broad yellowish-white supercilium, double yellowish-white wing-bars and whitish underparts. Distinguished from those species by smaller and more compact appearance, yellowish crown-stripe contrasting with dark olive sides of crown (which are clearly darker than mantle), and well-defined yellowish (sometimes almost whitish) rump. Possibly confusable with Ashy-throated Warbler (p.728), but lacks white on tail, has yellowish supercilium and crown-stripe, and underparts are uniform whitish or yellowish-white. *P. c. simlaensis* (see below) is possibly confusable with Brooks's Leaf Warbler (below), but has clearly defined yellow crown-stripe and rump band, and dark crown sides which contrast with mantle, and lacks strong yellow wash to throat and breast of that species. **Racial variation** *P. c. simlaensis* of W Himalayas has brighter yellowish-green upperparts, and brighter yellow supercilium, crown-stripe and cheeks, compared with *P. c. chloronotus* of E Himalayas. **VOICE** Two different basic types of song: one is a drawn-out thin rattle followed by a series of stammering notes on the same pitch, *tsirrrrrrrrrrrr-tsi-tsi-tsi-tsi-tsi-tsi-tsi-tsi-tsi-tsi-tsi-tsi-tsi-tsi-tsi–tsi-tsi*; the other is somewhat variable, but is commonly a stuttering, 'endless' series of notes with alternating pitch, *tsi-tsi-tsi-tsi-tsi-tsu-tsu-tsi-tsi tsu-tsu tsi-tsi tsi-tsi-tsi-tsi-tsi tsirrp tsi-tsi tsu-tsu tsu-tsu tsi-tsi tsu-tsu-tsu*. The call is a high-pitched *uist* (Alström and Olsson 1990). **HABITS** Keeps in company with other insectivorous species in the non-breeding season. Extremely active; frequently hovers in and around foliage (showing yellow rump). Hunts chiefly in the upper half of trees, sometimes in bushes. **HABITAT** Breeds mainly in coniferous and mixed coniferous–broadleaved forest, sometimes in pure stands of oak or rhododendron; winters in forest and secondary growth. **BREEDING** April–July. Nest is a ball of moss, lichen and birch bark, hidden in the outer branch of a conifer, 2–15 m above ground. **DISTRIBUTION AND STATUS** Altitudinal migrant. Breeds in Himalayas from N Pakistan east to Arunachal Pradesh; winters lower down and in hills of NE India. **PK:** frequent in summer, breeds 2200–2700 m; winters in adjacent foothills. **NP:** common and widespread; summers mainly 2750–4000 m, winters 275–2750 m. **IN:** common; breeds 2200–4200 m, winters from 2100 m down to the foothills. **BT:** common; 335–3965 m. **BD:** vagrant. **REFERENCES** Ticehurst (1938), Williamson (1967).

BROOKS'S LEAF WARBLER *Phylloscopus subviridis* — Plate 126

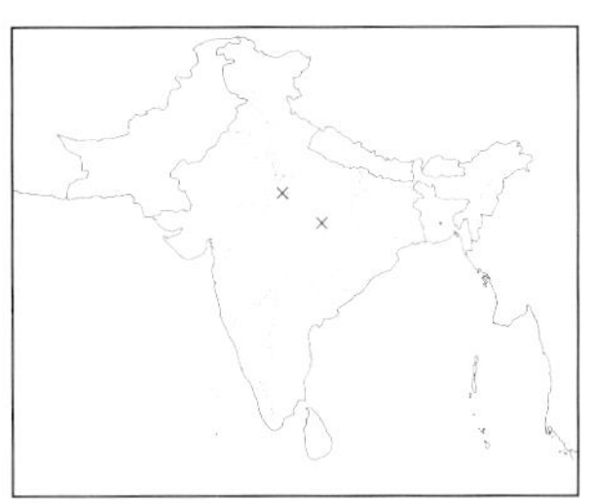

IDENTIFICATION 9 cm. Confusion is possible with Hume's, Yellow-browed and Lemon-rumped Warblers (p.730 and above), although can be separated from these by distinctive call. Told from Hume's by narrow, although sometimes poorly defined, greenish-yellow crown-stripe, yellow supercilium and yellow wash to cheeks and throat, and brighter yellowish-olive upperparts. Yellow supercilia are frequently brighter in front of eye, and can appear to join across forehead. Has ill-defined paler yellowish rump, which can be apparent when hovering, but is frequently not a very useful distinction from Hume's. In fresh plumage, entire underparts are washed with buffish-yellow. In worn plumage, underparts and wing-bars are whiter, and general coloration approaches that of worn Hume's, although upperparts are never quite so grey; supercilium and ear-coverts retain faint yellow wash (rather than being whitish or buffish-white), and crown-stripe is usually apparent. Brooks's Leaf has yellowish-horn basal half to lower mandible which is a good distinction from Hume's, which has a dark lower mandible (particularly useful when seen from below). Possibly confusable with Lemon-rumped, especially with *P. p. simlaensis* in NW Himalayas, but lacks a well-defined yellow rump, sides of crown are either concolorous with or just a shade darker than mantle (distinctly darker olive and contrasting with mantle on Lemon-rumped), and has strong yellow wash to throat and breast; further, has less distinct eye-stripe (which does not continue as dark border to rear of ear-coverts), and bases of median and greater coverts are not so dark (and do not form dark panels across wing as on Lemon-rumped). **VOICE** Call is different from that of Hume's, a monosyllabic, loud and piercing (higher-pitched) *chwee*, or *pseo* or *psee*; song is often long and complicated, and contains distinctive sibilant trills, with phrases recalling Tree Pipit (p.817), e.g. *chif-chif-chif...chu-chu-chu-tsi-tsi-tsi-ti-tchsrrrrrr...chitu-chitu-chit chu chu tsit-tsit-tsit tr-r-r-r-r-r* (Roberts 1992). **HABITS** Found singly or in pairs in the breeding season; otherwise in mixed itinerant parties. Very active. Keeps to the middle and upper storeys. **HABITAT** Summers in coniferous forest and mixed fir–broadleaved forest, typically in Blue Pine on south-facing slopes; winters in bushes, olive groves, acacias and plantations along roads and canals. **BREEDING** Very poorly known. May–July. Only nest described was a dome of coarse grass, built in a hollow under a bush on a steep ravine bank. **DISTRIBUTION AND STATUS** Breeds in Himalayas in N Pakistan; winters in plains and hills in N Pakistan and N India, mainly from Punjab south to W Uttar Pradesh. **PK:** breeding range is largely confined to Pakistan; locally frequent in summer, 2100–2700 m; fairly widespread but uncommon winter visitor to Punjab. **IN:** uncommon and local.

YELLOW-BROWED WARBLER *Phylloscopus inornatus* Plate 126

Plain Leaf Warbler (F,I), Inornate Warbler (K)

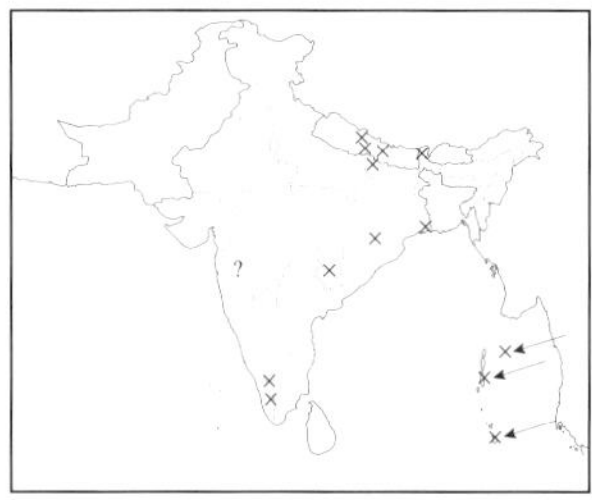

IDENTIFICATION 10–11 cm. Distinguished from Lemon-rumped Warbler (p.729) by lack of yellow rump and absence of a well-defined yellowish-white crown-stripe (although can show a diffuse paler line down centre of crown). From Buff-barred (p.728) by yellowish or whitish wing-bars, and lack of white on tail. For further differences, as well as distinguishing features from Brooks's Leaf Warbler (p.729), see those species. In fresh plumage, has brighter greenish-olive upperparts (especially on crown) compared with Hume's (below), and has yellowish-white supercilium, ear-coverts and wing-bars; further, the median-covert wing-bar is typically well defined, and underparts are very white with variable amounts of yellow. In worn plumage, supercilium, wing-bars and underparts are whiter, and upperparts become greyer, and is then very similar in plumage to worn Hume's, but bill has extensive pale (often orangish) base to lower mandible, and legs are paler flesh-brown or greyish-brown (bill and legs are darker on Hume's). **VOICE** Call is a loud *cheweest*, with a distinct rising inflection, and typically quite different from that of Hume's. **HABITS** Very similar to those of Hume's Warbler. **HABITAT** Gardens, groves and open forest. **DISTRIBUTION AND STATUS** Uncertain, because often considered conspecific with Hume's Warbler. Winters from C Nepal east to NE India and Bangladesh, and in Kerala, Tamil Nadu, and Andaman and Nicobar Is. **NP:** uncommon winter visitor and passage migrant; 915–2590 m. **IN:** status uncertain; from foothills up to 1525 m in Himalayas. **BT:** uncommon winter visitor; 1980 m, 2255 m. **BD:** winter visitor, status uncertain. **REFERENCES** Alström and Colston (1991), Crosby (1995), Shirihai and Madge (1993), Ticehurst (1938).

HUME'S WARBLER *Phylloscopus humei* Plate 126

Plain Leaf Warbler (F,I), Yellow-browed Warbler (N,R), *P. inornatus humei*

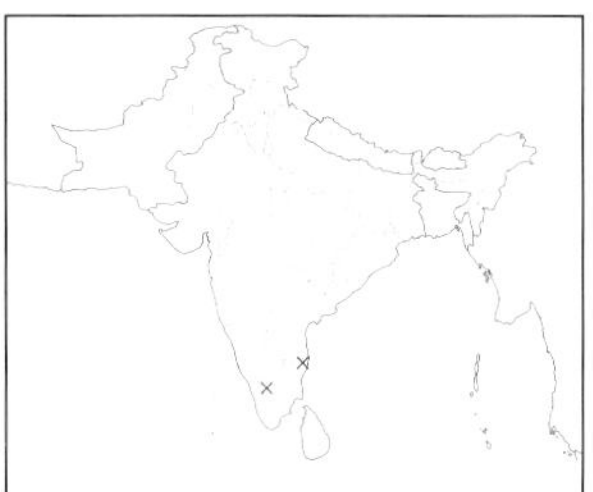

IDENTIFICATION 10–11 cm. Distinguished from Lemon-rumped Warbler (p.729) by lack of yellow rump and absence of a well-defined yellowish-white crown-stripe (although can show a diffuse paler line down centre of crown). From Buff-barred Warbler (p.728) by buffish or whitish wing-bars, and lack of white in tail. For further differences, as well as distinguishing features from Brooks's Leaf Warbler (p.729), see those species. The following features help separate Hume's from Yellow-browed (above; see that species for comparative details). In fresh plumage, has greyish-olive upperparts, with variable yellowish-green suffusion on mantle and back, and browner crown, while supercilium, ear-coverts and greater-covert wing-bar are buffish-white; the median-covert bar tends to be poorly defined, but a double wing-bar can be apparent (perhaps more so in worn plumage). In worn plumage, supercilium, wing-bars and underparts are white (often heavily sullied with grey), and upperparts are much greyer. Bill appears all dark, and legs are normally blackish-brown. **Racial variation** *P. h. mandellii*, which winters in NE India, has darker olive-green upperparts than the nominate race, described above, with dirty yellowish-white supercilium and underparts; the median-covert bar is poorly defined as in the nominate; shows more distinct (but still diffuse) pale crown-stripe, and lateral crown-stripes are darker than mantle. **VOICE** Calls of *P. h. humei* are usually quite different from those of Yellow-browed, and include a rolling disyllabic *whit-hoot* or *visu-visu*, and a sparrow-like, flat *chwee* (latter call is similar to, but weaker, than that of Greenish Warbler, p.731); does occasionally have a *seest* or *sweest* call, but this is shorter, flatter and less strident than Yellow-browed's. Song of *P. h. humei* is a repeated *wesoo...*, often followed by a lengthy, descending high-pitched *zweeeeeeeeeeeoooo*. Call of *P. h. mandellii* is a strikingly disyllabic, repeated *tjis-ip*; song is like that of nominate (P. Holt). **HABITS** A frequent member of mixed foraging flocks in winter. Hunts actively in trees and bushes, occasionally descending to the ground. Favours sunny edges of forest clearings. **HABITAT** Breeds in coniferous forest and subalpine shrubberies; winters in open broadleaved forest, secondary growth, groves, orchards and gardens. **BREEDING** End May–early September. Nest is a ball of grass and moss, built on the ground on a steep bank or at the base of a bush or tree. **DISTRIBUTION AND STATUS** Breeds in Himalayas from N Pakistan east to Bhutan; winters south to N Pakistan, Bangladesh and Karnataka, but absent from most of

NW and WC India. **PK:** widespread and locally common in summer, 2700–3500 m; common in winter in N Punjab, fairly common in NW Pakistan. **NP:** widespread; common in summer, 3280–3980 m, fairly common in winter below 2135 m (–2560 m). **IN:** widespread and common on breeding grounds; breeds 2100–3600 m, winters in plains and hills up to 1800 m. **BT:** fairly common; 305–4000 m. **BD:** winter visitor, status uncertain. **REFERENCES** Alström and Colston (1991), Shirihai and Madge (1993), Ticehurst (1938).

ARCTIC WARBLER *Phylloscopus borealis* Plate 126

Arctic Leaf Warbler (I)

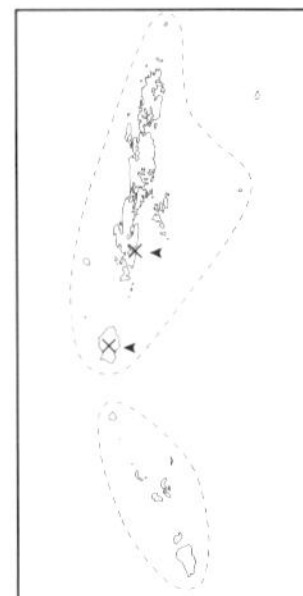

IDENTIFICATION 12 cm. Extremely similar to *viridanus* race of Greenish Warbler (below). Best identified by very distinctive call. There are further subtle differences, but great caution is needed as both species are variable and none of the following features is diagnostic. Typically, Arctic appears larger and more elongated, with a longer and deeper bill. It generally has a longer and finer supercilium, but in front of eye this falls noticeably short of forehead (on Greenish, the supercilium is usually wide in front of eye and extends to side of forehead to reach nostril). Also tends to have a darker and broader eye-stripe, which usually reaches unbroken to base of bill (usually broken, falling short of base of bill and forming a distinct dark spot in front of eye on Greenish), has more pronounced dusky mottling on ear-coverts, and frequently has a distinct greyish wash, or diffuse grey streaking, on breast sides and flanks. Further, legs and feet are generally paler, sometimes orangey (typically darker grey-brown on Greenish), and usually has dark tip to lower mandible (lower mandible of Greenish is frequently unmarked). Some of the above features of Arctic which help to separate it from *viridanus* Greenish are, however, shown by *trochiloides* Greenish and by Large-billed Leaf Warbler (p.732), which can cause further confusion. Arctic is paler green above (generally lacking distinctly darker crown) and whiter below, and colour of bill, legs and feet, and shape of supercilium in front of eye, are helpful features. Distinctive call is, however, the safest means of identification. **VOICE** Call is a buzzing *dziit* or *dzipp* (and sometimes a double note, *dzipp-ip*), similar to one of the calls of Purple Sunbird (p.803). **HABITS** Details unknown in the region. Similar to those of other *Phylloscopus*, but more dashing than most species; also hovers. Found singly, usually in canopy foliage. **HABITAT** Mango groves and mangroves. **DISTRIBUTION AND STATUS IN:** vagrant to Andaman Is. **REFERENCES** Alström and Olsson (1987), Svensson (1992).

GREENISH WARBLER *Phylloscopus trochiloides* Plate 126

Dull Green Warbler (F,I), Greenish Tree Warbler, Green Leaf Warbler (P), Green Warbler (N,R), Green Tree Warbler, *P. nitidus*

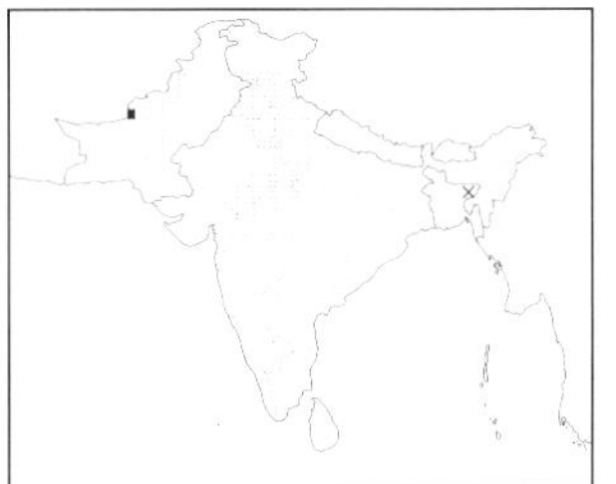

IDENTIFICATION 10–11 cm. This is a very variable *Phylloscopus* warbler, with four races recognised from the subcontinent and presumably much intergradation. Familiarisation with this species, especially its distinctive call, is essential as a sound basis for the identification of other species. Rather uniform wings, with one (sometimes two) fine wing-bar(s), and lack of crown-stripe are common to all races, although wing-bars can be lost through wear. Differences from other species are covered below. **Racial variation** *P. t. nitidus*, which occurs widely on passage throughout the subcontinent (except northeast) and winters in S India and Sri Lanka, is generally brighter and yellower than *P. t. ludlowi*/*viridanus*: in fresh plumage, upperparts are a brighter and purer green, and has one, sometimes two, slightly broader and yellower wing-bars, while supercilium and cheeks are noticeably yellow and underparts have a much stronger suffusion of yellow (on some, extending to undertail-coverts, although strength of yellow on underparts varies considerably); when worn, upperparts are duller, although still brighter than on worn-plumaged *ludlowi* and *viridanus*, and supercilium and, to a lesser extent, underparts retain a distinct yellowish wash. *P. t. ludlowi* and *P. t. viridanus*, which breed in W Himalayas and winter widely throughout the subcontinent, have duller green upperparts and whiter underparts compared with *P. t. nitidus*: in fresh plumage, upperparts are olive-green, and they have a single, narrow but well-defined white wing-bar, yellowish-white supercilium and wash to cheeks, and whitish underparts with faint yellowish suffusion; in worn plumage, the upperparts are duller and greyer (although traces of purer green, or even a strong greenish cast, can still be apparent) and underparts whiter. Confusion is possible with Tytler's Leaf Warbler (p.733), but that species has a slender all-dark bill (lower mandible is largely pale on *viridanus* Greenish), has a shorter tail, and always lacks white greater-covert bar. Tickell's Leaf Warbler (p.726) also lacks a wing-bar and is almost always much brighter yellow on supercilium and underparts, although a few can have rather washed-out appearance to the underparts, but have darker, browner upperparts and much shorter primary projection. For differences from Arctic Warbler (above), see that species. *P. t. trochiloides*, which breeds in the C and E Himalayas and NE India and winters south of this range, although not into the peninsula, is rather different from the other races described above: compared with *viridanus*, it has darker oily green upperparts, with noticeably darker olive crown and mottled ear-coverts, often shows a trace of a second (median-covert) wing-bar, has duskier underparts with greyish cast to throat, breast and flanks (and with diffuse oily yellow wash on breast, belly and undertail-coverts), and has darker bill (with orange at base, or basal two-thirds, of lower mandible). This race is extremely similar to Large-billed Leaf Warbler (p.732), and is identifiable with complete confidence only by different call; see that species for full account of differences. **VOICE** Call of *P. t. viri-*

danus is a loud, slurred and abrupt *chit-wee*; song is a loud, repeated, vehement *chi-chi-chi-chiwee-chiweee*. Call of *P. t. nitidus* is a more trisyllabic *chis-ru-weet*. Call of *P. t. trochiloides* is a *chis-weet*, and song is a *chis-weet, chist-weet*. **HABITS** Similar to those of Common Chiffchaff (p.724). Very active. Forages from the canopy down to low bushes, mainly by gleaning; also hovers, and darts out to catch flying insects. **HABITAT** Summers in pure birch or coniferous forest, also coniferous–birch–rhododendron forest, and subalpine shrubberies of dwarf junipers and willows; winters in mixed forest, gardens, orchards, trees and bushes in cultivation, and, in Bangladesh, also mangroves. **BREEDING** May–August. Nest is a ball of moss, lichen and dry grass, built on sloping ground among tree roots, or in a tree hollow up to 3 m above ground. **DISTRIBUTION AND STATUS** Breeds in Himalayas from N Pakistan east to Arunachal Pradesh, and in NE Indian hills; winters throughout much of the subcontinent, except parts of the northwest. **PK:** widespread passage migrant, common in N Punjab; winters in S Sindh; breeds rather sparsely in N Himalayas, 3200–3650 m, has also bred in Baluchistan. **NP:** common; widespread summer visitor, chiefly 3000–4270 m, winter visitor below 1830 m, and passage migrant. **IN:** common; breeds 2700–4300 m; winters in plains and hills, to 2200 m in Himalayas, to summits of peninsular hills. **BT:** fairly common; 250–4180 m. **BD, LK:** common winter visitor throughout. **REFERENCES** Pfister (1997).

PALE-LEGGED LEAF WARBLER *Phylloscopus tenellipes* Plate 126

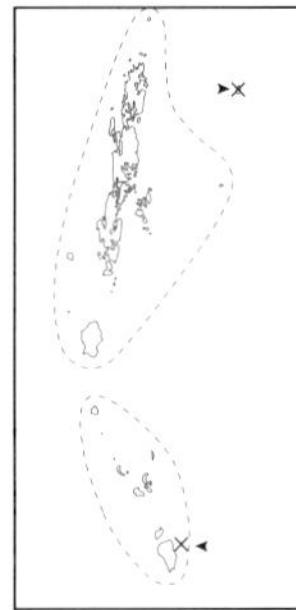

IDENTIFICATION 10 cm. Superficially resembles Greenish Warbler (p.731). Always safely distinguished by very pale grey-pink legs, feet and claws, whitish tip to rather short and stout, mainly dark bill, and distinctive call. Rather variable in plumage, many being very different from Greenish. Prominent supercilium is buff, cream or white, and contrasts strongly with broad, dark eye-stripe. Ear-coverts are frequently washed with buff, and distinctly mottled, and sides of neck can also be washed with buff. Upperparts vary from olive-green to olive-brown, and some individuals have bronze cast (especially to rump and to edges of rectrices). Buffish-white tips to median and greater coverts form double wing-bar (often appearing as lines of well-defined spots). Crown is distinctly greyer (and may show paler centre), and usually contrasts with mantle. Underparts are whitish (never showing any yellow), and may show slight buffish wash to flanks. Told from Dusky Warbler (p.726) by double wing-bar, greenish-olive cast to upperparts, and different call. **VOICE** Call is a high-pitched, clear, metallic *pink* or *peet* (J. Scharringa). **HABITS** Usually keeps close to the ground in the forest understorey, and has diagnostic habit of frequently pumping tail. **HABITAT** Collected on a boat in the region; elsewhere inhabits deciduous forest. **DISTRIBUTION AND STATUS IN:** vagrant; Narcondam I, and on a boat 16 km east of Great Nicobar I. **REFERENCES** Leader (1993).

LARGE-BILLED LEAF WARBLER *Phylloscopus magnirostris* Plate 126

Large-billed Tree Warbler

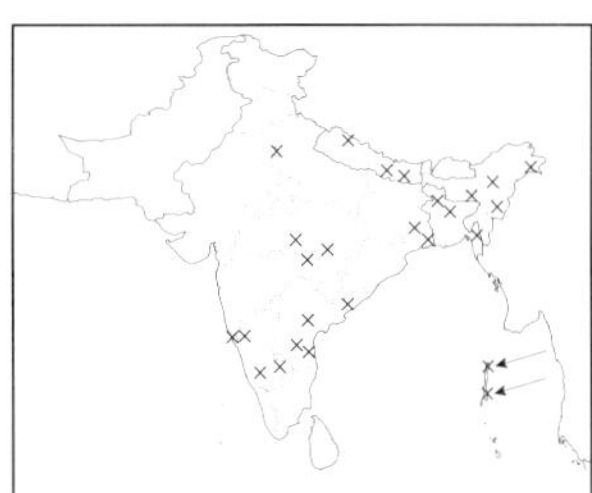

IDENTIFICATION 13 cm. Very similar to nominate race of Greenish Warbler (p.731), although in W Himalayas and in the peninsula (on passage and in winter) it is most likely to be found alongside *viridanus* and *ludlowi* races of Greenish. Distinguished from those races by combination of larger size and stockier appearance, larger and mainly dark bill (with orange at very base of lower mandible), darker oily green upperparts, with noticeably darker crown, more striking yellowish-white supercilium (owing to dark crown and eye-stripe), and broader dark eye-stripe with greyish mottling on ear-coverts. Underparts tend to look rather dirty, and there is often diffuse streaking on breast and flanks and oily yellow wash on breast, belly and undertail-coverts (note, however, that underparts can look whiter and much as on Greenish). Has yellowish-white greater-covert wing-bar, often with a trace of a second (median-covert) bar. Where ranges overlap (C and E Himalayas, and adjacent plains on passage), best distinguished from nominate Greenish by distinctive call and song; in addition, is larger, and on some birds bill can appear strikingly long, stout and mainly dark. Tends to show a broader dark stripe behind eye and longer, more striking yellowish-white supercilium (although some Greenish can have very similar head pattern). Some, but not all, birds have a hook-like tip to upper mandible, but this can also be apparent (although perhaps less noticeably so) on *trochiloides* Greenish. **VOICE** Call is a clear, whistled, upward-inflected *der-tee*, as well as a shortened three-noted version of song; song (also given in winter and on passage) is very distinctive, a clear series of five notes, the second and third of which are lower on the scale than the first note, with the fourth and fifth lower again than the preceding pair (Bates and Lowther 1952). **HABITS** Usually solitary. Rather less active than most *Phylloscopus* species. Forages mainly in trees, sometimes in undergrowth. Nearly always found near running water in breeding season. **HABITAT** Summers in deciduous, coniferous or mixed coniferous–deciduous forest along mountain streams and rivers; winters in evergreen sholas. **BREEDING** May–August. Nest is a dome of grass, moss and dead leaves, built under a log, rock or overhanging bank or among roots of a fallen tree. **DISTRIBUTION AND STATUS** Breeds in Himalayas from N Pakistan east to Bhutan; winters mainly in S India and Sri Lanka, chiefly on passage elsewhere. **PK:** scarce and local summer visitor; usually 2100–3000 m (–3200 m). **NP:** summer visitor, fairly common in the centre and east, uncommon in the west, 2440–3600 m; reported in winter up to 2750 m, but further confirmation is desirable. **IN:** fairly common summer visitor to Himalayas, 1800–3600 m; regularly winters in the south. **BT:** common summer visitor; 2135–3710 m. **BD:** scarce winter visitor. **LK:** common winter visitor throughout.

TYTLER'S LEAF WARBLER *Phylloscopus tytleri* Plate 126

Slender-billed Warbler (N)

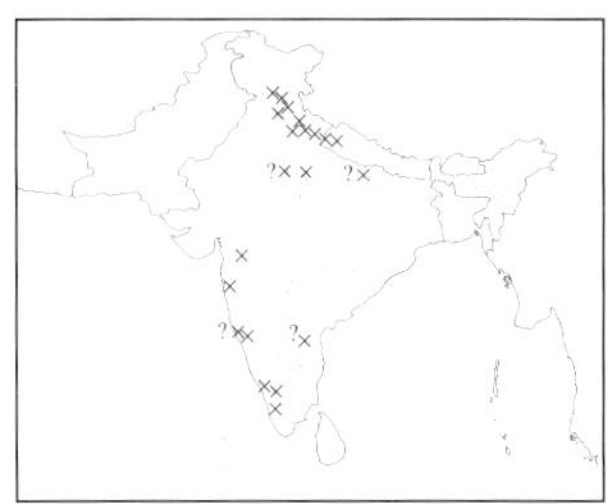

IDENTIFICATION 11 cm. Confusion is most likely with *viridanus* and *ludlowi* races of Greenish Warbler (p.731), but can always be distinguished by long, slender, mainly dark bill (lower mandible is largely pale in those races of Greenish), shorter tail, which gives rise to distinctive top-heavy appearance, lack of well-defined, white greater-covert wing-bar (although this can be lacking on worn-plumaged Greenish), and different call. The slender bill is accentuated by the reduced feathers at bill base compared with Greenish, and the rictal bristles are short, fine and inconspicuous (rictal bristles are particularly strong on Greenish). Supercilium tends to look finer, and is offset by rather broad and well-defined dark olive lores and eye-stripe. In fresh plumage, has dark greenish cast to upperparts (a slightly darker green than *viridanus*), supercilium is yellowish-white, and has variable yellowish wash to ear-coverts and underparts. In worn plumage, supercilium and underparts are whitish, and upperparts are greyer; closely resembles worn *viridanus* Greenish in plumage, although underparts tend to be more sullied with grey and always lacks wing-bar. **VOICE** Call is a double *y-it*; song is a distinctive, regularly repeated *pi-tsi-pi-tsu*. **HABITS** Very active. Often found in thickets and undergrowth, also in conifer trees. Forages mainly by gleaning, and also makes aerial sallies. **HABITAT** Breeds in coniferous forest, also in subalpine dwarf willows and birches; wintering habitat little described, but found in middle forest storey in a shola in S India. **BREEDING** May–July. Nest is a dome made of moss and lichen, well hidden among foliage of a fir branch, 6–9 m above ground. **DISTRIBUTION AND STATUS** Breeds in W Himalayas in Pakistan and Kashmir; winters mainly in Western Ghats. **PK:** scarce to locally common summer visitor to the inner N Himalayas; up to 3000 m. **NP:** rare, status uncertain, probably only a passage migrant; recorded 2135–3050 m in April. **IN:** locally common in Kashmir, breeds 2400–3600 m; rarely recorded in winter; regular southward migrant through the Himachal Pradesh Himalayas, with a more easterly route in spring in Uttar Pradesh and north and south of the Satpura Range. **REFERENCES** Harrap and Redman (1990), Neelakantan *et al.* (1993), Rasmussen (in prep.).

WESTERN CROWNED WARBLER *Phylloscopus occipitalis* Plate 127

Large Crowned Leaf Warbler (F,I)

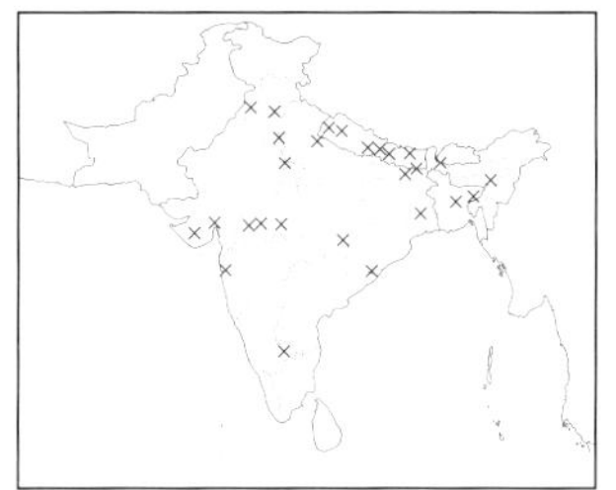

IDENTIFICATION 11 cm. Most likely to be confused with Blyth's Leaf Warbler (p.734), showing prominent crown-stripe as that species, but appears larger and more elongated, with larger and longer-looking bill. Upperparts are generally duller greyish-green, with stronger grey cast to nape, and whitish underparts are strongly suffused with grey, especially on throat and breast. Can show touch of yellow on ear-coverts and traces of yellow on breast and belly, but Blyth's Leaf is generally more strongly washed with yellow in these areas. Median- and greater-covert wing-bars are narrower (median-covert bar may be lacking) and tend to be less prominent than on Blyth's, in part because the bases of these feathers are not so dark (and tend not to show as dark panel across wing as is often the case on Blyth's). Head pattern also tends to be less striking: supercilium is generally duller yellow, and crown-stripe is greyish-white to pale yellow and tends to contrast less with dusky olive lateral crown-stripes (which may be darker towards nape). There is, however, much variation in patterning of head (in part through wear), and on some it is identical to that of Blyth's. For differences from Eastern Crowned Warbler (below), see that species. **VOICE** Call is a constantly repeated *chit-weei*; song consists of several calls run together, *chit-wee chit-wee chit-wee chit-wee-wee-wee*. **HABITS** In the breeding season, has a diagnostic habit of flicking alternately one wing and then the other half open. Joins mixed hunting flocks of insectivorous species in winter, and also in the breeding season when these pass through its nesting territory. Hunts at all levels of the vegetation, mainly by gleaning, occasionally by making aerial sallies. **HABITAT** Breeds in coniferous and mixed coniferous–deciduous forest; winters in moist deciduous and evergreen broadleaved forest. **BREEDING** May–July. Nest varies from a cup to a globe; it is made mainly of moss, and built in a hole in a wall, old rodent burrow, or hollow in a dead stump, or under tree roots. **DISTRIBUTION AND STATUS** Breeds in N Pakistan hills and in Himalayas from N Pakistan east to N Uttar Pradesh; winters chiefly in S Nepal, Eastern and Western Ghats and Bangladesh; winter distribution elsewhere is uncertain. **PK:** common and widespread summer visitor; 1800–3200 m. **NP:** uncommon spring passage migrant and rare winter visitor, possibly breeds; 75–2900 m. **IN:** common summer visitor to Himalayas, breeds 1800–3200 m; winters mainly in hills below 2100 m. **BD:** regular winter visitor.

EASTERN CROWNED WARBLER *Phylloscopus coronatus* Plate 127

***P. occipitalis* (E,I)**

IDENTIFICATION 11 cm. Extremely similar to Western Crowned Warbler (above), although, given wintering range, is most likely to be confused with Blyth's Leaf Warbler (p.734). Best told from Western Crowned by yellowish wash to undertail-coverts (although this can sometimes be difficult to see in the field, and underparts can

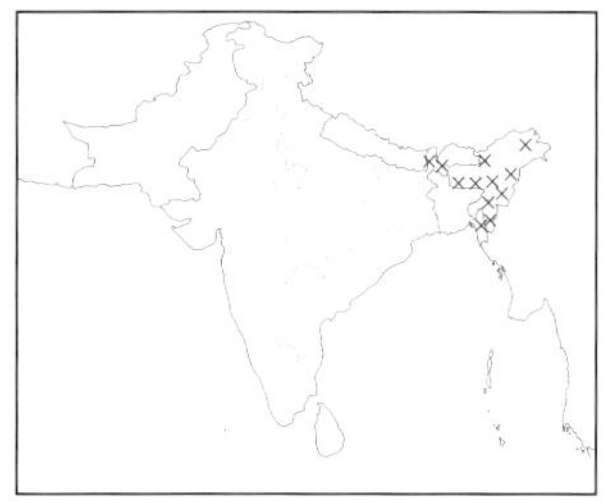

appear entirely white even at close range); also has slightly darker and purer green coloration to upperparts. There are possibly slight differences in head pattern, with Eastern Crowned tending to show broader dark olive eye-stripe and more uniform dark olive sides to crown, and having supercilium which is typically yellow in front of eye and white behind. Yellowish-white crown-stripe can be very indistinct and difficult to see, and confusion with Greenish and Large-billed Warblers (p.731 and p.732) is easily possible, but dark olive crown sides contrast strongly with mantle. Distinguished from Blyth's Leaf by combination of larger size and more elongated appearance, larger and longer-looking bill, whiter underparts with yellow undertail-coverts, and less striking wing pattern (with only a single, narrower greater-covert bar generally apparent, and tending to lack dark panel across greater coverts); supercilium is whiter behind eye, and dark sides of crown tend to be more uniform (frequently becoming darker, almost blackish, towards nape on Blyth's). **VOICE** Song is a *pitschu-pitsch-wii* (Ticehurst 1938); call is an occasional harsh, buzzy nasal *dwee* (P. Holt). **HABITS** In winter, very silent and unobtrusive. Keeps to the lower boughs of trees and bushes. **HABITAT** Dense broadleaved evergreen and semi-evergreen forest. **DISTRIBUTION AND STATUS** Winter visitor to Sikkim foothills and hills of NE India (Arunachal Pradesh, Assam, Manipur, Mizoram). **IN:** rare; foothills up to 2000 m. **BD:** vagrant. **REFERENCES** Leader (1992), Raman (1995), Ticehurst (1938).

BLYTH'S LEAF WARBLER *Phylloscopus reguloides* — Plate 127

Crowned Leaf Warbler (F)

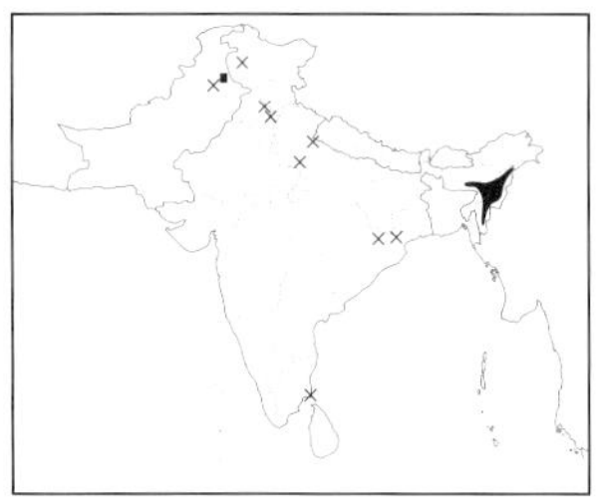

IDENTIFICATION 11 cm. Most likely to be confused with Western Crowned Warbler (p.733) and usually shows prominent crown-stripe as that species. Is smaller in size and appears more compact than Western Crowned, with smaller and shorter-looking bill. Head pattern tends to be more striking, with yellower supercilium and crown-stripe, contrasting with darker lateral crown-stripes (which can be almost black on some birds, especially towards nape). Underparts generally have distinct yellowish wash, especially on cheeks and sides of breast, and upperparts are a darker and purer green. Blyth's Leaf can, however, appear rather grey on mantle and show diffuse greyish streaking on breast. Wing-bars are more prominent (being broader, and often divided by a dark panel across greater coverts). For differences from Eastern Crowned and Yellow-vented Warblers (p.733 and below), see those species. **Racial variation** *P. r. kashmiriensis* of the W Himalayas tends to have brighter yellowish-green upperparts than the nominate race of the C Himalayas, and lateral crown-stripes tend to be less dark, whereas *P. r. assamensis* of the NE subcontinent tends to be a darker green on the upperparts. **VOICE** Call is a constantly repeated *kee-kew-i*; song is a trill of nine or ten notes, *ch-ti-ch-ti-ch-ti-chi-chi-ti-chee*. **HABITS** Found singly, in pairs or in mixed hunting parties of insectivorous species. A typical *Phylloscopus*, but unlike the others has a habit of clinging upside-down to trunks like a nuthatch. **HABITAT** Breeds in oak–rhododendron and coniferous forest and in mixed coniferous–broadleaved forest, in the Khasi Hills also in evergreen wet forest; winters in open forest and forest edges. **BREEDING** April–August. Nest is like that of Western Crowned Warbler, built in a hollow of a tree or bank or between stones in a wall. **DISTRIBUTION AND STATUS** Breeds in Himalayas from N Pakistan (Murree hills) east to Arunachal Pradesh, and in NE Indian hills; winters in adjacent foothills and in Bangladesh. **PK:** presumed rare; very local. **NP:** common and widespread; summers 1980–3800 m, winters mainly below 1500 m (–2750 m). **IN:** uncommon in the west, fairly common in the east; breeds 2000–3700 m in Himalayas, above 1400 m in NE hills, winters from 1500 m (2200 m in the far east) down to the plains. **BT:** common; 305–3715 m. **BD:** scarce winter visitor.

YELLOW-VENTED WARBLER *Phylloscopus cantator* — Plate 127

Black-browed Leaf Warbler (I), Yellow-throated Leaf Warbler (F)

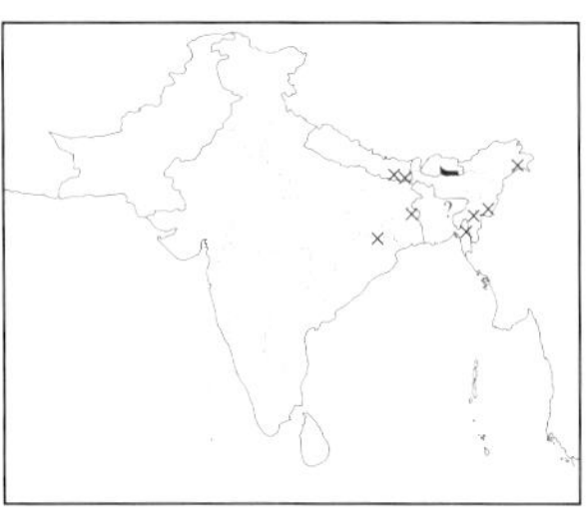

IDENTIFICATION 10 cm. Superficially resembles Blyth's Leaf Warbler (above). Distinguished from that species, and from other 'crowned leaf warblers', by yellow throat, upper breast and undertail-coverts contrasting with white lower breast and belly. In addition, is smaller in size, has brighter yellow supercilium and crown-stripe contrasting with darker lateral crown-stripes, and has brighter yellowish-green upperparts. **VOICE** The song consists of several single notes on the same pitch and ending in two slurred notes, *seep, seep, seep to-you*, with the accent downslurred on *you*; call is a double note, softer than those of other species of *Phylloscopus*, with the accent on the second note (S. Connop). **HABITS** Keeps singly or in pairs in the breeding season, often in mixed itinerant flocks in winter. Forages actively in the lower storey in bamboo clumps, bushes and lower branches of large trees. Has a habit of spreading the tail and flicking it upwards when calling. **HABITAT** Breeds in dense, moist broadleaved evergreen forest; also occurs in more open deciduous forest in winter. **BREEDING** End April–June. Nest is a ball of green moss, hidden on ground among fallen leaves or in a hollow in a bank. **DISTRIBUTION AND STATUS** Resident. Breeding and winter distributions are uncertain. Himalayas from E Nepal east to Arunachal Pradesh, and NE Indian hills and Bangladesh. **NP:** uncommon and very local in the east, 75–1525 m; probably mainly a winter visitor, has bred. **IN:** locally frequent; breeds in N Cachar, Assam (1200–1800 m), and probably Sikkim (1890 m in June, 305 m in November), Arunachal Pradesh and Manipur. **BT:** common, probably breeds; 300–1840 m. **BD:** scarce winter visitor. **REFERENCES** Choudhury (1996c), Lama (1995a, 1995b).

***SEICERCUS* AND *ABROSCOPUS* WARBLERS** Small and active warblers. They feed in a similar manner to *Phylloscopus* warblers, by gleaning from foliage and twigs and making frequent aerial sallies, but have a broader bill and brighter plumage than those species.

GOLDEN-SPECTACLED WARBLER *Seicercus burkii* Plate 127

Black-browed Flycatcher Warbler (I), Yellow-eyed Warbler (F)

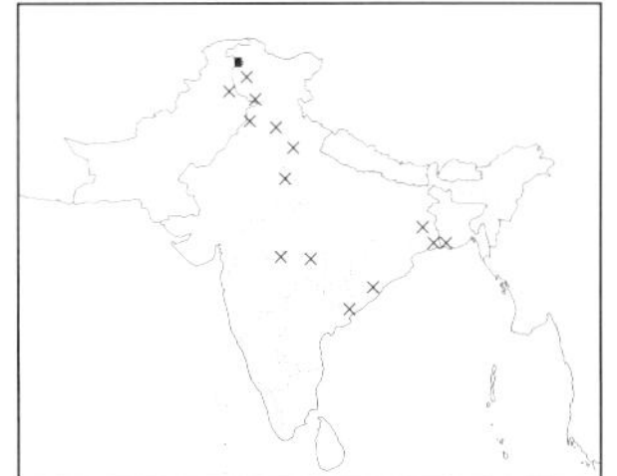

IDENTIFICATION 10 cm. Like a number of other *Seicercus* warblers, has domed head with blackish lateral crown-stripes, and beady black eye with prominent eye-ring. Upperparts are olive-green and underparts are bright yellow. Told from White-spectacled and Grey-cheeked Warblers (p.000 and p.736) by yellow (rather than white) eye-ring, and yellowish-green supercilium, lores and ear-coverts which are concolorous with sides of neck and mantle. Has yellowish-green to greyish centre to crown, and fine yellow greater-covert wing-bar in fresh plumage. **VOICE** Calls include *pillip* or *wee-up* and a single sharp *chiw*, uttered frequently. There are two populations with different songs. The one at higher altitude has a simple *witchu-witchu*; the one at lower altitude has a variety of quite rich phrases e.g. *weet-weeta-weeta-weet* and *weet-wit-wit-wit-wit* interspersed with short trills. **HABITS** Similar to those of other *Seicercus* warblers. Found in pairs or in mixed feeding flocks of warblers, tits and babblers. Forages actively in the forest understorey. **HABITAT** Understorey in broadleaved, coniferous and mixed broadleaved–coniferous forest, either open or dense. **BREEDING** April–July. Nest is a ball of green moss, leaves, grass and bark fibres, built on sloping ground or among tree roots. **DISTRIBUTION AND STATUS** Altitudinal and short-range migrant. Breeds in Himalayas from N Pakistan (Kagan valley) east to Arunachal Pradesh, and in NE Indian hills; winters mainly in adjacent foothills and in Bangladesh. **PK:** very rare and local; 2400–2900 m. **NP:** common and widespread; summers 1550–3800 m and winters 250–2135 m, occasionally down to 150 m. **IN:** in summer locally common in the west, common in the east, breeds 1800–3700 m, mainly above 2400 m in Himalayas, above 1000 m in NE hills; winters from 2100 m down to the foothills and plains. **BT:** common; 305–3810 m. **BD:** locally common winter visitor. **REFERENCES** Martens and Eck (1995).

GREY-HOODED WARBLER *Seicercus xanthoschistos* Plate 127

Grey-headed Flycatcher Warbler (I), Grey-headed Warbler (F)

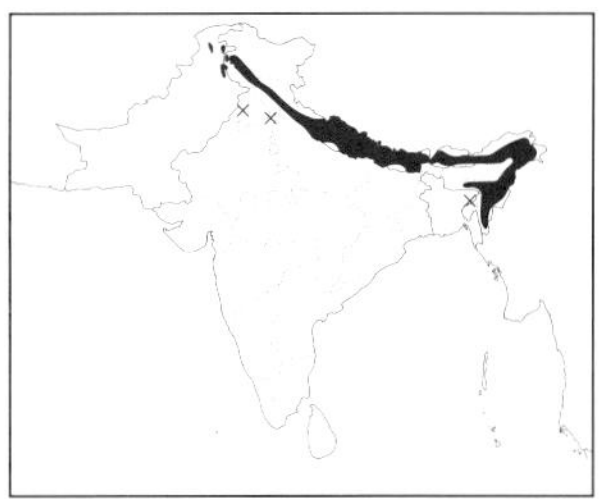

IDENTIFICATION 10 cm. Distinguished from other *Seicercus* warblers by combination of *Phylloscopus*-like appearance, greyish-white supercilium, and grey crown and mantle. Has diffuse pale grey central crown-stripe, and darker lateral crown-stripes. From Yellow-bellied Warbler (p.738), which also has a white supercilium, by yellow throat which is concolorous with bright yellow underparts, and by prominent white on outer rectrices which is frequently flashed as tail is constantly flicked open. From all *Phylloscopus* warblers by combination of uniform bright yellow underparts, lack of wing-bars, and grey crown and mantle. **Racial variation** Birds in the W Himalayas (*S. x. albosuperciliaris*) have paler grey lateral crown-stripes and mantle (with brownish cast) compared with those in the E Himalayas and NE India (e.g. nominate), which are purer and darker grey in these areas, with noticeable contrast between grey of mantle and green of back. **VOICE** Call is a high-pitched *psit-psit*, and alarm is a plaintive *tyee-tyee*; song is a brief, but incessantly repeated, high-pitched warble, *ti-tsi-ti-wee-tee* or *tsi-weetsi-weetsi-weetu-ti-tu* (Roberts 1992). **HABITS** Similar to those of other *Seicercus* warblers. In the non-breeding season, often keeps in groups of three or four, accompanying other small insectivorous birds. Arboreal; hunts restlessly, mainly in the middle storey. Feeds by gleaning, making short aerial sallies and hovering in front of sprigs. **HABITAT** Breeds in open broadleaved and coniferous forest; winters in forest, secondary growth, gardens and orchards. **BREEDING** March–August. Nest is a ball of green moss and grass, hidden on the ground or low down among moss on a boulder or old stump. **DISTRIBUTION AND STATUS** Resident, subject to altitudinal movements. Himalayas from N Pakistan east to Arunachal Pradesh; NE Indian hills. **PK:** locally common; breeds 900–2100 m, winters in adjacent foothills and plains. **NP:** common and widespread; summers 1000–2750 m (–3050 m), winters down to 750 m (to 245 m). **IN:** locally common in the west, common in the east; breeds 900–2700 m (down to 300 m), winters from 2000 m down to the foothills. **BT:** common; 305–2295 m. **BD:** rare passage migrant.

WHITE-SPECTACLED WARBLER *Seicercus affinis* Plate 127

Allied Flycatcher Warbler (I), Allied Warbler (F)

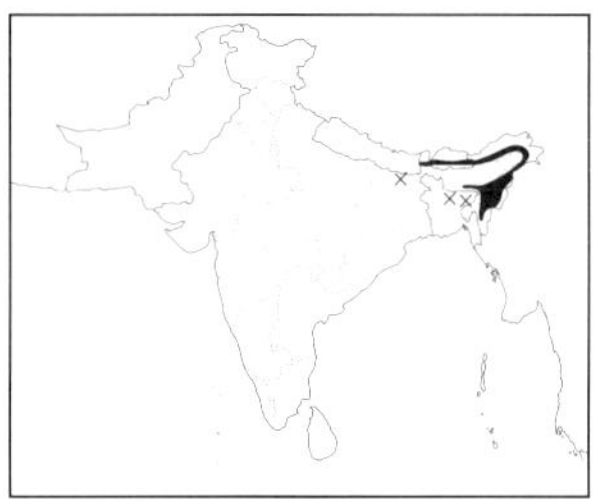

IDENTIFICATION 10 cm. Told from Golden-spectacled Warbler (p.735) by white eye-ring, grey supercilium, rear ear-coverts and sides of neck, and broader yellow greater-covert wing-bar. From Grey-cheeked Warbler (below) by yellow chin and upper throat, clearer grey supercilium and crown-stripe contrasting with well-defined dark grey lateral crown-stripes, greenish (rather than grey) lower ear-coverts, and yellowish lores. Can show touch of yellow on anterior edge of white eye-ring, which is not apparent on Grey-cheeked. **VOICE** Call is a sharp *che-wheet*. Song is a combination of sweet, variable phrases, each consisting usually of five to eight rapidly delivered notes, the phrases alternating after pauses of several seconds; phrases include: *sweet-sweet-sweet-sweet-sweet-sweet-sweet*; *tutitutitutituti*; *tit-twi-twi-twi-twi*; *tu-swit-swee-sisisisisi*, etc. **HABITS** Similar to those of other *Seicercus* warblers. Often joins mixed hunting parties in the non-breeding season. Flits actively about undergrowth and bushes of dense forest. Frequently makes aerial sallies, and flutters and hovers among foliage and twigs. **HABITAT** Dense moist broadleaved evergreen and pine forest. **BREEDING** April–June. Nest is a green ball of moss, with rootlets and leaves, built in a hollow in a mossy bank or among moss growing on a fallen log or dead stump. **DISTRIBUTION AND STATUS** Resident, subject to altitudinal movements. Himalayas from Nepal? and Darjeeling, West Bengal, east to Arunachal Pradesh; hills of NE India and Bangladesh. **NP:** possibly recorded in 19th century, but the specimen may have originated in India. **IN:** locally fairly common; 1500–2300 m in breeding season in Himalayas, above 1400 m in hills south of the Brahmaputra R; winters in foothills and adjacent plains. **BT:** frequent; 825–2285 m. **BD:** rare winter visitor.

GREY-CHEEKED WARBLER *Seicercus poliogenys* Plate 127

Grey-cheeked Flycatcher Warbler (I)

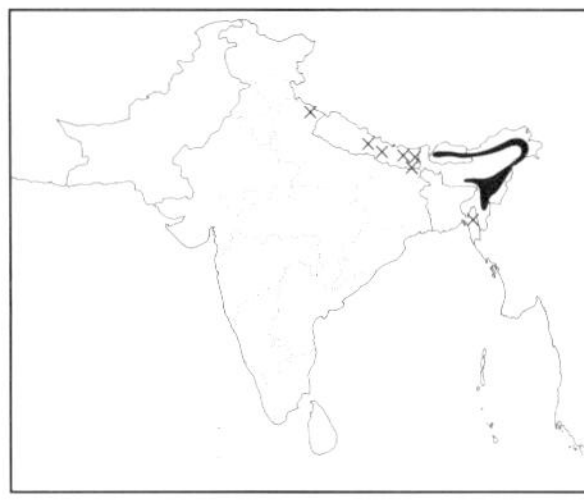

IDENTIFICATION 10 cm. As White-spectacled Warbler (above), with prominent white eye-ring, but has whitish chin and upper throat, dark grey lower ear-coverts and grey lores (on some, lores have small patch of white). Further, has more uniform dark grey head, with poorly defined (or completely non-existent) paler grey supercilium and central crown-stripe, and less distinct dark lateral crown-stripes. Told from Golden-spectacled Warbler (p.735) by white eye-ring, grey sides of head and crown, and broader yellow greater-covert wing-bar. **VOICE** Song is similar to White-spectacled's, but less melodic, more *Phylloscopus*-like, with notes more slurred together; phrases include: *titsi-titsi-chi*; *chi-chi-chi-chi-chi*; *tewchi-chewchi-chew*; *switu-switu-switu-switu*, etc. Calls include a thin, sibilant *tsew....tsew....tsew...* and an explosive *twit...twit...* (sometimes combined with song). **HABITS** Similar to those of White-spectacled Warbler. **HABITAT** Evergreen broadleaved forest and bamboo jungle. **BREEDING** May and June. Nest is a ball of green moss, built on the ground or among moss-covered rocks. **DISTRIBUTION AND STATUS** Resident, subject to altitudinal movements. Himalayas from N Uttar Pradesh east to Arunachal Pradesh; hills of NE India and Bangladesh. **NP:** probably resident, rare in the centre and east; 2440–3200 m. **IN:** locally fairly common; 1700 m up to at least 3050 m in breeding season in Himalayas, down to 1200 m in hills south of the Brahmaputra R; winters from 1890 m down to the foothills. **BT:** frequent; 1825–3400 m. **BD:** ?former winter visitor; no recent records, but could still occur in hill tracts.

CHESTNUT-CROWNED WARBLER *Seicercus castaniceps* Plate 127

Chestnut-headed Flycatcher Warbler (I)

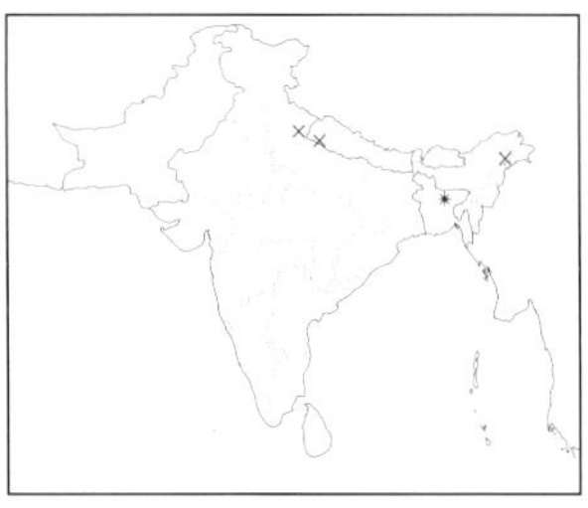

IDENTIFICATION 9.5 cm. Separated from other *Seicercus* warblers by combination of small size, chestnut crown with diffuse dark brown lateral crown-stripes, bright lemon-yellow rump, grey sides of head with white eye-ring, grey throat and upper breast contrasting with white lower breast and belly, and bright yellow flanks. Grey on sides of head, double yellow wing-bar, prominent yellow rump and lack of white supercilium are the best features for separation from Broad-billed Warbler (p.737); see that species for further differences. **VOICE** Calls include a *chi-chi* and a *tsik* (Ali and Ripley 1987); song of five to seven notes, extremely high-pitched and sibilant, and slightly undulating, *see see see see see...* (J. Scharringa). **HABITS** Similar to those of other *Seicercus* warblers. Keeps singly, in pairs or with mixed foraging flocks of warblers and tits. Very active. Flits restlessly about the middle and upper storeys; frequently flutters, hovers and makes aerial sallies. Often flicks wings. **HABITAT** Oak and oak–rhododendron forest. **BREEDING** April–June. Nest is a ball of green moss, hidden on the ground among overhanging moss and creepers. **DISTRIBUTION AND STATUS** Resident, subject to altitudinal movements. Himalayas from N Uttar Pradesh east to Arunachal Pradesh; hills of NE India and Bangladesh. **NP:** frequent; summers 1800–2750 m, winters 250–2285 m. **IN:** locally fairly common; in Himalayas summers 1200–2500 m, winters 150–2300 m; in Meghalaya breeds 750–1800 m. **BT:** fairly common; 610–2745 m. **BD:** ?former visitor; no recent records, but could still occur in hill tracts.

BROAD-BILLED WARBLER *Tickellia hodgsoni* — Plate 127

Broad-billed Flycatcher Warbler (I), ***Abroscopus hodgsoni*** **(F,I,K)**

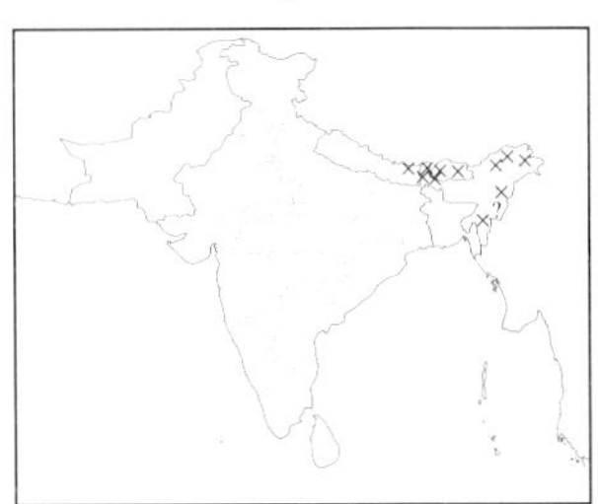

IDENTIFICATION 10 cm. A distinctive warbler with chestnut forehead and crown, greyish-white supercilium and dark grey eye-stripe, greyish ear-coverts, throat and breast, and yellow belly, flanks and vent. Has slightly yellower rump. Chestnut crown, grey throat and breast, and white on tail are best features to separate it from Yellow-bellied Warbler (p.738). Very similar in plumage to Mountain Tailorbird (p.722); best distinguished from that by shorter (and broader) bill, darker and more extensive chestnut on crown, uniform olive-green mantle and nape (lacking grey nape of Mountain Tailorbird), and greyish-white supercilium. **VOICE** Song is a series of very thin, high-pitched whistles repeated at intervals, *si.seeee-ee-eee.......si.seeee-ee-eee.......siiiiiiiiiiii.......siiiiiiiiiiii...*, etc; notes may increase in pitch and become difficult to hear. Also rapid, rather metallic jumbled notes: *witiwiwitiwi-chu-witiwiwitiwit; chitiwichitiwit-chit-chitiwichitiwit-chit-chitiwichitiwit...*, etc. **HABITS** Poorly known. Often in company with itinerant mixed parties of small birds. Frequents the forest understorey. **HABITAT** Bamboo and other undergrowth in dense evergreen broadleaved forest. **BREEDING** Little known. May and June. Only one nest described, a ball of dry leaves, chiefly bamboo, built 2 m above ground in a young tree. **DISTRIBUTION AND STATUS** Resident, possibly subject to altitudinal movements, but these are poorly known. Himalayas from E Nepal east to Arunachal Pradesh; NE Indian hills. **NP:** rare; recorded only in the Arun valley watershed, 2195 m (November) and 2300 m (September), probably resident. **IN:** generally uncommon, but locally fairly common; summers 1100–2700 m. **BT:** uncommon; 1370 m (October), 1830 m (November), 1865–2360 m in April and May. **REFERENCES** Alström (1997).

RUFOUS-FACED WARBLER *Abroscopus albogularis* — Plate 127

White-throated Flycatcher Warbler (I), White-throated Warbler (F)

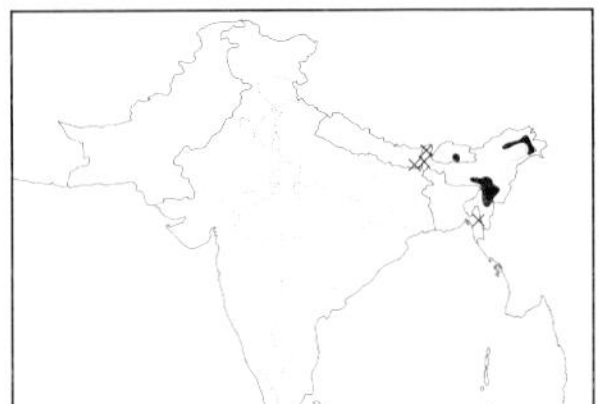

IDENTIFICATION 8 cm. Superficially resembles Chestnut-crowned Warbler (p.736). Readily distinguished by pale rufous face, lacking prominent white eye-ring, and by buff crown (with blackish lateral crown-stripes, as on that species), blackish mottling on throat, yellow band across breast, whitish rump, absence of double yellow wing-bar, and lack of white on tail. **VOICE** Sibilant, high-pitched, repetitive whistles: *titiriiiii...titiriiiii...titiriiiii...titiriii-ii...* etc (C. Robson). **HABITS** Similar to those of White-spectacled Warbler (p.736), but even more active. Often in small parties and with other small insectivorous species. Usually keeps to the undergrowth and lower branches of trees. **HABITAT** Bamboo clumps at edges and in more open areas of moist deciduous and evergreen broadleaved forest; also bamboo and scrub jungle. **BREEDING** April–June. Nest is a pad of moss on top of a layer of bamboo fibres, roots and leaves, placed in a hollow in a bamboo stem, usually near a stream. **DISTRIBUTION AND STATUS** Resident. Himalayas from E Nepal east to Arunachal Pradesh; hills of NE India and Bangladesh. **NP:** very rare; recorded only in the far east below 1220 m, possibly resident. **IN:** locally fairly common; 300–1400 m in Himalayas, up to 1800 m in Cachar (Assam). **BT:** locally fairly common; 700–935 m. **BD:** ?former resident; no recent records, but could still occur in hill tracts.

BLACK-FACED WARBLER *Abroscopus schisticeps* — Plate 127

Black-faced Flycatcher Warbler (I)

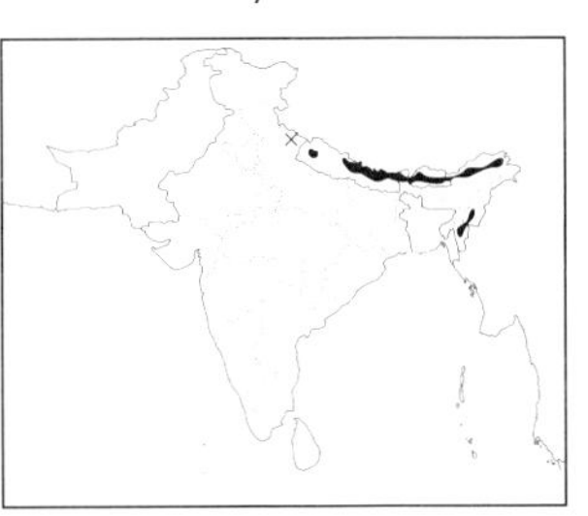

IDENTIFICATION 9 cm. Distinguished from the *Seicercus* and from other *Abroscopus* warblers by yellow supercilium and black mask. In addition, has grey crown, nape and rear of ear-coverts, and uniform olive-green upperparts lacking any wing-bar. Superficially resembles Yellow-bellied Fantail (p.608), but has much shorter tail. **Racial variation** The nominate race of the C Himalayas has yellow throat and breast and whitish rest of underparts, whereas the more widely distributed *A. s. flavimentalis*, which occurs to the east, has yellow of underparts restricted to throat. **VOICE** Alarm call is a rapid, high-pitched *tz-tz-tz-tz-tz-tz* (Fleming *et al.* 1984). **HABITS** Similar to those of *Seicercus* warblers. Usually in fast-moving parties of 10–15 birds, often with other warblers and small babblers. Forages actively in the middle storey and in tall bushes in forest. **HABITAT** Moist oak and mixed broadleaved forest, especially with moss-covered trees, creepers, bamboo and thick undergrowth. **BREEDING** Little known. April–June. Only two nests described: one was a pad of bamboo leaves, placed 5 m up in a hole in a small tree; the other was a pad of moss roots and fibres, placed in a small bamboo. **DISTRIBUTION AND STATUS** Resident. Himalayas from N Uttar Pradesh east to Arunachal Pradesh; NE Indian hills. **NP:** local, fairly common in the centre and east, rare in the west; 1525–2700 m, probably descends from higher altitudes in winter. **IN:** locally fairly common in the east; 1450–2500 m in Himalayas, sometimes down to 600 m in Cachar (Assam). **BT:** frequent; from 1370 m up to at least 2440 m.

YELLOW-BELLIED WARBLER *Abroscopus superciliaris* Plate 127

Yellow-bellied Flycatcher Warbler (I)

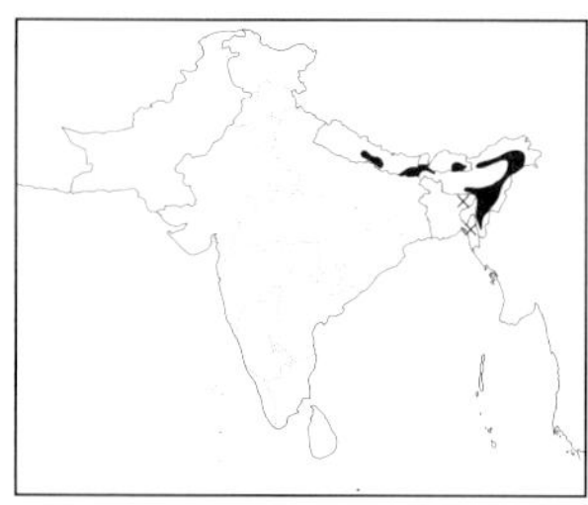

IDENTIFICATION 9 cm. Dull-coloured compared with the *Seicercus* and with other *Abroscopus* warblers. Has white supercilium, yellowish-olive upperparts, white throat and yellow rest of underparts. Confusable really only with Grey-hooded Warbler (p.735), which also has a white supercilium, and best distinguished from that species by white throat, yellowish-olive (rather than grey) mantle, and lack of white on tail. Separated from all *Phylloscopus* warblers by combination of rather long bill, brownish-grey on crown, white throat and yellow rest of underparts, and by fairly narrow tail, lacking prominent undertail-coverts, which gives rise to rather distinctive profile. Tail appears pale brownish-buff from below. **VOICE** Call is a typical *chrrt chrrt chrrt* (P. Morris); song is a halting, cheery ditty of six notes, ascending at the end, *tue-do-du-do-di-dee* (P. Holt). **HABITS** Similar to those of *Seicercus* warblers. Found singly, in pairs or in mixed, roving flocks of insectivorous species. Very active. Feeds chiefly by making short aerial sallies from bamboos, bushes and lower branches. **HABITAT** Bamboo jungle and bamboo in forest, often near streams. **BREEDING** April–June. Nest is pad of bamboo leaves and moss or rootlets, placed in a hollow in a bamboo stem within 2 m of ground. **DISTRIBUTION AND STATUS** Resident, subject to short altitudinal movements. Himalayas from WC Nepal east to Arunachal Pradesh; hills of NE India and Bangladesh. **NP:** locally fairly common in the far east, uncommon farther west; mainly 245–1525 m (–2285 m). **IN:** locally fairly common in summer; in Himalayas breeds 500–900 m, from base of the hills to 1500 m in Arunachal Pradesh; in hills south of the Brahmaputra R summers 900–1800 m; winters down to adjacent plains. **BT:** frequent; 825–2200 m. **BD:** scarce and local in the northeast and southeast.

GRASSBIRDS Subfamily Megalurinae

Brownish warblers with a longish tail which inhabit damp tall grassland. The males perform song flights in the breeding season.

STRIATED GRASSBIRD *Megalurus palustris* Plate 123

Striated Marsh Warbler (F,I,N), Striated Warbler (K,R)

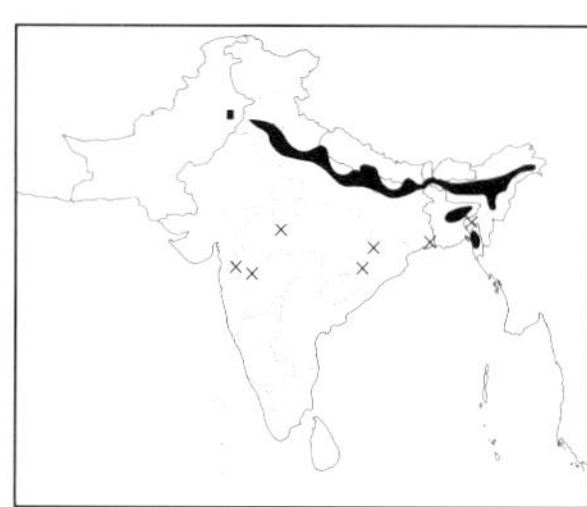

IDENTIFICATION 25 cm. A large, babbler-like 'warbler' with brownish-buff upperparts prominently streaked with black, whitish supercilium, whitish underparts with fine brown streaking on breast and flanks, and long, graduated tail. In fresh plumage, supercilium and underparts are strongly washed with pale yellow and streaking on crown and nape and underparts is partially obscured. Confusable with Bristled Grassbird (p.739), and is best distinguished from that by larger size, longer and finer bill, more prominent supercilium, which is clearly defined behind eye, and longer and narrower tail (becoming pointed when worn); tail differs from that of Bristled in having dark feather shafts, and less distinct cross-barring on upperside, and in lacking whitish tips. **VOICE** Call is a loud, harsh *chat*; song, which can be delivered in aerial display, is a clear, drawn-out whistle, ending in a short, explosive *wheeechoo* (Ali and Ripley 1987). **HABITS** Usually solitary or in pairs. Often perches conspicuously on top of reeds or bushes, and has a habit of jerking its tail and flicking one wing half open and then the other. Feeds in thick vegetation, and can climb rapidly up and down reed and grass stems. In the breeding season, males frequently sing from exposed perches and in short gliding song flight. **HABITAT** Tall damp grassland, reedbeds and tamarisks along large rivers and around ponds; also inhabits grassland near cultivation and villages (Assam) and gardens (Manipur). **BREEDING** April–July. Nest is a large, roughly built ball of coarse grass, placed low down in a grass clump or bush. **DISTRIBUTION AND STATUS** Resident. NE Pakistan, and from Punjab, India, east through N India and S Nepal to Arunachal Pradesh, also Bangladesh; scattered records south to Maharashtra and Orissa. **PK:** rare and very local. **NP:** local in the terai, fairly common at Kosi Tappu, rare elsewhere. **IN, BD:** locally common.

BRISTLED GRASSBIRD *Chaetornis striatus* Plate 123

Bristled Grass Warbler (I,N,R)

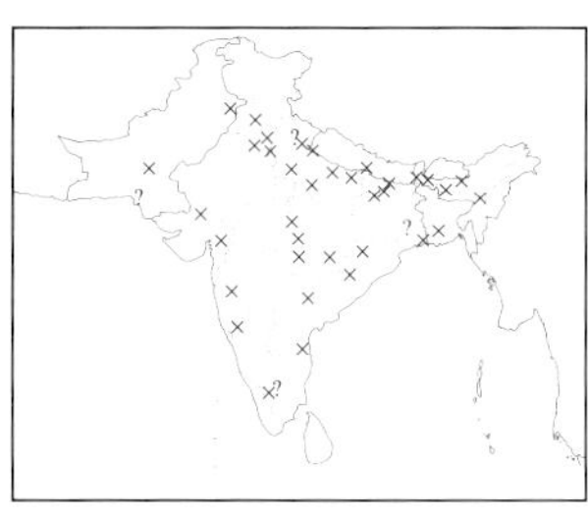

IDENTIFICATION 20 cm. Superficially resembles Striated Grassbird (p.738), with brownish-buff upperparts prominently streaked with black, and buffish-white underparts with fine dark streaking on lower throat. Has prominent black rictal bristles. Distinguished from Striated by smaller size, short, stout bill, less distinct supercilium (barely apparent behind eye), and shorter, broader tail with pale shafts and buffish-white tips (except on central pair) and with more prominent dark cross-barring (undertail appears blackish with broad whitish tips, although these can be lost through wear). In addition, breast and flanks lack the streaking which is apparent on worn Striated. In fresh plumage, underparts are washed with buff and feathers of upperparts and wings have broad buff fringes. Upperparts become greyer-brown and underparts whiter when worn. Larger size and brownish-buff (streaked dark brown) coloration to upperparts readily distinguish Bristled from Rufous-rumped Grassbird (below). **Immature** birds possibly have yellowish wash to underparts. **VOICE** Song, delivered from an exposed perch or in sustained song flight, is a disyllabic *trew-treuw* repeated monotonously at 2–3-second intervals (Grewal 1996). **HABITS** Spends most of the time skulking in dense grassland. In the breeding season, and less frequently at other times, males perform a song flight, rising about 20 m or more and circling widely for ten minutes or longer before descending; also sings from an exposed perch, and appears to have favourite perches. **HABITAT** Grassland with scattered bushes in riverain or swampy areas; short, dry grassland; also standing paddy-fields. **BREEDING** May–September. Nest is a ball of dry grass, placed on or near the ground in grass or scrub. **DISTRIBUTION AND STATUS** Endemic to the subcontinent. Resident, subject to local movements. Now recorded mainly from India and Nepal. Globally threatened. **PK:** vagrant. **IN:** widespread, but very local; formerly common in Gujarat, Andhra Pradesh and West Bengal, but very few recent published records. **NP:** rare and local, but probably overlooked; recorded mainly in summer. **BD:** ?former resident; could still occur locally. **REFERENCES** Baral (1997), Grewal (1996), Inskipp (1996).

RUFOUS-RUMPED GRASSBIRD *Graminicola bengalensis* Plate 123

Large Grass Warbler (F,I,K,N)

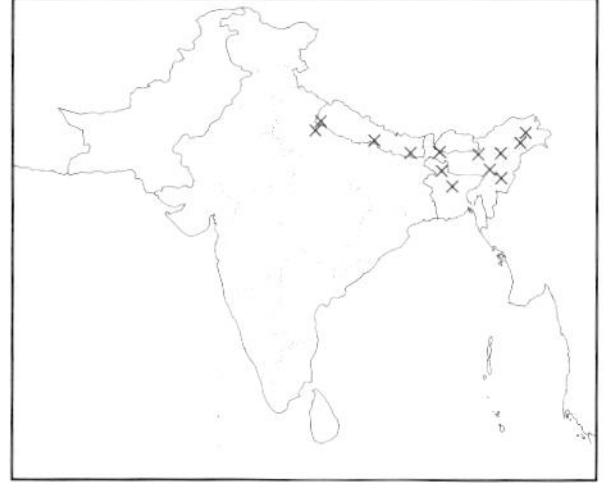

IDENTIFICATION 18 cm. Most likely to be confused with Bristled Grassbird (above). Separated from that species by black crown, nape and mantle (with rufous streaking on crown, white or buff streaking on nape and upper mantle, and broader and more prominent rufous streaking on lower mantle and back). In addition, has black-streaked rufous rump, blackish tail broadly tipped with white, and white underparts with rufous-buff breast sides and flanks. In fresh plumage, has broad rufous fringes to wing-coverts and remiges (wings appear rufous, with dark-centred tertials). **VOICE** Probable song is a subdued high *er-wi-wi-wi* or *bzz-wi-wi-wi, you-wuoo, yu-wuoo,* followed by series of usual call-notes or *er-wit-wit-wit,* and ending with curious, subdued, strained wheezy sounds. Usual call-notes are subdued, harsh, and scolding (sometimes rising at end): *err-err-err-errrr, jjjerrreali,* etc, reminiscent of distant Eurasian Jay (p.591); also *wirrruu,* interspersed with wheezy notes and (probable) song phrases (C. Robson from H. S. Baral recording). **HABITS** Outside the breeding season, skulks and creeps about quietly in dense grassland. When breeding, during the monsoon, males are very noisy, singing from the tops of reeds and soaring into the air. **HABITAT** Tall grass and reeds near water. **BREEDING** July and August. Nest is a bulky cup of grass and rushes, fixed low down between grass or reed stems standing in deep water. **DISTRIBUTION AND STATUS** Resident. From W Nepal terai and N Uttar Pradesh east through the floodplains of the Brahmaputra R (Arunachal Pradesh, Assam, Manipur, West Bengal), and south in the plains of Bangladesh. **NP:** very local in the terai, frequent at Chitwan, rare at Sukla Phanta. **IN:** local and common. **BD:** rare and local resident. **REFERENCES** Crosby (1995), Javed and Rahmani (in prep.).

BROAD-TAILED GRASSBIRD *Schoenicola platyura* Plate 123

Broad-tailed Grass Warbler (I,P)

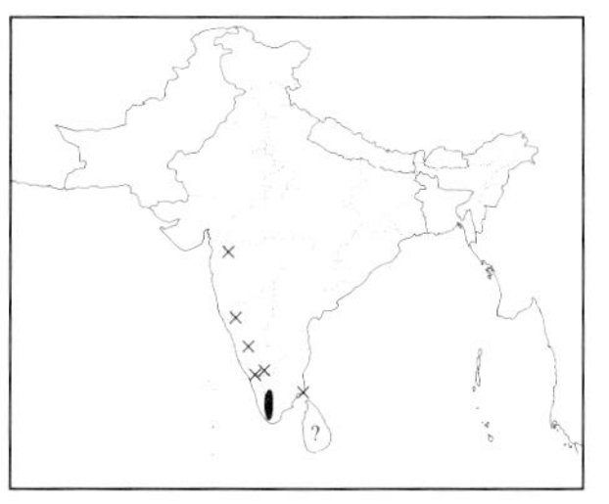

IDENTIFICATION 18 cm. Readily identified by stout bill, long, broad tail, uniform rufous-brown upperparts, and whitish underparts with rufous-buff wash to breast and flanks. Has buffish supercilium. Tail is diffusely cross-barred, and all but central pair of feathers have buffish tips. Rump and uppertail-coverts and tertials can also appear very faintly barred. When worn, upperparts are a paler, sandy greyish-brown, with sandy edges to wing-coverts and remiges, and underparts are whiter. **VOICE** Song, which can be delivered in aerial display, is a shrill and sweet trill, ending with a few warbling and *chack* notes (Ali and Ripley 1987); call is a sharp metallic *zink,* occasionally doubled (P. Holt). **HABITS** Very skulking except in the breeding season, when males sing from tops of bushes and in flight while soaring with tail fanned. At other seasons, seen most easily in the early morning or at sunset, when birds may perch on tops of grass stems. **HABITAT** Dense, tall grass and reeds on open hillsides, often around damp depressions. **BREEDING** July and August. Nest is a ball of coarse grass, placed up to 1 m above ground in tussocks of long grass. **DISTRIBUTION AND STATUS** Resident, endemic to the subcontinent. Western Ghats (Maharashtra, Karnataka, Kerala and Tamil Nadu) and Sri Lanka. **IN:** status uncertain; rare or uncommon, but probably overlooked, in higher hills; 900–2000 m. **LK:** status uncertain; probably a vagrant to lowlands and lower hills. **REFERENCES** Gaston and Zacharias (1996).

LAUGHINGTHRUSHES Subfamily Garrulacinae

Medium-sized, long-tailed passerines which are gregarious even in the breeding season. At the first sign of danger, they characteristically break into a concert of loud hissing, chattering and squealing. When really alarmed, some species call in a communal chorus of laughter-like noises, which gives the genus *Garrulax* its vernacular name. They often feed on the ground, moving along with long springy hops, rummaging among leaf litter, flicking leaves aside and into the air, and digging for food with their strong bill. Their flight is short and clumsy, the birds flying from tree to tree in follow-my-leader fashion.

ASHY-HEADED LAUGHINGTHRUSH *Garrulax cinereifrons* Plate 128

Ashy-headed Babbler

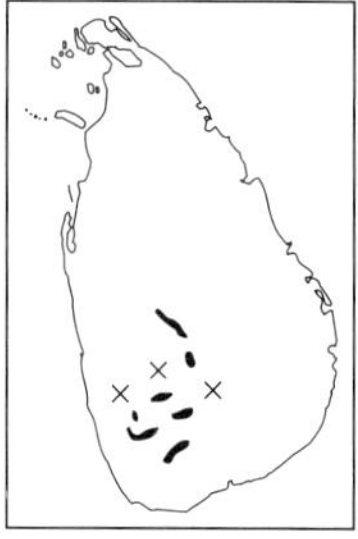

IDENTIFICATION 23 cm. A rather plain-coloured laughingthrush with greyish head, rufous-brown upperparts and tail, tawny underparts with paler throat, and dark bill and legs. **Juvenile** has brighter rufous underparts. **VOICE** Breaks out constantly into a harsh chattering, which is taken up in turn by all members of the troop, and ceases just as suddenly; this chattering usually terminates with a kind of hurried scream (Legge 1880). Can easily be mistaken for calls of Rufous Babbler (p.766) (Henry 1971). **HABITS** Usually keeps in flocks of four to six, sometimes up to 16 birds. Often joins mixed feeding flocks of other species, and then generally found close to the ground. Shy, but noisy when feeding. **HABITAT** Interior of dense wet forest and bamboo thickets. **BREEDING** March–July. Only one nest known: an untidy mass of leaves, placed 4–6 m above ground in a sapling fork in tall grass on a fairly steep hillside. **DISTRIBUTION AND STATUS** Globally threatened. **LK:** endemic resident, rare in wet lowlands and adjacent lower hills. **REFERENCES** Banks and Banks (1987).

WHITE-THROATED LAUGHINGTHRUSH *Garrulax albogularis* Plate 128

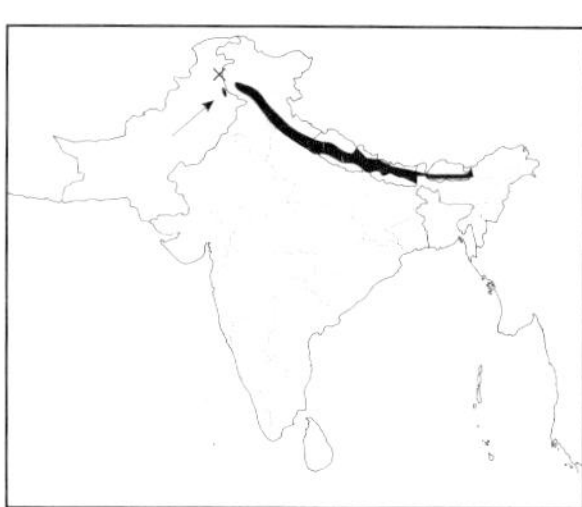

IDENTIFICATION 28 cm. A large, distinctive laughingthrush, best identified by striking white throat and upper breast, contrasting with brownish-olive lower breast-band, and pale rufous-orange underparts. Additional features include black lores and rufous-orange forehead, uniform brownish-olive upperparts, and indistinct grey panel on wing formed by grey outer fringes to primaries. In flight, shows broad white tips to tail feathers. **Juvenile** is similar to adult, but has less distinct breast-band and paler rufous-buff belly and flanks. **VOICE** A wheezy call when following each other through bushes and middle of trees; alarm calls *tzzzzzzzzz* and *koil-tzeee*; a gentle *teer-teer* contact note when feeding (Fleming *et al.* 1984). A variety of squeals, hisses and shrill, squeaky laughter when alarmed or excited (Ali and Ripley 1987). **HABITS** Similar to those of other laughingthrushes. Keeps in parties of six to a dozen in the breeding season, and in flocks of up to 50 or more in winter. Often with other laughingthrushes and other species. Fairly tame, more so than most others of genus. Forages on the ground, also frequently in bushes and in the low to middle level of trees, searching crevices and tearing off moss; sometimes feeds also in the open, in fields. **HABITAT** Broadleaved and mixed coniferous–broadleaved forest, open secondary growth, and scrub. **BREEDING** March–July. Builds a typical laughingthrush nest, one to a few metres above ground in a bush, at the top of a small tree or on a horizontal branch. **DISTRIBUTION AND STATUS** Resident. Himalayas from Murree, Pakistan, east to W Arunachal Pradesh; Assam. Subject to altitudinal movements: in the west summers 1800–2900 m, chiefly up to 2440 m, and in the centre and east mainly 1800–2700 m, occasionally to 3500 m; winters from 1200 m up to at least 2400 m, occasionally down to 450 m. **PK:** rare and local, or recently extirpated? **NP:** common and widespread. **IN:** locally frequent in Himalayas; very rare in NE hills. **BT:** common.

WHITE-CRESTED LAUGHINGTHRUSH *Garrulax leucolophus* Plate 128

IDENTIFICATION 28 cm. A large, unmistakable laughingthrush, with white crest, throat and upper breast contrasting with black mask, grey nape, chestnut mantle and band across lower breast, and dark olive-brown wings, tail and belly. **VOICE** Very noisy, with flocks uttering sudden bursts of cackling laughter-like sound, *pick-wo..pick-wo* etc. **HABITS** Similar to those of other laughingthrushes. Usually keeps in parties of eight to ten, sometimes in larger flocks

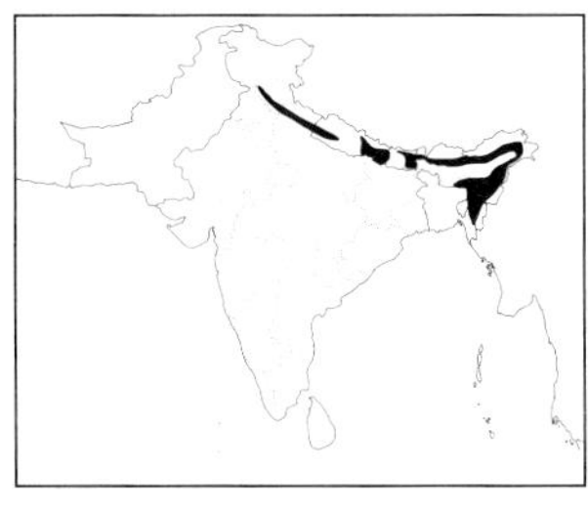

of up to 20 or more birds. Particularly noisy and quite wary, often bursting into a chorus of cackling until the noise reaches a crescendo. Forages chiefly on the ground, also in low bushes, and sometimes up to medium height of forest trees. **HABITAT** Broadleaved forest with dense undergrowth, secondary scrub and bamboo thickets. **BREEDING** March–September. Builds a typical laughingthrush nest in a bush, a few metres above ground. **DISTRIBUTION AND STATUS** Resident. Himalayas from NW Himachal Pradesh east to Arunachal Pradesh; NE India and Bangladesh. Possibly has some altitudinal movements: in Himalayas mainly 600–1565 m, uncommon down to 305 m and up to 2135 m (–2745 m in Bhutan); in NE hills from the base up to 1800 m. **NP, IN, BT:** common and widespread. **BD:** locally common in SE coastal forest?

LESSER NECKLACED LAUGHINGTHRUSH *Garrulax monileger* Plate 128

Necklaced Laughing Thrush (I), *G. moniligerus* (F,I)

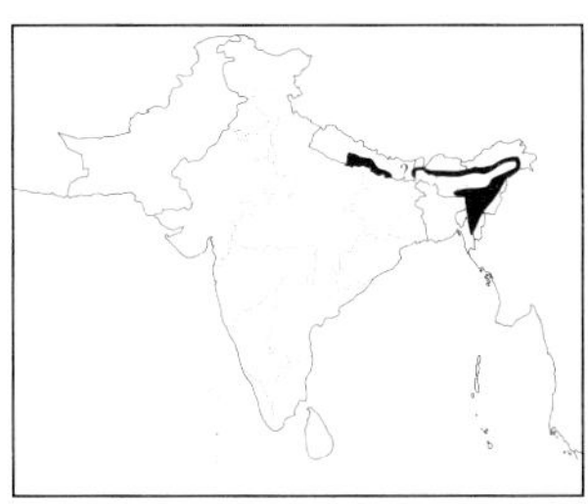

IDENTIFICATION 27 cm. Very similar to Greater Necklaced Laughingthrush (p.742), with black necklace, rufous-orange flanks, white centre of breast and belly, greyish-white panel on wing, and bold white tips to largely blackish outer tail feathers. Separated from that species by smaller size, with finer, all-dark bill, lower black border of ear-coverts not extending to bill, white throat, bordered with rufous-orange where throat adjoins necklace, olive-brown (rather than dark grey) primary coverts which are concolorous with rest of coverts, narrower necklace thinning and often almost obscured by fulvous at centre (although necklace can be uniformly broad on some birds), white of breast sides extending as crescent beneath black necklace, and brownish (rather than slate-grey) legs and feet. **Juvenile** is said to be similar, but with dusky necklace. **VOICE** Song is a loud, mellow *tee-too-ka-kew-kew-kew*; calls include a subdued *turrrr* and a *kaaaaaa* (Fleming *et al.* 1984). **HABITS** Similar to those of other laughingthrushes, but more wary and less conspicuous. Keeps in pairs in breeding season, and otherwise in flocks of ten to 20 birds. Shares the same ecological niche as Greater Necklaced, and often with that species. Feeds chiefly on the ground, and if disturbed hides in bushes and trees. **HABITAT** Dense broadleaved evergreen and moist deciduous forest with thick undergrowth, dense secondary growth and bamboo thickets. **BREEDING** March–July. Builds a typical laughingthrush nest in bushes or small trees, up to 6 m above ground. **DISTRIBUTION AND STATUS** Resident. Himalayas from WC Nepal east to Arunachal Pradesh; NE India and Bangladesh. From edge of the plains up to 1000 m, locally to 1400 m (–1800 m in Bhutan). **NP:** local and uncommon in C Himalayas, becoming more frequent farther east. **IN:** frequent up to 1000 m. **BT:** frequent. **BD:** local.

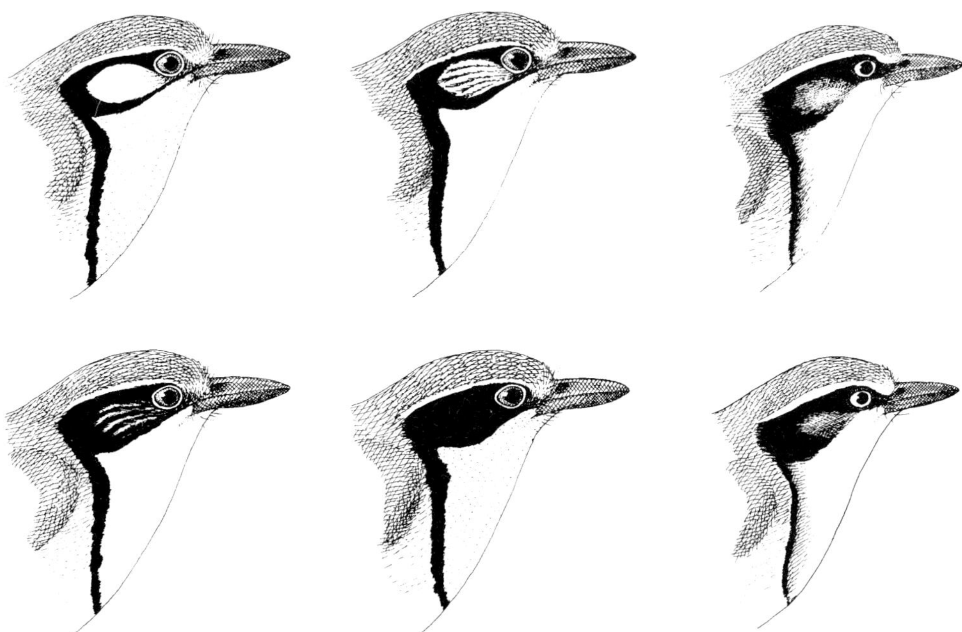

Greater Necklaced Laughingthrush Garrulax pectoralis *(centre and left-hand pair) and Lesser Necklaced Laughingthrush* Garrulax monileger *to show variation in head pattern (Drawing by Nigel Bean)*

GREATER NECKLACED LAUGHINGTHRUSH *Garrulax pectoralis* Plate 128

Black-gorgeted Laughing Thrush (I), Large Necklaced Laughing-thrush (F)

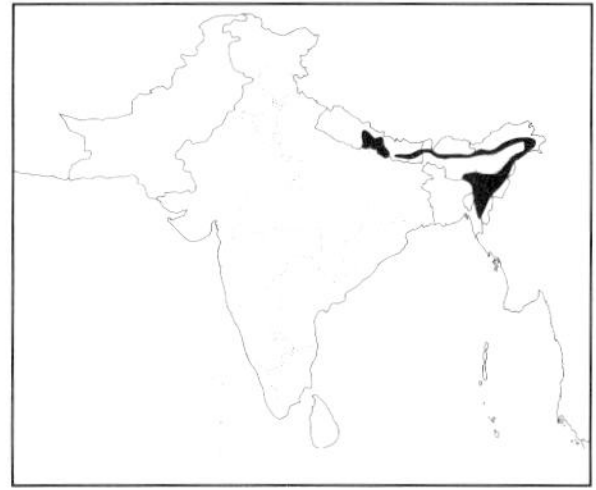

IDENTIFICATION 29 cm. Like Lesser Necklaced Laughingthrush (p.741), has black necklace, white centre of breast and belly with pale rufous-orange flanks, and greyish-white panel on wing, and shows broad white tip to blackish outer tail in flight. Distinguished from that species by larger size, with stouter, paler-based bill, complete black moustachial stripe (bordering either black or white, or streaked black-and-white ear-coverts), uniform buff or white throat without two-toned appearance shown by Lesser Necklaced, blackish primary coverts which contrast with mantle and wings, broader necklace which is clearly defined at centre, and slate-grey (rather than brownish) legs and feet. **VOICE** Song is a loud *what-what-who-who*; alarm call is a *pukreeeeeee pa-kak-kak-kak* (Fleming *et al.* 1984). **HABITS** Like those of Lesser Necklaced, and often associates with that species. **HABITAT** Very similar to that of Lesser Necklaced Laughingthrush. **BREEDING** March–August. Builds a typical laughingthrush nest in bushes or small trees, up to 6 m above ground. **DISTRIBUTION AND STATUS** Resident. Himalayas from WC Nepal east to Arunachal Pradesh; NE India and Bangladesh. From the plains edge up to 1220 m, locally to 1700 m. **NP:** local and uncommon in W Himalayas, becoming more frequent farther east. **IN, BT:** frequent. **BD:** locally common.

RUFOUS-NECKED LAUGHINGTHRUSH *Garrulax ruficollis* Plate 128

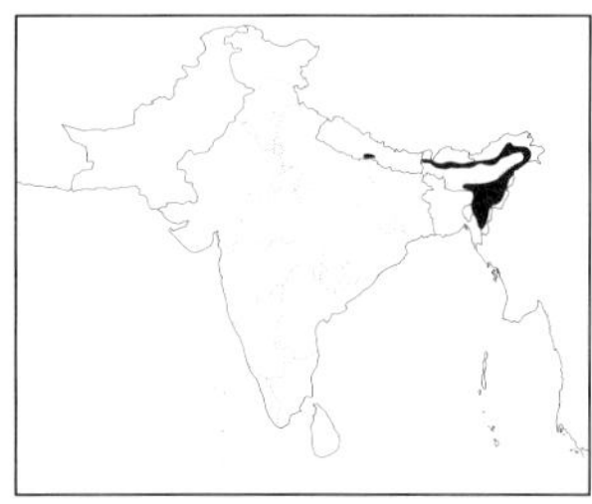

IDENTIFICATION 23 cm. A small, mainly olive-brown laughingthrush, readily identified by prominent rufous patch on sides of neck, black forehead, face and throat, grey crown and nape, and rufous vent and centre of lower belly. Tail is uniform brownish-black. **Juvenile** is duller, with browner crown. **VOICE** An incredibly varied and vocal songster. One territorial song is a shrill whistle that runs up the scale and then ends with several downslurred double notes. Punctuates its song with many 'conversational' calls, from scolding whistles and descending trills to chittering babbles and hoarse squawks (S. Connop). **HABITS** Similar to those of other laughingthrushes. Keeps in pairs in the breeding season, and in groups or flocks of up to 20 birds at other times. Skulks on the ground and in undergrowth or low bushes. **HABITAT** Forest margins, bushes at the edge of cultivation, secondary growth, tea gardens and bamboo thickets. **BREEDING** March–August. Builds a typical laughingthrush nest in bushes. **DISTRIBUTION AND STATUS** Resident. Himalayas in C Nepal and from Sikkim east to Arunachal Pradesh; NE India and Bangladesh. From base of the hills and adjacent plains up to 1525 m in Himalayas; from the plains up to 600 m (–1250 m) in NE Indian hills. **NP:** very local; mainly at Chitwan, where locally frequent. **IN:** locally common. **BT:** frequent. **BD:** locally common.

STRIATED LAUGHINGTHRUSH *Garrulax striatus* Plate 128

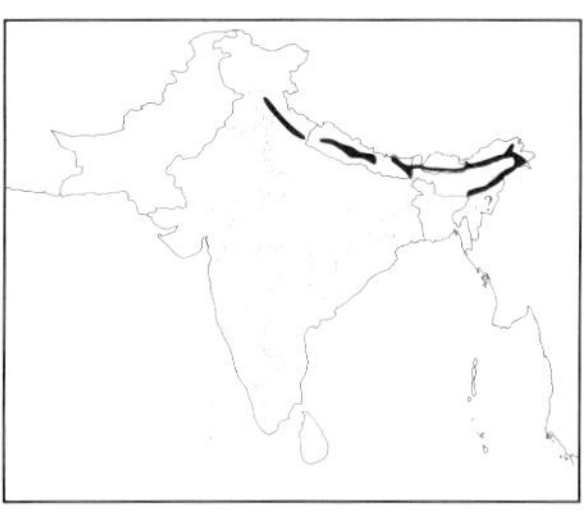

IDENTIFICATION 28 cm. A large laughingthrush with stout black bill and floppy crest, giving rise to dome-headed appearance. Chestnut crown, russet upperparts and brownish underparts are profusely covered with white to buffish-white streaking; wings are more rufous-brown, with greyish-white panel. Not really confusable with any other laughingthrush, although see Striped (p.747) for differences from that species. Could possibly be mistaken for one of the barwings (p.771–772), but it lacks dark barring on wings and tail. **Racial variation** *G. s. cranbrooki* of the NE subcontinent has broad black stripe behind the eye, not shown by other races in the subcontinent, and, compared with those, white streaking on crown is indistinct or absent and white streaking on mantle and underparts is much finer. **VOICE** A variety of calls: a whistled *hoo-wee... chew-chew* and *hooooooo-weeeeee-chew*, a gurgling *which-we-we-heet-chuuu, per-far-rigger* and a soft *poor-poor* (Fleming *et al.* 1984). **HABITS** Similar to those of other laughingthrushes, but is more arboreal. Found in pairs in the breeding season; otherwise singly or in small parties, often with other species. Forages at all forest levels, from the canopy of tall trees down to lower branches. **HABITAT** Dense broadleaved forest. **BREEDING** April–July. Builds a typical laughingthrush nest, 1–6 m above ground. **DISTRIBUTION AND STATUS** Resident. Himalayas from C Himachal Pradesh east to Arunachal Pradesh; NE India. Subject to altitudinal movements: in W Himalayas 1200–2700 m, summers mainly above 2000 m; in C and E Himalayas and NE hills, summers 1200–2850 m (950–3060 m) and winters 600–2700 m. **NP, IN:** locally common. **BT:** common. **REFERENCES** Martens and Eck (1995).

CHESTNUT-BACKED LAUGHINGTHRUSH *Garrulax nuchalis* Plate 128

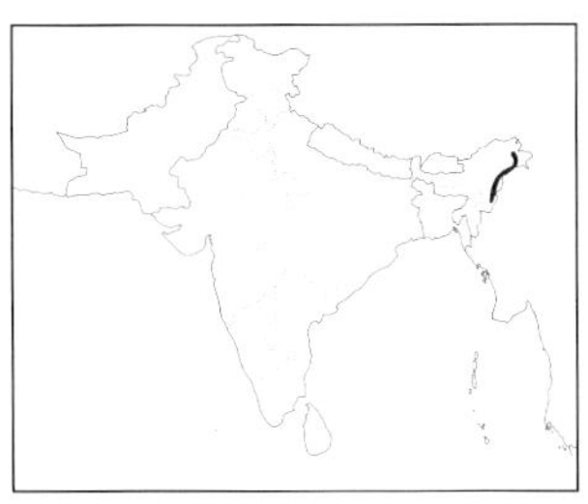

IDENTIFICATION 23 cm. A small laughingthrush, readily identified by white ear-coverts and sides of throat, white spot on forecrown, black forehead, lores, chin and centre of throat, blue-grey crown, bright rufous mantle, and grey breast. Shows diffuse blackish terminal band to tail. **VOICE** A rich whistled song of four or five notes, a soft *chip* call, and an unmistakable *churr* when alarmed (Ali and Ripley 1987). **HABITS** Similar to those of other laughingthrushes. Associates in small groups, sometimes with other laughingthrushes. Forages on the ground and in dense scrub. **HABITAT** Chiefly dense bushes on stony scrub-covered ravines and hills, also tall grass. **BREEDING** March–July. Builds a typical laughingthrush nest in dense bushes, about 1 m above ground. **DISTRIBUTION AND STATUS IN:** resident in NE hills (Assam, Manipur, Nagaland, Arunachal Pradesh), from the base up to 900 m; current status uncertain, and very few recent records. **REFERENCES** Barua (1995a), Singh (1995).

YELLOW-THROATED LAUGHINGTHRUSH *Garrulax galbanus* Plate 128

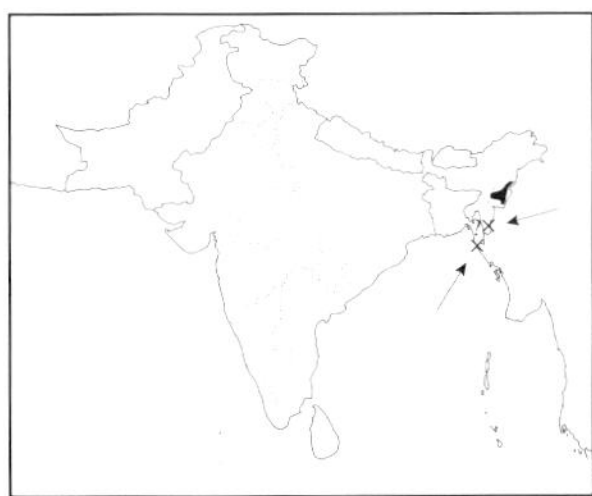

IDENTIFICATION 23 cm. A small laughingthrush with yellow underparts, black mask, and grey crown and nape. Told from the similar Rufous-vented Laughingthrush (below) by greyish-olive flanks and yellowish (rather than rufous) lower belly and vent, pale olive-brown (rather than rufous-brown) upperparts, paler grey crown and nape, greyish tail becoming blacker towards the tip and with broad white tips to outer feathers, noticeable black chin, greyish outer webs of primaries forming indistinct panel on wing, and greyish legs and feet. **VOICE** A frequently uttered feeble call (Ali and Ripley 1987). **HABITS** Similar to those of other laughingthrushes. Usually found in pairs or in small parties of up to six birds, sometimes in larger flocks. Feeds on the ground, and flies into trees when disturbed. **HABITAT** Tall grass interspersed with trees and shrubs, open scrub jungle, and margins of dense evergreen broadleaved forest. **BREEDING** April - July. Builds a typical laughingthrush nest in the fork of a low bush. **DISTRIBUTION AND STATUS** Resident in the hills of NE India (Assam, Manipur, Mizoram, Nagaland) and Bangladesh. **IN:** 800–1800 m; current status uncertain, and only one recent published record, from Manipur. **BD:** rare resident?; only one recent record, in the southeast. **REFERENCES** Long *et al.* (1994).

WYNAAD LAUGHINGTHRUSH *Garrulax delesserti* Plate 128

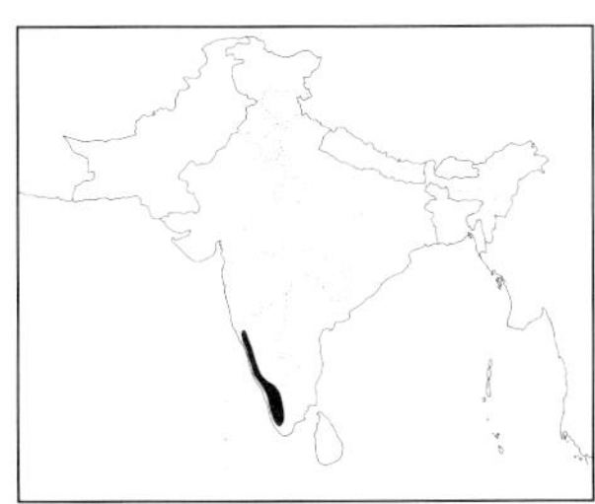

IDENTIFICATION 23 cm. Distinguishable from other laughingthrushes occurring in the peninsula by noticeable yellowish or pink lower mandible, black mask, with slightly paler slate-grey crown and nape, chestnut-brown back and wing-coverts, white throat and greyish breast and belly, rufous vent, and blackish-brown tail. **VOICE** Particularly frenzied, discordant series of screeches, squeals and cracked rattles from a flock; penetrating nasal whistled song of two to four descending notes, *tree-tree-true* (P. Holt). **HABITS** Similar to those of other laughingthrushes. Keeps in small flocks of six to 15, sometimes up to 50 birds. Skulking; clambers through undergrowth and forages on the ground below. **HABITAT** Humid broadleaved evergreen forest; also cardamom sholas; favours patches of dense *Strobilanthes* undergrowth. **BREEDING** Extended season, mainly during monsoon; April–September, varying locally. Nest is a partly domed cup, placed up to 2 m above ground in *Strobilanthes* undergrowth, bushes or small trees. **DISTRIBUTION AND STATUS IN:** resident, endemic to Western Ghats, from N Karnataka south to S Kerala and east to W Tamil Nadu; uncommon to common throughout, from base of the hills up to 1500 m. **REFERENCES** Gaston and Zacharias (1996).

RUFOUS-VENTED LAUGHINGTHRUSH *Garrulax gularis* Plate 128

***G. delesserti* (I,K)**

IDENTIFICATION 23 cm. A small laughingthrush with yellowish underparts, black mask and grey crown and nape. Distinguished from Yellow-throated (above) by rufous flanks and vent, rufous-brown upperparts (especially rump and uppertail-coverts), rufous outer tail feathers (lacking white at tip) contrasting with brown central feathers (which are darker blackish-brown towards the tip), grey sides to breast, darker grey crown and nape, yellow chin (with a tiny amount of black at base of bill), and orange legs and feet. **Juvenile** is similar to adult, but has blackish crown and rufous markings on grey breast. **VOICE** A loud whistle, in addition to cackling laughter (Ali and Ripley 1987). **HABITS** Similar to those of others of the subfamily, and very like those of Wynaad Laughingthrush (above). **HABITAT** Mainly dense evergreen undergrowth, dense scrub and secondary growth; also bamboo and scrub. **BREEDING** April–July. Nest and nest site as those of Wynaad Laughingthrush. **DISTRIBUTION AND STATUS** Resident, endemic to the subcontinent. Himalayan foothills from E Bhutan east to E Arunachal

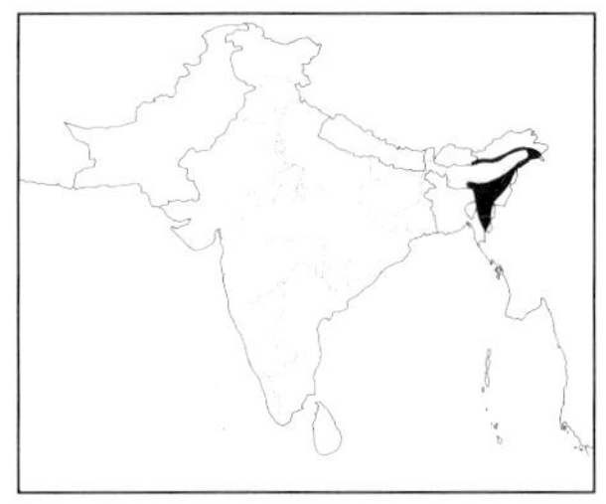

Pradesh, and south through the hills of NE India (Assam, Meghalaya, Mizoram, Nagaland) and Bangladesh. **IN:** mainly 100–1800 m, winters locally down to base of hills; current status uncertain, very few recent records. **BT:** local; 550–610 m. **BD:** rare resident in the southeast?; only one recent record. **REFERENCES** Athreya *et al.* (1997), Kaul *et al.* (1995), Singh (1995).

MOUSTACHED LAUGHINGTHRUSH *Garrulax cineraceus* Plate 128

Ashy Laughing Thrush (I)

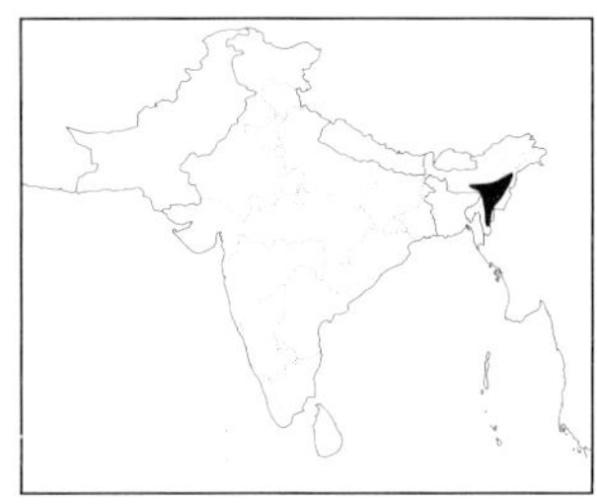

IDENTIFICATION 22 cm. A small, mainly greyish olive-brown laughingthrush, distinguished by greyish-buff supercilium and ear-coverts, black eye-stripe, crown and broad moustachial stripe, the latter breaking up into black streaking on sides of throat, black subterminal bands and white tips to tertials and secondaries, grey panel on wing with black primary-covert patch, and white-tipped black subterminal band to tail. **VOICE** Song is a loud *du-duuid,* and a variety of low, rather musical calls (Ali and Ripley 1987). **HABITS** Similar to those of other laughingthrushes. Keeps in pairs in breeding season, otherwise in small parties. Forages chiefly on the ground. **HABITAT** Dense undergrowth and bushes in moist forest, secondary growth and dense scrub at the edges of cultivation. **BREEDING** April–June. Builds a typical laughingthrush nest in thick bushes, up to 2 m above ground. **DISTRIBUTION AND STATUS IN:** resident in NE hills (Assam, Manipur, Meghalaya, Mizoram, Nagaland), subject to some altitudinal movements; breeds from 1500 m up to at least 2400 m, winters at lower levels; current status uncertain, and very few recent records.

RUFOUS-CHINNED LAUGHINGTHRUSH *Garrulax rufogularis* Plate 128

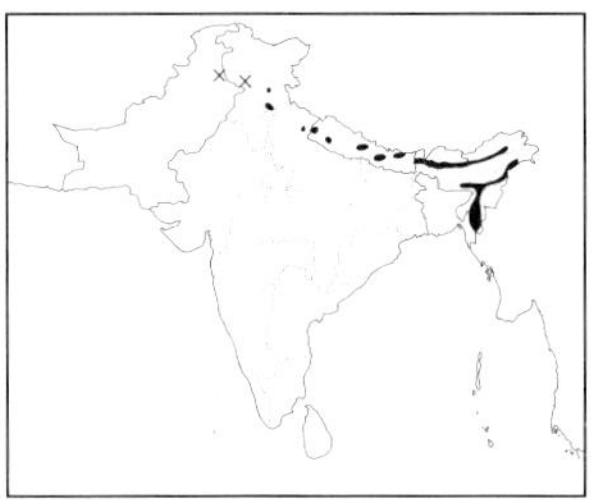

IDENTIFICATION 22 cm. A complex-patterned and variable laughingthrush. Common features include rufous chin and upper throat, blackish cap, diffuse black moustachial stripe, buff to rufous lores, irregular black spotting and barring on breast and flanks, bold black barring on upperparts, black and grey (or buff) banding across wings, and black subterminal band and rufous tip to tail. **Juvenile** is said to lack black scaling on upperparts. **Racial variation** Five races are described for the subcontinent. These include *G. r. occidentalis* of the W and C Himalayas, which has olive-brown upperparts, rufous ear-coverts and buffish-olive supercilium; *G. r. rufogularis* of the E Himalayas, which is more rufescent olive-brown on upperparts and tail, has grey ear-coverts and has dull rufous supercilium; *G. r. rufitinctus* of the Meghalaya hills, similar to *occidentalis* but with pale rufous (rather than buff) lores, entire throat rufous, buff rather than grey panelling on wing, and buff (rather than greyish-olive) wash to breast and belly. **VOICE** Extensive range of squeals, chuckles and chatters; pleasant song often recalls a farmer whistling his dog, *swee-tu..tu-tu-wee-u* (P. Holt). **HABITS** Similar to those of other laughingthrushes, but not so gregarious and less noisy compared with most species. Found singly, in pairs or in small parties. Secretive, and usually keeps out of sight in low bushes; feeds mainly on the ground. **HABITAT** Dense undergrowth in subtropical broadleaved forest, and bushes at edges of forest and cultivation. **BREEDING** April–September, varying locally. Builds a typical laughingthrush nest in the fork of a tree or bush, up to 6 m above ground. **DISTRIBUTION AND STATUS** Resident in Himalayas from N Pakistan east to Arunachal Pradesh; NE India and Bangladesh. Subject to altitudinal movements: in W Himalayas 600–1800 m; in E Himalayas mainly 600–1980 m (–3500 m in Sikkim?); in NE hills 900–1800 m. **PK:** extirpated; no records since 19th century. **NP:** local and frequent. **IN:** uncommon. **BT:** frequent. **BD:** former resident in the southeast?

SPOTTED LAUGHINGTHRUSH *Garrulax ocellatus* Plate 128

White-spotted Laughing Thrush (F,I)

IDENTIFICATION 32 cm. A very large laughingthrush, easily identified by profuse black-based white spotting on chestnut upperparts, along with blackish cap, rufous supercilium, lores and chin, deep chestnut ear-coverts, blackish throat diffusing into black barring on breast, buff lower breast and belly, chestnut-and-black wings with grey panel and with white tips to primaries, and white tips to chestnut, grey and black tail. **VOICE** A whistled *tu wee, tu wee, tu witty-o* song with human-like quality; also a *q-twe-twe-tweee-koi-koi* and a subdued *pie, pie, pie, pie* (Ali and Ripley 1987). **HABITS** Similar to those of other laughingthrushes. Keeps in pairs or small parties. Often associates with Black-faced (p.749). Inquisitive and easily observed. **HABITAT** Undergrowth and bamboo in broadleaved and coniferous forest and rhododendron shrubberies. **BREEDING** May and June. Builds a

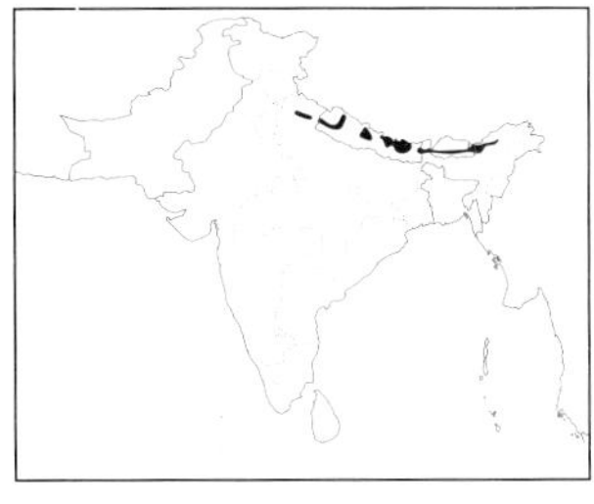

typical laughingthrush nest in bushes or saplings, up to 2 m above ground. **DISTRIBUTION AND STATUS** Resident. Himalayas from N Uttar Pradesh east to Arunachal Pradesh. Mainly 2135–3660 m (1800–4530 m); breeds chiefly above 2800 m. **NP, IN, BT:** fairly common.

GREY-SIDED LAUGHINGTHRUSH *Garrulax caerulatus* Plate 129

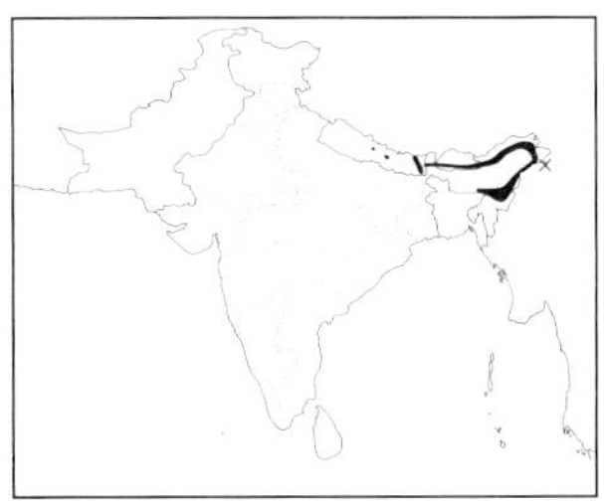

IDENTIFICATION 25 cm. A plain-coloured but distinctive laughingthrush, with white throat, breast and belly, grey breast sides and flanks, bluish-slate eye-ring and patch behind eye, black forehead, lores and submoustachial stripe, black scaling on rufous-brown crown, and uniform rufous olive-brown mantle, with more rufescent edges to flight feathers and tail. **Juvenile** is said to lack black scaling on crown and has brown flanks. **Racial variation** *G. c. subcaerulatus* of Meghalaya has white tips to outer tail feathers, which are lacking on the two other races in the subcontinent. **VOICE** A squealing *klee-loo*, a jovial *ovik-chor-r-r*, a loud *joy-to-weep, poo-ka-ree, new-jeriko*, and a *chik-chik-chik* alarm call (Fleming *et al.* 1984). **HABITS** Similar to those of other laughingthrushes. Found singly, in pairs or in small parties. Forages on the ground and in low bushes. **HABITAT** Undergrowth in dense humid forest and bamboo thickets. **BREEDING** May and June. Builds a typical laughingthrush nest in bushes, bamboo or small trees, 1–3 m above ground. **DISTRIBUTION AND STATUS** Resident. Himalayas from WC Nepal east to Arunachal Pradesh; NE India. Subject to some altitudinal movements: local in Himalayas, summers 1000–2700 m, winters down to 600 m; 1200–2300 m in NE hills. **NP:** uncommon in the centre and east. **IN:** uncommon in Himalayas, fairly common in NE hills. **BT:** uncommon.

SPOT-BREASTED LAUGHINGTHRUSH *Garrulax merulinus* Plate 129

Spotted-breasted Laughing Thrush (I)

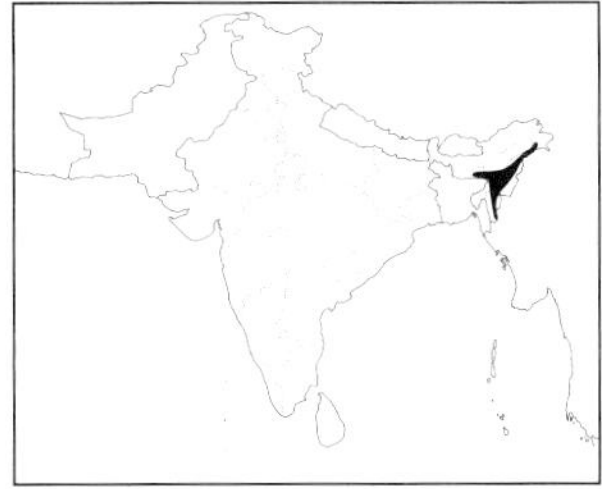

IDENTIFICATION 22 cm. Distinguishable from all other laughingthrushes by bold brown spotting on buff or rufous-buff throat and breast, along with narrow buff supercilium behind eye, uniform rufescent olive-brown upperparts, wings and tail (lacking panel on wing and pale tip to tail), and olive-brown flanks. **VOICE** Has a variety of clear, beautiful notes, and a coughing, oft-repeated chuckle (Ali and Ripley 1987). **HABITS** Similar to those of other laughingthrushes. Very secretive, and keeps in parties of ten to 20 birds. Feeds on the ground, hidden below thick undergrowth. **HABITAT** Dense undergrowth in heavy moist forest, bamboo thickets and overgrown forest clearings. **BREEDING** April–July. Builds a typical laughingthrush nest low down in a thick bush or bamboo clump. **DISTRIBUTION AND STATUS IN:** rare resident in NE hills (Arunachal Pradesh, Assam, Manipur, Meghalaya, Mizoram, Nagaland), very few recent records; 900–2400 m. **REFERENCES** Majumdar and Roy (1995).

WHITE-BROWED LAUGHINGTHRUSH *Garrulax sannio* Plate 129

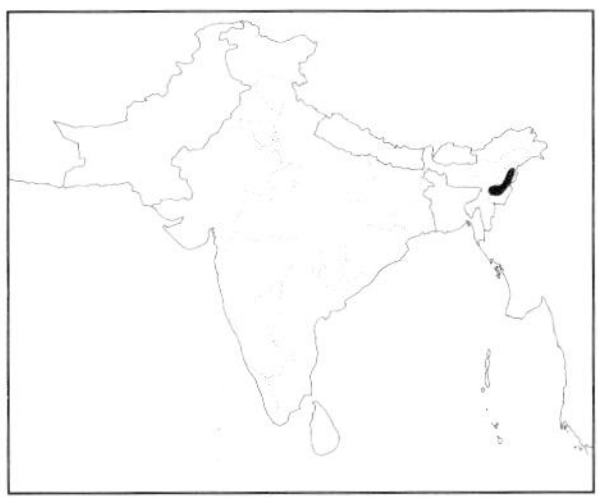

IDENTIFICATION 23 cm. A small, mainly brown laughingthrush, distinguishable from all others by broad buffish-white supercilium, lores and patch on cheeks, chestnut-brown crown and nape, cinnamon-brown ear-coverts, sides of neck and throat, dirty buff underparts, uniform olive-brown upperparts and tail, and rufous undertail-coverts. **VOICE** Harsh, shrill, explosive *tcheu* or *tchow* notes: *tcheu...tcheu...tcheu...* etc; pairs may call antiphonally. Alarm call is a harsh *tcheurrrr* or *chrrrrik*, sometimes a continuous grumbling *chrrreeerraow* etc, interspersed with shrill, sharp *chrrr-ik..chrrr-ik* (C. Robson). **HABITS** Similar to those of other laughingthrushes, but less wary than most species. Usually keeps in small parties; also singly and in pairs. **HABITAT** Undergrowth in dense forest, secondary growth, bamboo thickets and scrub-covered hillsides. **BREEDING** March–June. Builds a typical laughingthrush nest low down in thick bushes or small trees. **DISTRIBUTION AND STATUS IN:** resident in NE hills (Assam, Manipur, Nagaland), 1000–1800 m; current status uncertain, and no recent published records.

NILGIRI LAUGHINGTHRUSH *Garrulax cachinnans* Plate 129

Rufous-breasted Laughingthrush

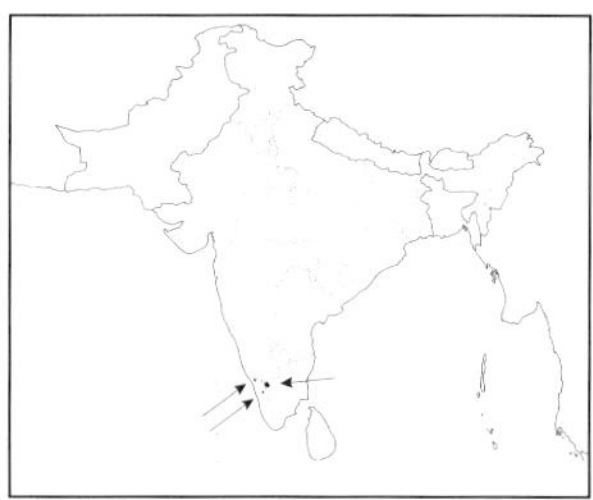

IDENTIFICATION 20 cm. A small, distinctive laughingthrush. The main features are bright rufous underparts, white supercilium contrasting with dark grey-brown crown, and black eye-stripe, lores and chin. Possibly confusable with the nominate race of Grey-breasted Laughingthrush (below), which has a black chin, although that species is not known to occur in the Nilgiri Hills; best told from Grey-breasted by rufous (rather than grey) ear-coverts, and by almost entire underparts being rufous, including lower throat and breast (which are grey on Grey-breasted). **VOICE** A laughing *pee-ko-ko* and a harsh *ke-ke-ke* (Ali and Ripley 1987). **HABITS** Similar to those of other laughingthrushes. Lives in small parties of about 12 birds. Very shy; spends most of its time on the ground under dense undergrowth. **HABITAT** Dense undergrowth in forest, also gardens and patches of scrub in the Nilgiris; hill guava trees *Rhodomyrtus tomentosa* in Kerala. **BREEDING** February–July. Builds a typical laughingthrush nest in the fork of a bush or tree, up to 3 m above ground. **DISTRIBUTION AND STATUS IN:** endemic resident, chiefly in the Nilgiri Hills, W Tamil Nadu, where common from 1200 m up to the summits; also in N Kerala, 1800 m.

GREY-BREASTED LAUGHINGTHRUSH *Garrulax jerdoni* Plate 129

White-breasted Laughing Thrush (I)

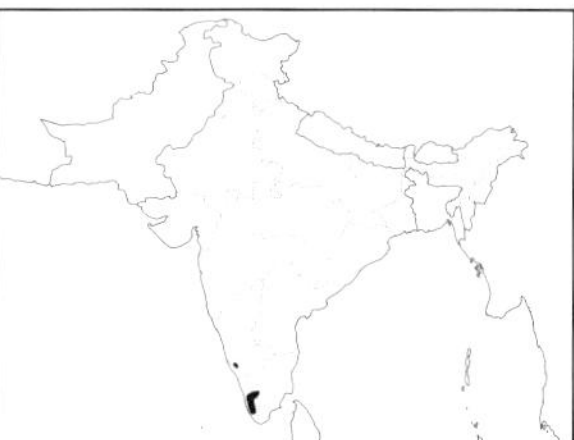

IDENTIFICATION 20 cm. A small olive-brown, grey and rufous laughingthrush with prominent white supercilium. The nominate race bears a superficial resemblance to Nilgiri Laughingthrush (above), with slate-grey crown, black eye-stripe and chin, and dull rufous belly and vent. Best told from that species by grey ear-coverts and grey (rather than rufous) throat and breast. **Racial variation** *G. c. fairbanki*, the most widely distributed of the subspecies, has a browner crown and brighter rufous belly and flanks, and lacks the black chin of the nominate form. *G. c. meridionale* is similar to *fairbanki*, but has shorter white supercilium which barely extends behind eye, lacks noticeably dark crown, has grey-streaked white breast, and has white belly with rufous restricted to the flanks. **VOICE** Cheeky nasal song, *qwee-te-qwee-tu-tu*; variety of calls, including gruff scolding, and sputtered, bubbling notes (P. Holt). **HABITS** Similar to those of other laughingthrushes. Keeps in flocks of six to 12 birds. Very skulking. **HABITAT** Occurrence is linked to that of the wild raspberry. Undergrowth and low bushes, raspberry and bracken thickets growing along banks of streams and edges of sholas, and tea and cardamom plantations. **BREEDING** December–June. Builds a typical laughingthrush nest, up to 2 m above ground and well hidden in a dense bush or thicket. **DISTRIBUTION AND STATUS IN:** endemic to Western Ghats, in the hills of S Kerala, W Tamil Nadu and S Karnataka; locally common from 1100 m up to the summits. **REFERENCES** Gaston and Zacharias (1996).

STREAKED LAUGHINGTHRUSH *Garrulax lineatus* Plate 129

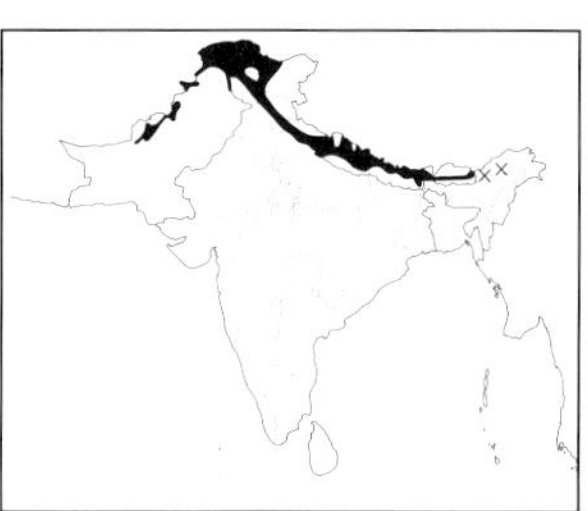

IDENTIFICATION 20 cm. A small, finely streaked laughingthrush. All races occurring in the subcontinent are readily identified by small size, fine dark streaking on crown and nape, fine white streaking on mantle and underparts, and grey-tipped olive-brown tail with diffuse black subterminal band on outer feathers. Striated Laughingthrush (p.742) is much larger and much browner in coloration, is more boldly streaked with white, and has dome-headed appearance owing to chestnut crest. Streaked does not occur south of the Brahmaputra, where it is replaced by the similar Striped Laughingthrush (p.747); see that species for main differences. **Racial variation** Five races are recognised in the subcontinent. The nominate race has greyish cast to crown and nape, which are streaked with brown, rufous ear-coverts, grey underparts with white shaft streaking bordered by rufous-brown, and largely rufous-brown wings. In comparison, *G. l. imbricatus* of the E Himalayas is uniformly brown in coloration, with brown crown and nape with indistinct darker shaft streaking, grey-brown ear-coverts with white streaking, brown underparts finely streaked with white, and more olive-brown coloration to wings. **VOICE** Song is a short rapid trill followed by loud ringing whistle, *trit-it-it-it chu-wheeeah*, higher in pitch than that of Variegated Laughingthrush (p.749); another vocalisation is a plaintive whistle, *peah-tee-teeh-teeh* (Roberts 1992). **HABITS** Keeps in pairs or in small parties of three to six birds. Usually found close to the ground and in or near thick cover; shuffles on the ground like a rodent, and creeps systematically through grass clumps and low bushes, often flicking its wings and tail. Flies only a short distance and, if disturbed, dives into cover. Not shy, despite its skulking habits. **HABITAT** Bushes at edges of cultivation and along roadsides, scrub-covered hillsides and secondary growth; in Pakistan also found in juniper scrub and patches of thick undergrowth in open coniferous forest, and in winter enters gardens and orchards at lower altitudes. **BREEDING** March–September, varying locally. Builds a typical laughingthrush nest, well concealed 1–3 m above ground in a low bush, sapling or pollarded tree, or on the ground. **DISTRIBUTION AND STATUS** Resident. Hills of W Pakistan, and Himalayas from N Pakistan east to Arunachal Pradesh. Subject to altitudinal movements: in W Himalayas breeds mainly 2100–3000 m (–3600 m), but varying locally, and winters 1000–2700 m (down to 600 m); in C and E Himalayas breeds chiefly 2440–3905 m (–2100 m), winters from 1065 m up to at least 2745 m; in W Arunachal Pradesh breeds 1500–3000 m, winters down to the duars. **PK:** widespread and common in Himalayas. **NP:** common in EC Himalayas and westwards, frequent farther east. **IN:** common in the west, locally common in the east. **BT:** common.

STRIPED LAUGHINGTHRUSH *Garrulax virgatus* — Plate 129

Manipur Streaked Laughing Thrush (I)

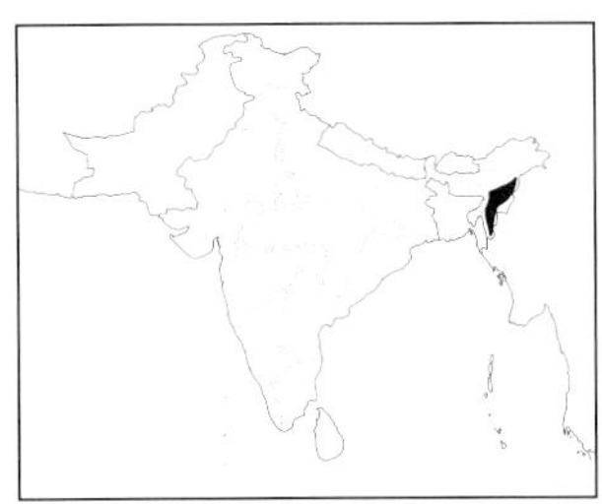

IDENTIFICATION 25 cm. A medium-sized laughingthrush with white streaking on upperparts and underparts. Care is needed not to confuse it with the smaller Streaked Laughingthrush (p.746), although that is a Himalayan species and there is no overlap of ranges. Easily told from that species by broad greenish-white supercilium (buffish in front of eye), broad buff patch on ear-coverts, rufous lores, deep chestnut throat contrasting with rufous-buff breast and belly, chestnut-brown crown and nape, fine but considerably more distinct white shaft streaking on upperparts and underparts, uniform olive-brown tail (without prominent pale tips to outer feathers), and white-tipped chestnut wing-coverts forming prominent wing panel. From White-browed Laughingthrush (p.745) by white streaking on upperparts and underparts, and chestnut wing-coverts. **VOICE** Has two territorial calls, often given antiphonally by pair-members: 1) (males?) a plaintive, hurried *chwi-pieu* or *wiwi-weu*; 2) (females?) a loud staccato, rattling trill, usually with shorter introductory note, *cho-prrrrrrt* or *chrrru-prrrrrr*. Calls include harsh *chit* and *chrrrrrr* notes (C. Robson). **HABITS** Similar to those of other laughingthrushes, but less noisy, and usually seen in pairs. **HABITAT** Dense undergrowth in moist broadleaved evergreen forest and thick secondary growth. **BREEDING** April–July. Has typical laughingthrush nest, well hidden in thick bushes up to 2 m above ground. **DISTRIBUTION AND STATUS IN:** resident in NE hills (Assam, Manipur, Meghalaya?, Mizoram, Nagaland), 900–2400 m; current status uncertain, with very few recent records. **REFERENCES** Robson (1991).

BROWN-CAPPED LAUGHINGTHRUSH *Garrulax austeni* — Plate 129

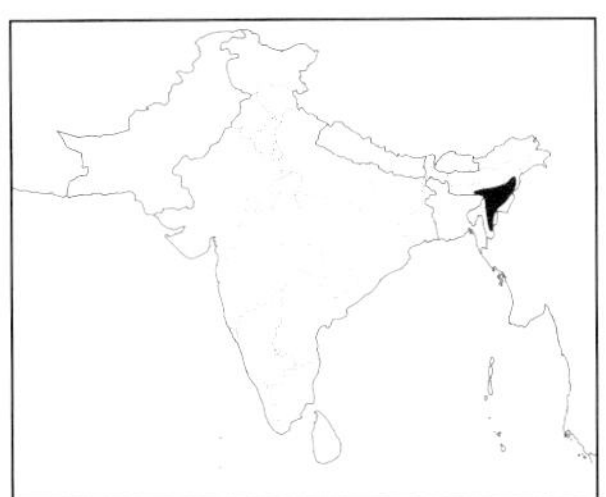

IDENTIFICATION 22 cm. A rufous-brown laughingthrush, most likely to be confused with Chestnut-crowned Laughingthrush (p.749). Best told by plain brownish face and throat without any grey, rufous-brown crown and nape with irregular buff shaft streaking, barred/scaled rufous-brown and white underparts, rufous olive-brown mantle without black spotting, and rufous-brown (rather than predominantly olive-yellow) wings and tail. In flight, tail shows narrow white tips to blackish outer feathers, with rufous-brown central feathers. **VOICE** Sings with loud, plaintive, jolly phrases, *whit-wee-wi-weeoo, whit-wi-chooee, whichi-wi-chooee whiwiwi-weeee-weeoo* etc, sometimes more rapid *whi-wi-wi-wi-wi-wi-wi-weee*; often given antiphonally with fairly harsh *jee-jee-jee* or *jee-jee...jee-jee* etc, presumably from females. A subdued but harsh *grrrret-grrrret-grrrret...* when alarmed. (C. Robson) **HABITS** Similar to those of other laughingthrushes, but less gregarious than many species; keeps singly, in pairs or in family parties. Skulks on the ground under dense cover, and is reluctant to fly. **HABITAT** Undergrowth in oak and rhododendron forest, bushes and bamboo thickets at edges and clearings of forest and in ravines. **BREEDING** April–August. Builds a usual laughingthrush nest, up to 2–3 m above ground in bushes or small trees. **DISTRIBUTION AND STATUS IN:** resident in hills of NE India (Assam, Manipur, Meghalaya, Mizoram, Nagaland), 1200–2700 m; current status uncertain, and no recent published records.

BLUE-WINGED LAUGHINGTHRUSH *Garrulax squamatus* — Plate 129

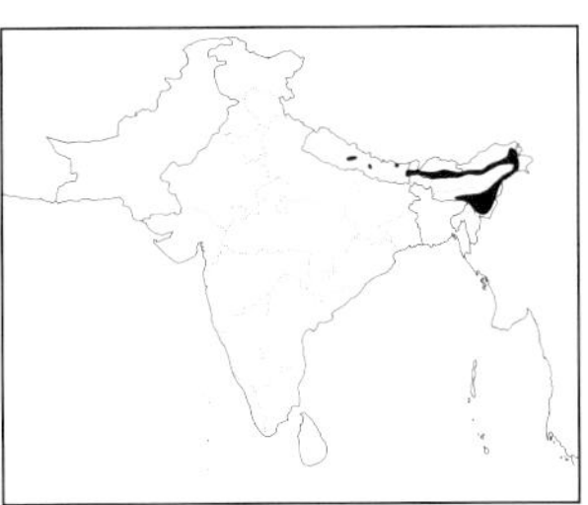

IDENTIFICATION 25 cm. A black-scaled olive-brown and grey laughingthrush bearing a superficial resemblance to Scaly Laughingthrush (p.748). Told from that species by black supercilium, silvery-blue outer webs to primaries forming prominent wing panel (which is brighter and more extensive than on Scaly), rufous greater coverts and rufous-brown fringes to secondaries and tertials, which form prominent patch on wing, black of tertials and secondaries forming noticeable dark rear edge to wing, chestnut-brown flanks and vent, chestnut undertail-coverts, and rufous-tipped black tail. Has striking white iris (brown in **juvenile**). Some birds have grey cast to crown, and/or dark olive tail, which are features also shown by Scaly Laughingthrush. **VOICE** Song is a *cur-white-to-go*, and alarm a scratchy *seek* (Fleming *et al.* 1984). **HABITS** Similar to those of other laughingthrushes. Usually found in pairs or family parties, sometimes singly. Very secretive; if alarmed, dives into thick cover. **HABITAT** Dense undergrowth in humid broadleaved evergreen forest and bamboo thickets, especially near water. **BREEDING** April–July. Builds a typical laughingthrush nest in bushes, up to 2 m above ground. **DISTRIBUTION AND STATUS** Resident. Himalayas from WC Nepal east to Arunachal Pradesh; NE India. In Himalayas, recorded chiefly 500–2400 m; in NE Indian hills, found mainly 800–1200 m (–1500 m). **NP:** scarce and local. **IN:** uncommon in Himalayas, more frequent in NE hills. **BT:** frequent. **REFERENCES** Athreya *et al.* (1997), Kaul *et al.* (1995), Lama (1995a), Singh (1995).

SCALY LAUGHINGTHRUSH *Garrulax subunicolor* Plate 129

Plain-coloured Laughing Thrush (F,I)

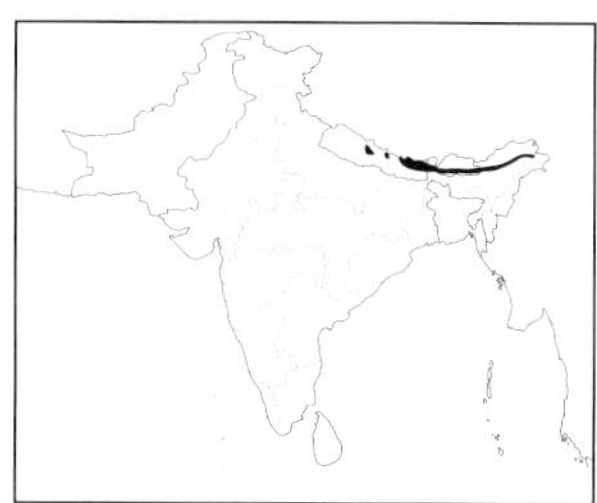

IDENTIFICATION 23 cm. A black-scaled olive-brown and rather plain laughingthrush, most likely to be confused with Blue-winged Laughingthrush (p.747). Told from that species by greyish crown, without prominent black supercilium, yellowish-olive outer webs to inner primaries and secondaries and olive tertials, which form prominent patch on wing (lacking Blue-winged's rufous and black on wings), less extensive and paler blue-grey panel on primaries, olive to olive-buff belly and vent, olive uppertail-coverts and central tail feathers which are concolorous with rest of upperparts, and white tips to outer tail feathers. Has striking yellow iris. **VOICE** Normal song is a two- or three-part wolf-whistle (descends on accented last note) that is buzzy and more slurred than several similar laughingthrush songs; variable, sometimes a single downslurred note or pairs of rolling triplets (S. Connop). **HABITS** Similar to those of other laughingthrushes. Keeps in pairs or in flocks of ten to 20 birds, depending on the season. **HABITAT** Thick undergrowth in moist broadleaved and mixed broadleaved–coniferous forest, and rhododendron shrubberies. **BREEDING** April–June. Builds a typical laughingthrush nest in bushes or on a branch, up to 1 m above ground. **DISTRIBUTION AND STATUS** Resident. Himalayas from WC Nepal east to Arunachal Pradesh. Subject to some altitudinal movements: breeds from 1800 m up to at least 3600 m, winters from 800 m (1500 in Nepal) up to 3400 m. **NP:** local and frequent in WC and C Himalayas, fairly common in the east. **IN:** scarce. **BT:** frequent.

ELLIOT'S LAUGHINGTHRUSH *Garrulax elliotii*

IDENTIFICATION cm. A mainly grey-brown laughingthrush, lacking prominent markings on head and body. Has faint whitish fringes to ear-coverts, throat and breast (difficult to see in the field), yellowish-olive outer webs to secondaries and inner primaries forming a prominent patch on otherwise mainly grey wings, cinnamon rear flanks and undertail-coverts, and yellowish-olive sides to white-tipped grey tail. **VOICE** Haunting, interrogative, whistled brassy song, *tu weir..tee-u*, repeated, often for long periods (P. Holt). **HABITS** A group of 20 was observed together in the forest understorey and scrub; often joined a group of Black-faced Laughingthrushes (p.749). **HABITAT** Mixed temperate forest and adjacent scrub on the edge of a clearing. **BREEDING** Details unknown in the region. **DISTRIBUTION AND STATUS IN:** probably a rare and local resident; a group seen in September 1994, at 3200 m in NE Arunachal Pradesh. **REFERENCES** Singh (1995, 1996).

Elliot's Laughingthrush Garrulax elliotii *(left-hand bird) and Brown-cheeked Laughingthrush* Garrulax henrici
(Drawing by Nigel Bean)

VARIEGATED LAUGHINGTHRUSH *Garrulax variegatus* Plate 129

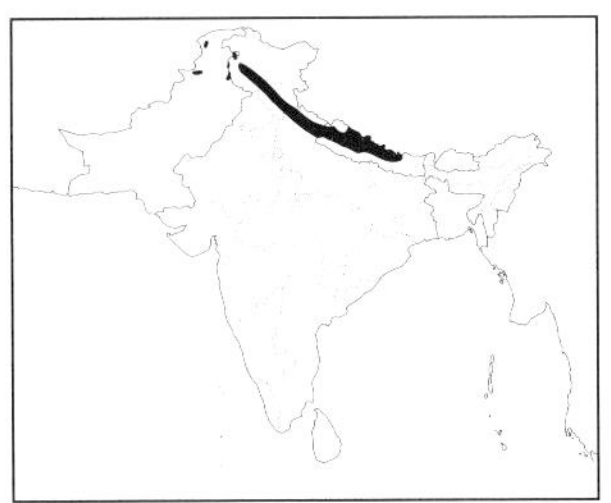

IDENTIFICATION 24 cm. A complex-patterned, mainly grey and olive laughingthrush without spotting or scaling. Plumage characteristics include rufous-buff forehead and malar stripe, black lores, chin and centre of throat, pale olive-grey crown and nape, rufous greater coverts, mainly grey wings with black primary coverts and patch on secondaries, and white tip to largely blackish tail. **Racial variation** *G. v. similis* of the W Himalayas has grey outer webs to primaries and grey subterminal band to tail. *G. v. variegatus* of the C and E Himalayas has olive-buff outer webs to primaries forming panel on wing, olive (rather than grey) mantle and back, olive subterminal band to tail (except on central feathers), and deeper rufous-buff belly and vent. **VOICE** A loud, penetrating whistle, *pit-we-weer*, which may be preceded by a softer *whi-chu-whi-wheeear*, lower-pitched than that of Streaked Laughingthrush (p.746); alarm calls include a rapid, squeaking *qweek-qweek-qweek-qweek* (Roberts 1992). **HABITS** Similar to those other laughingthrushes. In pairs in breeding season, otherwise in flocks of up to 20 birds. Very secretive. Prefers to forage in the forest understorey, although will also feed on the ground and in tall trees. **HABITAT** Thick undergrowth in open coniferous, broadleaved and mixed broadleaved–coniferous forest, bushes at edges of forest, rhododendron shrubberies and bushes around cultivation. **BREEDING** April–August. Builds a typical laughingthrush nest in a bush or branch of a tree, 1–6 m above ground. **DISTRIBUTION AND STATUS** Endemic to the subcontinent. Resident. Himalayas from N Pakistan east to EC Nepal. Subject to altitudinal movements: in W Himalayas, breeds 1700–3355 m, mainly above 2400 m, winters from 1200 m up to at least 2100 m (down to 400 m in India); in C Himalayas, breeds 2100–4100 m, winters up to at least 3200 m. **PK:** locally common on moister, better-forested slopes. **NP:** common in the west and centre, scarce farther east. **IN:** locally fairly common. **REFERENCES** Martens and Eck (1995).

BROWN-CHEEKED LAUGHINGTHRUSH *Garrulax henrici*

Prince Henry's Laughing-thrush (I)

IDENTIFICATION 25 cm. A mainly olive-grey laughingthrush with chestnut-brown lores and ear-coverts, short greyish-white supercilium behind eye, broad whitish malar stripe, black primary-covert patch and short olive panel on otherwise mainly blue-grey wings, rufous-cinnamon vent and undertail-coverts, and white-tipped blue-grey tail. Bill is nut-brown; legs are dark plumbeous. **VOICE** Song consists of repetition, at intervals of 4–10 seconds, of a plaintive phrase, e.g. *wichi-pi-choo* or *whi-pi-choo* or *whi-choo-it*, etc; often given antiphonally, with a cheerful *djeu-djeu* or *peu-peu*, presumably from females (C. Robson). **HABITS** A group observed in bushy growth; seemed to be shy. In Tibet, keeps in pairs in the breeding season, otherwise in small parties; skulks in low cover, always on the move. **HABITAT** Degraded broadleaved forest. **BREEDING** Unknown in the region. **DISTRIBUTION AND STATUS IN:** probably a rare resident in NE Arunachal Pradesh; recorded once, in January 1995 at 1500 m.

BLACK-FACED LAUGHINGTHRUSH *Garrulax affinis* Plate 129

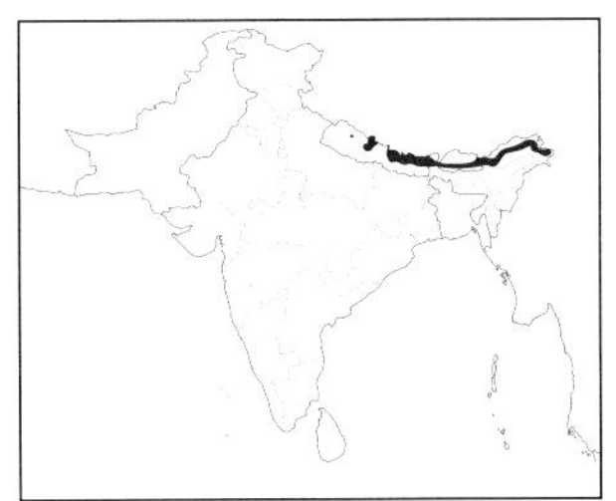

IDENTIFICATION 25 cm. A distinctive, mainly rufous-brown laughingthrush with black supercilium and ear-coverts, and white malar stripe, crescent behind eye and patch on sides of neck. Has black chin and centre of throat, greyish-white scaling on breast, variable grey mottling on mantle and back, olive-yellow panel on mainly blue-grey wings, black primary-covert patch, and olive-yellow tail with broad grey tip. **Racial variation** *G. a. bethelae* of the E Himalayas has deeper rufous-brown underparts with indistinct greyish fringes to breast compared with the nominate race. **VOICE** Song is a loud *tew-wee-to-whee-to-whee-you-whee*; alarm is a repeated, rapid *dze* (Fleming *et al.* 1984). **HABITS** Similar to those of other laughingthrushes, but less shy and more conspicuous than most species. Found in pairs in breeding season and in small parties at other times; often with White-browed Fulvetta (p.774). Forages chiefly low down in bushes; also on the ground and in small trees. Runs and scuttles through the undergrowth, and rarely takes flight. **HABITAT** Broadleaved, coniferous and mixed forest, and shrubberies above the treeline. **BREEDING** April–June. Builds a typical laughingthrush nest, 1–2.5 m above ground. **DISTRIBUTION AND STATUS** Resident. Himalayas from W Nepal east to Arunachal Pradesh. Subject to altitudinal movements: summers 2750–4000 m (–4600 m) in Nepal, 2440–4265 m (–4500 m) farther east; winters from 1250 m up to at least 3660 m. **NP, IN, BT:** common.

CHESTNUT-CROWNED LAUGHINGTHRUSH *Garrulax erythrocephalus* Plate 129

Red-headed Laughing Thrush (F,I)

IDENTIFICATION A variable laughingthrush. Distinguishing features common to the seven races described from the subcontinent are chestnut on head, dark spotting/scaling on mantle and breast, mainly olive-yellow wings with maroon greater coverts (often obscured), and olive-yellow sides to tail. **Racial variation** is considerable. For example, the nominate race of the W Himalayas has chestnut crown and nape, chestnut ear-coverts with white fringes

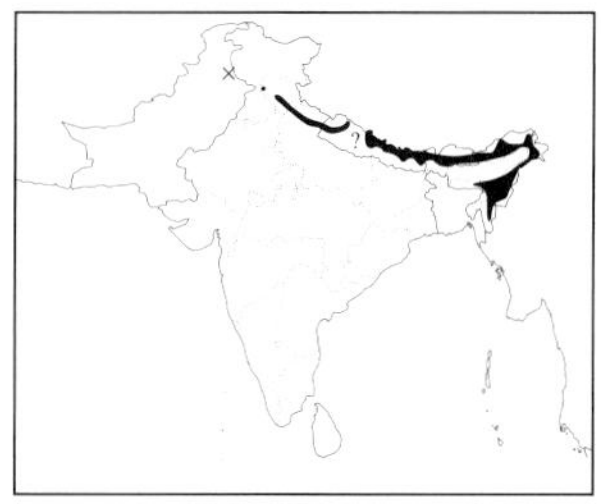

and variable black spotting, and buffish-olive breast and belly; juvenile of this race lacks spotting on upperparts and underparts. *G. e. nigrimentus* of the E Himalayas has chestnut forehead and nape but black-streaked grey crown, blackish ear-coverts with white fringes, and rufous-brown lower throat and breast. *G. e. chrysopterus* of Meghalaya has brighter rufous-chestnut crown, grey supercilium and streaking on ear-coverts, chestnut throat merging into rufous breast, and diffuse brown/rufous-brown spotting/scaling on mantle and breast. **VOICE** Song is a repeated *to-ree-a-rear*, and alarm is a *m-u-r-r* (Fleming *et al.* 1984). **HABITS** Similar to those of other laughingthrushes. Keeps in pairs or in small parties, depending on the season. Secretive, and rarely comes into the open. Feeds mainly in the forest understorey; also at medium height of trees. **HABITAT** Dense undergrowth in broadleaved forest, and thick bushes at edges of fields and pastures. **BREEDING** May–August. Builds a typical laughingthrush nest, up to 2 m above ground. **DISTRIBUTION AND STATUS** Resident. Himalayas from N Pakistan east to Arunachal Pradesh; NE India. Subject to altitudinal movements: in Himalayas, summers mainly 1800–3400 m, but chiefly to 3000 m in Nepal (–3500 m), and winters mainly above 1200 m (down to 600 m), to 2000 m in the west, to at least 2750 m in Nepal and to over 3000 m in the east; in NE India, occurs 1200–2800 m. **PK:** extirpated; one 19th-century record. **NP:** common and fairly widespread. **IN:** locally frequent in W Himalayas, common farther east; locally common in NE hills. **BT:** common.

RED-FACED LIOCICHLA *Liocichla phoenicea* — Plate 129

Crimson-winged Laughing Thrush (F,I), *G. phoenicea* (I)

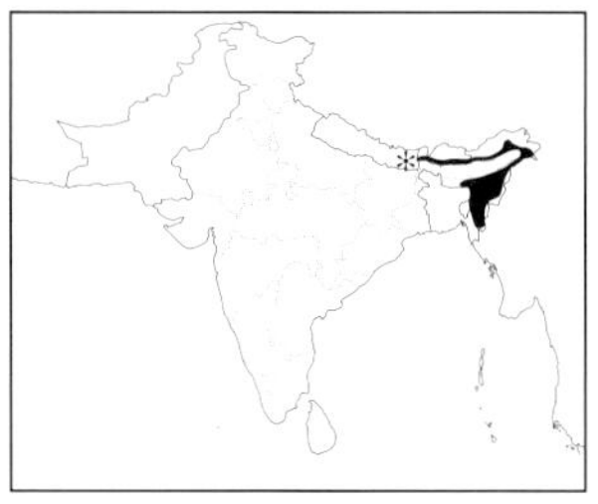

IDENTIFICATION 23 cm. A striking, mainly olive-brown laughingthrush with crimson ear-coverts and sides to neck, black supercilium, extensive crimson on wings, with outer webs of primaries becoming orange towards tip, grey panel on secondaries, crimson undertail-coverts, and rufous-orange tip to black tail (with undertail appearing entirely rufous-orange from below). **VOICE** Loud, plaintive, cheerful song of three to eight notes: *chewi-ter-twi-twitoo; chi-cho-choee-wi-chu-chooee; chu-wu-wi-yu-wher; chi-wee-ee-ee-weeoo; pwi-i-wi-chor-wu; toee-i-wi-chor-weeoo; pwi-i-wi*, etc. Harsh, grating, rasping *chrrrt-chrrrt* when alarmed; also a curious mewing call, *ji-uuuu* or *chi-uuuu* (C. Robson). **HABITS** Similar to those of other laughingthrushes. Found in pairs in the breeding season; otherwise usually in small parties, sometimes with other species. Very skulking and often difficult to observe. Feeds chiefly in thick undergrowth and on ground beneath; also at medium height of trees. **HABITAT** Dense undergrowth in broadleaved evergreen or moist deciduous forest, thickets along streams and edges of cultivation. **BREEDING** April–July. Builds a laughingthrush-type nest, low down in bushes or 2–3 m above ground in a small tree. **DISTRIBUTION AND STATUS** Resident. Himalayas from Nepal east to Arunachal Pradesh; NE India and Bangladesh. Subject to small altitudinal movements: 900–1850 m all year, sometimes winters down to 500 m. **NP:** extirpated; recorded only in 19th century. **IN:** locally common in Himalayas, fairly common in NE hills. **BT:** frequent. **BD:** former resident in the northeast and southeast?

BABBLERS Subfamily Sylviinae, tribe Timaliini

A large and diverse group of small to medium-sized passerines. They are characterised by their soft, loose plumage, short or fairly short wings, and strong feet and legs. The sexes are alike in most species. With the exception of most wren babblers, the members of this tribe typically associate in flocks outside the breeding season, and some species do so throughout the year. Such flocks often have a constant membership and defend territories against their neighbours. Babbler flocks are frequently a component of mixed-species feeding parties. Most babblers are noisy and have a wide range of chatters, rattles and whistles; some have a melodious song. Many are terrestrial or inhabit bushes or grass close to the ground, while other species are arboreal. Babblers are chiefly insectivorous, and augment their diet with fruits, seeds and nectar. Arboreal species collect food from leaves, moss, lichen and bark; terrestrial species forage by probing, digging, and tossing aside dead foliage.

ABBOTT'S BABBLER *Malacocincla abbotti* — Plate 130

***Trichastoma abbotti* (F,I,K)**

IDENTIFICATION 17cm. A short-tailed, rather top-heavy babbler with olive-brown upperparts and unstreaked underparts. Possibly confusable with Spot-throated and Buff-breasted Babblers (p.751), but is larger, with bigger head and larger bill, and has rufous cast to uppertail-coverts and tail. Further told from Buff-breasted by greyish (rather than buff) lores and more pronounced grey supercilium, white throat and upper breast, and proportionately shorter tail; and from Spot-throated by lack of grey spotting on throat and by rufous-buff breast sides, flanks and undertail-coverts. Coloration of legs and feet does not appear to be a useful feature (*contra* Boonsong and Round 1991). **VOICE** Three to four whistled notes, rendered as *three cheers for me*, with the last note highest; sometimes duets, with mate giving

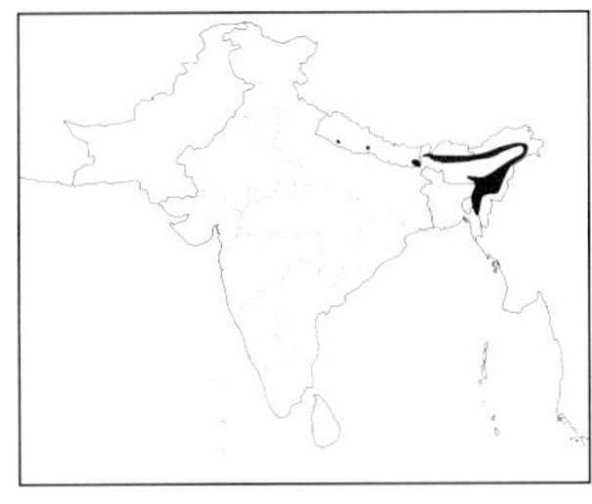

one or two *peep* notes (Boonsong and Round 1991). **HABITS** Occurs singly or in pairs in the same area day after day. Mainly terrestrial, skulking below thick undergrowth. Reluctant to fly, and if disturbed hides in dense cover. Eats insects. **HABITAT** Dense thickets in moist broadleaved evergreen forest; favours stream banks and palm ferns. **BREEDING** April and May. Builds a large cup nest close to the ground in bushes or dwarf palms. **DISTRIBUTION AND STATUS** Resident. Himalayan foothills from W Nepal east to Arunachal Pradesh; NE India and Bangladesh. From base of the hills up to 600 m (to 275 m in Nepal). **NP:** very local; common in the far east, rare farther west. **IN:** locally common. **BT:** fairly common, but very local. **BD:** local. **REFERENCES** Lama (1993).

BUFF-BREASTED BABBLER *Pellorneum tickelli* — Plate 130

Tickell's Babbler, *Trichastoma tickelli* (I,K), [Enigmatic Shortwing *Brachypteryx cryptica*]

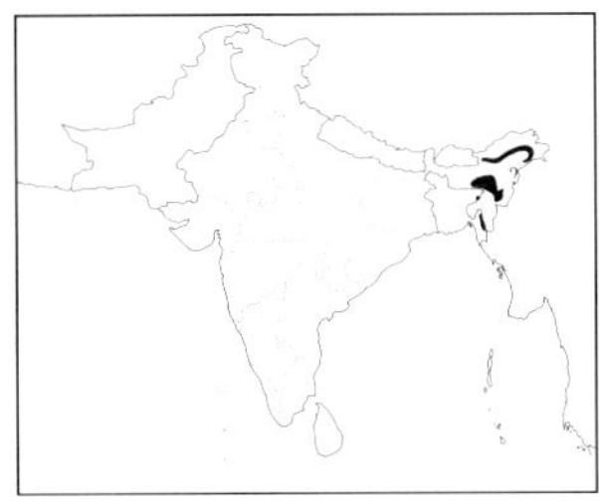

IDENTIFICATION 15 cm. A rather plain, well-proportioned babbler with dark olive-brown upperparts with slight rufescent cast, and mainly buff underparts except for white belly. Confusable with Abbott's Babbler (p.750), but is more neatly proportioned, with smaller head and proportionately longer tail, has smaller bill, buff lores, throat and breast (some with quite noticeable brown streaking), lacks rufous coloration to uppertail-coverts and sides of tail, and has duller buff to olive-brown flanks and darker olive-brown upperparts. Confusable also with the more similarly sized Spot-throated Babbler (below), but has buff lores, buff-coloured throat and breast, and longer and square-ended tail, and has faint whitish shaft streaking on more rufescent crown. **VOICE** Song is a loud, sharp, quick *wi-twee* or *wi-choo* or *witweewitweewitwee...*, also a loud *tchew-tchew.....tchew* etc, sometimes interspersed with high-pitched, jolly, laughing *swi-tit-tit-titchoo* or rattling *trrrrit-it..trrrrrt* (probably antiphonal calls of females). Calls include a harsh repeated *prrree* mixed with higher *pieu* notes, an explosive repeated *whit* mixed with rattling *prrrt* notes, and a rattling *trrrit-trrrit-trrrit....* (C. Robson) **HABITS** Similar to those of Abbott's Babbler. **HABITAT** Dense scrub, and thick undergrowth in moist broadleaved evergreen forest; favours bamboo thickets along streams. **BREEDING** March–June. Nest is a neat dome or half-dome, placed on the ground or low down in bushes or bamboo clumps. **DISTRIBUTION AND STATUS** Resident. Hills of NE India (Arunachal Pradesh, Assam, Manipur, Meghalaya, ?Nagaland) and Bangladesh. Subject to altitudinal movements: chiefly 1000–1400 m (–2100 m), winters down to the plains. **IN, BD:** locally common.

SPOT-THROATED BABBLER *Pellorneum albiventre* — Plate 130

Brown Babbler (I)

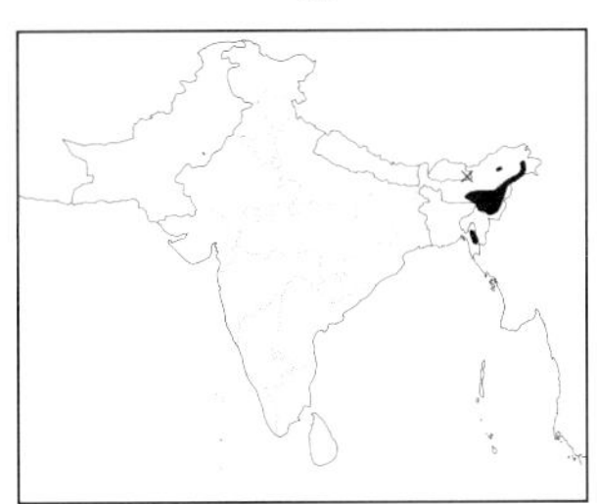

IDENTIFICATION 14 cm. A rather plain, well-proportioned babbler with dark olive-brown upperparts and short rounded tail. It is noticeably smaller than Abbott's Babbler (p.750), with smaller head and bill, and is similar in size and shape to Buff-breasted (above), but has shorter tail with rounded tip. In terms of plumage, is best told by combination of white throat with faint arrowhead-shaped grey spotting and olive-brown breast and flanks. Additional features which separate it from Abbott's are lack of rufous on uppertail-coverts and tail, and darker olive-brown coloration to upperparts. Further distinctions from Buff-breasted are grey lores and supercilium, and absence of rufescent cast to upperparts. **Racial variation** *P. a. ignotum* of Mishmi Hills has more extensive white belly and faint greyish-brown breast-band, and throat is mostly unspotted. **VOICE** Surprisingly rich thrush-like or chat-like song, quickly delivered and complicated, including much repetition; pairs may call antiphonally, the song being interspersed with fast high *tchu-tchu-tchu-tchu-tchu-tchu...* etc, dying away at the end or speeding up. Calls include a harsh *chrrr-chrrr-chrrr-chrrrit...* and slightly explosive *tip-tip-tip....* (C. Robson) **HABITS** Similar to those of Puff-throated Babbler (p.752). Very secretive, and keeps close to ground in dense undergrowth, usually in pairs. **HABITAT** Scrub and thickets of secondary growth or bamboo; avoids dense forest. **BREEDING** May–July. Nest is a dome, semi-dome or deep cup, placed in bamboo bushes or grass clumps. **DISTRIBUTION AND STATUS** Resident. Himalayan foothills in E Bhutan, and hills of NE India (Arunachal Pradesh, Assam, Manipur, Meghalaya, Nagaland) and Bangladesh. Subject to slight altitudinal movements: 500–1500 m, wintering down to the plains. **IN:** locally common. **BT:** very local. **BD:** rare? resident.

MARSH BABBLER *Pellorneum palustre* — Plate 130

Marsh Spotted Babbler (I)

IDENTIFICATION 15 cm. A marsh-dwelling babbler with white throat, grey supercilium back to eye, olive-brown upperparts, and bold brown streaking on breast and flanks. Superficially resembles Puff-throated Babbler (p.752), but is smaller, lacks rufous crown and buff supercilium of that species, and has rufous-buff wash to sides of throat, breast and flanks. Possibly confusable with the forest-dwelling Spot-throated Babbler

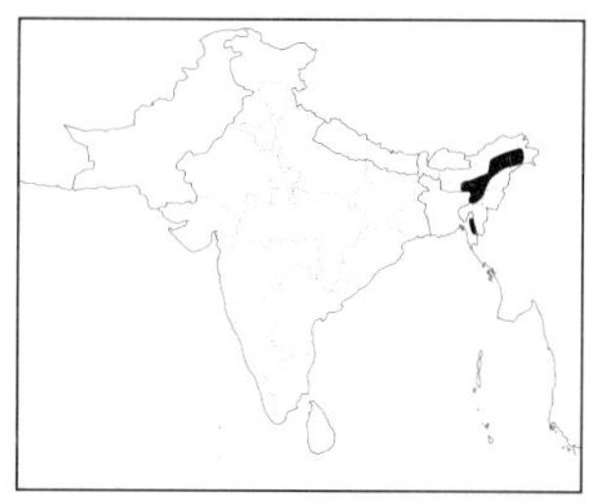

(p.751), but streaking is much bolder and is mainly on breast and flanks and, additionally, it has a noticeably longer tail. **VOICE** A loud, double chirp, *chi-chew* (Ali and Ripley 1987); has a series of undistinguished, unobtrusive churrs (P. Holt from D. Allen recording). **HABITS** Similar to those of Puff-throated Babbler. Very skulking and difficult to observe, although it calls frequently. **HABITAT** Extensive reedbeds and tall grassland at the edges of marshes and rivers, and bushes in swampy ground. **BREEDING** Monsoon from end of May onwards. Nest is a ball of grass, placed on the ground among grasses and roots. **DISTRIBUTION AND STATUS** Resident, endemic to the subcontinent. NE India (Arunachal Pradesh, Assam, Meghalaya) and Bangladesh; from the plains up to 800 m. Globally threatened. **IN:** current status uncertain, but very few recent records. **BD:** rare resident?; only one recent record. **REFERENCES** Barooah (1994).

PUFF-THROATED BABBLER *Pellorneum ruficeps* — Plate 130

Spotted Babbler (F,I)

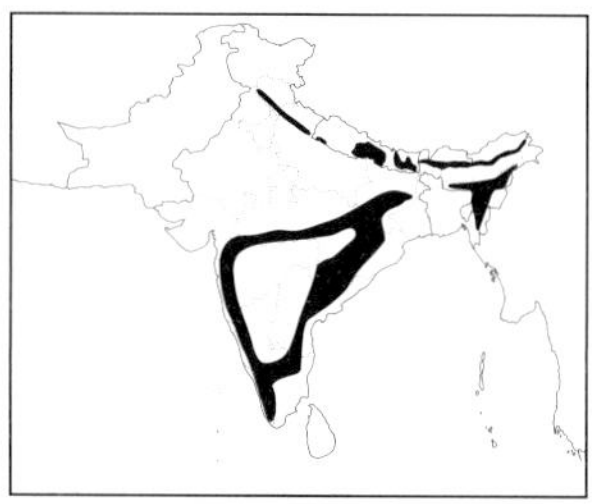

IDENTIFICATION 15 cm. A rather long-tailed babbler, readily distinguished from other *Pellorneum* babblers (p.751–p.752) by combination of rufous or chestnut crown, prominent buff supercilium, white throat (often puffed out), and heavily streaked whitish underparts. **Racial variation** Considerable, with much variation in the colour of crown (which can be rufous-brown to chestnut), ear-coverts (vary from buff and concolorous with supercilium to chestnut and concolorous with crown), darkness and size of brown spotting, colour of mantle (can be olive-brown to rufous-brown), and whether the mantle and sides of neck are unstreaked (e.g. *P. r. ruficeps*) or streaked (*P. r. mandellii*). **VOICE** Halting, impulsive song, *swee ti-ti-hwee hwee hwee ti swee-u*, rambles up and down the scale often for minutes on end; calls include a plaintive whistled *ne-menue*, like that of Common Iora (p.615), and subdued throaty churrs (P. Holt). **HABITS** Found mainly in pairs or family parties. A great skulker, staying on or near the ground in thick undergrowth. Runs over the forest floor or makes long hops when foraging; seeks insects by sifting and flicking aside dead leaves. **HABITAT** Dense thickets, bamboo and undergrowth in broadleaved forest, secondary growth, sholas and well-vegetated ravines. **BREEDING** Mainly during the monsoon, November–July, varying locally. Nest is a large untidy ball, placed on the ground among fallen leaves. **DISTRIBUTION AND STATUS** Resident. Himalayan foothills from W Himachal Pradesh east to Arunachal Pradesh; hills of NE and peninsular India and Bangladesh. In the Himalayas, occurs above 300 m up to 1200 m in the west, to 1675 m in Nepal, to 2000 m farther east; in NE Indian hills, occurs from the plains up to 1800 m; in the peninsular hills, occurs mainly from sea level up to 1350 m, to 1800 m in Kerala. **NP:** locally fairly common below 915 m in the centre and east, rare higher up. **IN:** common. **BT:** frequent. **BD:** locally common.

BROWN-CAPPED BABBLER *Pellorneum fuscocapillum* — Plate 130

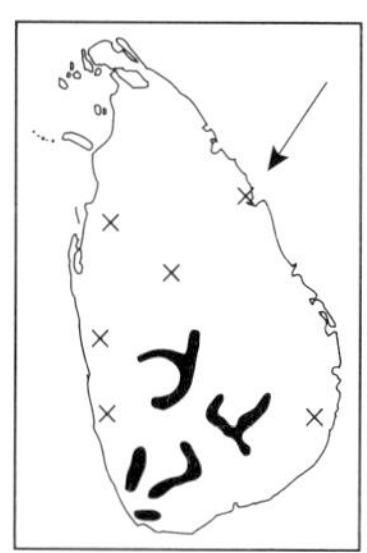

IDENTIFICATION 16 cm. Has brownish-black crown and nape with faint buff shaft streaking, dark olive-brown upperparts, wings and tail, and deep cinnamon sides of head and underparts. **Racial variation** *P. f. babaulti* (found in low country dry zone) is quite different from the nominate race (found in hills), described above, having paler cinnamon-buff sides of head and underparts and paler greyish-brown upperparts, wings and tail. **VOICE** Song and calls probably not distinguishable from those of Puff-throated Babbler (above) (P. Holt). **HABITS** Usually keeps in pairs or small parties. Shy and retiring. Feeds on or near the ground, rarely showing itself in the open. Heard more often than seen; calls mainly in the mornings and evenings, and intensely during the breeding season. **HABITAT** Thick ground cover, such as scrub, low jungle and forest undergrowth. **BREEDING** February-April, September-December, varying locally. Nest is a domed structure built on the ground, often at the foot of a large tree or under bushes. **DISTRIBUTION AND STATUS LK:** endemic resident, common in lowlands and hills.

LARGE SCIMITAR BABBLER *Pomatorhinus hypoleucos* — Plate 130

IDENTIFICATION 28 cm. Largest of the scimitar babblers. Best told by combination of larger size, lack of white supercilium, stouter, straighter and dull-coloured bill, grey ear-coverts, variable rufous mottling on supercilium and sides of neck, triangular white streaking on grey sides of breast, dark olive-brown upperparts with slight rufous tinge, and stout grey legs and feet. **VOICE** Sings with loud, hollow, variable piping notes (usually three notes per phrase), with pairs often calling antiphonally, i.e.: *wiu-pu-pu--wup-up-piu; wiu-pu-pu--wo-hu; whiu-pu-pu--whip-up-up; wiwiu-pu-pu--hu-hu-whahu; wuipupu--puh-pu-poi; ho-woi-pu--hiu-pu-pu*. Loud, harsh, grating alarm: *whit-tchtchtchtch; tchtchtchtchtchtchtch; hekhekhekhekhekhek* etc. (C. Robson) **HABITS** Very secretive, and most easily located by its call. Mainly terrestrial, progressing in ungainly hops. **HABITAT** Cane brakes, bamboo thickets, reeds, elephant grass and dense undergrowth in

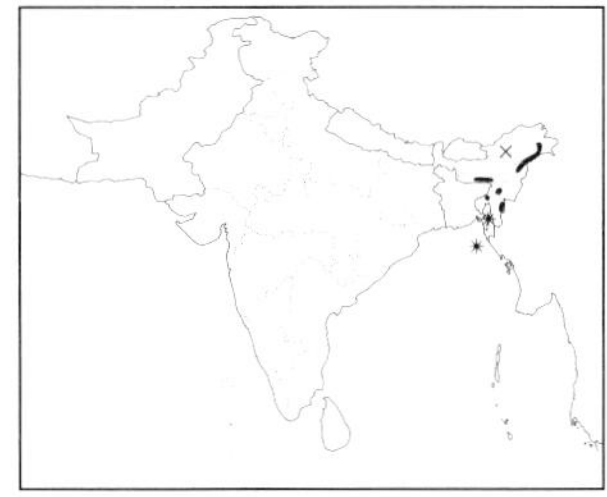

broadleaved evergreen forest. **BREEDING** January–April. Nest is a large semi-dome, placed on the ground in undergrowth or among bushes. **DISTRIBUTION AND STATUS** Resident. Hills of NE India (Arunachal Pradesh, Assam, Manipur, Meghalaya, Nagaland, Tripura) and Bangladesh; from foothills and adjacent plains locally up to 1200 m. **IN:** current status uncertain; very few recent records. **BD:** rare and local. **REFERENCES** Athreya *et al.* (1997), Raman (1995).

SPOT-BREASTED SCIMITAR BABBLER *Pomatorhinus erythrocnemis* Plate 130

***P. erythrogenys* (I,V)**

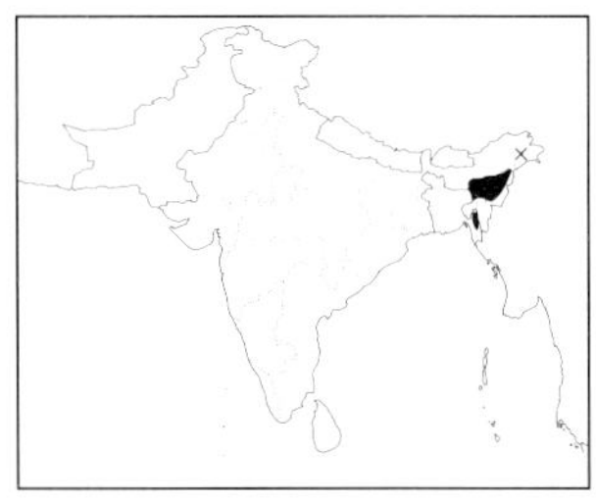

IDENTIFICATION 25 cm. The only scimitar babbler with both brown spotting on underparts and no white supercilium. Given its range, likely to be confused only with Large Scimitar Babbler (p.752). Distinguished from that species by smaller size, finer bill, rufous lores and ear-coverts, bold brown spotting on white breast, uniform olive-brown breast sides and flanks, paler olive-brown upperparts, and brownish rather than lead-grey legs and feet. Care is needed not to pass it off as Rusty-cheeked Scimitar Babbler (below), which occurs as far east as Bhutan, but Spot-breasted has white throat, well-defined brown spotting on breast, and olive-brown (rather than rufous) on sides of breast and flanks. **VOICE** Song/call is a quite low-pitched and persistent, fluty *tíuu-tuu*, first note stressed, followed by a higher-pitched *tíuuk*; apparently a duet with the mate (Taiwan) (J. Scharringa). **HABITS** Very similar to those of Rusty-cheeked Scimitar Babbler. **HABITAT** Undergrowth in forest, scrub jungle, thickets in forest clearings and abandoned cultivation. **BREEDING** April–June. Nest is like that of Rusty-cheeked Scimitar Babbler. **DISTRIBUTION AND STATUS** Resident. Hills of NE India (Arunachal Pradesh, Assam, Manipur, Meghalaya, Nagaland) and Bangladesh. **IN:** from 750 m to over 1800 m; current status uncertain, and no recent published records. **BD:** rare resident?; only one recent record.

RUSTY-CHEEKED SCIMITAR BABBLER *Pomatorhinus erythrogenys* Plate 130

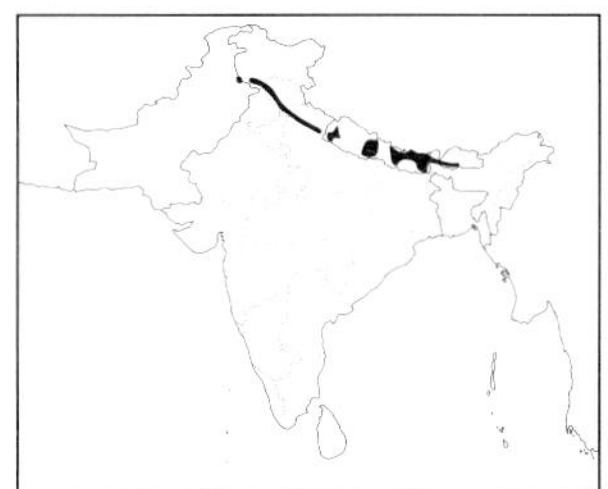

IDENTIFICATION 25 cm. Unmistakable throughout W and C Himalayan range: lacks white supercilium, and has rufous lores, ear-coverts, sides of breast, flanks and vent. Confusion possible with Large and Spot-breasted Scimitar Babblers (p.752 and above), although note different ranges. Large is best told by grey ear-coverts, breast sides and flanks; Spot-breasted by combination of white throat, brown-spotted breast, and olive-brown rather than rufous breast sides and flanks. **Racial variation** *P. e. haringtoni* of the E Himalayas has greyer or noticeably grey-streaked/spotted throat and upper breast, compared with the nominate race; grey spotting on breast can be well defined, but patterning is continuous with that of throat (throat is always white on Spot-breasted). **VOICE** Loud and far-carrying three-noted *quoit* or *khwoi* calls, followed immediately by staccato *quit* or *quip* call from female; also a ringing *khwir jot-khwir jot*, often followed by *khuwiyiu*, and quickly answered by female (Roberts 1992). **HABITS** Found in pairs in the breeding season, and in small parties at other times. A great skulker, mostly keeping out sight on the ground or in low bushes, but can be readily located by its loud and characteristic calls. Excels at moving rapidly through undergrowth while keeping well concealed. Rummages and probes among dead leaves for insects, and also eats seeds and berries; moves on the ground in long springing hops. Makes only short flights from bush to bush or across gaps in the undergrowth. **HABITAT** Thick undergrowth at forest edges, bush-covered hillsides and ravines and overgrown nullahs. **BREEDING** March–June. Nest is an untidy dome or cup, placed on an embankment or at the base of a tree, bush or grass tussock. **DISTRIBUTION AND STATUS** Sedentary resident. Himalayas from Margalla Hills and adjoining valleys, N Pakistan, east to Bhutan. **PK:** frequent but very local; 450–1800 m. **NP:** common and widespread; 305–2440 m. **IN:** common; 450–2200 m. **BT:** common; from foothills up to 2000 m.

WHITE-BROWED SCIMITAR BABBLER *Pomatorhinus schisticeps* Plate 130

Slaty-headed Scimitar Babbler (F)

IDENTIFICATION 22 cm. Striking white supercilium contrasting with blackish ear-coverts, and downcurved yellow bill, distinguish this scimitar babbler from all others in its range except Indian and Streak-breasted (p.754). Told from the latter by clean white centre to breast and belly, chestnut sides to breast with variable white streaking, larger size, and larger, more downcurved bill. Crown is typically slate-grey, but can be entirely rufescent olive-brown or have grey restricted to forehead and sides of crown (especially in *P. s. cryptanthus*) and be as that of Streak-breasted. Resembles Indian Scimitar Babbler (p.754), although there is no overlap in

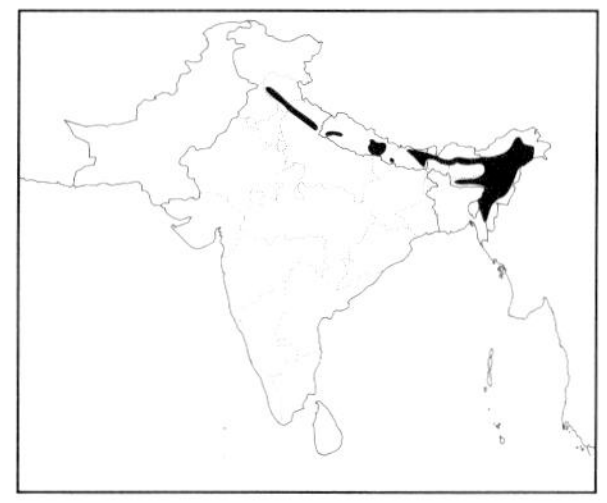

ranges; see that species for additional notes. **Juvenile** is smaller, with smaller bill and olive-brown crown; more closely resembles Streak-breasted, but centre of breast is white and sides of breast are chestnut. **VOICE** A quick single introductory note followed by a trilled hoot, or, more commonly, an evenly spaced three-noted call that varies in quality from a hoot to a whistle. This call resembles the hooting of Streak-breasted Scimitar Babbler to a limited extent (S. Connop). **HABITS** Often in hunting parties with other babblers. Forages chiefly in thick undergrowth; sometimes climbs into trees. Probes among leaf litter, bark crevices and moss. **HABITAT** Dense bushes, secondary growth, bamboo thickets, thick understorey in forest and well-vegetated ravines. **BREEDING** March–August, varying locally. Nest is a dome or semi-dome, placed on a sloping bank among undergrowth or low down in thick bushes or a bamboo clump. **DISTRIBUTION AND STATUS** Sedentary resident. Himalayas from W Himachal Pradesh east to Arunachal Pradesh; NE India and Bangladesh. **NP:** frequent 245–915 m, rare up to 1500 m. **IN:** fairly common in W Himalayas from plains edge up to 1500 m, locally common farther east up to 2000 m. **BT:** fairly common; 400–1590 m. **BD:** local.

INDIAN SCIMITAR BABBLER *Pomatorhinus horsfieldii* Plate 130

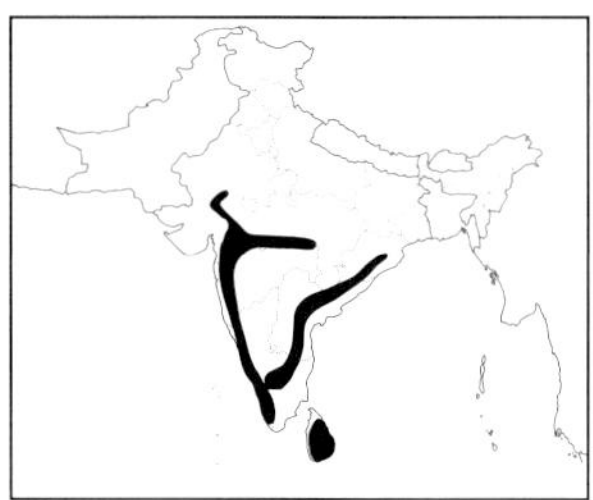

IDENTIFICATION 22 cm. The only scimitar babbler occurring in peninsular India and Sri Lanka. Has striking white supercilium contrasting with grey to blackish ear-coverts, and downcurved yellow bill. **Racial variation** Four races are described from the peninsula. The palest is *P. h. obscurus* (Rajasthan, Gujarat and Madhya Pradesh), which has grey upperparts with slightly darker grey crown, ear-coverts and breast sides and flanks. The darkest is *P. h. travancoreensis* (Western Ghats and adjoining parts of Tamil Nadu), which has brownish-black crown, darker olive upperparts, and black ear-coverts, sides of breast and flanks; juvenile *travancoreensis,* however, may show rufous on sides of neck and breast, recalling White-browed Scimitar Babbler (p.753), but is smaller, with shorter and straighter bill and fluffier plumage (and ranges of the two species do not overlap). The two races from Sri Lanka, *P. h. holdsworthi* and *P. h. melanurus* have olive-brown to chestnut-brown sides to breast, flanks and vent, and olive-brown to chestnut-brown upperparts: Sri Lankan birds, as well as some juveniles from the peninsula, resemble White-browed, but that species has brighter chestnut sides of neck, breast and flanks, is more olive-brown on the upperparts, and typically has a slate-grey rather than rufous-brown or dark olive crown. **VOICE** Male has a musical flute-like *wot-ho-ho-ho,* this immediately followed by a quiet *krukru* or *krokant* uttered by the female; alarm is a sharp *kir-r-r-r* (Ali and Ripley 1987). **HABITS** Very similar to those of White-browed Scimitar Babbler. **HABITAT** Dense scrub and undergrowth, bamboo thickets, thick understorey of forest, and well-wooded gardens. **BREEDING** October–May, varying locally. Nest and nest site are similar to those of White-browed Scimitar Babbler; nest is occasionally built in hole of tree trunk or in bushes. **DISTRIBUTION AND STATUS** Sedentary resident. Hills of peninsular India and Sri Lanka. **IN:** locally common in peninsular hills, from near sea level up to summits of Western Ghats. **LK:** common in lowlands and hills.

STREAK-BREASTED SCIMITAR BABBLER *Pomatorhinus ruficollis* Plate 130

Rufous-necked Scimitar Babbler (F,I)

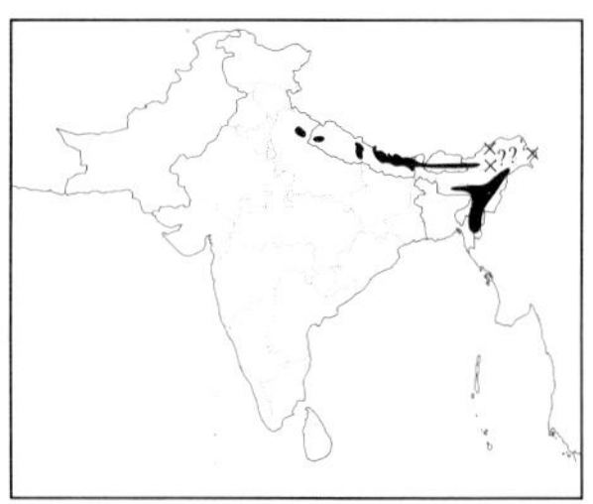

IDENTIFICATION 19 cm. Striking white supercilium contrasting with black ear-coverts, and downcurved yellow bill, distinguish this scimitar babbler from all others in its range except White-browed (p.753). Told from that species by diffuse olive-brown streaking on breast and belly, merging into olive-brown on flanks, distinct rufous patch on sides of neck which extends across nape as a narrow, diffuse band, smaller size, and smaller and less downcurved bill. Crown is rufescent olive-brown and concolorous with mantle (with some birds showing greyer coronal bands), and is never slate-grey as on most White-browed. **Juvenile** has brighter rufous upperparts, rufous breast with some white streaking, and smaller, almost straight bill. **VOICE** Call is a soft, musical *of-an-on*; song is varied, typically including a rising *pouki-wurki pouki-wurki* or falling *prrurti-witeu-witeu* (Ali and Ripley 1987). **HABITS** Similar to those of Rusty-cheeked Scimitar Babbler (p.753). Sometimes in company with other babblers. **HABITAT** Dense undergrowth in open forest, thick broadleaved forest, dense scrub on hillsides. **BREEDING** April–July. Nest is a loose dome, placed on bank or low down in bushes. **DISTRIBUTION AND STATUS** Resident, subject to some altitudinal movements. Himalayas from N Uttar Pradesh east to Arunachal Pradesh; NE India and Bangladesh. **NP:** fairly common; 1500–2590 m. **IN:** locally common in W Himalayas, mainly 1400–3300 m, winters down to 800 m; fairly common in E Himalayas, mainly 1500–3000 m, winters down to 700 m; locally common in NE hills, 900–1500 m. **BT:** fairly common; 1500–3000 m (down to 1370 m). **BD:** ?former resident; no recent records, but could still occur in hill tracts.

RED-BILLED SCIMITAR BABBLER *Pomatorhinus ochraceiceps* Plate 130

Lloyd's Scimitar Babbler (I)

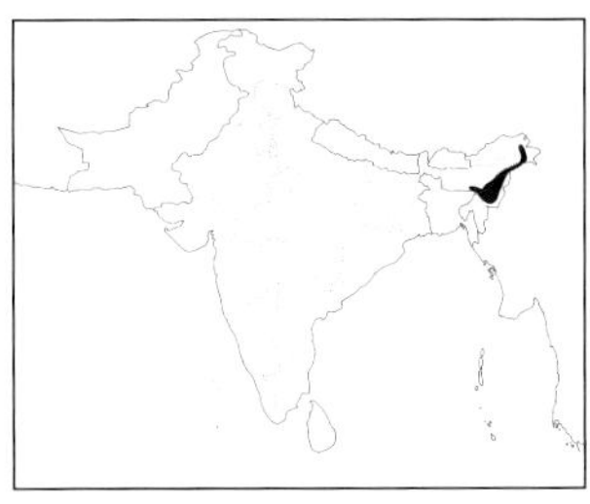

IDENTIFICATION 23 cm. Downcurved reddish bill and striking white supercilium distinguish this scimitar babbler from all others in its range except Coral-billed (below). Red-billed has a longer, finer and orange-red bill, narrower black mask, white or paler buff breast and belly (lacks Coral-billed's contrast between white malar stripe and deep buff to rufous lower throat and breast), and paler olive-brown upperparts with brighter ginger-buff cast to crown (lacking dark lateral crown-stripes). **Racial variation** *P. o. stenorhynchus* (Mishmi Hills, Arunachal Pradesh) has pale buff rather than white breast and belly, and gingery-buff cast to sides of neck, compared with *P. o. austeni* (hills south of the Brahmaputra in Assam, Manipur, Meghalaya and Nagaland). **VOICE** Typically, gives hurried, hollow piping, e.g. *wu-wu-wu* or *wu-wu-whip* or *pu-pu*, sometimes combined with antiphonal nasal *wyee*; also, very rapid *wi-wuwu* and more spaced, human-like whistle, *u-wip*. Harsh, scratchy alarm, *whi-chutututut* or *whi-trrrrrt.....whi-trrrrrt.. tchrrrtutututut.....tchrrrt* etc (C. Robson). **HABITS** Usually found singly, in pairs or in small parties. Very skulking. Searches for insects on the ground, in bushes or on lower branches of trees; also probes flowers of trees and bushes for nectar. **HABITAT** Dense undergrowth in broadleaved evergreen forest and bamboo thickets. **BREEDING** May–July. Builds a loose oval nest, concealed among leaf litter on the ground or low down in undergrowth. **DISTRIBUTION AND STATUS IN:** uncommon resident in NE hills (Arunachal Pradesh, Assam, Manipur, Meghalaya, Mizoram, Nagaland); 1500–2400 m, winters down to the foothills. **REFERENCES** Athreya *et al.* (1997), Katti *et al.* (1992), Singh (1995).

CORAL-BILLED SCIMITAR BABBLER *Pomatorhinus ferruginosus* Plate 130

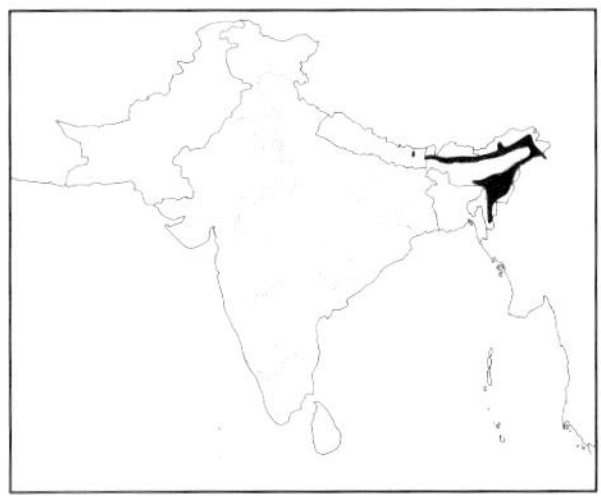

IDENTIFICATION 22 cm. Downcurved red bill and striking white supercilium distinguish this from all scimitar babblers in its range except Red-billed (above). Coral-billed has a stouter, shorter and blood-red bill, and broader supercilium. In E Himalayan range, the nominate race is further separated by brownish-black crown and nape, deep rufous breast and belly, larger and broader white supercilium, and bright rufous feathering on forehead and lores. Confusion is most likely where ranges overlap (in the hills south and east of the Brahmaputra R.), where Coral-billed, of the races *P. f. formosus* and *P. f. phayrei*, have rufescent olive-brown crown and buff underparts: main plumage differences from Red-billed are rich buff lower throat and breast contrasting with white upper throat and malar stripe, broader black mask, darker olive-brown upperparts, and slate-grey sides of crown; supercilium is typically buff in front of eye (white on Red-billed). **VOICE** Soft, questioning whistles: *whu, whiu...whiu* and *whoiee*; oriole-like mewing *weeeaaa* or *whheeeei*; shrill, short *yep-yep-yep...*; and short squeaky notes combined with harsh, scolding *tchrrrt-tchrrrrt, whitchitit* etc. Also a scratchy *weeitch-oo* and a shrill *wheep-wheep*. Harsh, dry alarm, *krrrrrt, kru-ruruttt, krrrrirrrurut* etc, less scratchy and piercing than Red-billed's (C. Robson). **HABITS** Similar to those of Rusty-cheeked Scimitar Babbler (p.753), but less shy and more easily observed. Keeps in pairs or small parties, depending on the season; often not associated with other species. **HABITAT** Bamboo thickets, dense undergrowth in moist broadleaved forest and at forest edges, thick secondary growth. **BREEDING** End April–July. Nest is an oval structure, placed on the ground or low down in bushes or clumps of grass or bamboo. **DISTRIBUTION AND STATUS** Resident. Himalayas from E Nepal east to Arunachal Pradesh; NE India. In Himalayas, 600–3800 m, usually above 1200 m; in NE Indian hills, 900–2400 m. **NP:** only one record in 20th century, from Arun valley. **IN:** rare in the west, locally frequent in the east. **BT:** frequent.

SLENDER-BILLED SCIMITAR BABBLER *Xiphirhynchus superciliaris* Plate 130

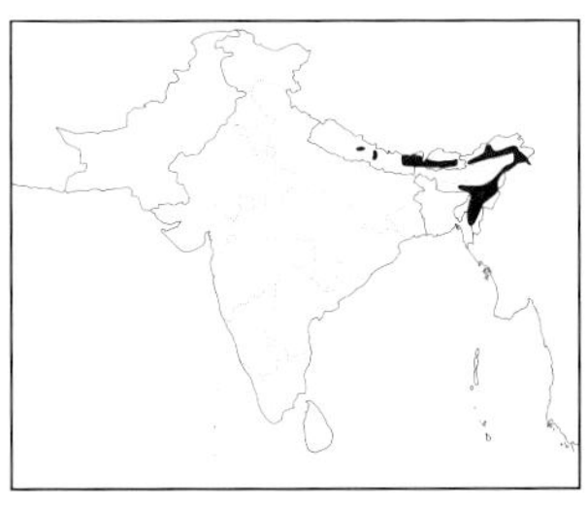

IDENTIFICATION 20 cm. Most distinctive of the scimitar babblers, with long, slender, downcurved black bill, fine and feathery white supercilium contrasting with slate-grey crown and ear-coverts, grey-streaked white throat, and deep rufous underparts. **VOICE** Male's song is a repeated powerful, tremulous *pwooorrr* or a slower *toop-toop-toop-toop*; both types used in duets, with female interjecting a two- to four-noted whistle, *bu-tu-wheip-wheip*. Excited staccato chittering interspersed with piercing rapid *pee-pee-pee* phrases (latter nuthatch-like in quality) from agitated party (S. Madge). **HABITS** Skulking and shy; usually keeps out of sight among thick undergrowth. Forages in a similar fashion to other scimitar babblers, by probing among leaf litter, moss and bark crevices for insects and ants; also sometimes climbs into flowering trees to feed on nectar. **HABITAT** Bamboo thickets and dense undergrowth in moist broadleaved forest. **BREEDING** April–July. Builds a large globular nest, usually on or close to the ground. **DISTRIBUTION AND STATUS** Resident, subject to altitudinal movements. Himalayas from WC Nepal east to

Arunachal Pradesh; NE India and Bangladesh. **NP:** scarce; 1500–3350 m. **IN:** uncommon in Himalayas, breeds 2100–3400 m, winters down to 600 m; in NE hills breeds up to 2700 m, winters down to the foothills. **BT:** generally frequent, locally fairly common; 1300–3505 m. **BD:** ?former resident; no recent records, but could still occur in hill tracts. **REFERENCES** Martens and Eck (1995).

LONG-BILLED WREN BABBLER *Rimator malacoptilus* Plate 131

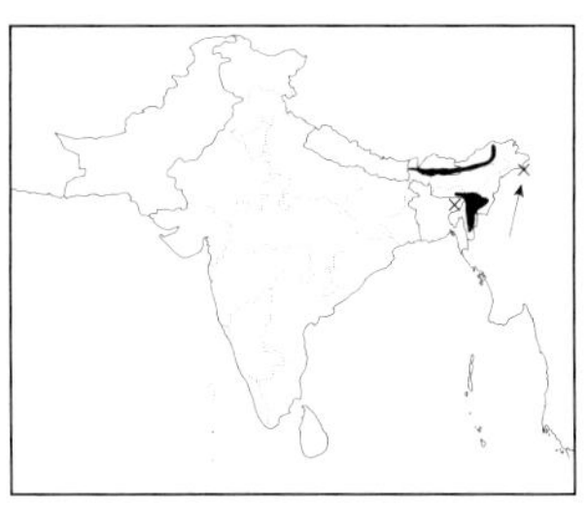

IDENTIFICATION 12 cm. A large wren babbler with short tail. Readily identified by combination of long, downcurved bill, buffish-white throat and buff belly merging into broadly buff-streaked brown breast and flanks, and brown upperparts with fine buff shaft-streaking. Has narrow dark moustachial stripe and less distinct malar stripe, and rufous-brown vent and undertail-coverts. **VOICE** A sweet chirping whistle (Ali and Ripley 1987) is the only vocalisation recorded from the subcontinent. Alarm is a churring *prurr prurr prrit* etc, or a quickly repeated *ker-wickit ker wickit*; `song' is a series of short, clear, bell-like whistles, *pee*, repeated every 3–4 seconds (P. Morris). **HABITS** Usually found in pairs. Very skulking, and adept at remaining out of sight. Keeps mainly to the ground, hopping about among low bushes and poking among leaf litter in search of insects. Has a weak flight. **HABITAT** Forest undergrowth on rocky ground, steep ravines, and overgrown, abandoned clearings. **BREEDING** May and June. Builds a globular nest on the ground among leaf litter. **DISTRIBUTION AND STATUS** Resident. Himalayas from Sikkim and West Bengal east to Arunachal Pradesh; NE India. Probably makes altitudinal movements; recorded 900–2700 m. **NP:** possibly recorded in 19th century, but the specimen may have originated in India. **IN:** scarce. **BT:** rare. **BD:** vagrant.

STREAKED WREN BABBLER *Napothera brevicaudata* Plate 131

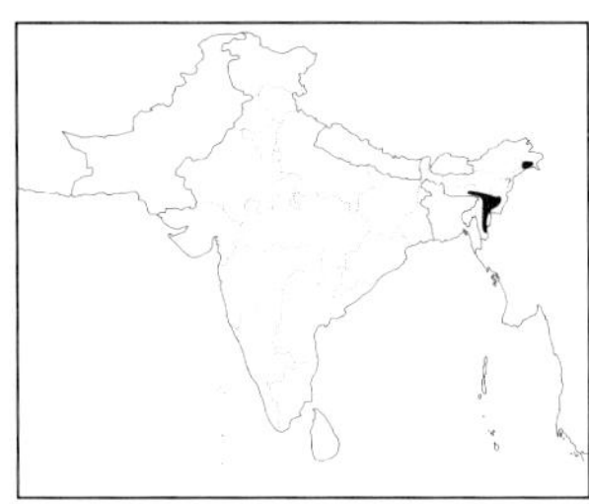

IDENTIFICATION 12 cm. A large, rather untidy-looking wren babbler with prominent tail, large bill and less rotund appearance compared with *Pnoepyga* species. Plumage differs from that of other wren babblers, with grey lores, supercilium and ear-coverts (resulting in grey-faced appearance), whitish throat diffusely streaked with grey, olive-brown breast, becoming brighter rufous-brown on flanks and vent, olive-brown upperparts with dark brown fringes (resulting in an untidy streaked or scaled appearance), and prominent buff tips to wing-coverts and tertials. Greyish edges to primaries form panel on wing. **VOICE** Sings with variable, clear, ringing whistled notes: *peee-oo, pu-ee, chiu-ree, chewee-ee, pee-wi* etc, sometimes single *pweeee*. Harsh, prolonged, scolding alternating rattles, *trrreeettt, chrrreerrrrt* etc, in alarm often mixed with plaintive *wher* notes (C. Robson). **HABITS** Keeps in pairs. Not shy. Hops quickly around moss-covered boulders on the forest floor, seeking insects. Reluctant to fly. **HABITAT** Moist, thick forest on rocky ground on steep slopes and in ravines. **BREEDING** May–July. Nest is a dome or semi-dome, placed on the ground between boulders, among tree roots or on mossy banks. **DISTRIBUTION AND STATUS IN:** locally fairly common resident in NE hills (Arunachal Pradesh, Assam, Manipur, Meghalaya, Mizoram, ?Nagaland), subject to some altitudinal movements; 300–2100 m. **REFERENCES** Athreya *et al.* (1997), Kaul *et al.* (1995), Singh (1995).

EYEBROWED WREN BABBLER *Napothera epilepidota* Plate 131

Small Wren Babbler

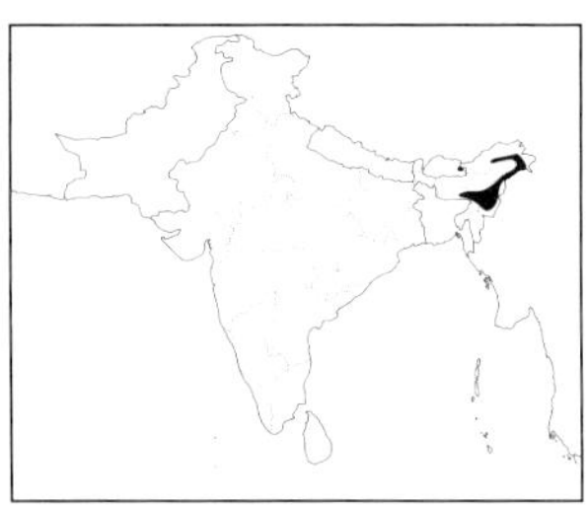

IDENTIFICATION 10 cm. The only wren babbler in the subcontinent with a prominent supercilium and dark eye-stripe. Additional features include dark brown upperparts, indistinctly scaled with black, prominent white spotting on wing-coverts, and bold dark spotting on throat and breast. **Racial variation** *N. e. roberti* of hills south of the Brahmaputra R has buff coloration to supercilium, sides of throat and breast, rather than the white of *N. e. guttaticollis* of the NE Himalayas. **VOICE** Song is a thin, plaintive, falling whistle, *cheeeeeu* or *piiiiiu*, repeated at 2–5-second intervals; when excited, song phrases may be interspersed with curious, slightly nasal *chikachik-chikachik-chikachik....* Rather subdued but prolonged rattles when alarmed, e.g. *prrrt-prrrt-prrrt, wprrrt.wprrrt.wprrrt, chrrut.chrrut chrrut,* etc (C. Robson). **HABITS** Keeps to the forest floor, usually around fallen logs, normally in pairs. Hops about among leaf litter or runs in and out of boulders, searching for insects. Loath to fly. **HABITAT** Moss- and fern-covered boulders, fallen logs and stumps in dense, moist shady forest. **BREEDING** April–June. Nest is a dome or very deep cup, placed among boulders. **DISTRIBUTION AND STATUS** Resident. Himalayas from E Bhutan eastwards; NE Indian hills (Arunachal Pradesh, Assam, Manipur, Meghalaya, Nagaland). Subject to altitudinal movements: breeds 1000–1800 m, winters down to the plains. **IN:** rare; very few recent records. **BT:** rare. **REFERENCES** Athreya *et al.* (1997), Kaul *et al.* (1995), Raman (1995).

SCALY-BREASTED WREN BABBLER *Pnoepyga albiventer* Plate 131

Greater Scaly-breasted Wren Babbler

IDENTIFICATION 10 cm. A rotund, tailless wren babbler with boldly scaled underparts, occurring in white and fulvous colour morphs. Told from the very similar Pygmy Wren Babbler (below) by larger size (appears noticeably larger than Winter Wren, p.680, or Grey-bellied Tesia, p.710), more rounded appearance, and more ponderous movements. Usually shows well-defined buff spotting on sides of crown and sides of neck (occasionally on entire crown and mantle), which is lacking on Pygmy; spotting on head and upperparts can, however, be much reduced on Scaly-breasted. Song is distinctive. Also very similar to Nepal Wren Babbler (below); see that species for main differences. **Juvenile** is considerably smaller and has uniform dark chestnut-brown upperparts, while underparts are sooty-grey to brown and lack bold scaling. **Racial variation** *P. a. pallidior* of the W and C Himalayas has paler olive-brown upperparts than nominate race. **VOICE** Song is a fine, strong warble, *tzee-tze-zit-tzu-stu-tzit*, rising and then ending abruptly; call is a high-pitched *tzit* (Fleming *et al.* 1984). **HABITS** Very skulking; keeps on or very close to the ground. Hops about among moss, boulders and roots, searching for insects; restless, and frequently flicks wings. Usually remains concealed except in the breeding season, when males sometimes sing in the open, perched on a rock or tree root. Reluctant to fly; if disturbed, slips away through dense undergrowth, keeping out of sight. **HABITAT** Moist, shady broadleaved forest among ferns and other tall herbage and moss-covered boulders and logs; favours ravines and edges of streams. **BREEDING** April–June. Nest is a ball of green moss and fine roots, placed near base of a moss-covered tree trunk on a mossy bank or under a rock. **DISTRIBUTION AND STATUS** Resident. Himalayas from W Himachal Pradesh east to Arunachal Pradesh; NE India. Subject to altitudinal movements: in W Himalayas, summers 2400–3600 m, winters down to 1000 m; in E Himalayas, summers 2745–3900 m, winters mainly 700–2285 m (275–2700 m); in Meghalaya, breeds down to 1000 m. **NP, IN:** fairly common. **BT:** common.

NEPAL WREN BABBLER *Pnoepyga immaculata* Plate 131

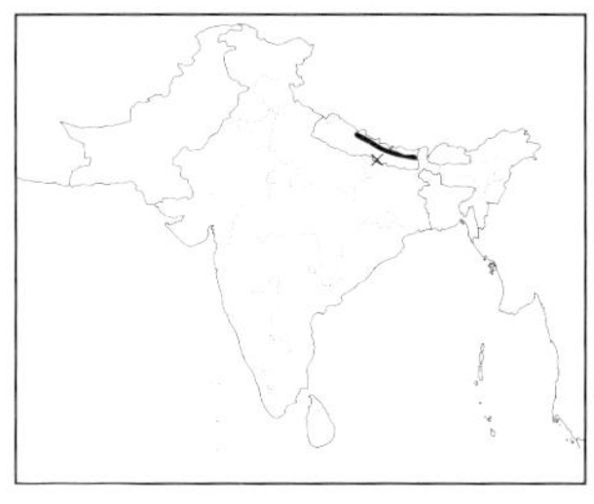

IDENTIFICATION 10 cm. A recently discovered wren babbler from the Nepal Himalayas: the same size as and very similar in appearance to Scaly-breasted Wren Babbler (above), although with comparatively longer and heavier bill; best separated by song. The feathers of underparts differ in shape from those of Scaly-breasted, being more elongated, resulting in narrower arrowhead-shaped black centres and pale fringes to feathers. Upperparts are more uniform, lacking buff spotting on crown, mantle and wing-coverts which is usually apparent on Scaly-breasted; particularly characteristic are the unmarked areas above and behind the eye and on neck sides. Note, however, that some Scaly-breasted (probably immature birds) may lack spotting on coverts, but otherwise have heavily spotted head and neck, while others may have reduced spotting on head and back. Occurs in white and fulvous colour morphs: the whitish feather edges on underparts of white morph are tinged ochre, appearing distinctly dirty compared with most Scaly-breasted; the fulvous morph is deep rusty-yellow on underparts, with coloration less saturated than the deep rusty colour of Scaly-bellied. Upperparts are a paler olive-brown than nominate Scaly-breasted (where ranges overlap); coloration is similar to that of *P. a. pallidior,* although there is no known overlap in ranges. Larger size and longer bill, and patterning of underparts, are best distinctions from Pygmy Wren Babbler (below). **VOICE** Eight high-pitched piercing notes, fairly quickly delivered, sometimes speeding up slightly towards the end, *tsi-tsu-tsi-tsi-si-tsu-tsi-tsi* or *si-su-si-si-swi-si-si-si,* c. 2–2.5 seconds in duration, sometimes a little faster (c. 2 seconds), repeated every 12–25 seconds, and sometimes every 5–8 seconds when excited; individual notes recall those of Pygmy Wren Babbler, although sometimes the first note is slightly more stressed (C. Robson from P. Davidson recording). **HABITS** Little known. Typical wren babbler feeding behaviour, hopping about low vegetation and boulders. Fairly confiding, but mostly keeps out of sight; occasionally sings from boulders. **HABITAT** Favours boulders and herbaceous and fern vegetation near running water with sparse tree cover or at forest edge or in open forest. **BREEDING** Unknown. Female in breeding condition collected in May. **DISTRIBUTION AND STATUS NP:** Resident, endemic to Nepal: a recently described species, currently known only from the Nepal Himalayas from WC areas eastwards, but may well occur farther east in Himalayas; recorded mainly 1730–3100 m from April to July, once at 250 m in March; locally fairly common. **REFERENCES** Harrap (1989), Martens (1992), Martens and Eck (1995).

PYGMY WREN BABBLER *Pnoepyga pusilla* Plate 131

Brown Wren Babbler (I), Lesser Scaly-breasted Wren Babbler (F,N)

IDENTIFICATION 9 cm. A rotund, tailless wren babbler with boldly scaled underparts, occurring in white and fulvous colour morphs. Distinguished from the very similar Scaly-breasted Wren Babbler (above) by smaller size (appears similar in size to Winter Wren, p.680, or Grey-bellied Tesia, p.710) and by distinctive song. Spotting on

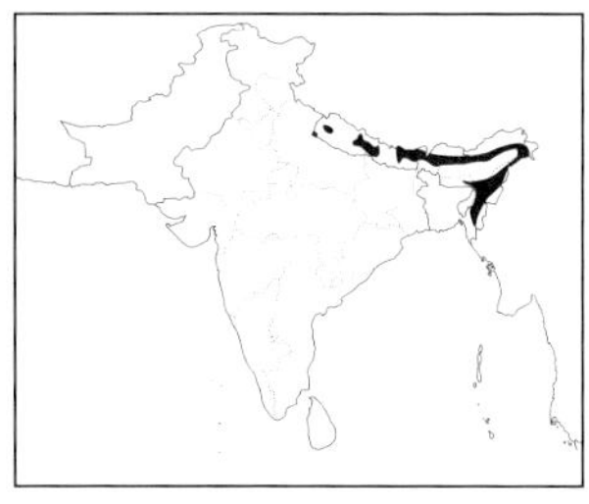

upperparts is confined to lower back and wing-coverts (lacking well-defined buff spotting on crown and neck which is usually present on Scaly-breasted). See Nepal Wren Babbler (p.758) and Rufous-throated and Rusty-throated Wren Babblers (below) for differences from those species. **Juvenile** has uniform dark brown upperparts, and underparts are sooty-grey and lack bold scaling. **VOICE** Song is a loud, slowly drawn-out *see–saw*, 1 second long, repeated up to 30 times at 2-second intervals; call is a *tzit* and *tzook* (Fleming *et al.* 1984). **HABITS** Very similar to those of Scaly-breasted Wren Babbler. **HABITAT** Very similar to that of Scaly-breasted Wren Babbler. **BREEDING** April–July. Nest is a ball of green moss and fine roots, placed on mossy tree trunks or among moss-covered rocks. **DISTRIBUTION AND STATUS** Resident. Himalayas from W Nepal east to Arunachal Pradesh; NE India and Bangladesh. Subject to altitudinal movements: in Himalayas, summers from 1500 m up to 2640 m in Nepal, to 2850 m in Bhutan, favouring 2000–2500 m, usually at lower altitudes than Scaly-breasted; in Meghalaya, breeds down to 1000 m; winters mainly 915–1770 m, sometimes down to the foothills and plains (–3500 m?) **NP:** frequent. **IN:** fairly common. **BT:** common. **BD:** former resident; no recent records, but could still occur in hill tracts.

RUFOUS-THROATED WREN BABBLER *Spelaeornis caudatus* — Plate 131

Tailed Wren Babbler (F,I)

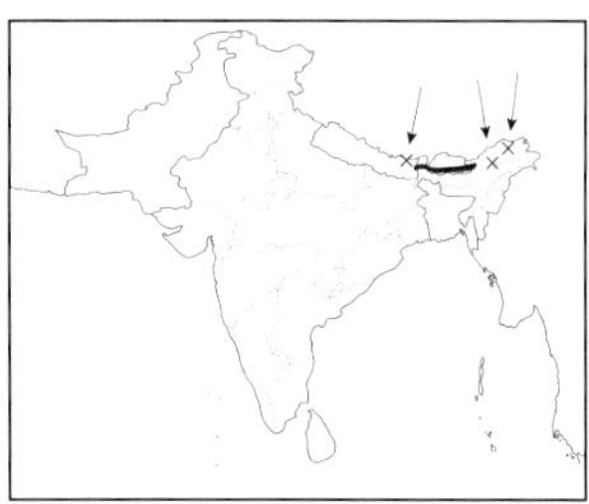

IDENTIFICATION 9 cm. A small, rotund and stub-tailed wren babbler. Distinguished from Pygmy Wren Babbler (p.757) by grey ear-coverts, whitish chin, rufous-orange throat and breast (latter with some dark streaking and barring), with paler rufous-orange extending onto flanks, white spotting (rather than scaling) on belly, no buff spotting on back and wing-coverts, and more noticeable short, square-ended tail. Some individuals are paler orange-buff on throat and breast. See Rusty-throated Wren Babbler (below) for differences from that species. **Juvenile** superficially resembles adult, but is smaller, lacks dark scaling on upperparts, and lacks white spotting and black barring on underparts. **VOICE** Sudden outburst, each phrase lasting some 1.5 seconds and consisting of three to five rapidly repeated *swediddy* notes (S. Madge). Intense simple warble of two to four (usually three) notes, *swichu-wichu-wichu* or *wichity-wichity-wu*. A *dzik* call very similar to that of Scaly-breasted Wren Babbler (p.757) (P. Holt from K. D. Bishop recording). **HABITS** Terrestrial and very secretive, usually keeping out of sight among ferns and moss-covered boulders. Male seen perched on a rock while singing. **HABITAT** Moist dense broadleaved forest among thick undergrowth, especially ferns and mossy rocks and fallen trees; dense thickets in narrow gullies. **BREEDING** Poorly known; published records give differing data. **DISTRIBUTION AND STATUS** Local resident, endemic to the subcontinent. Himalayas from E Nepal east to Arunachal Pradesh. Globally threatened. **NP:** very rare; 2135–2440 m. **IN:** locally common; 1800–2500 m (–3100 m?). **BT:** uncommon; 1500–2500 m. **REFERENCES** Singh (1995).

RUSTY-THROATED WREN BABBLER *Spelaeornis badeigularis* — Plate 131

Mishmi Wren (I)

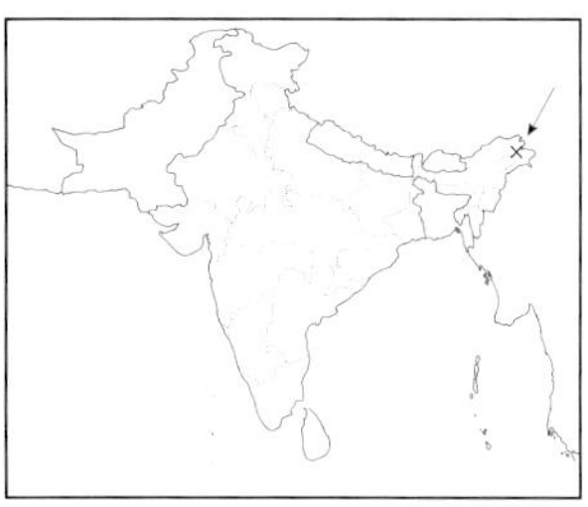

IDENTIFICATION 9 cm. A small, rotund and stub-tailed wren babbler. Told from Pygmy Wren Babbler (p.757) by white chin, rusty-chestnut throat with some dark streaking, white-barred or -spotted rather than scaled appearance to breast and belly, lack of buff spotting on back and wing-coverts, and presence of short, stubby tail. Main plumage differences from Rufous-throated Wren Babbler (above) include deeper rusty-chestnut throat, and this coloration not extending onto breast and flanks (with flanks and breast barred/spotted with white on black). **VOICE** Undocumented. **HABITS** Very poorly known. Presumably similar to those of Rufous-throated Wren Babbler. Shy and skulking. **HABITAT** Moist subtropical forest in winter. **BREEDING** Unknown. **DISTRIBUTION AND STATUS** Globally threatened. **IN:** endemic to the subcontinent; known only from one specimen, collected in Mishmi Hills, E Arunachal Pradesh, at 1600 m.

BAR-WINGED WREN BABBLER *Spelaeornis troglodytoides* — Plate 131

Long-tailed Spotted Wren Babbler (I)

IDENTIFICATION 10 cm. A very distinctive, long-tailed wren babbler with finely barred dark brown and grey wings and tail. Crown and nape are mottled with chestnut and black and are boldly spotted with white, with white spotting also prominent on sides of neck and continuing onto chestnut mantle. Has white throat diffusely spotted with black, with white merging into chestnut-splashed breast, has chestnut flanks marked with white, and has irregular dark spotting on white belly. **VOICE** Powerful, mellow, rapid warble of five repeated notes, regularly reiterated at 2–3-second intervals, *tu-lulu-lulu-lulu-lulu* (P. Holt from K. D. Bishop recording).

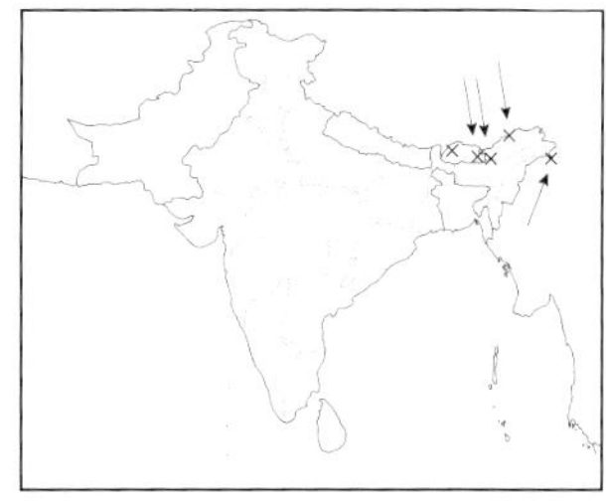

Calls with a faint *churr* (Smythies 1986). **HABITS** Forages in bushes, undergrowth, bamboo and moss-covered branches, rather than on the ground like other wren babblers. **HABITAT** Undergrowth and bamboo in moist temperate forest and rhododendron–bamboo scrub. **BREEDING** Unknown. **DISTRIBUTION AND STATUS** Resident. Himalayas in Bhutan and Arunachal Pradesh. **IN, BT:** rare; 2400–3355 m. **REFERENCES** Inskipp and Inskipp (1996), Singh (1995).

SPOTTED WREN BABBLER *Spelaeornis formosus* Plate 131

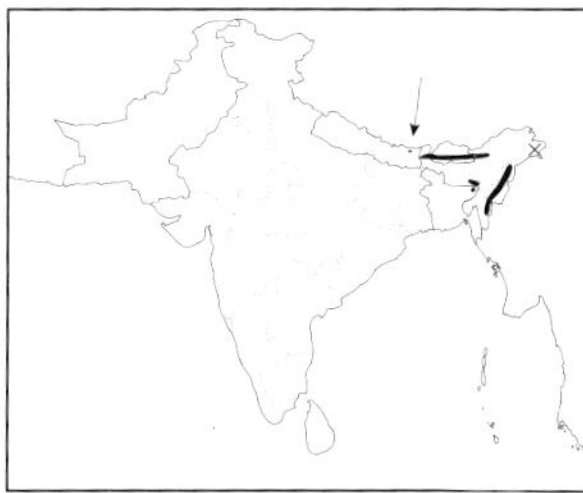

IDENTIFICATION 10 cm. A dark brown wren babbler with a more noticeable tail compared with the *Pnoepyga* species. Told from other wren babblers by broad dark brown barring on rufous-brown wings and tail, which gives rise to appearance not unlike that of Winter Wren (p.680). Lacks white throat and breast and bold white spotting on crown and nape of Bar-winged (p.758), and is readily told from Pygmy (p.758) by barred wings and tail and lack of bold scaling on underparts. Confusion is most likely with Winter Wren, but has irregular white flecking on grey-brown sides of head and upperparts (especially prominent on nape, sometimes forming collar, and wing-coverts), and has white and dark brown mottling and dark brown vermiculations on buffish underparts (not unlike Eurasian Wryneck, p.380). Underparts can appear dark, with patterning difficult to see, in the field. It lacks the intense barring on mantle, back, wing-coverts and underparts of Winter Wren. **VOICE** Call is a spluttering *put-put-put...* trill, and quite different from hard *chick* of Pygmy. A high-pitched, faltering whistle song, *did-did-did-dit, did-di-di-did*, incessantly repeated, with little variation (P. Holt from K. D. Bishop recording). **HABITS** Poorly known; similar to those of Pygmy Wren Babbler. **HABITAT** Poorly known. Moist temperate and subtropical broadleaved forest with dense undergrowth, ferns and moss-covered rocks; also long grass and scrub in winter. **BREEDING** Not authentically recorded. **DISTRIBUTION AND STATUS** Resident. Himalayas from E Nepal east to Arunachal Pradesh; NE India and Bangladesh; 500–2300 m. **NP:** rare and very local. **IN:** rare. **BT:** locally frequent. **BD:** rare resident; no recent records. **REFERENCES** Inskipp and Inskipp (1996), Singh (1995).

LONG-TAILED WREN BABBLER *Spelaeornis chocolatinus* Plate 131

Streaked Long-tailed Wren Babbler (I)

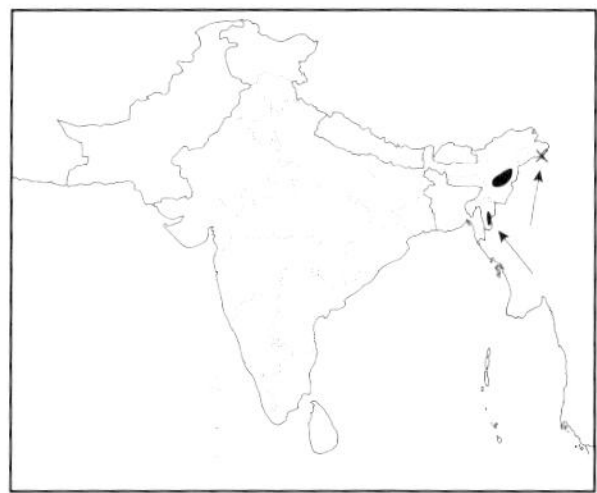

IDENTIFICATION 10 cm. A comparatively slim and long-tailed wren babbler with scaly appearance to brown upperparts, occurring as two distinct races. Distinguished from Tawny-breasted Wren Babbler (below) by smaller size and by patterning of throat and breast (see below). **Racial variation** *S. c. chocolatinus* of the S Assam and Manipur hills has rufous-buff throat, breast and flanks, with fine brown and buff spotting on sides of throat and sides of breast. *S. c. oatesi* of the Mizoram hills has white throat, centre of breast and belly with diffuse black spotting, and olive-brown flanks. **VOICE** *S. c. chocolatinus*: described as a loud, melodic, explosive whistle, *wheeuw*, and a soft *chir* alarm note (Ali and Ripley 1987). *S. c. oatesi*: sings with loud, abrupt, undulating phrases, *chiwi-chiwi-chiwi-chew* or *witchi-witchi-witchi-wu*, sometimes extended, but also may be shortened or hurried; song may be answered antiphonally with rather buzzy, hoarse *titcher.tcher-tcher* or *titcher-tcher-tcher-tcher-tcher*. Calls include soft *tuc..tuc...tuc...*, *chit-chit-chit...* and very quiet *ik..ik.ik* (C. Robson). **HABITS** Usually seen foraging among undergrowth within half a metre of the ground. **HABITAT** Ferns, bamboo thickets and other dense undergrowth in shady broadleaved evergreen forest and on steep hillsides strewn with moss-covered rocks; in the Mizoram hills found in thick bushes and dwarf bamboo, especially in clearings and at forest edges. **BREEDING** April–June. Nest is a dome, placed on the ground among dense undergrowth. **DISTRIBUTION AND STATUS IN:** resident in NE hills (Arunachal Pradesh, Assam, Manipur, Meghalaya, Mizoram, Nagaland), from 1200 m in winter to at least 3100 m in summer; current status uncertain, and very few recent records. **REFERENCES** Robson (1991), Singh (1995).

TAWNY-BREASTED WREN BABBLER *Spelaeornis longicaudatus* Plate 131

Long-tailed Wren Babbler (I,N)

IDENTIFICATION 10 cm. A comparatively slim and long-tailed wren babbler with scaly appearance to brown upperparts. Told from Long-tailed Wren Babbler by uniform orange-buff underparts without prominent black flecking or white spotting, and pale grey lores and ear-coverts (with whitish streak above eye). Possibly confusable with Buff-breasted Babbler (p.751), but is considerably smaller, has diffuse dark scaling and paler centres to feathers of upperparts, and has dark grey lores and ear-coverts. **Juvenile** has rufous-brown upperparts, lacking

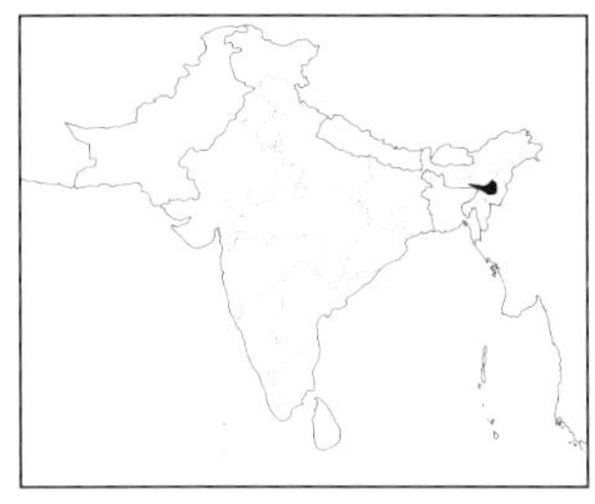

dark scaling. **VOICE** A loud clear whistle, and a soft churring alarm call (Ali and Ripley 1987). **HABITS** Poorly known. Creeps about among moss-covered boulders, and forages among undergrowth. **HABITAT** Deep, moist broadleaved evergreen forest with thick undergrowth, keeping to rocky ravines; steep hillsides with rock outcrops densely covered with moss, ferns and orchids. **BREEDING** April–June. Nest is a loose domed or oval structure, placed on the ground or among boulders. **DISTRIBUTION AND STATUS** Resident, endemic to the subcontinent. Globally threatened. **IN:** NE hills (Assam, Manipur, Meghalaya, Nagaland), 1000–2000 m; current status uncertain, with only one recent record.

WEDGE-BILLED WREN BABBLER *Sphenocichla humei* Plate 131

Wedge-billed Wren (I)

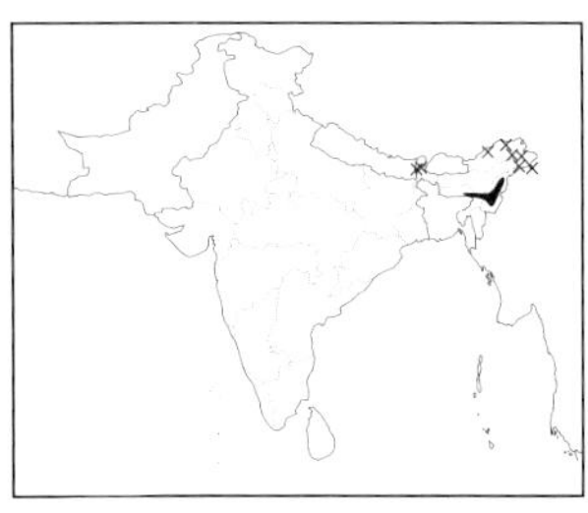

IDENTIFICATION 18 cm. An extraordinary-looking babbler, occurring as two distinct races. Common features are wedge-shaped yellow bill, broad but diffuse grey supercilium and spotting on sides of neck (more apparent in *humei*), dark brown upperparts, diffuse brown barring across wings and tail, and sturdy blackish legs and feet. **Racial variation** *S. h. humei* of Sikkim and Arunachal Pradesh has black face and most of underparts (becoming greyish-white on belly) with fine white shaft streaking, and white shaft streaking on olive-buff-centred feathers of crown and mantle (lacking pale tips to nape and mantle of *roberti*). *S. h. roberti* of the hills south of the Brahmaputra R is much paler and heavily scaled on the underparts, with feathers of throat and breast subterminally lined with white and fringed with black; has rufous-brown forehead, and paler, more olive-brown upperparts, with diffuse whitish tips to feathers of nape and mantle. **VOICE** Undocumented. **HABITS** Poorly known. Found in parties of 10–15 birds. Seeks insect prey by actively climbing up trunks of larger trees, like a treecreeper; also forages in undergrowth in the manner of other babblers. Prefers to use its legs rather than fly, but can fly well and makes short aerial excursions from tree to tree, unlike other wren babblers. **HABITAT** Broadleaved evergreen forest with large trees and bamboo. **BREEDING** May and June. Only one nest described: a pad of moss on top of a mass of fine grasses, wedged in a tree crevice 6 m above ground. **DISTRIBUTION AND STATUS** Resident. **IN:** Himalayas of Sikkim (not since 19th century), West Bengal and Arunachal Pradesh, and NE hills (Assam, Manipur, Meghalaya, Nagaland); from 1500 m up to at least 2300 m, winters down to 800 m; current status uncertain, and very few recent records. **REFERENCES** Athreya *et al.* (1997), Robson (1991), Singh (1995).

RUFOUS-FRONTED BABBLER *Stachyris rufifrons* Plate 132

Red-fronted Babbler (I) Buff-chested Babbler, *S. ambigua*

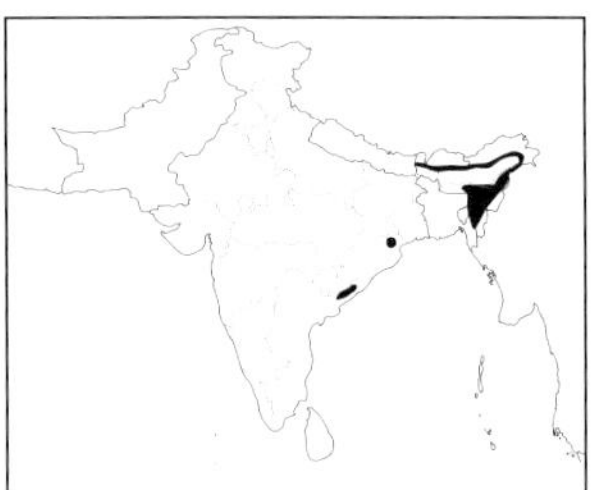

IDENTIFICATION 12 cm. A small, rufous-capped babbler with olive-brown mantle and buff-coloured underparts. Most likely to be confused with Rufous-capped Babbler (below), but rufous cap is less sharply defined and does not extend onto rear crown. In addition, has white throat (faintly streaked with black, as on Rufous-capped), fine grey supercilium and greyish lores, olive-brown (rather than buff) ear-coverts which are concolorous with mantle, and buffish breast and flanks, becoming paler on belly. **Juvenile** as adult, but has more rufous fringes to wings and tail, has paler underparts, and rufous cap is paler. **VOICE** Halting series of five to seven mellow, monotone piping whistles, separated from the next series by a pause of 4–8 seconds, *tu-tu-tu-tu-tu-tu-tu*; indistinguishable from the song of Rufous-capped Babbler and very similar to, but slightly higher-pitched and purer than, that of Golden Babbler (p.761) (P. Holt). **HABITS** Found in pairs in the breeding season; otherwise in small actively moving parties with other babblers and other species. Hunts for insects and sometimes berries in the undergrowth in typical babbler fashion; also in tops of bamboo clumps and medium-sized trees. Feeding actions are sometimes tit-like. **HABITAT** Bushes and bamboo thickets in deserted clearings, thick undergrowth in open forest, and densely vegetated ravines. **BREEDING** April–July. Nest is a dome, semi-dome or deep cup, placed in a bamboo clump. **DISTRIBUTION AND STATUS** Resident. Himalayan foothills from Sikkim east to Arunachal Pradesh; NE India, N Orissa, Andhra Pradesh and Bangladesh. **IN:** locally common from the plains edge up to 900 m; locally 1000–1200 m. **BT:** uncommon; 800–2500 m (down to 610 m). **BD:** locally common.

RUFOUS-CAPPED BABBLER *Stachyris ruficeps* Plate 132

Red-headed Babbler (F,I)

IDENTIFICATION 12 cm. A small, rufous-capped babbler with olive-coloured mantle and yellowish-buff underparts. Most likely to be confused with Rufous-fronted Babbler (above), but rufous cap is more sharply defined and extends farther onto rear crown. In addition, has brighter olive upperparts, pale yellow throat (faintly

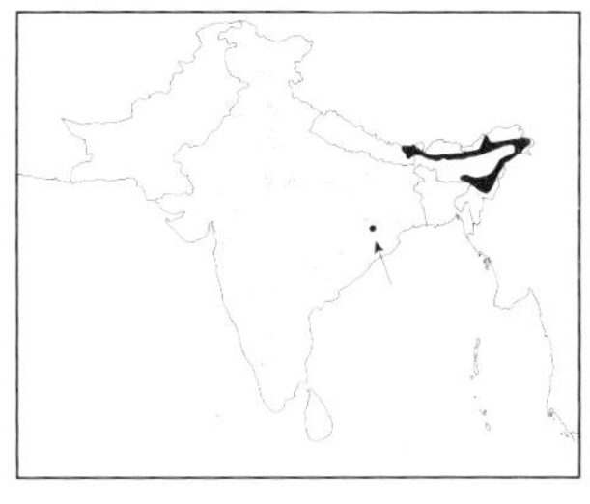

streaked with black, as on Rufous-fronted), yellowish-buff lores, supercilium and ear-coverts which contrast with mantle, and yellowish-buff underparts. **Juvenile** as adult, but duller, with paler underparts and a paler crown; more closely resembles Rufous-fronted. **VOICE** Song is similar to that of Golden Babbler (below), but without a pause after the first note: a series of seven or eight notes, *pee-pi-pi-pi-pi-pi pi.* Call is a four-noted whistle, *whi-whi-whi-whi,* and flocks utter a conversational chittering. **HABITS** Similar to those of Rufous-fronted Babbler. Keeps to low bushes. **HABITAT** Bamboo thickets and dense undergrowth in humid broadleaved forest. **BREEDING** April–July. Nest is a dome or deep cup, placed in low bushes or bamboo clumps. **DISTRIBUTION AND STATUS** Resident. Himalayas from E Nepal east to Arunachal Pradesh; NE India and N Orissa. Occurs 1000–2800 m, mainly 1525–2440 m (610–2890 in Bhutan). **NP:** fairly common in the far east. **IN:** fairly common. **BT:** common.

BLACK-CHINNED BABBLER *Stachyris pyrrhops* — Plate 132

Red-billed Babbler (I)

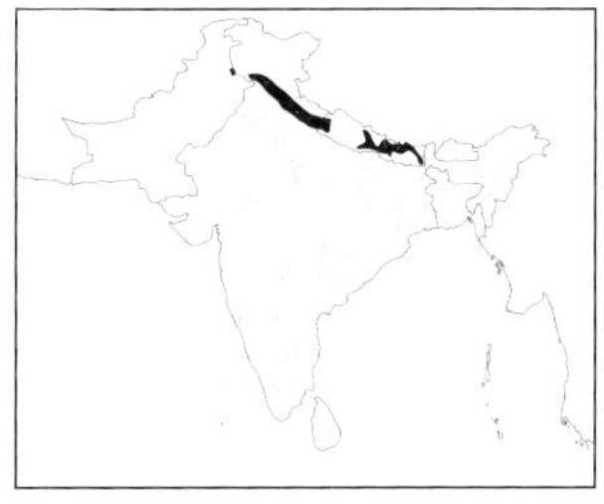

IDENTIFICATION 10 cm. A small, rather bull-headed babbler. Very distinctive, with black chin and lores, olive-buff crown with dark streaking, buffish ear-coverts, orange-buff underparts and olive-brown upperparts (lacking any rufous in plumage). **VOICE** A pleasant bell-like piping, *whit-whit-whit-whit,* which is very short and repeated at irregular intervals; normal contact call is a soft, melodious churring *t-r-r-r-r tr-eee tu-r-r-r,* which varies in pitch (Roberts 1992). **HABITS** Depending on the season, found in pairs or in small parties of about eight birds, often with other species. Active and restless. Feeds mainly in bushes and undergrowth. **HABITAT** Undergrowth in open forest and at forest edges, secondary growth, and bushes in abandoned cultivation. **BREEDING** April–July. Builds a globular nest, low down in bushes. **DISTRIBUTION AND STATUS** Resident, endemic to the subcontinent. Himalayas from Murree, Pakistan, east to E Nepal. Subject to some altitudinal movements: 245–2440 m, chiefly above 915 m, breeds mainly 1500–2000 m. **PK:** frequent but very local; 460–1500 m. **NP:** fairly common east to EC areas, rare farther east. **IN:** fairly common.

GOLDEN BABBLER *Stachyris chrysaea* — Plate 132

Gold-headed Babbler (I), Golden-headed Babbler (F)

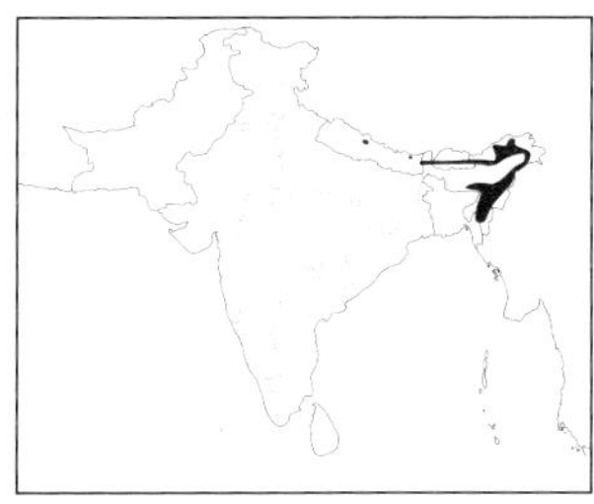

IDENTIFICATION 10 cm. A distinctive babbler, with yellow forehead and black-streaked yellow crown, black lores and moustachial stripe (giving rise to masked appearance), olive-green upperparts and yellow underparts. **Racial variation** *S. c. chrysaea* of the eastern Himalayas and south to Manipur has yellowish-olive upperparts and bright chrome-yellow underparts. *S. c. binghami* of Mizoram and south to the hills of Bangladesh has duller olive-green upperparts and duller yellow underparts. **VOICE** The song is very like some of the slower variations of that of Rufous-capped Babbler (p.760); Golden almost always has a single introductory note, and hesitates before it strings together five to eight toots on the same pitch. Has a dry, scolding chitter that is relatively quiet compared with that of other babblers, including Rufous-capped (S. Connop). **HABITS** Usually in mixed hunting parties outside the breeding season. Very active and continually on the move, flitting from one twig to another, hovering near flowers and searching under leaves. **HABITAT** Bamboo thickets and dense undergrowth in humid broadleaved forest, and overgrown deserted cultivation clearings. **BREEDING** April–July. Nest is a dome, placed in a bamboo clump or among undergrowth on a bank. **DISTRIBUTION AND STATUS** Resident. Himalayas in WC and E Nepal, and from Sikkim east to Arunachal Pradesh; NE India and Bangladesh. **NP:** rare and local; 1800–2440 m. **IN:** locally fairly common in Himalayas, 400–2600 m, mainly 1500–2000 m; locally common in NE hills, 300–1800 m. **BT:** fairly common; 500–2620 m. **BD:** ?rare resident; no recent records, but could still occur in hill tracts.

GREY-THROATED BABBLER *Stachyris nigriceps* — Plate 132

Black-throated Babbler (F,I)

IDENTIFICATION 12 cm. Readily distinguished from other *Stachyris* babblers (p.760–p.762) by combination of blackish crown with white streaking, black lateral crown-stripe and greyish supercilium, and black-and-white or grey chin and throat. **Racial variation** Differences are mainly in the patterning of throat and the colour of ear-coverts and underparts: e.g. *S. n. nigriceps* of the C and E Himalayas has chin and throat grey, edged with white, buff-brown ear-coverts and buff underparts, whereas *S. n. coltarti* of Nagaland has chin and throat mainly black, with white malar stripe, and bright orange-buff ear-coverts and underparts. **VOICE** A high-pitched, tinkling trill that can ascend, descend or remain on the same pitch; the trill is always prefaced with a single introductory note and a brief pause. Also noted is a shorter, less musical, descending trill (S. Connop). **HABITS**

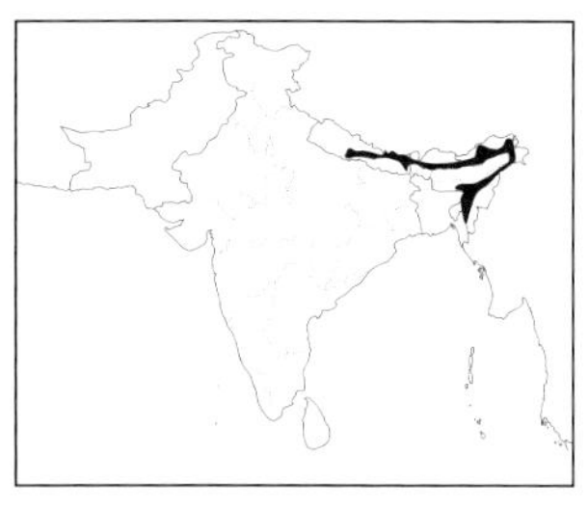

Skulks in thick undergrowth, often in itinerant foraging parties with other species in the non-breeding season. **HABITAT** Undergrowth and bamboo thickets in open or dense broadleaved forest, and secondary growth; often near water. **BREEDING** March–July, varying locally. Nest is a dome, hidden among vegetation on the ground, often on a bank. **DISTRIBUTION AND STATUS** Resident. Himalayas from WC Nepal east to Arunachal Pradesh; NE India and Bangladesh. Subject to altitudinal movements: in the west, breeds mainly 1000–1830 m (–2000 m), winters 245–1830 m; in the far east, occurs from the plains edge up to 1800 m. **NP:** local; frequent east of Kathmandu valley, rare farther west. **IN, BT:** fairly common. **BD:** local.

SNOWY-THROATED BABBLER *Stachyris oglei* — Plate 132

Austen's Spotted Babbler (I)

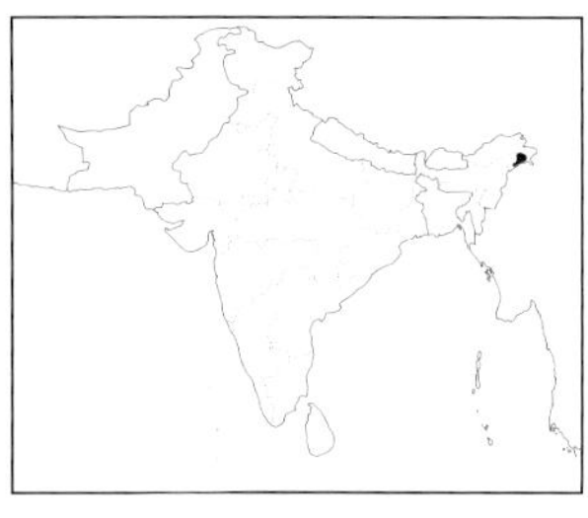

IDENTIFICATION 13 cm. A large, distinctive *Stachyris* babbler. Has white supercilium bordered above with black, broad black eye-stripe and white throat, black-bordered white spotting on sides of neck and mantle, chestnut crown and nape, rufous-brown upperparts, with fine black barring across wings and tail, grey breast and belly, and olive-brown flanks. **VOICE** Undescribed. **HABITS** Very poorly known. Found in flocks of 10–25 birds. Keeps to the heaviest undergrowth; is vocal, skulking and very wary. **HABITAT** Breeds in moist dense scrub in rocky ravines; in winter, in broadleaved evergreen forest and also in bamboo. **BREEDING** April–June. Builds a globular nest on the ground under bushes in rocky ravines. **DISTRIBUTION AND STATUS** Globally threatened. **IN:** resident, endemic to the Patkai and Mishmi hills, Arunachal Pradesh; generally rare, but locally frequent, 400–1800 m. **REFERENCES** Athreya *et al.* (1997).

TAWNY-BELLIED BABBLER *Dumetia hyperythra* — Plate 132

Rufous-bellied Babbler (F,I), White-throated Babbler (P)

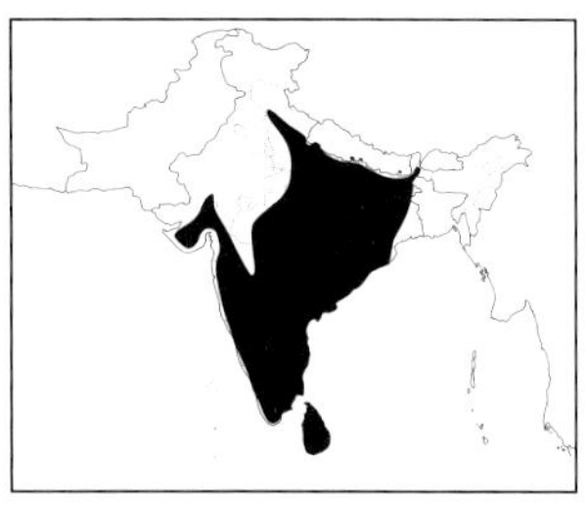

IDENTIFICATION 13 cm. A fairly long-tailed, rufous-coloured babbler. Forehead and forecrown are rufous-buff, sides of head and underparts are orange-buff, mantle is olive-brown, and wings and tail are brown, the tail with faint barring. Bill is pale pinkish-brown. **Juvenile** has brighter, more rufous-brown upperparts, lacking rufous-brown forehead; has only traces of white on throat, and duller underparts. **Racial variation** Four races are described from the subcontinent, three of which have white throat and show subtle differences in coloration of crown and underparts. *D. h. hyperythra* of E peninsular India has throat concolorous with rest of the underparts. **VOICE** A clear whistling song of seven notes; has a soft *tack-tack* call, and flocks utter a sunbird-like cheeping *sweech-sweech* call (Ali and Ripley 1987). **HABITS** Found in loose flocks of about ten birds, which restlessly follow each other through tall grass and bushes. Skulking and, if alarmed, the flock disperses and dives into thick cover. Feeds chiefly on insects taken in the undergrowth or on the ground; also on nectar. **HABITAT** Tall grass and scrub; avoids evergreen biotope. **BREEDING** Has an extended season, mainly during the monsoon. Builds a neat globular nest in a thorny bush, up to 2 m above ground. **DISTRIBUTION AND STATUS** Resident, endemic to the subcontinent. From SE Himachal Pradesh east through the Nepal terai to West Bengal and Bangladesh, and south through Uttar Pradesh, C and E Madhya Pradesh, S Rajasthan and Gujarat, and throughout the peninsula; Sri Lanka. **NP:** rare and local; below 305 m. **IN:** common; from the plains up to 900 m in Himalayas, to 1800 m in peninsular hills. **BD:** former resident; no recent records. **LK:** rare resident throughout, more in the dry zone.

DARK-FRONTED BABBLER *Rhopocichla atriceps* — Plate 132

Black-headed Babbler (I), Black-fronted Babbler (P)

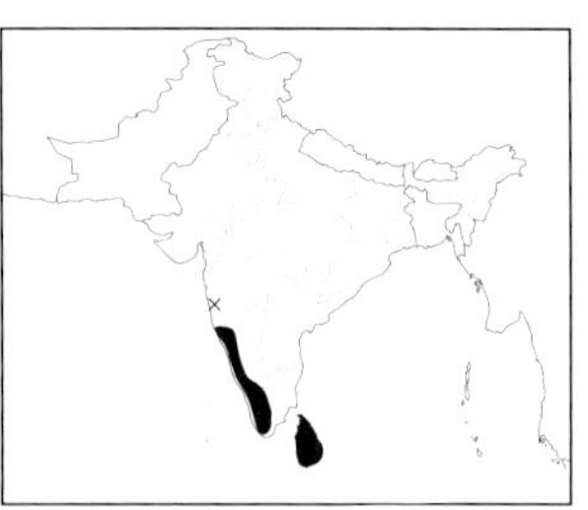

IDENTIFICATION 13 cm. A stocky, rather short-tailed and bull-headed babbler. The only babbler which has a combination of black on head, rufous-brown to olive-brown upperparts, and whitish underparts (with olive-brown to buffish flanks and vent). **Racial variation** Four races are described for the subcontinent. The two from the Western Ghats have dark crown and ear-coverts (crown is black in *R. a. atriceps* and sooty-brown in *R. a. bourdilloni*), while the two races in Sri Lanka have black of head restricted to forehead and ear-coverts (with *R. a. nigrifrons* having more rufous upperparts than *R. a. siccatus*). **VOICE** Unobtrusive *tup*, scolding *churr* and a plaintive nasal mewing (P. Holt); also a loud, throaty grating (R. Grimmett). **HABITS** Similar to those of Tawny-bellied Babbler (above). In small parties, often with other babblers. Keeps in thick undergrowth, diligently searching for insects. **HABITAT** Evergreen biotope in dense undergrowth, thickets near streams, reedbeds, bamboo, and cardamom cultivation. **BREEDING** Almost all year. Builds a globular nest, concealed in thick bushes. **DISTRIBUTION AND STATUS** Resident, endemic to the subcontinent. Western Ghats in Goa, Karnataka, Kerala and W Tamil Nadu; Sri Lanka. **IN:** from the plains up to 1800 m, common 600–1200 m. **LK:** widespread in lowlands and hills.

STRIPED TIT BABBLER *Macronous gularis* Plate 132

Yellow-breasted Babbler (F,I)

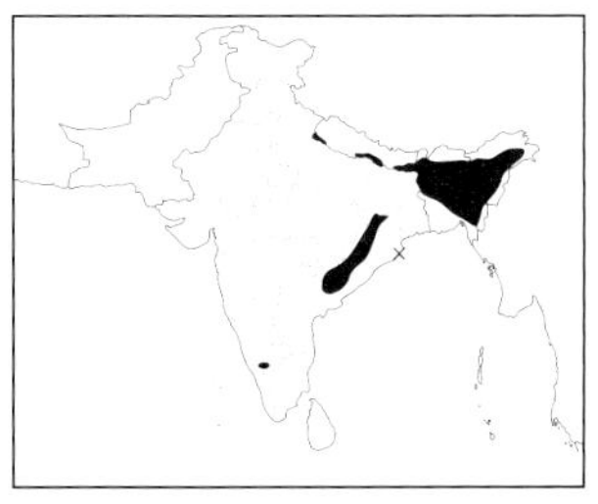

IDENTIFICATION 11 cm. A well-proportioned, typically rather scruffy-looking babbler with rufous-brown cap, pale yellow lores and supercilium, olive mantle, brown wings and tail, and pale yellow underparts with fine black streaking on throat and breast. **VOICE** A loud, monotonous *chuk-chuk-chuk*, repeated up to 15 times at the rate of five per second; also an alarm, *bizz-chir-chur* (Fleming *et al.* 1984). **HABITS** Depending on the season, found in pairs or parties, often with other species. A particularly noisy babbler, readily located by its distinctive call. Creeps and clambers about unobtrusively, searching for insects. **HABITAT** Bushes, creepers, tangles and undergrowth in open and dense broadleaved forest and thin bamboo jungle. **BREEDING** April–July. Builds a globular nest, fairly low down in bushes or bamboo. **DISTRIBUTION AND STATUS** Resident. Himalayan foothills from W Nepal east to Arunachal Pradesh; E and NE India, S Karnataka and Bangladesh. **NP:** common from C areas eastwards, frequent farther west; from the terai up to 760 m. **IN:** common; usually below 600 m, up to 900 m in the peninsula. **BT:** common; 245–825 m. **BD:** locally common.

CHESTNUT-CAPPED BABBLER *Timalia pileata* Plate 132

Red-capped Babbler (F,I)

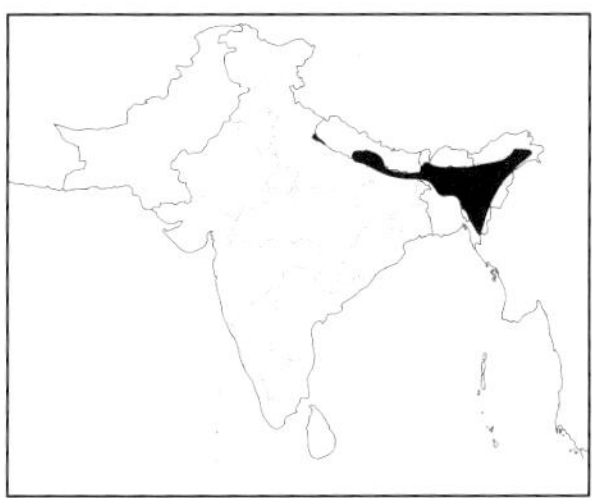

IDENTIFICATION 17 cm. A stocky, thick-necked babbler with bright chestnut cap, reddish-brown to crimson iris, thick black bill and black lores (resulting in masked appearance) contrasting with white forehead and supercilium, white ear-coverts and white throat and breast (streaked finely with black), bordered with slate-grey on sides of neck, olive-brown upperparts, faintly barred tail, buffish-olive flanks and vent, and buff belly. **VOICE** A fast, high-pitched, descending trill, varying in length, not so high-pitched as that of Grey-throated (p.7610) (S. Connop); contact note a *tzt*, and alarm call a *pic-pic-pic* (Fleming *et al.* 1984). **HABITS** Associates in small parties in the non-breeding season. Usually keeps out of sight in thick cover; may sun itself or sing in the open for a few seconds. Clambers up and down stems, systematically searching for insects. **HABITAT** Tall grass, reedbeds and scrub in low-lying wet areas; also grass-covered plateaux in the Khasi Hills. **BREEDING** March–October. Nest is a roughly made ball, placed low down in a bush or on the ground under a bush. **DISTRIBUTION AND STATUS** Resident. Himalayan terai and foothills and Brahmaputra floodplains from W Nepal east through N Uttar Pradesh and N Bihar to E Arunachal Pradesh and Bangladesh. **NP:** common at Chitwan, uncommon elsewhere; below 305 m. **IN:** locally common in plains and foothills; also at 1200 m on plateaux of Khasi Hills, Meghalaya. **BD:** local.

YELLOW-EYED BABBLER *Chrysomma sinense* Plate 132

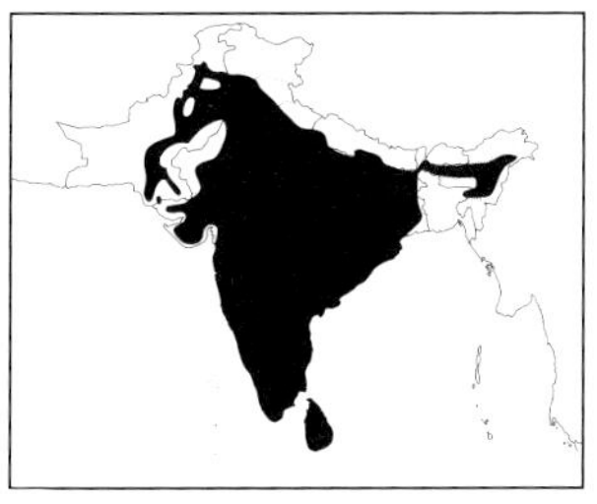

IDENTIFICATION 18 cm. A long-tailed babbler with rounded head and stout, dark bill (recalling a giant prinia in shape). Most distinctive features are yellow iris and thick orange orbital ring, white lores and fine white supercilium, striking white throat and breast, merging into buffish underparts, and yellow legs and feet. For differences from the restricted-range Jerdon's Babbler (p.764), see that species. **Racial variation** Birds of the NW subcontinent (*C. s. hypoleucum*) are paler, more olive-brown on upperparts, with more striking rufous-brown wings, compared with those occurring in the E and S subcontinent (*C. s. sinense*), which have richer, more chestnut-brown upperparts and richer buff lower belly and flanks. **VOICE** Song consists of a variable, rapid twittering trill, *trit-rit-ri-ri-ri-r-r*, ending in a plaintive two-noted *toway-twoh*, typically uttered from the top of a grass stem in rather prinia-like fashion; call is a loud and plaintive *teeuw-teeuw-teeuw*, repeated two to four times (Roberts 1992). **HABITS** Found in parties of 12 or more outside the breeding season. Skulking; spends most of its time concealed in thick bushes and tall grass, often foraging for insects close to the ground. Often calls briefly from a conspicuous perch before diving into the undergrowth again. Has a laboured, jerky flight. **HABITAT** Tall grass and bushes, reeds, thickets and sugarcane fields. **BREEDING** Almost all year, varying locally. Nest is a neat cone-shaped cup, hung between plant stems or wedged in a bush. **DISTRIBUTION AND STATUS** Sedentary resident. Throughout much of the subcontinent, except parts of the northwest, northeast and Himalayas. **PK:** uncommon and local along Indus R and its tributaries. **NP:** fairly common at Chitwan, frequent in the west; locally distributed below 365 m. **IN:** widespread and locally common; from base of the hills up to 1200 m. **BD:** local. **LK:** rare throughout.

JERDON'S BABBLER *Chrysomma altirostre* Plate 132

Jerdon's Moupinia (R), *Moupinia altirostre* (K)

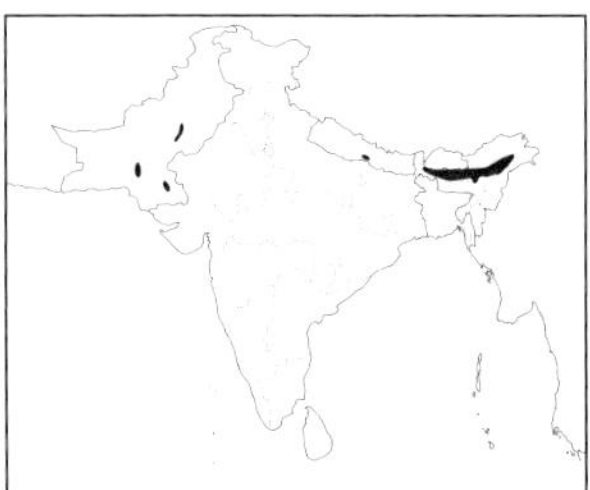

IDENTIFICATION 17 cm. A stocky, long-tailed babbler with rounded head and stout bill. Main differences from Yellow-eyed Babbler (p.763) are paler yellowish-brown bill, brown iris and dull yellowish-green orbital ring, lack of white lores and supercilium, and fleshy-brown legs and feet. See below for further differences from Yellow-eyed. **Racial variation** Two distinct races occur in the subcontinent. *C. a. altirostre* of the Indus plains has greyish lores and supercilium, grey-brown ear-coverts and olive-brown upperparts; throat and breast are pale grey, rather than brilliant white as on Yellow-eyed, and lacks the bright rufous-brown on the wing of that species. *C. a. griseigulare* of the NE subcontinent has slate-grey lores and supercilium, darker grey throat and breast and richer chestnut-brown underparts, and is richer buff on belly, flanks and vent compared with *altirostre*; grey supercilium and coloration of underparts readily distinguish this race from *sinense* race of Yellow-eyed. **VOICE** Song of *C. a. altirostre* typically comprises a series of plaintive, undulating, two-toned whistles, *twee-too whit-tooh tuwhit-toooh two-whit*, lacking the rapid trills of Yellow-eyed; call is a piercing *tew-tew-tew-tew-tew...*, starting slowly but ending more rapidly and slightly falling in tone (Roberts 1992). **HABITS** Poorly known; similar to those of Yellow-eyed Babbler. Found in pairs or small parties, according to the season. Seeks insects in reedbeds and mostly keeps out of sight, but male climbs to the top of a tall reed to sing in the breeding season. **HABITAT** Reedbeds and extensive tracts of elephant grass. **BREEDING** Mainly June and July. Nest is a deep cup, built on a stout stem at the junction of leaf blades. **DISTRIBUTION AND STATUS** Sedentary resident in the Indus plains, Pakistan, C Nepal, Brahmaputra plains in N West Bengal, Assam, Nagaland and Bangladesh. Globally threatened. **PK:** rare and local along Indus R and its tributaries. **NP:** rare; recorded only at Chitwan, c. 250 m. **IN:** current status uncertain, and no recent published records. **BD:** ?former resident; no recent records, but could still occur very locally.

SPINY BABBLER *Turdoides nipalensis* Plate 133

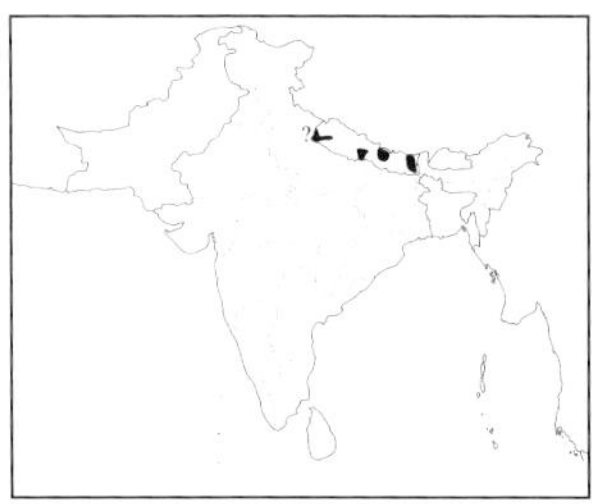

IDENTIFICATION 25 cm. Superficially resembles Striated Babbler (p.765), but is a bird of scrub-covered hillsides rather than lowland grassland. Best distinguished by downcurved black bill, white on face, dark brown upperparts which lack prominent streaking, white iris, and strong, fine black streaking on throat and breast. There is noticeable variation in patterning of head and coloration of underparts: some show largely white face and throat, and white centre of breast and belly with dark shaft streaking restricted to lower throat and breast; others have white restricted to lores and malar region, with buff lower throat and breast which are more extensively covered in dark shaft streaking. **VOICE** Song is a distinctive, harsh, ringing whistling: it starts with a few fine whistles, and then ascends the scale, *ter-ter-ter-ter-ter-ter*; also rendered as *right-here, right-here, right-here*. Call is usually a clear *el-el-el-el-el*, and alarm a low *churrrr*; female has a loud *wick-er-wick-er-wick-er*; pair will sometimes burst into a wild crescendo of screaming calls, reminiscent of Jungle Babbler (p.765) (Ali and Ripley 1987). **HABITS** Found in pairs from March to May; otherwise in small scattered groups. Very skulking and difficult to observe except early in the breeding season, when males often sing in the open, usually from the side of a bush. Seeks insects almost entirely on the ground among dense bushes, appearing only occasionally. If disturbed, slips into thick cover. **HABITAT** Dense scrub on hillsides; favours thicker areas, away from cultivation. **BREEDING** April–June. Nest is a deep cup, placed in a small bush or grass clump. **DISTRIBUTION AND STATUS NP:** endemic resident (may occur west into India, but there are no definite records); frequent; summers 1500–2135 m, winters 915–1830 m.

COMMON BABBLER *Turdoides caudatus* Plate 133

IDENTIFICATION 23 cm. A brownish-buff babbler with dark-streaked upperparts and cross-barred tail. Told from Striated Babbler (p.765) by unstreaked whitish throat and unstreaked centre to breast (with any streaking on underparts restricted to sides of breast). Additional features are slightly smaller size, colder whitish or greyish-buff coloration to underparts, yellowish legs and feet, and darker, more orange-brown iris. **VOICE** A series of pleasant, rapidly reiterated fluty whistles, and a louder, more drawn-out *pieuu-u-u pie-u-u pi-e-u-u*; also a higher-pitched *qwee qwe-e-e qwe-e-e* alarm. *T. c. huttoni*, which occurs in the Quetta region of Pakistan, has a distinctive, two-noted whistle, *qwee-yur-qweeyur* (Roberts 1992). **HABITS** A typical *Turdoides* babbler. Associates in small flocks of six to 20 birds, each flock maintaining its own territory all year. Flock-members keep up a constant conversation of whistles, trills and squeaks as they move about. Feeds chiefly on the ground, moving with springing hops; sometimes also hunts in bushes and in the lower branches of trees. Has a weak flight, with a few

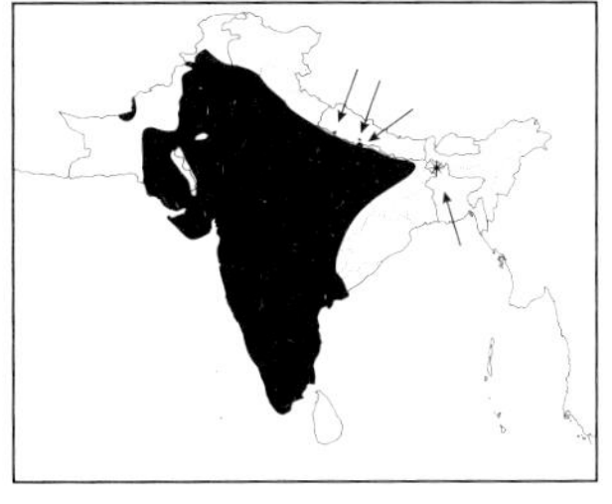

rapid wingbeats followed by a long glide, usually close to the ground, the birds usually flying after each other one at a time. **HABITAT** Thorn scrub, open country with scattered low bushes and grass clumps, and low arid hills with a sparse cover of thorn bushes and stunted trees; occasionally gardens and dry cultivation with open areas and bushes. **BREEDING** March–October, varying locally. Nest is a neat, thick-walled cup, usually placed low down in a thorn bush. **DISTRIBUTION AND STATUS** Sedentary resident. Throughout much of the subcontinent, except the northeast, Himalayas, W Pakistan, E India and Sri Lanka. **PK:** common; occurs almost throughout the cultivated plains, deserts and outer foothills. **NP:** very local, but fairly common in the W terai. **IN:** common and widespread; up to 900 m in the peninsula, sometimes to 2100 m in Himalayas. **BD:** former resident, possibly still occurs.

STRIATED BABBLER *Turdoides earlei* — Plate 133

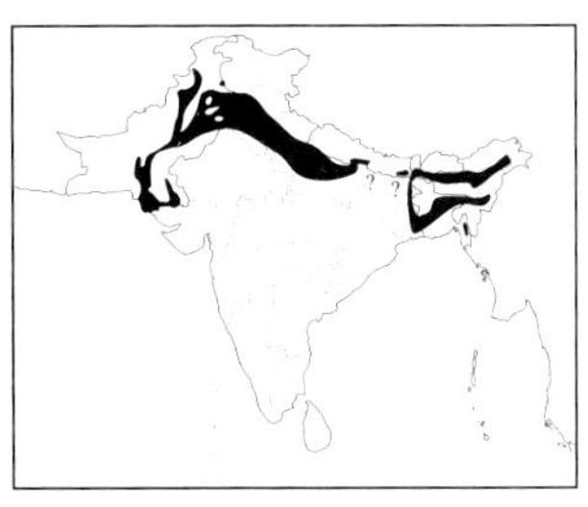

IDENTIFICATION 21 cm. A brown babbler with dark-streaked upperparts and cross-barred tail. Told from Common Babbler (p.764) by streaked or mottled appearance to fulvous throat and breast (which are unstreaked and white on Common). Additional features are slightly larger size, deeper buff breast and belly, blue-grey legs and feet (varying to olive-brown), and golden-yellow iris. In flight, the outer tail appears greyish-buff, which is not so apparent on Common. **VOICE** Song is a loudly repeated series of *tiew-tiew-tiew-tiew* calls, interspersed with *quip-quip-quip* calls from other birds of the group (Roberts 1992). **HABITS** Similar to those of Common Babbler. Keeps in noisy flocks, the individuals of which follow each other through reeds and tall grass. Clambers about vegetation when foraging. **HABITAT** Reedbeds, tall grass and rushes along rivers, irrigation canals and marshes; usually in wet habitats, where it replaces the Common Babbler. **BREEDING** March–October or later. Nest is a compact, thick-walled cup, placed in a small bush among tall grass. **DISTRIBUTION AND STATUS** Resident. Plains of the Indus, Ganges and Brahmaputra R systems. **PK:** common and widespread. **NP:** locally common in the east, uncommon elsewhere; below 305 m. **IN:** locally common. **BD:** locally common.

SLENDER-BILLED BABBLER *Turdoides longirostris* — Plate 133

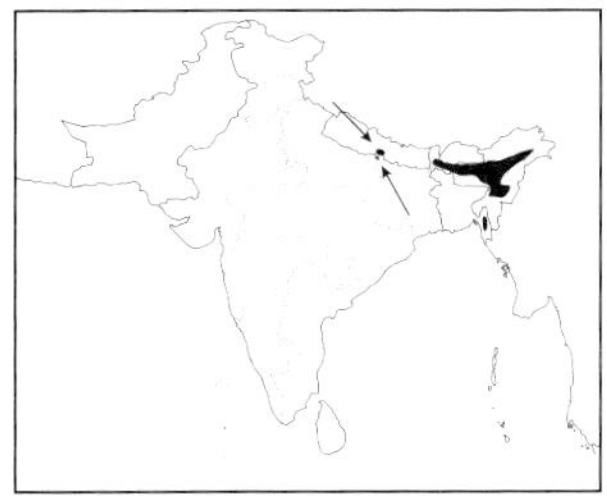

IDENTIFICATION 23 cm. A grass-dwelling, skulking, unstreaked, rufous babbler. Readily distinguished from other babblers by fine, downcurved blackish bill, whitish lores and buff ear-coverts, unstreaked dark rufous-brown upperparts, whitish throat, and unstreaked deep buff underparts. **VOICE** Has at least two song types: a shrill, rather high-pitched, quite strident series of notes, with short introduction, *yi, chiwiyu, chiwiyu chiwiyu chiwiyu chiwiyu chiwiyu...*; and a rather clear, high-pitched *wiii-wii-jiu-di*. Other vocalisations include even, fairly strident four- to six-noted *chiu-chiu-chiu-chiu-chiu* (possibly a song type), and discordant high-pitched *tiu-tiu-tiu, tiu-tiu-tiu-tiu-tiu-tiu...* (C. Robson). **HABITS** Found in noisy flocks outside the breeding season; also singly and in pairs. Skulks in tall thick grass, and usually remains hidden. Forages mainly for insects, both on the ground and in vegetation. **HABITAT** Tall grass and reeds, especially near water. **BREEDING** May and June. Nest is a neat cup, placed in a small bush among grass. **DISTRIBUTION AND STATUS** Resident. C Nepal, NW Bihar, NE India, and Bangladesh. **NP:** recorded only at Chitwan, where locally fairly common. **IN:** current status uncertain; very few recent records, and only from Assam. **BD:** rare? resident; no recent records.

LARGE GREY BABBLER *Turdoides malcolmi* — Plate 133

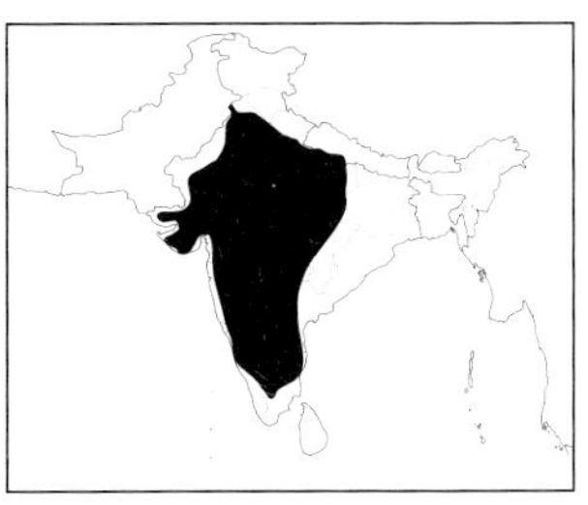

IDENTIFICATION 28 cm. A large, pale grey babbler with darker grey mottling on upperparts and prominent white sides to tail. Separated from Jungle Babbler (p.766) by larger size, greyish-pink throat and breast, lacking dark mottling, pale grey forehead (created by ashy shaft streaks), more prominent grey mottling on mantle, longer and more graduated tail with dull white outer feathers (especially prominent in flight), brownish-grey legs and feet, darker-coloured bill, dark grey lores, and pale yellow iris. **Juvenile** is smaller, and has paler grey upperparts which lack dark mottling. **VOICE** A monotonous, plaintive, drawling *kay-kay-kay-kay* (flatter and less squeaky than that of Jungle Babbler), and a noisy chattering when alarmed (Ali and Ripley 1987). **HABITS** Similar to those of Jungle Babbler, but less skulking. **HABITAT** Open dry, scrubby areas, cultivation, gardens and around villages; generally avoids wooded areas favoured by Jungle Babblers, and prefers less dry habitats than Common Babbler (p.764), but locally shares the same habitats as both species. **BREEDING** March–September, varying locally, but may breed in any month. Nest is an untidy cup, placed low down in scrub or 3–20 m above ground in trees. **DISTRIBUTION AND STATUS** Resident, endemic to the subcontinent. From Pakistan and Punjab and Gujarat, India, east to WC Nepal and E Uttar Pradesh and south through the peninsula to S Tamil Nadu. **PK:** rare and local. **NP:** local and frequent in the W terai. **IN:** common, but local, most frequent in the Deccan; plains and hills, up to 1200 m in the peninsula.

RUFOUS BABBLER *Turdoides subrufus* — Plate 133

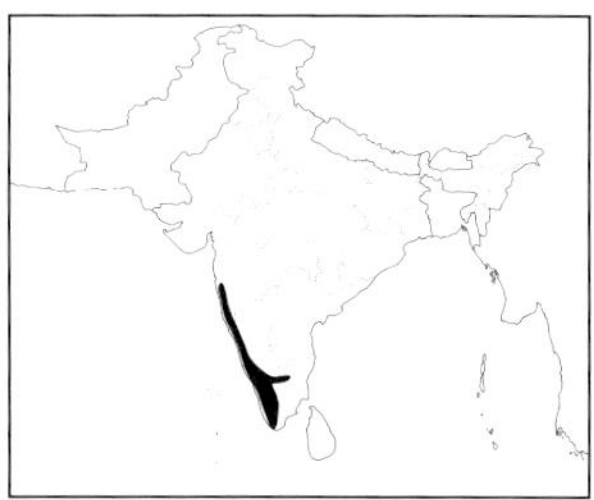

IDENTIFICATION 25 cm. An unstreaked, rufous babbler. Has grey forehead and forecrown, blackish lores, black upper mandible contrasting with yellow lower mandible, chestnut-brown upperparts, and uniform, unstreaked rufous underparts. Some (immatures?) lack grey forehead and forecrown. **Juvenile** has dark grey (rather than creamy-white) iris. Orange-billed Babbler (p.766) of Sri Lanka is similar, but Rufous has brighter rufous underparts, blackish lores and black upper mandible, and the two species do not overlap in range. **VOICE** High-pitched, shrill, sometimes frenzied squabbling or scolding squeaks (P. Holt). **HABITS** Keeps in small parties. Very secretive; usually creeps about out of sight in undergrowth. **HABITAT** Thick cover, edges of forest clearings and plantations in broadleaved evergreen and moist deciduous biotope; favours habitats intermixed with tall grass and bamboo. **BREEDING** February–November. Nest is a large deep cup, placed in the fork of a bush or small tree. **DISTRIBUTION AND STATUS IN:** resident, endemic to the southwest from C Maharashtra south throughout the Western Ghats and east to NC Tamil Nadu; rare in the north, fairly common in Kerala and W Tamil Nadu; from plains up to 1000 m.

JUNGLE BABBLER *Turdoides striatus* — Plate 133

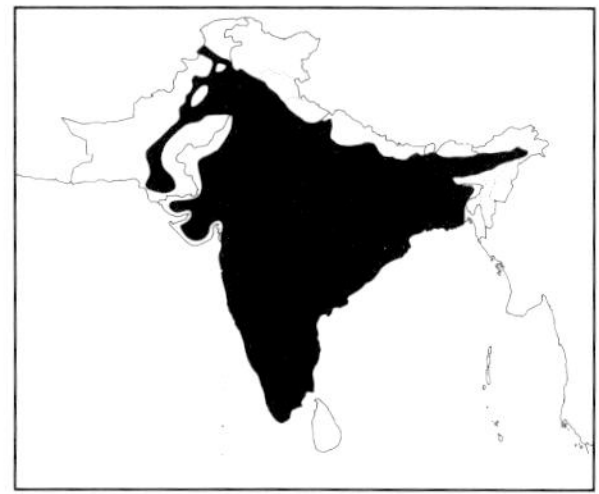

IDENTIFICATION 25 cm. A stocky, ash-grey to grey-brown babbler with stout yellowish bill. Throat and breast appear lightly mottled with grey, or streaked with grey or brown, and upperparts are lightly streaked. Distinguished from Large Grey Babbler (p.765) by smaller and stockier appearance, shorter, broader-looking tail lacking prominent white sides, mottling on throat and breast, and yellowish bill (although bill can be horn-brown in winter). From Yellow-billed Babbler (p.767) by lack of contrasting buffish-white crown, lack of buff streaking on mantle, and less heavily mottled throat and breast. **Racial variation** Six races are recognised in the subcontinent, varying in coloration and in prominence of mottling/streaking on underparts. *T. s. sindianus* and *T. s. striatus* of the N subcontinent have grey-brown upperparts and pale greyish underparts, with light grey mottling on throat and breast (*sindianus* being the paler and greyer of the two). *T. s. orientalis,* which occurs across most of the peninsula, has prominent, but diffuse, grey-brown streaking on throat and breast (can appear as buff streaking on grey-brown throat), and has more prominent greyish-buff streaking on upperparts; juvenile *orientalis* has more uniform grey-brown throat and breast. *T. s. somervillei* of Maharashtra is a very distinctive race, with prominent diffuse brown mottling or streaking on throat and breast, orange-buff coloration to lower belly, vent, rump and uppertail-coverts, orange-brown tail, dark brown primaries contrasting with paler grey-brown wing-coverts, and more uniform mantle (than *orientalis*). *T. s. malabaricus* appears intermediate between *somervillei* and *orientalis,* while *T. s. orissae* is similar to *striatus* but has brown mantle and tail and buff mottling on browner breast. **VOICE** A harsh *ke-ke-ke,* which frequently becomes a chorus of excited, discordant squeaking and chattering. **HABITS** Gregarious, noisy and excitable, birds calling to each other almost continuously and joining in a chorus of squeaking and chattering when alarmed. Feeds chiefly on the ground, hopping about and busily turning over leaves; flies up into trees and bushes immediately if disturbed. Unlike other *Turdoides* babblers, has a characteristic habit of fluffing out its rump feathers and drooping its wings and tail. **HABITAT** Deciduous forest, cultivation, gardens; also plantations along roads and canals in Pakistan. **BREEDING** January–October, varying locally, but may breed in any month. Nest is a cup, placed 1–9 m above ground in bushes and trees. **DISTRIBUTION AND STATUS** Resident, endemic to the subcontinent. Occurs throughout, except parts of the northwest, northeast and N Himalayas. **PK:** common throughout the Indus plains, ascending N foothills. **NP:** fairly common; below 1220 m (–1500 m). **IN:** common and widespread; plains and hills up to 1200 m, locally to 1800 m in Himalayas and to 1600 m in peninsular hills. **BT:** uncommon. **BD:** common.

ORANGE-BILLED BABBLER *Turdoides rufescens* — Plate 133

Ceylon Rufous Babbler (I,P)

IDENTIFICATION 25 cm. A distinctive babbler with uniform orange bill and legs, chestnut-brown mantle, back, wings and tail, cinnamon-rufous lores, ear-coverts, throat and breast, becoming browner on belly and flanks, and greyish crown and nape. **Juvenile** has greyish chin and browner underparts. **VOICE** A continuous chattering, squeaking and chirping. **HABITS** Moves in troops of ten to 15 or more birds, which maintain cohesion by

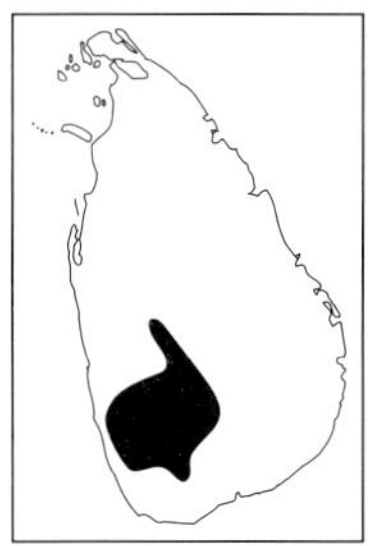

contact calls, the incessant chattering and squeaking indicating their presence a long distance away. They forage from about 2 m above ground to around the lower-canopy level. Often in mixed-species feeding flocks. **HABITAT** Confined to undisturbed forest in wet zone. **BREEDING** Little known. March–May. Nest is a cup, built in a low fork of a bushy tree. **DISTRIBUTION AND STATUS LK:** endemic resident; frequent in wet lowlands, very infrequent in adjacent hills.

YELLOW-BILLED BABBLER *Turdoides affinis* Plate 133

White-headed Babbler (I,P), Southern Common Babbler

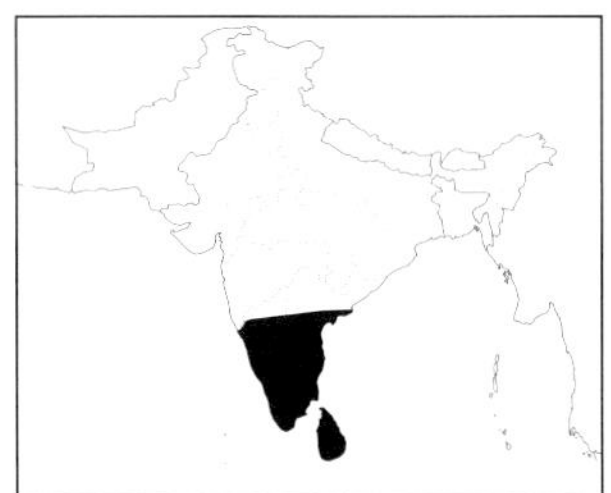

IDENTIFICATION 23 cm. In the Indian peninsula, differs from Jungle Babbler (p.766) in having creamy-white lores, forehead and crown (on some, sharply contrasting with grey-brown ear-coverts and throat), dark mottling on throat and breast (diffusely streaked on *orientalis* Jungle), pale grey panel on wings, paler, buff rump and base to tail contrasting more with darker brown terminal two-thirds of tail (which appear as a dark band across tail in flight), and also (in some birds) pale bluish-white iris. Among adult birds, paleness of head varies: on some, pale coloration extends onto nape and merges into brown of mantle; on others, crown contrasts noticeably with brown nape and mantle. Extent and darkness of mottling on throat and breast also vary. **Juvenile** has darker brownish-buff crown and nape which contrast less with brown mantle, lacks prominent buff streaking on mantle and back, and lacks darker mottling on throat and breast; there is no contrast between crown and ear-coverts as on adult birds. Juvenile more closely resembles Jungle Babbler, especially juvenile *orientalis* (with which it overlaps in range): best told by combination of paler crown and nape showing slight contrast with mantle, buff edges to primaries and secondaries which show as prominent panel on wing, and paler rump and base to tail which contrast with rest of tail. **Racial variation** *T. a. taprobanus* of Sri Lanka differs from the nominate race of the peninsula, described above, in having more uniform grey-brown upperparts and underparts, lacking whitish crown and nape and dark mottling on throat and breast (although see below): extremely similar to nominate race of Jungle Babbler (main difference being more striking greyish-white edges to remiges which show as prominent panel on wing), although that species does not occur in Sri Lanka. Variant *taprobanus* from a colony near Colombo have extensive black on throat and breast. **VOICE** Very high-pitched, intense, piercing piping calls (P. Holt). **HABITS** Similar to those of Jungle Babbler, and often with that species. Keeps in noisy excitable parties. **HABITAT** Low scrub, in drier and more open areas than Jungle Babbler. **BREEDING** January–November. Nest is a cup, placed 1–2 m above ground in bushes and trees. **DISTRIBUTION AND STATUS** Resident, endemic to peninsular India and Sri Lanka. From Goa east to NE Andhra Pradesh and south throughout the peninsula; Sri Lanka. **IN:** locally common; from the plains up to 300 m (–1000 m). **LK:** common throughout, except in the highest hills.

CHINESE BABAX *Babax lanceolatus* Plate 133

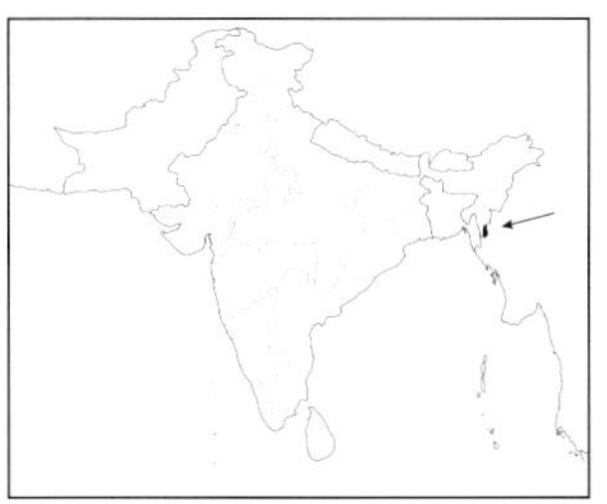

IDENTIFICATION 28 cm. A heavily streaked babbler with a downcurved bill. Although there is no known overlap in ranges, it can be told from Giant Babax (p.768) by smaller size, rufous-brown crown streaked with chestnut, bold chestnut-brown streaking on greyish mantle and back, buff (rather than grey) edges to primaries and tertials which form panelling on wings, brown tail, creamy-buff underparts with bold chestnut streaking on sides of breast, belly and flanks, broader, dark chestnut submoustachial stripe, and shorter and straighter bill. **Juvenile** is similar to adult, but streaking on upperparts is browner and more diffuse, wings and tail are browner, crown is more uniform rufous-brown, and underparts are less heavily streaked (with streaking confined mainly to breast); tail is shorter and squarer, and bill shorter and less decurved. **VOICE** Loud, full, plaintive whistle, given singly or in duet: *pu-i.pu-i.pu-i.pu-i.pu-i.pu-i...* or *tchu-wi.tchu-wi.tchu-wi...*, sometimes hurried to *pui-pui-pui-pui...* or *tchuwi-tchuwi-tchuwi-tchuwi...* etc. Contact calls consist of quiet chuntering *witchawitchawitcha-wit* and *whit* etc (C. Robson). **HABITS** Usually found in parties; rather shy. Can be seen on the ground, in bushes, and also in the tops of the highest trees, especially in mornings and evenings. **HABITAT** Open forest and hillsides covered with grass or bracken and brambles. **BREEDING** April–June. Nest is a cup, placed low down in bushes about 1 m above ground. **DISTRIBUTION AND STATUS IN:** resident in Mizoram above 1500 m; current status uncertain, and no recent published reports.

GIANT BABAX *Babax waddelli* Plate 133

IDENTIFICATION 31 cm. A heavily streaked, grey-coloured babbler with strong downcurved bill. Distinguished from Chinese Babax (p.763) (although there is no known overlap in ranges) by larger size, greyer head and mantle, boldly streaked with blackish-brown, grey (rather than buff) greater coverts and edges to tertials and primaries (forming grey panelling on wing), greyish (rather than buff) underparts with finer dark brown streaking which is strongest on lower breast and belly (rather than concentrated on breast sides and flanks as on Chinese), dark-spotted (and therefore less prominent) or non-existent submoustachial stripe, stronger and more downcurved bill, and blackish tail. **VOICE** A rapid series of quavering whistles, a pleasant thrush-like song, and a harsh grating call (Ali and Ripley 1987). **HABITS** Associates in small parties of five or six birds. Very secretive. Forages mainly on the ground; otherwise skulks in thick cover. **HABITAT** Dry scrub; favours *Hippophae rhamnoides*. **BREEDING** Unknown in the region. In Tibet, April–June; builds a large, untidy nest in a thorn bush, about 2 m above ground. **DISTRIBUTION AND STATUS IN:** extreme NE Sikkim; pre-

SILVER-EARED MESIA *Leiothrix argentauris* Plate 133

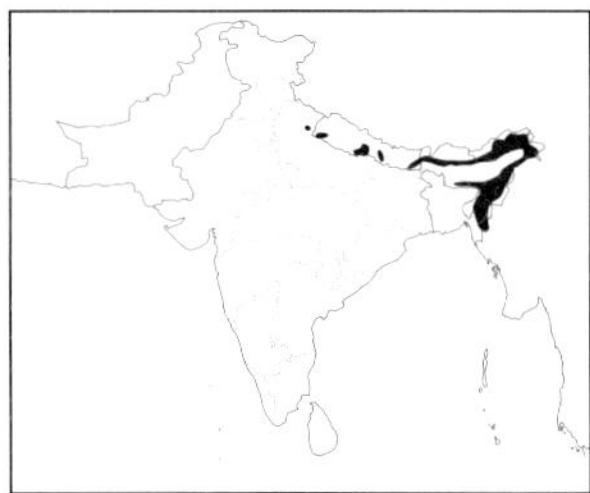

IDENTIFICATION 15 cm. A strikingly coloured babbler with orange-yellow forehead, black cap and submoustachial stripe, silver-grey ear patch, orange-yellow throat and breast, rusty-orange upper mantle merging into grey of rest of mantle and back, crimson and yellow panels on wing, and yellow sides to black tail. **Male** has crimson uppertail- and undertail-coverts. **Female** has olive-yellow uppertail-coverts and orange-buff undertail-coverts. **Juvenile** is similar to female, but has brown crown, and rusty-orange band across upper mantle is much less distinct. **VOICE** Cheerful, twangy, clearly spaced and descending whistled song, *che tchu-tchu che-rit*; calls include a flat piping *pe-pe-pe-pe-pe* and chattering notes (P. Holt). **HABITS** Keeps in pairs or in foraging parties of up to 30 birds, often mixed with other species. Constantly on the move. Seeks insects and fruit among foliage, usually in bushes, occasionally quite high in trees. **HABITAT** Evergreen biotope: bushes in forest, especially at edges and in more open areas, also bushes in clearings and in tea plantations. **BREEDING** April–August. Nest is a cup, placed within 2 m of the ground in a bush. **DISTRIBUTION AND STATUS** Resident, subject to small altitudinal movements. Himalayas from N Uttar Pradesh east to Arunachal Pradesh; NE India and Bangladesh. **NP:** local; frequent in the far east, rare farther west; mainly 365–1220 m (205–1830 m). **IN:** from the plains edge up to 2135 m in Himalayas, fairly common from Sikkim eastwards, less common farther west; common in NE hills, 300–1500 m. **BT:** common; 250–1600 m. **BD:** ?former resident; no recent records, but could still occur in hill tracts. **REFERENCES** Athreya *et al.* (1997).

RED-BILLED LEIOTHRIX *Leiothrix lutea* Plate 133

Pekin Robin

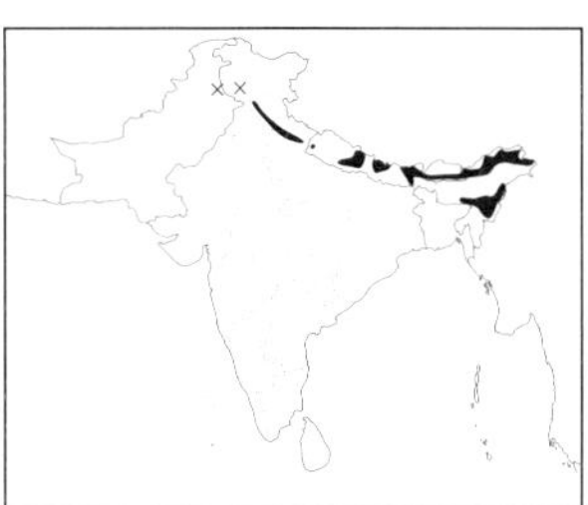

IDENTIFICATION 13 cm. A stocky babbler with domed head and forked tail. Readily identified by scarlet bill, creamy-white lores and eye-ring, yellowish-olive forehead and forecrown merging into greyish-olive of nape and mantle, dark moustachial stripe, bright yellow throat, becoming more orange on breast, black flight feathers edged with orange, yellow and crimson, forked black tail (partly overlaid by long, white-tipped chestnut-brown uppertail-coverts), and yellow undertail-coverts. **Female** has crimson of wing replaced by yellow, and paler throat and breast. **Juvenile** has buff throat and grey breast and flanks, and lacks yellow on underparts of adult. **Racial variation** *L. l. kumaiensis* of the W Himalayas differs from *L. l. calipyga* of the C and E Himalayas in having greyer upperparts. **VOICE** Rapid, chatty, thrush-like warbled song of up to 15 fluted notes. Harsh, scolding rattled calls like those of Rufous Sibia (P. Holt); also a clear, piping *pe-pe-pe-pa* and rapid *pu-pu-pu-pu-pu* (Ali and Ripley 1987). **HABITS** Found in pairs in the breeding season; otherwise in small groups of about six birds. A lively babbler; actively forages in undergrowth, sometimes moving up into trees or on to the ground. **HABITAT** Thick undergrowth in broadleaved forest and ravines, overgrown forest clearings, and bushes in tea plantations. **BREEDING** April–October. Nest is a bulky cup, placed low down in bushes. **DISTRIBUTION AND STATUS** Resident, subject to small altitudinal movements. Himalayas, mainly from NW Himachal Pradesh east to Arunachal Pradesh; NE India. **PK:** vagrant. **NP:** fairly common; chiefly 1220–2440 m (915–2745 m). **IN:** uncommon in W Himalayas, 1000–2400 m; locally common in east, breeds 1000–2700 m, winters 350–2100 m. **BT:** common; 620–3390 m. **REFERENCES** Athreya *et al.* (1997).

CUTIA *Cutia nipalensis* Plate 134

Nepal Cutia (F,I)

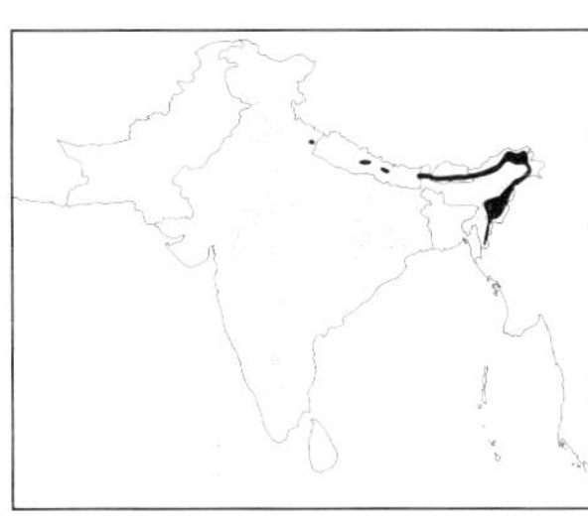

IDENTIFICATION 20 cm. A stocky, slow-moving nuthatch-like babbler. Both sexes are striking. **Male** has blue-grey crown and blue-black mask, white underparts with bold blackish barring on buff flanks, blue-grey panel on blue-black wings, rufous mantle, back and rump, black tail (just showing as dark tip beyond long rufous uppertail-coverts), and bright orange legs and feet. **Female** has duller grey crown, brown mask, and olive-brown mantle and back which are boldly spotted with black. **Juvenile** is similar to respective adult, but duller, and black barring is much reduced (restricted to lower flanks). **VOICE** A loud, ringing series of 10–15 sharp *toot* notes, falling off towards the end. Pair-members will converse with short, buzzy squawks and single or double toots as they travel (S. Connop), and also a querulous, upturned *hweet* and scolding *trt* (King *et al.* 1975). **HABITS** Found in pairs or small parties, sometimes with other babblers. Arboreal; usually keeps to the forest canopy. Forages among foliage and on mossy branches and trunks. **HABITAT** Dense, humid, mossy broadleaved evergreen and oak forest. **BREEDING** Nest not recorded. In Myanmar, young found in June. **DISTRIBUTION AND STATUS** Resident. Himalayas in N Uttar Pradesh, C Nepal and from E Nepal east to Arunachal Pradesh; NE India. Recorded 700–2500 m, probably breeds above 1500 m, favours 2100–2300-m zone. **NP:** scarce and very local. **IN:** local and uncommon. **BT:** frequent.

BLACK-HEADED SHRIKE BABBLER *Pteruthius rufiventer* Plate 134

Rufous-bellied Shrike Babbler (F,I)

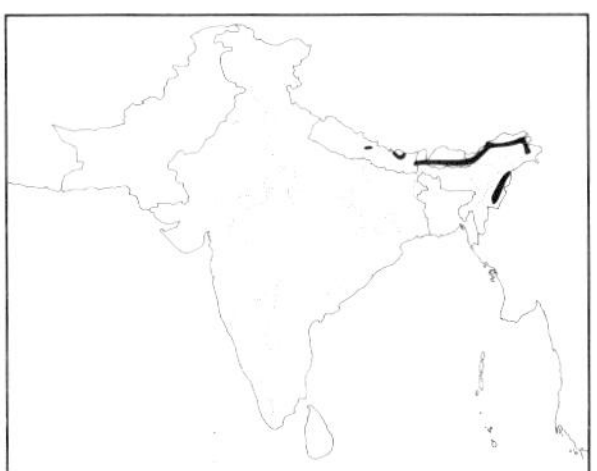

IDENTIFICATION 17 cm. **Male** told from male White-browed Shrike Babbler (below) by larger size and more elongated appearance, black head without white supercilium, rufous-brown mantle, back and rump, largely black wings (lacking all-rufous tertials), grey throat and breast, olive-yellow patch on sides of breast, pinkish-buff rest of underparts, and rufous tips to tertials and tail. **Female** from female White-browed by blue-black rear crown and nape, olive-green mantle (variably marked with black), rufous rump and uppertail-coverts, lack of rufous tertial patch, grey throat and breast, brownish-pink rest of underparts, and rufous tip to tail. **Juvenile male** superficially resembles adult male, but has greenish mantle and back (mixed with some rufous), green tips to coverts of otherwise black wings, and entirely greyish-white underparts. **VOICE** Song is a bright *pew-pew-peee-tu*, repeated without much variation (Fleming *et al.* 1984). **HABITS** Found in bushes near the ground and at other levels up to the forest canopy; often in small groups and with other babblers. Lethargic. **HABITAT** Dense, mossy, humid broadleaved evergreen forest. **BREEDING** Unknown. **DISTRIBUTION AND STATUS** Resident. Himalayas from WC Nepal east to Arunachal Pradesh; NE India. **NP:** scarce and local; mainly 2135–2500 m. **IN:** generally scarce, locally frequent; 1100–2200 m. **BT:** rare; 1960–2440 m. **REFERENCES** Allen *et al.* (1997), Kaul *et al.* (1995), Singh (1995).

WHITE-BROWED SHRIKE BABBLER *Pteruthius flaviscapis* Plate 134

Red-winged Shrike Babbler (F,I)

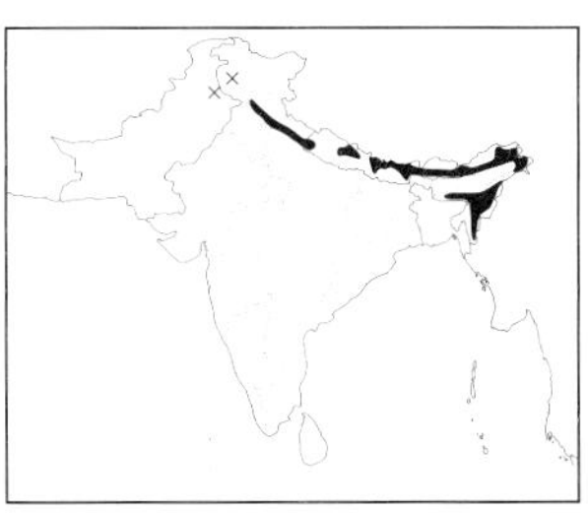

IDENTIFICATION 16 cm. **Male** distinguished from male Black-headed Shrike Babbler (above) by broad white supercilium behind eye, contrasting with blue-black crown, nape and ear-coverts, and by grey mantle, back and rump, rufous tertials (which form striking patch on wing) and white tips to primaries and secondaries, shorter black tail, and whitish underparts with pinkish flanks. **Female** from female Black-headed by uniform grey crown, nape and ear-coverts, unmarked brownish-olive mantle and rump, rufous tertial patch, uniform buffish-white underparts, yellowish tip to tail, and white tips to primaries. Female is possibly confusable with Green Shrike Babbler (p.770), but is considerably larger, has rufous tertials, and does not have a white greater-covert wing-bar. **Juvenile male** is similar to adult male, with black mask and white supercilium, but has brownish-grey crown and nape, brownish-olive upperparts (becoming greenish on uppertail-coverts), yellowish tips to black wing-coverts, and yellow tip to tail. **Juvenile female** is similar to adult female, but has crown and nape concolorous with mantle and has darker grey ear-coverts; best told from juvenile male by broad yellowish-green edges to greater coverts and secondaries, which form a prominent wing panel (as on adult female). **VOICE** Song is a rhythmic three-noted *yip-yip-yip* or *yip-dip-dip* with stress on the first or last note, and sometimes extended to six notes (Martens and Eck 1995); a short *pink*, and grating *churr* notes in alarm (Boonsong and Round 1991). **HABITS** Found in pairs in the breeding season; otherwise singly or in small parties, often mixed with other species. Arboreal; feeds mainly in the canopy. Rather slow-moving. **HABITAT** Mainly broadleaved forest; also in conifers. **BREEDING** April–June. Nest is a loosely made cup, placed very high up in trees. **DISTRIBUTION AND STATUS** Resident, subject to some altitudinal movements. Himalayas from N Pakistan, Kashmir and NW Himachal Pradesh east to Arunachal Pradesh; NE India. **PK:** rare and local, recently known only from Neelum valley; 900–2000 m. **NP:** fairly common; summers mainly 1800–2200 m, winters 1500–2135 m (down to 305 m). **IN:** frequent; breeds 1500–2700 m, winters 350–2000 m (down to 305 m). **BT:** fairly common; 600–2410 m.

GREEN SHRIKE BABBLER *Pteruthius xanthochlorus* Plate 134

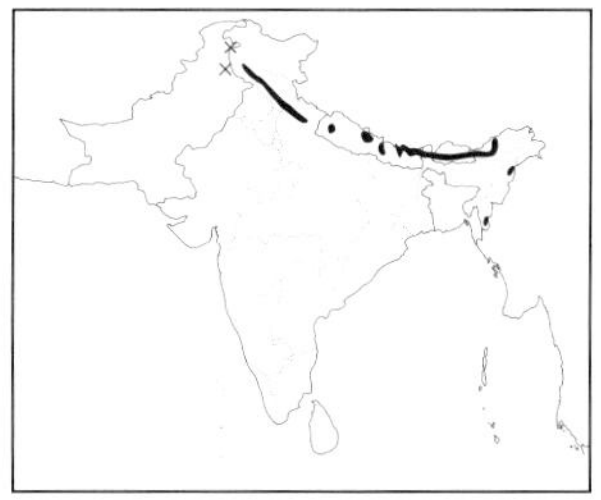

IDENTIFICATION 13 cm. A stocky, bull-headed shrike babbler. Has grey crown and ear-coverts, stubby blackish bill, olive-green mantle, wings and tail, narrow but prominent white or yellowish-white greater-covert wing-bar, blackish primary coverts showing as noticeable patch on wing, greyish-white throat and breast and pale yellow belly, and olive breast sides and flanks. Possibly confusable with female White-browed Shrike Babbler (p.769), but that species is considerably larger, has rufous tertial patch, and lacks wing-bar. Sexes are similar, but **female** has paler olive-grey crown which contrasts less with mantle. **Juvenile** has olive-brown crown and mantle, paler underparts, and yellowish tips to greater and median coverts forming double wing-bar. **Racial variation** *P. x. occidentalis* of the W Himalayas has blue-grey crown, which is dark grey on male of *P. x. xanthochlorus* of the E Himalayas (although female is much as male *xanthochlorus*). *P. x. hybridus* of hills south of the Brahmaputra R has a prominent white eye-ring. **VOICE** Song is a rapid, tit-like *whee-tee whee-tee whee-tee*; also utters a grating *chaa* (Fleming *et al.* 1984). **HABITS** Forages unobtrusively in trees, usually in pairs or in mixed roving parties. Rather sluggish compared with the other species it accompanies. **HABITAT** Broadleaved, coniferous and mixed broadleaved–coniferous forest. **BREEDING** April–August, varying locally. Builds a cup-shaped nest in a bush or tree, 0.5–8 m above ground. **DISTRIBUTION AND STATUS** Resident. Himalayas from N Pakistan east to C Arunachal Pradesh; NE India. Subject to some altitudinal movements: in W Himalayas, breeds 1800–3000 m, winters from 1200 m up to at least 2400 m; in C and E Himalayas, recorded 2100–3600 m (2135–3050 m all year in Nepal). **PK:** rare and very local. **NP:** frequent. **IN:** uncommon in the west, locally frequent in the east. **BT:** frequent.

BLACK-EARED SHRIKE BABBLER *Pteruthius melanotis* Plate 134

Chestnut-throated Shrike Babbler (F,I)

IDENTIFICATION 11 cm. A small, stocky shrike babbler. **Male** is striking and colourful, with yellow forehead, green crown and mantle, chestnut throat and breast, black rear edge to yellow ear-coverts, black-bordered white eye-ring and black stripe through eye, grey supercilium and nape, black wing-coverts with double white wing-bar and blue-grey wing panel, and yellow belly and flanks. **Female** is duller, with chestnut reduced to malar region, and has broad orange-buff (rather than white) tips to greater and median coverts; some birds have yellowish-green edges to remiges and therefore lack blue-grey panel on wing. **Juvenile** is similar to female, but has olive-brown upperparts (lacking grey patch on nape) and lacks chestnut on underparts, while some (younger?) lack bright yellow on underparts. Confusable really only with Chestnut-fronted Shrike Babbler (p.770); see that species for main differences. **VOICE** Song is a bright *tew wee, tew we, tew-wee*; also gives a *dz-wee-tik* and a rasping alarm note (Fleming *et al.* 1984). **HABITS** Outside the breeding season, found in small groups, usually in mixed hunting parties. Arboreal, and rather lethargic. **HABITAT** Humid broadleaved evergreen forest. **DISTRIBUTION AND STATUS** Resident. Himalayas from WC Nepal east to Arunachal Pradesh; NE India and Bangladesh. Subject to altitudinal movements: breeds 1800–2700 m (–2440 m in Nepal), winters 450–2200 m (down to 305 m). **NP:** local and frequent. **IN:** locally frequent. **BT:** frequent. **BD:** ?former resident; no recent records, but could still occur in hill tracts. **REFERENCES** Athreya *et al.* (1997), Kaul *et al.* (1995).

CHESTNUT-FRONTED SHRIKE BABBLER *Pteruthius aenobarbus* Plate 134

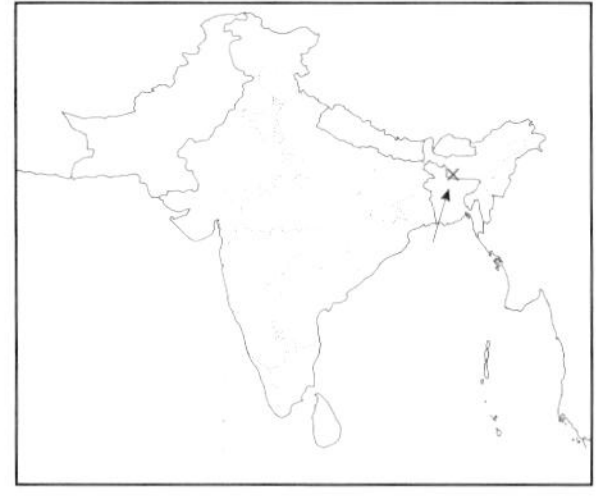

IDENTIFICATION 11 cm. A small, stocky shrike babbler which is similar in appearance to Black-eared (above). Main differences from that species are chestnut forehead and yellow forecrown, darker chestnut throat and upper breast, lack of black rear edge to ear-coverts and lack of grey nape; and has silvery-white (rather than blue-grey) edges to primaries, which form a panel on wing. **Female** of the race *aenobarbulus* (the race recorded in the region) has never been described; female *P. a. intermedius* of Myanmar differs from female Black-eared in dull chestnut forehead, lack of black rear edge to ear-coverts, lack of grey hindcollar and lack of chestnut in malar region, and has whitish (rather than yellow) underparts (although juvenile Black-eared also has whitish underparts). **VOICE** Song is a monotonously repeated *chip-chip-chip-chip...*; *wheet-wheet-wheet..wheet-wheet-wheet-wheet...*; *whit-whit-whit-whit....whit-whit-whit-whit-whit-whit-whit...*; *wchip-wchip-wchip-wchip...*, etc. Calls with short, buzzy, slightly nasal *jer-jer-jer, jwi-jwi-jwi* etc (C. Robson). **HABITS** Similar to those of Black-eared Shrike Babbler. **HABITAT** Fairly open forest and edges of broadleaved evergreen forest. **BREEDING** Probably April and May. Nest unknown in the region. **DISTRIBUTION AND STATUS IN:** in the subcontinent, known only from a specimen collected in the Garo Hills, Meghalaya.

WHITE-HOODED BABBLER *Gampsorhynchus rufulus* Plate 134

White-headed Shrike Babbler (F,I)

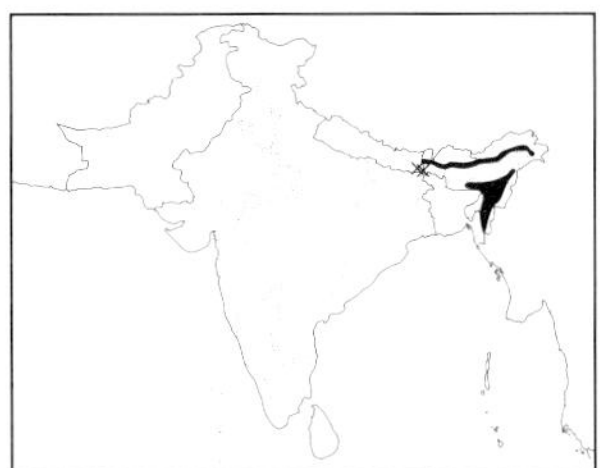

IDENTIFICATION 23 cm. A bull-headed, long-tailed babbler. **Adult** has white head and underparts (with buff wash on flanks), contrasting with rufous-brown upperparts and tail; tail is tipped with pale buff. Iris and bill are strikingly pale. Has variable amount of white on wing-coverts, but this is usually obscured in field by feathers of mantle. **Juvenile** has rufous-orange crown and ear-coverts, rufous-brown upperparts, and whitish throat, becoming buff on underparts; possibly confusable with Greater Rufous-headed Parrotbill (p.783), but has much thinner bill, and ear-coverts do not contrast so strongly with white throat. **VOICE** The usual call is a harsh, hard, stuttering rattle or cackle, e.g. *rrrrtchu-rrrrtchu-rrrrtchu*, *rrrrut-rrrrut* or *rrrt-rrrt-rrrt*; contact calls are soft and very quiet *wit*, *wet* and *wyee* notes (C. Robson). **HABITS** Gregarious, usually in flocks of ten to 15 birds, often with other species. Forages in thick undergrowth and bamboo thickets. **HABITAT** Bamboo jungle and undergrowth in moist broadleaved evergreen forest; also secondary growth. **BREEDING** April–August. Nest is a shallow saucer, placed 2 m above ground in a bush. **DISTRIBUTION AND STATUS** Resident. Himalayas from far E Nepal east to Arunachal Pradesh; NE India and Bangladesh. Recorded from the plains edge up to 1200 m. **NP:** very rare, possibly resident. **IN:** locally frequent. **BT:** uncommon. **BD:** ?former resident; no recent records, but could still occur in hill tracts.

RUSTY-FRONTED BARWING *Actinodura egertoni* Plate 134

Spectacled Barwing (F,I)

IDENTIFICATION 23 cm. Separated from other barwings by combination of rufous forehead, lores and chin, stout yellowish bill, uniform grey crown and nape contrasting with mantle and without pale streaking, rufous greater coverts lacking grey tips (which form fine wing-bar on other species), greyish-buff (rather than rufous-brown) barring on primaries and secondaries, rufous-brown and more diffusely barred tail (lacking blackish terminal band), and slimmer and longer-tailed appearance. **Juvenile** has crown and nape rufous-brown and concolorous with mantle, making rufous forehead less prominent. **Racial variation** Four races are described from the subcontinent, differing slightly in coloration of mantle (olive-brown to rufous-brown) and in greyness of crown and ear-coverts. **VOICE** A three-noted whistle, *ti-ti-ta*, the first note accentuated, the last lower, and reminiscent of Great Tit (p.683); also a feeble *cheep* when feeding (Ali and Ripley 1987). **HABITS** Found in pairs or small parties, usually not with other species. Hunts by clambering about among bushes and undergrowth; sometimes moves up into the canopy. **HABITAT** Dense understorey in broadleaved evergreen forest and thick secondary growth. **BREEDING** April–July. Nest is a cup, placed in bushes or trees 1-6 m above ground. **DISTRIBUTION AND STATUS** Resident. Himalayas from WC Nepal east to Arunachal Pradesh; NE India. In Himalayas, breeds 1200–2400 m; winters from the duars up to 1800 m; in NE hills, breeds 800–2200 m. **NP:** rare and local; 1785–2400 m. **IN:** locally fairly common. **BT:** fairly common. **BD:** one 19th-century specimen.

HOARY-THROATED BARWING *Actinodura nipalensis* Plate 134

Hoary Barwing (F,I)

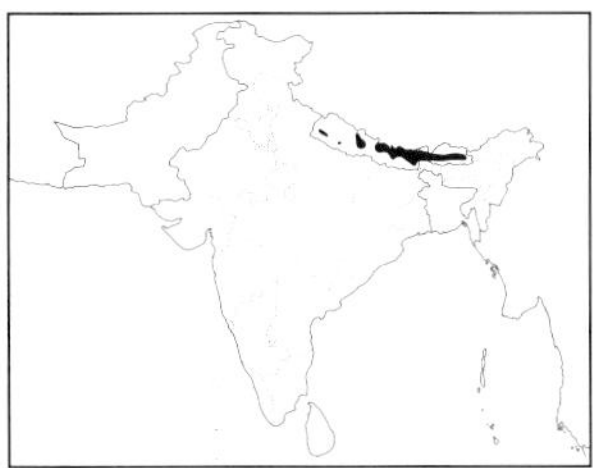

IDENTIFICATION 20 cm. Distinguished from other barwings by combination of unstreaked greyish throat and breast, prominent buffish-white shaft streaking on dark brown crown and nape, grey ear-coverts contrasting with dark moustachial stripe, and diffuse white streaking on olive-brown mantle and scapulars. In addition, has shorter, more strongly barred tail, and lacks rufous front to head of Rusty-fronted (above). Very similar to *daflaensis* race of Streak-throated Barwing (p.772), although there is no known overlap in ranges; subtle differences are buff streaking on crown and unstreaked throat and breast. **VOICE** Two types of territorial song: the first starts with one or two whistling notes, followed by a soft trill, *liou liou pre re re re..*, with whistles sometimes added to the end of the verse; the second is a series of long whistling notes (Martens and Eck 1995). Has a jay-like alarm note (Fleming *et al.* 1984). **HABITS** Found in pairs or in small parties with other babblers. Usually frequents the upper half of forest trees. Forages among ferns and mosses growing on trees, often clinging to the trunk or hanging upside-down from branches. **HABITAT** Mainly mossy oak forest, also mixed broadleaved–coniferous forest. **BREEDING** Little known. Nest is a cup, placed up to 10 m above ground. **DISTRIBUTION AND STATUS** Resident, endemic to the subcontinent. Himalayas from W Nepal east to E Bhutan. Subject to altitudinal movements: 1500–3500 m, mainly 1980–3000 m, and up to 2750 m in winter. **NP:** fairly common. **IN:** fairly common in West Bengal, rare farther east. **BT:** fairly common.

STREAK-THROATED BARWING *Actinodura waldeni* — Plate 134

Austen's Barwing (I)

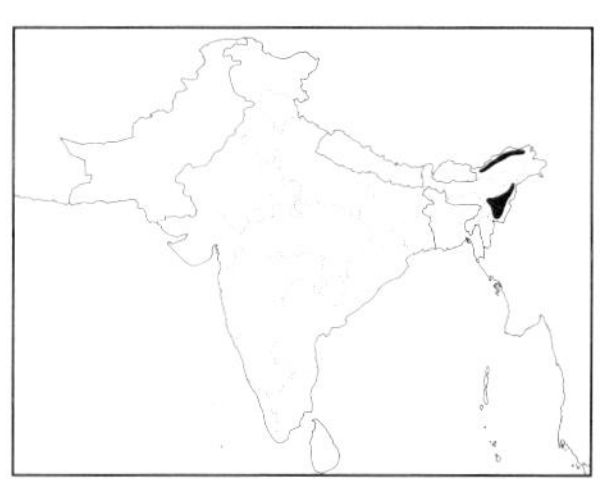

IDENTIFICATION 20 cm. Two races occur in the subcontinent which are very different in appearance, and confusion is therefore possible with both Hoary-throated and Rusty-fronted Barwings (p.771). **Racial variation** *A. w. daflaensis* of the E Himalayas has greyish-white throat, breast and belly diffusely streaked with brownish-grey, and is similar in appearance to Hoary-throated Barwing (although there is no known overlap in ranges): best told by streaking on underparts, lack of bold shaft streaking on crown and nape (crown feathers have narrow pale fringes, although these are not likely to be striking in field), absence of pronounced moustachial stripe, and uniform rufous-brown mantle. *A. w. waldeni* of the hills south of the Brahmaputra R has tawny-brown throat, breast and belly with fulvous streaks, and coloration of underparts could lead to confusion with Rusty-fronted Barwing: best told by lack of rusty 'front' to head, and by brown crown and nape faintly streaked with buff, streaked underparts, and blackish terminal band to shorter tail. **VOICE** Nominate subspecies has two song types: 1) loud, strident, slightly wavering and rising phrase beginning with a slight rattle, *tchrrrr-jo-jwiee* or *dddrrt-juee-iwee*, sometimes shortened to *jorr-dwidu*; 2) an undulating phrase ending with an even-pitched tremolo, *dwu-dwi-jwijwijwi* or *jo-dwi-jwijwijwijwijwi*. Contact calls are rather nasal, grumbling *grrr-ut..grrr-ut...* and *grr-grr-grr-grr-grr...* etc, intermixed with higher *wi-wee* or *wi-wee-wee-wee-wee-wee*.... Song and calls of *A. w. daflaensis* are unknown (C. Robson). **HABITS** Similar to those of Hoary-throated Barwing. Usually found at the middle height of trees, sometimes in low bushes. **HABITAT** Mossy broadleaved evergreen and mixed forest. **BREEDING** Details not recorded. **DISTRIBUTION AND STATUS IN:** locally fairly common resident in NE hills (Arunachal Pradesh, Assam, Manipur, Nagaland), subject to altitudinal movements; summers 2400–3300 m, winters down to 1500 m (to 500 m).

BLUE-WINGED MINLA *Minla cyanouroptera* — Plate 134

Blue-winged Siva (I)

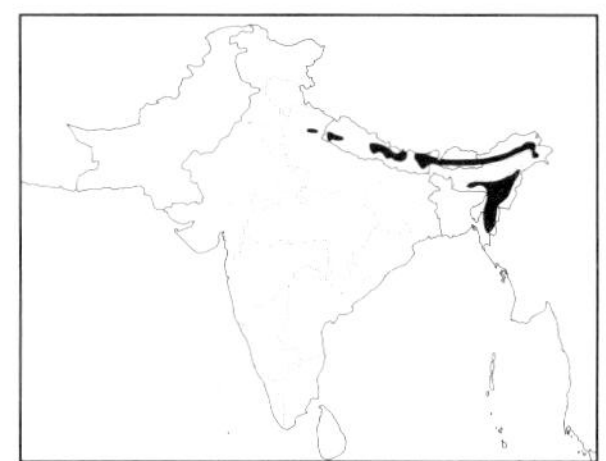

IDENTIFICATION 15 cm. A distinctive, slim babbler with long square-ended tail. Although colourful, can appear rather drab at long range. Has pale violet-grey crown and nape, with violet-blue streaking on forehead and sides of crown, white supercilium and buffish-white cheeks (resulting in 'pale-faced' appearance), fulvous-brown mantle, blue wings with pale violet-grey panel formed by fringes to tertials and secondaries, blue sides to tail, and pale vinous-grey underparts. White underside to dark-bordered tail very noticeable when viewed from below. **Juvenile** has duller, brownish-grey crown and nape, and buffish underparts. **VOICE** A clear, whistled *pi-piu* with emphasis on first note, and a loud *swit* (Boonsong and Round 1991). **HABITS** Usually keeps in small parties associated with other species, often babblers, warblers and flycatchers. Typically feeds in bushes, and sometimes at middle height of trees. **HABITAT** Mainly bushes in broadleaved forest or in mixed broadleaved–coniferous forest; also well-wooded country. **BREEDING** May and June. Nest is a cup, well concealed in bushes within 2 m of the ground, often on a stream bank. **DISTRIBUTION AND STATUS** Resident. Himalayas from N Uttar Pradesh east to Arunachal Pradesh; NE India and Bangladesh. Subject to altitudinal movements: probably summers mainly 1500–2500 m (–3010 m), winters chiefly 1000–2200 m, down to 245 m in the east. **NP:** fairly common. **IN:** locally fairly common. **BT:** common. **BD:** ?former resident; no recent records, but could still occur in hill tracts.

CHESTNUT-TAILED MINLA *Minla strigula* — Plate 134

Bar-throated Siva (I), Bar-throated Minla (F)

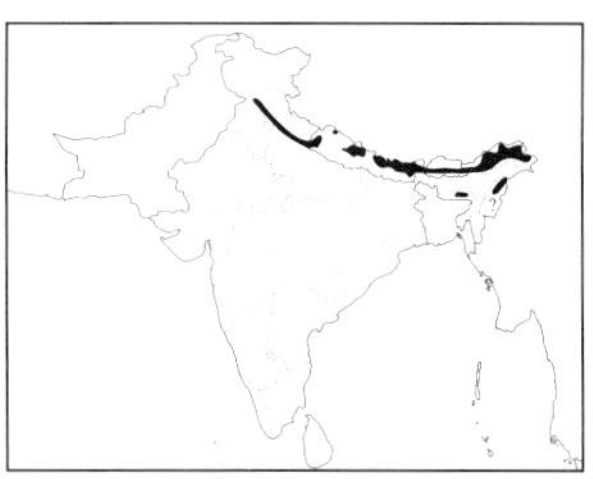

IDENTIFICATION 14 cm. A strikingly patterned minla with dull orange crown and nape, orange-yellow panel on wing and yellow sides to uppertail, grey ear-coverts with black moustachial stripe, black-and-white barring on throat, yellow underparts, black primary-covert patch, grey fringes to black-centred tertials, and olive-brown mantle and rump. Shows yellow at sides and tip of undertail when viewed from below. **Juvenile** has less distinct throat barring and duller crown and nape. **VOICE** A slurred whistle, *jo-ey, jo-ey dii*, the last note highest; also a ringing, metallic *chew* (Boonsong and Round 1991). **HABITS** Gregarious; keeps in small noisy flocks, usually with other species, and continually on the move. Frequents bushes and the lower canopy. **HABITAT** Broadleaved oak–rhododendron and mixed broadleaved–coniferous forest. **BREEDING** April–July. Nest is a cup, placed within 3 m of the ground in bushes. **DISTRIBUTION AND STATUS** Resident. Himalayas from NW Himachal Pradesh east to Arunachal Pradesh; NE India. Subject to altitudinal movements: in the west, summers 2100–3600 m, winters 1300–2250 m; in the east, summers from 1800 m (2440 m in Nepal) to 3750 m, winters 800–3700 m (1400–2745 m in Nepal). **NP:** common. **IN:** fairly common in the west, common in the east. **BT:** common.

RED-TAILED MINLA *Minla ignotincta* Plate 134

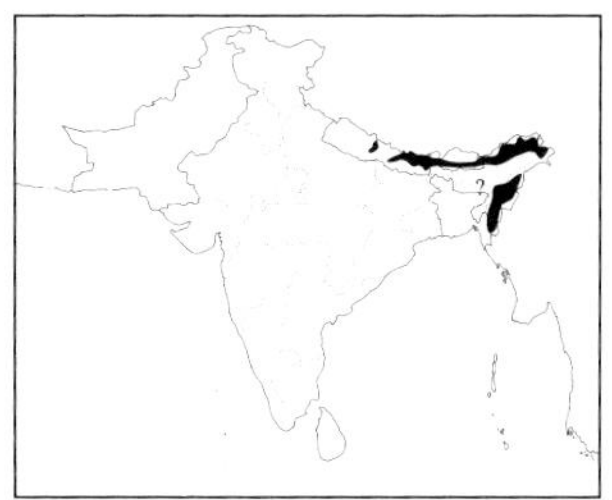

IDENTIFICATION 14 cm. A striking, slim, long-tailed babbler with black crown and ear-coverts and contrasting broad white supercilium, prominent white tips to black tertials, and yellowish underparts. Visible from below, the tips and sides to undertail are red on male and pink on female. **Male** differs from **female** in having deep maroon-brown (rather than olive-brown) mantle and back, scarlet (rather than orange-yellow) edges to secondaries forming striking panel on wing, stronger yellow wash to breast and belly, and brighter red sides and tip to tail. **VOICE** A variety of calls has been described, including a high-pitched *wi-wi-wi*, a loud, repeated *chik*, a high-pitched *tsi*, a high-pitched *chitititit*, and a tit-like *whi-whi-te-sik-sik*. Song is a loud ringing *twiyi-twiyuwi...* (Ali and Ripley 1987). **HABITS** Found in roving parties with other species. Forages in trees; often searches mossy trunks and branches like a treecreeper, or clings upside-down to small twigs like a tit, but is more slow-moving. **HABITAT** Moist, dense forest, broadleaved or mixed broadleaved–coniferous. **BREEDING** Little known. May and June. Nest is a cup, placed in a bushy tree. **DISTRIBUTION AND STATUS** Resident. Himalayas from WC Nepal east to Arunachal Pradesh; NE India and Bangladesh. Subject to altitudinal movements: breeds 1800–3400 m (–3770 m in Bhutan), winters from foothills to 2400 m, mainly below 1800 m. **NP:** fairly common in the far east, frequent farther west. **IN:** locally fairly common. **BT:** common. **BD:** ?former resident; no recent records, but could still occur in hill tracts.

GOLDEN-BREASTED FULVETTA *Alcippe chrysotis* Plate 135

Golden-breasted Tit Babbler (F,I)

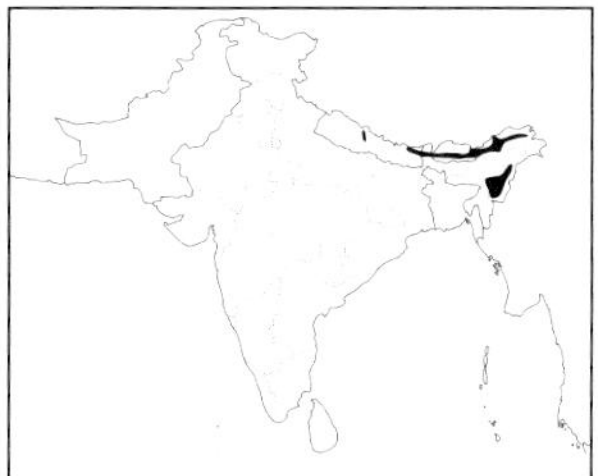

IDENTIFICATION 11 cm. A colourful, blue-grey and yellow fulvetta. Has blackish crown and blue-grey mantle (with olive lores), with silver-grey ear-coverts, dark grey throat and golden-yellow underparts, and bold patterning of orange-yellow, yellow, black and white on wings, and golden-yellow basal two-thirds to dark tail. **Racial variation** *A. c. albilineata* of the hills south of the Brahmaputra R has a white rear crown-stripe, which is lacking in the nominate race. **VOICE** Poorly known. A thin, high-pitched series of five notes, slightly descending (S. Connop); alarm call is a high-pitched buzz (Fleming *et al.* 1984). **HABITS** In non-breeding season, found in flocks of up to 50 birds, often in company with parrotbills and White-browed Fulvettas (p.774). Tame and active. Often hangs upside-down like a tit when foraging. Keeps at low and medium heights in bamboo or undergrowth. **HABITAT** Bamboo stands, understorey of bamboo in broadleaved temperate and subalpine forest. **BREEDING** May and June. Nest is egg-shaped, placed about 1 m above ground in a bamboo clump. **DISTRIBUTION AND STATUS** Resident. Himalayas in WC Nepal and from E Nepal east to Arunachal Pradesh; NE India. Subject to some altitudinal movements: in Himalayas, summers 2400–3050 m, winters down to 1800 m; in NE hills, 1800–2700 m. **NP:** very local; 2435–3050 m. **IN:** local and fairly common. **BT:** uncommon; 1800–2750 m.

YELLOW-THROATED FULVETTA *Alcippe cinerea* Plate 135

Dusky-green Tit Babbler (F,I)

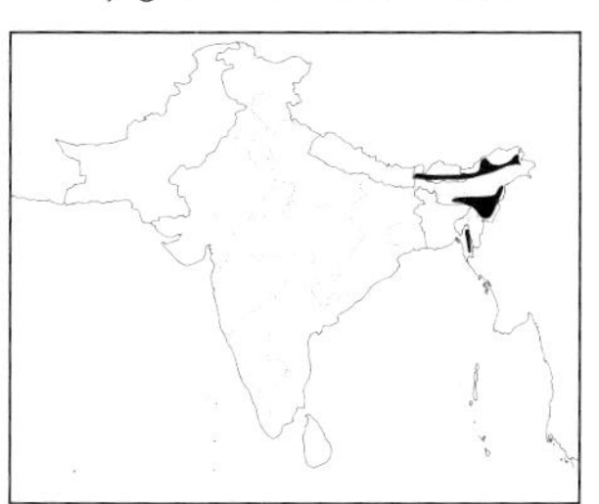

IDENTIFICATION 10 cm. Rather *Phylloscopus*-like in plumage, with prominent yellow supercilium contrasting with long, broad, black lateral crown-stripe, grey crown mottled with black, yellowish ear-coverts heavily mottled with grey, dark olive-green upperparts and brown wings, and yellow throat and undertail-coverts, with yellowish-olive breast and belly, becoming darker greyish-olive on breast sides and flanks. **VOICE** High-pitched, pulsed trill, *tsi-tsi-tsi-tsi-tsi-tsi*, often descending and trailing off; also a coarse rattle, *chrt-trrt* (P. Holt). **HABITS** Usually in mixed feeding parties with other small babblers. Forages low down in forest undergrowth; confiding and active, constantly darting about the vegetation. Bears a resemblance to a *Phylloscopus* warbler in both general appearance and behaviour. **HABITAT** Undergrowth in dense subtropical broadleaved evergreen forest. **BREEDING** April–July. Nest is a deep cup, sometimes domed or semi-domed, placed on the ground in bamboo clumps or between boulders. **DISTRIBUTION AND STATUS** Resident. Himalayas from Nepal? and Sikkim east to Arunachal Pradesh; NE India and Bangladesh. Recorded 500–2500 m, mainly above 1000 m. **NP:** possibly recorded in 19th century, but the specimen may have originated in India. **IN:** locally frequent. **BT:** frequent. **BD:** ?former resident; no recent records, but could still occur in hill tracts.

RUFOUS-WINGED FULVETTA *Alcippe castaneceps* Plate 135

Chestnut-headed Tit Babbler (F,I)

IDENTIFICATION 10 cm. Distinguished from other fulvettas by combination of dark chestnut crown and nape (streaked with buffish-white) contrasting with olive-brown mantle, white supercilium contrasting with black

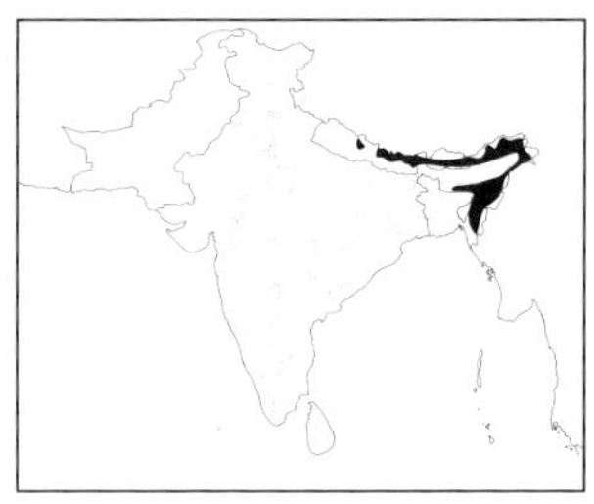

eye-stripe, short black moustachial stripe, black band across wing (formed by black greater and primary coverts) and rufous wing panel (formed by edges of primaries), and unmarked whitish throat and underparts, with buff flanks. **VOICE** Usual call is a wheezy, descending trill, *tsi-tsi-tsi-tsi-tsirr*, also a quiet *chip*; song is a rich, undulating and descending warble, *tju-tji-tju-tji-tju-tji-tju* (Thailand) (J. Scharringa). **HABITS** Keeps in flocks of up to 30 birds, often in mixed feeding parties with other small babblers, tits and warblers. Constantly on the move. Hunts at low and medium heights in forest, sometimes among foliage of bushes and undergrowth; also climbs up mossy trunks like a nuthatch. Feeds on insects and tree sap. **HABITAT** Undergrowth in moist broadleaved subtropical and temperate forest and in overgrown forest clearings. **BREEDING** April–July. Nest is domed or a deep cup, placed among moss against a tree trunk, among creepers or on a sloping bank. **DISTRIBUTION AND STATUS** Resident, subject to some altitudinal movements. Himalayas from WC Nepal east to Arunachal Pradesh; NE India and Bangladesh. **NP:** common; summers 1825–2745 m (–3505 m), winters from 1525 m up to at least 2745 m. **IN:** locally fairly common; breeds 1500–3000 m, winters down to foothills. **BT:** common; 500–3200 m. **BD:** ?former resident; no recent records, but could still occur in hill tracts.

WHITE-BROWED FULVETTA *Alcippe vinipectus* — Plate 135

White-browed Tit Babbler (F,I)

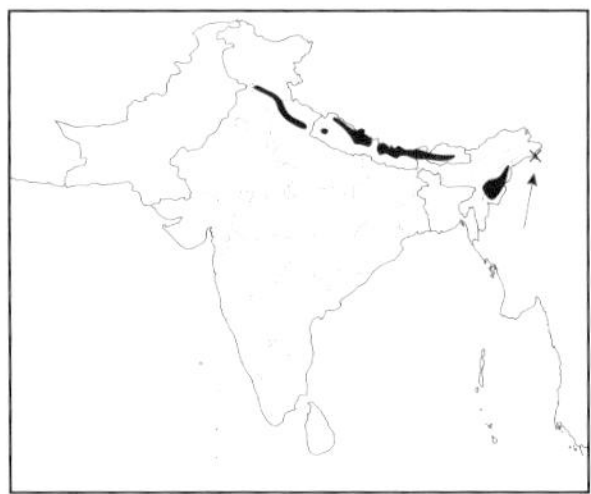

IDENTIFICATION 11 cm. A variable fulvetta with broad white supercilium, bordered by a dark lateral crown-stripe. Distinguished from Rufous-winged Fulvetta (p.773) by grey-brown to dark chestnut-brown crown (lacking prominent buff streaking), grey-brown to blackish-brown ear-coverts, rufous rather than black greater coverts, and black and silvery-grey panels on wing. From Streak-throated and Brown-throated Fulvettas (below and p.775) by prominent white supercilium (see those species for further differences). **Racial variation** Four races are described from the subcontinent. The two W races have a white throat: *A. v. kangrae* of the W Himalayas has a chestnut-brown crown and darker ear-coverts compared with *A. v. vinipectus* of Nepal, which has duller crown concolorous with ear-coverts. The two E races have a streaked throat, with *A. v. chumbiensis* of the E Himalayas having grey-brown crown and mantle, dark-brown lateral crown-stripes and brown streaking on throat, while *A. v. austeni* of the hills south of the Brahmaputra has brown crown and mantle, reddish-brown lateral crown-stripes and reddish-brown streaking on throat. **VOICE** Song is a rapid *chit-it-it-it-or-key* and a *tew-tu-tu-wheeee*; alarm is a *vek vek vek* and a faint *czzzzzz* (Fleming *et al.* 1984). **HABITS** When not breeding, keeps in flocks, sometimes with other babblers and tits. Inquisitive and tame. Forages restlessly low down in bushes and undergrowth. Tit-like in its actions, but is slower-moving. **HABITAT** Subalpine shrubberies of rhododendron, birch, willow and juniper; bushes and bamboo in temperate and subalpine broadleaved and coniferous forest and at forest edges. **BREEDING** April–July. Nest is a deep cup, placed within 1 m of ground in low bushes or in a bamboo clump in forest. **DISTRIBUTION AND STATUS** Resident. Himalayas from NW Himachal Pradesh east to Arunachal Pradesh; NE India. Subject to some altitudinal movements: in W Himalayas, summers from 2700 m to over 3300 m, winters from 1500 m to at least 2700 m; in C and E Himalayas, summers from 2400 m to the treeline, winters 2135–3000 m (down to 1525 m); in NE Hills, winters from 1500 m to at least 2700 m, probably occurs higher in summer. **NP:** common. **IN:** fairly common. **BT:** common.

STREAK-THROATED FULVETTA *Alcippe cinereiceps* — Plate 135

Brown-headed Tit Babbler (I)

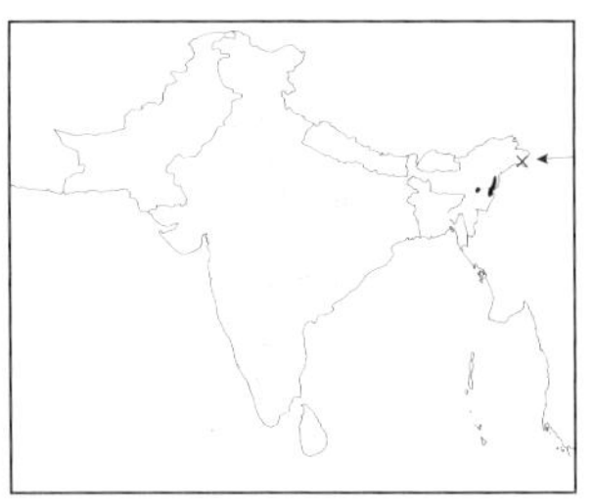

IDENTIFICATION 11 cm. A grey-brown fulvetta with prominent brown lateral crown-stripes and diffuse pinkish-brown streaking on throat. Range overlaps with that of *austeni* race of White-browed (above), which also has a streaked throat, but Streak-throated lacks the broad white supercilium of that species; further differences include brownish-buff crown and mantle (lacking chestnut tone of *austeni*), and greyish ear-coverts which are noticeably paler than crown and nape (rather than concolorous). It is extremely similar to Brown-throated Fulvetta (p.775), except for greyish ear-coverts and buffish coloration to crown, mantle and breast, and less prominent throat streaking. **VOICE** A rattling song of three or four notes, and a tit-like *cheep* (Ali and Ripley 1987). **HABITS** Found in small flocks of six to ten, often with other small babblers or warblers. Creeps about in undergrowth and bushes, sometimes in trees, rarely showing itself; usually very tame. **HABITAT** Dense secondary scrub, favouring brambles; also dense bamboo in the subtropical and temperate zone. **BREEDING** Unknown. Probably begins in April. **DISTRIBUTION AND STATUS IN:** rare resident in NE hills (Arunachal Pradesh, Assam, Manipur, Nagaland); from 1500 m in winter to 3500 m in summer. **REFERENCES** Ripley *et al.* (1991).

BROWN-THROATED FULVETTA *Alcippe ludlowi* Plate 135

Brown-headed Tit-Babbler (I), Ludlow's Fulvetta, *A. cinereiceps* (E,I)

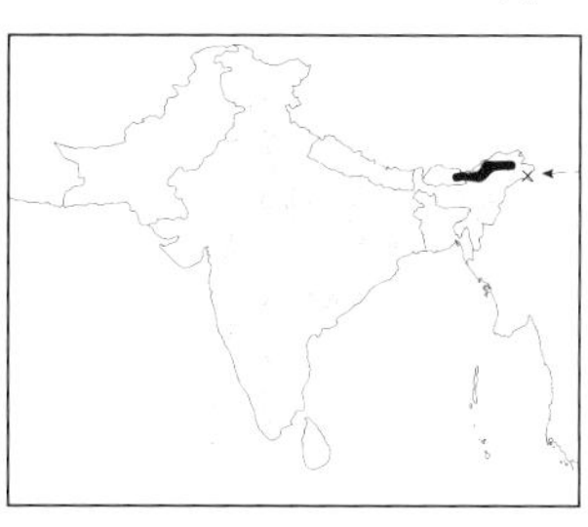

IDENTIFICATION 11 cm. A warm brown fulvetta with streaked throat. Range overlaps with that of *chumbiensis* race of White-browed Fulvetta (p.774). It lacks the broad white supercilium of that species, but is otherwise similar in plumage, with chestnut greater coverts and pale grey and black panels on wing; additional differences from that race of White-browed include lack of obvious lateral crown-stripes and more prominent rufous-brown streaking on throat. Extremely similar to Streak-throated Fulvetta (p.774); best told by brown ear-coverts, browner crown and mantle, and more prominent throat streaking. **VOICE** Poorly known. Alarm is rattling *trri, tchrrr* and *trrrrt* notes, more continuous when agitated and interspersed with two to four thin high-pitched *tsi* notes (C. Robson). **HABITS** Very similar to those of Streak-throated Fulvetta. **HABITAT** Low bushes and bamboo in rhododendron forest. **BREEDING** Unknown. **DISTRIBUTION AND STATUS** Resident. Himalayas in E Bhutan and Arunachal Pradesh. Subject to altitudinal movements: from 2100 m in winter up to 3505 m in summer. **IN:** locally fairly common. **BT:** common in the extreme east. **REFERENCES** Singh (1995).

RUFOUS-THROATED FULVETTA *Alcippe rufogularis* Plate 135

Red-throated Tit Babbler (I)

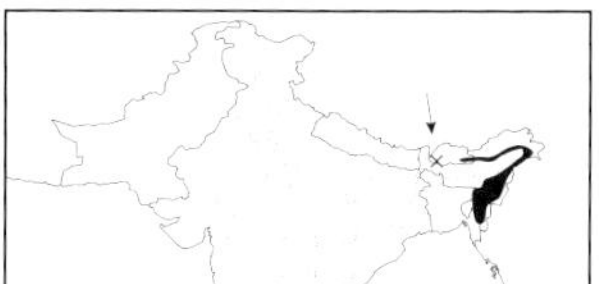

IDENTIFICATION 12 cm. A strikingly patterned and rather skulking fulvetta. More boldly patterned than Rufous-winged (p.773). Has rufous crown and blackish lateral crown-stripes, broad white supercilium contrasting with brown ear-coverts, white throat and breast with rufous collar, and uniform brown wings. **VOICE** Sings with fairly loud, shrill, quickly delivered *wichu-wichu-wichoi; wi-chuw-i-chewi-cheeu; wi-chi-wichi-chwi; wi-ti-ti-tuee; chuu-chu-wichu-chi-chu*, etc; song may be answered antiphonally with low, harsh *jrrjrrjrrjrrjrrjrr* or *jujujujujujuju*. Alarm calls are a constant, worried low chattering, *wrrr-it.wrrr.wrrr.wrrr.it* or *wrrititit*, etc, undulating *chrr-chrrr-chrr...*, whining *whiri-whiri-whiri-whiri...*, and loud, shrill explosive *whit....whit-whit...* and *wiwit-wiwit.wit...* (C. Robson). **HABITS** In the non-breeding season, keeps in small flocks, often mixed with other babblers. Skulking; hunts close to and sometimes on the ground among dense vegetation. Mainly insectivorous. **HABITAT** Bamboo stands, dense secondary growth and undergrowth in broadleaved tropical evergreen forest. **BREEDING** March–June. Builds a domed nest on the ground or on fallen debris. **DISTRIBUTION AND STATUS** Resident. Himalayas from Bhutan east to Arunachal Pradesh; NE India and Bangladesh. Recorded from plains up to 900 m. **IN:** locally frequent. **BT:** rare. **BD:** ?former resident; no recent records, but could still occur in hill tracts. **REFERENCES** Anon. (1993).

RUSTY-CAPPED FULVETTA *Alcippe dubia* Plate 135

Rufous-headed Tit-Babbler (I)

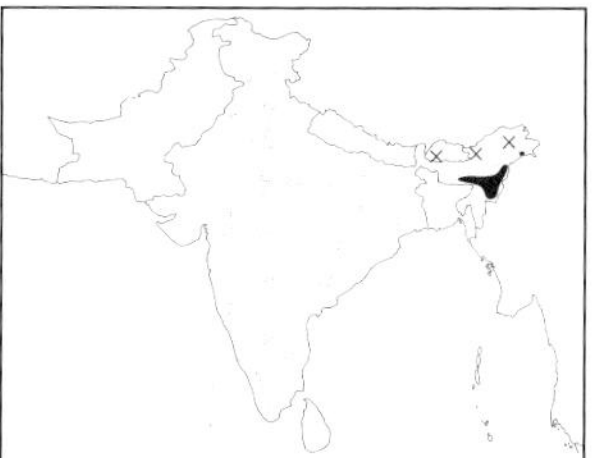

IDENTIFICATION 13 cm. A large, rather long-tailed, skulking fulvetta. Has noticeably bright rufous forehead, rufous crown and nape with dark brown scaling, broad white supercilium contrasting with black lateral crown-stripes, and dark brown ear-coverts and neck sides, the latter having prominent buff streaking. Uniform olive-brown wings help quickly to separate this species from Rufous-winged Fulvetta (p.773). Buffish underparts and lack of chestnut breast-band help separate it from Rufous-throated Fulvetta (above). **VOICE** Song is similar to that of Rufous-throated, but less shrill, with fewer notes per phrase and less variation: e.g. *chu-chi-chiu; chu-witee-wee; chu-witchi-chu; chu-witchu-chiu; wi-chi-chiu; wi-witu-chu*; sometimes hurried to *chu-witchiu* etc. Alarm call is a low grumbling rattle, sometimes with high squeaky note at end, e.g. *chrrr-rr..., chrrr-rrr-ritz* (C. Robson). **HABITS** Found in pairs or in small parties with other babblers, depending on the season. Usually forages on the ground among dense undergrowth or in low bushes; sometimes on the lower part of a tree trunk, like a nuthatch. Restless, active and tit-like in its actions. Chiefly insectivorous. **HABITAT** Bushes and dense undergrowth, especially ferns and brambles, in both thick and open forest; also at forest edges. **BREEDING** April–June. Nest is oval-shaped, placed on the ground or on fallen debris, usually on a slope. **DISTRIBUTION AND STATUS** Resident. Hills of NE India (Arunachal Pradesh, Assam, Manipur, Meghalaya, Nagaland) and Bhutan. **IN:** 900–2500 m; current status uncertain, very few recent records. **BT:** rare. **REFERENCES** Crosby (1995), Kaul *et al.* (1995).

BROWN-CHEEKED FULVETTA *Alcippe poioicephala* Plate 135

Quaker Babbler (I)

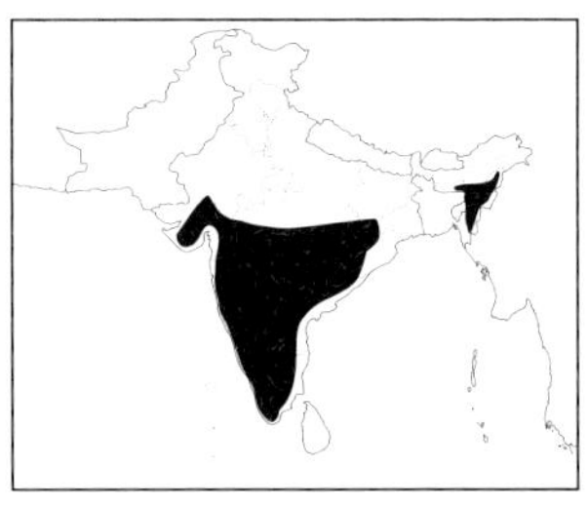

IDENTIFICATION 15 cm. A large, rather nondescript fulvetta, lacking any patterning to head. Has greyish crown and nape, grey-brown to olive-brown mantle, brown to rufous-brown wings and tail, and greyish-white to buff-coloured underparts, with paler throat and centre of breast. **VOICE** Attractive, bustling, whistled song, *tiew-teuw-tu-tee-tiu-tiu-wheet,* repeated at length with deliberate gaps between identical phrases; unassuming *churr* (P. Holt). **HABITS** Found in energetic parties, continually calling as they move about; often with other insectivorous species. Hunts chiefly in the undergrowth, sometimes quite high in the trees. Often hangs upside-down like a tit. **HABITAT** Undergrowth in moist broadleaved mixed deciduous or evergreen forest, bamboo stands, scrub and secondary growth. **BREEDING** January–November, varying locally. Nest is a cup, placed 1–2 m above ground in a tree fork or suspended from a branch. **DISTRIBUTION AND STATUS** Resident. Hills of NE and peninsular India and Bangladesh. **IN:** locally common; up to 1000 m in NE hills and to 2100 m in the peninsula. **BD:** locally common.

NEPAL FULVETTA *Alcippe nipalensis* Plate 135

Nepal Babbler (F,I)

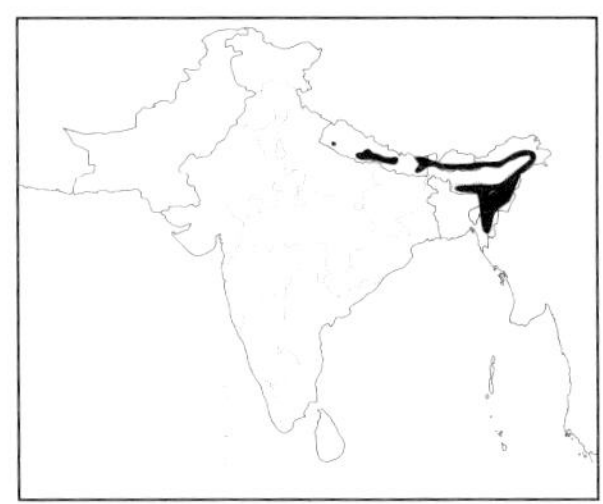

IDENTIFICATION 12 cm. A distinctive fulvetta with grey head and blackish lateral crown-stripe, prominent white eye-ring, olive-brown upperparts, whitish throat, centre of breast and belly, and buff flanks. **VOICE** Short buzzes and metallic *chit* notes, plus a short, fast trill of varying speed (S. Connop). **HABITS** Similar to those of Brown-cheeked Fulvetta (above). Forages mainly in bushes, undergrowth and small trees, sometimes on the ground. Usually quite shy, coming into the open infrequently. **HABITAT** Dense undergrowth in moist broadleaved deciduous and evergreen forest, bamboo stands and secondary growth. **BREEDING** March–July. Nest is a cup, placed 0.5–1.3 m above ground in bushes or bamboo clumps. **DISTRIBUTION AND STATUS** Resident. Himalayas from Nepal east to Arunachal Pradesh; NE India and Bangladesh. Subject to altitudinal movements in Himalayas: winters 245–1800 m, summers up to 2400 m, mainly above 1400 m; from foothills up to 1800 m in NE hills. **NP, IN:** locally common. **BT:** common. **BD:** locally common.

RUFOUS-BACKED SIBIA *Heterophasia annectans* Plate 136

Chestnut-backed Sibia (F,I)

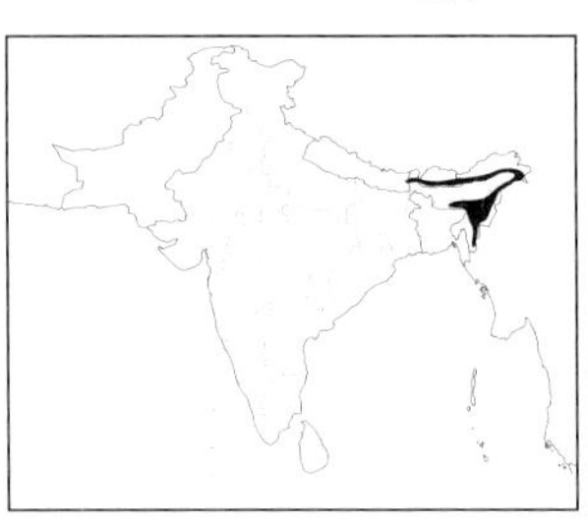

IDENTIFICATION 18 cm. Smallest and shortest-tailed of the sibias. Separated from other sibias by combination of black cap and mantle sides, black-and-white-streaked nape, white throat, breast and belly with deep buff flanks and vent, rufous back, rump and uppertail-coverts, black wings with rufous greater-covert bar, white fringes to tertials and grey edges to primaries and secondaries (forming a panel on wing), and white-tipped black tail (from below, showing as large white spots at tip of undertail). **VOICE** Sings with loud, strident, jolly phrases, repeated after intervals of 5–11 seconds, sample phrases including: *chwee-chwee-chui; wi-wi-chi-chui; wi-wi-chi-chi-chui; wi-chi-chew-chui; wi-chi-chew-chew* (C. Robson). **HABITS** Keeps in small parties. Arboreal, spending most of its time in the canopy of tall trees. Creeps along branches and flits from branch to branch, sometimes climbs like a nuthatch; tends to keep close to the trunk. **HABITAT** Dense, moist broadleaved evergreen forest in the subtropical and temperate zones. **BREEDING** May and June. Nest is a cup, built 3–7 m above ground on a branch of a small tree. **DISTRIBUTION AND STATUS** Resident. Himalayas from E Nepal east to Arunachal Pradesh; NE India. Subject to altitudinal movements: summers 1200–2300 m (–2650 m), winters down to the foothills. **NP:** rare and local. **IN:** generally scarce, locally frequent. **BT:** uncommon.

RUFOUS SIBIA *Heterophasia capistrata* Plate 136

Black-capped Sibia (F,I,N)

IDENTIFICATION 21 cm. Told from other sibias by combination of black cap, rufous or cinnamon-buff nape and underparts, grey terminal band and black subterminal band to rufous tail, and grey panelling on mainly black wings. **Juvenile** is similar, but has brownish-black cap. **Racial variation** *H. c. capistrata* of the W Himalayas has paler cinnamon-buff nape and underparts, and grey-brown mantle and back. *H. c. nigriceps* and *H. c. bayleyi* of the C and E Himalayas have deeper rufous nape and underparts; *bayleyi* has a brighter rufous-brown mantle which is almost concolorous with nape. **VOICE** Song is a clear, flute-like *tee-dee-dee-dee-dee-o-lu,* the first five notes on the same pitch, the sixth lowest and the last in between; call-note is a rapid *chi-chi,* and alarm is a harsh *chrai-chrai-chrai...*

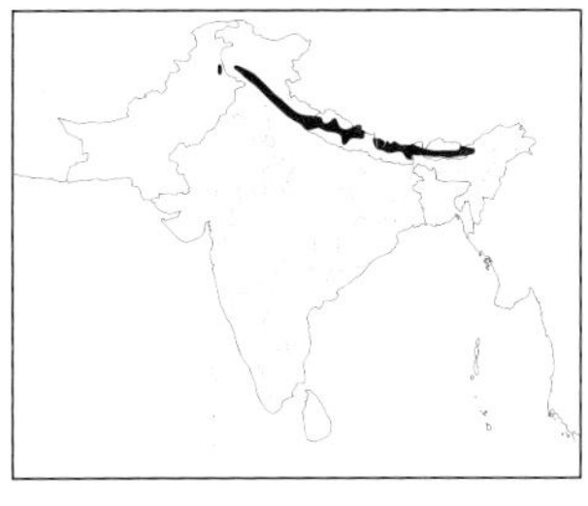

(Ali and Ripley 1987). **HABITS** Keeps in pairs or small parties, depending on the season. Conspicuous and noisy; its cheery call is one of the most familiar sounds of Himalayan oak forest. Arboreal. Forages actively among foliage or on moss-covered branches and trunks in middle levels and the canopy, sometimes moving lower down; hops rapidly from branch to branch; can cling to slender stems while probing flowers, and to tree trunks while searching bark crevices. Sometimes sallies out to catch flying insects. **HABITAT** Mainly moist broadleaved forest in the subtropical and temperate zones; favours oaks, also conifers. **BREEDING** April–August. Nest is a cup, placed 2–20 m above ground in trees or bushes. **DISTRIBUTION AND STATUS** Resident. Himalayas from Murree, N Pakistan, east to W Arunachal Pradesh. Subject to altitudinal movements: in the west, summers 1800–2700 m, winters 1200–2100 m (down to 460 m); in the centre and east, summers 1980–3000 m (–3400 m), winters 1050–2700 m (down to 600 m). **PK:** locally frequent. **NP, IN, BT:** common.

GREY SIBIA *Heterophasia gracilis* — Plate 136

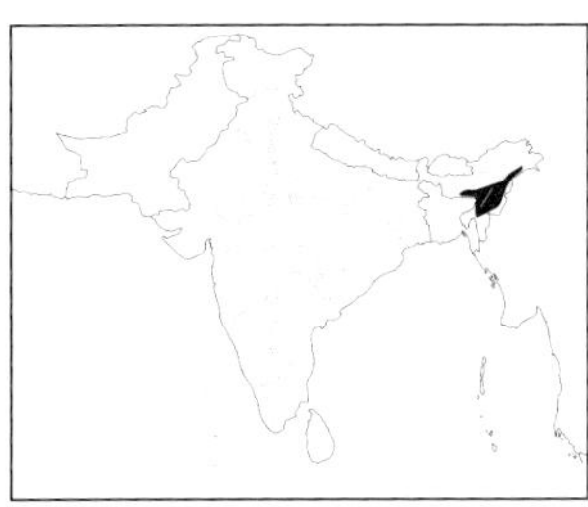

IDENTIFICATION 21 cm. A black-capped sibia without any rufous in plumage. Told from other sibias by combination of black crown and ear-coverts, grey nape, mantle and back, white underparts with buff rear flanks and undertail-coverts, largely black wings, with black fringes to grey tertials and grey greater coverts, and mainly grey tail with broad black subterminal band. **VOICE** Song is loud, strident, far-carrying series of well-spaced high-pitched, shrill whistled notes (usually descending towards end or from beginning): *tu-tu-ti-ti-ti-tu*; *ti-ti-ti-ti-tiu-tu*; *tiu-tiu-tiu-tiu-tiu*, etc. Has harsh, grating, slightly metallic calls typical of the genus, e.g. *trrit-trrit*. Contact calls include quiet, hurried, rather squeaky *witwit-witarit*, along with soft sibilant *ti-tew* (C. Robson). **HABITS** Found in small parties in the non-breeding season. Arboreal and lively; hunts restlessly in the canopy, sometimes descending to bushes. **HABITAT** Deciduous and evergreen broadleaved forest; mainly pine forest in the Khasi Hills. **BREEDING** Mainly May and June. Nest is a deep cup, made of moss, roots, leaves and fibres and lined with fine roots, usually placed in the crown of a tree. **DISTRIBUTION AND STATUS IN:** resident in NE hills (Arunachal Pradesh, Assam, Manipur, Meghalaya, Mizoram, Nagaland), subject to altitudinal movements; occurs from 1200 m to the summits, winters down to 900 m; current status uncertain, and very few recent records.

BEAUTIFUL SIBIA *Heterophasia pulchella* — Plate 136

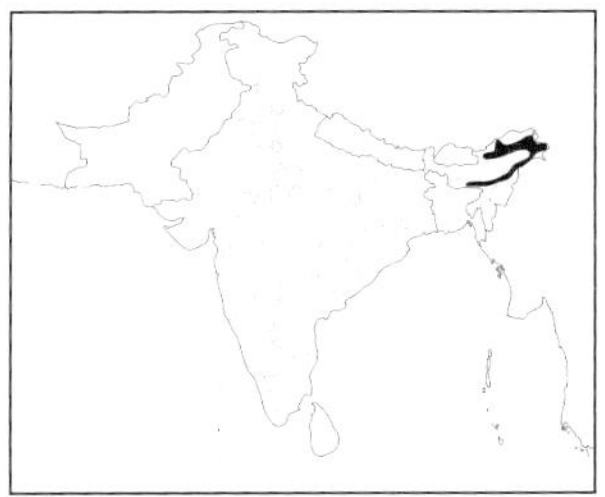

IDENTIFICATION 22 cm. Distinguished from other sibias by combination of bluish-slate crown and black lores, slate-grey upperparts and slightly paler underparts, contrasting black wing patch (formed by black greater and primary coverts), chestnut-brown tertials, blue-grey secondaries and silvery-grey edges to primaries forming panelling on wing, and brown, black and grey pattern to tail. **Racial variation** *H. p. nigroaurita* from north of the Brahmaputra has black ear-coverts. **VOICE** Song is a loud, strident *ti-ti-titi-tu-ti*, descending slightly towards end, the first part more hurried and the whole generally less descending, higher-pitched and more shrill than song of Grey Sibia (above); calls include continuous low, rattling *chrrrrrrrrr* or *churrururrr* (C. Robson). **HABITS** Keeps in pairs or small parties, depending on the season. Forages actively in tall trees on moss- and lichen-covered branches and trunks; hops jerkily up branches. Often probes tree blossoms. **HABITAT** Moist broadleaved forest. **BREEDING** Only one nest known: found in May, a cup-shaped structure built on a horizontal branch of a small tree. **DISTRIBUTION AND STATUS IN:** locally common resident in the NE hills (Arunachal Pradesh, Assam, Meghalaya, Nagaland), subject to altitudinal movements; 300–2700 m. **REFERENCES** Athreya *et al.* (1997).

LONG-TAILED SIBIA *Heterophasia picaoides* — Plate 136

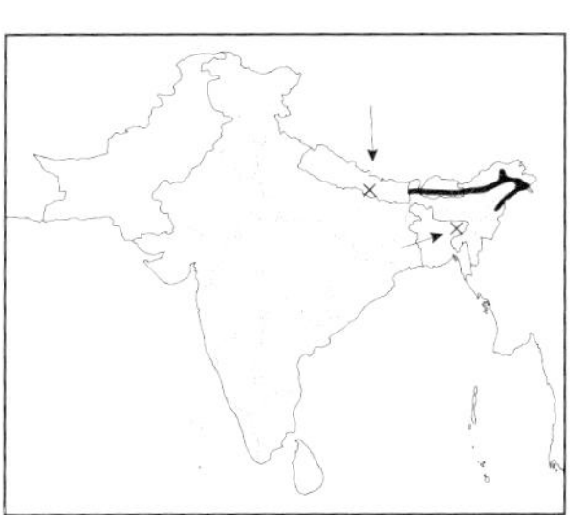

IDENTIFICATION 30 cm. Readily distinguished from other sibias by long tail with greyish-white tips, grey head and upperparts (with slightly darker lores) and paler grey underparts, and dark grey wings with white patch on secondaries. **VOICE** Calls include thin, metallic, high-pitched *tsittsit* and *tsic* notes, interspersed with dry, even-pitched rattling: *tsittsit-tsic-tsic-tsic-tsic..... chrrrrrrrt....tsitsitsittsit-tsic-tsic-chrrrrrrrt...* (C. Robson). **HABITS** In the non-breeding season, found in single-species flocks, birds flying after each other from tree to tree. Arboreal, and frequents mainly the middle levels and canopy. Often feeds on nectar of flowering trees; also on flower buds, insects and seeds. **HABITAT** Dense or open broadleaved evergreen forest in tropical and subtropical zones. **BREEDING** Poorly known. April–June. Nest is a deep cup, built high up on a horizontal branch of a tree. **DISTRIBUTION AND STATUS** Resident, subject to some altitudinal movements. Himalayas in EC Nepal and from Sikkim east to Arunachal Pradesh; NE India. **NP:** only 19th-century records. **IN:** locally fairly common; summers 760–1525 m, winters from base of the hills to 900 m. **BT:** fairly common; summers 540–1525 m, winters 305–1250 m. **BD:** vagrant.

STRIATED YUHINA *Yuhina castaniceps* Plate 135

White-browed Yuhina (I)

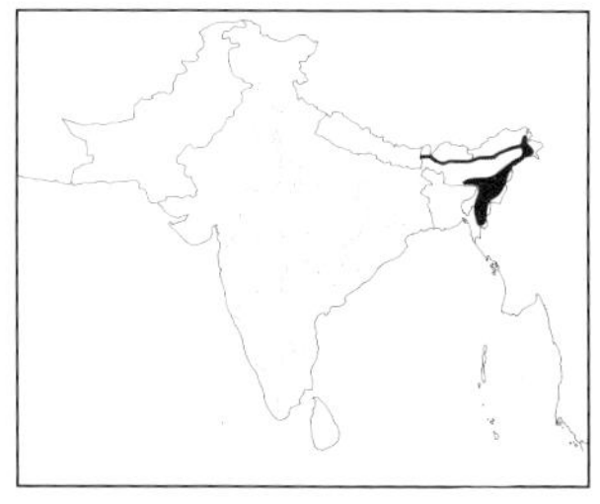

IDENTIFICATION 13 cm. Not so crested as other yuhinas, and the only one to show white on tail. Main plumage features are very short white supercilium, rufous ear-coverts with fine white streaking, white streaking on greyish-olive mantle, uniform greyish-white underparts, and white tips to graduated tail. **Racial variation** Three races occur in the subcontinent. The two predominantly Himalayan races, *Y. c. rufigenis* and *Y. c. plumbeiceps,* have a grey crown which is finely scaled with greyish-white; *Y. c. castaniceps* of hills east and south of the Brahmaputra R (ranges meet in Nagaland) has a rufous crown which is finely scaled with pale buff and concolorous with ear-coverts. **VOICE** A loud cheeping or twittering *chir-chit...chir-chit* (Ali and Ripley 1987); also a short, nasal descending *chrrr,* not unlike that of several *Alcippe* species (S. Connop). **HABITS** Found in parties of up to 30 birds, sometimes with other small insectivorous species. Particularly fast-moving; works rapidly through the middle forest level. Actions more tit-like than those of other yuhinas. **HABITAT** Open and dense broadleaved forest with a thick, bushy understorey; secondary growth in tropical and subtropical zones. **BREEDING** April–July. Nest is a cup, usually placed in a hole in a roadside cutting. **DISTRIBUTION AND STATUS** Resident. Himalayas from West Bengal east to Arunachal Pradesh; NE India and Bangladesh. Recorded 350–1600 m. **IN:** locally frequent. **BT:** fairly common. **BD:** ?former resident; no recent records, but could still occur in hill tracts. **REFERENCES** Athreya *et al.* (1997), Singh (1995).

WHITE-NAPED YUHINA *Yuhina bakeri* Plate 135

Chestnut-headed Yuhina (F)

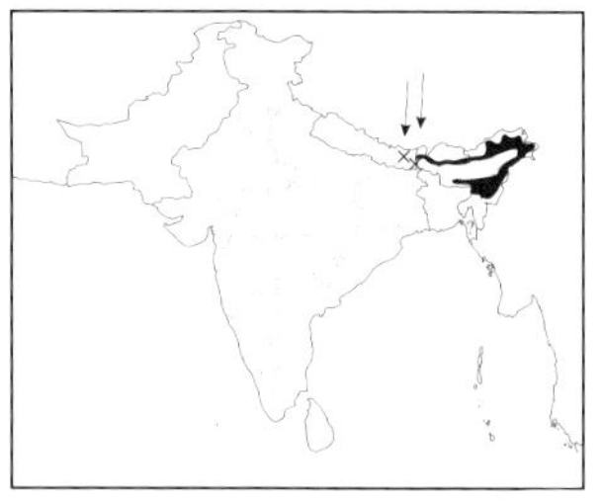

IDENTIFICATION 13 cm. Told from other yuhinas by combination of stout bill, rufous crest, white nape (especially prominent when crest raised), blackish lores, white streaking on rufous ear-coverts, lack of dark moustachial stripe, rufous wash to upper mantle, with white shaft streaking on olive-brown of lower mantle, and fine brown streaking on pinkish-buff breast. **Juvenile** is said to have paler underparts, with less distinct streaking. **VOICE** A ringing *zee-zee* or *zeuu-zuee,* as well as high-pitched alarm notes (Fleming *et al.* 1984). **HABITS** Found in pairs or small parties, depending on the season; often with other small babblers, tits and warblers. Forages actively, mainly in the middle level of forest and in bushes. **HABITAT** Broadleaved evergreen subtropical forest. **BREEDING** April–July. Nest is a cup or dome, built in a bank, low in bushes or against a mossy trunk. **DISTRIBUTION AND STATUS** Resident, subject to altitudinal movements. Himalayas from E Nepal east to Arunachal Pradesh; NE India and Bangladesh. **NP:** very rare and local; 1525 m, 2200 m. **IN:** locally fairly common; 500–2000 m. **BT:** frequent; summers 550–2200 m, winters down to 455 m. **BD:** ?former resident; no recent records, but could still occur very locally.

WHISKERED YUHINA *Yuhina flavicollis* Plate 135

Yellow-naped Yuhina (F,I)

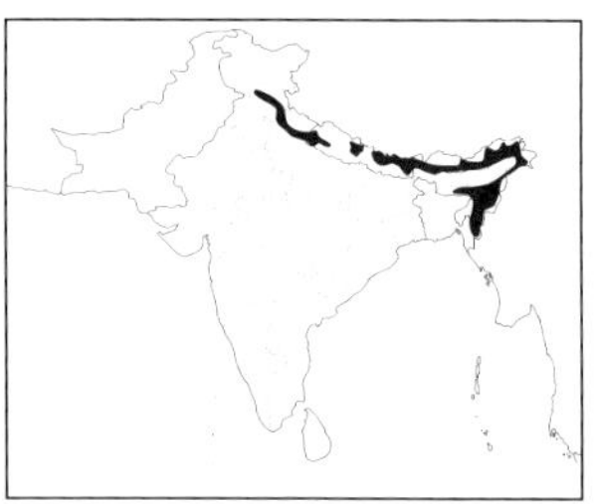

IDENTIFICATION 13 cm. Told from other yuhinas by combination of grey-brown crest, prominent black moustachial stripe, yellowish to rufous hind-collar, and prominent white eye-ring. Sides of breast and flanks are olive-brown, streaked with white. **Racial variation** *Y. f. albicollis* of W Himalayas has a paler hindcollar which is yellowish-buff in centre. *Y. f. flavicollis* of C and E Himalayas and the similar *Y. f. rouxi* of the hills south and east of the Brahmaputra have a more rufous hindcollar, the latter also having yellower underparts. **VOICE** A thin, squeaky *swii swii-swii,* also a metallic ringing note; loud, ringing notes in chorus from flocks (J. Scharringa). The most commonly heard call is a nasal *zi gra* (Martens and Eck 1995). **HABITS** In the non-breeding season, keeps in mixed feeding parties with other small insectivorous species. Not shy. Hunts energetically in bushes and the middle level of forest; flits from branch to branch, and sometimes makes aerial sallies after insects. **HABITAT** Broadleaved subtropical and temperate forest and secondary growth. **BREEDING** May and June. Nest is domed or cup-shaped, placed on a bank among roots or suspended from a branch. **DISTRIBUTION AND STATUS** Resident. Himalayas from NW Himachal Pradesh east to Arunachal Pradesh; NE India and Bangladesh. Subject to some altitudinal movements: in W Himalayas, summers 1700–3000 m, winters from 1200 m to at least 2300 m; in C and E Himalayas, summers 1800–3000 m, winters from 2745 m down to 800 m in Nepal, to 600 m in Bhutan and to plains edge in E India; in NE hills, occurs from plains edge (winter) to 2600 m (summer). **NP:** common and widespread. **IN:** locally common in the west, common in the east. **BT:** common. **BD:** ?former resident; no recent records, but could still occur in hill tracts.

STRIPE-THROATED YUHINA *Yuhina gularis* Plate 135

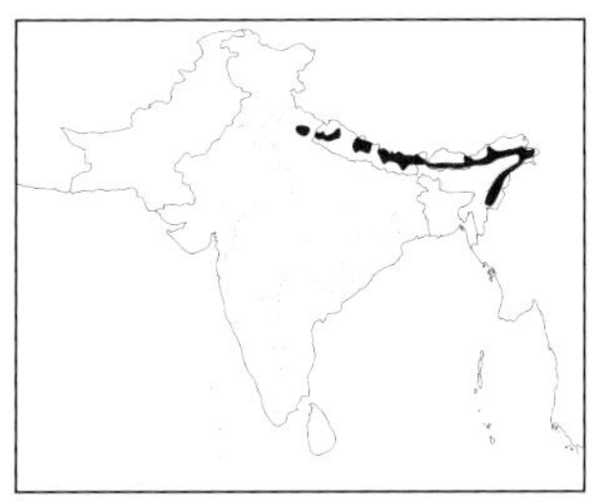

IDENTIFICATION 14 cm. Largest of the yuhinas, and best distinguished by combination of olive-brown crest concolorous with mantle (and lacking nape patch or hindcollar), rufous-orange secondaries forming prominent panel on wing, contrasting black primaries, black streaking on pale vinaceous throat, and brownish-orange belly and vent. **VOICE** Call-note is a nasal, descending *queee* (Martens and Eck 1995). **HABITS** In the non-breeding season, typically found in parties, often with other small babblers, tits and warblers. Usually frequents higher bushes and lower branches in forest. Often feeds on nectar of flowering rhododendrons. **HABITAT** Temperate broadleaved and broadleaved–coniferous forest; favours oak and rhododendron forest. **BREEDING** Little known. Probably May and June. One nest described as a cradle of roots attached to plant roots overhanging a bank. **DISTRIBUTION AND STATUS** Resident. Himalayas from N Uttar Pradesh east to Arunachal Pradesh; NE India. Subject to altitudinal movements: summers mainly 2400–3700 m (down to 1700 m), winters 1700–3300 m, rarely in the duars (down to 1255 m in Bhutan, to 1400 m in Nepal). **NP:** common and widespread. **IN:** uncommon in N Uttar Pradesh, common farther east. **BT:** common.

RUFOUS-VENTED YUHINA *Yuhina occipitalis* Plate 135

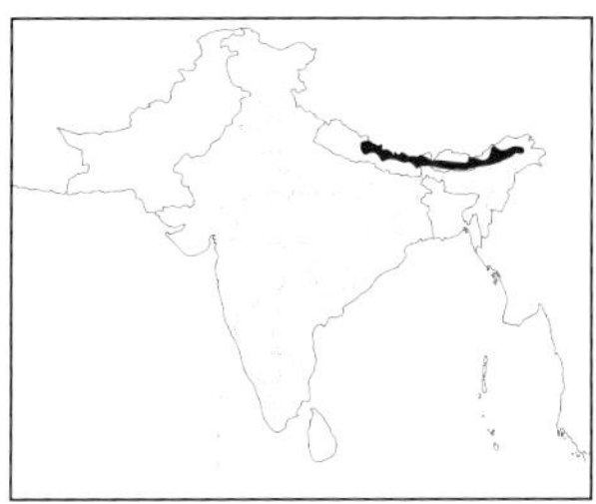

IDENTIFICATION 13 cm. Told from other yuhinas by combination of rufous lores, nape patch, vent and belly, grey crest, ear-coverts and hindneck, fine black moustachial stripe, grey throat and breast (though former slightly paler), and vinaceous underparts. **Juvenile** has a shorter crest, rufous of nape is paler, and vinaceous of breast is less prominent. **VOICE** A constant chittering; song is a high-pitched strong *zee-zu-drrrrr, tsip-che-e-e-e-e*; also *z-e-e.....zit* alarm (Fleming *et al.* 1984). **HABITS** Similar to those of Stripe-throated Yuhina (above), but forages more in the treetops. **HABITAT** Broadleaved temperate and subalpine forest, especially oak and rhododendrons. **BREEDING** April–June. Only one nest described: a cup, placed 1 m above ground in the fork of a small tree. **DISTRIBUTION AND STATUS** Resident. Himalayas from WC Nepal east to Arunachal Pradesh. Subject to altitudinal movements: summers from 2400 m to at least 3900 m, most frequent 3050–3400 m, and winters from 1500 m (1830 m in Nepal) to at least 2745 m. **NP:** common. **IN:** locally fairly common. **BT:** common.

BLACK-CHINNED YUHINA *Yuhina nigrimenta* Plate 135

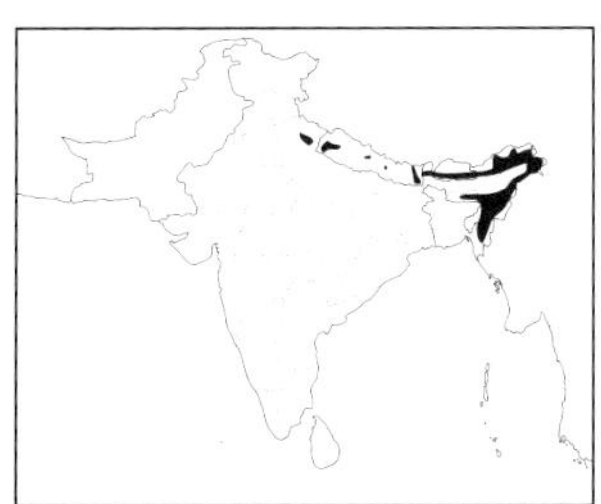

IDENTIFICATION 11 cm. A small, short-tailed, mainly olive-brown yuhina with grey-streaked black crest, black chin and lores, grey ear-coverts, nape and hindneck, and white to pale grey throat and upper breast contrasting with buffish of rest of underparts. Red lower mandible with dark tip is typically prominent, and legs and feet are orange-yellow. **Juvenile** has a shorter black crest with less distinct greyish fringes, and warmer brown upperparts and edges to wings and tail. **VOICE** Flock gives a constant twittering and buzzing, calls including a high *de-de-de-de* and a *zee-zoe-zen*; song is a soft *whee-to-whee-de-der-n-whee-yer* (Fleming *et al.* 1984). **HABITS** When not breeding, keeps in constantly twittering flocks of up to 20 birds, often in mixed parties with other small insectivorous species. Very restless, and ever on the move. Forages busily, mainly in low bushes, sometimes moving into the canopy; hangs upside-down on twigs in tit-like fashion. **HABITAT** Subtropical broadleaved evergreen forest, secondary growth and overgrown clearings. **BREEDING** March–July. Nest is a cup, suspended from lichen hanging from tree branches or fastened to exposed hanging roots on a bank. **DISTRIBUTION AND STATUS** Resident. Himalayas from N Uttar Pradesh east to Arunachal Pradesh; NE India and Bangladesh. Subject to some altitudinal movements: in Himalayas, 610–2200 m; south of Brahmaputra R, breeds 1000–1800 m. **NP:** rare. **IN:** locally fairly common. **BT:** common. **BD:** ?former resident; no recent records, but could occur in hill tracts.

WHITE-BELLIED YUHINA *Yuhina zantholeuca* Plate 135

IDENTIFICATION 11 cm. A small, olive-yellow and white yuhina with beady black eye. Easily told by olive-yellow crest, olive-yellow mantle, wings and tail, white underparts, pinkish bill and legs, and yellow undertail-

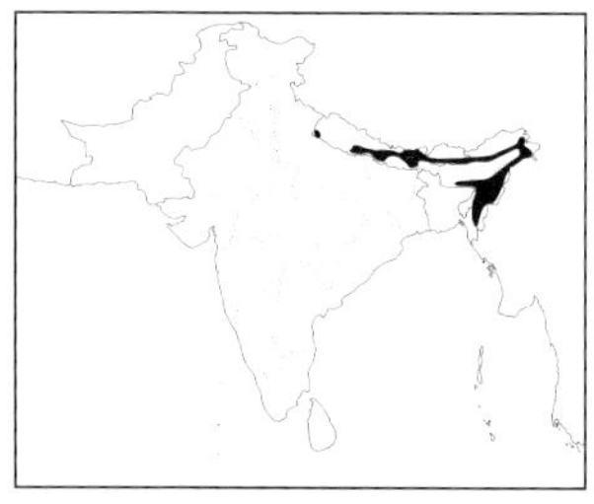

coverts. **Juvenile** is duller, with brownish cast to upperparts. **VOICE** A high, subdued, metallic *chit* and a *cheaan* alarm call (Fleming *et al.* 1984); a nasal tit-like *na-na* (R. Grimmett); sings with a short, high-pitched, descending trill, *si-i-i-i-i-i* (Boonsong and Round 1991). **HABITS** Often found singly, occasionally in small parties and sometimes with other small birds. Although lively, it is quiet and unobtrusive. Forages chiefly in the middle levels, also in the undergrowth and canopy. **HABITAT** Broadleaved forest, especially clearings and edges; secondary growth. **BREEDING** March–May. Nest is a cup, suspended between horizontal twigs, 0.5–2 m above ground. **DISTRIBUTION AND STATUS** Resident. Himalayas from Nepal east to Arunachal Pradesh; NE India and Bangladesh. Subject to poorly understood altitudinal movements: recorded 180–2600 m, locally down to plains in winter. **NP:** frequent, locally fairly common; mainly above 1600 m. **IN:** locally fairly common. **BT:** frequent. **BD:** local.

FIRE-TAILED MYZORNIS *Myzornis pyrrhoura* — Plate 135

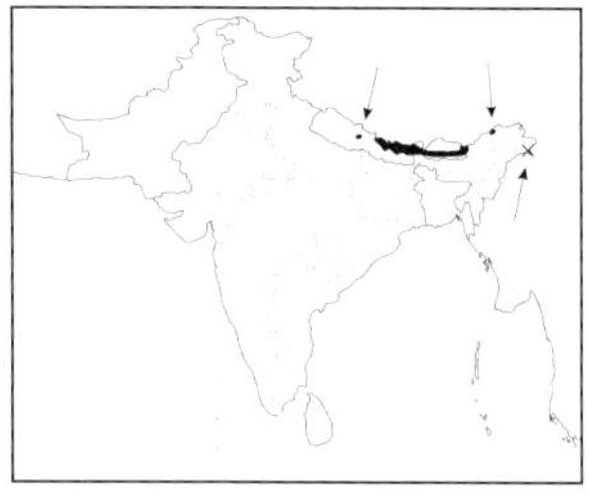

IDENTIFICATION 12 cm. Mainly brilliant emerald-green, with fine black bill, and black eye-stripe and scaling on crown. **Male** has red-and-orange panel on black wings, white tips to primary coverts, secondaries and primaries, red sides and black tip to tail, red patch on throat and breast, and orange on lower belly and undertail-coverts. **Female** is similar, but throat is orange-buff and lacks the red on throat/upper breast of male; has greyish belly and flanks, less extensive white tips to secondaries and primaries, and duller red sides to tail. **VOICE** A *trrrr-trrrr-trrr* preceded by a high-pitched squeak, and a repeated *tzip* in alarm (Fleming *et al.* 1984); very high-pitched, fine Goldcrest-like *tsi-tsi* contact notes (P. Holt). **HABITS** Usually found singly, also in pairs or small groups associated with mixed hunting parties of other small birds. Forages chiefly in bushes, sometimes in trees. Has a specially adapted bristled tongue for nectar-feeding, and also takes insects and spiders. Often probes blossoms of trees and shrubs, especially rhododendrons; also feeds by methodically searching foliage, hovering in front of flowers and sprigs, and sometimes by making short flights like a flycatcher. Clings to and creeps up mossy trunks and rocks, exploring crevices. **HABITAT** Rhododendron and juniper shrubberies; mossy oak–rhododendron forest and bamboo stands. **BREEDING** Poorly known. May; fledged young on 1 June in Nepal. Nest is an untidy ball of moss, lined with rhododendron bark, and placed against a mossy bank or trunk, 1–2 m above the ground. **DISTRIBUTION AND STATUS** Resident, subject to some altitudinal movements. Himalayas from WC Nepal east to Arunachal Pradesh. **NP:** uncommon and local; 2000–3950 m, up to at least 2745 m in winter. **IN:** local and rare; 1600–3600 m, probably breeds above 2700 m. **BT:** frequent; from 1800 m up to at least 3665 m. **REFERENCES** Lama (1995c).

BEARDED PARROTBILL *Panurus biarmicus* — Plate 136

Bearded Tit Babbler (I), Bearded Reedling (R), Bearded Tit

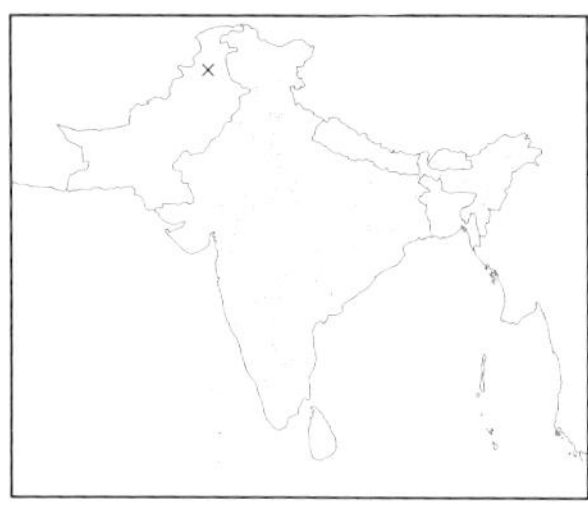

IDENTIFICATION 16–17 cm. **Male** is striking, with grey head and black moustache, yellow bill, black and white patterning on wings, rufous mantle and tail, rufous flanks, and black undertail-coverts. **Female** has buff head without black moustache and lacks black undertail-coverts, but is otherwise similar in pattern to male, although duller. **Juvenile** is similar to female, but is brighter yellowish-buff in coloration; has black centre to mantle, black primary coverts and black centres to other coverts, and black sides to tail (with prominent white tips to outer rectrices). Juvenile male has yellow bill and black lores. **VOICE** A ringing, twanging *ping ping*; also ticking and churring notes when feeding. **HABITS** Gregarious, birds keeping together by constant contact calls. Moves about reed stems actively and with agile tit-like actions. Feeds on seeds in winter. Has a whirring direct flight just above the reed tops. **HABITAT** Reedbeds; flock recorded in Pakistan was in tall *Saccharum spontaneum* grass and tamarisk bushes. **DISTRIBUTION AND STATUS PK:** winter vagrant.

GREAT PARROTBILL *Conostoma oemodium* — Plate 136

***C. aemodium* (F,I)**

IDENTIFICATION 28 cm. Largest of the parrotbills, and rather laughingthrush-like in shape and behaviour. Told from Brown (p.781) by larger size and paler grey-brown coloration, much larger, cone-shaped yellow or orange bill, buffish-white forehead contrasting with brown lores, paler and more uniform grey-brown sides of head, throat and breast, and grey sides to tail. Lacks dark lateral crown-stripes of Brown. **VOICE** Halting, loud, simple song of two to four clear whistled notes, e.g. *truu-dree-dreeu*; also more plaintive nasal wheezes, squeals, cackles and churrs (P. Holt from B. Demeulemester recording); alarm is a *churrrrrrr* (Fleming *et al.* 1984). **HABITS** Found singly, in pairs or in small parties, sometimes with laughingthrushes. Tends to keep out of sight, although

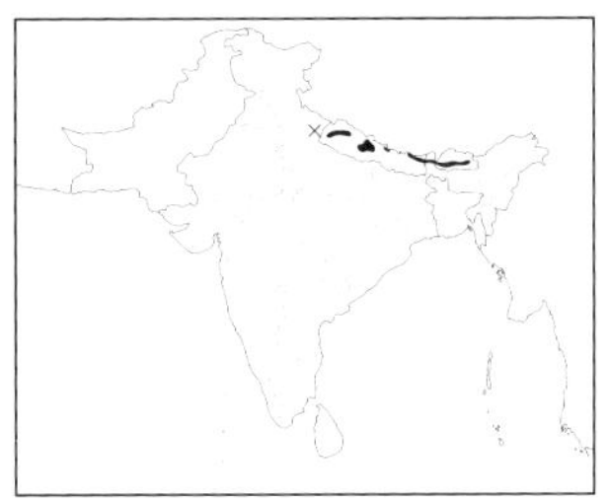

not shy. Keeps mainly to the undergrowth, occasionally ascending tall trees. Slow-moving; hops and clambers about more like a laughingthrush than a parrotbill. **HABITAT** Ringal bamboo stands in forest, usually of oak–rhododendron or fir–rhododendron. **BREEDING** Poorly known. May–July. Nest is a cup, placed in a bamboo clump. **DISTRIBUTION AND STATUS** Resident. Himalayas from N Uttar Pradesh east to E Bhutan. Shows little if any altitudinal movement; 2600–3660 m. **NP:** uncommon. **IN:** rare. **BT:** uncommon.

BROWN PARROTBILL *Paradoxornis unicolor* — Plate 136

Brown Suthora (I)

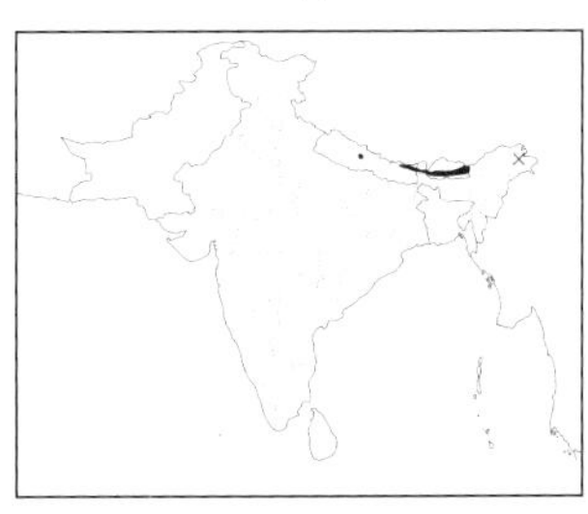

IDENTIFICATION 21 cm. A medium-sized, stocky, square-headed and dull-coloured parrotbill. Distinguished from other similar-sized parrotbills by dull brown upperparts, with darker mottling on crown and nape, and dull grey underparts. From Great Parrotbill (p.780) by smaller size and stocky shape, smaller and much stouter greyish or pale yellow bill, diffuse grey mottling on dull brown ear-coverts, dusky grey and rather untidy-looking throat and breast merging into olive-brown of flanks and belly, black lateral crown-stripe broadening on nape, diffuse grey supercilium behind eye and pale eye-ring, and browner tail. Has warmer, rufous-brown panel on wings, as Great Parrotbill. **VOICE** Call is a *chirrup*, and loud *churrrr-churrrrr* in alarm (Fleming *et al.* 1984). **HABITS** Usually keeps in small parties of four to six birds, which skulk in the undergrowth and frequently call to each other. Sometimes hangs upside-down when feeding. Has a weak fluttering flight. **HABITAT** Mainly stands of dense bamboo *Arundinaria*; also rhododendron and other bushes in the temperate and subalpine zones. **BREEDING** Little known. Probably May. **DISTRIBUTION AND STATUS** Resident, showing little altitudinal movement. Himalayas in WC Nepal and from E Nepal east to Arunachal Pradesh. **NP:** uncommon and very local; 2590–3300 m. **IN:** rare; 2700–3400 m, down to 2000 m in winter. **BT:** frequent; 2000–3355 m.

GREY-HEADED PARROTBILL *Paradoxornis gularis* — Plate 136

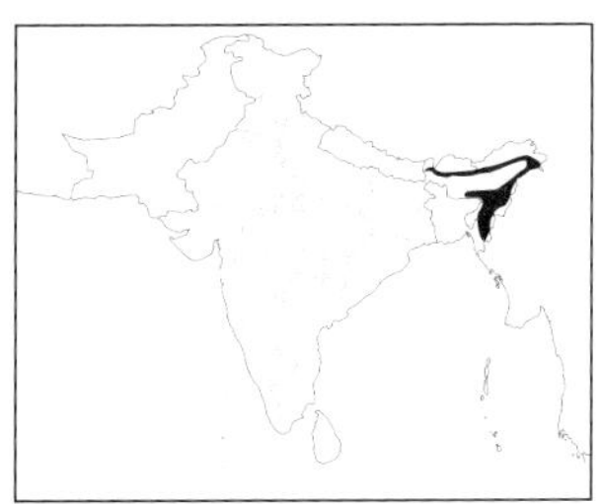

IDENTIFICATION 21 cm. A medium-sized, stocky parrotbill with stout orange bill. Readily separated from other parrotbills by mainly grey head, with black lateral crown-stripe broadening towards nape, black throat, white surround to eye and white malar stripe, rufous-brown mantle and wings, and white or buffish-white underparts. **VOICE** Usual calls are short, quite harsh, rather slurred *jieu* or *jiow* notes, e.g. *jiow-jiow, jieu-jieu-jieu* etc, and less harsh *djer* notes, sometimes interspersed with rapid low twittering, soft *chip* notes, and very soft, short rattled *chrrrat* etc. (C. Robson). **HABITS** Found in pairs or small flocks of four to eight birds. Less skulking than other parrotbills. Frequents the middle and lower forest storeys in trees, bushes and bamboo. **HABITAT** Open and closed broadleaved forest, bushes and bamboo stands. **BREEDING** April–July. Nest is a cup, placed 2–3 m above ground in young trees. **DISTRIBUTION AND STATUS** Resident. Himalayas from West Bengal east to Arunachal Pradesh; NE India and Bangladesh. **IN:** scarce and local in Himalayas, 500–1500 m (–2400 m), winters down to the plains; common in NE hills, 600–2100 m. **BT:** frequent; 915–1250 m (–2050 m). **BD:** ?former resident; no recent records, but could still occur in hill tracts.

BLACK-BREASTED PARROTBILL *Paradoxornis flavirostris* — Plate 136

Gould's Parrotbill (F,I)

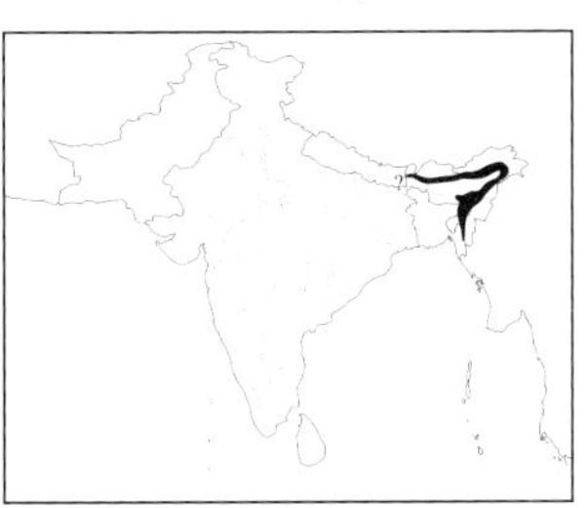

IDENTIFICATION 19 cm. A medium-sized, stocky parrotbill with rufous-brown head and olive-brown upperparts, black patch on ear-coverts, and huge orange bill. Likely to be confused only with Spot-breasted Parrotbill (p.782), although note different distribution. Best told by black breast and solid black chin (with black barring on white throat and malar area), rufous-buff (rather than pale buff) underparts, darker rufous-brown crown and nape, even stouter bill, and different call. **VOICE** A striking, whistled *phew, phew, phew, phuit*, ascending in pitch and volume; also a bleating or mewing cry, and a mellow, three-noted warble (Ali and Ripley 1987). **HABITS** Keeps in small parties in the non-breeding season. Skulking, and usually keeps low down in vegetation; occasionally flies up into the air, calling, perhaps in display. Loath to fly, and normally flutters only a few metres into thicker cover if disturbed. **HABITAT** Mixed grass and bamboo in the hills, and dense reedbeds, elephant grass and grasses along river banks in the lowlands;

mainly in the tropical and subtropical zones. **BREEDING** April–July. Nest is a deep cup, built in reeds or bamboo. **DISTRIBUTION AND STATUS** Resident, endemic to the subcontinent. Recently recorded only in Assam; formerly found also in Nepal, NE India (Arunachal Pradesh, Meghalaya, Nagaland, West Bengal) and Bangladesh. Globally threatened. **NP:** recorded only in the 19th century, in the terai. **IN:** plains and foothills (–2400 m in Nagaland, –1900 m in Sikkim?); now very rare and local. **BD:** ?former resident; no recent records, but could still occur in hill tracts. **REFERENCES** Choudhury (1994).

SPOT-BREASTED PARROTBILL *Paradoxornis guttaticollis* Plate 136

White-throated Parrotbill (I)

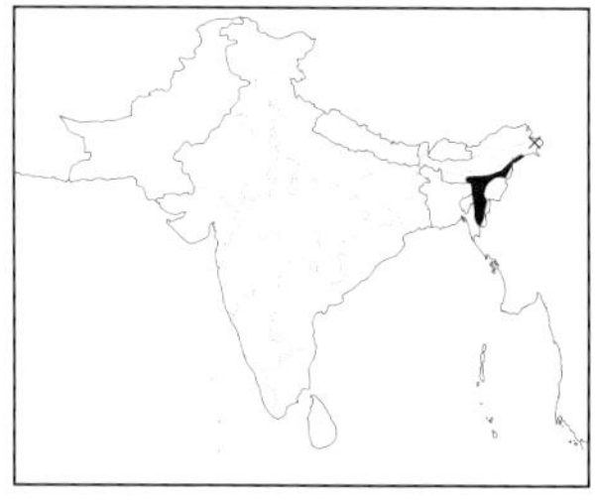

IDENTIFICATION 19 cm. A medium-sized, stocky parrotbill with rufous head and upperparts, black patch on ear-coverts, and large orange bill. Likely to be confused only with Black-breasted Parrotbill (p.782), although note distribution. Best told by black arrowhead-shaped spotting on buffish-white throat and breast (lacking bold black patch on breast), pale buff (rather than rufous-buff) underparts, brighter rufous crown and nape, less stout bill, and different call. **VOICE** Typical territorial calls consist of three to seven loud, even-pitched staccato notes, *whit-whit-whit-whit-whit*; or more plaintive series, e.g. *wui-wui-wui-wui* or *whi-whi-whi-whi-whi-whi-whi* or *dri-dri-dri-dri-dri-dri*, etc. Also makes coarse sounds, harsher than territorial calls, e.g. *chow-chow-chow-chow-chow, juju-dui-dui-dui* etc. Low contact calls include *ruk-ruk, ruk-uk-uk, chi-cho-cho* and sibilant *chu-chu* and *chut-chut-chut* (C. Robson). **HABITS** Similar to those of Black-breasted Parrotbill. **HABITAT** Grass and scrub, bushes and bamboo stands, mainly in the subtropical zone. **BREEDING** April–June. Nest is like that of Black-breasted Parrotbill. **DISTRIBUTION AND STATUS** Resident. Hills of NE India (Arunachal Pradesh, Assam, Meghalaya, Mizoram, Nagaland) and Bangladesh. Recorded from 900 m to over 2100 m, mainly 1500–1800 m. **IN:** current status uncertain; very few recent records. **BD:** ?former resident; no recent records, but could still occur in hill tracts. **REFERENCES** Singh (1995).

FULVOUS PARROTBILL *Paradoxornis fulvifrons* Plate 136

Fulvous-fronted Suthora (I), Fulvous-fronted Parrotbill (F)

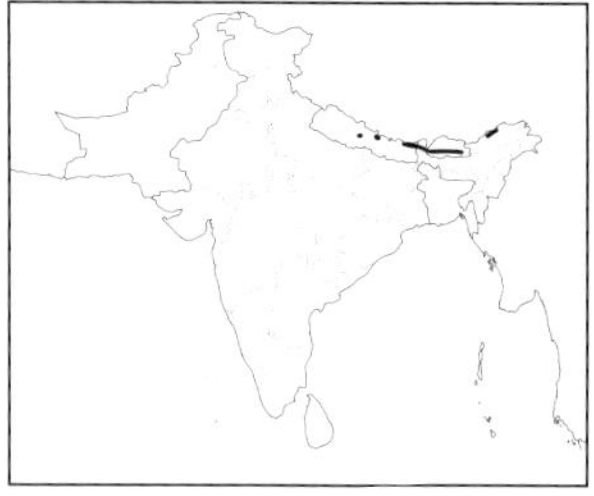

IDENTIFICATION 12 cm. A small, bull-headed and comparatively long-tailed parrotbill, lacking black, white and grey patterning of Black-throated (below). Main differences from that species are fulvous (rather than grey or rufous) crown and supercilium, olive-brown (rather than black) lateral crown-stripes, olive-brown ear-coverts, lack of striking white malar patch, fulvous throat and breast, and less rufescent upperparts. **VOICE** Probable song type: thin, high pitched *si-si ssuuu-juuu*, with *suuu* part rising and with harsher-sounding final note; also, *si-si-sissu-suu-u* and *si-si-sissu-suue*, with thin last notes. Short contact calls, and soft *twip.tip.tip.tip trritip-tip* etc (C. Robson). **HABITS** Keeps in flocks of 20–30 birds, which move rapidly through the bamboo and maintain contact with a continual twitter. Climbs with agility about bamboo stems, sometimes hanging upside-down. Quite tame. **HABITAT** Dense bamboo in temperate and sub-alpine zones. **BREEDING** Probably June and July. Nest unknown. **DISTRIBUTION AND STATUS** Local resident. Himalayas from WC Nepal east to Arunachal Pradesh. Not known to move altitudinally with the seasons; 2745–3555 m. **NP:** uncommon **IN:** rare. **BT:** uncommon.

BLACK-THROATED PARROTBILL *Paradoxornis nipalensis* Plate 136

Orange Suthora (I), Nepal Parrotbill (F)

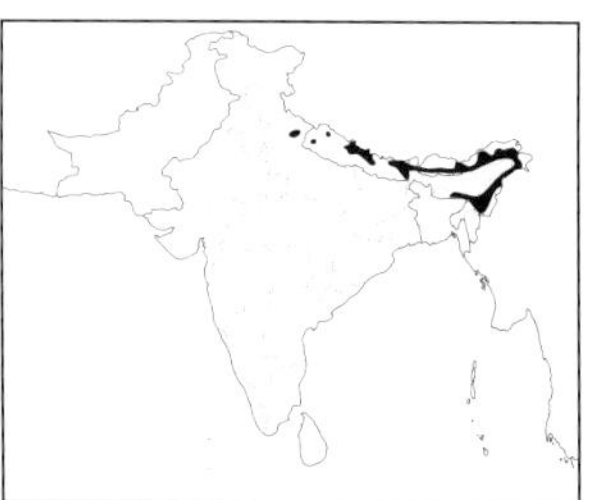

IDENTIFICATION 10 cm. A small, bull-headed parrotbill. All races show broad blackish lateral crown-stripes and black throat, fine white supercilium and white malar patch, and black primary-covert patch, which distinguish this species from Fulvous Parrotbill (above). **Racial variation** Considerable in the subcontinent: *P. n. nipalensis* and *P. n. garhwalensis* of the C Himalayas have grey crown and ear-coverts; *P. n. humii* to the east has brownish-orange crown and ear-coverts and brighter orange-brown mantle; *P. n. crocotius* of E Bhutan is similar to *humii*, but has cinnamon-orange crown and duller ear-coverts and mantle; *P. n. poliotis* of E Himalayas south to Manipur has rufous crown, slate-grey ear-coverts, more extensively black throat and grey underparts; and *P. n. patriciae* of the Mizoram hills is similar to *poliotis*, but has deep fulvous (rather than grey) breast. **VOICE** Flocks emit a general hubbub of dry, chattering trills (S. Buckton). **HABITS** Similar to those of Fulvous Parrotbill, but more fast-moving. Often in mixed feeding parties with other babblers and tits. Hunts almost feverishly among bamboo and bushes; sometimes a few birds pause briefly to perch close together on a branch. **HABITAT** Bamboo and dense undergrowth in deciduous and evergreen broadleaved forest, especially oaks; bamboo stands. **BREEDING** Known only from Assam. May and June. Nest is a tiny cup, placed up to

0.6 m above ground in a bamboo clump or thick bushes. **DISTRIBUTION AND STATUS** Resident. Himalayas from N Uttar Pradesh east to Arunachal Pradesh; NE India. **NP:** frequent; 2000–3000 m (down to 1050 m). **IN:** generally uncommon, locally fairly common; 2100–2700 m in N Uttar Pradesh, 1200–3300 m in E Himalayas, from 530 m up to at least 2600 m in NE hills. **BT:** frequent. **REFERENCES** Athreya *et al.* (1997).

LESSER RUFOUS-HEADED PARROTBILL *Paradoxornis atrosuperciliaris* Plate 136

Lesser Red-headed Suthora (I), Black-browed Parrotbill

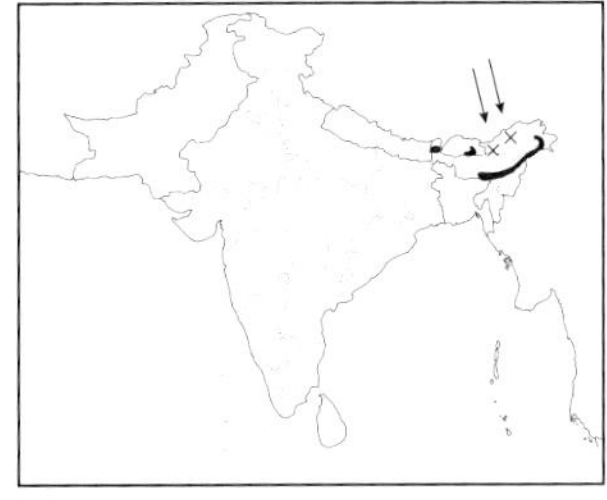

IDENTIFICATION 15 cm. A smallish, rather stocky parrotbill with rufous-orange crown and nape and buffish-white underparts, and a stout pale bill. Told from the similar Greater Rufous-headed Parrotbill (below) by smaller size, smaller and stouter bill, whitish lores and paler buffish-orange ear-coverts. **Racial variation** *P. a. oatesi* of the E Himalayas has no apparent black eyebrow, and whiter underparts. Black eyebrow is prominent (a further difference from Greater Rufous-headed) and underparts buff in *P. a. atrosuperciliaris*, which occurs south and east of the Brahmaputra R. **VOICE** Possible song consists of sharp, rapidly repeated chipping *tit-tit-tit-tit-tit-tit-tit-tit...*, *chit-chit-chit-chit-chit-chit...*, *tsu-tsu-tsu-tsu-tsu-tsu...* etc. Flocks call with subdued, rapid, jumbled chattering, interspersed with harsher, more metallic *chut-chut-chut* or *chip-chip-chip*. Soft *wik-wik* and *tchip-tchip-tchip-tchip* contact calls. **HABITS** Found in flocks of six to 15 birds, often with White-hooded Babblers (p.771) or Greater Rufous-headed or Black-breasted Parrotbills (above and p.781). Tends to keep out of sight in bamboo stands. Hangs upside-down from bamboo stems in tit-like fashion. Has a weak flight. **HABITAT** Bamboo stands, tall reeds and grass and scrub jungle, mainly in the tropical and subtropical zones. **BREEDING** April–July. Nest is a deep cup, placed about 2 m above ground in a bamboo clump or reeds. **DISTRIBUTION AND STATUS** Resident. Himalayas from Nepal? and West Bengal east to Arunachal Pradesh; NE India (Assam, Meghalaya, Nagaland). Subject to some altitudinal movements: recorded 500–1500 m, winters down to the foothills. **NP:** possibly recorded in 19th century, but the specimen may have originated in India. **IN:** generally rare, but locally frequent in Himalayan foothills; uncommon in NE hills. **BT:** probably uncommon. **REFERENCES** Allen *et al.* (1997), Athreya *et al.* (1997).

GREATER RUFOUS-HEADED PARROTBILL *Paradoxornis ruficeps* Plate 136

Greater Red-headed Parrotbill (I), Rufous-headed Parrotbill

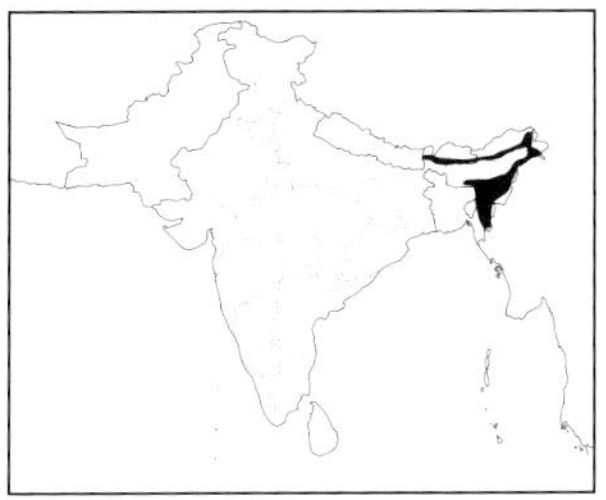

IDENTIFICATION 18 cm. A medium-sized, rather stocky parrotbill with rufous-orange crown, ear-coverts and nape and a stout pale bill. Told from the very similar Lesser Rufous-headed Parrotbill (above) by larger size, longer and less stubby bill, and deep rufous-orange ear-coverts (which are well demarcated from throat), without whitish lores. In addition, birds south and east of the Brahmaputra R lack the noticeable black eyebrow shown by the Lesser Rufous-headed which occur in that region. Possibly confusable with juvenile White-hooded Babbler (p.771), but has much stouter bill. **Juvenile** is said to be paler rufous-orange on head. **Racial variation** *P. r. ruficeps* of the E Himalayas has whiter underparts, with buff restricted to the flanks, compared with *P. r. bakeri*, which occurs south and east of the Brahmaputra R and has mainly buff underparts. **VOICE** A strong, whistled *swee-swee-swee-swo*, and a harsh, buzzing and metallic *dzaw-dzaw* (R. Grimmett); also nasal *tchip*, *chit* and doubled *chit-it* notes (P. Holt). **HABITS** Goes about in pairs or small parties, often with other babblers. Typically skulks in the undergrowth and lower level of forest. Flight is weak. **HABITAT** Bamboo stands, bamboo and other undergrowth in moist broadleaved forest, reedbeds and tall grass in the tropical and subtropical zones. **BREEDING** April–July. Nest is a deep cup, placed 1–2 m above ground in bamboo, reeds or a small tree. **DISTRIBUTION AND STATUS** Resident. Himalayas from Darjeeling, West Bengal, east to Arunachal Pradesh; NE India. From plains up to 1830 m all year (–1930 m in Bhutan). **IN:** locally frequent. **BT:** uncommon. **BD:** vagrant? **REFERENCES** Athreya *et al.* (1997), Raman (1995), Singh (1995).

SYLVIA WARBLERS Subfamily Sylviinae, tribe Sylviini

Small to medium-sized passerines with a fine bill, closely resembling the true warblers. Typically, they inhabit bushes and scrub and feed chiefly by gleaning insects from foliage and twigs; they sometimes also consume berries in autumn and winter.

GARDEN WARBLER *Sylvia borin* Plate 124

IDENTIFICATION 14 cm. A rather stocky, stout-billed, very plain warbler. Has olive-brown to grey-brown upperparts and buffish-white underparts, with white throat. Comparatively featureless, but has dark eye with whitish eye-ring and narrow pale fringes to tertials. Stout bill, stocky appearance and plain face, with just a faint sug-

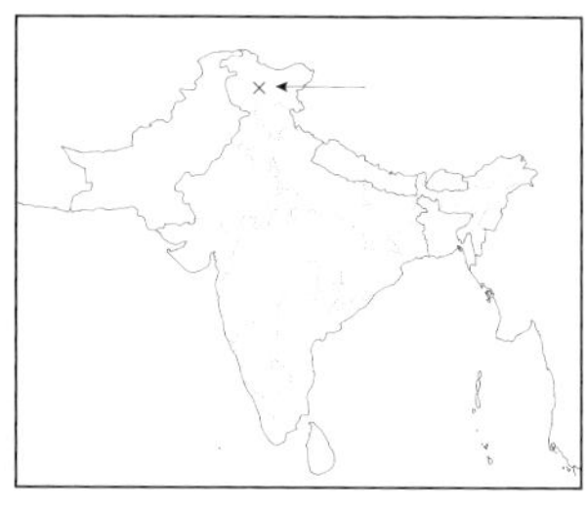

gestion of a greyish supercilium, help separate it from the *Hippolais* and *Acrocephalus* warblers. For differences from Barred Warbler (p.785), see that species. **VOICE** Has strong, rapidly delivered and melodious song; calls include a *check-check* and low *tchur-r-r*. **HABITS** Not described from the region, but well studied in Europe. Forages mainly in bushes, occasionally moving into the tree canopy. Quiet and unobtrusive, keeping within cover for long periods. Flicks wings and tail only when excited. Flight is fast and generally straight. **HABITAT** Undescribed in the region. Elsewhere, frequents undergrowth in forest clearings and edges and bushes. **DISTRIBUTION AND STATUS IN:** vagrant to Ladakh.

GREATER WHITETHROAT *Sylvia communis* — Plate 124

Whitethroat (I), Common Whitethroat (R)

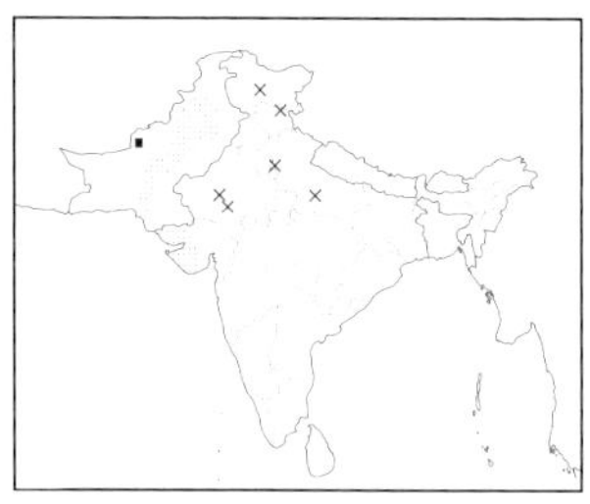

IDENTIFICATION 14 cm. Superficially resembles Lesser Whitethroat (below), but is larger and longer-tailed, has broad, well-defined sandy-brown to pale rufous-brown fringes to greater coverts and tertials, pale base to lower mandible, and orange-brown to pale brown (not grey) legs and feet. Unlike Lesser, does not show darker ear-coverts. **Adult male** has grey crown and ear-coverts merging into greyish mantle; breast and flanks can show pinkish wash, and has orange- or reddish-brown iris. **Adult female** and **first-winter** have pale grey-brown crown, ear-coverts and mantle, and iris is dull brown or olive. Larger size and broad fringes to coverts and tertials help separate both from female Ménétries's Warbler (p.785). **VOICE** A hurried, scratchy warbling, *cheeechiwee-cheechiweechoo-chiwichoo*; calls include a sharp *tack tack*, and harsh *tcharr* and lower-pitched *chur* when alarmed. **HABITS** Found singly or in pairs in the breeding season; often in loose groups when on passage. Feeding behaviour is similar to that of other *Sylvia* warblers. Chiefly keeps low down in vegetation, often coming into the open. If flushed, flies low and jerkily into cover. Has a horizontal carriage, with the head and tail usually held up. Raises crown feathers when excited. **HABITAT** On passage, found in scattered bushes in semi-desert, standing crops and bushes, hedges and herbaceous plants around cultivation and at roadsides; has bred in thorn bushes on hillsides. **BREEDING** May–July. Nest is a cup of grass, placed in a low bush. **DISTRIBUTION AND STATUS** Has bred in Baluchistan, Pakistan, and collected once in Ladakh in June; passage migrant in Pakistan and NW India (from Jammu and Kashmir south to Gujarat and east to C Uttar Pradesh). **PK:** fairly widespread and frequent, late August–mid September; only two breeding records, once at 2300 m. **IN:** common on northward migration.

LESSER WHITETHROAT *Sylvia curruca* — Plate 124

Hume's Lesser Whitethroat (P), Hume's Whitethroat, Small Whitethroat, *S. althaea*, *S. minula*

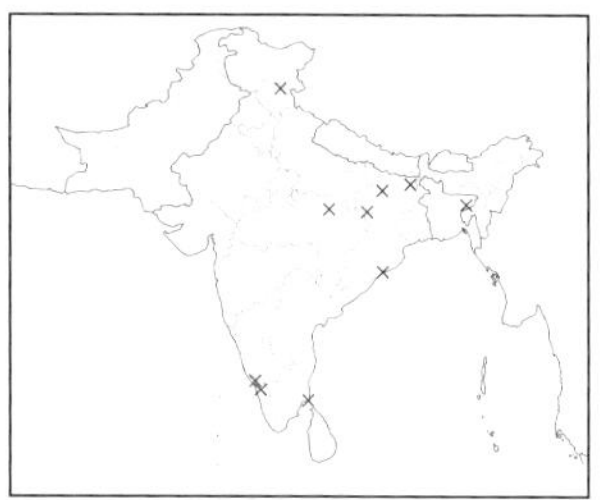

IDENTIFICATION 13 cm. Variable, with brownish-grey upperparts, dull whitish underparts (can have pinkish flush to breast in fresh plumage), slate-grey crown (greyer and slightly darker than mantle) with darker lores and ear-coverts, blackish bill, and dark grey legs and feet. Can show suggestion of paler supercilium and pale buffish fringes to tertials and secondaries in fresh plumage. For differences from Greater Whitethroat (above) and Orphean Warbler (p.786), see those species. **Racial variation** *S. c. blythi*, which winters widely through the subcontinent, is covered by the description above. *S. c. althaea*, which breeds in the W Himalayas and winters widely through the peninsula, closely resembles *blythi*, but appears slightly larger, with larger and stouter bill, has darker, purer grey mantle, and has darker grey crown with blackish ear-coverts; on some *althaea*, whole crown can be dark grey, with little contrast against dark ear-coverts (giving rise to dark-headed appearance), and can show strong greyish wash to sides of breast; does not generally show a noticeable contrast between grey of crown and ear-coverts and brownish coloration of nape and sides of neck, which is usually the case in *blythi*. *S. c. minula*, which is a passage migrant and winter visitor to NW subcontinent, is slightly smaller and more finely built than *blythi*, with finer bill: compared with *blythi*, has paler, sandy grey-brown upperparts with sandy fringes to coverts and remiges, the fringes to secondaries forming sandy panel on wing; tail is slightly darker grey-brown than rump/uppertail-coverts, but shows little contrast (unlike *blythi*); forehead and crown are pale grey (paler than in *blythi*) and, as in that form, often shows slightly darker 'mask'; lores may be paler grey than ear-coverts and concolorous with forecrown, and darker 'mask' is frequently barely apparent or lacking, giving rise to rather 'plain-faced' appearance; underparts, especially breast sides and flanks, are frequently washed with warm buff (more so than in *blythi*). All three races vary, however, and racial identity cannot always be ascertained. **VOICE** *S. c. blythi*: song is a soft, low-pitched, rather scratchy warble, and a distinctive dry, throbbing rattle, the two often run together; call is a hard *teck-teck*. *S. c. althaea*: song lacks the rattle, and is a loud, continuous bubbling warble, usually starting off with a rapidly bubbling *wrichoo-wrichoo-wrichoo-wrichoo-richoo-tiee-diee-dee-dee* (Roberts 1992). *S. c. minula*: song lacks the rattle of *blythi*, and is a pleasant, rather quiet and varied warbling; calls include a *chee-chee-chee* and a *tirritic* (Wallace 1973).

HABITS Has a horizontal carriage and feeding behaviour similar to those of Greater Whitethroat, but unlike that species often hunts in trees, is more secretive and has a less jerky flight. Also frequently feeds in bushes. **HABITAT** Breeds in scattered juniper scrub and Holly Oak scrub in Pakistan, low scattered bushes of cotoneaster and berberis in Kashmir, and *Lonicera*, willows and fruit trees in Ladakh; winters in scrub, acacias, roadside and canalside plantations, bushes in semi-desert and deciduous woodland. **BREEDING** End April–August. Nest is a loose cup of dry grass, placed in a low bush or tree, 0.5–1.5 m above ground. **DISTRIBUTION AND STATUS** Breeds in hills of W Pakistan, and in Himalayas from N Pakistan east to Kashmir; winters mainly from Pakistan east to E Nepal and south to N Tamil Nadu and N Sri Lanka. **PK:** common and widespread winter visitor; breeds uncommonly in drier N areas. **NP:** uncommon and widespread winter visitor and passage migrant; regularly recorded below 1500 m (–2750 m on passage). **IN:** locally common on breeding grounds, 1500–3700 m; common and widespread winter visitor to the plains and hills, up to 900 m (–3300 m on passage). **BD:** vagrant. **LK:** winter visitor to dry lowlands, especially NW coastal areas. **REFERENCES** Svensson (1992), Wallace (1973).

MÉNÉTRIES'S WARBLER *Sylvia mystacea* — Plate 124

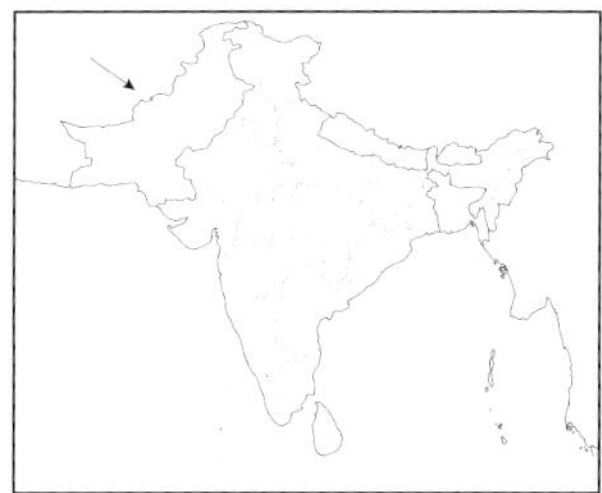

IDENTIFICATION 12 cm. A small, active *Sylvia* warbler with comparatively long tail which is frequently cocked and swung. **Male** is distinctive, with blackish crown and ear-coverts, orange-brown iris and reddish-brown orbital ring, pinkish-buff to deep pink throat and breast with white submoustachial line, blue-grey mantle and rump with contrastingly dark blackish tail, and brownish-red legs and feet. Some (younger?) males have whitish underparts and paler grey head (showing less contrast with mantle). **Female/first-winter** has rather uniform sandy grey-brown upperparts and whitish underparts; iris is yellowish-brown (female) or dark/olive-brown (first-winter). Differs from *minula* Lesser Whitethroat (p.784) in lacking any suggestion of darker mask, and in having strikingly dark tail, and pale (typically orange-brown) legs and feet; often has rufous-brown coloration to feathers of forehead, which is lacking on Lesser Whitethroat. Distinguished from female Greater Whitethroat (p.784) by smaller size, darker tail, uniform sandy grey-brown coverts (lacking prominent fringes), and much less distinct (paler) fringes to tertials. **VOICE** Song is a dry, chattering warble; calls include a *dack* and dry, harsh rattling *tzerrr* (Alström and Colston 1991). **HABITS** Feeding behaviour is similar to that of other *Sylvia* warblers. Forages restlessly in bushes or low herbaceous plants, usually within cover. Sometimes perches on the top of bushes; when perched, has a habit of raising its tail above the body and waving it from side to side and up and down. Flight is weak and jerky. Males sing from inside bushes and in short, steep, jerky song flight. **HABITAT** Semi-desert, favouring valley bottoms with much scrub cover. **BREEDING** Unknown in the region. Probably nests April–June, in thickets. In the CIS, nest is a deep cup made of grasses and thin twigs, placed low down in a bush. **DISTRIBUTION AND STATUS PK:** rare summer visitor, recorded only from the Surkhab valley, Baluchistan, at 1670 m. **REFERENCES** Alström and Colston (1991), Svensson (1992).

DESERT WARBLER *Sylvia nana* — Plate 124

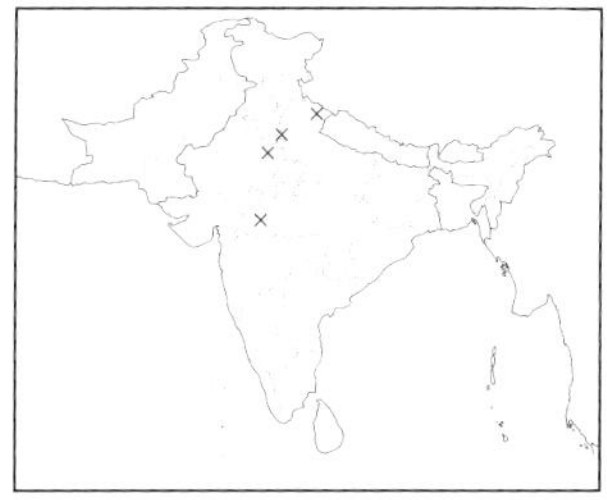

IDENTIFICATION 11.5 cm. A small, very distinctive *Sylvia* with sandy-brown upperparts, rufous rump, uppertail-coverts and central tail feathers, whitish underparts, yellow iris, yellow base to bill, and yellowish legs and feet. First-winter plumage is as adult. **VOICE** Song is a pleasant *tiri-tityu-tyu-tyu-tyuyu*; call is a nasal rattle. **HABITS** Feeds mainly on the ground, progressing in short hops or creeping about like a mouse; methodically seeks insects around the roots of small bushes. Sometimes also feeds in bushes in a similar manner to other *Sylvia* warblers. Often holds the tail cocked. Occasionally perches on the top of bushes. Flight is fast, with whirring wingbeats, low over the ground. **HABITAT** Scattered scrub in sandy or stony desert, rocky hills and escarpments, and low vegetation on coastal mudflats. **DISTRIBUTION AND STATUS** Winter visitor, mainly to Pakistan and extreme NW India (from Punjab south to W Gujarat); may breed in S Baluchistan, but confirmation is required. **PK:** common and very widespread in the more barren, uncultivated areas. **IN:** locally common.

BARRED WARBLER *Sylvia nisoria* — Plate 124

IDENTIFICATION 15 cm. A large, stout-billed *Sylvia*. In flight, appears heavy, with long, broad tail, recalling Eurasian Wryneck (p.380). **Adult** is greyish above and whitish below, with yellowish iris. Underparts are variably barred with grey (more heavily on older males, and more faintly/less extensively on females and younger males); scapulars and uppertail-coverts are faintly barred with white, and has broad whitish fringes to median and greater coverts, and tertials. **First-winter** has greyish olive-brown upperparts and buffish underparts, and resembles Garden Warbler (p.783). Distinguished from that species by larger size and more elongated appearance, with longer tail, larger bill, pale greyish-white fringes to tertials and median/greater coverts (forming narrow double wing-bars), faint whitish barring on uppertail-coverts, and dark barring on undertail-coverts and occasionally flanks. **VOICE** Song is a hurried warble, often interspersed with dry rattling; call is a harsh *charr* or *tchad-tchad.*

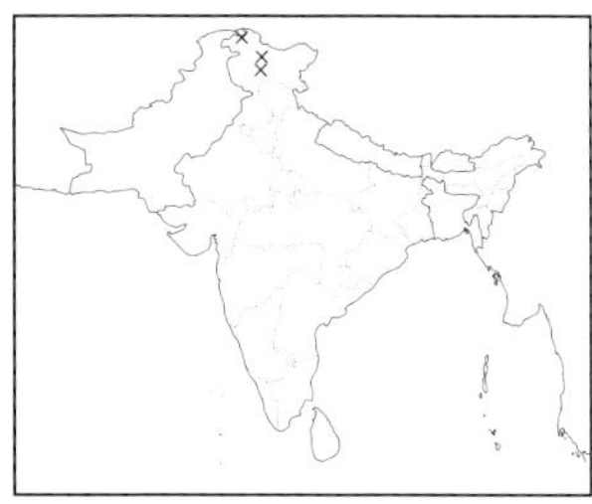

HABITS Shy, and skulks within thick low cover. Often lethargic on passage, but can move rapidly through vegetation. **HABITAT** Bushes. **DISTRIBUTION AND STATUS PK:** vagrant to the north. **IN:** vagrant to Ladakh.

ORPHEAN WARBLER *Sylvia hortensis* Plate 124

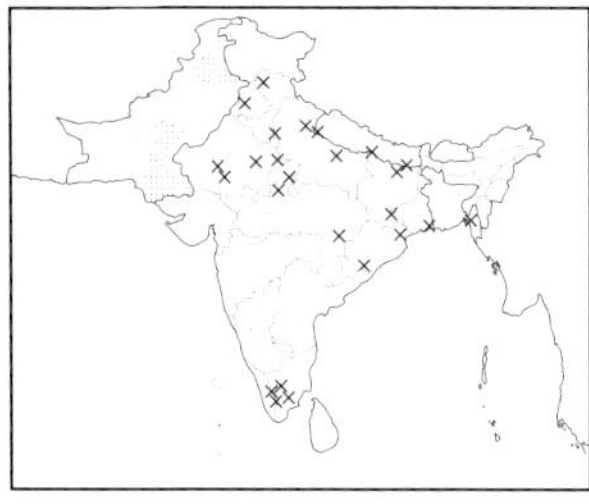

IDENTIFICATION 15 cm. A large, big-billed *Sylvia*, most likely to be confused with Lesser Whitethroat (p.784). **Adult** is readily told by larger size and longer, stouter-looking bill, noticeable contrast between blackish crown and paler grey mantle, blackish tail which contrasts noticeably with grey rump and uppertail-coverts, and (on adult male) white or yellowish-white iris. Bill of some birds can look very long and slightly downcurved, while on others it is large but evenly proportioned. **Adult male** has black crown which is concolorous with ear-coverts and is clearly demarcated from much paler, bluish-grey upperparts. **Adult female** can be much as adult male, but others have duller dark grey crown (with blacker ear-coverts) and sandy-brown cast to mantle; still shows strong contrast between crown and mantle, which is lacking on Lesser Whitethroat. Iris is pale grey-brown (but may show whitish spotting or narrow broken ring). **First-year** has crown concolorous with mantle (or slightly darker or greyer), with darker grey ear-coverts, and is very similar in plumage to many Lesser Whitethroats; like that species, has dark iris. Much larger size and more ponderous movements, heavier appearance in flight, with longer-looking tail, and larger bill should be sufficient to separate it from Lesser Whitethroat, but can be surprisingly difficult to judge on occasions. Orphean often shows darker-looking uppertail (contrasting with paler grey uppertail-coverts, and with purer white on outer rectrices), shows indistinct (or lacks) white eye-ring (usually quite distinct and more complete on Lesser Whitethroat), and has greyish centres and diffuse whitish fringes to undertail-coverts (generally uniformly white on Lesser Whitethroat). Some birds, however, are not safely separable in the field by any of these plumage features. **VOICE** Song is a strong, varied, thrush-like warble; call is a *tack* or *tchak*, which is deeper and harder than calls of Lesser Whitethroat, and has a loud *trrr* rattle. **HABITS** Usually solitary. Forages chiefly in trees and bushes, and much less likely than other *Sylvia* warblers to be found close to the ground. Has slower and more deliberate movements than other warblers. Carriage is slightly above the horizontal, and sometimes cocks its tail. **HABITAT** Breeds on bush-covered hillsides; winters in dense scrub jungle, riverain forest, groves and bushes in semi-desert. **BREEDING** End April–July. Nest is a flimsy cup of grasses, covered in cobwebs, built in a low bush. **DISTRIBUTION AND STATUS** Summer visitor to Baluchistan and NW Pakistan; winters mainly from Gujarat east to E Maharashtra and south to S Karnataka, with scattered records from elsewhere; also a passage migrant, mainly to Pakistan and India. **PK:** in summer, fairly widespread and locally common in C and N Baluchistan, less frequent in NW Pakistan, breeds 760–2400 m; passage migrant in Punjab; a few winter records in S Sind. **NP:** vagrant. **IN:** widespread and locally common winter visitor; common passage migrant in the northwest. **BD:** vagrant. **REFERENCES** Svensson (1992), Harris *et al.* (1996).

LARKS Alaudidae

Terrestrial passerines, generally small-sized, which usually walk and run on the ground and often have a very elongated hindclaw. Their plumage is cryptically coloured in brownish or buff, with dark streaks below, and the colour of the upperparts is often the same as that of the local soil. Juveniles of most lark species differ from adults in having rounded dark-centred feathers to the upperparts, with prominent pale fringes. Typically, their flight is strong and undulating. As a family, larks take a wide variety of food, including insects, molluscs, arthropods, seeds, flowers, buds and leaves. Larks are ground-nesters and defend breeding territories. Many species have a melodious song, which is often delivered in a distinctive, steeply climbing or circling aerial display, but also from a conspicuous low perch. They live in a wide range of open habitats, including grassland, desert and cultivation.

SINGING BUSHLARK *Mirafra cantillans* Plate 137

Singing Lark, *M. javanica* (I)

IDENTIFICATION (See also summary table, p.788.) 14 cm. A stocky, stout-billed, broad-winged lark with slight crest. Like other *Mirafra* larks shows rufous on wing, although this is less extensive than on other species. Distinguished from Indian and Rufous-winged Bushlarks (p.787) by comparatively uniform brownish-buff ear-coverts, weaker and less extensive spotting on breast, and whitish outer tail feathers; upperparts are generally

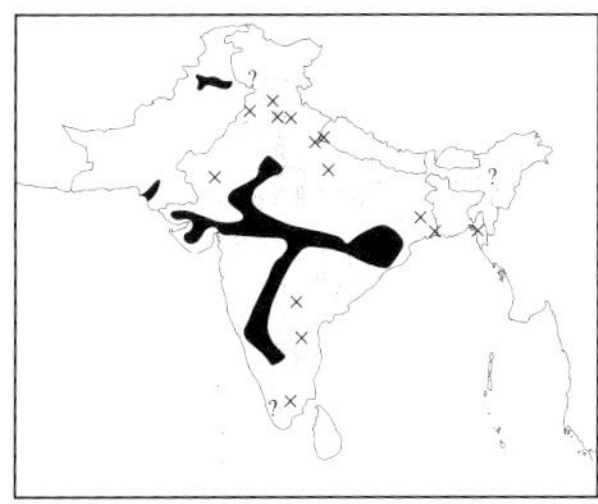

more diffusely streaked, and colder grey-brown in coloration; throat is whiter than rest of underparts, and often shows diffuse brownish- to rufous-buff breast-band. Further differences from Rufous-winged are slimmer build and longer tail, and smaller and shorter bill. See table (p.788) for further details. Compared with other *Mirafra* larks, has more varied song and distinctive display flight, towering high on winnowing or flickering wings. Also sings when perched. Bill is distinctly shorter and stouter than that of Oriental Skylark (p.797); further, shows more rufous on wing, breast generally appears spotted rather than streaked, and has shorter crest. **VOICE** Song is described as sweet and full, with much mimicry (Baker 1926), similar to those of Oriental Skylark and Sykes's Lark (p.797 and p.796). **HABITS** Usually found singly. Like other bushlarks, feeds by running about actively on the ground, picking up seeds and small insects and sometimes digging for insect larvae. Often perches on bushes if disturbed, in common with other *Mirafra* species, but unlike other larks. Males sing from the top of a bush and in a prolonged song flight, drifting over a large area before descending steeply to the ground. **HABITAT** Open thorn scrub and edges of fallow or abandoned cultivation, grassland, and semi-desert with scattered bushes. **BREEDING** March–September. Nest is a shallow cup of grass, sometimes partly domed, usually sheltered under an earth overhang or a plant. **DISTRIBUTION AND STATUS** Resident. Mainly N and S Pakistan, and India from E Rajasthan south to S Karnataka and from Gujarat east to Orissa, but apparently absent from many areas. **PK:** scarce resident and local migrant. **NP:** rare and local. **IN:** frequent but very local resident; plains and foothills, locally up to 350 m. **BD:** very local resident or summer visitor to the southeast. **REFERENCES** Giri and Choudhary (1997).

INDIAN BUSHLARK *Mirafra erythroptera* — Plate 137

Red-winged Bush Lark (I), Indian Lark

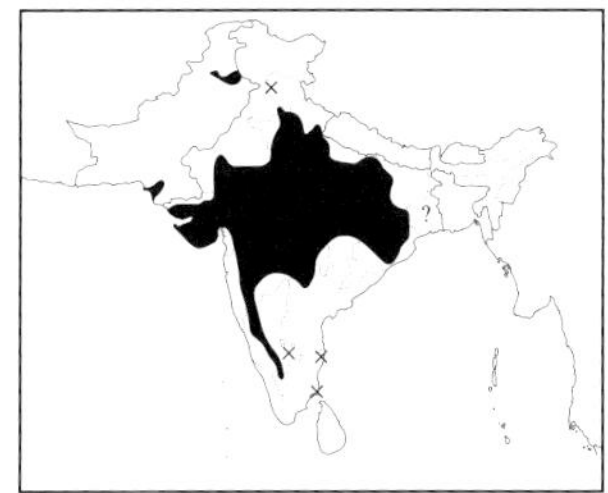

IDENTIFICATION (See also summary table, p.788.) 14 cm. A stocky, stout-billed, broad-winged lark with slight crest. Most similar to Singing Bushlark (p.786) in structure and appearance, although bill looks slightly longer and tail shorter. Main differences from Singing are more prominent spotting on ear-coverts and malar region (with more pronounced dark border to ear-coverts), more pronounced dark spotting on breast, more extensive rufous on wing (very prominent in flight), and rufous-buff outer webs to outer tail feathers. Upperparts are generally more heavily streaked, and warmer sandy-buff to rufous-buff in coloration, with rufous cast to crown often apparent; underparts tend to be more uniform whitish to buffish-white than on Singing. Told from *affinis* race of Rufous-winged (below) by smaller and shorter bill, smaller size, more rufous on win, and shorter hindclaw. **Racial variation** *M. e. sindiana* of NW subcontinent has sandy-buff coloration to upperparts, whereas the more southerly and easterly *M. e. erythroptera* is more rufous-buff above. **VOICE** A *tit-tit-tit*, followed by long, drawn-out, upward-inflected whistles, *tsweeeih-tsweeeih-tsweeeih*, occasionally uttering a variety of *Alauda*-like melodious phrases; call is a drawn-out *swee* (Roberts 1992). **HABITS** Similar to those of Singing Bushlark, except for its display flight. The male displays almost all day in the breeding season, beginning his song flight from the top of a bush or post, flying upwards with rapid wingbeats, and parachuting down with wings held motionless and raised in a wide V. **HABITAT** Sparse stony scrub, and fallow land in open plains and plateaux; in Pakistan and NW India, found among *Euphorbia* clumps in low hills and barren clay flats. **BREEDING** March–October. Nest is a shallow cup or dome of grass, placed in a small depression or at the base of a bush or stone. **DISTRIBUTION AND STATUS** Resident, endemic to the subcontinent. Mainly N and S Pakistan and from S Punjab, India, south to N Tamil Nadu, N Andhra Pradesh and Orissa, and from Gujarat east to Orissa. **PK:** locally frequent resident in S Sindh, winter visitor to Salt Range, Punjab. **IN:** widespread and locally common resident in the plains.

RUFOUS-WINGED BUSHLARK *Mirafra assamica* — Plate 137

Bush Lark (F,I), Rufous-winged Lark

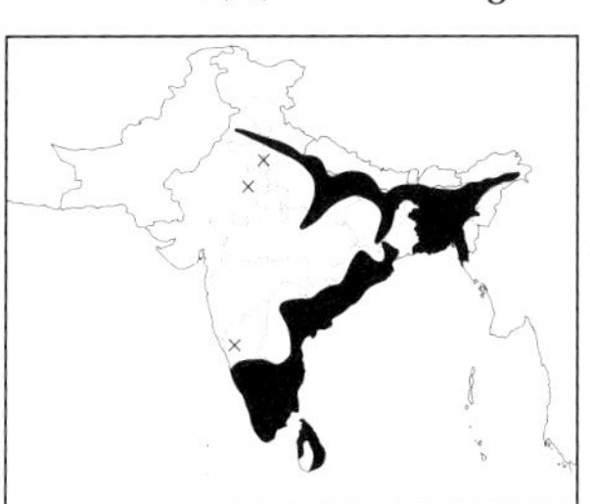

IDENTIFICATION (See also summary table, p.788.) 15 cm. Similar to Singing and Indian Bushlarks (p.787 and above) in general appearance, but is larger and stockier, with larger and longer bill and shorter tail (especially compared with Singing). Confusion is unlikely with Singing owing to heavily spotted breast, greater amount of rufous on wing, rufous-buff outer webs to outer tail feathers, and different song and display flight. **Racial variation** *M. a. assamica* of N subcontinent has brownish-grey, diffusely streaked upperparts; the underparts are dirty rufous, with paler throat and greyish flanks, and the bill is deep-based. *M. a. affinis* of peninsular India and Sri Lanka has rufous-buff upperparts with prominent dark streaks; the underparts are generally paler, and the bill is thinner. Alström *et al.* (1998) treat the latter as a separate species. **VOICE** The song of *M. a. assamica* typically consists of repetition of a series of thin, high-pitched disyllabic notes, usually delivered in a prolonged song flight. *M. a. affinis* has a very different song, a dry, metallic rattle lasting several seconds, and delivered either from a perch or in a short song flight. The call of *M. a. assam-*

IDENTIFICATION OF LARKS

Species	Structural features	Head pattern	Upperpart pattern and coloration
Singing Bushlark *Mirafra cantillans*	Well proportioned, with moderately long tail. Bill short and stout. Smallest of the bushlarks	Strong buffish-white supercilium. Ear-coverts comparatively uniform brownish-buff (some with diffuse and indistinct dark border at rear and with indistinct spotting in malar region)	Generally more diffusely streaked than Singing, with colder grey-brown coloration to upperparts
Indian Bushlark *M. e. erythroptera* *M. e. sindiana*	Much as Singing. Bill looks slightly larger and tail shorter	Supercilium possibly not so prominent as on Singing. Spotted ear-coverts and malar region, with variable, diffuse dark border at rear of ear-coverts	More clearly and heavily streaked than Singing. Crown with slight rufous cast. Upperparts warm sandy-buff (*sindiana*) to rufous-buff (*erythroptera*)
Rufous-winged Bushlark *M. a. assamica*	Stocky and comparatively short-tailed. Bill large and stout	Buffish to rufous-buff supercilium. Ear-coverts with variable rufous tinge. Ear-coverts and malar region with bold, diffuse blackish spotting and barring, with diffuse dark border to ear-coverts	Brownish-greyish and diffusely streaked (streaking strongest on crown and back)
Rufous-winged Bushlark *M. a. affinis*	Stocky and comparatively short-tailed. Bill large and long; larger than Indian Bushlark's	Buffish supercilium. Boldly spotted ear-coverts and malar region, with prominent dark border to ear-coverts	Heavily streaked crown with slight rufous cast. Upperparts rufous-buff (similar in overall appearance to *M. e. erythroptera*). Often shows prominent buffish (and heavily streaked) nape

Species	Primary projection	Bill	Upperparts and wings
Greater Short-toed Lark *C. brachydactyla dukhunensis/ C. b. longipennis*	Tertials reach or almost reach tip of primaries	Proportionately shorter and broader than Hume's. Usually pale pinkish, with indistinct dark culmen and tip to lower mandible	Warm sandy-buff and heavily streaked. Dark centres to median coverts strongly defined. Race *longipennis* is a shade colder and greyer on upperparts
Hume's Short-toed Lark *C. a. acutirostris/ C. a. tibetana*	Tertials reach (or almost reach) tip of primaries	Proportionately slightly longer and slimmer than in Greater's. Usually brownish-yellow, with distinct dark culmen and tip	Pale brownish-grey, and less heavily streaked than Greater. Streaking can be very poorly defined in fresh plumage. Uppertail-coverts usually have warm rufous-pink coloration. Dark centres to median coverts less pronounced than on Greater

Breast markings	Underpart coloration	Outer tail feathers	Wings	Hindclaw
Comparatively weak, diffuse and small brown spotting, indistinct or almost lacking on some	Typically, white throat, brownish-buff breast and buffish rest of underparts	Outer tail feathers mainly whitish, some with buffish tinge. Penultimate feathers with whitish outer webs	Comparatively weak rufous panel. Rufous fringes to primary coverts, and narrow rufous edges to outer webs of primaries and secondaries, with only a small amount of rufous on inner webs of these feathers	Shorter than or roughly equal in length to hindtoe
Strong, clearly defined blackish drop-shaped spots	Uniform whitish to buffish-white, some with stronger buff wash to breast	Rufous-buff outer web to outer tail feathers. Penultimate pair with narrow rufous-buff edge to outer webs	Extensive and prominent panel, showing much rufous in flight. Primary coverts rufous except for dark line along shaft. Almost whole and of outer web of primaries of secondaries rufous; most for inner webs rufous except tips	Shorter than or roughly equal in length to hindtoe
Large, diffuse spotting, not so bold as in *affinis*	Dirty rufous-buff, with paler throat and grey on flanks	Diffuse rufous edges to outer webs of outer tail feathers	Less extensive and prominent panel than on Indian. Primary coverts with diffuse rufous fringes. Primaries and secondaries with rufous edges to outer webs; broad diffuse edges to inner webs (except primary tips). Black centres to tertials contrast markedly with rufous-buff fringes	Long, usually distinctly longer than hindtoe
Very strong, bold blackish drop-shaped spots	Uniform whitish to buff, with variable rufous-buff wash to breast, belly and flanks	Rufous-buff outer web to outer tail feathers. Rest of tail feathers with narrow rufous-buff fringe	Less extensive and prominent panel than on Indian. Primary coverts with rufous fringe. Primaries and secondaries with rufous edges to outer webs; broad diffuse edge to inner webs (except primary tips)	Long, usually distinctly longer than hindtoe

Underparts	Head pattern
Variable dark patch on side of upper breast (lacking on some); some with a few streaks on upper breast. *C. b. dukhunensis* has buffish-white underparts with variable rufous-buff breast-band (often strongest, and distinctly rufous, on breast sides). *C. b. longipennis* has breast washed with brownish-buff (again, often strongest on breast sides). Flanks often buffish	Crown heavily streaked, some with distinct rufous cast. Broader supercilium than on Hume's and Lesser and lores usually appear pale. Typically, shows dark eye-stripe and patch on rear ear-coverts, with pale patch on lower ear-coverts and crescent below eye
Variable diffuse dark patch on breast side, some with a few diffuse streaks. Breast washed with cold greyish-buff, although breast warmer and buffier on some. Rest of underparts whitish	Compared with Greater Short-toed: crown less heavily streaked, often appearing almost unstreaked; supercilium narrower and more poorly defined in front of eye; ear-coverts more uniform, usually without prominent dark eye-stripe. Lores usually show dark stripe

continued overleaf

IDENTIFICATION OF LARKS continued

Species	Primary projection	Bill	Upperparts and wings
Lesser Short-toed Lark *C. rufescens persica*	3–4 primary tips clearly visible beyond longest tertial	Shorter and stouter than in Greater's, more distinctly curved on both mandibles	Paler, sandy-buff (almost pinkish-buff), compared with Greater, and generally more finely and sparsely streaked. Dark centres to median coverts usually less pronounced than on Greater
Asian Short-toed Lark	3–4 primary tips clearly visible beyond longest tertial	Short and stout, but distinctly smaller than that of *persica* race of Lesser	Generally even paler than Lesser, and streaking more diffuse. Base colour of some cream. Dark centres to median coverts usually less pronounced than on Greater
Sand Lark *C. r. raytal/ C. r. adamsi*	3 primary tips clearly visible beyond longest tertial	Finer than in Greater's. Bill of *adamsi* is distinctly longer and finer than that of nominate	Cold sandy-grey and diffusely streaked (streaking really distinct only on scapulars). Wings rather uniform, lacking pronounced dark centres to median coverts

ica consists of a series of variable, thin, high-pitched short notes, whereas that of *M. a. affinis* is typically a short, high-pitched trill (Alström 1998). **HABITS** Generally similar to those of Indian Bushlark. *M. a. assamica* is typically terrestrial, whereas *M. a. affinis* frequently perches on bushes, trees and telegraph wires. **HABITAT** *M. a affinis* inhabits dry, open areas with bushes and trees, while *M. a. assamica* favours more open, grassy areas which are often slightly wet. **BREEDING** December–May and September, varying locally. Nest and nest site are like those of Indian Bushlark. **DISTRIBUTION AND STATUS** Resident. From Punjab, India, east to NE India and Bangladesh and south through much of the E and S peninsula and Sri Lanka. **NP:** common and widespread throughout the terai. **IN:** common and widespread in plains and low country. **BT:** rare. **BD:** common throughout. **LK:** common in lowlands, more frequent in dry zone. **REFERENCES** Alström (1998).

BLACK-CROWNED SPARROW LARK *Eremopterix nigriceps* Plate 137

Black-crowned Finch Lark (I,R)

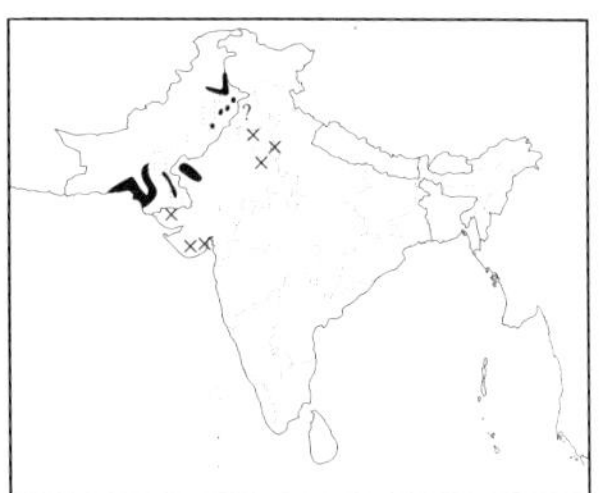

IDENTIFICATION 13 cm. A small, stocky lark with a stout bill. **Male** has brownish-black underparts and white cheeks. Distinguished from the similar Ashy-crowned (below) by brownish-black crown and nape, with whitish forehead; nape is white on some, forming collar, with brownish-black patch on upper mantle. Upperparts are sandier than on Grey-crowned. **Female** is probably inseparable in the field from female Ashy-crowned, although upperparts are more sandy-brown. Much stouter bill, more uniform upperparts (with almost unstreaked mantle and scapulars) and dark grey underwing-coverts separate it from Sand Lark (p.795). **VOICE** Song is brief and stereotyped, although more varied than that of Ashy-crowned: a short, repeated, warbled *dwee-di-ul-twee-e-h* uttered on the rise, followed by a lower-pitched *d-e-e-e-eh de-e-e-e-h* as it parachutes down, and sometimes interspersed with a third sequence, *chip-di-di-dee-eh* (Roberts 1992). **HABITS** In the non-breeding season, keeps in flocks of up to 40 birds. Walks and runs quickly and erratically, and crouches close to the ground to feed. The male displays almost all day during the nesting period: he flies upwards with fast wingbeats, his flight becoming undulating at the peak of his ascent, and then makes a stepped descent with wings slightly raised. Feeds on seeds and insects, either picked from the ground or taken directly from vegetation, usually by reaching up from the ground, also by fluttering up to seed heads. **HABITAT** Sandy deserts. **BREEDING** February–September. Nest is like that of Ashy-crowned Sparrow Lark, placed in a depression and usually sheltered by a grass clump. **DISTRIBUTION AND STATUS** Resident, subject to local movements. C and E Pakistan and NW India (Haryana, Gujarat and Rajasthan). **PK:** common to frequent in the more extensive deserts, including the Thar and Cholistan deserts and sand hills bordering the Nara canal. **IN:** locally common.

ASHY-CROWNED SPARROW LARK *Eremopterix grisea* Plate 137

Ashy-crowned Finch Lark (F,I,N,P,R)

IDENTIFICATION 12 cm. A small, stocky lark with a stout bill. **Male** has brownish-black underparts as Black-crowned (above), but occurs widely throughout subcontinent. Told from Black-crowned by grey crown and nape, contrasting with brownish-black lores and supercilium; for further differences, see that species. **Female** told from Sand Lark (p.795) by much stouter greyish bill, more uniform head (lacking dark eye-stripe), rather uniform

Underparts	Head pattern
Relatively broad band of fine dark streaking. Lacking dark patches on sides of breast and with variable buffish wash. Some with streaking on flanks, streaking continuing onto lower throat on some	Crown strongly streaked, but more finely so than on Greater. Less striking head pattern than Greater, with less prominent supercilium and streaked ear-coverts. Typically, white supercilium continues across forehead (broken at culmen base on Greater)
As Lesser, although streaking generally more diffuse	Much as Lesser
Fine, sparse dark streaking on otherwise rather uniform white or creamy-white underparts	Crown more strongly streaked than rest of upperparts. Prominent whitish supercilium and broad crescent below eye-stripe, with whitish patch on ear-coverts

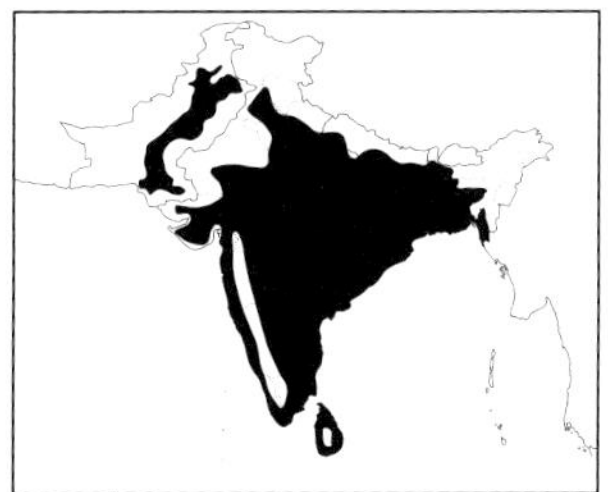

upperparts (with almost unstreaked mantle and scapulars), indistinct and diffuse breast streaking, and blackish underwing-coverts (latter can be difficult to see in field). **Juvenile** has rufous cast to upperparts and underparts, with rufous-buff fringes to upperwing-coverts and tertials. **VOICE** Song less varied than Black-crowned's: a short, flute-like *tweedle-deedle-deedle* as the bird rises, followed by a drawn-out whistled *wheeh* in descent (Roberts 1992). Call is a rolling *chulp* (R. Grimmett). **HABITS** Similar to those of Black-crowned Sparrow Lark, including display flight, but rather less gregarious. Can often be seen on dusty tracks and collecting grit from roadsides. **HABITAT** Uncultivated tracts with scattered thorn bushes and grass clumps, cultivation and fallow and ploughed fields around villages, stony scrub and dry tidal mudflats. **BREEDING** Almost all year, varying locally. Builds a saucer-shaped nest of grasses in a depression in the ground, often rimmed with a wall of small stones and placed in the shelter of a stone or small bush. **DISTRIBUTION AND STATUS** Endemic to the subcontinent. Resident, subject to local movements. Widespread, but apparently absent from Himalayas, Western Ghats and parts of the northwest and northeast. **PK:** locally common and very widespread throughout the Indus plains from N Punjab to the Karachi coast. **NP:** fairly common and widespread throughout the terai (–730 m). **IN:** common and widespread; mainly in the plains, occasionally up to 1000 m. **BD:** occurs locally throughout. **LK:** common in the coastal dry zone, visitor to the wet zone.

BAR-TAILED LARK *Ammomanes cincturus* — Plate 137

Bar-tailed Desert Lark (I)

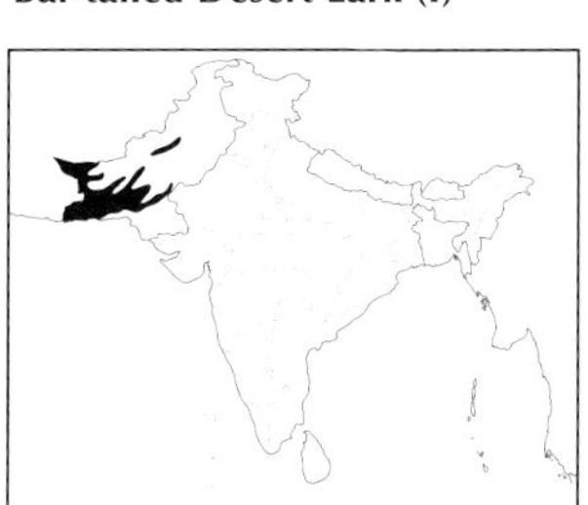

IDENTIFICATION 15 cm. Superficially similar to Desert Lark (p.792), with unstreaked sandy-grey upperparts, pinkish-buff breast and belly, and rufous on wings and uppertail-coverts. Crown is finely streaked, and breast has diffuse greyish streaking. Most useful feature is blackish terminal bar to rufous tail. Tertials are orangey-buff (colder grey-brown on Desert) and contrast more markedly with blackish primaries. Further, is smaller and stockier than Desert, with more upright stance, and has shorter and finer bill (which is mainly pinkish-horn). Primary projection is about one-quarter to one-third the length of exposed tertials. Upperparts and underparts are quite different in coloration of from those of Rufous-tailed Lark (p.792), and there is no known overlap in ranges. **Juvenile** is similar to adult, although looks scruffier, and paler, more creamy-coloured, with a less distinct tail-bar. **VOICE** Song comprises quiet fluty notes, with louder, mournful *see-oo-lee* like a creaking door (Cramp 1988); flight call (and some contact calls) a *twer* (Harris *et al.* 1996). **HABITS** Found in pairs or scattered flocks, according to the season. Runs quickly, and often prefers to escape in this way. Frequently adopts an upright posture on the ground, rather like a bunting. In song flight, the male rises steeply, then flies with deep undulations on a roughly circular path, ending with a steep descent to the ground. Direct flight is fast and rather jerky, with rapid wingbeats alternating with glides. Feeds on insects, seeds and other plant material, picked from the surface; will also dig for food. **HABITAT** Low stony hills and barren gravelly plains. **BREEDING** March and April. Builds a shallow cup-shaped nest of grass in a depression under a stone or lump of earth. **DISTRIBUTION AND STATUS PK:** resident, confined to the montane plateau regions of Baluchistan, where locally common and widespread in the south. **REFERENCES** Harris *et al.* (1996).

RUFOUS-TAILED LARK *Ammomanes phoenicurus* Plate 137

Rufous-tailed Finch Lark (I)

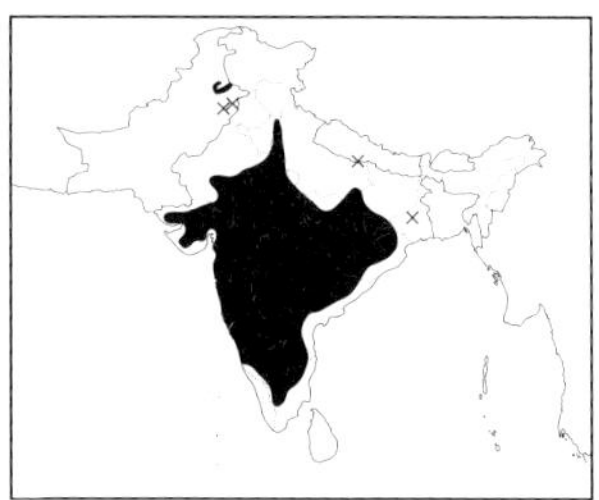

IDENTIFICATION 16 cm. Distinguished from Bar-tailed and Desert Larks (p.791 and below) by much darker grey-brown upperparts, rufous-orange underparts and underwing-coverts, and more prominent dark spotting/streaking on throat and breast. Has rufous-orange uppertail-coverts, and rufous-orange tail has broad and well-defined dark terminal bar. **VOICE** Song combines sweet *tee-hoo* phrases with low-pitched husky whistles and chirrups (Ali and Ripley 1987). **HABITS** Similar to those of Bar-tailed Lark. Runs about in rapid zigzags when feeding. During aerial display, the male rises to about 30 m, flies around with deeply flapping wingbeats, and then plunges to the ground in a stepped descent. **HABITAT** Cultivation, fallow and ploughed fields, stubbles, and open country with scattered bushes and stony outcrops. **BREEDING** February–May. Builds a shallow cup-shaped nest of grass, sometimes with a wall of pebble and sticks around it, hidden in a depression under a grass tuft, earth clod or small bush. **DISTRIBUTION AND STATUS** Resident, endemic to the subcontinent. N Punjab, Pakistan, S Nepal and much of India except the Himalayas and parts of the northwest, north, northeast and E coastal strip. **PK:** status uncertain, but seems to be an erratic monsoon visitor in N Punjab. **NP:** rare and local in the W terai. **IN:** plains and plateaux, locally common in the north. **REFERENCES** Anon. (1992a).

DESERT LARK *Ammomanes deserti* Plate 137

Desert Finch Lark (I)

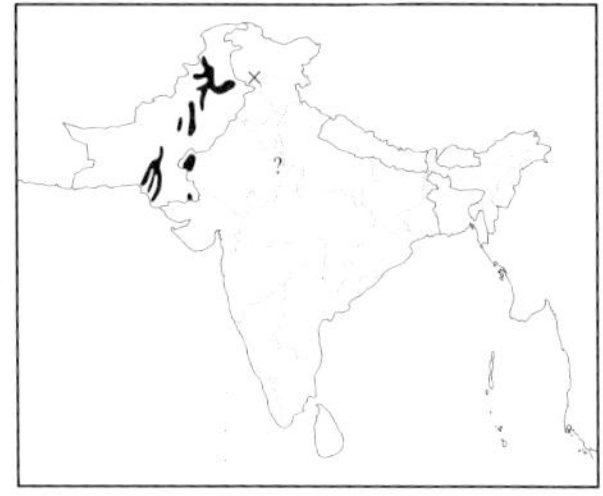

IDENTIFICATION 17 cm. Similar to Bar-tailed Lark (p.791), with rather uniform brownish-grey upperparts, buffish underparts with diffuse breast streaking, and rufous on wings and uppertail-coverts. Lacks dark tail-bar, and tail is largely grey-brown with rufous at sides. Tertials are grey-brown and show little contrast with primaries, and primary projection is about half length of exposed tertials. Distinguished also by larger size and slimmer appearance, and longer and broader bill (which has dark culmen and tip, with pale yellow lower mandible). Told from Rufous-tailed Lark (above) by much paler upperparts, buffish to greyish-white underparts (with weak breast streaking), and lack of dark bar on tail. **Juvenile** has buff-brown upperparts with faint buff fringes, and tail lacks blackish centre. **VOICE** Song comprises well-spaced, rising and falling, flute-like whistles, *pee-pyooh* or *peef-poof,* interspersed with warbling phrases (Roberts 1992); call is a *cuu* or *puu* (Cramp 1988). **HABITS** Usually progresses on the ground with a fast walk; runs occasionally. Searches busily for seeds and insects among stones. Well camouflaged on the ground, but often perches on rocks and utters calls, then becoming more conspicuous. The male's song flight is circular and long-sustained, with undulations, peaks of which coincide with bursts of song; he also sings from a prominent perch. **HABITAT** Low, very arid, rocky foothills, nullahs, also fallow land in desert-canal cultivation. **BREEDING** April–July. Nest and nest site are like those of Rufous-tailed Lark. **DISTRIBUTION AND STATUS** Resident. Mainly Pakistan and W Rajasthan. **PK:** common and sedentary in the foothills; 760–1800 m in Baluchistan, up to 900 m in Kohat and Kurram Agency. **IN:** uncommon. **REFERENCES** Harris *et al.* (1996).

GREATER HOOPOE LARK *Alaemon alaudipes* Plate 137

Bifasciated Lark (I), Hoopoe Lark (R)

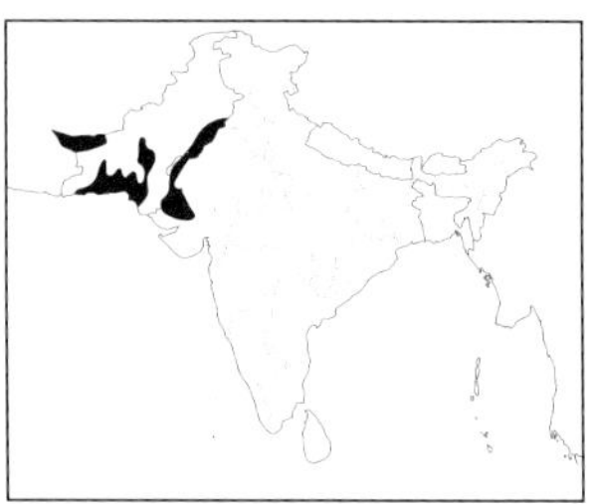

IDENTIFICATION 19 cm. A very distinctive lark, with long slightly downcurved bill and long legs. Has prominent white supercilium, black eye-stripe and moustachial stripe, indistinct black malar stripe, black-spotted breast, and sandy grey-brown upperparts. In flight, white at base and tips of black primaries and secondaries shows as prominent banding across wings, and black tail with white sides contrasts with pale upperparts. **Female** is smaller than male, with shorter bill and poorly defined head pattern and breast spotting. **Juvenile** differs from adult in having shorter, straighter bill, and whitish fringes and dark grey subterminal crescents to feathers of upperparts; underparts as female. **VOICE** Song is a series of flute-like whistles: the first series is repeated quickly, the second is more vehement and drawn out in a high key, followed by a third, more rapid series of piping whistles (Roberts 1992). **HABITS** Found singly or in pairs. Can run very swiftly and prefers to escape in this way, often running several hundred metres; reluctant to fly, except when displaying. Forages by walking slowly and then suddenly stopping to dig and probe for insects; also picks food from the ground and plants. In aerial display, the male typically flutters vertically upwards from the top of a bush or sand knoll, flips over, and then nose-dives back to the same perch, opening his wings at the last moment. **HABITAT** Extensive areas of arid desert, especially low sand dunes and barren clay flats. **BREEDING** March–July. Builds an untidy nest with a base of sticks and a deep cup of grass, up to 0.6 m above ground in a small bush. **DISTRIBUTION AND STATUS** Resident.

Pakistan and Rann of Kutch, Gujarat. **PK:** scarce; Sindh, S Baluchistan and E Bahawalpur. **IN:** patchily distributed and generally sparse, locally fairly common. **REFERENCES** Cramp (1988).

BIMACULATED LARK *Melanocorypha bimaculata* Plate 137

Eastern Calandra Lark (I)

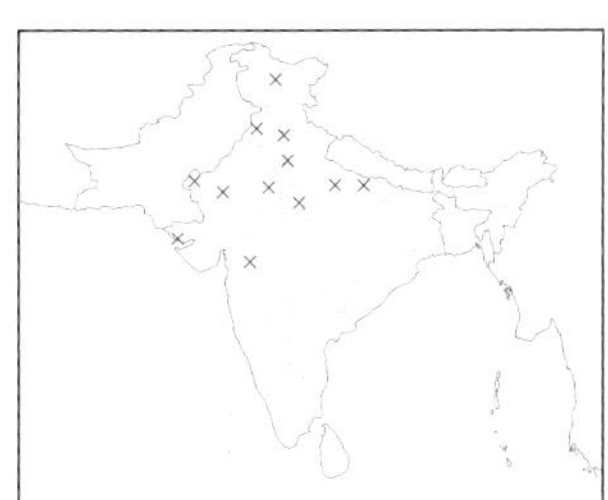

IDENTIFICATION 17 cm. A large, stout-billed and stocky lark with long, broad-based wings and comparatively short tail. Readily distinguished from other larks recorded in the subcontinent by prominent white supercilium and eye-ring, black patch on side of breast, dark grey underwing lacking white trailing edge, and whitish tip to tail. For differences from Tibetan Lark (below), see that species. **VOICE** A guttural *prrp* or *chirp*. **HABITS** Highly gregarious on its wintering grounds, sometimes hundreds together. Habits similar to those of other larks. Runs when feeding, picking up seeds and insects from the ground; also digs for pupae. Generally has a fairly upright stance, but will hide by squatting and freezing. **HABITAT** Semi-desert, paddy stubbles, fallow fields, edges of jheels and dry coastal mudflats. **DISTRIBUTION AND STATUS** Winter visitor. Mainly Pakistan, also NW and N India (from Jammu and Kashmir south to N Maharashtra and east to Uttar Pradesh). **PK:** local and erratically frequent winter visitor and passage migrant. **IN:** locally common winter visitor.

TIBETAN LARK *Melanocorypha maxima* Plate 137

Long-billed Calandra Lark (I)

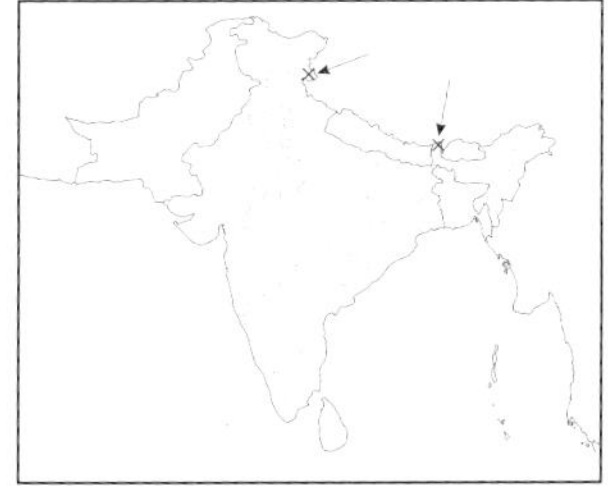

IDENTIFICATION 21 cm. A very large lark of the Tibetan plateau, which superficially resembles Bimaculated Lark (above) because of black patch on side of breast. Is much larger than that species, with rather small-headed, long-necked appearance, and has much longer and thinner bill. Has rather uniform head, lacking prominent supercilium or eye-stripe (crown and nape are diffusely streaked), and crown, ear-coverts and rump can be distinctly rufous. Breast is diffusely spotted and/or washed with grey. Further, has white trailing edge to secondaries, and white sides and broad white tip to outer tail feathers (with all but central tail feathers showing pale tips). **Juvenile** has dark blackish-brown upperparts with whitish fringes, and yellowish underparts with diffuse dark spotting on breast. **VOICE** Song similar to that of Bimaculated Lark, but generally poorer, being slower, more of a disjointed staccato, hiccuping, impulsive stutter; also includes repetition of more pleasant warbled phrases and call-notes, and is rich in mimicry (e.g. of Rosy Pipit, p.819, Oriental Skylark, p.797, Red-billed Chough, p.596). Call is a coarse rippled *tchui-lip*, very similar to one of the calls of Bimaculated Lark (P. Holt). **HABITS** Very little known in the region. Male sings from the top of a grassy hump, twitching open his wings excitedly. **HABITAT** Grassy marshland around high-altitude lakes and bogs in Tibetan plateau country. **BREEDING** Unknown in the region. June and July in Tibet. Nest is a hollow on the ground, lined with grass, among drier humps at the edge of a bog. **DISTRIBUTION AND STATUS IN:** breeding resident in Ladakh, 4300 m, where locally common, and in N Sikkim above 3600 m.

GREATER SHORT-TOED LARK *Calandrella brachydactyla* Plate 138

Short-toed Lark (F,I), *C. cinerea* (F,I,K)

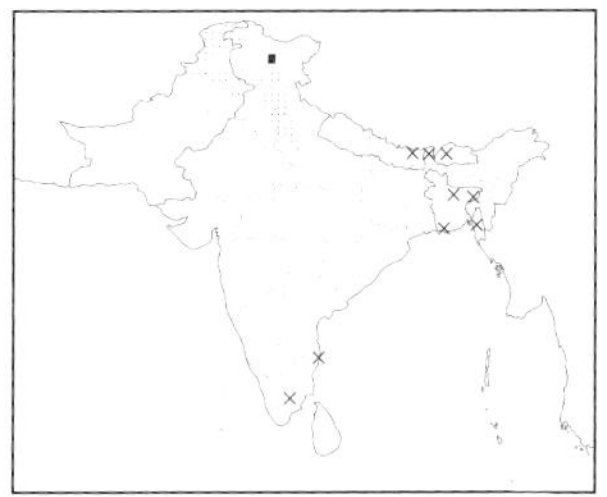

IDENTIFICATION (See also summary table, p.788.) 14 cm. Very similar in structure and appearance to Hume's Short-toed (p.794). Features which usually help in separation from Hume's are subtle differences in head pattern and bill shape/coloration, warmer-coloured and more heavily streaked upperparts, prominent dark centres to median coverts, warmer-coloured breast often with well-defined streaking, and different call. Told from Sand Lark (p.795) by larger size and slimmer appearance, faster and more direct flight with longer tail and slimmer wings, heavily streaked mantle and dark centres to wing-coverts and tertials, warmer coloration to upperparts, dark patch on side of breast (if present) and buffier breast and flanks, and different call. For differences from the very similar Lesser and Asian Short-toed Larks (p.794), see those species. **Racial variation** Two races winter in the subcontinent. *C. b. dukhunensis*, which is more easily separated from other small larks, has warm sandy-buff upperparts, variable rufous-buff breast-band, and rufous-buff ear-coverts and wash on flanks. *C. b. longipennis* is slightly colder and greyer in coloration of upperparts, and has breast washed with brownish-buff. **VOICE** Flight call is a dry *tchirrup* or *chichirrup* which recalls Northern House Martin (p.693). **HABITS** Similar to those of other larks. Gregarious on its wintering grounds, running and flying about restlessly, and birds twisting and turning in unison. Unobtrusive on the ground; will squat and freeze if alarmed. Feeds on insects and seeds picked from the ground or low plants; often digs with the bill. **HABITAT** Open stony grassland, grassy margins of lakes, semi-desert, fallow fields, paddy stubbles and dry coastal mudflats. **DISTRIBUTION AND STATUS** Widespread winter visitor to the subcontinent, but apparently absent from parts of NE, C and S India and Sri Lanka. Breeding records require confirmation. **PK:** common winter visitor to the plains of Punjab and Sindh; also found on passage in Chitral, Gilgit and Baltistan. **NP:** frequent; mainly a passage migrant, also a winter visitor, 750–4575 m; two monsoon records, including one at 5000 m. **IN:** common and widespread winter visitor to low country. **BT:** rare passage migrant. **BD:** scarce winter visitor. **REFERENCES** Shirihai and Alström (1990).

HUME'S SHORT-TOED LARK *Calandrella acutirostris* — Plate 138

Hume's Lark

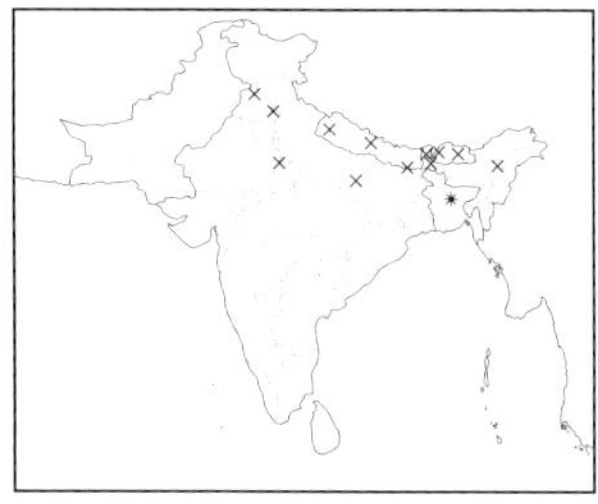

IDENTIFICATION (See also summary table, p.788.) 14 cm. Very similar in structure and appearance to Greater Short-toed (p.793). Identification features which usually hold are subtle differences in head pattern (with dark lores, and less pronounced supercilium and eye-stripe), slight differences in bill shape/coloration, greyer and less heavily streaked upperparts contrasting with pinkish uppertail-coverts, greyish breast-band, and different call. Differences in structure and behaviour (as Greater Short-toed), dark patch on side of breast (usually present), greyish-buff breast-band, and different call are main distinctions from Sand Lark (p.795). For differences from Lesser and Asian Short-toed (below), see those species. **VOICE** Flight call is a rather full, rolling *tiyrr* or *tiurr* (Shirihai and Alström 1990). Birds breeding in Nepal have a mellow, variable song, *tee-leu-ee-lew* (Fleming *et al.* 1984). **HABITS** Very similar to those of Greater Short-toed Lark. Usually keeps in pairs in the breeding season and in flocks in winter. In his song flight, the male spirals upwards high in the air and flies around in wide circles with dipping glides, before parachuting to the ground; also sings from a permanent rock or ridge. **HABITAT** Breeds in semi-desert in Tibetan plateau country, and in Pakistan in the lower rocky hills; winters in fallow cultivation and open wasteland. **BREEDING** May–August. Nest is slight depression on the ground, lined with grass and vegetable down, sometimes with a rim of gravel, sited in the shelter of a plant or stone. **DISTRIBUTION AND STATUS** Summer visitor to Baluchistan, Pakistan, and Himalayas from N Pakistan east to Sikkim; recorded in winter mainly from S Nepal and Madhya Pradesh, with scattered records from elsewhere. **PK:** widespread and frequent to scarce summer visitor. **NP:** common in summer in the N Dolpo (in northwest); uncommon in winter and on passage, 75–4800 m. **IN:** common in Ladakh, where summers 2000–5000 m; not very common in Sikkim, 4575–5030 m. **BT:** rare, status uncertain. **BD:** probably a regular winter visitor. **REFERENCES** Pfister (1997), Shirihai and Alström (1990).

LESSER SHORT-TOED LARK *Calandrella rufescens* — Plate 138

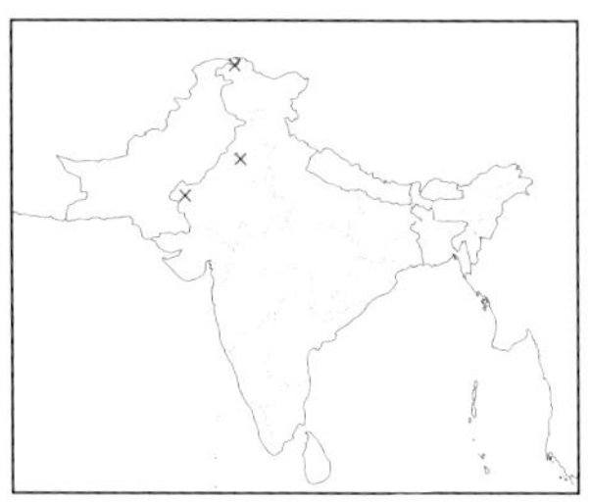

IDENTIFICATION (See also summary table, p.788.) 13 cm. Distinguished from Greater and Hume's (p.793 and above) by noticeable extension of primaries beyond tertials, with at least three primary tips visible (tertials reach or almost reach wing-point on Greater). Bill is shorter and stouter. Has a broad gorget of well-defined streaking across breast, with streaking often apparent on lower throat and flanks, more finely streaked upperparts which are pale, sandy-buff in coloration, less striking head pattern with less prominent supercilia (which appear to join across bill) and streaked ear-coverts; lacks prominent dark centres to median coverts (which can show distinct dark bar on Greater), and has different call. For differences from the very similar Asian Short-toed (below), see that species. **VOICE** Calls include a rattling *prrt* or *prrirrick* or *chirrit*, which are distinct from those of Greater. **HABITS** Very like those of Greater Short-toed Lark, but less gregarious in winter. **HABITAT** Stony foothills. **DISTRIBUTION AND STATUS** Probably under-recorded. Winter visitor to Pakistan; vagrant to Haryana, and possibly winters in Rajasthan. **PK:** locally frequent winter visitor to Sindh/Baluchistan border regions; possibly breeds in NW Baluchistan or NW Pakistan. **IN:** status uncertain; one record from Haryana, and possibly from Desert National Park, Rajasthan. **REFERENCES** Harris *et al.* (1996).

ASIAN SHORT-TOED LARK *Calandrella cheleensis* — Plate 138

***C. rufescens* (I)**

IDENTIFICATION (See also summary table, p.788.) 13 cm. Separated from Greater and Hume's (p.793 and p.794) by noticeable extension of primaries beyond tertials (as Lesser, above)). Does not show dark breast-side patch which is frequently present on those two species. Compared with Lesser, at least in the case of *C. c. leucophaea* (which is the race of Asian recorded in the subcontinent), upperparts are generally paler sandy-buff (on some, almost cream) and streaking is more diffuse; underparts are similar, although streaking on breast is more diffuse, and shows more white on outer tail feathers (outer rectrices are mainly white; half of inner web dark on Lesser); bill is also distinctly smaller. **VOICE** Dry rolling call-note, *trrrrt* or *prrrrt-up*, is probably indistinguishable from that of Lesser Short-toed Lark. Song is pleasant, lengthy and varied, often consisting of a long series of

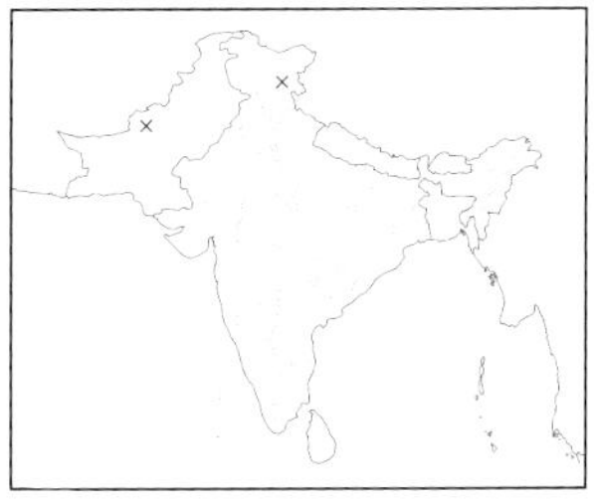

repeated call-notes, but may then suddenly accelerate into attractive vivacious phrases containing excellent mimicry of e.g. Crested Lark (below) (P. Holt). **HABITS** Very like those of Greater Short-toed Lark. **HABITAT** Undescribed in subcontinent. **DISTRIBUTION AND STATUS PK, IN:** vagrant.

SAND LARK *Calandrella raytal* — Plate 138

Indian Short-toed Lark, Indian Sandlark (K)

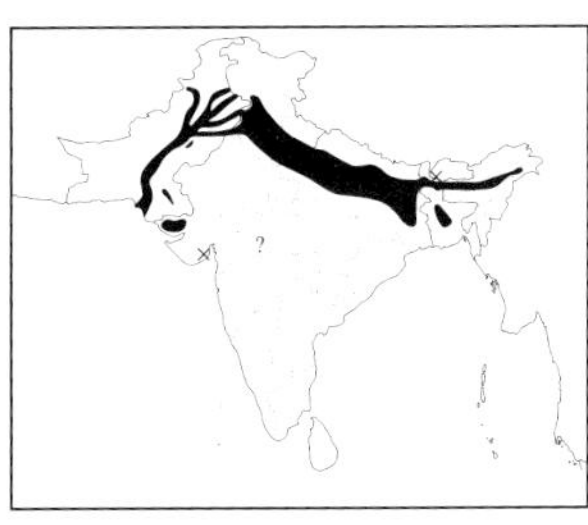

IDENTIFICATION (See also summary table, p.788.) 12 cm. Distinguished from other *Calandrella* larks occurring in the subcontinent by smaller size and stockier appearance, comparatively short tail, and rather rounded wings with distinctive, rather jerky and fluttering flight action. Additional features are finer bill (especially *adamsi*), rather uniform, cold sandy-grey upperparts (with streaking most prominent on crown), whitish underparts with fine sparse streaking across breast (and lacking dark patches on breast side), and prominent blackish sides to tail contrasting with white outer tail feathers and very pale rump and uppertail-coverts. **Racial variation** Bill of *C. r. adamsi* of NW subcontinent is distinctly finer than that of the nominate race. *C. r. krishnakumarsinhji*, known only from the type locality (Bhavnagar in Gujarat), has dark grey upperparts, which are more heavily streaked. **VOICE** Call is a rolling, deep and guttural *prrr..prrr* (R. Grimmett). The aerial display song is a series of short, rapidly delivered and repeated undulating warbling notes, *treet-truit-it-it-du-du-du-du-di-di-di-dit*. **HABITS** Runs about in zigzagging spurts on bare sand and mud close to water. During his aerial display, the male swoops repeatedly over his territory before shooting steeply to the ground. **HABITAT** Sandy and muddy banks and islands of lakes, rivers and tidal creeks; sand dunes adjacent to water, and coastal dunes. **BREEDING** February–September. Nest is a depression, lined with fine grasses, hairs and vegetable down, and sited in the shelter of a small bush, grass clump or earth clod. **DISTRIBUTION AND STATUS** Resident. From Pakistan east through Punjab, India, Uttar Pradesh and West Bengal to Assam and Bangladesh; also Gujarat. **PK:** common along the Indus R system and on the coast around Karachi and the Makran. **NP:** locally common; below 305 m. **IN:** locally common in the north. **BT:** fairly common, but very local. **BD:** local.

CRESTED LARK *Galerida cristata* — Plate 138

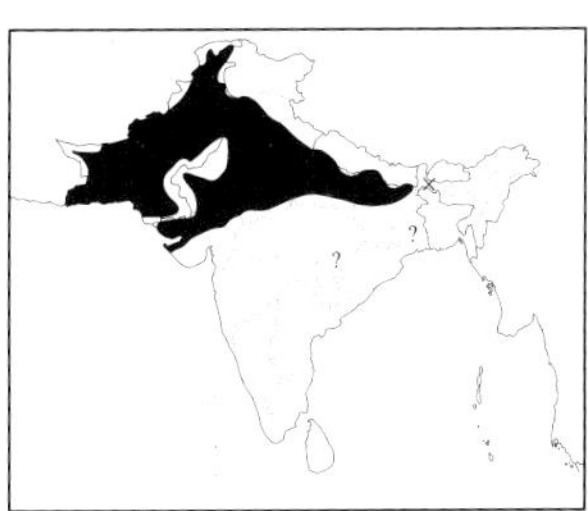

IDENTIFICATION 18 cm. A large, sandy to sandy-grey lark with prominent crest. Upperparts and breast are well streaked. Readily distinguished from Oriental Skylark (p.797) by larger size and erect crest, broader rounded wings, rather buoyant, fluttering flight, rufous-buff outer tail feathers and underwing, and different calls and song. Although not known from peninsular India, it is possibly confusable with Malabar Lark (below), but is much larger and paler, and much less heavily streaked on upperparts and breast. **Racial variation** *G. c. magna* of NW Pakistan is warmer, more sandy-coloured on upperparts than other two races (which are greyer) occurring in the subcontinent. **VOICE** Take-off call is a pleasant, fluty *du-ee*, and also utters a similar *tuee-tuu-teeooo*. Song is prolonged and complex, with much mimicry and interspersed with variations of call; slower and clearer than Oriental Skylark's. **HABITS** Keeps singly, in pairs or in small scattered flocks. Quite tame; freezes if approached too closely. Walks or runs swiftly in search of plant material and invertebrates, taken mainly from the ground surface. Perches readily on rocks, low bushes and telegraph wires. The male circles during his song display, either briefly and low over the ground or for a few minutes at a great height; he also sings while standing in open ground or perched on a bush. **HABITAT** Desert, semi-desert, dry fallow fields and cultivation in dry areas, and dry coastal mudflats. **BREEDING** March–August. Builds a shallow cup-shaped nest in a depression on the ground under an earth clod or at the base of a small plant. **DISTRIBUTION AND STATUS** Resident, subject to local movements. Mainly from Pakistan east through N India and S Nepal to E Bihar. **PK:** common and very widespread; locally to 2400 m in summer. **NP:** fairly common in the west, rare in the east; below 275 m. **IN:** locally common in the north, mainly in the plains, also the Kashmir foothills.

MALABAR LARK *Galerida malabarica* — Plate 138

Malabar Crested Lark (I)

IDENTIFICATION 16 cm. Similar to Crested Lark (above), with prominent crest, but has a more southerly distribution. Smaller than Crested, with darker, more rufescent upperparts with much stronger blackish streaking.

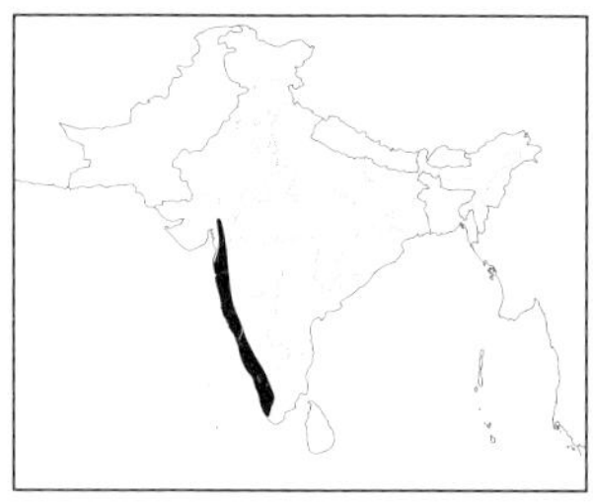

Breast is heavily spotted, and washed with buff or rufous-buff. Is buffish to rufous-buff and less heavily streaked on nape and upper mantle, and has pale rufous outer tail feathers and underwing-coverts. Told from Sykes's Lark (below) by larger size, much longer bill, paler but more heavily streaked breast, and buffish-white belly and flanks. Confusable also with *australis* race of Oriental Skylark (p.797), which is similar in general coloration; best told by stouter bill, longer crest, larger breast streaking, pale rufous (rather than buffish-white) outer tail feathers, and different call. **VOICE** Call is a pleasant, undulating *chew-chew-you*. Song consists of a variety of melancholy and fluty calls, *tuee* and *du-ee* etc, all very similar to those of Crested Lark, if perhaps a trifle coarser, although equally varied and probably not distinguishable in the field (P. Holt). **HABITS** Similar to those of Crested Lark, but sometimes found in larger flocks of up to 30 birds in the non-breeding season. **HABITAT** Cultivation, grass-covered hills, grassy edges of coastal mudflats, forest clearings, and open scrub. **BREEDING** Almost all year, varying locally. Nest and nest site are like those of Crested Lark. **DISTRIBUTION AND STATUS IN:** endemic resident, subject to local movements; Western Ghats from S Gujarat south to S Kerala and W Tamil Nadu; locally common in plains and hills up to 2000 m.

SYKES'S LARK *Galerida deva* — Plate 138

Sykes's Crested Lark (I), Tawny Lark

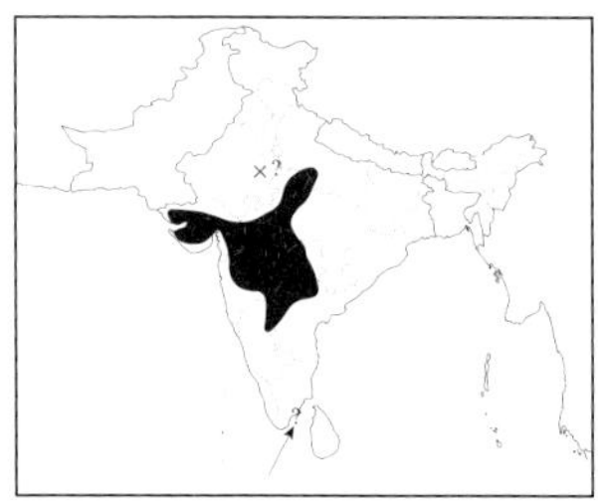

IDENTIFICATION 14 cm. A small lark of the peninsula with prominent upstanding crest as Malabar Lark (p.795). Smaller than that species (similar in size to Greater Short-toed Lark, p.793). Entire underparts are uniform pale rufous to rufous-buff (lacking whitish belly), and streaking on breast is finer and much less extensive (confined to narrow band across upper breast, and almost lacking on some). Has rather uniform pale rufous uppertail-coverts which contrast with buffish and heavily streaked back and rump (uppertail-coverts of Malabar are much as rump/back, with slight rufescent cast on some). Further, bill is shorter and stouter, and has different calls and song. Much as Malabar, is buffish to rufous-buff and less heavily streaked on nape and upper mantle, and has pale rufous outer tail feathers and underwing-coverts. Possibly confusable with *australis* race of Oriental Skylark (p.797), which is similar in general coloration; best told from that species by distinctly stouter bill, longer crest, less extensive breast streaking, and pale rufous (rather than buffish-white) outer tail feathers, in addition to which underparts are a more uniform and deeper pale rufous, and generally lacks fine streaking and spotting on lower throat and malar region which is shown by Oriental. **VOICE** Song is similar to that of Singing Bushlark (p.786), a spirited, melodious, stumbling song very rich in mimicry and reminiscent of Oriental Skylark's; calls similar to those of Crested Lark (p.795) (P. Holt). **HABITS** Similar to those of Crested Lark except for song flight, which is very like that of Singing Bushlark. **HABITAT** Stony plateaux with sparse scrub, and dry cultivation. **BREEDING** March–September. Nest and nest site are similar to those of Crested Lark. **DISTRIBUTION AND STATUS IN:** endemic resident, subject to local movements; mainly from Gujarat and S Uttar Pradesh south to N Karnataka and east to N Andhra Pradesh; locally common in plains and hills up to 1000 m, mainly in the C plateau.

EURASIAN SKYLARK *Alauda arvensis* — Plate 138

Skylark (I), Common Skylark (K)

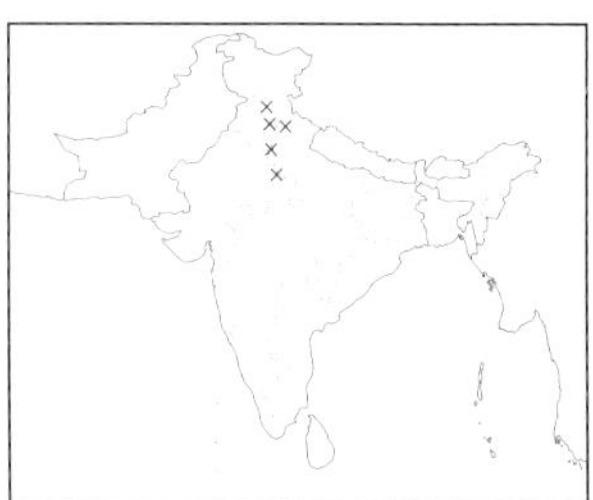

IDENTIFICATION 18 cm. Larger than Oriental Skylark (p.797), although very similar to some races of that species in plumage, and with slight crest. Told from that species by longer tail, noticeable extension of primaries beyond closed tertials (tertials almost reach primary tips on Oriental), white outer tail feathers (more buffish on Oriental), pronounced whitish trailing edge to secondaries, and proportionately shorter and stouter bill. In flight, appears larger, longer-tailed and longer-winged, and flight action is more powerful and direct (over long distances, flight has an erratic rhythm). Upperparts are paler sandy-brown (than on most races of Oriental), and underparts whiter. Oriental has rufous cast to ear-coverts, and more pronounced rufous edges to fringes of primary coverts, primaries and secondaries which form panel on wing. Crested Lark (p.795), with its broader, rounded wings, very prominent crest, cinnamon outer tail feathers and underwing, and very different call, should not cause confusion. **VOICE** Calls include a grating *chirriup* or liquid *trruwee*. **HABITS** Similar behaviour to that of Oriental Skylark. Gregarious on its wintering grounds, often in large flocks. Walks steadily when feeding; consumes seeds and other plant material, and insects when available, picked either from the ground or directly from plants. **HABITAT** Cultivation, favouring young wheat, paddy stubbles and fallow fields, and grass meadows. **DISTRIBUTION AND STATUS** Winter visitor. Mainly Pakistan, also N India from Punjab east to W Uttar Pradesh and south to

E Rajasthan. **PK:** fairly widespread; common in Baluchistan and parts of Punjab, less common in Sindh. **IN:** locally fairly common.

ORIENTAL SKYLARK *Alauda gulgula* Plate 138

Eastern Skylark (I,P), Oriental Lark, Indian Lark, Little Skylark (F)

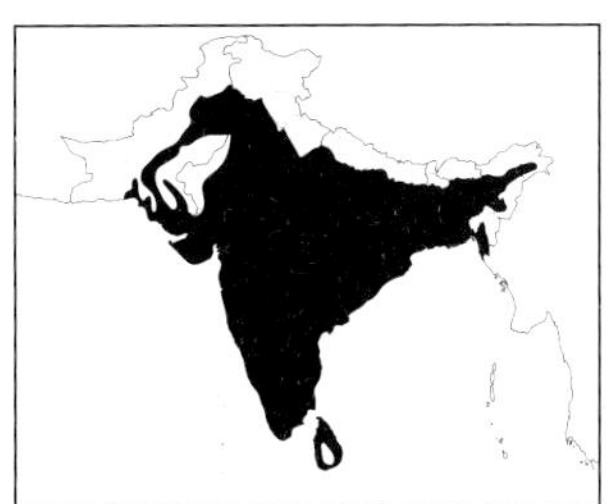

IDENTIFICATION 16 cm. Variable in coloration and in prominence of streaking on upperparts and underparts (see racial variation). Some races very similar to Eurasian Skylark (p.796) in overall coloration, but Oriental is smaller, has shorter tail and more rounded wings, and buffish outer tail feathers, and lacks prominent white trailing edge to secondaries. See Eurasian for further details. Possibly confusable with Singing and Indian Bushlarks (p.786 and p.787), but has much slimmer bill, and rufous on wing is much less prominent and extensive (lacking rufous on inner webs of primaries and secondaries). For differences from Malabar and Sykes's Larks (p.795 and p.796), see those species. Crested Lark (p.795) should not cause confusion, having broader, rounded wings, very prominent crest, cinnamon outer tail feathers and underwing, and very different call. **Racial variation** Six races occur in the subcontinent. Greatest divergence is shown by *A. g. inconspicua* of NW and N subcontinent, which has sandy-buff base colour to upperparts, and whitish underparts with rufous-buff wash across breast. By comparison, *A. g. australis* of W peninsula and Sri Lanka has warmer rufous-buff base colour to more heavily streaked upperparts, and base colour of underparts is a uniform rufous-buff. **VOICE** Song is a sustained repertoire of bubbling warbles and shorter whistling notes, with much variation; call is a grating, throaty *bazz bazz.* **HABITS** A typical lark. Found in pairs or scattered flocks. Walks about methodically, seeking insects and seeds from the ground and on plants. Perches freely on stone walls, low stumps and stones. Crouches and freezes to escape notice. During his song flight, the male sings for several minutes while circling, then nearly closes his wings and descends to the ground in a steep dive. **HABITAT** Open grassland, cultivation, upland pastures, grass bordering saltpans and coastal mudflats, and damp grassland at the edges of lakes, tanks and jheels. **BREEDING** March–August and November–May, varying locally. Builds a cup-shaped nest of grass in a depression on the ground, usually under an earth clod or grass tuft. **DISTRIBUTION AND STATUS** Resident, subject to local and altitudinal movements, and winter visitor. Throughout much of the subcontinent, except parts of the northwest and northeast. **PK:** common and widespread resident in the plains of Sindh and Punjab, and a summer visitor to the broader valleys and lower foothills of Baluchistan and NW Pakistan; also a sparse summer visitor to the Himalayas, breeds 3000–3300 m. **NP:** fairly common resident and winter visitor; resident below 150 m, also breeds up to at least 3600 m, and winters 1280–1700 m. **IN:** widespread and locally common resident and winter visitor; breeds 1600–4300 m in Himalayas, winters down to the foothills; resident in the peninsula, in plains and hills up to 1600 m. **BT:** frequent resident and winter visitor. **BD:** resident; occurs locally throughout. **LK:** common resident in the dry lowlands and higher hills, also a winter visitor to wet and dry lowlands.

HORNED LARK *Eremophila alpestris* Plate 138

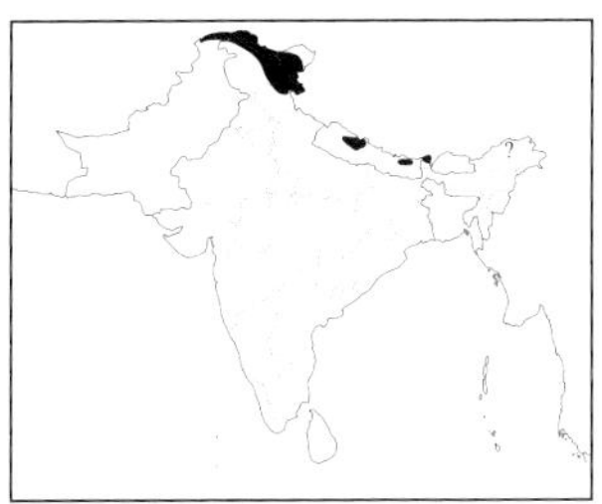

IDENTIFICATION 18 cm. **Adult male** has striking black-and-white head pattern, with black mask, 'horns' and band across crown. Underparts are creamy-white with black breast-band, and upperparts are sandy, with strong pinkish to vinous cast to upper mantle and/or nape. **Adult female** has black breast and diffuse dark mask, but crown and mantle are heavily streaked, and lacks pinkish cast to nape/mantle. **Juvenile** has suggestion of dark mask; upperparts are extensively and diffusely spotted with yellowish-buff, and underparts have pale yellowish wash; tertials and wing-coverts have broad yellowish-buff fringes and dark subterminal crescents. **Racial variation** Black mask joins black of breast in *E. a. albigula* of NW subcontinent. **VOICE** Song comprises a series of *tsit-tsit-tsit* notes, followed by short warbling phrases which are interspersed with longer inflected whistles (Roberts 1992); call is a quiet *tsit tsit.* **HABITS** Found in pairs or small flocks. Very tame. Constantly on the move when foraging, walking or running in short spurts; often adopts a crouching posture. Takes insects and seeds from the ground or plant stems. Perches readily on raised ground and rocks. Male occasionally performs a song flight, but usually sings from rocks. **HABITAT** Breeds in high-altitude stony screes, stony plateaux, stony steppe, bare stony mountainsides and alpine pastures; winters in fallow land in terraced cultivation, bare sand stretches along mountain rivers and barren stony slopes of lower mountain valleys. **BREEDING** May–July. Nest is a cup-shaped depression on the ground, well lined with dry grass, hair and vegetable down, and sited in the shelter of a tiny plant or stone. **DISTRIBUTION AND STATUS** Resident, subject to altitudinal movements. Himalayas from N Pakistan east to Sikkim. **PK:** common; breeds in innermost N valleys and upland plateaux, 3300–5100 m; winters mainly in the broader N valleys and occasionally in the foothills, 1500–3000 m (down to 450 m). **NP:** fairly common; 3965–5490 m (2600–5900 m). **IN:** common; breeds from the treeline up to 5400 m, winters down to 3000 m.

FLOWERPECKERS, SUNBIRDS AND SPIDERHUNTERS
Nectariniidae, subfamily Nectariniinae

More work is needed to advance the identification of female and immature flowerpeckers and sunbirds, and many of the characters mentioned here need to be tested more thoroughly in the field. These birds are represented in the region by two discrete tribes.

FLOWERPECKERS Tribe Dicaeini

Very small passerines with short beak and tail, with a tongue adapted for nectar-feeding, and resembling sunbirds in behaviour. Strictly arboreal, they usually frequent the canopy and feed mainly on soft fruits, berries and nectar; also on small insects and spiders. Many species are especially fond of mistletoe *Loranthus* berries. Typically, flowerpeckers are very active, continually flying about restlessly, and twisting and turning in different attitudes when perched, while calling frequently with high-pitched notes. They build a purse-like nest of vegetable down, often bound together with cobwebs, rootlets and grass; the nest is suspended from the end of a branch, well hidden among leaves and usually high in a tree. Flowerpeckers normally live singly or in pairs; some species form small parties in the non-breeding season. All are sedentary.

THICK-BILLED FLOWERPECKER *Dicaeum agile* — Plate 139

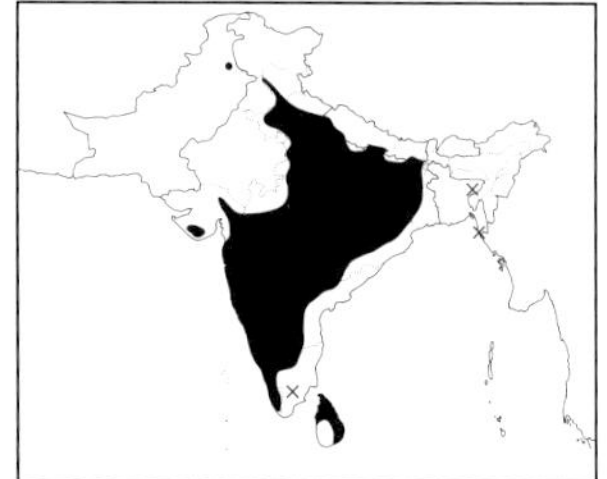

IDENTIFICATION 10 cm. A dull, olive-grey and whitish flowerpecker. In fresh plumage, has olive-green cast to back, rump, and edges of wings and tail. **Adult** distinguished from other flowerpeckers by combination of stout bluish-grey bill, indistinct dark malar stripe, lightly streaked breast, comparatively long and broad, fairly dark tail with white tip (which can be rather indistinct), and orange-red iris. **Juvenile** has pinkish bill. **VOICE** Has a *tchup-tchup* call, which is not so hard as *chick* call of Pale-billed (p.799). **HABITS** A typical flowerpecker. Has a distinctive habit of jerking its tail from side to side as it feeds or hops about. Frequently flies from one tree to the next, and is known to follow a regular feeding circuit. Feeds mainly on figs of peepul and banyan; also on berries of mistletoe. **HABITAT** Forest, well-wooded country, groves, orchards and gardens, mainly of broadleaved trees, but in Pakistan found in Chir Pine and *Pistacia integerrima*. **BREEDING** January–August. Has a distinctive nest: a hanging purse resembling a dead leaf, made of reddish vegetable down and spiders' cocoons, suspended from a twig 1.5–9 m up in a tree. **DISTRIBUTION AND STATUS** Resident, subject to altitudinal movements in Himalayas. Himalayan foothills in NE Punjab, Pakistan, and from Himachal Pradesh east to Arunachal Pradesh and south through much of the subcontinent, except parts of the northwest, northeast and E coastal strip. **PK:** rare and very local; apparently resident. **NP:** widespread and frequent; resident below 800 m, summers up to 2135 m. **IN:** locally common in plains and foothills; summers up to 1500 m (–3000 m), winters in foothills below 800 m. **BD:** local? resident. **LK:** infrequent in dry lowlands and hills, scarce in the wet zone.

YELLOW-VENTED FLOWERPECKER *Dicaeum chrysorrheum* — Plate 139

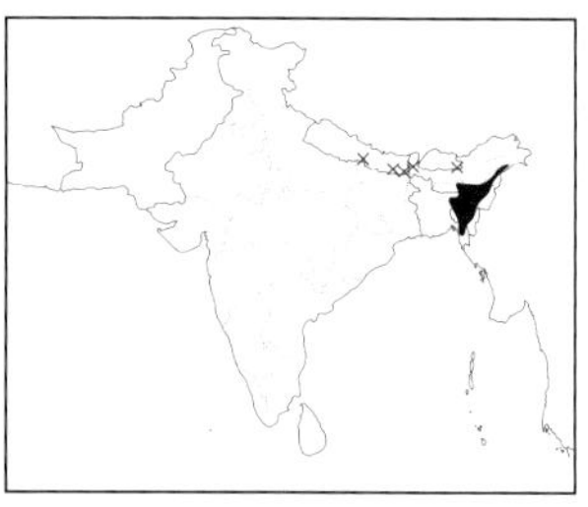

IDENTIFICATION 10 cm. Told from other flowerpeckers by combination of well-defined blackish malar stripe and streaking on white or yellowish-white underparts, orange-yellow vent, fine black bill, noticeably downcurved at tip, black lores and whitish supercilium to eye, bright olive-green upperparts with contrasting blackish primary coverts and primaries, and blackish tail (lacking white tip). **Juvenile** similar to adult, but has duller upperparts, and greyish-white underparts with paler yellow vent and less prominent streaking. **VOICE** A short, distinctive *dzeep* (Boonsong and Round 1991). **HABITS** A typical flowerpecker. Especially fond of mistletoe berries. Has a strong flight, and appears to travel considerable distances. **HABITAT** Open forest, forest edges and orchards. **BREEDING** April–July. Has a typical flowerpecker nest, usually placed within 6 m of ground. **DISTRIBUTION AND STATUS** Resident. Himalayan foothills from C Nepal east to Arunachal Pradesh; hills of NE India and Bangladesh. **NP:** rare and very local in the centre and east at c. 245 m. **IN:** common south of the Brahmaputra R; from foothills up to 2000 m. **BT, BD:** rare.

YELLOW-BELLIED FLOWERPECKER *Dicaeum melanoxanthum* — Plate 139

IDENTIFICATION 13 cm. A large, stout-billed flowerpecker. Has white spots at tip of undertail. **Male** has bluish-black upperparts and breast sides, white centre of throat and breast, and yellow rest of underparts. Has bright red iris. **Female** is like a dull version of male, with upperparts olive-brown, sides of breast olive-grey, and belly and vent dull olive-yellow. **Juvenile male** is similar to female, but has brighter yellow underparts and blue-black cast to mantle and back. Legge's Flowerpecker (p.799) superficially resembles Yellow-bellied, but is smaller, lacks dis-

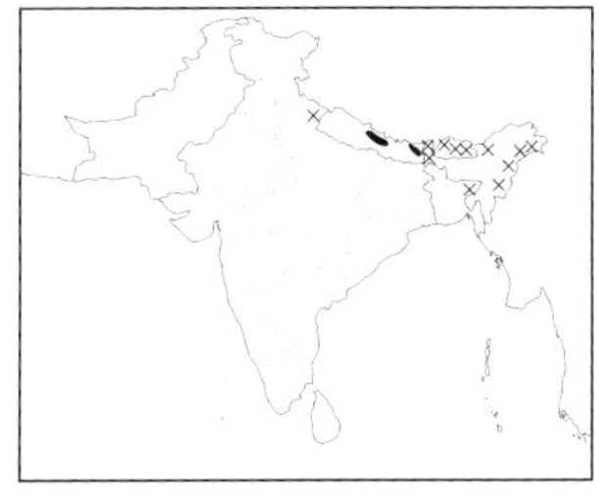

tinctive dark sides to breast, and is found only in Sri Lanka. **VOICE** Call is an agitated *zit-zit-zit-zit* (Fleming *et al.* 1984). **HABITS** Similar to those of other flowerpeckers, but slower-moving. **HABITAT** Broadleaved forest, both open forest and clearings and edges of dense forest. **BREEDING** Details unknown. **DISTRIBUTION AND STATUS** Resident, subject to altitudinal movements. Himalayas from N Uttar Pradesh and from C Nepal east to Arunachal Pradesh; NE Indian hills. **NP:** local and frequent from WC areas eastwards; summers 2350–3000 m, winters from 1050 m up to at least 1550. **IN:** scarce and local; summers from 2000 m up to at least 2745 m (–3600 m?), winters 1600–1830 m. **BT:** rare. **BD:** vagrant. **REFERENCES** Martens and Eck (1995).

LEGGE'S FLOWERPECKER *Dicaeum vincens* — Plate 139

White-throated Flowerpecker

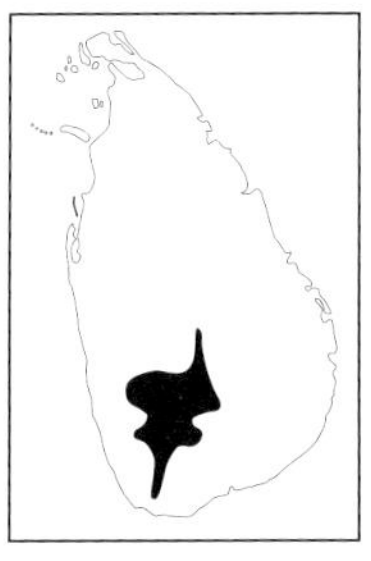

IDENTIFICATION 10 cm. A stout-billed flowerpecker. **Male** has bluish-black upperparts, white throat, upper breast and undertail-coverts, yellow lower breast and belly, and white tips to outer tail feathers. **Female** is like a dull version of male, although underparts are similar; crown, ear-coverts and nape are blue-grey, becoming dark olive on mantle and back. **Juvenile** resembles female, but has yellow wash to throat, which is therefore more concolorous with rest of underparts, and upperparts are more uniform olive-brown. **VOICE** A weak *tze-tze-tze.* **HABITS** Similar to those of other flowerpeckers. Keeps singly, in pairs or in small family parties. Feeds on nectar and fruits, especially bowitiya and Screw Pine; also eats insects and spiders. **HABITAT** Forest and wooded gardens close to forest. **BREEDING** January–August. Has a typical flowerpecker nest, suspended 18–38 m above ground in a dipterocarp tree. **DISTRIBUTION AND STATUS LK:** common endemic resident in wet lowlands and adjacent low hills, below 900 m.

ORANGE-BELLIED FLOWERPECKER *Dicaeum trigonostigma* — Plate 139

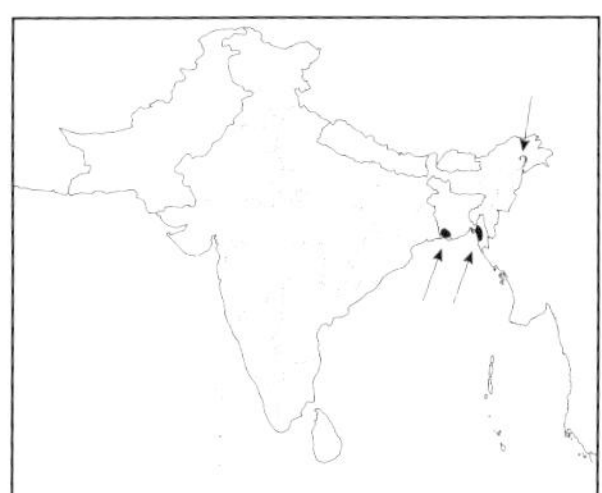

IDENTIFICATION 9 cm. Orange coloration to rump of adult distinguishes it from other flowerpeckers in the region. **Male** has blue-grey crown, mantle, wings and tail, flame-orange back, becoming more yellowish-orange on rump and uppertail-coverts, grey throat and upper breast, and orange lower breast, belly and vent. **Female** told from other female flowerpeckers by combination of olive-grey throat and upper breast, yellowish-orange on lower breast, belly and vent (with olive breast sides and flanks), greenish upperparts (with variable blue-grey cast to crown and mantle), blue-grey edges to primaries and secondaries forming panel on wing, and dull orange rump contrasting with dark tail. **Juvenile** is similar to female, but duller, with olive-brown upperparts, olive-yellow rump, and olive-yellow centre to belly and undertail-coverts; bill is orange with dark tip. Juvenile male has blue edges to rectrices, which are barely apparent on juvenile female. **VOICE** Call is a harsh *dzit.* Song is a sharp, high-pitched, metallic *ptit.ptit.ptit.ptit.tsi* or *tit.tit.tit.tit.tit-tit*; also, a high, thin, rapid *psee-psee-psee-psee-psee-psee,* each note with an upward inflection. **HABITS** A typical flowerpecker. **HABITAT** Clearings and edges of evergreen forest and mangroves. **BREEDING** April and May. Has a typical flowerpecker nest, usually suspended 10–12 m above ground. **DISTRIBUTION AND STATUS** Resident in Bangladesh; reported from Arunachal Pradesh by Baker (1922-30), but no other records. **IN:** occurrence uncertain. **BD:** locally common in the southeast and south.

PALE-BILLED FLOWERPECKER *Dicaeum erythrorynchos* — Plate 139

Tickell's Flowerpecker (F,I,P), Small Flowerpecker

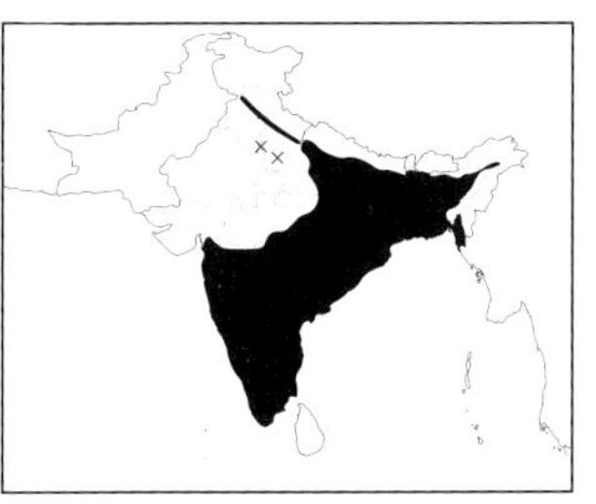

IDENTIFICATION 8 cm. A plain-coloured flowerpecker with greyish-olive upperparts with slight greenish cast, and pale greyish underparts with variable yellowish-buff wash. Told from Plain Flowerpecker (p.800) by flesh-coloured bill; for further differences from races of Plain occurring in the subcontinent, see that species. Possibly confusable also with juvenile Scarlet-backed Flowerpecker (p.800), but that species has an orange-red base to bill, with noticeably darker tip, a white supercilium to eye, and pale fringes to wing-coverts and tertials. **Juvenile** as adult, but bill is more orange-yellow, and has greyer upperparts and underparts. **Racial variation** *D. e. ceylonense* of Sri Lanka differs from the nominate race in having a dark brown upper mandible and darker, more olive upperparts. **VOICE** Hurried chittering song lower than that of Thick-billed Flowerpecker (p.798); call is a sharp *chik chik chik,* and also utters a high-pitched *pseep.* **HABITS** Keeps in pairs in the breeding season; otherwise in parties of up to ten birds. Constantly on the move, all the while uttering its sharp call. Flits about actively, usually in the canopy. Has a strong bounding and dipping flight, and covers large distances in the day. Feeds chiefly on berries of mistletoe. **HABITAT** Open broadleaved forest and groves, plantations, orchards and coastal mangroves; its distribution is dependent on the presence of mistletoe. **BREEDING** January–September, varying locally. Has a typical flowerpecker nest, suspended 3–12 m above ground. **DISTRIBUTION AND STATUS** Resident. Himalayan foothills from Himachal Pradesh east to West Bengal, Assam and south through much of the subcontinent, except parts of NW and NE India. **NP:** widespread and frequent; below 305 m. **IN:** widespread and generally common; in plains and hills, up to the summits in the south, most frequent in the plains. **BD, LK:** common throughout.

PLAIN FLOWERPECKER *Dicaeum concolor* Plate 139

Plain-colored Flowerpecker (F,I)

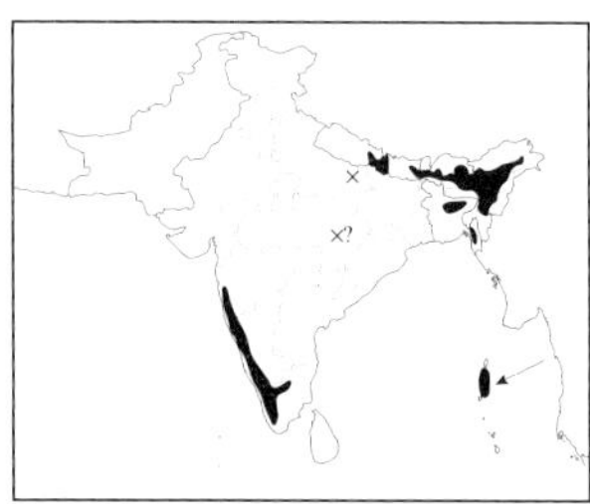

IDENTIFICATION 9 cm. A plain-coloured flowerpecker with olive-brown to olive-green upperparts and greyish-olive to pale yellow underparts. Distinguished from Pale-billed Flowerpecker (p.799) by dark bill (grey, with darker tip); see racial variation for further differences from that species. Possibly confusable with female Fire-breasted Flowerpecker (below), but that species has orange-buff wash to entire underparts. **Juvenile** has paler bill, especially on lower mandible, but bill is not so strikingly pale as on Pale-billed. **Racial variation** *D. c. olivaceum* of C and E Himalayas and NE subcontinent has olive-green upperparts and edges to flight feathers and dusky greyish-olive underparts, which are further differences from Pale-billed; juvenile has browner upperparts and greyish-white underparts. *D. c. concolor* of the Western Ghats has darker olive-brown upperparts and paler greyish-white underparts, with faint yellowish-buff wash on breast and belly; upperparts are darker and browner than Pale-billed's and contrast more strongly with underparts. *D. c. virescens* of the Andaman Is has brighter green upperparts than *olivaceum*, and grey throat and breast contrasting with yellow lower belly, flanks and vent. **VOICE** Staccato *tzik*, more piercing than call of Pale-billed Flowerpecker, repeated sometimes metronomically; distinctive penetrating *tzierrr* is repeated as song (P. Holt). **HABITS** A typical flowerpecker. An extremely active and restless species, usually in pairs or small parties. Very fond of mistletoe berries; also eats nectar, insects and spiders. **HABITAT** Edges and clearings of broadleaved forest, groves, orchards and tea and coffee plantations; its distribution is closely linked to the presence of mistletoe. **BREEDING** January–August. Nest is a very small purse of white vegetable down, suspended 6–12 m up in a tree, sometimes in a high bush or plant. **DISTRIBUTION AND STATUS** Resident. Mainly Himalayan foothills from C Nepal east to Arunachal Pradesh; hills of NE and SW India, and Bangladesh. **NP:** patchily distributed in the centre and east, locally fairly common; 305–1525 m (150–2500 m). **IN:** common; from the foothills up to 1800 m in Himalayas, in low country and hills up to the summits in the southwest. **BT:** fairly common; 250–1800 m. **BD:** local.

FIRE-BREASTED FLOWERPECKER *Dicaeum ignipectus* Plate 139

Buff-bellied Flowerpecker (K)

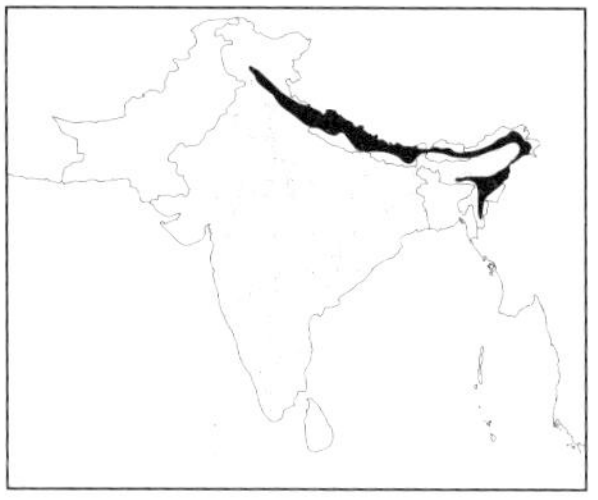

IDENTIFICATION 9 cm. **Male** is distinctive, with dark metallic blue or green upperparts (can look black in poor light), buff-coloured underparts, and scarlet breast patch with a black patch in centre of belly. **Female** has olive-green upperparts, orange-buff throat, centre of breast and belly, and olive breast sides and flanks. Orange-buff on underparts separates female from Plain Flowerpecker (above). **Juvenile** has whiter throat merging into pale greyish-olive of rest of underparts, and has duller olive upperparts than female. Very similar to Plain, although different altitudinal range and habitat should aid identification. **VOICE** Song is a shrill *titty-titty-titty*; call is a clicking *chip* (Ali and Ripley 1987). **HABITS** A typical flowerpecker. Solitary or in pairs in the breeding season; at other times occasionally in small parties. Favours mistletoe berries. **HABITAT** Broadleaved forest, secondary growth and orchards; its distribution is linked to the presence of mistletoe berries. **BREEDING** March–June. Has a typical flowerpecker nest, suspended from a twig at the end of a branch 3–9 m up, and well concealed among leaves. **DISTRIBUTION AND STATUS** Resident, subject to altitudinal movements. Himalayas from Kashmir east to Arunachal Pradesh; NE Indian hills. **NP:** widespread and common; summers mainly 1830–2700 m, winters 915–2285 m. **IN:** common; breeds mainly 1400–2500 m, locally to 3000 m, winters from foothills up to 2500 m. **BT:** common; from 2895 m down to 1110 m and probably lower.

SCARLET-BACKED FLOWERPECKER *Dicaeum cruentatum* Plate 139

IDENTIFICATION 9 cm. **Male** is distinctive, with scarlet upperparts contrasting with black ear-coverts, sides of neck and mantle sides, and blue-black wings and tail. Underparts are pale buff, with grey on sides of breast and flanks. **Female** told from other female flowerpeckers by scarlet rump and uppertail-coverts contrasting with blackish tail, olive-brown upperparts, and faint buffish wash to whitish underparts. **Juvenile** as female, but lacks scarlet rump and uppertail-coverts (the latter having distinct orange cast). Possibly confusable with Pale-billed

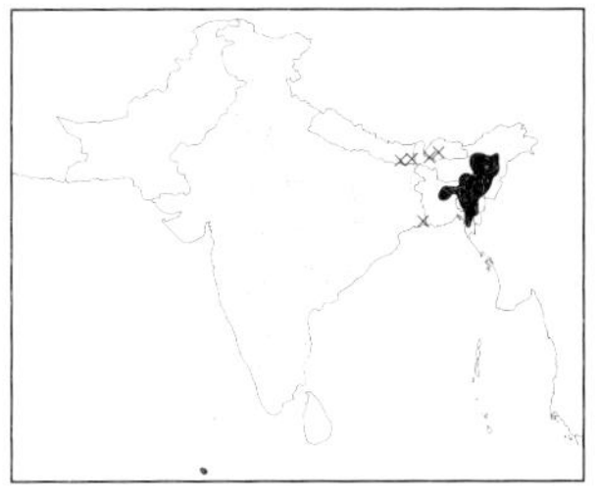

Flowerpecker (p.799), but has bright orange-red bill with dark tip, and fine whitish supercilium to eye. Bill colour separates juvenile from Plain and from juvenile Fire-breasted Flowerpeckers (p.799 and p.800). Orange coloration to uppertail-coverts suggests Orange-bellied (p.799), but has buff fringes to wing-coverts and tertials, lacks blue-grey edges to remiges (which form variable panel on wing of Orange-bellied), and has whitish throat and centre of belly. **VOICE** Song is a thin, repeated *tissit, tissit...* (Boonsong and Round 1991); call is a hard, metallic *tip..tip..tip* etc (C. Robson). **HABITS** A typical flowerpecker. Solitary or in pairs in the breeding season; occasionally in small parties at other times. Fond of mistletoe berries. **HABITAT** Broadleaved forest, secondary growth and orchards; its distribution is linked to the presence of mistletoe. **BREEDING** March–June. Has a typical flowerpecker nest, suspended 3–9 m above ground. **DISTRIBUTION AND STATUS** Resident. Himalayan foothills in E Nepal, Bhutan and hills of NE India and Bangladesh. **NP:** rare and very local in the east; 305 m, 2135 m. **IN:** status uncertain; foothills up to 1400 m, also in plains in the northeast. **BT:** rare. **BD:** locally common.

SUNBIRDS AND SPIDERHUNTERS Tribe Nectariniini

Sunbirds and spiderhunters have a bill and tongue adapted to feed on nectar; they also eat small insects and spiders. The bill is long, thin and curved for probing the corollas of flowers, and has fine serrations near the tip, probably to help in capturing hard-bodied insects. The tongue is very long, tubular and extensible far beyond the bill, and is used to draw out nectar. These birds have a curious habit of stretching and contracting their neck and at the same time swaying their body from side to side.

SUNBIRDS Small to very small passerines, the males having bright iridescence in parts of their plumage and the females usually being much duller and without metallic lustre. Males of some species, after breeding, moult into a dull-coloured plumage, resembling females. Sunbirds are purely arboreal and feed mainly at the blossoms of flowering trees and shrubs. They flit and dart actively from flower to flower, clambering over the blossoms, often hovering momentarily in front of them, and clinging acrobatically to twigs. The nectar of large-petalled flowers, such as hibiscus and canna, is reached by piercing a hole at the base of the calyx. Sunbirds are pugnacious and vigorously defend their territories against intruders. They usually keep singly or in pairs, although several may congregate in flowering trees, and some species join mixed foraging flocks. They build a pear-shaped or oval purse-like nest, with a side entrance near the top and often sheltered by a projecting porch; the nest is made of fibres, rootlets and grasses, decorated or held together with cobwebs and usually with a loose tail of material hanging below, and is typically suspended from a twig fairly near the ground. Sunbirds have sharp, metallic calls and high-pitched trilling and twittering songs.

RUBY-CHEEKED SUNBIRD *Anthreptes singalensis* Plate 139

Rubycheek (F,I)

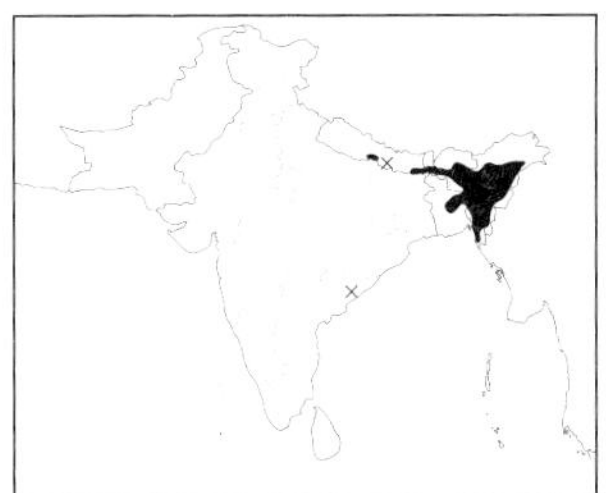

IDENTIFICATION 11 cm. **Male** told from other sunbirds by short flowerpecker-like bill, metallic green upperparts, coppery-red ear-coverts bordered below by purplish moustachial stripe, rufous-orange throat, and yellow rest of underparts. **Female** lacks coppery-red ear-coverts and has dull olive-green upperparts. Separated from all other flowerpeckers by rufous-orange throat and breast and yellow rest of underparts. **Juvenile** as female, but entire underparts are yellow. **VOICE** A disyllabic *wee-eest* with rising inflection, and similar to call of Yellow-browed Warbler (p.730) (Boonsong and Round 1991). Probable song is a rapid high-pitched *switi-ti-chi-chu...tusi-tit....swit-swit....switi-ti-chi-chu....switi-ti-chi-chu...* (C. Robson). **HABITS** A small active sunbird, continually flitting about on low branches and bushes. Unlike other sunbirds, sometimes associates in small parties in winter. **HABITAT** Favours evergreen biotope: open forest, forest clearings and edges and along tracks, scrub jungle and mangroves. **BREEDING** End March–June. Nest is similar to that of other sunbirds, but with a rather large entrance, hung from a bush up to 2 m above ground. **DISTRIBUTION AND STATUS** Resident. Mainly Himalayan foothills from C Nepal east to Arunachal Pradesh; hills of NE India and Bangladesh. **NP:** very local and rare; below 455 m. **IN:** locally frequent; foothills up to 700 m, and in adjacent plains. **BT:** rare; 245–400 m. **BD:** locally common.

PURPLE-RUMPED SUNBIRD *Nectarinia zeylonica* Plate 139

IDENTIFICATION 10 cm. **Male** is similar to Crimson-backed (p.802), with metallic green crown and purple throat and rump. Best told by larger size, brighter yellow lower breast and belly with distinctive greyish-white flanks, narrow maroon band across upper breast (reaching bend of wing), metallic green shoulder patch, and

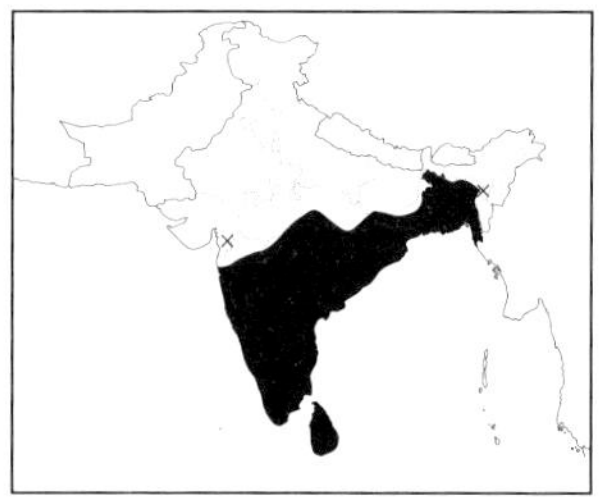

maroon (rather than crimson) sides of head and mantle. Male appears to retain breeding plumage throughout the year. **Female** distinguished from female Crimson-backed by larger size, greyish-white throat, olive rump, greyish-white flanks contrasting with yellow belly, and grey-brown upperparts (with faint greenish cast) with rufous-brown fringes to tertials and secondaries forming panel on wing. From female Purple (p.803) by greyish-white throat which merges with grey of ear-coverts, greyish-white flanks, and rufous-brown on wing (last feature can be difficult to see); usually shows a more prominent supercilium than Purple, but lacks 'masked' appearance shown by many female Purple. **Juvenile** as female, but entire underparts are yellow. Rump colour separates it from juvenile and female Crimson-backed (below), and rufous-brown on wings from juvenile Purple. **VOICE** Calls include a high-pitched *ptsee..ptsee*, and a metallic *chit* (recalling Grey Wagtail, p.814), which are different from calls of Crimson-backed and Purple (R. Grimmett). High broken twittering song comprises calls strung together, *tu-witou-titou-switou* etc (P. Holt). **HABITS** A typical sunbird. Usually keeps in pairs throughout the year. Constantly on the move, flitting from tree to tree and calling incessantly. **HABITAT** Cultivation, gardens, secondary growth and open deciduous woodland. **BREEDING** Throughout the year, varying locally. Nest is very like that of Purple Sunbird, suspended 2–15 m up in a tree or shrub. **DISTRIBUTION AND STATUS** Resident. From N Maharashtra northeast through C Madhya Pradesh to S Assam and south through much of the subcontinent. **IN:** locally common; plains and hills up to 1000 m (–2100 m). **BD:** common throughout. **LK:** common in lowlands and lower hills, less frequent in higher hills.

CRIMSON-BACKED SUNBIRD *Nectarinia minima* — Plate 139

Small Sunbird (I,P)

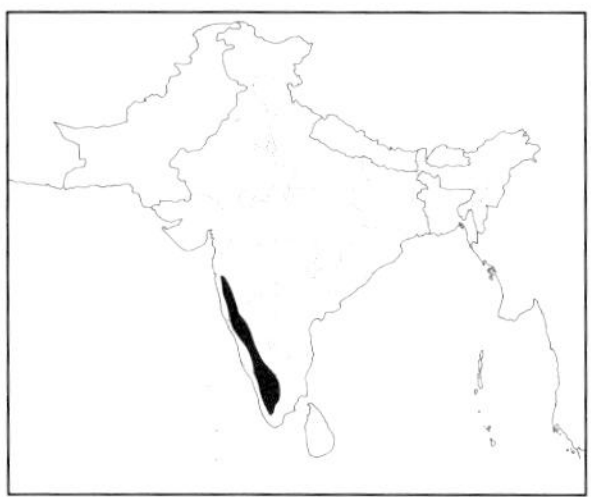

IDENTIFICATION 8 cm. Distinguished from Purple-rumped Sunbird (p.801) by smaller size and finer, more downcurved bill, and by flowerpecker-like call. **Male** is similar to Purple-rumped, having metallic green crown, purple rump and purple throat. Best told by broad crimson breast-band (extending well below bend of wing), with pale yellow of underparts (which can appear white in some views) restricted to belly, by crimson (rather than maroon) sides of head and mantle, and by lack of metallic green shoulder patch. **Eclipse male** as female, but has metallic purple rump and crimson scapulars and back. **Female** told from other female sunbirds by combination of small size, crimson rump, olive-green upperparts and edges to wings, and uniform yellowish underparts. Some (worn?) females have duller, greyer upperparts and greyish-white underparts. **Juvenile female** is similar to adult female, but has brighter yellow underparts and brighter olive-green upperparts. **Juvenile male** appears to be similar to eclipse male, but with duller greyish underparts. **VOICE** Calls include a flowerpecker-like *thlick-thlick*, although not quite so hard as that of Plain Flowerpecker (R. Grimmett), and a nasal *spziew*. Fast song lacks power and variety of those of larger species; introduction often stereotypic *tsee-sit-see-su..tse-sit-swee...*, then breaks down into erratic twitters and trills (P. Holt). **HABITS** A typical sunbird. Favours flowers of *Erythrina* and Loranthaceae species. **HABITAT** Evergreen biotope, chiefly in the foothills: forest, sholas, gardens, and flowering shade trees in tea and coffee plantations. **BREEDING** December–April, September and October. Nest is similar to that of other sunbirds, but smaller, neater and rounder and usually lacking a tail of dangling material, suspended in a bush or small tree within 2 m of the ground. **DISTRIBUTION AND STATUS IN:** resident, endemic to the Western Ghats and adjacent hills from Maharashtra south to Kerala and W Tamil Nadu; locally common, from 300 m to summits.

PURPLE-THROATED SUNBIRD *Nectarinia sperata* — Plate 140

Van Hasselt's Sunbird

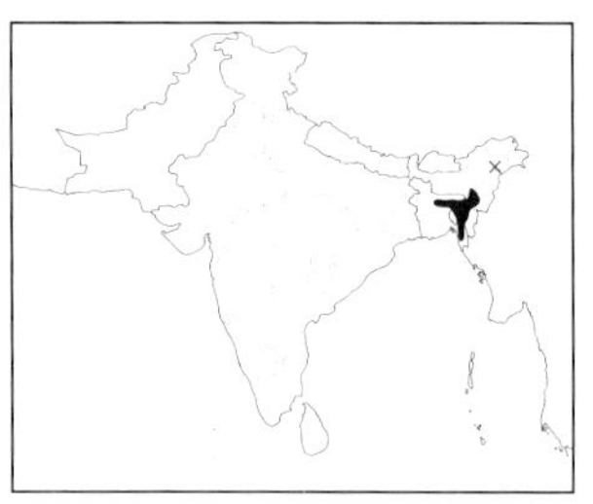

IDENTIFICATION 10 cm. A small, short-billed sunbird. **Male** is readily identified by crimson breast and upper belly, becoming sooty-brown on lower belly, and blackish sides of head and mantle. In addition, has metallic green crown, purple throat, and metallic blue-green back and rump. Can sometimes appear almost black in poor light. **Female** told from other female sunbirds by a combination of small size, dull yellowish underparts with more olive-coloured throat, and olive-green upperparts. **VOICE** Has a feeble *chip chip* call. Song? is a thin, high-pitched *psweet.psweet.psweet.psweet-psweet.psweet..psit-it..psweet.psweet...* etc; also a high-pitched *ti-swit...titwitwitwitwitit...* (C. Robson). **HABITS** A typical sunbird. **HABITAT** Thin forest, gardens and dense cover in swampy land. **BREEDING** Very little known in the region. February and May in Bangladesh. **DISTRIBUTION AND STATUS** Resident, subject to seasonal movements. Plains of NE India (Assam, Manipur, Mizoram, Tripura) and Bangladesh. **IN:** rare and local. **BD:** local.

OLIVE-BACKED SUNBIRD *Nectarinia jugularis* Plate 140

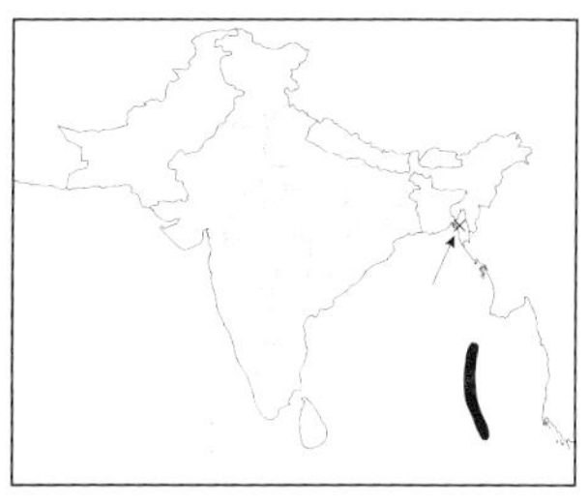

IDENTIFICATION 11 cm. **Male** is distinctive, with olive-green upperparts, metallic blue or purple and blue-green throat and breast, with narrow chestnut-brown breast-band, and yellow belly and vent. **Eclipse male** is as female, but has broad blackish stripe down centre of throat and breast. **Female** has olive upperparts and yellow underparts. **Racial variation** Male *N. j. klossi* of the Nicobar Is has brown crown and nape contrasting with olive mantle, metallic purple or blue feathers on crown, browner throat, and brighter orange-yellow breast compared with *N. j. andamanica* of the Andaman Is (which has uniform olive forehead, crown and nape concolorous with mantle); female *klossi* is brighter yellow on underparts than female *andamanica. N. j. proselia* of Car Nicobar is similar to *klossi*, but has stronger metallic purple throat and olive crown and nape, and is smaller in size. **VOICE** Call is a loud *sweet*; song consists of alternating, varied, thin, high-pitched phrases, rapidly delivered at intervals (C. Robson). **HABITS** A typical sunbird. **HABITAT** Forest, scrub and coastal mangroves. **BREEDING** January–February and May–July. Has a typical sunbird nest, often hung from a grass stem close to the ground, also from a shrub or tree. **DISTRIBUTION AND STATUS IN:** common in Andaman and Nicobar Is. **BD:** vagrant?; only one probable record. **REFERENCES** Anon. (1994), Sankaran and Vijayan (1993).

PURPLE SUNBIRD *Nectarinia asiatica* Plate 140

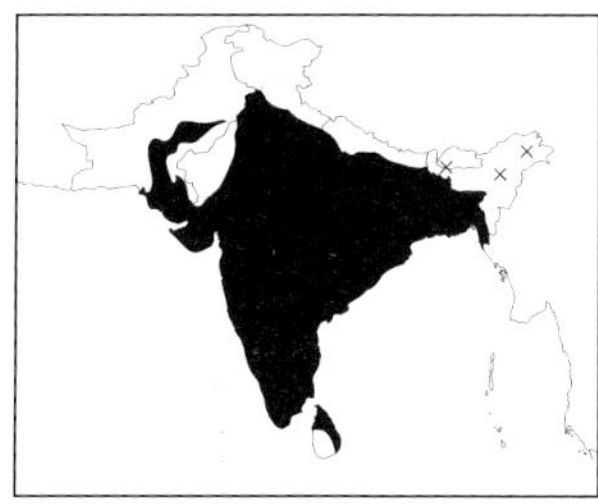

IDENTIFICATION 10 cm. **Male** is a metallic blue-green and purple sunbird, often looking black in poor light. In S India and Sri Lanka, confusable with Loten's (below), but has a shorter and only slightly downcurved bill, and dark metallic blue or purple belly and vent (which appear concolorous with rest of underparts). **Eclipse male** is as female, but has a broad blackish stripe down centre of throat and breast, metallic blue-green wing-coverts and brownish-black remiges which contrast with greyish-green mantle, and metallic blue tail. Told from eclipse Loten's by bill shape and size, and paler greyish-green upperparts. **Female** has greenish upperparts and yellow underparts. Some (worn?) females have very grey upperparts and show only a trace of yellow on underparts. Told from female Loten's by bill size and shape. As with eclipse male, often shows a fine supercilium and/or darker olive lores and ear-coverts (often giving rise to poorly defined 'mask'), which are not apparent on female (and eclipse male) Loten's. From female Purple-rumped (p.801) by yellow throat concolorous with breast, strong contrast between ear-coverts and throat, and lack of prominent greyish-white flanks. **Juvenile** is brighter yellow on entire underparts than female. Differs from juvenile Purple-rumped in lacking rufous-brown on wing. **VOICE** Song is a pleasant, descending *swee-swee-swee swit zizi-zizi*, and has a low, twittering subsong; call is a buzzing *zit* and a high-pitched, upward-inflected and slightly wheezy *swee* or *che-wee* (R. Grimmett). **HABITS** A typical sunbird, but probably more insectivorous than other species. Sometimes makes short aerial sallies like a flycatcher. The male sings from the top of a bare tree or telegraph wire, while occasionally jerking from side to side and raising his wings to reveal his bright orange-and-yellow pectoral tufts. **HABITAT** Open deciduous forest and gardens. **BREEDING** Throughout the year, varying locally. Nest is similar to that of other sunbirds, but untidy and covered with small bark pieces, caterpillar droppings and bits of paper, string and other rubbish; suspended within 2 m of ground in a shrub or tree, often within greyish masses of spiders' webs. **DISTRIBUTION AND STATUS** Resident, subject to local and altitudinal movements, and partial migrant. Throughout much of the subcontinent, except parts of the northwest and northeast. **PK:** widespread and common throughout the plains; rare or absent from N Punjab in winter, resident farther south; ascends the foothills locally to 1200 m in summer. **NP:** widespread and common below 365 m; mainly a summer visitor 900–2135 m. **IN:** common and widespread; in plains and foothills, up to 1700 m in Himalayas, to 2400 m in peninsular hills. **BT:** rare and local. **BD:** locally common throughout. **LK:** common in the dry lowlands, visitor to the wet lowlands and hills.

LOTEN'S SUNBIRD *Nectarinia lotenia* Plate 140

Long-billed Sunbird

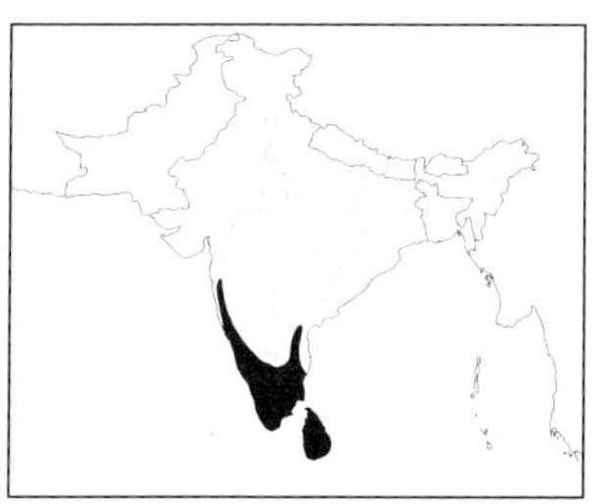

IDENTIFICATION 13 cm. Closely resembles Purple Sunbird (above), but is larger and has a longer, sharply downcurved bill. **Male** much as Purple Sunbird, with blackish upperparts, glossed green and purple, and metallic green-and-purple throat and breast. Plumage differences from Purple include broad maroon band across breast and dusky brown belly and flanks which contrast noticeably with breast. **Eclipse male** is as female, but has broad blackish stripe down centre of throat and breast and metallic blue-green wing-coverts. Told from eclipse Purple by bill size and shape, and darker olive-green upperparts which do not contrast noticeably with wings. **Female** has dark olive-green upperparts and pale yellow underparts. Some (worn?) females are almost white on the underparts and have grey-brown upperparts.

As with eclipse male, lacks the paler supercilium and masked appearance which are often apparent on Purple; upperparts are generally darker than on Purple, and ear-coverts and sides of neck contrast with throat and breast, giving rise to hooded appearance. Separated from female Purple-rumped (p.801) by longer bill, uniform yellow underparts, absence of supercilium, strong contrast between ear-coverts and throat, and lack of rufous-brown on wing. **Juvenile** as female. **VOICE** Song a slow *tichit-wut...tichit-wu-eet...wue-wue-wue-wue*, last notes accelerated (P. Holt); also a repeated *cheewit-cheewit cheewit.* Call is a harsh *chit chit,* similar to that of Little Spiderhunter (p.806), lacking the buzzing quality of call of Purple (R. Grimmett). **HABITS** A typical sunbird. Has a habit of continually jerking its head to and fro.**HABITAT** Well-wooded country and gardens in moist deciduous biotope. **BREEDING** Throughout the year. Nest is similar to that of other sunbirds, but is very untidy and covered in wood chips, bark and caterpillar excreta; usually suspended from a shady tree 3 m or more above ground, but also sometimes built among creepers inside a mass of spiders' webs or in a bush. **DISTRIBUTION AND STATUS** Resident, endemic to India and Sri Lanka. Indian peninsula from W Maharashtra, W Karnataka and S Andhra Pradesh south through the peninsula and Sri Lanka. **IN:** fairly common in the low country and hills up to 1600 m. **LK:** common in the lowlands and lower hills, less frequent in higher hills.

MRS GOULD'S SUNBIRD *Aethopyga gouldiae* Plate 140

Gould's Sunbird

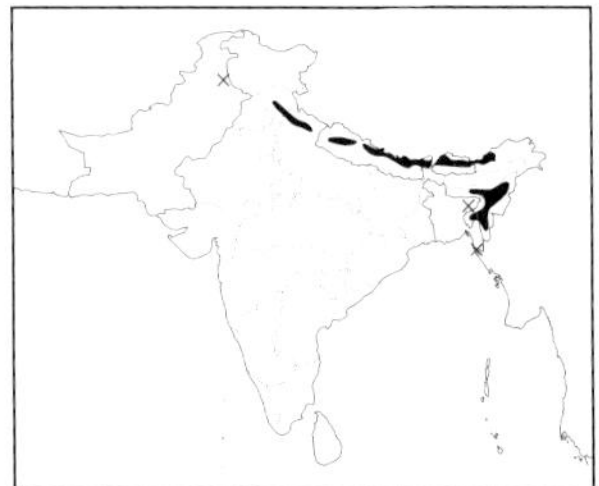

IDENTIFICATION 10 cm. **Male** is confusable with both Green-tailed and Crimson Sunbirds (p.804 and p.805). Like Green-tailed has yellow on underparts, but has crimson mantle and back (with crimson extending as far as yellow rump), metallic purplish-blue crown, ear-covert patch and throat, crimson sides of neck, supercilium and malar stripe, and blue to purplish-blue uppertail-coverts and tail. Told from Crimson by metallic purple throat, yellow on underparts (with scarlet streaking on breast), and blue uppertail-coverts and tail. **Female** distinguished from other female sunbirds except Black-throated (p.805) by prominent pale yellow rump band (as on Lemon-rumped Warbler, p.729). From Black-throated by yellowish underparts, especially lower breast and belly (some have greyish throat and breast), broad and well-defined white tips to outer tail feathers, and shorter, straighter bill with noticeably pale lower mandible. Short bill, yellow rump, yellower underparts and shorter, squarer tail should separate from female Green-tailed. **Juvenile** male is similar to female, but has bright yellow breast and belly. **Racial variation** *A. e. dabryii*, which has been recorded in NE subcontinent, has scarlet (rather than yellow) breast. **VOICE** Call is a quick-repeated *tzip*; alarm a *tshi-stshi-ti-ti-ti*, and a lisping *squeeeeee* which rises in the middle (Fleming *et al.* 1984). **HABITS** A typical sunbird. Very lively. Forages at all levels, from bushes up to the canopy. **HABITAT** Rhododendron and other flowering trees and shrubs in forest. **BREEDING** April–August. Nest is like that of other sunbirds, but with the edge of the entrance reinforced to form a firm rim, suspended rather low in bushes. **DISTRIBUTION AND STATUS** Resident, subject to altitudinal movements. Mainly the Himalayas, from Himachal Pradesh east to Arunachal Pradesh; NE India. **PK:** vagrant. **NP:** widespread and uncommon; summers chiefly 2500–3655 m, winters from 1830 m up to at least 2700 m. **IN:** generally uncommon, but locally fairly common in the east; breeds 1800–3300 m, winters from 2700 m down to the base of hills in the Himalayas; mainly 900–2400 m south of the Brahmaputra R. **BT:** frequent; 1000–3355 m. **BD:** vagrant.

GREEN-TAILED SUNBIRD *Aethopyga nipalensis* Plate 140

Nepal Yellow-backed Sunbird (I), Nepal Sunbird (F)

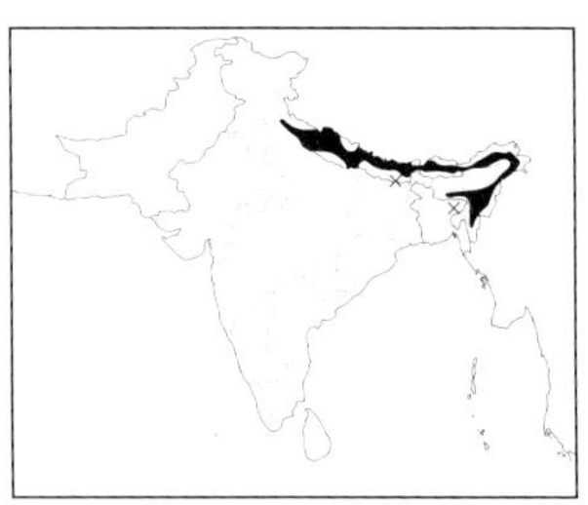

IDENTIFICATION 11 cm. **Male** is likely to be confused only with Mrs Gould's Sunbird (above). Distinguished from that species by maroon mantle (almost absent in *A. n. horsfieldi*) and olive-green back, dark metallic blue-green crown and throat, and blackish sides of head (whole head looks dark, lacking crimson on sides). Has blue-green uppertail-coverts and tail (tail can appear blue, but not purplish-blue as on Mrs Gould's). **Female** has greyish-olive throat and breast (very grey on some birds), becoming yellowish-olive on belly and flanks. Lack of well-defined yellow rump band (although rump and uppertail-coverts are slightly yellowish-green) and longer, noticeably graduated tail (with slim central feathers extending noticeably beyond the rest) separate it from female Mrs Gould's and Black-throated (above and p.805). For differences from female Fire-tailed (p.805), see that species. **Juvenile** is apparently similar to female, but has square tail and narrower white tip to rectrices. Juvenile male can have orange wash on breast. **Racial variation** *A. n. horsfieldi* of W Himalayas has maroon of upperparts restricted to narrow band below metallic green nape. **VOICE** Song is a *tchiss......tchiss-iss-iss-iss* (Ali and Ripley 1987); call is a loud *chit chit.* **HABITS** A typical sunbird. Often associates with mixed foraging flocks in the non-breeding season. **HABITAT** Oak–rhododendron and mixed forest, secondary growth and gardens. **BREEDING** May and June. Has a typical sunbird nest, suspended within 2 m of the ground. **DISTRIBUTION AND STATUS** Resident, subject to altitudinal movements. Himalayas from N Uttar Pradesh east to Arunachal Pradesh; NE India. **NP:** widespread and common; summers chiefly 1830–3000 m, infrequent up to 3505 m, winters 915–2745 m (down to 305 m). **IN:** uncommon in the west, common in the east; in Himalayas, breeds 1800–2900 m, winters down to 150 m (–3600 m). **BT:** common; 1220–3665 m. **BD:** status uncertain, and only one recent record.

BLACK-THROATED SUNBIRD *Aethopyga saturata* Plate 140

Black-breasted Sunbird (F,I)

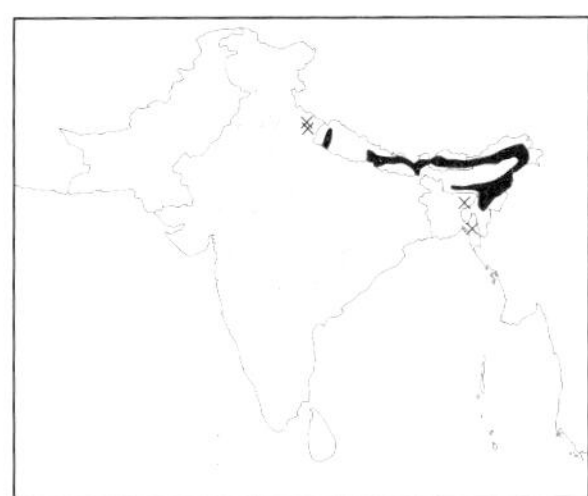

IDENTIFICATION 11 cm. **Male** is readily told from other male sunbirds by blackish throat and breast merging into greyish-olive of underparts. In addition, has dark metallic purple tail, metallic purple crown, malar stripe and nape, black sides of head, and crimson mantle and sides of neck. **Female** told from other female sunbirds except Mrs Gould's (p.804) by well-defined pale yellow rump which is usually apparent. From Mrs Gould's by uniform, greyish-olive underparts (without any yellow), longer, dark and noticeably downcurved bill, and narrow or indistinct pale tips to outer tail feathers. **VOICE** A rapid *ti-ti-ti-ti-ti-ti-ti-ti-ti-ti-ti* (S. Buckton). **HABITS** A typical sunbird. Usually feeds in bushes and lower branches. **HABITAT** Bushes in open forest, at the edges of dense forest and in secondary growth. **BREEDING** May–July. Has a typical sunbird nest, suspended in bushes or creepers, usually within 2 m of ground. **DISTRIBUTION AND STATUS** Resident, subject to altitudinal movements. Himalayas from N Uttar Pradesh east to Arunachal Pradesh; NE India and Bangladesh. **NP:** widespread and frequent, mainly 1000–1830 m; occasionally summers up to 2200 m and winters down to 305 m. **IN:** fairly common in Himalayas, from the base of the hills in winter up to 2000 m in summer; from the foothills and adjacent plains up to 1800 m in the northeast. **BT:** common; 510–2285 m. **BD:** ?former resident; no recent records, but could still occur in hill tracts.

CRIMSON SUNBIRD *Aethopyga siparaja* Plate 140

Yellow-backed Sunbird (I), Scarlet-breasted Sunbird (F)

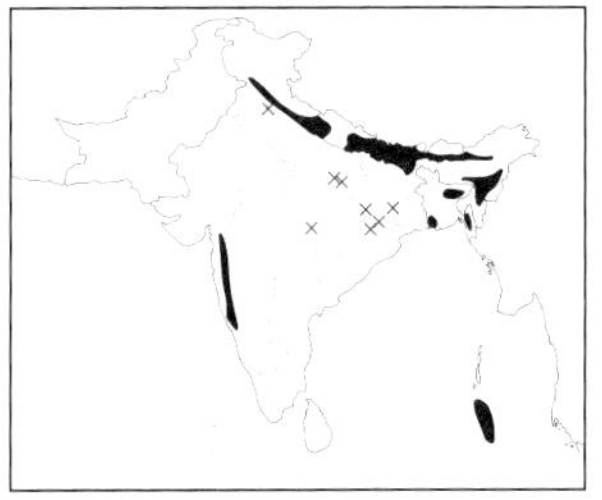

IDENTIFICATION 11 cm. **Male** distinguished from other sunbirds by largely crimson head and mantle, scarlet throat and breast, and dusky yellowish-olive belly and vent. Crown, malar stripe and tail are metallic bottle-green. **Female** has yellowish-olive underparts variably washed with grey, and with stronger yellow coloration to centre of belly. Told from female Black-throated (above) and Mrs Gould's (p.804) by lack of yellow rump. Most likely to be confused with female Green-tailed (p.804), but has shorter and squarer tail with indistinct pale tips to outer feathers, and slightly shorter and broader-based bill with paler lower mandible. **Juvenile male** is similar to female, but has scarlet wash to throat and breast. **Racial variation** Four races are described from the subcontinent. *A. s. seheriae* and *A. s. labecula* of the Himalayas and NE subcontinent are covered by the description above. Male *A. s. vigorsii* of the Western Ghats is larger, and central tail feathers extend only just beyond rest of tail; further, has scarlet throat and breast mixed with fine yellow streaking, uniform grey lower breast, belly and flanks, and uniform grey-brown wings lacking yellowish-olive edges to flight feathers and coverts. Female *vigorsii* is also different, having greyer underparts lacking strong yellow or olive tones of female *seheriae*. As in *seheriae*, males can be similar to female, but with dull scarlet throat and breast contrasting with grey rest of underparts. Male *A. s. nicobarica* of the Nicobar Is has violet-purple (rather than green) crown and tail, further to which it appears smaller than *seheriae*, with brighter, purer scarlet throat and breast and grey belly and vent, and seems not to show elongated central tail feather; females possibly always show dull scarlet on throat and breast. **VOICE** Rapid, tripping song of three to six sharp and clearly enunciated notes, *tsip-it-sip-it-sit*, lacking the intense chittering that usually characterises the songs of Black-throated and Green-tailed, and is very different from Mrs Gould's powerful, pulsed seesawing song (P. Holt). **HABITS** A typical sunbird. Especially fond of red flowers. Forages mainly low down in bushes, also in coconut palms when in flower, and occasionally in flowering trees. **HABITAT** Bushes in open broadleaved forest, groves and gardens; also in mangroves in Bangladesh. **BREEDING** February, April–July. Has a typical sunbird nest, usually attached to roots of bushes dangling from an overhanging bank. **DISTRIBUTION AND STATUS** Resident, subject to seasonal and altitudinal movements. Mainly the Himalayas, from Himachal Pradesh east to Arunachal Pradesh, also hills of NE, E and SW India, and Bangladesh; spreads to adjacent plains of N and NE India in winter. **NP:** widespread and fairly common below 915 m, frequent up to 1200 m, scarce up to 2100 m. **IN:** locally fairly common; in the Himalayas and NE hills, breeds from the foothills up to 1800 m, winters down to adjacent plains; c. 900 m in Western Ghats. **BT:** fairly common; 250–1830 m. **BD:** locally common. **REFERENCES** Martens and Eck (1995).

FIRE-TAILED SUNBIRD *Aethopyga ignicauda* Plate 140

IDENTIFICATION 12 cm. **Male** distinguished from other sunbirds by scarlet uppertail-coverts and very long central tail feathers. Nape and mantle are also scarlet. Crown and throat are metallic purple, and underparts are yellow (washed with orange on breast). **Eclipse male** is similar to female, but has brighter yellow belly and scarlet uppertail-coverts and sides to tail. **Female** is most similar to female Green-tailed (p.804), but has straighter bill, squarer tail (lacking white tips to rectrices) with trace of brownish-orange at sides, more noticeable olive-yellow on rump (distinct from back, but not forming prominent band as on Black-throated, above, or Mrs Gould's, p.804), and slightly brighter yellow on breast and belly. **VOICE** Song is a high-pitched, monot-

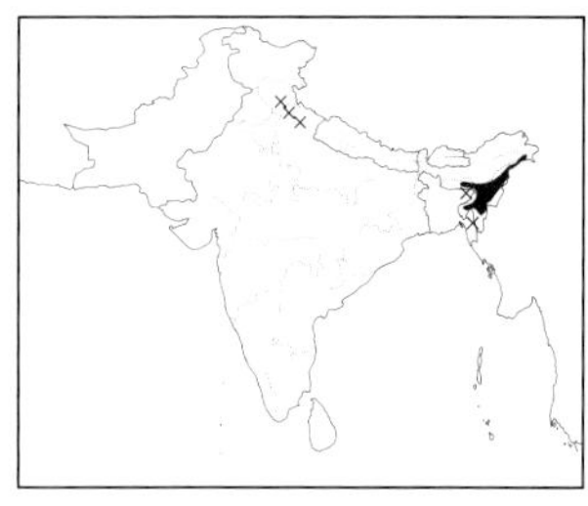

onous *dzidzi-dzidzidzidzi.* **HABITS** A typical sunbird, but a particularly vivacious one. In breeding plumage, the long red tail of the male swirls in flight. **HABITAT** Breeds in rhododendron shrubberies above the treeline, and open coniferous forest with an understorey of rhododendrons; winters in broadleaved and mixed broadleaved–coniferous forest. **BREEDING** April–June. Has a typical sunbird nest, suspended from a dwarf bamboo or other bush and within 2 m of ground. **DISTRIBUTION AND STATUS** Resident, subject to altitudinal movements. Himalayas from S Himachal Pradesh east to Bhutan; NE India and Bangladesh. **NP:** widespread and fairly common; summers mainly 3000–4000 m, winters 1050–2135 m (610–2895 m). **IN:** fairly common in Himalayas; common south of the Brahmaputra R in winter, uncommon in summer; breeds 3000–4000 m, winters 1200–2900 m. **BT:** fairly common; summers 3000–4120 m, winters down to 1000 m. **BD:** ?former resident; no recent records, but could still occur in hill tracts.

SPIDERHUNTERS The sexes are alike, having similar dull-coloured plumage, the males lacking iridescence. The spiderhunters have similar foraging behaviour to the sunbirds, but are larger and bulkier, have a longer bill and utter explosive chattering calls. They are usually found singly or in pairs.

LITTLE SPIDERHUNTER *Arachnothera longirostra* — Plate 140

A. longirostris **(F)**

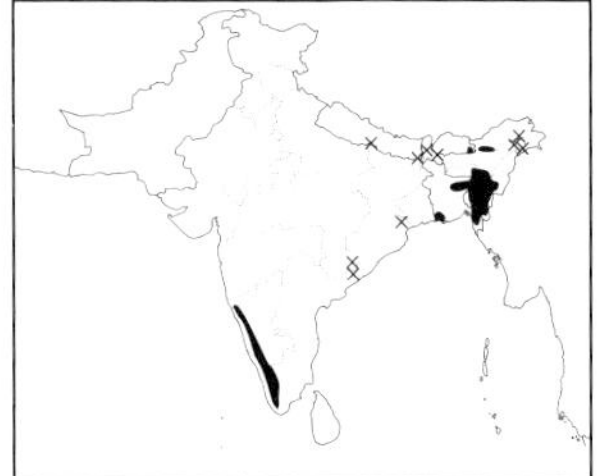

IDENTIFICATION 16 cm. Told from Streaked Spiderhunter (below) by smaller size and proportionately longer bill, unstreaked olive-green upperparts, whitish throat and breast merging into pale yellow of rest of underparts, and whitish eye-ring, with dark moustachial stripe. Similar in plumage to some female/juvenile sunbirds, but is larger, with a much longer bill. **Juvenile** has yellowish-olive tinge to throat. **VOICE** Song is a rapidly repeated *wit-wit-wit-wit...*; call is an abrasive *itch* (R. Grimmett). **HABITS** Keeps to the lower storey of forest. Restless and noisy. Especially fond of the nectar of wild banana flowers. Frequently clings upside-down while probing blossoms for nectar. **HABITAT** Wild bananas and bamboos in broadleaved evergreen and moist deciduous forest, secondary growth and sholas; often along streams. **BREEDING** Throughout the year, varying locally. Nest is a cup made of skeleton leaves, grass and vegetable down, and sewn by its rim to the underside of a banana or other broad leaf. **DISTRIBUTION AND STATUS** Resident. From SC Nepal east to Arunachal Pradesh; NE India and Bangladesh; Simlipal Hills, E India; Eastern and Western Ghats. **NP:** rare and very local in the centre and east; below 305 m. **IN:** patchily distributed; locally frequent in Western Ghats, locally common in the northeast; mainly in the foothills, most frequent below 610 m, scarce up to 1800 m, also in adjacent plains. **BT:** rare. **BD:** locally common.

STREAKED SPIDERHUNTER *Arachnothera magna* — Plate 140

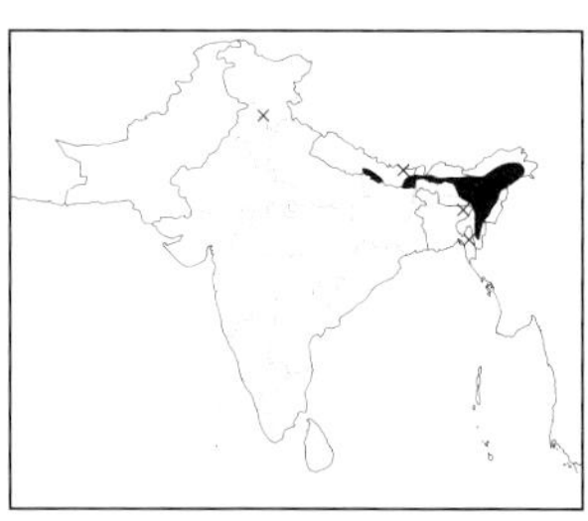

IDENTIFICATION 19 cm. Distinguished from Little Spiderhunter (above) by larger size, bold streaking on dark olive-green upperparts, and bold streaking on yellowish-white underparts. Has rather plain face, lacking paler cheeks and darker moustachial stripe, and has orange legs and feet. Has undulating, almost woodpecker-like flight. **Juvenile** as adult, although streaking is less apparent. **VOICE** Song is a strident chatter; call is a sharp *chirirrik* or *chirik chirik.* **HABITS** A typical spiderhunter. Usually found singly or in pairs, often with mixed itinerant hunting parties. Forages in the upper storey. Fast-moving, flies strongly and swiftly from one tree to the next. Very fond of the nectar of wild banana flowers. **HABITAT** Broadleaved evergreen and moist deciduous forest with dense undergrowth, especially of bananas. **BREEDING** March–July. Nest is a compact inverted dome made of skeleton leaves, bound together with cobwebs and sewn to the underside of a broad leaf. **DISTRIBUTION AND STATUS** Resident, subject to seasonal movements. Himalayas in Sutlej valley, Himachal Pradesh, in 19th century, and from C Nepal east to Arunachal Pradesh; NE India and Bangladesh. **NP:** patchily distributed and locally fairly common in the centre and east; below 450 m (–2135 m). **IN:** common east of Sikkim; breeds 600–1500 m, occasionally up to 2200 m, spreading into plains in winter. **BT:** fairly common; 245–1930 m. **BD:** ?rare winter visitor to northeast and southeast.

SPARROWS AND SNOWFINCHES Passeridae, subfamily Passerinae

Small passerines with a thick conical bill. There are four genera: *Passer*, the true sparrows, some of which are closely associated with human habitation; *Petronia*, the rock sparrows, which inhabit dry rocky country or light scrub; and *Montifringilla* and *Pyrgilauda*, the snowfinches, which occur in mountains. They are mainly brown and grey in coloration, sometimes with black, except for the snowfinches, which have some conspicuous white in the plumage. Most species feed on seeds, taken on or near the ground; snowfinches also consume a high proportion of insects when available. Many *Passer* and *Petronia* species are gregarious all year, and some nest in loose colonies; the snowfinches gather in flocks outside the breeding season. *Passer* species often form large communal roosts outside the breeding season. Sparrows and snowfinches usually nest in bushes or in holes in buildings, trees, earth banks or rock faces. The *Passer* sparrows are rather noisy, using a variety of harsh, chirping notes; the others have more varied songs and rather harsh calls. The main references used are Clement *et al.* (1993) and Summers-Smith (1988).

HOUSE SPARROW *Passer domesticus* Plate 141

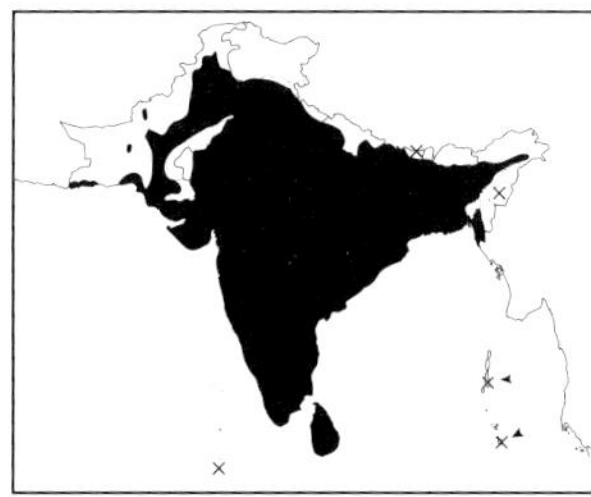

IDENTIFICATION 15 cm. **Adult male breeding** has grey crown, chestnut nape, and black throat and upper breast. Grey crown, browner upperparts and less black on underparts are best distinctions from male Spanish Sparrow (below). Bill is blackish. **Male non-breeding** can be much duller, with chestnut nape often obscured by greyish fringes, and black throat much reduced owing to greyish-white fringes. Bill becomes brownish-horn. **Adult female** has pale buff supercilium, dark brown streaking on buffish mantle, and unstreaked greyish-white underparts (faintly washed with buff on flanks). For differences from female Spanish, Sind, Russet and Dead Sea Sparrows (below and p.808), see those species. **Juvenile** as female, with broader buff-brown fringes to upperparts; juvenile male can have more prominent buff supercilium and greyish chin and throat. **VOICE** Call is a monotonous *chirrup*, and alarm is a *chur-r-r-it-it*; song is a long series of *chirrup*, *cheep* and *churp* notes (Clement *et al.* 1993). **HABITS** Markedly gregarious outside the breeding season, forming large communal roosts in favourite trees in woods. Flocks numbering hundreds or thousands forage in grain or stubble fields. Feeds chiefly on seeds, especially of crops such as cereals; also takes shoots, buds, food scraps, refuse and insects; nestlings are often fed insects and caterpillars. Forages mainly by hopping about on the ground; also perches on ripening cereal heads and systematically pecks out seeds. **HABITAT** Breeds in human habitation, ranging from city centres to isolated houses in forest; in autumn and winter also occurs in cultivation, sometimes far from habitation. **BREEDING** Throughout the year, varying locally. Nest is a bulky, unwoven, domed structure of straw and plant stems, usually placed in a hole in a building, often under eaves, sometimes inside occupied rooms; also in a tree, earth bank or cliff. **DISTRIBUTION AND STATUS** Resident, subject to some seasonal movements. Throughout most of the subcontinent, except parts of the northwest and northeast. **PK:** very widespread and common; partly a sedentary resident in the plains, some ascending the outer foothills in summer; also a passage migrant in huge numbers, some remaining to breed in Baluchistan (up to 3000 m) and the inner dry valleys of the northwest. **NP:** common and widespread; below 1600 m, occasionally up to 2135 m (–4350 m). **IN:** widespread and common; plains and hills, breeds up to 4500 m in Ladakh, withdraws from higher altitudes in winter. **BT:** common and local; 250 m. **BD, LK:** common throughout. **MV:** introduced to K. Malé.

SPANISH SPARROW *Passer hispaniolensis* Plate 141

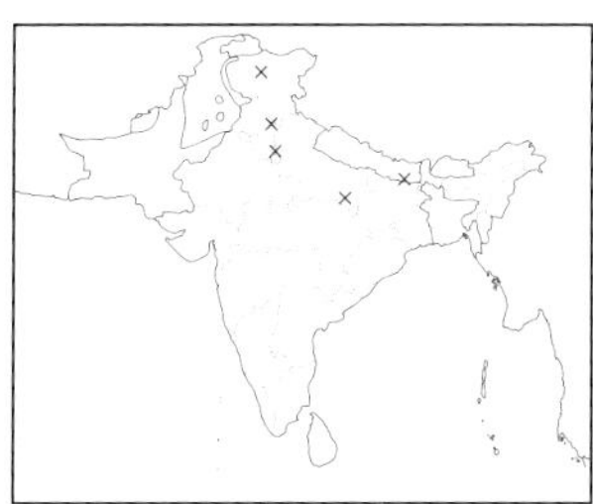

IDENTIFICATION 15.5 cm. **Adult male breeding** distinguished from male House Sparrow (above) by chestnut crown concolorous with nape, fine white supercilium (often broken above eye), more extensive black on breast and black streaking on flanks, and largely black mantle with distinct buffish-white 'braces'. Bill is black. **Male non-breeding** is much duller, with chestnut of crown partially obscured by greyish-buff fringes, black breast and flank streaking much reduced owing to greyish-white fringes, and black of mantle less apparent owing to pale buff fringes. Bill is yellowish-horn with darker tip. Breast and flank markings, and chestnut on crown, are best features for separation from non-breeding House Sparrow. **Adult female** is easily confusable with female House Sparrow, but generally has longer whitish supercilium, fine grey streaking on breast and flanks, and buffish-white stripes or 'braces' on mantle. **Juvenile** as female House Sparrow, and probably not separable in the field. **VOICE** Call is similar to House Sparrow's, but with more metallic *chweeng chweeng* notes or squeaky *cheela-cheeli* notes ; song is also similar but more rhythmic, *chuet-chuet-chuet-tchuet* (Clement *et al.* 1993). **HABITS** Tends to be more shy than House Sparrow, and is not commensal with man. Highly gregarious, forming large foraging flocks and communal roosts; often associated with House Sparrows. **HABITAT** Cultivation, especially cereal crops, semi-desert, and riverain areas, especially reedbeds and marshes. **DISTRIBUTION AND STATUS** Winter visitor. Pakistan, SE Nepal and India (mainly Punjab, N Rajasthan and N Gujarat). **PK:** mainly a locally common passage migrant, also a winter visitor. **NP:** vagrant or very rare winter visitor to Kosi, 75 m. **IN:** locally common but erratic winter visitor.

SIND SPARROW *Passer pyrrhonotus* Plate 141

Sind Jungle Sparrow (I)

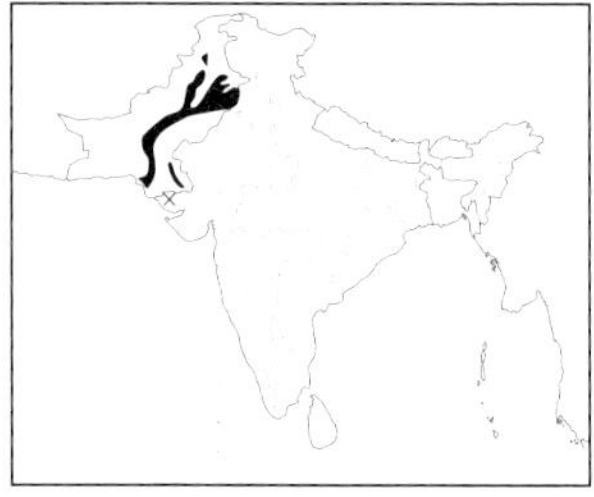

IDENTIFICATION 13 cm. **Adult male** separated from male House Sparrow (p.807) by smaller size and slimmer appearance, with finer bill. Has grey (rather than chestnut) nape, with chestnut of head brighter and reduced to broad crescent surrounding ear-coverts; also has grey cheeks, smaller black throat patch (which does not extend onto breast), and chestnut (rather than grey) lower back (extending onto rump on some birds). Bill is black when breeding; in non-breeding season becomes brownish-horn, with yellow tinge to lower mandible. **Adult female** is very similar to female House Sparrow, and is best told by smaller size and slimmer structure. Other features include generally more prominent buffish-white supercilium which extends to sides of nape, warmer buffish-brown (rather than brownish-grey) lower back and rump, and greyer cast to ear-coverts contrasting with whiter throat. **Juvenile** as female. **VOICE** Call is similar to House Sparrow's, but is a higher-pitched *chu-wit chu-wit*; song is more tuneful and complex compared with that of House, comprising higher-pitched chirrups interspersed with rapid grating *t-rr-r-r-rt* with short twitters and whistles (Roberts 1992). **HABITS** Non-commensal, but confiding in human presence. Usually in small groups of four to six, but may be found in flocks of up to 20 in the non-breeding season; sometimes joins foraging flocks with House Sparrow. More arboreal than House Sparrow. Feeds on seeds, including cereal grain, and insects. **HABITAT** Trees alongside water: groves on river and canal banks, riverain forest and other areas which are seasonally flooded. **BREEDING** April and July–September. Nest is a bulky, untidy globe of twigs, grass and roots with an entrance near the top, usually placed 2–5 m above ground in the top of a tamarisk or acacia. **DISTRIBUTION AND STATUS** Resident. Largely confined to Pakistan, also recorded from Punjab and Gujarat; has spread with the development of irrigation systems. **PK:** frequent in the floodplain of the Indus and its tributaries; has also spread north and away from rivers. **IN:** locally fairly common in Punjab. **REFERENCES** Bapat (1993).

RUSSET SPARROW *Passer rutilans* Plate 141

Cinnamon Tree Sparrow (I), Cinnamon Sparrow (F, N)

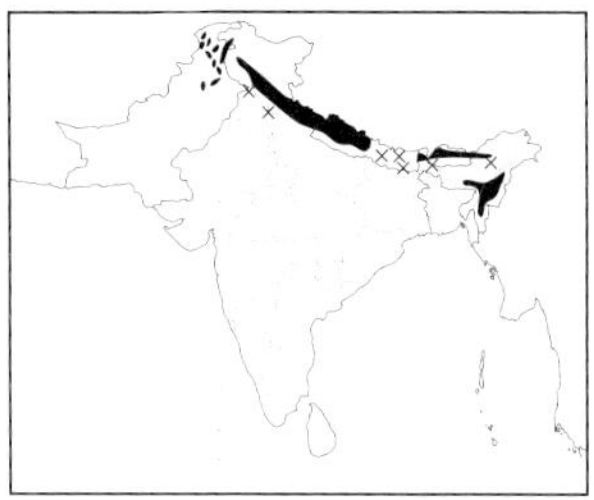

IDENTIFICATION 14.5 cm. **Adult male** is distinctive and likely to be mistaken only for Eurasian Tree Sparrow (p.809). Russet lacks that species' black cheek patch, and has bright chestnut coloration to mantle and variable yellow wash on ear-coverts and underparts. Bill is black when breeding, becoming greyish-horn in non-breeding season. **Adult female** is possibly confusable with female House Sparrow (p.807), but is slimmer, with finer and more pointed bill; has more prominent supercilium and stronger dark eye-stripe, unstreaked brown or rufous-brown scapulars, rufous-brown lower back and rump, and faint yellowish wash to underparts. **Juvenile** as female, but is duller; crown and nape are more sandy (less olive), and underparts are whiter. **VOICE** Call is similar to House Sparrow's, but is a more musical and softer *cheeep* or *chilp*; also has a *swee...swee* alarm, and a rapid *chit-chit-chit*. Song is *cheep-chirrup-cheweep* or *chwe-cha-cha*, frequently repeated (Clement *et al.* 1993). **HABITS** Usually in pairs or loose flocks in the breeding season; in large flocks in winter. Less aggressive than House Sparrow. Closely associated with towns and villages in areas where House Sparrow is absent. Quite tame and confiding. Forages on the ground or in low vegetation; flies into neighbouring trees if disturbed. Feeds chiefly on seeds, also berries and insects. **HABITAT** Open forest and forest clearings and edges, and cultivation near upland villages; also grassland in winter. A bird of upland villages where House Sparrow is absent. **BREEDING** April–August. Nest is an untidy pad of dry grass and plant stems, placed up to 9 m from the ground in a hole in a tree, in thatching or under eaves; in Bhutan, also nests in walls of dzongs and monasteries alongside Eurasian Tree Sparrows. **DISTRIBUTION AND STATUS** Resident, subject to altitudinal movements. Himalayas from N Pakistan east to Arunachal Pradesh; NE India. **PK:** locally frequent to common; from 1200 m in winter up to 2700 m in summer. **NP:** fairly common from WC areas westwards, uncommon farther east; mainly 915–2900, also common at 4270 m (75–4350 m). **IN:** common; in Himalayas, summers 1200–2900 m, winters 500–1500 m; in NE hills, breeds from the base to over 1400 m. **BT:** common; 1100–3965 m.

DEAD SEA SPARROW *Passer moabiticus* Plate 141

Scrub Sparrow (I)

IDENTIFICATION 12.25 cm. **Adult male** is a very distinctive sparrow. Has largely grey head with prominent supercilium and black stripe through eye, small black throat patch, broad white submoustachial stripe, and yellow patch on side of neck. Supercilium is white in front of eye, broadening and becoming warm buff behind. Further, has pale olive-grey breast-band, yellow wash to belly and flanks, and chestnut median and greater coverts forming panel on wing. Bill is black. **Male non-breeding** has grey of head heavily suffused with sandy-olive, and black of chin and throat are tipped with whitish. Bill is brownish-horn with paler base. **Adult female** is possibly confusable with female House Sparrow (p.807), but is smaller and slimmer, and has more prominent buffish-white supercilium, indistinct yellow spot on side of neck, warmer sandy-buff underparts (including rump), and yellow-

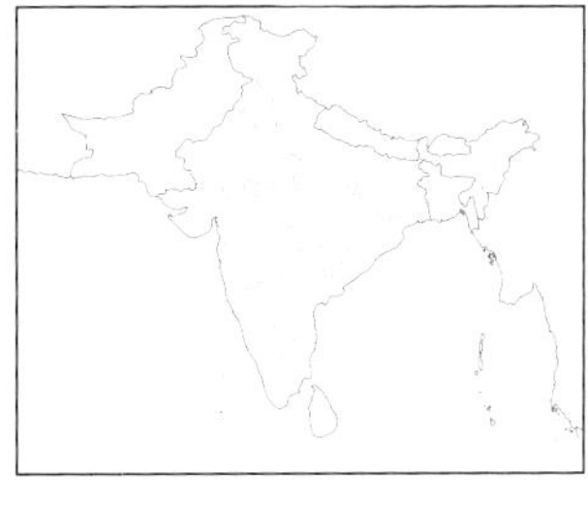

ish wash to underparts. **Juvenile** as female, but is duller; lacks yellow spot on neck side, and supercilium is less prominent. **VOICE** Calls include a *chet-chet-chet*, a harsher *chip-chip-chip*, a slurred *chiz-chiz-chiz*, and a liquid *chrelp*; song is a far-carrying and rhythmic *chillung-chillung-chillung* (Clement *et al.* 1993). **HABITS** Gregarious, living in large flocks in winter. Feeds mainly on seeds of grasses, herbs and shrubs, including *Suaeda*; also on insects. Rather wary. **HABITAT** Bushes, especially tamarisks, near streams; usually in rather saline areas. **BREEDING** Not recorded in the region, but could possibly breed. In Iran, typically builds a bulky nest in tamarisks, about 1.5 m above ground. **DISTRIBUTION AND STATUS PK:** winter visitor; very local but common in C and W edges of the Chagai desert, Baluchistan.

EURASIAN TREE SPARROW *Passer montanus* — Plate 141

Tree Sparrow (F,I)

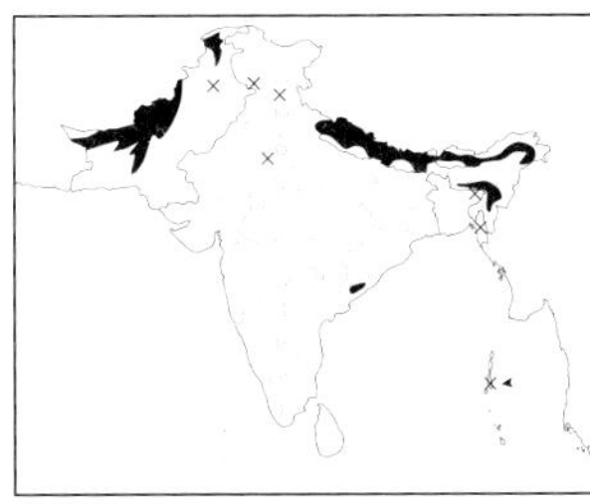

IDENTIFICATION 14 cm. **Adult** has dull chestnut crown, black spot on whitish ear-coverts, small black throat patch not extending onto breast, and white collar separating chestnut nape from brown-streaked mantle. Black ear-covert patch is best distinction from male House and Russet Sparrows (p.807 and p.808). Unlike other sparrows, sexes are alike. **Juvenile** is similar to adult, but has paler chestnut crown and diffuse black patches on ear-coverts and throat. **Racial variation** Rather subtle. *P. m. dilutus* of NW subcontinent is palest race, with sandy-brown upperparts, paler chestnut crown, and clean white underparts (with some buff wash on breast sides and flanks). *P. m. malaccensis* of N and NE subcontinent has darker brown or rufous-brown upperparts, darker crown, and greyish wash to underparts. *P. m. tibetanus* of N Himalayas from Nepal eastwards is somewhat intermediate between the two. **VOICE** Call is a monotonous *chip chip*, which is harder than the similar call of House Sparrow; song is a running-together of this note, interspersed with *tsweep* or similar calls. **HABITS** Very similar to those of House Sparrow; sometimes found alongside that species, and replaces it in many areas. Very gregarious; occurs in small flocks in the breeding season and gathers in large flocks at other times. Closely associated with human habitation and cultivation. **HABITAT** Towns, villages, cultivation and orchards. **BREEDING** March–August, varying locally. Sometimes loosely colonial. Nest is like that of House Sparrow, placed under eaves in roof thatching, or in a hole in a tree, wall or earth bank; in Bhutan, also in a hole in monastery or dzong wall. **DISTRIBUTION AND STATUS** Resident, subject to altitudinal movements. Baluchistan, Pakistan, and NW Pakistan Himalayas; also from N Uttar Pradesh east to Arunachal Pradesh, NE India and Bangladesh; Eastern Ghats. **PK:** locally common in main drier mountain valleys; locally up to 3000 m. **NP:** common and widespread; chiefly 610–4270 m, up to 3795 m in winter, also breeds at 75 m. **IN:** common; breeds up to 2700 m. **BT:** common. **BD:** rare in the northeast.

CHESTNUT-SHOULDERED PETRONIA *Petronia xanthocollis* — Plate 141

Yellow-throated Sparrow (F,I,P), Chestnut-shouldered Rock Sparrow (R)

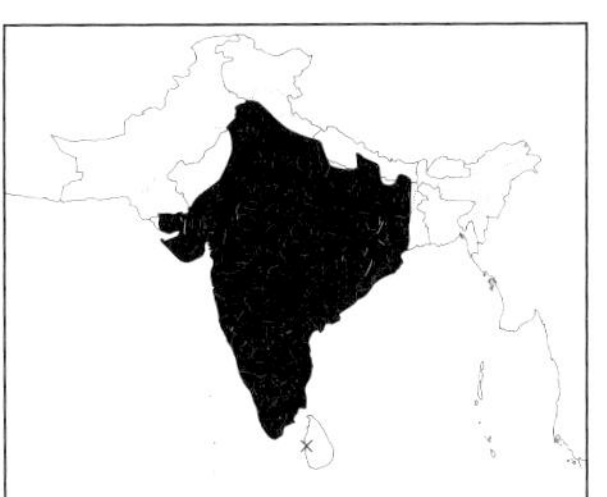

IDENTIFICATION 13.5 cm. **Adult male** distinguished from other sparrows by long, fine bill, uniform brownish-grey head and upperparts (lacking any streaking), and yellow patch on lower throat. Has chestnut lesser coverts, which can be obscured, and white tips to median and greater coverts which form double wing-bar. Bill is black when breeding, becoming brown with yellowish base in non-breeding season. **Adult female** is similar to male, but has brown lesser coverts, buff-tinged tips to median coverts, and yellow throat patch either reduced to a faint yellow wash or absent. **Juvenile** is similar to female, but upperpart coloration is more sandy-brown, with pale buffish supercilium, and lacks any yellow on throat. **VOICE** Calls similar to House Sparrow's (p.807), but song is a repetitive series of *chip, chillup* and *chalp* notes, slightly higher-pitched and more liquid than those of House (Roberts 1992; Clement *et al.* 1993). **HABITS** Usually in pairs or small groups in the breeding season. Gait and perching behaviour are rather finch-like. In the breeding season forages more in trees than *Passer* sparrows, consuming plant material, nectar and insects. At other times eats fallen seeds on the ground, often in large flocks with *Passer* sparrows, finches and Black-headed Buntings (p.856). Roosts communally with these species in thickets. Has an undulating flight, rather more dipping than that of other sparrows. **HABITAT** Open dry forest, thorn scrub, hedges, trees at the edge of cultivation, riverain forest, and in Pakistan also irrigated forest plantations. **BREEDING** End February–June, varying locally. Often forms loose colonies. Nest is a small pad of hair, feathers and grass, usually placed in a hole 1–6 m up in a tree, sometimes in a hole in a mud wall or under a roof. **DISTRIBUTION AND STATUS** Resident, subject to local movements, and partial migrant. Mainly from C Pakistan east through S Nepal to West Bengal and south through the peninsula. **PK:** mainly a common summer visitor to the Indus plains and outer foothills, up to 1200 m; resident in lower Sindh, Makran and S Baluchistan. **NP:** widespread; frequent in the far west and at Chitwan, uncommon elsewhere. **IN:** common and widespread resident and local migrant; plains and hills, up to 750 m in Himalayas, to 1200 m in peninsular hills. **LK:** vagrant.

ROCK SPARROW *Petronia petronia* Plate 141

Streaked Rock Sparrow (R)

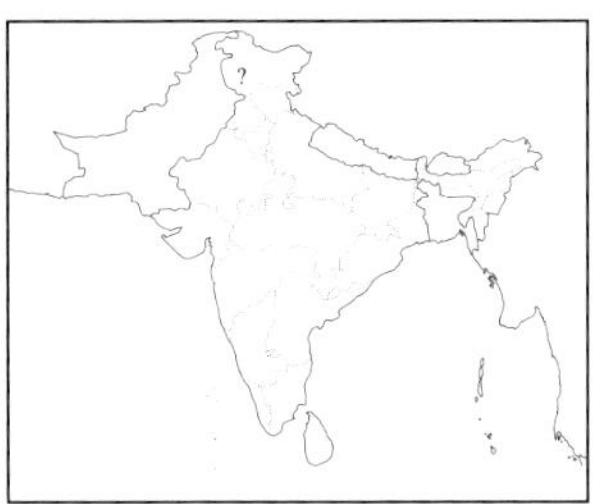

IDENTIFICATION 17 cm. **Adult** separated from other sparrows by combination of stocky, short-tailed appearance, striking head pattern, and white tips to tail feathers and patch at base of primaries which are especially noticeable in flight. Has broad whitish supercilium, dark brown lateral crown-stripe and eye-stripe, and pale central crown-stripe. Also shows buffish-white stripes or 'braces' on mantle, diffuse grey-brown streaking on breast and flanks, whitish fringes to grey-brown undertail-coverts, and yellow patch on lower throat (which can be difficult to see). **Juvenile** is similar to adult, but has warmer brown upperparts and lacks yellow throat patch. **VOICE** Song is drawn-out, sibilant *vee-viep*; calls include nasal *waip* or *uee*, a *kriep*, and a metallic *zveeh-vu* (Jonsson 1992). **HABITS** Similar to those of other sparrows. Rather shy. Keeps in small flocks, which forage on the ground for fallen seeds; more active than the *Passer* sparrows, and hops strongly. Has a bounding flight, faster than that of *Passer* species. **HABITAT** Dry stony ground in mountain regions, especially near cliffs. **DISTRIBUTION AND STATUS PK:** local winter visitor; fairly common in the Gilgit main valley, 1500 m, occasionally recorded in Baluchistan and the Indus valley.

TIBETAN SNOWFINCH *Montifringilla adamsi* Plate 141

Tibet Snow Finch (I), Black-winged Snowfinch

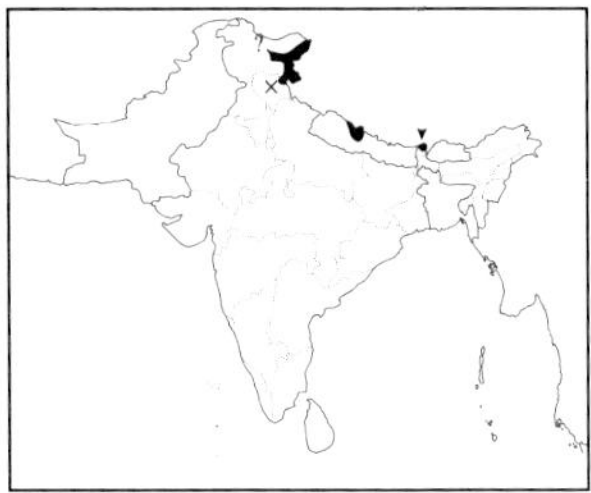

IDENTIFICATION 17 cm. **Adult** distinguished from other snowfinches by largely white greater and median coverts and white fringes to inner secondaries and outermost tertial (forming broad white panels on otherwise mainly black wing). Additional features are combination of whitish-tipped black throat with plain grey-brown lores and forehead, and dull grey-brown coloration to head and upperparts. Adult non-breeding has pale (rather than blackish) bill. **Juvenile** lacks black throat; has warmer buffish-brown upperparts, buffish wash to breast and flanks, and warm buffish (rather than white) sides to tail. Told from juveniles of other snowfinches by buffish-white greater coverts and panel at base of secondaries. **VOICE** Rapid, jolty, sparrow-like, staccato chattering song repeats only a few notes (occasionally up to 20 in succession), *chi-di-chi-di-dzeu...chi-di-dzeu...chi-di-chi-di-chi-di-chi-di-chi-di-dzeu...* etc; usually delivered from a prominent perch (P. Holt). **HABITS** In winter gathers in large flocks, sometimes of up to 3000 birds. Walks and runs like a lark. Perches readily on rocks, walls of houses and prayer flags. Feeds on insects and seeds, often at the edges of melting snow. Tame in some areas. Has a strong, swift, undulating flight interspersed with glides. **HABITAT** Barren, rocky Tibetan semi-desert, often near villages and upland cultivation. **BREEDING** May–August. Builds nest in a deep hollow in a rock fissure, wall, or pika burrow, or under a rock. **DISTRIBUTION AND STATUS** Resident, subject to poorly understood altitudinal movements. N Himalayas in Ladakh, N Himachal Pradesh, N Sikkim and NW Nepal. **NP:** common in the Tibetan plateau region in the northwest; summers 4200–5100 m, winters 2530–3445 m. **IN:** common in the west; recorded 3800 m to almost 5000 m. **REFERENCES** Martens and Eck (1995), Pfister (1997).

WHITE-RUMPED SNOWFINCH *Pyrgilauda taczanowskii* Plate 141

Mandelli's Snow Finch (F,I), ***Montifringilla taczanowskii***

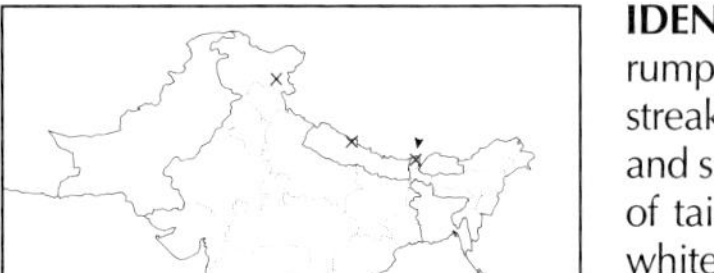

IDENTIFICATION 17 cm. **Adult** separated from other snowfinches by white rump (very conspicuous in flight) and pale greyish coloration to upperparts (with streaked mantle and scapulars). Additional features are black lores, white throat and supercilia (which join across forehead, and extend onto nape), white on sides of tail (lacking dark terminal bar found on the other four species), and diffuse white panel at base of secondaries and inner primaries (with secondaries broadly tipped whitish). Bill is pale yellowish-horn with darker tip. **Juvenile** has warmer brown coloration to mantle and wings, has buffish breast and flanks, and is buff on sides of tail. Told from juveniles of other snowfinches by pale rump, dark brown crown and paler greyish nape, and heavily streaked mantle and scapulars. **VOICE** Simple weak song of clipped notes, asthmatic wheezes and more pleasant whistles, irregularly and loosely woven together in a hiccuping series delivered in a circling undulating song flight, and usually lasting 1–1.5 minutes (P. Holt). **HABITS** Associates closely with colonies of pikas, sharing their burrows for breeding, roosting and shelter. Keeps in flocks in winter, often with Rufous-necked Snowfinches (p.811). Skims low over the ground in flight; characteristically bows and bobs its tail after landing. **HABITAT** Stony plateaux in Tibetan steppe country and among pika colonies at the drier edges of marshes. **BREEDING** Breeding season unknown. Builds nest in a pika burrow. **DISTRIBUTION AND STATUS** Resident? and winter visitor. N Himalayas in Ladakh, N Sikkim and NW Nepal and N India. **NP:** status uncertain, possibly a rare resident; one collected in June at 4815 m in Mustang, in the northwest. **IN:** probably breeds in N Sikkim, where juveniles ringed in August at c. 5000 m, also collected there in September/October; recorded occasionally in Ladakh in summer. **REFERENCES** Pfister (1997).

SMALL SNOWFINCH *Pyrgilauda davidiana* — Plate 141

Père David's Snow Finch (I), *Montifringilla davidiana*

IDENTIFICATION 15 cm. A small, compact, short-tailed snowfinch. **Adult** superficially resembles Plain-backed (below), with black lores and throat (extending onto upper breast on some individuals). Told from that species by black forehead, pale sandy-brown (not cinnamon) nape and sides of neck, white patch at base of primary coverts, and darker streaking on warm buff-brown mantle and scapulars. Has small blackish bill with a yellowish base to both mandibles. **Juvenile** lacks black head pattern of adult. Told from juvenile Plain-backed by slightly greyer upperparts, with darker streaking on mantle and scapulars, and by lack of warm cinnamon tinge to sides of neck. Juvenile Rufous-necked (below) has warm cinnamon tinge to ear-coverts and whitish supercilium. **VOICE** Strident, bouncy song starts with two or three House Sparrow-like calls followed by a regular repetition of up to ten *til-chu-lip...til-chu-lip* Tawny Pipit-like notes (P. Holt). **DISTRIBUTION AND STATUS IN:** recorded in Sikkim by Meinertzhagen (1952), but the record is now considered doubtful.

RUFOUS-NECKED SNOWFINCH *Pyrgilauda ruficollis* — Plate 141

Red-necked Snow Finch (F,I), *Montifringilla ruficollis*

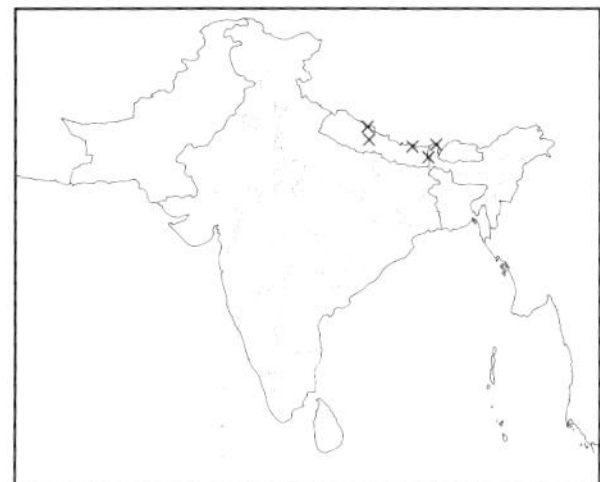

IDENTIFICATION 15 cm. **Adult** is superficially similar to Plain-backed Snowfinch (below), having cinnamon nape and sides of neck/breast, white cheeks, and largely white underparts. Distinguished from that species by bright rufous patch at rear of ear-coverts, greyish-white forehead (lacking blackish centre), and fine black malar stripe and white throat. Also has largely white median coverts, broad whitish-buff tips to greater coverts forming prominent wing-bar, and conspicuous streaking on mantle and scapulars. **Juvenile** is duller, with buffish tinge to breast and flanks, warm cinnamon tinge to ear-coverts and neck sides, and whitish-buff fringes and tips to median and greater coverts. Told from juvenile Plain-backed by whitish-buff wing-bars and streaked mantle and scapulars. **VOICE** Song is an erratic repetition of simple sparrow-like notes, *dishu-tchelu-tischu-delu* etc, repeated almost monotonously; calls include a harsh *tishik-ik* (P. Holt) and also a soft *duuid* (Clement *et al.* 1993). **HABITS** Closely associated with pika burrows; feeds around the entrance holes. Usually in pairs during the breeding season, and in small flocks, often with Plain-backed Snowfinch and White-rumped Snowfinch (p.810) at other times. Flight is weak and low over the ground. **HABITAT** Barren, stony Tibetan steppe and grassy plateaux. **BREEDING** Breeding season unknown. Builds nest in a pika burrow or rock fissure. **DISTRIBUTION AND STATUS** Resident? N Himalayas in N Nepal, N Sikkim and Darjeeling, West Bengal. **NP:** status uncertain; possibly a rare resident, several records June–November, 3290–4850 m. **IN:** probably breeds, juveniles ringed in August in Sikkim, c. 5000 m; recorded 4200–4800 m near Darjeeling in October.

PLAIN-BACKED SNOWFINCH *Pyrgilauda blanfordi* — Plate 141

Blanford's Snow Finch, *Montifringilla blanfordi*

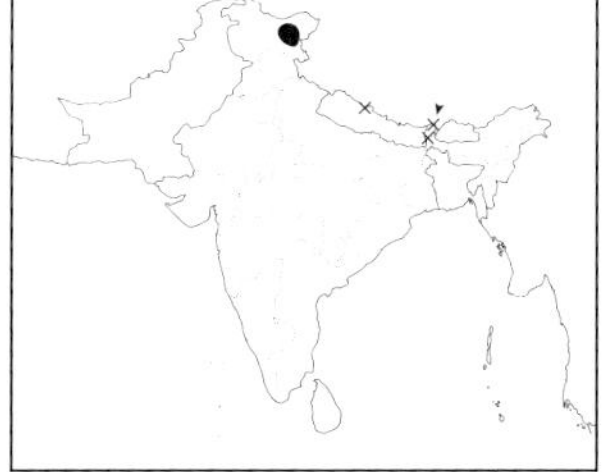

IDENTIFICATION 15 cm. **Adult** resembles Rufous-necked Snowfinch (above), having cinnamon nape and sides of neck/breast, and white cheeks. Compared with Rufous-necked, lacks rufous patch at rear of ear-coverts, and has black centre to white forehead and forecrown, black 'spur' in front of eye dividing white supercilium, and black chin and centre of throat. Has rather uniform wing-coverts (lacking prominent wing-bars), and mantle and scapulars are unstreaked (or, rarely, very faintly streaked). Bill is blackish, occasionally with bluish tinge. **Juvenile** is duller and lacks head pattern of adult. Told from juvenile Rufous-necked by uniform, unstreaked warm buffish-brown mantle, scapulars and back, lack of whitish-buff greater- and median-covert wing-bars, and whiter cheeks. For differences from juvenile Small Snowfinch (above), see that species. **VOICE** Poorly described; flocks give rapid twittering call on ground and in flight (Clement *et al.* 1993). **HABITS** Lives in company with colonies of pikas, and nests in their burrows. Gathers in large flocks in winter, often with Rufous-necked Snowfinch and sparrows; usually in pairs in the breeding season. Behaviour is reminiscent of a sparrow. Tame and active; runs quickly on the ground. **HABITAT** Tibetan steppe country. **BREEDING** Breeding season unknown. Builds nest in a pika burrow. **DISTRIBUTION AND STATUS** Resident? and winter visitor. Pakistan?, N Nepal, N Sikkim, near Darjeeling, West Bengal, and Ladakh. **PK:** occurrence uncertain, but likely in NW Baltistan. **NP:** status uncertain, possibly a rare resident; one collected in June at 4815 m in Mustang, in the northwest. **IN:** probably resident; recorded 4300 m (December) and 4880–5030 m (July–October) in N Sikkim; locally common in Ladakh, pair observed feeding young in June at 4500 m. **REFERENCES** Pfister (1997), Robson (1993b).

WAGTAILS AND PIPITS Passeridae, subfamily Motacillinae

Small, slender, terrestrial birds with long legs, relatively long toes and a thin, pointed bill. Pipits are mainly dull-coloured, and wagtails generally have brighter and more contrasting patterns; some wagtails exhibit wide geographical variation. All walk with a deliberate gait and run rapidly. The flight is undulating and strong, especially in the case of the wagtails. Most wagtails wag the tail up and down, and so do some pipits, but usually to a lesser extent. They feed mainly by picking insects from the ground as they walk along, or by making short rapid runs to capture insects they have flushed; they also make short flights from the ground, catching prey in mid-air. Song flights are characteristic of many pipits, often consisting of a fluttering ascent and a rapid, parachuting descent. Both wagtails and pipits call in flight, and this is often a useful identification feature. They are usually found singly or in pairs in the breeding season and in scattered flocks in autumn and winter. Wagtails roost communally in the non-breeding season, often in large numbers and with other wagtails, in reedbeds, trees, shrubs and sugarcane fields. Pipits and wagtails nest on the ground; wagtails also nest in holes in banks of streams or crevices in rocks or walls.

FOREST WAGTAIL *Dendronanthus indicus* — Plate 142

***Motacilla indica* (F,I,P)**

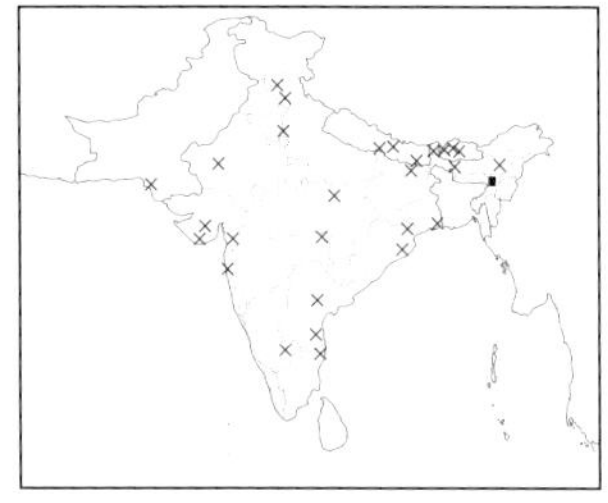

IDENTIFICATION 18 cm. A forest-dwelling wagtail, readily distinguished from other wagtails by combination of broad yellowish-white median- and greater-covert wing-bars and white patch on secondaries, double black breast-band (lower band broken at centre of breast), olive upperparts, white supercilium, and whitish underparts. Sexes alike. **VOICE** Call is a strident metallic *pink* or *dzink-dzzt*; song is a repetitive, intense Great Tit-like see-sawing series of usually three to six notes, *dzi-chu...dzi-chu...dzi-chu* (P. Holt). **HABITS** Has a characteristic habit of swaying its tail and the hindpart of its body from side to side with a rather deliberate motion, instead of wagging the tail up and down. Forages chiefly on the ground on forest paths and glades with rather a sedate walk; also captures insects by running along horizontal branches. Flies up on to the lower branches of trees when disturbed, often calling. **HABITAT** Paths and glades in tropical broadleaved evergreen forest; also shady coffee and cardamom plantations, deciduous forest and mangroves in winter. **BREEDING** May. Nest is a small, neat cup, covered in lichens and matching supporting branches, built 2–3 m above ground in a small tree. **DISTRIBUTION AND STATUS** Breeds in N Cachar, Assam; mainly a winter visitor, chiefly to NE and SW India, Bangladesh and Sri Lanka. **PK, NP:** vagrant. **IN:** very local; breeds above 1525 m in Assam; winters mainly above 1000 m in the northeast, locally common in the southwest from the foothills up to 2100 m. **BT:** rare passage migrant. **BD:** local winter visitor and passage migrant. **LK:** common winter visitor to all zones. **REFERENCES** Inskipp and Inskipp (1996), Tymstra *et al.* (1997).

WHITE WAGTAIL *Motacilla alba* — Plate 142

Pied Wagtail (F,I)

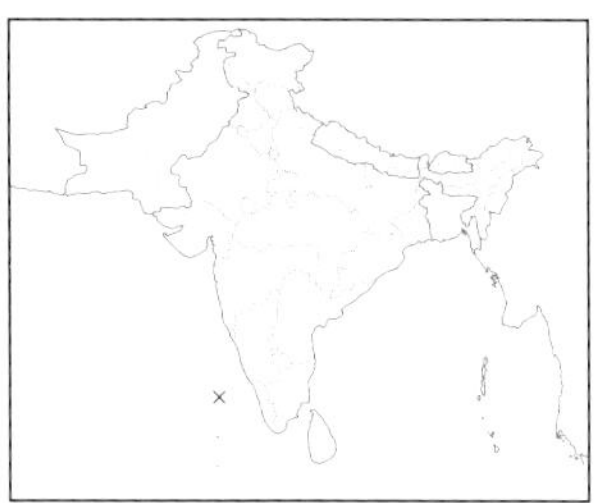

IDENTIFICATION 19 cm. Extremely variable, with black-and-white head pattern, grey or black mantle, and largely white to largely black wing-coverts. Black-backed birds are possibly confusable with White-browed Wagtail (p.813), but that species is much larger and has a largely black head with a broad white supercilium. Racial variation among breeding adults (sexes are similar) is covered below. There is considerable variation in patterning of black on head and breast of non-breeding and first-winter birds, although in some races non-breeding birds retain characteristics of breeding plumage. **Juveniles** of the two breeding races have grey head, mantle and breast with whitish supercilium. **Racial variation** *M. a. dukhunensis* (a widespread winter visitor to the subcontinent) has grey mantle, white forehead and face, and black hind-crown/nape, throat and breast. *M. a. personata* (breeding NW subcontinent and wintering widely across subcontinent) has grey mantle and black head and breast, with white forehead and face patch, giving rise to pale-masked appearance. *M. a. alboides* (breeding N subcontinent and wintering more widely in north and northeast) is much as *personata*, but has black mantle and back, although upperparts of female are variably mixed with grey. *M. a. leucopsis* (winter visitor to N and NE subcontinent and Andamans) has black mantle and back, but otherwise has head pattern as breeding male *dukhunensis* but with white throat. *M. a. ocularis* (uncommon to rare winter visitor to N and NE subcontinent) has grey mantle and back and is much as *dukhunensis*, but has a black eye-stripe in all plumages. *M. a. baicalensis* (recorded as passage migrant in Nepal) has grey mantle and back and is much as *dukhunensis*, but has white chin and upper throat contrasting with black breast. **VOICE** Call is a loud *tslee-vit*; song is a lively twittering and chattering with call-like notes. **HABITS** A typical wagtail. Readily perches on telegraph wires, roofs of buildings and, less commonly, in trees. **HABITAT** Summers by streams and rivers in open country in hills and mountains; winters in open country near water, e.g. marshes, rivers, streams, canals, lakes and wet fields, also lawns, and fallow cultivation. **BREEDING** April–early August. Nest is a cup made of dry grass, roots and leaves, placed under a rock, bush, grass clump or heap of washed-up debris on river banks, or in a hole in a wall or under eaves. **DISTRIBUTION AND STATUS** Resident, with altitudinal and short-range movements, and a winter visitor. Breeds in Himalayas from N Pakistan east to Arunachal Pradesh; winters in Himalayan foothills and south throughout most of the subcontinent except parts of Pakistan. **PK:** frequent in summer in the main Himalayan valleys, 1500–3200 m; common winter visitor throughout the Indus basin, also widespread in Baluchistan; common on passage throughout NW Pakistan, Chitral and Gilgit. **NP:** widespread and common passage migrant, winter visitor and resident; summers 2400–4800 m, winters mainly below 1500 m (–5000 m on passage). **IN:** widespread and common; breeds mainly 1500–5000 m in Himalayas; winters in plains and hills, mainly up to 1500 m, locally to 2700 m in Himalayas. **BT:** common; 250–4265 m. **BD:** common winter visitor. **LK:** rare winter visitor to lowlands. **REFERENCES** Martens and Eck (1995).

WHITE-BROWED WAGTAIL *Motacilla maderaspatensis* Plate 142

Large Pied Wagtail (F,I,P)

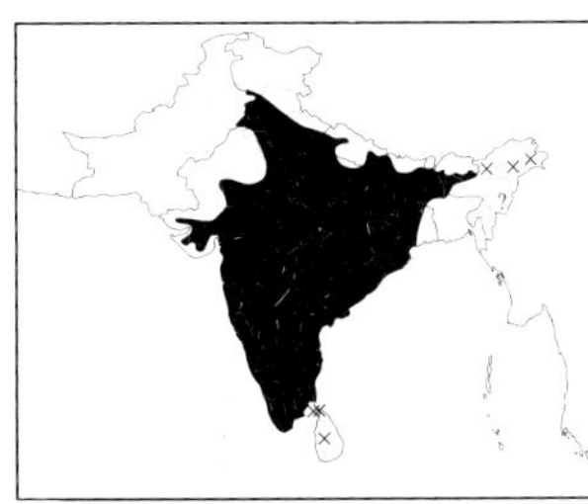

IDENTIFICATION 21 cm. A very large wagtail. **Adult** is black and white: head is black, with white supercilium, neck, mantle and breast are also black, and wing-coverts are largely white. Combination of black mantle and black head broken only by white supercilium separates it from all races of White Wagtail (p.812). Sexes are similar. **First-winter** is similar, but with greyer crown and mantle. **Juvenile** has brownish-grey head, mantle and breast, with white supercilium. **VOICE** Call is a distinctive, loud *chiz-zat*; song is a clear, high-pitched jumble of loud, pleasant whistling notes (Ali and Ripley 1987). **HABITS** A typical wagtail. Usually keeps in pairs throughout the year. **HABITAT** Banks of rivers, pools, lakes, canals, and around irrigation barrages. **BREEDING** March–October, varying locally. Nest is a substantial structure of roots and grass with a neat cup, placed near water on a ledge under a bridge, in a hollow in a river bank or in a hole in a tree or wall. **DISTRIBUTION AND STATUS** Resident locally throughout much of the subcontinent, except parts of the northwest, northeast, Himalayas and Sri Lanka. **PK:** resident, locally common in N Punjab; occurs sparingly in S Punjab and the lower streams flowing into the Indus in NW Pakistan. **NP:** fairly common and widespread resident; mainly below 915 m, uncommon up to 1700 m, a summer visitor at higher altitudes. **IN:** locally common and widespread resident; in plains and hills, locally to 1500 m in Himalayas, to 2200 m in the peninsula. **BT:** local and fairly common. **BD:** scarce resident; occurs throughout. **LK:** rare winter visitor to the N coastal lowlands and lower hills, mainly in dry zone.

CITRINE WAGTAIL *Motacilla citreola* Plate 142

Yellow-headed Wagtail (F,I), Yellow-hooded Wagtail

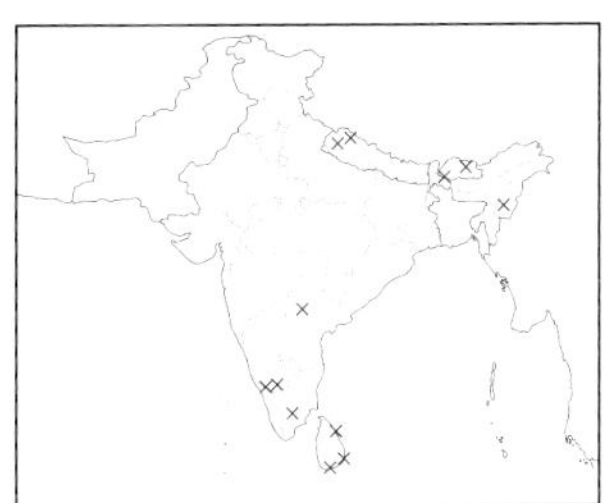

IDENTIFICATION 19 cm. **Adult male breeding** is readily distinguished from Yellow Wagtail (p.814) by yellow head and underparts, black or grey mantle, and broad white tips to median and greater coverts. **Female breeding** and **adult non-breeding** have broad yellow supercilium that surrounds ear-coverts to join yellow of throat, and have greyish crown, nape, ear-coverts and mantle, and mainly yellow underparts. Some breeding females show yellow crown and ear-coverts and more closely resemble breeding males. Non-breeding females can be very pale buffish-yellow on underparts. Yellow surround to ear-coverts, pale lores, broad white wing-bars (although narrower when worn), greyish upperparts including rump and uppertail-coverts, white undertail-coverts, and greyish breast sides and flanks are features of Citrine, but, since considerable variation exists in plumages of Yellow, some of these can also be shown by that species. **Juvenile** lacks any yellow, and has brownish crown, ear-coverts and mantle, buffish supercilium (with dark upper edge) and surround to ear-coverts, and buffish-white underparts with gorget of black spotting across breast. **First-winter** has grey upperparts and is similar to some first-winter Yellow, but has broader white supercilium, especially behind eye, which usually (although not always) surrounds ear-coverts (on Yellow, eye-stripe joins, and is usually concolorous with, grey of sides of neck). The following are useful features, but are not conclusive: dark border to supercilium; pale brown forehead; pale lores; all-dark bill; broader white wing-bars; and white undertail-coverts. Grey-and-white first-winter birds are possibly confusable with some plumages of White Wagtail (p.812), but lack black breast-band and have more prominent supercilium and different call. By early November, first-winter Citrine have yellowish supercilium, ear-covert surround and throat. **Racial variation** Three races are recorded from the subcontinent. Breeding male *M. c. calcarata*, the only one to breed in the subcontinent, has black mantle and back and deeper yellow underparts (including undertail-coverts). Breeding male *M. c. citreola* and *M. c. werae* have grey mantle and back with variable black collar; *werae* may lack collar and has paler yellow underparts. **VOICE** Call is a harsh *brrzzreep*, typically more buzzing than that of Yellow (although some calls of Yellow can be very similar); song is a repetition of similar sounds; also gives a metallic *pzeeow*. **HABITS** A typical wagtail, but with a rather sedate gait and less tail-wagging than White Wagtail. Highly gregarious when feeding in winter. Closely associated with wet habitats, more so than other wagtails; sometimes forages on floating vegetation on lakes, far from the shore. **HABITAT** Summers in wet grassland in Himalayan valleys and on marshy patches on alpine slopes below glaciers and melting snow; winters on marshes, around lakes, tanks and jheels, and on wet fields. **BREEDING** May–August. Nest is a compact cup, made of dry grass, rootlets and moss, placed on the ground under a bush, stone or grass tussock. **DISTRIBUTION AND STATUS** Breeds in Baluchistan, Pakistan, and in Himalayas from N Pakistan east to Himachal Pradesh; winters widely in the subcontinent, mainly south to C Karnataka, S Maharashtra, E Orissa and Bangladesh. **PK:** common overall; breeds in the inner Himalayan ranges and sparingly in Baluchistan, 2400–3900 m; winter visitor to Sindh and Punjab; also a passage migrant to Baluchistan and Punjab. **NP:** mainly a winter visitor to lowlands (–5200 m on passage). **IN:** common in summer, mainly 3000–5000 m, also down to 1500 m; widespread and locally common in winter, chiefly in the plains. **BT:** uncommon winter visitor and passage migrant. **BD:** locally common winter visitor. **LK:** status uncertain; probably a winter vagrant. **REFERENCES** Alström and Colston (1991), Pfister (1997), Svensson (1992).

YELLOW WAGTAIL *Motacilla flava* — Plate 142

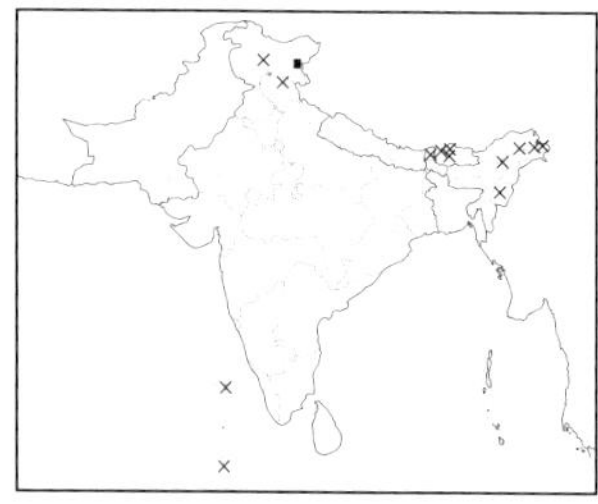

IDENTIFICATION 18 cm. **Male breeding** has olive-green upperparts and yellow underparts, with considerable variation in coloration of head depending on race (see racial variation). **Female** in breeding plumage usually shows some features of breeding male. **First-winter** birds typically have brownish-olive upperparts, whitish underparts with variable yellowish wash, and buff or whitish median- and greater-covert wing-bars and fringes to tertials. Some first-winters, however, have greyish upperparts and whitish underparts (lacking any yellow) and have broader white wing-bars, and can closely resemble first-winter Citrine Wagtail (p.813). Compared with latter, grey-and-white first-winter Yellow have narrower white supercilium which does not extend around ear-coverts to join white of throat; additionally, they typically lack a dark upper border to supercilium, and have grey forehead concolorous with crown, dark lores resulting in complete dark eye-stripe, pale base to lower mandible, and narrower white wing-bars. **Juvenile** has a dark malar stripe and band across breast. **Racial variation** About seven races have been recorded in the subcontinent; breeding males are most distinctive, but female and non-breeding birds of some races may also be identifiable. *M. f. beema* has pale bluish-grey head, complete and distinct white supercilium, white chin, and usually a white submoustachial stripe contrasting with yellow throat; ear-coverts are grey or brown, usually with some white feathers. *M. f. leucocephala* has whole head to nape white, with a variable blue-grey cast on the ear-coverts and rear crown; chin is white, and throat yellow as rest of underparts. *M. f. melanogrisea* has black head, lacking any supercilium, and white chin and poorly defined submoustachial stripe contrasting with yellow throat. *M. f. taivana* differs from all other races in having olive-green crown, concolorous with mantle, and broad yellow supercilium contrasting with blackish lores and ear-coverts. *M. f. plexa* has dark blue-grey crown and nape (darker than *beema*), and narrow white supercilium contrasting with blackish lores and dark grey ear-coverts; chin is white. *M. f. thunbergi* has dark slate-grey crown with darker ear-coverts, lacking supercilium (although may show faint trace behind eye). *M. f. lutea* has mainly yellow head, with variable amounts of yellowish-green on crown and nape and ear-coverts (concolorous with mantle). *M. f. zaissanensis* has head slate-grey, with narrow white supercilium. *M. f. superciliaris* is probably a hybrid between *beema* and *melanogrisea* and looks like the latter, but with a white supercilium. **VOICE** Call is typically a loud disyllabic *tswee-ip*, usually quite distinct from the harsher, buzzing call of Citrine; some races have harsher *tsreep* call which more closely resembles that of Citrine. **HABITS** A typical wagtail. When foraging, characteristically associates with grazing domestic livestock, capturing insects disturbed by the animals' hooves. **HABITAT** Damp pastures, especially near grazing livestock, irrigated fodder crops, and grassy margins of lakes and marshes. **BREEDING** June. Nest is a cup made of grass and roots, placed within the base of grass tussocks. **DISTRIBUTION AND STATUS** Breeds in W Himalayas (Ladakh) and possibly Kashmir; winters throughout most of the subcontinent, except parts of the northwest, northeast and Himalayas. **PK:** common passage migrant in Punjab, Sindh and NW Pakistan, also in Baluchistan; small numbers overwinter, mainly in Sindh. **NP:** widespread and frequent; mainly a winter visitor below 1350 m (–3800 m on passage). **IN:** breeds 3600–4500 m; common and widespread winter visitor in plains and hills, up to at least 1200 m in Himalayas; common on passage in W Himalayas. **BT:** uncommon passage migrant; recorded up to 4850 m. **BD, LK:** common winter visitor throughout. **MV:** irregular winter visitor in small numbers; probably also a passage migrant. **REFERENCES** Dittberner and Dittberner (1984), Grant and Mackworth-Praed (1952).

GREY WAGTAIL *Motacilla cinerea* — Plate 142

***M. caspica* (E,F)**

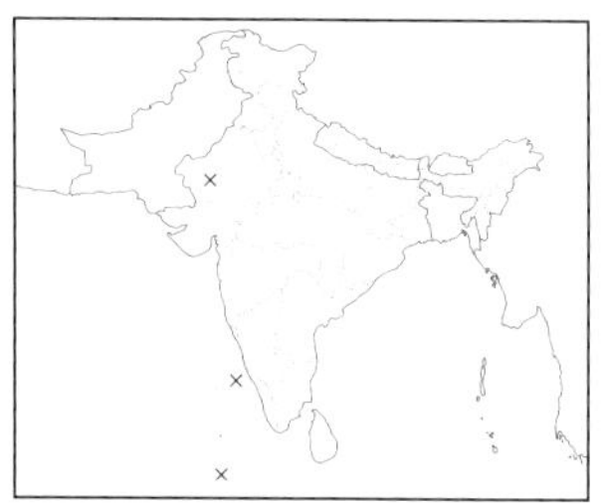

IDENTIFICATION 19 cm. Much longer-tailed than other wagtails, a feature especially noticeable in flight. In all plumages, has white supercilium, grey upperparts and yellow vent and undertail-coverts. In flight, shows narrow white wing-bar (due to white bases of primaries and secondaries) and yellow rump. At rest, shows whitish fringes to tertials but otherwise wings appear contrastingly blackish, lacking broad fringes to coverts present on Yellow and Citrine Wagtails (above and p.813). **Male breeding** has black throat, with rest of underparts yellow. **Female breeding** lacks well-defined black bib, but may show black mottling on chin/throat. **Adult non-breeding** and **first-winter** have white throat and pale yellowish to buffish-white underparts, with yellow vent. **Juvenile** much as non-breeding, but with brownish cast to upperparts, buffish supercilium, and dark mottling on breast sides. **VOICE** Call is a sharp *stit* or *zee-fit*; song is a series of call-like notes. **HABITS** A typical wagtail, but usually found singly throughout the year; sometimes forms roosts of up to 50 birds in winter. Forages by delicately tripping among stones of river beds, wading in the shallows, and fly-catching from a perch or on the ground; wags its tail incessantly. Has a strong bounding flight, often following the course of the stream. Perches readily in trees. **HABITAT** Fast-flowing, rocky mountain streams in summer; slower streams in the lowlands and foothills in winter. **BREEDING** April–July. Nest is a cup of dry plant stems, usually built near water under a stone, among exposed roots on a bank or in a stone wall. **DISTRIBUTION AND STATUS** Breeds in Baluchistan, Pakistan, and in Himalayas from N Pakistan east to Bhutan; winters throughout most of the subcontinent, except parts of the northwest. **PK:** frequent to locally common in summer in Himalayas, sparse in Baluchistan, breeds 1820–3960 m; uncommon in winter in the plains. **NP:** common and widespread; breeds mainly 1110–3550 m (–4115 m), winters below 365 m, occasionally up to 1550 m. **IN:** common in summer in Himalayas, 1800–3900 m, locally down to 1200 m; winters in plains and foothills, up to 1500 m, locally to 2000 m in Himalayas (–4000 m). **BT:** fairly common. **BD:** uncommon winter visitor throughout. **LK:** common winter visitor throughout. **MV:** vagrant. **REFERENCES** Martens and Eck (1995).

RICHARD'S PIPIT *Anthus richardi* — Plate 143

A. novaeseelandiae **(F,I,K,N)**

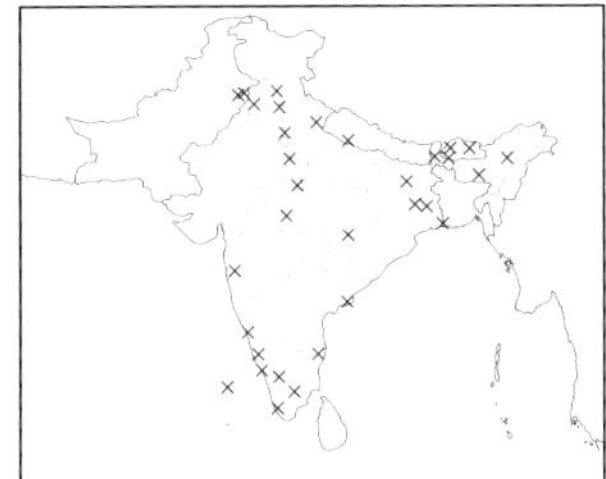

IDENTIFICATION 17 cm. As Paddyfield Pipit (below) in plumage, but is larger, with longer legs and hindclaw and more erect carriage, and has heavier bill and longer tail. Take-off behaviour and call are different: on being flushed. typically gains height and distance quickly with deep, bounding undulations, and drops down at long range, often after hovering lark-like with tail spread. Extremely similar to Blyth's Pipit (p.816); see that species for main differences. Compared with juvenile and well-streaked first-winter Tawny Pipit (p.816), is larger and longer-tailed, and has more upright carriage, larger bill (often held above horizontal), longer legs and longer hindclaw, as well as different 'plain-faced' facial pattern, with pale lores and surround to eye; ear-coverts are also often pale-centred and supercilium often extends to surround ear-coverts (ear-coverts of Tawny tend to be more uniform, and supercilium broad and square-ended at rear), while malar stripe and patch tend to be more prominent. Richard's is usually distinctly browner above, and deeper and more contrastingly buff on breast and flanks (underparts are more uniformly buffish-white on Tawny). **First-winter** is very similar to adult, but retains white-fringed (rather than brownish-buff-fringed) wing-coverts which contrast with rest of wing. **Juvenile** plumage can be retained until early winter; is more heavily and prominently marked than adult on upperparts, blackish feathers of which have narrow whitish fringes (worn birds can appear almost blackish on crown and mantle), and breast is strongly spotted. **VOICE** Call is a loud explosive *dschreep* or *schreep*, which is very different from the call of Paddyfield and Tawny Pipits; can also give a softer *chup* call. **HABITS** Similar to those of other pipits. Rather wary. On the ground, progresses with swift runs combined with a strutting walk on strong legs; often has an upright carriage, except when moving quickly. Has a powerful flight, more undulating than that of other large pipits, with bursts of flapping beats alternating with long bounds; before landing, may hover above the ground, fluttering with dangling legs. Has a long escape flight. Uses low perches, such as rocks and low mounds. **HABITAT** Moist grassy areas and cultivation. **DISTRIBUTION AND STATUS** Winters widely in the subcontinent, but probably under-recorded. **PK:** recorded, but status uncertain. **NP:** winter visitor and passage migrant; frequent below 1500 m. **IN:** widespread, but status uncertain. **BT:** uncommon passage migrant; recorded up to 4850 m. **BD:** common winter visitor throughout. **LK:** common winter visitor to lowlands and up to middle altitudes. **REFERENCES** Britton (1984), Harris *et al.* (1989), Vittery (1994).

PADDYFIELD PIPIT *Anthus rufulus* — Plate 143

Indian Pipit (P), ***A. novaeseelandiae*** **(F,I,K,N,R)**

IDENTIFICATION 15 cm. Very similar to Richard's Pipit (above) in plumage. Compared with Richard's, is much smaller, with shorter tail, and has shorter legs and hindclaw, smaller bill and more horizontal carriage. When flushed, has comparatively weak, rather fluttering flight and distinctive call (see Richard's for comparison). Shape and carriage more closely resemble those of Tawny Pipit (p.816), although is shorter-tailed, and flight is weaker. Well-streaked upperparts, malar region and breast of Paddyfield readily distinguish it from most Tawny (although that species is often distinctly streaked on upperparts, especially on crown). Juvenile plumage of Tawny can be retained until midwinter (with spotted breast and well-streaked upperparts) and can very closely resemble Paddyfield: by comparison, Paddyfield is generally pale on lores and around eye (although lores may be, or appear, dark), and supercilium frequently appears to extend around ear-coverts; in addition, often shows warm ginger-buff wash across breast and down flanks (underparts more uniform on Tawny), and pure white on outer tail feathers (more buffish on Tawny), and call is different. **Juvenile** has more scalloped appearance to upperparts, and darker and heavier spotting on breast. **Racial variation** Three races are described from the subcontinent. *A. r. waitei* of the NW subcontinent is paler and more sandy-grey on the upperparts compared with the widely distributed nominate race, and is less heavily streaked above and below. *A. r. malayensis* of the S peninsula and Sri Lanka is darker and more heavily streaked than the nominate race. **VOICE** Call is a weak *chup-chup-chup* or *chip-chip-chip* or *chilt-chilt* with almost chattering quality; song, given perched or in aerial display, is a repetitive *chip-chip-chip* etc. **HABITS** Forages by running rapidly on the ground, wagging its tail; has a less powerful gait than Richard's Pipit. When flushed, usually flies a short distance. Readily perches on bushes, rocks and clods of earth. In song flight, the male rises in a series of fluttering ascents, circles high over his territory, and then descends steeply on stiff wings held above the back like a parachute; he also sings from a prominent perch. **HABITAT** Short grassland, green fodder crops, stubbles, ploughed and fallow fields, and grassy and stony ground. **BREEDING** November–September, varying locally. Nest is a cup, sometimes partly domed, made of grass and grass roots, usually sheltered among grass clumps, often in a hoof print. **DISTRIBUTION AND STATUS** Resident, subject to local movements. Throughout most of the subcontinent, except parts of the northwest, northeast and Himalayas. **PK:** widespread and locally common in the Indus basin; spreads to the foothills of NW Pakistan and Himalayas in summer. **NP:** widespread and common resident; below 1830 m (–2440 m in summer). **IN:** widespread and common; breeds in plains and hills, up to 1800 m (–2100 m) in Himalayas. **BT:** uncommon; 250–1620 m. **BD, LK:** common throughout.

TAWNY PIPIT *Anthus campestris* — Plate 143

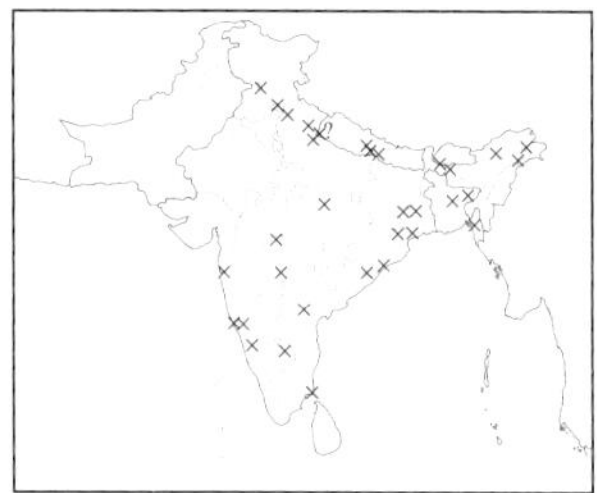

IDENTIFICATION 16 cm. Smaller and shorter-legged than Richard's Pipit (p.815), with more horizontal, often rather wagtail-like carriage. Shape and carriage more closely resemble those of Paddyfield (p.815), although has longer tail. **Adult** is distinctive, with faintly streaked sandy-grey upperparts (usually more strongly streaked on crown), black-centred median coverts which contrast with upperparts, and unstreaked or only very faintly streaked breast with pale buffish wash. Possibly confusable with Long-billed Pipit (p.817), but is much smaller and proportionately longer-legged, with less richly coloured wings and underparts; see that species for further details. **First-winter** is similar to adult, but some retain dark-streaked juvenile feathers, especially on crown, scapulars and breast. **Juvenile** plumage can be largely retained until midwinter, and upperparts and breast are as heavily streaked as on Richard's and Paddyfield. Subtle plumage differences are dark lores and eye-stripe contrasting with supercilium, which tends to be broader and square-ended at rear, more uniform buffish-white underparts, and (generally) buffish outer tail feathers; dark lores can be indistinct, or lacking on some moulting birds. Has shorter hindclaw than Richard's. **VOICE** Loud song is a slow, somewhat melancholy and monotonous *cher-lee*; calls (usually given in flight) include a clear House Sparrow-like *tchilip* and a mellow *chep* (P. Holt). **HABITS** Similar to those of other pipits. Walks and runs swiftly with occasional alert pauses; frequently wags its tail up and down, like a wagtail or small pipit. Flight is undulating, but less powerful than that of Richard's Pipit (and flight silhouette recalls a wagtail); escape flight is quite long. Sometimes uses higher perches, such as telegraph wires and bushes, than those preferred by Richard's. **HABITAT** Uncultivated bare ground, stony semi-desert with scattered scrub, and fallow and ploughed fields. **DISTRIBUTION AND STATUS** Winter visitor, mainly to Pakistan and NW India; scattered records from elsewhere. **PK:** common and widespread winter visitor in the plains and lower outer valleys in NW Pakistan. **NP:** vagrant. **IN:** widespread winter visitor; common in the northwest, generally uncommon elsewhere. **BT:** rare. **BD:** rare passage migrant. **REFERENCES** Britton (1984), Harris *et al.* (1989), Svensson (1992).

BLYTH'S PIPIT *Anthus godlewskii* — Plate 143

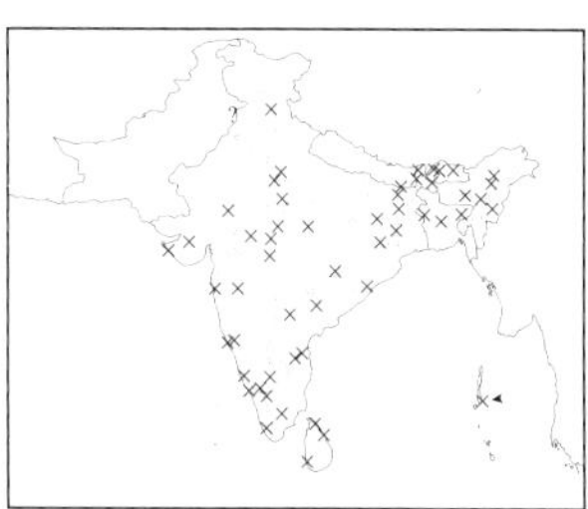

IDENTIFICATION 16.5 cm. Extremely similar in plumage to Richard's and Paddyfield Pipits (p.815). Compared with Richard's, very subtle differences are slightly smaller size and more compact appearance, shorter tail, shorter hindclaw, shorter and more pointed bill, and shorter legs; upperparts tend to look more heavily streaked, and underparts more uniformly buffish, although many appear identical. Square-shaped, well-defined black centres to adult median coverts are diagnostic, these feathers generally also having paler and broader tips resulting in more prominent median-covert wing-bar (black centres to median coverts are more triangular in shape and more diffuse on Richard's); this feature can, however, be extremely difficult to judge in the field. White on inner web of penultimate tail feather is typically restricted to a wide and short wedge at tip (on Richard's, inner web typically is largely white; rarely, white is limited to a short wedge, but this is then narrow and pointed), although this feature is likely to be noted only on a preening bird (or in the hand). Best distinctions from Paddyfield are call, larger size, patterning of median coverts, and more cleanly and heavily streaked upperparts (at least in *A. r. waitei*). **First-winter** is as adult, but most retain juvenile median coverts and cannot be separated from Richard's on this feature (see juvenile). **Juvenile** plumage, which can be retained until midwinter, is more heavily streaked on upperparts and breast; median coverts are fringed with white (rather than buff as on fresh adult) and shape of dark centres is identical to that of juvenile Richard's. **VOICE** Two basic calls: one is a mellow *chup* or *chep* (very similar to one of the notes of both Tawny and Paddyfield Pipits), and the other a diagnostic, powerful buzzy *spzeeu* reminiscent of the common flight call of

Richard's Pipit, but higher-pitched, a little softer and with a slight drop at the end; both calls commonly combined (P. Holt). **HABITS** Gait resembles that of Tawny Pipit, and lacks the strutting walk of Richard's; in frequency of tail-wagging is intermediate between those two species. Flight is similar to that of Richard's Pipit, but without the fluttering pause before landing. **HABITAT** Cultivation, fallow fields, grassland and marshes. **DISTRIBUTION AND STATUS** Winters widely in the subcontinent, but probably under-recorded. **PK:** possibly recorded. **NP:** passage migrant in the east; recorded up to 4250 m. **IN:** widespread winter visitor; plains and hills, up to 750 m in the peninsula. **BT:** rare. **BD:** rare passage migrant? **LK:** status uncertain, probably a rare winter visitor to all zones. **REFERENCES** Alström and Colston (1991), Bradshaw (1994), Svensson (1992).

LONG-BILLED PIPIT *Anthus similis* — Plate 143

Brown Rock Pipit (F,I)

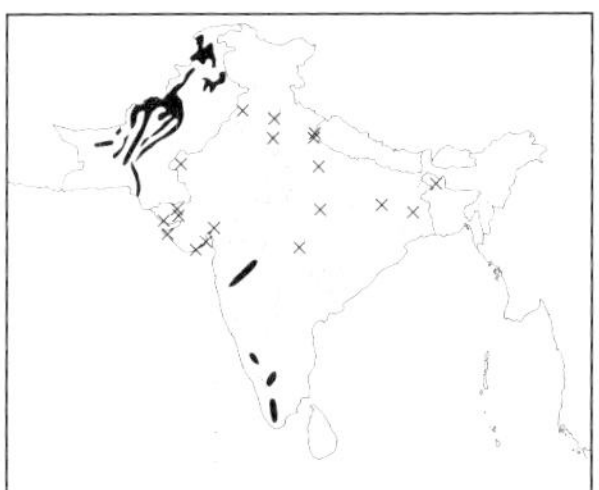

IDENTIFICATION 20 cm. Considerably larger than Tawny Pipit (p.816), with very large bill (which has pronounced curve to culmen) and shorter-looking legs. Like that species, has dark lores. Appears large and powerful in flight, with deep undulations. The race *decaptus* is most similar to Tawny in coloration, but upperparts are colder, darker and greyer, lacks distinct dark malar or moustachial stripe, and has warmer buff underparts. Other races are more distinct, with deeper orange-buff underparts, rufous-buff fringes to tertials and coverts, and rufous-buff outer edge to tail. Not likely to be confused with Richard's, Blyth's or Paddyfield Pipits (p.815, p.816 and p.815), which are either more heavily streaked on upperparts and breast (compared with northern races) or less richly coloured on underparts (compared with races in the peninsula). **Juvenile** has dark spotting on breast, and rounded dark centres to upperparts have distinct pale fringes. **Racial variation** Four races are known from the subcontinent. *A. s. decaptus* of the NW subcontinent has paler and greyer upperparts than *A. s. jerdoni* of N subcontinent, which is deeper orange-buff on underparts; both these subspecies can have unstreaked or lightly streaked breast. *A. s. similis* and *A. s. travancoriensis* of the peninsula have darker grey-brown upperparts and warm rufous-buff underparts; breast is more heavily streaked/spotted. **VOICE** Calls include a deep *chup* and a loud, ringing *che-vlee*; song is a slow, measured *chirrit-chirrit-chirrit-teeweeh-pr-chirrit-chirrit-tweeweeh chirrit-teweeh-chirrit-teeweeh* (Roberts 1992). **HABITS** Non-gregarious; usually keeps singly or in pairs. Has an upright posture when alert, more horizontal when feeding. Flicks tail upwards while simultaneously fanning it; does not wag tail downwards like most pipits. Escapes in flight, or runs off a long distance before skulking in cover. Flight is strong and bounding, very similar to that of Richard's Pipit, including habit of hovering above the ground before landing. In song flight, the male flaps upwards, then flies in an undulating path high over his territory, before gliding down on stiff wings; also sings from a prominent boulder or bush. **HABITAT** Breeds on dry grassy, rocky or scrub-covered slopes; winters in dry cultivation, fallow fields and scattered scrub. **BREEDING** April–August. Nest is a shallow cup made of coarse grass, well hidden under a grass tuft, stone or small bush. **DISTRIBUTION AND STATUS** Resident, subject to altitudinal movements, and partial migrant. Hills of Pakistan, Himalayan foothills from N Pakistan east to W Nepal, and hills of W and SW India; winter visitor to Madhya Pradesh and scattered records from elsewhere. **PK:** common and widespread in the drier lower hills up to 2400 m, locally to 2900 m; spreads into the Indus plains in winter. **NP:** rare breeder, possibly resident; recorded below 1700 m, mainly in the west. **IN:** in Himalayas, common on breeding grounds, 600–1800 m, occasionally higher, winters below 900 m; uncommon in the southwest, breeds above 1000 m. **BD:** ?former resident in the northwest.

TREE PIPIT *Anthus trivialis* — Plate 144

Eurasian Tree Pipit (F)

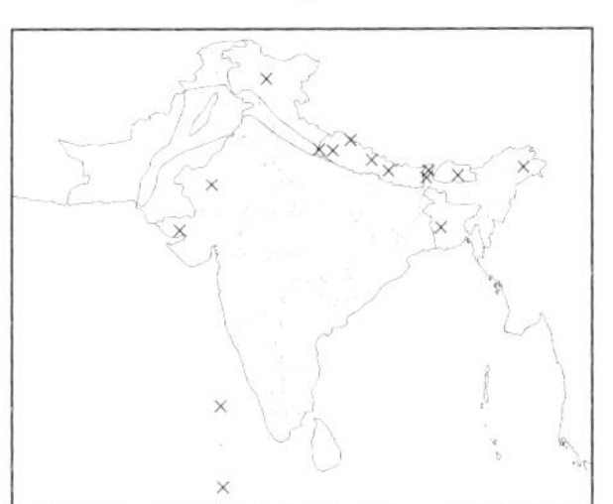

IDENTIFICATION 15 cm. Most likely to be confused with Olive-backed (p.817), but has buffish-brown to greyish coloration to upperparts (lacking greenish-olive cast), and buffish fringes to greater coverts, tertials and secondaries (greenish-olive on Olive-backed). Typically, has less striking face pattern: Tree Pipit has less prominent and wholly buffish-white supercilium, indistinct dark upper edge to supercilium and diffuse dark eye-stripe, and usually ear-coverts are rather plain and without prominent pale and dark spots (face pattern can, however, approach that of Olive-backed). In worn plumage, upperparts are browner (lacking grey or warm buff cast) and underparts whiter. For differences from Meadow and Red-throated Pipits (p.818 and p.819), see those species. **Racial variation** Two races occur in the subcontinent. *A. t. haringtoni*, which breeds in NW Himalayas and winters widely across the subcontinent, differs from the nominate race, which also winters widely across the subcontinent, in having colder and greyer coloration to upperparts, and generally lacking buff tones to supercilium, submoustachial stripe and breast (although they are much the same in worn plumage). **VOICE** Call is typically a harsher *teez* than Olive-backed's, although there is much overlap; song is louder and far-carrying, ending in finch-like trill, *chik-chik....chia-chia-wich-wich-tsee-a-tsee-a tsee-a* (Cramp 1988). **HABITS** Habitually perches in trees, and readily walks along branches; usually flies into trees if disturbed. Feeds mainly on the ground among low vegetation and leaf litter, walking rather deliberately, with intervening short runs; frequently wags the tail gently up and down. Has a rather upright stance and a buoyant, undulating flight. In song flight, the male flutters upwards a short distance from the top of a tree, then glides down on stiff, upheld wings with legs dangling and tail held forward; also sings from a prominent tree or bush. **HABITAT** Breeds on grassy slopes at edge of the treeline; winters in groves, fallow fields, stubbles and open country with scattered trees. **BREEDING** May–July. Nest is a neat cup made of grass stems, placed in a natural hollow under a stone or grass tuft. **DISTRIBUTION AND STATUS** Resident, short-range migrant and winter visitor. Breeds in NW Himalayas from Pakistan east to N Himachal Pradesh; winters widely in the subcontinent, except parts of the Himalayas, northwest, northeast and south. **PK:** locally frequent; breeds 2700–4550 m; passage migrant in Sindh and Punjab; also winters in lower Sindh. **NP:** uncommon and widespread winter visitor and passage migrant; recorded up to 3050 m. **IN:** summers rather sparsely, 2700–4200 m in Himalayas; winter visitor to the plains, mainly in C areas. **BT:** rare passage migrant. **BD, MV:** vagrant. **REFERENCES** Harris *et al.* (1989).

OLIVE-BACKED PIPIT *Anthus hodgsoni* — Plate 144

Indian Tree Pipit (I), Olive Tree Pipit (K), Hodgson's Tree Pipit (F)

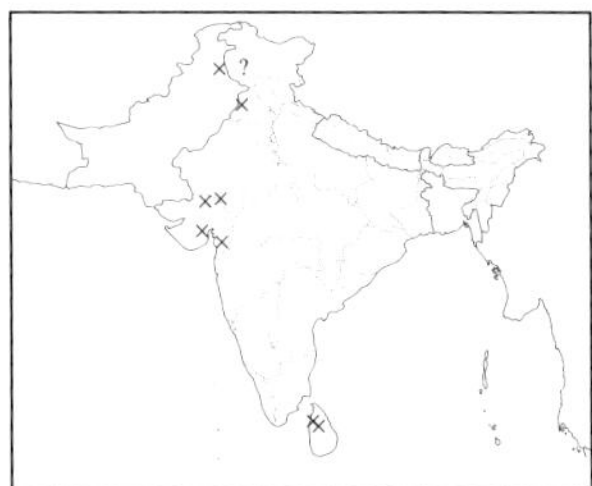

IDENTIFICATION 15 cm. Similar to Tree Pipit (p.817), but in fresh plumage has greenish-olive cast to crown, mantle and scapulars and greenish-olive fringes to greater coverts, tertials and secondaries. Typically, shows more prominent supercilium which is buffish in front of eye and white behind, has stronger dark eye-stripe and dark upper edge to supercilium, and shows distinct whitish spot and blackish patch on rear ear-coverts which are usually lacking on Tree Pipit. Some Tree Pipits can, however, show suggestion of similar head pattern. In worn plumage, upperparts lose greenish coloration and become more greyish-olive, and breast loses warm buff wash; separation from Tree then becomes more difficult. **Racial variation** *A. h. yunnanensis*, which is a widespread winter visitor to the subcontinent, is much less heavily streaked on upperparts than the nominate race (a further difference from Tree Pipit, which has a well-streaked mantle). **VOICE** Flight call is a weak *see*, slightly finer and fainter than Tree Pipit's, although Tree can utter similar flight calls; song is faster and higher-pitched, and the trills are slightly harder and drier, recalling Winter Wren (p.680) (Alström and Colston 1991). **HABITS** Flight, gait, posture and carriage are like those of Tree Pipit. Vigorously pumps tail up and down, more strongly so than other pipits. In song flight, the male flies upwards a short distance from a tree top on quivering wings, then parachutes down with wings and tail spread. **HABITAT** Breeds in clearings of open forest, scrub with scattered trees and shrubberies above the treeline; winters in forest clearings, coffee and cardamom plantations, groves and cultivation with scattered trees. **BREEDING** March–July. Nest is a cup of moss and dry grass, placed on the ground, usually under a grass tuft. **DISTRIBUTION AND STATUS** Resident, subject to altitudinal movements, also partial migrant and winter visitor. Breeds in Himalayas from Himachal Pradesh east to Arunachal Pradesh; winters mainly in N, NE, E and SW India, S Nepal, Bhutan and Bangladesh. **PK:** vagrant. **NP:** common and widespread; summers mainly 2200–4000 m (down to 1800 m), winters below 2560 m. **IN:** common and widespread; breeds 2700–4000 m, winters in plains and hills, up to 2000 m in Himalayas. **BT:** common; 250–4125 m. **BD:** common winter visitor throughout. **LK:** winter vagrant to dry lowlands. **REFERENCES** Martens and Eck (1995), Robson (1996b).

MEADOW PIPIT *Anthus pratensis* — Plate 144

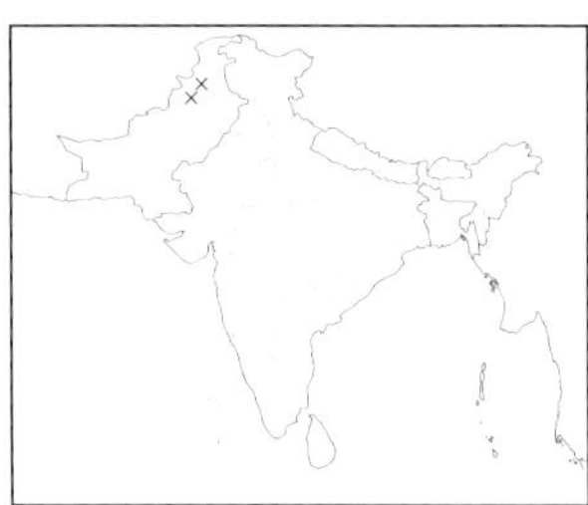

IDENTIFICATION 15 cm. Very similar to Tree Pipit (p.817) in appearance, and best told by distinctive call. Subtle differences from Tree are slimmer build, weaker, more fluttering flight, slimmer and weaker bill, less distinct supercilium, and less boldly streaked breast but more boldly streaked flanks. Hindclaw is much longer and straighter on Meadow (short and arched on Tree), although this is difficult to see in field, and legs and feet tend to be browner (not so strikingly pink). In fresh plumage, upperparts are warm buffish olive-brown (may show greenish tint) and has yellowish-buff wash to breast and flanks, these areas respectively becoming greyer-brown and whiter when worn. Because of a similarity of calls, possibly confusable with Rosy and Buff-bellied Pipits (p.8190 and p.820) in non-breeding plumage. Lacks Rosy's prominent white supercilium, broad white wing-bars and distinct greenish edges to tertials and secondaries, and is smaller and less heavily streaked on upperparts and underparts. Very similar to Buff-bellied, but is smaller, has more olive-brown and more heavily streaked crown, nape and mantle, lacks prominent white median- and greater-covert wing-bars, has less prominent white supercilium, and has less distinct dark malar patch and spotting on upper breast. **VOICE** Call is a soft, slightly squeaky *sip-sip-sip*. **HABITS** Similar to those of other pipits. Has a distinctive creeping walk, and holds body almost horizontal when perched; wags tail less often than Tree Pipit. Keeps in loose flocks, sometimes with Water Pipit (p.819). Flight is undulating; escape flight is usually high, and ends by dropping into low vegetation cover or on to open ground. **HABITAT** Keeps to open area: grass fields and open grass margins of lakes. **DISTRIBUTION AND STATUS PK:** vagrant.

RED-THROATED PIPIT *Anthus cervinus* Plate 144

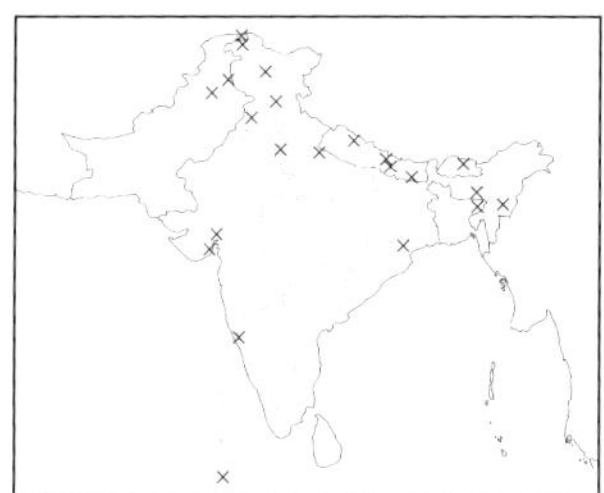

IDENTIFICATION 15 cm. **Adult** readily distinguished from other pipits by brick-red to pinkish-red supercilium, throat, upper breast and sides of neck. Reddish coloration tends to be less extensive and paler on females and in autumn/winter. Upperparts are very heavily streaked and typically show pale 'braces' on sides of mantle. **First-year** is similar in coloration to nominate race of Tree Pipit (p.817), but typically has more heavily streaked upperparts, often with pale 'braces', heavily streaked rump, well-defined and broad white tips to median and greater coverts forming prominent wing-bars, strongly contrasting blackish centres and whitish fringes to tertials, more pronounced dark malar patch, and more boldly streaked breast and (especially) flanks. Nominate Tree tends to have warmer buff wash to breast and flanks, while *haringtoni* race of Tree is more similar in appearance. Above features should be applied with caution owing to variation and the effects of wear. Some first-year males can show a little pinkish-buff on throat. Heavily streaked appearance may possibly cause confusion with non-breeding Rosy Pipit (below), but has different call, has browner (less olive) coloration to upperparts, and lacks olive-green fringes to greater coverts/tertials and secondaries. **VOICE** Call is typically a long, drawn-out *seeeeee*, although can be more abbreviated and recall Tree Pipit. **HABITS** Usually keeps in small flocks. Gait and carriage are intermediate between those of Tree Pipit and Meadow Pipit, including the creeping walk of the latter. If disturbed, usually flies off high before dropping into low vegetation or on to open ground. Flight is like that of Tree Pipit. **HABITAT** Keeps to open ground: marshes, wet grassland and stubbles. **DISTRIBUTION AND STATUS** Winter visitor and passage migrant, mainly to Pakistan, N India, Nepal, Bhutan, Bangladesh and Maldives. **PK:** rare passage migrant. **NP:** uncommon winter visitor and passage migrant; recorded up to 5180 m. **IN:** rare passage migrant. **BT:** rare. **BD:** probably a scarce winter visitor to the northeast. **MV:** autumn passage migrant and winter visitor in small numbers.

ROSY PIPIT *Anthus roseatus* Plate 144

Vinaceous-breasted Pipit (I), Rose-breasted Pipit (F)

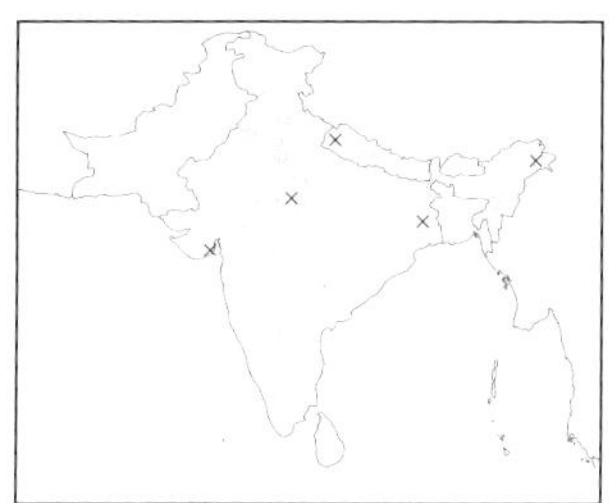

IDENTIFICATION 15 cm. **Adult breeding** distinguished from Water and Buff-bellied Pipits (below and p.820) by bold dark streaking on olive (to almost blue-grey) crown and mantle, mauve-pink wash to underparts, variable bold, irregular black spotting on breast and flanks (almost lacking on some, except on flanks), and olive to olive-green edges to greater coverts, secondaries and tertials. Pinkish to buff supercilium is very prominent, with broad dark eye-stripe and moustachial stripe, and whitish eye-ring. In **non-breeding** plumage, boldly streaked upperparts with distinct olive cast, and olive to olive-green edges to coverts, secondaries and tertials (less apparent when worn), separate Rosy from non-breeding Water and Buff-bellied Pipits. Underparts are considerably more heavily streaked than on Water Pipit and may also have buffish or pinkish wash; lores are dark (pale on Buff-bellied and often on Water). For differences from non-breeding Meadow and Red-throated Pipits (p.818 and above), see those species. **VOICE** Call is a weak *seep-seep*, very similar to those of Meadow and Buff-bellied Pipits, but slightly less strident than call of Water Pipit; song, usually uttered in display flight, is *tit-tit-tit-tit-tit teedle-teedle* as the bird flutters upwards, followed by *sweet-sweet-sweet* as it parachutes down (Roberts 1992). **HABITS** In summer behaves much as Water Pipit; in winter is rather skulking, running and creeping on the ground with body held almost horizontal, in contrast to the more erect posture typical of many other pipits in the region. Forages among grass clumps, boulders and bushes, and along edges of small streams. **HABITAT** Summers on alpine meadows, on grass and boulder-strewn slopes and grassy scrub-covered slopes above the treeline; winters in marshes, cultivation, and damp grassland along stream banks. **BREEDING** End May–September. Nest is a cup of grass, placed in a depression under a stone or grass tuft. **DISTRIBUTION AND STATUS** Breeds Himalayas from N Pakistan east to Arunachal Pradesh; winters mainly south to N Pakistan, E Rajasthan, S Nepal, Bhutan, Bangladesh and Assam. **PK:** common in Himalayas in summer, breeds mainly 3300–3650 m (3275–4275 m); winters chiefly in the outer foothills and valleys of N Punjab and NW Pakistan. **NP:** fairly common and widespread; summers mainly 4000–5050 m and winters 760–1500 m, occasionally down to the terai. **IN:** common on breeding grounds from the timberline up to 4200 m; winters in plains and foothills, up to 1500 m in Himalayas. **BT:** common; 610–4850 m. **BD:** local winter visitor.

WATER PIPIT *Anthus spinoletta* Plate 144

IDENTIFICATION 15 cm. Like Rosy and Buff-bellied Pipits (above and p.820), shows prominent supercilium and median- and greater-covert wing-bars. Lightly streaked upperparts and lack of olive-green on wing separate it from Rosy Pipit in all plumages, and lores are usually pale in subspecies occurring in the subcontinent (dark on Rosy); in non-breeding plumage, is considerably less heavily marked on underparts than Rosy Pipit. Lacks distinct moustachial stripe, and generally has dark legs, which are features which help separation from Buff-bellied in all plumages. In breeding plumage, has orange-buff wash to supercilium and underparts, the latter being less

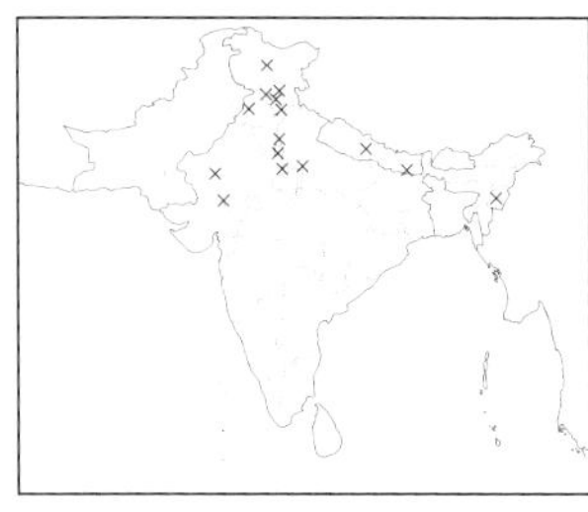

heavily marked than on breeding Buff-bellied Pipit, with indistinct (or non-existent) dark malar stripe and patch, and unstreaked or only faintly streaked breast sides and flanks (there is, however, some overlap); upperparts are a shade paler (more buffish) and more noticeably streaked on Water, and underparts are slightly paler and a shade pinker. In non-breeding plumage, told from non-breeding Buff-bellied by paler, buffier and more distinctly streaked upperparts, rather diffuse and indistinct malar stripe and patch, and diffuse streaking on breast and flanks (underparts considerably more heavily marked on Buff-bellied); background colour of underparts varies from white to pale buff. **VOICE** Call is similar to that of Rosy Pipit, perhaps thinner and sharper. **HABITS** Usually keeps in small scattered flocks. Forages by walking in low ground vegetation and in swift short runs, often wagging the tail up and down. Flight is undulating and buoyant; escape flight is usually low and short. Rarely perches on bushes, trees or telegraph wires. **HABITAT** Marshes, irrigated cultivation, rice stubbles and damp grassy edges of jheels, canals and ditches. **DISTRIBUTION AND STATUS** Winter visitor to Pakistan, N India (mainly from Rajasthan, C Uttar Pradesh) and Nepal. **PK:** status uncertain; probably locally common throughout Punjab and Sindh plains, Baluchistan and N Himalayan valleys, 1500 m. **NP:** probably a rare winter visitor and passage migrant; recorded below 915 m. **IN:** locally fairly common in N plains and foothills. **REFERENCES** Alström and Mild (1996).

BUFF-BELLIED PIPIT *Anthus rubescens* — Plate 144

Water Pipit, *A. spinoletta japonicus* (F,I,K,R)

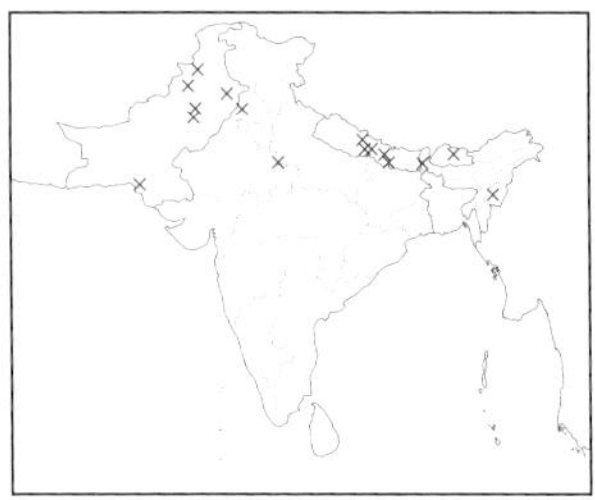

IDENTIFICATION 15 cm. Similar to Rosy and Water Pipits (p.819). Lightly streaked upperparts, lack of olive-green on wing, and pale lores help separate it from Rosy in all plumages. In breeding plumage, has deeper orange-buff wash to underparts than Water Pipit; breast and flanks are more heavily (but irregularly) spotted with black and has more pronounced malar stripe and malar patch, although there is some overlap (some Buff-bellied being more lightly streaked). In non-breeding plumage, has darker greyish-brown upperparts which are slightly less prominently streaked; black malar stripe and patch, and bold black spotting/streaking on breast and flanks, are much more pronounced than on Water Pipit. For differences from Meadow Pipit (p.818), see that species. **VOICE** Call is much as Rosy Pipit's, but perhaps thinner and sharper. **HABITS** Very similar to those of Water Pipit. **HABITAT** Like that of Water Pipit. **DISTRIBUTION AND STATUS** Winter visitor, mainly to Pakistan, N India and Nepal. **PK:** status uncertain; probably uncommon. **NP:** probably a rare winter visitor and passage migrant; recorded below 2715 m. **IN, BT:** rare. **REFERENCES** Alström and Colston (1991), Alström and Mild (1996).

UPLAND PIPIT *Anthus sylvanus* — Plate 143

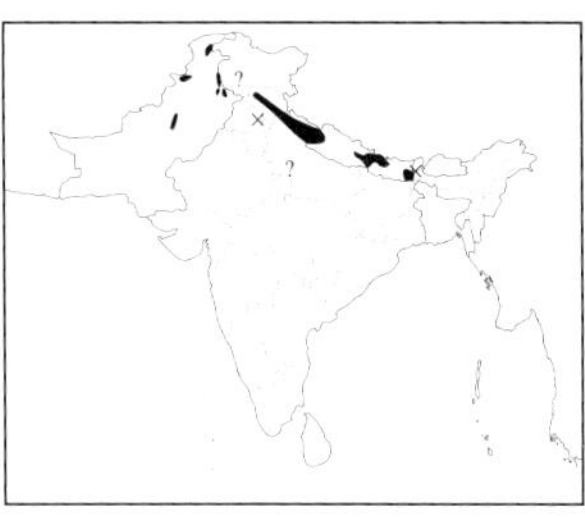

IDENTIFICATION 17 cm. A distinctive, large, very heavily streaked pipit. Distinguished from other pipits by combination of very boldly streaked buffish upperparts, profuse but fine black streaking on underparts, and prominent whitish supercilium. Bill is short and broad (with distinctly curved culmen and slight hook at tip), and tail feathers are narrow and pointed. Base of lower mandible and legs are reddish. Underparts vary from being washed with warm buff to being rather cold and grey in coloration. On **juvenile**, dark brown centres to feathers of upperparts are rounded and neatly fringed with rufous-buff. **VOICE** Call is a sparrow-like *chirp*; song is distinctive, a high-pitched penetrating two-noted whistle, *whit-tsee, whit-tsee...* etc, repeated monotonously (Roberts 1992). **HABITS** Usually keeps singly or in pairs. Flicks tail quite sharply, instead of wagging it like other pipits. Readily perches on rocks and clods of earth with fairly upright stance. Male usually sings from a prominent perch such as a rock or low bush, sometimes from quite high in a tree; occasionally performs song flights like other pipits, fluttering into the air, circling while singing, and then parachuting down. **HABITAT** Steep rocky and grassy slopes, abandoned terraced cultivation with scattered trees and open pine forest. **BREEDING** March–July. Nest is a cup of coarse grass, placed under a stone or grass clump. **DISTRIBUTION AND STATUS** Resident, subject to some altitudinal movements. Pakistan hills and Himalayas in N Pakistan, and India (Punjab, Himachal Pradesh, Uttar Pradesh and West Bengal) and Nepal. **PK:** scarce and local in the drier foothills; 1500–2000 m, locally to 2300 m. **NP:** widespread and locally fairly common; summers 1830–2900 m, winters 1350–2000 m. **IN:** frequent; breeds 1200–3000 m, locally down to 900 m. **REFERENCES** Martens and Eck (1995).

NILGIRI PIPIT *Anthus nilghiriensis* — Plate 143

IDENTIFICATION 17 cm. A large, heavily streaked pipit. Given its range and high-altitude grassland habitat, most likely to be confused with Paddyfield Pipit (p.815), but has shorter tail, boldly streaked crown and mantle,

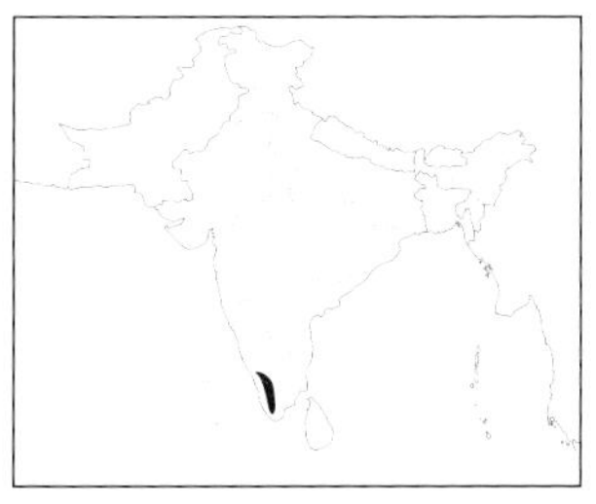

broader and more distinct buffish supercilium, and rich buff underparts with boldly spotted breast, upper belly and flanks. May show some spotting in malar region, but lacks malar stripe and patch. When perched in tree, has distinctive habit of bobbing rear end like Olive-backed Pipit (p.818). **VOICE** Call is a weak *see-see*, quite unlike Paddyfield's; feeble song, initially quiet and hesitant, accelerating into a trill, *tsip-tsip-tsip-sip-sip-sip...*, and ending abruptly, is given from the ground (P. Holt). **HABITS** Keeps singly or in pairs. When flushed, flies up on to the nearest bush or tree. **HABITAT** Grassy upland slopes interspersed with bushes and trees. **BREEDING** April–July. Nest is a cup of coarse grass and roots, placed on sloping ground under a bush or among coarse grass. **DISTRIBUTION AND STATUS IN:** resident, endemic to the SW hills (Kerala and W Tamil Nadu); locally fairly common; breeds mainly above 1500 m, locally at c. 1000 m.

ACCENTORS Passeridae, subfamily Prunellinae

Small, compact, sombre-coloured birds resembling *Passer* sparrows in appearance, but with a more slender and pointed bill. Typically, they forage quietly and unobtrusively on the ground, moving by hopping or in shuffling walk; some species also run. In summer accentors are chiefly insectivorous, and in winter they feed mainly on seeds. Their flight is usually low over the ground and sustained only over short distances, although it is strong and swift in most species. Accentors build cup-shaped nests of plant materials, lined with hair, wool or feathers, which are usually placed in shrubs, in low tree branches, in a rock crevice or on the ground. Some species in the region are migratory, while others make altitudinal movements in the Himalayas.

ALPINE ACCENTOR *Prunella collaris* — Plate 145

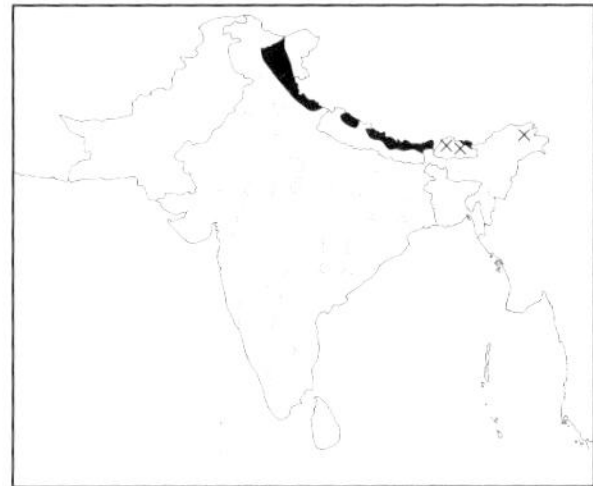

IDENTIFICATION 15.5–17 cm. **Adult** superficially resembles Altai Accentor (below), but has close black barring on narrow white throat patch, comparatively uniform grey head, breast and centre of belly, diffusely streaked mantle, and (white-tipped) black greater and primary coverts which form dark panel across wing. Has chestnut streaking on flanks but, unlike on Altai, streaks usually merge so that flanks appear wholly chestnut. Both species show white or buffish tips to rectrices which are usually prominent in flight. **Juvenile** superficially resembles adult, with dark barring on throat and similar wing pattern; has dark mottling on crown and nape, and buffish mantle, breast and flanks streaked with dark brown (lacking chestnut flank streaking). **VOICE** Song is varied and melodious, with ringing, whistling and squeaking notes; calls include a rolling *churrupp* and a finch-like *chu-chu-chu* (Jonsson 1992). **HABITS** Found singly, in pairs or in family groups, according to the season. Usually tame. A typical accentor, but has a more erect carriage than the other species. Forages among rocks, grassy vegetation and the edges of melting snow. Walks quickly, alternating this with short runs or hops; sometimes makes aerial sallies. Unobtrusive, particularly in winter, but more conspicuous in the breeding season, when males often sing from the top of prominent stones or dwarf shrubs. **HABITAT** Breeds in alpine zone on open stony slopes, scree, moraines, cliffs and rocky pastures; also occurs near upland villages in winter. **BREEDING** May–August. Nest is a compact cup, placed under a stone, in a rock crevice or on a rock ledge. **DISTRIBUTION AND STATUS** Resident, subject to altitudinal movements. Himalayas from N Pakistan east to Arunachal Pradesh. **PK:** breeds in inner mountain ranges, 3500–5000 m; locally common in winter (down to 1800 m). **NP:** frequent; summers chiefly 4200–5500 m (–7900 m), winters from 2440 m to at least 3795 m. **IN:** common; summers 3600–5500 m, winters from 2400 m up to at least 4800 m (down to 2000 m). **BT:** common.

ALTAI ACCENTOR *Prunella himalayana* — Plate 145

Rufous-streaked Accentor

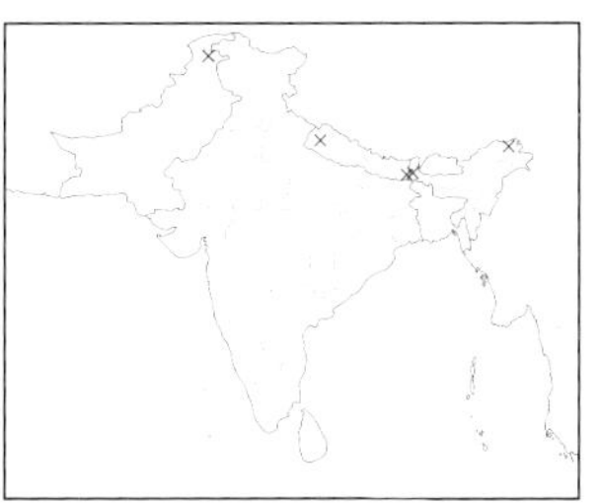

IDENTIFICATION 15–15.5 cm. **Adult** resembles Alpine Accentor (above), but has white throat and whitish underparts, with diffuse rufous spotting across breast and streaking on flanks. Also typically has diffuse malar stripe of black spotting, and black gorget across lower throat, which can be well defined on some birds (with malar stripe offset by white submoustachial stripe), while on others spotting is irregular and extends onto centre of throat. Also has brownish ear-coverts (sometimes forming distinct patch at rear), and variable, sometimes striking, greyish supercilium. Like Alpine, has white tips to greater and primary coverts, but has broad buffish and chestnut fringes to these feathers and therefore usually lacks striking black panel across wing. Mantle is more heavily streaked, with blackish centres and rufous and buff fringes, and can show prominent pale 'braces'. **Juvenile** (although there is no confirmed breeding in subcontinent) lacks distinctive patterning on throat and underparts of adult, having these areas diffusely spotted with brown and washed with buff; warm brown spotting on breast and adult-like patterning to wings help separate it from juvenile Alpine. **VOICE** Song is a short trilling warble; flight call is a double *tee-tee* (Roberts 1992). **HABITS** A typical accentor, but more gregarious than other species in winter, often gathering in flocks of over 100 birds, sometimes with Rufous-breasted Accentors (below) and Plain Mountain Finches (p.834). In flight, they resemble a flock of finches, flying up and circling together and keeping up a constant twitter. Forages on stony or grassy slopes and is very unobtrusive, crouching low with body parallel to the ground. **HABITAT** Grassy slopes, stony slopes and plateaux. **BREEDING** Unknown in the region. In the CIS, May–August, with nest a cup, mainly of grass, placed in a hollow under a tussock. **DISTRIBUTION AND STATUS** Winter visitor. Himalayas from N Pakistan east to Arunachal Pradesh. **PK:** uncommon winter visitor to N foothills; one summer record at 3650 m, but breeding not proven. **NP:** fairly common; 2135–4300 m (down to 1200 m). **IN:** fairly common, especially in the west; 2000–4000 m, occasionally down to 1500 m (1000 m); one summer record in Kashmir. **BT:** uncommon.

ROBIN ACCENTOR *Prunella rubeculoides* Plate 145

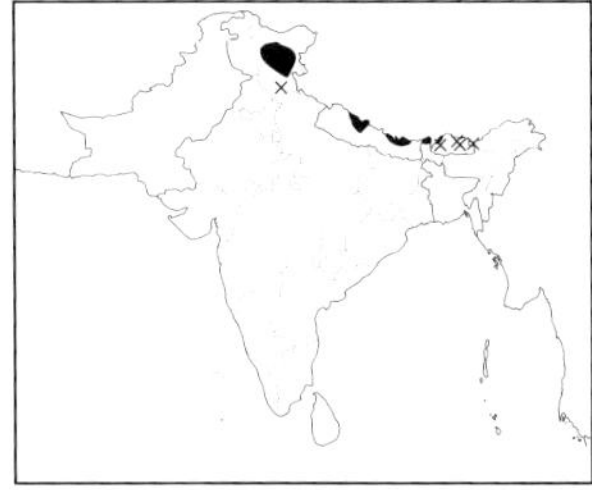

IDENTIFICATION 16–17 cm. **Adult** has well-defined, unstreaked rusty-orange band across breast. Possibly confusable with Rufous-breasted Accentor (below), but has uniform brownish-grey head including throat, diffusely streaked upperparts, and unstreaked white belly (with limited streaking on flanks). **Juvenile** is very different from adult: has pale supercilium, buffish throat mottled with brown, dark streaking on crown and nape, and buff breast streaked with brown. Very similar to juvenile Rufous-breasted, but has more diffusely streaked underparts (with streaking hardly apparent on belly and flanks) and less well-defined supercilium. **VOICE** Song is a high-pitched *tzwe-e-you, tzwe-e-you*; alarm call is a ringing *pi-pi-pi-pi* (Fleming *et al.* 1984). **HABITS** A typical accentor. Usually found singly, or in twos or threes. Tame and confiding. Forages by hopping about in open grassy areas. Often perches in bushes and on walls. Several males chase each other in spring, and quiver wings in courtship display. **HABITAT** Summers in dwarf willows, *Caragana* scrub and sedge tussocks around streams and lakes; winters on stony ground and around upland villages. **BREEDING** May–early September. Builds nest on the ground among sedge clumps or low down in a *Caragana* bush bordering a stream. **DISTRIBUTION AND STATUS** Resident, subject to altitudinal movements. Himalayas from N Pakistan (SW Baltistan and E Gilgit) east to Bhutan. **PK:** local, frequent only on the Deosai Plateau; breeds 3600–4260 m. **NP:** fairly common; summers mainly 4200–5000 m, winters from 2655 m up to at least 3960 m. **IN:** common; breeds 3600–5300 m, locally down to 3000 m, winters down to 2000 m (to 1500 m). **BT:** uncommon. **REFERENCES** Pfister (1997).

RUFOUS-BREASTED ACCENTOR *Prunella strophiata* Plate 145

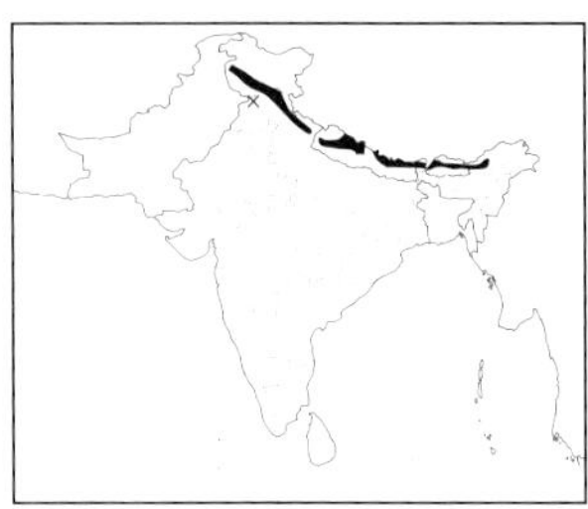

IDENTIFICATION 15 cm. **Adult** possibly confusable with Robin Accentor (above), with rufous band across breast, but has prominent supercilium which is whitish in front of eye, becoming broader and rufous behind eye, and has blackish ear-coverts (with prominent white crescent or spotting below eye, and mottled with rufous at rear). In addition, has blackish lateral crown-stripes, with dark streaking on crown and nape, whitish throat (with variable black streaking, typically forming diffuse malar stripe and band across lower throat), and black streaking on grey neck sides, often shows streaking across rufous breast, and has dark streaking on belly and flanks. Some variation exists, and females (and probably first-winters) typically have duller (streaked) and less extensive rufous on breast, and less well-marked head pattern. **Juvenile** lacks rufous on breast and has less distinct whitish supercilium; underparts are whitish and extensively (and cleanly) streaked with dark brown, with variable fulvous wash across breast. More heavily streaked underparts and more prominent supercilium (offset by brown ear-coverts and crown sides) help separate it from juvenile Robin Accentor. **VOICE** Song is a melodious warbling, reminiscent of Winter Wren (p.680) but not quite so shrill or vehement, and with some pretty trills and warbles; call is a penetrating *trr-r-rit trrr-r-it* (Roberts 1992). **HABITS** A typical accentor. Found singly, in pairs or in small parties. Tame and confiding. Inconspicuous when feeding, shuffling, hopping or running along the ground in a mouse-like fashion, often inside thickets. Frequently flicks wings. Often perches on bushtops. **HABITAT** Summers in subalpine and alpine zone: dwarf rhododendron or juniper; and *Berberis* or *Viburnum* bushes at the edge of coniferous forest and birch scrub. Winters in bushes around fallow fields and upland pastures and scrub forest. **BREEDING** May–August. Builds a neat, thick-walled cup in a small bush, occasionally in the lower branches of a conifer tree, up to 3 m above ground. **DISTRIBUTION AND STATUS** Resident, subject to altitudinal movements. Himalayas from N Pakistan east to Arunachal Pradesh. **PK:** mainly in Himalayas, locally frequent; summers 2700–3600 m (down to 2300 m), winters in the outer foothills. **NP:** fairly common; summers chiefly 3500–4930 m and winters from 1600 m up to at least 3650 m. **IN:** common; summers 2700–4000 m in the west, up to at least 4880 m in the east; winters down to 600 m in the west, to 1300 m in the east. **BT:** common; from 1450 m up to at least 4420 m.

SIBERIAN ACCENTOR *Prunella montanella* Plate 145

IDENTIFICATION 15 cm. **Adult** most likely to be confused with Black-throated Accentor (below), having broad orange-buff supercilium contrasting with blackish sides to crown and ear-coverts. Best told from that species by orange-buff throat (although black throat can be obscured on some Black-throated, and throat is then whitish and distinct from breast), and additionally by chestnut streaking on mantle (although streaking can be dark brown as on Black-throated, but is still chestnut at edges). Breast sides and flanks are streaked with chestnut (a further distinction from Black-throated), or streaked blackish and usually with some chestnut at edges (when much as Black-throated). Supercilium is usually deeper orange-buff than Black-throated's, and even when worn (or on duller individuals: see below) is typically brighter in front of than behind eye, whereas the supercilium of Black-throated is generally whitish in front of eye, becoming more buffish behind. Some individuals (first-winter?) have paler brownish-black ear-coverts, paler crown with darker sides, and duller buff supercilium and throat/breast; even on dull birds, however, crown is not noticeably streaked, and ear-coverts are mainly blackish, which are further distinctions from Black-throated lacking the black throat. Often shows black mottling on breast. Broad orange-buff supercilium and the chestnut streaking on mantle and flanks, although all variable, are best features for separation from Brown Accentor (below). **VOICE** Call is a weak, ringing trill, *si-si-si-si*. **DISTRIBUTION AND STATUS IN:** One published record for Ladakh (Meinertzhagen) now considered doubtful. **REFERENCES** Alström and MacKay (1995).

RADDE'S ACCENTOR *Prunella ocularis* Plate 145

Spot-throated Accentor, *P. fulvescens* (I)

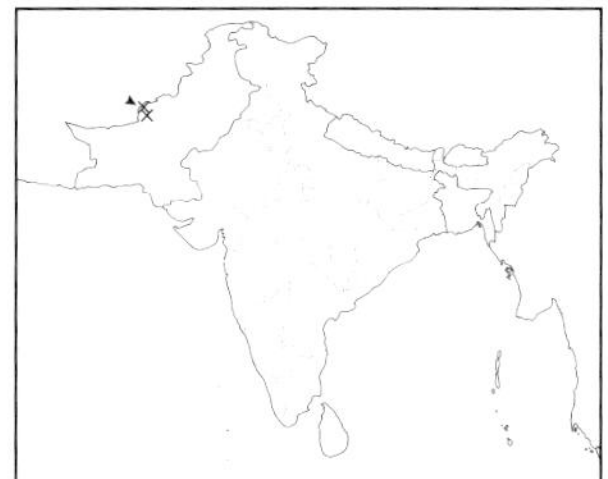

IDENTIFICATION 15–16 cm. Most likely to be confused with Brown Accentor (p.823), and has similar head pattern (with broad whitish supercilium, slightly buffish when fresh, contrasting with crown and ear-coverts). Distinguished from that species by dark brown crown, which is almost concolorous with ear-coverts (crown is distinctly paler than ear-coverts and almost concolorous with mantle on Brown), and dark brown streaking on mantle. Note, however, that *sushkini* race of Brown, which has been recorded as a winter visitor to N Nepal and Sikkim, has darker streaking on mantle compared with nominate race, and crown can also be dark. Radde's further differs from Brown (including *sushkini*) in typically showing dark-spotted malar stripe (lacking on Brown) and diffuse brown streaking on sides of breast and flanks (lacking or very faint on Brown), and also has orange-buff on breast which forms a comparatively well-defined pectoral band (breast, belly and flanks of Brown are more concolorous and paler buff); some Radde's, however, show no dark markings on malar and flanks. Confusion is also possible with Black-throated (p.823) lacking black throat, but Radde's has whitish supercilium, more extensively white throat, and dark brown crown and ear-coverts (crown is paler and prominently streaked on such Black-throated, and ear-coverts are distinctly mottled with white or buff on those birds). **VOICE** Song is a weak, rising and falling *slee-vit-chur-chur-tui* (Porter *et al.* 1996); call is a weak, ringing trill, *si-si-si-si*. **HABITS** Similar to those of Brown Accentor. **HABITAT** Unknown in the region. Favours dry rocky areas in mountainous country. **DISTRIBUTION AND STATUS PK:** vagrant. **REFERENCES** Alström and MacKay (1995).

BROWN ACCENTOR *Prunella fulvescens* Plate 145

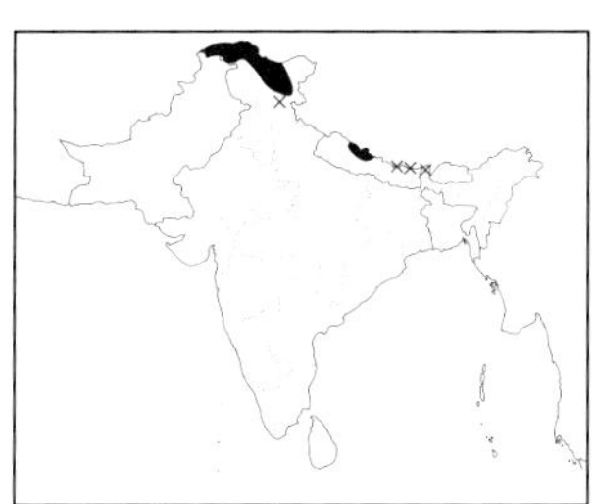

IDENTIFICATION 14.5–15 cm. **Adult** usually readily told by combination of broad whitish supercilium (contrasting with blackish ear-coverts), grey-brown upperparts with only very faint streaking, pale orange-buff underparts with whiter throat, and absence of (or only very light) streaking on flanks. For differences from Black-throated (below), which can occasionally lack or have very indistinct black throat, and Radde's and Siberian Accentors (p.824 and above), see those species. **Juvenile** is similar to adult, but (in the nominate race at least) has more heavily streaked upperparts with rufous-buff cast, brown mottling on supercilium and crown, browner ear-coverts (with less striking head pattern), and brown streaking across breast. **Racial variation** *P. f. sushkini* from Tibet has been recorded in the N subcontinent and differs from the nominate race, described above, in having more prominent brown streaking on upperparts and deeper buff underparts. *P. f. dresseri*, recorded from the NW subcontinent, has paler, sandy-brown upperparts compared with the nominate race, with warm sandy-buff tones especially to edges of remiges and rump. **VOICE** Song is a variable warbling *tuk-tileep-tilee-tileep-tileep* (Fleming *et al.* 1984); call is a weak, ringing trill, *si-si-si-si*. **HABITS** A typical accentor. Keeps in pairs in the breeding season and singly or in small scattered parties in winter, sometimes with Tibetan Snowfinches (p.810). Feeds mainly by creeping and hopping about on the ground, also occasionally in lower branches of bushes. Sings from the tops of bushes. **HABITAT** Dwarf *Caragana* and willows and other low scrub on dry rocky slopes; also around upland villages and nearby fallow fields in winter. **BREEDING**

May–August. Builds nest in a hole in a wall, or on the ground under shelter of a bush or stone. **DISTRIBUTION AND STATUS** Resident, subject to altitudinal movements, and local migrant. Breeds in Himalayas in N Pakistan, Ladakh and NW Nepal; winters mainly from N Pakistan east to WC Nepal. **PK:** locally common in winter in the lower valleys of Chitral, Baltistan and Gilgit; probably breeds in small numbers. **NP:** common in the Tibetan plateau region in the northwest; summers up to 4880 m, winters from 2300 m up to at least 3800 m. **IN:** locally common; 3300–5100 m in summer, winters down to 1500 m. **REFERENCES** Pfister (1997).

BLACK-THROATED ACCENTOR *Prunella atrogularis* Plate 145

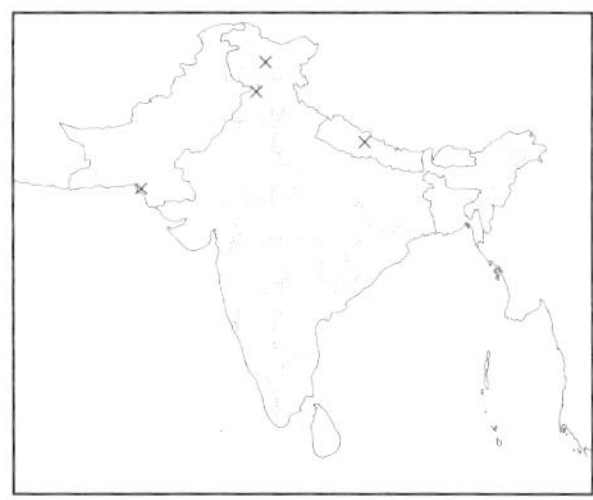

IDENTIFICATION 14.5–15 cm. Typically very distinctive, with broad orange-buff supercilium and submoustachial stripe, blackish crown sides and ear-coverts, black chin and upper throat, dark brown streaking on mantle, and orange-buff breast and flanks. Black throat patch separates it from all other accentors, although on some (first-winter?) birds black throat can be partly obscured by pale fringes (when it is difficult to see in side-on view) or, rarely, is completely absent. Birds lacking black throat could easily be mistaken for Siberian or Radde's Accentors (above and p.824); for differences see those species. Buff supercilium, rather pale or patchy ear-coverts, and dark streaking on mantle and flanks separate such birds from nominate Brown Accentor (above). **VOICE** Call is a weak, ringing trill, *si-si-si-si*. **HABITS** A typical accentor. Usually in small parties, sometimes with finches, buntings or other accentors. Tame and confiding. Shuffles mouse-like around the bottom of bushes or stone walls, while simultaneously flicking wings. Often perches in the open on the tops of bushes. **HABITAT** Bushes near cultivation, dry scrub-covered hills, orchards and semi-desert near cultivation. **DISTRIBUTION AND STATUS** Winters in the hills of Pakistan, and in Himalayas from N Pakistan east to WC Nepal. **PK:** locally common, mainly in semi-arid hills. **NP:** fairly common in the far northwest; 2440–3050 m. **IN:** locally fairly common in the hills up to 2500 m, mainly below 1800 m.

MAROON-BACKED ACCENTOR *Prunella immaculata* Plate 145

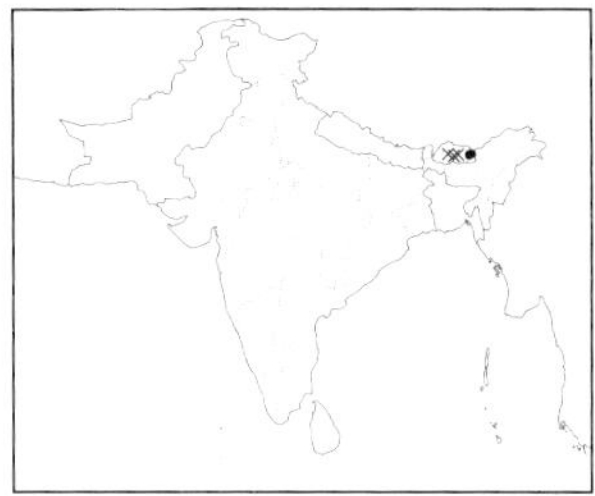

IDENTIFICATION 16 cm. A distinctive accentor, **adult** having slate-grey head, neck and breast, white scaling on forehead and forecrown, yellow iris, maroon-brown mantle and tertials, maroon-chestnut belly and vent, grey wing-coverts with contrasting black primary coverts, and grey edges to primaries forming panel on wing. **Juvenile** has similar wing pattern to adult, but is otherwise rather different: head is olive-grey (lacking white scaling on crown), mantle is rufous-brown with black streaking, throat is white with black spotting, and breast is buff, streaked with dark brown. **VOICE** Very high and feeble *tzip* calls, often doubled (P. Holt). **HABITS** Similar to those of other accentors. Keeps in small parties in winter. Forages chiefly inconspicuously on the ground among forest undergrowth or under bushes; rarely comes into the open. **HABITAT** Moist forest of rhododendrons or mixed conifers–rhododendrons, bushes at forest clearings and edges, and edges of terraced fields at forest margins. **BREEDING** Not satisfactorily recorded. **DISTRIBUTION AND STATUS** Resident, subject to altitudinal movements. Himalayas from WC Nepal east to Arunachal Pradesh. **NP:** frequent winter visitor; 1830–2700 m (3600–4400 m in September). **IN:** scarce resident; altitudinal range uncertain, winters 2135–2440 m (–3385 m; –3690 m?). **BT:** scarce in summer, 3355 m and probably higher; locally common in winter, 1705–3000 m. **REFERENCES** Lama (1995a).

WEAVERS Passeridae, subfamily Ploceinae

Small, rather plump, finch-like passerines with a large, conical bill. Adults feed chiefly on seeds and grain, supplemented by invertebrates; the young are often fed on invertebrates. Males in the region have brilliant yellow in the plumage in the breeding season, and at other times are dull-coloured and streaked like the females. Weavers inhabit grassland, marshes, cultivation and very open woodland. They are highly gregarious, roosting and nesting communally, and are noted for their elaborate roofed nests, woven with coarse grass strips by the males.

BLACK-BREASTED WEAVER *Ploceus benghalensis* Plate 146

Black-throated Weaver Bird (I), Black-throated Weaver (F)

IDENTIFICATION 14 cm. **Male breeding** has lemon-yellow to golden-yellow crown, similar to other male weavers, but has broad black band across breast contrasting with whitish rest of underparts (with variable faint streaking on flanks). Additional differences from Streaked Weaver (p.825) include smaller size, unstreaked grey-brown nape, and more uniform, grey-brown rump (only faintly streaked) which contrasts with heavily streaked mantle/back. There is an interesting variation: some show white ear-coverts and throat, contrasting with black breast, while others have grey-

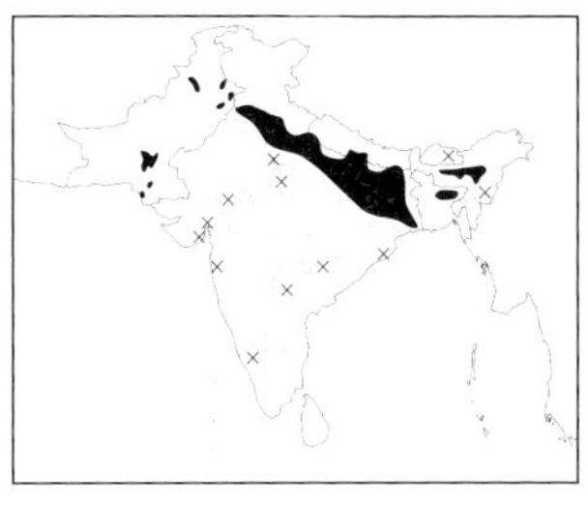

brown ear-coverts and sides of throat which merge with black of breast and grey-brown of nape. Bill is pale bluish-grey. **Male non-breeding**, **female** and **juvenile** lack yellow on crown, but always show black on breast, which can be a well-defined broad band, variably broken by whitish fringes to feathers, or can be restricted to black patches on sides; upper breast is never streaked as on Streaked Weaver, but may show indistinct, diffuse streaking on lower breast and flanks. As Streaked, have yellow supercilium (often white behind eye), distinct yellow patch on side of neck, and yellow submoustachial stripe (with black malar), but crown, nape and sides of neck are more uniform, and indistinctly streaked; ear-coverts are unstreaked, often with pale centre (with distinct dark eye-stripe and rear edge); rump is also plain and indistinctly streaked and, like nape, contrasts with heavily streaked mantle/back. Juveniles tend to be more strongly washed with buff (e.g. on breast and flanks). Head pattern and black on breast distinguish them from all plumages of Baya (below). **VOICE** Song is a soft, barely audible *tsi tsi tsisik tsisik tsik tsik*; call is a soft *chit-chit* (Ali and Ripley 1987). **HABITS** Very similar to those of Baya Weaver. Gregarious all year; often associates with other weavers. **HABITAT** Tall, damp, seasonally flooded grassland, and reedy marshes along rivers and canals; also well-irrigated cultivation in winter. **BREEDING** June–September. Nest is similar to that of Baya Weaver but, instead of hanging by a long thin neck, the top dome of the nest is interwoven into a number of standing reed stems and there is a shorter vertical entrance tube; the nests are always built close to or above water in tall, dense *Saccharum* grass or reeds, and in small scattered clusters. **DISTRIBUTION AND STATUS** Endemic to the subcontinent. Resident, subject to local movements. Mainly in the Indus and Gangetic plains east to NE India and Bangladesh; also very locally in Pakistan and in the peninsula, south to Andhra Pradesh and Karnataka. **PK:** widespread in the Indus floodplain, but only in a few scattered localities. **NP:** local and fairly common; below 245 m. **IN:** common, but local. **BT:** rare. **BD:** local, occurs in the northeast and centre.

STREAKED WEAVER *Ploceus manyar* — Plate 146

Streaked Weaver Bird (I), Striated Weaver (P)

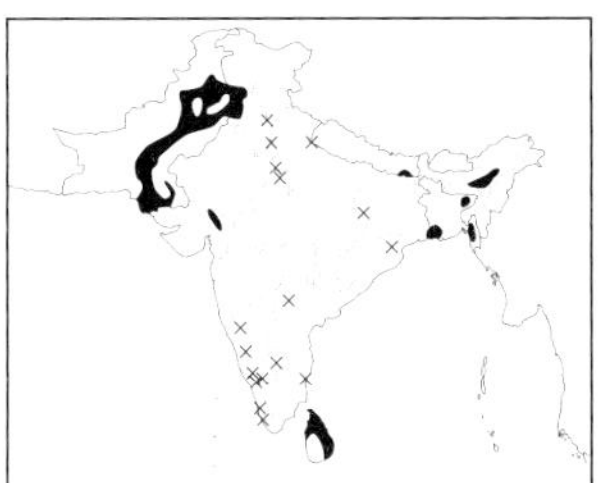

IDENTIFICATION 14 cm. **Male breeding** has golden-yellow crown contrasting with dark brown sides of head and throat. Told from male Black-breasted and Baya (p.825 and below) by heavily streaked breast and flanks. Bill is brownish-black. **Male non-breeding**, **female** and **juvenile** typically have boldly streaked throat, breast and flanks, usually sufficient to separate them from other weavers. Some birds are only lightly streaked on underparts and then easily confusable with Baya, although streaking is typically stronger and more arrowhead-shaped; useful features are prominent yellow supercilium and crescent below eye, well-defined yellow patch on side of neck, heavily streaked crown, dark or heavily streaked ear-coverts, and pronounced dark malar and moustachial stripes. It is possible that some (juveniles?) have no streaking on underparts, when patterning of head is likely to be best means of identification. Compared with Black-breasted, crown, nape, sides of neck and rump are heavily streaked, and that species always shows at least a small patch of black on side of breast. **VOICE** Song is a soft, continuous trill, *see-see-see-see-see*, ending in an *o-cheee*, also a *tre tre cherrer cherrer*; call is a loud *chirt, chirt*. **HABITS** Similar to those of Baya Weaver. In winter, feeds chiefly on the flowering heads of *Phragmites* reeds, *Typha* bulrushes and *Saccharum* grasses by clinging to the upright stems. Roosts communally in reedbeds in winter. **HABITAT** Reedbeds and seasonally flooded areas. **BREEDING** February–October, varying locally. Nest is similar to that of Baya Weaver, but has the top dome interwoven into standing reed stems and lacks a long thin neck; usually built in *Typha* growing in water and in small scattered colonies, but sometimes in large colonies with the nests close together, and often mixed with Black-breasted Weaver nests. **DISTRIBUTION AND STATUS** Resident. Mainly Pakistan, SE Nepal, Assam, Gujarat, Bangladesh and Sri Lanka; scattered records elsewhere. **PK:** common resident throughout the Indus floodplain. **NP:** rare and very local migrant. **IN:** common and widespread, but local resident. **BD:** rare resident in northeast, south and southeast. **LK:** common and local in the dry lowlands, mainly near coasts.

BAYA WEAVER *Ploceus philippinus* — Plate 146

Baya (I)

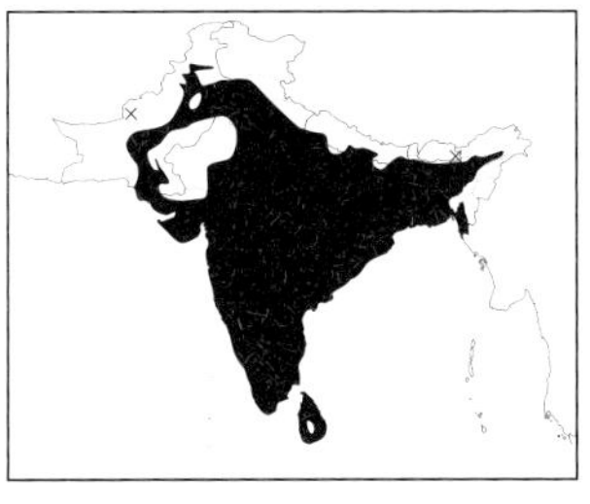

IDENTIFICATION 15 cm. **Male breeding** has yellow crown and dark brown ear-coverts and throat. Told from other male weavers in breeding plumage by unstreaked yellow breast and dark-streaked yellow mantle and scapulars (although see *P. p. burmanicus*). Bill is dark blackish-brown. **Male non-breeding**, **female** and **juvenile** have brownish-buff upperparts, boldly streaked with dark brown, and buff to pale yellowish underparts which are either unstreaked or show sparse, diffuse streaking, usually on sides of breast and flanks (can show streaking as prominent as on some poorly marked Streaked Weavers, above, although streaks tend to finer). Compared with Streaked, supercilium is generally less prominent and typically warm buff in coloration, lacks well-defined yellow patch on side of neck, and has paler and more uniform ear-coverts, lacking pronounced dark moustachial and malar stripes; head pattern of some (non-breeding males?) can, however, be rather similar to that of Streaked, with yellowish supercilium, dark ear-coverts and heavily streaked crown. Different head pattern and lack of black on breast separate them from Black-breasted (p.824). See Finn's Weaver (below) for differences from that species. **Racial variation** Breeding male *P. p. burmanicus* of NE subcontinent generally has buff rather than yellow breast (although some may have a trace of yellow), lacks yellow on mantle, which is (dark-streaked) brownish-buff, and has buff or pale grey throat. Female *burmanicus* tends to be rufous-buff on supercilium, breast and flanks. **VOICE** Song is a soft *chit chit chit* followed by a drawn-out wheezy whistle, *chec-ee-ee*; call is a *chit-chit-chit* (Ali and Ripley 1987). **HABITS** A typical weaver. Highly gregarious throughout the year. Feeds extensively on ripening cereal crops and does much damage, but this is largely compensated for by the huge numbers of insect pests eaten, especially when feeding young. Forages by hopping on the ground seeking fallen seeds, and by picking seeds from the tops of upright grass stems. Roosts communally all year and, although it may wander locally in winter, often returns to traditional roosts; often with wagtails and hirundines in winter. Males call together noisily when nest-building. **HABITAT** Cultivation, paddy-fields, grassland and scrub with scattered trees, and mangroves. **BREEDING** March–October, varying locally and depending on arrival of the monsoon. Colonial. Builds a retort-shaped nest with a long vertical entrance tube, made of finely woven strips of leaves and coarse grass; nest is suspended from a palm frond or tip of a branch, usually of an isolated tree growing at the edge of water. **DISTRIBUTION AND STATUS** Resident, subject to seasonal movements. Throughout much of the subcontinent, except parts of the northwest, northeast and Himalayas. **PK:** locally common throughout the Indus plains from Karachi up to N Punjab, mainly in the floodplain. **NP:** common and widespread; recorded below 1370 m, mainly a summer visitor in the Himalayas. **IN:** common and widespread; plains and hills up to 1200 m in Himalayas, locally to 1000 m in the peninsular hills. **BT:** rare. **BD:** locally common throughout. **LK:** lowlands and lower hills; common in the dry zone, infrequent in the wet zone.

FINN'S WEAVER *Ploceus megarhynchus* — Plate 146

Finn's Baya (I), Yellow Weaver

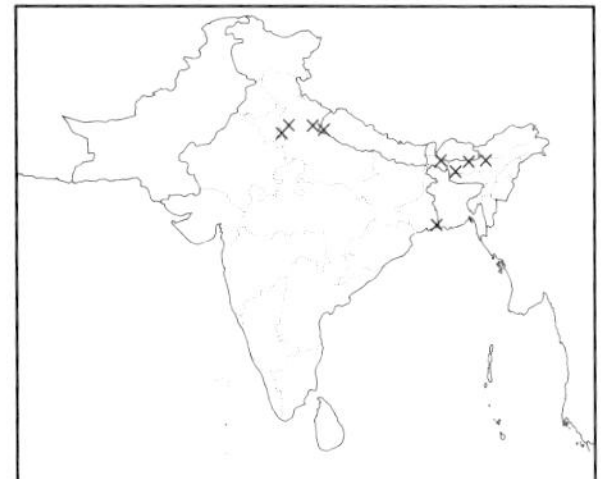

IDENTIFICATION 17 cm. **Male breeding** told from other weavers by bright yellow head with dark-brown ear-coverts, golden-yellow underparts, and yellow rump and uppertail-coverts. Mantle and back are boldly streaked dark brown. Has dark patches on breast, which can show as complete breast-band. **Female breeding** and **first-year male** have pale yellow to yellowish-brown head, and pale yellow to buffish-white underparts; mantle is rich brown with dark streaking. **Adult non-breeding** and **immature** lack yellow and are very similar to respective plumages of Baya Weaver (p.825), and separable possibly only by larger size and bill, and by harsher call. **Racial variation** Breeding male *P. m. salimalii* of NE subcontinent differs from nominate race in having purer yellow head, less yellow on rump, and white undertail-coverts (sometimes also white belly); on breeding female, yellow of underparts extends to undertail-coverts (lower belly and undertail-coverts white in nominate). **VOICE** Song is louder and harsher than Baya Weaver's, a *twit-twit-tit-t-t-t-t-t-trrrrr wheeze whee wee we*; call is a harsh *twit-twit* (Ali and Ripley 1987). **HABITS** Similar to those of Baya Weaver. Roosts in tall grass and sugarcane stands. **HABITAT** *Imperata* and *Saccharum* grassland with well-scattered trees, especially those seasonally flooded; also rice and sugarcane cultivation. **BREEDING** End May–August. Nests colonially 9–10 m up in treetops or in reedbeds. Nest is a large untidy ball woven of coarse grass and supported by twigs or reed stems, not suspended like the nests of other Indian weavers; many nests are often linked together by connecting walls or by long separate strands of vegetation. **DISTRIBUTION AND STATUS** Resident, endemic to India and Nepal. Occurs mainly in India (N Uttar Pradesh, Meerut, Delhi, West Bengal and Assam); also Sukla Phanta, SW Nepal. Globally threatened. **NP:** rare and very local. **IN:** resident; uncommon and very local in the plains and terai. **REFERENCES** Baral (1998), Choudhury (1996b), Giri and Choudhary (1997), Majumdar and Brahmachari (1988), Robson (1993b).

ESTRILDINE FINCHES Passeridae, subfamily Estrildinae

Small, slim passerines with a short, stout, conical beak. They feed chiefly on small seeds, which they pick up from the ground or gather by clinging to stems and pulling the seeds directly from seed heads. Their gait is a hop or occasionally a walk. Outside the breeding season all species are gregarious, and many form communal roosts and feed or roost with other munias and weavers. If disturbed, they typically fly up together in a close-knit pack and move off with fast, whirring wingbeats to the cover of nearby trees, bushes or reedbeds. The flight of individuals is undulating, but the flock as a whole maintains a fairly direct course. They build an untidy, unwoven ball-shaped nest with a side entrance, which usually has a short projecting entrance tunnel. The main references specific to estrildine finches are Goodwin (1982) and Restall (1996).

RED AVADAVAT *Amandava amandava* — Plate 146

Red Munia (F,I), *Estrilda amandava* (F,I)

IDENTIFICATION 10 cm. **Male breeding** is mainly bright red with irregular white spotting (primarily on breast sides, flanks and lower scapulars). Crown, nape and mantle are mottled with olive-brown; has dark brown

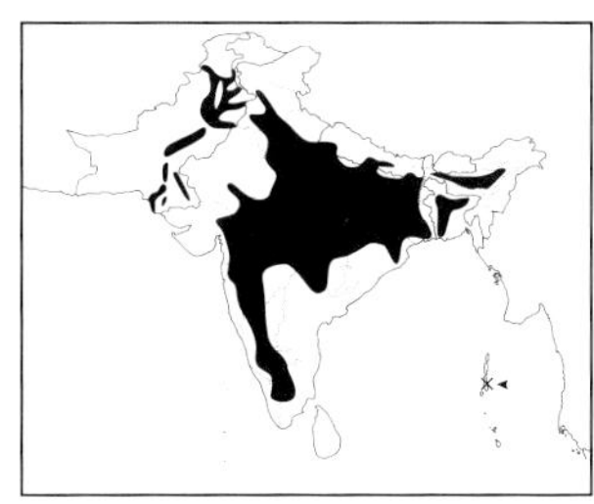

wings with white-tipped coverts and tertials, and blackish undertail-coverts and tail. Otherwise, has red bill, black lores, and pink legs and feet. **Male non-breeding** as female, but has white spotting on red uppertail-coverts, larger white tips to greater coverts, and scattered red on breast and belly. **Female** has red bill, but lacks red in plumage except for red rump and uppertail-coverts (which have a few indistinct white spots); wings are browner than male's, with smaller white or pale buff tips to greater and median coverts, as well as tertials; upperparts are grey-brown and underparts are buffish-white, with buff wash to sides of breast and flanks. **Juvenile** lacks any red and is possibly confusable with other juvenile munias, but has double buff wing-bars and buff fringes to tertials; additional features are fawn-brown upperparts, including rump, with blackish tail, pink base to lower mandible, and pink legs and feet. **VOICE** Song is a weak, high-pitched warble; calls include a thin *teei* and a variety of high-pitched chirps and squeaks (Clement *et al.* 1993). **HABITS** A typical estrildine finch. When not breeding, forms flocks of up to 30 birds and often joins other munias, weavers and *Passer* sparrows; at this season, roosts communally in sugarcane fields and reedbeds. **HABITAT** Tall wet grassland, reedy marshes, sugarcane fields, and tamarisk scrub near cultivation; in Assam, also villages, gardens and cultivation. **BREEDING** Mainly June-December, varying locally. Builds a typical estrildine nest, very well concealed low down in a thorny bush overgrown with grass or in a reed clump. **DISTRIBUTION AND STATUS** Widespread resident in the subcontinent, absent in parts of the northwest, northeast, east and Sri Lanka. **PK:** locally frequent; occurs irregularly throughout the Indus plains and extends west into the riverain tracts of NW Pakistan. **NP:** local, and frequent; below 305 m (–670 m). **IN:** widespread and fairly common, but local. **BD:** rare.

GREEN AVADAVAT *Amandava formosa* — Plate 146

Green Munia (I), *Estrilda formosa* (I)

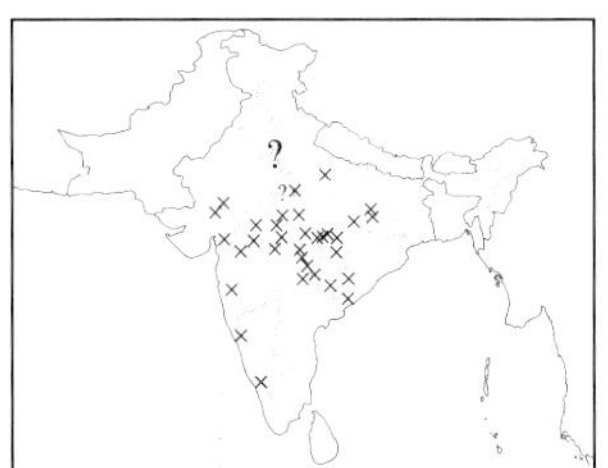

IDENTIFICATION 10 cm. **Male breeding** has red bill. Plumage is striking, with lime-green upperparts, bold black-and-white barring on flanks, and yellowish underparts (brightest on belly, vent and undertail-coverts). Black tail contrasts with greenish-yellow uppertail-coverts. **Female** is similar to male, but has duller greyish-green upperparts, less prominent grey-and-white barring on flanks, greyish throat and breast, and duller yellow vent and undertail-coverts. **Juvenile** lacks bright green in plumage and could be confused with other juvenile munias. Best distinguished by combination of red at base of blackish bill, olive-green cast to upperparts (especially rump and uppertail-coverts), greyish cast to head and breast, buff wash on flanks, yellow wash on undertail-coverts, and pink legs and feet. **VOICE** Song is similar to that of Red Avadavat (p.826), but louder, ending in a prolonged trill; calls include a weak, twittering *seee* or *swee swee*, as well as *cheep* and *chirp* (Clement *et al.* 1993). **HABITS** Little studied; presumably similar to those of other estrildine finches. Keeps in small flocks or family parties, and in the non-breeding season in flocks of up to 50 birds. Feeds on the ground, mainly on small seeds, also on small insects, usually close to cover; flies up into trees and low bushes if disturbed. **HABITAT** Grass and low bushes, tall grassland, sugarcane fields, and open forest with bushes; often near water. **BREEDING** Recorded in May and January. Breeds in small colonies. Nest is a large ball made of coarse grass, attached to sugarcane leaves. **DISTRIBUTION AND STATUS** Globally threatened. **IN:** endemic resident; widespread in C areas, occurring from S Rajasthan, C Uttar Pradesh and S Bihar south to N Kerala and N Andhra Pradesh (also Delhi, probably escaped cagebirds); scarce and very local. A small colony which formerly bred in Lahore, Pakistan, is believed to have originated from escaped cagebirds. **REFERENCES** Neelakantan *et al.* (1993).

INDIAN SILVERBILL *Lonchura malabarica* — Plate 147

Common Silverbill (I), White-throated Silverbill, White-throated Munia (F,P)

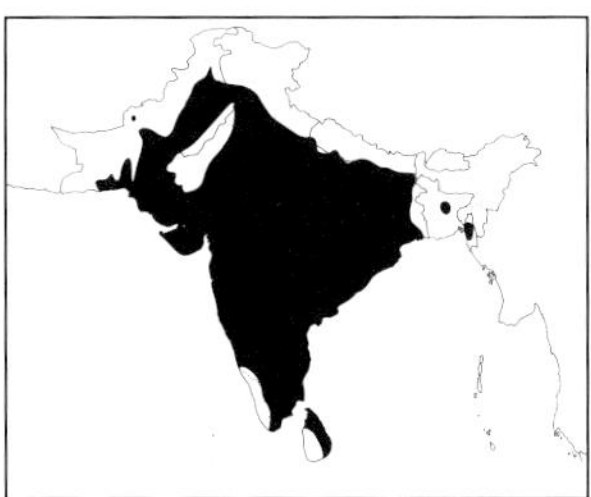

IDENTIFICATION 11–11.5 cm. **Adult** distinguished from other munias by combination of fawn-brown upperparts, whitish underparts, long black tail with elongated and pointed central rectrices, and white rump and uppertail-coverts. Also has narrow whitish supercilium, and flanks are finely barred with rufous-buff. Bill is blue-grey bill, and legs and feet vary from vinous to grey-brown. Female has a less prominent supercilium than male, and the flanks are less barred. **Juvenile** is similar, but is more buffish on underparts; has brown mottling on rump and uppertail-coverts, lacks barring on flanks, and the central rectrices are shorter and more rounded. **VOICE** Contact call is a *tchrip!* or *tchreep!*; flight call is a repeated *chir-rup!* (sounding like *zip!*); and song is a series of short, abrupt trills (Restall 1996). **HABITS** A typical estrildine finch. When not breeding, roosts communally in old nests, usually of weavers, or their own. May be found in flocks of up to 60 birds after the monsoon and in early winter; otherwise in small parties when not breeding. Often found around nesting colonies of Baya Weaver (p.825). **HABITAT** Prefers drier habitats than other estrildine finches: cultivation, dry grassland, open thorn scrub and scrub desert. **BREEDING** Throughout the year, varying locally. Builds a typical estrildine nest, usually 2–3 m up in a leafless thorn bush or small tree; often uses an old Baya Weaver nest. **DISTRIBUTION AND STATUS** Resident, subject to local movements. Throughout most of the subcontinent, except parts of the northwest, northeast and Himalayas. **PK:** widespread and locally common in plains; spreads into dry valleys and foothills up to 600 m in summer. **NP:** uncommon; below 305 m. **IN:** widespread and common; in plains and hills up to 600 m. **BD:** locally common in southeast and centre. **LK:** common in dry lowlands. **REFERENCES** Restall (1996).

WHITE-RUMPED MUNIA *Lonchura striata* — Plate 147

White-backed Munia (I,P), Striated Munia (N), Sharp-tailed Munia (F)

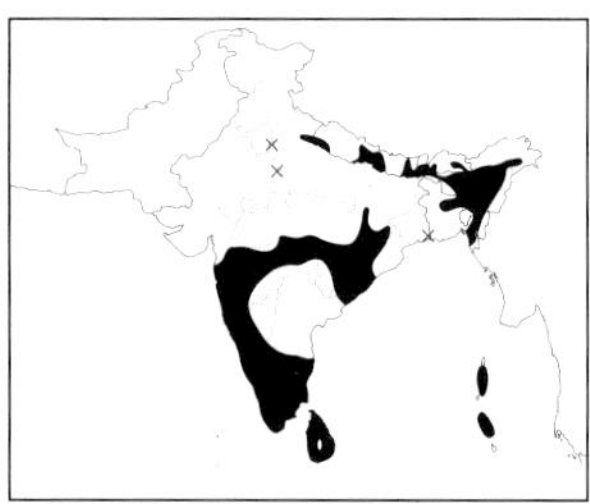

IDENTIFICATION 10–11 cm. The only munia in the subcontinent which has a dark breast and white rump. **Racial variation** *L. s. striata* of the peninsula and Sri Lanka has brown upperparts with pale shaft streaking, uniform blackish-brown ear-coverts and blackish throat and breast (lacking mottling on ear-coverts and pale fringes to breast), and unstreaked creamy-white or white belly; juvenile is less cleanly marked than adult, with streaking lacking or only very faint on upperparts, and has buff fringes to breast feathers. *L. s. acuticauda* of the Himalayan foothills and NE subcontinent has rufous-brown sides of face and neck, with pale shaft streaking/mottling on ear-coverts, and rufous-brown to whitish fringes on dark brown breast, along with greyish-buff to greyish-white flanks and belly with faint brownish streaking and mottling; juvenile has brown and buff barring on throat and breast. *L. s. fumigata* and *L. s. semistriata* of the Andaman and Nicobar Is, respectively, are similar to *L. s. striata*: the former differs in lacking streaking on the upperparts, and underparts are warm buff, while the latter has pale fringes to breast and also has pale buffish underparts; juvenile *fumigata* has whitish throat barred with brown, and rufous-buff fringes to brown breast. **VOICE** Song is a rising and falling series of twittering notes; calls include a twittering *tr-tr-tr, prrrit* and *brrt* (Clement *et al.* 1993). **HABITS** A typical estrildine finch. In the non-breeding season usually keeps in small parties, sometimes in quite large flocks; roosts communally at this season, often with Scaly-breasted Munias (p.829) and weavers, in sugarcane fields and thickets. **HABITAT** Open wooded areas and scrub near cultivation. **BREEDING** Almost all year, mainly during the monsoon. Nest is a small untidy ball made of coarse grass or bamboo leaves, placed 2–6 m up in a small tree. **DISTRIBUTION AND STATUS** Resident, subject to seasonal movements. Himalayan foothills from N Uttar Pradesh east to Arunachal Pradesh; NE India and Bangladesh; from S Gujarat east to S Bihar and C Orissa and south through the peninsula, but apparently absent from large areas; also occurs in Sri Lanka. **NP:** local resident below 1220 m; mainly a summer visitor at higher altitudes, up to 2135 m. **IN:** widespread and common; plains and hills, up to 1675 m in Himalayas (–1800 m), to 900 m in peninsular hills (–1800 m). **BT:** fairly common; 240–1770 m. **BD:** locally common in the northeast, southeast and centre. **LK:** common throughout, except highest hills. **REFERENCES** Restall (1996).

BLACK-THROATED MUNIA *Lonchura kelaarti* — Plate 147

Rufous-bellied Munia (I), Ceylon Hill Munia (P)

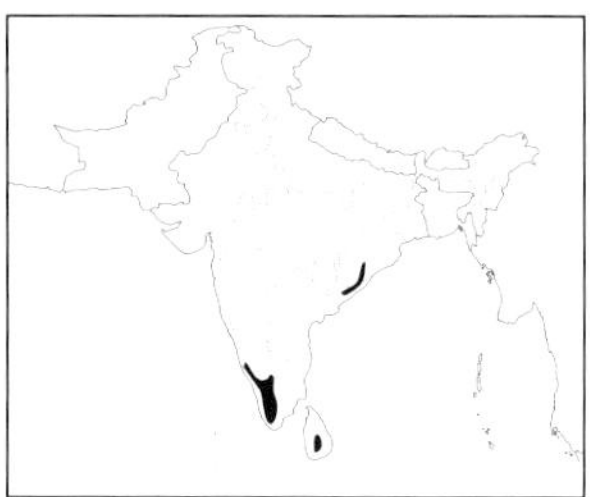

IDENTIFICATION 12 cm. **Adult** told from other munias by combination of blackish face, throat, and upper breast, pinkish-cinnamon sides of neck and rest of underparts, and dark brown upperparts with fine white shaft streaking. Shorter uppertail-coverts are brown, diffusely spotted with pinkish-buff, and longer uppertail-coverts are orangish, contrasting with blackish-brown tail. **Juvenile** lacks adult's black on head and breast, and has uniform brown upperparts (lacking pale shaft streaking and orangish uppertail-coverts); underparts are warm buffish-brown with diffuse buff streaking and mottling. **Racial variation** Adult *L. k. kelaarti* of Sri Lanka differs from *L. k. jerdoni*, described above, in having white underparts which are boldly spotted and barred with brownish-black; shorter uppertail-coverts are blackish, spotted with white, and longer uppertail-coverts are olive-yellow. Blackish throat and upper breast help separate it from Scaly-breasted Munia (p.829). Juvenile *kelaarti* has pale shaft streaking on ear-coverts, white throat with blackish barring, and diffuse brown and rufous-buff barring on underparts. **VOICE** Song is a barely audible series of five notes; calls include a high-pitched nasal *tay* and a *chirp* (Clement *et al.* 1993). **HABITS** Very like those of other estrildine finches, but travels about more than other species, often flying at considerable heights. Usually in pairs or family parties, and often with White-rumped Munias (above) and Scaly-breasted Munias. Sometimes uses its nest for roosting. **HABITAT** Usually at higher altitudes and in wetter habitats than White-rumped Munia: forest clearings, lantana scrub, tea estates, gardens, and grassland. **BREEDING** Almost all year, mainly February–September. In India the nest is like that of White-rumped Munia; in Sri Lanka it is often smaller, more compact, and made of green moss, ferns and fine grasses, built in a bush, small tree, or large hole in a tree trunk, or under the eaves of a thatched house. **DISTRIBUTION AND STATUS** Resident, subject to local movements. Endemic to SW India (from N Karnataka south through Kerala and W Tamil Nadu), Eastern Ghats (Andhra Pradesh and Orissa) and Sri Lanka. **IN:** locally fairly common; from foothills up to 2100 m, descends from higher levels in winter. **LK:** common in hills, more frequent at higher altitudes.

SCALY-BREASTED MUNIA *Lonchura punctulata* Plate 147

Nutmeg Mannikin (I), Spotted Munia (F,P)

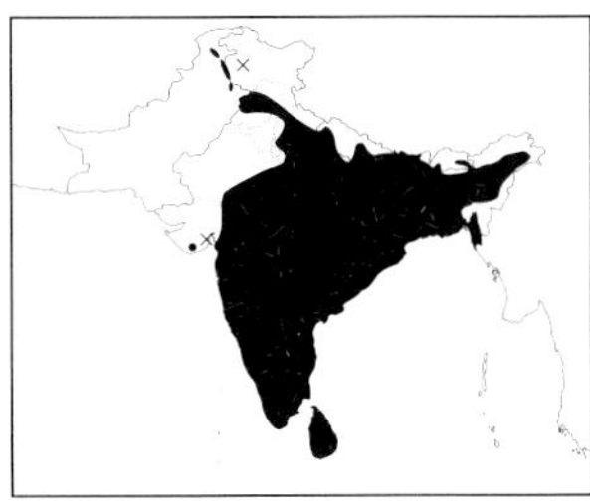

IDENTIFICATION 10.7–12 cm. **Adult** is distinctive, with chestnut-brown face, throat and upper breast, whitish underparts boldly scaled with black, olive-brown upperparts, and olive-yellow to rufous-orange on uppertail-coverts and edges of tail. **Juvenile** has uniform brown upperparts and buff to rufous-buff underparts, with whitish belly. Very similar to juvenile Black-headed (below), but is said to have black rather than grey bill. **Racial variation** *L. p. subundulata* of the NE subcontinent has brown rather than black scaling on lower breast and belly. **VOICE** Typical song is a series of *klik-klik-klik* or *tit-tit-tit* notes, followed by a short series of whistles and churs, and ending with a longer *weee*; contact calls include a repeated *tit-ti tit-ti* and a loud *kit-teee kit-teee*, and also utters a *sieuw sieuw* (Restall 1996). **HABITS** A typical estrildine finch. In the non-breeding season, associates in flocks and roosts communally in sugarcane fields and lantana thickets, sometimes with other munias and weavers. Feeds on small berries, as well as seeds. Often roosts in nests, either those previously used for breeding or nests built for that purpose. **HABITAT** Open secondary forest interspersed with grassland patches and bushes, bush-covered hillsides, and cultivation and gardens. **BREEDING** Throughout the year, mainly May–September. Builds a typical estrildine nest, large for the size of the bird, usually 2–5 m up and hidden in a bush, small tree, or creeper growing on a trellis. **DISTRIBUTION AND STATUS** Resident. Pakistan (Murree and Margalla hills) and most of the rest of the subcontinent east and south from Punjab, W Uttar Pradesh, E Rajasthan and E Gujarat. **PK:** very local and frequent; summers up to 1800 m. **NP:** fairly common and widespread resident; below 1525 m (–2680 m in summer). **IN:** common and widespread; plains and hills, up to 2400 m in Himalayas, to 1800 m in the northeast, to 2100 m in peninsular hills. **BT:** fairly common; 620–2285 m. **BD, LK:** common throughout. **REFERENCES** Restall (1996).

BLACK-HEADED MUNIA *Lonchura malacca* Plate 147

Chestnut Munia (N)

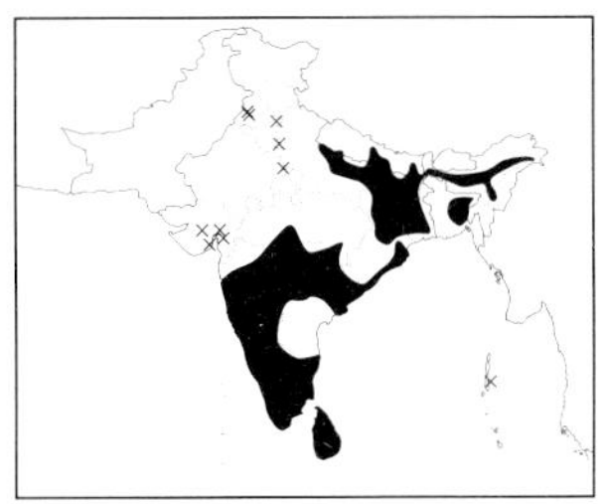

IDENTIFICATION 11.5 cm. **Adult** distinguished from other munias by combination of black head, neck and upper breast, rufous-brown upperparts, white or chestnut (depending on race) lower breast and flanks, and black centre of belly, vent and undertail-coverts. **Juvenile** has uniform brown upperparts and buff to whitish underparts; has blue-grey bill. **Racial variation** *L. m. malacca* of peninsular India and Sri Lanka typically has white lower breast and flanks (morphs with diffuse rufous or greyish scaling on white lower breast and flanks, and with cinnamon rather than white lower breast and flanks, have been recorded); juvenile of this race is possibly whiter on underparts than juvenile Scaly-breasted (above). *L. m. atricapilla* of lowland NE India and *L. m. rubroniger* of Himalayan foothills of India and Nepal both have chestnut lower breast and flanks, while lower belly and vent can be dark chestnut-brown rather than black; juveniles of these races are warmer buff on underparts than juvenile nominate. **VOICE** Song is a barely audible series of bill-snapping, followed by a faint but long drawn-out, descending *peeeeee* (*L. m. malacca*), or an extended *weee* ending with a series of slurred notes (*L. m. atricapilla*); calls include a weak *peekt*, a whistling *veet-veet*, and a triple *chirp* in flight (Restall 1996). **HABITS** A typical estrildine finch. When not breeding, associates in flocks of up to 100 or more, sometimes with Scaly-breasted Munias. **HABITAT** Cultivation, grass fields, marshes and tall grassland. **BREEDING** Almost any month, varying locally. Nests in small colonies, often with Streaked Weavers (p.825). Builds a typical estrildine nest, usually in reeds standing in water, in bushes or in sugarcane, within 2 m of the ground or water. **DISTRIBUTION AND STATUS** Resident. Mainly from C Uttar Pradesh east to NE India and Bangladesh; also E, C and S India (but absent from some areas), and Sri Lanka. **NP:** local and frequent; mainly below 1220 m (–1370 m). **IN:** widespread and locally common; from plains and hills up to 2100 m in the peninsula. **BD:** local in the northeast, east-centre and centre. **LK:** common throughout, more frequent in E hills.

JAVA SPARROW *Lonchura oryzivora* Plate 147

Padda oryzivora

IDENTIFICATION 12.5–13 cm. **Adult** is very striking, with pinkish-red bill and eye-ring, black crown and throat contrasting with white cheeks, grey upperparts and breast, pink belly and flanks, and black rump/uppertail-coverts and tail. **Juvenile** is much duller, with dark grey crown and dusky white cheeks, pink base to grey bill, brownish-grey upperparts with rufous fringes to tertials and secondaries, and buffish underparts with diffuse greyish breast. **VOICE** Song is a mixture of *dik, tchuk* and *wee* notes that are uttered at first slowly and then in a continuous rattling or jangling, and usually ending in a drawn-out *weeee*; calls include a liquid *tup* or *ch,luk* and a sharp *tack* (Restall 1996). **HABITS** Similar to those of other estrildine finches. Gregarious; often found in flocks, feeding in paddy-fields. When available, cultivated rice is its main food; also eats other small seeds, fruits and

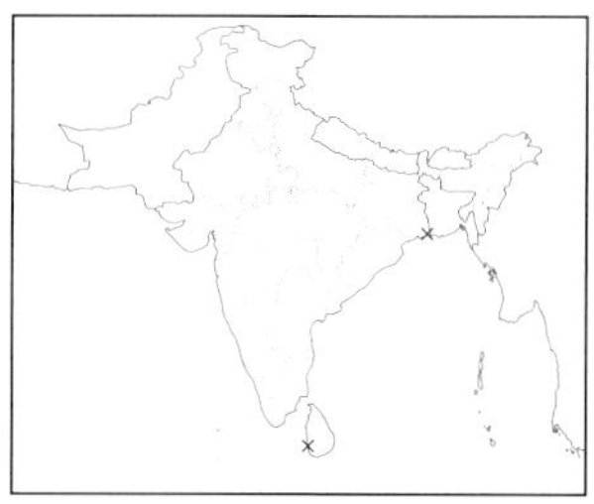

insects. **HABITAT** Cultivation, gardens and reedbeds. **BREEDING** Around Colombo, Sri Lanka. Not described from the region; in Java nest is more or less rounded, or a half-ball-shaped structure, made of grass stems, built under eaves of houses. **DISTRIBUTION AND STATUS** Introduced resident in India and Sri Lanka. **IN:** a colony formerly occurred around Calcutta, West Bengal, and formerly reported also near Madras, Tamil Nadu. **LK:** breeds occasionally in and around Colombo.

FINCHES Fringillidae, subfamily Fringillinae

Small to medium-sized passerines with a strong, conical bill used for shelling seeds, their main diet. In the cardueline finches (i.e. finches other than Chaffinch and Brambling), the bill is also used for extracting seeds from plant seed heads. Many species differ in the types of seed they prefer, and these differences are related to the size and shape of their bill. Chaffinch and Brambling forage for seeds mainly on the ground, in a quick walk interspersed with hops. The gait of cardueline finches is typically a hop, or sometimes a shuffling walk; they forage by picking seeds from the ground, by clinging to the stalks and seed heads of tall herbs, or by taking seeds, buds, nectar, blossoms or berries in bushes or trees. The young are fed on seeds or a mixture of seeds and invertebrates. Most finches are highly gregarious outside the breeding season, and some cardueline species gather in flocks even when breeding, especially for feeding or drinking. The flight of finches is fast and undulating. Their nest is typically an open compact cup, usually hidden in a tree or bush. The main reference specific to finches is Clement *et al.* (1993); measurements have been taken from this reference, as have calls, unless otherwise stated.

CHAFFINCH *Fringilla coelebs* — Plate 147

Common Chaffinch

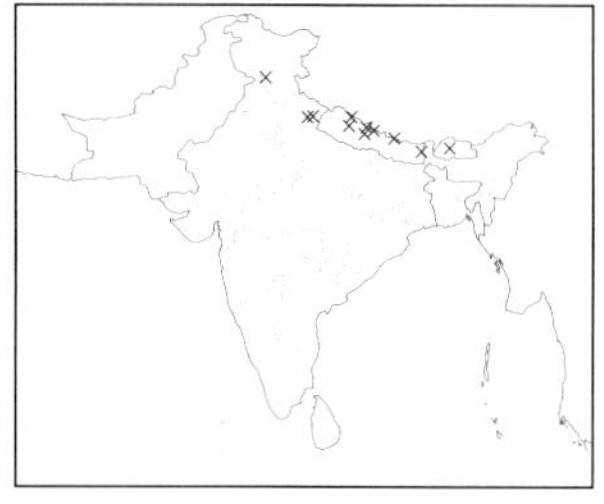

IDENTIFICATION 16 cm. **Male non-breeding** distinguished from Brambling (below) by blue-grey crown and nape, orange-pink face and underparts, maroon-brown mantle, and absence of white rump. Plumage becomes brighter towards breeding season as brown-buff feather fringes are lost with wear. **Female** is considerably duller than female Brambling, with greyish-brown mantle and scapulars, dull greyish-buff underparts, yellowish-white (rather than orange) greater-covert wing-bar, and greenish (rather than white) rump. **VOICE** Typical call is a metallic *chink*, and flight call is a quiet *chap*; song is a descending chattering rattle with a cheerful final flourish. **HABITS** Found singly or in small flocks, often with other finches or buntings. Seeks seeds on the ground, often from freshly turned soil, feeding with a rapid pecking action. Hops and walks with distinctive short, quick steps accompanied by slightly nodding head movements. Flight is bounding and undulating. **HABITAT** Upland fields bordered by bushes or coniferous forest, and orchards. **DISTRIBUTION AND STATUS** Winter visitor. Mainly N and W Pakistan and N Nepal. **PK:** irregular, common in some years in Baluchistan; also occurs in small numbers in the Salt Range, around Kohat and in Gilgit. **NP:** uncommon from WC areas westwards; 2000–2750 m (1555–3050 m). **IN, BT:** vagrant. **REFERENCES** Madge (1985).

BRAMBLING *Fringilla montifringilla* — Plate 147

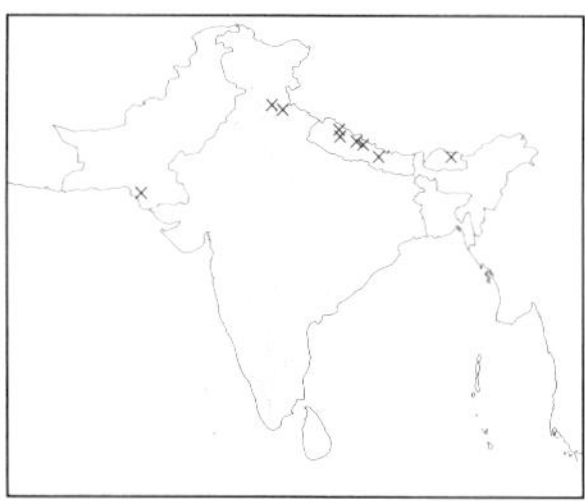

IDENTIFICATION 16 cm. **Male non-breeding** and **female** told from Chaffinch (above) by orange scapulars, pale orange breast and flanks (contrasting with white belly), orange greater-covert wing-bar, and white rump. Non-breeding male has pale yellow bill with black tip. Non-breeding female has less orange on scapulars, duller orange breast and flanks, and duller bill. Head and mantle of male become progressively blacker towards breeding season as rufous feather fringes are lost with wear, and bill becomes black. **VOICE** Call is a Chaffinch-like *chup*, usually accompanied by a distinctive deep nasal *zweee*; song is a drawn-out *wheeze*, but in spring can utter a wide variety of other song and call notes. **HABITS** Similar to those of Chaffinch. Gleans seeds on the ground, often in small flocks mixed with Chaffinches and buntings. Flies up into nearby bushes and trees if disturbed. Its flight has more pronounced undulations than that of Chaffinch. **HABITAT** Fields bordered by bushes and coniferous forest, orchards. **DISTRIBUTION AND STATUS** Winter visitor and passage migrant. Mountains of W Pakistan, and Himalayas from N Pakistan east to EC Nepal. **PK:** locally common in winter in Baluchistan, and on spring passage in NW Pakistan and Chitral. **NP:** erratic winter visitor, mainly in the north and northwest; 2135–3050 m (down to 1500 m). **IN:** status uncertain, and no recent published records. **BT:** vagrant.

FIRE-FRONTED SERIN *Serinus pusillus* Plate 148

Gold-fronted Finch (F,I), Red-fronted Serin (R)

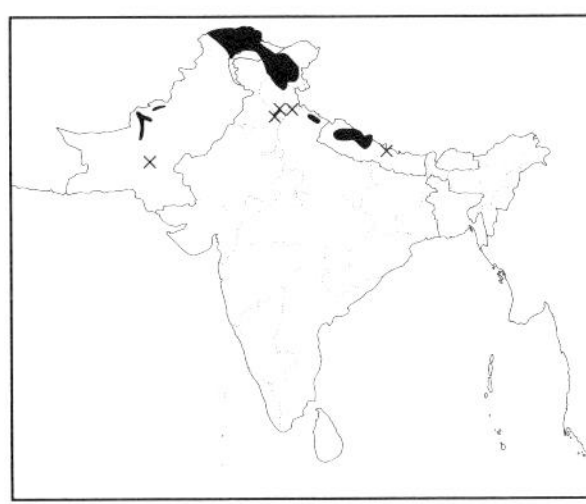

IDENTIFICATION 12.5 cm. **Male** is very distinctive, with scarlet forehead and largely black head and breast. Mantle and belly/flanks are boldly streaked with black, and washed with olive-yellow. Has double buffish-orange wing-bars and olive-yellow rump/uppertail-coverts. **Female** is generally duller, with less red on forehead, and black of head and breast is browner (although some are as striking as male). In fresh plumage (autumn/winter), black of head on both sexes is partly obscured by buff fringes and forehead is duller. **Juvenile** has cinnamon-brown crown, ear-coverts and throat, with crown lightly streaked; has buffish tips to median and greater coverts which show as broad double wing-bars, and (as adult) has yellowish edges to remiges and rectrices. **VOICE** Song is a melodious, rippling trill interspersed with twittering; call is a rapid, ringing *trillit-drillt* and a soft *dueet* (Clement *et al.* 1993). **HABITS** Gregarious throughout the year, forming large flocks in winter. Flocks keep up a continual twittering when feeding and in flight. Eats seeds and berries. A lively and restless forager. Frequently feeds on the ground; also jumps up to pick seeds from low herbs and grasses, or clings to stalks to peck at seed heads. Has a bouncing, undulating flight. **HABITAT** Dry habitats: summers near the treeline in dwarf juniper and birch scrub, dwarf bushes on rocky hillsides and in Tibetan steppe habitat; winters on open slopes and stony ground with bushes and stubbles of upland terraced cultivation. **BREEDING** June–August. Builds nest of grass, bark strips and rootlets, covered on the outside with spiders' webs, usually 1–6 m up in a small bush. **DISTRIBUTION AND STATUS** Resident, subject to altitudinal movements. Mountains of Baluchistan, Pakistan, and Himalayas from N Pakistan east to NC Nepal. **PK:** common in NE Baluchistan, N Dir, Chitral, Swat, Gilgit and Baltistan; summers 2000–4700 m, winters down to 1370 m. **NP:** fairly common, mainly from WC areas westwards; summers 2440–4575 m, occasionally winters down to 2100 m. **IN:** fairly common; breeds 2400–4300 m, winters mainly 750–3300 m.

YELLOW-BREASTED GREENFINCH *Carduelis spinoides* Plate 148

Himalayan Greenfinch (I), Himalayan Goldfinch (F)

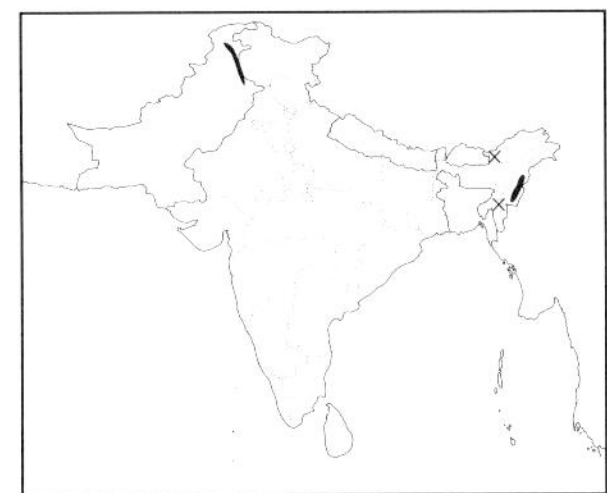

IDENTIFICATION 14 cm. **Male** is distinctive, with blackish-olive crown, ear-coverts and malar stripe, yellow supercilium and crescent behind ear-coverts, blackish-olive mantle, yellow underparts and rump, yellow tips to wing-coverts and at base of primaries forming broad panels across wing, and yellow sides to base of tail. **Adult female** is similarly patterned, but has paler olive upperparts with faint dark streaking, less distinct head pattern, and duller yellow underparts. **Juvenile** has wings and tail similar in pattern to adult female's, but has heavy streaking on buffish-olive upperparts and buffish-yellow underparts; shows faint yellowish supercilium and sub-moustachial stripe (with head pattern shadowing that of adult female). This plumage is retained until first summer. For differences from Black-headed Greenfinch (below), see that species. **Racial variation** *C. s. heinrichi*, which occurs in Nagaland and Manipur, lacks yellow submoustachial stripe and crescent below eye of the nominate race, described above. **VOICE** Call is a light twittering, followed by a harsh *tsswee*; song is an extended and more varied version of the call, often given in display flight. **HABITS** A typical cardueline finch. Gregarious throughout the year; frequently found in small parties, and in winter gathers in large flocks, sometimes of over 100 birds. Favours downy seed heads of herbs, and also forages for berries and insects in bushes and trees; if disturbed, the flock flies up into nearby trees. Undulating flight is accompanied by soft twittering notes. **HABITAT** Open forest and forest edges, shrubberies above the treeline, cultivation with nearby trees, open slopes, and gardens in hill villages. **BREEDING** June–October. Builds nest of grass and rootlets, well concealed 2–20 m up near the end of a horizontal branch. **DISTRIBUTION AND STATUS** Resident, subject to altitudinal movements. Himalayas from N Pakistan east to W Arunachal Pradesh; NE India. **PK:** locally frequent and locally nomadic; summers 1500–3300 m, winters 300–1800 m. **NP:** common and widespread; summers chiefly 2440–3700 m (–4400 m), winters 915–1850 m (down to 75 m). **IN:** in W Himalayas, breeds 1800–3300 m (from 1100 m?), locally common in Kashmir; local and frequent in Sikkim, breeds 2100–3800 m, winters mainly below 1500 m, locally to 2700 m; in the northeast, summers 2300–2400 m, winters down to 1400 m at least. **BT:** common; 610–4000 m.

BLACK-HEADED GREENFINCH *Carduelis ambigua* Plate 148

***C. spinoides* (I)**

IDENTIFICATION 12.5–14 cm. Like Yellow-breasted (above), has yellow at base of primaries and secondaries forming broad panel across wing, and yellow sides to base of tail. **Male** distinguished from that species by dull black head, dull greenish nape and mantle, greenish rump and grey uppertail-coverts, and greyish-white (rather than yellow) greater-covert wing-bar. Underparts are greyish, variably marked with greenish-yellow (especially

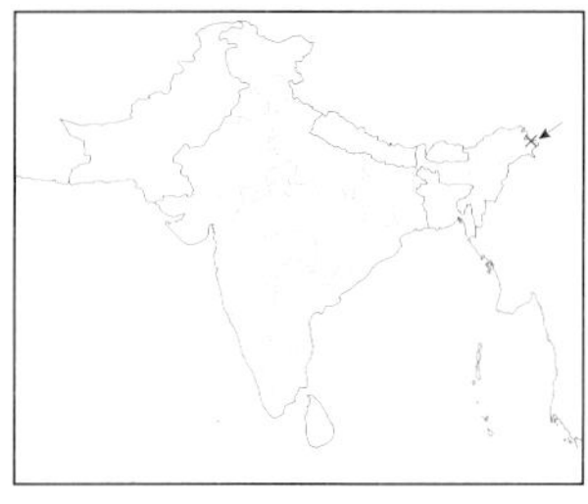

on throat and centre of breast). **Female** has brownish-grey crown and mantle, with diffuse dark streaking, and grey ear-coverts; underparts lack greenish-yellow of male, and also lacks greenish rump. **Juvenile** is similar to juvenile Yellow-breasted, but has broader yellow band across base of primaries and secondaries, colder grey-brown coloration to streaked upperparts, and heavier black streaking on whitish underparts (lacking strong yellow wash to underparts of juvenile Yellow-breasted); also lacks suggestion of yellowish supercilium and submoustachial stripe shown by that species. **VOICE** Song is a long wheeze, *wheeeeeu, wheeeeee* or *jjjjjj*, usually repeated at intervals amid call notes; typical call is a jumbled, jingling sound, *titutitu, titu-titu..titu-tittrititititit* etc, mixed with harder *chututut* or *jututut*, quiet, rising, buzzy *jieuu* and soft *chu-chu* etc (C. Robson). **HABITS** Very like those of Yellow-breasted Greenfinch. **HABITAT** Cultivation and nearby forest edges, pastures. **BREEDING** Unknown in the region. Similar to that of Yellow-breasted Greenfinch. **DISTRIBUTION AND STATUS IN:** possibly resident in NE Arunachal Pradesh; very locally fairly common; 1300 m, 2800–3110 m, subject to altitudinal movements. **REFERENCES** Singh (1995).

EURASIAN SISKIN *Carduelis spinus* — Plate 148

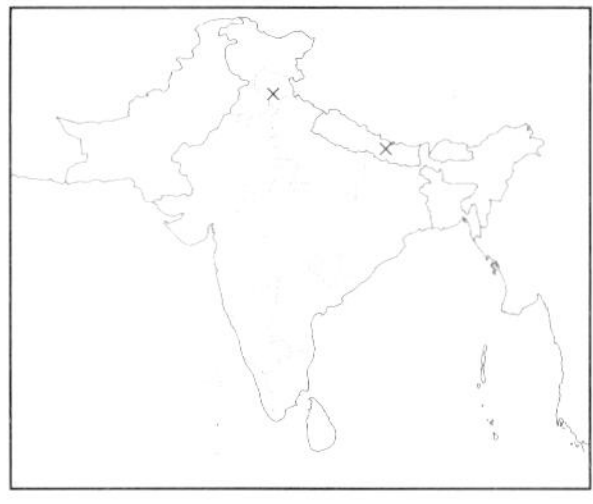

IDENTIFICATION 11–12 cm. Most likely to be confused with female Tibetan Siskin (below). **Male** is readily distinguished from that species by black crown and chin, and black-and-yellow patterning on wing. Has greenish-yellow median- and greater-covert wing-bars, with black band across greater coverts, and yellow patches at base of secondaries which are offset by black band across middle of wing. **First-winter male** resembles adult, but is more heavily streaked on mantle. **Female** lacks male's black on head, and is more heavily streaked on upperparts and underparts. Easily confused with female Tibetan Siskin and best separated by wing pattern, with yellow or yellowish-white patches at bases of secondaries and primaries (which can be obscured on closed wing, but show as prominent yellow wing patches in flight); rump and uppertail-coverts are a brighter yellow, contrasting more with back, and yellow at sides of tail-base is more pronounced; bill is marginally longer and slimmer. First-winter female has buff background coloration to head and mantle. **VOICE** Call is a *tet-tet* and distinctive, wheezy *toolee*, and in flight also a trilling *tirrillilit*; song is a mixture of trills, twitters and wheezy notes (Clement *et al.* 1993). **HABITS** Not described from the region, but well studied in Europe. Gregarious, and often associates with other small finches. Forages mainly in trees, moving restlessly about branches, and hanging upside-down tit-like from cones and seed heads while extracting seeds; also feeds on seed heads of herbs. Flight is light, rapid and undulating. **HABITAT** Usually inhabits conifers, alders and birches. **DISTRIBUTION AND STATUS NP, IN:** vagrant. **REFERENCES** Cramp and Perrins (1994), Gaston and Chattopadhyay (1981).

TIBETAN SISKIN *Carduelis thibetana* — Plate 148

Tibetan Serin, *Serinus thibetanus*

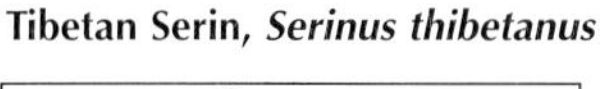

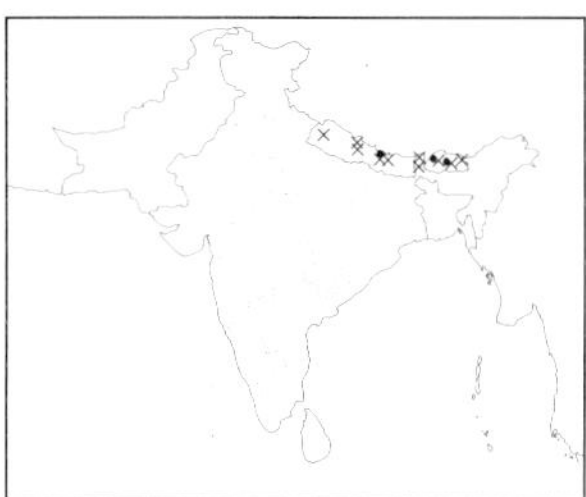

IDENTIFICATION 12 cm. In all plumages, lacks yellow patches on wing shown by Yellow-breasted and Black-headed Greenfinches (p.831). For differences from the vagrant Eurasian Siskin (above), see that species. **Adult male** is distinctive, with olive-green crown, ear-coverts and mantle, yellow supercilium and border behind ear-coverts, yellowish-green rump, and yellow underparts. Wing and tail feathers are broadly edged with yellowish-green. **First-winter male** shows slight streaking on mantle and flanks. **Adult female** superficially resembles male, but has blackish streaking on darker, greyish-green upperparts, more clearly defined yellowish-green wing-bars, paler yellow throat and breast, and whitish lower breast and belly (with black streaking on breast and flanks). **Juvenile** as adult female, but is generally duller green or tinged brownish-buff on upperparts, and has duller rump, buff fringes and tips to greater coverts, and paler (more heavily streaked) underparts. **VOICE** Call is a soft dry chattering, interspersed with an occasional wheezy *twang* (R. Grimmett); song is a nasal buzzing *zeezle-eezle-eeze*, interspersed with trills (Clement *et al.* 1993). Flocks indulge in high-pitched twittering and wheezing commotions, particularly in flight; heard at close range, these wheezy chitterings are interspersed with varied nasal *sweeo* and *cheek* notes and high-pitched nasal *ti-ti-tweeoo* song phrases (S. Madge). **HABITS** In winter keeps in flocks, sometimes of several hundred; found in pairs in the breeding season. Feeds mainly in the treetops, often in alders or birches, occasionally on the ground. **HABITAT** Summers in hemlock, birch and mixed fir–birch forest; winters chiefly in alders. **BREEDING** Unknown in the region. Little known elsewhere; in pairs May and June. **DISTRIBUTION AND STATUS** Possibly breeds in Nepal and Bhutan; winters in Himalayas from Nepal east to Bhutan. **NP:** local, regularly recorded in the Kathmandu valley, uncommon elsewhere; 1050–3500 m. **IN:** rare; 1000–3050 m. **BT:** frequent; possibly breeds 1500–3530 m. **REFERENCES** Inskipp and Inskipp (1980).

EUROPEAN GOLDFINCH *Carduelis carduelis* **Plate 148**

Goldfinch (I), Eurasian Goldfinch (F,N,R)

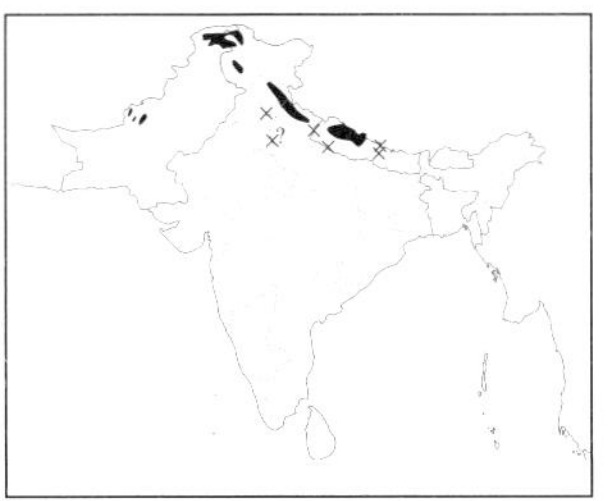

IDENTIFICATION 13–15.5 cm. **Adult** is distinctive, with red face, grey-brown crown, nape and mantle, black wings with yellow panel and with white on tertials, white rump, and grey-brown breast and flanks. **Juvenile** lacks red face of adult; grey-brown upperparts have faint streaking, as does breast; wings are similar to adult's, but has buffish tips to coverts and tertial markings. **Racial variation** *C. c. major* has been recorded as a vagrant to subcontinent: this has white sides to face and throat (bordering red), black crown and sides of head, ginger-brown nape and mantle, and ginger breast and flanks. **VOICE** Flight call is a liquid twitter, *tswitt-witt-witt*; song is varied mix of twittering, interspersed with repeated *tew-tew-tew* and *tuwee-it* phrases (Roberts 1992). **HABITS** May be found in small parties all year, and often in larger flocks in winter, but rarely with other finches. Feeds chiefly on herb seeds; perches acrobatically on seed heads, and hangs upside-down on the taller plants. Flight is light and bouncing and accompanied by continual twittering. **HABITAT** Upland cultivation and orchards, shrubberies above the treeline, and open coniferous forest. **BREEDING** April–August, varying with altitude. Builds nest of wool, moss and grass, usually well hidden 2–9 m up near the end of a branch. **DISTRIBUTION AND STATUS** Resident, subject to altitudinal movements. Hills of N and W Pakistan, and Himalayas from N Pakistan east to NC Nepal; winters in Pakistan and in adjacent Indian plains. **PK:** locally common resident and common winter visitor, but erratic and nomadic in occurrence, depending on food supply; occurs mainly in inner drier mountains; summers 1800–3600 m (down to 1500 m), winters in foothills and adjacent plains. **NP:** uncommon resident; summers mainly 2450–4250 m and winters 1920–2440 m (down to 75 m). **IN:** common; breeds 2400–3900 m (from 1500 m), descends in winter, occasionally to the plains.

TWITE *Carduelis flavirostris* **Plate 148**

Tibetan Twite, *Acanthis flavirostris* (E,F)

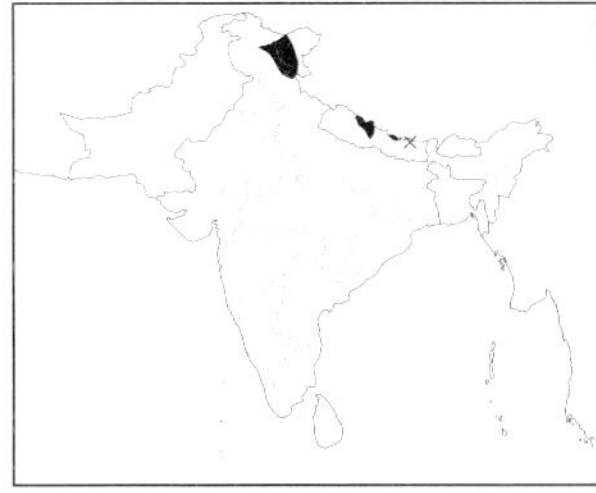

IDENTIFICATION 13–13.5 cm. A small finch with streaked upperparts, buff supercilium, cheeks and throat, white panel on wing (formed by white edges to primaries), and white edges to tail feathers. Bill is yellowish. In fresh plumage (autumn and winter), has broad buff or whitish median- and greater-covert wing-bars. **Male** has pink rump, which is partly obscured in fresh plumage. For differences from Eurasian Linnet (below), see that species. **Racial variation** Two races occur in the subcontinent. *C. f. montanella* from the westernmost Himalayas is sandy-buff in coloration, and is only lightly streaked on breast and flanks. *C. f. rufostrigata,* which occurs from Ladakh eastwards, is much darker: upperparts, breast and flanks are heavily streaked, and throat, breast and flanks are rich buff. **VOICE** Call is a weak nasal twittering interspersed with distinctive wheezy *tweee* notes, while *C. f. rufostrigata* has a distinctive *ditoo, didoowit* and twanging *twayee*; song is an extended and more varied repetition of the call, interspersed with quiet trills (Clement *et al.* 1993). **HABITS** Gregarious in the non-breeding season, often in large compact flocks and with Horned Lark (p.7970), Fire-fronted Serin (p.831) or Brandt's Mountain Finch (p.834). Usually keeps in pairs when breeding. Feeds chiefly on small seeds picked from the ground; also feeds on the seed heads of herbs and eats some insects in summer. Flight is light, rapid and undulating, with some erratic movements, and accompanied by an excited twittering chorus. **HABITAT** Dry country: Tibetan plateau semi-desert and stony slopes with *Caragana* scrub. **BREEDING** May–August. Builds nest of dry grass, low down in dwarf bushes. **DISTRIBUTION AND STATUS** Resident, subject to altitudinal movements. N Himalayas from N Pakistan east to Himachal Pradesh and N Nepal. **PK:** locally frequent in restricted habitat in N Chitral, N Gilgit and Baltistan, 3000–4200 m; winters in adjacent valleys, sometimes down to 1450 m. **NP:** probably resident, fairly common in Dolpo and Mustang in the northwest, uncommon farther east; 3965–4575 m. **IN:** locally common; summers mainly 3600–5000 m, winters down to 3000 m. **REFERENCES** Pfister (1997).

EURASIAN LINNET *Carduelis cannabina* **Plate 148**

Linnet (F,I), Common Linnet (F,N), Brown Linnet (R), *Acanthis cannabina* (F)

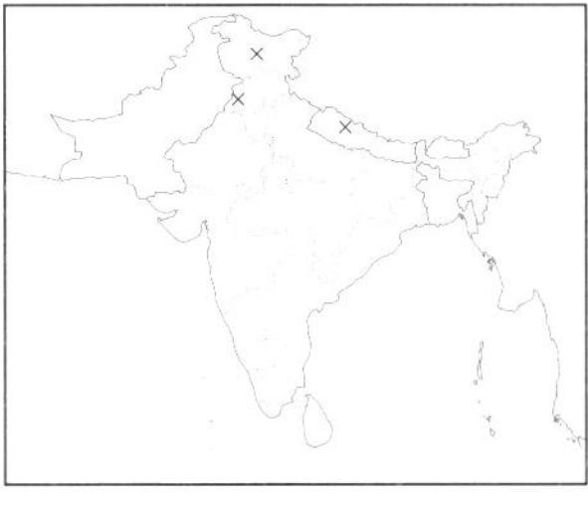

IDENTIFICATION 13–14 cm. Similar to Twite (above), with white edges to primaries and white at sides of tail. Distinguished from that species by greyish crown, ear-coverts and nape contrasting with browner mantle, absence of warm buff on face and throat (latter usually with broad greyish streaking), whitish lower rump and uppertail-coverts (streaked with black), and larger greyish bill. **Male** has chestnut-brown mantle and wing-coverts, with variable dark streaking on mantle. In breeding plumage, crown, nape and ear-coverts are purer grey and has crimson on forehead and breast. **Female** and **first-winter** have duller brown mantle, with dark brown streaking, and dark streaking on breast and flanks. **VOICE** is a rapid *chi-chi-chi-chi,* but does not give wheezy *twee* notes of Twite; song is a variable musical twittering and trilling.

HABITS Found in flocks, often with other finches and buntings. Feeds chiefly on the ground, but perches readily in bushes. Flight is similar to that of Twite, undulating and fast, and accompanied by frequent twitters, but is less erratic than that species'. **HABITAT** Open stony slopes, upland meadows and fallow fields. **DISTRIBUTION AND STATUS** Winter visitor, mainly to Pakistan. **PK:** erratic winter visitor to N and W hills and Himalayas; common in some years. **NP, IN:** vagrant. **REFERENCES** Robson (1996a).

PLAIN MOUNTAIN FINCH *Leucosticte nemoricola* Plate 148

Hodgson's Mountain Finch (F,I)

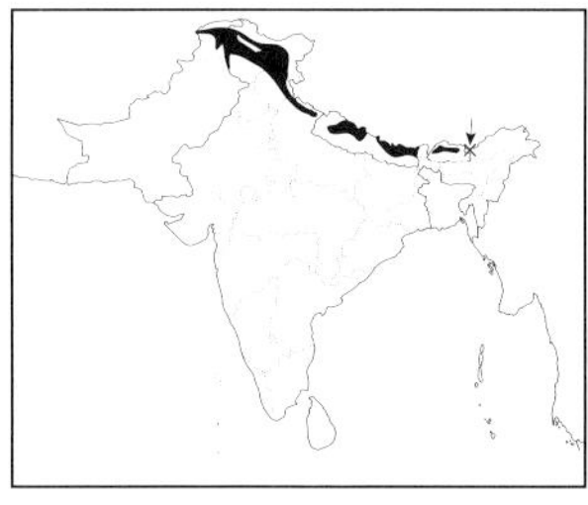

IDENTIFICATION 15 cm. **Adult** distinguished from Brandt's Mountain Finch (below) by pale supercilium (indistinct on some), boldly streaked crown and mantle, with pale 'braces', and distinct patterning to coverts. Crown can be unstreaked or only lightly streaked on some birds. Median coverts are dark-centred, with bold white fringes, and greater coverts are tipped with white (forming well-defined wing-bar) and show dark central panel. Unstreaked grey rump contrasts with browner, streaked mantle/back, and has prominent white tips to uppertail-coverts. Tertials and inner secondaries are edged with white, forming narrow panel on closed wing, but this is less prominent than on Brandt's. **Juvenile** is a warmer rufous-buff on crown, ear-coverts, mantle and underparts than adult; crown and nape are only lightly streaked, buffish supercilium is indistinct or absent, and mantle is less heavily streaked and lacks 'braces'; has rufous-buff fringes to tertials and tips to coverts. **First-winter** as adult, but with rufous on crown and ear-coverts. **VOICE** is a soft twittering *chi-chi-chi-chi*; song is a sharp twitter, *rick-pi-vitt* or *dui-dip-dip-dip* (Clement *et al.* 1993). **HABITS** In the non-breeding season keeps in large compact flocks, often numbering over 200 birds; found in smaller flocks when breeding. Often takes flight, the flocks circling, twisting and turning in unison, all the while twittering loudly. Forages by hopping and running on open ground, keeping a horizontal posture. Feeds chiefly on small seeds, also some invertebrates. Perches readily on trees, bushes, rocks and stone walls. **HABITAT** Summers above the treeline on alpine meadows, screes, moraines, and grassy and stony slopes, favouring edges of melting snow; winters in forest clearings and upland terraced cultivation. **BREEDING** July and August. Nest is a shallow cup made of grass, well sheltered in a deep crevice or marmot burrow, or under a rock. **DISTRIBUTION AND STATUS** Resident, subject to altitudinal movements. N Himalayas from Pakistan east to W Arunachal Pradesh. Breeds above the treeline and generally at lower altitudes than Brandt's Mountain Finch. **PK:** locally common; breeds 3000–4275 m, winters down to 1500 m. **NP:** common and widespread; summers chiefly 4200–5200 m, winters from 2000 m up to at least 3650 m. **IN:** common; breeds above 3300 m in Kashmir, up to 5000 m in Ladakh and Spiti, and 4200–5300 m in the east; winters down to 1000 m, but some birds remain at high altitudes. **BT:** common. **REFERENCES** Pfister (1997).

BRANDT'S MOUNTAIN FINCH *Leucosticte brandti* Plate 148

Black-headed Mountain Finch (F,I)

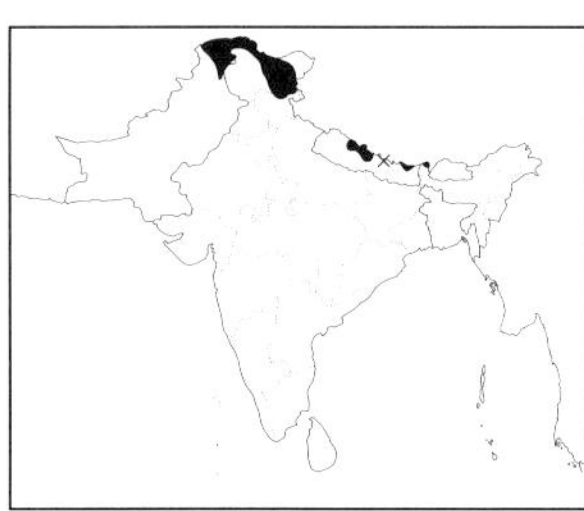

IDENTIFICATION 16.5–19 cm. Told from Plain Mountain Finch (above) in all plumages by lack of supercilium, unstreaked to lightly streaked mantle (lacking pale 'braces'), and rather pale and comparatively uniform greyish wing-coverts (lacking dark centres and white tips to median coverts and well-defined greater-covert bar). Has broad white edges to primary coverts and to tertials/secondaries, which form more striking white panel on wing compared with Plain, and has more prominent white edges to outer rectrices. **Adult breeding** has sooty-black head and nape, and brownish-grey mantle with poorly defined streaking. Male has pink on rump, but this is indistinct on female. **Adult non-breeding** is similar, but head is not so dark (although forehead, lores and ear-coverts are brownish-black and darker than rest of head). **Juvenile** and **first-summer** have brownish-buff to greyish-buff head and mantle, latter with indistinct streaking, and tertials and wing-coverts have warm buff edgings. **Racial variation** Three races are recorded from the subcontinent, although *L. b. haematopygia*, described above, is by far the most widely distributed. The vagrant *L. b. brandti* is noticeably paler, with paler sandy-grey back and purer grey uppertail-coverts, broader white tips and edges to remiges and rectrices, paler coverts with pink fringes to lesser coverts, and paler grey and more uniform tertials (which show as more striking pale area on wing); only forecrown and lores are black in breeding plumage. *L. b. pamirensis*, a winter visitor to NW subcontinent, is intermediate in appearance. **VOICE** Call is a loud *twitt-twitt*, *twee-ti-ti* or *peek-peek* and a harsh *churr*; song is undescribed. **HABITS** Very similar to those of Plain Mountain Finch. Tame and confiding. Readily perches on rocks, stone walls and bushes. Feeds on small seeds. **HABITAT** Alpine meadows and open stony slopes, screes and moraines; favours the edges of melting snow. **BREEDING** June–August. Nest is a rough cup made of grass, well sheltered in a deep crevice under a boulder, in a rodent burrow or in a pile of stones. **DISTRIBUTION AND STATUS** Resident, subject to altitudinal movements. N Himalayas from Pakistan east to Himachal Pradesh, Nepal and Sikkim. **PK:** scarce and local; summers 3660–4800 m, straggles down to 1500 m in winter. **NP:** fairly common; summers mainly 4200–5250 m (–6000 m), usually winters above 3500 m (down to 2350 m). **IN:** common; breeds mainly 3900–5400 m; winters down to 3000 m in the west, to 3600 m in Sikkim.

SPECTACLED FINCH *Callacanthis burtoni* Plate 149

Red-browed Finch (F,I,R)

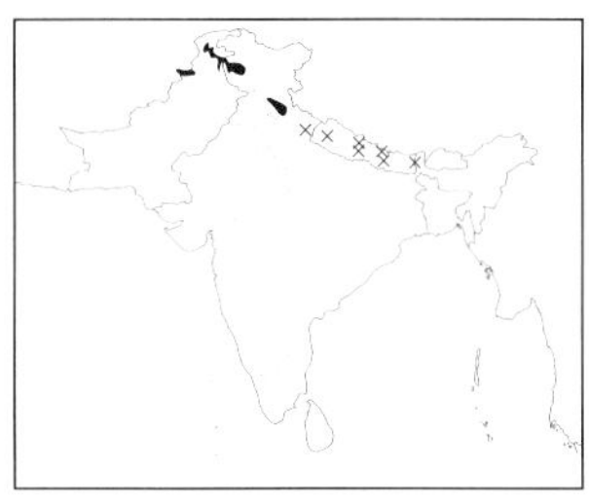

IDENTIFICATION 17–18 cm. A large, stocky finch with dark head and with red or yellow forehead and mask through eye. Wings are black, with bold whitish tips to greater coverts, tertials, secondaries and primaries, and has white tip to black tail. **Male** has pinkish-red 'spectacles', maroon-brown mantle, and pinkish-red wash to underparts. 'Spots' on wing-coverts are pinkish-white. **Female** has paler head with orange-yellow 'spectacles', olive-brown mantle, and buffish-brown underparts with yellowish wash to breast; white tips to wing feathers are less prominent than on male. **Juvenile** is similar to female, but lacks prominent 'spectacles' (head is browner, with buff or rufous-buff eye-patch), and has buffish 'spots' on wings. Underparts on juvenile male are warm cinnamon-brown. **VOICE** A loud, clear *pwee*, and a softer *tew-tew* when foraging; song is long sequence of mainly downward-inflected whistles, *teee-uh-tee-e-uh-te-ee-uh tee-yih te-te-eih twa teee-yih* (Roberts 1992). **HABITS** Usually found in pairs or small parties, according to the season. Very confiding. Feeds unobtrusively, mainly on the ground but also in low bushes, chiefly on seeds; flies up into nearby bushes or trees if disturbed. **HABITAT** Open forest of fir, oak, hemlock and rhododendron; mixed deciduous and coniferous forest. **BREEDING** May–July. Builds a large nest of moss, lichen, grass and ferns, 3–21 m up in a conifer. **DISTRIBUTION AND STATUS** Endemic to the subcontinent. Resident and winter visitor, subject to altitudinal movements. Himalayas from N Pakistan east to Sikkim. **PK:** local and generally scarce resident, but locally fairly common; has small altitudinal movements, summers from 2740 m up to the treeline. **NP:** chiefly a local and erratic winter visitor; one summer record. **IN:** locally frequent in Kashmir; breeds from 2400 m to the treeline, winters 1800–3000 m (down to 800 m).

CRIMSON-WINGED FINCH *Rhodopechys sanguinea* Plate 149

Crimson-winged Desert Finch (I), *Callacanthis sanguinea*

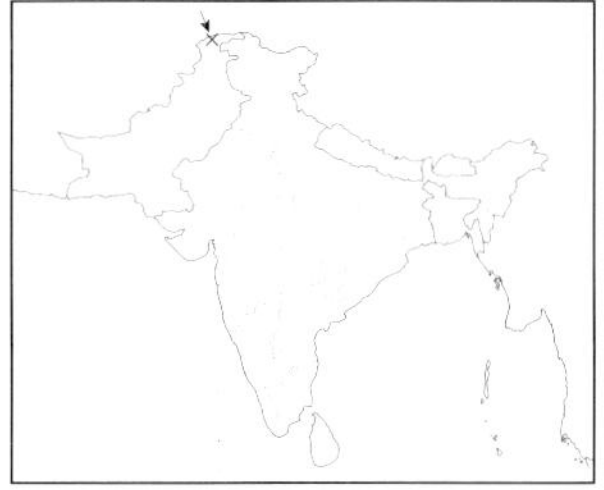

IDENTIFICATION 15–18 cm. A large, stout-billed finch with pink on wing. Superficially resembles Mongolian or Desert Finches (p.836). Is larger, with longer, stouter (yellowish) bill, has blackish crown, giving rise to capped appearance, and has dark streaking on brown mantle, dark-streaked ear-coverts, and brown breast-band and streaking on flanks. Belly and crescent below brown breast are strikingly white. **Male** has much pink on wings (owing to pink edges to coverts and remiges), pink rump, and black mottling on breast. Has pink face in breeding plumage. **Female** lacks pink on face and rump; breast and flanks are less heavily marked, and shows less (and paler) pink on wing. **Juvenile** is similar to female, but lacks dark cap, and pink on wing is restricted to bases of secondaries. **VOICE** Call is a chat-like *wee-tll-ee*, and flight call is a soft *chee-rup* or *toik* or *dy-lit-dy-lit*; song is a clear, melodious *tchwili-tchwilichip* (Clement *et al.* 1993). **HABITS** Found in pairs or small groups in summer; larger flocks in the non-breeding season. **HABITAT** Two birds found in alpine grassland. **DISTRIBUTION AND STATUS PK:** vagrant (July).

TRUMPETER FINCH *Bucanetes githagineus* Plate 149

Trumpeter Bullfinch (I,R), *Carpodacus githagineus, Rhodopechys githaginea*

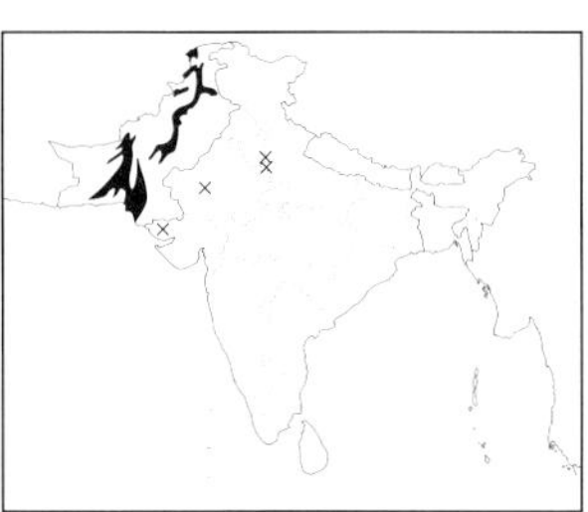

IDENTIFICATION 14–15 cm. A small, stocky, stout-billed finch. Most likely to be confused with Mongolian Finch (p.836), but has comparatively uniform wings and tail in all plumages, stouter bill, and distinctive nasal calls. **Male breeding** is unmistakable, with reddish bill, pinkish forehead, lores and wash to underparts, grey cast to crown, nape and ear-coverts, pink edges to greater coverts and remiges, pink rump, and pink edges to tail feathers. Is much duller and greyer on head and body in non-breeding plumage, when bill is yellow. **Female** is more uniform sandy-brown, with only traces of pink in plumage (e.g. on greater coverts, remiges and rectrices); bill is also yellow. **Juvenile** as female, but lacking any pink; has buff fringes to tertials and greater coverts. Very similar to juvenile Mongolian, but has stouter bill. **VOICE** Call is an abrupt *chee* or *chit* and flight call is a soft *weechp*; song is a drawn-out buzzing *cheeeee*, rising on scale, and can be followed by toy-trumpet-like phrases, or interspersed with metallic clicks and whistles (Clement *et al.* 1993). **HABITS** Found in pairs or small flocks, according to the season. Tame and confiding. Terrestrial; hops, creeps or shuffles along, keeping a low posture when feeding, but very upright when alert. Readily perches on rocks. Flight is swift, light and bounding. Regularly flies some distance to water. **HABITAT** Dry rocky hills and stony semi-desert. **BREEDING** Little known. April–June. Builds nest of plant stems and grasses in holes under rocks, in crevices between stones or in walls of old buildings. **DISTRIBUTION AND STATUS** Resident, subject to local movements, in Pakistan; winter visitor to NW India (Haryana, Rajasthan and Gujarat). **PK:** locally common in hilly regions, but nomadic and very erratic in distribution. **IN:** very local. **REFERENCES** Sangha (1995).

MONGOLIAN FINCH *Bucanetes mongolicus* — Plate 149

Mongolian Trumpeter Bullfinch (I), Mongolian Desert Finch (F), *Rhodopechys mongolica*

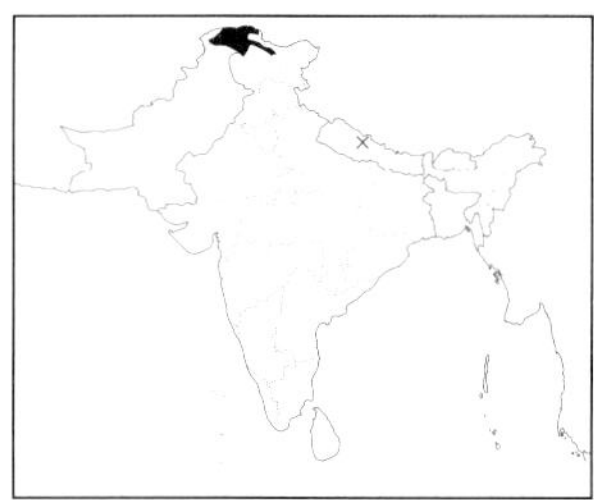

IDENTIFICATION 14–15 cm. Similar to Trumpeter Finch (p.835), but usually shows pronounced whitish or buffish edges to bases of greater coverts and tertials/secondaries which form pale panels on wing, as well as more pronounced whitish or buffish outer edges to rectrices that are prominent in flight. Crown and mantle are usually more prominently streaked, tends to look slimmer and larger-tailed, and has smaller and less stout bill. **Adult male breeding** has pinkish-red on supercilium, lores, throat and breast, pink edges to greater coverts and primaries, prominent white panels on wing, and pink rump. **Male non-breeding** and **female** have less pink in plumage (e.g. with uniform buffish underparts, and just traces of pink on tips of greater coverts and edges of primaries). Pale wing panels can be buffish and less distinct (but are usually sufficiently pronounced to aid separation from Trumpeter). **Juvenile** is similar to female, but lacks pink in plumage and has buff fringes to tertials and greater coverts. May be very similar to juvenile Trumpeter Finch (although bill is finer). **VOICE** Calls lack nasal quality of those of Trumpeter Finch, although is often silent. Typical contact call is a *deedjud*, and gives a quiet four-noted rattle in flight; song is a pleasant, repeated *doe-mi-sol-mi* (Kirwan and Konrad 1995). **HABITS** Tame and confiding. Feeds chiefly by gleaning seeds on the ground, also from low bushes. Perches readily on rocks and bushes, but usually keeps on the ground. Flight is similar to that of Trumpeter Finch, but is more powerful. Makes regular journeys to drink. **HABITAT** Dry stony slopes, and gravelly ground in the hills. **BREEDING** Undescribed from the region. Elsewhere, nest is a shallow cup made of grass and plant stems, placed in a small hollow under a stone or in an earth cliff. **DISTRIBUTION AND STATUS** Resident in Pakistan Himalayas and Ladakh; winter visitor to Baluchistan and Nepal. **PK:** nomadic and erratic in distribution, with some altitudinal movements, up to 3000 m in summer; locally frequent in Gilgit and Chitral, uncommon in Baluchistan. **NP:** vagrant or very rare local winter visitor to upper Kali Gandaki valley; 2745–3505 m. **IN:** locally fairly common in winter, 1500–3000 m; summers 3000–3900 m. **REFERENCES** Kirwan and Konrad (1995).

DESERT FINCH *Rhodospiza obsoleta* — Plate 149

Lichtenstein's Desert Finch (I), Black-billed Finch (R), *Rhodopechys obsoleta*

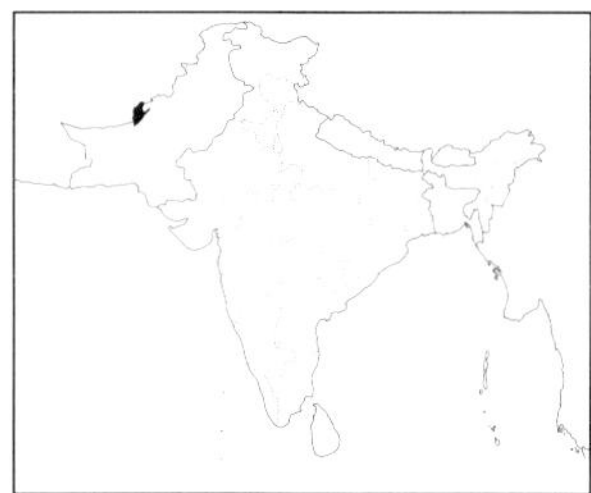

IDENTIFICATION 14.5–15 cm. A sandy-brown finch lacking any obvious pink on head and body. Has pink edges to greater coverts and secondaries, white edges to primaries, striking black centres to tertials, and white outer edges to tail. Combination of these features, plus black bill in spring/summer, help separate it from other 'pink-winged' finches. Bill of non-breeding adult is yellow-horn; that of juvenile is straw-coloured, becoming pale horn. **Male** has black lores. **Female** lacks black lores and has duller wing pattern than male (white of primary edges is tinged greyer, and pink edges to coverts are duller and less extensive). **Juvenile** is similar to female, but wings are duller and has buffish edges to coverts and tertials. White edges and blackish centres to primaries help separate from juvenile Trumpeter and Mongolian Finches (p.835 and above). **VOICE** Call is distinctive, a rippling or purring *r-r-r-r-r-ee* or *prrrt-prrrt*; also a harsh *turr* and sharp *shreep*. Song is a rambling mixture of call-notes and harsh trills and rolls (Clement *et al.* 1993). **HABITS** Keeps in pairs in the breeding season, and in small flocks at other times. Forages mainly by hopping on the ground. Readily perches in bushes and trees, and adopts an upright posture. Flight is swift and undulating. **HABITAT** Dry, open habitat with scattered trees, such as along streams, at edges of cultivation, and in gardens, irrigated orchards and roadside plantations. **BREEDING** March–July. Builds an untidy nest of grass stems in grape vines or in the fork of a tree, 1–2 m above ground. **DISTRIBUTION AND STATUS PK:** resident in C and N Baluchistan, where locally frequent, but erratic in occurrence; irregular winter visitor to Kohat, Kurram and Chitral.

BLANFORD'S ROSEFINCH *Carpodacus rubescens* — Plate 149

Crimson Rosefinch

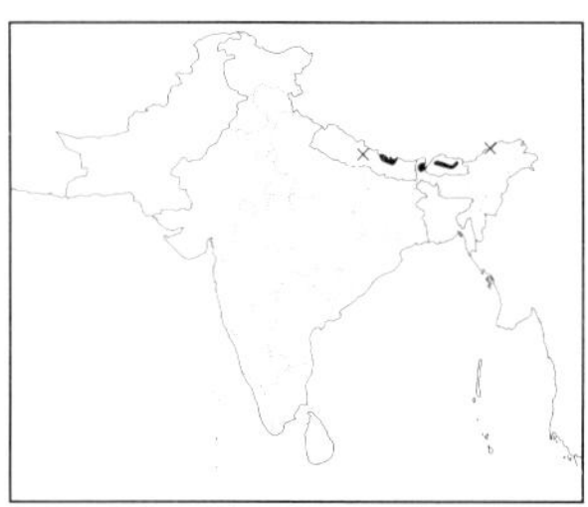

IDENTIFICATION (See also summary tables, p.838.) 15 cm. **Male** distinguished from *roseatus* Common (p.837) by slimmer and more pointed bill. Has a more uniform head, with ear-coverts only slightly browner (Common tends to show contrasting dark brown lores and ear-coverts), and duller crimson coloration to crown (glistening geranium-red on Common). Underparts are a more uniform dull pinkish-crimson, often with distinct greyish cast to breast and belly (Common being a brighter geranium-red, especially on throat and upper breast). **First-summer male** is similar but duller (browner), especially on mantle, wings and underparts. **Female** told from all other female rosefinches except Dark-breasted (p.837) by rather plain, dark appearance and lack of supercilium. From Dark-breasted by slightly stouter bill, more uniform wings, more uniform upperparts, with indistinct streaking on crown, reddish or bright olive cast to rump and uppertail-coverts (and also to rest of crown and mantle on some birds), and paler underparts; may show slightly paler tips to median and greater coverts and tertials, but these are not so prominent as on Dark-breasted. **Juvenile** resembles female, but lacks crimson tinge to rump and uppertail-coverts, and has paler underparts. **VOICE** Call is different from that of Common Rosefinch, a short, thin, high-pitched *sip*; also a series of abrupt, rising and falling notes, *pitch-ew, pitch-it, chit-it, chit-ew,...* (Clement *et al.* 1993), also described as a hard, metallic *ti-tip, tu-tip* or *du-dip* and *tu-tiptiptip* etc (C. Robson). Song is undescribed. **HABITS** Poorly known. Found in small flocks in the non-breeding season, and singly or in pairs when breeding. Forages chiefly on the ground in forest clearings. Diet is unknown. **HABITAT** Glades in conifer and mixed conifer–birch forest. **BREEDING** Unknown. Young out of the nest and adults in breeding condition in April. **DISTRIBUTION AND STATUS** Resident, subject to poorly known altitudinal movements. Himalayas from WC Nepal east to Arunachal Pradesh. **NP:** rare, possibly resident; 2950 m in May, 2745–3050 m in August and September, 2135–3050 m in winter. **IN:** rare; 3100–3800 m in summer, 1300–1800 m in winter. **BT:** uncommon; 3200–3700 m. **REFERENCES** Martens and Eck (1995).

DARK-BREASTED ROSEFINCH *Carpodacus nipalensis* Plate 149

Nepal Rosefinch (F,I)

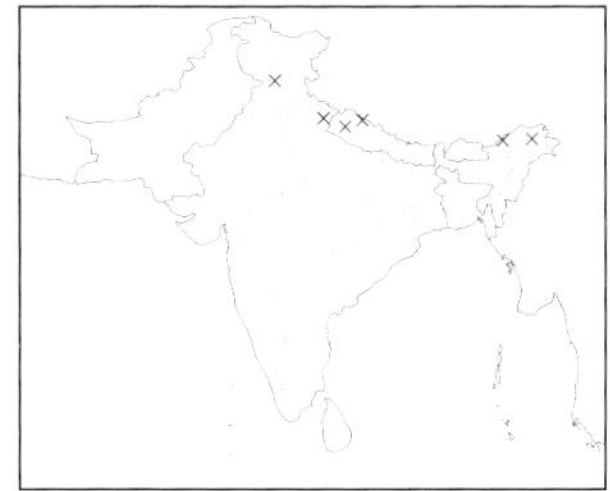

IDENTIFICATION (See also summary tables, p.838.) 15–16 cm. A slim-bodied rosefinch with slender bill. **Male** told from other rosefinches by combination of maroon-brown breast-band contrasting with rosy-pink throat and belly, reddish-pink forehead/forecrown and supercilium contrasting with dark maroon stripe through eye, and maroon-brown upperparts with (indistinct) darker streaking. Superficially resembles Dark-rumped (p.843), lacking pink or red rump, but that species has paler pink supercilium, cheeks and throat, is stockier and larger, has prominently streaked mantle, and lacks well-defined breast-band. **First-winter/first-summer male** is similar to female, but has maroon-brown upperparts. **Female** distinguished from other rosefinches except Blanford's (p.836) by unstreaked underparts, almost concolorous with upperparts, and lack of supercilium. From Blanford's by broad, diffuse streaking on mantle, broad buffish wing-bars and tips to tertials (although these may be less distinct and brownish-buff, or almost lacking through wear), darker greyish-brown underparts, and dark greyish olive-brown rump and uppertail-coverts. **Juvenile** is much as female. **VOICE** Calls are a plaintive wailing double whistle, a sparrow-like twitter and a *cha-a-rrr* alarm; song is a monotonous chipping (Clement *et al.* 1993). **HABITS** Keeps in pairs or small flocks (often single-sex), according to the season. Quite shy. Forages on the ground or in bushes, seeking seeds, berries and rhododendron nectar. **HABITAT** Summers in open oak–rhododendron and fir–rhododendron forest, shrubberies above the treeline and steep grassy slopes with scattered bushes or boulders; winters in forest clearings, and cultivation with nearby bushes. **BREEDING** Unknown. Collected in breeding condition in late June and July. **DISTRIBUTION AND STATUS** Resident, subject to altitudinal movements. Himalayas from Kashmir east to Arunachal Pradesh. **NP:** fairly common; summers mainly 3050–3900 m (–4270 m) and winters 1830–2745 m (down to 1370 m). **IN:** fairly common; summers from 3000 m up to the treeline in the west, 3400–4400 m in the east; winters mainly 1800–2700 m (down to 1200 m). **BT:** common; 1200–4265 m.

COMMON ROSEFINCH *Carpodacus erythrinus* Plate 149

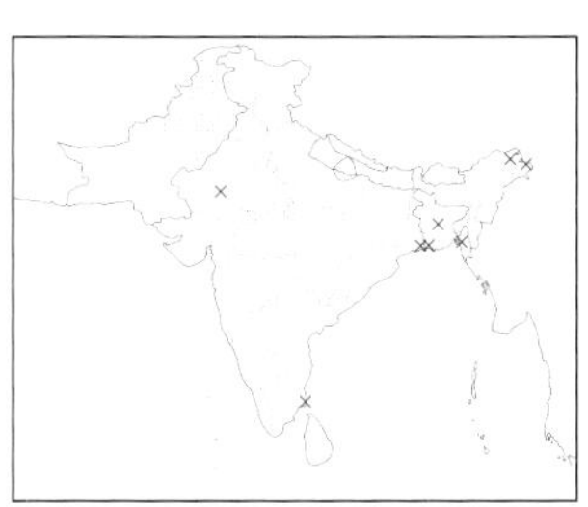

IDENTIFICATION (See also summary tables, p.838.) 14.5–15 cm. A compact, stout-billed rosefinch. **Male** is rather plain-faced, with deep red head, breast and rump, red wash to streaked upperparts, and red of underparts extending onto flanks and lower belly. Tends to show darker brownish ear-coverts. Confusable really only with Blanford's (p.836); see that species for differences. **Female** told from other rosefinches with streaked underparts by combination of short, stout bill, rather plain face with beady black eye (lacking supercilium or dark eye-stripe), bold streaking on whitish underparts (although see racial variation below), and narrow whitish or buff median- and greater-covert wing-bars. **Juvenile** and **first-winter/first-summer** are very similar to female, but with more prominent streaking on upperparts and underparts. **First-summer male** can show some red on head, rump and breast. **Racial variation** *C. e. erythrinus* occurs as a winter visitor to the subcontinent. Compared with *C. e. ferghanensis* and *C. e. roseatus*, described above, which are Himalayan breeders and winter across the subcontinent, the nominate race has browner mantle and whiter underparts, and red in plumage is less intense and largely restricted to head, breast and rump; female *erythrinus* is paler olive-grey on mantle, with only faint streaking, and breast and flanks are also only faintly streaked. **VOICE** Call is a distinctive, clear, rising *ooeet* or *too-ee*, and alarm is a sharp *chay-eeee*; song is a monotonous clear whistling *weeeja-wu-weeeja* (Clement *et al.* 1993). **HABITS** Gregarious in the non-breeding season, often in flocks of up to 30 birds; in pairs when breeding. Forages by hopping on the ground, gleaning seeds, and by clambering among foliage of bushes and trees in search of berries, flower buds and nectar. Sometimes perches inactively for quite long periods. Has an undulating flight like other rosefinches.

IDENTIFICATION OF FEMALE ROSEFINCHES

Species	Most likely confusion species	Size/structure	Supercilium	Wing-coverts and tertials
Blandford's	Dark-breasted and Vinaceous	Small and compact	Lacking	Relatively uniform, with indistinct pale fringing
Dark-breasted	Blandford's and Vinaceous	Relatively small, slim-bodied, with slender bill	Lacking	Variable, broad buffish wing-bars and tips to tertials
Common	Beautiful	Small and compact, with stout, stubby bill	Lacking	Narrow, whitish or buff tips to coverts, forming narrow double wing-bar
Beautiful	Common	Small and compact	Whitish, but very poorly defined	Indistinct pale tips to median and greater coverts
Pink-browed	Dark-rumped, Spot-winged and White-browed	Relatively small and compact	Prominent buff supercilium, contrasting with dark ear-coverts	Relatively uniform, lacking wing-barred effect
Vinaceous	Blandford's and Dark-breasted	Relatively small and compact	Lacking	Uniform wing-coverts, but conspicuous whitish tips to tertials
Dark-rumped	Pink-browed, Spot-winged and White-browed	Medium-sized	Prominent buff supercilium	Buffish tips to greater coverts and outer edge of tertials
Three-banded	Unmistakable	Medium large	Lacking	Broad, double white wing-bars and scapular line, and prominent white tips to tertials
Spot-winged	Pink-browed, Dark-rumped and White-browed	Medium-sized and rather stocky	Prominent, very broad, buff, supercilium	Prominent pale buff tips to greater coverts and outer edge of tertials
White-browed	Pink-browed, Dark-rumped and Spot-winged	Medium-large	Prominent, long, white supercilium, contrasting with dark lower border and rear of ear-coverts	Whitish to buff tips to median and greater coverts, forming narrow double wing-bar
Red-mantled	Streaked and Great	Large, with stout, heavy bill and long tail	Rather faint whitish supercilium, weakly offset against greyish eye-stripe	Lacks wing-bars, but has indistinct paler tips to median and coverts
Streaked	Great and Red-mantled	Large, with stout bill	Lacking	Lacks prominent wing-bars but has dark centres to median and greater coverts and tertials
Great	Streaked and Red-mantled	Large, with stout bill	Lacking	Relatively uniform, pale grey-brown
Red-fronted	Streaked	Very large, with rather long, conical bill	Lacking	Lacks wing-bars or obvious tertial contact
Crimson-browed Finch	Unmistakable	Large grosbeak-like shape with heavy, stout, stubby bill	Bright olive-yellow, extending across forehead	Relatively uniform

Underparts	Upperparts	Other features
Unstreaked, pale greyish-brown	Uniform grey-brown, unstreaked but for indistinct crown streaking	Reddish or bright olive cast to rump and uppertail-coverts
Unstreaked, dark greyish-brown Whitish with variable, bold, dark streaking	Relatively uniform dark greyish-brown, with diffuse mantle streaking	Dark greyish olive-brown rump
Whitish, with variable, bold, dark streaking	Grey-brown with some dark streaking	Beady-eyed appearance
Whitish, quite heavily streaked	Buffish-grey, heavily-streaked darker	
Heavily streaked, with strong fulvous wash from breast to undertail-coverts	Warm brownish-buff with heavy dark streaking	Fulvous coloration on rump
Warm brownish-buff, lightly streaked	Warm brown, almost concolorous with underparts, with diffuse streaking	Plain-faced appearance
Brownish-fulvous, heavily streaked	Rather dark brown with heavy dark streaking	Lacks well-defined dark ear-coverts
Dull orange-yellow breast contrasting with whitish belly to undertail-coverts; some faint flank streaking	Dull orange-yellow, extensively mixed with grey on mantle and streaked darker	Short, whitish streaks on grey ear-coverts and throat
Brownish-fulvous, very heavily streaked, including on throat	Rather dark brown with heavy dark streaking	Well-defined dark ear-coverts contrasting with supercilium
White, heavily streaked, with racially variable ginger-buff wash to throat and breast	Mid to dark brown with heavy dark streaking	Deep olive-yellow rump, heavily streaked
Whitish underparts, heavily streaked	Pale grey, heavily streaked	
Whitish underparts, heavily streaked	Dark grey, rather heavily streaked	
Whitish, heavily streaked	Sandy-brown with faint streaking	
Greyish, very heavily streaked, with variable pale yellow wash on breast	Very dark grey with bold, heavy dark streaking	Rump and uppertail-coverts more olive than black, or yellow
Grey, with olive-yellow breast	Greenish-olive with some diffuse streaking	Often shows olive-yellow rump

IDENTIFICATION OF MALE ROSEFINCHES

Species	Most likely confusion species	Size/structure	General coloration	Supercilium
Blandford's	Common	Small and compact, with relatively slender bill	Pinkish-crimson	Lacking
Dark-breasted	Dark-rumped	Relatively small, slim-bodied, with long, slender bill	Dark maroon-pink and brown	Quite prominent, reddish-pink, contrasting with dark maroon eye-stripe
Common	Blandford's	Small and compact, with short, stubby bill	Bright geranium-red	Lacking
Beautiful	Pink-browed	Small and compact	Cold greyish-pink	Rather indistinct, pale lilac-pink
Pink-browed	Beautiful	Smallish and compact	Deep, warm pink	Prominent, deep pink, contrasting with dark maroon-pink eye-stripe
Vinaceous	Unmistakable	Relatively small and compact	Dark crimson	Prominent, pale pink
Dark-rumped	Dark-breasted and Spot-winged	Medium-sized	Brownish-maroon	Prominent, bright pink, contrasting with pinkish-maroon ear-coverts
Three-banded	Unmistakable	Medium large	Pinkish-crimson, white and blackish	Lacking
Spot-winged	Dark-rumped	Medium-sized and rather stocky	Maroon and pink	Prominent, pale pink, contrasting with crown and ear-coverts
White-browed	Red-mantled and Pink-browed	Medium-large	Brownish and pale pink	Prominent, long, pinkish with splashes of white, extends across forehead
Red-mantled	White-browed	Large, with stout, heavy bill and long tail	Pink and pale brownish-grey	Prominent, pink
Streaked	Great	Large, with stout bill	Crimson-pink	Lacking
Great	Streaked	Large with stout bill	Rose-pink and sandy-grey	Lacking
Red-fronted	Streaked	Very large, with rather long, conical bill	Red and dark grey-brown	Short and red, extending across forehead
Crimson-browed Finch	Confusion very unlikely	Grosbeak-like shape with large, stout, stubby bill	Red and brownish-green	Red, extending across forehead

Wing-coverts and tertials	Underparts	Upperparts	Rump
Lacks wing-bars and contrasting tertial fringes	Dull pinkish-crimson, unstreaked, often with greyish cast	Unstreaked, dull crimson	Unstreaked, dull crimson
Uniform; lacks wing-bars and contrasting tertial fringes	Maroon-brown breast band contrasting with rosy-pink throat and belly	Maroon-brown, with indistinct darker streaks, and reddish-brown forecrown	Maroon-brown, concolorous with rest of upperparts
Rather indistinct bright red fringes to wing-coverts and tertials	Bright geranium-red, especially on throat and breast	Diffusely streaked bright geranium-red	Unstreaked, bright red
Indistinct paler fringes to wing-coverts and tertials	Cold greyish-pink with pronounced dark shaft streaks, especially on flanks	Cold pinkish-grey, with conspicuous dark crown and mantle streaking	Contrasting, unstreaked pale lilac-pink
Rather uniform; lacks prominent paler fringing to wing-coverts and tertials	Unstreaked, warm pink	Pinkish-brown mantle and back streaked darker; unstreaked or lightly streaked maroon-pink crown	Unstreaked, deep pink
Uniform coverts; lacks wing-bars but has prominent pinkish-white tertial tips	Uniform dark crimson	Dark crimson, with diffuse dark mantle streaking	Paler, dull crimson, contrasting with rest of upperparts
Rather indistinct pinkish tips to coverts and buffish tips to tertials	Indistinctly streaked, with brownish-maroon breast and flanks	Pink-tinged brown and broad diffuse streaks	Pinkish-brown, concolorous with rest of upperparts
Broad, double white wing-bars and scapular line, bold white outer edges to tertials	Pinkish-crimson breast contrasting with white belly and lower flanks	Pinkish-crimson crown and nape, with greyish mantle	Pinkish-crimson
Very prominent pink tips to median and greater coverts and tertials	Rather uniform pink, with some darker mottling	Rather uniform maroon, indistinctly streaked, with irregular pink splashes	Maroon, prominently splashed with pink
Pronounced pale tips to greater and median coverts forming narrow wing-bars	Pink, with some white streaking	Brown, with conspicuous darker streaking	Pink, well defined contrasting with rest of upperparts
Very indistinct paler fringing	Pink, with some streaking	Brownish-grey, with pink tinge, streaked darker	Uniform pink
Very indistinct paler fringing	Crimson-pink, with clearly defined white spotting	Grey-brown, washed pink, and with conspicuous darker streaking	Uniform deep pink
Very indistinct paler fringing	Rose-pink, with large diffuse white spots	Sandy-grey, washed pink, with narrow front streaking	Uniform rose-pink
Very indistinct paler fringing	Grey-brown, with bold dark streaks	Red throat and breast, contrasting with dark-streaked grey-brown remainder of underside	Deep pink, contrasting with rest of upperparts
Very indistinct paler fringing	Red throat and upper breast, contrasting with pale olive-grey remainder of underparts	Warm olive-brown, tinged with red, and diffusely streaked	Quite bright red, uniform

HABITAT Summers in shrubberies above the treeline, on alpine slopes with tall herbs and bush-covered slopes with scattered birches or firs, and in open coniferous forest and bushes at the edges of terraced cultivation; winters in cultivation with nearby bushes and open wooded country. **BREEDING** June–September. Builds nest of grass, well hidden in bushes, within 2 m of the ground. **DISTRIBUTION AND STATUS** Resident, subject to altitudinal and migratory movements in the subcontinent; also winter visitor. Breeds in N Baluchistan, Pakistan, and Himalayas from N Pakistan east to Arunachal Pradesh; winters throughout most of the subcontinent, except parts of the northwest and northeast, SE India and Sri Lanka; in winter, numbers increased by a major influx of visitors. **PK:** locally common on spring passage, less common on autumn passage; locally common breeding bird in Himalayas and higher mountains of Baluchistan. **NP:** fairly common and widespread altitudinal migrant and winter visitor; summers mainly 3350–4000 m, winters 275–2000 m. **IN:** fairly common; summers 3900–4200 m, down to 2700 m in the west; winters from 1500 m down to the foothills and plains. **BT:** common; 380–4420 m. **BD:** rare winter visitor to the southwest and southeast.

BEAUTIFUL ROSEFINCH *Carpodacus pulcherrimus* — Plate 149

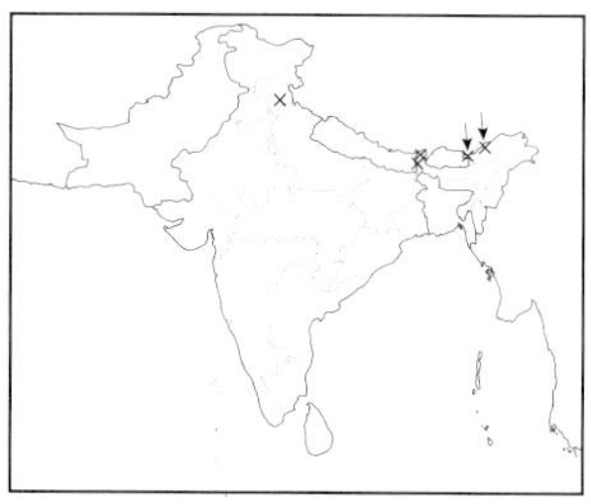

IDENTIFICATION (See also summary tables, p.838.) 15 cm. A small, compact rosefinch. **Male** is confusable really only with male Pink-browed (below), but has paler lilac-pink supercilium, rump and underparts, cold pinkish-grey coloration to heavily streaked crown and mantle, and pronounced shaft streaking on underparts (especially flanks and undertail-coverts). Smaller size, heavily streaked pinkish-grey upperparts, pink rump and pale pink underparts are best distinctions from male Dark-rumped (p.843). **First-winter/first-summer male** as adult female. **Female** has heavily streaked buffish-grey upperparts, and whitish underparts which are also heavily streaked; has very poorly defined supercilium (not apparent on some) which is whitish and finely streaked with dark brown, and ear-coverts are rather pale and well streaked. Similar to female Pink-browed, but lacks prominent supercilium (unstreaked, and offset against dark ear-coverts on that species), has whiter background coloration to underparts, and rump and uppertail-coverts are concolorous with back. **Racial variation** *C. p. waltoni* of Arunachal Pradesh has brighter and more reddish-pink supercilium and underparts (closer in coloration to Pink-browed), and paler sandy-brown upperparts. **VOICE** Call is a soft *trip* or *trillip*, and has a soft twitter; flight call is a harsh *chaaannn* (Clement *et al.* 1993). **HABITS** Keeps in pairs or small flocks, depending on the season. Forages quietly on the ground or low down in bushes, eating small seeds and buds. Often perches inactively in bushes, and freezes if disturbed. **HABITAT** Summers in rhododendron shrubberies, *Caragana* scrub and stony slopes above the treeline; winters on open bush-covered slopes and upland terraced cultivation with nearby bushes. **BREEDING** July–September. Builds nest of grass, roots and fibres close to the ground in a low shrub. **DISTRIBUTION AND STATUS** Resident, subject to altitudinal movements. Himalayas from N Uttar Pradesh east to W Arunachal Pradesh. Breeds 3600–4650 m, winters from 2100 m up to at least 3600 m. **NP:** common and widespread. **IN:** locally frequent in Arunachal Pradesh; status uncertain elsewhere, with very few recent published records. **BT:** local and frequent. **REFERENCES** Singh (1995).

PINK-BROWED ROSEFINCH *Carpodacus rodochrous* — Plate 149

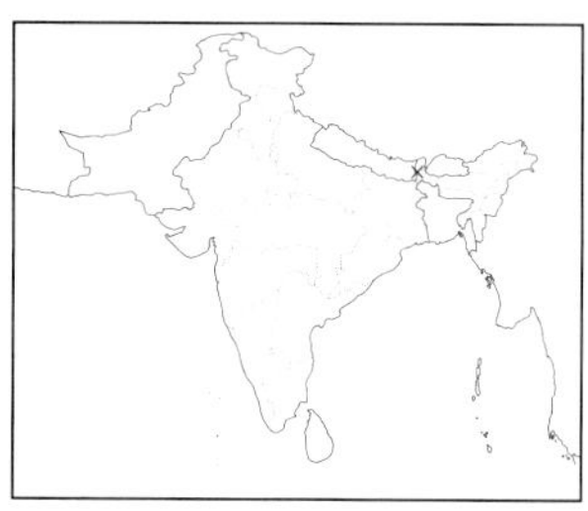

IDENTIFICATION (See also summary tables, p.838.) 14–15 cm. A small, compact rosefinch. **Male** is best told from male Beautiful (above) by deeper pink supercilium, rump and underparts, unstreaked (or lightly streaked) maroon-pink crown, eye-stripe and nape, warmer pinkish-brown coloration to streaked mantle and back, and absence of streaking on flanks, vent and undertail-coverts. Smaller size and shorter tail, uniform pink supercilium and throat (not splashed with white), crown coloration, and lack of prominent whitish tips to greater coverts are best distinctions from White-browed Rosefinch (p.844). Pink rump and uniform pink underparts separate it from Dark-rumped Rosefinch (p.843). **First-winter/first-summer male** as female. **Female** has heavily streaked upperparts and underparts. Distinguished from female Beautiful by prominent buff supercilium contrasting with dark ear-coverts, warmer brownish-buff coloration to mantle, fulvous coloration to rump, and strong fulvous wash from breast to undertail-coverts. Smaller size and shorter tail, coloration of supercilium and underparts, and absence of wing-bars are best distinctions from female White-browed (see that species for more details). For differences from female Dark-rumped and Spot-winged (p.843 and p.844), see those species. **VOICE** A loud *per-lee* or *chew-wee* and *sweet*; song is sweet and lilting (Clement *et al.* 1993). **HABITS** Found in pairs in the breeding season, and in small flocks at other times. Feeds unobtrusively on the ground or in bushes, taking small seeds, berries and rhododendron nectar. **HABITAT** Summers in open fir and birch forest and rhododendron and juniper shrubberies; winters in oak forest and on bush-covered slopes, also locally around upland villages. **BREEDING** July–September. Builds nest of twiglets and grass in a low bush or small tree. **DISTRIBUTION AND STATUS** Resident, subject to altitudinal movements. Mainly Himalayas from N Pakistan east to E Nepal. **PK:** scarce and local; recorded mainly in summer around 3000 m, winters 470–1200 m. **NP:** fairly common and widespread; summers mainly 3050–3965 m and winters 915–3000 m. **IN:** locally fairly common in the west, rare in West Bengal; summers 2745–3660 m, winters 1220–3000 m.

VINACEOUS ROSEFINCH *Carpodacus vinaceus* Plate 150

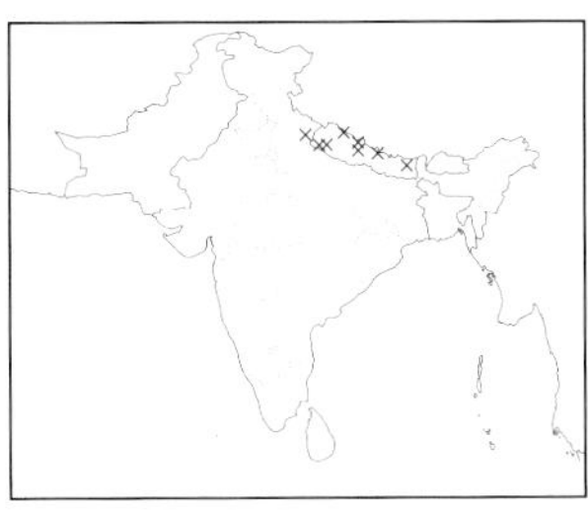

IDENTIFICATION (See also summary tables, p.838.) 13–16 cm. **Male** is mainly dark crimson, with diffuse dark streaking on mantle. Combination of prominent pink supercilium, pinkish-white tips to tertials, and coloration of upperparts and underparts distinguishes it from other male rosefinches. In winter, some males have browner lower breast and belly. **Female** is told from other female rosefinches by absence of supercilium (giving rise to plain-faced appearance), by whitish tips to tertials, and by warm brownish-buff coloration to underparts, which are almost concolorous with upperparts; pale tips to tertials may be indistinct or lacking in worn plumage. Lightly streaked underparts, as well as wing pattern, are best distinctions from female Crimson-browed and Dark-breasted (p.846 and p.837). **VOICE** Call is a hard *pwit* or *zieh* with a whiplash-like quality, and also gives a high-pitched *tip* and faint *tink* or *zick*; song is a simple *pee-dee, be do-do* (Clement *et al.* 1993). **HABITS** Keeps singly, in pairs or in small flocks, foraging on the ground or low down in bushes. Diet is unknown. Perches quietly and still in bushes for long periods. **HABITAT** Bamboo and dense bushes in moist forest; rhododendron and bamboo. **BREEDING** Details unknown. Collected in breeding condition in July. **DISTRIBUTION AND STATUS** Resident? Himalayas. Nepal and India. **NP:** scarce; recorded 3050–3200 m in probable breeding season, 1065–3050 m in winter. **IN:** very rare winter visitor to Naini Tal, Uttar Pradesh, 2500 m; two pairs in August in Uttar Pradesh, 3500 m. **REFERENCES** Jepson (1987).

DARK-RUMPED ROSEFINCH *Carpodacus edwardsii* Plate 150

Large Rosefinch (I), Edwards's Rose Finch (F)

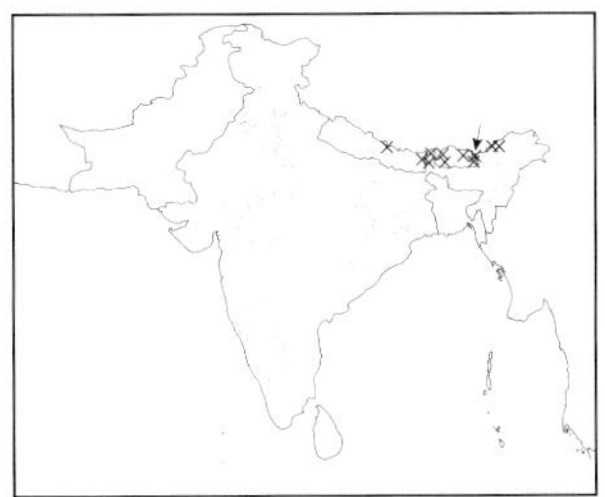

IDENTIFICATION (See also summary tables, p.838.) 16–17 cm. **Male** has bright pink supercilium and throat contrasting with pinkish-maroon crown and ear-coverts, and brownish-maroon breast and flanks. Mantle, back and rump are brown (faintly tinged pink), and broadly (but diffusely) streaked. Has pinkish tips to median and greater coverts and buffish tips to tertials, and fine (and indistinct) dark shaft streaking on underparts. Confusable with Spot-winged (p.844), but tips to coverts and tertials are much less prominent, lacks prominent pink on rump, and breast and flanks are clearly darker and browner than throat and belly. Brownish-maroon breast and lack of well-defined pink rump separate it from Pink-browed (p.842). Compared with Dark-breasted (p.837), has paler pink supercilium, cheeks and throat, is larger and stockier, has browner and more prominently streaked mantle, band across breast is browner and more diffuse, and has pale tips to coverts and tertials. **First-summer male** is similar to female, but has pinkish tinge to mantle and back, and supercilium, ear-coverts and breast are washed with pink. **Female** is well streaked on upperparts and underparts, with prominent buff supercilium. Told female from Pink-browed by larger size and stockier appearance, with stouter bill, and by darker brown upperparts and deeper brownish-fulvous underparts (with breast tending to be a shade darker than belly), while pale fringes to tertials have distinctly paler tip to outer edge (more even on female Pink-browed). Buffish tips to greater coverts and outer webs of tertials are less prominent than on female Spot-winged, other differences from which include darker, browner coloration to underparts, finer supercilium, which is much less pronounced behind eye, lack of well-defined dark ear-coverts, and more finely and sparsely streaked throat and breast. **VOICE** Call is an abrupt, short, rather shrill and high-pitched, metallic *zwiiih* or *tswii* (C. Robson from E. Vercruysse recording). **HABITS** Usually keeps singly, in pairs or in small parties. Often shy. Forages on the ground, under cover or in low bushes. Feeds mainly on seeds and nectar of rhododendron flowers. **HABITAT** Summers in rhododendron and juniper shrubberies and rhododendron and fir forest; winters in open rhododendron or birch forest, and slopes with thickets of bamboo, rose bushes and other scrub. **BREEDING** Details unknown. **DISTRIBUTION AND STATUS** Resident, subject to altitudinal movements. Himalayas from C Nepal east to Arunachal Pradesh. **NP:** scarce and local, status uncertain; recorded only in Langtang National Park and upper Mai valley, 2440–3635 m in March and May. **IN:** uncommon; breeds 3400–3900 m, winters 2000–3700 m. **BT:** uncommon; 2000–3965 m.

THREE-BANDED ROSEFINCH *Carpodacus trifasciatus* Plate 150

IDENTIFICATION (See also summary tables, p.838.) 17–19.5 cm. **Male** has broad double wing-bars (white, variably washed with pink) and white tips to scapulars, which form prominent banding. Upperparts and underparts are mainly pinkish-crimson, with variable grey edges to feathers of mantle, and has striking pinkish-white tips to blackish ear-coverts and throat. Belly and lower flanks are white, contrasting with pinkish-crimson breast, and shows prominent white on outer edges of tertials. **First-summer male** is duller than adult male, with crimson replaced by reddish-brown, and has buffish wing-bars. **Female** is similar in pattern to male; crimson of male is replaced by dull orange-yellow, with upperparts more extensively mixed with grey, and greater-covert wing-bar is washed with orange-yellow. **VOICE** Generally silent; song is unknown (Clement *et al.* 1993). **HABITS** Not recorded in the region. Lethargic, spending long periods perched motionless in bushes or trees. Quite tame.

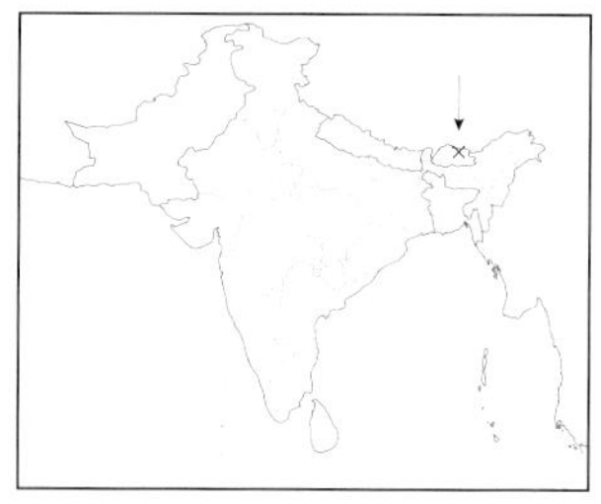

Feeds chiefly on the ground, gleaning seeds. **HABITAT** The Bhutan record was from fields near an upland village; recorded elsewhere in orchards and hedges. **DISTRIBUTION AND STATUS BT:** vagrant; once at 2800 m in Bumthang in March. Possibly winters in some of the higher, drier valleys of C and E Bhutan and in Arunachal Pradesh. **REFERENCES** Clement (1992).

SPOT-WINGED ROSEFINCH *Carpodacus rodopeplus* Plate 150

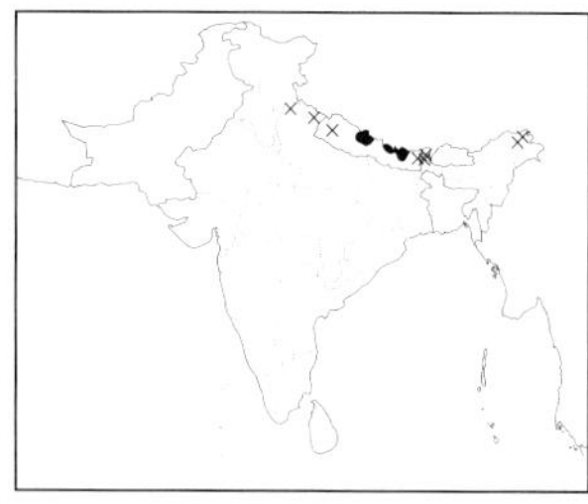

IDENTIFICATION (See also summary tables, p.838.) 15 cm. **Male** is confusable really only with Dark-rumped Rosefinch (p.843), but has very prominent pink tips to median and greater coverts and tertials. In addition, has darker and more uniform maroon upperparts, with irregular splashes of pink (and indistinct streaking) on mantle, more uniformly pink underparts (with darker mottling sometimes apparent through wear, although not showing as band across breast), and splashes of pink on rump. **Female** has broad buff supercilium, and heavily streaked upperparts and underparts. Distinguished from female Pink-browed (p.842) by larger size and bill, more heavily streaked throat and breast, and well-defined pale buff tips to greater coverts and outer edges of tertials (pale tertial fringes are more even and narrower on female Pink-browed). Main differences from female Dark-rumped include broader and more distinct supercilium behind eye, contrasting with well-defined dark ear-coverts, paler and more heavily streaked throat (some showing suggestion of dark malar stripe) and breast, and more prominent tips to greater coverts and tertials. In worn plumage, tertial 'spots' may be less distinct or lacking. **VOICE** Song is unknown (Clement *et al.* 1993); call is a nasal, disyllabic *churr-weee*, the second part of the call being higher-pitched (P. Morris). **HABITS** Usually keeps singly, in pairs or in small scattered flocks. Quite shy. Feeds on the ground or in bushes, on seeds. Perches inactively for quite long periods. **HABITAT** Summers in rhododendron shrubberies above the treeline and in alpine meadows; winters in bushes and bamboo thickets in forest, and in damp forest ravines. **BREEDING** Very little known. August. **DISTRIBUTION AND STATUS** Resident, subject to altitudinal movements. Himalayas from Himachal Pradesh east to Arunachal Pradesh. **NP:** local and fairly common; summers mainly 3050–4000 m and winters 2000–3050 m. **IN:** rare.

WHITE-BROWED ROSEFINCH *Carpodacus thura* Plate 150

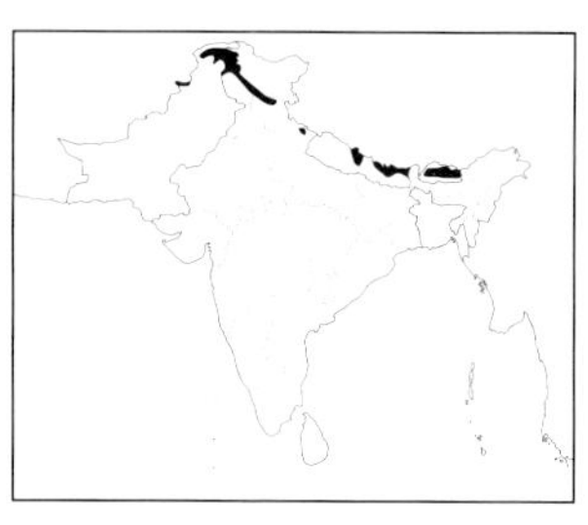

IDENTIFICATION (See also summary tables, p.838.) 17 cm. Combination of large size, well-defined pink rump, and contrast between brown upperparts and pink underparts/supercilium helps separate **male** from most rosefinches having pink supercilium. Most likely to be confused with Pink-browed (p.842), but is larger and longer-tailed, has (iridescent) whitish upper edge and rear end to pink supercilium, dark-streaked brown crown, nape and mantle (lacking pinkish coloration), and prominent pale tips to wing-coverts (pinkish to median and buffish to greater coverts). Lores are deep crimson, and contrast markedly with supercilium, and throat has iridescent white streaking. For differences from Red-mantled (p.845), see that species. **First-winter/first-summer male** resembles female, but has lower back and rump rich buff-brown or reddish-brown (and can breed in this plumage). **Female** told from other female rosefinches by combination of large size and long tail, prominent supercilium, deep olive-yellow (and heavily streaked) rump, and whitish to buff tips to median and greater coverts which form comparatively distinct double wing-bar. **Racial variation** Three races are known from the subcontinent, the males of which vary to a small degree in the intensity of brown of upperparts and pink of underparts. Female of nominate race, of C Himalayas, has the most prominent supercilium, contrasting markedly with broad, dark eye-stripe, and has ginger-brown coloration to throat and breast, with whitish cheeks and whitish belly; it is very different from other female rosefinches. Female *C. t. blythi* of W Himalayas has colder grey-brown upperparts than female of nominate, has less prominent supercilium and eye-stripe (ear-coverts are more extensively streaked), and has orange-buff wash to throat; streaking on underparts is stronger than on Pink-browed, and shows contrast between buff wash on breast and white background colour of belly. Female *C. t. feminus* of Arunachal Pradesh differs from nominate in having white background colour to more heavily streaked underparts. **VOICE** Calls include a sharp, buzzing *deep-deep, deep-de-de-de-de*, a loud, harsh whistling *pwit pwit*, and a loud piping *pupupipipipi*; song is a weak twittering (Clement *et al.* 1993). **HABITS** Very similar to those of Spot-winged Rosefinch (above), but is tame and confiding, and feeds on seeds, berries and buds. **HABITAT** Summers in dwarf rhododendron and juniper shrubberies, on steep slopes with dwarf juniper and willow, on alpine meadows and in open fir, juniper and rhododendron forest near the treeline; winters on open hills with bushes. **BREEDING** July–August. Nest is a large cup made of fine grasses and seed pods, placed low in bushes. **DISTRIBUTION AND STATUS** Resident, subject to altitudinal movements.

Himalayas from N Pakistan east to W Arunachal Pradesh. **PK:** scarce; breeds 2400–3350 m, rarely descends below 2400 m in winter. **NP:** fairly common from WC areas eastwards; summers mainly 3800–4200 m and winters 2440–3660 m (down to 1830 m). **IN:** locally fairly common; in the west, summers 3000–4200 m, winters above 1800 m; in the east, summers 3800–4200 m, winters 2400–3900 m (down to 1900 m). **BT:** common; 3355–4570 m.

RED-MANTLED ROSEFINCH *Carpodacus rhodochlamys* Plate 150

Blyth's Rosefinch, *C. grandis*

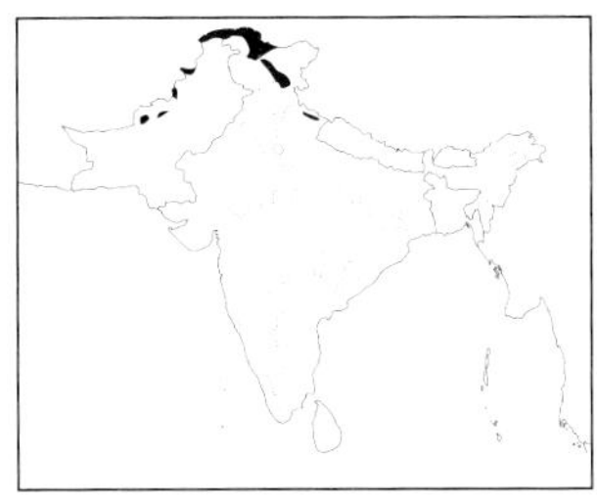

IDENTIFICATION (See also summary tables, p.838.) 18 cm. Large, long-tailed rosefinch. Stockier than White-browed (p.844), with much larger bill. **Male**'s crown and mantle are paler and greyer, with pinkish wash, and streaking on upperparts is less prominent (almost absent on crown). Pink of supercilium generally does not extend across forehead. Does not show prominent wing-bars as on White-browed. Much larger size and bill and paler overall coloration are best distinctions from Pink-browed (p.842). **Female** told from other female rosefinches by combination of large size and huge bill, pale grey coloration to (heavily streaked) upperparts including rump, indistinct supercilium weakly offset against greyish eye-stripe (much less prominent than on White-browed), and heavily streaked whitish underparts. **VOICE** Flight call is a rather metallic-toned twitter or disyllabic *twit-twit*; song is feeble, and consists of a series of rather short wheezy *chirp* and *twit* notes, interspersed with single-noted squeaky whistles (Roberts 1992). **HABITS** Found singly, in pairs or in small groups. Tame and confiding. Forages chiefly on the ground, also in low bushes. Takes a variety of tree seeds and berries, including juniper, wild olive, *Hippophae* and rose; also buds and dandelion flowers. Its flight is powerful, fast and undulating, and accompanied by a soft twittering. **HABITAT** Breeds in drier mountain forest and shrubberies of juniper, rose and other bushes; winters lower down in wild olive trees, thorn scrub, orchards and gardens. **BREEDING** Poorly known. May–July. Builds nest of soft juniper-bark strips and grasses, 1–1.5 m up in a low bush. **DISTRIBUTION AND STATUS** Resident, subject to altitudinal movements. Mountains of W and N Pakistan, and Himalayas from N Pakistan east to N Uttar Pradesh. **PK:** locally frequent; breeds 2700–3500 m, winters 300–2400 m. **IN:** locally frequent; breeds 3400–4000 m, winters 2200–2600 m.

STREAKED ROSEFINCH *Carpodacus rubicilloides* Plate 150

Eastern Great Rosefinch (F,I)

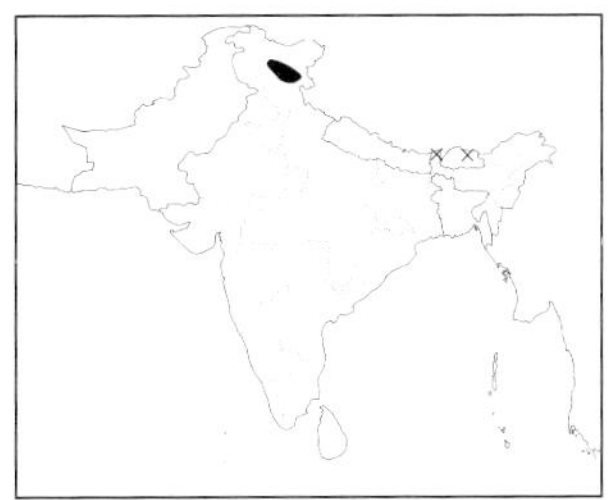

IDENTIFICATION (See also summary tables, p.838.) 19 cm. **Male** is confusable really only with male Great (below), but has deeper crimson-pink head and underparts, and prominently streaked nape, mantle and scapulars. Coloration of upperparts is a darker (pink-washed) grey-brown, and rump is also a deeper pink. White spotting on crown and underparts is narrower and more clearly defined. **Female** is rather nondescript, lacking supercilium. Distinguished from female Great by darker grey upperparts with heavier streaking on nape, mantle and scapulars, more heavily streaked ear-coverts and underparts, and faintly streaked rump and uppertail-coverts; centres to wing-coverts and remiges (especially tertials) are much darker brownish-black (decidedly washed-out grey-brown on female Great). Possibly confusable with female Red-fronted (p.846), but is slimmer and longer-tailed, has stouter (deeper and less pointed) bill, always has greyish rump, and is paler on upperparts. **VOICE** Call is a loud *twink*, a soft *sip* and a melancholy bullfinch-like *dooid dooid*; song is a slowly descending *tsee-tsee-soo-soo-soo* (Clement *et al.* 1993). **HABITS** Keeps singly, in pairs or in small scattered flocks, depending on the season; sometimes with Great Rosefinch or White-winged Grosbeak (p.850). Quite shy. Feeds on the ground, and perches on bushes if alarmed. Flight is powerful, swift and bounding. **HABITAT** Arid country: stony ground well above the treeline with sparse *Caragana*, willow and *Hippophae* scrub, screes and moraines; also thickets and *Caragana* scrub in winter. **BREEDING** June and July. Builds a large nest of roots and grass on a base of sticks and twigs, usually in a bush within 3 m of the ground. **DISTRIBUTION AND STATUS** Resident, subject to altitudinal movements. N Himalayas from Ladakh east to Bhutan. **NP:** frequent; up to 4700 m in summer, winters 2800–3660 m (down to 2440 m). **IN:** locally common; summers 3700–5000 m, winters down to 3000 m. **BT:** very rare. **REFERENCES** Pfister (1997).

GREAT ROSEFINCH *Carpodacus rubicilla* Plate 150

IDENTIFICATION (See also summary tables, p.838.) 19–20 cm. **Male** is confusable really only with Streaked (above), but has paler rose-pink head and underparts and paler (pink-washed) sandy-grey upperparts. Extent and prominence of streaking on upperparts is variable; typically, only back and scapulars are noticeably faintly streaked, and nape appears unstreaked, creating shawl-like effect. Wing-coverts are almost uniform sandy-grey, with only slightly darker centres, and appear paler than rest of wing. White spotting on crown and underparts is larger and more diffuse than on Streaked. In flight, both sexes show white edge to outer tail feathers, which is bare-

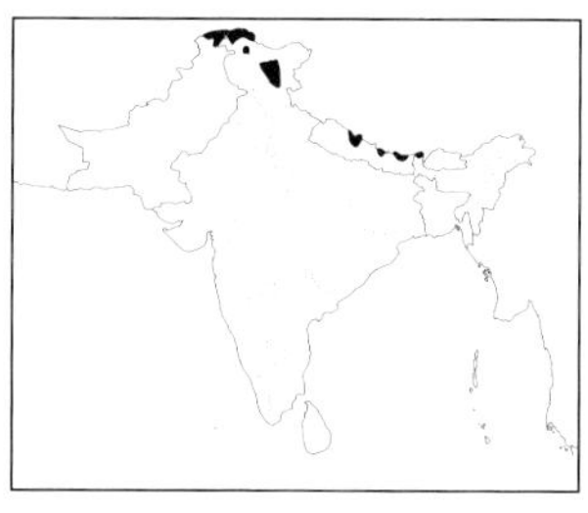

ly apparent on Streaked. **First-summer male** is as female, and can breed in this plumage. **Female** is similar to female Streaked and Red-mantled (p.845), but has paler, sandy-brown upperparts which are only faintly streaked, less heavily streaked ear-coverts and underparts, and unstreaked rump and uppertail-coverts; streaking on crown and throat tends to be more prominent than on mantle and rest of underparts, and centres to coverts and remiges (especially tertials) are paler grey-brown (much darker brownish-black on female Streaked). **VOICE** Contact call is a loud *tooey tooey*, and flocks in flight give rapid twittering calls; song is a brief stereotyped *twee-twee-twe-cho-chush-u* (Roberts 1992). **HABITS** Found singly, in pairs, and in winter in flocks of up to 30 birds. Habits similar to those of Streaked Rosefinch, and sometimes associates with that species in winter. Forages mainly on the ground, also on bushes, seeking seeds and berries. Flight is deeply undulating. **HABITAT** Arid, sparsely vegetated and rocky ground in alpine zone; also *Caragana* scrub in winter. **BREEDING** Poorly known. July and August. Nest is built in a rock crevice or under stones. **DISTRIBUTION AND STATUS** Resident, usually with only small altitudinal movements. N Himalayas from N Pakistan east to Sikkim. **PK:** locally common in Chitral, Gilgit, Hunza and Baltistan; summers 3000–4200 m (down to 1500 m in winter). **NP:** frequent; chiefly 3660–5000 m (down to 2650 m). **IN:** uncommon; summers 3300–4800 m.

RED-FRONTED ROSEFINCH *Carpodacus puniceus* — Plate 150

Red-breasted Rosefinch (F,I,R)

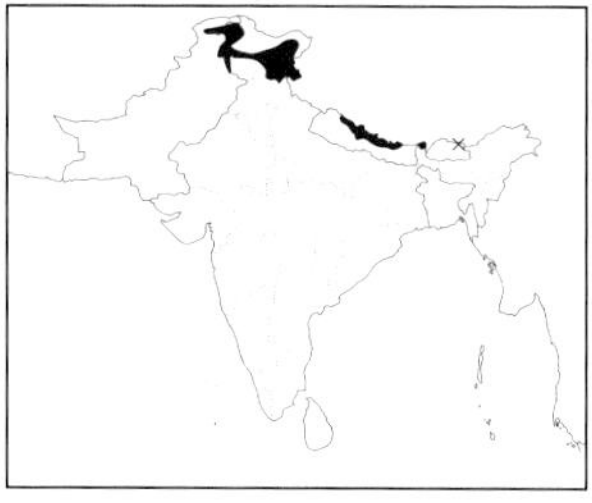

IDENTIFICATION (See also summary tables, p.838.) 20 cm. **Male** distinguished from other male rosefinches by combination of large size, comparatively long, conical bill, red forehead/supercilium and grey-brown eye-stripe, and red lower ear-coverts, throat and breast contrasting with dark-streaked grey-brown belly, flanks and vent. Crown, nape and mantle are grey-brown with dark streaking, lack pinkish wash, and contrast strongly with red of plumage. Has deep pink rump. Bill shape, heavily streaked grey-brown upperparts, and very different habitat and habits separate it from Crimson-browed Finch (below). **Female** is heavily streaked and lacks supercilium. Resembles female Streaked (p.845), but is considerably darker on underparts, has long conical bill, and is stockier, with shorter tail; breast is variably washed with pale yellow, and rump and uppertail-coverts are more olive than back or are yellow. **Juvenile** is similar to female, but lacks yellow on underparts and rump, and is generally more heavily streaked; throat and breast are yellowish by second winter, with males showing red on underparts by second summer. **VOICE** Call is a bulbul-like cheery whistle, *are-you-quite-ready*, and also has a cat-like grating *m-a-a-a-u* and a sparrow-like *chirp*; song is a short *twiddle-le-de* (Clement *et al.* 1993). **HABITS** Keeps singly or in pairs in the breeding season, and in parties of up to ten birds in winter. Shy. Feeds on the ground among large boulders, often at the edge of melting snow. Spends long periods digging with its powerful bill. **HABITAT** Well above the treeline on steep rocky mountainsides with patches of dwarf juniper and grassy and stony slopes. **BREEDING** Poorly known. July and August. Nest is a thick cup made of coarse grass, placed on a cliff ledge. **DISTRIBUTION AND STATUS** Resident, subject to some altitudinal movements. N Himalayas from N Pakistan east to Bhutan. **PK:** scarce and sedentary; mainly 3300–4400 m, rarely winters below 2700–3000 m (down to 1500 m). **NP:** frequent; summers mainly 4265–5490 m, winters from 2745 m up to at least 4575 m. **IN:** uncommon; breeds 3900–5200 m, winters down to 2700 m (to 1500 m). **BT:** very rare.

CRIMSON-BROWED FINCH *Propyrrhula subhimachala* — Plate 150

Red-headed Rosefinch (I), Juniper Finch (F), *Pinicola subhimachalus*

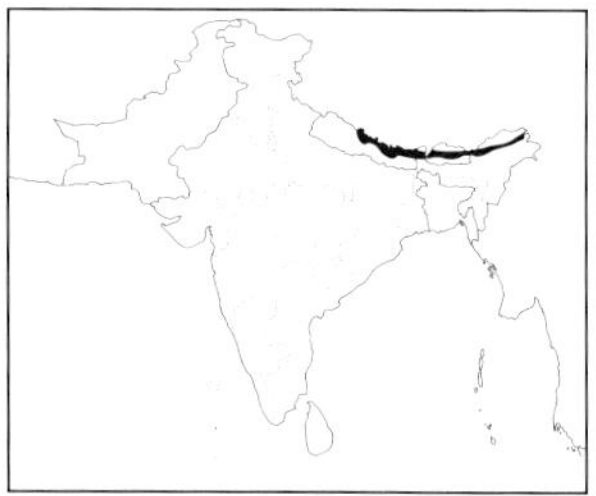

IDENTIFICATION (See also summary tables, p.838.) 19–20 cm. Rather grosbeak-like in shape and behaviour, with short stubby bill. **Male** has red forehead, throat and upper breast; upperparts and rump are variegated green, and underparts are grey mixed with olive. Red of breast is spotted with pinkish-white. **Female** has bright olive-yellow forehead and supercilium, greyish nape, ear-coverts and throat, olive-yellow breast and grey rest of underparts, and greenish-olive upperparts, often with olive-yellow rump; forehead, supercilium and breast can be orange on some (older) females. **VOICE** Has melodic sparrow-like *chirp*; song is a bright and varied warble, also a *ter-ter-tee* (Clement *et al.* 1993). **HABITS** Found singly, in pairs or in small parties, according to the season. Quiet, rather sluggish and shy. Feeds in bushes and low trees, chiefly on seeds and berries, especially barberries. **HABITAT** Summers in shrubberies, especially junipers near the treeline; winters in forest with thick undergrowth. **BREEDING** Unknown. Collected in breeding condition in August. **DISTRIBUTION AND STATUS** Resident, subject to altitudinal movements. Himalayas from WC Nepal east to Arunachal Pradesh; NE India (winter only). **NP:** uncommon; summers mainly 3500–4000 m, winters from 2590 m up to at least 3050 m. **IN:** uncommon; summers 3500–4200 m, winters up to at least 3600 m (down to 1800 m). **BT:** uncommon; 1790–4265 m.

SCARLET FINCH *Haematospiza sipahi* — Plate 150

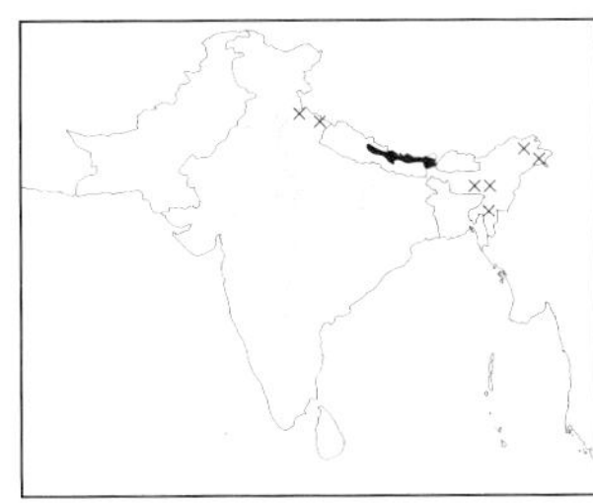

IDENTIFICATION 18 cm. A stocky, stout-billed, short-tailed finch. **Male** is mainly bright scarlet, with darker wings and tail. **First-summer male** resembles female, but has orange rump and orange-brown tinge to crown, nape and mantle. **Female** has bright yellow rump; upperparts are olive-green with diffuse dark feather centres, and may show white mottling on crown and mantle; underparts are similar, but greyer, and become paler towards vent. **VOICE** A loud, pleasant *too-eee* and a *kwee-i-iu*; song is a clear, liquid *par-ree-reeeeeee* (Clement *et al.* 1993). **HABITS** Keeps singly, in pairs and, in winter, in flocks of up to 25 birds. Forages on the ground, in bushes and in treetops. Eats a variety of seeds, berries, buds and some insects. Flight is swift, powerful and undulating. **HABITAT** Edges, clearings and ravines in broadleaved forest, especially near streams. **BREEDING** Poorly known. May and June in Meghalaya. Builds a large nest of twigs and coarse roots, 7–12 m up in a tree. **DISTRIBUTION AND STATUS** Resident, subject to altitudinal movements. Himalayas in N Uttar Pradesh and from WC Nepal east to Arunachal Pradesh; NE India. **NP:** uncommon and local from WC areas eastwards; 2135–3100 m in May, and winters from 1220 m up to at least 2560 m (down to 520 m). **IN:** uncommon; breeds 1600–2000 m in Meghalaya; breeding range in Himalayas is poorly known, 1660 m and 2710 m (May) and 3850 m (August) in Sikkim; 550–2400 m in the non-breeding season. **BT:** frequent; 800–3180 m. **REFERENCES** Athreya *et al.* (1997).

RED CROSSBILL *Loxia curvirostra* — Plate 149

Crossbill (F,I,R), Common Crossbill (N)

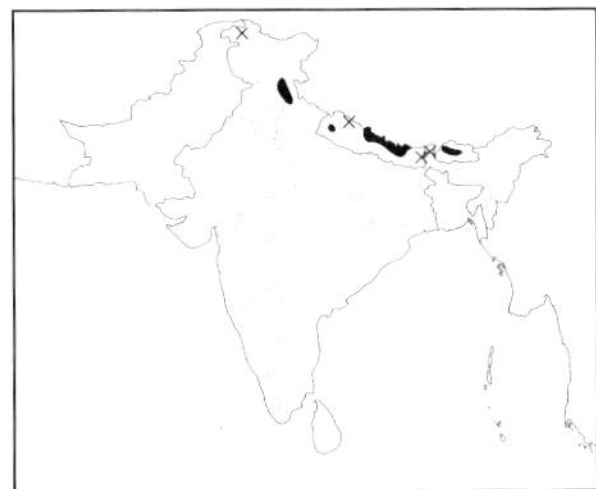

IDENTIFICATION 16–17 cm. Told from other finches by distinctive bill shape: upper and lower mandibles cross over towards tip. In addition, tail is deeply forked. **Male** is rusty-red, with darker wings and tail. **First-winter/summer male** is duller orangey-red, although there is much variation (some being greenish-yellow). **Female** is olive-green, with brighter greenish-yellow rump, and with dark wings and tail. **Juvenile** resembles female, but is duller, more olive-green, and is boldly streaked on upperparts and underparts; mandibles initially are not crossed. Possibly confusable with some female/immature rosefinches, but tail is sharply forked and it has very different call. **VOICE** Call is a hard *chip-chip*; song is a loud series of call-notes developing into *cheeree-cheeree-choop-chip-chip-cheeree*, often given as subdued subsong (Clement *et al.* 1993). **HABITS** Gregarious when not breeding, forming restless, noisy flocks. Feeds in the tops of tall conifers, where it is difficult to see; most easily detected by its distinctive, constant chipping calls. Uses its specially adapted bill to extract seeds from cones. Very agile when foraging; clambers about branches, often using the bill as an aid in the manner of a parrot, and hangs upside-down from cones. Flight is fast, powerful and bounding. **HABITAT** Coniferous forest; favours hemlocks. **BREEDING** Little known in the region. Presumably breeds in any month, depending on food supply, as elsewhere in range. **DISTRIBUTION AND STATUS** Resident, subject to erratic movements. Himalayas in N Pakistan, Himachal Pradesh, Sikkim, Nepal and Bhutan. **PK:** irregular visitor, probably breeding; recorded only in Gilgit, 3025–3235 m. **NP:** frequent; movements are poorly understood, probably resident; mainly 2590–3660 m (from 2100 m). **IN:** uncommon; 2700–4000 m (down to 1500 m in winter, Sikkim). **BT:** frequent; 2550–3570 m.

BROWN BULLFINCH *Pyrrhula nipalensis* — Plate 151

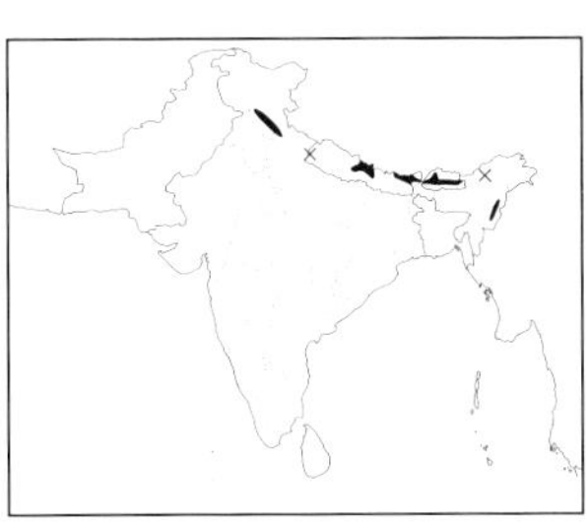

IDENTIFICATION 16–17 cm. **Adult** distinguished from other bullfinches by greyish upperparts and underparts, lacking any extensive red, yellow or orange in plumage (mantle has brownish cast). Also has black upper rump, reducing white rump band to narrow crescent, and longer tail. Additional features include narrow black surround to bill, black lores and scaling on forehead and crown, white patch below eye, glossy blue back, wings and tail, and buffish patch on greater coverts. At close range, male can be separated from female by crimson-pink (rather than yellow) outer edge to inner tertials. **Juvenile** is similar to adult, but has orange-buff wing-bar, buff-brown upperparts, warm buff underparts, and lacks black surround to bill and black lores. **Racial variation** *P. n. ricketti* of Arunachal Pradesh is darker, with blackish crown, and lacks (or has indistinct) white patch below eye. **VOICE** Mellow *per-lee* and soft whistling twitter when feeding; song is a repeated mellow *her-dee-a-duuee* (Clement *et al.* 1993). **HABITS** Found in pairs or small parties. Quite tame. Arboreal; feeds unobtrusively in the tops of trees and bushes, on berries, seeds, blossoms, buds and rhododendron nectar. Flight is fast and direct. **HABITAT** Dense moist forest or thick undergrowth in fir, oak and rhododendron forest. **BREEDING** Details unknown. Noted with nesting material in June. **DISTRIBUTION AND STATUS** Resident, with small altitudinal movements. Himalayas in Himachal Pradesh, NW Uttar Pradesh and from Nepal east to Arunachal Pradesh; NE India. **NP:** local and frequent; 1600–3050 m in winter and up to 3200 m in summer. **IN:** uncommon; summers 2100–3000 m, winters down to 1500 m. **BT:** uncommon; 1800–3320 m.

ORANGE BULLFINCH *Pyrrhula aurantiaca* Plate 151

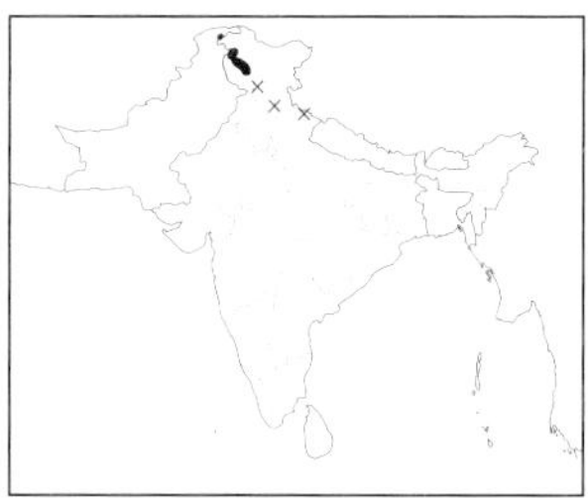

IDENTIFICATION 14 cm. **Male** told from Red-headed (below) by brownish-orange (rather than grey) mantle, scapulars and back, orange-buff wing-bars, lack of white surround to black face, and deep orange underparts. Some (first-year?) males are paler orange on upperparts and underparts. **Female** separated from female Red-headed by grey (rather than yellow) crown and nape, buff-brown upperparts, brownish-orange underparts, and buffish wing-bars. **Juvenile** is similar to female, but head and body are almost uniform pale orange, and black of face is much reduced. **VOICE** An upward-inflected *tewtya*; song opens with a *tew-tew*, followed by rising and falling metallic warbling phrases (Roberts 1992). **HABITS** Keeps singly, in pairs or in small flocks. Tame and confiding. Usually forages on the ground, gleaning seeds at the base of trees and bushes; also eats shoots, buds and berries, taken from bushes. Perches quietly and motionless in trees for quite long periods. **HABITAT** Open coniferous forest and birch–coniferous forest. **BREEDING** June–August. Builds nest of fine twigs and rootlets, well concealed in a sapling or in the lower branches of a large tree. **DISTRIBUTION AND STATUS** Endemic to the subcontinent. Resident, subject to altitudinal movements. W Himalayas from Pakistan east to N Uttar Pradesh. **PK:** scarce and local; summers 2400–3000 m, winters down to 1550 m. **IN:** locally frequent; summers 2745–3505 m, winters 1675–2135 m. **REFERENCES** Shah (1979).

RED-HEADED BULLFINCH *Pyrrhula erythrocephala* Plate 151

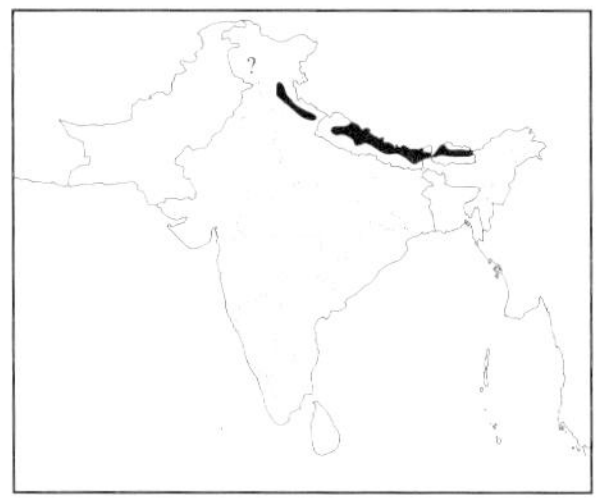

IDENTIFICATION 17 cm. **Male** distinguished from male Orange (above) by grey mantle, scapulars and back, greyish-white wing-bars, white surround to black face, and paler orange underparts with white belly. Also confusable with male Grey-headed (below), but has reddish-orange crown and nape, and lacks blackish band across upper rump. **First-year male** is similar to female, but has olive-yellow on breast and upper flanks. **Female** told from female Orange and Grey-headed by olive-yellow crown and nape, grey mantle, scapulars and back, greyish-white wing-bars, and pale grey underparts. **Juvenile** is similar to female, but browner, and head and upperparts are warm brown or rufous-brown. **VOICE** A soft, mellow *pew-pew*; song is a low, mellow *terp-terp-tee* (Clement *et al.* 1993). **HABITS** Usually found singly, in pairs or in small parties. Feeds in bushes, trees or on the ground, chiefly on seeds, also taking buds, catkins, berries and nectar and blossoms of rhododendrons. Lethargic, spending much time scarcely moving on the same perch. **HABITAT** Breeds in deciduous forest, especially of birch, and winters in rhododendron, oak–rhododendron and conifer–rhododendron forest; often found near streams. **BREEDING** July and August. Builds nest of twigs and moss, 3 m up in a small tree. **DISTRIBUTION AND STATUS** Resident, subject to some altitudinal movements. Himalayas from Himachal Pradesh east to W Arunachal Pradesh. **NP:** fairly common and widespread; summers mainly 3050–4000 m, winters 1830–3865 m. **IN:** fairly common; breeds 2400–3300 m in the west, 3300–3900 m in Sikkim, and winters 1500–3900 m (down to 1000 m). **BT:** common; 1600–4100 m.

GREY-HEADED BULLFINCH *Pyrrhula erythaca* Plate 151

Beavan's Bullfinch

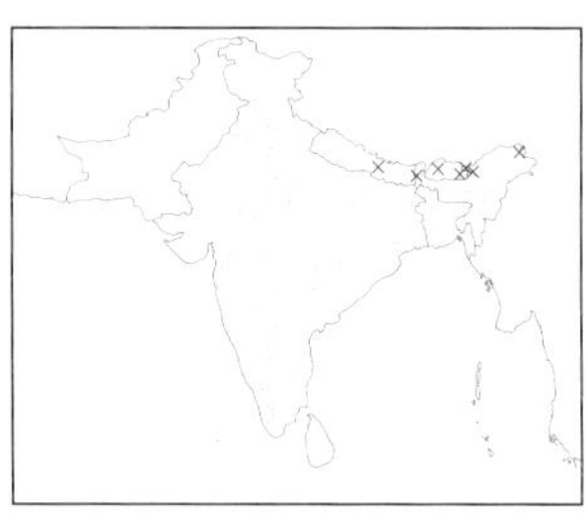

IDENTIFICATION 17 cm. **Male** distinguished from Red-headed (above) by grey crown, nape and foreneck, deeper orange-red breast, belly and flanks, black band across upper rump, and longer tail. **Female** from female Red-headed by grey crown and nape, fawn-brown mantle, scapulars and back, pinkish-brown underparts, and blackish band across upper rump. **Juvenile** is very similar to female, but crown and nape are more greyish-olive, mantle is dull grey-brown and underparts are dull brown, and has broad buffish-brown tips to greater coverts; has dark grey lores, with pale buff above and below eye. **VOICE** A soft *soo-ee* or *poo-ee*, which can be given as triple whistle; song is undescribed (Clement *et al.* 1993). **HABITS** Similar to those of other bullfinches. Keeps in pairs in the breeding season, and in small parties at other times. Tame and confiding. Feeds in bushes or on the ground, on seeds, buds, insects and rhododendron nectar. **HABITAT** Conifer–rhododendron forest and willow and buckthorn thickets. **BREEDING** Little known. One nest found in July, 3.6 m up in a young pine. **DISTRIBUTION AND STATUS** Resident, subject to altitudinal movements. Himalayas from Darjeeling, West Bengal, east to Arunachal Pradesh. **NP:** vagrant. **IN:** locally frequent; summers 2500–3800 m, winters 2000–3200 m, occasionally down to 1700 m. **BT:** rare. **REFERENCES** Giri and Choudhary (1996).

HAWFINCH *Coccothraustes coccothraustes* **Plate 151**

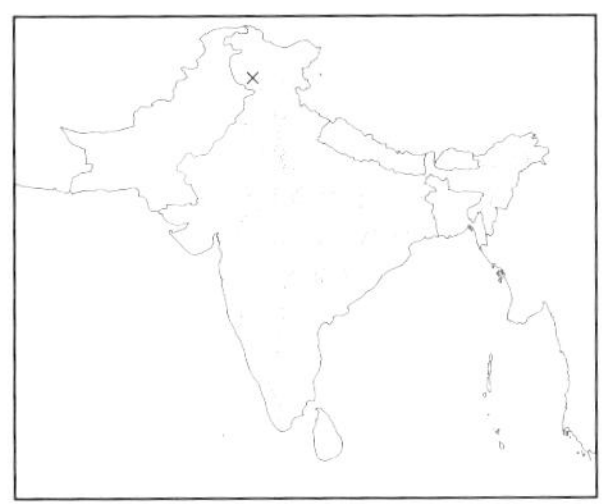

IDENTIFICATION 16–18 cm. Fawn- and brown-coloured finch with huge stout bill. **Male** has black chin and lores, orange-brown head and underparts, grey nape and sides of neck, white and orange-buff wing-coverts, and blue-black rest of wing. In flight, shows white band across primaries and white tip to tail. In breeding plumage, mantle is deeper brown and bill is blue-black (rather than yellowish). **Female** has duller, pale brown head and underparts, and secondaries are broadly edged with grey. **Juvenile** resembles female, but has brown streaking and spotting on underparts. **VOICE** Call is a distinctive *see-tic* or *tic*, and also has a hoarse whistle, *tzeep*; song, which is seldom heard, is a bunting-like *deek-waree-ree-ree*. **HABITS** In the region, usually found in small parties. Unobtrusive and shy; often perches quietly in bushes and trees for quite long periods. Feeds in trees and on the ground beneath, mainly on wild olive berries, also on other berries and seeds. Makes regular journeys to drink. Flight is rapid, powerful and bounding, and often at a considerable height, and is accompanied by distinctive, but rather quiet, call. **HABITAT** Wild olive forest, orchards and old graveyards. **DISTRIBUTION AND STATUS** Local winter visitor in irregular numbers, mainly to Pakistan. **PK:** locally frequent, especially in the Punjab Salt Range. **IN:** vagrant.

BLACK-AND-YELLOW GROSBEAK *Mycerobas icterioides* **Plate 151**

***Coccothraustes icterioides* (I,K)**

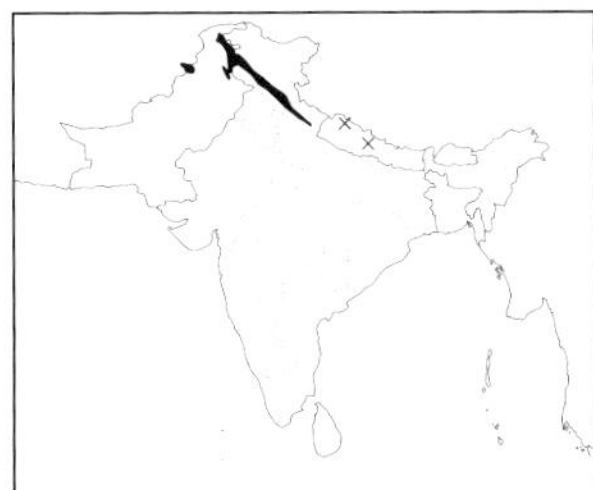

IDENTIFICATION 22 cm. **Male** is yellow, with black head, wings and tail, and is very similar to male Collared (below), although has different calls and song. Black of plumage is duller (less glossy), and has black (not yellow) thighs. Neck and upperparts are generally a purer, paler lemon-yellow, although some (older?) males may show orange tinge to mantle similar to Collared, and rump tends to be a purer yellow (washed with orange on Collared). **Female** is very different from female Collared, lacking olive-green and yellow in plumage; mantle and breast are pale grey and concolorous with head, and belly, flanks and rump are pale peachy-orange. **Juvenile male** is similar to adult female, but has yellow rump and blackish wings and tail, with patches of black on scapulars and throat. **VOICE** A throaty whistle, *pi-riu, pir-riu, pir-riu*; song is a rich, clear *prr-trweeet-a-troweeet* or a clear, rich *tookiyu, tookiyu* (Clement *et al.* 1993). **HABITS** Keeps in pairs or small loose flocks. Birds frequently call noisily to each other, both when perched and in flight. Feeds on the ground, in bushes and in trees, on a variety of food: berries, seeds, shoots and small invertebrates. Flight is strong, swift and undulating, usually at treetop level. **HABITAT** Fir–spruce and pine forest. **BREEDING** April–September. Nest is a large, shallow saucer, made of fine twigs, plant stems, moss and lichen, placed 3–18 m up in a conifer, usually close to the trunk. **DISTRIBUTION AND STATUS** Resident, subject to altitudinal movements. Mainly Himalayas from N Pakistan east to N Uttar Pradesh. **PK:** common and sedentary; mainly 2000–3350 m, down to 1500 m in winter. **NP:** rare and local in the west; possibly breeds. **IN:** fairly common; breeds mainly 1800–3000 m, winters down to 1500 m (to 750 m). **REFERENCES** Giri and Choudhary (1997), Lewis (1994b).

COLLARED GROSBEAK *Mycerobas affinis* **Plate 151**

Allied Grosbeak (F,I), *Coccothraustes affinis* (I,K)

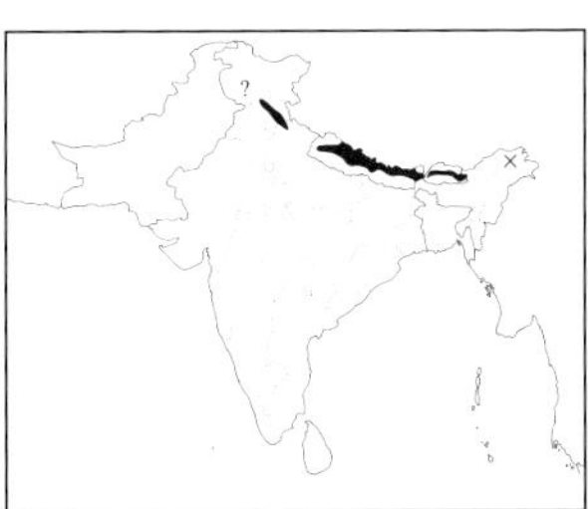

IDENTIFICATION 22 cm. **Male** is very similar to male Black-and-yellow Grosbeak (above), mainly orange-yellow with black head, wings and tail. Compared with that species, black of plumage is strongly glossed, has yellow thighs, song and calls are different, and upper mantle has strong orange cast (although Black-and-yellow may show orange wash to mantle). **Female** is very different from female Black-and-yellow: grey head is well demarcated from olive-yellow of underparts, and has greyish-olive mantle, largely yellowish-olive wings, and olive-yellow rump contrasting with black tail. **Juvenile male** resembles adult male, but yellow is duller and more olive, black of head is browner (with chin and throat mottled with grey-brown), and mantle is mottled with black. **Juvenile female** is similar to adult female, but chin and throat are paler, underparts are duller, and rump shows variable amount of yellow. **VOICE** Call is a mellow but rapid *pip-pip-pip-pip-pip-pip-ugh*, and alarm a sharp *kurr*; song is a clear, loud and rising whistle, *ti-di-li-ti-di-li-um* (Clement *et al.* 1993). **HABITS** Found in pairs in the breeding season, and in small parties at other times. Like other grosbeaks is often first located by its calls, which can be heard some distance away. Usually seen in flight or perched on the tops of tall trees, but also feeds in low bushes and on the ground. Flight is swift and undulating, with birds flying close together. **HABITAT** Coniferous and mixed broadleaved–coniferous forest. **BREEDING** Very poorly known. Observed carrying nest material in May; adult with fledged young in late July. **DISTRIBUTION AND STATUS** Resident, subject to altitudinal movements. Himalayas from N Himachal Pradesh east to Arunachal Pradesh. **NP:** widespread, fairly common from EC areas eastwards, uncommon farther east;

summers mainly 3000–3900 m and winters down to 2440 m (to 1065 m). **IN:** locally fairly common; breeds from 2700 m up to the treeline, occasionally winters down to 1800 m. **BT:** fairly common; 2000–4265 m. **REFERENCES** Martens and Eck (1995).

SPOT-WINGED GROSBEAK *Mycerobas melanozanthos* Plate 151

Spotted-winged Grosbeak (I), *Coccothraustes melanozanthos* (I,K)

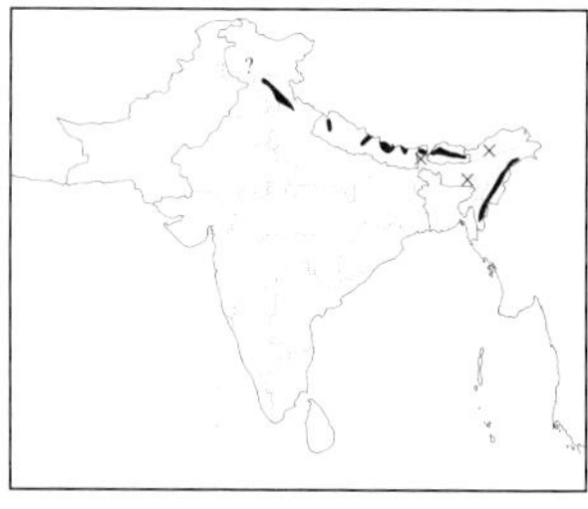

IDENTIFICATION 22 cm. A stocky, comparatively short-tailed and stout-billed grosbeak. **Male** has dark grey head, upperparts and breast, and yellow underparts. Distinguished from other grosbeaks by broad white tips to greater coverts, tertials and secondaries, and black rump and uppertail-coverts. **Female** is very distinctive, with bold blackish streaking on yellowish crown and mantle, yellow underparts with boldly streaked breast and flanks, and striking head pattern with yellow supercilium, broad black stripe through ear-coverts and black malar stripe; wings are blackish, with broad whitish tips to greater coverts, tertials and secondaries. **Juvenile** as female, but yellow of plumage is replaced by pale yellow, whitish or buff. **First-summer male** is similarly marked to juvenile, but has warm buff to rufous-brown tinge to throat and breast. **VOICE** Call is a rattling *krrrr* or *charrarauk*; song is a loud, melodious whistle, *tew-tew-teeeu*, also an oriole-like *tyop-tiu* or *tyu-tio* (Clement *et al.* 1993). **HABITS** Depending on the season, keeps in pairs or in flocks of up to 80 birds. Feeds in trees, also in bushes and on the ground. Eats seeds, fruits and berries, especially wild cherry. Has a strong undulating flight, the birds keeping in a compact flock. **HABITAT** Breeds in mixed coniferous–broadleaved forest, and winters in broadleaved forest. **BREEDING** May–July. Builds a shallow, saucer-shaped nest of twigs and moss, 4 m up in a tree. **DISTRIBUTION AND STATUS** Resident, with poorly understood altitudinal movements. Himalayas from Murree hills, Pakistan, east to Arunachal Pradesh; NE India. **PK:** scarce, very local and erratic in occurrence; recorded only in summer, around 2700 m. **NP:** uncommon resident; recorded 1400–2135 m in winter and up to 3355 m in summer. **IN:** uncommon; 1830 m (January and June) up to 3355 m (September). **BT:** frequent; 610–3660 m.

WHITE-WINGED GROSBEAK *Mycerobas carnipes* Plate 151

***Coccothraustes carnipes* (I,K)**

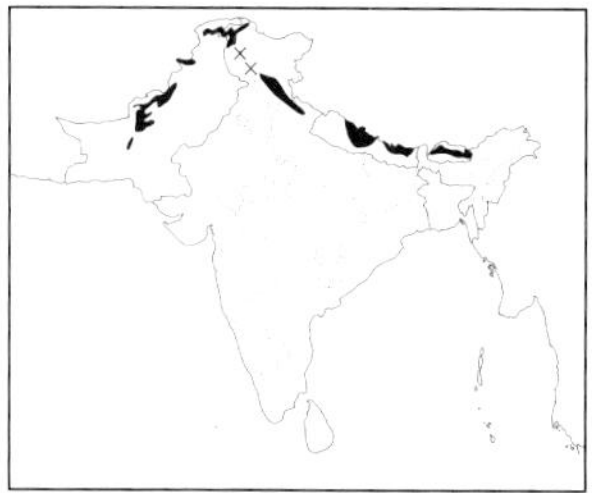

IDENTIFICATION L 22 cm. A long-tailed grosbeak with deeply undulating flight. **Male** told from other grosbeaks by dark grey head, mantle and breast, olive-yellow rest of underparts and rump, black wings with yellow tips to greater coverts and tertials, and large white patch at base of primaries (which is very prominent in flight). **Female** resembles male, with distinctive white patch at base of primaries, but black of plumage is replaced by sooty-grey, grey underparts become dull yellowish-olive on lower belly and vent, and has dull olive-yellow rump; white patch on wing is smaller, and yellow greater-covert bar is narrower. **Juvenile** similar to adult female, but is browner, with paler fringes to upperparts and olive-yellow tips to median (as well as greater) coverts. **First-winter** as female. **First-summer male** has yellower rump and vent and belly, and more olive mantle. **VOICE** Call is a soft, nasal *schwenk* or squawking *wit*, the latter often extended to *wet-et-et*; song is a *wet-et-et-un-di-di-di-dit* (Clement *et al.* 1993). **HABITS** Keeps singly, in pairs or in scattered flocks. Noisy, like all grosbeaks. Quite tame. Often seen perched in treetops or in flight. Has a strongly undulating flight, interspersed with glides, and with fast whirring wingbeats, rather like that of a woodpecker. Feeds chiefly on juniper seeds, also on other seeds and berries, taken on the ground, in bushes and in trees. **HABITAT** Closely associated with junipers: dwarf juniper shrubberies near the treeline, mixed juniper–fir–rhododendron forest and pine–juniper forest. **BREEDING** June–September, varying locally. Builds a deep nest of twigs and plant stems, well concealed in a juniper or spruce within 2 m of ground. **DISTRIBUTION AND STATUS** Resident, subject to some altitudinal movements, but some remain at higher levels all year. Mountains of W and N Pakistan, and Himalayas from N Pakistan east to W Arunachal Pradesh. **PK:** locally frequent and sedentary; mainly 2400–3650 m (down to 1500 m). **NP:** fairly common; summers mainly 3050–4270 m (–4600 m), winters down to 2745 m. **IN:** locally fairly common; breeds 3000–4200 m, winters mainly down to 2700 m (to 1500 m). **BT:** common; 2440–4265 m. **REFERENCES** Inskipp and Inskipp (1994).

GOLD-NAPED FINCH *Pyrrhoplectes epauletta* Plate 151

Gold-headed Black Finch (I), Gold-crowned Black Finch (F)

IDENTIFICATION 15 cm. A small, stocky finch. **Male** is all black but for orange-yellow rear crown and nape, orange flash at sides of breast, and white inner webs to tertials. In flight, shows white on underwing-coverts. **Female** is very different, with olive-green head, grey nape and mantle, rufous-brown wing-coverts and scapulars, white inner webs to tertials (as male), and rufous-brown underparts. **Juvenile** as female, but duller. **First-winter male** can show scattering of orange feathers on nape and black feathers on underparts. **VOICE** Call is a thin, high-pitched *teeu*, and also a *purl-lee* and a squeaky *plee-e-e*; song is a rapid *pi-pi-pi-pi*, and gives a soft

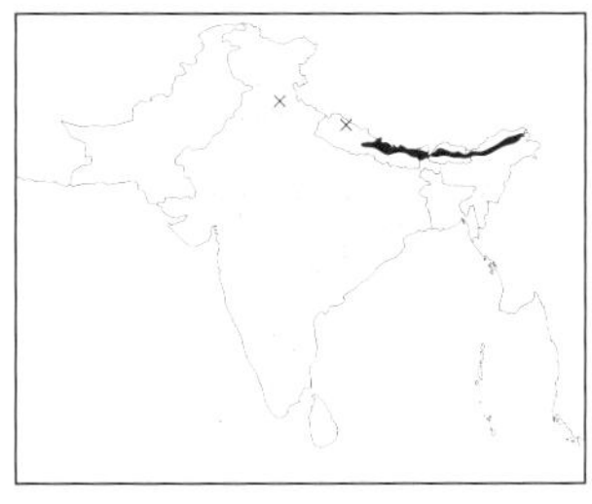

bullfinch-like piping (Clement *et al.* 1993). **HABITS** Keeps singly or in pairs in the breeding season, and in small groups, sometimes with rosefinches, in winter. Very quiet and unobtrusive. Forages on the ground or in bushes, often low down and within the foliage. Eats seeds, berries and insects. **HABITAT** Dense undergrowth in oak and rhododendron forest, also rhododendron shrubberies and bamboo thickets in summer. **BREEDING** Details unknown. Noted carrying nest material in March. **DISTRIBUTION AND STATUS** Resident. Mainly Himalayas from C Nepal east to Arunachal Pradesh. **NP:** uncommon; subject to poorly understood altitudinal movements, 3260–3355 m in May, 1525–3000 m in winter. **IN:** uncommon; summers 2800–3900 m, winters 1400–3600 m. **BT:** locally fairly common; 1600–3965 m.

BUNTINGS Fringillidae, subfamily Emberizinae

Small to medium-sized, terrestrial passerines with a strong, conical bill designed for shelling seeds. Generally, the breeding plumage of males is attained through wear, and the patterning is obscured during autumn/winter when plumage is fresh. Unlike finches, buntings prefer the seeds of grasses; adults also eat insects in summer, and feed insects to their young. They forage by hopping or creeping on the ground and picking up food items. Their flight is undulating. Buntings are usually gregarious outside the breeding season, feeding and roosting in flocks, often with other species. When breeding, they form pairs and are territorial. Their nests are cup-shaped, made mainly of grasses and rootlets, and are usually placed on the ground or low down in a bush. Buntings occur in a wide variety of open habitats. Many species in the region are only winter visitors. Byers *et al.* (1995) has been extensively used as the main reference.

CRESTED BUNTING *Melophus lathami* Plate 152

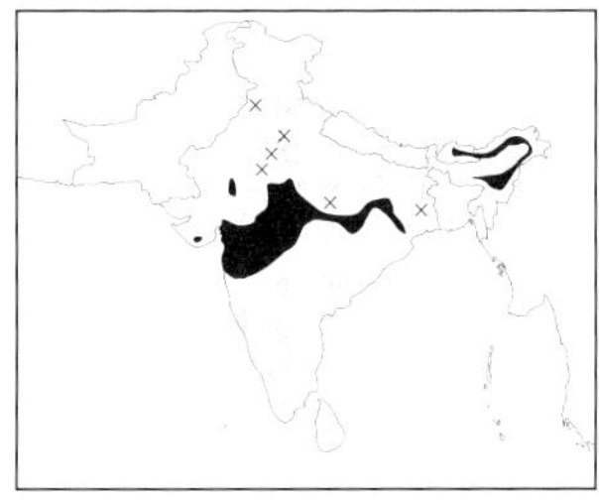

IDENTIFICATION 17 cm. **Male** is bluish-black with prominent crest, and with mainly chestnut wings and tail. **Female** has shorter crest, and chestnut edges to feathers of wings and tail (chestnut may be very indistinct when worn); upperparts are sandy-brown with dark brown streaking, and underparts are paler, with diffuse dark malar stripe and dark streaking across breast and flanks; lacks white on tail. **First-winter male** as female, but upperparts are darker brown and more heavily streaked, and underparts are olive-grey and heavily streaked with blackish-brown. **Juvenile** as female, but with buffier and more heavily streaked underparts, and shorter crest. **VOICE** Call is a *tip* or *pink*; song is a *tsri-tsri-tsi-tsu-tsu-tsu*, last three notes descending (Ali and Ripley 1987). **HABITS** Very similar to those of other buntings. Keeps singly or in pairs in the breeding season, and in small loose parties at other times. Lively and quite tame. Perches readily on the tops of bushes or boulders, in upright posture. **HABITAT** Dry grassy and rocky hillsides, dry grassy slopes with scattered trees and bushes, and terraced cultivation. **BREEDING** April–August. Builds nest on the ground under a rock or in hollow in a bank or stone wall. **DISTRIBUTION AND STATUS** Resident, subject to altitudinal movements in the Himalayas and local movements in the C Indian hills. Himalayan foothills from N Pakistan east to Arunachal Pradesh, and south to C Maharashtra, C Madhya Pradesh and N Orissa; NE India. **PK:** frequent summer visitor; 1000–1800 m. **NP:** fairly common and widespread resident; summers 2440–1220 m and possibly lower, winters 75–1460 m. **IN:** fairly common but local; summers up to 1800 m in Himalayas, to 2400 m in Nagaland. **BT:** fairly common. **BD:** vagrant. **REFERENCES** Sarker and Sarker (1986).

YELLOWHAMMER *Emberiza citrinella* Plate 152

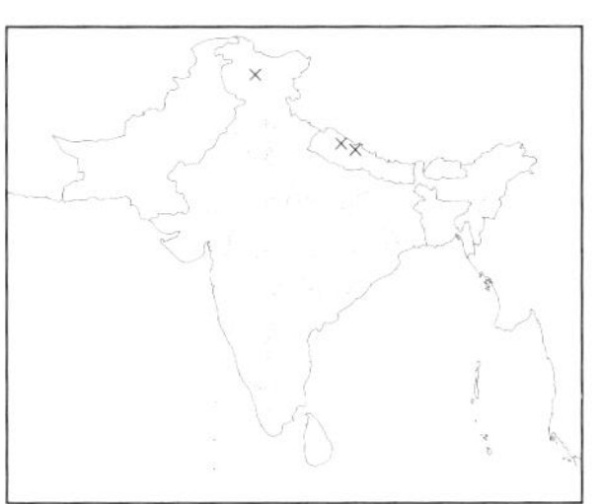

IDENTIFICATION 16.5 cm. A long-tailed, rufous-rumped bunting. Regularly hybridises with Pine Bunting (p.852), and can show mixture of characters. **Male** non-breeding has yellow crown, supercilium and throat, blackish sides to crown and surround to ear-coverts, much yellow on underparts, and rufous streaking on breast which may form ill-defined band. Head and underparts are more extensively yellow (through wear) in breeding plumage. **Female** non-breeding is similar to non-breeding male, but generally with less yellow on head and underparts. Distinguished from female/first-winter Pine by yellow on throat, supercilium, belly and edges to rectrices, olive-yellow tinge to crown, and olive tinge to mantle. Compared with Yellow-breasted Bunting (p.855), underparts are more heavily streaked (usually including some rufous), head pattern is less striking (with less distinct supercilium, lateral crown-stripe and dark border to ear-coverts), and is longer-tailed. **First-winter** as non-breeding adult. Some (mainly first-winter) females lack yellow and are then very difficult to separate from female Pine: however, belly is not pure white as on Pine, usually has more evenly streaked crown and narrower supercilium (on Pine, streaks are more restricted to lateral crown, and thus tends to show more pronounced pale crown-stripe), malar stripe and breast tend to be less prominently streaked, and has yellowish (rather than whitish or whitish-buff) edges to primaries and to base of outer tail feathers. **VOICE** As that of Pine. **HABITS** In the region, found singly or in small groups. A typical bunting; behaviour is very like that of Pine Bunting, and often associates with that species. **HABITAT** Upland cultivation. **DISTRIBUTION AND STATUS NP:** rare and irregular winter visitor. **IN:** vagrant. **REFERENCES** Alström and Colston (1991), Harris *et al.* (1996).

PINE BUNTING *Emberiza leucocephalos* — Plate 152

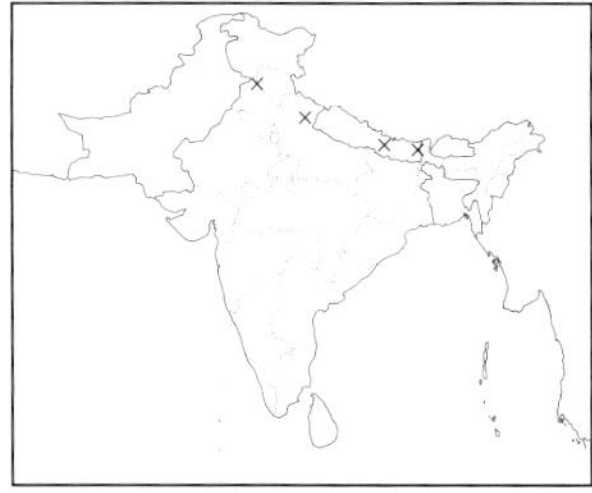

IDENTIFICATION 17 cm. A long-tailed, chestnut-rumped bunting. **Male** non-breeding has mainly chestnut supercilium and throat, whitish crown and patch on ear-coverts, whitish gorget below chestnut throat, and chestnut streaking across breast and flanks. Pale fringes to head feathers wear to reveal stronger white, black and chestnut head pattern in breeding plumage. Chestnut on supercilium and throat aids separation from male White-capped Bunting (p.853). **Female** lacks chestnut patterning to head (except for touch on supercilium and throat in worn plumage), and has dark streaking (mixed with some chestnut) across breast. Has more strongly marked head pattern than female White-capped, with prominent greyish supercilium, dark border to ear-coverts, and (usually) a pronounced pale spot at rear of ear-coverts; breast is more diffusely streaked, often with whitish patch on lower throat, and has white (rather than buff) belly and undertail-coverts. Pine Bunting is much larger than White-capped, and has very different call; further differences given under that species. Chestnut rump and streaking on breast/flanks, and different call are best distinctions from female Reed Bunting (p.857). For differences from Yellowhammer (p.851) and Rustic Bunting (p.855), see those species. **First-winter** as fresh-plumaged adult; head pattern of male more obscured by broader pale fringes. **VOICE** Calls include a short *dzik*, rasping *dzuh* and rolling *prullullu*; song is a rattling *tzi-tzi-tzi-tzi-tzi-tzuuh*. **HABITS** A typical bunting. Keeps in loose flocks of 20 or more, sometimes with Rock Bunting (below) or White-capped Bunting. Quite shy, often flying some distance if disturbed. Has a very upright stance when perched, but horizontal when foraging on the ground. Perches readily in bushes. Flocks often roost with other buntings and finches. **HABITAT** Stubble or fallow fields in dry hills. **DISTRIBUTION AND STATUS** Winter visitor. Hills of W and N Pakistan, and Himalayas from N Pakistan east to E Nepal. **PK:** locally frequent; recorded in the main far N valleys, Baluchistan and valleys and foothills around Peshawar, Kohat and Bannu. **NP:** irregular, fairly common in most years in the upper Kali Gandaki valley and in the northwest; mainly 2440–3050 m, occasionally down to 915 m. **IN:** fairly common; usually up to 1500 m, occasionally to 2700 m.

ROCK BUNTING *Emberiza cia* — Plate 152

Eurasian Rock-Bunting (K)

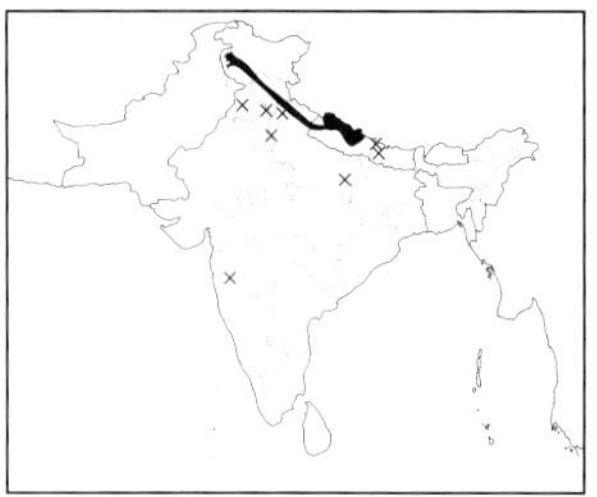

IDENTIFICATION 16 cm. **Male** has grey head and breast, with black lateral crown-stripes, supercilium and border to ear-coverts. Rest of underparts are deep rufous, mantle is rufous-brown, streaked with dark brown, and rump is deep rufous. Non-breeding and first-winter male are similar to breeding male, although head pattern is slightly obscured by buff fringes. **Female** is dull version of male, with similar although less striking head pattern (with grey of head/breast suffused with brown); belly and flanks are pale rufous and faintly streaked with brown. Head pattern and rufous underparts readily separate it from female White-capped (p.853). For differences from female Godlewski's and House Buntings (p.853 and p.854), see those species. **Juvenile** is warm buff, heavily streaked with brown, with dark border to ear-coverts; has rufous tinge to rump and belly. **Racial variation** Compared with *E. c. stracheyi* of W and C Himalayas, male *E. c. par* of extreme NW subcontinent has paler, more rufous-orange underparts and coloration to mantle; juvenile *par* is relatively pale, with sandy-buff belly and rump. **VOICE** Song is a fast and ringing *zit ziterit zit zit ziterit zit* (Jonsson 1992); calls include a sharp *tsee* and soft *yip*. **HABITS** A typical bunting. Depending on the season, found singly, in pairs or in small scattered flocks, often with finches, sparrows or Pine Bunting (p.852). Rather unobtrusive, but not shy. Usually has a half-upright posture. Hops and creeps on the ground when foraging, and flies up into trees or to rocky outcrops if disturbed. **HABITAT** Summers on dry, open grassy and rocky hillsides, edges of open coniferous forest and margins of terraced cultivation; winters also on stubbles and fallow fields in the lowlands. **BREEDING** May–August, varying with altitude. Builds nest on a steep slope at the base of a bush, under a grass tussock, or in a stone wall. **DISTRIBUTION AND STATUS** Resident, subject to altitudinal movements. Breeds in mountains of N and W Pakistan, and Himalayas from N Pakistan east to WC Nepal; winter visitor mainly to N Pakistan. **PK:** common and widespread; breeds in drier N mountains, 2000–4500 m, winters in N foothills and broader valleys and N plains. **NP:** common and widespread in WC areas and westwards; summers mainly 2440–4600 m, occasionally winters down to 1800 m. **IN:** common; breeds 2000–4200 m, winters in hills mainly up to 2100 m, vagrant to plains.

GODLEWSKI'S BUNTING *Emberiza godlewskii* Plate 152

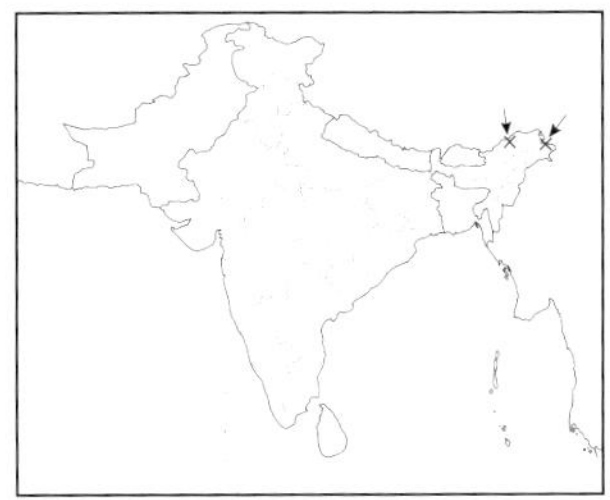

IDENTIFICATION Closely resembles Rock Bunting (p.852), but has E Himalayan distribution. **Male** as male Rock, but has dark chestnut (rather than black) lateral crown-stripes, stripe behind eye and rear border to ear-coverts. Lores and moustachial stripe are black, as on Rock. Median-covert wing-bar is white (rufous in races of Rock occurring in subcontinent). Male non-breeding and first-winter are similar to breeding male, but paler, with less striking head pattern. **Female** is very similar in plumage to respective male. **VOICE** Song is variable, with differences from Rock's not well understood, although apparently begins with higher-pitched *tsitt* notes; call as that of Rock (Byers *et al.* 1995). **HABITS** Like those of Rock Bunting. **HABITAT** Dry slopes with bushes and rocks. **BREEDING** June and July. Nest and nest site are like those of Rock Bunting. **DISTRIBUTION AND STATUS IN:** fairly common resident in N Arunachal Pradesh; breeds 2700–4200 m, winters 1500–3300 m.

GREY-NECKED BUNTING *Emberiza buchanani* Plate 152

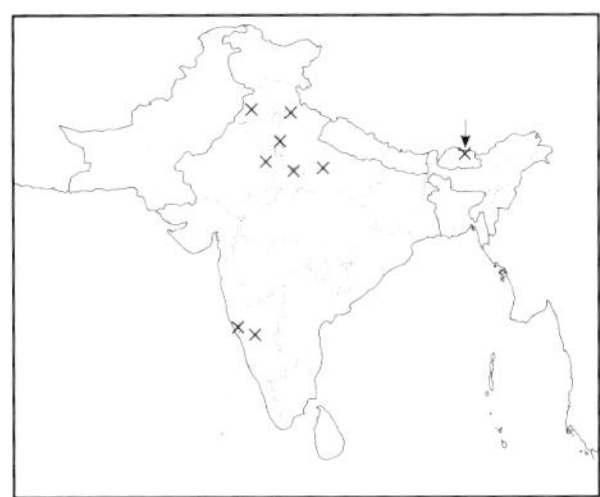

IDENTIFICATION 15 cm. In all plumages, has pinkish-orange bill and rather plain head with whitish eye-ring (and lacks supercilium and eye-stripe). For differences from the similar Ortolan Bunting (p.853), see that species. **Male** has blue-grey head with buffish or whitish submoustachial stripe and throat, deep rusty-pink breast and belly with variable diffuse whitish fringes, and diffusely streaked sandy-brown mantle with pronounced rufous scapulars. Rump is sandy-grey. **Female** is very similar to male, but generally paler, with buffish cast to grey head and nape (often with some streaking) which contrast less with mantle, which is less heavily streaked, and with paler/less extensive rusty-pink on breast; may show some dark spotting on breast. **First-winter/juvenile** often have only slight greyish cast to head, and underparts are warm buff (with variable rufous cast), while crown, malar region, breast and flanks are faintly streaked; many first-winter birds, however, are much as adult female. **VOICE** Song is a *sti-sti-stüe ste-stüe* (Jonsson 1992); call is a soft *click.* **HABITS** A typical bunting. Keeps in small flocks in winter, and in pairs when breeding. Hops and creeps inconspicuously on the ground. Has a half-upright to horizontal posture. Males sing from quite low bushes, stones or open ground. Flight is usually rather low over the ground. **HABITAT** Dry rocky hills with sparse bushes, and stony ground with scattered *Euphorbia* and *Acacia* bushes. **BREEDING** May and June. Builds nest on the ground under a stone, grass tussock or bush. **DISTRIBUTION AND STATUS** Summer visitor and passage migrant to Pakistan; winters mainly in Pakistan and C and W India. **PK:** scarce; mainly a passage migrant, breeds irregularly in Baluchistan, small numbers overwinter; recorded chiefly 1650–2000 m. **IN:** locally frequent. **BT:** vagrant.

ORTOLAN BUNTING *Emberiza hortulana* Plate 152

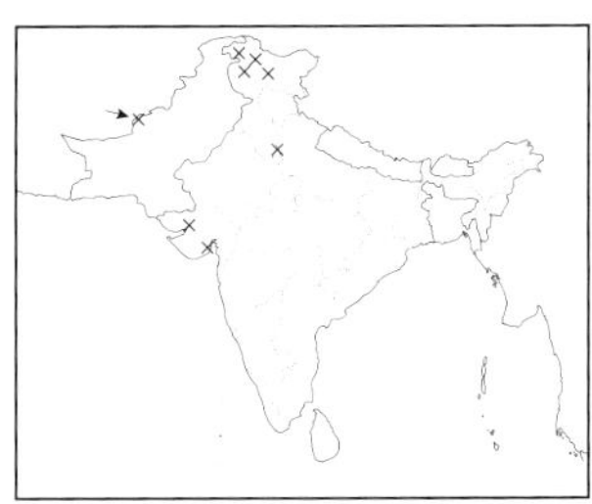

IDENTIFICATION 16 cm. Very similar to Grey-necked Bunting (p.853), with rather plain head, pinkish-orange bill, and prominent eye-ring. **Male** told from Grey-necked by olive cast to grey head, greyish-olive breast-band, pale yellow submoustachial stripe and throat, and more boldly streaked brown mantle. **Female** is similar to male, but duller, with dark streaking on more olive crown and nape, streaked malar stripe and dark streaking on breast; breast is greyish-yellow with a faint tinge of olive. Sexing is difficult, however, with some males inseparable from females. **First-winter/juvenile** have upperparts varying from greyish-brown to warm brown, submoustachial stripe and throat are buffish-white (often with touch of yellow, which helps separation from Grey-necked), and underparts are gingery-yellow; upperparts are more heavily streaked than on Grey-necked, and has heavily streaked malar stripe and patch and boldly streaked breast (with streaking continuing onto flanks). By comparison, first-winter/juvenile Grey-necked are inconspicuously and finely streaked above, and malar and upper breast are only finely streaked. Tertials of Ortolan have sharply defined black centres with distinctive 'step' shape (centres less well defined and more evenly shaped on Grey-necked). **VOICE** Song is a *tsie-tsie-tsie-tsie, truh-truh-truh* (Jonsson 1992); call is a soft *dip* or *plit.* **HABITS** A typical bunting, with behaviour very like that of Grey-necked. **HABITAT** Orchards, and grassy slopes with scattered bushes and trees. **DISTRIBUTION AND STATUS PK, IN:** vagrant. **REFERENCES** Harris *et al.* (1996), Svensson (1992).

WHITE-CAPPED BUNTING *Emberiza stewarti* Plate 152

Chestnut-breasted Bunting

IDENTIFICATION 15 cm. **Male** is readily told from male Rock Bunting (p.852) by grey head and upper breast, with black eye-stripe and throat. Mantle is chestnut, unstreaked or lightly streaked with dark brown, and breast-band and flanks are chestnut. In fresh (non-breeding) plumage, head and body patterns are partly obscured by

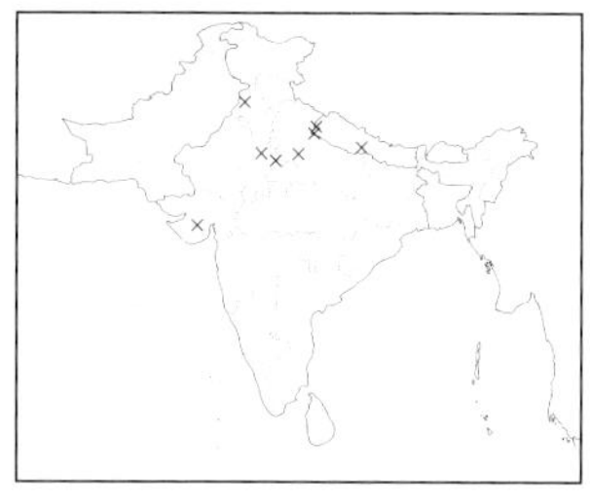

grey and buff feather fringes. Suggestion (at least) of black throat and supercilium, and chestnut on breast, always separate it from Rock Bunting. **Female** is a rather nondescript but well-streaked bunting which most closely resembles the larger female Pine Bunting (p.852), with chestnut rump and uppertail-coverts. However, call is very different; head looks plainer than on female Pine, with (generally) rather indistinct dark border to ear-coverts and less pronounced supercilium, but with rather prominent white pale eye-ring; crown and mantle are more uniformly and diffusely streaked; and, further, has more finely streaked breast and flanks, and underparts are washed with buff when fresh and greyish-white when worn (lacking striking white belly of Pine). May show chestnut on breast, which can be prominent and form breast-band in breeding plumage. **Juvenile** similar to female, but head is rather pale with indistinct streaking. **VOICE** Calls include a distinctive twitter, *chua-chua-chua*, very different from those of similar species; song is a monotonous *jing jing jing*. **HABITS** A typical bunting. Gathers in small flocks in winter, when often with other finches and buntings. Adopts a crouched horizontal posture when feeding; flies up into trees if disturbed. Perches freely on bushes, boulders or trees. **HABITAT** Dry grassy and rocky slopes on low hills, and dry scrub forest of juniper, olives or Chilgoza Pine; also fallow fields and waste ground with scattered bushes in winter. **BREEDING** Mid April–July. Builds nest on the ground under a bush, grass tussock or rock on a steep slope. **DISTRIBUTION AND STATUS** Breeds in mountains of W and N Pakistan, and Himalayas from N Pakistan east to N Uttar Pradesh; winters mainly in the foothills and lower valleys of N Pakistan and in NC India (E Rajasthan, Madhya Pradesh and N Maharashtra). **PK:** common; breeds 1675–3000 m. **NP:** vagrant. **IN:** locally common; breeds 1200–2700 m, winters in plains and hills up to 1800 m (–2500 m).

HOUSE BUNTING *Emberiza striolata* — Plate 152

Striolated Bunting (I)

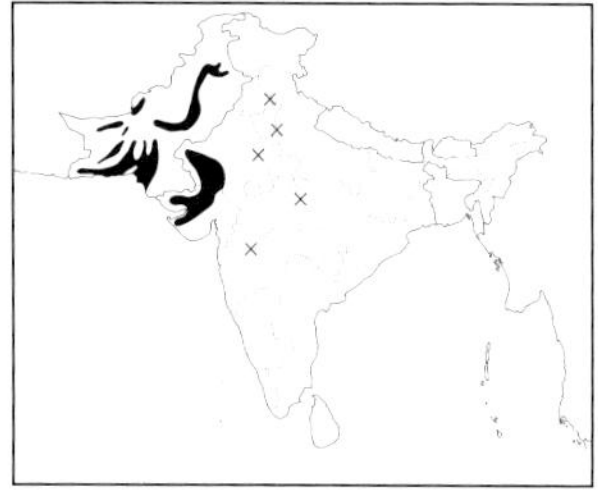

IDENTIFICATION 13–14 cm. Smaller and shorter-tailed than Rock Bunting (p.852). Lacks white on tail (Rock has much white on outer tail feathers), and has orange lower mandible (bill all grey on Rock). **Male** has different head pattern from Rock: has blackish eye-stripe and moustachial stripe, prominent whitish supercilium and submoustachial stripe, and blackish streaking on greyish crown, throat and breast. Further, underparts are brownish-buff (with variable rufous tinge), and wings appear mainly rufous and contrast with sandy-brown mantle and scapulars. **Female** is a dull version of male, with head pattern ghosting that of male (base colour of head is more sandy-brown and head stripes and streaking are browner). Most of above-mentioned features hold for separation from female Rock. **Juvenile** is browner than female, with less distinct head pattern, and with darker underparts (more yellowish-cinnamon). **VOICE** Song is a *which-which-wheech-whichy-which* (Ali and Ripley 1987); calls include a nasal *dschu* and a sparrow-like *tchiele* (Byers *et al.* 1995). **HABITS** A typical bunting. Found singly, in pairs or in small flocks, depending on the season. Tame and approachable. Forages unobtrusively, hopping about on the ground, adopting a rather level stance. Makes regular journeys to drink. Males sing from the tops of bushes or prominent boulders. Flight is fast and flitting. **HABITAT** Low, dry rocky hills with very sparse *Euphorbia* or thorn scrub, and ancient ruins; winters also in sandy plains and tamarisk scrub. Despite its name, does not frequent human habitation in the region. **BREEDING** End February–November. Builds nest under a rock on the ground. **DISTRIBUTION AND STATUS** Resident, subject to local movements. Pakistan and NW India (mainly W Rajasthan and Gujarat). **PK:** widespread and locally frequent; subject to local and erratic movements. **IN:** local and uncommon.

CHESTNUT-EARED BUNTING *Emberiza fucata* — Plate 153

Grey-headed Bunting (F,I)

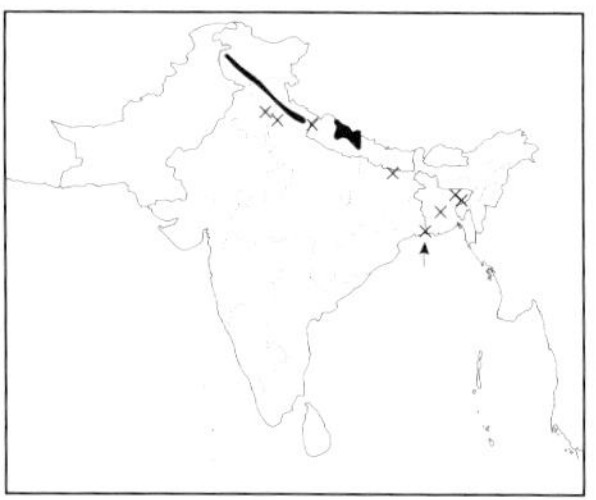

IDENTIFICATION 16 cm. **Male** distinguished from other buntings by combination of chestnut ear-coverts, finely streaked grey crown and nape, black streaking on white breast, and unstreaked chestnut lower breast and flanks. In fresh (non-breeding plumage) patterning is much obscured, although chestnut ear-coverts, black breast streaking and some chestnut on breast sides are usually apparent. **Female** in breeding and non-breeding plumages is similar in pattern to respective plumage of male, but duller and more washed out (e.g. crown and nape are more olive-grey, chestnut breast-band may be lacking, and chestnut ear-coverts are duller). **First-winter** male is much as adult male non-breeding. Some first-winter birds (mainly female?) are rather nondescript, with well-streaked olive-brown upperparts and buffish underparts with heavily streaked malar and breast: best identified by combination of rather plain head with warmer brown ear-coverts and slightly paler supercilium (lacking pronounced dark border to ear-coverts and dark lateral crown-stripes), prominent pale eye-ring, rufous rump, and pinkish lower mandible. **Juvenile** has a prominent white supercilium and dark-bordered whitish ear-coverts **VOICE** Song is rapid twittering *zwee zwizwezwizizi trup-*

trup; calls include an explosive *pzick*, a higher-pitched *zii* and a lower-pitched *chutt*. **HABITS** Very like those of other buntings. Keeps in small flocks in winter, and singly or in pairs in summer. Males sing from the top of a bush or the lower branches of a tree. Often roosts communally in reedbeds in winter. **HABITAT** Low hills with bushes, and dry rocky and grassy slopes; winters also in marshes, wet stubbles and grassland with bushes. Found in same habitat as White-capped Bunting (p.853) in Kashmir and Pakistan. **BREEDING** May–July. Builds nest on a steep slope under a grass tussock or in a grass clump under a bush. **DISTRIBUTION AND STATUS** Resident, subject to altitudinal movements, and winter visitor. Breeds in Himalayas from N Pakistan (Azad Kashmir, Kagan valley and N Chitral) east to C Nepal; winters in adjacent foothills and plains east to NE India and Bangladesh. **PK:** rare and local summer breeder, 1800–2400 m; winter movements are unknown. **NP:** uncommon, probably resident; has poorly understood altitudinal movements; recorded mainly in the west, 2135–2300 m in breeding season (–5000 m, presumably on passage), below 915 m in winter. **IN:** uncommon in Himalayas, locally common in winter in the northeast; breeds 1800–2700 m, winters in plains and foothills up to at least 1500 m. **BD:** locally common winter visitor. **REFERENCES** Lama (1993), Martens and Eck (1995).

LITTLE BUNTING *Emberiza pusilla* — Plate 153

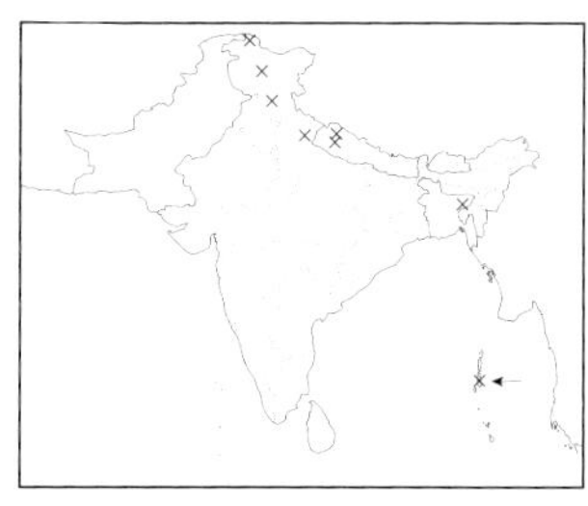

IDENTIFICATION 13 cm. A small bunting, confusable really only with female of the larger Reed Bunting (p.857). **Adult** has distinctive head pattern: has chestnut crown-stripe, supercilium and ear-coverts when worn (e.g. spring), although supercilium and crown can be paler buffish-white in fresh non-breeding plumage; lateral crown-stripes become blacker (with wear) in breeding plumage; also has prominent pale eye-ring, and lacks dark moustachial stripe. Further, has more pointed bill than Reed, with almost straight culmen, and has uniform grey-brown mantle, lightly streaked with dark brown (lacking pale 'braces'), more finely streaked breast and flanks, and more prominent pale median- and greater-covert wing-bars. **First-winter** much as adult, although head pattern duller. **VOICE** Call is a sharp *tzic*. **HABITS** A typical bunting. Usually found in small flocks. Unobtrusive. Flocks hop about on the ground with a horizontal posture. Readily perches in trees and bushes. **HABITAT** Stubbles, and ploughed or grass fields. **DISTRIBUTION AND STATUS** Winter visitor. Mainly from WC Nepal east to NE India. **PK:** vagrant. **NP:** fairly common and widespread; mainly below 2000 m (–3560 m). **IN:** common; chiefly below 1800 m. **BT:** fairly common; 400–3200 m. **BD:** rare in the northeast and southwest. **REFERENCES** Inskipp and Inskipp (1994).

RUSTIC BUNTING *Emberiza rustica* — Plate 153

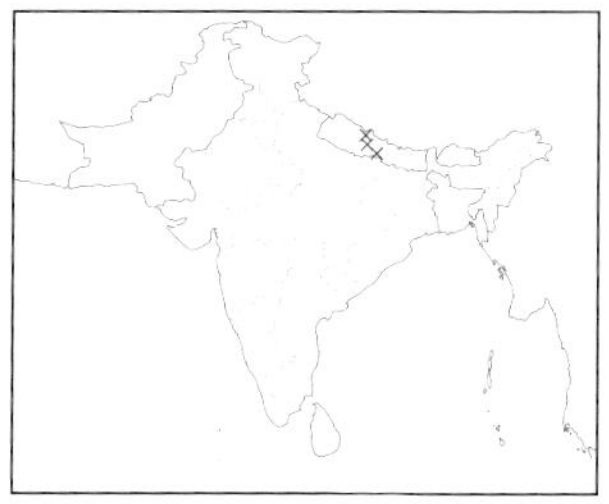

IDENTIFICATION 14–15 cm. Most likely to be confused with female Reed Bunting (p.857), but in all plumages separated by rufous streaking on breast and flanks, with whiter lower breast and belly, white tips to median and greater coverts which form well-defined wing-bars, pale spot on rear ear-coverts, pale spot on rear crown, at least a touch of rufous on nape, and larger bill with straighter culmen. Supercilium is typically whiter and more pronounced than on Reed. Crown feathers are frequently raised, resulting in crested appearance. Compared with Pine Bunting (p.852), is smaller and shorter-tailed, has rufous patch on nape (although this may be indistinct) and has more striking head pattern. Variable in winter (e.g. adult males showing strong head pattern with black lateral crown-stripes, broader white supercilium and more extensive rufous breast streaking). Through wear, male in breeding plumage has black ear-coverts and lateral crown-stripes strongly contrasting with white crown-stripe and supercilium, and rufous nape and breast-band. **VOICE** Call is a sharp *tzic*, similar to that of Little Bunting (above). **HABITS** Not described from the region, but very like those of other buntings. Restless and active, feeding quickly. Has a fairly horizontal stance on the ground, and often holds tail up. Rather upright when perched. **HABITAT** Mainly damp habitats. **DISTRIBUTION AND STATUS NP:** vagrant.

YELLOW-BREASTED BUNTING *Emberiza aureola* — Plate 153

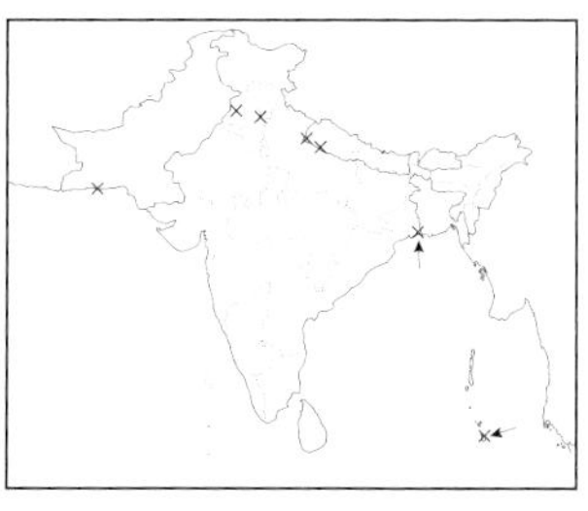

IDENTIFICATION 15 cm. A stocky, comparatively short-tailed bunting. Has more direct, less undulating flight compared with other buntings, when appears more weaver- or sparrow-like. **Male** is very distinctive, with yellow underparts, chestnut band across breast and streaking on flanks, and white shoulder patch. Black and chestnut of head are largely obscured by buffish fringes in fresh (non-breeding) plumage, and head pattern may then be similar to female's (with prominent supercilium, dark lateral crown-stripes and dark border to ear-coverts), but shows breast-band and white inner wing-coverts. In breeding plumage, black face and throat and chestnut of crown and mantle are revealed through wear. **Female** and **first-winter** have broad yellowish-white to pale yellow supercilium and a pale crown-stripe, yellowish-white to pale yellow breast and flanks, boldly streaked mantle (with pale 'braces' often apparent), and prominent white median-covert wing-bar; flanks may be lightly streaked. **Juvenile** as female, but underparts are paler yellowish-buff, and with fine, dense streaking on breast and flanks. Female, first-winter and juvenile confusable really only with Chestnut Bunting (below), but have more striking head pattern (with more prominent supercilium and dark border to ear-coverts), more heavily marked upperparts (e.g. with pronounced 'braces'), white median-covert bar, much white on tail, and indistinct or non-existent malar stripe; lack bright chestnut rump of that species. **VOICE** Calls include a soft *chup* or *tup*, and a metallic *tick* very like Little Bunting's (p.855). **HABITS** A typical bunting. Gregarious, often in large flocks, sometimes of many hundreds; can form huge roosts, e.g. over 7000 birds recorded in the Nepal terai. Not shy, and is easily observed. Hops and creeps inconspicuously on the ground, and flies up into bushes and trees if disturbed. **HABITAT** Cultivation and grassland. **DISTRIBUTION AND STATUS** Winter visitor and passage migrant. Nepal, India (mainly northeast) and Bangladesh. **PK:** vagrant. **NP:** common below 1370 m; mainly a passage migrant, some birds overwinter. **IN:** common winter visitor to the northeast, rare elsewhere. **BD:** local winter visitor and passage migrant to the northeast and southeast. **REFERENCES** Alström and Colston (1991).

CHESTNUT BUNTING *Emberiza rutila* — Plate 153

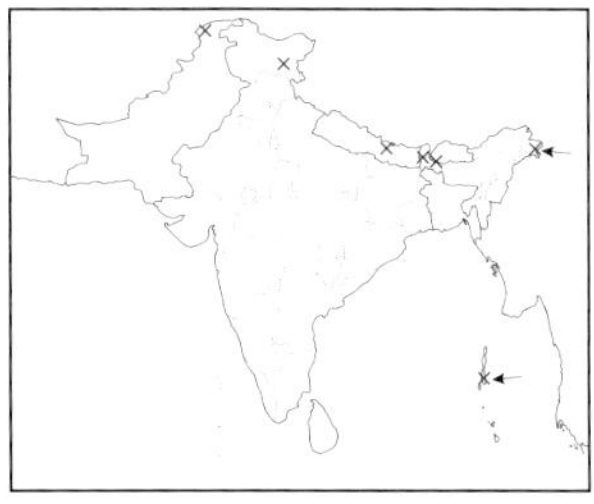

IDENTIFICATION 14 cm. A small, short-tailed bunting. **Male** is very distinctive, with chestnut head, breast and upperparts, and pale yellow belly. In fresh non-breeding plumage, chestnut of head and upperparts appears duller owing to pale fringes. **Female** and **first-winter** have yellowish underparts, and are most likely to be confused with female/first-winter Yellow-breasted Bunting (p.855). Chestnut is smaller and slighter, with finer bill; also has less striking head pattern (with indistinct buffish supercilium, and lacking prominent dark border to ear-coverts), more finely streaked mantle, and bright and unstreaked chestnut rump, and there is little or no white on tail. Throat is creamy-white or buff and never yellow (often so on Yellow-breasted), and contrasts markedly with yellow of rest of underparts. Some first-winter males can show chestnut on crown, ear-coverts and/or breast. **Juvenile** is similar to female, but is more heavily streaked, and has a whiter and more prominent supercilium. Female and first-winter can be separated from respective plumages of Black-faced Bunting (p.857) by chestnut rump, buffish throat and brighter yellow underparts (lacking bold dark streaking on flanks shown by Black-faced), and lack of prominent white on tail. **VOICE** Call is a *tick*, as Little Bunting's (p.855). **HABITS** Very like those of other buntings. Unobtrusive. **HABITAT** Rice stubbles, forest clearings, and open forest and scrub. **DISTRIBUTION AND STATUS** Winter visitor, mainly to NE India (Arunachal Pradesh, Assam, Manipur, Mizoram, West Bengal). **PK:** vagrant. **IN:** scarce. **NP:** vagrant.

BLACK-HEADED BUNTING *Emberiza melanocephala* — Plate 153

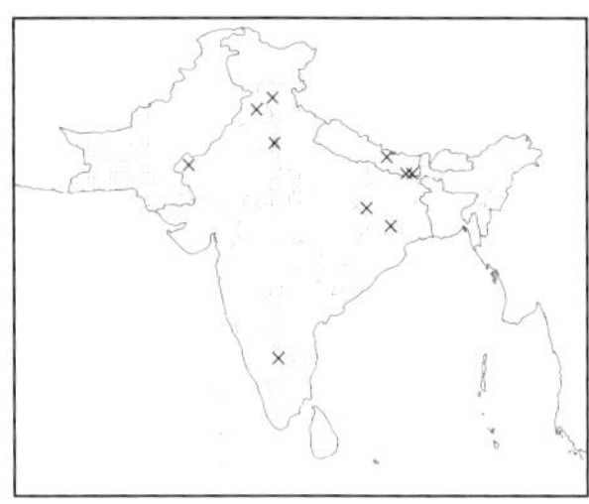

IDENTIFICATION 16–18 cm. A large bunting with a long, full tail that lacks any white. **Male** told from Red-headed Bunting (below) by largely black head and chestnut upperparts, including rump. In fresh (non-breeding) plumage, black of head and chestnut of upperparts are largely obscured by pale fringes. **Female/ first-year** in breeding (worn) plumage show ghost pattern of male, with greyish-olive head and rufous tinge to mantle and back. In fresh plumage, adult female and first-year birds of both sexes are variable, and very difficult to separate from Red-headed (and often not safely distinguishable in field). Features for Black-headed which can be apparent include larger size and longer bill, rufous tinge to mantle and/or back, slight contrast between throat and greyish ear-coverts, and more uniform yellowish underparts. Further details are given under Red-headed. **First-winter** birds are usually streaked or spotted on breast, with this plumage moulted during winter. **VOICE** Call is a *pyiup* or *tyilp*; flight call is a *pchlü* or *plüt* (Jonsson 1992). **HABITS** A typical bunting. Highly gregarious in winter and on passage, sometimes forming huge flocks with Red-headed Buntings which inflict widespread damage on standing crops. Forms large communal roosts in thickets, often with finches and sparrows. Hops on the ground with a fairly upright stance. **HABITAT** Cereal crops. **DISTRIBUTION AND STATUS** Winter visitor and passage migrant. Pakistan, India (mainly from Gujarat east to C Madhya Pradesh and E Maharashtra, and south to C Karnataka) and Nepal. **PK:** common and widespread passage migrant in lower Sindh and S Baluchistan. **NP:** scarce winter visitor, recorded mainly from the E terai (–1340 m). **IN:** common winter visitor in the west and centre.

RED-HEADED BUNTING *Emberiza bruniceps* — Plate 153

IDENTIFICATION 16 cm. A large bunting with long, full tail which lacks any white. **Male** told from male Black-headed Bunting (above) by mainly rufous head and breast, yellowish-green mantle and scapulars with dark streaking, and yellow rump and uppertail-coverts. In fresh (non-breeding) plumage, rufous of head is partly obscured by pale fringes. **Female** and **first-year** have sandy-brown crown and mantle, rather plain head with whitish eye-ring, pale-fringed black-centred median coverts, and buffish-white to pale yellowish underparts with yellow vent. Some (worn) females show rufous on head and breast, or yellow tinge to crown or mantle, and are

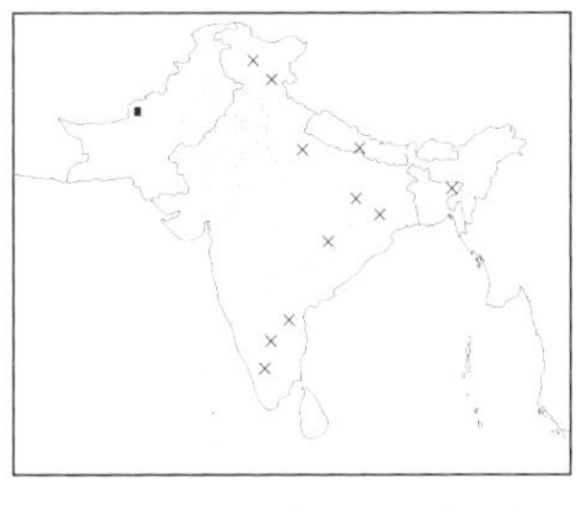

then distinguishable. Others are very difficult to separate from Black-headed, and often indistinguishable (following differences after Byers *et al.* 1996, which see for further details). Red-headed is slightly smaller, with a slightly shorter primary projection (four instead of five primaries showing, although with some overlap); bill of Red-headed is slightly shorter and more conical. On Black-headed, the ear-coverts are a shade darker, often greyer, particularly below and in front of eye, and contrast more with throat than on Red-headed, which has browner ear-coverts. The mantle tends to be more distinctly streaked on Red-headed (although much overlap), and the back probably never has a rufous tinge, which it often does on Black-headed. After a complete winter moult, there are two different female-type plumages in both species: one with most of underparts yellow (possibly adult female), the other with underparts mainly whitish or buff with yellow undertail-coverts (possibly first-year). Red-headed with yellow underparts has a paler yellow or whitish-buff throat than breast, with a (shade) darker buff breast-band (these areas generally concolorous on Black-headed); forehead and crown are, on average, less prominently streaked (often virtually unstreaked); and rump is usually brighter yellow; the wing-bars tend to be buffier. Black-headed with yellow underparts often shows greyer crown and rufous-tinged mantle (Red-headed shows no significant colour difference between crown and mantle). Birds with whitish or buff underparts are even more difficult and many are probably best left unidentified; although the differences mentioned above apply, they are even more subtle. **First-winter** birds are usually streaked or spotted on breast, with this plumage moulted during winter: in this plumage, characters of the two species overlap to such an extent that identification is usually not possible (although differences in crown streaking and contrast between ear-coverts and throat, mentioned above, are indicative). **VOICE** Call is a *tliip* or *tlyp*, a rather harsh *jyp* and a *prrit* (Alström and Colston 1991). **HABITS** Very like those of Black-headed Bunting, and often associates with that species. **HABITAT** Cultivation, especially cereals. **BREEDING** May and June. Nest well hidden, usually low down in a bush. **DISTRIBUTION AND STATUS** Winter visitor and passage migrant; has bred. Mainly Pakistan and India from S Jammu south to C Karnataka and east to W Uttar Pradesh and N Andhra Pradesh. **PK:** common passage migrant, mainly in N Sindh and S Punjab, also passes through N Baluchistan and NW Pakistan in spring; small numbers have bred in Baluchistan, but not recently. **NP:** vagrant. **IN:** common winter visitor in the west and centre. **BD:** ?former winter visitor to the northeast; no recent records.

BLACK-FACED BUNTING *Emberiza spodocephala* — Plate 153

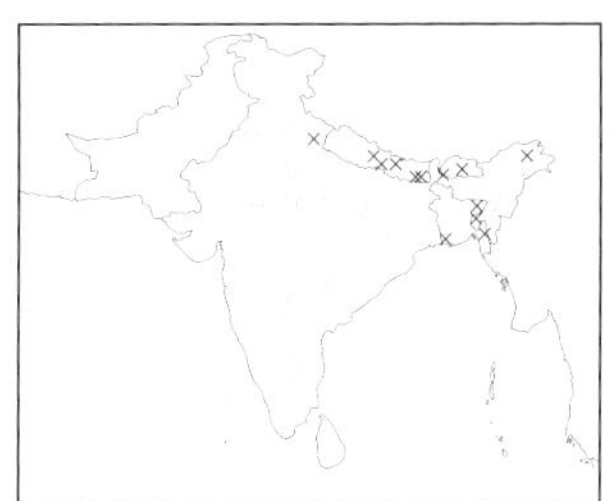

IDENTIFICATION 15cm. A small bunting with rather fine bill. **Male** is very distinctive, with blackish lores and chin forming indistinct mask, greenish-grey head and breast, and yellow rest of underparts. In non-breeding (fresh) plumage, head is duller and may show yellowish throat and submoustachial stripe, indistinct yellowish supercilium, and dark malar stripe. **Female** typically has yellowish supercilium and submoustachial stripe, and pale oily yellow underparts with variable olive-grey on neck sides and wash across breast (breast is diffusely streaked, with strong streaking on flanks); yellow wash may be faint on some; upperparts are a rather cold grey-brown and strongly streaked. May lack supercilium, when sides of head and crown rather uniform. Told from Chestnut Bunting (p.856) by greyish-olive (rather than chestnut) rump and uppertail-coverts and prominent white on tail; pale yellow background colours of throat and breast are concolorous (lacking striking contrast between buffish throat and yellow underparts shown by Chestnut), and olive-grey wash to breast and strong streaking on flanks are further differences. **VOICE** Call is a soft *tsip* or a slightly sharper *tzit.* **HABITS** A typical bunting. Found singly, in pairs or in small flocks. Usually forages in or near cover. **HABITAT** Stands of long grass, edges of marshes, paddy stubbles and standing paddy; also mangroves in Bangladesh. Often near water. **DISTRIBUTION AND STATUS** Winter visitor and passage migrant. Mainly from C Nepal east to NE India and Bangladesh. **NP:** uncommon and local; occurs below 1280 m. **IN:** common in the northeast in hills; up to 1000 m. **BT:** vagrant. **BD:** rare in the southeast, south and northeast.

REED BUNTING *Emberiza schoeniclus* — Plate 153

Common Reed-Bunting (K)

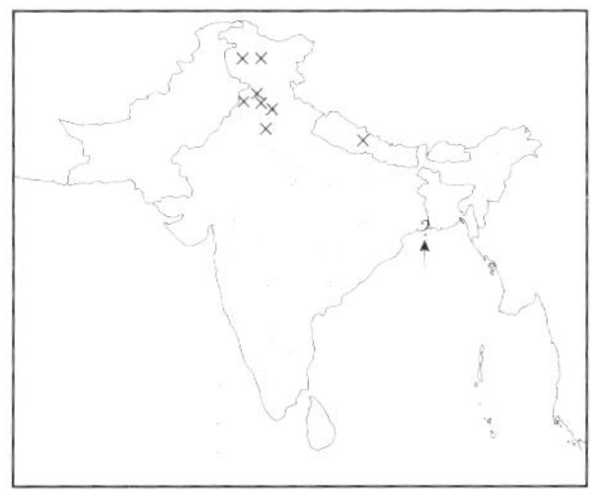

IDENTIFICATION 14–15 cm. **Male** in breeding plumage distinguished from other buntings by blackish head and breast with prominent white submoustachial stripe. In fresh (non-breeding) plumage, black of head and throat/breast is obscured by brownish fringes and shows dark lateral crown-stripes and buffish supercilium and submoustachial stripe. **Female** superficially resembles Little Bunting (p.855), but lacks warm chestnut on lores, ear-coverts and supercilium, and black moustachial stripe and malar stripe reach bill; further, has more boldly streaked mantle, often showing pale 'braces', less prominent rufous-brown wing-bars, bolder but more diffuse streaking on breast and flanks, and stouter bill with convex culmen. In worn (breeding) plumage, crown and ear-coverts of female appear uniformly dark, contrasting with white supercilium and submoustachial stripe. **First-winter male** usually shows black on throat and breast. For differences from Rustic and Black-faced Buntings (p.855 and p.857), see those species. **Racial variation** There is one record of a large-billed race *E. s. pyrrhuloides*, but this is now considered doubtful. **VOICE** Call is a distinctive *tseeu* and a harsh *chirp*. **HABITS** A typical bunting. Keeps singly, in pairs or in small flocks. Has a very upright stance when perched. Frequently flicks and spreads tail, showing white outer feathers. Hops and creeps when foraging, with body horizontal and tail held up. Flight is jerky and undulating. **HABITAT** Reedbeds, irrigated crops. **DISTRIBUTION AND STATUS** Winter visitor. Mainly Pakistan, also NW India (Jammu and Kashmir, Punjab, Haryana and Delhi). **PK:** locally frequent, mainly in riverain tracts in N Punjab. **IN:** rare. **NP:** vagrant.

CORN BUNTING *Miliaria calandra* — Plate 153

***Emberiza calandra* (I)**

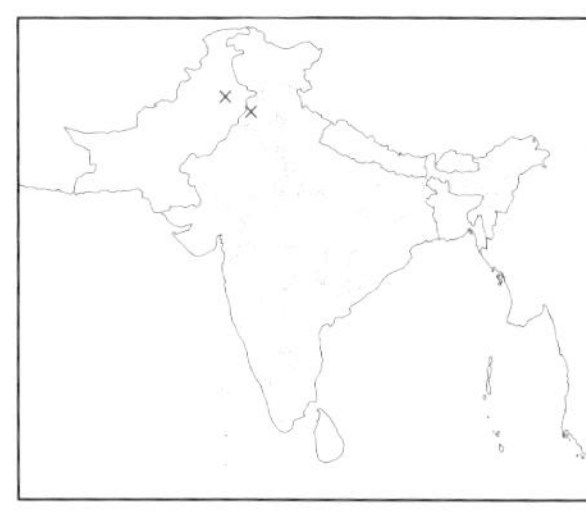

IDENTIFICATION 18 cm. A large, buff-brown and well-streaked bunting. Lacks white on tail. Distinguished from female and first-year Red-headed and Black-headed Buntings (p.856) by stockier shape and shorter tail, stouter pale (rather than grey) bill, boldly streaked upperparts and underparts (with streaks often coalescing on breast to form patch), indistinct buffish supercilium contrasting slightly with dark-streaked crown, absence of any yellow on underparts, with off-white (rather than yellow) vent, and brownish (rather than rufous or yellowish) rump concolorous with rest of upperparts. Some first-year Red-headed may be almost as heavily streaked, but other features still hold. **VOICE** Call is a very hard *tik* and a rolling *dchrrut*. **HABITS** Usually in small flocks in winter. Perches readily on telegraph wires and bushes; occasionally flicks wings and tail. Has a powerful undulating flight. **HABITAT** Cultivation, especially stubbles. **DISTRIBUTION AND STATUS PK, IN:** vagrant. **REFERENCES** Robson (1996a).

REFERENCES

A huge number of references was used to write this book and it is not possible to list all of them. The main references specific to the Indian subcontinent are marked with an asterisk (*).

Anon. (1979) *University of Southampton Himalayan Expedition 1977 Report.* University of Southampton.

Anon. (1992a) Recently seen! *Nepal Bird Watching Club Bull.* 1–2: 6.

Anon. (1992b) Recently seen! *Nepal Bird Watching Club Bull.* 3: 2–3.

Anon. (1993) Manas...and the jungles of Bhutan. P.9 in *Naturetrek 1993.* Alresford.

Anon. (1994) From the field: India. *Oriental Bird Club Bull.* 19: 65–66.

Abdulali, H. (1964) Some notes on the Painted Partridge [*Francolinus pictus* (Jardine & Selby)] around Bombay. *J. Bombay Nat. Hist. Soc.* 61: 444–449.

Abdulali, H. (1966) Notes on Indian birds, 5 – The races of *Apus affinis* (J.E. Gray) in the Indian region. *J. Bombay Nat. Hist. Soc.* 62: 521–528.

***Abdulali, H.** (1973) *Checklist of the Birds of Maharashtra with Notes on their Status around Bombay.* Bombay Natural History Society, Bombay.

Abdulali, H. (1976) On the validity of *Riparia riparia indica* Ticehurst and extension of range of *Riparia riparia ijimae* (Lönnberg). *J. Bombay Nat. Hist. Soc.* 72: 853–854.

Abdulali, H. (1980) A catalogue of the birds in the collection of the Bombay Natural History Society. Parts 1–17 – Non-Passeriformes. Errata. *J. Bombay Nat. Hist. Soc.* 77: 145–148.

Abdulali, H., and Hussain, S. A. (1971) Extension of the breeding range of Sykes's Nightjar (*Caprimulgus mahrattensis* Sykes) in Indian limits. *J. Bombay Nat. Hist. Soc.* 68: 452.

***Abdulali, H., and Panday, J. D.** (1978) *Checklist of the Birds of Delhi, Agra and Bharatpur with Notes on their Status in the Neighbourhood.* Published by the author, Bombay.

Abdulali, H., and Unnithan, S. (1985) Removal of the Northern Leaf Warbler *Phylloscopus trochilus acredula* (Linnaeus) from the Indian avifauna. *J. Bombay Nat. Hist. Soc.* 83: 209.

***Ali, S.** (1945) *The Birds of Kutch.* Oxford University Press, Bombay.

Ali, S. (1949) *Indian Hill Birds.* Oxford University Press, Bombay. (Reprinted 1979)

***Ali, S.** (1954–1955) The birds of Gujarat. *J. Bombay Nat. Hist. Soc.* 52: 374–458, 735–802.

***Ali, S.** (1962) *The Birds of Sikkim.* Oxford University Press, Madras.

***Ali, S.** (1969) *Birds of Kerala.* Oxford University Press, New Delhi.

Ali, S. (1977) *Field Guide to the Birds of the Eastern Himalayas.* Oxford University Press, Delhi.

Ali, S. (1996) *The Book of Indian Birds.* Twelfth revised and enlarged centenary edition. Bombay Natural History Society, Bombay.

***Ali, S., and Abdulali, H.** (1941) *The Birds of Bombay and Salsette.* Prince of Wales Museum, Bombay.

***Ali, S., and Ripley, S. D.** (1948) The birds of the Mishmi Hills. *J. Bombay Nat. Hist. Soc.* 48: 1–37.

***Ali, S., and Ripley, S. D.** (1987) *Compact Handbook of the Birds of India and Pakistan.* Oxford University Press, Bombay.

***Ali, S., and Whistler, H.** (1933–1934) The Hyderabad State ornithological survey. *J. Bombay Nat. Hist. Soc.* 36: 356–390, 707–725, 898–919; 37: 124–142, 425–454.

***Ali, S., and Whistler, H.** (1939–1940) The birds of central India. *J. Bombay Nat. Hist. Soc.* 41: 82–106, 470–488.

***Ali, S., and Whistler, H.** (1942–1943) The birds of Mysore. *J. Bombay Nat. Hist. Soc.* 43: 130–147, 318–341, 573–595; 44: 9–26, 206–220.

Ali, S., Biswas, B., and Ripley, S. D. (1996) The birds of Bhutan. *Rec. Zool. Surv. India, Occ. Pap.* 136.

Allen, D., Anderton, J., and Kazmierczak, K. (1997) Report on an ornithological visit to Buxa Tiger Reserve, West Bengal, India, 17 February to 6 March 1992. *Forktail* 12: 31–48.

Alström, P [= Alstom] (1994) Common Gull *Larus canus* Linnaeus recorded in India. *J. Bombay Nat. Hist. Soc.* 90: 509–510.

Alström, P. (1997) Field identification of Asian *Gyps* vultures. *Oriental Bird Club* 25: 32–49.

Alström, P. (1998) Taxonomy of the *Mirafra assamica* complex. *Forktail* 13: 97–107.

Alström, P., and Colston, P. (1991) *A Field Guide to the Rare Birds of Britain and Europe.* HarperCollins, London.

Alström, P., and Hirschfeld, E. (1991) Field identification of Brown, Siberian and Grey-streaked Flycatchers. *Birding World* 4: 271–278.

Alström, P., and MacKay, A. (1995) Identification of Siberian, Black-throated, Arabian and Brown Accentors. *Birding World* 8: 108–112.

Alström, P., and Mild, K. (1987) Some notes on the taxonomy of the Water Pipit complex. *Proc. 4th Int. Ident. Meeting,* Eilat: 47–48.

Alström, P., and Mild, K. (1996) The identification of Rock, Water and Buff-bellied Pipits. *Alula* 2: 161–175.

Alström, P., and Olsson, U. (1987) Field identification of Arctic and Greenish Warblers. *Proc. 4th Int. Ident. Meeting,* Eilat: 54–59.

Alström, P., and Olsson, U. (1994) Identification of Tickell's and Buff-throated Warblers. *Dutch Birding* 16: 89–94.

***Ara, J.** (1953) Field notes on the birds of the Kolhan Forest Division (Singbhum District, Bihar). *J. Bengal Nat.*

Hist. Soc. 26: 9–20, 56–67.
***Ash, J. S., and Shafeeg, A.** (1995) The birds of the Maldives. *Forktail* 10: 3–31.
Aspinall, S. (1996) Yellow-eyed Stock Dove. *Birding World* 9: 148–149.
Athreya, R. M., Captain, A. S., and Athreya, V. R. (1997) A Faunal Survey of Namdapha Tiger Reserve, Arunachal Pradesh, India. Unpublished report to Oriental Bird Club.

Baker, E. C. S. (1922–1930) *The Fauna of British India. Birds.* Second edition. 8 vols. Taylor and Francis, London.
Bakewell, D. N., Carey, G. J., and Williams, M. D. (1988) Some notes on `ringtail' harriers occurring in Hong Kong. *Hong Kong Bird Report 1987*: 64–67.
Balachandran, S. (1991) Bird records from Mandapam and neighbouring islands, Tamil Nadu. *J. Bombay Nat. Hist. Soc.* 87: 456–457.
Balachandran, S. (1992) Occurrence of White or Longtailed Tropic-bird *Phaethon lepturus* on the south-east coast of India. *J. Bombay Nat. Hist. Soc.* 88: 441–442.
Banks, J., and Banks, J. (1987) A note on the first discovery of the nest and eggs of the Ashy-headed Babbler *Garrulax cinereifrons*, an endemic species of Sri Lanka, in 1984. *J. Bombay Nat. Hist. Soc.* 84: 682–684.
Bapat, N. N. (1993) Sind Jungle Sparrow *Passer pyrrhonotus* Blyth in north-west Gujarat. *J. Bombay Nat. Hist. Soc.* 89: 378.
Baral, H. S. (1993) Status of storks, ibises and spoonbills in Nepal. *Specialist Group on Storks, Ibises, and Spoonbills Newsletter* 6(1/2): 6–8.
Baral, H. S. (1996) Grassland birds of Nepal. *Bird Conservation Nepal Newsletter* 4(4)/5(1): 4.
Baral, H. S. (1997) Bristled Grassbirds *Chaetornis striatus* in Nepal. *Danphe* 6(2): 5.
Baral, H. S. (1998) Finn's Weaver *Ploceus megarhynchus* and Singing Bushlark *Mirafra cantillans*: two new species for Nepal. *Forktail* 13: 129–131.
Barooah, D. (1994) Birds of Panidihing. *Newsletter for Birdwatchers* 34: 83–86.
Barua, M (1995a) Bird observations from Chakrashila Wildlife Sanctuary and adjacent areas. *Newsletter for Birdwatchers* 35: 93–94.
Barua, M. (1995b) Occurrence of the Rufous-vented Prinia (*Prinia burnesii*) in Pabitora Wildlife Sanctuary, Assam. *Newsletter for Birdwatchers* 35: 115.
***Bates, R. S. P., and Lowther, E. H. N.** (1952) *Breeding Birds of Kashmir.* Oxford University Press, Bombay.
Becking, J. H. (1981) Notes on the breeding of Indian cuckoos. *J. Bombay Nat. Hist. Soc.* 78: 201–231.
van den Berg, A., Smeenk, C., Bosman, C. A. W., Haase, B. J. M., van der Niet, A. M., and Cadée, G. C. (1991) Barau's Petrel *Pterodroma baraui*, Jouanin's Petrel *Bulweria fallax* and other seabirds in the northern Indian Ocean in June–July 1984 and 1985. *Ardea* 79: 1–14.
***Betts, F. N.** (1947) Bird life in an Assam jungle. *J. Bombay Nat. Hist. Soc.* 46: 667–684.
***Betts, F. N.** (1951) The birds of Coorg. *J. Bombay Nat. Hist. Soc.* 50: 20–63, 224–263.
Bhattacharjee, P. C., and Saikia, P. (1995) Greater Adjutant Stork – conservation in Assam. Pp. 37–38 in L. Vijayan (ed.), *Avian Conservation in India.* SACON, Coimbatore.
Bhushan, B. (1986) Rediscovery of the Jerdon's or Double-banded Courser *Cursorius bitorquatus* (Blyth). *J. Bombay Nat. Hist. Soc.* 83: 1–14.
Bhushan, B. (1990a) Jerdon's Courser – rediscovery and survey. Pp. 127–134 in Anon., *Status and Ecology of the Lesser and Bengal Floricans with Reports on Jerdon's Courser and Mountain Quail.* Bombay Natural History Society, Bombay.
Bhushan, B. (1990b) Report on the rediscovery of the Jerdon's or Doublebanded Courser *Cursorius bitorquatus* by the Bombay Natural History Society. *Mayura* 7 & 8: 1–3.
Biswas, B. (1959) On the parakeet *Psittacula intermedia* (Rothschild) (Aves: Psittacidae). *J. Bombay Nat. Hist. Soc.* 56: 558–562.
Biswas, B. (1968) The female of Molesworth's Tragopan *Tragopan blythii molesworthi* Baker. *J. Bombay Nat. Hist. Soc.* 65: 216–217.
Boonsong Lekagul and Round, P. D. (1991) *A Guide to the Birds of Thailand.* Saha Karn Bhaet, Bangkok.
Bradshaw, C. (1994) Blyth's Pipit identification. *British Birds* 87: 136–142.
***Briggs, F. S.** (1931) A note on the birds in the neighbourhood of Mhow. *J. Bombay Nat. Hist. Soc.* 35: 382–404.
Britton, D. J. (1984) Identification pitfalls and assessment problems 9. Richard's Pipit *Anthus novaeseelandiae* and Tawny Pipit *A. campestris. British Birds* 77: 412–415.
Britton, P. L. (1982) Identification of White-cheeked Tern. *Dutch Birding* 4: 55–57.
Brooks, W. E. (1875) Notes on a new *Dumeticola*, and on *Tribura luteoventris*, Hodgson, and *Dumeticola affinis*, Hodgson. *Stray Feathers* 3: 284–287.
Brown, L., and Amadon D. (1968) *Eagles, Hawks and Falcons of the World.* 2 vols. Country Life Books, Feltham.
Buckton, S., and Morris, P. (1990) India and Nepal, Dec 1989–June 1990. Unpublished.
Buckton, S., and Morris, P. (1993) Observations of Wood Snipe *Gallinago nemoricola* in Nepal. *Oriental Bird Club Bull.* 17: 31–35.
Burton, J. A. (ed.) (1984) *Owls of the World: their Evolution, Structure and Ecology.* Revised edition. Peter Lowe, London.
Butler, A. L. (1899–1900) The birds of the Andaman and Nicobar Islands. *J. Bombay Nat. Hist. Soc.* 12: 386–403, 555–571, 684–696; 13: 144–154.
***Butler, E. A.** (1875–1876) Notes on the avifauna of Mount Aboo and northern Guzerat. *Stray Feathers* 3: 437–500; 4: 1–41.

*__Butler, E. A.__ (1881) A tentative catalogue of the birds of the Deccan and south Mahratta country. *Stray Feathers* 9: 367–442.

Byers, C., Olsson, U., and Curson, J. (1995) *Buntings and Sparrows: a Guide to the Buntings and North American Sparrows.* Pica Press, Mountfield.

Carey, G. J. (1993) The status and field identification of snipe in Hong Kong. *Hong Kong Bird Report* 1992: 139–152.

Carey, G. J., and Leader, P. J. (1994) Juvenile terns in Hong Kong: a summary of identification. *Hong Kong Bird Report* 1993: 184–189.

Carey, G., and Olsson, U. (1995). Field identification of Common, Wilson's, Pintail and Swinhoe's Snipes. *Birding World* 8: 179–190.

Chacko, T. (1992) Black-necked Cranes wintering in Bhutan. *Oriental Bird Club Bull.* 16: 36–38.

Chakravarthy, A. K., Sandhu, P. S., and Rao, P. K. A. (1981) Lesser Grey Shrike (*Lanius minor*) off Sukhna Lake. *Newsletter for Birdwatchers* 21(6): 11.

*__Chakravarthy, A. K., and Tejasri, K. P. P. C.__ (1992) *Birds of Hill Region of Karnataka: An Introduction.* Narbarath Enterprises, Bangalore.

Chantler, P., and Driessens, G. (1995) *Swifts, A Guide to the Swifts and Treeswifts of the World.* Pica Press, Mountfield.

Choudhary, H. (1996a) Additional sightings! *Bird Conservation Nepal Bull.* 4(4)/5(1): 2–3.

Choudhary, H. (1996b) Additional sightings! *Bird Conservation Nepal Bull.* 5(2): 2–3.

Choudhary, H. (1996c) Additional sightings! *Bird Conservation Nepal Bull.* 5(4): 2.

*__Choudhury, A.__ (1990) *Checklist of the Birds of Assam.* Sofia Publishers, Guwahati.

Choudhury, A. (1994) Bird Survey of Dibru-Saikhowa Wildlife Sanctuary, Assam, India. Unpublished report to Oriental Bird Club.

Choudhury, A. (1996a) *Survey of the White-winged Duck and the Bengal Florican in Tinsukia District and adjacent areas of Assam and Arunachal Pradesh.* The Rhino Foundation for Nature in North-East India, Guwahati.

Choudhury, A. (1996b) Status and conservation of the cranes in north-east India. Paper presented at the Bombay Natural History Society Salim Ali Centenary Seminar on Conservation of Avifauna of Wetlands and Grasslands, February 12–15 1996, Mumbai.

Choudhury, A. (1996c) Recent records of the White-bellied Heron from Assam and Arunachal Pradesh. Abstract. Paper presented at the Salim Ali Centenary Seminar on Conservation of Avifauna of Wetlands and Grasslands, February 12–15 1996, Mumbai.

Choudhury, A. (1997) New localities for Blyth's Tragopan from Nagaland, India. *Tragopan* 6: 11–12.

Clark, W. S. (1992) The taxonomy of Steppe and Tawny Eagles, with criteria for separation of museum specimens and live eagles. *Bull. Brit. Orn. Club* 112: 150–156.

Clark, W. S., and Khan, A. A. (1995) Sightings of two rare raptors, Lesser Spotted Eagle *Aquila pomarina* and Pied Harrier *Circus melanoleucos*, in Pakistan. *Forktail* 10: 173–175.

Clark, W. S., and Schmitt, N. J. (1993) Field identification of the Rufous-bellied Eagle *Hieraaetus kienerii. Forktail* 8: 7–9.

Clark, W. S., and Shirihai, H. (1995) Identification of Barbary Falcon. *Birding World* 8: 336–343.

Clarke, R. (1996) *Montagu's Harrier.* Arlequin Press, Chelmsford.

Clement, P. (1987) Field identification of Western Palearctic wheatears. *British Birds* 80: 137–157, 187–238.

Clement, P., Harris, A., and Davis, J. (1993) *Finches and Sparrows.* Christopher Helm, London.

Clement, P., and Worfolk, T. (1995) Southern and eastern Great Grey Shrikes in northwest Europe. *Birding World* 8: 300–309.

Clements, F. A. (1992) Recent records of birds from Bhutan. *Forktail* 7: 57–73.

Collar, N. J., and Andrew, P. (1988) *Birds to Watch.* International Council for Bird Preservation, Cambridge.

Collar, N. J., Crosby, M. J., and Stattersfield, A. J. (1994) *Birds to Watch 2, the World List of Threatened Birds.* BirdLife International, Cambridge.

Colston, P., and Burton, P. (1988) *A Field Guide to the Waders of Britain and Europe with North Africa and the Middle East.* Hodder and Stoughton, London.

Cramp, S. (ed.) (1985) *The Birds of the Western Palearctic.* 4. Oxford University Press, Oxford.

Cramp, S. (ed.) (1988) *The Birds of the Western Palearctic.* 5. Oxford University Press, Oxford.

Cramp, S., and Perrins, C. (eds) (1993) *The Birds of the Western Palearctic.* 7. Oxford University Press, Oxford.

Cramp, S., and Perrins, C. (eds) (1994) *The Birds of the Western Palearctic.* 8. Oxford University Press, Oxford.

Cramp, S., and Simmons, K. E. L. (eds) (1977) *The Birds of the Western Palearctic.* 1. Oxford University Press, Oxford.

Cramp, S., and Simmons, K. E. L. (eds) (1980) *The Birds of the Western Palearctic.* 2. Oxford University Press, Oxford.

Cramp, S., and Simmons, K. E. L. (eds) (1983) *The Birds of the Western Palearctic.* 3. Oxford University Press, Oxford.

Cronin, E. W., Jr, and Sherman, P. W. (1976) A resource-based mating system: the Orange-rumped Honeyguide. *Living Bird* 15: 5–32.

Crosby, M. (1995) From the field: India. *Oriental Bird Club Bull.* 21: 70.

*__D'Abreu, E. A.__ (1935) A list of the birds of the Central Provinces. *J. Bombay Nat. Hist. Soc.* 38: 95–116.

Daniel, J. C., and Hussain, S. A. (1975) The Brownwinged Storkbilled Kingfisher *Pelargopsis amauroptera* (Pearson) in Orissa. *J. Bombay Nat. Hist. Soc.* 71: 304–305.

Davidar, P., Yoganand, T. R. K., Ganesh, T., and Joshi, N. (1997) An assessment of common and rare forest bird species of the Andaman islands. *Forktail* 12: 99–105.

***Davidson, J.** (1882) Rough list of the birds of western Khandesh. *Stray Feathers* 10: 279–326.

Delacour, J. (1977) *The Pheasants of the World.* Second edition. World Pheasant Association and Spur Publications, Hindhead.

del Hoyo, J., Elliott, A., and Sargatal, J. (eds) (1992) *Handbook of the Birds of the World.* 1. Lynx Edicions, Barcelona.

De Silva, R. I. (1990) The seabirds of Sri Lanka (an annotated checklist). *Ceylon J. Sci. (Biol. Sci.)* 21: 28–33.

De Silva, R., and Perera, L. (1993) Long-billed Plover *Charadrius placidus*: a new species for Sri Lanka. *Forktail* 9: 154–155.

Devillers, P. (1977) The skuas of the Northern American Pacific Coast. *Auk* 94: 417–429.

Dhindsa, M. S., Sandhu, P. S., and Sandhu, J. S. (1991) Some additions to the checklist of birds of Punjab. *Pavo* 28: 23–28.

Dittberner, H., and Dittberner, W. (1984) *Die Schafstelze.* A. Ziemsen Verlag, Wittenberg Lutherstadt.

Drijvers, R. (1995) Horned Grebe *Podiceps auritus*: a new species for India. *Forktail* 10: 175– 176.

Dubois, P. J., and Yésou, P. (1995) Identification of Western Reef Egrets and dark Little Egrets. *British Birds* 88: 307–319.

Eldridge, M., and Harrop, A. (1992) Identification and status of Baikal Teal. *Birding World* 5(11): 417–423.

Eriksen, J. (1988) Identification and status of the Plain Leaf Warbler. *Sandgrouse* 10: 107–109.

***Fairbank, S. B.** (1876) List of birds collected in the vicinity of Khandala, Mahabaleshwar, and Belgaw along the Sahyadri Mountains; and near Ahmednagar in the Dakhan. *Stray Feathers* 4: 250–268.

***Fleming, R. L., Sr, Fleming, R. L., Jr, and Bangdel, L. S.** (1984) *Birds of Nepal.* Third edition. Avalok, Kathmandu.

Flint, V. E., Boehme, R. L., Kostin, Y. V., and Kuznetsov, A. A. (1984) *A Field Guide to Birds of the USSR.* Princeton University Press, Princeton.

Forshaw, J. M. (1989) *Parrots of the World.* Third edition. Blandford, London.

Forsman, D. (1994) Field identification of Crested Honey Buzzard. *Birding World* 7: 396–403.

Forsman, D. (1995) Field identification of female and juvenile Pallid Harrier and Montagu's Harrier. *Dutch Birding* 17: 41–54.

Friedmann, H. (1976) The Asian honeyguides. *J. Bombay Nat. Hist. Soc.* 71: 426–431.

Frith, C. B, and Frith, D. W. (1983) A systematic review of the hornbill genus *Anthracoceros* (Aves, Bucerotidae). *Zoological Journal of the Linnean Society* 78: 29–71.

Frith, H. J. (ed.) (1976) *Reader's Digest Complete Book of Australian Birds.* Reader's Digest Services, Sydney.

Fry, C. H., Fry, K., and Harris, A. (1992) *Kingfishers, Bee-eaters and Rollers. A Handbook.* Christopher Helm, London.

Ganguli-Lachungpa, U. (1996) Baseline bird survey in proposed Kitam Wildlife Sanctuary and other lowland forests of South Sikkim, India. March–April and September–October 1996. Unpublished report to Oriental Bird Club.

Garner, M. (1997) Identification of Yellow-legged Gulls in Britain. *Brit. Birds* 90: 25–62.

Garson, P. J., Young, L., and Kaul, R. (1992) Ecology and conservation of the Cheer Pheasant *Catreus wallichii*, studies in the wild and the progress of a reintroduction project. *Biol. Conserv.* 59: 25–35.

Gaston, A. J., and Chattopadhyay, S. (1981) Siskin (*Carduelis spinus*) in Solang Nalla, Himachal Pradesh. *J. Bombay Nat. Hist. Soc.* 78: 386–387.

Gaston, A. J., and Zacharias, V. J. (1996) The recent distribution of endemic and disjunct birds in Kerala state: preliminary results of an ongoing survey. *J. Bombay Nat. Hist. Soc.* 93(3): 389–400.

Gaston, A. J., Garson, P. J., and Hunter, M. L. (1983) The status and conservation of forest wildlife in Himachal Pradesh, western Himalayas. *Biol. Conserv.* 27: 291–314.

Gay, P. H. (1996) Indian Pitta *Pitta brachyura*: first for Kathmandu Valley. *Bird Conservation Nepal Bull.* 5(2): 1.

Gee, B. (1995) South India, Sri Lanka and the Andaman Islands. Unpublished.

***George, J.** (ed.) (1992) *Checklist of the Birds of Bangalore.* Second edition. Birdwatchers' Field Club of Bangalore, Bangalore.

***Ghorpade, K. D.** (1974) Preliminary notes on the ornithology of Sandur, Karnataka. *J. Bombay Nat. Hist. Soc.* 70: 499–531.

Gibbs, D., Barnes, E., and Cox, J. (in prep.) *Pigeons and Doves.* Pica Press, Mountfield.

Ginige, P., and Kotagama, S. W. (1993) The distribution, status and conservation of hornbills in Sri Lanka. Pp.422–428 in P. Poonswad and A. Kemp (eds), *Manual of the Status and Study of Asian Hornbills.* Hornbill Project Thailand, Bangkok.

Giri, T. R., and Choudhary, H. (1996) Additional sightings! *Bird Conservation Nepal Bull.* 5(3): 2–3.

Giri, T. R., and Choudhary, H. (1997) Additional sightings! *Danphe* 6(2): 7–8.

Gole, P. (1992) On the trail of wintering Black-necked Cranes in India. *J. Ecol. Soc.* 6: 7–22.

Gole, P. (1996) *Environment and Ornithology in India.* Rawat Publications, Jaipur.

Goodwin, D. (1967) *Pigeons of the World.* Oxford University Press, Oxford.

Goodwin, D., and Vaurie, C. (1956) Are *Luscinia pectardens* (David & Oustalet) and *Luscinia obscura* (Berezowsky & Bianchi) colour phases of a single species? *Bull. Brit. Orn. Club* 76: 141–143.

Goroshko, O. A. (1993) [Taxonomic status of the Pale (Sand?) Martin *Riparia (riparia) diluta* (Sharpe and Wyatt 1893).] *Russ. J. Ornithol.* 2: 303–323. (In Russian)

Grant, C. H. B., and Mackworth-Praed, C. W. (1952) On the species and races of the Yellow Wagtails from western Europe to western North America. *Bull. Brit. Mus. (Nat. Hist.)* 1: 255–268.

Grant, P. J. (1986) *Gulls: a Guide to Identification.* Second edition. T. & A. D. Poyser, Calton.

Green, A. J. (1993) Status and habitat of the White-winged Wood Duck *Cairina scutulata. Bird Conservation International* 3: 119–143.

Grewal, B. (1994) *Threatened Birds of India.* Privately published.

Grewal, B. (1996) Bristled Grassbird *Chaetornis striatus* at Okhla, Delhi. *Oriental Bird Club Bull.* 24: 43–44.

Grewal, B., and Sahgal, B. (eds) (1995) *Birds of Corbett Tiger Reserve and its environs.* Unpublished.

Gruber, D. (1995) Die Kennzeichen und das Vorkommen der Weisskopfmöwe *Larus cachinnans* in Europa. *Limicola* 9: 121–165.

***Grubh, R. B., and Ali, S.** (1976) Birds of Goa. *J. Bombay Nat. Hist. Soc.* 73: 42–53.

Hall, B. P. (1957) The taxonomic importance of variation in non-breeding plumage in *Aegithina tiphia* and *A. nigrolutea. Ibis* 99: 143–156.

Hancock, J., and Kushlan, J. (1984) *The Herons Handbook.* Croom Helm, London and Sydney.

Hancock, J. A., Kushlan, J. A., and Kahl, M. P. (1992) *Storks, Ibises and Spoonbills of the World.* Academic Press, London.

Hargitt, E. (1890) *Catalogue of the birds in the collection of the British Museum,* 18 – Picidae. British Museum, London.

Haribal, M. (1992) Yellowrumped Flycatcher *Ficedula* (*Muscicapa*) *zanthopygia* (*narcissina*): a new addition to the avifauna of the Indian subcontinent. *J. Bombay Nat. Hist. Soc.* 88: 456–458.

Harrap, S. (1989) Identification, vocalisations and taxonomy of *Pnoepyga* wren-babblers. *Forktail* 5: 61–70.

Harrap, S. (1993) Identification of Mugimaki, Narcissus and Yellow-rumped Flycatchers. *Birding World* 6: 406–412.

Harrap, S., and Quinn, D. (1996) *Tits, Nuthatches and Treecreepers.* Christopher Helm, London.

Harrap, S. C., and Redman, N. J. (1990) Some observations of scarce birds in Kerala and Tamil Nadu. *J. Bombay Nat. Hist. Soc.* 86: 460–461.

Harris, A., Tucker, L., and Vinicombe, K. (1989) *The Macmillan Field Guide to Bird Identification.* Macmillan, London.

Harris, A., Shirihai, H., and Christie, D. (1996) *The Macmillan Birder's Guide to European and Middle Eastern Birds.* Macmillan, London.

***Harris, P.** (1996) *Goa, the Independent Birders' Guide.* Eastern Publications, Lowestoft.

Harrison, P. (1983) *Seabirds: an identification guide.* Croom Helm, Beckenham.

Harrison, P. (1987) *Seabirds of the World: a photographic guide.* Christopher Helm, London.

***Harvey, W. G.** (1990) *Birds in Bangladesh.* University Press Ltd, Dhaka.

Hayman, P., Marchant, J., and Prater, T. (1986) *Shorebirds. An Identification Guide to the Waders of the World.* Christopher Helm, London.

Heath, P. (1988) Little known Oriental bird: Rusty-bellied Shortwing. *Oriental Bird Club Bull.* 8: 16–19.

Heath, P. J. (1989) A Short-billed Minivet *Pericrocotus brevirostris* nest in Nepal. *Forktail* 4: 117–118.

***Henry, G. M.** (1971) *A Guide to the Birds of Ceylon.* Second edition. Oxford University Press, London.

***Hewetson, C. E.** (1956) Observations on the bird life of Madhya Pradesh. *J. Bombay Nat. Hist. Soc.* 53: 595–645.

Higgins, P. J., and Davies, S. J. J. F. (1996) *Handbook of Australian, New Zealand and Antarctic Birds.* 3. Oxford University Press, Melbourne.

Hirschfeld, E. (1992) Identification of Rufous Turtle Dove. *Birding World* 5: 52–57.

Hirschfeld, E. (1994) First record of Plain Leaf Warbler *Phylloscopus neglectus* in Bahrain. *Sandgrouse* 14: 120–121.

Hirschfeld, E., Kjellén, N., and Ullman, M. (1988) Birdwatching in Pakistan, Feb. 14th to March 6th, 1988. Unpublished.

Hirst, P., and Procter, B. (1995) Identification of Wandering and Grey-tailed Tattlers. *Birding World* 8: 91–97.

Hoffmann, T. H. (1984) *National Red Data List of Endangered and Rare Birds of Sri Lanka.* Ceylon Bird Club and Wild Life and Nature Protection Society of Sri Lanka, Colombo.

Hoffmann, T. H. (1996) New bird records in Sri Lanka and some connected matters. *J. Bombay Nat. Hist. Soc.* 93(3): 382–388.

Hollom, P. A. D., Porter, R. F., Christensen, S., and Willis, I. (1988) *Birds of the Middle East and North Africa.* T. & A. D. Poyser, Calton.

Hume, A. O. The birds of a drought. *Stray Feathers* 7: 52–68.

Husain, K. Z. (1959) Is *Psittacula intermedia* (Rothschild) a valid species? *Bull. Brit. Orn. Club* 79: 89–92.

Husain, K. Z., and Haque, M. N. (1981) *The White-winged Wood Duck Project. Study of the Ecology and Breeding Biology of the White-winged Wood Duck* Cairina scutulata *(Müller) in Pablakhali, the Chittagong Hill Tracts, 1976–1978.* Report to the University Grants Commission, Dhaka.

Husain, K. Z., and Sarker, S. U. (1971) Notes on a collection of birds from Pabna (Bangladesh). *J. Asiatic Soc.*

Bangladesh 16: 259–288.

Hussain, S. A. (1984) Some aspects of the biology and ecology of Narcondam Hornbill *(Rhyticeros narcondami). J. Bombay Nat. Hist. Soc.* 81(1): 1–18.

Hussain, S. A. (1986) Status of Blacknecked Crane in Ladakh – 1983 problems and prospects. *J. Bombay Nat. Hist. Soc.* 82: 449–458.

Hussain, S. A. (1993) The distribution, status and conservation of hornbills in India. Pp.296–304 in P. Poonswad and A. Kemp (eds), *Manual of the Status and Study of Asian Hornbills.* Hornbill Project Thailand, Bangkok.

Hussain, S. A., and Khan, M. A. R. (1977) A new subspecies of Bay Owl [*Phodilus badius* (Horsfield)] from peninsular India. *J. Bombay Nat. Hist. Soc.* 74: 334–335.

Hussain, S. A., Akhtar, S. A., and Tiwari, J. K. (1992) Status and distribution of White-winged Black Tit *Parus nuchalis* in Kachchh, Gujarat, India. *Bird Conservation International* 2: 115–122.

***Inglis, C. M.** (1901–1904) The birds of the Madhubani subdivision of the Darbhanga district, Tirhut, with notes on species noticed elsewhere in the district. *J. Bombay Nat. Hist. Soc.* 13: 621–631; 14: 132–139, 362–371, 554–563, 764–771; 15: 70–77, 337–343; 16: 70–75.

***Inglis, C. M., Travers, W. L., O'Donel, H. V., and Shebbeare, E. O.** (1920) A tentative list of the vertebrates of the Jalpaiguri district, Bengal. Birds. *J. Bombay Nat. Hist. Soc.* 26: 988–999; 27: 151–158.

Inskipp, C., and Inskipp, T. (1983) *Results of a Preliminary Survey of Bengal Floricans* Houbaropsis bengalensis *in Nepal and India, 1982.* International Council for Bird Preservation, Study Report 2, Cambridge.

***Inskipp, C., and Inskipp, T.** (1991) *A Guide to the Birds of Nepal.* Second edition. Christopher Helm, London.

Inskipp, C., and Inskipp, T. (1993) Birds recorded during a visit to Bhutan in spring 1993. *Forktail* 9: 121–142.

Inskipp, C., and Inskipp, T. (1994) Birds of Sagarmatha National Park. Unpublished report to WWF Nepal and Department of National Parks and Wildlife Conservation, Nepal.

Inskipp, C., and Inskipp, T. P. (1995a) Little-known Oriental bird. Intermediate Parakeet *Psittacula intermedia. Oriental Bird Club Bull.* 22: 29–31.

***Inskipp, C., and Inskipp, T.** (1995b) *An Introduction to Birdwatching in Bhutan.* World Wildlife Fund Bhutan Program, Thimphu.

Inskipp, C., and Inskipp, T. (1996) Avifauna Survey-cum-Training Programme in Jigme Dorji National Park, April–May 1996. Unpublished report to WWF Bhutan and Royal Government of Bhutan Forestry Department.

Inskipp, C., and Inskipp, T. (1997) Eastern Blossom-headed Parakeet *Psittacula roseata* – an additional species for the Nepal list. *Danphe* 6(2): 3.

Inskipp, T. (1996) Little known Oriental bird: Bristled Grassbird *Chaetornis striatus. Oriental Bird Club Bull.* 24: 46–47.

Inskipp, T. P., and Inskipp, C. (1980) Notes on birds recorded in Nepal, April–May 1980. Unpublished.

Inskipp, T., Lindsey, N., and Duckworth, W. (1996) *An Annotated Checklist of the Birds of the Oriental Region.* Oriental Bird Club, Sandy.

Jakobsen, O. F. (1995) Eyebrowed Thrush *Turdus obscurus*: a new species for Sri Lanka. *Forktail* 10: 176–177.

Javed, S. (1993) Swamp Francolin: conservation prospects. *World Pheasant Association, India, News* 1(2): 5–6.

Javed, S., and Rahmani, A. R. (1991) Swamp Francolin in the north Indian terai. *WPA News* 34: 15–18.

Javed, S., and Rahmani, A. R. (in prep.) Conservation of the avifauna of Dudwa National Park, India. *Forktail.*

Jepson, P. (1987) Recent reports. *Oriental Bird Club Bull.* 6: 36–40.

Jepson, P. (1991) The occurrence of Kessler's Thrush *Turdus kessleri* in Nepal. *Forktail* 6: 83–85.

***Jesse, W.** (1902–1903) A list of the birds of Lucknow. *Ibis* (8)2: 470–490, 531–566; (8)3: 49–81, 148–178.

Johnsgard, P. A. (1983) *Cranes of the World.* University of Indiana Press, Bloomington.

Johnsgard, P. A. (1986) *The Pheasants of the World.* Oxford University Press, Oxford.

Johnsgard, P. A. (1988) *The Quails, Partridges and Francolins of the World.* Oxford University Press, Oxford.

Johnsgard, P. A. (1991) *Bustards, Hemipodes and Sandgrouse, Birds of Dry Places.* Oxford University Press, Oxford.

Johnsgard, P. A. (1993) *Cormorants, Darters and Pelicans of the World.* Smithsonian Institution Press, Washington DC.

***Johnson, D., Thompson, P., and Woolner, J.** (1992) *Birds of Bangladesh.* Revised. University Press Ltd, Dhaka.

***Jones, A. E.** (1947–1948) The birds of the Simla and adjacent hills. *J. Bombay Nat. Hist. Soc.* 47: 117–125, 219–249, 409–432.

Jones, D. N., Dekker, R. W. R. J., and Roselaar, C. S. (1995) *The Megapodes.* Oxford University Press, Oxford.

Jonsson, L. (1992) *Birds of Europe with North Africa and the Middle East.* Christopher Helm, London.

Jonsson, L. (1996) "Gulfotade trutar". Räkna med både medelhavstrut och kaspisk trut. *Vår Fågelvärld* 55(8): 12–26.

Kannan, R. (1993a) Rediscovery of the Oriental Bay-Owl *Phodilus badius* in peninsular India. *Forktail* 8: 148–149.

Kannan, R. (1993b) Recent sightings of the Ceylon Frogmouth in India. *Oriental Bird Club Bull.* 17: 37–38.

Kannan, R. (1994) Ecology and Conservation of the Great Pied Hornbill (*Buceros bicornis*) in the Western Ghats of Southern India. D.Ph. dissertation, University of Arkansas. Unpublished.

Karthikeyan, S. (1996) Bird attracting trees and birds of Shevaroys and Kolli Hills. *Newsletter for Birdwatchers* 36: 49–51.

Karthikeyan, S., and Athreya, V. R. (1993) Kashmir Redbreasted Flycatcher *Muscicapa subrubra* Hartert and Steinbacher at Ooty. *J. Bombay Nat. Hist. Soc.* 89: 376–377.

Katju, D. (1996) Pheasants in Mizoram, India: an impression. *Tragopan* 5: 9–10.

Katti, M., Singh, P., Manjrekar, N., Sharma, D., and Mukherjee, S. (1992) An ornithological survey in eastern Arunachal Pradesh, India. *Forktail* 7: 75–89.

Kaul, R. (1992) Indian Mountain Quail, can we learn from Cheer Pheasant studies. *WPA News* 38: 18–19.

***Kaul, R., and Ahmed, A.** (1992) Pheasant Studies in North-East India – 1, Arunachal Pradesh. Report to Peter Scott Trust, Jamnagar. Unpublished.

***Kaul, R., Ahmed, A., and Katju, D.** (1996) Wildlife Studies in North-East India – IV [Mizoram]. Report to WPA/Peter Scott Trust, Jamnagar. Unpublished.

Kaul, R., and Howman, S. (1991) Quail and francolin studies in western India. *WPA News* 32: 19–22.

***Kaul, R., Raza, R., and Kalsi, R.** (1995) Wildlife Studies in North-East India – II [Jan.–Feb., 1994]. Report to Peter Scott Trust, Jamnagar. Unpublished.

Kazmierczak, K. (1991) Pied Ground Thrushes in south India. *Newsletter for Birdwatchers* 31(7 & 8): 13.

Kazmierczak, K., Balachandran, S., and Rosalind, L. (1993) Caspian Plover *Charadrius asiaticus* Pallas at Point Calimere, Tamil Nadu. *J. Bombay Nat. Hist. Soc.* 89: 373.

Kemp, A. (1995) *The Hornbills.* Oxford University Press, Oxford.

Kennerley, P. R., and Bakewell, D. N. (1991) Identification and status of Nordmann's Greenshank. *Dutch Birding* 13(1): 1–8.

Kennerley, P. R., and Leader, P. J. (1992) The identification, status and distribution of small *Acrocephalus* warblers in eastern China. *Hong Kong Bird Report* 1991: 143–187.

Kennerley, P. R., and Leader, P. J. (1993) Russet Bush Warbler and Brown Bush Warbler: two new species to Hong Kong. *Hong Kong Bird Report* 1992: 114–130.

Kennerley, P. R., Hoogendoorn, W., and Chalmers, M. L. (1995) Identification and systematics of large white-headed gulls in Hong Kong. *Hong Kong Bird Report* 1994: 127–156.

Khaling, S. (1997) Satyr Tragopan in the Singhalila National Park, Darjeeling, India. *Tragopan* 6: 13–14.

Khan, M. A. R. (1981) The endangered birds of Bangladesh. *Newsletter for Birdwatchers* 21(12): 4–7.

Khan, M. A. R. (1982) *Wildlife of Bangladesh: A Checklist.* University of Dhaka, Dhaka.

Khan, M. A. R. (1986) Wildlife in Bangladesh mangrove ecosystem. *J. Bombay Nat. Hist. Soc.* 83: 32–47.

King, B. F., Dickinson, E. C., and Woodcock, M. W. (1975) *A Field Guide to the Birds of South-East Asia.* Collins, London.

King, B. F., and Rasmussen, P. C. (1998) The rediscovery of the Forest Owlet *Athene* (*Heteroglaux*) *blewitti*. *Forktail* 14.

Kirwan, G., and Konrad, V. (1995) Little known Western Palearctic birds: Mongolian Trumpeter Finch. *Birding World* 8: 139–144.

Klein, R. (1994) Silbermöwen *Larus argentatus* und Weisskopfmöwen *Larus cachinnans* auf Mülldeponien in Mecklenburg – erste Ergebnisse einer Ringfundanalyse. *Vogelwelt* 115: 267–286.

***Koelz, W.** (1948) Notes on a collection of birds from Madras Presidency. *J. Bombay Nat. Hist. Soc.* 47: 128–142.

***Kotagama, S., and Fernando, P.** (1994) *A Field Guide to the Birds of Sri Lanka.* The Wildlife Heritage Trust of Sri Lanka, Colombo.

***Kurup, D. N., and Zacharias, V. J.** (1995) Birds of Lakshadweep Islands, India. *Forktail* 10: 49–64.

Kylänpää, J. (1998) Black-capped Kingfisher *Halcyon pileata*: a new species for Pakistan. *Forktail* 13: 126.

Lama, S. (1993) Recently seen! *Nepal Bird Watching Club Bull.* 2(4): 3.

Lama, S. (1994a) Additional sightings! *Nepal Bird Watching Club Bull.* 3(1): 3–4.

Lama, S. (1994b) Additional sightings! *Nepal Bird Watching Club Bull.* 3(2): 2–3.

Lama, S. (1994c) Additional sightings! *Bird Conservation Nepal Bull.* 3(3): 4–5.

Lama, S. (1995a) Additional sightings! *Bird Conservation Nepal Bull.* 4(1): 2–4.

Lama, S. (1995b) Additional sightings! *Bird Conservation Nepal Bull.* 4(2): 2–3.

Lama, S. (1995c) Additional sightings! *Bird Conservation Nepal Bull.* 4(3): 2–3.

Lambert, F. R., and Woodcock, M. (1996) *Pittas, Broadbills and Asities.* Pica Press, Mountfield.

Leader, P. J. (1993) The field identification of Arctic, Eastern Crowned, Two-barred Greenish and Pale-legged Warblers in Hong Kong. *Hong Kong Bird Report* 1992: 153–159.

Leader, P. J. (1995a) Plain Martin: the first record for Hong Kong. *Hong Kong Bird Report* 1994: 115–117.

Leader, P. J. (1995b) Field identification of Dusky, Radde's and Yellow-streaked Warblers. *Hong Kong Bird Report* 1994: 170–180.

Leader, P. J., and Carey, G. J. (1995) Identification and status of Japanese Sparrowhawk and Besra in Hong Kong. *Hong Kong Bird Report* 1994: 157–169.

Lefranc, N., and Worfolk, T. (1997) *Shrikes. A Guide to the Shrikes of the World.* Pica Press, Mountfield.

***Legge, W. V.** (1983) *A History of the Birds of Ceylon.* 4 vols. Second edition (reprint of 1880 edition updated with a modern introduction, appendices and checklist). Tisara Prakasakayo, Dehiwala.

Lewis, A. (1994a) Asian Stubtail *Urosphena squameiceps*: a new species for Nepal and the Indian subcontinent. *Forktail* 6: 155.

Lewis, A. (1994b) Black-and-yellow Grosbeak *Mycerobas icterioides*: a new species for Nepal. *Forktail* 6: 156.

Lister, M. D. (1951) Some bird associations of Bengal. *J. Bombay Nat. Hist. Soc.* 49: 695–728.

Lister, M. D. (1954) A contribution to the ornithology of the Darjeeling area. *J. Bombay Nat. Hist. Soc.* 52: 20–68.

Long, A., Crosby, M., and Inskipp, T. (1994) A review of the taxonomic status of the Yellow-throated Laughingthrush *Garrulax galbanus. Oriental Bird Club Bull.* 19: 41–47.

Long, A. J., Eames, J. C., and Robson, C. R. (1992) Some hints on the identification of five *Alcedo* kingfishers in the Orient. *Oriental Bird Club Bull.* 15: 18–23.

*__Ludlow, F., and Kinnear, N.__ (1937) The birds of Bhutan and adjacent territories of Sikkim and Tibet. *Ibis* (14)1: 1–46, 249–293, 467–504.

*__Ludlow, F., and Kinnear, N.__ (1944) The birds of south-eastern Tibet. *Ibis* 86: 43–86, 176–208, 348–389.

Madge, S. (1992) Identification of Moustached Warbler. *Birding World* 5: 299–303.

Madge, S. (1995) A record of Goliath Heron in Assam. *Oriental Bird Club Bull.* 21: 47.

Madge, S., and Burn, H. (1988) *Wildfowl: An Identification Guide to the Ducks, Geese and Swans of the World.* Christopher Helm, London.

Madge, S., and Burn, H. (1993) *Crows and Jays: A Guide to the Crows, Jays and Magpies of the World.* Christopher Helm, London.

Mahabal, A. (1992) Avifauna of Chamba District (Himachal Pradesh) with emphasis on their altitudinal distribution. *Pavo* 30: 17–25.

Majumdar, N., and Brahmachari, G. K. (1988) Major grassland types of India and their bird communities: a conservation perspective. Pp.205–214 in P. D. Goriup (ed.), *Ecology and Conservation of Grassland Birds.* Techn. Publ. no. 7. International Council for Bird Preservation, Cambridge.

Majumdar, N., and Roy, C. S. (1995) Aves. Pp.129–377 in Anon. (ed.), *Fauna of Meghalaya.* Part 1 (Vertebrates). Zoological Survey of India, Calcutta.

Majumdar, N., Roy, C. S., Ghosal, D. K., Dasgupta, J. M., Basuroy, S., and Dutta, B. K. (1992) Aves. Pp.171–418 in Anon., *Fauna of West Bengal – Part 1 (Overview, Mammalia, Aves & Wild Life).* Zoological Survey of India, Calcutta.

Malhotra, Y. R., and Pathania, P. S. (1981) The Chukar Partridge in Leh (Ladakh). *TigerPaper* 8(3): 20–22.

Malling Olsen, K. (1989) Field identification of the smaller skuas. *British Birds* 82: 143–176.

Malling Olsen, K., and Larsson, H. (1995) *Terns of Europe and North America.* Christopher Helm, London.

Malling Olsen, K., and Larsson, H. (1997) *Skuas and Jaegers. A Guide to the Skuas and Jaegers of the World.* Pica Press, Mountfield.

Marchant, S., and Higgins, P. (1990) *The Handbook of Australian, New Zealand and Antarctic Birds.* 1. Oxford University Press, Melbourne.

Marchant, S., and Higgins, P. J. (1996) *The Handbook of Australian, New Zealand and Antarctic Birds.* 3. Oxford University Press, Melbourne.

Martens, J., and Eck, S. (1991) *Pnoepyga immaculata* n. sp. eine neue bodenbewohnende Timalie aus dem Nepal – Himalaya. *J. Orn.* 132: 179–198.

Martens, J., and Eck, S. (1995) Towards an ornithology of the Himalayas: systematics, ecology and vocalizations of Nepal birds. *Bonner Zoologische Monographien* 38: 1–445.

Mathew, D. N., and Ambedkar, V. C. (1964) A bird study trip to the Laccadive Islands. *J. Bombay Nat. Hist. Soc.* 61: 185–190.

Mathew, D. N., Mathew, G., and Gandhi, T. (1996) Breeding seasons and conservation of the terns *Sterna fuscata* and *Anous stolidus* in the Lakshadweep. *J. Bombay Nat. Hist. Soc.* 93(3): 507–510.

*__Matthews, W. H., and Edwards, V. S.__ (1944) *A List of Birds of Darjeeling and Neighbourhood.* Published by the authors, Darjeeling.

McGowan, P. J. K., Dowell, S. D, Carroll, J. P., and Aebischer, N. J., and the WPA/BirdLife/SSC Partridge, Quail and Francolin Specialist Group (1995) *Partridges, Quails, Francolins, Snowcocks and Guineafowl Status Survey and Conservation Action Plan 1995–1999.* IUCN, Gland.

McGowan, P. J. K., and Garson, P. J. (1995) *Pheasants, Status Survey and Conservation Action Plan 1995–1999.* IUCN, Gland.

Mees, G. F. (1981) The sparrow-hawks (*Accipiter*) of the Andaman Islands. *J. Bombay Nat. Hist. Soc.* 77: 371–412.

Meine, C. D., and Archibald, G. W. (1996) *The Cranes: Status Survey and Conservation Action Plan.* IUCN, Gland and Cambridge.

Meinertzhagen, R. (1900) Reported occurrence of the Greater Black-backed Gull (*Larus marinus*) in Rajputana. *J. Bombay Nat. Hist. Soc.* 13: 374.

Meinertzhagen, R. (1952) A new bird for India – *Montifringilla davidiana potanini* (Sushkin). *J. Bombay Nat. Hist. Soc.* 51: 273–274.

Melville, D. S., Galsworthy, A. C., and Leader, P. J. (1991) Pale-footed Bush Warbler: a species new to Hong Kong. *Hong Kong Bird Report* 1990: 111–116.

Mitra, S. (1996) Eastern White Storks visit West Bengal. *Newsletter for Birdwatchers* 36: 32.

Mohan, D. (1990) Shortwings and grosbeaks in Mandakini valley. *Newsletter for Birdwatchers* 30(7&8): 8.

Mohan, D., and Chellam, R. (1991) New call record of Greenbreasted Pitta *Pitta sordida* (P. L. S. Muller) in Dehra Dun, Uttar Pradesh. *J. Bombay Nat. Hist. Soc.* 87: 453–454.

Mohapatra, K. K., and Rao, P. (1994) Further evidence on the occurrence of the Black Tern *Chlidonias niger* (Linnaeus) on India's eastern coast. *J. Bombay Nat. Hist. Soc.* 90: 511.

Morioka, T., Yamagata, N., Kanouchi, T., and Kawata, T. (1995) *The Birds of Prey of Japan.* Bun-ichi Sogo Shuppan, Tokyo.

Mudappa, D. C. (1994) Nesting Habitat of the Malabar Grey Hornbill *Ocyceros griseus* (Aves: Bucerotidae) in

the Anaimalai Hills of the Western Ghats, South India. Unpublished report to Oriental Bird Club.
Mudappa, D. C., and Kannan, R. (1997) Nest site characteristics and nesting success of Malabar Gray Hornbill in the southern Western Ghats, India. *Wilson Bull.* 109: 102–111.
Mundkur, T. (1985) Observations on the roof-nesting habit of the Redwattled Lapwing (*Vanellus indicus*) in Poona, Maharashtra. *J. Bombay Nat. Hist. Soc.* 82: 194–196.
Mundkur, T. (1990) Extension of breeding range of Brown Flycatcher *Muscicapa latirostris. J. Bombay Nat. Hist. Soc.* 87: 148.
Mundkur, T. (1991a) Prey items of the Great Thick-knee *Esacus recurvirostris. Forktail* 6: 71–72.
Mundkur, T. (1991b) Nesting and feeding ecology of aquatic birds in Saurashtra and Gulf of Kachchh. PhD thesis, Saurashtra University, Rajkot. Unpublished.
Mundkur, T., and Pravez, R. (1986) Rediscovery of the Great Crested Grebe (*Podiceps cristatus*) breeding in Gujarat. *J. Bombay Nat. Hist. Soc.* 83: 429–431.
Mundkur, T., and Pravez, R. (1990) Sight record of Rednecked Grebe *Podiceps griseigena* near Rajkot, Gujarat. *J. Bombay Nat. Hist. Soc.* 86: 440.
Mundkur, T., Pandya, P., Jhala, N., Pravez, R., and Khachar, S. (1992) Snow Goose *Anser caerulescens* – an addition to the Indian avifauna. *J. Bombay Nat. Hist. Soc.* 88: 446–447.
Mundkur, T., Pravez, R., Khachar, S., and Naik, R. M. (1990) Hitherto unreported nest site of Lesser Flamingo *Phoeniconaias minor* in the Little Rann of Kutch, Gujarat. *J. Bombay Nat. Hist. Soc.* 86: 281–285.
Mundkur, T., Raol, L. M., and Varu, S. N. (1988) Distribution of the Slenderbilled Gull (*Larus genei* Breme) in the Gulf of Kachchh, Gujarat. *J. Bombay Nat. Hist. Soc.* 85: 420–422.

Naoroji, R. (1991) Sighting of Least Frigate Bird *Fregata ariel* in Bombay. *J. Bombay Nat. Hist. Soc.* 88: 109–110.
Naoroji, R. (1995) Conservation issues of some raptor species in the Himalayan foothills with emphasis on Mountain Hawk-Eagle and Lesser Greyheaded Fishing Eagle. Pp.32–34 in L. Vijayan (ed.), *Avian Conservation in India.* SACON, Coimbatore.
Naoroji, R. (1996) Breeding of the Red-thighed Falconet. Abstract. Pp.92–93 in Pan-Asian Ornithological Congress and XII BirdLife Asia Conference Coimbatore, India, 9–16 November 1996.
Narayan, G. (1990) General ecology and behaviour of the Bengal Florican. Pp.17–34 in Anon., *Status and ecology of the Lesser and Bengal Floricans with reports on Jerdon's Courser and Mountain Quail.* Bombay Natural History Society, Bombay.
***Neelakantan, K. K., Sashikumar, C., and Venugopalan, R.** (1993) *A Book of Kerala Birds.* Part 1. World Wide Fund for Nature – India, Kerala State Committee, Trivandrum.
Nelson, J. B. (1978) *The Sulidae: Gannets and Boobies.* Oxford University Press, Oxford.
***Nichols, E. G..** (1943–1945) Occurrence of birds in Madura district. *J. Bombay Nat. Hist. Soc.* 44: 387–407, 574–584; 45: 122–132.

Osborne, P., Collar, N., and Goriup, P. (1984) *Bustards.* Dubai Wildlife Research Centre, Dubai.
***Osmaston, B. B., and Sale, J. B.** (1989) *Wildlife of Dehra Dun and Adjacent Hills.* Natraj, Dehra Dun.

Palmes, P., and Briggs, C. (1986) Crab-plovers in the Gulf of Kutch. *Forktail* 1: 21–28.
Pandav, B. (1997) Birds of Bhitarkanika mangroves, eastern India. *Forktail* 12: 7–17.
Parasharya, B. M., and Naik, R. M. (1987) Changes in the soft part coloration of the Indian Reef Heron, *Egretta gularis* (Bosc) related to age and breeding status. *J. Bombay Nat. Hist. Soc.* 84: 1–6.
Parasharya, B. M., and Naik, R. M (1988) Breeding biology of the Indian Reef Heron. *J. Bombay Nat. Hist. Soc.* 85: 251–262.
Paynter, R. A., Jr. (1970) Species with Malaysian affinities in the Sundarbans, East Pakistan. *Bull. Brit. Orn. Club* 90(5): 118–119.
Perennou, C., Mundkur, T., Scott, D. A., Folkestad, A., and Kvenild, L. (1994) *The Asian Waterfowl Census 1987–91: Distribution and Status of Asian Waterfowl.* AWB Publication 86. IWRB Publication 24. AWB, Kuala Lumpur, and IWRB, Slimbridge.
Pfister, O. (1997) Introduction to the Birds of Ladakh. Dissertation. University of Hull. Unpublished.
Pierce, R. (1986) Observations of behaviour and foraging of the Ibisbill *Ibidorhyncha struthersii* in Nepal. *Ibis* 128(1): 37–47.
Porter, R. F., Willis, I., Christensen, S., and Nielsen, B. P. (1974) *Flight Identification of European Raptors.* T. & A. D. Poyser, London.
Porter, R. F., Christensen, S., and Schiermacker-Hansen, P. (1996). *Field Guide to the Birds of the Middle East.* T. & A. D. Poyser, London.
Prakash, V. (1995) Conservation of the Narcondam Hornbill. Pp.44–45 in L. Vijayan (ed.), *Avian Conservation in India.* SACON, Coimbatore.
Prasad, J. N., Karthikeyan, S., Srinivasa, T. S., Subramanya, S., and Shyamal, L. (1992) Distribution of Painted Spurfowl in Karnataka. *Newsletter for Birdwatchers* 32(7 & 8): 11.
***Price, T. D.** (1980) The seasonality and occurrence of birds in the Eastern Ghats of Andhra Pradesh. *J. Bombay Nat. Hist. Soc.* 76: 379–422.

Rahmani, A. R. (1989a) *The Great Indian Bustard: Final Report.* Bombay Natural History Society, Bombay.
Rahmani, A. R. (1989b) Status of the Black-necked Stork *Ephippiorhynchus asiaticus* in the Indian subcontinent.

Forktail 5: 99–110.

Rahmani, A. R. (1995) Conservation of the Houbara and Great Indian Bustards. Pp.19–20 in L. Vijayan (ed.), *Avian Conservation in India.* SACON, Coimbatore.

Rahmani, A. R. (1996) *Present Status of the Bengal Florican* Houbaropsis bengalensis *in Dudwa Tiger Reserve.* Centre of Wildlife and Ornithology, Aligarh.

Rahmani, A. R. (1997) Status and distribution of Stoliczka's Bushchat *Saxicola macrorhyncha* in India. *Forktail* 12: 61–77.

Rahmani, A. R., and Arora, V. M. (1991) Wetlands of Uttar Pradesh – Part 1. *Newsletter for Birdwatchers* 31(7 & 8): 4–5.

Rahmani, A. R., and Manakadan, R. (1990a) The past and present distribution of the Great Indian Bustard *Ardeotis nigriceps* (Vigors) in India. *J. Bombay Nat. Hist. Soc.* 87: 175–194.

Rahmani, A. R., and Manakadan, R. (1990b) Breeding records of Creamcoloured Courser *Cursorius cursor cursor* (Latham) from India. *J. Bombay Nat. Hist. Soc.* 86: 447.

Rahmani, A. R., Narayan, G., and Rosalind, L. (1990) Status of the Greater Adjutant Stork (*Leptoptilos dubius*) in the Indian subcontinent. *Colonial Waterbirds* 13: 138–142.

Rahmani, A. R., Narayan, G., Rosalind, L., Sankaran, R., and Ganguli-Lachungpa, U. (1992) Status of the Bengal Florican *Houbaropsis bengalensis* in India. *J. Bombay Nat. Hist. Soc.* 88: 349–375.

Ranjitsinh, M. K. (1992) Breeding of Caspian Tern *Hydroprogne caspia* in the Little Rann of Kutch, Gujarat. *J. Bombay Nat. Hist. Soc.* 88: 283–284.

Rao, P., and Mohapatra, K. K. (1994) Occurrence of the Lesser Frigate Bird *Fregata minor* (Gmelin) in Andhra Pradesh. *J. Bombay Nat. Hist. Soc.* 90: 284.

Rasmussen, P. (1996) Buff-throated Warbler *Phylloscopus subaffinis* restored to the avifauna of the Indian subcontinent. *Forktail* 11: 173–175.

Rasmussen, P. C. (1998) Tytler's Leaf Warbler *Phylloscopus tytleri*: non-breeding distribution, morphological discrimination, and ageing. *Forktail* 14.

Rasmussen, P. C., and Collar, N. J. (1998) Identification, distribution and status of the Forest Owlet *Athene (Heteroglaux) blewitti. Forktail* 14.

Redman, N. (1992) Little-known bird: Blue-fronted Robin. *Oriental Bird Club Bull.* 16: 32–35.

Restall, R. (1996) *Munias and Mannikins.* Pica Press, Mountfield.

Richmond, C. W. (1903) Birds collected by Dr. W. L. Abbott and Mr. C. B. Kloss in the Andaman and Nicobar Islands. *Proc. U.S. Nat. Mus.* 25: 287–314.

Riddiford, N., Harvey, P. V., and Shepherd, K. B. (1989) Daurian Starling: new to the Western Palearctic. *British Birds* 82: 603–612.

Rieger, I., and Walzthöny, D. (1992) The distribution of the Mountain Quail (*Ophrysia superciliosa*) in the last century. *Gibier Faune Sauvage* 9 (Numéro Spécial): 585–590.

***Ripley, S. D.** (1961) *A Synopsis of the Birds of India and Pakistan.* Bombay Natural History Society, Bombay.

Ripley, S. D. (1976) Reconsideration of *Athene blewitti* (Hume). *J. Bombay Nat. Hist. Soc.* 73: 1–4.

Ripley, S. D., and Beehler, B. M. (1987) Species status of the Malaysian Three-toed Kingfishers *(Ceyx)* – a reassessment. *Bull. Brit. Orn. Club* 107: 145–147.

***Ripley, S. D., Beehler, B. M., and Krishna Raju, K. S. R.** (1988) Birds of the Vishakhapatnam Ghats, Andhra Pradesh. *J. Bombay Nat. Hist. Soc.* 84: 540–559; 85: 90–107.

Ripley, S. D., Saha, S. S., and Beehler, B. M. (1991) Notes on birds from the Upper Noa Dihing, Arunachal Pradesh, northeastern India. *Bull. Brit. Orn. Club* 111: 19–28.

***Roberts, T. J.** (1991–1992) *The Birds of Pakistan.* 2 vols. Oxford University Press, Karachi.

Roberts, T. J., and King, B. (1986) Vocalizations in the owls of the genus *Otus* in Pakistan. *Ornis Scand.* 17: 299–305.

Robertson, A. (1995) Occurrence of some pelagic seabirds (Procellariiformes) in waters off the Indian subcontinent. *Forktail* 10: 129–140.

***Robertson, A., and Jackson, M. C. A.** (1992) *Birds of Periyar: An Aid to Birdwatching in the Periyar Sanctuary.* Tourism and Wildlife Society of India.

Robson, C. (1985) Recent reports: India. *Oriental Bird Club Bull.* 2: 36–37.

Robson, C. (1991) Recent reports: India. *Oriental Bird Club Bull.* 13: 49–50.

Robson, C. (1993a) From the field: India. *Oriental Bird Club Bull.* 17: 51.

Robson, C. (1993b) From the field: India. *Oriental Bird Club Bull.* 18: 67.

Robson, C. (1994) From the field: India. *Oriental Bird Club Bull.* 20: 57.

Robson, C. (1996a) From the field: India. *Oriental Bird Club Bull.* 23: 50.

Robson, C. (1996b) From the field: India. *Oriental Bird Club Bull.* 24: 59–65.

Round, P. D. (1992) The identification and status of Russet Bush Warbler in China and continental Southeast Asia. *Hong Kong Bird Report* 1991: 188–194.

Round, P. D., and Loskot, V. (1994) A reappraisal of the taxonomy of the Spotted Bush-Warbler *Bradypterus thoracicus. Forktail* 10: 159–172.

Saikia, P., and Bhattacharjee, P. C. (1993) Status, diversity and decline of waterbirds in Brahmaputra valley, Assam, India. Pp.20–27 in A. Verghese, S. Sridhar and A. K. Chakravarthy (eds), *Bird Conservation, Strategies for the Nineties and Beyond.* Ornithological Society of India, Bangalore.

Sane, S. R., Kannan, P., Rajendran, C. G., Ingle, S. T., and Bhagwat, A. M. (1987) On the taxonomic status of

Psittacula intermedia (Rothschild). *J. Bombay Nat. Hist. Soc.* 83 (Suppl.): 127–134.

Sangha, H. (1995) Birds recorded in the Desert National Park, Rajasthan, India. Unpublished report to Oriental Bird Club.

Sankaran, R. (1990a) Mountain Quail – a preliminary survey. Pp.135–137 in Anon., *Status and ecology of the Lesser and Bengal Floricans with reports on Jerdon's Courser and Mountain Quail.* Bombay Natural History Society, Bombay.

Sankaran, R. (1990b) Ecology and behaviour of the Lesser Florican. Pp.85–93 in Anon., *Status and ecology of the Lesser and Bengal Floricans with reports on Jerdon's Courser and Mountain Quail.* Bombay Natural History Society, Bombay.

Sankaran, R. (1993) *The Status and Conservation of the Nicobar Scrubfowl* Megapodius nicobariensis. SACON, Coimbatore.

Sankaran, R. (1995a) Distribution, status and conservation of the Nicobar Megapode. Pp.43–44 in L. Vijayan (ed.), *Avian Conservation in India.* SACON, Coimbatore.

Sankaran, R. (1995b) The status and conservation of the Lesser Florican. Pp.22–24 in L. Vijayan (ed.), *Avian Conservation in India.* SACON, Coimbatore.

Sankaran, R. (1996) Conservation of the Lesser Florican. Background paper for workshop, 28th July 1996. Hadothi Naturalists Society, Kota, in collaboration with SACON, Department of Forests and Wildlife, Rajasthan, and Centre for Wildlife and Ornithology, Aligarh.

Sankaran, R. (1997) Developing a protected area network in the Nicobar islands: the perspective of endemic avifauna. *Biodiversity and Conservation* 6: 797–815.

Sankaran, R. (1998) An annotated list of the endemic avifauna of the Nicobar islands. *Forktail*: 13: 17–22.

Sankaran, R., Rahmani, A. R., and Ganguli-Lachungpa, U. (1992) The distribution and status of the Lesser Florican *Sypheotides indica* (J. F. Miller) in the Indian subcontinent. *J. Bombay Nat. Hist. Soc.* 89: 156–179.

***Sankaran, R., and Vijayan, L.** (1993) The avifauna of the Andaman and Nicobar Islands: A review and the current scenario. Pp. 255–274 in A. Verghese, S. Sridhar and A. K. Chakravarthy (eds), *Bird Conservation, Strategies for the Nineties and Beyond.* Ornithological Society of India, Bangalore.

Santharam, V. (1983) Coastal birds in and around Madras. *Newsletter for Birdwatchers* 23(11 & 12): 5–7.

Santharam, V., and Nameer, P. O. (1992) The Lesser Coucal – a less-known bird. *Newsletter for Birdwatchers* 32(7 & 8): 9–10.

Sarker, S. U., and Sarker, N. J. (1986) Status and distribution of birds of the Sundarbans, Bangladesh. *J. Noami* 3: 19–33.

***Sawarkar, V. B.** (1987) Bird survey of the Melghat Tiger Reserve. *Cheetal* 29: 4–27.

Saxena, A. (1994) Sighting of Christmas Island Frigate Bird (*Fregata andrewsi* Mathews) in the Andamans. *J. Bombay Nat. Hist. Soc.* 91: 138.

Serrao, J. S. (1989) Pied Crested Cuckoos. *Newsletter for Birdwatchers* 29(9 & 10): 9–10.

Shah, S. R. (1979) Orange Honeyguide and Bullfinch, two unusual birds near the Valley of Flowers. *Newsletter for Birdwatchers* 19(5): 5–6.

Shankar Raman, T. R. (1995) Shifting Cultivation and Conservation of Tropical Forest Bird Communities in North-East India. Unpublished report to Oriental Bird Club.

Shirihai, H., and Alström, P. (1990) Identification of Hume's Short-toed Lark. *British Birds* 83: 262–272.

Shirihai, H., and Madge, S. (1993) Identification of Hume's Yellow-browed Warbler. *Birding World* 6: 439–443.

Shirihai, H., Christie, D. A., and Harris, A. (1996) Identification of *Hippolais* warblers. *British Birds* 89: 114–138.

Shirihai, H., Roselaar, C. S., Helbig, A. J., Barthel, P. H., and van Loon, A. J. (1995) Identification and taxonomy of large *Acrocephalus* warblers. *Dutch Birding* 17: 229–239.

Short, L. L. (1973) Habits of some Asian Woodpeckers (Aves, Picidae). *Bulletin of the American Museum of Natural History.* 152(5). American Museum of Natural History, New York.

Short, L. L. (1982) *Woodpeckers of the World.* Delaware Museum of Natural History, Greenville, Delaware.

Shrestha, M. K. (1993) Hornbill distribution and status in Nepal. Pp.388–391 in P. Poonswad and A. Kemp (eds), *Manual of the Status and Study of Asian Hornbills.* Hornbill Project Thailand, Bangkok.

Sinclair, J. C. (1977) Sight records of unusual birds from Colaba Point, Bombay, Maharashtra. *J. Bombay Nat. Hist. Soc.* 73: 530–531.

***Singh, P.** (1995) Recent bird records from Arunachal Pradesh, India. *Forktail* 10: 65–104.

Slater, P., Slater, P., and Slater, R. (1986) *The Slater Field Guide to Australian Birds.* Rigby, Dee Why West.

Smythies, B. E. (1986) *The Birds of Burma.* Third edition. Oliver and Boyd, London.

Sonobe, K., and Usui, S. (eds) (1993) *A Field Guide to the Waterbirds of Asia.* Wild Bird Society of Japan, Tokyo.

Stanford, J. K. (1937) On the breeding of the Oystercatcher (*Haematopus ostralegus* subsp.) and other birds in the Bengal Sunderbunds. *J. Bombay Nat. Hist. Soc.* 39: 867–868.

Stanford, J. K. (1954) *A Bewilderment of Birds.* Hart-Davis, London.

***Stevens, H.** (1915) Notes on the birds of upper Assam. *J. Bombay Nat. Hist. Soc.* 23: 234–268, 547–570, 721–736.

***Stevens, H.** (1923–1925) Notes on the birds of the Sikkim Himalayas. *J. Bombay Nat. Hist. Soc.* 29: 503–518 (+ 3 pp. unpaginated corrections), 723–740, 1007–1030; 30: 54–71, 352–379, 664–685, 872–893.

Stonor, C. R. (1952) Distribution of Lord Derby's Parrakeet. *Ibis* 94: 162.

Subramanya, S., Prasad, J. N., and Karthikeyan, S. (1995) In search of the Yellow-throated Bulbul. *Sanctuary* 15(5): 68–70.

Sugathan, R. (1981) A survey of the Ceylon Frogmouth (*Batrachostomus moniliger*) habitat in the Western Ghats of India. *J. Bombay Nat. Hist. Soc.* 78: 309–316.

Summers-Smith, J. D. (1988) *The Sparrows.* T. & A. D. Poyser, Calton.

Svensson, L. (1992). *Identification of European Passerines.* Fourth edition. Published by the author, Stockholm.

***Taher, S. A., and Pittie, A.** (1989) *A Checklist of the Birds of Andhra Pradesh.*

Talukdar, B. K. (1995) Spot-billed Pelican in Assam. *Oriental Bird Club Bull.* 22: 46–47.

***Thompson, P. M., Harvey, W. G., Johnson, D. L., Millin, D. J., Rashid, S. M. A., Scott, D. A., Stanford, C., and Woolner, J. D.** (1994) Recent notable records from Bangladesh. *Forktail* 9: 13–44.

Ticehurst, C. B. (1938) *A Systematic Review of the Genus Phylloscopus.* British Museum (Natural History), London.

Tiwari, J. K., and Rahmani, A. R. (1997) The current status and biology of the White-winged Black Tit *Parus nuchalis* in Kutch, Gujarat, India. *Forktail* 12: 79–85.

Tiwari, J. K., Varu, S. N., and Himmatsinhji, M. K. (1996) The occurrence of the Grey Hypocolius *Hypocolius ampelinus* in India. *Forktail* 11: 33–38.

Turner, A., and Rose, C. (1989) *A Handbook to the Swallows and Martins of the World.* Christopher Helm, London.

***Tyabji, H. N.** (1994) *Bandhavgarh National Park, A Guide.* Privately published.

Tyler, S. J., and Ormerod, S. J. (1994) The ecology of river birds in Nepal. *Forktail* 9: 59–82.

Tymstra, R., Connop, S., and Tshering, C. (1997) Some bird observations from central Bhutan, May 1994. *Forktail* 12: 65–76.

Uddin S. R. (1995) Birds of Cuddapah district, Andhra Pradesh. *Mayura* 10: 28–33.

Ullman, M. (1991) Distinguishing Demoiselle Crane from Crane. *Dutch Birding* 13: 90–93.

Vaid, K. M. (1965) Wire-tailed Swallow's nest – a new record of altitude. *Indian Forester* 91: 804.

Vittery, A. (1994) The birds of Pakistan: supplementary observations from the northern Punjab and hills. *Forktail* 9: 143–147.

Voous, K. H. (1988) *Owls of the Northern Hemisphere.* Collins, London.

Voous, K. H., and Bijleveld, M. F. I. J. (1964) A note on the Himalayan buzzards *Buteo buteo* (Aves). *Beaufortia* 11: 37–43.

Vyas, R. (1992) Checklist of the birds of Kota district in south-east Rajasthan. *Newsletter for Birdwatchers* 32(11 & 12): 8–10.

***Vyawahare, P. M.** (1992) Checklist of birds from Dhule district, Maharashtra, with a note on migratory birds. *Pavo* 29(1–2): 77–106.

Wallace, D. I. M. (1973) Identification of some scarce or difficult west Palearctic species in Iran. *British Birds* 66: 376–390.

Walters, M. (1985) On the status of *Psittacula intermedia* (Rothschild). *J. Bombay Nat. Hist. Soc.* 82: 197–199.

Walton, H. J. (1900) Notes on birds collected in Kumaon. *J. Asiatic Soc. Bengal* 69: 155–168.

Warakagoda, D. (1994) Annotated checklist of the seabirds of Sri Lanka. *Ceylon Bird Club Notes* April 1994, pp.39–54.

Whistler, H. (1922) Birds of Jhang District. *Ibis* 4: 259–309.

Whistler, H. (1935) *Popular Handbook of Indian Birds.* Second edition. Gurney and Jackson, London.

***Whistler, H.** (1938) The ornithological survey of Jodhpur state. *J. Bombay Nat. Hist. Soc.* 40: 213–235.

***Whistler, H., and Kinnear, N. B.** (1931–1937) The Vernay Scientific Survey of the Eastern Ghats (Ornithological Section). *J. Bombay Nat. Hist. Soc.* 35: 505–524, 737–760; 36: 67–93, 334–352, 561–590, 832–844; 37: 96–105, 281–297, 515–528, 751–763; 38: 26–40, 232–240, 418–437, 672–698; 39: 246–263, 447–463.

***Whitehead, C. H. T.** (1911) Notes on the birds of Sehore, Central India, with special reference to migration. *J. Bombay Nat. Hist. Soc.* 21: 153–170.

***Wijesinghe, D. P.** (1991) *Checklist of the Birds of Sri Lanka.* Ceylon Bird Club, Colombo.

Williamson, K. (1967) *Identification for Ringers 2. The Genus* Phylloscopus. Second edition. BTO Guide No. 8, Tring.

Williamson, K. (1968) *Identification for Ringers 1. The Genera* Cettia, Locustella, Acrocephalus *and* Hippolais. Third edition. BTO Guide No. 7, Tring.

Winkler, H., Christie, D. A., and Nurney, D. (1995) *Woodpeckers. A Guide to the Woodpeckers, Piculets and Wrynecks of the World.* Pica Press, Mountfield.

WWF INDIA and AWB (1993) *Directory of Indian Wetlands.* WWF INDIA, New Delhi; AWB, Kuala Lumpur.

Yahya, H. S. A. (1994) A survey of the White-winged (Wood) Duck *Cairina scutulata* in India. *IWRB Threatened Waterfowl Research Group Newsletter* 5: 7–8.

Young, L., and Kaul, R. (1987) Conservation of Himalayan pheasants in Kumaon. Pp.684–691 in Y. P. S. Pangley and S. C. Joshi (eds), *Western Himalaya: Environment, Problems and Development*, 2. Gyanodaya Prakashan, Nainital.

Zacharias, V. J., and Gaston, A. J. (1993) The birds of Wynaad, southern India. *Forktail* 8: 11–23.

INDEX OF ENGLISH NAMES

Numbers in **bold** refer to plate numbers. Alternative names of species are shown in parentheses.

INDEX OF SCIENTIFIC NAMES

Numbers in **bold** refer to plate numbers.